SOLUTIONS MANUAL

Mary Beth Kramer

University of Delaware

Kathleen Thrush Shaginaw

Particular Solutions, Inc.

CHEMISTRY
A MOLECULAR APPROACH

Nivaldo J. Tro

PEARSON

Prentice Hall

Upper Saddle River, NJ 07458

Editor-in-Chief, Science: Nicole Folchetti
Editor: Jeff Howard
Assistant Editor: Carol G. DuPont
Senior Managing Editor, Science: Kathleen Schiaparelli
Assistant Managing Editor, Science: Gina M. Cheselka
Project Manager: Ed Thomas
Supplement Cover Manager: Paul Gourhan
Supplement Cover Designer: Victoria Colotta
Senior Operations Supervisor: Alan Fischer
Director of Operations: Barbara Kittle

© 2008 Pearson Education, Inc.

Pearson Prentice Hall

Pearson Education, Inc.

Upper Saddle River, NJ 07458

Pearson Prentice Hall™ is a trademark of Pearson Education, Inc.

The author and publisher of this book have used their best efforts in preparing this book. These efforts include the development, research, and testing of the theories and programs to determine their effectiveness. The author and publisher make no warranty of any kind, expressed or implied, with regard to these programs or the documentation contained in this book. The author and publisher shall not be liable in any event for incidental or consequential damages in connection with, or arising out of, the furnishing, performance, or use of these programs.

Printed in the United States of America

10 9 8 7 6 5 4 3 2 1

ISBN 13: 978-0-13-615110-4

ISBN 10:   0-13-615110-8

Pearson Education Ltd., *London*
Pearson Education Australia Pty. Ltd., *Sydney*
Pearson Education Singapore, Pte. Ltd.
Pearson Education North Asia Ltd., *Hong Kong*
Pearson Education Canada, Inc., *Toronto*
Pearson Educación de Mexico, S.A. de C.V.
Pearson Education—Japan, *Tokyo*
Pearson Education Malaysia, Pte. Ltd.

Table of Contents

Chapter 1
Matter, Measurement, and Problem Solving

1. "The properties of the substances around us depend on the atoms, ions, or molecules that compose them" means that the specific types of atoms and molecules that compose something tell us a great deal about the properties to expect. A material composed of only sodium and chlorine ions will have the properties of table salt. A material composed of molecules with one carbon atom and two oxygen atoms will have the properties of the gas carbon dioxide. If the atoms and molecules change, so do the properties that we expect the material to have.

2. The main goal of chemistry is to seek to understand the behavior of matter by studying the behavior of atoms and molecules.

3. The scientific approach to knowledge is based on observation and experiment. Scientists observe and perform experiments on the physical world to learn about it. Observations often lead scientists to formulate a hypothesis, a tentative interpretation or explanation of the observations. Hypotheses are tested by experiments, highly controlled procedures designed to generate such observations. The results of an experiment may support a hypothesis or prove it wrong—in which case the hypothesis must be modified or discarded. A series of similar observations can lead to the development of scientific law, a brief statement that summarizes past observations and predicts future ones. One or more well-established hypotheses may form the basis for a scientific theory. A scientific theory is a model for the way nature is and tries to explain not merely what nature does, but why.

    The Greek philosopher Plato (427 - 347 B.C.) took an opposite approach. He thought that the best way to learn about reality was not through the senses, but through reason. He believed that the physical world was an imperfect representation of a perfect and transcendent world (a world beyond space and time). For him, true knowledge came, not through observing the real physical world, but through reasoning and thinking about the ideal one.

4. A hypothesis is a tentative interpretation or explanation of the observed phenomena. A law is a concise statement that summarizes observed behaviors and observations and predicts future observations. A theory attempts to explain why the observed behavior is happening.

5. Antoine Lavoisier studied combustion and made careful measurements of the mass of objects before and after burning them in closed containers. He noticed that there was no change in the total mass of material within the container during combustion. Lavoisier summarized his observations on combustion with the law of conservation of mass, which states that, "In a chemical reaction, matter is neither created nor destroyed."

6. John Dalton formulated the atomic theory of matter. Dalton explained the law of conservation of mass, as well as other laws and observations of the time, by proposing that matter was composed of small, indestructible particles called atoms. Since these particles were merely rearranged in chemical changes (and not created or destroyed), the total amount of mass would remain the same.

7. The statement "that is just a theory" is generally taken to mean that there is no scientific proof behind the statement. This statement is the opposite of the meaning in the context of the scientific theory, where theories are tested again and again.

8. Matter can be classified according to its state—solid, liquid, or gas—and according to its composition.

9. In solid matter, atoms or molecules pack close to each other in fixed locations. Although the atoms and molecules in a solid vibrate, they do not move around or past each other. Consequently, a solid has a fixed volume and rigid shape.

    In liquid matter, atoms or molecules pack about as closely as they do in solid matter, but they are free to move relative to each other, giving liquids a fixed volume but not a fixed shape. Liquids assume the shape of their container.

    In gaseous matter, atoms or molecules have a lot of space between them and are free to move relative to one another, making gases compressible. Gases always assume the shape and volume of their container.

10. Solid matter may be crystalline, in which case its atoms or molecules are arranged in patterns with long-range, repeating order, or it may be amorphous, in which case its atoms or molecules do not have any long-range order.

11. A pure substance is composed of only one type of atom or molecule. In contrast, a mixture is a substance composed of two or more different types of atoms or molecules that can be combined in variable proportions.

12. An element is a pure substance which is not decomposable into simpler substances. A compound is composed of two or more elements in fixed proportions.

13. A homogeneous mixture has the same composition throughout, while a heterogeneous mixture has different compositions in different regions.

14. If a mixture is composed of an insoluble solid and a liquid, the two can be separated by filtration, in which the mixture is poured through filter paper usually held in a funnel.

15. Mixtures of miscible liquids (substances that easily mix) can usually be separated by distillation, a process in which the mixture is heated to boil off the more volatile (easily vaporizable) liquid. The volatile liquid is then recondensed in a condenser and collected in a separate flask.

16. A physical property is one that a substance displays without changing its composition, whereas a chemical property is one that a substance displays only by changing its composition via a chemical change.

17. Changes that alter only state or appearance, but not composition, are called physical changes. The atoms or molecules that compose a substance *do not change* their identity during a physical change. For example, when water boils, it changes its state from a liquid to a gas, but the gas remains composed of water molecules, so this a physical change. When sugar dissolves in water, the sugar molecules are separated from each other, but the molecules of sugar and water remain intact.

    In contrast, changes that alter the composition of matter are called chemical changes. During a chemical change, atoms rearrange, transforming the original substances into different substances. For example, the rusting of iron, the combustion of natural gas to form carbon dioxide and water, and the denaturing of proteins when an egg is cooked are examples of chemical changes.

18. In chemical and physical changes, matter often exchanges energy with its surroundings. In these exchanges, the total energy is always conserved; energy is neither created nor destroyed. Systems with high potential energy tend to change in the direction of lower potential energy, releasing energy into the surroundings.

19. Chemical energy is a potential energy. It is the energy that is contained in the bonds that hold the molecules together. This energy arises primarily from electrostatic forces between the electrically charged particles (protons and electrons) that compose atoms and molecules. Some of these arrangements—such as the one within the molecules that compose gasoline—have a much higher potential energy than others. When gasoline undergoes combustion the arrangement of these particles changes, creating molecules with much lower potential energy and transferring a great deal of energy (mostly in the form of heat) to the surroundings. A raised weight has a certain amount of potential energy (dependent on the height the weight is raised) that can be converted to kinetic energy when the weight is released.

20. The SI base units include the meter (m) for length, the kilogram (kg) for mass, the second (s) for time, and the Kelvin (K) for temperature.

21. The three different temperature scales are Kelvin (K), Celsius (°C), and Fahrenheit (°F). The size of the degree is the same in the Kelvin and the Celsius scales, and they are 1.8 times larger than the degree size for the Fahrenheit scale.

22. Prefix multipliers are used with the standard units of measurement to change the value of the unit by powers of 10.
    For example, the kilometer has the prefix "kilo," meaning 1000 or 10^3. Therefore:
    1 kilometer = 1000 meters = 10^3 meter

Similarly, the millimeter has the prefix "milli," meaning 0.001 or 10^{-3}.

1 millimeter = 0.001 meters = 10^{-3} meters

23. A derived unit is a combination of other units. Examples of derived units are: speed in meters per second (m/s); volume in meters cubed (m^3), and density in grams per cubic centimeter (g/cm^3).

24. The density (d) of a substance is the ratio of its mass (m) to its volume (V):

$$\text{Density} = \frac{\text{mass}}{\text{Volume}} \quad \text{or} \quad d = \frac{m}{V}$$

The density of a substance is an example of an intensive property, one that is independent of the amount of the substance. Mass is one of the properties used to calculate the density of a substance. Mass, in contrast, is an extensive property, one that depends on the amount of the substance.

25. An intensive property is a property that is independent of the amount of the substance. An extensive property is a property that depends on the amount of the substance.

26. Measured quantities are reported so that the number of digits reflects the uncertainty in the measurement. The non-place-holding digits in a reported number are called significant figures.

27. In multiplication or division, the result carries the same number of significant figures as the factor with the fewest significant figures.

28. In addition or subtraction, the result carries the same number of decimal places as the quantity with the fewest decimal places.

29. When rounding to the correct number of significant figures, round down if the last (or left-most) digit dropped is four or less; and round up if the last (or left-most) digit dropped is five or more.

30. Accuracy refers to how close the measured value is to the actual value. Precision refers to how close a series of measurements are to one another or how reproducible they are. A series of measurements can be precise (close to one another in value and reproducible) but not accurate (not close to the true value).

31. Random error is error that has equal probability of being too high or too low. Almost all measurements have some degree of random error. Random error can, with enough trials, average itself out. Systematic error is error that tends towards being either too high or too low. Systematic error does not average out with repeated trials.

32. Using units as a guide to solving problems is often called dimensional analysis. Units should always be included in calculations; they are multiplied, divided, and canceled like any other algebraic quantity.

33. a) This statement is a theory because it attempts to explain why. It is not possible to observe individual atoms.

    b) This statement is an observation.

    c) This statement is a law, because it summarizes many observations and can explain future behavior.

    d) This statement is an observation.

34. a) This statement is a law, because it summarizes many observations and can explain future behavior.

    b) This statement is a law, because it summarizes many observations and can explain future behavior.

    c) This statement is a law, because it summarizes many observations and can explain future behavior.

    d) This statement is a theory because it attempts to explain why.

35. a) If we divide the mass of the oxygen by the mass of the carbon the result is always 4/3.

    b) If we divide the mass of the oxygen by the mass of the hydrogen the result is always 16.

c) These observations suggest that the masses of elements in molecules are ratios of whole numbers (4 and 3; and 16 and 1, respectively).

d) Atoms combine in small whole number ratios and not as random weight ratios.

36. There are many hypotheses that may be developed. One hypothesis is that a large explosion generated galaxies with fragments that are still moving away from each other.

37. a) Sweat is a homogeneous mixture of water, sodium chloride, and other components.

b) Carbon dioxide is a pure substance that is a compound (two or more elements bonded together).

c) Aluminum is a pure substance that is an element (element #13 in the periodic table).

d) Vegetable soup is a heterogeneous mixture of broth, chunks of vegetables, and extracts from the vegetables.

38. a) Wine is a generally homogeneous mixture of water, ethyl alcohol, and other components from the grapes. In some cases, there may be sediment present and so it would be a heterogeneous mixture.

b) Beef stew is a heterogeneous mixture of thick broth, and chunks of vegetables.

c) Iron is a pure substance that is an element (element #26 in the periodic table).

d) Carbon monoxide is a pure substance that is a compound (two or more elements bonded together).

39.

substance	pure or mixture	Type
aluminum	pure	element
apple juice	mixture	homogeneous
hydrogen peroxide	pure	compound
chicken soup	mixture	heterogeneous

40.

substance	pure or mixture	Type (element or compound)
water	pure	compound
coffee	mixture	neither
ice	pure	compound
carbon	pure	element

41. a) pure substance that is a compound (one type of molecule that contains two different elements)

b) heterogeneous mixture (two different molecules that are segregated into regions)

c) homogeneous mixture (two different molecules that are randomly mixed)

d) pure substance is an element (individual atoms of one type)

42. a) pure substance that is an element (individual atoms of one type)

b) homogeneous mixture (two different molecules that are randomly mixed)

c) pure substance is a compound (one type of molecule that contains two different elements)

d) pure substance is a compound (one type of molecule that contains two different elements)

43. a) physical property (color can be observed without making or breaking chemical bonds)

b) chemical property (must observe by making or breaking chemical bonds)

c) physical property (the phase can be observed without making or breaking chemical bonds)

d) physical property (density can be observed without making or breaking chemical bonds)

e) physical property (mixing does not involve making or breaking chemical bonds, so this can be observed without making or breaking chemical bonds)

44. a) physical property (color can be observed without making or breaking chemical bonds)

b) physical property (odor can be observed without making or breaking chemical bonds)

c) chemical property (must observe by making or breaking chemical bonds)

d) chemical property (decomposition involves breaking bonds, so bonds must be broken to observe this property)

e) physical property (the phase of a substance can be observed without making or breaking chemical bonds)

45. a) chemical property (burning involves breaking and making bonds, so bonds must be broken and made to observe this property)

b) physical property (sublimation is a phase change and so can be observed without making or breaking chemical bonds)

c) physical property (odor can be observed without making or breaking chemical bonds)

d) chemical property (burning involves breaking and making bonds, so bonds must be broken and made to observe this property)

46. a) physical property (vaporization is a phase change and so can be observed without making or breaking chemical bonds)

b) physical property (sublimation is a phase change and so can be observed without making or breaking chemical bonds)

c) chemical property (rusting involves the reaction of iron with oxygen to form iron oxide; observing this process involves making and breaking chemical bonds)

d) physical property (color can be observed without making or breaking chemical bonds)

47. a) chemical change (new compounds are formed as methane and oxygen react to form carbon dioxide and water)

b) physical change (vaporization is a phase change and does not involve the making or breaking of chemical bonds)

c) chemical change (new compounds are formed as propane and oxygen react to form carbon dioxide and water)

d) chemical change (new compounds are formed as the metal in the frame is converted to oxides)

48. a) chemical change (new compounds are formed as the sugar burns)

b) physical change (dissolution is a phase change and does not involve the making or breaking of chemical bonds)

c) physical change (this is simply the rearrangement of the atoms)

d) chemical change (new compounds are formed as the silver converts to an oxide)

49. a) physical change (vaporization is a phase change and does not involve the making or breaking of chemical bonds)

   b) chemical change (new compounds are formed)

   c) physical change (vaporization is a phase change and does not involve the making or breaking of chemical bonds)

50. a) physical change (vaporization of butane is a phase change and does not involve the making or breaking of chemical bonds)

   b) chemical change (new compounds are formed as the butane combusts)

   c) physical change (vaporization of water is a phase change and does not involve the making or breaking of chemical bonds)

51. a) To convert from °F to °C, first find the equation that relates these two quantities. $°C = \dfrac{°F - 32}{1.8}$ Now substitute °F into the equation and compute the answer. Note: The number of digits reported in this answer follow significant figure conventions, covered in section 1.6. $°C = \dfrac{°F - 32}{1.8} = \dfrac{0.}{1.8} = 0. \, °C$

   b) To convert from K to °F, first find the equations that relates these two quantities.
   $K = °C + 273.15$ and $°C = \dfrac{°F - 32}{1.8}$ Since these equations do not directly express K in terms of °F, you must combine the equations and then solve the equation for °F. Substituting for °C:
   $K = \dfrac{°F - 32}{1.8} + 273.15$ rearrange $K - 273.15 = \dfrac{°F - 32}{1.8}$ rearrange $1.8 \, (K - 273.15) = (°F - 32)$
   finally $°F = 1.8 \, (K - 273.15) + 32$ Now substitute K into the equation and compute the answer.
   $°F = 1.8 \, (77 \, K - 273.15) + 32 = 1.8 \, (-196 \, K) + 32 = -353 + 32 = -321 \, °F$

   c) To convert from °F to °C, first find the equation that relates these two quantities. $°C = \dfrac{°F - 32}{1.8}$ Now substitute °F into the equation and compute the answer. $°C = \dfrac{-109°F - 32°F}{1.8} = \dfrac{-141}{1.8} = -78.3 \, °C$

   d) To convert from °F to K, first find the equations that relates these two quantities.
   $K = °C + 273.15$ and $°C = \dfrac{°F - 32}{1.8}$ Since these equations do not directly express K in terms of °F, you must combine the equations and then solve the equation for K. Substituting for °C
   $K = \dfrac{°F - 32}{1.8} + 273.15$
   Now substitute °F into the equation and compute the answer.
   $K = \dfrac{(98.6 - 32)}{1.8} + 273.15 = \dfrac{66.6}{1.8} + 273.15 = 37.0 + 273.15 = 310.2 \, K$

52. a) To convert from °F to °C, first find the equation that relates these two quantities. $°C = \dfrac{°F - 32}{1.8}$
   Now substitute °F into the equation and compute the answer. Note: The number of digits reported in this answer follow significant figure conventions, covered in section 1.6.
   $°C = \dfrac{212°F - 32°F}{1.8} = \dfrac{180.}{1.8} = 100. \, °C$

   b) Begin by finding the equation that relates the quantity that is given (°C) and the quantity you are trying to find (K). $K = °C + 273.15$ Since this equation gives the temperature in K directly, simply substitute in the correct value for the temperature in °C and compute the answer.
   $K = 22 \, °C + 273.15 = 295 \, K$

c) To convert from K to °F, first find the equations that relates these two quantities. $K = °C + 273.15$ and $°C = \dfrac{°F - 32}{1.8}$ Since these equations do not directly express K in terms of °F, you must combine the equations and then solve the equation for °F. Substituting for °C: $K = \dfrac{°F - 32}{1.8} + 273.15$, rearrange $K - 273.15 = \dfrac{°F - 32}{1.8}$, rearrange $1.8(K - 273.15) = (°F - 32)$, rearrange $°F = 1.8(K - 273.15) + 32$. Now substitute K into the equation and compute the answer. $°F = 1.8(0.00\ K - 273.15) + 32 = 1.8(-273.15\ K) + 32 = -491.67 + 32 = -459.67\ °F$

d) Begin by finding the equation that relates the quantity that is given (°C) and the quantity you are trying to find (K). $K = °C + 273.15$ Since this equation does not directly express °C in terms of K, you must solve the equation for °C. $°C = K - 273.15$ Now substitute K into the equation and compute the answer. $°C = 2.735 - 273.15 = -270.42\ °C$

53. To convert from °F to °C, first find the equation that relates these two quantities. $°C = \dfrac{°F - 32}{1.8}$ Now substitute °F into the equation and compute the answer. Note: The number of digits reported in this answer follow significant figure conventions, covered in section 1.6. $°C = \dfrac{-80.°F - 32°F}{1.8} = \dfrac{-112}{1.8} = -62.2\ °C$

Begin by finding the equation that relates the quantity that is given (°C) and the quantity you are trying to find (K). $K = °C + 273.15$ Since this equation gives the temperature in K directly, simply substitute in the correct value for the temperature in °C and compute the answer. $K = -62.2\ °C + 273.15 = 210.9\ K$.

54. To convert from °F to °C, first find the equation that relates these two quantities. $°C = \dfrac{°F - 32}{1.8}$ Now substitute °F into the equation and compute the answer. Note: The number of digits reported in this answer follow significant figure conventions, covered in section 1.6. $°C = \dfrac{134°F - 32°F}{1.8} = \dfrac{102}{1.8} = 56.6\ °C$

Begin by finding the equation that relates the quantity that is given (°C) and the quantity you are trying to find (K). $K = °C + 273.15$ Since this equation gives the temperature in K directly, simply substitute in the correct value for the temperature in °C and compute the answer. $K = 56.6\ °C + 273.15 = 329.8\ K$

55. Use Table 1.2 to determine the appropriate prefix multiplier and substitute the meaning into the expressions.
a) 10^{-9} implies "nano" so $1.2 \times 10^{-9}\ m = 1.2$ nanometers $= 1.2$ nm

b) 10^{-15} implies "femto" so $22 \times 10^{-15}\ s = 22$ femtoseconds $= 22$ fs

c) 10^{9} implies "giga" so $1.5 \times 10^{9}\ g = 1.5$ gigagrams $= 1.5$ Gg

d) 10^{6} implies "mega" so $3.5 \times 10^{6}\ L = 3.5$ megaliters $= 3.5$ ML

56. Use Table 1.2 to determine the appropriate prefix multiplier and substitute the meaning into the expressions.
a) 10^{-9} implies "nano" so 4.5 ns $= 4.5$ nanoseconds $= 4.5 \times 10^{-9}\ s$

b) 10^{-15} implies "femto" so 18 fs $= 18$ femtoseconds $= 18 \times 10^{-15}\ s = 1.8 \times 10^{-14}\ s$
Remember that in scientific notation the first number should be smaller than 10.

c) 10^{-12} implies "pico" so 128 pm $= 128 \times 10^{-12}\ m = 1.28 \times 10^{-10}\ m$
Remember that in scientific notation the first number should be smaller than 10.

d) 10^{-6} implies "micro" so $35\ \mu m = 35$ micrograms $= 35 \times 10^{-6}\ g = 3.5 \times 10^{-5}\ m$
Remember that in scientific notation the first number should be smaller than 10.

57. b) **Given:** 515 km   **Find:** dm
Conceptual plan: km → m → dm

$$\dfrac{1000\ m}{1 km} \qquad \dfrac{10\ dm}{1 m}$$

7

Solution: $515 \ \cancel{km} \times \dfrac{1000 \ \cancel{m}}{1 \ \cancel{km}} \times \dfrac{10 \ dm}{1 \ \cancel{m}} = 5.15 \times 10^6 \ dm$

Check: The units (dm) are correct. The magnitude of the answer (10^6) makes physical sense because a decimeter is a much smaller unit than a kilometer.

Given: 515 km   **Find:** cm

Conceptual plan: km $\rightarrow$ m $\rightarrow$ cm

$$\dfrac{1000 \ m}{1 km} \qquad \dfrac{100 \ cm}{1 m}$$

Solution: $515 \ \cancel{km} \times \dfrac{1000 \ \cancel{m}}{1 \ \cancel{km}} \times \dfrac{100 \ cm}{1 \ \cancel{m}} = 5.15 \times 10^7 \ cm$

Check: The units (cm) are correct. The magnitude of the answer (10^7) makes physical sense because a centimeter is a much smaller unit than a kilometer and a decimeter.

c) **Given:** 122.355 s   **Find:** ms

Conceptual plan: s $\rightarrow$ ms

$$\dfrac{1000 \ ms}{1s}$$

Solution: $122.355 \ \cancel{s} \times \dfrac{1000 \ ms}{1 \ \cancel{s}} = 1.22355 \times 10^5 \ ms$

Check: The units (ms) are correct. The magnitude of the answer (10^5) makes physical sense because a millisecond is a much smaller unit than a second.

Given: 122.355 s   **Find:** ks

Conceptual plan: s $\rightarrow$ ks

$$\dfrac{1 \ ks}{1000 \ s}$$

Solution: $122.355 \ \cancel{s} \times \dfrac{1 \ ks}{1000 \ \cancel{s}} = 1.22355 \times 10^{-1} \ ks = 0.122355 \ ks$

Check: The units (ks) are correct. The magnitude of the answer (10^{-1}) makes physical sense because a kilosecond is a much larger unit than a second.

d) **Given:** 3.345 kJ   **Find:** J

Conceptual plan: kJ $\rightarrow$ J

$$\dfrac{1000 \ J}{1kJ}$$

Solution: $3.345 \ \cancel{kJ} \times \dfrac{1000 \ J}{1 \ \cancel{kJ}} = 3.345 \times 10^3 \ J$

Check: The units (J) are correct. The magnitude of the answer (10^3) makes physical sense because a joule is a much smaller unit than a kilojoule.

Given: 3.345×10^3 J (from above)   **Find:** mJ

Conceptual plan: J $\rightarrow$ mJ

$$\dfrac{1000 \ mJ}{1 \ J}$$

Solution: $3.345 \times 10^3 \ \cancel{J} \times \dfrac{1000 \ mJ}{1 \ \cancel{J}} = 3.345 \times 10^6 \ mJ$

Check: The units (mJ) are correct. The magnitude of the answer (10^6) makes physical sense because a millijoule is a much smaller unit than a joule.

58. a) **Given:** 254,998 m   **Find:** km

Conceptual plan: m $\rightarrow$ km

$$\dfrac{1 \ km}{1000 \ m}$$

Solution: $254,998 \ \cancel{m} \times \dfrac{1 \ km}{1000 \ \cancel{m}} = 2.54998 \times 10^2 \ km = 254.998 \ km$

Check: The units (km) are correct. The magnitude of the answer (10^2) makes physical sense because a kilometer is a much larger unit than a meter.

b) **Given**: 254,998 m   **Find**: Mm
   Conceptual plan: m → Mm

$$\frac{1 \text{ Mm}}{10^6 \text{ m}}$$

Solution: 254,998 m x $\dfrac{1 \text{ Mm}}{10^6 \text{ m}}$ = = 2.54998 x 10^{-1} Mm = 0. 254998 Mm

Check: The units (Mm) are correct. The magnitude of the answer (10^{-1}) makes physical sense because a megameter is a much larger unit than a meter or kilometer.

c) **Given**: 254,998 m   **Find**: mm
   Conceptual plan: m → mm

$$\frac{1000 \text{ mm}}{1 \text{ m}}$$

Solution: 254,998 m x $\dfrac{1000 \text{ mm}}{1 \text{ m}}$ = = 2.54998 x 10^8 mm

Check: The units (mm) are correct. The magnitude of the answer (10^8) makes physical sense because a millimeter is a much smaller unit than a meter.

d) **Given**: 254,998 m   **Find**: cm
   Conceptual plan: m → cm

$$\frac{100 \text{ cm}}{1 \text{ m}}$$

Solution: 254,998 m x $\dfrac{100 \text{ cm}}{1 \text{ m}}$ = = 2.54998 x 10^7 cm

Check: The units (cm) are correct. The magnitude of the answer (10^7) makes physical sense because a centimeter is a much smaller unit than a meter, but larger than a millimeter.

59. **Given**: 1 m square 1 m^2 **Find**: cm^2
    Conceptual plan: 1 m^2 → cm^2

$$\frac{100 \text{ cm}}{1 \text{ m}}$$

Notice that for squared units, the conversion factors must be squared.

Solution: 1 m^2 x $\dfrac{(100 \text{ cm})^2}{(1 \text{ m})^2}$ = 1 x 10^4 cm^2

Check: The units of the answer are correct and the magnitude makes sense. The unit centimeter is smaller than a meter, so the value in square centimeters should be larger than in square meters.

60. **Given**: 4 cm on each edge cube   **Find**: cm^3
    Conceptual plan: Read the information given carefully. The cube is 4 cm on each side.

$$l, w, h → V$$
$$V = l \times w \times h$$
$$in\ a\ cube\ l = w = h$$

Solution: 4 cm x 4 cm x 4 cm = $(4 \text{ cm})^3$ = 64 cm^3 = 60 cm^3

Check: The units of the answer are correct and the magnitude makes sense. The unit 4 centimeter is larger than 1 centimeter, so the value in cubic centimeters should be larger.

61. **Given**: $m = 2.49$ g, $V = 0.349$ cm^3 **Find**: d in g/cm^3 and compare to pure copper.
    Conceptual plan: m, V → d

$$d = m/V$$

Compare to the published value. d (pure copper) = 8.96 g/cm^3 (This value is in Table 1.4.)

Solution: d = $\dfrac{2.49 \text{ g}}{0.349 \text{ cm}^3}$ = 7.13 $\dfrac{\text{g}}{\text{cm}^3}$

The density of the penny is much smaller than the density of pure copper (= 7.13 g/cm^3 < 8.96 g/cm^3) so the penny is not pure copper.

Check: The units (g/cm^3) are correct. The magnitude of the answer seems correct. Many coins are layers of metals, so it is not surprising that the penny is not pure copper.

62. **Given:** $m = 1.41$ kg, $V = 0.314$ L   **Find:** d in g/cm^3 and compare to pure titanium.
    Conceptual plan: m, V → d   then   kg → g   then   L → cm^3

$$d = m/V \qquad \frac{1000\ g}{1\ kg} \qquad \frac{1000\ cm^3}{1\ L}$$

Compared to the published value. d (pure titanium) = 4.51 g/cm^3 (This value is in Table 1.4.)

Solution: $d = \dfrac{1.41\ kg}{0.314\ L} \times \dfrac{1000\ g}{1\ kg} \times \dfrac{1\ L}{1000\ cm^3} = 4.49\ \dfrac{g}{cm^3}$

Check: The units (g/cm^3) are correct. The magnitude of the answer seems correct. The density of the frame is almost exactly the density of pure titanium (4.49 g/cm^3 versus 4.51 g/cm^3) so the frame could be titanium.

63. **Given:** $m = 4.10$ x 10^3 g, $V = 3.25$ L   **Find:** d in g/cm^3
    Conceptual plan: m, V → d   then   L → cm^3

$$d = m/V \qquad \frac{1000\ cm^3}{1\ L}$$

Solution: $d = \dfrac{4.10 \times 10^3\ g}{3.25\ L} \times \dfrac{1\ L}{1000\ cm^3} = 1.26\ \dfrac{g}{cm^3}$

Check: The units (g/cm^3) are correct. The magnitude of the answer seems correct.

64. **Given:** $m = 371$ grams, $V = 19.3$ mL   **Find:** d in g/cm^3 and compare to pure gold.
    Conceptual plan: m, V → d

$$d = m/V$$

Compared to the published value. d (pure gold) = 19.3 g/mL (This value is in Table 1.4.)

Solution: $d = \dfrac{371\ g}{19.3\ mL} = 19.2\ \dfrac{g}{mL}$

The density of the nugget is essentially the same as the density of pure gold (= 19.2 g/mL versus 19.3 g/mL) so the nugget could be gold.

Check: The units (g/cm^3) are correct. The magnitude of the answer seems correct and is essentially the same as the density of pure gold.

65. a) **Given:** d = 1.11 g/cm^3, V = 417 mL   **Find:** m
    Conceptual plan: d, V → m   then   cm^3 → mL

$$d = m/V \qquad \frac{1\ mL}{1\ cm^3}$$

Solution: $d = m/V$ Rearrange by multiplying both sides of equation by V. $m = d \times V$

$m = 1.11\ \dfrac{g}{cm^3} \times \dfrac{1\ cm^3}{1\ mL} \times 417\ mL = 4.63 \times 10^2$ g

Check: The units (g) are correct. The magnitude of the answer seems correct considering the value of the density is about 1 g/cm^3.

b) **Given:** d = 1.11 g/cm^3, m = 4.1 kg   **Find:** V in L
   Conceptual plan: d, V → m   then   kg → g   and   cm^3 → L

$$d = m/V \qquad \frac{1000\ g}{1\ kg} \qquad \frac{1\ L}{1000\ cm^3}$$

Solution: $d = m/V$ Rearrange by multiplying both sides of equation by V and dividing both sides of the equation by d.

$$V = \frac{m}{d} = \frac{4.1 \text{ kg}}{1.11 \frac{\text{g}}{\text{cm}^3}} \text{ x } \frac{1000 \text{ g}}{1 \text{ kg}} = 3.7 \text{ x } 10^3 \text{ cm}^3 \text{ x } \frac{1 \text{ L}}{1000 \text{ cm}^3} = 3.7 \text{ L}$$

Check: The units (L) are correct. The magnitude of the answer seems correct considering the value of the density is about 1 g/cm^3.

66. a) **Given:** $d = 0.7857$ g/cm^3, $V = 28.56$ mL   **Find:** m
       Conceptual plan: d, V   →   m
                               $d = m/V$

       Solution: $d = m/V$ Rearrange by multiplying both sides of equation by V. $m = d \text{ x } V$

$$m = \left(0.7857 \frac{\text{g}}{\text{cm}^3} \right) \text{ x } \frac{1 \text{ cm}^3}{1 \text{ mL}} \text{ x } (28.56 \text{ mL}) = 22.44 \text{ g}$$

       Check: The units (g) are correct. The magnitude of the answer seems correct considering the value of the density is less than 1 g/cm^3.

    b) **Given:** d = 0.7857 g/cm^3, m = 6.54 g   **Find:** V
       Conceptual plan: d, m   →   V then   cm^3 → mL

$$d = m/V \qquad\qquad\qquad \frac{1 \text{ mL}}{1 \text{ cm}^3}$$

       Solution: $d = m/V$ Rearrange by multiplying both sides of equation by V and dividing both sides of the equation by d.

$$V = \frac{m}{d} = \frac{6.54 \text{ g}}{0.7857 \frac{\text{g}}{\text{cm}^3}} = 8.32 \text{ cm}^3 \text{ x } \frac{1 \text{ mL}}{1 \text{ cm}^3} = 8.32 \text{ mL}$$

       Check: The units (mL) are correct. The magnitude of the answer seems correct considering the value of the density is less than 1 g/cm^3.

67. In order to obtain the readings look to see where the bottom of the meniscus lies. Estimate the distance between two markings on the device.
    a)   73.5 mL – the meniscus appears to be about half way between the 73 mL and the 74 mL marks.

    b)   88.2 °C – the mercury is between the 84 °C mark and the 85 °C mark, but it is closer to the lower number.

    c)   645 mL - the meniscus appears to be just above the 640m mL mark.

68. In order to obtain the readings look to see where the bottom of the meniscus lies. Estimate the distance between two markings on the device. Use all digits on a digital device.
    a)   4.50 mL – the meniscus appears to be on the 4.5 mL mark.

    b)   27.43 °C – the mercury is just above the 27.4 °C mark. Note that the 10's digit is only labeled every 10 °C.

    c)   0.873 g – read all the places on the digital display.

69.   Remember that
   1.   Interior zeroes (zeroes between two numbers) are significant.
   2.   Leading zeroes (zeroes to the left of the of the first non-zero number) are not significant. They only serve to locate the decimal point.
   3.   Trailing zeroes (zeroes at the end of a number) are categorized as follows:
        o   trailing zeroes after a decimal point are always significant.
        o   trailing zeroes before an implied decimal point are ambiguous and should be avoided by using scientific notation or by inserting a decimal point at the end of the number.
    a)   1,050,501 km
    b)   0.00020 m

c) 0.0000000000000002 s

d) 0.001090 cm

70. Remember that
    1. Interior zeroes (zeroes between two numbers) are significant.
    2. Leading zeroes (zeroes to the left of the of the first non-zero number) are not significant. They only serve to locate the decimal point.
    3. Trailing zeroes (zeroes at the end of a number) are categorized as follows:
        o trailing zeroes after a decimal point are always significant.
        o trailing zeroes before an implied decimal point are ambiguous and should be avoided by using scientific notation or by inserting a decimal point at the end of the number.
    a) 180,701 mi
    b) 0.001040 m
    c) 0.005710 km
    d) 90,201 m

71. Remember all of the rules from section 1.7
    a) Three significant figures. The 3, 1, and the 2 are significant (rule 1). The leading zeroes only mark the decimal place and are therefore not significant (rule 3).

    b) Ambiguous. The 3, 1 and the 2 are significant (rule 1). The trailing zeroes occur before an implied decimal point and are therefore ambiguous (rule 4). Without more information, we would assume 3 significant figures. It is better to write this as 3.12×10^5 to indicate three significant figures or as 3.12000×10^5 to indicate six (rule 4).

    c) Three significant figures. The 3, 1, and the 2 are significant (rule 1).

    d) Five significant figures. The 1's, 3, 2, and 7 are significant (rule 1).

    e) One significant figure. The 2 is significant (rule 1). The 0's are not significant because of there is no decimal point (rule 4).

72. Remember all of the rules from section 1.7
    a) Four significant figures. The 1's are significant (rule 1). The leading zeroes only mark the decimal place and are therefore not significant (rule 3).

    b) One significant figure. The 7 is significant (rule 1). The leading zeroes only mark the decimal place and are therefore not significant (rule 3).

    c) Ambiguous. The 1, 8, and the 7 are significant (rule 1). The first 0 is significant, since it is an interior 0 (rule 2). The trailing zeroes occur before an implied decimal point and are therefore ambiguous (rule 4). Without more information, we would assume 4 significant figures. It is better to write this as 1.087×10^5 to indicate 4 significant figures or as 1.08700×10^5 to indicate six (rule 4).

    d) Seven significant figures. The 1, 5, 6, and 3's are significant (rule 1). The trailing zero's are significant because they are to the right of the decimal point and non-zero numbers (rule 4)

    e) Three significant figures. The 3 and 8 are significant (rule 1). The first 0 is significant because the first one is an interior zero and the last two are not significant because there is no decimal point (rule 4).

73. a) This is not exact because π is an irrational number. 3.14 only shows three of the infinite number of significant figures that π has.

    b) This is an exact conversion, because it comes from a definition of the units, and so has an unlimited number of significant figures.

    c) This is a measured number and so it is not an exact number. There are 2 significant figures.

d)   This is an exact conversion, because it comes from a definition of the units, and so has an unlimited number of significant figures.

74. a)   This is a measured number and so it is not an exact number. There are 9 significant figures.

    b)   This is a an exact conversion, so has an unlimited number of significant figures

    c)   This is a measured number and so it is not an exact number. There are 3 significant figures.

    d)   This is an exact conversion, because it comes from a definition of the units and so has an unlimited number of significant figures.

75. a)   156.9 – the 8 is rounded up since the next digit is a 5.

    b)   156.8 – the last two digits are dropped since 4 is less than 5.

    c)   156.8 – the last two digits are dropped since 4 is less than 5.

    d)   156.9 – the 8 is rounded up since the next digit is a 9 which is greater than 5.

76. a) 7.98×10^4 – the last digits are dropped since 4 is less than 5.

    b) 1.55×10^7 – the 8 is rounded up since the next digit is a 9 which is greater than 5.

    c)   2.35 – the 4 is rounded up since the next digit is a 9 which is greater than 5.

    d)   0.0000454 – the 3 is rounded up since the next digit is a 8 which is greater than 5.

77. a) $9.15 \div 4.970 = 1.84$ – Three significant figures are allowed to reflect the three significant figures in the least precisely known quantity (9.15).

    b) $1.54 \times 0.03060 \times 0.69 = 0.033$ – Two significant figures are allowed to reflect the two significant figures in the least precisely known quantity (0.69). The intermediate answer (0.03251556) is rounded up since the first non-significant digit is a 5.

    c) $27.5 \times 1.82 \div 100.04 = 0.500$ – Three significant figures are allowed to reflect the three significant figures in the least precisely known quantity (27.5 and 1.82). The intermediate answer (0.50029988) is truncated since the first non-significant digit is a 2, which is less than 5.

    d) $(2.290 \times 10^6) \div (6.7 \times 10^4) = 34$ – Two significant figures are allowed to reflect the two significant figures in the least precisely known quantity (6.7×10^4). The intermediate answer (34.17910448) is truncated since the first non-significant digit is a 1, which is less than 5.

78. a) $89.3 \times 77.0 \times 0.08 = 6 \times 10^2$ – One significant figure is allowed to reflect the one significant figure in the least precisely known quantity (0.08). The intermediate answer (5.50088×10^2) is rounded up since the first non-significant digit is a 5.

    b) $(5.01 \times 10^5) \div (7.8 \times 10^2) = 6.4 \times 10^2$ – Two significant figures are allowed to reflect the two significant figures in the least precisely known quantity (7.8×10^2). The intermediate answer (6.423076923×10^2) is truncated since the first non-significant digit is a 2, which is less than 5.

    c) $4.005 \times 74 \times 0.007 = 2$ – One significant figure is allowed to reflect the one significant figure in the least precisely known quantity (0.007). The intermediate answer (2.07459) is truncated since the first non-significant digit is a 0, which is less than 5.

    d) $453 \div 2.031 = 223$ – Three significant figures are allowed to reflect the three significant figures in the least precisely known quantity (453). The intermediate answer (223.042836) is truncated since the first non-significant digit is a 0, which is less than 5.

79. a)
$$
\begin{array}{r}
43.7 \\
- \quad 2.341 \\
\hline
41.359 = \quad 41.4
\end{array}
$$
Round the intermediate answer to one decimal place to reflect the quantity with the fewest decimal places (43.7). Round the last digit up since the first non-significant digit is 5.

   b)
$$
\begin{array}{r}
17.6 \\
+ \quad 2.838 \\
+ \quad 2.3 \\
+ \quad 110.77 \\
\hline
133.508 = \quad 133.5
\end{array}
$$
Round the intermediate answer to one decimal place to reflect the quantity with the fewest decimal places (2.3). Truncate non-significant digits since the first non-significant digit is 0.

   c)
$$
\begin{array}{r}
19.6 \\
+ \quad 58.33 \\
- \quad 4.974 \\
\hline
72.956 = \quad 73.0
\end{array}
$$
Round the intermediate answer to one decimal place to reflect the quantity with the fewest decimal places (19.6). Round the last digit up since the first non-significant digit is 5.

   d)
$$
\begin{array}{r}
5.99 \\
- \quad 5.572 \\
\hline
0.418 = \quad 0.42
\end{array}
$$
Round the intermediate answer to two decimal places to reflect the quantity with the fewest decimal places (5.99). Round the last digit up since the first non-significant digit is 8.

80. a)
$$
\begin{array}{r}
0.004 \\
+ \quad 0.09879 \\
\hline
0.10279 = \quad 0.103
\end{array}
$$
Round the intermediate answer to three decimal places to reflect the quantity with the fewest decimal places (0.004). Round the last digit up since the first non-significant digit is 9.

   b)
$$
\begin{array}{r}
1239.3 \\
+ \quad 9.73 \\
+ \quad 3.42 \\
\hline
1252.45 = \quad 1252.5
\end{array}
$$
Round the intermediate answer to one decimal place to reflect the quantity with the fewest decimal places (1239.3). Round the last digit up since the first non-significant digit is 5.

   c)
$$
\begin{array}{r}
2.4 \\
- \quad 1.777 \\
\hline
0.623 = \quad 0.6
\end{array}
$$
Round the intermediate answer to one decimal place to reflect the quantity with the fewest decimal places (2.4). Truncate non-significant digits since the first non-significant digit is 2.

   d)
$$
\begin{array}{r}
532 \\
+ \quad 7.3 \\
- \quad 48.523 \\
\hline
490.777 = \quad 491
\end{array}
$$
Round the intermediate answer to zero decimal places to reflect the quantity with the fewest decimal places (532). Round the last digit up since the first non-significant digit is 7.

81. Perform operations in parentheses first. Keep track of significant figures in each step, by noting which is the last significant digit in an intermediate result.

   a) $(24.6681 \times 2.38) + 332.58 =$
$$
\begin{array}{r}
58.\underline{7}10078 \\
+ \quad 332.58 \\
\hline
391.290078 = \quad 391.3
\end{array}
$$

14

The first intermediate answer has one significant digit to the right of the decimal, because it is allowed three significant figures (reflecting the quantity with the fewest significant figures (2.38).) Underline the most significant digit in this answer. Round the next intermediate answer to one decimal place to reflect the quantity with the fewest decimal places (58.7). Round the last digit up since the first non-significant digit is 9.

b) $\dfrac{(85.3 - 21.489)}{0.0059} = \dfrac{63.\underline{8}11}{0.0059} = 1.\underline{0}81542 \times 10^4 = 1.1 \times 10^4$

The first intermediate answer has one significant digit to the right of the decimal, to reflect the quantity with the fewest decimal places (85.3). Underline the most significant digit in this answer. Round the next intermediate answer to two significant figures to reflect the quantity with the fewest significant figures (0.0059). Round the last digit up since the first non-significant digit is 8.

c) $(512 \div 986.7) + 5.44 = $
$$\begin{array}{r} 0.5\underline{1}89014 \\ +\quad 5.44 \\ \hline 5.9589014 = \quad 5.96 \end{array}$$

The first intermediate answer has three significant figures and three significant digits to the right of the decimal, reflecting the quantity with the fewest significant figures (512). Underline the most significant digit in this answer. Round the next intermediate answer to two decimal places to reflect the quantity with the fewest decimal places (5.44). Round the last digit up since the first non-significant digit is 8.

d) $[(28.7 \times 10^5) \div 48.533] + 144.99 = $
$$\begin{array}{r} 59\underline{1}35.01 \\ +\quad 144.99 \\ \hline 59280.01 = 59300 = 5.93 \times 10^4 \end{array}$$

The first intermediate answer has three significant figures, reflecting the quantity with the fewest significant figures (28.7×10^5). Underline the most significant digit in this answer. Since the number is so large this means that when the addition is performed, the most significant digit is the 100's place. Round the next intermediate answer to the 100's places and put in scientific notation to remove any ambiguity. Note that the last digit is rounded up since the first non-significant digit is 8.

82. Perform operations in parentheses first. Keep track of significant figures in each step, by noting which is the last significant digit in an intermediate result.

a) $[(1.7 \times 10^6) \div [(2.63 \times 10^5)] + 7.33 = $
$$\begin{array}{r} 6.\underline{4}63878 \\ +\quad 7.33 \\ \hline 13.793878 = 13.8 \end{array}$$

The first intermediate answer has one significant digit to the right of the decimal, because it is allowed two significant figures (reflecting the quantity with the fewest significant figures (1.7×10^6).) Underline the most significant digit in this answer. Round the next intermediate answer to one decimal place to reflect the quantity with the fewest decimal places (6.5). Round the last digit up since the first non-significant digit is 9.

b) $(568.99 - 232.1) \div 5.3 = 336.\underline{8}9 \div 5.3 = 63.564151 = 64$

The first intermediate answer has one significant digit to the right of the decimal, to reflect the quantity with the fewest decimal places (232.1). Underline the most significant digit in this answer. Round the next intermediate answer to two significant figures to reflect the quantity with the fewest significant figures (5.3). Round the last digit up since the first non-significant digit is 5.

c) $(9443 + 45 - 9.9) \times 8.1 \times 10^6 = = 947\underline{8}.1 \times 8.1 \times 10^6 = 7.67726 \times 10^{10} = 7.7 \times 10^{10}$

The first intermediate answer only has significant digits to the left of the decimal, reflecting the quantity with the fewest significant figures (9443 & 45). Underline the most significant digit in this answer. Round the next intermediate answer to two significant figures to reflect the quantity with the fewest significant figures (8.1×10^6). Round the last digit up since the first non-significant digit is 7.

d) $(3.14 \times 2.4367) - 2.34 = $
$$\begin{array}{r} 7.6\underline{5}1238 \\ -\quad 2.34 \\ \hline 5.311238 = 5.31 \end{array}$$

The first intermediate answer has three significant figures, reflecting the quantity with the fewest significant figures (3.14). Underline the most significant digit in this answer. This number has two significant digits to the right of the decimal point. Round the next intermediate answer to two significant digits to the right of the decimal point, since both numbers have two significant digits to the right of the decimal point. Note that the last digit is truncated since the first non-significant digit is 1.

83. a) **Given:** 154 cm **Find:** in
Conceptual plan: cm → in

$$\frac{1 \text{ in}}{2.54 \text{ cm}}$$

Solution: 154 cm x $\dfrac{1 \text{ in}}{2.54 \text{ cm}}$ = 60.62992 in = 60.6 in

Check: The units (in) are correct. The magnitude of the answer (60.6) makes physical sense because an inch is a larger unit than a cm. Three significant figures are allowed because 154 cm has three significant figures.

b) **Given:** 3.14 kg **Find:** g
Conceptual plan: kg → g

$$\frac{1000 \text{ g}}{1 \text{ kg}}$$

Solution: 3.14 kg x $\dfrac{1000 \text{ g}}{1 \text{ kg}}$ = 3.14 x 10³ g

Check: The units (g) are correct. The magnitude of the answer (10³) makes physical sense because a kg is a much larger unit than a gram. Three significant figures are allowed because 3.14 kg has three significant figures.

c) **Given:** 3.5 L **Find:** qt
Conceptual plan: L → qt

$$\frac{1.057 \text{ qt}}{1 \text{ L}}$$

Solution: 3.5 L x $\dfrac{1.057 \text{ qt}}{1 \text{ L}}$ = 3.6995 qt = 3.7 qt

Check: The units (qt) are correct. The magnitude of the answer (3.7) makes physical sense because a L is a smaller unit than a qt. Two significant figures are allowed because 3.5 L has two significant figures. Round the last digit up because the first non-significant digit is a 9.

d) **Given:** 109 mm **Find:** in
Conceptual plan: mm → m → in

$$\frac{1 \text{ m}}{1000 \text{ mm}} \qquad \frac{39.37 \text{ in}}{1 \text{ m}}$$

Solution: 109 mm x $\dfrac{1 \text{ m}}{1000 \text{ mm}}$ x $\dfrac{39.37 \text{ in}}{1 \text{ m}}$ = 4.29133 in = 4.29 in

Check: The units (in) are correct. The magnitude of the answer (4) makes physical sense because a mm is a much smaller unit than an in. Three significant figures are allowed because 109 mm has three significant figures.

84. a) **Given:** 1.4 in **Find:** mm
Conceptual plan: in → cm → m → mm

$$\frac{2.54 \text{ cm}}{1 \text{ in}} \qquad \frac{1 \text{ m}}{100 \text{ cm}} \qquad \frac{1000 \text{ mm}}{1 \text{ m}}$$

Solution: 1.4 in x $\dfrac{2.54 \text{ cm}}{1 \text{ in}}$ x $\dfrac{1 \text{ m}}{100 \text{ cm}}$ x $\dfrac{1000 \text{ mm}}{1 \text{ m}}$ = 35.56 mm = 36 mm

Check: The units (mm) are correct. The magnitude of the answer (36) makes physical sense because a mm is smaller than an in. Two significant figures are allowed because 1.4 in has two significant figures. Round the last digit up because the first non-significant digit is a 5.

b) **Given:** 116 ft **Find:** cm

16

Conceptual plan: ft → in → cm

$$\frac{12 \text{ in}}{1 \text{ ft}} \qquad \frac{2.54 \text{ cm}}{1 \text{ in}}$$

Solution: $116 \text{ ft} \times \dfrac{12 \text{ in}}{1 \text{ ft}} \times \dfrac{2.54 \text{ cm}}{1 \text{ in}} = 3.5\underline{3}57 \times 10^3 \text{ cm} = 3.54 \times 10^3 \text{ cm}$

Check: The units (cm) are correct. The magnitude of the answer (10^3) makes physical sense because a ft is a much larger unit than a cm. Three significant figures are allowed because 116 ft has three significant figures. Round the last digit up because the first non-significant digit is a 5.

c) **Given:** 1845 kg **Find:** lb
   Conceptual plan: kg → g → lb

$$\frac{1000 \text{ g}}{1 \text{ kg}} \qquad \frac{1 \text{ lb}}{453.6 \text{ g}}$$

Solution: $1845 \text{ kg} \times \dfrac{1000 \text{ g}}{1 \text{ kg}} \times \dfrac{1 \text{ lb}}{453.6 \text{ g}} = 4.06\underline{7}5 \times 10^3 \text{ lb} = 4.068 \times 10^3 \text{ lb}$

Check: The units (lb) are correct. The magnitude of the answer (10^3) makes physical sense because a lb is a smaller unit than a kg. Four significant figures are allowed because 1845 kg and 453.6 g/lb each have four significant figures. Round the last digit up because the first non-significant digit is a 5.

d) **Given:** 815 yd **Find:** km
   Conceptual plan: yd → m → km

$$\frac{1 \text{ m}}{1.094 \text{ yd}} \qquad \frac{1 \text{ km}}{1000 \text{ m}}$$

Solution: $815 \text{ yd} \times \dfrac{1 \text{ m}}{1.094 \text{ yd}} \times \dfrac{1 \text{ km}}{1000 \text{ m}} = 0.74\underline{4}9726 \text{ km} = 0.745 \text{ km}$

Check: The units (km) are correct. The magnitude of the answer (0.7) makes physical sense because a yd is a much smaller unit than an km. Three significant figures are allowed because 815 yd has three significant figures. Round the last digit up because the first non-significant digit is a 9.

85. **Given:** 10.0 km **Find:** minutes **Other:** running pace = 7.5 miles per hour
    Conceptual plan: km → mi → hr → min

$$\frac{0.6214 \text{ mi}}{1 \text{ km}} \qquad \frac{1 \text{ hr}}{7.5 \text{ mi}} \qquad \frac{60 \text{ min}}{1 \text{ hr}}$$

Solution: $10.0 \text{ km} \times \dfrac{0.6214 \text{ mi}}{1 \text{ km}} \times \dfrac{1 \text{ hr}}{7.5 \text{ mi}} \times \dfrac{60 \text{ min}}{1 \text{ hr}} = 49.\underline{7}12 \text{ min} = 50. \text{ min} = 5.0 \times 10^1 \text{ min}$

Check: The units (min) are correct. The magnitude of the answer (50) makes physical sense because she is running almost 7.5 miles (which would take her 60 min = 1 hr). Two significant figures are allowed because of the limitation of 7.5 mi/hr (two significant figures). Round the last digit up because the first non-significant digit is a 7.

86. **Given:** 195 km **Find:** hours **Other:** riding pace = 24 miles per hour
    Conceptual plan: km → mi → hr

$$\frac{0.6214 \text{ mi}}{1 \text{ km}} \qquad \frac{1 \text{ hr}}{24 \text{ mi}}$$

Solution: $195 \text{ km} \times \dfrac{0.6214 \text{ mi}}{1 \text{ km}} \times \dfrac{1 \text{ hr}}{24 \text{ mi}} = 5.0\underline{4}8875 \text{ hr} = 5.0 \text{ hr}$

Check: The units (hr) are correct. The magnitude of the answer (5) makes physical sense because she is riding over 100 miles (which would take her over 4 hr). Two significant figures are allowed because of the limitation of 24 mi/hr (two significant figures). Truncate after the last digit up because the first non-significant digit is a 4.

87. **Given:** 14 km/L **Find:** miles per gallon

Conceptual plan: $\dfrac{\textbf{km}}{\textbf{L}}$ → $\dfrac{\textbf{mi}}{\textbf{L}}$ → $\dfrac{\textbf{mi}}{\textbf{gal}}$

$$\dfrac{0.6214 \text{ mi}}{1 \text{ km}} \qquad \dfrac{3.785 \text{ L}}{1 \text{ gallon}}$$

Solution: $\dfrac{14 \text{ km}}{1 \text{ L}} \times \dfrac{0.6214 \text{ mi}}{1 \text{ km}} \times \dfrac{3.785 \text{ L}}{1 \text{ gallon}} = 32.927986 \dfrac{\text{miles}}{\text{gallon}} = 33 \dfrac{\text{miles}}{\text{gallon}}$

Check: The units (mi/gal) are correct. The magnitude of the answer (33) makes physical sense because the dominating factor is that a L is much smaller than a gallon, so the answer should go up. Two significant figures are allowed because of the limitation of 14 km/L (two significant figures). Round up the last digit up because the first non-significant digit is a 9.

88. **Given:** 5.0 gallons **Find:** cm^3

   Conceptual plan: **gal** → **L** → $\textbf{cm}^3$

$$\dfrac{3.785 \text{ L}}{1 \text{ gallon}} \qquad \dfrac{1000 \text{ cm}^3}{1 \text{ L}}$$

   Solution: $5.0 \text{ gallons} \times \dfrac{3.785 \text{ L}}{1 \text{ gallon}} \times \dfrac{1000 \text{ cm}^3}{1 \text{ L}} = 1.8925 \times 10^4 \text{ cm}^3 = 1.9 \times 10^4 \text{ cm}^3$

   Check: The units (cm^3) are correct. The magnitude of the answer (10^4) makes physical sense because cm^3 is much smaller than a gallon, so the answer should go up several orders of magnitude. Two significant figures are allowed because of the limitation of 15.0 gallons (two significant figures). Round up the last digit up because the first non-significant digit is a 9.

89. a) **Given:** 195 m^2 **Find:** km^2

   Conceptual plan: m^2 → km^2

$$\dfrac{(1 \text{ km})^2}{(1000 \text{ m})^2}$$

   Notice that for squared units, the conversion factors must be squared.

   Solution: $195 \text{ m}^2 \times \dfrac{(1 \text{ km})^2}{(1000 \text{ m})^2} = 1.95 \times 10^{-4} \text{ km}^2$

   Check: The units (km^2) are correct. The magnitude of the answer (10^{-4}) makes physical sense because a kilometer is a much larger unit than a meter.

   b) **Given:** 195 m^2 **Find:** dm^2

   Conceptual plan: m^2 → dm^2

$$\dfrac{(10 \text{ dm})^2}{(1 \text{ m})^2}$$

   Notice that for squared units, the conversion factors must be squared.

   Solution: $195 \text{ m}^2 \times \dfrac{(10 \text{ dm})^2}{(1 \text{ m})^2} = 1.95 \times 10^4 \text{ dm}^2$

   Check: The units (dm^2) are correct. The magnitude of the answer (10^4) makes physical sense because a decimeter is a much smaller unit than a meter.

   c) **Given:** 195 m^2 **Find:** cm^2

   Conceptual plan: m^2 → cm^2

$$\dfrac{(100 \text{ cm})^2}{(1 \text{ m})^2}$$

   Notice that for squared units, the conversion factors must be squared.

   Solution: $195 \text{ m}^2 \times \dfrac{(100 \text{ cm})^2}{(1 \text{ m})^2} = = 1.95 \times 10^6 \text{ cm}^2$

   Check: The units (cm^2) are correct. The magnitude of the answer (10^6) makes physical sense because a centimeter is a much smaller unit than a meter.

90. a) **Given:** 115 m^3 **Find:** km^3
   Conceptual plan: m^3 → km^3

   $$\frac{(1\text{ km})^3}{(1000\text{ m})^3}$$

   Notice that for cubed units, the conversion factors must be cubed.

   Solution: 115 m^3 x $\dfrac{(1\text{ km})^3}{(1000\text{ m})^3}$ = 1.15 x 10^{-7} km^3

   Check: The units (km^3) are correct. The magnitude of the answer (10^{-7}) makes physical sense because a kilometer is a much larger unit than a meter.

   b) **Given:** 115 m^3 **Find:** dm^3
   Conceptual plan: m^3 → mm^3

   $$\frac{(10\text{ dm})^3}{(1\text{ m})^3}$$

   Notice that for cubed units, the conversion factors must be cubed.

   Solution: 115 m^3 x $\dfrac{(10\text{ dm})^3}{(1\text{ m})^3}$ = 1.15 x 10^5 dm^3

   Check: The units (dm^3) are correct. The magnitude of the answer (10^5) makes physical sense because a decimeter is a much smaller unit than a meter.

   c) **Given:** 115 m^3 **Find:** cm^3
   Conceptual plan: m^3 → cm^3

   $$\frac{(100\text{ cm})^3}{(1\text{ m})^3}$$

   Notice that for cubed units, the conversion factors must be cubed.

   Solution: 115 m^3 x $\dfrac{(100\text{ cm})^3}{(1\text{ m})^3}$ = 1.15 x 10^8 cm^3

   Check: The units (cm^3) are correct. The magnitude of the answer (10^8) makes physical sense because a centimeter is a much smaller unit than a meter.

91. **Given:** 435 acres   **Find:** square miles   **Other:** 1 acre = 43,560 ft^2, 1 mile = 5280 ft
   Conceptual plan: acres → ft^2 → mi^2

   $$\frac{43560\text{ ft}^2}{1\text{ acre}} \qquad \frac{(1\text{ mi})^2}{(5280\text{ ft})^2}$$

   Notice that for squared units, the conversion factors must be squared.

   Solution: 435 acres x $\dfrac{43560\text{ ft}^2}{1\text{ acre}}$ x $\dfrac{(1\text{ mi})^2}{(5280\text{ ft})^2}$ = 0.6796875 mi^2 = 0.680 mi^2

   Check: The units (mi^2) are correct. The magnitude of the answer (0.7) makes physical sense because an acre is much smaller than a mi^2, so the answer should go down several orders of magnitude. Three significant figures are allowed because of the limitation of 435 acres (three significant figures). Round up the last digit up because the first non-significant digit is a 7.

92. a) **Given:** 954 million acres **Find:** square miles   **Other:** 1 acre = 43,560 ft^2, 1 mile = 5280 ft
   Conceptual plan: **Substitute 10^6 for million**   then   acres → ft^2 → mi^2

   $$\frac{43560\text{ ft}^2}{1\text{ acre}} \qquad \frac{(1\text{ mi})^2}{(5280\text{ ft})^2}$$

   Notice that for squared units, the conversion must be squared.
   Solution: 954 million acres = 954 x 10^6 acres

   954 x10^6 acres x $\dfrac{43560\text{ ft}^2}{1\text{ acre}}$ x $\dfrac{(1\text{ mi})^2}{(5280\text{ ft})^2}$ = 1.490625 x 10^6 mi^2 = 1.49 x 10^6 mi^2

   Check: The units (mi^2) are correct. The magnitude of the answer (10^6) makes physical sense because an acre is much smaller than a mi^2, so the answer should go down several orders of magnitude. Three significant figures are allowed because of the limitation of 435 acres (three significant figures). Truncate the last digit up because the first non-significant digit is a 0.

b) **Given:** 3.537 million square miles   **Find:** percentage of U.S. land is farmland
Conceptual plan: Substitute 10^6 for million   then   % farm = $\underline{\text{farmland}}$ x 100%
Note - units of farmland and total land must be the same.   **total land**
Solution: 3.537 million mi^2 =   3.537 x 10^6 mi^2

% farmland = $\dfrac{1.49 \times 10^6 \ mi^2}{3.537 \times 10^6 \ mi^2}$ x 100 % = 42.1437659 % farmland   = 42.1 % farmland

Check: The units (%) are correct. The magnitude of the answer (4 %) makes physical sense because less and less of our land is devoted to farmland. Three significant figures are allowed because of the limitation of 435 acres (three significant figures). Truncate the last digit up because the first non-significant digit is a 4.

93. **Given:** 14 lbs   **Find:** mL   **Other:** 80 mg/0.80 mL & 15 mg/kg body
Conceptual plan: lb → kg body → mg → mL

$\dfrac{1 \ kg \ body}{2.205 \ lb}$ $\dfrac{15 \ mg}{1 \ kg \ body}$ $\dfrac{0.80 \ mL}{80 \ mg}$

Solution: 14 lb x $\dfrac{1 \ kg \ body}{2.205 \ lb}$ x $\dfrac{15 \ mg}{1 \ kg \ body}$ x $\dfrac{0.80 \ mL}{80 \ mg}$ = 0.9523809524 mL = 0.95 mL

Check: The units (cm^3) are correct. The magnitude of the answer (1 mL) makes physical sense because it is reasonable amount of liquid to give to a baby. Two significant figures are allowed because of the statement in the problem. Truncate the last digit because the first non-significant digit is a 2.

94. **Given:** 18 lbs   **Find:** mL   **Other:** 100 mg/5.0 mL & 10 mg/kg body
Conceptual plan: lb → kg body → mg → mL

$\dfrac{1 \ kg \ body}{2.205 \ lb}$ $\dfrac{10 \ mg}{1 \ kg \ body}$ $\dfrac{5.0 \ mL}{100 \ mg}$

Solution: 18 lb x $\dfrac{1 \ kg \ body}{2.205 \ lb}$ x $\dfrac{10 \ mg}{1 \ kg \ body}$ x $\dfrac{5.0 \ mL}{100 \ mg}$ = 4.081632653 mL = 4.1 mL

Check: The units (cm^3) are correct. The magnitude of the answer (4 mL) makes physical sense because it is reasonable amount of liquid to give to a baby.
Two significant figures are allowed because of the statement in the problem. Round up the last digit because the first non-significant digit is an 8.

95. **Given:** solar year   **Find:** seconds   **Other:**   60 seconds/minute; 60 minutes/ hour; 24 hours/solar day; and 365.24 solar days/solar year
Conceptual plan: yr → day → hr → min → sec

$\dfrac{365.24 \ day}{1 \ solar \ yr}$ $\dfrac{24 \ hr}{1 day}$ $\dfrac{60 \ min}{1 \ hr}$ $\dfrac{60 \ sec}{1 \ min}$

Solution:

1 solar yr x $\dfrac{365.24 \ day}{1 \ solar \ yr}$ x $\dfrac{24 \ hr}{1 day}$ x $\dfrac{60 \ min}{1 \ hr}$ x $\dfrac{60 \ sec}{1 \ min}$ = 3.1556736 x 10^7 sec = 3.1557 x 10^7 sec

Check: The units (seconds) are correct. The magnitude of the answer (10^7) makes physical sense because each conversion factor increases the value of the answer – a second is many orders of magnitude smaller than a year. Five significant figures are allowed because all conversion factors are assumed to be exact, except for the 365.24 days/ solar year (five significant figures). Round up the last digit because the first non-significant digit is a 7.

96. a) "Million" translates to 10^6 in Table 1.2. Substitute this quantity into the expression and move the decimal point to be in proper scientific notation. Fifty million Frenchmen = 50 x 10^6 Frenchmen = 5 x 10^7 Frenchmen (assuming one significant figure in fifty.)

b) This can be expressed as two different ratios: 10 jokes / 100 enemies = 1.0 x 10^{-1} jokes per enemy or 100 enemies / 10 jokes = 1 x 10^1 enemies per joke

20

c) "Hundred" translates as 10^{-2} (since this modifies millionth, something less than 1) and "millionth" translates to 10^{-6} in Table 1.2. Substitute this quantity into the expression and move the decimal point to be in proper scientific notation. $1.8 \times 10^{-2} \times 10^{-6} \, cm = 1.8 \times 10^{-8} \, cm$

d) "Thousand" translates to 10^3 in Table 1.2. Substitute this quantity into the expression and move the decimal point to be in proper scientific notation. Sixty thousand dollars $= 60 \times 10^3$ dollars $= 6 \times 10^4$ dollars (assuming one significant figure in sixty.)

e) The density of platinum (Table 1.4) $= 21.4 \, g/mL = 2.14 \times 10^1 \, g/mL$ moving the decimal point to be in proper scientific notation.

97. a) Extensive - the volume of a material depends on how much there is present.

   b) Intensive – the boiling point of a material is independent of how much material you have, so these values can be published in reference tables.

   c) Intensive - the temperature of a material depends on how much there is present.

   d) Intensive – the electrical; conductivity of a material is independent of how much material you have, so these values can be published in reference tables.

   e) Extensive - the energy contained in material depends on how much there is present. Many times energy is expressed in terms of Joules/mole, which then turns this quantity into an intensive property.

98. **Given:** $°C = \dfrac{°F - 32}{1.8}$ **Find:** temperature where $°F = °C$

   Conceptual plan: $°C = \dfrac{°F - 32}{1.8}$ set $°C = °F = x$ and solve for x

   Solution: $x = \dfrac{x - 32°F}{1.8}$ → $1.8 \, x = x - 32$ → $1.8 \, x - x = -32$ → $0.8 \, x = -32$ →
   $x = -32/0.8 = -40.$ → $-40. \, °F = -40. \, °C$
   Check: The units (°F & °C) are correct. Plugging the result back into the equation confirms that the calculations were done correctly. The magnitude of the answer seems correct, since it is known that the result is not between 0°C and 100 °C. The numbers are getting closer together as the temperature is dropped.

99. **Given:** $130 \, °X = 212 \, °F$ and $10 \, °X = 32 \, °F$ **Find:** temperature where $°X = °F$.
   Conceptual plan: Use data to derive an equation relating °X and °F. Then set $°F = °X = z$ and solve for z.
   Solution: Assume a linear relationship between the two temperatures $(y = mx + b)$.
   Let $y = °F$ and let $x = °X$.
   The slope of the line (m) is the relative change in the two temperature scales:
   $$m = \dfrac{\Delta \, °F}{\Delta \, °X} = \dfrac{212 \, °F - 32 \, °F}{130 \, °X - 10 \, °X} = \dfrac{180 \, °F}{120 \, °X} = 1.5$$
   Solve for intercept (b) by plugging one set of temperatures into the equation:
   $y = 1.5 \, x + b$ → $32 = (1.5)(130) + b$ → $32 = 15 + b$ → $b = 17$ → $°F = (1.5) \, °X + 17$
   Set $°F = °X = z$ and solve for z.
   $z = 1.5 \, z + 17$ → $-17 = 1.5 \, z - z$ → $-17 = 0.5 \, z$ → $z = -34$ → $-34°F = -34 \, °X$
   Check: The units (°F & °X) are correct. Plugging the result back into the equation confirms that the calculations were done correctly. The magnitude of the answer seems correct, since it is known that the result is not between 32°F and 212 °F. The numbers are getting closer together as the temperature is dropped.

100. **Given:** $17 \, °J = 0 \, °H$ and $97 \, °J = 120 \, °H$ **Find:** temperature where methyl alcohol boils in °J
   Other: methyl alcohol boils at 84° H
   Conceptual plan: Use data to derive an equation relating °J and °H. Then set $°H = 84 \, °H$ and solve for °J.
   Solution: Assume a linear relationship between the two temperatures $(y = mx + b)$.
   Let $y = °J$ and let $x = °H$.

The slope of the line (m) is the relative change in the two temperature scales:

$$m = \frac{\Delta \,^\circ J}{\Delta \,^\circ H} = \frac{97\,^\circ J - 17\,^\circ J}{120\,^\circ H - 0\,^\circ H} = \frac{80\,^\circ J}{120\,^\circ H} = 0.667$$ Solve for intercept (b) by plugging one set of temperatures into

the equation:

$y = 0.6\underline{6}7\,x + b$ → $17 = (0.6\underline{6}7)(0) + b$ → $b = 17$ → $^\circ J = (0.6\underline{6}7)\,^\circ H + 17$

Set $^\circ H = 84\,^\circ H$ and solve for $^\circ J$.

$^\circ J = (0.6\underline{6}7)(84) + 17$ → $^\circ J = 56 + 17 = 73\,^\circ J$

Check: The units ($^\circ J$) are correct. Plugging the original data points back into the equation confirms that the calculations were done correctly. The magnitude of the answer seems correct, since the result should be between $17^\circ J$ and $97\,^\circ J$ and closer to $97^\circ J$, than $17^\circ J$.

101. 1G. $F = ma = kg(m/s^2)$. Let's call it N for Newton. Ten tons = 20,000 lb = 2.2 kg/lb x 20,000 lb = 4.4 x 10 x 10^4 kg, deceleration = 55 mi x .6 km/mi x 10^3 m/km x 1/3.6 x 10^3 s^2 Exponents = 10^4 x10^3 x 10^{-3} = 10^4. So the kN is convenient.

For one molecule, the mass is 10^{-20} kg and deceleration is 3 x 10^8 m/s^2. So Exponents = 10^{-20} x 10^8 = 10^{-12}. So the pN is convenient.

102. **Given:** $25\,^\circ C$ and $-196\,^\circ C$ **Find:** Why significant figures are 3 and 2, respectively.
Conceptual plan: The problem is stated in units of $^\circ C$, so it must be converted to another temperature unit to see if the significant figures can change. Try K. Begin by finding the equation that relates the quantity that is given ($^\circ C$) and the quantity you are trying to find (K). $K = \,^\circ C + 273.15$
$K = 25\,^\circ C + 273.15 = 298\,K$ → $K = -196\,^\circ C + 273.15 = 77\,K$
A small positive temperature in $^\circ C$ gains significant figures, because of the rules of addition for significant figures – going from 2 to 3. A very negative temperature in $^\circ C$ loses significant figures, because of the rules of addition for significant figures – going from 3 to 2.

103.a) 1.76 x $10^{-3}/8.0$ x 10^2 $= 2.2$ x 10^{-6} Two significant figures are allowed to reflect the quantity with the fewest significant figures (8.0 x 10^2).

b)   Write all figures so that the decimal points can be aligned:

```
   0.0187
+  0.0002     All quantities are known to four places to the right of the decimal place,
-  0.0030     so the answer should be reported to four places to the right of the
   0.0159     decimal place or three significant figures.
```

c) $[(136000)(0.000322)/0.082)](129.2) = 6.899910244$ x $10^4 = 6.9$ x 10^4 Round the intermediate answer to two significant figures to reflect the quantity with the fewest significant figures (0.082). Round up the last digit since the first non-significant digit is 9.

104. **Given:** one gallon of gasoline   **Find:** US dollars   **Other:** 1 Euro = $1.25 US and
$\qquad\qquad\qquad\qquad\qquad\qquad\qquad\qquad\qquad\qquad\qquad\qquad$ 1 liter of gasoline in France = 0.97 Euro

Conceptual plan: gal → L → Euro → $ US

$$\frac{3.785\,L}{1\text{ gallon}} \quad \frac{0.97\text{ Euro}}{1\,L} \quad \frac{\$1.25\text{ US}}{1\text{ Euro}}$$

Solution: $1\text{ gallon} \times \dfrac{3.785\,L}{1\text{ gallon}} \times \dfrac{0.97\text{ Euro}}{1\,L} \times \dfrac{\$1.25\text{ US}}{1\text{ Euro}} = \$4.\underline{5}893125\text{ US} = \$4.6\text{ US}$

Check: The units ($ US) are correct. The magnitude of the answer ($ 4.5 US) makes physical sense because dominating conversion factor is ~ 4. Two significant figures are allowed because of the limitation of 0.94 Euro (two significant figures). Round up the last digit because the first non-significant digit is an 8.

105.a)   **Given:** cylinder dimensions - length = 22 cm, radius = 3.8 cm, d(gold) = 19.3 g/cm^3 & *d(sand)* = 3.00 g/cm^3
Find: m(gold) and m(sand)
Conceptual plan: L, r → V   then   d, V → m
$\qquad\qquad\qquad\qquad\qquad V = l\,\pi\,r^2 \qquad\qquad\qquad d = m/V$
Solution: V(gold) = V(sand) = (22 cm)(π)(3.8 cm)^2 $= 9\underline{9}.80212\ cm^3$ $d = m/V$ Rearrange by multiplying both sides of equation by V.   → $m = d\ x\ V$

22

$$m(\text{gold}) = \left(19.3 \frac{g}{cm^3}\right) \times (99.80212 \text{ cm}^3) = 1.926181 \times 10^4 \text{ g} = 1.9 \times 10^4 \text{ g}$$

Check: The units (g) are correct. The magnitude of the answer seems correct considering the value of the density is ~20 g/cm³. Two significant figures are allowed to reflect the significant figures in 22 cm and 3.8 cm. Truncate the non-significant digits because the first non-significant digit is a 2.

$$m(\text{sand}) = \left(3.00 \frac{g}{cm^3}\right) \times (99.80212 \text{ cm}^3) = 2.99206 \times 10^3 \text{ g} = 3.0 \times 10^3 \text{ g}$$

Check: The units (g) are correct. The magnitude of the answer seems correct considering the value of the density is 3 g/cm³. This number is much lower that the gold mass. Two significant figures are allowed to reflect the significant figures in 22 cm and 3.8 cm. Round the last digit up because the first non-significant digit is a 9.

b) Comparing the two values 1.9×10^4 g versus 3.0×10^3 g shows a difference in weight of almost a factor of 10. This difference should be enough to trip the alarm and alert the authorities to the presence of the thief.

106. **Given:** $r = 1.0 \times 10^{-13}$ cm, $m = 1.7 \times 10^{-24}$ g **Find:** density **Other:** $V = (4/3) \pi r^3$
Conceptual plan: $r \rightarrow V$ then $m, V \rightarrow d$
$$V = (4/3)\pi r^3 \qquad\qquad d = m/V$$
Solution: $V = (4/3) \pi r^3 = (4/3)(\pi)(1.0 \times 10^{-13} \text{ cm})^3 = 4.188790205 \times 10^{-39} \text{ cm}^3$

$$d = \frac{m}{V} = \frac{1.7 \times 10^{-24} \text{ g}}{4.188790205 \times 10^{-39} \text{ cm}^3} = 4.058451049 \times 10^{14} \frac{g}{cm^3} = 4.1 \times 10^{14} \frac{g}{cm^3}$$

Check: The units (g/cm³) are correct. The magnitude of the answer seems correct considering how small a nucleus is compared to an atom. Two significant figures are allowed to reflect the significant figures in 1.0 $\times 10^{-13}$ cm. Round the last digit up because the first non-significant digit is a 5.

107. **Given:** 3.5 lb of titanium **Find:** volume in in³ **Other:** density of titanium is 4.5 g/cm³
Conceptual plan: lb $\rightarrow$ g   then   m, d $\rightarrow$ V   then cm³ $\rightarrow$ in³
$$\frac{453.6 \text{ g}}{1 \text{ lb}} \qquad\qquad d = m/V \qquad\qquad \frac{(1 \text{ in})^3}{(2.54 \text{ cm})^3}$$
Solution: $3.5 \text{ lb} \times \dfrac{453.6 \text{ g}}{1 \text{ lb}} = 1.5876 \times 10^3 \text{ g}$

$d = m/V$ Rearrange by multiplying both sides of the equation by V and dividing both sides of the equation by d. $\rightarrow$

$$V = \frac{m}{d} = \frac{1.5876 \times 10^3 \text{ g}}{4.5 \frac{g}{cm^3}} = 3.520177384 \times 10^2 \text{ cm}^3 = 3.5 \times 10^2 \text{ cm}^3 \times \frac{(1 \text{ in})^3}{(2.54 \text{ cm})^3} = 21 \text{ in}^3$$

Check: The units (in³) are correct. The magnitude of the answer seems correct considering many grams we have. Two significant figures are allowed to reflect the significant figures in 3.5 lb. Truncate the non-significant digits because the first non-significant digit is a 2.

108. **Given:** density (g/cm³) **Find:** density (lb/in³) **Other:** density of iron is 7.86 g/cm³
Conceptual plan: $\dfrac{g}{cm^3} \rightarrow \dfrac{lb}{cm^3} \rightarrow \dfrac{lb}{in^3}$
$$\frac{1 \text{ lb}}{453.6 \text{ g}} \qquad \frac{(2.54 \text{ cm})^3}{(1 \text{ in})^3}$$
Solution: $\dfrac{7.86 \text{ g}}{cm^3} \times \dfrac{1 \text{ lb}}{453.6 \text{ g}} \times \dfrac{(2.54 \text{ cm})^3}{(1 \text{ in})^3} = 0.2839557386 \dfrac{lb}{in^3} = 0.284 \dfrac{lb}{in^3}$

Check: The units (lb/in³) are correct. The magnitude of the answer seems correct considering that the dominating factor is that a gram is smaller than a pound, so the answer should go down. Three significant figures are allowed to reflect the significant figures in 7.86 lb. Round the last digit up because the first non-significant digit is a 9.

109. **Given:** cylinder dimensions: length = 2.16 in, radius = 0.22 in, m= 41 g **Find:** density (g /cm³)

23

Conceptual plan: in → cm   then   l, r → V   then   m, V → d

$$\frac{2.54 \text{ cm}}{1 \text{ in}} \qquad V = l\pi r^2 \qquad d = m/V$$

Solution: $2.16 \text{ in} \times \dfrac{2.54 \text{ cm}}{1 \text{ in}} = 5.4\underline{8}64 \text{ cm} = l$ $\qquad 0.22 \text{ in} \times \dfrac{2.54 \text{ cm}}{1 \text{ in}} = 0.5\underline{5}88 \text{ cm} = r$

$V = l\,\pi\, r^2 = (5.4\underline{8}64 \text{ cm})(\pi)(0.5\underline{5}88 \text{ cm})^2 = 5.\underline{3}820798 \text{ cm}^3$

$d = \dfrac{m}{V} = \dfrac{41 \text{ g}}{5.\underline{3}820798 \text{ cm}^3} = 7.\underline{6}178729 \dfrac{\text{g}}{\text{cm}^3} = 7.6 \dfrac{\text{g}}{\text{cm}^3}$

Check: The units (g/cm³) are correct. The magnitude of the answer seems correct considering the value of the density of iron (a major component in steel) is 7.86 g/cm³. Two significant figures are allowed to reflect the significant figures in 0.22 in and 41 g. Truncate the non-significant digits because the first non-significant digit is a 2.

110. **Given:** m = 85 g **Find:** radius of the sphere (inches) **Other:** density (aluminum) = 2.7 g /cm³
Conceptual plan: m, d → V   then   V → r   then   cm → in

$$d = m/V \qquad V = (4/3)\pi r^3 \qquad \frac{1 \text{ in}}{2.54 \text{ cm}}$$

Solution: $d = m/V$ Rearrange by multiplying both sides of the equation by V and dividing both sides of the equation by d.

$$V = \frac{m}{d} = \frac{85 \text{ g}}{2.7 \dfrac{\text{g}}{\text{cm}^3}} = 3\underline{1}.48148148 \text{ cm}^3$$

$V = (4/3)\pi r^3$ Rearrange by dividing both sides of the equation by (4/3) π. $r^3 = \dfrac{3V}{4\pi}$

Take the cube root of both sides of the equation.

$$r = \left(\frac{3V}{4\pi}\right)^{1/3} = \left(\frac{(3)\,(3\underline{1}.48148148 \text{ cm}^3)}{4\pi}\right)^{1/3} = (7.\underline{5}1565009 \text{ cm}^3)^{1/3} = 1.\underline{9}58794386 \text{ cm}$$

$1.\underline{9}58794386 \text{ cm} \times \dfrac{1 \text{ in}}{2.54 \text{ cm}} = 0.7\underline{7}11788923 \text{ in} = 0.77 \text{ in}$

Check: The units (in) are correct. The magnitude of the answer seems correct. The magnitude of the volume is about a third of the mass (density is about 3 g/cm³). The radius in cm seems right considering the geometry involved. The magnitude goes down when we convert from cm to inches, because inches are bigger than cm's. Two significant figures are allowed to reflect the significant figures in 2.7 g/cm³ and 85 g. Truncate the non-significant digits because the first non-significant digit is a 1.

111. **Given:** 185 cubic yards (yd³) of H_2O **Find:** mass of the H_2O (pounds) **Other:** d(H_2O) = 1.00 g/cm³ at 0°C
Conceptual plan: yd³ → m³ → cm³ → g → lb

$$\frac{(1\text{m})^3}{(1.094 \text{ yd})^3} \quad \frac{(100 \text{ cm})^3}{(1\text{m})^3} \quad \frac{1.00 \text{ g}}{1.00 \text{ cm}^3} \quad \frac{1 \text{ lb}}{453.59 \text{ g}}$$

Solution:

$$185 \text{ yd}^3 \times \frac{(1\text{m})^3}{(1.094 \text{ yd})^3} \times \frac{(100 \text{ cm})^3}{(1\text{m})^3} \times \frac{1.00 \text{ g}}{1.00 \text{ cm}^3} \times \frac{1 \text{ lb}}{453.59 \text{ g}} = 3.1\underline{1}4987377 \times 10^5 \text{ lbs} = 3.11 \times 10^5 \text{ lbs}$$

Check: The units (lb) are correct. The magnitude of the answer (10⁵) makes physical sense because a pool is not a small object. Three significant figures are allowed because the conversion factor with the least precision is the density (1.00 g/cm³ - 3 significant figures) and the initial size has three significant figures. Truncate after the last digit because the first non-significant digit is a 4.

112. **Given:** 7655 cubic feet (ft³) of ice **Find:** mass of the ice (kg)   **Other:** 1.00 cm³ ice = 0.917 g ice at 0°C
Conceptual plan: ft³ → cm³ → g → kg

$$\frac{(30.48 \text{ cm})^3}{(1 \text{ ft})^3} \quad \frac{0.917 \text{ g}}{1.00 \text{ cm}^3} \quad \frac{1 \text{ kg}}{1000 \text{ g}}$$

Solution: $7655 \, \text{ft}^3 \times \dfrac{(30.48 \, \text{cm})^3}{(1 \, \text{ft})^3} \times \dfrac{0.917 \, \text{g}}{1.00 \, \text{cm}^3} \times \dfrac{1 \, \text{kg}}{1000 \, \text{g}} = 1.987739274 \times 10^5 \, \text{kg} = 1.99 \times 10^5 \, \text{kg}$

Check: The units (kg) are correct. The magnitude of the answer (10^5) makes physical sense because an iceberg is a large object. Three significant figures are allowed because the conversion factor with the least precision is the density ($0.917 \, \text{g/cm}^3$ - 3 significant figures). Round up the last digit because the first non-significant digit is a 7.

113. **Given:** 15 liters of gasoline **Find:** kilometers **Other:** 52 mi/gal in the city
   Conceptual plan: L $\rightarrow$ gal $\rightarrow$ mi $\rightarrow$ km

$$\dfrac{1 \, \text{gallon}}{3.785 \, \text{L}} \qquad \dfrac{52 \, \text{mi}}{1.0 \, \text{gallon}} \qquad \dfrac{1 \, \text{km}}{0.6214 \, \text{mi}}$$

Solution: $15 \, \text{L} \times \dfrac{1 \, \text{gallon}}{3.785 \, \text{L}} \times \dfrac{52 \, \text{mi}}{1.0 \, \text{gallon}} \times \dfrac{1 \, \text{km}}{0.6214 \, \text{mi}} = 3.316327941 \times 10^2 \, \text{km} = 3.3 \times 10^2 \, \text{km}$

Check: The units (km) are correct. The magnitude of the answer (10^2) makes physical sense because the dominating conversion factor is the mileage, which increases the answer. Two significant figures are allowed because the conversion factor with the least precision is 52 mi/gallon (2 significant figures) and the initial volume (15 L) has 2 significant figures. Truncate the last digit because the first non-significant digit is a 1. It is best to put the answer in scientific notation so that it is unambiguous how many significant figures are expressed.

114. **Given:** 355 mL of gasoline **Find:** kilometers **Other:** 57 mi/gal in the city
   Conceptual plan: mL $\rightarrow$ L $\rightarrow$ gal $\rightarrow$ mi $\rightarrow$ km

$$\dfrac{1 \, \text{L}}{1000 \, \text{mL}} \qquad \dfrac{1 \, \text{gallon}}{3.785 \, \text{L}} \qquad \dfrac{57 \, \text{mi}}{1.0 \, \text{gallon}} \qquad \dfrac{1 \, \text{km}}{0.6214 \, \text{mi}}$$

Solution: $355 \, \text{mL} \times \dfrac{1 \, \text{L}}{1000 \, \text{mL}} \times \dfrac{1 \, \text{gallon}}{3.785 \, \text{L}} \times \dfrac{57 \, \text{mi}}{1.0 \, \text{gallon}} \times \dfrac{1 \, \text{km}}{0.6214 \, \text{mi}} = 8.603319984 \, \text{km} = 8.6 \, \text{km}$

Check: The units (km) are correct. The magnitude of the answer (8.6) makes physical sense because the dominating conversion factor is the conversion from mL to L, which decreases the answer. Two significant figures are allowed because the conversion factor with the least precision is 57 mi/gallon (2 significant figures). Truncate the last digit because the first non-significant digit is a 0.

115. **Given:** radius of nucleus of the hydrogen atom = 1.0×10^{-13} cm; radius of the hydrogen atom = 52.9 pm.
   Find: percent of volume occupied by nucleus (%)
   Conceptual plan: cm $\rightarrow$ m   then pm $\rightarrow$ m then r $\rightarrow$ V then V_{atom}, $V_{nucleus}$ $\rightarrow$ % $V_{nucleus}$

$$\dfrac{1 \, \text{m}}{100 \, \text{cm}} \qquad \dfrac{1 \, \text{m}}{10^{12} \, \text{pm}} \qquad V = (4/3)\pi r^3 \qquad \% \, V_{nucleus} = \dfrac{V_{nucleus}}{V_{atom}} \times 100\%$$

Solution: $1.0 \times 10^{-13} \, \text{cm} \times \dfrac{1 \, \text{m}}{100 \, \text{cm}} = 1.0 \times 10^{-15} \, \text{m}$ and $52.9 \, \text{pm} \times \dfrac{1 \, \text{m}}{10^{12} \, \text{pm}} = 5.29 \times 10^{-11} \, \text{m}$

$V = (4/3)\pi r^3$ Substitute into %V equation.

$\% \, V_{nucleus} = \dfrac{V_{nucleus}}{V_{atom}} \times 100\% \rightarrow \quad \% \, V_{nucleus} = \dfrac{(4/3) \, \pi r^3_{nucleus}}{(4/3) \, \pi r^3_{atom}} \times 100\%$ Simplify equation.

$\% \, V_{nucleus} = \dfrac{r^3_{nucleus}}{r^3_{atom}} \times 100\%$ Substitute numbers and calculate result.

$\% \, V_{nucleus} = \dfrac{(1.0 \times 10^{-15} \, \text{m})^3}{(5.29 \times 10^{-11} \, \text{m})^3} \times 100\% = (1.890359168 \times 10^{-5})^3 \times 100\% = 6.755118685 \times 10^{-13} \, \% = 6.8 \times 10^{-13} \, \%$

Check: The units (%) are correct. The magnitude of the answer seems correct (10^{-13} %), since a proton is so small. Two significant figures are allowed to reflect the significant figures in 1.0×10^{-13} cm. Round up the last digits because the first non-significant digit is a 5.

116. **Given:** radius of neon = 69 pm; 2.69×10^{22} atoms per liter **Find:** percent of volume occupied by neon (%)
   Conceptual plan: Assume 1L total volume.

$$pm \rightarrow m \rightarrow cm \quad then \quad r \rightarrow V \quad then \quad cm^3 \rightarrow L \quad then \quad L/atom \rightarrow \quad L \quad then \quad V_{Ne}, V_{Total} \rightarrow \%V_{Ne}$$

$$\frac{1\,m}{10^{12}\,pm} \qquad \frac{100\,cm}{1\,m} \qquad V = (4/3)\pi r^3 = 1\,atom \qquad \frac{1\,L}{1000\,cm^3} \qquad 2.69 \times 10^{22}\,atoms$$

$$\%\,V_{Ne} = \frac{V_{Ne}}{V_{Total}} \times 100\%$$

Solution: $69\,\cancel{pm} \times \dfrac{1\,\cancel{m}}{10^{12}\,\cancel{pm}} \times \dfrac{100\,cm}{1\,\cancel{m}} = 6.9 \times 10^{-9}\,cm$

$V = (4/3)\pi r^3 = (4/3)\pi(6.9 \times 10^{-9}\,cm)^3 = 1.\underline{3}7605528 \times 10^{-24}\,cm^3$

$1.\underline{3}7605528 \times 10^{-24}\,\cancel{cm^3} \times \dfrac{1\,L}{1000\,\cancel{cm^3}} = 1.\underline{3}7605528 \times 10^{-27}\,L$

$\dfrac{1.\underline{3}7605528 \times 10^{-27}\,L}{atom} \times 2.69 \times 10^{22}\,atoms = 3.\underline{7}01588707 \times 10^{-5}\,L$ \qquad Substitute into %V equation.

$\%\,V_{Ne} = \dfrac{V_{Ne}}{V_{Total}} \times 100\% = \dfrac{3.\underline{7}01588707 \times 10^{-5}\,\cancel{L}}{1\,\cancel{L}} \times 100\% = 3.\underline{7}01588707 \times 10^{-3}\,\% = 3.7 \times 10^{-3}\,\%$

Check: This says that the separation between atoms is very large in the gas phase. The units (%) are correct. The magnitude of the answer seems correct (10^{-3} %), it is known that gases are primarily empty space. Two significant figures are allowed to reflect the significant figures in 69 pm. Truncate the non-significant digits because the first non-significant digit is a 0.

117. **Given:** mass of black hole (BH) = 1x 10^3 suns; radius of black hole = one-half the radius of our moon.
Find: density (g/cm^3) **Other:** radius of our sun = 7.0×10^5 km; average density of our sun = 1.4×10^3 kg/m^3; diameter of the moon = 2.16×10^3 miles
Conceptual plan: $d_{BH} = m_{BH}/V_{BH}$
Calculate m_{BH}: $r_{sun} \rightarrow V_{sun}$ $km^3_{sun} \rightarrow m^3_{sun}$ $V_{sun}, d_{sun} \rightarrow m_{sun}$ $m_{sun} \rightarrow m_{BH}$ kg $\rightarrow$ g

$$V = (4/3)\pi r^3 \qquad \frac{(1000\,m)^3}{(1\,km)^3} \qquad d_{sun} = \frac{m_{sun}}{V_{sun}} \qquad m_{BH} = (1 \times 10^3) \times m_{sun} \qquad \frac{1000\,g}{1\,kg}$$

Calculate V_{BH}: $d_{moon} \rightarrow r_{moon} \rightarrow r_{BH}$ mi $\rightarrow$ km $\rightarrow$ m $\rightarrow$ cm $r \rightarrow V$

$$r_{moon} = \tfrac{1}{2}\,d_{moon} \qquad r_{BH} = \tfrac{1}{2}\,r_{moon} \qquad \frac{1\,km}{0.6214\,mi} \qquad \frac{1000\,m}{1\,km} \qquad \frac{100\,cm}{1\,m} \qquad V = (4/3)\pi r^3$$

Substitute into $d_{BH} = m_{BH}/V_{BH}$
Solution: Calculate m_{BH} $\quad V_{sun} = (4/3)\pi r_{sun}^3 = (4/3)\pi(7.0 \times 10^5\,km)^3 = 1.\underline{4}3675504 \times 10^{18}\,km^3$

$1.\underline{4}3675504 \times 10^{18}\,\cancel{km^3} \times \dfrac{(1000\,m)^3}{(1\,\cancel{km})^3} = 1.\underline{4}3675504 \times 10^{27}\,m^3$

$d_{sun} = m_{sun}/V_{sun}$ \quad Solve for m by multiplying both sides of the equation by V_{sun}. \quad $m_{sun} = V_{sun} \times d_{sun}$
$m_{sun} = (1.\underline{4}3675504 \times 10^{27}\,m^3)(1.4 \times 10^3\,kg/m^3) = 2.\underline{0}11457056 \times 10^{30}\,kg$
$m_{BH} = (1 \times 10^3) \times m_{sun} = (1 \times 10^3) \times (2.\underline{0}11457056 \times 10^{30}\,kg) = 2.\underline{0}11457056 \times 10^{33}\,kg$

$2.\underline{0}11457056 \times 10^{33}\,\cancel{kg} \times \dfrac{1000\,g}{1\,\cancel{kg}} = 2.\underline{0}11457056 \times 10^{36}\,g$

Calculate V_{BH} $\quad r_{moon} = \tfrac{1}{2}\,d_{moon} = \tfrac{1}{2}(2.16 \times 10^3\,miles) = 1.08 \times 10^3\,miles$
$r_{BH} = \tfrac{1}{2}\,r_{moon} = \tfrac{1}{2}(1.08 \times 10^3\,miles) = 540.\,miles$

$540.\,\cancel{miles} \times \dfrac{1\,\cancel{km}}{0.6214\,\cancel{mi}} \times \dfrac{1000\,\cancel{m}}{1\,\cancel{km}} \times \dfrac{100\,cm}{1\,\cancel{m}} = 8.\underline{6}900547 \times 10^7\,cm$

$V = (4/3)\pi r^3 = (4/3)\pi(8.\underline{6}900547 \times 10^7\,cm)^3 = 2.7\underline{4}888228 \times 10^{24}\,cm^3$

Substitute into $\quad d_{BH} = \dfrac{m_{BH}}{V_{BH}} = \dfrac{2.\underline{0}11457056 \times 10^{36}\,g}{2.7\underline{4}888228 \times 10^{24}\,cm^3} = 7.\underline{3}1737339 \times 10^{11}\,\dfrac{g}{cm^3} = 7.3 \times 10^{11}\,\dfrac{g}{cm^3}$

Check: The units (g/cm^3) are correct. The magnitude of the answer seems correct (10^{12}), since we expect extremely high numbers for black holes. Two significant figures are allowed to reflect the significant figures in the radius of our sun (7.0×10^5 km) and the average density of sun (1.4×10^3 kg/m^3). Truncate the non-significant digits because the first non-significant digit is a 4.

118. **Given:** 15.0 ppm CO; eight hour period **Find:** milligrams of carbon monoxide

Other: 0.50 L of air per breath; 20 breaths per minute; carbon monoxide has a density of 1.2 g/L; and 15.0 ppm CO means 15.0 L CO per 10^6 L air

Conceptual plan: hr $\rightarrow$ min $\rightarrow$ breaths $\rightarrow$ L_{air} $\rightarrow$ L_{CO} $\rightarrow$ g_{CO} $\rightarrow$ mg_{CO}

$$\frac{60 \text{ min}}{1 \text{ hr}} \quad \frac{20 \text{ breath}}{1 \text{ min}} \quad \frac{0.50 \text{ } L_{air}}{1 \text{ breath}} \quad \frac{15.0 \text{ } L_{CO}}{1 \times 10^6 \text{ } L_{air}} \quad \frac{1.2 \text{ } g_{CO}}{1 \text{ } L_{CO}} \quad \frac{1000 \text{ } mg_{CO}}{1 \text{ } g_{CO}}$$

Solution:

$$8 \text{ hr} \times \frac{60 \text{ min}}{1 \text{ hr}} \times \frac{20 \text{ breath}}{1 \text{ min}} \times \frac{0.50 \text{ } L_{air}}{1 \text{ breath}} \times \frac{15.0 \text{ } L_{CO}}{1 \times 10^6 \text{ } L_{air}} \times \frac{1.2 \text{ } g_{CO}}{1 \text{ } L_{CO}} \times \frac{1000 \text{ } mg_{CO}}{1 \text{ } g_{CO}} = 86.4 \text{ } mg_{CO} = 9 \times 10^1 \text{ } mg_{CO}$$

Check: The units (mg) are correct. The magnitude of the answer (10^2) makes physical sense because there are more than 6 powers of 10 visible in these conversion factors in the numerator and one factor of 10^6 in the denominator. This means that most of the conversions cancel each other out, but there is still some left in the numerator. One significant figure is allowed because the conversion factor with the least precision is 20 breaths/minute (1 significant figure) and the starting time (8 hours) also has one significant figure. Round up the last digit because the first non-significant digit is a 6.

119. **Given:** cubic nanocontainers with an edge length = 25 nanometers

Find: a) volume of one nanocontainer; b) grams of oxygen could be contained by each nanocontainer; c) grams of oxygen inhaled per hour; d) minimum number of nanocontainers per hour; and e) minimum volume of nanocontainers.

Other: (pressurized oxygen) = 85 g/L; 0.28 g of oxygen per liter; average human inhales about 0.50 L of air per breath and takes about 20 breaths per minute; and adult total blood volume = ~ 5 L.

Conceptual Plan:

a) nm $\rightarrow$ m $\rightarrow$ cm   then l $\rightarrow$ V   then cm^3 $\rightarrow$ L

$$\frac{1 \text{ m}}{10^9 \text{ nm}} \quad \frac{100 \text{ cm}}{1 \text{ m}} \qquad V = l^3 \qquad \frac{1 \text{ L}}{1000 \text{ cm}^3}$$

b) L $\rightarrow$ g pressurized oxygen

$$\frac{85 \text{ g oxygen}}{1 \text{ L nanocontainers}}$$

c)   hr $\rightarrow$ min $\rightarrow$ breaths $\rightarrow$ L_{air} $\rightarrow$ g_{O2}

$$\frac{60 \text{ min}}{1 \text{ hr}} \quad \frac{20 \text{ breath}}{1 \text{ min}} \quad \frac{0.50 \text{ } L_{air}}{1 \text{ breath}} \quad \frac{0.28 \text{ } g_{CO}}{1 \text{ } L_{air}}$$

d) grams oxygen $\rightarrow$ number nanocontainers

$$\frac{1 \text{ nanocontainer}}{\text{part (b) grams of oxygen}}$$

e) number nanocontainers $\rightarrow$ volume nanocontainers

$$\frac{\text{part (a) volume}}{\text{of 1 nanocontainer}}$$

Solution:

a) $25 \text{ nm} \times \dfrac{1 \text{ m}}{10^9 \text{ nm}} \times \dfrac{100 \text{ cm}}{1 \text{ m}} = 2.5 \times 10^{-6} \text{ cm}$

$V = l^3 = (2.5 \times 10^{-6} \text{ cm})^3 = 1.\underline{5}625 \times 10^{-17} \text{ cm}^3 \times \dfrac{1 \text{ L}}{1000 \text{ cm}^3} = 1.\underline{5}625 \times 10^{-20} \text{ L} = 1.6 \times 10^{-20} \text{ L}$

b)

$1.\underline{5}625 \times 10^{-20} \text{ L} \times \dfrac{85 \text{ g oxygen}}{1 \text{ L nanocontainers}} = 1.\underline{3}28125 \times 10^{-18} \dfrac{\text{g pressurized O}_2}{\text{nanocontainer}} = 1.3 \times 10^{-18} \dfrac{\text{g pressurized O}_2}{\text{nanocontainer}}$

c) $1 \text{ hr} \times \dfrac{60 \text{ min}}{1 \text{ hr}} \times \dfrac{20 \text{ breath}}{1 \text{ min}} \times \dfrac{0.50 \text{ } L_{air}}{1 \text{ breath}} \times \dfrac{0.28 \text{ } gO_2}{1 \text{ } L_{air}} = 1.\underline{6}8 \times 10^2 \text{ g oxygen} = 1.7 \times 10^2 \text{ g oxygen}$

d)

$$1.\underline{6}8 \times 10^2 \text{ g oxygen} \times \frac{1 \text{ nanocontainer}}{1.3 \times 10^{-18} \text{ g of oxygen}} = 1.\underline{2}92307692 \times 10^{20} \text{ nanocontainers} = 1.3 \times 10^{20} \text{ nanocontainers}$$

e) $1.\underline{2}92307692 \times 10^{20} \text{ nanocontainers} \times \dfrac{1.5625 \times 10^{-20} \text{ L}}{\text{nanocontainer}} = 2.\underline{0}19230769 \text{ L} = 2.0 \text{ L}$

This volume is much too large to be feasible, since the volume of blood in the average human is 5 L.

Check:

a) The units (L) are correct. The magnitude of the answer (10^{-20}) makes physical sense because these are very, very tiny containers. Two significant figures are allowed reflecting the significant figures in the starting dimension (25 nm – 2 significant figures). Round up the last digit because the first non-significant digit is a 6.

b) The units (g) are correct. The magnitude of the answer (10^{-18}) makes physical sense because these are very, very tiny containers and very few molecules can fit inside. Two significant figures are allowed reflecting the significant figures in the starting dimension (25 nm) and the given concentration (85 g/L) – 2 significant figures in each. Truncate the non-significant digits because the first non-significant digit is a 2.

c) The units (g oxygen) are correct. The magnitude of the answer (10^2) makes physical sense because of the conversion factors involved and the fact that air is not very dense. Two significant figures are allowed because it is stated in the problem. Round up the last digit because the first non-significant digit is an 8.

d) The units (nanocontainers) are correct. The magnitude of the answer (10^{20}) makes physical sense because these are very, very tiny containers and we need a macroscopic quantity of oxygen in these containers. Two significant figures are allowed reflecting the significant figures in both of the quantities in the calculation – 2 significant figures. Round up the last digit because the first non-significant digit is a 9.

e) The units (L) are correct. The magnitude of the answer (2) makes physical sense because the magnitudes of the numbers in this step. Two significant figures are allowed reflecting the significant figures in both of the quantities in the calculation – 2 significant figures. Truncate the non-significant digits because the first non-significant digit is a 1.

120. No. Since the container is sealed the atoms and molecules can move around, but they can not leave. If no atoms or molecules can leave, the mass must be constant.

121. c) is the best representation. When solid carbon dioxide (dry ice) sublimes it changes phase from a solid to a gas. Phase changes are physical changes, so no molecular bonds are broken. This diagram shows molecules with one carbon atom and two oxygen atoms bonded together in every molecule. The other diagrams have no carbon dioxide molecules.

122. This problem is similar to problem #60, only the dimension is changes to 7 cm on each edge.
    Given: 7 cm on each edge cube   **Find:** cm^3
    Conceptual plan: Read the information given carefully. The cube is 7 cm on each side.
        l , w , h $\rightarrow$ V
            $V = l \times w \times h$
            in a cube $l = w = h$
    Solution: 7 cm x 7 cm x 7 cm = $(7 \text{ cm})^3 =$ = 343 cm^3 or 343 cubes

123. In order to determine which number is large, the units need to be compared. There is a factor of 1000 between grams and kg, in the numerator. There is a factor of $(100)^3$ or 1,000,000 between cm^3 and m^3. This second factor more than compensates for the first factor. Thus Substance A with a density of 1.7 g/cm^3 is more dense than Substance B with a density of 1.7 kg/m^3.

124. Remember that density = mass/volume.

a) The darker colored box has a heavier mass, but a smaller volume, so it is more dense than the lighter colored box.

b) The lighter colored box is heavier than the darker colored box and both boxes have the same volume, so the lighter colored box is more dense.

c) The larger box is the heavier box, so it can not be determined with this information which box is denser.

125. Remember that: An observation is the information collected when studying phenomena. A law is a concise statement that summarizes observed behaviors and observations and predicts future observations. A theory attempts to explain why the observed behavior is happening.

a) This statement is most like a law, because it summarizes many observations and can explain future behavior – many places and many days.

b) This statement is a theory because it attempts to explain why – gravitational forces.

c) This statement is most like an observation, because it is information collected in order to understand tidal behavior.

d) This statement is most like a law, because it summarizes many observations and can explain future behavior – many places and many days and months.

Chapter 2
Atoms and Elements

1. Scanning tunneling microscopy is a technique that can image, and even move, individual atoms and molecules. A scanning tunneling microscope works by moving an extremely sharp electrode over a surface and measuring the resulting tunneling current, the electrical current that flows between the tip of the electrode and the surface even though the two are not in physical contact.

2. It is important to understand the nature of atoms because they are the keys to connecting the macroscopic and microscopic worlds.

3. The first people to propose that matter was composed of small, indestructible particles were Leucippus and Democritus. These Greek philosophers theorized that matter was ultimately composed of small, indivisible particles called atomos. In the sixteenth century modern science began to emerge. A greater emphasis on observation brought rapid advancement as the scientific method became the established way to learn about the physical world. By the early 1800's certain observations led the English chemist John Dalton to offer convincing evidence that supported the early atomic ideas of Leucippus and Democritus. The theory that all matter is composed of atoms grew out of observations and laws. The three most important laws that led to the development and acceptance of the atomic theory were the law of conservation of mass, the law of definite proportions, and the law of multiple proportions. John Dalton explained the laws with his atomic theory.

4. The law of conservation of mass states: In a chemical reaction, matter is neither created nor destroyed. In other words, when you carry out any chemical reaction, the total mass of the substances involved in the reaction does not change.

5. The law of definite proportions states: All samples of a given compound, regardless of their source or how they were prepared, have the same proportions of their constituent elements. This means that elements composing a given compound always occur in fixed (or definite) proportions in all samples of the compound.

6. The law of multiple proportions states: When two elements (call them A and B) form two different compounds, the masses of element B that combine with 1 g of element A can be expressed as a ratio of small whole numbers. This means that when two atoms (A and B) combine to form more than one compound, the ratio of B in one compound to B in the second compound will be a small whole number.

7. The law of definite proportions applies to two or more samples of the same compound and states that the ratio of one element to the other in the samples will always be the same. The law of multiple proportions applies to two different compounds containing the same two elements (A and B) and states that the masses of B that combine with 1 g of A are related as a small whole number ratio.

8. The main ideas of John Daltons atomic theory are: 1) Each element is composed of tiny, indestructible particles called atoms. 2) All atoms of a given element have the same mass and other properties that distinguish them from the atoms of other elements. 3) Atoms combine in simple, whole number ratios to form compounds. 4) Atoms of one element cannot change into atoms of another element. In a chemical reaction, atoms change the way that they are bound together with other atoms to form a new substance. The law of conservation of mass is explained by the 4th idea. Since the atoms cannot change into another element, and just change how they are bound together, the total mass will remain constant. The law of constant composition is supported by idea 2 and 3. Since the atoms of a given element always have the same mass and other distinguishing properties, and they combine in simple whole number ratios, different samples of the same compound will have the same properties and the same composition. The law of multiple proportions is also supported by ideas 2 and 3 since the atoms can combine in simple whole number ratios, the ratio of the mass of B in one compound to the mass of B in a second compound will also be a small whole number.

9. In the late 1800's, an English physicist named J.J. Thomson performed experiments to probe the properties of cathode rays. Thomson found that these rays were actually streams of particles with the following properties: they traveled in straight lines; they were independent of the composition of the material from

which they originated; and they carried a negative electrical charge. He measured the charge to mass ratio of the particles and found that the cathode ray particle was about 2000 times lighter than hydrogen.

10. In Millikan's oil drop experiment, oil was sprayed into fine droplets using an atomizes. The droplets were allowed to fall under the influence of gravity through a small hole into the lower portion of the apparatus where they could be viewed. During their fall, the drops would acquire electrons that had been produced by the interaction of high energy radiation with air. These charged drops interacted with two electrically charged plates within the apparatus. The negatively charged plate at the bottom of the apparatus repelled the negatively charged drops. By varying the voltage on the plates, the fall of the charged drops could be slowed, stopped, or even reversed. From the voltage required to halt the free fall of the drops, and from the masses of the drops themselves, Millikan calculated the charge of each drop. He then reasoned that, since each drop must contain an integral number of electrons, the charge of each drop must be a whole number multiple of the electron's charge. The magnitude of the charge of the electron is of tremendous importance because it determines how strongly an atom holds its electrons.

11. The plum – pudding model of the atom, proposed by J.J. Thomson said the negatively charged electrons were small particles electrostatically held within a positively charged sphere.

12. Rutherford's gold foil experiment directed positively charged α particles at an ultrathin sheet of gold foil. These particles were to act as probes of the gold atoms' structure. If the gold atoms were indeed like plum pudding – with their mass and charge spread throughout the entire volume of the atom – these speeding probes should pass right through the gold foil with minimum deflection. A majority of the particles did pass directly through the foil, but some particles were deflected, and some even bounced back. He realized that to account for the deflections, the mass and positive charge of an atom must all be concentrated is a space much smaller than the size of the atom itself.

13. Rutherford's nuclear model of the atom has three basic parts: 1) Most of the atom's mass and all of its positive charge are contained in a small core called the **nucleus.** 2) Most of the volume of the atom is empty space, throughout which, time, negatively charged electrons are dispersed. 3) There are as many negatively charged electrons outside the nucleus as there are positively charged particles within the nucleus, so that the atom is electrically neutral. The revolutionary part of this theory is the idea that matter – at its core – is much less uniform than it appears.

14. Matter appears solid because the variation in its density is on such a small scale that our eyes cannot see it.

15. The three subatomic particles that compose atoms are:
    Protons, which have a mass of 1.67262 x 10^{-27} kg or 100727 amu and a relative charge of +1.
    Neutrons, which have a mass of 1.67493 x 10^{-27} kg or 100866 amu and a relative charge of 0.
    Electrons, which have a mass of 0.00091 x 10^{-27} kg or 0.00055 amu and a relative charge of – 1.

16. The number of protons in the nucleus defines the element.

17. The atomic number, Z, is the number of protons in an atom's nucleus. The atomic mass number (A) is the sum of the neutrons and protons in an atom.

18. The names of the elements were often given to describe their properties. For example, argon originates from the Greek word argos meaning inactive. Other elements were named after figures from Greek or Roman mythology or astronomical bodies. Still others were named for the places where they were discovered or where their discoverer was born. More recently, elements have been named after scientists.

19. Isotopes are atoms with the same number of protons but different numbers of neutrons. Natural abundance is the relative amount of each different isotope in a naturally occurring sample of a given element.

20. Isotopes can be symbolized: $^{A}_{Z}X$. Where A is the mass number, Z is the atomic number, and X is the chemical symbol. A second notation is the chemical symbol (or chemical name) followed by a dash and the mass number of the isotope:
    X – A, where X is the chemical symbol or name and A is the mass number. The carbon isotope with a mass of 12 would have the symbol: $^{12}_{6}C$ or C – 12.

21. An ion is a charged particle. Positively charged ions are called cations. Negatively charged ions are called anions.

22. The periodic law states: When elements are arranged in order of increasing mass, certain sets of properties recur periodically. Mendeleev organized all the known elements in a table consisting of a series of rows in which mass increased from left to right. The rows were arranged so that elements with similar properties were aligned in the same vertical column.

23. Metals are found on the left side and the middle of the periodic table. They are good conductors of heat and electricity, they can be pounded into flat sheets (malleability); they can be drawn into wires (ductility); they are often shiny; and they tend to lose electrons when they undergo chemical change.
    Nonmetals are found on the upper right side of the periodic table. Their properties are more varied: some are solids at room temperature, others are liquids or gases. As a whole they tend to be poor conductors of heat and electricity and they all tend to gain electrons when they undergo chemical changes.
    Metalloids lie along the zigzag diagonal line that divides metals and nonmetals. They show mixed properties. Several metalloids are also classified as semiconductors because of their intermediate and temperature dependent electrical conductivity.

24. a) Noble gases are in group 8A and are mostly unreactive. As the name implies, they are all gases in their natural state.

    b) Alkali metals are in group 1A and are all reactive metals.

    c) Alkaline earth metals are in group 2A and are also fairly reactive..

    d) Halogens are in group 7A and are very reactive nonmetals.

25. Main group metals tend to lose electrons, forming a cation with the same number of electrons as the nearest noble gas. A main group nonmetal tends to gain electrons, forming an anion with the same number of electrons as the nearest, previous noble gas.

26. Atomic mass represents the average mass of the isotopes that compose that element. The average calculated is weighted according to the natural abundance of each isotope.
    Atomic mass $= \sum_n$ (fraction of isotope n) x (mass of isotope n)

27. In a mass spectrometer, the sample is injected into the instrument and vaporized. The vaporized atoms are then ionized by an electron beam. The electrons in the beam collide with the vaporized atoms, removing electrons from the atoms and creating positively charged ions. Charged plates with slits in them accelerate the positively charged ions into a magnetic field, which deflects them. The amount of deflection depends on the mass of the ions, - lighter ions are deflected more than heavier ones. Finally, the ions strike a detector and produce an electrical signal that is recorded.

28. The result of the mass spectrometer is the separation of the atoms in the sample according to their mass, producing a mass spectrum. The position of each peak on the x – axis gives the mass of the isotope, and the intensity (indicated by the height of the peak) gives the relative abundance of that isotope.

29. A mole is an amount of material. It is defined as the amount of material containing 6.0221421×10^{23} particles (Avogadro's number). The numerical value of the mole is defined as being equal to the number of atoms in exactly 12 grams of pure carbon – 12. It is useful for converting number of atoms to moles of atoms and moles of atoms to number of atoms.

30. The mass corresponding to a mole of one element is different from the mass corresponding to a mole of another element because the mass of the atom of each element is different. A mole is a specific number of atoms, so the heavier the mass of each atom, the heavier the mass of one mole of atoms.

31. **Given:** 1.50 g hydrogen; 12.0 g oxygen **Find:** grams water vapor
    Conceptual Plan: total mass reactants = total mass products
    Solution: Mass of reactants = 1.50 g hydrogen + 12.0 g oxygen = 13.5 grams
    Mass of products = mass of reactants = 13.5 grams water vapor.

Check: According to the Law of Conservation of Mass, matter is not created or destroyed in a chemical reaction, so, since water vapor is the only product the masses of hydrogen and oxygen must combine to form the mass of water vapor.

32. **Given:** 21 kg gasoline; 84 kg oxygen   **Find:** mass of carbon dioxide and water
    Conceptual Plan: total mass reactants = total mass products
    Solution: Mass of reactants = 21 kg gasoline + 84 kg oxygen = 105 kg mass
                     Mass of products = mass of reactants = 105 kg of mass of carbon dioxide and water.
    Check: According to the Law of Conservation of Mass, matter is not created or destroyed in a chemical reaction, so, since carbon dioxide and water are the only products the masses of gasoline and oxygen must combine to form the mass of carbon dioxide and water.

33. **Given:** sample 1: 38.9 g carbon, 448 g chlorine; sample 2: 14.8 g carbon, 134 g chlorine
    Find: consistent with definite proportions.
    Conceptual Plan: determine mass ratio of sample 1 and 2 and compare.
    $$\frac{\text{mass of chlorine}}{\text{mass of carbon}}$$
    Solution: Sample 1: $\dfrac{448\,\text{g chorine}}{38.9\,\text{g carbon}} = 11.5$ Sample 2: $\dfrac{134\,\text{g chlorine}}{14.8\,\text{g carbon}} = 9.05$

    Results are not consistent with the law of definite proportions because the ratio of chlorine to carbon is not the same.
    Check: According to the Law of Definite Proportions, the mass ratio of one element to another is the same for all samples of the compound.

34. **Given:** sample 1: 6.98 grams sodium, 10.7 grams chlorine; sample 2: 11.2 g sodium, 17.3 grams chlorine

    Find: consistent with definite proportions.
    Conceptual Plan: determine mass ratio of sample 1 and 2 and compare.
    $$\frac{\text{mass of chlorine}}{\text{mass of sodium}}$$
    Solution: Sample 1: $\dfrac{10.7\,\text{g chorine}}{6.98\,\text{g sodium}} = 1.53$ Sample 2: $\dfrac{17.3\,\text{g chlorine}}{11.2\,\text{g sodium}} = 1.54$

    Results are consistent with the law of definite proportions.
    Check: According to the Law of Definite Proportions, the mass ratio of one element to another is the same for all samples of the compound.

35. **Given:** mass ratio sodium to fluorine = 1.21:1; sample = 28.8 g sodium   **Find:** g fluorine
    Conceptual Plan: g sodium → g fluorine
    $$\frac{\text{mass of fluorine}}{\text{mass of sodium}}$$
    Solution: $28.8\,\text{g sodium} \times \dfrac{1\,\text{g fluorine}}{1.21\,\text{g sodium}} = 23.8\,\text{g fluorine}$

    Check: The units of the answer, g fluorine are correct. The magnitude of the answer is reasonable since it is less than the grams of sodium.

36. **Given:** sample 1: 1.65 kg magnesium, 2.57 kg fluorine; sample 2: 1.32 kg magnesium
    Find: g fluorine in sample 2.
    Conceptual Plan:
        mass magnesium and mass fluorine → mass ratio → mass fluorine(kg) → mass fluorine(g)
    $$\frac{\text{mass of fluorine}}{\text{mass of magnesium}} \qquad\qquad \frac{1000\,\text{g}}{\text{kg}}$$
    Solution: $\text{mass ratio} = \dfrac{2.57\,\text{kg fluorine}}{1.65\,\text{kg magnesium}} = \dfrac{1.56\,\text{kg fluorine}}{1.00\,\text{kg magnesium}}$

    $1.32\,\text{kg magnesium} \times \dfrac{1.56\,\text{kg fluorine}}{1.00\,\text{kg magnesium}} \times \dfrac{1000\,\text{g}}{\text{kg}} = 2.06 \times 10^3\ \text{g fluorine}$

    Check: The units of the answer, g fluorine, are correct. The magnitude of the answer is reasonable since it is greater that the mass of magnesium and the ratio is greater than 1.

37. **Given:** 1 gram osmium: sample 1 = 0.168 g oxygen; sample 2 = 0.3369 g oxygen
Find: consistent with multiple proportions.
Conceptual Plan: determine mass ratio of oxygen

$$\frac{\text{mass of oxygen sample 2}}{\text{mass of oxygen sample 1}}$$

Solution: $\dfrac{0.3369\,\text{g oxygen}}{0.168\,\text{g oxygen}} = 2.00$ \quad Ratio is a small whole number. Results are consistent with multiple proportions

Check: According to the Law of Multiple Proportions, when two elements form two different compounds, the masses of element B that combine with 1 g of element A can be expressed as a ratio of small whole numbers.

38. **Given:** 1 g palladium: compound A: 0.603 g S, compound B: 0.301 g S; compound C: 0.151 g S
Find: consistent with multiple proportions
Conceptual Plan: determine mass ratio of sulfur in the 3 compounds

$$\frac{\text{mass of sulfur sample A}}{\text{mass of sulfur sample B}} \quad \frac{\text{mass of sulfur sample A}}{\text{mass of sulfur sample C}} \quad \frac{\text{mass of sulfur sample B}}{\text{mass of sulfur sample C}}$$

Solution: $\dfrac{0.603\,\text{g S in compound A}}{0.301\,\text{g S in compound B}} = 2.00 \quad \dfrac{0.603\,\text{g S in compound A}}{0.151\,\text{g S in compound C}} = 3.99 \sim 4 \quad \dfrac{0.301\,\text{g S in compound B}}{0.151\,\text{g S in compound C}} = 1.99 \sim 2$

Ratio of each is a small whole number. Results are consistent with multiple proportions.

Check: According to the Law of Multiple Proportions, when two elements form two different compounds, the masses of element B that combine with 1 g of element A can be expressed as a ratio of small whole numbers.

39. **Given:** sulfur dioxide = 3.49 g oxygen and 3.50 g sulfur, sulfur trioxide = 6.75 g oxygen and 4.50 g sulfur.
Find: mass oxygen per g S for each compound and then determine the mass ratio of oxygen

$$\frac{\text{mass of oxygen in sulfur dioxide}}{\text{mass of sulfur in sulfur dioxide}} \quad \frac{\text{mass of oxygen in sulfur trioxide}}{\text{mass of sulfur in sulfur trioxide}} \quad \frac{\text{mass of oxyen in sulfur trioxide}}{\text{mass of oxyen in sulfur dioxide}}$$

Solution: $\text{sulfur dioxide} = \dfrac{3.49\,\text{g oxygen}}{3.50\,\text{g sulfur}} = \dfrac{0.997\,\text{g oxygen}}{1\,\text{g sulfur}} \qquad \text{sulfur trioxide} = \dfrac{6.75\,\text{g oxygen}}{4.50\,\text{g sulfur}} = \dfrac{1.50\,\text{g oxygen}}{1\,\text{g sulfur}}$

$\dfrac{1.50\,\text{g oxygen in sulfur trioxide}}{0.997\,\text{g oxygen in sulfur dioxide}} = \dfrac{1.50}{1} = \dfrac{3}{2}$ \quad Ratio is in small whole numbers and is consistent with multiple proportions.

Check: According to the Law of Multiple Proportions, when two elements form two different compounds, the masses of element B that combine with 1 g of element A can be expressed as a ratio of small whole numbers.

40. **Given:** sulfur hexafluoride = 4.45 g fluorine and 1.25 g sulfur, sulfur tetrafluoride = 4.43 g fluorine and 1.87 g sulfur.
Find: mass fluorine per g S for each compound and then determine the mass ratio of fluorine

$$\frac{\text{mass of fluorine in sulfur hexafluoride}}{\text{mass of sulfur in sulfur hexafluoride}} \quad \frac{\text{mass of fluorine in sulfur tetrafluoride}}{\text{mass of sulfur in sulfur tetrafluoride}} \quad \frac{\text{mass of oxyen in sulfur hexafluoride}}{\text{mass of oxyen in sulfur tetrafluoride}}$$

Solution: $\text{sulfur hexafluoride} = \dfrac{4.45\,\text{g fluorine}}{1.25\,\text{g sulfur}} = \dfrac{3.56\,\text{g fluorine}}{1\,\text{g sulfur}} \qquad \text{sulfur tetrafluoride} = \dfrac{4.43\,\text{g fluorine}}{1.87\,\text{g sulfur}} = \dfrac{2.369\,\text{g fluorine}}{1\,\text{g sulfur}}$

$\dfrac{3.56\,\text{g fluorine in sulfur hexafluoride}}{2.369\,\text{g fluorine in sulfur tetrafluoride}} = \dfrac{1.50}{1} = \dfrac{3}{2}$ \quad Ratio is in small whole numbers and is consistent with multiple proportions.

Check: According to the Law of Multiple Proportions, when two elements form two different compounds, the masses of element B that combine with 1 g of element A can be expressed as a ratio of small whole numbers.

41. a) Sulfur and oxygen atoms have the same mass. INCONSISTENT with Dalton's atomic theory because only atoms of the same element have the same mass.

   b) All cobalt atoms are identical. CONSISTENT with Dalton's atomic theory because all atoms of a given element have the same mass and other properties that distinguish them from atoms of other elements.

c) Potassium and chlorine atoms combine in a 1:1 ratio to form potassium chloride. CONSISTENT with Dalton's atomic theory because atoms combine in simple whole number ratios to form compounds.

d) Lead atoms can be converted into gold. INCONSISTENT with Dalton's atomic theory because atoms of one element cannot change into atoms of another element.

42. a) All carbon atoms are identical. CONSISTENT with Dalton's atomic theory because all atoms of a given element have the same mass and other properties that distinguish them from atoms of other elements.

b) An oxygen atom combines with 1.5 hydrogen atoms to form a water molecule. INCONSISTENT with Dalton's atomic theory because atoms combine in simple whole number ratios to form compounds. An oxygen atom actually combines with 2 hydrogen atoms to form a water molecule.

c) Two oxygen atoms combine with a carbon atom to form a carbon dioxide molecule. CONSISTENT with Dalton's atomic theory because atoms combine in simple whole number ratios to form compounds.

d) The formation of a compound often involves the destruction of one or more atoms. INCONSISTENT with Dalton's atomic theory because atoms change the way that they are bound together with other atoms when they form a new substance.

43. a) The volume of an atom is mostly empty space. CONSISTENT with Rutherford's nuclear theory because most of the volume of the atom is empty space, throughout which tiny, negatively charged electrons are dispersed.

b) The nucleus of an atom is small compared to the size of the atom. CONSISTENT with Rutherford's nuclear theory because most of the atom's mass and all of its positive charge are contained in a small core called the nucleus.

c) Neutral lithium atoms contain more neutrons than protons. INCONSISTENT with Rutherford's nuclear theory because it did not distinguish where the mass of the nucleus came from other than from the protons.

d) Neutral lithium atoms contain more protons than electrons. INCONSISTENT with Rutherford's nuclear theory because there are as many negatively charged particles outside the nucleus as there are positively charged particles within the nucleus.

44. a) Since electrons are smaller than protons, and since a hydrogen atom contains only one proton and one electron, it must follow that the volume of a hydrogen atom is mostly due to the proton. INCONSISTENT with Rutherford's nuclear theory because most of the volume of the atom is empty space, throughout which tiny, negatively charged electrons are dispersed.

b) A nitrogen atom has seven protons in its nucleus and seven electrons outside of its nucleus. CONSISTENT with Rutherford's nuclear theory because there are as many negatively charged particles outside the nucleus as there are positively charged particles within the nucleus.

c) A phosphorus atom has 15 protons in its nucleus and 150 electrons outside of its nucleus. INCONSISTENT with Rutherford's nuclear theory because there are as many negatively charged particles outside the nucleus as there are positively charged particles within the nucleus.

d) The majority of the mass of a fluorine atom is due to its nine electrons. INCONSISTENT with Rutherford's nuclear theory because most of the atom's mass and all of its positive charge are contained in a small core called the nucleus.

45. **Given:** drop A = - 6.9×10^{-19} C; drop B = - 9.2×10^{-19} C; drop C = - 11.5×10^{-19} C; drop D = - 4.6×10^{-19} C
Find: The charge on a single electron
Conceptual Plan: determine the ratio of charge for each set of drops.

$$\frac{\text{charge on drop 1}}{\text{charge on drop 2}}$$

Solution: $\dfrac{-6.9 \times 10^{-19}\text{C drop A}}{-4.6 \times 10^{-19}\text{ C drop D}} = 1.5$ $\dfrac{-9.2 \times 10^{-19}\text{C drop B}}{-4.6 \times 10^{-19}\text{ C drop D}} = 2$ $\dfrac{-11.5 \times 10^{-19}\text{C drop C}}{-4.6 \times 10^{-19}\text{ C drop D}} = 2.5$

The ratios obtained are not whole numbers, but, can be converted to whole numbers by multiplying by 2. Therefore, the charge on the electron has to be 1/2 the smallest value experimentally obtained. The charge on the electron = $- 2.3 \times 10^{-19}$C.

Check: The units of the answer, Coulombs, are correct. The magnitude of the answer is reasonable since all the values experimentally obtained are integer multiples of $- 2.3 \times 10^{-19}$.

46. **Given:** drop A = $- 4.8 \times 10^{-9}$z; drop B = $- 9.6 \times 10^{-9}$z; drop C = $- 6.4 \times 10^{-9}$z; drop D = $- 12.8 \times 10^{-9}$z
Find: The charge on a single electron
Conceptual Plan:
   determine the ratio of charge for each set of drops then determine the charge on an electron
$$\frac{\text{charge on drop 1}}{\text{charge on drop 2}}$$
   then determine the number of electrons in each drop
$$\frac{\text{charge on drop}}{\text{charge on one electron}}$$

Solution: $\dfrac{-9.6 \times 10^{-9}\text{z drop B}}{-4.8 \times 10^{-9}\text{ z drop A}} = 2$ $\dfrac{-6.4 \times 10^{-9}\text{z drop C}}{-4.8 \times 10^{-9}\text{ z drop A}} = 1.33$ $\dfrac{-12.8 \times 10^{-9}\text{z drop B}}{-4.8 \times 10^{-9}\text{ z drop A}} = 2.66$

The ratios obtained are not whole numbers, but, can be converted to whole numbers by multiplying by 3. Therefore, the charge on the electron has to be 1/3 the smallest value experimentally obtained. The charge on the electron = $\dfrac{1}{3}$ x $- 4.8 \times 10^{-9}$ z = $- 1.6 \times 10^{-9}$ z .

Number of electrons in:

Drop A: $\dfrac{-4.8 \times 10^{-9}\ z}{-1.6 \times 10^{-9}\ z} = 3$ electrons   Drop B: $\dfrac{-9.6 \times 10^{-9}\ z}{-1.6 \times 10^{-9}\ z} = 6$ electrons

Drop C: $\dfrac{-6.4 \times 10^{-9}\ z}{-1.6 \times 10^{-9}\ z} = 4$ electrons   Drop D: $\dfrac{-12.8 \times 10^{-9}\ z}{-1.6 \times 10^{-9}\ z} = 8$ electrons

Check: The units of the answer, zorg, are correct. The magnitude of the answer is reasonable since all the values experimentally obtained are integer multiples of $- 1.6 \times 10^{-9}$.

47. **Given:** charge on body = $- 15\ \mu$C.   **Find:** number of electrons, mass of the electrons
Conceptual Plan: μC → C → number of electrons → mass of electrons
$$\frac{1\ C}{10^6 \mu C} \qquad \frac{1\ \text{electron}}{-1.60 \times 10^{-19} C} \qquad \frac{9.10 \times 10^{-28}\ g}{1\ \text{electron}}$$

Solution: $- 15\ \mu C \times \dfrac{1\ C}{10^6\ \mu C} \times \dfrac{1\ \text{electron}}{-1.60 \times 10^{-19}\ C} = 9.\underline{3}75 \times 10^{13}$ electrons = 9.4×10^{13} electrons

$9.\underline{3}75 \times 10^{13}$ electrons $\times \dfrac{9.10 \times 10^{-28}\ g}{1\ \text{electron}} = 8.5 \times 10^{-14}$ g

Check: The units of the answers, number of electrons and grams, are correct. The magnitude of the answers are reasonable since the charge on an electron and the mass of an electron are very small.

48. **Given:** charge = $- 1.0$ C.   **Find:** number of electrons, mass of the electrons
Conceptual Plan: C → number of electrons → mass of electrons
$$\frac{1\ \text{electron}}{-1.60 \times 10^{-19} C} \qquad \frac{9.10 \times 10^{-28}\ g}{1\ \text{electron}}$$

Solution: $- 1.0\ C \times \dfrac{1\ \text{electron}}{-1.60 \times 10^{-19}\ C} = 6.\underline{2}5 \times 10^{18}$ electrons = 6.3×10^{18} electrons

$6.\underline{2}5 \times 10^{18}$ electrons $\times \dfrac{9.10 \times 10^{-28}\ g}{1\ \text{electron}} = 5.7 \times 10^{-9}$ g

Check: The units of the answers, number of electrons and grams, are correct. The magnitude of the answers are reasonable since the charge on an electron and the mass of an electron are very small.

49. a) True: protons and electrons have equal and opposite charges

    b) True: protons and electrons have opposite charge so they will attract each other

    c) True: the mass of the electron is much less than the mass of the neutron

    d) False: the mass of the proton and the mass of the neutron are about the same

50. a) True: protons and electrons have equal and opposite charges.

    b) True: the mass of the proton and the mass of the neutron are about the same.

    c) False: all atoms contain protons. The lightest element, hydrogen, contains 1 proton.

    d) False: protons have a positive charge, neutrons are neutral

51. **Given:** mass of proton   **Find:** number of electron in equal mass
    Conceptual Plan: mass of protons → number of electrons

$$\frac{1 \text{ electron}}{0.00091 \times 10^{-27} \text{ kg}}$$

Solution: $1.67262 \times 10^{-27} \text{ kg} \times \dfrac{1 \text{ electron}}{0.00091 \times 10^{-27} \text{ kg}} = 1.8 \times 10^3 \text{ electrons}$

Check: The units of the answer, electrons, are correct. The magnitude of the answer is reasonable since the mass of the electron is much less than the mass of the proton.

52. **Given:** helium nucleus   **Find:** number of electrons in equal mass
    Conceptual Plan:
    # protons → mass of protons and # neutrons → mass of neutrons → total mass → number of electrons

$$\frac{1.67262 \times 10^{-27} \text{ kg}}{1 \text{ proton}} \qquad \frac{1.67493 \times 10^{-27} \text{ kg}}{1 \text{ neutron}} \qquad \text{mass protons + mass neutrons} \quad \frac{1 \text{ electron}}{0.00091 \times 10^{-27} \text{ kg}}$$

Solution: $2 \text{ protons} \times \dfrac{1.67262 \times 10^{-27} \text{ kg}}{\text{proton}} = 3.34524 \times 10^{-27} \text{ kg}$

$2 \text{ neutrons} \times \dfrac{1.67493 \times 10^{-27} \text{ kg}}{\text{neutron}} = 3.34986 \times 10^{-27} \text{ kg}$

$(3.34524 \times 10^{-27} \text{ kg} + 3.34986 \times 10^{-27} \text{ kg}) \times \dfrac{1 \text{ electron}}{0.00091 \times 10^{-27} \text{ kg}} = 7.4 \times 10^3 \text{ electrons}$

Check: The units of the answer, electrons, are correct. The magnitude of the answer is reasonable since the mass of the electrons is much less than the mass of the proton and neutron.

53. For each of the isotopes: determine Z(the number of protons) from the periodic table then determine A(protons + neutrons). Then, write the symbol in the form $^{A}_{Z}X$.

    a)   the sodium isotope with 12 neutrons: Z = 11; A = 11 + 12 = 23. $^{23}_{11}Na$

    b)   the oxygen isotope with 8 neutrons: Z = 8; A = 8 + 8 = 16. $^{16}_{8}O$

    c)   the aluminum isotope with 14 neutrons: Z = 13; A = 13 + 14 = 27 $^{27}_{13}Al$

    d)   the iodine isotope with 74 neutrons: Z = 53; A = 53 + 74 = 127 $^{127}_{53}I$

54. For each of the isotopes: determine Z(the number of protons) from the periodic table then determine A(protons + neutrons). Then, write the symbol in the form X – A.

    a)   the argon isotope with 22 neutrons: Z = 18; A = 18 + 22 =40.   Ar – 40

b)   the plutonium isotope with 145 neutrons: $Z = 94$: $A = 94 + 145 = 239$. Pu – 239

c)   the phosphorus isotope with 16 neutrons: $Z = 15$; $A = 15 + 16 = 31$.   P – 31

d)   the fluorine isotope with 10 neutrons: $Z = 9$: $A = 9 + 10 = 19$ F – 19

55. a) $^{14}_{7}N$: $Z = 7$; $A = 14$: protons = $Z = 7$; neutrons = $A - Z = 14 - 7 = 7$

    b) $^{23}_{11}Na$: $Z = 11$: $A = 23$: protons = $Z = 11$; neutrons = $A - Z = 23 - 11 = 12$

    c) $^{222}_{86}Rn$: $Z = 86$: $A = 222$: protons = $Z = 86$; neutrons = $A - Z = 222 - 86 = 136$

    d) $^{208}_{82}Pb$: $Z = 82$: $A = 208$: protons = $Z = 82$; neutrons = $A - Z = 208 - 82 = 126$

56. a) $^{40}_{19}K$: $Z = 19$; $A = 40$: protons = $Z = 19$; neutrons = $A - Z = 40 - 19 = 21$

    b) $^{226}_{88}Ra$: $Z = 88$; $A = 226$: protons = $Z = 88$; neutrons = $A - Z = 226 - 88 = 138$

    c) $^{99}_{43}Tc$: $Z = 43$; $A = 99$: protons = $Z = 43$; neutrons = $A - Z = 99 - 43 = 56$

    d) $^{33}_{15}P$: $Z = 15$; $A = 33$: protons = $Z = 15$; neutrons = $A - Z = 33 - 15 = 18$

57. Carbon – 14: $A = 14$, $Z = 6$: $^{14}_{6}C$ # protons = $Z = 6$ # neutrons = $A - Z = 14 - 6 = 8$

58. Uranium – 235: $A = 235$, $Z = 92$: $^{235}_{92}U$ # protons = $Z = 92$ # neutrons = $A - Z = 235 - 92 = 143$

59. In a neutral atom the number of protons = the number of electrons = Z. For an ion, electrons are lost (cations) or gained (anions)

    a) Ni^{2+}: $Z = 28$ = protons; $Z - 2 = 26$ = electrons

    b) S^{2-}: $Z = 16$ = protons; $Z + 2 = 18$ = electrons

    c) Br^{-}: $Z = 35$ = protons; $Z + 1 = 36$ = electrons

    d) Cr^{3+}: $Z = 24$ = protons; $Z - 3 = 21$ = electrons

60. In a neutral atom the number of protons = the number of electrons = Z. For an ion, electrons are lost (cations) or gained (anions)

    a) Al^{3+}: $Z = 13$ = protons; $Z - 3 = 10$ = electrons

    b) Se^{2-}: $Z = 34$ = protons; $Z + 2 = 36$ = electrons

    c) Ga^{3+}: $Z = 31$ = protons; $Z - 3 = 28$ = electrons

    d) Sr^{2+}: $Z = 38$ = protons; $Z - 2 = 36$ = electrons

61. Main group metal atoms will lose electrons to form a cation with the same number of electrons as the nearest, previous noble gas.
Nonmetal atoms will gain electrons to form an anion with the same number of electrons as the nearest noble gas.

    a) O^{2-} O is a nonmetal and has 8 electrons. It will gain electrons to form an anion. The nearest noble gas is neon with 10 electrons, so O will gain 2 electrons.

    b) K^{+} K is a main group metal and has 19 electrons. It will lose electrons to form a cation. The nearest noble gas is argon with 18 electrons, so K will lose 1 electron.

    c) Al^{3+} Al is a main group metal and has 13 electrons. It will lose electrons to form a cation. The nearest noble gas is neon with 10 electrons, so Al will lose 3 electrons.

d) Rb^+ Rb is a main group metal and has 37 electrons. It will lose electrons to form a cation. The nearest noble gas is krypton with 36 electrons, so Rb will lose 1 electron.

62. Main group metal atoms will lose electrons to form a cation with the same number of electrons as the nearest, previous noble gas.
Nonmetal atoms will gain electrons to form an anion with the same number of electrons as the nearest noble gas.

a) Mg^{2+} Mg is a main group metal and has 12 electrons. It will lose electrons to form a cation. The nearest noble gas is neon with 10 electrons, so Mg will lose 2 electrons

b) N^{3-} N is a nonmetal and has 7 electrons. It will gain electrons to form an anion. The nearest noble gas is neon with 10 electrons, so N will gain 3 electrons.

c) F^- F is a nonmetal and has 9 electrons. It will gain electrons to form an anion. The nearest noble gas is neon with 10 electrons, so F will gain 1 electron.

d) Na^+ Na is a main group metal and has 11 electrons. It will lose electrons to form a cation. The nearest noble gas is neon with 10 electrons, so Na will lose 1 electron.

63. Main group metal atoms will lose electrons to form a cation with the same number of electrons as the nearest, previous noble gas.
Nonmetal atoms will gain electrons to form an anion with the same number of electrons as the nearest noble gas.

Symbol	Ion formed	Number of Electrons in Ion	Number of Protons in Ion
Ca	Ca^{2+}	**18**	**20**
Be	Be^{2+}	2	**4**
Se	Se^{2-}	**36**	34
In	In^{3+}	**46**	49

64. Main group metal atoms will lose electrons to form a cation with the same number of electrons as the nearest, previous noble gas.
Nonmetal atoms will gain electrons to form an anion with the same number of electrons as the nearest noble gas.

Symbol	Ion formed	Number of Electrons in Ion	Number of Protons in Ion
Cl	Cl^-	**18**	17
Te	Te^{2-}	54	**52**
Br	Br^-	**36**	**35**
Sr	Sr^{2+}	**36**	38

65. a)   Na   Sodium is a metal

    b)   Mg   Magnesium is a metal

    c)   Br   Bromine is a nonmetal

    d)   N   Nitrogen is a nonmetal

    e)   As   Arsenic is a metalloid

66. a)   lead   Pb is a metal

    b)   iodine   I is a nonmetal

    c)   potassium   K is a metal

d) silver   Ag is a metal

e) xenon   Xe is a nonmetal

67. a) tellurium   Te is in group 6A and is a main group element

b) potassium   K is in group 1A and is a main group element

c) vanadium   V is in group 5B and is a transition element

d) manganese   Mn is in group 7B and is a transition element

68. a) Cr   chromium is in group 6B and is a transition element

b) Br   bromine is in group 7A and is a main group element

c) Mo   molybdenum is in group 6B and is a transition element

d) Cs   cesium is in group 1A and is a main group element

69. a) sodium   Na is in group 1A and is an alkali metal

b) iodine   I is in group 7A and is a halogen

c) calcium   Ca is in group 2A and is an alkaline earth metal

d) barium   Ba is in group 2A and is an alkaline earth metal

e) krypton   Kr is in group 8A and is a noble gas

70. a) F   fluorine is in group 7A and is a halogen

b) Sr   strontium is in group 2A and is an alkaline earth metal

c) K   potassium is in group 1A and is an alkali metal

d) Ne   neon is in group 8A and is a noble gas

e) At   astatine is in group 7A and is a halogen

71. a) N and Ni would not be similar. Nitrogen is a nonmetal, nickel is a metal

b) Mo and Sn would not be most similar. Although both are metals, molybdenum is a transition metal and tin is a main group metal.

c) Na and Mg would not be similar. Although both are main group metals, sodium is in group 1A and magnesium is in group 2A.

d) Cl and F would be most similar. Chlorine and fluorine are both in group 7A. Elements in the same group have similar chemical properties.

e) Si and P would not be most similar. Silicon is a metalloid and phosphorus is a nonmetal.

72. a) Nitrogen and oxygen would not be most similar. Although both are nonmetals, N is in group 5A and O is in group 6A.

b) Titanium and gallium would not be most similar. Although both are metals, Ti is a transition metal and Ga is a main group metal.

c) Lithium and sodium would be most similar. Li and Na are both in group 1A. Elements in the same group have similar chemical properties.

d) Germanium and arsenic would not be the most similar. Ge and As are both metalloids and would share some properties, but Ge is in group 4A and As is in group 5A.

e) Argon and bromine would not be most similar. Although both are nonmetals, Ar is in group 8A and Br is in group 7A.

73. **Given:** Rb – 85; mass = 84.9118 amu; 72.15%: Rb – 87; mass = 86.9092 amu; 27.85 %   **Find:** atomic mass Rb

Conceptual Plan: % abundance → fraction and then find atomic mass

$$\frac{\% \text{ abundance}}{100}$$ $$\text{Atomic mass} = \sum_{n} (\text{fraction of isotope n}) \times (\text{mass of isotope n})$$

Solution: $\text{Fraction Rb - 85} = \dfrac{72.15}{100} = 0.7215$ $\text{Fraction Rb - 87} = \dfrac{27.85}{100} = 0.2785$

$\text{Atomic mass} = \sum_{n} (\text{fraction of isotope n}) \times (\text{mass of isotope n}) = 0.7215(84.9116 \text{ amu}) + 0.2785(86.9092 \text{ amu}) = 85.47 \text{ amu}$

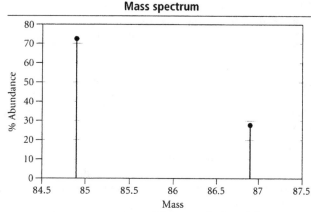

Check: Units of the answer, amu, are correct. The magnitude of the answer is reasonable because it lies between 84.9116 amu and 86.9092 amu and is closer to 84.9118, which has the higher % abundance. The mass spectrum is reasonable because it has two mass lines corresponding to the two isotopes and the line at 84.9116 is about 2.5 times larger than the line at 86.9092.

74. **Given:** Si – 28: mass = 27.9769 amu; 92.2%: Si – 29: mass = 28.9765 amu; 4.67 %: Si – 30: mass = 29.9737 amu; 3.10%
Find: atomic mass Si
Conceptual Plan: % abundance → fraction and then find atomic mass

$$\frac{\% \text{ abundance}}{100}$$ $$\text{Atomic mass} = \sum_{n} (\text{fraction of isotope n}) \times (\text{mass of isotope n})$$

Solution:

$\text{Fraction Si - 28} = \dfrac{92.2}{100} = 0.922$ $\text{Fraction Si - 29} = \dfrac{4.67}{100} = 0.0467$ $\text{Fraction Si - 30} = \dfrac{3.10}{100} = 0.0310$

Atomic mass $= \sum_{n}$ (fraction of isotope n) x (mass of isotope n)

$$= 0.922(27.9769 \text{ amu}) + 0.0467(28.9765 \text{ amu}) + 0.0310(29.9737 \text{ amu}) = 28.1 \text{ amu}$$

Check: Units of the answer, amu, are correct. The magnitude of the answer is reasonable because it lies between 27.9769 amu and 29.9737 amu and is closer to 27.9769 which has the highest % abundance. The mass spectrum is reasonable because it has three mass lines corresponding to the three isotopes and the line at 27.9769 is about 20 times larger than the other two lines.

75. Fluorine has an isotope F –19 with a very large abundance so that the mass of fluorine is very close to the mass of the isotope and the line in the mass spectrum reflects the abundance of F – 19. Chlorine has 2 isotopes Cl – 35 and Cl – 37 and the mass of 35.45 amu is the weighted average of these two isotopes so there is no line at 35.45 amu.

76. Copper would have no isotope with a mass of 63.546 amu. Since the mass of the isotope comes primarily from the sum of the protons and neutrons, the mass of the isotope has to have a value close to a whole number. Copper must be composed of 2 or more isotopes, one with a mass less than 63.546 amu and one with a mass greater than 63.546 amu.

77. **Given:** Isotope – 1; mass = 120.9038 amu; 57.4%: Isotope – 2; mass = 122.9042 amu;
    Find: atomic mass of the atom and identify the atom
    Conceptual Plan:
    % abundance isotope 2 → and then % abundance → fraction and then find atomic mass

    $$100\% - \% \text{ abundance Isotope 1} \qquad \frac{\% \text{ abundance}}{100} \qquad \text{Atomic mass} = \sum_{n}(\text{fraction of isotope n}) \text{ x (mass of isotope n)}$$

    Solution: 100.0% - 57.4 % Isotope 1 = 42.6 % Isotope 2

    $$\text{Fraction Isotope 1} = \frac{57.4}{100} = 0.574 \qquad \text{Fraction Isotope 2} = \frac{42.6}{100} = 0.426$$

    Atomic mass $= \sum_{n}$ (fraction of isotope n) x (mass of isotope n) $= 0.574(120.9038 \text{ amu}) + 0.426(122.9042 \text{ amu}) = 121.8 \text{ amu}$

    From the periodic table Sb has a mass of 121.757 amu, so it is the closest mass and the element is antimony.

    Check: The units of the answer, amu, are correct. The magnitude of the answer is reasonable because it lies between 120.9038 and 122.9042 and is slightly less than halfway between the two values because the lower value has a slightly greater abundance.

78. **Given:** Br – 81; mass = 80.9163 amu, 49.31 %, atomic mass Br = 79.904 amu
    Find: mass and abundance Br – 79
    Conceptual Plan: % abundance Br – 79 → then % abundance → fraction → mass Br – 79

    $$100\% - \% \text{ Br} - 81 \qquad \frac{\% \text{ abundance}}{100} \qquad \text{Atomic mass} = \sum_{n}(\text{fraction of isotope n}) \text{ x (mass of isotope n)}$$

    Solution: 100.00% - 49.31 % = 50.69% Br – 79

    $$\text{Fraction Br - 79} = \frac{50.69}{100} = 0.5069 \qquad \text{Fraction Br - 81} = \frac{49.31}{100} = 0.4931$$

    Let X be the mass of Br – 79

$$\text{Atomic mass} = \sum_{n} (\text{fraction of isotope n}) \times (\text{mass of isotope n})$$

$$79.904 \text{ amu} = 0.5069(X \text{ amu}) + 0.4931(80.9163 \text{ amu})$$

$$X = 78.91 \text{ amu} = \text{mass Br - 79}$$

Check: The units of the answer amu, are correct. The magnitude of the answer is reasonable because it is less than the mass of the atom and the second isotope (Br – 81) has a mass greater than the mass of the atom.

79. **Given:** 3.8 mol sulfur   **Find:** atoms of sulfur
    Conceptual Plan: mol S → atoms S

$$\frac{6.022 \times 10^{23} \text{ atoms}}{\text{mol}}$$

Solution: $3.8 \text{ mol S} \times \dfrac{6.022 \times 10^{23} \text{ atoms S}}{\text{mol S}} = 2.3 \times 10^{24} \text{ atoms S}$

Check: The units of the answer, atoms S, are correct. The magnitude of the answer is reasonable since there is more than 1 mole of material present.

80. **Given:** 5.8×10^{24} aluminum atoms   **Find:** mol Al
    Conceptual Plan: atoms Al → mol Al

$$\frac{1 \text{ mol}}{6.022 \times 10^{23} \text{ atoms}}$$

Solution: $5.8 \times 10^{24} \text{ atoms Al} \times \dfrac{1 \text{ mol Al}}{6.022 \times 10^{23} \text{ atoms Al}} = 9.6 \text{ mol Al}$

Check: The units of the answer, mol Al, are correct. The magnitude of the answer is reasonable since there is greater than Avogadro's number of atoms present.

81. a) **Given:** 11.8 g Ar   **Find:** mol Ar
    Conceptual Plan: g Ar → mol Ar

$$\frac{1 \text{ mol Ar}}{39.948 \text{ g Ar}}$$

Solution: $11.8 \text{ g Ar} \times \dfrac{1 \text{ mol Ar}}{39.948 \text{ g Ar}} = 0.295 \text{ mol Ar}$

Check: The units of the answer, mol Ar, are correct. The magnitude of the answer is reasonable since there is less than the mass of 1 mol present.

b) **Given:** 3.55 g Zn   **Find:** mol Zn
    Conceptual Plan: g Zn → mol Zn

$$\frac{1 \text{ mol Zn}}{65.39 \text{ g Zn}}$$

Solution: $3.55 \text{ g Zn} \times \dfrac{1 \text{ mol Zn}}{65.39 \text{ g Zn}} = 0.0543 \text{ mol Zn}$

Check: The units of the answer, mol Zn, are correct. The magnitude of the answer is reasonable since there is less than the mass of 1 mol present.

c) **Given:** 26.1 g Ta   **Find:** mol Ta
    Conceptual Plan: g Ta → mol Ta

$$\frac{1 \text{ mol Ta}}{180.948 \text{ g Ta}}$$

Solution: $26.1 \text{ g Ta} \times \dfrac{1 \text{ mol Ta}}{180.948 \text{ g Ta}} = 0.144 \text{ mol Ta}$

Check: The units of the answer, mol Ta, are correct. The magnitude of the answer is reasonable since there is less than the mass of 1 mol present.

d) **Given:** 0.211 g Li   **Find:** mol Li

Conceptual Plan: g Li → mol Li

$$\frac{1\,\text{mol Li}}{6.941\,\text{g Li}}$$

Solution: $0.211\ \cancel{\text{g Li}} \times \dfrac{1\ \text{mol Li}}{6.941\ \cancel{\text{g Li}}} = 0.0304$ mol Li

Check: The units of the answer, mol Li, are correct. The magnitude of the answer is reasonable since there is less than the mass of 1 mol present.

82. a) **Given:** 2.3×10^{-3} mol Sb   **Find:** grams Sb
   Conceptual Plan: mol Sb → g Sb

$$\frac{121.757\ \text{g Sb}}{1\,\text{mol Sb}}$$

   Solution: $2.3 \times 10^{-3}\ \cancel{\text{mol Sb}} \times \dfrac{121.757\ \text{g Sb}}{1\ \cancel{\text{mol Sb}}} = 0.28$ grams Sb

   Check: The units of the answer, grams Sb, are correct. The magnitude of the answer is reasonable since there is less than 1 mol of Sb present.

   b) **Given:** 0.0355 mol Ba   **Find:** grams Ba
   Conceptual Plan: mol Ba → g BA

$$\frac{137.327\ \text{g Ba}}{1\,\text{mol Ba}}$$

   Solution: $0.0355\ \cancel{\text{mol Ba}} \times \dfrac{137.327\ \text{g Ba}}{1\ \cancel{\text{mol Ba}}} = 4.88$ grams Ba

   Check: The units of the answer, grams Ba, are correct. The magnitude of the answer is reasonable since there is less than 1 mol of Ba present.

   c) **Given:** 43.9 mol Xe   **Find:** grams Xe
   Conceptual Plan: mol Xe → g Xe

$$\frac{131.29\ \text{g Xe}}{1\,\text{mol Xe}}$$

   Solution: $43.9\ \cancel{\text{mol Xe}} \times \dfrac{131.29\ \text{g Xe}}{1\ \cancel{\text{mol Xe}}} = 5.76 \times 10^{3}$ grams Xe

   Check: The units of the answer, grams Xe, are correct. The magnitude of the answer is reasonable since there is much more than 1 mol of Xe present.

   d) **Given:** 1.3 mol W   **Find:** grams W
   Conceptual Plan: mol W → g W

$$\frac{183.85\ \text{g W}}{1\,\text{mol W}}$$

   Solution: $1.3\ \cancel{\text{mol W}} \times \dfrac{183.85\ \text{g W}}{1\ \cancel{\text{mol W}}} = 2.4 \times 10^{2}$ grams W

   Check: The units of the answer, grams W, are correct. The magnitude of the answer is reasonable since there is slightly over 1 mol of W present.

83. **Given:** 3.78 g silver   **Find:** atoms Ag
   Conceptual Plan: g Ag → mol Ag → atoms Ag

$$\frac{1\,\text{mol Ag}}{107.868\,\text{g Ag}} \quad \frac{6.022 \times 10^{23}\,\text{atoms}}{\text{mol}}$$

   Solution: $3.78\ \cancel{\text{g Ag}} \times \dfrac{1\ \cancel{\text{mol Ag}}}{107.868\ \cancel{\text{g Ag}}} \times \dfrac{6.022 \times 10^{23}\ \text{atoms Ag}}{1\ \cancel{\text{mol Ag}}} = 2.11 \times 10^{22}$ atoms Ag

   Check: The units of the answer, atoms Ag, are correct. The magnitude of the answer is reasonable since there is less than the mass of 1 mol of Ag present.

84. **Given:** 4.91×10^{21} Pt atoms   **Find:** g Pt

Conceptual Plan: atoms Pt → mol Pt → g Pt

$$\frac{1\,mol}{6.022 \times 10^{23}\,atoms} \qquad \frac{195.08\,g\,Pt}{1\,mol\,Pt}$$

Solution: $4.91 \times 10\ atoms\ Pt\ \times\ \dfrac{1\ mol\ Pt}{6.022 \times 10^{23}\ atoms\ Pt}\ \times\ \dfrac{195.08\ g\ Pt}{1\ mol\ Pt} = 1.59\ g\ Pt$

Check: The units of the answer, g Pt, are correct. The magnitude of the answer is reasonable since there is less than 1 mol of Pt atoms present.

85. a) **Given:** 5.18 g P   **Find:** atoms P
     Conceptual Plan: g P → mol P → atoms P

$$\frac{1\,mol\,P}{30.9738\,g\,P} \qquad \frac{6.022 \times 10^{23}\,atoms}{mol}$$

     Solution: $5.18\ g\ P\ \times\ \dfrac{1\ mol\ P}{30.9738\ g\ P}\ \times\ \dfrac{6.022 \times 10^{23}\ atoms\ P}{1\ mol\ P} = 1.01 \times 10^{23}\ atoms\ P$

     Check: The units of the answer, atoms P, are correct. The magnitude of the answer is reasonable since there is slightly less than the mass of 1 mol of P present.

   b) **Given:** 2.26 g Hg   **Find:** atoms Hg
     Conceptual Plan: g Hg → mol Hg → atoms Hg

$$\frac{1\,mol\,Hg}{200.59\,g\,Hg} \qquad \frac{6.022 \times 10^{23}\,atoms}{mol}$$

     Solution: $2.26\ g\ Hg\ \times\ \dfrac{1\ mol\ Hg}{200.59\ g\ Hg}\ \times\ \dfrac{6.022 \times 10^{23}\ atoms\ Hg}{1\ mol\ Hg} = 6.78 \times 10^{21}\ atoms\ Hg$

     Check: The units of the answer, atoms Hg, are correct. The magnitude of the answer is reasonable since there is less than the mass of 1 mol of Hg present.

   c) **Given:** 1.87 g Bi   **Find:** atoms Bi
     Conceptual Plan: g Bi → mol Bi → atoms Bi

$$\frac{1\,mol\,Bi}{208.98\,g\,Bi} \qquad \frac{6.022 \times 10^{23}\,atoms}{mol}$$

     Solution: $1.87\ g\ Bi\ \times\ \dfrac{1\ mol\ Bi}{208.98\ g\ Bi}\ \times\ \dfrac{6.022 \times 10^{23}\ atoms\ Bi}{1\ mol\ Bi} = 5.39 \times 10^{21}\ atoms\ Bi$

     Check: The units of the answer, atoms Bi, are correct. The magnitude of the answer is reasonable since there is less than the mass of 1 mol of Bi present.

   d) **Given:** 0.082 g Sr   **Find:** atoms Sr
     Conceptual Plan: g Sr → mol Sr → atoms Sr

$$\frac{1\,mol\,Sr}{87.62\,g\,Sr} \qquad \frac{6.022 \times 10^{23}\,atoms}{mol}$$

     Solution: $0.082\ g\ Sr\ \times\ \dfrac{1\ mol\ Sr}{87.62\ g\ Sr}\ \times\ \dfrac{6.022 \times 10^{23}\ atoms\ Sr}{1\ mol\ Sr} = 5.6 \times 10^{20}\ atoms\ Sr$

     Check: The units of the answer, atoms Sr, are correct. The magnitude of the answer is reasonable since there is less than the mass of 1 mol of Sr present.

86. a) **Given:** 1.1×10^{23} gold atoms   **Find:** grams Au
     Conceptual Plan: atoms Au → mol Au → g Au

$$\frac{1\,mol}{6.022 \times 10^{23}\,atoms} \qquad \frac{196.97\,g\,Au}{1\,mol\,Au}$$

     Solution: $1.1 \times 10^{23}\ atoms\ Au\ \times\ \dfrac{1\ mol\ Au}{6.022 \times 10^{23}\ atoms\ Au}\ \times\ \dfrac{196.97\ g\ Au}{1\ mol\ Au} = 36\ g\ Au$

     Check: The units of the answer, g Au, are correct. The magnitude of the answer is reasonable since there is less than Avogadro's number of atoms in the sample.

45

b) **Given:** 2.82×10^{22} helium atoms   **Find:** grams He

Conceptual Plan: atoms He → mol He → g He

$$\frac{1\,\text{mol}}{6.022 \times 10^{23}\,\text{atoms}} \quad \frac{4.002\,\text{g He}}{1\,\text{mol He}}$$

Solution: $2.82 \times 10^{22}\ \cancel{\text{atoms He}} \times \dfrac{1\ \cancel{\text{mol He}}}{6.022 \times 10^{23}\ \cancel{\text{atoms He}}} \times \dfrac{4.002\ \text{g He}}{1\ \cancel{\text{mol He}}} = 0.187\ \text{g He}$

Check: The units of the answer, g He, are correct. The magnitude of the answer is reasonable since there is less than Avogadro's number of atoms in the sample.

c) **Given:** 1.8×10^{23} lead atoms   **Find:** grams Pb

Conceptual Plan: atoms Pb → mol Pb → g Pb

$$\frac{1\,\text{mol}}{6.022 \times 10^{23}\,\text{atoms}} \quad \frac{207.2\,\text{g Pb}}{1\,\text{mol Pb}}$$

Solution: $1.8 \times 10^{23}\ \cancel{\text{atoms Pb}} \times \dfrac{1\ \cancel{\text{mol Pb}}}{6.022 \times 10^{23}\ \cancel{\text{atoms Pb}}} \times \dfrac{207.2\ \text{g Pb}}{1\ \cancel{\text{mol Pb}}} = 62\ \text{g Pb}$

Check: The units of the answer, g Pb, are correct. The magnitude of the answer is reasonable since there is less than Avogadro's number of atoms in the sample.

d) **Given:** 7.9×10^{21} uranium atoms   **Find:** grams U

Conceptual Plan: atoms U → mol U → g U

$$\frac{1\,\text{mol}}{6.022 \times 10^{23}\,\text{atoms}} \quad \frac{238.029\,\text{g U}}{1\,\text{mol U}}$$

Solution: $7.9 \times 10^{21}\ \cancel{\text{atoms U}} \times \dfrac{1\ \cancel{\text{mol U}}}{6.022 \times 10^{23}\ \cancel{\text{atoms U}}} \times \dfrac{238.029\ \text{g U}}{1\ \cancel{\text{mol U}}} = 3.1\ \text{g U}$

Check: The units of the answer, g U, are correct. The magnitude of the answer is reasonable since there is less than Avogadro's number of atoms in the sample.

87. **Given:** 52 mg diamond (carbon)   **Find:** atoms C

Conceptual Plan: mg C → g C → mol C → atoms C

$$\frac{1\,\text{g C}}{1000\,\text{mg C}} \quad \frac{1\,\text{mol C}}{12.011\,\text{g C}} \quad \frac{6.022 \times 10^{23}\,\text{atoms}}{\text{mol}}$$

Solution: $52\ \cancel{\text{mg C}} \times \dfrac{1\ \cancel{\text{g C}}}{1000\ \cancel{\text{mg C}}} \times \dfrac{1\ \cancel{\text{mol C}}}{12.011\ \cancel{\text{g C}}} \times \dfrac{6.022 \times 10^{23}\ \text{atoms C}}{1\ \cancel{\text{mol C}}} = 2.6 \times 10^{21}\ \text{atoms C}$

Check: The units of the answer, atoms C, are correct. The magnitude of the answer is reasonable since there is less than the mass of 1 mol of C present.

88. **Given:** 536 kg helium   **Find:** atoms He

Conceptual Plan: kg He → g He → mol He → atoms He

$$\frac{1000\,\text{g He}}{1\,\text{kg He}} \quad \frac{1\,\text{mol He}}{4.0026\,\text{g He}} \quad \frac{6.022 \times 10^{23}\,\text{atoms}}{\text{mol}}$$

Solution: $536\ \cancel{\text{kg He}} \times \dfrac{1000\ \cancel{\text{g He}}}{1\ \cancel{\text{kg He}}} \times \dfrac{1\ \cancel{\text{mol He}}}{4.0026\ \cancel{\text{g He}}} \times \dfrac{6.022 \times 10^{23}\ \text{atoms He}}{1\ \cancel{\text{mol He}}} = 8.06 \times 10^{28}\ \text{atoms He}$

Check: The units of the answer, atoms He, are correct. The magnitude of the answer is reasonable since there is much more than the mass of 1 mol of He present.

89. **Given:** 1 atom platinum   **Find:** g Pt

Conceptual Plan: atoms Pt → mol Pt → g Pt

$$\frac{1\,\text{mol}}{6.022 \times 10^{23}\,\text{atoms}} \quad \frac{195.08\,\text{g Pt}}{1\,\text{mol Pt}}$$

Solution: $1 \ \cancel{\text{atom Pt}} \ \text{x} \ \dfrac{1 \ \cancel{\text{mol Pt}}}{6.022 \ \text{x} \ 10^{23} \ \cancel{\text{atoms Pt}}} \ \text{x} \ \dfrac{195.08 \ \text{g Pt}}{1 \ \cancel{\text{mol Pt}}} = 3.239 \ \text{x} \ 10^{-22} \ \text{g Pt}$

Check: The units of the answer, g Pt, are correct. The magnitude of the answer is reasonable since there is only 1 atom in the sample.

90. **Given:** 35 atoms xenon   **Find:** g Xe
    Conceptual Plan: atoms Xe → mol Xe → g Xe

$$\dfrac{1 \text{mol}}{6.022 \ \text{x} \ 10^{23} \ \text{atoms}} \qquad \dfrac{131.29 \ \text{g Xe}}{1 \ \text{mol Xe}}$$

Solution: $35 \ \cancel{\text{atom Xe}} \ \text{x} \ \dfrac{1 \ \cancel{\text{mol Xe}}}{6.022 \ \text{x} \ 10^{23} \ \cancel{\text{atoms Xe}}} \ \text{x} \ \dfrac{131.29 \ \text{g Xe}}{1 \ \cancel{\text{mol Xe}}} = 7.631 \ \text{x} \ 10^{-21} \ \text{g Xe}$

Check: The units of the answer, g Xe, are correct. The magnitude of the answer is reasonable since there are only 35 atoms in the sample.

91. **Given:** 7.83 g HCN sample 1: 0.290 g H; 4.06 g N. 3.37 g HCN sample 2   **Find:** g C in sample 2
    Conceptual Plan:
       g HCN sample 1 → g C in HCN sample 1 → ratio g C to g HCN → g C in HCN sample 2

$$\text{g HCN} - \text{g H} - \text{g N} \qquad \dfrac{\text{g C}}{\text{g HCN}} \qquad \text{g HCN} \ \text{x} \ \dfrac{\text{g C}}{\text{g HCN}}$$

Solution: $7.83 \ \text{g HCN} - 0.290 \ \text{g H} - 4.06 \ \text{g N} = 3.48 \ \text{g C}$

$$3.37 \ \cancel{\text{g HCN}} \ \text{x} \ \dfrac{3.48 \ \text{g C}}{7.83 \ \cancel{\text{g HCN}}} = 1.50 \ \text{g C}$$

Check: The units of the answer, g C, are correct. The magnitude of the answer is reasonable since the sample size is about half the original sample size, the g C are about half the original g C.

92. a)   **Given:** mass ratio S:O = 1.0:1.0 in SO_2 **Find:** mass ratio S:O in SO_3
        Conceptual Plan: determine the ratio of O:O in SO_3 and SO_2 then determine g O per g S in SO_3
        Solution: for a fixed amount of S, the ratio of O is $\dfrac{3 \ O}{2 \ O} = 1.5$. So, for 1 gram S, SO_3 would have 1.5 g
        O. The mass ratio of S:O = 1.0:1.5 in SO_3.
        Check: The answer is reasonable since the ratio is smaller than the ratio for SO_2 and SO_3 has to contain more O per gram of S.

    b)   **Given:** mass ratio S:O = 1.0:1.0 in SO_2 **Find:** mass ratio S:O in S_2O
        Conceptual Plan: determine the ratio of S:S in S_2O and SO_2 then determine g O per g S in S_2O
        Solution: for a fixed amount of O, the ratio of S is $\dfrac{2 \ S}{0.5 \ S} = 4.0$. So, for 1 gram O, S_2O would have 4
        gram S. The mass ratio of S:O = 4.0:1.0 in S_2O.
        Check: The answer is reasonable since the ratio is larger than the ratio for SO_2 and S_2O has to contain more S per gram of O.

93. **Given:** In CO mass ratio O:C = 1.33:1; In compound X, mass ratio O:C = 2:1.   **Find:** formula of X
    Conceptual Plan: determine the mass ratio of O:O in the 2 compounds.
    Solution:

    For 1 gram of C: $\dfrac{2 \ \text{g O in compound X}}{1.33 \ \text{g O in CO}} = 1.5$ So, the ratio of O to C in compound X has to be 1.5:1 and the formula is C_2O_3.

    Check: The answer is reasonable since it fulfills the criteria of multiple proportions and the mass ratio of O:C is 2:1.

94. **Given:** mass ratio 1 atom N:1 atom ^{12}C = 7:6; mass ratio 2 mol N:1 mol O in N_2O = 7:4
       Find: mass of 1 mol O
    Conceptual Plan: determine the mass ratio of O to ^{12}C from the mass ratio of N to ^{12}C and the mass ratio of N to O and then determine the mol ratio of ^{12}C to O then use the mass of 1 mol ^{12}C to determine mass 1 mol O

$$\frac{12.00 \text{ g }^{12}\text{C}}{1 \text{ mol }^{12}\text{C}}$$

Solution: From the mass ratios: for every 7 grams N there are 6 grams ^{12}C and for every 7 grams N there are 4 grams O. So, the mass ratio of O:^{12}C is 4:6.

$$\frac{1 \text{ atom }^{12}\text{C}}{1 \text{ atom N}} \times \frac{6.022 \times 10^{23} \text{ atom N}}{1 \text{ mol N}} \times \frac{1 \text{ mol }^{12}\text{C}}{6.022 \times 10^{23} \text{ atom }^{12}\text{C}} \times \frac{2 \text{ mol N}}{1 \text{ mol O}} = \frac{2 \text{ mol }^{12}\text{C}}{1 \text{ mol O}}$$

$$\frac{2 \text{ mol }^{12}\text{C}}{1 \text{ mol O}} \times \frac{12.00 \text{ g }^{12}\text{C}}{1 \text{ mol }^{12}\text{C}} \times \frac{4 \text{ g O}}{6 \text{ g }^{12}\text{C}} = 16.00 \text{ g O/ mol O}$$

Check: The units of the answer, g O/mol O, are correct. The magnitude of the answer is reasonable since it is close to the value on the periodic table.

95. **Given:** $^{4}\text{He}^{2+} = 4.00151$ amu;   **Find:** charge to mass ratio C/kg

     Conceptual Plan: determine total charge on $^{4}\text{He}^{2+}$ and then amu $^{4}\text{He}^{2+} \rightarrow$ g $^{4}\text{He}^{2+} \rightarrow$ kg $^{4}\text{He}^{2+}$

$$\frac{+1.60218 \times 10^{-19} \text{ C}}{\text{proton}} \qquad \frac{1 \text{ g}}{1.66054 \times 10^{-24} \text{ amu}} \qquad \frac{1 \text{ kg}}{1000 \text{ g}}$$

Solution:

$$\frac{2 \text{ protons}}{1 \text{ atom }^{4}\text{He}^{2+}} \times \frac{+1.60218 \times 10^{-19} \text{ C}}{\text{proton}} = \frac{3.20436 \times 10^{-19} \text{ C}}{\text{atom }^{4}\text{He}^{2+}}$$

$$\frac{4.00151 \text{ amu}}{1 \text{ atom }^{4}\text{He}^{2+}} \times \frac{1.66054 \times 10^{-24} \text{ g}}{1 \text{ amu}} \times \frac{1 \text{ kg}}{1000 \text{ g}} = \frac{6.64466742 \times 10^{-27} \text{ kg}}{1 \text{ atom }^{4}\text{He}^{2+}}$$

$$\frac{3.20436 \times 10^{-19} \text{ C}}{\text{atom }^{4}\text{He}^{2+}} \times \frac{1 \text{ atom }^{4}\text{He}^{2+}}{6.64466742 \times 10^{-27} \text{ kg}} = 4.82245 \times 10^{7} \text{ C/kg}$$

Check: the units of the answer, C/kg, are correct. The magnitude of the answer is reasonable when compared to the charge to mass ratio of the electron.

96. **Given:** 12.3849 g sample I; atomic mass I = 126.9045 amu; 1.00070g ^{129}I; mass ^{129}I = 128.9050 amu
     Find: mass of contaminated sample

     Conceptual Plan: total mass of sample $\rightarrow$ fraction I and ^{129}I in the sample $\rightarrow$ apparent "atomic

     mass" mass I + mass ^{129}I $\dfrac{\text{g I}}{\text{g sample}}; \dfrac{\text{g }^{129}\text{I}}{\text{g sample}}$ Atomic mass $= \sum_{n}$ (fraction of isotope n) x (mass of isotope n)

Solution: 12.3849 g I + 1.00070 g ^{129}I = 13.3856 g sample

$$\frac{12.3849 \text{ g}}{13.3856 \text{ g}} = 0.925240557 \text{ fraction I} \qquad \frac{1.00070 \text{ g}}{13.3856 \text{ g}} = 0.07475944 \text{ fraction }^{129}\text{I}$$

$$\text{Atomic mass} = \sum_{n} \text{(fraction of isotope n) x (mass of isotope n)}$$

$$= (0.925240557)(126.9045 \text{ amu}) + (0.07475944)(128.9050 \text{ amu})$$

$$= 127.055 \text{ amu}$$

Check: The units of the answer, amu, are correct. The magnitude of the answer is reasonable because it is between 126.9045 and 128.9050 and only slightly higher than the naturally occurring value.

97. $^{236}_{90}\text{Th}$ A – Z = number of neutrons. 236 – 90 = 146 neutrons. So, any isotope with 146 neutrons is an isotone of $^{236}_{90}\text{Th}$.

Some would be: $^{238}_{92}\text{U}$; $^{239}_{93}\text{Np}$; $^{241}_{95}\text{Am}$; $^{237}_{91}\text{Pa}$; $^{235}_{89}\text{Ac}$; $^{244}_{98}\text{Cf}$ etc.

98.

Symbol	Z	A	Number protons	Number electrons	Number neutrons	Charge
Si	14	28	14	14	14	0
S^{2-}	16	32	16	18	16	2 −
Cu^{2+}	29	63	29	27	34	2+
P	15	28	15	15	13	0

99.

Symbol	Z	A	Number protons	Number electrons	Number neutrons	Charge
O^{2-}	8	16	8	10	8	2 −
Ca^{2+}	20	40	20	18	20	2+
Mg^{2+}	12	25	12	10	13	2+
N^{3-}	7	14	7	10	7	3 −

100. **Given:** r (neutron) = 1.0 x 10^{-13} cm; r(star piece) = 0.10 mm   **Find:** density of neutron, mass (kg) of star piece

Conceptual Plan:

r (neutron) → vol (neutron) → density (neutron) and then r (star piece) → vol (star piece)

$$V = \frac{4}{3}\pi r^3 \qquad d = \frac{m}{v} \qquad V = \frac{4}{3}\pi r^3$$

→ mass (star piece)

$$m = dv$$

Solution:

For the neutron:

$$\text{Vol(neutron)} = \frac{4}{3}\pi(1.0 \times 10^{-13}\,\text{cm})^3 = 4.19 \times 10^{-39}\,\text{cm}^3 \qquad d = \frac{1.00727\,\text{amu}}{4.19 \times 10^{-39}\,\text{cm}^3} \times \frac{1.661 \times 10^{-24}\,\text{g}}{\text{amu}} = 3.99 \times 10^{14}\,\text{g/cm}^3$$

For the star piece:

$$\text{Vol(star piece)} = \frac{4}{3}\pi(0.10\,\text{mm})^3 \frac{(1\text{cm})^3}{(10\,\text{mm})^3} = 4.19 \times 10^{-4}\,\text{cm}^3 \qquad m = 4.19 \times 10^{-4}\,\text{cm}^3 \times \frac{3.99 \times 10^{14}\,\text{g}}{\text{cm}^3} \times \frac{1\text{kg}}{1000\,\text{g}} = 1.7 \times 10^8\,\text{kg}$$

Check: The units of the answer, kg, are correct. The magnitude of the answer shows the great mass of the neutron star.

101. **Given:** r(nucleus) = 2.7 fm; r(atom) = 70 pm   (assume 2 significant figures)
Find: vol(nucleus); vol(atom), % vol(nucleus)

Conceptual Plan:

r(nucleus)(fm) → r(nucleus)(pm) → vol(nucleus) and then r(atom) → vol(atom) and then % vol

$$\frac{10^{-15}\text{m}}{1\text{fm}}\quad\frac{1\text{pm}}{10^{-12}\text{m}} \qquad V = \frac{4}{3}\pi r^3 \qquad V = \frac{4}{3}\pi r^3 \qquad \frac{\text{vol(nucleus)}}{\text{vol(atom)}} \times 100$$

Solution:

$$2.7\,\text{fm} \times \frac{10^{-15}\,\text{m}}{\text{fm}} \times \frac{1\,\text{pm}}{10^{-12}\,\text{m}} = 2.7 \times 10^{-3}\,\text{pm} \qquad V_{\text{nucleus}} = \frac{4}{3}\pi(2.7 \times 10^{-3}\,\text{pm})^3 = 8.2 \times 10^{-8}\,\text{pm}^3$$

$$V_{\text{atom}} = \frac{4}{3}\pi(70\,\text{pm})^3 = 1.4 \times 10^6\,\text{pm}^3 \qquad \frac{8.2 \times 10^{-8}\,\text{pm}^3}{1.4 \times 10^6\,\text{pm}^3} \times 100\% = 5.9 \times 10^{-12}\%$$

Check: The units of the answer, % vol, are correct. The magnitude of the answer is reasonable because the nucleus only occupies a very small % of the vol of the atom.

102. **Given:** 1 penny = 1.0 mm   **Find:** height in km of Avogadro's number of pennies

Conceptual Plan: height of 1 penny → height of Avogadro's number of pennies

$$6.022 \times 10^{23}$$

Solution: $\dfrac{1.0 \text{ mm}}{\text{penny}} \times 6.022 \times 10^{23} \text{ pennies} \times \dfrac{1 \text{ m}}{1000 \text{ mm}} \times \dfrac{1 \text{ km}}{1000 \text{ m}} = 6.022 \times 10^{17} \text{ km}$

Check: The units of the answer, km, are correct. The magnitude of the answer shows just how large Avogadro's number is.

103. **Given:** 6.022×10^{23} pennies   **Find:** the amount in dollars; the dollars/person
     Conceptual Plan: pennies → dollars → dollars/person

$$\dfrac{1 \text{ dollar}}{100 \text{ pennies}} \qquad 6.5 \text{ billion people}$$

Solution:

$6.022 \times 10^{23} \text{ pennies} \times \dfrac{1 \text{ dollar}}{100 \text{ pennies}} = 6.022 \times 10^{21} \text{ dollars} \qquad \dfrac{6.022 \times 10^{21} \text{ dollars}}{6.5 \times 10^{9} \text{ people}} = 9.3 \times 10^{11} \text{ dollars / person}$,

billionaires

104. **Given:** 1 mol blueberries, m = 0.75 g; m(automobile) = 2.0×10^3 kg   **Find:** number of autos for 1 mol blueberries
     Conceptual Plan:
          mol blueberries → mass blueberries (g) → mass blueberries (kg) → number of automobiles

$$\dfrac{0.75 \text{ g}}{\text{blueberry}} \qquad \dfrac{\text{kg}}{1000 \text{ g}} \qquad \dfrac{1 \text{ automobile}}{2.0 \times 10^3 \text{ kg}}$$

Solution:

$1 \text{ mol blueberries} \times \dfrac{6.022 \times 10^{23} \text{ blueberries}}{\text{mol blueberries}} \times \dfrac{0.75 \text{ g}}{\text{blueberry}} \times \dfrac{1 \text{ kg}}{1000 \text{ g}} \times \dfrac{1 \text{ automobile}}{2.0 \times 10^3 \text{ kg}} = 2.3 \times 10^{17} \text{ automobiles}$

Check: The units of the answer, automobiles, are correct. The magnitude of the answer is reasonable because Avogadro's number is so large.

105. **Given:** O = 15.9994 amu when C = 12.011 amu **Find:** mass O when C = 12.00 amu
     Conceptual Plan: determine ratio O:C for ^{12}C system then use the same ratio when C = 12.00

$$\dfrac{\text{mass O}}{\text{mass C}}$$

Solution: Based on ^{12}C = 12.00; O = 15.9994 and C = 12.011 so, $\dfrac{\text{mass O}}{\text{mass C}} = \dfrac{15.9994 \text{ amu}}{12.011 \text{ amu}} = \dfrac{1.33206 \text{ amu O}}{1 \text{ amu C}}$

Based on C = 12.00, the ratio has to be the same,

$$12.000 \text{ amu C} \times \dfrac{1.33206 \text{ amu O}}{1 \text{ amu C}} = 15.985 \text{ amu O}$$

Check: The units of the answer, amu O, are correct. The magnitude of the answer is reasonable because the value for the new mass basis is smaller then the original mass basis, therefore, the mass of O should be less.

106. **Given:** Ti cube: d = 4.50 g/cm^3; e = 2.78 in.   **Find:** number Ti atoms
     Conceptual Plan: e in inch → e in cm → vol cube → g Ti → mol Ti → atoms Ti

$$\dfrac{2.54 \text{ cm}}{1 \text{ inch}} \qquad V = e^3 \qquad \dfrac{4.50 \text{ g}}{\text{cm}^3} \quad \dfrac{1 \text{ mol Ti}}{47.867 \text{ g}} \qquad \dfrac{6.022 \times 10^{23} \text{ atoms}}{\text{mol}}$$

Solution: $2.78 \text{ in} \times \dfrac{2.54 \text{ cm}}{\text{in}} = 7.061 \text{ cm}$

$(7.061 \text{ cm})^3 \times \dfrac{4.50 \text{ g}}{\text{cm}^3} \times \dfrac{1 \text{ mol Ti}}{47.867 \text{ g}} \times \dfrac{6.022 \times 10^{23} \text{ atoms Ti}}{1 \text{ mol Ti}} = 4.00 \times 10^{23} \text{ atoms Ti}$

Check: The units of the answer, atoms Ti, are correct. The magnitude of the answer is reasonable because there is about 30 mol of Ti in the cube.

107. **Given:** Cu sphere: r = 0.935 in; d = 8.96 g/cm^3 **Find:** number of Cu atoms
     Conceptual Plan: r in inch → r in cm → vol sphere → g Cu → mol Cu → atoms Cu

$$\frac{2.54\,\text{cm}}{1\,\text{inch}} \qquad V = \frac{4}{3}\pi r^3 \qquad \frac{8.96\,\text{g}}{\text{cm}^3} \quad \frac{1\,\text{mol Cu}}{63.546\,\text{g}} \quad \frac{6.022 \times 10^{23}\,\text{atoms}}{\text{mol}}$$

Solution: $0.935\,\text{in} \times \dfrac{2.54\,\text{cm}}{\text{in}} = 2.3\underline{7}49\,\text{cm}$

$$\frac{4}{3}\pi(2.3\underline{7}49\,\text{cm})^3 \times \frac{8.96\,\text{g}}{\text{cm}^3} \times \frac{1\,\text{mol Cu}}{63.546\,\text{g}} \times \frac{6.022 \times 10^{23}\,\text{atoms Cu}}{1\,\text{mol Cu}} = 4.76 \times 10^{24}\,\text{atoms Cu}$$

Check: The units of the answer, atoms Cu, are correct. The magnitude of the answer is reasonable because there are about 8 mol Cu present.

108. **Given:** B – 10 = 10.01294 amu; B – 11 = 11.00931 amu; B = 10.811 amu
Find: % abundance B – 10 and B – 11
Conceptual Plan: Let x = fraction B – 10 then 1 – x = fraction B – 11 → abundances
$$\text{Atomic mass} = \sum_n (\text{fraction of isotope n}) \times (\text{mass of isotope n})$$

Solution:
$$\text{Atomic mass} = \sum_n (\text{fraction of isotope n}) \times (\text{mass of isotope n})$$

$10.811 = (x)(10.01294\,\text{amu}) + (1 - x)(11.00931\,\text{amu})$

$0.19\underline{8}31 = 0.99637\,x$

$x = 0.19\underline{9}0 \qquad 1 - x = 0.80\underline{0}96$

B – 10 = 0.199 x 100 = 19.9 % and B – 11 = 0.801 x 100 = 80.1 %

Check: The units of the answer, %, abundance are correct. The relative abundances are reasonable because B has an atomic mass closer to the mass of B - 11 than to B - 10.

109. **Given:** Li – 6 = 6.01512 amu; Li – 7 = 7.01601 amu; B = 6.941 amu
Find: % abundance Li – 6 and Li – 7
Conceptual Plan: Let x = fraction Li – 6 then 1 – x = fraction Li – 7 → abundances
$$\text{Atomic mass} = \sum_n (\text{fraction of isotope n}) \times (\text{mass of isotope n})$$

Solution:
$$\text{Atomic mass} = \sum_n (\text{fraction of isotope n}) \times (\text{mass of isotope n})$$

$6.941 = (x)(6.01512\,\text{amu}) + (1 - x)(7.01601\,\text{amu})$

$0.07501 = 1.00089\,x$

$x = 0.07494 \qquad 1 - x = 0.92506$

Li – 6 = 0.07494 x 100 = 7.494 % and Li – 7 = 0.92506 x 100 = 92.506 %

Check: The units of the answer, %, abundance are correct. The relative abundances are reasonable because Li has an atomic mass closer to the mass of Li – 7 than to Li – 6.

110. **Given:** 1 mol sand grains; e(cube) = 0.10 mm; area Texas = 268,601 sq mi. **Find:** height of sand ft
Conceptual Plan:
mol sand → grains sand → vol sand mm^3 → vol sand ft^3 and then area Texas mi^2 → area ft^2

$$\frac{6.022 \times 10^{23}\,\text{grains}}{\text{mol}} \qquad V = e^3 \qquad \text{mm}^3 \times \left(\frac{\text{cm}}{10\,\text{mm}}\right)^3 \left(\frac{1\,\text{in}}{2.54\,\text{cm}}\right)^3 \left(\frac{1\,\text{ft}}{12\,\text{in}}\right)^3 \qquad \left(\frac{5280\,\text{ft}}{1\,\text{mi}}\right)^2$$

and then → height ft.
$$h = \frac{\text{Volume}}{\text{Area}}$$

Solution:

$$1\,\text{mol sand grains} \times \frac{6.022 \times 10^{23}\,\text{grains}}{\text{mol}} \times \frac{(0.10\,\text{mm})^3}{\text{grain}} \times \left(\frac{\text{cm}}{10\,\text{mm}}\right)^3 \times \left(\frac{1\,\text{in}}{2.54\,\text{cm}}\right)^3 \times \left(\frac{1\,\text{ft}}{12\,\text{in}}\right)^3 = 2.12\underline{6}6 \times 10^{13}\,\text{ft}^3\,\text{sand}$$

$$\frac{2.12\underline{6}6 \times 10^{13}\,\text{ft}^3\,\text{sand}}{268,601\,\text{mi}^2} \times \left(\frac{1\,\text{mi}}{5280\,\text{ft}}\right)^2 = 2.84\,\text{ft of sand}$$

Check: The units of the answer, ft sand, are correct. The magnitude of the answer seems reasonable.

111. **Given:** sun: d = 1.4 g/cm^3; r = 7 x 10^8 m; 100 billion stars/galaxy; 10 billion galaxies/universe
    Find: number of atoms in the universe
    Conceptual Plan: r (star) in m → r (star) in cm → vol (star) → g H/star → mol H star → atoms H/star

$$\frac{100\,cm}{m} \qquad V = \frac{4}{3}\pi r^3 \quad \frac{1.4\,gH}{cm^3} \qquad \frac{1\,mol\,H}{1.008\,g} \qquad \frac{6.022 \times 10^{23}\,atoms}{mol}$$

→ atoms H/galaxy → atoms H/universe

$$\frac{100 \times 10^9\,stars}{galaxy} \quad \frac{10 \times 10^9\,galaxies}{universe}$$

Solution: $7 \times 10^8\,\cancel{m} \times \dfrac{100\,cm}{\cancel{m}} = 7 \times 10^{10}\,cm$

$$\frac{4}{3}\pi \frac{(7 \times 10^{10}\,\cancel{cm})^3}{\cancel{star}} \times \frac{1.4\,\cancel{gH}}{\cancel{cm^3}} \times \frac{1\,\cancel{mol\,H}}{1.008\,\cancel{gH}} \times \frac{6.022 \times 10^{23}\,\cancel{atoms\,H}}{\cancel{mol\,H}} \times \frac{100 \times 10^9\,\cancel{stars}}{\cancel{galaxy}} \times \frac{10 \times 10^9\,\cancel{galaxies}}{universe}$$

$= 1 \times 10^{78}$ atoms/universe

Check: The units of the answer, atoms/universe, are correct.

112.a) **Given:** 37 Wt – 296; 2 Wt – 297; 12 Wt – 298   **Find:** % abundance of each
    Conceptual Plan: total atoms → fraction of each isotope → % abundance

$$\text{Sum of atoms} \qquad \frac{\text{number of each isotope}}{\text{total atoms}} \qquad \text{fraction x 100}$$

Solution: Total atoms = 37 + 2 + 12 = 51

$$\frac{37}{51} \times 100 = 72.55\%\,Wt - 296 \qquad \frac{2}{51} \times 100 = 3.922\%\,Wt - 297 \qquad \frac{12}{51} \times 100 = 23.53\%\,Wt - 298$$

Check: The units of the answers, % abundance, are correct. The values of the answers are reasonable since they add up to 100 %

b)

c) **Given:** Wt – 296, m = 24.6630 x mass ^{12}C; 72.55%: Wt – 297, m = 24.7490 x mass ^{12}C; 3.922%: Wt – 298, m = 24.8312 x mass ^{12}C; 23.53 %   **Find:** atomic mass Wt
   Conceptual Plan:
   mass of isotope relative to ^{12}C → mass of isotope and then % abundance → fraction

$$(\text{Mass relative to }^{12}\text{C})(12.00\,amu) \qquad \frac{\%\,abundance}{100}$$

   abundance then determine atomic mass

$$\text{Atomic mass} = \sum_n (\text{fraction of isotope n}) \times (\text{mass of isotope n})$$

   Solution:
   Wt – 296 = 24.6630 x 12.00 amu = 295.956 amu; Wt – 297 = 24.7490 x 12.00 amu = 296.988 amu; Wt – 298 = 24.8312 x 12.00 amu = 297.974 amu

$$\text{fraction}\,Wt - 296 = \frac{72.55}{100} = 0.7255 \quad \text{fraction}\,Wt - 297 = \frac{3.922}{100} = 0.03922 \quad \text{fraction}\,Wt - 298 = \frac{23.53}{100} = 0.2353$$

$$\text{Atomic mass} = \sum_{n} (\text{fraction of isotope n}) \times (\text{mass of isotope n})$$

$$= (0.7255)(295.956 \text{ amu}) + (0.03922)(296.988 \text{ amu}) + (0.2353)(297.974 \text{ amu})$$

$$= 296.477 \text{ amu}$$

Check: The units of the answer, amu, are correct. The magnitude of the answer is reasonable because it lies between 295.956 and 297.974 and is closer to 296 which has the highest abundance.

113.a) This is the Law of Definite Proportions: All samples of a given compound, regardless of their source or how they were prepared, have the same proportions of their constituent elements.

b) This is the Law of Conservation of Mass: In a chemical reaction, matter is neither created nor destroyed.

c) This is the Law of Multiple Proportions: When two elements form two different compounds, the masses of element B that combine with 1 g of element A can be expressed as a ratio of small whole numbers. In this example the ratio of O from hydrogen peroxide to O from water = 16:8 → 2:1, a small whole number ratio.

114. If the amu and mole were not based on the same isotope, the numerical values obtained for an atom of material and a mole of material would not be the same. If, for example, the mole was based on the number of particles in C – 12 but the amu was changed to a fraction of the mass of an atom of Ne – 20 the number of particles and the number of amu that make up one mole of material would no longer be the same. We would no longer have the relationship where the mass of an atom in amu is numerically equal to the mass of a mole of those atoms in grams.

115. **Given:** a. Cr: 55.0 g; atomic mass = 52 g/mol b. Ti: 45.0 g; atomic mass = 48 g/mol and
c. Zn: 60.0 g; atomic mass = 65 g/mol   **Find:** which has the greatest mol, and which has the greatest mass
Conceptual Plan: without calculation, compare grams of material to g/mol for each.
Solution: Cr would have the greatest mole amount of the elements. It is the only one whose mass is greater than the molar mass. Zn would be the greatest mass amount because it is the largest mass value.

116. The different isotopes of the same element have the same number of protons and electrons, so the attractive forces between the nucleus and the electrons is constant and there is no difference in the radii of the isotopes. Ions, on the other hand, have a different number of electrons than the parent atom from which they are derived. Cations have fewer electrons than the parent atom. The attractive forces are greater because there is a larger positive charge in the nucleus than the negative charge in the electron cloud. So, cations are smaller than the atom the derived from. Anions have more electrons than the parent. The electron cloud has a greater negative charge than the nucleus, so the anions have larger radii than the parent.

Chapter 3
Molecules, Compounds, and Chemical Equations

1. The properties of compounds are generally very different from the properties of the elements that compose them. When two elements combine to form a compound, an entirely new substance results.

2. Chemical bonds are the result of interactions between charged particles – electrons and protons – that compose atoms. Ionic bonds – which occur between metals and nonmetals – involve the transfer of electrons from one atom to another. Covalent bonds – which occur between two or more nonmetals – involve the sharing of electrons between two atoms.

3. Chemical compounds can be represented by chemical formulas and molecular models. The type of formula or model you use depends on how much information you know about the compound and how much you want to communicate An empirical formula gives the relative number of atoms of each element in the compound. It contains the smallest whole number ratio of the elements in the compound. A molecular formula gives the actual number of atoms of each element in the compound. A structural formula shows how the atoms are connected. A ball and stick model shows the geometry of the compound. A space – filling model shows the relative sizes of the atoms and how they merge together.

4. An empirical formula gives the relative number of atoms of each element in a compound.
    A molecular formula gives the actual number of atoms of each element in a molecule of a compound.

5. Atomic elements are those that exist in nature with single atoms as their base units. Neon (Ne), gold (Au), potassium (K) are a few examples of atomic elements
    Molecular elements do not normally exist in nature with single atoms as their base unit, rather they exist as molecules, two or more atoms of the same element bonded together. Most exist as diatomic molecules, for example hydrogen (H_2), nitrogen (N_2), oxygen (O_2). Some exist as polyatomic molecules; phosphorus (P_4) and sulfur (S_8).
    Ionic compounds are generally composed of a one or more metal cations (usually one type of metal) and one or more nonmetal anions bound together by ionic bonds. Sodium chloride (NaCl), potassium sulfate (Na_2SO_4) would be examples of ionic compounds.
    Molecular compounds are composed of two or more covalently bonded nonmetals. Examples would be water (H_2O), sulfur dioxide (SO_2), nitrogen dioxide (NO_2).

6. To write a formula for an ionic compound: 1) Write the symbol for the metal cation and its charge followed by the symbol for the nonmetal or polyatomic anion and its charge. 2) Adjust the subscript on each cation and anion to balance the overall charge. 3) Check that the sum of the charges of the cations equals the sum of the charges of the anions.

7. Binary ionic compounds are named by using the name of the cation (metal) and the base name of the anion (nonmetal) + the suffix – ide. Ionic compounds that contain a polyatomic anion are named by using the name of the cation (metal) and the name of the polyatomic anion.

8. Ionic compounds formed from metals that can form more than one cation must include the charge of the cation in the name. The charge is indicated by putting the charge of the metal in roman numerals in parentheses after the metal name. Metals that can form only one cation do not need the charge specified.

9. To name a binary molecular inorganic compound: list the name of the first element with a prefix to indicate the number of atoms in the compound if there is more than one, followed by the base name of the second element with a prefix to indicate the number of atoms in the compound if there are more than one, followed by the suffix – ide.

10. The prefix mono = 1; di = 2; tri = 3; tetra = 4; penta = 5; hexa = 6.

11. Binary acids are composed of hydrogen and a nonmetal. The names for binary acids have the form: hydro plus the base name of the nonmetal + ic acid. Oxyacids contain hydrogen and an oxyanion. The names of oxyacids depend on the ending of the oxyanion and have the following forms: oxyanions ending with – ate: base name of the oxyanion + ic acid; oxyanions ending with – ite: base name of the oxyanion + ous acid.

12. The formula mass is the average mass of the molecule (or formula unit) of a compound. The formula mass allows the conversion between the mass of molecules and the number of molecules present.

13. The chemical formula indicates the elements present in the compound and the relative number of atoms of each.

14. Mass percent composition is the mass of an element of the compound divided by the total mass of the compound times 100. Mass percent composition is used as a conversion factor between the mass of the element and the mass of the compound.

15. Chemical formulas contain within them inherent relationships between atoms (or moles of atoms) and molecules (or moles of molecules). For example, the formula CCl_2F_2 tells us that one mole of CCl_2F_2 contains one mole of C atoms, two moles of Cl atoms and two moles of F atoms.

16. The experimental data showing the relative masses of the elements in a compound can be used to obtain an empirical formula.

17. The molecular formula is a whole number multiple of the empirical formula. To find the molecular formula the molar mass of the compound must be known. The molar mass divided by the empirical formula molar mass gives the whole number multiple used to convert the empirical formula to the molecular formula.

18. In combustion analysis, the unknown compound undergoes combustion (burning) in the presence of pure oxygen. All of the carbon in the sample is converted to CO_2 and all of the hydrogen is converted to H_2O.

19. To early chemist organic compounds came from living things, they were easily decomposed, and could not be synthesized in the laboratory. Inorganic compounds came from the earth, were more difficult to decompose and could be synthesized in the laboratory.

20. An alkane is a hydrocarbon containing only single C to C bonds. An alkene contains a double C to C bond and an alkyne contains a triple C to C bond.

21. Functionalized hydrocarbons are hydrocarbons in which a functional group – a characteristic atom or group of atoms – has been incorporated into the hydrocarbon. The family or organic compounds known as alcohols have an – OH functional group.

22. a) alcohol: R— OH

    b) ethers: R— O— R'

    c) aldehyde:
$$R-\overset{\displaystyle \overset{O}{\|}}{C}-H$$

    d) ketone:
$$R-\overset{\displaystyle \overset{O}{\|}}{C}-R'$$

    e) carboxylic acid:
$$R-\overset{\displaystyle \overset{O}{\|}}{C}-OH$$

    f) ester:
$$R-\overset{\displaystyle \overset{O}{\|}}{C}-OR'$$

    g) amines: RNH_2

23. The chemical formula gives you the kind of atom and the number of each atom in the compound.
    a) $Ca_3(PO_4)_2$ contains: 3 calcium atoms, 2 phosphorus atoms and 8 oxygen atoms
    b) $SrCl_2$ contains: 1 strontium atom and 2 chlorine atoms
    c) KNO_3 contains: 1 potassium atom, 1 nitrogen atom and 3 oxygen atoms
    d) $Mg(NO_2)_2$ contains: 1 magnesium atom, 2 nitrogen atoms and 4 oxygen atoms

24. The chemical formula gives you the kind of atom and the number of each atom in the compound.
   a) $Ba(OH)_2$ contains: 1 barium atom, 2 oxygen atoms and 2 hydrogen atoms.
   b) NH_4Cl contains: 1 nitrogen atom, 4 hydrogen atoms and 1 chlorine atom
   c) NaCN contains: 1 sodium atom, 1 carbon atom and 1 nitrogen atom
   d) $Ba(HCO_3)_2$ contains: 1 barium atom, 2 hydrogen atoms, 2 carbon atoms, and 6 oxygen atoms.

25. a) 1 blue = nitrogen, 3 white = hydrogen: NH_3
   b) 2 black = carbon, 6 white = hydrogen: C_2H_6
   c) 1 yellow – green = sulfur, 3 red = oxygen: SO_3

26. a) 1 blue = nitrogen, 2 red = oxygen: NO_2
   b) 1 yellow – green = sulfur, 2 white = hydrogen: SH_2
   c) 1 black = carbon, 4 white = hydrogen: CH_4

27. a) Neon is an element and it is not one of the elements that exist as diatomic molecules therefore it is an atomic element
   b) Fluorine is one of the elements that exist as diatomic molecules therefore it is a molecular element.
   c) Potassium is not one of the elements that exist as diatomic molecules therefore it is an atomic element.
   d) Nitrogen is one of the elements that exist as diatomic molecules therefore it is a molecular element.

28. a) Hydrogen is one of the elements that exist as diatomic molecules therefore it has a molecule as its basic unit.
   b) Iodine is one of the elements that exist as diatomic molecules therefore it has a molecule as its basic unit.
   c) Lead is not one of the elements that exist as a diatomic molecule therefore it does not have a molecule as its basic unit.
   d) Oxygen is one of the elements that exist as diatomic molecules therefore it has a molecule as its basic unit.

29. a) CO_2 is a compound composed of a nonmetal and a nonmetal therefore it is a molecular compound.
   b) $NiCl_2$ is a compound composed of a metal and a nonmetal therefore it is an ionic compound.
   c) NaI is a compound composed of a metal and a nonmetal therefore it is an ionic compound.
   d) PCl_3 is a compound composed of a nonmetal and a nonmetal therefore it is a molecular compound.

30. a) CF_2Cl_2 is a compound composed of a nonmetal and 2 other nonmetals therefore it is a molecular compound.
   b) CCl_4 is a compound composed of a nonmetal and a nonmetal therefore it is a molecular compound.
   c) PtO_2 is a compound composed of a metal and a nonmetal therefore it is an ionic compound.
   d) SO_3 is a compound composed of a nonmetal and a nonmetal therefore it is a molecular compound.

31. a) white – hydrogen: a molecule composed of two of the same element, therefore it is a molecular element.
   b) blue – nitrogen, white – hydrogen: a molecule composed of a nonmetal and a nonmetal therefore it is a molecular compound.
   c) purple – sodium: a substance composed of all the same atoms, therefore it is an atomic element.

32. a) green – chlorine, purple - sodium: a compound composed of metal and nonmetal, therefore it is an ionic compound.
   b) green – chlorine: a molecule composed of two of the same element, therefore it is a molecular element.
   c) red – oxygen, black – carbon, white – hydrogen: a molecule composed of nonmetals, therefore it is a molecular compound.

33. To write the formula for an ionic compound: 1) Write the symbol for the metal cation and its charge and the symbol for the nonmetal anion and its charge. 2) Adjust the subscript on each cation and anion to balance the overall charge. 3) Check that the sum of the charges of the cations equals the sum of the charges of the anions.
   a) magnesium and sulfur: Mg^{2+} S^{2-} MgS   cations 2+; anions 2-
   b) barium and oxygen: Ba^{2+} O^{2-} BaO   cations 2+; anions 2-
   c) strontium and bromine: Sr^{2+} Br^{-} $SrBr_2$ cation 2+; anions 2(1-) = 2-
   d) beryllium and chlorine: Be^{2+} Cl^{-} $BeCl_2$ cations 2+; anions 2(1-) = 2-

34. To write the formula for an ionic compound: 1) Write the symbol for the metal cation and its charge and the symbol for the nonmetal anion and its charge. 2) Adjust the subscript on each cation and anion to balance the overall charge. 3) Check that the sum of the charges of the cations equals the sum of the charges of the anions.
   a) aluminum and sulfur: Al^{3+} S^{2-} Al_2S_3 cation2(3+) = 6+; anions3(2-) = 6-
   b) aluminum and oxygen: Al^{3+} O^{2-} Al_2O_3 cation2(3+) = 6+; anion 3(2-) = 6-
   c) sodium and oxygen: Na^+ O^{2-} Na_2O cation 2(1+) = 2+: anion 2-
   d) strontium and iodine: Sr^{2+} I^- SrI_2 cation 2+; anion 2(1-) = 2-

35. To write the formula for an ionic compound: 1) Write the symbol for the metal cation and its charge and the symbol for the polyatomic anion and its charge. 2) Adjust the subscript on each cation and anion to balance the overall charge. 3) Check that the sum of the charges of the cations equals the sum of the charges of the anions.
   Cation = barium: Ba^{2+}
   a) hydroxide: OH^- $Ba(OH)_2$ cation 2+, anion 2(1-) = 2-
   b) chromate: CrO_4^{2-} $BaCrO_4$ cation 2+; anion 2-
   c) phosphate: PO_4^{3-} $Ba_3(PO_4)_2$ cation 3(2+)=6+; anion 2(3-) = 6-
   d) cyanide: CN^- $Ba(CN)_2$ cation 2+; anion 2(1-) = 2-

36. To write the formula for an ionic compound: 1) Write the symbol for the metal cation and its charge and the symbol for the nonmetal anion and its charge. 2) Adjust the subscript on each cation and anion to balance the overall charge. 3) Check that the sum of the charges of the cations equals the sum of the charges of the anions.
   Cation = sodium: Na^+
   a) carbonate: CO_3^{2-} Na_2CO_3 cation 2(1+) = 2+; anion 2-
   b) phosphate: PO_4^{3-} Na_3PO_4 cation 3(1+) = 3+; anion 3-
   c) hydrogen phosphate: HPO_4^{2-} Na_2HPO_4 cation 2(1+) = 2+; anion 2-
   d) acetate: $C_2H_3O_2^-$ $NaC_2H_3O_2$ cation 1+; anion 1-

37. To name a binary ionic compound: name the metal cation followed by the base name of the anion + ide.
   a) Mg_3N_2: the cation is magnesium, the anion is from nitrogen which becomes nitride: magnesium nitride
   b) KF: the cation is potassium, the anion is from fluorine which becomes fluoride: potassium fluoride.
   c) Na_2O: the cation is sodium, the anion is from oxygen which becomes oxide: sodium oxide.
   d) Li_2S: the cation is lithium, the anion is from sulfur which becomes sulfide: lithium sulfide.

38. To name a binary ionic compound: name the metal cation followed by the base name of the anion + ide.
   a) CsF: the cation is cesium, the anion is from fluorine which becomes fluoride: cesium fluoride
   b) KI the cation is potassium, the anion if from iodine which becomes iodide: potassium iodide.
   c) $SrCl_2$: the cation is strontium, the anion is from chlorine which becomes chloride: strontium chloride.
   d) $BaCl_2$: the cation is barium, the anion is from chlorine which becomes chloride: barium chloride.

39. To name an ionic compound with a metal cation that can have more than one charge: name the metal cation followed by parentheses with the charge in roman numerals followed by the base name of the anion + ide.
   a) $SnCl_4$: the charge on Sn must be 4+ for the compound to be charge neutral: the cation is tin(IV), the anion is from chlorine which becomes chloride; tin(IV) chloride
   b) PbI_2: the charge on Pb must be 2+ for the compound to be charge neutral: the cation is lead(II), the anion is from iodine which becomes iodide; lead(II) iodide
   c) Fe_2O_3: the charge on Fe must be 3+ for the compound to be charge neutral; the cation is iron(III), the anion is from oxygen which becomes oxide: iron(III) oxide
   d) CuI_2: the charge on Cu must be 2+ for the compound to be charge neutral; the cation is copper(II), the anion is from iodine which becomes iodide: copper(II) iodide.

40. To name an ionic compound with a metal cation that can have more than one charge: name the metal cation followed by parentheses with the charge in roman numerals followed by the base name of the anion + ide.
   a) SnO_2: the charge on Sn must be 4+ for the compound to be charge neutral: the cation is tin(IV), the anion is from oxygen which becomes oxide: tin(IV) oxide.
   b) $HgBr_2$: the charge of Hg must be 2+ for the compound to charge neutral: the cation is mercury(II), the anion is from bromine which become bromide: mercury(II) bromide

c) $CrCl_2$:   the charge on Cr must be 2+ for the compound to be charge neutral: the cation is chromium(II), the anion is from chlorine which becomes chloride: chromium(II) chloride.

d) $CrCl_3$:   the charge on Cr must be 3+ for the compound to be charge neutral; the cation is chromium(III), the anion is from chlorine which become chloride: chromium(III) chloride.

41. To name these compounds you must first decide if the metal cation is invariant or can have more than one charge. Then, name the metal cation followed by the base name of the anion + ide.

   a) SnO: Sn can have more than one charge. The charge on Sn must be 2+ for the compound to be charge neutral: the cation is tin(II), the anion is from oxygen which becomes oxide: tin(II) oxide.

   b) Cr_2S_3:   Cr can have more than one charge. The charge on Cr must be 3+ for the compound to be charge neutral: the cation is chromium(III), the anion is from sulfur which become sulfide: chromium(III) sulfide.

   c) RbI: Rb is invariant. The cation is rubidium, the anion is from iodine which becomes iodide: rubidium iodide.

   d) $BaBr_2$:   Ba is invariant. The cation is barium, the anion is from bromine which becomes bromide: barium bromide.

42. To name these compounds you must first decide if the metal cation is invariant or can have more than one charge. Then, name the metal cation followed by the base name of the anion + ide.

   a) BaS: Ba is invariant. The cation is barium, the anion is from sulfur which becomes sulfide: barium sulfide.

   b) $FeCl_3$:   Fe can have more than one charge. The charge on Fe must be 3+ for the compound to be charge neutral. The cation is iron(III), the anion is from chlorine which becomes chloride: iron(III) chloride.

   c) PbI_4:   Pb can have more than one charge. The charge on Pb must be 4+ for the compound to be charge neutral. The cation is lead(IV), the anion is from iodine which becomes iodide: lead(IV) iodide.

   d) $SrBr_2$:   Sr is invariant. The cation is strontium, the anion is from bromine which becomes bromide: strontium bromide.

43. To name these compounds you must first decide is the metal cation is invariant or can have more than one charge. Then, name the metal cation followed by the name of the polyatomic anion.

   a) $CuNO_2$:   Cu can have more than one charge. The charge on Cu must be 1+ for the compound to be charge neutral. The cation is copper(I), the anion is nitrite: copper(I) nitrite

   b) $Mg(C_2H_3O_2)_2$:   Mg is invariant. The cation is magnesium, the anion is acetate: magnesium acetate.

   c) $Ba(NO_3)_2$:   Ba is invariant. The cation is barium, the anion is nitrate: barium nitrate.

   d) $Pb(C_2H_3O_2)_2$:   Pb can have more than one charge. The charge on Pb must be 2+ for the compound to be charge neutral. The cation is lead(II), the anion is acetate: lead(II) acetate.

   E $KClO_3$:   K is invariant. The cation is potassium, the anion is chlorate: potassium chlorate.

   f) $PbSO_4$:   Pb can have more than one charge. The charge on Pb must be 2+ for the compound to be charge neutral. The cation is lead(II), the anion is sulfate: lead(II) sulfate.

44. To name these compounds you must first decide is the metal cation is invariant or can have more than one charge. Then, name the metal cation followed by the name of the polyatomic anion.

   a) $Ba(OH)_2$:   Ba is invariant. The cation is barium, the anion is hydroxide; barium hydroxide.

   b) NH_4I: The cation is ammonium, the anion is from iodine which becomes iodide; ammonium iodide.

   c) $NaBrO_4$:   Na is invariant. The cation is sodium, the anion is perbromate; sodium perbromate.

   d) $Fe(OH)_3$:   Fe can have more than one charge. The charge on Fe must be 3+ for the compound to be charge neutral. The cation is iron(III), the anion is hydroxide; iron(III) hydroxide.

   e) $CoSO_4$:   Co can have more than one charge. The charge on Co must be 2+ for the compound to be charge neutral. The cation is cobalt(II), the anion is sulfate: cobalt(II) sulfate.

   f) $KClO$:   K is invariant. The cation is potassium, the anion is hypochlorite; potassium hypochlorite.

45. To write the formula for an ionic compound: 1) Write the symbol for the metal cation and its charge and the symbol for the nonmetal anion or polyatomic anion and its charge. 2) Adjust the subscript on each cation and anion to balance the overall charge. 3) Check that the sum of the charges of the cations equals the sum of the charges of the anions.

a)	sodium hydrogen sulfite:	Na^+	HSO_3^-	$NaHSO_3$	cation 1+; anion 1-
b)	lithium permanganate:	Li^+	MnO_4^-	$LiMnO_4$	cation 1+; anion 1-
c)	silver nitrate:	Ag^+	NO_3^-	$AgNO_3$	cation 1+; anion 1-
d)	potassium sulfate:	K^+	SO_4^{2-}	K_2SO_4	cation 2(1+) = 2+; anion 2-
e)	rubidium hydrogen sulfate:	Rb^+	HSO_4^-	$RbHSO_4$	cation 1+; anion 1-
f)	potassium hydrogen carbonate:	K^+	HCO_3^-	$KHCO_3$	cation 1+; anion 1-

46. To write the formula for an ionic compound: 1) Write the symbol for the metal cation and its charge and the symbol for the nonmetal anion or polyatomic anion and its charge. 2) Adjust the subscript on each cation and anion to balance the overall charge. 3) Check that the sum of the charges of the cations equals the sum of the charges of the anions.

a)	copper(II) chloride:	Cu^{2+}	Cl^-	$CuCl_2$	cation 2+; anion 2(1-) = 2-
b)	copper(I) iodate:	Cu^+	IO_3^-	$CuCl$	cation 1+; anion 1-
c)	lead(II) chromate:	Pb^{2+}	CrO_4^{2-}	$PbCrO_4$	cation 2+; anion 2-
d)	calcium fluoride:	Ca^{2+}	F^-	CaF_2	cation 2+; anion 2(1-) = 2-
e)	potassium hydroxide:	K^+	OH^-	KOH	cation 1+; anion 1-
f)	iron(II) phosphate:	Fe^{2+}	PO_4^{3-}	$Fe_3(PO_4)_2$	cation 3(2+)=6+;anion 2(3-) =6-

47. Hydrates are named the same way as other ionic compounds with the addition of the term *prefix*hydrate, where the prefix is the number of water molecules associated with each formula unit.
   a) $CoSO_4 \bullet 7H_2O$ cobalt(II) sulfate heptahydrate
   b) iridium(III) bromide tetrahydrate $IrBr_3 \bullet 4H_2O$
   c) $Mg(BrO_3)_2 \bullet 6H_2O$ magnesium bromate hexahydrate
   d) potassium carbonate dihydrate $K_2CO_3 \bullet 2H_2O$

48. Hydrates are named the same way as other ionic compounds with the addition of the term *prefix*hydrate, where the prefix is the number of water molecules associated with each formula unit.
   a) cobalt(II) phosphate octahydrate $Co_3(PO_4)_2 \bullet 8H_2O$
   b) $BeCl_2 \bullet 2H_2O$ beryllium chloride dihydrate
   c) chromium(III) phosphate trihydrate $CrPO_4 \bullet 3H_2O$
   d) $LiNO_2 \bullet H_2O$ lithium nitrite monohydrate

49. a) CO The name of the compound is the name of the first element, *carbon*, following by the base name of the second element, *ox*, prefixed by *mono-* to indicate one and given the suffix – *ide*; carbonmonoxide

   b) NI_3 The name of the compound is the name of the first element, *nitrogen*, followed by the base name of the second element, *iod*, prefixed by *tri-* to indicate three and given the suffix – *ide*.: nitrogen triiodide.

   c) $SiCl_4$ The name of the compound is the name of the first element, *silicon*, followed by the base name of the second element, *chlor*, prefixed by *tetra-* to indicate four and given the suffix – *ide*.: silicon tetrachloride.

   d) N_4Se_4 The name of the compound is the name of the first element, *nitrogen*, prefixed by *tetra-* to indicate four followed by the base name of the second element, *selen*, prefixed by *tetra-* to indicate four and given the suffix – *ide*.: tetranitrogen tetraselenide.

   e) I_2O_5 The name of the compound is the name of the first element, *iodine*, prefixed by di to indicate two followed by the base name of the second element, *ox*, prefixed by *penta-* to indicate five and given the suffix – *ide*.: diiodine pentaoxide.

50. a) SO_3 The name of the compound is the name of the first element, *sulfur*, followed by the base name of the second element, *ox*, prefixed by *tri-* to indicate three and given the suffix – *ide*.: sulfur trioxide

   b) SO_2 The name of the compound is the name of the first element, *sulfur*, followed by the base name of the second element, *ox*, prefixed by *di-* to indicate two and given the suffix – *ide*.: sulfur dioxide.

   c) BrF_5 The name of the compound is the name of the first element, *bromine*, followed by the base name of the second element, *fluor*, prefixed by *penta-* to indicate five and given the suffix – *ide*.: bromine pentafluoride.

   d) NO The name of the compound is the name of the first element, *nitrogen*, followed by the base name of the second element, *ox*, prefixed by *mono-* to indicate one and given the suffix – *ide*.: nitrogen monoxide.

e) XeO_3 The name of the compound is the name of the first element, *xenon*, followed by the base name of the second element, *ox*, prefixed by *tri-* to indicate three and given the suffix – *ide*.: xenon trioxide.

51. a) phosphorus trichloride: PCl_3
    b) chlorine monoxide: ClO
    c) disulfur tetrafluoride: S_2F_4
    d) phosphorus pentafluoride: PF_5
    e) diphosphorus pentasulfide: P_2S_5

52. a) boron tribromide: BBr_3
    b) dichlorine monoxide: Cl_2O
    c) xenon tetrafluroide: XeF_4
    d) carbon tetrabromide: CBr_4
    e) diboron tetrachloride: B_2Cl_4

53. a) HI: the base name of I is *iod* so the name is hydroiodic acid
    b) HNO_3:   the oxyanion is *nitrate*, which ends in –*ate;* therefore, the name of the acid is nitric acid.
    c) H_2CO_3:   the oxyanion is *carbonate*, which ends in –*ate;* therefore, the name of the acid is carbonic acid.
    d) $HC_2H_3O_2$: the oxyanion is *acetate*, which ends in –*ate;* therefore, the name of the acid is acetic acid.

54. a) HCl: the base name of Cl is *chlor* so the name is hydrochloric acid.
    b) $HClO_2$:   the oxyanion is *chlorite*, which ends in –*ite;* therefore, the name of the acid is chlorous acid.
    c) H_2SO_4:   the oxyanion is *sulfate*, which ends in –*ate;* therefore, the name of the acid is sulfuric acid.
    d) HNO_2:   the oxyanion is *nitrite*, which ends in –*ite;* therefore, the name of the acid is nitrous acid.

55. a) hydrofluoric acid: HF
    b) hydrobromic acid: HBr
    c) sulfurous acid: H_2SO_3

56. a) phosphoric acid: H_3PO_4
    b) hydrocyanic acid: HCN
    c) chlorous acid: $HClO_2$

57. To find the formula mass, we sum the atomic masses of each atom in the chemical formula.
    a) NO_2 formula mass   = 1 x (atomic mass N) + 2 x (atomic mass O)
                                = 1 x (14.01 amu) + 2 x (16.00 amu)
                                = 46.01 amu
    b) C_4H_{10} formula mass   = 4 x (atomic mass C) + 10 x (atomic mass H)
                                = 4 x (12.01 amu) + 10 x (1.008 amu)
                                = 58.12 amu
    c) $C_6H_{12}O_6$ formula mass = 6 x (atomic mass C) + 12 x (atomic mass H) + 6 x (atomic mass O)
                                = 6 x (12.01 amu) + 12 x (1.008 amu) + 6 x (16.00 amu)
                                = 180.16 amu
    d) $Cr(NO_3)_3$ formula mass   = 1 x (atomic mass Cr) + 3 x (atomic mass N) + 9 x (atomic mass O)
                                = 1 x (52.00 amu) + 3 x (14.01 amu) + 9 x (16.00 amu)
                                = 238.0 amu

58. To find the formula mass, we sum the atomic masses of each atom in the chemical formula.
    a) $MgBr_2$ formula mass = 1 x (atomic mass Mg) + 2 x (atomic mass Br)
                                = 1 x (24.30 amu) + 2 x (79.90 amu)
                                = 184.1 amu
    b) HNO_2 formula mass = 1 x (atomic mass H) + 1 x (atomic mass N) + 2 x (atomic mass O)
                                = 1 x (1.008 amu) + 1 x (14.01 amu) + 2 x (16.00 amu)

$= 47.02$ amu

c) CBr_4 formula mass $= 1$ x (atomic mass C) $+ 4$ x (atomic mass Br)

                                    $= 1$ x $(12.01$ amu$) + 4$ x $(79.90$ amu$)$

                                      $= 331.6$ amu

d) $Ca(NO_3)_2$ formula mass $= 1$ x (atomic mass Ca) $+ 2$ x (atomic mass N) $+ 6$ x (atomic mass O)

                                      $= 1$ x $(40.08$ amu$) + 2$ x $(14.01$ amu$) + 6$ x $(16.00$ amu$)$

                                      $= 164.10$ amu

59. a) **Given:** 6.5 g H_2O **Find:** number of molecules

       Conceptual Plan: g H_2O $\rightarrow$ mole H_2O $\rightarrow$ number H_2O molecules

$$\frac{1\ mol}{18.02\ g\ H_2O} \qquad \frac{6.022\times10^{23}\ H_2O\ molecules}{mol\ H_2O}$$

       Solution: $6.5\ g\ H_2O \times \dfrac{1\ mol\ H_2O}{18.02\ g\ H_2O} \times \dfrac{6.022\times10^{23}\ H_2O\ molecules}{mol\ H_2O} = 2.2\times10^{23}\ H_2O$ molecules

       Check: Units of the answer, H_2O molecules, are correct. The magnitude is a is appropriate because it is smaller than Avogadro's number as expected since we have less than 1 mole of H_2O.

    b) **Given:** 389 g CBr_4 **Find:** number of molecules

       Conceptual Plan: g CBr_4 $\rightarrow$ mole CBr_4 $\rightarrow$ number CBr_4 molecules

$$\frac{1\ mol}{331.6\ g\ CBr_4} \qquad \frac{6.022\times10^{23}\ CBr_4\ molecules}{mol\ CBr_4}$$

       Solution: $389\ g\ CBr_4 \times \dfrac{1\ mol\ CBr_4}{331.6\ g\ CBr_4} \times \dfrac{6.022\times10^{23}\ CBr_4\ molecules}{mol\ CBr_4} = 7.06\times10^{23}\ CBr_4$ molecules

       Check: Units of the answer, CBr_4 molecules, are correct. The magnitude is a is appropriate because it is large than Avogadro's number as expected since we have mare than 1 mole of CBr_4.

    c) **Given:** 22.1 g O_2 **Find:** number of molecules

       Conceptual Plan: g O_2 $\rightarrow$ mole O_2 $\rightarrow$ number O_2 molecules

$$\frac{1\ mol}{32.00\ g\ O_2} \qquad \frac{6.022\times10^{23}\ O_2\ molecules}{mol\ O_2}$$

       Solution: $22.1\ g\ O_2 \times \dfrac{1\ mol\ O_2}{32.00\ g\ O_2} \times \dfrac{6.022\times10^{23}\ O_2\ molecules}{mol\ O_2} = 4.16\times10^{23}\ O_2$ molecules

       Check: Units of the answer, O_2 molecules, are correct. The magnitude is a is appropriate because it is smaller than Avogadro's number as expected since we have less than 1 mole of O_2.

    d) **Given:** 19.3 g C_8H_{10} **Find:** number of molecules

       Conceptual Plan: g C_8H_{10} $\rightarrow$ mole C_8H_{10} $\rightarrow$ number C_8H_{10} molecules

$$\frac{1\ mol}{106.16\ g\ C_8H_{10}} \qquad \frac{6.022\times10^{23}\ C_8H_{10}\ molecules}{mol\ C_8H_{10}}$$

       Solution: $19.3\ g\ C_8H_{10} \times \dfrac{1\ mol\ C_8H_{10}}{106.16\ g\ C_8H_{10}} \times \dfrac{6.022\times10^{23}\ C_8H_{10}\ molecules}{mol\ C_8H_{10}} = 1.09\times10^{23}\ C_8H_{10}$ molecules

       Check: Units of the answer, C_8H_{10} molecules, are correct. The magnitude is a is appropriate because it is smaller than Avogadro's number as expected since we have less than 1 mole of C_8H_{10}.

60. a) **Given:** 5.94×10^{20} SO_3 molecules   **Find:** mass in g

       Conceptual Plan: number SO_3 molecules $\rightarrow$ mole SO_3 $\rightarrow$ g SO_3

$$\frac{1\ mol\ SO_3}{6.022\times10^{23}\ SO_3\ molecules} \qquad \frac{80.00\ g\ SO_3}{1\ mol\ SO_3}$$

       Solution: $5.94\times10^{20}\ SO_3\ molecules \times \dfrac{1\ mol\ SO_3}{6.022\times10^{23}\ SO_3\ molecules} \times \dfrac{80.00\ g\ SO_3}{1\ mol\ SO_3} = 0.0789\ g\ SO_3$

       Check: Units of the answer, grams SO_3 are correct. The magnitude is appropriate because there is less than Avogadro's number of molecules so we have less than 1 mole of SO_3.

b) **Given:** 2.8×10^{22} H_2O molecules **Find:** mass in g

   Conceptual Plan: number H_2O molecules $\rightarrow$ mole H_2O $\rightarrow$ g H_2O

$$\frac{1 \text{ mol } H_2O}{6.022 \times 10^{23} \ H_2O \text{ molecules}} \qquad \frac{18.02 \text{ g } H_2O}{1 \text{ mol } H_2O}$$

   Solution: 2.8×10^{22} H_2O molecules $\times \dfrac{1 \text{ mol } H_2O}{6.022 \times 10^{23} \ H_2O \text{ molecules}} \times \dfrac{18.02 \text{ g } H_2O}{1 \text{ mol } H_2O} = 0.84 \text{ g } H_2O$

   Check: Units of the answer, grams H_2O, are correct. The magnitude is appropriate because there is less than Avogadro's number of molecules so we have less than 1 mole of H_2O.

c) **Given:** 4.5×10^{25} O_3 molecules **Find:** mass in g

   Conceptual Plan: number O_3 molecules $\rightarrow$ mole O_3 $\rightarrow$ g O_3

$$\frac{1 \text{ mol } O_3}{6.022 \times 10^{23} \ O_3 \text{ molecules}} \qquad \frac{48.00 \text{ g } O_3}{1 \text{ mol } O_3}$$

   Solution: 4.5×10^{25} O_3 molecules $\times \dfrac{1 \text{ mol } O_3}{6.022 \times 10^{23} \ O_3 \text{ molecules}} \times \dfrac{48.00 \text{ g } O_3}{1 \text{ mol } O_3} = 3.6 \times 10^3 \text{ g } O_3$

   Check: Units of the answer, grams O_3, are correct. The magnitude is appropriate because there is more than Avogadro's number of molecules so we have more than 1 mole of O_3.

d) **Given:** 9.85×10^{19} CCl_2F_2 molecules **Find:** mass in g

   Conceptual Plan: number CCl_2F_2 molecules $\rightarrow$ mole CCl_2F_2 $\rightarrow$ g CCl_2F_2

$$\frac{1 \text{ mol } O_3}{6.022 \times 10^{23} \ O_3 \text{ molecules}} \qquad \frac{48.00 \text{ g } O_3}{1 \text{ mol } O_3}$$

   Solution: 9.85×10^{19} CCl_2F_2 molecules $\times \dfrac{1 \text{ mol } CCl_2F_2}{6.022 \times 10^{23} \ CCl_2F_2 \text{ molecules}} \times \dfrac{120.91 \text{ g } CCl_2F_2}{1 \text{ mol } CCl_2F_2} = 1.98 \times 10^2 \text{ g } CCl_2F_2$

   Check: Units of the answer, grams CCl_2F_2, are correct. The magnitude is appropriate because there is less than Avogadro's number of molecules so we have less than 1 mole of CCl_2F_2.

61. **Given:** 1 H_2O molecule   **Find:** mass in g

   Conceptual Plan: number H_2O molecules $\rightarrow$ mole H_2O $\rightarrow$ g H_2O

$$\frac{1 \text{ mol } H_2O}{6.022 \times 10^{23} \ H_2O \text{ molecules}} \qquad \frac{18.02 \text{ g } H_2O}{1 \text{ mol } H_2O}$$

   Solution: 1 H_2O molecules $\times \dfrac{1 \text{ mol } H_2O}{6.022 \times 10^{23} \ H_2O \text{ molecules}} \times \dfrac{18.02 \text{ g } H_2O}{1 \text{ mol } H_2O} = 2.992 \times 10^{-23} \text{ g } H_2O$

   Check: Units of the answer, grams H_2O, are correct. The magnitude is appropriate because there is much less than Avogadro's number of molecules so we have much less than 1 mole of H_2O.

62. **Given:** 1 $C_6H_{12}O_6$ molecule **Find:** mass in g

   Conceptual Plan: number $C_6H_{12}O_6$ molecules $\rightarrow$ mole $C_6H_{12}O_6$$\rightarrow$ g $C_6H_{12}O_6$

$$\frac{1 \text{ mol } C_6H_{12}O_6}{6.022 \times 10^{23} \ C_6H_{12}O_6 \text{ molecules}} \qquad \frac{180.16 \text{ g } C_6H_{12}O_6}{1 \text{ mol } C_6H_{12}O_6}$$

   Solution:

$$1 \ C_6H_{12}O_6 \text{ molecules} \times \frac{1 \text{ mol } C_6H_{12}O_6}{6.022 \times 10^{23} \ C_6H_{12}O_6 \text{ molecules}} \times \frac{180.16 \text{ g } C_6H_{12}O_6}{1 \text{ mol } C_6H_{12}O_6} = 2.992 \times 10^{-22} \text{ g } C_6H_{12}O_6$$

   Check: Units of the answer, grams $C_6H_{12}O_6$, are correct. The magnitude is appropriate because there is much less than Avogadro's number of molecules so we have much less than 1 mole of $C_6H_{12}O_6$.

63. **Given:** 1.8×10^{17} $C_{12}H_{22}O_{11}$ molecule **Find:** mass in mg

   Conceptual Plan:

   number $C_{12}H_{22}O_{11}$ molecules $\rightarrow$ mole $C_{12}H_{22}O_{11}$$\rightarrow$ g $C_{12}H_{22}O_{11}$ $\rightarrow$ mg $C_{12}H_{22}O_{11}$

$$\frac{1 \text{ mol } C_{12}H_{22}O_{11}}{6.022 \times 10^{23} \ C_{12}H_{22}O_{11} \text{ molecules}} \qquad \frac{342.3 \text{ g } C_{12}H_{22}O_{11}}{1 \text{ mol } C_{12}H_{22}O_{11}} \qquad \frac{1 \times 10^3 \text{ mg } C_{12}H_{22}O_{11}}{1 \text{ g } C_{12}H_{22}O_{11}}$$

Solution:

$$1.8 \times 10^{17} \text{ } \cancel{C_{12}H_{22}O_{11} \text{ molecules}} \times \frac{1 \text{ mol } C_{12}H_{22}O_{11}}{6.022 \times 10^{23} \text{ } \cancel{C_{12}H_{22}O_{11} \text{ molecules}}} \times \frac{342.3 \text{ g } \cancel{C_{12}H_{22}O_{11}}}{1 \text{ } \cancel{\text{mol } C_{12}H_{22}O_{11}}} \times \frac{1 \times 10^3 \text{ mg } C_{12}H_{22}O_{11}}{\cancel{\text{g } C_{12}H_{22}O_{11}}} = 0.10 \text{ mg } C_{12}H_{22}O_{11}$$

Check: Units of the answer, milligrams $C_{12}H_{22}O_{11}$, are correct. The magnitude is appropriate because there is much less than Avogadro's number of molecules so we have much less than 1 mole of $C_{12}H_{22}O_{11}$.

64. **Given:** 0.12 mg NaCl   **Find:** number of formula units

    Conceptual Plan: **mg NaCl   →   g NaCl → mole NaCl → number of formula units NaCl**

$$\frac{1 \text{ g NaCl}}{1 \times 10^3 \text{ mg NaCl}} \qquad \frac{1 \text{ mol NaCl}}{58.44 \text{ g NaCl}} \qquad \frac{6.022 \times 10^{23} \text{ NaCl formula units}}{1 \text{ mol NaCl}}$$

    Solution:

$$0.12 \text{ } \cancel{\text{mg NaCl}} \times \frac{1 \text{ } \cancel{\text{g NaCl}}}{1 \times 10^3 \text{ } \cancel{\text{mg NaCl}}} \times \frac{1 \text{ } \cancel{\text{mol NaCl}}}{58.44 \text{ } \cancel{\text{g NaCl}}} \times \frac{6.022 \times 10^{23} \text{ formula units NaCl}}{1 \text{ } \cancel{\text{mol NaCl}}} = 1.2 \times 10^{18} \text{ formula units NaCl}$$

    Check: Units of the answer, formula units NaCl, are correct. The magnitude is appropriate because there is less than 1 mole of NaCl so we have less than Avogadro's number of formula units.

65. a) **Given:** CH_4 **Find:** mass percent C

    Conceptual Plan: $\text{mass } \% \text{ C} = \dfrac{1 \times \text{molar mass C}}{\text{molar mass } CH_4} \times 100$

    $1 \times \text{molar mass C} = 1(12.01 \text{ g/mol}) = 12.01 \text{ g C}$

    Solution: $\text{molar mass } CH_4 = 1(12.01 \text{ g/mol}) + 4(1.008 \text{ g/mol}) = 16.04 \text{ g/mol}$

$$\text{mass } \% \text{ C} = \frac{1 \times \text{molar mass C}}{\text{molar mass } CH_4} \times 100\%$$

$$= \frac{12.01 \text{ } \cancel{\text{g/mol}}}{16.04 \text{ } \cancel{\text{g/mol}}} \times 100\%$$

$$= 74.87 \text{ \%}$$

    Check: Units of the answer, %, are correct. The magnitude is reasonable because it is between 0 and 100% and carbon is the heaviest element.

    b) **Given:** C_2H_6 **Find:** mass percent C

    Conceptual Plan: $\text{mass } \% \text{ C} = \dfrac{2 \times \text{molar mass C}}{\text{molar mass } C_2H_6} \times 100$

    $2 \times \text{molar mass C} = 2(12.01 \text{ g/mol}) = 24.02 \text{ g C}$

    Solution: $\text{molar mass } C_2H_6 = 2(12.01 \text{ g/mol}) + 6(1.008 \text{ g/mol}) = 30.07 \text{ g/mol}$

$$\text{mass } \% \text{ C} = \frac{2 \times \text{molar mass C}}{\text{molar mass } C_2H_6} \times 100\%$$

$$= \frac{24.02 \text{ } \cancel{\text{g/mol}}}{30.07 \text{ } \cancel{\text{g/mol}}} \times 100\%$$

$$= 79.89 \text{ \%}$$

    Check: Units of the answer, %, are correct. The magnitude is reasonable because it is between 0 and 100% and carbon is the heaviest element.

    c) **Given:** C_2H_2 **Find:** mass percent C

    Conceptual Plan: $\text{mass } \% \text{ C} = \dfrac{2 \times \text{molar mass C}}{\text{molar mass } C_2H_2} \times 100$

    $2 \times \text{molar mass C} = 2(12.01 \text{ g/mol}) = 24.02 \text{ g C}$

    Solution: $\text{molar mass } C_2H_2 = 2(12.01 \text{ g/mol}) + 2(1.008 \text{ g/mol}) = 26.04 \text{ g/mol}$

$$\text{mass } \% \text{ C} = \frac{2 \times \text{molar mass C}}{\text{molar mass } C_2H_2} \times 100\%$$

$$= \frac{24.02 \text{ } \cancel{\text{g/mol}}}{26.04 \text{ } \cancel{\text{g/mol}}} \times 100\%$$

$$= 92.26 \text{ \%}$$

    Check: Units of the answer, %, are correct. The magnitude is reasonable because it is between 0 and 100% and carbon is the heaviest element.

d) **Given:** C_2H_5Cl **Find:** mass percent C
Conceptual Plan: $\text{mass \% C} = \dfrac{2 \times \text{molar mass C}}{\text{molar mass } C_2H_5Cl} \times 100$

$2 \times \text{molar mass C} = 2(12.01 \text{g/mol}) = 24.02 \text{ g C}$

Solution: $\text{molar mass } C_2H_5Cl = 2(12.01 \text{ g/mol}) + 5(1.008 \text{ g/mol}) + 1(35.45 \text{ g/mol}) = 64.51 \text{ g/mol}$

$$\text{mass \% C} = \frac{2 \times \text{molar mass C}}{\text{molar mass } C_2H_5Cl} \times 100\%$$

$$= \frac{24.02 \text{ g/mol}}{64.51 \text{ g/mol}} \times 100\%$$

$$= 37.23 \%$$

Check: Units of the answer, %, are correct. The magnitude is reasonable because it is between 0 and 100% and chlorine is heavier than carbon.

66. a) **Given:** N_2O **Find:** mass percent N
Conceptual Plan: $\text{mass \% N} = \dfrac{2 \times \text{molar mass N}}{\text{molar mass } N_2O} \times 100$

$2 \times \text{molar mass N} = 2(14.01 \text{g/mol}) = 28.02 \text{ g N}$

Solution: $\text{molar mass } N_2O = 2(14.01 \text{ g/mol}) + (16.00 \text{ g/mol}) = 44.02 \text{ g/mol}$

$$\text{mass \% N} = \frac{2 \times \text{molar mass N}}{\text{molar mass } N_2O} \times 100\%$$

$$= \frac{28.02 \text{ g/mol}}{44.02 \text{ g/mol}} \times 100\%$$

$$= 63.65 \%$$

Check: Units of the answer, %, are correct. The magnitude is reasonable because it is between 0 and 100% and there are 2 nitrogen.

b) **Given:** NO   **Find:** mass percent N
Conceptual Plan: $\text{mass \% N} = \dfrac{1 \times \text{molar mass N}}{\text{molar mass NO}} \times 100$

$1 \times \text{molar mass N} = 1(14.01 \text{g/mol}) = 14.01 \text{ g N}$

Solution: $\text{molar mass NO} = (14.01 \text{ g/mol}) + (16.00 \text{ g/mol}) = 30.01 \text{ g/mol}$

$$\text{mass \% N} = \frac{1 \times \text{molar mass N}}{\text{molar mass NO}} \times 100\%$$

$$= \frac{14.01 \text{ g/mol}}{30.01 \text{ g/mol}} \times 100\%$$

$$= 46.68 \%$$

Check: Units of the answer, %, are correct. The magnitude is reasonable because it is between 0 and 100% and the mass of nitrogen is less than the mass of oxygen.

c) **Given:** NO_2 **Find:** mass percent N
Conceptual Plan: $\text{mass \% N} = \dfrac{1 \times \text{molar mass N}}{\text{molar mass } NO_2} \times 100$

$1 \times \text{molar mass N} = 1(14.01 \text{g/mol}) = 14.01 \text{ g N}$

Solution: $\text{molar mass } NO_2 = (14.01 \text{ g/mol}) + 2(16.00 \text{ g/mol}) = 46.01 \text{ g/mol}$

$$\text{mass \% N} = \frac{1 \times \text{molar mass N}}{\text{molar mass } NO_2} \times 100\%$$

$$= \frac{14.01 \text{ g/mol}}{46.01 \text{ g/mol}} \times 100\%$$

$$= 30.45 \%$$

Check: Units of the answer, %, are correct. The magnitude is reasonable because it is between 0 and 100% and the mass of nitrogen is less than the mass of oxygen and there are 2 oxygen.

d) **Given:** HNO_3 **Find:** mass percent N
Conceptual Plan: $\text{mass \% N} = \dfrac{1 \times \text{molar mass N}}{\text{molar mass } HNO_3} \times 100$

$$1 \text{ x molar mass N} = 1(14.01 \text{g/mol}) = 14.01 \text{ g N}$$

Solution:
$$\text{molar mass HNO}_3 = (1.008 \text{ g/mol}) + (14.01 \text{ g/mol}) + 3(16.00 \text{ g/mol}) = 63.02 \text{ g/mol}$$

$$\text{mass \% N} = \frac{1 \text{ x molar mass N}}{\text{molar mass HNO}_3} \times 100\%$$

$$= \frac{14.01 \text{ g/mol}}{63.02 \text{ g/mol}} \times 100\%$$

$$= 22.23 \%$$

Check: Units of the answer, %, are correct. The magnitude is reasonable because it is between 0 and 100% and the mass of nitrogen is less than the mass of oxygen and there are 3 oxygen.

67. **Given:** NH_3 **Find:** mass percent N
Conceptual Plan:
$$\text{mass \% N} = \frac{1 \text{ x molar mass N}}{\text{molar mass NH}_3} \times 100$$

$$1 \text{ x molar mass N} = 1(14.01 \text{g/mol}) = 14.01 \text{ g N}$$

$$\text{molar mass NH}_3 = 3(1.008 \text{ g/mol}) + (14.01 \text{ g/mol}) = 17.03 \text{ g/mol}$$

Solution:
$$\text{mass \% N} = \frac{1 \text{ x molar mass N}}{\text{molar mass NH}_3} \times 100\%$$

$$= \frac{14.01 \text{ g/mol}}{17.03 \text{ g/mol}} \times 100\%$$

$$= 82.27 \%$$

Check: Units of the answer, %, are correct. The magnitude is reasonable because it is between 0 and 100% and nitrogen is the heaviest

Given: $CO(NH_2)_2$ **Find:** mass percent N
Conceptual Plan:
$$\text{mass \% N} = \frac{2 \text{ x molar mass N}}{\text{molar mass CO(NH}_2)_2} \times 100$$

Solution:

$$2 \text{ x molar mass N} = 1(14.01 \text{g/mol}) = 28.02 \text{ g N}$$

$$\text{molar mass CO(NH}_2)_2 = (12.01 \text{ g/mol}) + (16.00 \text{ g/mol}) + 2(14.01 \text{ g/mol}) + 4(1.008 \text{ g/mol}) = 60.06 \text{ g/mol}$$

$$\text{mass \% N} = \frac{1 \text{ x molar mass N}}{\text{molar mass CO(NH}_2)_2} \times 100\%$$

$$= \frac{28.02 \text{ g/mol}}{60.06 \text{ g/mol}} \times 100\%$$

$$= 46.65 \%$$

Check: Units of the answer, %, are correct. The magnitude is reasonable because it is between 0 and 100% there are two nitrogen

Given: NH_4NO_3 **Find:** mass percent N
Conceptual Plan:
$$\text{mass \% N} = \frac{2 \text{ x molar mass N}}{\text{molar mass NH}_4NO_3} \times 100$$

Solution:
$$1 \text{ x molar mass N} = 2(14.01 \text{g/mol}) = 28.02 \text{ g N}$$

$$\text{molar mass NH}_4NO_3 = +2 (14.01 \text{ g/mol}) + 4(1.008 \text{ g/mol}) + 3(16.00 \text{ g/mol}) = 80.05 \text{ g/mol}$$

$$\text{mass \% N} = \frac{2 \text{ x molar mass N}}{\text{molar mass NH}_4NO_3} \times 100\%$$

$$= \frac{28.02 \text{ g/mol}}{80.05 \text{ g/mol}} \times 100\%$$

$$= 35.00 \%$$

Check: Units of the answer, %, are correct. The magnitude is reasonable because it is between 0 and 100% and the mass of nitrogen is less than the mass of oxygen and there are 3 oxygen.

Given: $(NH_4)_2SO_4$ **Find:** mass percent N

Conceptual Plan: $\text{mass \% N} = \dfrac{2 \times \text{molar mass N}}{\text{molar mass }(NH_4)_2SO_4} \times 100$

Solution:

$1 \times \text{molar mass N} = 2(14.01\text{g/mol}) = 28.02 \text{ g N}$

$\text{molar mass }(NH_4)_2SO_4 = 2(14.01 \text{ g/mol}) + 8(1.008 \text{ g/mol}) + (32.07 \text{ g/mol}) + 4(16.00 \text{ g/mol}) = 132.15 \text{ g/mol}$

$$\text{mass \% N} = \frac{2 \times \text{molar mass N}}{\text{molar mass }(NH_4)_2SO_4} \times 100\%$$

$$= \frac{28.02 \text{ g/mol}}{132.15 \text{ g/mol}} \times 100\%$$

$$= 21.20 \text{ \%}$$

Check: Units of the answer, %, are correct. The magnitude is reasonable because it is between 0 and 100% and the mass of nitrogen is less than the mass of oxygen and sulfur.

The fertilizer with the highest nitrogen content is NH_3 because is has the highest %N.

68. **Given:** Fe_2O_3 **Find:** mass percent Fe

    Conceptual Plan: $\text{mass \% Fe} = \dfrac{2 \times \text{molar mass Fe}}{\text{molar mass }Fe_2O_3} \times 100$

        $2 \times \text{molar mass Fe} = 2(55.85\text{g/mol}) = 111.7 \text{ g Fe}$

Solution: $\text{molar mass }Fe_2O_3 = 2(55.85 \text{ g/mol}) + 3(16.00 \text{ g/mol}) = 159.7 \text{ g/mol}$

$$\text{mass \% Fe} = \frac{1 \times \text{molar mass Fe}}{\text{molar mass }Fe_2O_3} \times 100\%$$

$$= \frac{111.7 \text{ g/mol}}{159.7 \text{ g/mol}} \times 100\%$$

$$= 69.94 \text{ \%}$$

Check: Units of the answer, %, are correct. The magnitude is reasonable because it is between 0 and 100% and iron is the heaviest

Given: Fe_3O_4 **Find:** mass percent Fe

Conceptual Plan: $\text{mass \% Fe} = \dfrac{3 \times \text{molar mass Fe}}{\text{molar mass }Fe_3O_4} \times 100$

        $3 \times \text{molar mass Fe} = 3(55.85\text{g/mol}) = 167.6 \text{ g Fe}$

Solution: $\text{molar mass }Fe_3O_4 = 3(55.85 \text{ g/mol}) + 4(16.00 \text{ g/mol}) = 231.6 \text{ g/mol}$

$$\text{mass \% Fe} = \frac{3 \times \text{molar mass Fe}}{\text{molar mass }Fe_3O_4} \times 100\%$$

$$= \frac{167.6 \text{ g/mol}}{231.6 \text{ g/mol}} \times 100\%$$

$$= 72.38 \text{ \%}$$

Check: Units of the answer, %, are correct. The magnitude is reasonable because it is between 0 and 100% and iron is the heaviest

Given: $FeCO_3$ **Find:** mass percent Fe

Conceptual Plan: $\text{mass \% Fe} = \dfrac{1 \times \text{molar mass Fe}}{\text{molar mass }FeCO_3} \times 100$

        $1 \times \text{molar mass Fe} = (55.85\text{g/mol}) = 55.85 \text{ g Fe}$

Solution: $\text{molar mass }FeCO_3 = 1(55.85 \text{ g/mol}) + 1(12.01 \text{ g/mol}) + 3(16.00 \text{ g/mol}) = 115.86 \text{ g/mol}$

$$\text{mass \% Fe} = \frac{1 \times \text{molar mass Fe}}{\text{molar mass }FeCO_3} \times 100\%$$

$$= \frac{55.85 \text{ g/mol}}{115.86 \text{ g/mol}} \times 100\%$$

$$= 48.20 \text{ \%}$$

Check: Units of the answer, %, are correct. The magnitude is reasonable because it is between 0 and 100% and iron is slightly less than the sum of carbon and oxygen.

69. **Given:** 55.5 g CuF_2: 37.42 % F   **Find:** g F in CuF_2
    Conceptual Plan: g CuF_2 $\rightarrow$ g F

$$\frac{37.42 \text{ g F}}{100.0 \text{ g } CuF_2}$$

    Solution: $55.5 \text{ g } CuF_2 \times \dfrac{37.42 \text{ g F}}{100.0 \text{ g } CuF_2} = 20.77 = 20.8 \text{ g F}$

    Check: Units of the answer, g F, are correct. The magnitude is reasonable because it is less than the original mass.

70. **Given:** 155 mg Ag; 75.27 % Ag in AgCl   **Find:** mg AgCl
    Conceptual Plan: mg Ag $\rightarrow$ g Ag $\rightarrow$ g AgCl $\rightarrow$ mg AgCl

$$\frac{1 \text{ g Ag}}{1000 \text{ mg Ag}} \quad \frac{100.0 \text{ g AgCl}}{75.27 \text{ g Ag}} \quad \frac{1000 \text{ mg AgCl}}{1 \text{ g AgCl}}$$

    Solution: $155 \text{ mg Ag} \times \dfrac{1 \text{ g Ag}}{1000 \text{ mg Ag}} \times \dfrac{100.0 \text{ g AgCl}}{75.27 \text{ g Ag}} \times \dfrac{1000 \text{ mg AgCl}}{1 \text{ g AgCl}} = 206 \text{ mg AgCl}$

    Check: Units of the answer, g AgCl, are correct. The magnitude is reasonable because it is greater than the original mass.

71. **Given:** 150 μg I; 76.45% I in KI   **Find:** μg KI
    Conceptual Plan: μg I $\rightarrow$ g I $\rightarrow$ g KI $\rightarrow$ μg KI

$$\frac{1 \text{ g I}}{1 \times 10^6 \ \mu\text{g I}} \quad \frac{100.0 \text{ g KI}}{76.45 \text{ g I}} \quad \frac{1 \times 10^6 \ \mu\text{g KI}}{1 \text{ g KI}}$$

    Solution: $150 \ \mu\text{g I} \times \dfrac{1 \text{ g I}}{1 \times 10^6 \ \mu\text{g I}} \times \dfrac{100.0 \text{ g KI}}{76.45 \text{ g I}} \times \dfrac{1 \times 10^6 \ \mu\text{g KI}}{1 \text{ g KI}} = 196 \ \mu\text{g KI}$

    Check: Units of the answer, μg KI, are correct. The magnitude is reasonable because it is greater than the original mass.

72. **Given:** 3.0 mg F; 45.24 % F in NaF   **Find:** mg NaF
    Conceptual Plan: mg F $\rightarrow$ g F $\rightarrow$ g NaF $\rightarrow$ mg NaF

$$\frac{1 \text{ g F}}{1000 \text{ mg F}} \quad \frac{100.0 \text{ g NaF}}{45.24 \text{ g F}} \quad \frac{1000 \text{ mg NaF}}{1 \text{ g NaF}}$$

    Solution: $3.0 \text{ mg F} \times \dfrac{1 \text{ g F}}{1000 \text{ mg F}} \times \dfrac{100.0 \text{ g NaF}}{45.24 \text{ g NaF}} \times \dfrac{1000 \text{ mg NaF}}{1 \text{ g NaF}} = 6.6 \text{ mg NaF}$

    Check: Units of the answer, mg NaF, are correct. The magnitude is reasonable because it is greater than the original mass.

73. a) red – oxygen, white – hydrogen: 2H:O H_2O
    b) black – carbon, white – hydrogen: 2H:C CH_2
    c) black – carbon, white – hydrogen, red – oxygen: 3C:O:H CH_3OH or CH_4O

74. a) black – carbon, red – oxygen: 2O:C CO_2
    b) red – oxygen, white – hydrogen :   2H:2O H_2O_2
    c) red – oxygen, white – hydrogen: 2H:O H_2O

75. a) **Given:** 0.0885 mol C_4H_{10} **Find:** mol H atoms
    Conceptual Plan: mol C_4H_{10} $\rightarrow$ mole H atom

$$\frac{10 \text{ mol H}}{1 \text{ mol } C_4H_{10}}$$

    Solution: $0.0885 \text{ mol } C_4H_{10} \times \dfrac{10 \text{ mol H}}{1 \text{ mol } C_4H_{10}} = 0.885 \text{ mol H atoms}$

    Check: Units of the answer, mol H atoms, are correct. The magnitude is reasonable because it is greater than the original mol C_4H_{10}.

b) **Given:** 1.3 mol CH_4 **Find:** mol H atoms

Conceptual Plan: mol CH_4 → mole H atom

$$\frac{4 \text{ mol H}}{1 \text{ mol CH}_4}$$

Solution: $1.3 \text{ mol CH}_4 \times \dfrac{4 \text{ mol H}}{1 \text{ mol CH}_4} = 5.2 \text{ mol H atoms}$

Check: Units of the answer, mol H atoms, are correct. The magnitude is reasonable because it is greater than the original mol CH_4.

c) **Given:** 2.4 mol C_6H_{12} **Find:** mol H atoms

Conceptual Plan: mol C_6H_{12} → mole H atom

$$\frac{12 \text{ mol H}}{1 \text{ mol C}_6H_{12}}$$

Solution: $2.4 \text{ mol C}_6H_{12} \times \dfrac{12 \text{ mol H}}{1 \text{ mol C}_6H_{12}} = 29 \text{ mol H atoms}$

Check: Units of the answer, mol H atoms, are correct. The magnitude is reasonable because it is greater than the original mol C_6H_{12}.

d) **Given:** 1.87 mol C_8H_{18} **Find:** mol H atoms

Conceptual Plan: mol C_8H_{18} → mole H atom

$$\frac{18 \text{ mol H}}{1 \text{ mol C}_8H_{18}}$$

Solution: $1.87 \text{ mol C}_8H_{18} \times \dfrac{18 \text{ mol H}}{1 \text{ mol C}_8H_{18}} = 33.7 \text{ mol H atoms}$

Check: Units of the answer, mol H atoms, are correct. The magnitude is reasonable because it is greater than the original mol C_8H_{18}.

76. a) **Given:** 4.88 mol H_2O_2 **Find:** mol O atoms

Conceptual Plan: mol H_2O_2 → mole O atom

$$\frac{2 \text{ mol O}}{1 \text{ mol H}_2O_2}$$

Solution: $4.88 \text{ mol H}_2O_2 \times \dfrac{2 \text{ mol O}}{1 \text{ mol H}_2O_2} = 9.8 \text{ mol O atoms}$

Check: Units of the answer, mol O atoms, are correct. The magnitude is reasonable because it is greater than the original mol H_2O_2.

b) **Given:** 2.15 mol N_2O **Find:** mol O atoms

Conceptual Plan: mol N_2O → mole O atom

$$\frac{1 \text{ mol O}}{1 \text{ mol N}_2O}$$

Solution: $2.15 \text{ mol N}_2O \times \dfrac{1 \text{ mol O}}{1 \text{ mol N}_2O} = 2.15 \text{ mol O atoms}$

Check: Units of the answer, mol O atoms, are correct. The magnitude is reasonable because it is the same as the original mol N_2O

c) **Given:** 0.0237 mol H_2CO_3 **Find:** mol O atoms

Conceptual Plan: mol H_2CO_3 → mole O atom

$$\frac{3 \text{ mol O}}{1 \text{ mol H}_2CO_3}$$

Solution: $0.0237 \text{ mol H}_2CO_3 \times \dfrac{3 \text{ mol O}}{1 \text{ mol H}_2CO_3} = 0.711 \text{ mol O atoms}$

Check: Units of the answer, mol O atoms, are correct. The magnitude is reasonable because it is greater than the original mol H_2CO_3.

d) **Given:** 24.1 mol CO_2 **Find:** mol O atoms

Conceptual Plan: mol CO_2 → mole O atom

$$\frac{2 \text{ mol O}}{1 \text{ mol CO}_2}$$

Solution: $24.1 \text{ mol } CO_2 \times \dfrac{2 \text{ mol } O}{1 \text{ mol } CO_2} = 48.2 \text{ mol } O \text{ atoms}$

Check: Units of the answer, mol O atoms, are correct. The magnitude is reasonable because it is greater than the original mol CO_2.

77. a) **Given:** 8.5 g NaCl **Find:** g Na

    Conceptual Plan: g NaCl $\rightarrow$ mole NaCl $\rightarrow$ mol Na $\rightarrow$ g Na

$$\dfrac{1 \text{ mol NaCl}}{58.44 \text{ g NaCl}} \quad \dfrac{1 \text{ mol Na}}{1 \text{ mol NaCl}} \quad \dfrac{22.99 \text{ g Na}}{1 \text{ mol Na}}$$

    Solution: $8.5 \text{ g NaCl} \times \dfrac{1 \text{ mol NaCl}}{58.44 \text{ g NaCl}} \times \dfrac{1 \text{ mol Na}}{1 \text{ mol NaCl}} \times \dfrac{22.99 \text{ g Na}}{1 \text{ mol Na}} = 3.3 \text{ g Na}$

    Check: Units of the answer, g Na, are correct. The magnitude is reasonable because it is less than the original g NaCl.

b) **Given:** 8.5 g Na_3PO_4 **Find:** g Na

    Conceptual Plan: g Na_3PO_4 $\rightarrow$ mole Na_3PO_4 $\rightarrow$ mol Na $\rightarrow$ g Na

$$\dfrac{1 \text{ mol } Na_3PO_4}{163.94 \text{ g } Na_3PO_4} \quad \dfrac{3 \text{ mol Na}}{1 \text{ mol } Na_3PO_4} \quad \dfrac{22.99 \text{ g Na}}{1 \text{ mol Na}}$$

    Solution: $8.5 \text{ g } Na_3PO_4 \times \dfrac{1 \text{ mol } Na_3PO_4}{163.94 \text{ g } Na_3PO_4} \times \dfrac{3 \text{ mol Na}}{1 \text{ mol } Na_3PO_4} \times \dfrac{22.99 \text{ g Na}}{1 \text{ mol Na}} = 3.6 \text{ g Na}$

    Check: Units of the answer, g Na, are correct. The magnitude is reasonable because it is less than the original g Na_3PO_4.

c) **Given:** 8.5 g $NaC_7H_5O_2$ **Find:** g Na

    Conceptual Plan: g $NaC_7H_5O_2$ $\rightarrow$ mole $NaC_7H_5O_2$ $\rightarrow$ mol Na $\rightarrow$ g Na

$$\dfrac{1 \text{ mol } NaC_7H_5O_2}{144.10 \text{ g } NaC_7H_5O_2} \quad \dfrac{1 \text{ mol Na}}{1 \text{ mol } NaC_7H_5O_2} \quad \dfrac{22.99 \text{ g Na}}{1 \text{ mol Na}}$$

    Solution: $8.5 \text{ g } NaC_7H_5O_2 \times \dfrac{1 \text{ mol } NaC_7H_5O_2}{144.10 \text{ g } NaC_7H_5O_2} \times \dfrac{1 \text{ mol Na}}{1 \text{ } NaC_7H_5O_2} \times \dfrac{22.99 \text{ g Na}}{1 \text{ mol Na}} = 1.4 \text{ g Na}$

    Check: Units of the answer, g Na, are correct. The magnitude is reasonable because it is less than the original g $NaC_7H_5O_2$.

d) **Given:** 8.5 g $Na_2C_6H_6O_7$ **Find:** g Na

    Conceptual Plan: g $Na_2C_6H_6O_7$ $\rightarrow$ mole $Na_2C_6H_6O_7$ $\rightarrow$ mol Na $\rightarrow$ g Na

$$\dfrac{1 \text{ mol } Na_2C_6H_6O_7}{236.1 \text{ g } Na_2C_6H_6O_7} \quad \dfrac{2 \text{ mol Na}}{1 \text{ mol } Na_2C_6H_6O_7} \quad \dfrac{22.99 \text{ g Na}}{1 \text{ mol Na}}$$

    Solution:

$8.5 \text{ g } Na_2C_6H_6O_7 \times \dfrac{1 \text{ mol } Na_2C_6H_6O_7}{236.1 \text{ g } Na_2C_6H_6O_7} \times \dfrac{2 \text{ mol Na}}{1 \text{ mol } Na_2C_6H_6O_7} \times \dfrac{22.99 \text{ g Na}}{1 \text{ mol Na}} = 1.7 \text{ g } Na_2C_6H_6O_7$

    Check: Units of the answer, g Na, are correct. The magnitude is reasonable because it is less than the original g $Na_2C_6H_6O_7$.

78. a) **Given:** 25 kg CF_2Cl_2 **Find:** kg Cl

    Conceptual Plan: kg CF_2Cl_2 $\rightarrow$ g CF_2Cl_2 $\rightarrow$ mole CF_2Cl_2 $\rightarrow$ mol Cl $\rightarrow$ g Cl $\rightarrow$ kg Cl

$$\dfrac{1000 \text{ g } CF_2Cl_2}{1 \text{ kg } CF_2Cl_2} \quad \dfrac{1 \text{ mol } CF_2Cl_2}{120.91 \text{ g } CF_2Cl_2} \quad \dfrac{2 \text{ mol Cl}}{1 \text{ mol } CF_2Cl_2} \quad \dfrac{35.45 \text{ g Cl}}{1 \text{ mol Cl}} \quad \dfrac{1 \text{ kg Cl}}{1000 \text{ g Cl}}$$

    Solution:

$25 \text{ kg } CF_2Cl_2 \times \dfrac{1000 \text{ g } CF_2Cl_2}{\text{kg } CF_2Cl_2} \times \dfrac{1 \text{ mol } CF_2Cl_2}{120.91 \text{ g } CF_2Cl_2} \times \dfrac{2 \text{ mol Cl}}{1 \text{ mol } CF_2Cl_2} \times \dfrac{35.45 \text{ g Cl}}{1 \text{ mol Cl}} \times \dfrac{1 \text{ kg Cl}}{1000 \text{ g Cl}} = 15 \text{ kg Cl}$

    Check: Units of the answer, kg Cl, are correct. The magnitude is reasonable because it is less than the original kg CF_2Cl_2.

b) **Given:** 25 kg $CFCl_3$ **Find:** kg Cl

Conceptual Plan: kg CFCl₃ → g CFCl₃ → mole CFCl₃ → mol Cl → g Cl → kg Cl

$$\frac{1000 \text{ g CFCl}_3}{1 \text{ kg CFCl}_3} \quad \frac{1 \text{ mol CFCl}_3}{137.4 \text{ g CFCl}_3} \quad \frac{3 \text{ mol Cl}}{1 \text{ mol CFCl}_3} \quad \frac{35.45 \text{ g Cl}}{1 \text{ mol Cl}} \quad \frac{1 \text{ kg Cl}}{1000 \text{ g Cl}}$$

Solution:

$$25 \text{ kg CFCl}_3 \times \frac{1000 \text{ g CFCl}_3}{\text{kg CFCl}_3} \times \frac{1 \text{ mol CFCl}_3}{137.4 \text{ g CFCl}_3} \times \frac{3 \text{ mol Cl}}{1 \text{ mol CFCl}_3} \times \frac{35.45 \text{ g Cl}}{1 \text{ mol Cl}} = 19 \text{ kg Cl}$$

Check: Units of the answer, kg Cl, are correct. The magnitude is reasonable because it is less than the original kg CF_2Cl_2.

c) **Given:** 25 kg $C_2F_3Cl_3$ **Find:** kg Cl
Conceptual Plan: kg $C_2F_3Cl_3$ → g $C_2F_3Cl_3$ → mole $C_2F_3Cl_3$ → mol Cl → g Cl → kg Cl

$$\frac{1000 \text{ g } C_2F_3Cl_3}{1 \text{ kg } C_2F_3Cl_3} \quad \frac{1 \text{ mol } C_2F_3Cl_3}{187.4 \text{ g } C_2F_3Cl_3} \quad \frac{3 \text{ mol Cl}}{1 \text{ mol } C_2F_3Cl_3} \quad \frac{35.45 \text{ g Cl}}{1 \text{ mol Cl}} \quad \frac{1 \text{ kg Cl}}{1000 \text{ g Cl}}$$

Solution:

$$25 \text{ kg } C_2F_3Cl_3 \times \frac{1000 \text{ g } C_2F_3Cl_3}{\text{kg } C_2F_3Cl_3} \times \frac{1 \text{ mol } C_2F_3Cl_3}{187.4 \text{ g } C_2F_3Cl_3} \times \frac{3 \text{ mol Cl}}{1 \text{ mol } C_2F_3Cl_3} \times \frac{35.45 \text{ g Cl}}{1 \text{ mol Cl}} = 14 \text{ kg Cl}$$

Check: Units of the answer, kg Cl, are correct. The magnitude is reasonable because it is less than the original kg $C_2F_3Cl_3$.

d) **Given:** 25 kg CF_3Cl **Find:** kg Cl
Conceptual Plan: kg CF_3Cl → g CF_3Cl → mole CF_3Cl → mol Cl → g Cl → kg Cl

$$\frac{1000 \text{ g } CF_3Cl}{1 \text{ kg } CF_3Cl} \quad \frac{1 \text{ mol } CF_3Cl}{104.46 \text{ g } CF_3Cl} \quad \frac{1 \text{ mol Cl}}{1 \text{ mol } CF_3Cl} \quad \frac{35.45 \text{ g Cl}}{1 \text{ mol Cl}} \quad \frac{1 \text{ kg Cl}}{1000 \text{ g Cl}}$$

Solution:

$$25 \text{ kg } CF_3Cl \times \frac{1000 \text{ g } CF_3Cl}{\text{kg } CF_3Cl} \times \frac{1 \text{ mol } CF_3Cl}{104.46 \text{ g } CF_3Cl} \times \frac{1 \text{ mol Cl}}{1 \text{ mol } CF_3Cl} \times \frac{35.45 \text{ g Cl}}{1 \text{ mol Cl}} = 8.5 \text{ kg Cl}$$

Check: Units of the answer, kg Cl, are correct. The magnitude is reasonable because it is less than the original kg CF_3Cl.

79. a) **Given:** 1.651 g Ag; 0.1224 g O   **Find:** empirical formula
Conceptual Plan:
convert mass to mol of each element → write pseudoformula → write empirical formula

$$\frac{1 \text{ mol Ag}}{107.9 \text{ g Ag}} \qquad \frac{1 \text{ mol O}}{16.00 \text{ g O}} \qquad \text{divide by smallest number}$$

Solution:

$$1.651 \text{ g Ag} \times \frac{1 \text{ mol Ag}}{107.9 \text{ g Ag}} = 0.01530 \text{ mol Ag}$$

$$0.1224 \text{ g O} \times \frac{1 \text{ mol O}}{16.00 \text{ g O}} = 0.007650 \text{ mol O}$$

$$Ag_{0.01530} O_{0.007650}$$

$$Ag_{\frac{0.01530}{0.007650}} O_{\frac{0.007650}{0.007650}} \rightarrow Ag_2O$$

The correct empirical formula is Ag_2O

b) **Given:** 0.672 g Co; 0.569 g As; 0.486 g O **Find:** empirical formula
Conceptual Plan:
convert mass to mol of each element → write pseudoformula → write empirical formula

$$\frac{1 \text{ mol Co}}{58.93 \text{ g Co}} \quad \frac{1 \text{ mol As}}{74.92 \text{ g As}} \quad \frac{1 \text{ mol O}}{16.00 \text{ g O}} \qquad \text{divide by smallest number}$$

Solution:

$$0.672 \text{ g Co} \times \frac{1 \text{ mol Co}}{58.93 \text{ g Co}} = 0.0114 \text{ mol Co}$$

$$0.569 \text{ g As} \times \frac{1 \text{ mol As}}{74.92 \text{ g As}} = 0.00759 \text{ mol O}$$

$$0.486 \text{ g O} \times \frac{1 \text{ mol O}}{16.00 \text{ g O}} = 0.0304 \text{ mol O}$$

$$Co_{0.0114}As_{0.00759}O_{0.0304}$$

$$Co_{\frac{0.0114}{0.00759}}As_{\frac{0.00759}{0.00759}}O_{\frac{0.0304}{0.00759}} \rightarrow Co_{1.5}As_1O_4$$

$$Co_{1.5}As_1O_4 \text{ x } 2 \rightarrow Co_3As_2O_8$$

The correct empirical formula is $Co_3As_2O_8$

c) **Given:** 1.443 g Se; 5.841 g Br   **Find:** empirical formula
Conceptual Plan:
convert mass to mol of each element → write pseudoformula → write empirical formula

$$\frac{1 \text{ mol Se}}{78.96 \text{ g Se}} \qquad \frac{1 \text{ mol Br}}{79.90 \text{ g Br}} \qquad \text{divide by smallest number}$$

Solution:

$$1.443 \text{ g Se x } \frac{1 \text{ mol Se}}{78.96 \text{ g Se}} = 0.01828 \text{ mol Se}$$

$$5.841 \text{ g Br x } \frac{1 \text{ mol Br}}{79.90 \text{ g Br}} = 0.07310 \text{ mol Br}$$

$$Se_{0.01828} Br_{0.07310}$$

$$Se_{\frac{0.01828}{0.01828}} Br_{\frac{0.07310}{0.01828}} \rightarrow SeBr_4$$

The correct empirical formula is $SeBr_4$

80. a) **Given:** 1.245 g Ni; 5.381 g I   **Find:** empirical formula
Conceptual Plan:
convert mass to mol of each element → write pseudoformula → write empirical formula

$$\frac{1 \text{ mol Ni}}{58.69 \text{ g Ni}} \qquad \frac{1 \text{ mol I}}{126.9 \text{ g I}} \qquad \text{divide by smallest number}$$

Solution:

$$1.245 \text{ g Ni x } \frac{1 \text{ mol Ni}}{58.69 \text{ g Ni}} = 0.02121 \text{ mol Ni}$$

$$5.381 \text{ g I x } \frac{1 \text{ mol I}}{126.9 \text{ g I}} = 0.04240 \text{ mol I}$$

$$Ni_{0.02121} I_{0.04240}$$

$$Ni_{\frac{0.02121}{0.02121}}I_{\frac{0.04240}{0.02121}} \rightarrow NiI_2$$

The correct empirical formula is NiI_2

b) **Given:** 2.677 g Ba; 3.115 g Br   **Find:** empirical formula
Conceptual Plan:
convert mass to mol of each element → write pseudoformula → write empirical formula

$$\frac{1 \text{ mol Ba}}{137.3 \text{ g Ba}} \qquad \frac{1 \text{ mol Br}}{79.90 \text{ g Br}} \qquad \text{divide by smallest number}$$

Solution:

$$\frac{2.677 \text{ g Ba}}{} \text{ x } \frac{1 \text{ mol Ba}}{137.3 \text{ g Ba}} = 0.01942 \text{ mol Ba}$$

$$\frac{3.115 \text{ g Br}}{} \text{ x } \frac{1 \text{ mol Br}}{79.90 \text{ g Br}} = 0.03899 \text{ mol Br}$$

$$Ba_{0.01942} Br_{0.03899}$$

$$Ba_{\frac{0.01942}{0.01942}}Br_{\frac{0.03899}{0.01942}} \rightarrow BaBr_2$$

The correct empirical formula is $BaBr_2$

c) **Given:** 2.128 g Be; 7.557 g S; 15.107 g O   **Find:** empirical formula
Conceptual Plan:
convert mass to mol of each element → write pseudoformula → write empirical formula

$$\frac{1 \text{ mol Be}}{9.012 \text{ g Be}} \qquad \frac{1 \text{ mol S}}{32.07 \text{ g S}} \qquad \frac{1 \text{ mol O}}{16.00 \text{ g O}} \qquad \text{divide by smallest number}$$

Solution:

$$2.128 \text{ g Be} \times \frac{1 \text{ mol Be}}{9.012 \text{ g Be}} = 0.2361 \text{ mol Be}$$

$$7.557 \text{ g S} \times \frac{1 \text{ mol S}}{32.07 \text{ g S}} = 0.2356 \text{ mol S}$$

$$15.107 \text{ g O} \times \frac{1 \text{ mol O}}{16.00 \text{ g O}} = 0.9442 \text{ mol O}$$

$$Be_{0.2361} S_{0.2356} O_{0.9442}$$

$$Be_{\frac{0.2361}{0.2356}} S_{\frac{0.2356}{0.2356}} O_{\frac{0.9442}{0.2356}} \rightarrow BeSO_4$$

The correct empirical formula is $BeSO_4$

81. a) **Given:** In a 100 g sample: 74.03 g C, 8.70 g H, 17.27 g N   **Find:** empirical formula
   Conceptual Plan:
   convert mass to mol of each element → write pseudoformula → write empirical formula

   $$\frac{1 \text{ mol C}}{12.01 \text{ g C}} \quad \frac{1 \text{ mol H}}{1.008 \text{ g H}} \quad \frac{1 \text{ mol N}}{14.01 \text{ g N}} \qquad \text{divide by smallest number}$$

   Solution:

   $$74.03 \text{ g C} \times \frac{1 \text{ mol C}}{12.01 \text{ g C}} = 6.164 \text{ mol C}$$

   $$8.70 \text{ g H} \times \frac{1 \text{ mol H}}{1.008 \text{ g H}} = 8.63 \text{ mol H}$$

   $$17.27 \text{ g N} \times \frac{1 \text{ mol N}}{14.01 \text{ g N}} = 1.233 \text{ mol N}$$

   $$C_{6.164} H_{8.63} N_{1.233}$$

   $$C_{\frac{6.164}{1.233}} H_{\frac{8.63}{1.233}} N_{\frac{1.233}{1.233}} \rightarrow C_5 H_7 N$$

   The correct empirical formula is C_5H_7N

   b) **Given:** In a 100 g sample: 49.48 g C, 5.19 g H, 28.85 g N, 16.48 g O   **Find:** empirical formula
   Conceptual Plan:
   convert mass to mol of each element → write pseudoformula → write empirical formula

   $$\frac{1 \text{ mol C}}{12.01 \text{ g C}} \quad \frac{1 \text{ mol H}}{1.008 \text{ g H}} \quad \frac{1 \text{ mol N}}{14.01 \text{ g N}} \quad \frac{1 \text{ mol O}}{16.00 \text{ g O}} \qquad \text{divide by smallest number}$$

   Solution:

   $$49.48 \text{ g C} \times \frac{1 \text{ mol C}}{12.01 \text{ g C}} = 4.120 \text{ mol C}$$

   $$5.19 \text{ g H} \times \frac{1 \text{ mol H}}{1.008 \text{ g H}} = 5.15 \text{ mol H}$$

   $$28.85 \text{ g N} \times \frac{1 \text{ mol N}}{14.01 \text{ g N}} = 2.059 \text{ mol N}$$

   $$16.48 \text{ g O} \times \frac{1 \text{ mol O}}{16.00 \text{ g O}} = 1.030 \text{ mol O}$$

   $$C_{4.120} H_{5.15} N_{2.059} O_{1.030}$$

   $$C_{\frac{4.120}{1.030}} H_{\frac{5.15}{1.030}} N_{\frac{2.059}{1.030}} O_{\frac{1.030}{1.030}} \rightarrow C_4 H_5 N_2 O$$

   The correct empirical formula is $C_4H_5N_2O$

82. a) **Given:** In a 100 g sample: 58.80g C, 9.87 g H, 31.33 g O   **Find:** empirical formula
   Conceptual Plan:
   convert mass to mol of each element → write pseudoformula → write empirical formula

   $$\frac{1 \text{ mol C}}{12.01 \text{ g C}} \quad \frac{1 \text{ mol H}}{1.008 \text{ g H}} \quad \frac{1 \text{ mol O}}{16.00 \text{ g O}} \qquad \text{divide by smallest number}$$

   Solution:

   $$58.80 \text{ g C} \times \frac{1 \text{ mol C}}{12.01 \text{ g C}} = 4.896 \text{ mol C}$$

   $$9.87 \text{ g H} \times \frac{1 \text{ mol H}}{1.008 \text{ g H}} = 9.79 \text{ mol H}$$

$$31.33 \text{ g O} \times \frac{1 \text{ mol O}}{16.00 \text{ g O}} = 1.958 \text{ mol O}$$

$$C_{4.896}H_{9.79}O_{1.958}$$

$$C_{\frac{4.896}{1.958}}H_{\frac{9.79}{1.958}}O_{\frac{1.958}{1.958}} \rightarrow C_{2.5}H_5O$$

$$C_{2.5}H_5O \times 2 = C_5H_{10}O_2$$

The correct empirical formula is $C_5H_{10}O_2$

b) **Given:** In a 100 g sample: 63.15 g C, 5.30 g H, 31.35 g O   **Find:** empirical formula
Conceptual Plan:
  convert mass to mol of each element → write pseudoformula → write empirical formula
$$\frac{1 \text{ mol C}}{12.01 \text{ g C}} \quad \frac{1 \text{ mol H}}{1.008 \text{ g H}} \quad \frac{1 \text{ mol O}}{16.00 \text{ g O}}$$
divide by smallest number

Solution:
$$63.15 \text{ g C} \times \frac{1 \text{ mol C}}{12.01 \text{ g C}} = 5.258 \text{ mol C}$$

$$5.30 \text{ g H} \times \frac{1 \text{ mol H}}{1.008 \text{ g H}} = 5.26 \text{ mol H}$$

$$31.35 \text{ g O} \times \frac{1 \text{ mol O}}{16.00 \text{ g O}} = 1.959 \text{ mol O}$$

$$C_{5.258}H_{5.26}O_{1.959}$$

$$C_{\frac{5.258}{1.959}}H_{\frac{5.26}{1.959}}O_{\frac{1.959}{1.959}} \rightarrow C_{2.68}H_{2.68}O$$

$$C_{2.68}H_{2.68}O \times 3 = C_8H_8O_3$$

The correct empirical formula is $C_8H_8O_3$

83. **Given:** 0.77 mg N, 6.61 mg N_xCl_y **Find:** empirical formula
Conceptual Plan:
  Find mg Cl → convert mg to g for each element → convert mass to mol of each element →
$$\frac{\text{mg } N_xCl_y - \text{mg N}}{} \quad \frac{1 \text{ g}}{1000 \text{ mg}} \qquad \frac{1 \text{ mol N}}{14.01 \text{ g N}} \quad \frac{1 \text{ mol Cl}}{35.45 \text{ g Cl}}$$
  write pseudoformula → write empirical formula
        divide by smallest number
Solution: 6.61 mg N_xCl_y – 0.77 mg N = 5.94 mg Cl

$$\frac{0.77 \text{ mg N}}{} \times \frac{1 \text{ g N}}{1000 \text{ mg N}} \times \frac{1 \text{ mol N}}{14.01 \text{ g N}} = 5.5 \times 10^{-5} \text{ mol N}$$

$$\frac{5.94 \text{ g Cl}}{} \times \frac{1 \text{ g Cl}}{1000 \text{ mg Cl}} \times \frac{1 \text{ mol Cl}}{35.45 \text{ g Cl}} = 1.7 \times 10^{-4} \text{ mol Cl}$$

$$N_{5.5 \times 10^{-5}}Cl_{1.7 \times 10^{-4}}$$

$$N_{\frac{5.5 \times 10^{-5}}{5.5 \times 10^{-5}}}Cl_{\frac{1.7 \times 10^{-4}}{5.5 \times 10^{-5}}} \rightarrow NCl_3$$

The correct empirical formula is NCl_3

84. **Given:** 45.2 mg P, 131.6 mg P_xSe_y **Find:** empirical formula
Conceptual Plan: Find mg Se → convert mg to g for each element → convert mass to mol of each element →
$$\frac{\text{mg } P_xSe_y - \text{mg P}}{} \quad \frac{1 \text{ g}}{1000 \text{ mg}} \qquad \frac{1 \text{ mol P}}{30.97 \text{ g P}} \quad \frac{1 \text{ mol Se}}{78.96 \text{ g Se}}$$
  write pseudoformula → write empirical formula
        divide by smallest number
Solution: 131.6 mg P_xSe_y – 45.2 mg P = 86.4 mg Se

$$45.2 \text{ mg P} \times \frac{1 \text{ g P}}{1000 \text{ mg P}} \times \frac{1 \text{ mol P}}{30.97 \text{ g P}} = 0.00146 \text{ mol P}$$

$$86.4 \text{ g Se} \times \frac{1 \text{ g Se}}{1000 \text{ mg Se}} \times \frac{1 \text{ mol Se}}{78.96 \text{ g Se}} = 0.00109 \text{ mol Se}$$

$$P_{0.00146} Se_{0.00109}$$

$$P_{\frac{0.00146}{0.00109}} Se_{\frac{0.00109}{0.00109}} \rightarrow P_{1.33}Se$$

$$P_{1.33}Se \times 3 = P_4Se_3$$

The correct empirical formula is P_4Se_3

85. a) **Given:** empirical formula = C_6H_7N, molar mass = 186.24 g/mol   **Find:** molecular formula
    Conceptual Plan: molecular formula = empirical formula x n

$$n = \frac{\text{molar mass}}{\text{empirical formula mass}}$$

   Solution: empirical formula mass = 6(12.01 g/mol) + 7(1.008 g/mol) + 1(14.01 g/mol) = 93.13 g/mol

$$n = \frac{\text{molar mass}}{\text{formula molar mass}} = \frac{186.24 \text{ g/mol}}{93.13 \text{ g/mol}} = 1.998 = 2$$

   molecular formula $= C_6H_7N \times 2$
                        $= C_{12}H_{14}N_2$

   b) **Given:** empirical formula = C_2HCl, molar mass = 181.44 g/mol   **Find:** molecular formula
    Conceptual Plan: molecular formula = empirical formula x n

$$n = \frac{\text{molar mass}}{\text{empirical formula mass}}$$

   Solution: empirical formula mass = 2(12.01 g/mol) + 1(1.008 g/mol) + 1(35.45 g/mol) = 60.48 g/mol

$$n = \frac{\text{molar mass}}{\text{formula molar mass}} = \frac{181.44 \text{ g/mol}}{60.48 \text{ g/mol}} = 3$$

   molecular formula $= C_2HCl \times 3$
                        $= C_6H_3Cl_3$

   c) **Given:** empirical formula = $C_5H_{10}NS_2$, molar mass = 296.54 g/mol   **Find:** molecular formula
    Conceptual Plan: molecular formula = empirical formula x n

$$n = \frac{\text{molar mass}}{\text{empirical formula mass}}$$

   Solution: empirical formula mass = 5(12.01 g/mol) + 10(1.008 g/mol) + 1(14.01 g/mol) + 2(32.07) = 148.28 g/mol

$$n = \frac{\text{molar mass}}{\text{formula molar mass}} = \frac{296.54 \text{ g/mol}}{148.28 \text{ g/mol}} = 2$$

   molecular formula $= C_5H_{10}NS_2 \times 2$
                        $= C_{10}H_{20}N_2S_4$

86. a) **Given:** empirical formula = C_4H_9, molar mass = 114.22 g/mol **Find:** molecular formula
    Conceptual Plan: molecular formula = empirical formula x n

$$n = \frac{\text{molar mass}}{\text{empirical formula mass}}$$

   Solution: empirical formula mass = 4(12.01 g/mol) + 9(1.008 g/mol) = 57.11 g/mol

$$n = \frac{\text{molar mass}}{\text{formula molar mass}} = \frac{114.22 \text{ g/mol}}{57.11 \text{ g/mol}} = 2$$

   molecular formula $= C_4H_9 \times 2$
                        $= C_8H_{18}$

   b) **Given:** empirical formula = CCl, molar mass = 284.77 g/mol **Find:** molecular formula
    Conceptual Plan: molecular formula = empirical formula x n

$$n = \frac{\text{molar mass}}{\text{empirical formula mass}}$$

   Solution: empirical formula mass = 1(12.01 g/mol) + 1(35.45 g/mol) = 47.46 g/mol

$$n = \frac{\text{molar mass}}{\text{formula molar mass}} = \frac{284.77 \text{ g/mol}}{47.46 \text{ g/mol}} = 6$$

   molecular formula $= CCl \times 6$
                        $= C_6Cl_6$

   c) **Given:** empirical formula = C_3H_2N, molar mass = 312.29 g/mol   **Find:** molecular formula
    Conceptual Plan: molecular formula = empirical formula x n

$$n = \frac{\text{molar mass}}{\text{empirical formula mass}}$$

   Solution: empirical formula mass = 3(12.01 g/mol) + 2(1.008 g/mol) + 1(14.01 g/mol) = 52.06 g/mol

$$n = \frac{\text{molar mass}}{\text{formula molar mass}} = \frac{312.29 \text{ g/mol}}{52.06 \text{ g/mol}} = 6$$

molecular formula $= C_3H_2N \times 6$

$= C_{18}H_{12}N_6$

87. **Given:** 33.01 g CO_2, 13.51 g H_2O **Find:** empirical formula

Conceptual Plan:

mass CO_2, H_2O → mol CO_2, H_2O → mol C, mol H → pseudoformula → empirical formula

$\dfrac{1 \text{ mol } CO_2}{44.01 \text{ g } CO_2}$ $\dfrac{1 \text{ mol } H_2O}{18.02 \text{ g } H_2O}$ $\dfrac{1 \text{ mol C}}{1 \text{ mol } CO_2}$ $\dfrac{2 \text{ mol H}}{1 \text{ mol } H_2O}$ divide by smallest number

Solution:

$$33.01 \text{ g } CO_2 \times \frac{1 \text{ mol } CO_2}{44.01 \text{ g } CO_2} = 0.7500 \text{ mol } CO_2$$

$$13.51 \text{ g } H_2O \times \frac{1 \text{ mol } H_2O}{18.02 \text{ g } H_2O} = 0.7497 \text{ mol } H_2O$$

$$0.7500 \text{ mol } CO_2 \times \frac{1 \text{ mol C}}{1 \text{ mol } CO_2} = 0.7500 \text{ mol C}$$

$$0.7497 \text{ mol } H_2O \times \frac{2 \text{ mol H}}{1 \text{ mol } H_2O} = 1.499 \text{ mol H}$$

$C_{0.7500} H_{1.499}$

$C_{\frac{0.7500}{0.7500}} H_{\frac{1.499}{0.7500}} \rightarrow CH_2$

The correct empirical formula is CH_2

88. **Given:** 8.80 g CO_2, 1.44 g H_2O **Find:** empirical formula

Conceptual Plan:

mass CO_2, H_2O → mol CO_2, H_2O → mol C, mol H → pseudoformula → empirical formula

$\dfrac{1 \text{ mol } CO_2}{44.01 \text{ g } CO_2}$ $\dfrac{1 \text{ mol } H_2O}{18.02 \text{ g } H_2O}$ $\dfrac{1 \text{ mol C}}{1 \text{ mol } CO_2}$ $\dfrac{2 \text{ mol H}}{1 \text{ mol } H_2O}$ divide by smallest number

Solution:

$$8.80 \text{ g } CO_2 \times \frac{1 \text{ mol } CO_2}{44.01 \text{ g } CO_2} = 0.200 \text{ mol } CO_2$$

$$1.44 \text{ g } H_2O \times \frac{1 \text{ mol } H_2O}{18.02 \text{ g } H_2O} = 0.0799 \text{ mol } H_2O$$

$$0.200 \text{ mol } CO_2 \times \frac{1 \text{ mol C}}{1 \text{ mol } CO_2} = 0.200 \text{ mol C}$$

$$0.0799 \text{ mol } H_2O \times \frac{2 \text{ mol H}}{1 \text{ mol } H_2O} = 0.160 \text{ mol H}$$

$C_{0.200} H_{0.160}$

$C_{\frac{0.200}{0.160}} H_{\frac{0.160}{0.160}} \rightarrow C_{1.25}H$

$C_{1.25}H \times 4 = C_5H_4$

The correct empirical formula is C_5H_4

89. **Given:** 4.30 g sample, 8.59 g CO_2, 3.52 g H_2O **Find:** empirical formula

Conceptual Plan:

mass CO_2, H_2O → mol CO_2, H_2O → mol C, mol H → mass C, mass H, mass O → mol O →

$\dfrac{1 \text{ mol } CO_2}{44.01 \text{ g } CO_2}$ $\dfrac{1 \text{ mol } H_2O}{18.02 \text{ g } H_2O}$ $\dfrac{1 \text{ mol C}}{1 \text{ mol } CO_2}$ $\dfrac{2 \text{ mol H}}{1 \text{ mol } H_2O}$ $\dfrac{12.01 \text{ g C}}{1 \text{ mol C}}$ $\dfrac{1.008 \text{ g H}}{1 \text{ mol H}}$ g sample - gC - g H $\dfrac{1 \text{ mol O}}{16.00 \text{ g O}}$

pseudoformula → empirical formula

divide by smallest number

Solution:

$$8.59 \text{ g CO}_2 \times \frac{1 \text{ mol CO}_2}{44.01 \text{ g CO}_2} = 0.195 \text{ mol CO}_2$$

$$3.52 \text{ g H}_2\text{O} \times \frac{1 \text{ mol H}_2\text{O}}{18.02 \text{ g H}_2\text{O}} = 0.195 \text{ mol H}_2\text{O}$$

$$0.195 \text{ mol CO}_2 \times \frac{1 \text{ mol C}}{1 \text{ mol CO}_2} = 0.195 \text{ mol C}$$

$$0.195 \text{ mol H}_2\text{O} \times \frac{2 \text{ mol H}}{1 \text{ mol H}_2\text{O}} = 0.390 \text{ mol H}$$

$$0.195 \text{ mol C} \times \frac{12.01 \text{ g C}}{1 \text{ mol C}} = 2.34 \text{ g C}$$

$$0.390 \text{ mol H}_2\text{O} \times \frac{1.008 \text{ g H}}{1 \text{ mol H}} = 0.393 \text{ g H}$$

$$4.30 \text{ g} - 2.34 \text{ g} - 0.393 \text{ g} = 1.57 \text{ g O}$$

$$1.57 \text{ g O} \times \frac{1 \text{ mol O}}{16.00 \text{ g O}} = 0.0979 \text{ mol O}$$

$$C_{0.195} H_{0.390} O_{0.0979}$$

$$C_{\frac{0.195}{0.0979}} H_{\frac{0.390}{0.0979}} O_{\frac{0.0979}{0.0979}} \rightarrow C_2H_4O$$

The correct empirical formula is C_2H_4O

90. **Given:** 12.01 g sample, 14.01 g CO_2, 4.32 g H_2O **Find:** empirical formula
Conceptual Plan:
mass CO_2, H_2O → mol CO_2, H_2O → mol C, mol H → mass C, mass H, mass O → mol O →

$$\frac{1 \text{ mol CO}_2}{44.01 \text{ g CO}_2} \quad \frac{1 \text{ mol H}_2\text{O}}{18.02 \text{ g H}_2\text{O}} \qquad \frac{1 \text{ mol C}}{1 \text{ mol CO}_2} \quad \frac{2 \text{ mol H}}{1 \text{ mol H}_2\text{O}} \qquad \frac{12.01 \text{ g C}}{1 \text{ mol C}} \quad \frac{1.008 \text{ g H}}{1 \text{ mol H}} \quad \text{g sample - gC - g H} \qquad \frac{1 \text{ mol O}}{16.00 \text{ g O}}$$

pseudoformula → empirical formula
divide by smallest number

Solution:

$$14.01 \text{ g CO}_2 \times \frac{1 \text{ mol CO}_2}{44.01 \text{ g CO}_2} = 0.3183 \text{ mol CO}_2$$

$$4.32 \text{ g H}_2\text{O} \times \frac{1 \text{ mol H}_2\text{O}}{18.02 \text{ g H}_2\text{O}} = 0.2397 \text{ mol H}_2\text{O}$$

$$0.3183 \text{ mol CO}_2 \times \frac{1 \text{ mol C}}{1 \text{ mol CO}_2} = 0.3183 \text{ mol C}$$

$$0.2397 \text{ mol H}_2\text{O} \times \frac{2 \text{ mol H}}{1 \text{ mol H}_2\text{O}} = 0.4795 \text{ mol H}$$

$$0.3183 \text{ mol C} \times \frac{12.01 \text{ g C}}{1 \text{ mol C}} = 3.823 \text{ g C}$$

$$0.4795 \text{ mol H}_2\text{O} \times \frac{1.008 \text{ g H}}{1 \text{ mol H}} = 0.4833 \text{ g H}$$

$$12.01 \text{ g} - 3.823 \text{ g} - 0.4833 \text{ g} = 7.70 \text{ g O}$$

$$7.70 \text{ g O} \times \frac{1 \text{ mol O}}{16.00 \text{ g O}} = 0.481 \text{ mol O}$$

$$C_{0.3183}H_{0.4795}O_{0.481}$$

$$C_{\frac{0.3183}{0.3183}}H_{\frac{0.4795}{0.3183}}O_{\frac{0.481}{0.3183}} \rightarrow C H_{1.5}O_{1.5}$$

$$C H_{1.5}O_{1.5} \times 2 = C_2H_3O_3$$

The correct empirical formula is $C_2H_3O_3$

91. **Conceptual Plan: write a skeletal reaction → balance atoms in more complex compounds → balance elements that occur as free elements → clear fractions**
Solution: Skeletal reaction: $SO_2(g) + O_2(g) + H_2O(l) \rightarrow H_2SO_4(aq)$

| | Balance O: | $SO_2(g) + 1/2O_2(g) + H_2O(l) \rightarrow H_2SO_4(aq)$ |
| | Clear fraction: | $2SO_2(g) + O_2(g) + 2H_2O(l) \rightarrow 2H_2SO_4(aq)$ |

Check:

left side	right side
2 S atoms	2 S atoms
8 O atoms	8 O atoms
4 H atoms	4 H atoms

92. **Conceptual Plan: write a skeletal reaction → balance atoms in more complex compounds → balance elements that occur as free elements → clear fractions**

Solution: Skeletal reaction: $NO_2(g) + O_2(g) + H_2O(l) \rightarrow HNO_3(aq)$

Balance H: $NO_2(g) + O_2(g) + H_2O(l) \rightarrow 2HNO_3(aq)$

Balance N: $2NO_2(g) + O_2(g) + H_2O(l) \rightarrow 2HNO_3(aq)$

Balance O: $2NO_2(g) + 1/2O_2(g) + H_2O(l) \rightarrow 2HNO_3(aq)$

Clear fraction: $4NO_2(g) + O_2(g) + 2H_2O(l) \rightarrow 4HNO_3(aq)$

Check:

left side	right side
4 N atoms	4 N atoms
12 O atoms	12 O atoms
4 H atoms	4 H atoms

93. **Conceptual Plan: write a skeletal reaction → balance atoms in more complex compounds → balance elements that occur as free elements → clear fractions**

Solution: Skeletal reaction: $Na(s) + H_2O(l) \rightarrow H_2(g) + NaOH(aq)$

Balance H: $Na(s) + H_2O(l) \rightarrow 1/2H_2(g) + NaOH(aq)$

Clear fraction: $2Na(s) + 2H_2O(l) \rightarrow H_2(g) + 2NaOH(aq)$

Check:

left side	right side
2 Na atoms	2 Na atoms
4 H atoms	4 H atoms
2 O atoms	2 O atoms

94. **Conceptual Plan: write a skeletal reaction → balance atoms in more complex compounds → balance elements that occur as free elements → clear fractions**

Solution: Skeletal reaction: $Fe(s) + O_2(g) \rightarrow Fe_2O_3(s)$

Balance O: $Fe(s) + 3O_2(g) \rightarrow 2Fe_2O_3(s)$

Balance Fe: $4Fe(s) + 3O_2(g) \rightarrow 2Fe_2O_3(s)$

Check:

left side	right side
4 Fe atoms	4 Fe atoms
6 O atoms	6 O atoms

95. **Conceptual Plan: write a skeletal reaction → balance atoms in more complex compounds → balance elements that occur as free elements → clear fractions**

Solution: Skeletal reaction: $C_{12}H_{22}O_{11}(aq) + H_2O(l) \rightarrow C_2H_5OH(aq) + CO_2(g)$

Balance H: $C_{12}H_{22}O_{11}(aq) + H_2O(l) \rightarrow 4C_2H_5OH(aq) + CO_2(g)$

Balance C: $C_{12}H_{22}O_{11}(aq) + H_2O(l) \rightarrow 4C_2H_5OH(aq) + 4CO_2(g)$

Check:

left side	right side
12 C atoms	12 C atoms
24 H atoms	24 H atoms
12 O atoms	12 O atoms

96. **Conceptual Plan: write a skeletal reaction → balance atoms in more complex compounds → balance elements that occur as free elements → clear fractions**

Solution: Skeletal reaction: $CO_2(g) + H_2O(l) \rightarrow C_6H_{12}O_6(aq) + O_2(g)$

Balance C: $6CO_2(g) + H_2O(l) \rightarrow C_6H_{12}O_6(aq) + O_2(g)$

Balance H: $6CO_2(g) + 6H_2O(l) \rightarrow C_6H_{12}O_6(aq) + O_2(g)$

Balance O: $6CO_2(g) + 6H_2O(l) \rightarrow C_6H_{12}O_6(aq) + 6O_2(g)$

Check:

left side	right side
6 C atoms	6 C atoms
18 O atoms	18 O atoms
12 H atoms	12 H atoms

97. a) **Conceptual Plan: write a skeletal reaction → balance atoms in more complex compounds → balance elements that occur as free elements → clear fractions**

Solution: Skeletal reaction: $PbS(s) + HBr(aq) \rightarrow PbBr_2(s) + H_2S(g)$

Balance Br: $\quad PbS(s) + 2HBr(aq) \rightarrow PbBr_2(s) + H_2S(g)$

Check:

left side	right side
1 Pb atom	1 Pb atom
1 S atom	1 S atom
2 H atoms	2 H atoms
2 Br atoms	2 Br atoms

b) Conceptual Plan: write a skeletal reaction → balance atoms in more complex compounds → balance elements that occur as free elements → clear fractions

Solution: Skeletal reaction: $CO(g) + H_2(g) \rightarrow CH_4(g) + H_2O(l)$

Balance H: $\quad CO(g) + 3H_2(g) \rightarrow CH_4(g) + H_2O(l)$

Check:

left side	right side
1 C atom	1 C atom
1 O atom	1 O atom
6 H atoms	6 H atoms

c) Conceptual Plan: write a skeletal reaction → balance atoms in more complex compounds → balance elements that occur as free elements → clear fractions

Solution: Skeletal reaction: $HCl(aq) + MnO_2(s) \rightarrow MnCl_2(aq) + H_2O(l) + Cl_2(g)$

Balance Cl $\quad 4HCl(aq) + MnO_2(s) \rightarrow MnCl_2(aq) + H_2O(l) + Cl_2(g)$

Balance O $\quad 4HCl(aq) + MnO_2(s) \rightarrow MnCl_2(aq) + 2H_2O(l) + Cl_2(g)$

Check:

left side	right side
4 H atoms	4 H atoms
4 Cl atoms	4 Cl atoms
1 Mn atom	1 Mn atom
2 O atoms	2 O atoms

d) Conceptual Plan: write a skeletal reaction → balance atoms in more complex compounds → balance elements that occur as free elements → clear fractions

Solution: Skeletal reaction: $C_5H_{12}(l) + O_2(g) \rightarrow CO_2(g) + H_2O(l)$

Balance C: $\quad C_5H_{12}(l) + O_2(g) \rightarrow 5CO_2(g) + H_2O(l)$

Balance H: $\quad C_5H_{12}(l) + O_2(g) \rightarrow 5CO_2(g) + 6H_2O(l)$

Balance O: $\quad C_5H_{12}(l) + 8O_2(g) \rightarrow 5CO_2(g) + 6H_2O(l)$

Check:

left side	right side
5 C atoms	5 C atoms
12 H atoms	12 H atoms
16 O atoms	16 O atoms

98. **a) Conceptual Plan: write a skeletal reaction → balance atoms in more complex compounds → balance elements that occur as free elements → clear fractions**

Solution: Skeletal reaction: $Cu(s) + S(s) \rightarrow Cu_2S(s)$

Balance Cu: $\quad 2Cu(s) + S(s) \rightarrow Cu_2S(s)$

Check:

left side	right side
2 Cu atoms	2 Cu atoms
1 S atom	1 S atom

b) Conceptual Plan: write a skeletal reaction → balance atoms in more complex compounds → balance elements that occur as free elements → clear fractions

Solution: Skeletal reaction: $Fe_2O_3(s) + H_2(g) \rightarrow Fe(s) + H_2O(l)$

Balance O: $\quad Fe_2O_3(s) + H_2(g) \rightarrow Fe(s) + 3H_2O(l)$

Balance Fe: $\quad Fe_2O_3(s) + H_2(g) \rightarrow 2Fe(s) + 3H_2O(l)$

Balance H: $\quad Fe_2O_3(s) + 3H_2(g) \rightarrow 2Fe(s) + 3H_2O(l)$

Check:

left side	right side
2 Fe atoms	2 Fe atoms
3 O atoms	3 O atoms
6 H atoms	6 H atoms

c) Conceptual Plan: write a skeletal reaction → balance atoms in more complex compounds → balance elements that occur as free elements → clear fractions

Solution: Skeletal reaction: $SO_2(g) + O_2(g) \rightarrow SO_3(g)$

Balance O: $SO_2(g) + 1/2O_2(g) \rightarrow SO_3(g)$
Clear fraction: $2SO_2(g) + O_2(g) \rightarrow 2SO_3(g)$

Check:

left side	right side
2 S atoms	2 S atoms
6 O atoms	6 O atoms

d) Conceptual Plan: write a skeletal reaction → balance atoms in more complex compounds → balance elements that occur as free elements → clear fractions

Solution: Skeletal reaction: $NH_3(g) + O_2(g) \rightarrow NO(g) + H_2O(g)$
Balance H: $2NH_3(g) + O_2(g) \rightarrow NO(g) + 3H_2O(g)$
Balance O: $2NH_3(g) + 5/2O_2(g) \rightarrow 2NO(g) + 3H_2O(g)$
Clear fraction: $4NH_3(g) + 5O_2(g) \rightarrow 4NO(g) + 6H_2O(g)$

Check:

left side	right side
4 N atoms	4 N atoms
6 H atoms	6 H atoms
10 O atoms	10 O atoms

99. **a) Conceptual Plan: balance atoms in more complex compounds → balance elements that occur as free elements → clear fractions**

Solution: Skeletal reaction: $CO_2(g) + CaSiO_3(s) + H_2O(l) \rightarrow SiO_2(s) + Ca(HCO_3)_2(aq)$
Balance C: $2CO_2(g) + CaSiO_3(s) + H_2O(l) \rightarrow SiO_2(s) + Ca(HCO_3)_2(aq)$

Check:

left side	right side
2 C atoms	2 C atoms
8 O atoms	8 O atoms
1 Ca atom	1 Ca atom
1 Si atom	1 Si atom
2 H atoms	2 H atoms

b) Conceptual Plan: balance atoms in more complex compounds → balance elements that occur as free elements → clear fractions

Solution: Skeletal reaction: $Co(NO_3)_3(aq) + (NH_4)_2S(aq) \rightarrow Co_2S_3(s) + NH_4NO_3(aq)$
Balance S: $Co(NO_3)_3(aq) + 3(NH_4)_2S(aq) \rightarrow Co_2S_3(s) + NH_4NO_3(aq)$
Balance Co: $2Co(NO_3)_3(aq) + 3(NH_4)_2S(aq) \rightarrow Co_2S_3(s) + NH_4NO_3(aq)$
Balance N: $2Co(NO_3)_3(aq) + 3(NH_4)_2S(aq) \rightarrow Co_2S_3(s) + 6NH_4NO_3(aq)$

Check:

left side	right side
2 Co atoms	2 Co atoms
12 N atoms	12 N atoms
18 O atoms	18 O atoms
24 H atoms	24 H atoms
3 S atoms	3 S atoms

c) Conceptual Plan: balance atoms in more complex compounds → balance elements that occur as free elements → clear fractions

Solution: Skeletal reaction: $Cu_2O(s) + C(s) \rightarrow Cu(s) + CO(g)$
Balance Cu: $Cu_2O(s) + C(s) \rightarrow 2Cu(s) + CO(g)$

Check:

left side	right side
2 Cu atoms	2 Cu atoms
1 O atom	1 O atom
1 C atom	1 C atom

d) Conceptual Plan: balance atoms in more complex compounds → balance elements that occur as free elements → clear fractions

Solution: Skeletal reaction: $H_2(g) + Cl_2(g) \rightarrow HCl(g)$
Balance Cl: $H_2(g) + Cl_2(g) \rightarrow 2HCl(g)$

Check:

left side	right side
2 H atom	2 H atom
2 Cl atom	2 Cl atom

100. **a) Conceptual Plan: balance atoms in more complex compounds → balance elements that occur as free elements → clear fractions**

Solution: Skeletal reaction: $Na_2S(aq) + Cu(NO_3)_2(aq) \rightarrow NaNO_3(aq) + CuS(s)$

	Balance Na:	$Na_2S(aq) + Cu(NO_3)_2(aq) \rightarrow 2NaNO_3(aq) + CuS(s)$	
Check:		left side	right side
		2 Na atom	2 Na atom
		1 S atom	1 S atom
		1 Cu atom	1 Cu atom
		2 N atom	2 N atom
		6 O atom	6 O atom

b) Conceptual Plan: balance atoms in more complex compounds → balance elements that occur as free elements → clear fractions

Solution:	Skeletal reaction: $N_2H_4(l) \rightarrow NH_3(g) + N_2(g)$	
	Balance H:	$3N_2H_4(l) \rightarrow 4NH_3(g) + N_2(g)$
Check:	left side	right side
	6 N atoms	6 N atoms
	12 H atoms	12 H atoms

c) Conceptual Plan: balance atoms in more complex compounds → balance elements that occur as free elements → clear fractions

Solution:	Skeletal reaction: $HCl(aq) + O_2(g) \rightarrow H_2O(l) + Cl_2(g)$	
	Balance Cl:	$2HCl(aq) + O_2(g) \rightarrow H_2O(l) + Cl_2(g)$
	Balance O:	$2HCl(aq) + 1/2O_2(g) \rightarrow H_2O(l) + Cl_2(g)$
	Clear fraction:	$4HCl(aq) + O_2(g) \rightarrow 2H_2O(l) + 2Cl_2(g)$
Check:	left side	right side
	4 H atoms	4 H atoms
	4 Cl atoms	4 Cl atoms
	2 O atoms	2 O atoms

d) Conceptual Plan: balance atoms in more complex compounds → balance elements that occur as free elements → clear fractions

Solution:	Skeletal reaction: $FeS(s) + HCl(aq) \rightarrow FeCl_2(aq) + H_2S(g)$	
	Balance Cl:	$FeS(s) + 2HCl(aq) \rightarrow FeCl_2(aq) + H_2S(g)$
Check:	left side	right side
	1 Fe atom	1 Fe atom
	1 S atom	1 S atom
	2 H atoms	2 H atoms
	2 Cl atoms	2 Cl atoms

101. a) composed of metal cation and polyatomic anion – inorganic compound
  b) composed of carbon and hydrogen – organic compound
  c) composed of carbon, hydrogen and oxygen – organic compound
  d) composed of metal cation and nonmetal anion – inorganic compound

102. a) composed of carbon and hydrogen – organic compound
  b) composed of carbon, hydrogen and nitrogen – organic compound
  c) composed of metal cation and nonmetal anion – inorganic compound
  d) composed of metal cation and polyatomic anion – inorganic compound

103. a) contains a double bond – alkene
  b) contains only single bonds – alkane
  c) contains triple bond – alkyne
  d) contains only single bonds – alkane

104. a) contains triple bond – alkyne
  b) contains double bond - alkene
  c) contains only single bonds – alkane
  d) contains triple bond – alkyne

105. a) prop = 3 C, ane = single bonds: $CH_3CH_2CH_3$
  b) 3 C = prop, single bonds = ane: propane
  c) oct = 8 C, and = single bonds: CH_3CH_2 CH_2 CH_2 CH_2 CH_2 CH_2 CH_3
  d) 5 C = pent, single bonds = ane: pentane

106.a) 2 C = eth, single bonds = ane: ethane

b) pent = 5 C, and = single bonds: $CH_3 CH_2 CH_2 CH_2 CH_3$

c) 6 C = hex, single bonds = ane: hexane

d) hept = 7 C, ane = single bonds: $CH_3 CH_2 CH_2 CH_2 CH_2 CH_2 CH_3$

107.a) contains O: functionalized hydrocarbon: alcohol

b) contains only C and H: hydrocarbon

c) contains O: functionalized hydrocarbon: ketone

d) contains N: functionalized hydrocarbon: amine

108.a) contains O: functionalized hydrocarbon: carboxylic acid

b) contains O: functionalized hydrocarbon: aldehyde

c) contains only C and H: hydrocarbon

d) contains O: functionalized hydrocarbon: ether

109. **Given:** 145 mL C_2H_5OH, d = 0.789 g/cm^3 **Find:** number of molecules

Conceptual Plan: cm^3 → mL: mL C_2H_5OH → g C_2H_5OH → mol C_2H_5OH → molecules C_2H_5OH

$$\frac{1\ cm^3}{1\ mL} \qquad \frac{1\ mL\ C_2H_5OH}{0.789\ g\ C_2H_5OH} \quad \frac{1\ mol\ C_2H_5OH}{46.07\ g\ C_2H_5OH} \quad \frac{6.022\ x\ 10^{23}\ molecules\ C_2H_5OH}{1\ mol\ C_2H_5OH}$$

Solution:

$$145\ mL\ C_2H_5OH \times \frac{0.789\ g}{cm^3} \times \frac{1\ cm^3}{1\ mL} \times \frac{1\ mol\ C_2H_5OH}{46.07\ g\ C_2H_5OH} \times \frac{6.022\ x\ 10^{23}\ molecules\ C_2H_5OH}{1\ mol\ C_2H_5OH} = 1.49\ x\ 10^{24}\ molecules\ C_2H_5OH$$

Check: Units of answer, molecules C_2H_5OH, are correct. The magnitude is reasonable because we had more than 2 moles of C_2H_5OH and we have more than 2 times Avogadro's number of molecules.

110. **Given:** 0.05 mL H_2O, d = 1.0 g/cm^3 **Find:** number of molecules

Conceptual Plan: cm^3 → mL: mL H_2O → g H_2O → mol H_2O → molecules H_2O

$$\frac{1\ cm^3}{1\ mL} \qquad \frac{1\ mL\ H_2O}{1.0\ g\ H_2O} \quad \frac{1\ mol\ H_2O}{18.02\ g\ H_2O} \quad \frac{6.022\ x\ 10^{23}\ molecules\ H_2O}{1\ mol\ H_2O}$$

Solution:

$$\frac{0.05\ mL\ H_2O}{} \times \frac{1\ cm^3}{1\ mL} \times \frac{1.0\ g}{cm^3} \times \frac{1\ mol\ H_2O}{18.02\ g\ H_2O} \times \frac{6.022\ x\ 10^{23}\ molecules\ H_2O}{1\ mol\ H_2O} = 2\ x\ 10^{21}\ molecules\ H_2O$$

Check: Units of answer, molecules H_2O, are correct. The magnitude is reasonable because we have less then 1 mole H_2O and we have less than Avogadro's number of molecules.

111.a) To write the formula for an ionic compound: 1) Write the symbol for the metal cation and its charge and the symbol for the nonmetal anion or polyatomic anion and its charge. 2) Adjust the subscript on each cation and anion to balance the overall charge. 3) Check that the sum of the charges of the cations equals the sum of the charges of the anions.

potassium chromate: K^+ CrO_4^{-2}; K_2CrO_4 cation 2(1+) = 2+; anion 2-

Given: K_2CrO_4 **Find:** mass percent of each element

Conceptual Plan: %K, then %Cr, then %O

$$mass\ \% K = \frac{2\ x\ molar\ mass\ K}{molar\ mass\ K_2CrO_4} \times 100 \quad mass\ \% Cr = \frac{1\ x\ molar\ mass\ Cr}{molar\ mass\ K_2CrO_4} \times 100$$

$$mass\ \% O = \frac{4\ x\ molar\ mass\ O}{molar\ mass\ K_2CrO_4} \times 100$$

molar mass of K = 39.10 g/mol, molar mass Cr = 52.00 g/mol, molar mass O = 16.00 g/mol

Solution: molar mass K_2CrO_4 = 2(39.10 g/mol) + 1(52.00 g/mol) + 4(16.00 g/mol) = 194.20 g/mol

$2 \times$ molar mass K $= 2(39.10 \text{ g/mol}) = 78.20 \text{ g K}$ $1 \times$ molar mass Cr $= 1(52.00 \text{ g/mol}) = 52.00 \text{ g Cr}$

$$\text{mass \% K} = \frac{2 \times \text{molar mass K}}{\text{molar mass K}_2\text{CrO}_4} \times 100\% \qquad \text{mass \% Cr} = \frac{1 \times \text{molar mass Cr}}{\text{molar mass K}_2\text{CrO}_4} \times 100\%$$

$$= \frac{78.20 \text{ g/mol}}{194.20 \text{ g/mol}} \times 100\% \qquad\qquad = \frac{52.00 \text{ g/mol}}{194.20 \text{ g/mol}} \times 100\%$$

$$= 40.27\% \qquad\qquad\qquad\qquad\qquad = 26.78\%$$

$4 \times$ molar mass O $= 4(16.00 \text{ g/mol}) = 64.00 \text{ g O}$

$$\text{mass \% O} = \frac{4 \times \text{molar mass O}}{\text{molar mass K}_2\text{CrO}_4} \times 100\%$$

$$= \frac{64.00 \text{ g/mol}}{194.20 \text{ g/mol}} \times 100\%$$

$$= 32.96\%$$

Check: Units of the answer, %, are correct. The magnitude is reasonable because each is between 0 and 100% and the total is 100%.

b) To write the formula for an ionic compound: 1) Write the symbol for the metal cation and its charge and the symbol for the nonmetal anion or polyatomic anion and its charge. 2) Adjust the subscript on each cation and anion to balance the overall charge. 3) Check that the sum of the charges of the cations equals the sum of the charges of the anions.
Lead(II)phosphate: Pb^{2+} PO_4^{3-} ; $Pb_3(PO_4)_2$ cation $3(2+) = 6+$; anion $2(3-) = 6-$
Given: $Pb_3(PO_4)_2$ **Find:** mass percent of each element
Conceptual Plan: %Pb, then % P, then %O

$$\text{mass \% Pb} = \frac{3 \times \text{molar mass Pb}}{\text{molar mass Pb}_3(\text{PO}_4)_2} \times 100 \quad \text{mass \% P} = \frac{2 \times \text{molar mass P}}{\text{molar mass Pb}_3(\text{PO}_4)_2} \times 100$$

$$\text{mass \% O} = \frac{8 \times \text{molar mass O}}{\text{molar mass Pb}_3(\text{PO}_4)_2} \times 100$$

Solution: molar mass $Pb_3(PO_4)_2 = 3(207.2 \text{ g/mol}) + 2(30.97 \text{ g/mol}) + 8(16.00 \text{ g/mol}) = 811.5 \text{ g/mol}$

$3 \times$ molar mass Pb $= 3(207.2 \text{ g/mol}) = 621.6 \text{ g Pb}$ $2 \times$ molar mass P $= 2(30.97 \text{ g/mol}) = 61.94 \text{ g P}$

$$\text{mass \% K} = \frac{2 \times \text{molar mass K}}{\text{molar mass Pb}_3(\text{PO}_4)_2} \times 100\% \qquad \text{mass \% P} = \frac{2 \times \text{molar mass P}}{\text{molar mass Pb}_3(\text{PO}_4)_2} \times 100\%$$

$$= \frac{78.20 \text{ g/mol}}{811.5 \text{ g/mol}} \times 100\% \qquad\qquad = \frac{61.94 \text{ g/mol}}{811.5 \text{ g/mol}} \times 100\%$$

$$= 76.60\% \qquad\qquad\qquad\qquad = 7.632\%$$

$4 \times$ molar mass O $= 8(16.00 \text{ g/mol}) = 128.0 \text{ g O}$

$$\text{mass \% O} = \frac{8 \times \text{molar mass O}}{\text{molar mass Pb}_3(\text{PO}_4)_2} \times 100\%$$

$$= \frac{128.0 \text{ g/mol}}{811.5 \text{ g/mol}} \times 100\%$$

$$= 15.77\%$$

Check: Units of the answer, %, are correct. The magnitude is reasonable because each is between 0 and 100% and the total is 100%.

c) sulfurous acid: H_2SO_3
Given: H_2SO_3 **Find:** mass percent of each element
Conceptual Plan: %H, then %S, then %O

$$\text{mass \% H} = \frac{2 \times \text{molar mass H}}{\text{molar mass HSO}_3} \times 100 \qquad \text{mass \% S} = \frac{1 \times \text{molar mass S}}{\text{molar mass HSO}_3} \times 100$$

$$\text{mass \% O} = \frac{3 \times \text{molar mass O}}{\text{molar mass HSO}_3} \times 100$$

Solution: molar mass $H_2SO_3 = 2(1.008 \text{ g/mol}) + 1(32.06 \text{ g/mol}) + 3(16.00 \text{ g/mol}) = 82.076 \text{ g/mol}$

$$2 \text{ x molar mass H} = 1(1.008 \text{ g/mol}) = 2.016 \text{ g H} \qquad 1 \text{ x molar mass S} = 1(32.06 \text{ g/mol}) = 32.06 \text{ g Cr}$$

$$\text{mass \%H} = \frac{2 \text{ x molar mass H}}{\text{molar mass H}_2\text{SO}_3} \text{ x } 100\% \qquad \text{mass \% S} = \frac{1 \text{ x molar mass S}}{\text{molar mass H}_2\text{SO}_3} \text{ x } 100\%$$

$$= \frac{2.016 \text{ g/mol}}{82.076 \text{ g/mol}} \text{ x } 100\% \qquad\qquad = \frac{32.06 \text{ g/mol}}{82.076 \text{ g/mol}} \text{ x } 100\%$$

$$= 2.456 \% \qquad\qquad\qquad = 39.06 \%$$

$$4 \text{ x molar mass O} = 3(16.00 \text{ g/mol}) = 48.00 \text{ g O}$$

$$\text{mass \% O} = \frac{3 \text{ x molar mass O}}{\text{molar mass H}_2\text{SO}_3} \text{ x } 100\%$$

$$= \frac{48.00 \text{ g/mol}}{82.076 \text{ g/mol}} \text{ x } 100\%$$

$$= 58.48 \%$$

Check: Units of the answer, %, are correct. The magnitude is reasonable because each is between 0 and 100% and the total is 100%.

d) To write the formula for an ionic compound: 1) Write the symbol for the metal cation and its charge and the symbol for the nonmetal anion or polyatomic anion and its charge. 2) Adjust the subscript on each cation and anion to balance the overall charge. 3) Check that the sum of the charges of the cations equals the sum of the charges of the anions.
cobalt(II)bromide: Co^{2+} Br^{-} ; $CoBr_2$ cation 2+ = 2+; anion 2(1-) = 2-
Given: $CoBr_2$ **Find:** mass percent of each element
Conceptual Plan: %Co, then %Br

$$\text{mass \% Co} = \frac{1 \text{ x molar mass Co}}{\text{molar mass CoBr}_2} \text{ x } 100 \qquad \text{mass \% Br} = \frac{2 \text{ x molar mass Br}}{\text{molar mass CoBr}_2} \text{ x } 100$$

Solution: molar mass $CoBr_2$ = (58.93 g/mol) + 2(79.90 g/mol) = 218.7 g/mol

$$2 \text{ x molar mass Co} = 1(58.93 \text{ g/mol}) = 58.93 \text{ g K} \quad 1 \text{ x molar mass Br} = 2(79.90 \text{ g/mol}) = 159.8 \text{ g Br}$$

$$\text{mass \% Co} = \frac{1 \text{ x molar mass Co}}{\text{molar mass CoBr}_2} \text{ x } 100\% \qquad \text{mass \% Br} = \frac{2 \text{ x molar mass Br}}{\text{molar mass CoBr}_2} \text{ x } 100\%$$

$$= \frac{58.93 \text{ g/mol}}{218.7 \text{ g/mol}} \text{ x } 100\% \qquad\qquad = \frac{159.8 \text{ g/mol}}{218.7 \text{ g/mol}} \text{ x } 100\%$$

$$= 26.94 \% \qquad\qquad\qquad = 73.07 \%$$

Check: Units of the answer, %, are correct. The magnitude is reasonable because each is between 0 and 100% and the total is 100%.

112. a) perchloric acid: $HClO_4$
Given: $HClO_4$
Find: mass percent of each element
Conceptual Plan: %H, then %Cl, then %O

$$\text{mass \% H} = \frac{1 \text{ x molar mass H}}{\text{molar mass HClO}_4} \text{ x } 100 \qquad\qquad \text{mass \% Cl} = \frac{1 \text{ x molar mass Cl}}{\text{molar mass HClO}_4} \text{ x } 100$$

$$\text{mass \% O} = \frac{4 \text{ x molar mass O}}{\text{molar mass HClO}_4} \text{ x } 100$$

Solution: molar mass $HClO_4$ = 1(1.008 g/mol) + 1(35.45 g/mol) + 4(16.00 g/mol) = 100.46 g/mol

$$1 \text{ x molar mass H} = 1(1.008 \text{ g/mol}) = 1.008 \text{ g H} \quad 1 \text{ x molar mass Cl} = 1(35.45 \text{ g/mol}) = 35.45 \text{ g Cr}$$

$$\text{mass \%H} = \frac{1 \text{ x molar mass H}}{\text{molar mass HClO}_4} \text{ x } 100\% \qquad \text{mass \% Cl} = \frac{1 \text{ x molar mass Cl}}{\text{molar mass HClO}_4} \text{ x } 100\%$$

$$= \frac{1.008 \text{ g/mol}}{100.46 \text{ g/mol}} \text{ x } 100\% \qquad\qquad = \frac{35.45 \text{ g/mol}}{100.46 \text{ g/mol}} \text{ x } 100\%$$

$$= 1.075 \% \qquad\qquad\qquad = 35.29 \%$$

$$4 \times \text{molar mass O} = 4(16.00 \text{ g/mol}) = 64.00 \text{ g K}$$

$$\text{mass \% O} = \frac{4 \times \text{molar mass O}}{\text{molar mass HSO}_3} \times 100\%$$

$$= \frac{64.00 \text{ g/mol}}{100.46 \text{ g/mol}} \times 100\%$$

$$= 63.71 \%$$

Check: Units of the answer, %, are correct. The magnitude is reasonable because each is between 0 and 100% and the total is 100%.

b) phosphorus pentachloride: PCl_5
   Given: PCl_5 **Find:** mass percent of each element
   Conceptual Plan: %P, then %Cl

$$\text{mass \% P} = \frac{1 \times \text{molar mass P}}{\text{molar mass PCl}_5} \times 100 \qquad \text{mass \% Cl} = \frac{5 \times \text{molar mass Cl}}{\text{molar mass PCl}_5} \times 100$$

Solution: molar mass $PCl_5 = 1(30.97 \text{ g/mol}) + 5(35.45 \text{ g/mol}) = 208.2 \text{ g/mol}$
1 x molar mass P $= 1(30.97 \text{ g/mol}) = 30.97 \text{ g P}$ 1 x molar mass Cl $= 5(35.45 \text{ g/mol}) = 177.25 \text{ g Cr}$

$$\text{mass \%P} = \frac{1 \times \text{molar mass P}}{\text{molar mass PCl}_5} \times 100\% \qquad\qquad \text{mass \% Cl} = \frac{5 \times \text{molar mass Cl}}{\text{molar mass PCl}_5} \times 100\%$$

$$= \frac{30.97 \text{ g/mol}}{208.2 \text{ g/mol}} \times 100\% \qquad\qquad\qquad = \frac{177.25 \text{ g/mol}}{208.2 \text{ g/mol}} \times 100\%$$

$$= 14.87 \% \qquad\qquad\qquad\qquad\qquad = 85.13 \%$$

Check: Units of the answer, %, are correct. The magnitude is reasonable because each is between 0 and 100% and the total is 100%.

c) nitrogen triiodide: NI_3
   Given: NI_3 **Find:** mass percent of each element
   Conceptual Plan: %N, then %I

$$\text{mass \%N} = \frac{1 \times \text{molar mass N}}{\text{molar mass NI}_3} \times 100 \qquad \text{mass \% I} = \frac{3 \times \text{molar mass I}}{\text{molar mass NI}_3} \times 100$$

Solution: molar mass $NI_3 = 1(14.01 \text{ g/mol}) + 3(126.9 \text{ g/mol}) = 394.7 \text{ g/mol}$

1 x molar mass N $= 1(14.01 \text{ g/mol}) = 14.01 \text{ g H}$ 1 x molar mass I $= 3(126.9 \text{ g/mol}) = 380.7 \text{ g I}$

$$\text{mass \%N} = \frac{1 \times \text{molar mass N}}{\text{molar mass NI}_3} \times 100\% \qquad\qquad \text{mass \% I} = \frac{3 \times \text{molar mass I}}{\text{molar mass NI}_3} \times 100\%$$

$$= \frac{14.01 \text{ g/mol}}{394.7 \text{ g/mol}} \times 100\% \qquad\qquad\qquad = \frac{380.7 \text{ g/mol}}{394.7 \text{ g/mol}} \times 100\%$$

$$= 3.549 \% \qquad\qquad\qquad\qquad\qquad = 96.45 \%$$

Check: Units of the answer, %, are correct. The magnitude is reasonable because each is between 0 and 100% and the total is 100%.

d) carbon dioxide: CO_2
   Given: CO_2 **Find:** mass percent of each element
   Conceptual Plan: %C, then %O

$$\text{mass \%C} = \frac{1 \times \text{molar mass C}}{\text{molar mass CO}_2} \times 100 \qquad \text{mass \%O} = \frac{2 \times \text{molar mass O}}{\text{molar mass CO}_2} \times 100$$

Solution: molar mass $CO_2 = 1(12.01 \text{ g/mol}) + 2(16.00 \text{ g/mol}) = 44.01 \text{ g/mol}$

1 x molar mass C $= 1(12.01 \text{ g/mol}) = 12.01 \text{ g C}$ 2 x molar mass O $= 2(16.00 \text{ g/mol}) = 32.00 \text{ g O}$

$$\text{mass \%C} = \frac{1 \times \text{molar mass C}}{\text{molar mass CO}_2} \times 100\% \qquad\qquad \text{mass \% O} = \frac{2 \times \text{molar mass O}}{\text{molar mass CO}_2} \times 100\%$$

$$= \frac{12.01 \text{ g/mol}}{44.01 \text{ g/mol}} \times 100\% \qquad\qquad\qquad = \frac{32.00 \text{ g/mol}}{44.01 \text{ g/mol}} \times 100\%$$

$$= 27.29 \% \qquad\qquad\qquad\qquad\qquad = 72.71 \%$$

Check: Units of the answer, %, are correct. The magnitude is reasonable because each is between 0 and 100% and the total is 100%.

113. **Given:** 25 g CF_2Cl_2/mo.   **Find:** g Cl /yr.

Conceptual Plan: g CF_2Cl_2/mo $\rightarrow$ g Cl/mo $\rightarrow$ g Cl/yr

$$\frac{70.09 \text{ g Cl}}{120.91 \text{ g } CF_2Cl_2} \qquad \frac{12 \text{ mo.}}{1 \text{ yr}}$$

Solution: $\dfrac{25 \text{ g } CF_2Cl_2}{\text{mo.}} \times \dfrac{70.90 \text{ g Cl}}{120.91 \text{ g } CF_2Cl_2} \times \dfrac{12 \text{ mo.}}{1 \text{ yr}} = 1.8 \times 10^2$ g Cl/yr

Check: Units of answer, g Cl, is correct. Magnitude is reasonable because it is less than the total CF_2Cl_2 /yr.

114. **Given:** 12 kg CHF_2Cl/mo.   **Find:** kg Cl /yr.

Conceptual Plan: kg CF_2Cl_2/mo $\rightarrow$ kg Cl/mo $\rightarrow$ kg Cl/yr

$$\frac{35.45 \text{ g Cl}}{86.47 \text{ g } CHF_2Cl} = \frac{35.45 \text{ kg Cl}}{86.47 \text{ kg } CHF_2Cl} \qquad \frac{12 \text{ mo.}}{1 \text{ yr}}$$

Solution: $\dfrac{12 \text{ kg } CHF_2Cl}{\text{mo.}} \times \dfrac{35.45 \text{ kg Cl}}{86.47 \text{ kg } CHF_2Cl} \times \dfrac{12 \text{ mo.}}{1 \text{ yr}} = 59$ kg Cl/yr

Check: Units of answer, kg Cl, is correct. Magnitude is reasonable because it is less than the total CHF_2Cl /yr.

115. **Given:** MCl_3, 65.57% Cl   **Find:** identify M

Conceptual Plan: g Cl $\rightarrow$ mol Cl $\rightarrow$ mol M $\rightarrow$ atomic mass M

$$\frac{1 \text{ mol Cl}}{35.45 \text{ g Cl}} \qquad \frac{1 \text{ mol M}}{3 \text{ mol Cl}} \qquad \frac{\text{g M}}{\text{mol M}}$$

Solution: in 100 g sample: 65.57 g Cl, 34.43 g M

65.57 g Cl $\times \dfrac{1 \text{ mol Cl}}{35.45 \text{ g}} \times \dfrac{1 \text{ mol M}}{3 \text{ mol Cl}} = 0.6165$ mol M $\dfrac{34.43 \text{ g M}}{0.6165 \text{ mol M}} = 55.84$ g/mol M

molar mass of 55.84 = Fe

The identity of M = Fe

116. **Given:** M_2O, 16.99% O   **Find:** identify M

Conceptual Plan: g O $\rightarrow$ mol O $\rightarrow$ mol M $\rightarrow$ atomic mass M

$$\frac{1 \text{ mol O}}{16.00 \text{ g Cl}} \qquad \frac{2 \text{ mol M}}{1 \text{ mol O}} \qquad \frac{\text{g M}}{\text{mol M}}$$

Solution: in 100 g sample: 16.99 g O, 83.01 g M

16.99 g O $\times \dfrac{1 \text{ mol O}}{16.00 \text{ g}} \times \dfrac{2 \text{ mol M}}{1 \text{ mol O}} = 2.124$ mol M $\dfrac{83.01 \text{ g M}}{2.124 \text{ mol M}} = 39.08$ g/mol M

molar mass of 39.08 = K

The identity of M = K

117. **Given:** In a 100 g sample: 79.37 g C, 8.88 g H, 11.75 g O, molar mass = 272.37g/mol

Find: molecular formula

Conceptual Plan:

convert mass to mol of each element $\rightarrow$ pseudoformula $\rightarrow$ empirical formula $\rightarrow$ molecular formula

$$\frac{1 \text{ mol C}}{12.01 \text{ g C}} \qquad \frac{1 \text{ mol H}}{1.008 \text{ g H}} \qquad \frac{1 \text{ mol O}}{16.00 \text{ g O}} \qquad \text{divide by smallest number} \qquad \text{empirical formula x n}$$

Solution:

79.37 g C $\times \dfrac{1 \text{ mol C}}{12.01 \text{ g C}} = 6.609$ mol C

8.88 g H $\times \dfrac{1 \text{ mol H}}{1.008 \text{ g H}} = 8.81$ mol H

11.75 g O $\times \dfrac{1 \text{ mol O}}{16.00 \text{ g O}} = 0.7344$ mol O

$$C_{6.609}H_{8.81}O_{0.7344}$$

$$C_{\frac{6.609}{0.7344}} H_{\frac{8.81}{0.7344}} O_{\frac{0.7344}{0.7344}} \rightarrow C_9H_{12}O$$

The correct empirical formula is $C_9H_{12}O$

empirical formula mass = 9(12.01 g/mol) + 12(1.008 g/mol) + 1(16.00 g/mol) = 136.19 g/mol

$$n = \frac{molar\ mass}{formula\ molar\ mass} = \frac{272.37\ g/mol}{136.19\ g/mol} = 2$$

molecular formula = $C_9H_{12}O$ x 2

= $C_{18}H_{24}O_2$

118. **Given:** In a 100 g sample: 40.00 g C, 6.72 g H, 53.29 g O, molar mass = 180.16g/mol
Find: molecular formula
Conceptual Plan:
convert mass to mol of each element → pseudoformula → empirical formula → molecular formula

$$\frac{1\ mol\ C}{12.01\ g\ C} \qquad \frac{1\ mol\ H}{1.008\ g\ H} \qquad \frac{1\ mol\ O}{16.00\ g\ O} \qquad divide\ by\ smallest\ number \qquad empirical\ formula\ x\ n$$

Solution:

$$40.00\ g\ C \times \frac{1\ mol\ C}{12.01\ g\ C} = 3.331\ mol\ C$$

$$6.72\ g\ H \times \frac{1\ mol\ H}{1.008\ g\ H} = 6.67\ mol\ H$$

$$53.29\ g\ O \times \frac{1\ mol\ O}{16.00\ g\ O} = 3.331\ mol\ O$$

$$C_{3.331}H_{6.67}O_{3.331}$$

$$C_{\frac{3.331}{3.331}}H_{\frac{6.67}{3.331}}O_{\frac{3.331}{3.331}} \rightarrow CH_2O$$

The correct empirical formula is CH_2O

empirical formula mass = 1(12.01 g/mol) + 2(1.008 g/mol) + 1(16.00 g/mol) = 30.03 g/mol

$$n = \frac{molar\ mass}{formula\ molar\ mass} = \frac{180.16\ g/mol}{30.03\ g/mol} = 6$$

molecular formula = CH_2O x 6

= $C_6H_{12}O_6$

119. **Given:** 13.42 g sample, 39.61 g CO_2, 9.01 g H_2O, molar mass = 268.34 g/mol
Find: molecular formula
Conceptual Plan:
mass CO_2, H_2O → mol CO_2, H_2O → mol C, mol H → mass C, mass H, mass O → mol O →

$$\frac{1\ mol\ CO_2}{44.01\ g\ CO_2} \quad \frac{1\ mol\ H_2O}{18.02\ g\ H_2O} \quad \frac{1\ mol\ C}{1\ mol\ CO_2} \quad \frac{2\ mol\ H}{1\ mol\ H_2O} \quad \frac{12.01\ g\ C}{1\ mol\ C} \quad \frac{1.008\ g\ H}{1\ mol\ H} \quad g\ sample\ -\ gC\ -\ g\ H \qquad \frac{1\ mol\ O}{16.00\ g\ O}$$

pseudoformula → empirical formula → molecular formula

divide by smallest number   empirical formula x ı

Solution:

$$39.61\ g\ CO_2 \times \frac{1\ mol\ CO_2}{44.01\ g\ CO_2} = 0.9000\ mol\ CO_2$$

$$9.01\ g\ H_2O \times \frac{1\ mol\ H_2O}{18.02\ g\ H_2O} = 0.5000\ mol\ H_2O$$

$$0.9000\ mol\ CO_2 \times \frac{1\ mol\ C}{1\ mol\ CO_2} = 0.9000\ mol\ C$$

$$0.5000\ mol\ H_2O \times \frac{2\ mol\ H}{1\ mol\ H_2O} = 1.000\ mol\ H$$

$$0.9000 \text{ mol C} \times \frac{12.01 \text{ g C}}{1 \text{ mol C}} = 10.81 \text{ g C}$$

$$1.000 \text{ mol H}_2\text{O} \times \frac{1.008 \text{ g H}}{1 \text{ mol H}} = 1.008 \text{ g H}$$

$$13.42 \text{ g} - 10.81 \text{ g} - 1.008 \text{ g} = 1.60 \text{ g O}$$

$$1.60 \text{ g O} \times \frac{1 \text{ mol O}}{16.00 \text{ g O}} = 0.100 \text{ mol O}$$

$$C_{0.9000} H_{1.000} O_{0.100}$$

$$C_{\frac{0.9000}{0.100}} H_{\frac{1.000}{0.100}} O_{\frac{0.100}{0.100}} \rightarrow C_9H_{10}O$$

The correct empirical formula is $C_9H_{10}O$

empirical formula mass = 9(12.01 g/mol) + 10(1.008 g/mol) + 1(16.00 g/mol) = 134.2 g/mol

$$n = \frac{\text{molar mass}}{\text{formula molar mass}} = \frac{268.34 \text{ g/mol}}{134.2 \text{ g/mol}} = 2$$

molecular formula $= C_9H_{10}O \times 2$

$\qquad\qquad\qquad = C_{18}H_{20}O_2$

120. **Given:** 1.893 g sample, 5.545 g CO_2, 1.388 g H_2O, molar mass = 270.36 g/mol

Find: molecular formula

Conceptual Plan:

mass CO_2, H_2O → mol CO_2, H_2O → mol C, mol H → mass C, mass H, mass O → mol O →

$$\frac{1 \text{ mol CO}_2}{44.01 \text{ g CO}_2} \quad \frac{1 \text{ mol H}_2\text{O}}{18.02 \text{ g H}_2\text{O}} \qquad \frac{1 \text{ mol C}}{1 \text{ mol CO}_2} \quad \frac{2 \text{ mol H}}{1 \text{ mol H}_2\text{O}} \qquad \frac{12.01 \text{ g C}}{1 \text{ mol C}} \quad \frac{1.008 \text{ g H}}{1 \text{ mol H}} \quad \text{g sample - gC - g H} \qquad \frac{1 \text{ mol O}}{16.00 \text{ g O}}$$

pseudoformula → empirical formula → molecular formula

$\qquad$ divide by smallest number $\qquad\qquad$ empirical formula x n

Solution:

$$5.545 \text{ g CO}_2 \times \frac{1 \text{ mol CO}_2}{44.01 \text{ g CO}_2} = 0.1260 \text{ mol CO}_2$$

$$1.388 \text{ g H}_2\text{O} \times \frac{1 \text{ mol H}_2\text{O}}{18.02 \text{ g H}_2\text{O}} = 0.07703 \text{ mol H}_2\text{O}$$

$$0.1260 \text{ mol CO}_2 \times \frac{1 \text{ mol C}}{1 \text{ mol CO}_2} = 0.1260 \text{ mol C}$$

$$0.07703 \text{ mol H}_2\text{O} \times \frac{2 \text{ mol H}}{1 \text{ mol H}_2\text{O}} = 0.1541 \text{ mol H}$$

$$0.1260 \text{ mol C} \times \frac{12.01 \text{ g C}}{1 \text{ mol C}} = 1.513 \text{ g C}$$

$$0.1541 \text{ mol H}_2\text{O} \times \frac{1.008 \text{ g H}}{1 \text{ mol H}} = 0.1553 \text{ g H}$$

$$1.893 \text{ g} - 1.513 \text{ g} - 0.1553 \text{ g} = 0.2247 \text{ g O}$$

$$0.2247 \text{ g O} \times \frac{1 \text{ mol O}}{16.00 \text{ g O}} = 0.01404 \text{ mol O}$$

$$C_{0.1260} H_{0.1541} O_{0.01404}$$

$$C_{\frac{0.1260}{0.01404}} H_{\frac{0.1541}{0.01404}} O_{\frac{0.01404}{0.01404}} \rightarrow C_9H_{11}O$$

The correct empirical formula is $C_9H_{11}O$

empirical formula mass = 9(12.01 g/mol) + 1(1.008 g/mol) + 1(16.00 g/mol) = 135.2 g/mol

$$n = \frac{\text{molar mass}}{\text{formula molar mass}} = \frac{270.36 \text{ g/mol}}{135.2 \text{ g/mol}} = 2$$

molecular formula $= C_9H_{11}O \times 2$

$\qquad\qquad\qquad = C_{18}H_{22}O_2$

121. **Given:** 4.93 g $MgSO_4 \bullet xH_2O$, 2.41 g $MgSO_4$ $\qquad$ **Find:** value of x

Conceptual Plan: g MgSO$_4$ → mol MgSO$_4$ g H$_2$O → mol H$_2$O   Determine mole ratio

$$\frac{1 \text{ mol MgSO}_4}{120.38 \text{ g MgSO}_4} \qquad \frac{1 \text{ mol H}_2\text{O}}{18.02 \text{ g H}_2\text{O}} \qquad \frac{\text{mol HO}_2}{\text{mol MgSO}_4}$$

Solution:

$$2.41 \text{ g MgSO}_4 \times \frac{1 \text{ mol MgSO}_4}{120.38 \text{ g MgSO}_4} = 0.0200 \text{ mol MgSO}_4$$

$$2.52 \text{ g H}_2\text{O} \times \frac{1 \text{ mol H}_2\text{O}}{18.02 \text{ g H}_2\text{O}} = 0.140 \text{ mol H}_2\text{O}$$

$$\frac{0.140 \text{ mol H}_2\text{O}}{0.0200 \text{ mol MgSO}_4} = 7$$

x = 7

122. **Given:** 3.41 g CuCl$_2$•xH$_2$O, 2.69 g CuCl$_2$ **Find:** value of x
Conceptual Plan: g CuCl$_2$ → mol CuCl$_2$ g H$_2$O → mol H$_2$O   Determine mole ratio

$$\frac{1 \text{ mol CuCl}_2}{134.45 \text{ g CuCl}_2} \qquad \frac{1 \text{ mol H}_2\text{O}}{18.02 \text{ g H}_2\text{O}} \qquad \frac{\text{mol HO}_2}{\text{mol CuCl}_2}$$

Solution:

$$2.69 \text{ g CuCl}_2 \times \frac{1 \text{ mol CuCl}_2}{134.45 \text{ g CuCl}_2} = 0.0200 \text{ mol CuCl}_2$$

$$0.72 \text{ g H}_2\text{O} \times \frac{1 \text{ mol H}_2\text{O}}{18.02 \text{ g H}_2\text{O}} = 0.040 \text{ mol H}_2\text{O}$$

$$\frac{0.040 \text{ mol H}_2\text{O}}{0.0200 \text{ mol CuCl}_2} = 2$$

x = 2

123. **Given:** molar mass = 177 g/mol, g C = 8(g H)   **Find:** molecular formula
Conceptual Plan: C$_x$H$_y$BrO
Solution: in 1 mol compound, let x = mol C and y = mol H, assume mol Br = 1, mol O = 1
177 g/mol = x(12.01 g/mol) + y(1.008 g/mol) + 1(79.90 g/mol) + 1(16.00 g/mol)
x(12.01 g/mol) = 8 {y(1.008 g/mol)}
177 g/mol = 8y(1.008 g/mol) + y(1.008 g/mol) + 79.90 g/mol + 16.00 g/mol
81 = 9y(1.008)
y = 9 = mol H
x(12.01) = 9(1.008)
x = 6 = mol C
molecular formula = C$_6$H$_9$BrO
Check: molar mass = 6(12.01 g/mol) + 9(1.008 g/mol) + 1(79.90 g/mol) + 1(16.00 g/mol) = 177.0 g/mol

124. **Given:** 3.54 g sample yields 8.49 g CO$_2$ and 2.14 g H$_2$O; 2.35 g sample yields 0.199 g N; molar mass = 165
Find: molecular formula
Conceptual Plan:
mass N → mol N; then mass CO$_2$, H$_2$O → mol CO$_2$, H$_2$O → mol C, mol H → mass C, mass H;

$$\frac{1 \text{ mol N}}{14.01 \text{ g N}} \quad \frac{1 \text{ mol CO}_2}{44.01 \text{ g CO}_2} \quad \frac{1 \text{ mol H}_2\text{O}}{18.02 \text{ g H}_2\text{O}} \quad \frac{1 \text{ mol C}}{1 \text{ mol CO}_2} \quad \frac{2 \text{ mol H}}{1 \text{ mol H}_2\text{O}} \quad \frac{12.01 \text{ g C}}{1 \text{ mol C}} \quad \frac{1.008 \text{ g H}}{1 \text{ mol H}}$$

mass O → mol O →   pseudoformula → empirical formula → molecular formula
g sample - gC - gH - gN $\frac{1 \text{ mol O}}{16.00 \text{ g O}}$ divide by smallest number   empirical formula x n

Solution:

$$\frac{0.199 \text{ g N}}{2.35 \text{ g sample}} = \frac{x \text{ g N}}{3.54 \text{ g sample}} \; ; x = 0.300 \text{ g N}$$

$$\frac{0.300 \text{ g N}}{} \times \frac{1 \text{ mol N}}{14.01 \text{ g N}} = 0.0214 \text{ mol N}$$

$$\frac{8.49 \text{ g CO}_2}{} \times \frac{1 \text{ mol CO}_2}{44.01 \text{ g CO}_2} = 0.193 \text{ mol CO}_2$$

$$\frac{2.14 \text{ g H}_2\text{O}}{} \times \frac{1 \text{ mol H}_2\text{O}}{18.02 \text{ g H}_2\text{O}} = 0.119 \text{ mol H}_2\text{O}$$

$$\frac{0.193 \text{ mol } CO_2}{} \times \frac{1 \text{ mol } C}{1 \text{ mol } CO_2} = 0.193 \text{ mol } C$$

$$\frac{0.119 \text{ mol } H_2O}{} \times \frac{2 \text{ mol } H}{1 \text{ mol } H_2O} = 0.238 \text{ mol } H$$

$$\frac{0.193 \text{ mol } C}{} \times \frac{12.01 \text{ g } C}{1 \text{ mol } C} = 2.32 \text{ g } C$$

$$\frac{0.238 \text{ mol } H_2O}{} \times \frac{1.008 \text{ g } H}{1 \text{ mol } H} = 0.239 \text{ g } H$$

$$3.54 \text{ g} - 2.32 \text{ gC} - 0.239 \text{ gH} - 0.300 \text{ gN} = 0.681 \text{ g } O$$

$$\frac{0.681 \text{ g } O}{} \times \frac{1 \text{ mol } O}{16.00 \text{ g } O} = 0.0426 \text{ mol } O$$

$$C_{0.193} H_{0.238} N_{0.0214} O_{0.0426}$$

$$C_{\frac{0.193}{0.0214}} H_{\frac{0.238}{0.0214}} N_{\frac{0.0214}{0.0214}} O_{\frac{0.0426}{0.0214}} \rightarrow C_9H_{11}NO_2$$

The correct empirical formula is $C_9H_{11}NO_2$

empirical formula mass = $9(12.01 \text{ g/mol}) + 11(1.008 \text{ g/mol}) + 1(14.01 \text{ g/mol}) + 2(16.00 \text{ g/mol}) = 165.19$ g/mol

$$n = \frac{\text{molar mass}}{\text{formula molar mass}} = \frac{165 \text{ g/mol}}{165.19 \text{ g/mol}} = 1$$

$$\text{molecular formula} = C_9H_{11}NO_2 \times 1$$
$$= C_9H_{11}NO_2$$

125. **Given:** 23.5 mg $C_{17}H_{22}ClNO_4$ **Find:** total number of atoms

Conceptual Plan: mg compound → g compound → mol compound → mol atoms → number of atoms

$$\frac{1000 \text{ mg}}{1 \text{ g}} \qquad \frac{1 \text{ mol}}{339.8 \text{ g}} \qquad \frac{45 \text{ mol atoms}}{1 \text{ mol compound}} \qquad \frac{6.022 \times 10^{23} \text{ atoms}}{1 \text{ mol atoms}}$$

Solution: $23.5 \text{ mg} \times \frac{1 \text{ g}}{1000 \text{ mg}} \times \frac{1 \text{ mol cpd}}{339.8 \text{ g}} \times \frac{45 \text{ mol atoms}}{1 \text{ mol cpd}} \times \frac{6.022 \times 10^{23} \text{ atoms}}{\text{mol}} = 1.87 \times 10^{21}$ atoms

Check: The units of the answer, number of atoms, is correct. The magnitude of the answer is reasonable since the molecule is so complex.

126. **Given:** In a 100 g sample: 76 g V, 24 g O **Find:** formula and name

Conceptual Plan:

convert mass to mol of each element → write pseudoformula → write empirical formula

$$\frac{1 \text{ mol } V}{50.94 \text{ g } V} \qquad \frac{1 \text{ mol } O}{16.00 \text{ g } O} \qquad\qquad \text{divide by smallest number}$$

Solution:

$$76 \text{ g } V \times \frac{1 \text{ mol } V}{50.94 \text{ g } V} = 1.5 \text{ mol } V$$

$$24 \text{ g } O \times \frac{1 \text{ mol } O}{16.00 \text{ g } O} = 1.5 \text{ mol } O$$

$$V_{1.5}O_{1.5}$$

$$V_{\frac{1.5}{1.5}}O_{\frac{1.5}{1.5}} \rightarrow VO$$

The correct formula is VO; vanadium(II) oxide

Given: In a 100 g sample: 68 g V, 32 g O **Find:** formula and name

Conceptual Plan:

convert mass to mol of each element → write pseudoformula → write empirical formula

$$\frac{1 \text{ mol } V}{50.94 \text{ g } V} \qquad \frac{1 \text{ mol } O}{16.00 \text{ g } O} \qquad\qquad \text{divide by smallest number}$$

Solution:

$$68 \text{ g } V \times \frac{1 \text{ mol } V}{50.94 \text{ g } V} = 1.33 \text{ mol } V$$

$$32 \ \cancel{g \ O} \times \frac{1 \ mol \ O}{16.00 \ \cancel{g \ O}} = 2 \ mol \ O$$

$$V_{1.33}O_2$$

$$V_{\frac{1.33}{1.33}}O_{\frac{2}{1.33}} \rightarrow VO_{1.5} \rightarrow V_2O_3$$

The correct formula is V_2O_3; vanadium(III) oxide

Given: In a 100 g sample: 61 g V, 39 g O   **Find:** formula and name
Conceptual Plan:

convert mass to mol of each element → write pseudoformula → write empirical formula
$$\frac{1 \ mol \ V}{50.94 \ g \ V} \qquad \frac{1 \ mol \ O}{16.00 \ g \ O}$$
divide by smallest number

Solution:

$$76 \ \cancel{g \ V} \times \frac{1 \ mol \ V}{50.94 \ \cancel{g \ V}} = 1.2 \ mol \ V$$

$$39 \ \cancel{g \ O} \times \frac{1 \ mol \ O}{16.00 \ \cancel{g \ O}} = 2.4 \ mol \ O$$

$$V_{1.2}O_{2.4}$$

$$V_{\frac{1.2}{1.2}}O_{\frac{2.4}{1.2}} \rightarrow VO_2$$

The correct formula is VO_2; vanadium(IV) oxide

Given: In a 100 g sample: 56 g V, 44 g O   **Find:** formula and name
Conceptual Plan:

convert mass to mol of each element → write pseudoformula → write empirical formula
$$\frac{1 \ mol \ V}{50.94 \ g \ V} \qquad \frac{1 \ mol \ O}{16.00 \ g \ O}$$
divide by smallest number

Solution:

$$56 \ \cancel{g \ V} \times \frac{1 \ mol \ V}{50.94 \ \cancel{g \ V}} = 1.1 \ mol \ V$$

$$44 \ \cancel{g \ O} \times \frac{1 \ mol \ O}{16.00 \ \cancel{g \ O}} = 2.75 \ mol \ O$$

$$V_{1.1}O_{2.75}$$

$$V_{\frac{1.1}{1.1}}O_{\frac{2.75}{1.1}} \rightarrow VO_{2.5} \rightarrow V_2O_5$$

The correct formula is V_2O_5; vanadium(V) oxide

127. **Given:** MCl_3, 2.395 g sample, 3.606×10^{-2} mol Cl   **Find:** atomic mass M
Conceptual Plan: mol Cl → g Cl → g X
$$\frac{35.45 \ g \ Cl}{1 \ mol \ Cl} \qquad g \ sample - \ g \ Cl$$

mol Cl → mol M → atomic mass M
$$\frac{1 \ mol \ M}{3 \ mol \ Cl} \qquad \frac{g \ M}{mol \ M}$$

Solution:

$$3.606 \times 10^{-2} \ \cancel{mol \ Cl} \times \frac{35.45 \ g}{1 \ \cancel{mol \ Cl}} = 1.278 \ g \ Cl$$

$$2.395 \ g - 1.278 \ g = 1.117 \ g \ M$$

$$3.606 \times 10^{-2} \ \cancel{mol \ Cl} \times \frac{1 \ mol \ M}{3 \ \cancel{mol \ Cl}} = 1.202 \times 10^{-2} \ mol \ M$$

$$\frac{1.117 \ g \ M}{0.01202 \ mol \ M} = 92.93 \ g/mol \ M$$

molar mass of M = 92.93 g/mol

H

128.

129. **Given:** g NaCl + g NaBr = 2.00 g, g Na = 0.75 g   **Find:** g NaBr

Conceptual Plan: Let x = mol NaCl, y = mol NaBr, then x(molar mass NaCl) = g NaCl, y(molar mass NaBr) = g NaBr

Solution: $x(58.4) + y(102.9) = 2.00$

$x(23.0) + y(23.0) = 0.75$ $y = 0.0326 - x$

$58.4x + 102.9(0.0326-x) = 2.00$

$58.4x + 3.354 - 102.9x = 2.00$

$44.5x = 1.354$

$x = 0.03043$ mol NaCl

$y = 0.0326 - 0.03043 = 0\ 00217$ mol NaBr

g NaBr = $(0.00217)(102.9$ g/mol$) = 0.224$ g NaBr

Check: The units of the answer, g NaBr, are correct. The magnitude is reasonable since it is less than the total mass.

130. **Given:** Sample 1: 1.00 g X, 0.472 g Z, X_2Z_3; Sample 2: 1.00 g X, 0.630 g Z; Sample 3: 1.00 g X, 0.789 g Z

Find: empirical formula for samples 2 and 3

Conceptual Plan: moles X remains constant, determine relative moles of Z for the 3 samples.

Solution: Let X = atomic mass X, Z = atomic mass Z

$$n_X = \frac{1.00\text{ g X}}{X} \qquad n_Z = \frac{0.472\text{ g Z}}{Z}$$

for sample 1: $\dfrac{n_X}{n_Z} = \dfrac{2}{3}$

for sample 2: $\dfrac{0.630\text{ g}}{0.472\text{ g}} = 1.33$, so, mol $= 1.33n_Z$

mol ratio: $\dfrac{n_X}{1.33n_Z} = \dfrac{2}{(1.33)3} = \dfrac{2}{4} = \dfrac{1}{2}$

Empirical formula sample 2: XZ_2

for sample 3: $\dfrac{0.789\text{ g}}{0.472\text{ g}} = 1.67$, so, mol $= 1.67n_Z$

mol ratio: $\dfrac{n_X}{1.67n_Z} = \dfrac{2}{(1.67)3} = \dfrac{2}{5}$

Empirical formula sample 3: X_2Z_5

131. **Given:** Sample of $CaCO_3$ and $(NH_4)_2CO_3$ is 61.9% CO_3^{2-} **Find:** % $CaCO_3$

Conceptual Plan: Let x = $CaCO_3$, y = $(NH_4)_2CO_3$, then x(molar mass $CaCO_3$) = g $CaCO_3$, y(molar mass $(NH_4)_2CO_3$) = g $(NH_4)_2CO_3$

then, a 100.0 g sample contains: x(100.0) g $CaCO_3$; y(96.1) g $(NH_4)_2CO_3$; and 61.9 g CO_3^{2-}

Solution: $x(100.0) + y(96.1) = 100.0$

$x(60.0) + y(60.0) = 61.9$ $y = 1.032 - x$

$100.0x + 96.1(1.032-x) = 100$

91

$$100.0x + 99.14 - 96.1x = 100$$
$$3.9x \quad\quad\quad = 0.96$$
$$x \quad\quad = 0.22 \text{ mol } CaCO_3$$
$$y \quad\quad = 1.032 - 0.22 = 0.81 \text{ mol } (NH_4)_2CO_3$$

g $CaCO_3$ = (0.22 mol)(100.0g/mol) = 22.0 g $CaCO_3$ in a 100 g sample:

mass % $CaCO_3$ = 22.0%

Check: The units of the answer, mass % $CaCO_3$, are correct. The magnitude is reasonable since it is between 0 and 100%

132. **Given:** 50.0 g S, 100 g Cl_2, 150 g mixture S_2Cl_2 and SCl_2 **Find:** % S_2Cl_2

Conceptual Plan: total mol S = 2(mol S_2Cl_2) + mol SCl_2; mol S_2Cl_2 → g S_2Cl_2 → %S_2Cl_2

$$\frac{134.9 \text{ g}}{1 \text{ mol } S_2Cl_2} \qquad \frac{\text{g } S_2Cl_2}{150 \text{ g sample}} \text{ x } 100$$

then, S_2Cl_2 = 134.9 g/mol, SCl_2 = 103.0 g/mol, let x = mol S_2Cl_2, y = mol SCl_2

x(134.9) = g S in S_2Cl_2, y(103.0) = g S in SCl_2

Solution:

$$\text{mol S } = 50.0 \text{ g S x } \frac{1 \text{ mol S}}{32.1 \text{ g}} = 1.56 \text{ mol S}$$

2x = mol S in S_2Cl_2, y = mol S in SCl_2

2x + y = 1.56

x(134.9) + y(103.0) = 150.0

134.9x+ 103.0(1.56 – 2x) = 150.0

$$71.1x = 10.44$$
$$x \quad = 0.147$$
$$y \quad = 1.27$$

$$0.147 \text{ mol } S_2Cl_2 \text{ x } \frac{134.9 \text{ g } S_2Cl_2}{1 \text{ mol } S_2Cl_2} = 19.8 \text{ g } S_2Cl_2$$

$$\frac{19.8 \text{ g } S_2Cl_2}{150 \text{ g sample}} \text{ x } 100 = 13.2 \text{ %}S_2Cl_2$$

Check: Units of answer, % S_2Cl_2, are correct. Magnitude is reasonable since it is between 0 and 100% and mol of S_2Cl_2 are less than mol SCl_2.

133. **Given:** 1.1 kg CF_2Cl_2/automobile, 25% leak/year, 100 x 10^6 automobiles **Find:** kg Cl/yr

Conceptual Plan: **kg CF_2Cl_2 /auto → kg CF_2Cl_2 leaked/yr → kg Cl/yr/auto → kg Cl**

$$\frac{25 \text{ kg } CF_2Cl_2}{100 \text{ kg } CF_2Cl_2} \quad \frac{70.9 \text{ g Cl}}{120.91 \text{ g } CF_2Cl_2} \quad \frac{100 \text{ x } 10^6 \text{ auto}}{}$$

Solution: $\dfrac{1.1 \text{ kg } CF_2Cl_2}{\text{auto}} \text{ x } \dfrac{25 \text{ kg } CF_2Cl_2}{100 \text{ kg } CF_2Cl_2} \text{ x } \dfrac{70.9 \text{ kg Cl}}{120.91 \text{ kg } CF_2Cl_2} \text{ x } \dfrac{100 \text{ x } 10^6 \text{ auto}}{} = 1.6 \text{ x } 10^7 \text{ kg Cl/yr}$

Check: Units of the answer, kg Cl, are correct. The magnitude is reasonable because it is less than the kg CF_2Cl_2 leaked per year.

134. **Given:** coal = 2.55%S, H_2SO_4,1.0 metric ton coal **Find:** metric ton H_2SO_4 produced

Conceptual Plan: metric ton coal → kg coal → kg S → kg H_2SO_4 → metric ton H_2SO_4

$$\frac{1000 \text{ kg}}{\text{metric ton}} \quad \frac{2.55 \text{ kg S}}{100 \text{ kg coal}} \quad \frac{98.09 \text{ kg } H_2SO_4}{32.07 \text{ kg S}} \quad \frac{\text{metric ton}}{1000 \text{ kg}}$$

Solution:

$$1.0 \text{ metric ton coal x } \frac{1000 \text{ kg coal}}{\text{metric ton coal}} \text{ x } \frac{2.55 \text{ kg S}}{100 \text{ kg coal}} \text{ x } \frac{98.09 \text{ kg } H_2SO_4}{32.07 \text{ kg S}} \text{ x } \frac{1 \text{ metric ton } H_2SO_4}{1000 \text{ kg } H_2SO_4} = 0.078 \text{ metric ton } H_2SO_4$$

Check: Units of the answer, metric ton H_2SO_4, are correct. Magnitude is reasonable since it is more than 2.55% of a metric ton and the mass of H_2SO_4 is greater than the mass of S.

135. **Given:** rock contains: 38.0% PbS, 25.0% $PbCO_3$, 17.4% $PbSO_4$, **Find:** kg rock needed for 5.0 metric ton Pb

Conceptual Plan: determine kg Pb/ 100 kg rock then ton Pb→ kg Pb → kg rock

$$\frac{1000 \text{ kg}}{\text{metric ton}} \quad \frac{100 \text{ kg rock}}{64.2 \text{ kg rock}}$$

Solution: in 100 kg rock:

$$\left(\frac{38.0 \ \cancel{\text{kg PbS}}}{} \times \frac{207.2 \text{ kg Pb}}{239.3 \ \cancel{\text{kg PbS}}}\right) + \left(\frac{25.0 \ \cancel{\text{kg PbCO}_3}}{} \times \frac{207.2 \text{ kg Pb}}{267.2 \ \cancel{\text{kg PbCO}_3}}\right) + \left(\frac{17.4 \ \cancel{\text{kg PbSO}_4}}{} \times \frac{207.2 \text{ kg Pb}}{303.2 \ \cancel{\text{kg PbSO}_4}}\right) = 64.2 \text{ kg Pb}$$

$$5.0 \ \cancel{\text{metric ton Pb}} \times \frac{1000 \ \cancel{\text{kg Pb}}}{\cancel{\text{metric ton Pb}}} \times \frac{100 \text{ kg rock}}{64.2 \ \cancel{\text{kg Pb}}} = 7.8 \times 10^3 \text{ kg rock}$$

Check: Units of answer, kg rock, are correct. Magnitude is reasonable since it is greater than the amount of Pb needed.

136. The sphere in the molecular models represents the electron cloud of the atom. On this scale, the nucleus wound be too small to see.

137. a) Atomic mass O > atomic mass C, % O would be higher.
  b) Atomic mass N and O close, molecule contains 2N to 1 O, % N would be higher.
  c) Atomic mass O > atomic mass C, same number of atoms, % O would be higher.
  d) Atomic mass N much greater than atomic mass H, % N would be higher.

138. The statement is incorrect because a chemical formula is based on the ratio of atoms combined not the ratio of grams combined. The statement should read: "The chemical formula for ammonia (NH_3) indicates that ammonia contains three hydrogen atoms to each nitrogen atom."

139. The statement is incorrect because equations are balanced based on the number and kind of atoms not molecules. The statement should read: "When a chemical equation is balanced, the number of atoms of each type on both sides of the equation will be equal."

140. H_2SO_4: Atomic mass S is approximately twice atomic mass O, both are much greater than atomic mass H. The order of % mass: % O > % S > % H

Chapter 4
Chemical Quantities and Aqueous Reactions

1. Reaction stoichiometry is the numerical relationships between chemical amounts in a balanced chemical equation. The coefficients in a chemical reaction specify the relative amounts in moles of each of the substances involved in the reaction.

2. The limiting reactant is the reactant that is completely consumed in a chemical reaction and limits the amount of product. The theoretical yield is the amount of product that can be made in a chemical reaction based on the amount of limiting reactant. The percent yield is calculated as $\dfrac{\text{actual yield}}{\text{theoretical yield}}$ x 100. The reactant in excess is any reactant that occurs in a quantity greater than that required to completely react with the limiting reactant.

3. No, the percent yield would not be different if the actual yield and theoretical yield were calculated in moles. The relationship between grams and moles is the molar mass. This would be the same value for the actual yield and the theoretical yield.

4. An aqueous solution is a solution in which water acts as the solvent. The solvent is the majority component of the mixture, and the solute is the minority component in the mixture.

5. Molarity is a concentration term. It is the amount of solute (in moles) divided by the volume of solution (in liters). The molarity of a solution can be used as a conversion factor between moles of the solute and liters of the solution.

6. Substances that completely dissociate into ions when they dissolve in water are called strong electrolytes and conduct electricity easily. Substances that do not completely dissociate in water are called weak electrolytes and conduct electricity only weakly. Compounds that do not dissociate into ions when dissolved in water are called nonelectrolytes and do not conduct electricity.

7. Acids are molecular compounds that ionize – form ions – when they dissolve in water. A strong acid is one that completely ionizes in solution. A weak acid is one that does not completely ionize in water. A solution of a weak acid is composed mostly of the nonionized acid.

8. A compound is termed soluble if it dissolves in water. A compound is insoluble is it does not dissolve in water.

9. The solubility rules are a set of empirical rules that have been inferred from observations on many ionic compounds. The solubility rules allow us to predict if a compound is soluble or insoluble.

10. Cations that usually form soluble compounds are: Li^+, Na^+, K^+, and NH_4^+. The anions that usually form soluble compounds are NO_3^-, and $C_2H_3O_2^-$ which have no exceptions; Cl^-, Br^-, I^- except when these ions pair with Ag^+, Hg_2^{2+}, or Pb^{2+} which result in insoluble compounds; SO_4^{2-} except with Sr^{2+}, Ba^{2+}, Pb^{2+}, Ag^+ or Ca^{2+} which form insoluble compounds. The anions that usually form insoluble compounds are OH^- and S^{2-} except with Li^+, Na^+, K^+, and NH_4^+ which form soluble compounds and when S^{2-} pairs with Ca^{2+}, Sr^{2+} or Ba^{2+} the compounds are soluble; CO_3^{2-} and PO_4^{3-} are insoluble except when paired with Li^+, Na^+, K^+, and NH_4^+.

11. A precipitation reaction is one in which a solid or precipitate forms upon mixing two solutions. An example is: $2\ KI(aq) + Pb(NO_3)_2(aq) \rightarrow PbI_2(s) + 2\ KNO_3(aq)$

12. The key to predicting precipitation reactions is to understand that only insoluble compounds form precipitates. In a precipitation reaction, two solutions containing soluble compounds combine and an insoluble compound precipitates.

13. A molecular equation is an equation showing the complete neutral formulas for each compound in the reaction as if they existed as molecules. Equations which list individually all of the ions present as either reactants or precuts in a chemical reaction are called complete ionic equation. Equations which show only the species that actually change during the reaction are called net ionic equations.

14. An acid is a substance that produces H^+ ions in aqueous solutions. A base is a substance that produces OH^- ions in aqueous solutions.

15. When an acid and base are mixed, the $H^+(aq)$ from the acid combines with the OH^- from the base to form $H_2O(l)$. An example is: $HCl(aq) + NaOH(aq) \rightarrow H_2O(l) + NaCl(aq)$

16. In a titration, a substance in a solution of known concentration is reacted with another substance in a solution of unknown concentration. The acid - base titration is continued until the neutralization is complete. At the equivalence point, the point when the number of moles of OH^- equals the number of moles of H^+, the titration is complete. An indicator is a dye whose color depends on the acidity or basicity of the solution.

17. Aqueous reactions that form a gas upon mixing two solutions are called gas – evolution reactions. An example is: $H_2SO_4(aq) + Li_2S(aq) \rightarrow H_2S(g) + Li_2SO_4(aq)$

18. The reactant types that give rise to gas – evolution reactions are: sulfides, carbonates, bicarbonate, sulfites, bisulfites, and ammonium compounds.

19. Oxidation – reduction reactions or redox reactions are reactions in which electrons are transferred from one reactant to the other. An example is: $4 Fe(s) + 3 O_2(g) \rightarrow 2 Fe_2O_3(s)$

20. The oxidation state or oxidation number is a number given to each atom based on the electron assignments. It is the "charge" an atom would have if all shared electrons were assigned to the atom with a greater attraction for those electrons.

21. To identify redox reactions by using oxidation states, begin by assigning oxidation states to each atom in the reaction. A change in oxidation state for the atoms indicates a redox reaction.

22. When a substance is oxidized it loses electrons, there is an increase in oxidation state. When a substance is reduced it gains electrons, there is a reduction in oxidation state.

23. A substance that causes the oxidation of another substance is called an oxidizing agent. A substance that causes the reduction of another substance is called a reducing agent.

24. Combustion reactions are characterized by the reaction of a substance with O_2 to form one or more oxygen containing compounds, often including water. Combustion reactions emit heat. Combustion reactions are important because most of our society's energy is derived from them.
An example is: $CH_4(g) + 2 O_2(g) \rightarrow CO_2(g) + 2 H_2O(g)$

25. **Given:** 4.9 moles C_6H_{14} **Find:** balanced reaction, moles O_2 required
Conceptual Plan: balance the reaction then mol C_6H_{14} $\rightarrow$ mol O_2

$$2 C_6H_{14}(g) + 19 O_2(g) \rightarrow 12 CO_2(g) + 14 H_2O(g) \quad \frac{19 \text{ mol } O_2}{2 \text{ mol } C_6H_{14}}$$

Solution: $4.9 \text{ mol } C_6H_{14} \times \dfrac{19 \text{ mol } O_2}{2 \text{ mol } C_6H_{14}} = 47 \text{ mol } O_2$

Check: The units, mol O_2, are correct. The magnitude is reasonable because much more O_2 is needed than C_6H_{14}.

26. **Given:** 1.07 moles $HC_2H_3O_2$ **Find:** balanced reaction, moles $Ba(OH)_2$ required
Conceptual Plan: balance the reaction then   **mol $HC_2H_3O_2$ $\rightarrow$ mol $Ba(OH)_2$**

$$2 HC_2H_3O_2 (aq) + Ba(OH)_2(aq) \rightarrow 2 H_2O(l) + Ba(C_2H_3O_2)_2(aq) \quad \frac{1 \text{ mol } Ba(OH)_2}{2 \text{ mol } HC_2H_3O_2}$$

Solution: $1.07 \text{ mol } HC_2H_3O_2 \times \dfrac{1 \text{ mol } Ba(OH)_2}{2 \text{ mol } HC_2H_3O_2} = 0.535 \text{ mol } HC_2H_3O_2$

Check: The units, mol $Ba(OH)_2$, are correct. The magnitude is reasonable because much less $Ba(OH)_2$ is needed than $HC_2H_3O_2$.

27. a) **Given:** 1.3 mol N_2O_5 **Find:** mol NO_2

Conceptual Plan: mol N_2O_5 → mol NO_2

$$\frac{4\,NO_2}{2\,N_2O_5}$$

Solution: $1.3\ \cancel{mol\,N_2O_5} \times \dfrac{4\ mol\ NO_2}{2\ \cancel{mol\,N_2O_5}} = 2.6\ mol\ NO_2$

Check: The units of the answer, mol NO_2, are correct. The magnitude is reasonable since it is greater than mol N_2O_5.

b) **Given:** 5.8 mol N_2O_5 **Find:** mol NO_2

Conceptual Plan: mol N_2O_5 → mol NO_2

$$\frac{4\,NO_2}{2\,N_2O_5}$$

Solution: $5.8\ \cancel{mol\,N_2O_5} \times \dfrac{4\ mol\ NO_2}{2\ \cancel{mol\,N_2O_5}} = 11.6\ mol\ NO_2 = 12\ mol\ NO_2$

Check: The units of the answer, mol NO_2, are correct. The magnitude is reasonable since it is greater than mol N_2O_5.

c) **Given:** 10.5 g N_2O_5 **Find:** mol NO_2

Conceptual Plan: g N_2O_5 → mol N_2O_5 → molNO_2

$$\frac{1\ mol\ N_2O_5}{108.02\ g\ N_2O_5} \qquad \frac{4\,NO_2}{2\,N_2O_5}$$

Solution: $10.5\ \cancel{g\,N_2O_5} \times \dfrac{1\ \cancel{mol\,N_2O_5}}{108.02\ \cancel{g\,N_2O_5}} \times \dfrac{4\ mol\ NO_2}{2\ \cancel{mol\,N_2O_5}} = 0.194\ mol\ NO_2$

Check: The units of the answer, mol NO_2, are correct. The magnitude is reasonable since 10 g is about 0.1 mol N_2O_5 and the answer is greater than mol N_2O_5.

d) **Given:** 1.55 kg N_2O_5 **Find:** mol NO_2

Conceptual Plan: kg N_2O_5 → g N_2O_5 → mol N_2O_5 → molNO_2

$$\frac{1000\ g\ N_2O_5}{kg\ N_2O_5} \quad \frac{1\ mol\ N_2O_5}{108.02\ g\ N_2O_5} \quad \frac{4\,NO_2}{2\,N_2O_5}$$

Solution: $1.55\ \cancel{kg\,N_2O_5} \times \dfrac{1000\ \cancel{g\,N_2O_5}}{kg\,N_2O_5} \times \dfrac{1\ \cancel{mol\,N_2O_5}}{108.02\ \cancel{g\,N_2O_5}} \times \dfrac{4\ mol\ NO_2}{2\ \cancel{mol\,N_2O_5}} = 28.7\ mol\ NO_2$

Check: The units of the answer, mol NO_2, are correct. The magnitude is reasonable since 1.5 kg is about 14 mol N_2O_5 and the answer is greater than mol N_2O_5.

28. a) **Given:** 5.3 mol N_2H_4 **Find:** mol NH_3

Conceptual Plan: mol N_2H_4 → mol NH_3

$$\frac{4\,NH_3}{3\,N_2H_4}$$

Solution: $5.3\ \cancel{mol\,N_2H_4} \times \dfrac{4\ mol\ NH_2}{3\ \cancel{mol\,N_2H_4}} = 7.1\ mol\ NH_3$

Check: The units of the answer, mol NH_3, are correct. The magnitude is reasonable since it is greater than mol N_2H_4.

b) **Given:** 2.28 mol N_2H_4 **Find:** mol NH_3

Conceptual Plan: mol N_2H_4 → mol NH_3

$$\frac{4\,NH_3}{3\,N_2H_4}$$

Solution: $2.28\ \cancel{mol\,N_2H_4} \times \dfrac{4\ mol\ NH_2}{3\ \cancel{mol\,N_2H_4}} = 3.04\ mol\ NH_3$

Check: The units of the answer, mol NH_3, are correct. The magnitude is reasonable since it is greater than mol N_2H_4.

c) **Given:** 32.5 g N_2H_4 **Find:** mol NH_3
   Conceptual Plan: g N_2H_4 → mol N_2H_4 → mol NH_3

$$\frac{1 \text{ mol } N_2H_4}{32.05 \text{ g } N_2H_4} \qquad \frac{4 \text{ } NH_3}{3 \text{ } N_2H_4}$$

Solution: $32.5 \text{ g } N_2H_4 \times \dfrac{1 \text{ mol } N_2H_4}{32.05 \text{ g } N_2H_4} \times \dfrac{4 \text{ mol } NH_2}{3 \text{ mol } N_2H_4} = 1.35 \text{ mol } NH_3$

Check: The units of the answer, mol NH_3, are correct. The magnitude is reasonable since there is about 1 mol N_2H_4 and the answer is greater than mol N_2H_4.

d) **Given:** 14.7 kg N_2H_4 **Find:** mol NH_3
   Conceptual Plan: kg N_2H_4 →g N_2H_4 → mol N_2H_4 → mol NH_3

$$\frac{1000 \text{ g } N_2H_4}{\text{kg } N_2H_4} \qquad \frac{1 \text{ mol } N_2H_4}{32.05 \text{ g } N_2H_4} \qquad \frac{4 \text{ } NH_3}{3 \text{ } N_2H_4}$$

Solution: $14.7 \text{ kg } N_2H_4 \times \dfrac{1000 \text{ g } N_2H_4}{\text{kg } N_2H_4} \times \dfrac{1 \text{ mol } N_2H_4}{32.05 \text{ g } N_2H_4} \times \dfrac{4 \text{ mol } NH_2}{3 \text{ mol } N_2H_4} = 612 \text{ mol } NH_3$

Check: The units of the answer, mol NH_3, are correct. The magnitude is reasonable since 15 kg is about 500 mol N_2H_4 and the answer is greater than mol N_2H_4.

29. **Given:** 3 mol SiO_2 **Find:** mol C, mol SiC, mol CO
    Conceptual Plan: mol SiO_2 → mol C → mol SiC → mol CO

$$\frac{3 \text{ C}}{SiO_2} \qquad \frac{SiC}{SiO_2} \qquad \frac{2 \text{ CO}}{SiO_2}$$

Solution:

$3 \text{ mol } SiO_2 \times \dfrac{3 \text{ mol C}}{\text{mol } SiO_2} = 9 \text{ mol C}$ $3 \text{ mol } SiO_2 \times \dfrac{\text{mol SiC}}{\text{mol } SiO_2} = 3 \text{ mol SiC}$ $3 \text{ mol } SiO_2 \times \dfrac{2 \text{ mol CO}}{\text{mol } SiO_2} = 6 \text{ mol CO}$

Given: 6 mol C   **Find:** mol SiO_2, mol SiC, mol CO
Conceptual Plan: mol C → mol SiO_2 → mol SiC → mol CO

$$\frac{SiO_2}{3 \text{ C}} \qquad \frac{SiC}{3 \text{ C}} \qquad \frac{2 \text{ CO}}{3 \text{ C}}$$

Solution:

$6 \text{ mol C} \times \dfrac{\text{mol } SiO_2}{3 \text{ mol C}} = 2 \text{ mol } SiO_2$ $6 \text{ mol C} \times \dfrac{\text{mol SiC}}{3 \text{ mol C}} = 2 \text{ mol SiC}$ $6 \text{ mol C} \times \dfrac{2 \text{ mol CO}}{3 \text{ mol C}} = 4 \text{ mol CO}$

Given: 10 mol CO   **Find:** mol SiO_2, mol C, mol SiC
Conceptual Plan: mol CO →mol SiO_2 → mol C → mol SiC

$$\frac{SiO_2}{2 \text{ CO}} \qquad \frac{3 \text{ C}}{2 \text{ CO}} \qquad \frac{SiC}{2 \text{ CO}}$$

Solution:

$10 \text{ mol CO} \times \dfrac{\text{mol } SiO_2}{2 \text{ mol CO}} = 5.0 \text{ mol } SiO_2$ $10 \text{ mol C} \times \dfrac{3 \text{ mol C}}{2 \text{ mol CO}} = 15 \text{ mol C}$ $10 \text{ mol CO} \times \dfrac{\text{mol SiC}}{2 \text{ mol CO}} = 5.0 \text{ mol SiC}$

Given: 2.8 mol SiO_2 **Find:** mol C, mol SiC, mol CO
Conceptual Plan: mol SiO_2 → mol C → mol SiC → mol CO

$$\frac{3 \text{ C}}{SiO_2} \qquad \frac{SiC}{SiO_2} \qquad \frac{2 \text{ CO}}{SiO_2}$$

Solution:

$2.8 \text{ mol } SiO_2 \times \dfrac{3 \text{ mol C}}{\text{mol } SiO_2} = 8.4 \text{ mol C}$ $2.8 \text{ mol } SiO_2 \times \dfrac{\text{mol SiC}}{\text{mol } SiO_2} = 2.8 \text{ mol SiC}$ $2.8 \text{ mol } SiO_2 \times \dfrac{2 \text{ mol CO}}{\text{mol } SiO_2} = 5.6 \text{ mol CO}$

Given: 1.55 mol C   **Find:** mol SiO_2, mol SiC, mol CO

Conceptual Plan: mol C → mol SiO$_2$ → mol SiC → mol CO

$$\frac{SiO_2}{3\,C} \qquad \frac{SiC}{3\,C} \qquad \frac{2\,CO}{3\,C}$$

Solution:

$$1.55\ \cancel{mol\ C} \times \frac{3\ mol\ SiO_2}{3\ \cancel{mol\ C}} = 0.517\ mol\ SiO_2 \qquad 1.55\ \cancel{mol\ C} \times \frac{mol\ SiC}{3\ \cancel{mol\ C}} = 0.517\ mol\ SiC \qquad 1.55\ \cancel{mol\ C} \times \frac{2\ mol\ CO}{3\ \cancel{mol\ C}} = 1.03\ mol\ CO$$

SiO$_2$	C	SiC	CO
3	9	3	6
2	**6**	2	4
5.0	15	5.0	**10**
2.8	8.4	2.8	5.6
0.517	**1.55**	0.517	1.03

30. **Given:** 2 mol N$_2$H$_4$ **Find:** mol N$_2$O$_4$, mol N$_2$, mol H$_2$O

Conceptual Plan: mol N$_2$H$_4$ → mol N$_2$O$_4$ → mol N$_2$ → mol H$_2$O

$$\frac{N_2O_4}{2\,N_2H_4} \qquad \frac{3\,N_2}{2\,N_2H_4} \qquad \frac{4\,H_2O}{2\,N_2H_4}$$

Solution:

$$2\ \cancel{mol\ N_2H_4} \times \frac{1\ mol\ N_2O_4}{2\ \cancel{mol\ N_2H_4}} = 1\ mol\ N_2O_4 \qquad 2\ \cancel{mol\ N_2H_4} \times \frac{3\ mol\ N_2}{2\ \cancel{mol\ N_2H_4}} = 3\ mol\ N_2 \qquad 2\ \cancel{mol\ N_2H_4} \times \frac{4\ mol\ H_2O}{2\ \cancel{mol\ N_2H_4}} = 4\ mol\ H_2O$$

Given: 5 mol N$_2$O$_4$ **Find:** mol N$_2$H$_4$, mol N$_2$, mol H$_2$O

Conceptual Plan: mol N$_2$O$_4$ → mol N$_2$H$_4$ → mol N$_2$ → mol H$_2$O

$$\frac{2\,N_2H_4}{N_2O_4} \qquad \frac{3\,N_2}{N_2O_4} \qquad \frac{4\,H_2O}{N_2O_4}$$

Solution:

$$5\ \cancel{mol\ N_2O_4} \times \frac{2\ mol\ N_2H_4}{\cancel{mol\ N_2O_4}} = 10\ mol\ N_2H_4 \qquad 5\ \cancel{mol\ N_2O_4} \times \frac{3\ mol\ N_2}{\cancel{mol\ N_2O_4}} = 15\ mol\ N_2 \qquad 5\ \cancel{mol\ N_2O_4} \times \frac{4\ mol\ H_2O}{\cancel{mol\ N_2O_4}} = 20\ mol\ H_2O$$

Given: 10 mol H$_2$O **Find:** mol N$_2$O$_4$, mol N$_2$O$_4$, mol N$_2$,

Conceptual Plan: mol H$_2$O → mol N$_2$H$_4$ → mol N$_2$ → mol N$_2$O$_4$

$$\frac{2\,N_2H_4}{4\,H_2O} \qquad \frac{3\,N_2}{4\,H_2O} \qquad \frac{1\,N_2O_4}{4\,H_2O}$$

Solution:

$$10\ \cancel{mol\ H_2O} \times \frac{2\ mol\ N_2H_4}{4\ \cancel{mol\ H_2O}} = 5.0\ mol\ N_2H_4 \qquad 10\ \cancel{mol\ H_2O} \times \frac{3\ mol\ N_2}{4\ \cancel{mol\ H_2O}} = 7.5\ mol\ N_2 \qquad 10\ \cancel{mol\ H_2O} \times \frac{1\ mol\ N_2O_4}{4\ \cancel{mol\ H_2O}} = 2.5\ mol\ H_2O$$

Given: 2.5 mol N$_2$H$_4$ **Find:** mol N$_2$O$_4$, mol N$_2$, mol H$_2$O

Conceptual Plan: mol N$_2$H$_4$ → mol N$_2$O$_4$ → mol N$_2$ → mol H$_2$O

$$\frac{N_2O_4}{2\,N_2H_4} \qquad \frac{3\,N_2}{2\,N_2H_4} \qquad \frac{4\,H_2O}{2\,N_2H_4}$$

Solution:

$$2.5\ \cancel{mol\ N_2H_4} \times \frac{1\ mol\ N_2O_4}{2\ \cancel{mol\ N_2H_4}} = 1.3\ mol\ N_2O_4 \quad 2.5\ \cancel{mol\ N_2H_4} \times \frac{3\ mol\ N_2}{2\ \cancel{mol\ N_2H_4}} = 3.8\ mol\ N_2 \quad 2.5\ \cancel{mol\ N_2H_4} \times \frac{4\ mol\ H_2O}{2\ \cancel{mol\ N_2H_4}} = 5.0\ mol\ H_2O$$

Given: 4.2 mol N$_2$O$_4$ **Find:** mol N$_2$H$_4$, mol N$_2$, mol H$_2$O

Conceptual Plan: mol N$_2$O$_4$ → mol N$_2$H$_4$ → mol N$_2$ → mol H$_2$O

$$\frac{2\,N_2H_4}{N_2O_4} \qquad \frac{3\,N_2}{N_2O_4} \qquad \frac{4\,H_2O}{N_2O_4}$$

Solution:

$$4.2 \ \cancel{\text{mol } N_2O_4} \ \times \ \frac{2 \ \text{mol } N_2H_4}{\cancel{\text{mol } N_2O_4}} = 8.4 \ \text{mol } N_2H_4 \qquad 4.2 \ \cancel{\text{mol } N_2O_4} \ \times \ \frac{3 \ \text{mol } N_2}{\cancel{\text{mol } N_2O_4}} = 12.6 \ \text{mol } N_2 = 13 \ \text{mol } N_2$$

$$4.2 \ \cancel{\text{mol } N_2O_4} \ \times \ \frac{4 \ \text{mol } H_2O}{\cancel{\text{mol } N_2O_4}} = 16.8 \ \text{mol } H_2O = 17 \ \text{mol } H_2O$$

Given: 11.8 mol N_2 **Find:** mol N_2H_4, mol N_2O_4, mol H_2O

Conceptual Plan: mol N_2 → mol N_2H_4 → mol N_2O_4 → mol H_2O

$$\frac{2 \ N_2H_4}{3 \ N_2} \qquad\qquad \frac{2 \ N_2O_4}{3 \ N_2} \qquad\qquad \frac{4 \ H_2O}{3 \ N_2}$$

Solution:

$$11.8 \ \cancel{\text{mol } N_2} \ \times \ \frac{2 \ \text{mol } N_2H_4}{3 \ \cancel{\text{mol } N_2}} = 7.87 \ \text{mol } N_2H_4 \quad 11.8 \ \cancel{\text{mol } N_2} \ \times \ \frac{\text{mol } N_2O_4}{3 \ \cancel{\text{mol } N_2}} = 3.93 \ \text{mol } N_2 \quad 11.8 \ \cancel{\text{mol } N_2} \ \times \ \frac{4 \ \text{mol } H_2O}{3 \ \cancel{\text{mol } N_2}} = 15.7 \ \text{mol } H_2O$$

N_2H_2	N_2O_4	N_2	H_2O
2	1	3	4
10	**5**	15	20
5	2.5	7.5	**10**
2.5	1.2	3.8	5.0
8.4	**4.2**	13	17
7.87	3.93	**11.8**	15.7

31. **Given:** 3.2 g Fe   **Find:** g HBr; g H_2

    Conceptual Plan: **g Fe → mol Fe → mol HBr → g HBr**

$$\frac{\text{mol Fe}}{55.8 \ \text{g Fe}} \qquad \frac{2 \ \text{mol HBr}}{\text{mol Fe}} \qquad \frac{80.9 \ \text{g HBr}}{\text{mol HBr}}$$

                         g Fe → mol Fe → mol H_2 → g H_2

$$\frac{\text{mol Fe}}{55.8 \ \text{g Fe}} \qquad \frac{1 \ \text{mol } H_2}{\text{mol Fe}} \qquad \frac{2.02 \ \text{g } H_2}{\text{mol } H_2}$$

    Solution:

$$3.2 \ \text{g} \ \times \ \frac{1 \ \text{mol Fe}}{55.8 \ \text{g Fe}} \ \times \ \frac{2 \ \text{mol HBr}}{1 \ \text{mol Fe}} \ \times \ \frac{80.9 \ \text{g HBr}}{1 \ \text{mol HBr}} = 9.3 \ \text{g HBr}$$

$$3.2 \ \text{g} \ \times \ \frac{1 \ \text{mol Fe}}{55.8 \ \text{g Fe}} \ \times \ \frac{1 \ \text{mol } H_2}{1 \ \text{mol Fe}} \ \times \ \frac{2.02 \ \text{g } H_2}{1 \ \text{mol } H_2} = 0.12 \ \text{g } H_2$$

Check: Units of answers, g HBr, g H_2, are correct. The magnitude of the answers is reasonable because molar mass HBr is greater than Fe and molar mass H_2 is much less than Fe.

32. **Given:** 15.2 g Al   **Find:** g H_2SO_4; g H_2

    Conceptual Plan: **g Al → mol Al → mol H_2SO_4 → g H_2SO_4**

$$\frac{\text{mol Al}}{26.98 \ \text{g Al}} \qquad \frac{3 \ \text{mol } H_2SO_4}{2 \ \text{mol Al}} \qquad \frac{98.09 \ \text{g } H_2SO_4}{\text{mol } H_2SO_4}$$

                         g Al → mol Al → mol H_2 → g H_2

$$\frac{\text{mol Al}}{26.98 \ \text{g Al}} \qquad \frac{3 \ \text{mol } H_2}{2 \ \text{mol Al}} \qquad \frac{2.016 \ \text{g } H_2}{\text{mol } H_2}$$

    Solution:

$$15.2 \ \text{g Al} \ \times \ \frac{1 \ \text{mol Al}}{26.98 \ \text{g Al}} \ \times \ \frac{3 \ \text{mol } H_2SO_4}{2 \ \text{mol Al}} \ \times \ \frac{98.09 \ \text{g } H_2SO_4}{1 \ \text{mol } H_2SO_4} = 82.9 \ \text{g } H_2SO_4$$

$$15.2 \ \text{g Al} \ \times \ \frac{1 \ \text{mol Al}}{26.98 \ \text{g Al}} \ \times \ \frac{3 \ \text{mol } H_2}{2 \ \text{mol Al}} \ \times \ \frac{2.016 \ \text{g } H_2}{1 \ \text{mol H}} = 1.71 \ \text{g } H_2$$

Check: Units of answers, g H_2SO_4, g H_2, are correct. The magnitude of the answers is reasonable because molar mass H_2SO_4 is greater than Al and molar mass H_2 is much less than Al.

33. a) **Given:** 2.5 g Ba   **Find:** g $BaCl_2$

Conceptual Plan: g Ba → mol Ba → mol $BaCl_2$ → g $BaCl_2$

$$\frac{mol\ Ba}{137.33\ g\ Ba} \qquad \frac{1\ mol\ BaCl_2}{1\ mol\ Ba} \qquad \frac{208.23\ g\ BaCl_2}{1\ mol\ BaCl_2}$$

Solution: $2.5\ g\ Ba \times \dfrac{1\ mol\ Ba}{137.33\ g\ Ba} \times \dfrac{1\ mol\ BaCl_2}{1\ mol\ Ba} \times \dfrac{208.23\ g\ BaCl_2}{1\ mol\ BaCl_2} = 3.8\ g\ BaCl_2$

Check: Units of answer, g $BaCl_2$, are correct. The magnitude of the answer is reasonable because it is larger than grams Ba.

b) **Given:** 2.5 g CaO   **Find:** g $CaCO_3$
   Conceptual Plan: g CaO → mol CaO → mol $CaCO_3$ → g $CaCO_3$

$$\frac{mol\ CaO}{56.08\ g\ CaO} \qquad \frac{mol\ CaCO_3}{1\ mol\ CaO} \qquad \frac{100.09\ g\ CaCO_3}{mol\ CaCO_3}$$

Solution: $2.5\ g\ CaO \times \dfrac{1\ mol\ CaO}{56.08\ g\ CaO} \times \dfrac{1\ mol\ CaCO_3}{1\ mol\ CaO} \times \dfrac{100.09\ g\ CaCO_3}{1\ mol\ CaCO_3} = 4.5\ g\ CaCO_3$

Check: Units of answer, g $CaCO_3$, are correct. The magnitude of the answer is reasonable because it is larger than grams CaO.

c) **Given:** 2.5 g Mg   **Find:** g MgO
   Conceptual Plan: g Mg → mol Mg → mol MgO → g MgO

$$\frac{mol\ Mg}{24.30\ g\ Mg} \qquad \frac{mol\ MgO}{mol\ Mg} \qquad \frac{40.30\ g\ MgO}{mol\ MgO}$$

Solution: $2.5\ g\ Mg \times \dfrac{1\ mol\ Mg}{24.30\ g\ Mg} \times \dfrac{1\ mol\ MgO}{1\ mol\ Mg} \times \dfrac{40.30\ g\ MgO}{1\ mol\ MgO} = 4.1\ g\ MgO$

Check: Units of answer, g MgO, are correct. The magnitude of the answer is reasonable because it is larger than grams Mg.

d) **Given:** 2.5 g Al   **Find:** g Al_2O_3
   Conceptual Plan: g Al → mol Al → mol Al_2O_3 → g Al_2O_3

$$\frac{mol\ Al}{26.98\ g\ Al} \qquad \frac{2\ mol\ Al_2O_3}{4\ mol\ Al} \qquad \frac{101.96\ g\ Al_2O_3}{mol\ Al_2O_3}$$

Solution: $2.5\ g\ Al \times \dfrac{1\ mol\ Al}{26.98\ g\ Al} \times \dfrac{1\ mol\ Al_2O_3}{1\ mol\ Al} \times \dfrac{101.96\ g\ Al_2O_3}{1\ mol\ Al_2O_3} = 4.7\ g\ Al_2O_3$

Check: Units of answer, g Al_2O_3, are correct. The magnitude of the answer is reasonable because it is larger than grams Al.

34. a) **Given:** 10.4 g K   **Find:** g KCl
   Conceptual Plan: g K → mol K → mol KCl → g KCl

$$\frac{mol\ K}{39.10\ g\ K} \qquad \frac{2\ mol\ KCl}{2\ mol\ K} \qquad \frac{74.55\ g\ KCl}{mol\ KCl}$$

Solution: $10.4\ g\ K \times \dfrac{1\ mol\ K}{39.10\ g\ K} \times \dfrac{2\ mol\ KCl}{2\ mol\ K} \times \dfrac{74.55\ g\ KCl}{1\ mol\ KCl} = 19.8\ g\ KCl$

Check: Units of answer, g KCl, are correct. The magnitude of the answer is reasonable because it is larger than grams K.

b) **Given:** 10.4 g K   **Find:** g KBr
   Conceptual Plan: g K → mol K → mol KBr → g KBr

$$\frac{mol\ K}{39.10\ g\ K} \qquad \frac{2\ mol\ KBr}{2\ mol\ K} \qquad \frac{119.00\ g\ KBr}{mol\ KBr}$$

Solution: $10.4\ g\ K \times \dfrac{1\ mol\ K}{39.10\ g\ K} \times \dfrac{2\ mol\ KBr}{2\ mol\ K} \times \dfrac{119.00\ g\ KBr}{1\ mol\ KBr} = 31.6\ g\ KBr$

Check: Units of answer, g KBr, are correct. The magnitude of the answer is reasonable because it is larger than grams K.

c) **Given:** 10.4 g Cr **Find:** g Cr_2O_3

Conceptual Plan: **g Cr → mol Cr → mol Cr_2O_3 → g Cr_2O_3**

$$\frac{\text{mol Cr}}{52.00 \text{ g Cr}} \qquad \frac{2 \text{ mol } Cr_2O_3}{4 \text{ mol Cr}} \qquad \frac{152.00 \text{ g } Cr_2O_3}{\text{mol } Cr_2O_3}$$

Solution: $10.4 \text{ g Cr} \times \dfrac{1 \text{ mol Cr}}{52.00 \text{ g Cr}} \times \dfrac{2 \text{ mol } Cr_2O_3}{4 \text{ mol Cr}} \times \dfrac{152.00 \text{ g } Cr_2O_3}{1 \text{ mol } Cr_2O_3} = 15.2 \text{ g } Cr_2O_3$

Check: Units of answer, g Cr_2O_3, are correct. The magnitude of the answer is reasonable because it is larger than g Cr.

d) **Given:** 10.4 g Sr **Find:** g SrO

Conceptual Plan: **g Sr → mol Sr → mol SrO → g SrO**

$$\frac{\text{mol Sr}}{87.62 \text{ g Sr}} \qquad \frac{2 \text{ mol SrO}}{2 \text{ mol Sr}} \qquad \frac{103.62 \text{ g SrO}}{\text{mol SrO}}$$

Solution: $10.4 \text{ g Sr} \times \dfrac{1 \text{ mol Sr}}{87.62 \text{ g Sr}} \times \dfrac{2 \text{ mol SrO}}{2 \text{ mol Sr}} \times \dfrac{103.62 \text{ g SrO}}{1 \text{ mol SrO}} = 12.3 \text{ g SrO}$

Check: Units of answer, g SrO, are correct. The magnitude of the answer is reasonable because it is larger than g Sr.

35. a) **Given:** 4.85 g NaOH **Find:** g HCl

Conceptual Plan: g NaOH → mol NaOH → mol HCl → g HCl

$$\frac{\text{mol NaOH}}{40.01 \text{ g NaOH}} \qquad \frac{1 \text{ mol HCl}}{1 \text{ mol NaOH}} \qquad \frac{36.46 \text{ g HCl}}{1 \text{ mol HCl}}$$

Solution: $4.85 \text{ g NaOH} \times \dfrac{1 \text{ mol NaOH}}{40.01 \text{ g NaOH}} \times \dfrac{1 \text{ mol HCl}}{1 \text{ mol NaOH}} \times \dfrac{36.46 \text{ g HCl}}{1 \text{ mol HCl}} = 4\ 42 \text{ g HCl}$

Check: Units of answer, g HCl, are correct. The magnitude of the answer is reasonable since it is less than g NaOH.

b) **Given:** 4.85 g $Ca(OH)_2$ **Find:** g HNO_3

Conceptual Plan: g $Ca(OH)_2$ → mol $Ca(OH)_2$ → mol HNO_3 → g HNO_3

$$\frac{\text{mol } Ca(OH)_2}{74.10 \text{ g } Ca(OH)_2} \qquad \frac{2 \text{ mol } HNO_3}{1 \text{ mol } Ca(OH)_2} \qquad \frac{63.02 \text{ g } HNO_3}{1 \text{ mol } HNO_3}$$

Solution: $4.85 \text{ g } Ca(OH)_2 \times \dfrac{1 \text{ mol } Ca(OH)_2}{74.10 \text{ g } Ca(OH)_2} \times \dfrac{2 \text{ mol } HNO_3}{1 \text{ mol } Ca(OH)_2} \times \dfrac{63.02 \text{ g } HNO_3}{1 \text{ mol } HNO_3} = 8.25 \text{ g } HNO_3$

Check: Units of answer, g HNO_3, are correct. The magnitude of the answer is reasonable since it is more than g $Ca(OH)_2$.

c) **Given:** 4.85 g KOH **Find:** g H_2SO_4

Conceptual Plan: g KOH → mol KOH → mol H_2SO_4 → g H_2SO_4

$$\frac{\text{mol KOH}}{56.11 \text{ g KOH}} \qquad \frac{1 \text{ mol } H_2SO_4}{2 \text{ mol KOH}} \qquad \frac{98.09 \text{ g } H_2SO_4}{1 \text{ mol } H_2SO_4}$$

Solution: $4.85 \text{ g NaOH} \times \dfrac{1 \text{ mol KOH}}{56.11 \text{ g KOH}} \times \dfrac{1 \text{ mol } H_2SO_4}{2 \text{ mol KOH}} \times \dfrac{98.09 \text{ g } H_2SO_4}{1 \text{ mol } H_2SO_4} = 4\ 24 \text{ g } H_2SO_4$

Check: Units of answer, g H_2SO_4, are correct. The magnitude of the answer is reasonable since it is less than g KOH.

36. a) **Given:** 55.8 g $Pb(NO_3)_2$ **Find:** g KI

Conceptual Plan: g $Pb(NO_3)_2$ → mol $Pb(NO_3)_2$ → mol KI → g KI

$$\frac{\text{mol } Pb(NO_3)_2}{331.2 \text{ g } Pb(NO_3)_2} \qquad \frac{2 \text{ mol KI}}{1 \text{ mol } Pb(NO_3)_2} \qquad \frac{166.00 \text{ g KI}}{1 \text{ mol KI}}$$

Solution: $55.8 \text{ g } Pb(NO_3)_2 \times \dfrac{1 \text{ mol } Pb(NO_3)_2}{331.2 \text{ g } Pb(NO_3)_2} \times \dfrac{2 \text{ mol KI}}{1 \text{ mol } Pb(NO_3)_2} \times \dfrac{166.00 \text{ g KI}}{1 \text{ mol KI}} = 55.9 \text{ g KI}$

Check: Units of answer, g KI, are correct. The magnitude of the answer is reasonable since there are 2 mol KI for each $Pb(NO_3)_2$.

b) **Given:** 55.8 g $CuCl_2$ **Find:** g Na_2CO_3
   Conceptual Plan: g $CuCl_2$ → mol $CuCl_2$ → mol Na_2CO_3 → g Na_2CO_3

$$\frac{\text{mol } CuCl_2}{134.45 \text{ g } CuCl_2} \quad\quad \frac{1 \text{ mol } Na_2CO_3}{1 \text{ mol } CuCl_2} \quad\quad \frac{106.01 \text{ g } Na_2CO_3}{1 \text{ mol } Na_2CO_3}$$

   Solution: $55.8 \text{ g } CuCl_2 \times \dfrac{1 \text{ mol } CuCl_2}{134.45 \text{ g } CuCl_2} \times \dfrac{1 \text{ mol } Na_2CO_3}{1 \text{ mol } CuCl_2} \times \dfrac{106.01 \text{ g } Na_2CO_3}{1 \text{ mol } Na_2CO_3} = 44.0 \text{ g } Na_2CO_3$

   Check: Units of answer, g Na_2CO_3, are correct. The magnitude of the answer is reasonable since it is less than g $CuCl_2$.

c) **Given:** 55.8 g $Sr(NO_3)_2$ **Find:** g K_2SO_4
   Conceptual Plan: g $Sr(NO_3)_2$ → mol $Sr(NO_3)_2$ → mol K_2SO_4 → g K_2SO_4

$$\frac{\text{mol } Sr(NO_3)_2}{211.64 \text{ g } Sr(NO_3)_2} \quad \frac{1 \text{ mol } K_2SO_4}{1 \text{ mol } Sr(NO_3)_2} \quad \frac{174.27 \text{ g } K_2SO_4}{1 \text{ mol } K_2SO_4}$$

   Solution:

$$55.8 \text{ g } Sr(NO_3)_2 \times \frac{1 \text{ mol } Sr(NO_3)_2}{211.64 \text{ g } Sr(NO_3)_2} \times \frac{1 \text{ mol } K_2SO_4}{1 \text{ mol } Sr(NO_3)_2} \times \frac{174.27 \text{ g } K_2SO_4}{1 \text{ mol } K_2SO_4} = 45.9 \text{ g } K_2SO_4$$

   Check: Units of answer, g K_2SO_4, are correct. The magnitude of the answer is reasonable since it is less than g $Sr(NO_3)_2$.

37. a) **Given:** 2 mol Na; 2 mol Br_2 **Find:** Limiting Reactant
   Conceptual Plan: mol Na → mol NaBr

$$\frac{2 \text{ mol NaBr}}{2 \text{ mol Na}}$$

   → **smallest mol amount determines limiting reactant**

   mol Br_2 → mol NaBr

$$\frac{2 \text{ mol NaBr}}{1 \text{ mol } Br_2}$$

$$2 \text{ mol Na} \times \frac{2 \text{ mol NaBr}}{2 \text{ mol Na}} = 2 \text{ mol NaBr}$$

   Solution: $2 \text{ mol } Br_2 \times \dfrac{2 \text{ mol NaBr}}{1 \text{ mol } Br_2} = 4 \text{ mol NaBr}$

    Na is Limiting Reactant

   Check: Answer is reasonable since Na produced smallest amount of product.

b) **Given:** 1.8 mol Na; 1.4 mol Br_2 **Find:** Limiting Reactant
   Conceptual Plan: mol Na → mol NaBr

$$\frac{2 \text{ mol NaBr}}{2 \text{ mol Na}}$$

   → **smallest mol amount determines limiting reactant**

   mol Br_2 → mol NaBr

$$\frac{2 \text{ mol NaBr}}{1 \text{ mol } Br_2}$$

$$1.8 \text{ mol Na} \times \frac{2 \text{ mol NaBr}}{2 \text{ mol Na}} = 1.8 \text{ mol NaBr}$$

   Solution: $1.4 \text{ mol } Br_2 \times \dfrac{2 \text{ mol NaBr}}{1 \text{ mol } Br_2} = 2.8 \text{ mol NaBr}$

    Na is Limiting Reactant

   Check: Answer is reasonable since Na produced smallest amount of product.

c) **Given:** 2.5 mol Na; 1 mol Br_2 **Find:** Limiting Reactant

Conceptual Plan: mol Na → mol NaBr

$$\frac{2 \text{ mol NaBr}}{2 \text{ mol Na}}$$

→ **smallest mol amount determines limiting reactant**

mol Br$_2$ → mol NaBr

$$\frac{2 \text{ mol NaBr}}{1 \text{ mol Br}_2}$$

$$2.5 \ \cancel{\text{mol Na}} \ \times \ \frac{2 \text{ mol NaBr}}{2 \ \cancel{\text{mol Na}}} = 2.5 \text{ mol NaBr}$$

Solution: $1 \ \cancel{\text{mol Br}_2} \ \times \ \dfrac{2 \text{ mol NaBr}}{1 \ \cancel{\text{mol Br}_2}} = 2 \text{ mol NaBr}$

Br$_2$ is Limiting Reactant

Check: Answer is reasonable since Br$_2$ produced smallest amount of product.

d) **Given:** 12.6 mol Na; 6.9 mol Br$_2$ **Find:** Limiting Reactant

Conceptual Plan: mol Na → mol NaBr

$$\frac{2 \text{ mol NaBr}}{2 \text{ mol Na}}$$

→ **smallest mol amount determines limiting reactant**

mol Br$_2$ → mol NaBr

$$\frac{2 \text{ mol NaBr}}{1 \text{ mol Br}_2}$$

$$12.6 \ \cancel{\text{mol Na}} \ \times \ \frac{2 \text{ mol NaBr}}{2 \ \cancel{\text{mol Na}}} = 12.6 \text{ mol NaBr}$$

Solution: $6.9 \ \cancel{\text{mol Br}_2} \ \times \ \dfrac{2 \text{ mol NaBr}}{1 \ \cancel{\text{mol Br}_2}} = 13.8 \text{ mol NaBr}$

Na is Limiting Reactant

Check: Answer is reasonable since Na produced smallest amount of product.

38. a) **Given:** 1 mol Al; 1 mol O$_2$ **Find:** Limiting Reactant

Conceptual Plan: mol Al → mol Al$_2$O$_3$

$$\frac{2 \text{ mol Al}_2\text{O}_3}{4 \text{ mol Al}}$$

→ **smallest mol amount determines limiting reactant**

mol O$_2$ → mol Al$_2$O$_3$

$$\frac{2 \text{ mol Al}_2\text{O}_3}{3 \text{ mol O}_2}$$

$$1 \ \cancel{\text{mol Al}} \ \times \ \frac{2 \text{ mol Al}_2\text{O}_3}{4 \ \cancel{\text{mol Al}}} = 0.5 \text{ mol Al}_2\text{O}_3$$

Solution: $1 \ \cancel{\text{mol O}_2} \ \times \ \dfrac{2 \text{ mol Al}_2\text{O}_3}{3 \ \cancel{\text{mol O}_2}} = 0.67 \text{ mol Al}_2\text{O}_3$

Al is Limiting Reactant

Check: Answer is reasonable since Al produced smallest amount of product.

b) **Given:** 4 mol Al; 2.6 mol O$_2$ **Find:** Limiting Reactant

Conceptual Plan: mol Al → mol Al$_2$O$_3$

$$\frac{2 \text{ mol Al}_2\text{O}_3}{4 \text{ mol Al}}$$

→ **smallest mol amount determines limiting reactant**

mol O$_2$ → mol Al$_2$O$_3$

$$\frac{2 \text{ mol Al}_2\text{O}_3}{3 \text{ mol O}_2}$$

$$4 \ \cancel{\text{mol Al}} \times \frac{2 \ \text{mol Al}_2\text{O}_3}{4 \ \cancel{\text{mol Al}}} = 2 \ \text{mol Al}_2\text{O}_3$$

Solution: $2.6 \ \cancel{\text{mol O}_2} \times \dfrac{2 \ \text{mol Al}_2\text{O}_3}{3 \ \cancel{\text{mol O}_2}} = 1.7 \ \text{mol Al}_2\text{O}_3$

O_2 is Limiting Reactant

Check: Answer is reasonable since O_2 produced smallest amount of product.

c) **Given:** 16 mol Al; 13 mol O_2 **Find:** Limiting Reactant
Conceptual Plan: mol Al → mol Al$_2$O$_3$

$$\frac{2 \ \text{mol Al}_2\text{O}_3}{4 \ \text{mol Al}}$$
→ smallest mol amount determines limiting reactant

mol O$_2$ → mol Al$_2$O$_3$

$$\frac{2 \ \text{mol Al}_2\text{O}_3}{3 \ \text{mol O}_2}$$

$$16 \ \cancel{\text{mol Al}} \times \frac{2 \ \text{mol Al}_2\text{O}_3}{4 \ \cancel{\text{mol Al}}} = 8.0 \ \text{mol Al}_2\text{O}_3$$

Solution: $13 \ \cancel{\text{mol O}_2} \times \dfrac{2 \ \text{mol Al}_2\text{O}_3}{3 \ \cancel{\text{mol O}_2}} = 8.67 \ \text{mol Al}_2\text{O}_3$

Al is Limiting Reactant

Check: Answer is reasonable since Al produced smallest amount of product.

d) **Given:** 7.4 mol Al; 6.5 mol O_2 **Find:** Limiting Reactant
Conceptual Plan: mol Al → mol Al$_2$O$_3$

$$\frac{2 \ \text{mol Al}_2\text{O}_3}{4 \ \text{mol Al}}$$
→ smallest mol amount determines limiting reactant

mol O$_2$ → mol Al$_2$O$_3$

$$\frac{2 \ \text{mol Al}_2\text{O}_3}{3 \ \text{mol O}_2}$$

$$7.4 \ \cancel{\text{mol Al}} \times \frac{2 \ \text{mol Al}_2\text{O}_3}{4 \ \cancel{\text{mol Al}}} = 3.7 \ \text{mol Al}_2\text{O}_3$$

Solution: $6.5 \ \cancel{\text{mol O}_2} \times \dfrac{2 \ \text{mol Al}_2\text{O}_3}{3 \ \cancel{\text{mol O}_2}} = 4.3 \ \text{mol Al}_2\text{O}_3$

Al is Limiting Reactant

Check: Answer is reasonable since Al produced smallest amount of product.

39. The greatest number of Cl_2 molecules will be formed from reaction mixture b and would be 3 molecules Cl_2.

a) **Given:** 7 molecules HCl, 1 molecule O_2 **Find:** Theoretical yield Cl_2
Conceptual Plan: molecule HCl → molecules Cl$_2$

$$\frac{2 \ \text{molecule Cl}_2}{4 \ \text{molecule HCl}}$$
→ smallest molecule amount determines limiting reactant

molecules O$_2$ → molecules Cl$_2$

$$\frac{2 \ \text{molecules Cl}_2}{1 \ \text{molecules O}_2}$$

Solution:

$$7 \ \cancel{\text{molecules HCl}} \times \frac{2 \ \text{molecules Cl}_2}{4 \ \cancel{\text{molecules HCl}}} = 3 \ \text{molecules Cl}_2$$

$$1 \ \cancel{\text{molecules O}_2} \times \frac{2 \ \text{molecules Cl}_2}{1 \ \cancel{\text{molecules O}_2}} = 2 \ \text{molecules Cl}_2$$

Theoretical Yield = 2 molecules Cl_2

b) **Given:** 6 molecules HCl, molecule O_2 **Find:** Theoretical yield Cl_2
   Conceptual Plan: molecule HCl → molecules Cl_2

$$\frac{2 \text{ molecule } Cl_2}{4 \text{ molecule HCl}} \rightarrow \text{ smallest molecule amount determines limiting reactant}$$

   molecules O_2 → molecules Cl_2

$$\frac{2 \text{ molecules } Cl_2}{1 \text{ molecules } O_2}$$

   Solution:

$$6 \text{ molecules HCl} \times \frac{2 \text{ molecules } Cl_2}{4 \text{ molecules HCl}} = 3 \text{ molecules } Cl_2$$

$$3 \text{ molecules } O_2 \times \frac{2 \text{ molecules } Cl_2}{1 \text{ molecules } O_2} = 6 \text{ molecules } Cl_2$$

   Theoretical Yield = 3 molecules Cl_2

c) **Given:** 4 molecules HCl, 5 molecule O_2 **Find:** Theoretical yield Cl_2
   Conceptual Plan: molecule HCl → molecules Cl_2

$$\frac{2 \text{ molecule } Cl_2}{4 \text{ molecule HCl}} \rightarrow \text{ smallest molecule amount determines limiting reactant}$$

   molecules O_2 → molecules Cl_2

$$\frac{2 \text{ molecules } Cl_2}{1 \text{ molecules } O_2}$$

   Solution:

$$4 \text{ molecules HCl} \times \frac{2 \text{ molecules } Cl_2}{4 \text{ molecules HCl}} = 2 \text{ molecules } Cl_2$$

$$5 \text{ molecules } O_2 \times \frac{2 \text{ molecules } Cl_2}{1 \text{ molecules } O_2} = 10 \text{ molecules } Cl_2$$

   Theoretical Yield = 2 molecules Cl_2
   Check: The units of the answer, molecules Cl_2, is correct. The answer is reasonable based on the limiting reactant in each mixture.

40. The greatest number of CO_2 molecules will be formed from reaction mixture a and would be 2 molecules CO_2.

   a) **Given:** 3 molecules CH_3OH, 3 molecule O_2 **Find:** Theoretical yield CO_2
      Conceptual Plan: molecule CH_3OH → molecules CO_2

$$\frac{2 \text{ molecule } CO_2}{2 \text{ molecule } CH_3OH} \rightarrow \text{ smallest molecule amount determines limiting reactant}$$

      molecules O_2 → molecules CO_2

$$\frac{2 \text{ molecules } CO_2}{3 \text{ molecules } O_2}$$

   Solution:

$$3 \text{ molecules } CH_3OH \times \frac{2 \text{ molecules } CO_2}{2 \text{ molecules } CH_3OH} = 3 \text{ molecules } CO_2$$

$$3 \text{ molecules } O_2 \times \frac{2 \text{ molecules } CO_2}{3 \text{ molecules } O_2} = 2 \text{ molecules } CO_2$$

   Theoretical Yield = 2 molecules CO_2

   b) **Given:** 1 molecules CH_3OH, 6 molecule O_2 **Find:** Theoretical yield CO_2

Conceptual Plan: molecule CH_3OH → molecules CO_2

$$\frac{2 \text{ molecule } CO_2}{2 \text{ molecule } CH_3OH}$$ → smallest molecule amount determines limiting reactant

molecules O_2 → molecules CO_2

$$\frac{2 \text{ molecules } CO_2}{3 \text{ molecules } O_2}$$

Solution:

$$1 \text{ molecules } CH_3OH \times \frac{2 \text{ molecules } CO_2}{2 \text{ molecules } CH_3OH} = 1 \text{ molecules } CO_2$$

$$6 \text{ molecules } O_2 \times \frac{2 \text{ molecules } CO_2}{3 \text{ molecules } O_2} = 4 \text{ molecules } CO_2$$

Theoretical Yield = 1 molecules CO_2

c) **Given:** 4 molecules CH_3OH, 2 molecule O_2 **Find:** Theoretical yield CO_2

Conceptual Plan: molecule CH_3OH → molecules CO_2

$$\frac{2 \text{ molecule } CO_2}{2 \text{ molecule } CH_3OH}$$ → smallest mol amount determines limiting reactant

molecules O_2 → molecules CO_2

$$\frac{2 \text{ molecules } CO_2}{3 \text{ molecules } O_2}$$

Solution:

$$4 \text{ molecules } CH_3OH \times \frac{2 \text{ molecules } CO_2}{2 \text{ molecules } CH_3OH} = 4 \text{ molecules } CO_2$$

$$2 \text{ molecules } O_2 \times \frac{2 \text{ molecules } CO_2}{3 \text{ molecules } O_2} = 1 \text{ molecules } CO_2$$

Theoretical Yield = 1 molecules CO_2

Check: The units of the answer, molecules CO_2, is correct. The answer is reasonable based on the limiting reactant in each mixture.

41. a) **Given:** 4 mol Ti, 4 mol Cl_2 **Find:** Theoretical yield $TiCl_4$

Conceptual Plan: mol Ti → mol $TiCl_4$

$$\frac{1 \text{ mol } TiCl_4}{1 \text{ mol Ti}}$$ → smallest mol amount determines limiting reactant

mol Cl_2 → mol $TiCl_4$

$$\frac{1 \text{ mol } TiCl_4}{2 \text{ mol } Cl_2}$$

$$4 \text{ mol Ti} \times \frac{1 \text{ mol } TiCl_4}{1 \text{ mol Ti}} = 4 \text{ mol } TiCl_4$$

Solution:

$$4 \text{ mol } Cl_2 \times \frac{1 \text{ mol } TiCl_4}{2 \text{ mol } Cl_2} = 2 \text{ mol } TiCl_4$$

Theoretical Yield = 2 mol $TiCl_4$

Check: Units of the answer, mol $TiCl_4$, are correct. Answer is reasonable since Cl_2 produced smallest amount of product and is the limiting reactant.

b) **Given:** 7 mol Ti, 17 mol Cl_2 **Find:** Theoretical yield $TiCl_4$

Conceptual Plan: mol Ti → mol $TiCl_4$

$$\frac{1 \text{ mol } TiCl_4}{1 \text{ mol Ti}}$$ → smallest mol amount determines limiting reactant

mol Cl_2 → mol $TiCl_4$

$$\frac{1 \text{ mol } TiCl_4}{2 \text{ mol } Cl_2}$$

$$7 \; \cancel{\text{mol Ti}} \times \frac{1 \; \text{mol TiCl}_4}{1 \; \cancel{\text{mol Ti}}} = 7 \; \text{mol TiCl}_4$$

Solution:
$$17 \; \cancel{\text{mol Cl}_2} \times \frac{1 \; \text{mol TiCl}_4}{2 \; \cancel{\text{mol Cl}_2}} = 8.5 \; \text{mol TiCl}_4$$

Theoretical Yield = 7 mol $TiCl_4$

Check: Units of the answer, mol $TiCl_4$, are correct. Answer is reasonable since Ti produced smallest amount of product and is the limiting reactant.

c) **Given:** 12.4 mol Ti, 18.8 mol Cl_2 **Find:** Theoretical yield $TiCl_4$
    Conceptual Plan: mol Ti → mol TiCl$_4$

$$\frac{1 \; \text{mol TiCl}_4}{1 \; \text{mol Ti}}$$

→ **smallest mol amount determines limiting reactant**

          mol Cl$_2$ → mol TiCl$_4$

$$\frac{1 \; \text{mol TiCl}_4}{2 \; \text{mol Cl}_2}$$

$$12.4 \; \cancel{\text{mol Ti}} \times \frac{1 \; \text{mol TiCl}_4}{1 \; \cancel{\text{mol Ti}}} = 12.4 \; \text{mol TiCl}_4$$

Solution:
$$18.8 \; \cancel{\text{mol Cl}_2} \times \frac{1 \; \text{mol TiCl}_4}{2 \; \cancel{\text{mol Cl}_2}} = 9.4 \; \text{mol TiCl}_4$$

Theoretical Yield = 9.4 mol $TiCl_4$

Check: Units of the answer, mol $TiCl_4$, are correct. Answer is reasonable since Cl_2 produced smallest amount of product and is the limiting reactant.

42. a) **Given:** 3 mol Mn, 3 mol O_2 **Find:** Theoretical yield MnO_2
    Conceptual Plan: mol Mn → mol MnO$_2$

$$\frac{2 \; \text{mol MnO}_2}{2 \; \text{mol Mn}}$$

→ **smallest mol amount determines limiting reactant**

          mol O$_2$ → mol MnO$_2$

$$\frac{2 \; \text{mol MnO}_2}{2 \; \text{mol O}_2}$$

$$3 \; \cancel{\text{mol Mn}} \times \frac{1 \; \text{mol MnO}_2}{1 \; \cancel{\text{mol Mn}}} = 3 \; \text{mol MnO}_2$$

Solution:
$$3 \; \cancel{\text{mol O}_2} \times \frac{1 \; \text{mol MnO}_2}{1 \; \cancel{\text{mol O}_2}} = 3 \; \text{mol MnO}_2$$

Theoretical Yield = 3 mol MnO_2

Check: Units of the answer, mol MnO_2, are correct. Answer is reasonable since equal mol are produced for both reactants

b) **Given:** 4 mol Mn, 7 mol O_2 **Find:** Theoretical yield MnO_2
    Conceptual Plan: mol Mn → mol MnO$_3$

$$\frac{2 \; \text{mol MnO}_2}{2 \; \text{mol Mn}}$$

→ **smallest mol amount determines limiting reactant**

          mol O$_2$ → mol MnO$_3$

$$\frac{2 \; \text{mol MnO}_2}{2 \; \text{mol O}_2}$$

$$4 \; \cancel{\text{mol Mn}} \times \frac{2 \; \text{mol MnO}_2}{2 \; \cancel{\text{mol Mn}}} = 4 \; \text{mol MnO}_2$$

Solution:
$$7 \; \cancel{\text{mol O}_2} \times \frac{2 \; \text{mol MnO}_2}{2 \; \cancel{\text{mol O}_2}} = 7 \; \text{mol MnO}_2$$

Theoretical Yield = 4 mol MnO_2

Check: Units of the answer, mol MnO_2, are correct. Answer is reasonable since Mn produced smallest amount of product and is the limiting reactant.

c) **Given:** 27.5 mol Mn, 43.8 mol O_2 **Find:** Theoretical yield MnO_2
    Conceptual Plan: mol Mn → mol MnO_3

$$\frac{2\ \text{mol } MnO_2}{2\ \text{mol Mn}}$$

→ **smallest mol amount determines limiting reactant**

mol O_2 → mol MnO_3

$$\frac{2\ \text{mol } MnO_2}{2\ \text{mol } O_2}$$

$$27.5\ \text{mol Mn} \times \frac{2\ \text{mol } MnO_2}{2\ \text{mol Mn}} = 27.5\ \text{mol } MnO_2$$

Solution:

$$43.8\ \text{mol } O_2 \times \frac{2\ \text{mol } MnO_2}{2\ \text{mol } O_2} = 43.8\ \text{mol } MnO_2$$

Theoretical Yield = 27.5 mol MnO_2

Check: Units of the answer, mol MnO_2, are correct. Answer is reasonable since Mn produced smallest amount of product and is the limiting reactant.

43. a) **Given:** 2.0 g Al, 2.0 g Cl_2 **Find:** Theoretical yield in g $AlCl_3$
    Conceptual Plan: g Al → mol Al → mol $AlCl_3$

$$\frac{1\ \text{mol Al}}{26.98\ \text{g Al}} \qquad \frac{2\ \text{mol } AlCl_3}{2\ \text{mol Al}}$$

→ **smallest mol amount determines limiting reactant**

g Cl_2 → mol Cl_2 → mol $AlCl_3$

$$\frac{1\ \text{mol } Cl_2}{70.91\ \text{g } Cl_2} \qquad \frac{2\ \text{mol } AlCl_3}{3\ \text{mol } Cl_2}$$

then: mol $AlCl_3$ → g $AlCl_3$

$$\frac{133.34\ \text{g } AlCl_3}{\text{mol } AlCl_3}$$

Solution:

$$2.0\ \text{g Al} \times \frac{1\ \text{mol Al}}{26.98\ \text{g Al}} \times \frac{2\ \text{mol } AlCl_3}{2\ \text{mol Al}} = 0.074\ \text{mol } AlCl_3$$

$$2.0\ \text{g } Cl_2 \times \frac{1\ \text{mol } Cl_2}{70.90\ \text{g } Cl_2} \times \frac{2\ \text{mol } AlCl_3}{3\ \text{mol } Cl_2} = 0.0188\ \text{mol } AlCl_3$$

$$0.0188\ \text{mol } AlCl_3 \times \frac{133.34\ \text{g } AlCl_3}{\text{mol } AlCl_3} = 2.5\ \text{g } AlCl_3$$

Check: Units of the answer, g $AlCl_3$, are correct. Answer is reasonable since Cl_2 produced smallest amount of product and is the limiting reactant.

b) **Given:** 7.5 g Al, 24.8 g Cl_2 **Find:** Theoretical yield in g $AlCl_3$
    Conceptual Plan: g Al → mol Al → mol $AlCl_3$

$$\frac{1\ \text{mol Al}}{26.98\ \text{g Al}} \qquad \frac{2\ \text{mol } AlCl_3}{2\ \text{mol Al}}$$

→ **smallest mol amount determines limiting reactant**

g Cl_2 → mol Cl_2 → mol $AlCl_3$

$$\frac{1\ \text{mol } Cl_2}{70.91\ \text{g } Cl_2} \qquad \frac{2\ \text{mol } AlCl_3}{3\ \text{mol } Cl_2}$$

then: mol $AlCl_3$ → g $AlCl_3$

$$\frac{133.34\ \text{g } AlCl_3}{\text{mol } AlCl_3}$$

Solution:

$$7.5\ \text{g Al} \times \frac{1\ \text{mol Al}}{26.98\ \text{g Al}} \times \frac{2\ \text{mol } AlCl_3}{2\ \text{mol Al}} = 0.2780\ \text{mol } AlCl_3$$

$$24.8\ \text{g } Cl_2 \times \frac{1\ \text{mol } Cl_2}{70.90\ \text{g } Cl_2} \times \frac{2\ \text{mol } AlCl_3}{3\ \text{mol } Cl_2} = 0.2332\ \text{mol } AlCl_3$$

$$0.23\underline{3}2 \text{ mol AlCl}_3 \text{ x } \frac{133.34 \text{ g AlCl}_3}{\text{mol AlCl}_3} = 31.1 \text{ g AlCl}_3$$

Check: Units of the answer, g $AlCl_3$, are correct. Answer is reasonable since Cl_2 produced smallest amount of product and is the limiting reactant.

c) **Given:** 0.235 g Al, 1.15 g Cl_2 **Find:** Theoretical yield in g $AlCl_3$
Conceptual Plan: g Al → mol Al → mol AlCl₃

$$\frac{1 \text{ mol Al}}{26.98 \text{ g Al}} \qquad \frac{2 \text{ mol AlCl}_3}{2 \text{ mol Al}} \rightarrow \textbf{smallest mol amount determines limiting reactant}$$

g Cl₂ → mol Cl₂ → mol AlCl₃

$$\frac{1 \text{ mol Cl}_2}{70.91 \text{ g Cl}_2} \qquad \frac{2 \text{ mol AlCl}_3}{3 \text{ mol Cl}_2}$$

then: mol AlCl₃ → g AlCl₃

$$\frac{133.34 \text{ g AlCl}_3}{\text{mol AlCl}_3}$$

Solution:

$$0.235 \text{ g Al x } \frac{1 \text{ mol Al}}{26.98 \text{ g Al}} \text{ x } \frac{2 \text{ mol AlCl}_3}{2 \text{ mol Al}} = 0.00871\underline{0} \text{ mol AlCl}_3$$

$$1.15 \text{ g Cl}_2 \text{ x } \frac{1 \text{ mol Cl}_2}{70.90 \text{ g Cl}_2} \text{ x } \frac{2 \text{ mol AlCl}_3}{3 \text{ mol Cl}_2} = 0.01081 \text{ mol AlCl}_3$$

$$0.00871\underline{0} \text{ mol AlCl}_3 \text{ x } \frac{133.34 \text{ g AlCl}_3}{\text{mol AlCl}_3} = 1.16 \text{ g AlCl}_3$$

Check: Units of the answer, g $AlCl_3$, are correct. Answer is reasonable since Al produced smallest amount of product and is the limiting reactant.

44. a) **Given:** 5.0 g Ti, 5.0 g F_2 **Find:** Theoretical yield in g TiF_4
Conceptual Plan: g Ti → mol Ti → mol TiF₄

$$\frac{1 \text{ mol Ti}}{47.87 \text{ g Ti}} \qquad \frac{1 \text{ mol TiF}_4}{1 \text{ mol Ti}} \rightarrow \textbf{smallest mol amount determines limiting reactant}$$

g F₂ → mol F₂ → mol TiF₄

$$\frac{1 \text{ mol F}_2}{38.00 \text{ g F}_2} \qquad \frac{1 \text{ mol TiF}_4}{2 \text{ mol F}_2}$$

then: mol TiF₄ → g TiF₄

$$\frac{123.87 \text{ g TiF}_4}{\text{mol TiF}_4}$$

Solution:

$$5.0 \text{ g Ti x } \frac{1 \text{ mol Ti}}{47.87 \text{ g Ti}} \text{ x } \frac{1 \text{ mol TiF}_4}{1 \text{ mol Ti}} = 0.10\underline{4} \text{ mol TiF}_4$$

$$5.0 \text{ g F}_2 \text{ x } \frac{1 \text{ mol F}_2}{38.00 \text{ g F}_2} \text{ x } \frac{1 \text{ mol TiF}_4}{2 \text{ mol F}_2} = 0.132 \text{ mol TiF}_4$$

$$0.10\underline{4} \text{ mol TiF}_4 \text{ x } \frac{123.87 \text{ g TiF}_4}{\text{mol TiF}_4} = 13 \text{ g TiF}_4$$

Check: Units of the answer, g TiF_4, are correct. Answer is reasonable since F_2 produced smallest amount of product and is the limiting reactant.

b) **Given:** 2.4 g Ti, 1.6 g F_2 **Find:** Theoretical yield in g TiF_4

Conceptual Plan: g Ti → mol Ti → mol TiF$_4$

$$\frac{1 \text{ mol Ti}}{47.87 \text{ g Ti}} \qquad \frac{1 \text{ mol TiF}_4}{1 \text{ mol Ti}} \qquad \rightarrow \textbf{smallest mol amount determines limiting reactant}$$

g F$_2$ → mol F$_2$ → mol TiF$_4$

$$\frac{1 \text{ mol F}_2}{38.00 \text{ g F}_2} \qquad \frac{1 \text{ mol TiF}_4}{2 \text{ mol F}_2}$$

then: mol TiF$_4$ → g TiF$_4$

$$\frac{123.87 \text{ g TiF}_4}{\text{mol TiF}_4}$$

Solution:

$$2.4 \text{ g Ti} \times \frac{1 \text{ mol Ti}}{47.87 \text{ g Ti}} \times \frac{1 \text{ mol TiF}_4}{1 \text{ mol Ti}} = 0.0501 \text{ mol TiF}_4$$

$$1.6 \text{ g F}_2 \times \frac{1 \text{ mol F}_2}{38.00 \text{ g F}_2} \times \frac{1 \text{ mol TiF}_4}{2 \text{ mol F}_2} = 0.0210 \text{ mol TiF}_4$$

$$0.0210 \text{ mol TiF}_4 \times \frac{123.87 \text{ g TiF}_4}{\text{mol TiF}_4} = 2.6 \text{ g TiF}_4$$

Check: Units of the answer, g TiF$_4$, are correct. Answer is reasonable since F$_2$ produced smallest amount of product and is the limiting reactant.

c) **Given:** 0.233 g Ti, 0.288 g F$_2$ **Find:** Theoretical yield in g TiF$_4$

Conceptual Plan: g Ti → mol Ti → mol TiF$_4$

$$\frac{1 \text{ mol Ti}}{47.87 \text{ g Ti}} \qquad \frac{1 \text{ mol TiF}_4}{1 \text{ mol Ti}} \qquad \rightarrow \textbf{smallest mol amount determines limiting reactant}$$

g F$_2$ → mol F$_2$ → mol TiF$_4$

$$\frac{1 \text{ mol F}_2}{38.00 \text{ g F}_2} \qquad \frac{1 \text{ mol TiF}_4}{2 \text{ mol F}_2}$$

then: mol TiF$_4$ → g TiF$_4$

$$\frac{123.87 \text{ g TiF}_4}{\text{mol TiF}_4}$$

Solution:

$$0.233 \text{ g Ti} \times \frac{1 \text{ mol Ti}}{47.87 \text{ g Ti}} \times \frac{1 \text{ mol TiF}_4}{1 \text{ mol Ti}} = 0.004867 \text{ mol TiF}_4$$

$$0.288 \text{ g F}_2 \times \frac{1 \text{ mol F}_2}{38.00 \text{ g F}_2} \times \frac{1 \text{ mol TiF}_4}{2 \text{ mol F}_2} = 0.003789 \text{ mol TiF}_4$$

$$0.003789 \text{ mol TiF}_4 \times \frac{123.87 \text{ g TiF}_4}{\text{mol TiF}_4} = 0.469 \text{ g TiF}_4$$

Check: Units of the answer, g TiF$_4$, are correct. Answer is reasonable since F$_2$ produced smallest amount of product and is the limiting reactant.

45. **Given:** 28.5 g KCl; 25.7 g Pb^{2+}; 29.4 g PbCl$_2$ **Find:** limiting reactant, theoretical yield PbCl$_2$, % yield

Conceptual Plan: g KCl → mol KCl → mol $PbCl_2$

$$\frac{1 \text{ mol KCl}}{74.55 \text{ g KCl}} \qquad \frac{1 \text{ mol } PbCl_2}{2 \text{ mol KCl}} \qquad → \text{ smallest mol amount determines limiting}$$

reactant

g Pb^{2+} → mol Pb^{2+} → mol $PbCl_2$

$$\frac{1 \text{ mol } Pb^{2+}}{207.2 \text{ g } Pb^{2+}} \qquad \frac{1 \text{ mol } PbCl_2}{1 \text{ mol } Pb^{2+}}$$

then: mol $PbCl_2$ → g $PbCl_2$ then: determine % yield

$$\frac{278.1 \text{ g } PbCl_2}{\text{mol } PbCl_2} \qquad\qquad \frac{\text{actual yield g } PbCl_2}{\text{theoretical yield g } PbCl_2} \text{ x } 100$$

Solution:

$$28.5 \text{ g KCl x } \frac{1 \text{ mol KCl}}{74.55 \text{ g KCl}} \text{ x } \frac{1 \text{ mol } PbCl_2}{2 \text{ mol KCl}} = 0.1911 \text{ mol } PbCl_2$$

$$25.7 \text{ g } Pb^{2+} \text{ x } \frac{1 \text{ mol } Pb^{2+}}{207.2 \text{ g } Pb^{2+}} \text{ x } \frac{1 \text{ mol } PbCl_2}{1 \text{ mol } Pb^{2+}} = 0.1240 \text{ mol } PbCl_2$$

$$0.1240 \text{ mol } PbCl_2 \text{ x } \frac{278.1 \text{ g } PbCl_2}{1 \text{ mol } PbCl_2} = 34.5 \text{ g } PbCl_2$$

$$\frac{34.5 \text{ g } PbCl_2}{53.14 \text{ g } PbCl_2} \text{ x } 100 = 85.3\%$$

Check: The theoretical yield has the correct units, g $PbCl_2$, and has a reasonable magnitude compared to the mass of KCl, the limiting reactant. The % yield is reasonable, under 100%.

46. **Given:** 10.1 g Mg; 10.5 g O_2; 11.9 g MgO   **Find:** limiting reactant, theoretical yield $PbCl_2$, % yield
    Conceptual Plan: g Mg → mol Mg → mol MgO

$$\frac{1 \text{ mol Mg}}{24.30 \text{ g Mg}} \qquad \frac{2 \text{ mol MgO}}{2 \text{ mol Mg}} \qquad → \text{ smallest mol amount determines limiting reactant}$$

g O_2 → mol O_2 → mol MgO

$$\frac{1 \text{ mol } O_2}{32.00 \text{ g } O_2} \qquad \frac{2 \text{ mol MgO}}{1 \text{ mol } O_2}$$

then: mol MgO → g MgO   then: determine % yield

$$\frac{40.30 \text{ g MgO}}{1 \text{ mol MgO}} \qquad\qquad \frac{\text{actual yield g MgO}}{\text{theoretical yield g MgO}} \text{ x } 100$$

Solution:

$$10.1 \text{ g Mg x } \frac{1 \text{ mol Mg}}{24.30 \text{ g Mg}} \text{ x } \frac{2 \text{ mol MgO}}{2 \text{ mol Mg}} = 0.4156 \text{ mol MgO}$$

$$10.5 \text{ g } O_2 \text{ x } \frac{1 \text{ mol } O_2}{32.00 \text{ g } O_2} \text{ x } \frac{2 \text{ mol MgO}}{1 \text{ mol } O_2} = 0.6562 \text{ mol MgO}$$

$$0.4156 \text{ mol MgO x } \frac{40.30 \text{ g MgO}}{1 \text{ mol MgO}} = 16.75 \text{ g MgO}$$

$$\frac{11.9 \text{ g MgO}}{16.75 \text{ g MgO}} \text{ x } 100 = 71.0\%$$

Check: The theoretical yield has the correct units, g MgO, and has a reasonable magnitude compared to the mass of Mg, the limiting reactant. The % yield is reasonable, under 100%.

47. **Given:** 136.4 kg NH_3; 211.4 kg CO_2; 168.4 kg CH_4N_2O **Find:** limiting reactant, theoretical yield CH_4N_2O, % yield

Conceptual Plan: kg NH$_3$ → g NH$_3$ → mol NH$_3$ → mol CH$_4$N$_2$O

$$\frac{1000 \text{ g}}{1 \text{ kg}} \qquad \frac{1 \text{ mol NH}_3}{17.03 \text{ g NH}_3} \qquad \frac{1 \text{ mol CH}_4\text{N}_2\text{O}}{2 \text{ mol NH}_3} \quad \rightarrow \textbf{ smallest amount determines limiting reactant}$$

kg CO$_2$ → g CO$_2$ → mol CO$_2$ → mol CH$_4$N$_2$O

$$\frac{1000 \text{ g}}{1 \text{ kg}} \qquad \frac{1 \text{ mol CO}_2}{44.01 \text{ g CO}_2} \qquad \frac{1 \text{ mol CH}_4\text{N}_2\text{O}}{1 \text{ mol CO}_2}$$

then: mol CH$_4$N$_2$O → g CH$_4$N$_2$O → kg CH$_4$N$_2$O   **then: determine % yield**

$$\frac{60.06 \text{ g CH}_4\text{N}_2\text{O}}{1 \text{ mol CH}_4\text{N}_2\text{O}} \qquad \frac{1 \text{ kg}}{1000 \text{ g}} \qquad\qquad \frac{\text{actual yield kg CH}_4\text{N}_2\text{O}}{\text{theoretical yield kg CH}_4\text{N}_2\text{O}} \times 100$$

Solution:

$$136.4 \text{ kg NH}_3 \times \frac{1000 \text{ g}}{\text{kg}} \times \frac{1 \text{ mol NH}_3}{17.03 \text{ g NH}_3} \times \frac{1 \text{ mol CH}_4\text{N}_2\text{O}}{2 \text{ mol NH}_3} = 4004.7 \text{ mol CH}_4\text{N}_2\text{O}$$

$$211.4 \text{ g CO}_2 \times \frac{1000 \text{ g}}{\text{kg}} \times \frac{1 \text{ mol CO}_2}{44.01 \text{ g CO}_2} \times \frac{1 \text{ mol CH}_4\text{N}_2\text{O}}{1 \text{ mol CO}_2} = 4803.2 \text{ mol CH}_4\text{N}_2\text{O}$$

$$4004.7 \text{ mol CH}_4\text{N}_2\text{O} \times \frac{60.06 \text{ g CH}_4\text{N}_2\text{O}}{1 \text{ mol CH}_4\text{N}_2\text{O}} \times \frac{\text{kg}}{1000 \text{ g}} = 240.52 \text{ kg CH}_4\text{N}_2\text{O}$$

$$\frac{168.4 \text{ kg CH}_4\text{N}_2\text{O}}{240.52 \text{ kg CH}_4\text{N}_2\text{O}} \times 100 = 70.01\%$$

Check: The theoretical yield has the correct units, kg CH$_4$N$_2$O, and has a reasonable magnitude compared to the mass of NH$_3$, the limiting reactant. The % yield is reasonable, under 100%.

48. **Given:** 155.8 kg SiO$_2$; 78.3 kg C; 66.1 kg Si   **Find:** limiting reactant, theoretical yield Si, % yield

Conceptual Plan: write and balance the reaction, then

kg SiO$_2$ → g SiO$_2$ → mol SiO$_2$ → mol Si

$$\frac{1000 \text{ g}}{1 \text{ kg}} \qquad \frac{1 \text{ mol SiO}_2}{60.085 \text{ g SiO}_2} \qquad \frac{1 \text{ mol Si}}{2 \text{ mol SiO}_2} \quad \rightarrow \textbf{ smallest amount determines limiting reactant}$$

kg C → g C → mol C → mol Si

$$\frac{1000 \text{ g}}{1 \text{ kg}} \qquad \frac{1 \text{ mol CO}_2}{44.01 \text{ g CO}_2} \qquad \frac{1 \text{ mol Si}}{2 \text{ mol C}}$$

then: mol Si → g Si → kg CH$_4$N$_2$O   **then: determine % yield**

$$\frac{26.981 \text{ g Si}}{1 \text{ mol Si}} \qquad \frac{1 \text{ kg}}{1000 \text{ g}} \qquad\qquad \frac{\text{actual yield kg Si}}{\text{theoretical yield kg Si}} \times 100$$

Solution: SiO$_2$(s) + 2C(s) → Si(s) + 2CO(g)

$$155.8 \text{ kg SiO}_2 \times \frac{1000 \text{ g}}{\text{kg}} \times \frac{1 \text{ mol SiO}_2}{60.085 \text{ g SiO}_2} \times \frac{1 \text{ mol Si}}{1 \text{ mol SiO}_2} = 2592.9 \text{ mol Si}$$

$$78.3 \text{ g C} \times \frac{1000 \text{ g}}{\text{kg}} \times \frac{1 \text{ mol C}}{12.01 \text{ g C}} \times \frac{1 \text{ mol Si}}{2 \text{ mol C}} = 6519.6 \text{ mol Si}$$

$$2592.9 \text{ mol Si} \times \frac{28.085 \text{ g Si}}{1 \text{ mol Si}} \times \frac{\text{kg}}{1000 \text{ g}} = 72.822 \text{ kg Si}$$

$$\frac{66.1 \text{ kg Si}}{72.82 \text{ kg Si}} \times 100\% = 90.8\%$$

Check: The theoretical yield has the correct units, kg Si, and has a reasonable magnitude compared to the mass of SiO$_2$, the limiting reactant. The % yield is reasonable, under 100%.

49. a) **Given:** 4.3 mol LiCl; 2.8 L solution   **Find:** Molarity LiCl

Conceptual Plan: mol LiCl, L solution → Molarity

$$\text{molarity (M)} = \frac{\text{amount of solute (in moles)}}{\text{volume of solution (in L)}}$$

Solution: $\dfrac{4.3 \text{ mol LiCl}}{2.8 \text{ L solution}} = 1.5 \text{ M}$

Check: The units of the answer, M, are correct. The magnitude of the answer is reasonable. Concentrations are usually between 0 M and 18 M.

b) **Given:** 22.6 g $C_6H_{12}O_6$; 1.08 L solution   **Find:** Molarity $C_6H_{12}O_6$

Conceptual Plan: g $C_6H_{12}O_6$ → mol $C_6H_{12}O_6$, L solution → Molarity

$$\frac{\text{mol } C_6H_{12}O_6}{180.16 \text{ g } C_6H_{12}O_6} \qquad \text{molarity (M)} = \frac{\text{amount of solute (in moles)}}{\text{volume of solution (in L)}}$$

Solution: $22.6 \text{ g } C_6H_{12}O_6 \times \dfrac{1 \text{ mol } C_6H_{12}O_6}{180.16 \text{ g } C_6H_{12}O_6} = 0.125\underline{4} \text{ mol } C_6H_{12}O_6$

$\dfrac{0.125\underline{4} \text{ mol } C_6H_{12}O_6}{1.08 \text{ L solution}} = 0.116 \text{ M}$

Check: The units of the answer, M, are correct. The magnitude of the answer is reasonable. Concentrations are usually between 0 M and 18 M.

c) **Given:** 45.5 mg NaCl; 154.4 mL solution   **Find:** Molarity NaCl

Conceptual Plan: mg NaCl → g NaCl → mol NaCl, and mL solution → L solution then Molarity

$$\frac{\text{g NaCl}}{1000 \text{ mg NaCl}} \qquad \frac{\text{mol NaCl}}{58.45 \text{ g NaCl}} \qquad \frac{\text{L solution}}{1000 \text{ mL solution}} \qquad \text{molarity (M)} = \frac{\text{amount of solute (in moles)}}{\text{volume of solution (in L)}}$$

Solution: $45.5 \text{ mg NaCl} \times \dfrac{1 \text{ g}}{1000 \text{ mg}} \times \dfrac{1 \text{ mol NaCl}}{58.45 \text{ g NaCl}} = 7.78\underline{4} \times 10^{-4} \text{ mol NaCl}$

$154 \text{ mL solution} \times \dfrac{1 \text{ L}}{1000 \text{ mL}} = 0.154 \text{ L}$

$\dfrac{7.784 \times 10^{-4} \text{ mol NaCl}}{0.154 \text{ L}} = 0.00505 \text{ M NaCl}$

Check: The units of the answer, M, are correct. The magnitude of the answer is reasonable. Concentrations are usually between 0 M and 18 M.

50. a) **Given:** 0.11 mol $LiNO_3$; 5.2 L solution   **Find:** Molarity $LiNO_3$

Conceptual Plan: mol $LiNO_3$, L solution → Molarity

$$\text{molarity (M)} = \frac{\text{amount of solute (in moles)}}{\text{volume of solution (in L)}}$$

Solution: $\dfrac{0.11 \text{ mol } LiNO_3}{5.2 \text{ L solution}} = 0.21 \text{ M}$

Check: The units of the answer, M, are correct. The magnitude of the answer is reasonable. Concentrations are usually between 0 M and 18 M.

b) **Given:** 61.3 g C_2H_6O; 2.44 L solution   **Find:** Molarity $C_6H_{12}O_6$

Conceptual Plan: g C_2H_6O → mol C_2H_6O, L solution → Molarity

$$\frac{\text{mol } C_2H_6O}{46.068 \text{ g } C_2H_6O} \qquad \text{molarity (M)} = \frac{\text{amount of solute (in moles)}}{\text{volume of solution (in L)}}$$

Solution: $61.3 \text{ g } C_2H_6O \times \dfrac{1 \text{ mol } C_2H_6O}{46.068 \text{ g } C_2H_6O} = 0.133\underline{1} \text{ mol } C_2H_6O$

$\dfrac{0.133\underline{1} \text{ mol } C_2H_6O}{2.44 \text{ L solution}} = 0.545 \text{ M}$

Check: The units of the answer, M, are correct. The magnitude of the answer is reasonable. Concentrations are usually between 0 M and 18 M.

c) **Given:** 15.2 mg KI; 102 mL solution   **Find:** Molarity KI

Conceptual Plan: mg KI → g KI → mol KI, and mL solution → L solution then Molarity

$$\frac{g\ KI}{1000\ mg\ KI} \qquad \frac{mol\ KI}{166.00\ g\ KI} \qquad\qquad \frac{L\ solution}{1000\ mL\ solution} \qquad molarity\ (M) = \frac{amount\ of\ solute\ (in\ moles)}{volume\ of\ solution\ (in\ L)}$$

Solution: $15.2\ mg\ KI \times \dfrac{1\ g}{1000\ mg} \times \dfrac{1\ mol\ KI}{166.00\ g\ KI} = 9.1\underline{5}7 \times 10^{-5}\ mol\ KI$

$102\ mL\ solution \times \dfrac{1\ L}{1000\ mL} = 0.102\ L$

$\dfrac{9.1\underline{5}7 \times 10^{-5}\ mol\ KI}{0.102\ L} = 8.98 \times 10^{-4}\ M\ KI$

Check: The units of the answer, M, are correct. The magnitude of the answer is reasonable. Concentrations are usually between 0 M and 18 M.

51. a) **Given:** 0.556 L; 2.3 M KCl   **Find:** mol KCl
    Conceptual Plan: volume solution x M = mol
    volume solution (L) x M = mol

    Solution: $0.556\ L\ solution \times \dfrac{2.3\ mol\ KCl}{L\ solution} = 1.3\ mol\ KCl$

    Check: Units of answer, mol KCl, are correct. The magnitude is reasonable since it is less than 1 L solution.

    b) **Given:** 1.8 L; 0.85 M KCl   **Find:** mol KCl
    Conceptual Plan: volume solution x M = mol
    volume solution (L) x M = mol

    Solution: $1.8\ L\ solution \times \dfrac{0.85\ mol\ KCl}{L\ solution} = 1.5\ mol\ KCl$

    Check: Units of answer, mol KCl, are correct. The magnitude is reasonable since it is less than 2 L solution.

    c) **Given:** 114 mL; 1.85 M KCl   **Find:** mol KCl
    Conceptual Plan: mL solution → L solution, then volume solution x M = mol
    $\frac{1\ L}{1000\ mL}$ volume solution (L) x M = mol

    Solution: $114\ mL\ solution \times \dfrac{1\ L}{1000\ mL} \times \dfrac{1.85\ mol\ KCl}{L\ solution} = 0.2109\ mol\ KCl$

    Check: Units of answer, mol KCl, are correct. The magnitude is reasonable since it is less than 1 L solution.

52. a) **Given:** 0.45 mol C_2H_5OH, 0.200 M C_2H_5OH **Find:** volume solution
    Conceptual Plan: mol C_2H_5OH → volume solution
    $\frac{mol\ C_2H_5OH}{M\ C_2H_5OH}$

    Solution: $\dfrac{0.45\ mol\ C_2H_5OH}{0.200\ \dfrac{mol\ C_2H_5OH}{L\ solution}} = 2.2\ L\ C_2H_5OH$

    Check: Units of answer, L C_2H_5OH, are correct. The magnitude is reasonable for the amount and volume of solution.

    b) **Given:** 1.22 mol C_2H_5OH, 0.200 M C_2H_5OH **Find:** volume solution
    Conceptual Plan: mol C_2H_5OH → volume solution
    $\frac{mol\ C_2H_5OH}{M\ C_2H_5OH}$

Solution:
$$\frac{1.22 \ \cancel{\text{mol C}_2\text{H}_5\text{OH}}}{0.200 \ \dfrac{\cancel{\text{mol C}_2\text{H}_5\text{OH}}}{\text{L solution}}} = 6.10 \text{ L C}_2\text{H}_5\text{OH}$$

Check: Units of answer, L C$_2$H$_5$OH, are correct. The magnitude is reasonable for the amount and volume of solution.

c) **Given:** 1.2×10^{-2} mol C$_2$H$_5$OH, 0.200 M C$_2$H$_5$OH   **Find:** volume solution
   Conceptual Plan: mol C$_2$H$_5$OH → volume solution
$$\frac{\text{mol C}_2\text{H}_5\text{OH}}{\text{M C}_2\text{H}_5\text{OH}}$$

Solution:
$$\frac{1.2 \times 10^{-2} \ \cancel{\text{mol C}_2\text{H}_5\text{OH}}}{0.200 \ \dfrac{\cancel{\text{mol C}_2\text{H}_5\text{OH}}}{\text{L solution}}} = 0.060 \text{ L C}_2\text{H}_5\text{OH}$$

Check: Units of answer, L C$_2$H$_5$OH, are correct. The magnitude is reasonable for the amount and volume of solution.

53. **Given:** 400.0 mL; 1.1 M NaNO$_3$ **Find:** g NaNO$_3$
    Conceptual Plan: mL solution → L solution, then volume solution x M = mol NaNO$_3$
$$\text{volume solution (L) x M = mol}$$

   then mol NaNO$_3$ → g NaNO$_3$
$$\frac{85.01 \text{ g NaNO}_3}{\text{mol NaNO}_3}$$

Solution: $400.0 \ \cancel{\text{mL solution}} \times \dfrac{1 \ \cancel{\text{L}}}{1000 \ \cancel{\text{mL}}} \times \dfrac{1.1 \ \cancel{\text{mol NaNO}_3}}{\cancel{\text{L solution}}} \times \dfrac{85.01 \text{ g}}{\cancel{\text{mol NaNO}_3}} = 37 \text{ g NaNO}_3$

Check: Units of answer, g NaNO$_3$, are correct. The magnitude is reasonable for the concentration and volume of solution.

54. **Given:** 5.5 L; 0.500 M CaCl$_2$ **Find:** g CaCl$_2$
    Conceptual Plan: volume solution x M = mol CaCl$_2$ then mol CaCl$_2$ → g CaCl$_2$
$$\text{volume solution (L) x M = mol} \qquad\qquad \frac{110.98 \text{ g CaCl}_2}{\text{mol CaCl}_2}$$

Solution: $5.5 \ \cancel{\text{L solution}} \times \dfrac{0.500 \ \cancel{\text{mol CaCl}_2}}{\cancel{\text{L solution}}} \times \dfrac{110.98 \text{ g}}{\cancel{\text{mol CaCl}_2}} = 3.1 \times 10^2 \text{ g CaCl}_2$

Check: Units of answer, g CaCl$_2$, are correct. The magnitude is reasonable for the concentration and volume of solution.

55. **Given:** $V_1 = 123$ mL; $M_1 = 1.1$ M; $V_2 = 500.0$ mL   **Find:** M_2
    Conceptual Plan: mL → L then V$_1$, M$_1$, V$_2$ → M$_2$
$$\frac{1 \text{ L}}{1000 \text{ mL}} \qquad\qquad V_1M_1 = V_2M_2$$

Solution: $123 \ \cancel{\text{mL}} \times \dfrac{1 \text{ L}}{1000 \ \cancel{\text{mL}}} = 0.123 \text{ L}$ $500.0 \ \cancel{\text{mL}} \times \dfrac{1 \text{ L}}{1000 \ \cancel{\text{mL}}} = 0.5000 \text{ L}$

$$M_2 = \frac{V_1M_1}{V_2} = \frac{(0.123 \ \cancel{\text{L}})(1.1 \text{ M})}{(0.5000 \ \cancel{\text{L}})} = 0.27 \text{ M}$$

Check: Units of the answer, M, are correct. The magnitude of the answer is reasonable since it is less than the original concentration.

56. **Given:** $V_1 = 3.5$ L; $M_1 = 4.8$ M; $V_2 = 45$ L   **Find:** M_2
    Conceptual Plan: V$_1$, M$_1$, V$_2$ → M$_2$
$$V_1M_1 = V_2M_2$$

Solution: $M_2 = \dfrac{V_1 M_1}{V_2} = \dfrac{(3.5 \text{ L})(4.8 \text{ M})}{(45 \text{ L})} = 0.37$ M

Check: Units of the answer, M, are correct. The magnitude of the answer is reasonable since it is less than the original concentration.

57. **Given:** $V_1 = 50$ mL; $M_1 = 12$ M; $M_2 = 0.100$ M **Find:** V_2
   Conceptual Plan: mL → L then V_1, M_1, M_2 → V_2

$$\dfrac{1 \text{ L}}{1000 \text{ mL}} \qquad\qquad V_1 M_1 = V_2 M_2$$

   Solution: $50 \text{ mL} \times \dfrac{1 \text{ L}}{1000 \text{ mL}} = 0.050 \text{ L}$

$$V_2 = \dfrac{V_1 M_1}{M_2} = \dfrac{(0.050 \text{ L})(12 \text{ M})}{(0.100 \text{ M})} = 6.0 \text{ L}$$

   Check: Units of the answer, L, are correct. The magnitude of the answer is reasonable since the new concentration is much less than the original, the volume must be larger.

58. **Given:** $V_1 = 25$ mL; $M_1 = 10.0$ M; $M_2 = 0.150$ M **Find:** V_2
   Conceptual Plan: mL → L then V_1, M_1, M_2 → V_2

$$\dfrac{1 \text{ L}}{1000 \text{ mL}} \qquad\qquad V_1 M_1 = V_2 M_2$$

   Solution: $25 \text{ mL} \times \dfrac{1 \text{ L}}{1000 \text{ mL}} = 0.025 \text{ L}$

$$V_2 = \dfrac{V_1 M_1}{M_2} = \dfrac{(0.025 \text{ L})(10.0 \text{ M})}{(0.150 \text{ M})} = 1.7 \text{ L}$$

   Check: Units of the answer, L, are correct. The magnitude of the answer is reasonable since the new concentration is much less than the original, the volume must be larger.

59. **Given:** 95.4 mL, 0.102 M $CuCl_2$; 0.175 M Na_3PO_4 **Find:** volume Na_3PO_4
   Conceptual Plan: mL $CuCl_2$ → L $CuCl_2$ → mol $CuCl_2$ → mol Na_3PO_4 → L Na_3PO_4 → mL Na_3PO_4

$$\dfrac{1 \text{ L}}{1000 \text{ mL}} \quad \dfrac{0.102 \text{ mol } CuCl_2}{\text{L}} \quad \dfrac{2 \text{ mol } Na_3PO_4}{3 \text{ mol } CuCl_2} \quad \dfrac{1 \text{ L}}{0.175 \text{ mol } Na_3PO_4} \quad \dfrac{1000 \text{ mL}}{\text{L}}$$

   Solution:

$$95.4 \text{ mL } CuCl_2 \times \dfrac{1 \text{ L}}{1000 \text{ mL}} \times \dfrac{0.102 \text{ mol } CuCl_2}{1 \text{ L}} \times \dfrac{2 \text{ mol } Na_3PO_4}{3 \text{ mol } CuCl_2} \times \dfrac{1 \text{ L}}{0.175 \text{ mol } Na_3PO_4} \times \dfrac{1000 \text{ mL}}{1 \text{ L}} = 37.1 \text{ mL } Na_3PO_4$$

   Check: Units of answer, mL Na_3PO_4, are correct. The magnitude of the answer is reasonable since the concentration of Na_3PO_4 is greater.

60. **Given:** 125 mL, 0.150 M $Co(NO_3)_2$; 0.150 M Li_2S **Find:** volume Li_2S
   Conceptual Plan: mL $Co(NO_3)_2$ → L $Co(NO_3)_2$ → mol $Co(NO_3)_2$ → mol Li_2S → L Li_2S → mL Li_2S

$$\dfrac{1 \text{ L}}{1000 \text{ mL}} \quad \dfrac{0.150 \text{ mol } Co(NO_3)_2}{\text{L}} \quad \dfrac{1 \text{ mol } Li_2S}{1 \text{ mol } Co(NO_3)_2} \quad \dfrac{1 \text{ L}}{0.155 \text{ mol } Li_2S} \quad \dfrac{1000 \text{ mL}}{\text{L}}$$

   Solution:

$$125 \text{ mL } Co(NO_3)_2 \times \dfrac{1 \text{ L}}{1000 \text{ mL}} \times \dfrac{0.150 \text{ mol } Co(NO_3)_2}{1 \text{ L}} \times \dfrac{1 \text{ mol } Li_2S}{1 \text{ mol } Co(NO_3)_2} \times \dfrac{1 \text{ L}}{0.150 \text{ mol } Li_2S} \times \dfrac{1000 \text{ mL}}{1 \text{ L}} = 125 \text{ mL } Li_2S$$

   Check: Units of answer, mL Li_2S, are correct. The magnitude of the answer is reasonable since the concentrations are the same and the mole ratio is 1:1.

61. **Given:** 25.0 g H_2; 6.0 M H_2SO_4 **Find:** volume H_2SO_4
   Conceptual Plan: g H_2 → mol H_2 → mol H_2SO_4 → L H_2SO_4

$$\dfrac{2.016 \text{ g } H_2}{1 \text{ mol } H_2} \quad \dfrac{3 \text{ mol } H_2SO_4}{3 \text{ mol } H_2} \quad \dfrac{1 \text{ L}}{6.0 \text{ mol } H_2SO_4}$$

Solution: $25.0 \ \cancel{g \ H_2} \times \dfrac{1 \ \cancel{mol \ H_2}}{2.016 \ \cancel{g \ H_2}} \times \dfrac{3 \ \cancel{mol \ H_2SO_4}}{3 \ \cancel{mol \ H_2}} \times \dfrac{1 \ L}{6.0 \ \cancel{mol \ H_2SO_4}} = 2.0 \ L \ H_2SO_4$

Check: The units, L H_2SO_4, are correct. The magnitude is reasonable since there are approximately 12 mol H_2 and the mole ratio is 1:1.

62. **Given:** 25.0 g Zn, 275 mL solution   **Find:** M $ZnCl_2$
    Conceptual Plan: g Zn → mol Zn → mol $ZnCl_2$ → M $ZnCl_2$

$$\dfrac{65.38 \ g \ Zn}{1 \ mol \ Zn} \qquad \dfrac{1 \ mol \ ZnCl_2}{1 \ mol \ Zn} \qquad \dfrac{mol \ ZnCl_2}{volume \ solution}$$

Solution:
$$25.0 \ \cancel{g \ Zn} \times \dfrac{1 \ \cancel{mol \ Zn}}{65.38 \ \cancel{g \ Zn}} \times \dfrac{1 \ mol \ ZnCl_2}{1 \ \cancel{mol \ Zn}} = 0.3824 \ mol \ ZnCl_2$$

$$\dfrac{0.3824 \ mol \ ZnCl_2}{275 \ \cancel{mL}} \times \dfrac{1000 \ \cancel{mL}}{L} = 1.39 \ M \ ZnCl_2$$

Check: Units of the answer, M $ZnCl_2$, are correct. The magnitude is reasonable because the stoichiometry is 1:1 and the mol Zn is less than 0.5.

63. a)   CsCl is an ionic compound. An aqueous solution is an electrolyte solution so, it conducts electricity.

    b) CH_3OH is a molecular compound. An aqueous solution is a non electrolyte solution, so it does not conduct electricity.

    c) $Ca(NO_3)_2$ is an ionic compound. An aqueous solution is an electrolyte solution so, it conducts electricity.

    d) $C_6H_{12}O_6$ is a molecular compound. An aqueous solution is a non electrolyte solution, so it does not conduct electricity.

64. a) $MgBr_2$ is an ionic compound. An aqueous solution is a strong electrolyte.

    b) $C_{12}H_{22}O_{11}$ is a molecular compound. An aqueous solution is a non electrolyte.

    c) Na_2CO_3 is an ionic compound. An aqueous solution is a strong electrolyte.

    d)   KOH is a strong base. An aqueous solution is a strong electrolyte.

65. a) $AgNO_3$ is soluble. Compounds containing NO_3^- are always soluble with no exceptions. The ions in solution are $Ag^+(aq)$ and $NO_3^-(aq)$.

    b) $Pb(C_2H_3O_2)_2$ is soluble. Compounds containing $C_2H_3O_2^-$ are always soluble with no exceptions. The ions in solution are $Pb^{+2}(aq)$ and $C_2H_3O_2^-(aq)$.

    c) KNO_3 is soluble. Compounds containing K^+ are always soluble with no exceptions. The ions in solution are $K^+(aq)$ and $NO_3^-(aq)$.

    d) $(NH_4)_2S$ is soluble. Compounds containing NH_4^+ are always soluble with no exceptions. The ions in solution are $NH_4^+(aq)$ and $S^{-2}(aq)$.

66. a)   AgI is insoluble. Compounds containing I^- are normally soluble but Ag^+ is an exception.

    b) $Cu_3(PO_4)_2$ is insoluble. Compounds containing PO_4^{-3} are normally insoluble and Cu^{+2} is not an exception.

    c) $CoCO_3$ is insoluble. Compounds containing CO_3^{-2} are normally insoluble and Co^{+2} is not an exception.

    d) K_3PO_4 is soluble. Compounds containing PO_4^{-3} are normally insoluble, but K^+ is an exception. The ions in solution are $K^+(aq)$ and $PO_4^{-3}(aq)$.

67. a) $LiI(aq) + BaS(aq) \rightarrow$ Possible products: Li_2S and BaI_2. Li_2S is soluble. Compounds containing S^{2-} are normally insoluble but Li^+ is and exception. BaI_2 is soluble. Compounds containing I^- are normally soluble and Ba^{2+} is not an exception. $LiI(aq) + BaS(aq) \rightarrow$ No Reaction.

   b) $KCl(aq) + CaS(aq) \rightarrow$ Possible products: K_2S and $CaCl_2$. K_2S is soluble. Compounds containing S^{2-} are normally insoluble but K^+ is an exception. $CaCl_2$ is soluble. Compounds containing Cl^- are normally soluble and Ca^{2+} is not an exception. $KCl(aq) + CaS(aq) \rightarrow$ No Reaction.

   c) $CrBr_2(aq) + Na_2CO_3(aq) \rightarrow$ Possible products: $CrCO_3$ and $NaBr$. $CrCO_3$ is insoluble. Compounds containing CO_3^{2-} are normally insoluble and Cr^{2+} is not an exception. $NaBr$ is soluble. Compounds containing Br^- are normally soluble and Na^+ is not an exception. $CrBr_2(aq) + Na_2CO_3(aq) \rightarrow CrCO_3(s) + 2\ NaBr(aq)$

   d) $NaOH(aq) + FeCl_3(aq) \rightarrow$ Possible products $NaCl$ and $Fe(OH)_3$. $NaCl$ is soluble. Compounds containing Na^+ are normally soluble, no exceptions. $Fe(OH)_3$ is insoluble. Compounds containing OH^- are normally insoluble and Fe^{3+} is not an exception. $3\ NaOH(aq) + FeCl_3(aq) \rightarrow 3\ NaCl(aq) + Fe(OH)_3(s)$

68. a) $NaNO_3(aq) + KCl(aq) \rightarrow$ Possible products: $NaCl$ and KNO_3. $NaCl$ is soluble. Compounds containing Na^+ are always soluble, no exceptions. KNO_3 is soluble. Compounds containing K^+ are always soluble, no exceptions. $NaNO_3(aq) + KCl(aq) \rightarrow NaCl(aq) + KNO_3(aq)$

   b) $NaCl(aq) + Hg_2(C_2H_3O_2)_2(aq) \rightarrow$ Possible products: $NaC_2H_3O_2$ and Hg_2Cl_2. $NaC_2H_3O_2$ is soluble. Compounds containing Na^+ are always soluble, no exceptions. Hg_2Cl_2 is insoluble. Compounds containing Cl^- are normally soluble but Hg_2^{2+} is an exception. $2\ NaCl(aq) + Hg_2(C_2H_3O_2)_2(aq) \rightarrow 2\ NaC_2H_3O_2(aq) + Hg_2Cl_2(s)$

   c) $(NH_4)_2SO_4(aq) + SrCl_2(aq) \rightarrow$ Possible products: NH_4Cl and $SrSO_4$. NH_4Cl is soluble. Compounds containing NH_4^+ are always soluble, no exceptions. $SrSO_4$ is insoluble. Compounds containing SO_4^{2-} are normally soluble but Sr^{2+} is an exception. $(NH_4)_2SO_4(aq) + SrCl_2(aq) \rightarrow 2\ NH_4Cl(aq) + SrSO_4(s)$

   d) $NH_4Cl(aq) + AgNO_3(aq) \rightarrow$ Possible products: NH_4NO_3 and $AgCl$. NH_4NO_3 is soluble. Compounds containing NH_4^+ are always soluble, no exceptions. $AgCl$ is insoluble. Compounds containing Cl^- are normally soluble, but Ag^+ is an exception. $NH_4Cl(aq) + AgNO_3(aq) \rightarrow NH_4NO_3(aq) + AgCl(s)$

69. a) $K_2CO_3(aq) + Pb(NO_3)_2(aq) \rightarrow$ Possible products: KNO_3 and $PbCO_3$. KNO_3 is soluble. Compounds containing K^+ are always soluble, no exceptions. $PbCO_3$ is insoluble. Compounds containing CO_3^{2-} are normally insoluble and Pb^{2+} is not an exception. $K_2CO_3(aq) + Pb(NO_3)_2(aq) \rightarrow 2\ KNO_3(aq)$ and $PbCO_3(s)$

   b) $Li_2SO_4(aq) + Pb(C_2H_3O_2)_2(aq) \rightarrow$ Possible products: $LiC_2H_3O_2$ and $PbSO_4$. $LiC_2H_3O_2$ is soluble. Compounds containing Li^+ are always soluble, no exceptions. $PbSO_4$ is insoluble. Compounds containing SO_4^{2-} are normally soluble but, Pb^{2+} is an exception. $Li_2SO_4(aq) + Pb(C_2H_3O_2)_2(aq) \rightarrow 2\ LiC_2H_3O_2(aq)$ and $PbSO_4(s)$

   c) $Cu(NO_3)_2(aq) + MgS(s) \rightarrow$ Possible products: CuS and $Mg(NO_3)_2$. CuS is insoluble. Compounds containing S^{-2} are normally insoluble and Cu^{2+} is not an exception. $Mg(NO_3)_2$ is soluble. Compounds containing NO_3^- are always soluble, no exceptions. $Cu(NO_3)_2(aq) + MgS(s) \rightarrow CuS(s)$ and $Mg(NO_3)_2(aq)$

   d) $Sr(NO_3)_2(aq) + KI(aq) \rightarrow$ Possible products: SrI_2 and KNO_3. SrI_2 is soluble. Compounds containing I^- are normally soluble and Sr^{2+} is not an exception. KNO_3 is soluble. Compounds containing K^+ are always soluble, no exceptions. $Sr(NO_3)_2(aq) + KI(aq) \rightarrow$ No Reaction.

70. a) $NaCl(aq) + Pb(C_2H_3O_2)_2(aq) \rightarrow$ Possible products $NaC_2H_3O_2$ and $PbCl_2$. $NaC_2H_3O_2$ is soluble. Compounds containing Na^+ are always soluble, no exceptions. $PbCl_2$ is insoluble. Compounds containing Cl^- are normally soluble but Pb^{2+} is an exception. $2\ NaCl(aq) + Pb(C_2H_3O_2)_2(aq) \rightarrow 2\ NaC_2H_3O_2(aq) + PbCl_2(s)$

b) $K_2SO_4(aq) + SrI_2(aq) \rightarrow$ Possible products: KI and $SrSO_4$. KI is soluble. Compounds containing K^+ are always soluble, no exceptions. $SrSO_4$ is insoluble. Compounds containing SO_4^{2-} are normally soluble, but Sr^{2+} is an exception. $K_2SO_4(aq) + SrI_2(aq) \rightarrow 2$ KI(aq) and $SrSO_4(s)$

c) $CsCl(aq) + CaS(aq) \rightarrow$ Possible products: Cs_2S and $CaCl_2$. Cs_2S is soluble. Compounds containing S^{2-} are normally insoluble but Cs^+ is an exception. $CaCl_2$ is soluble. Compounds containing Cl^- are normally soluble and Ca^{2+} is not an exception. $CsCl(aq) + CaS(aq) \rightarrow$ No Reaction

d) $Cr(NO_3)_3 + Na_3PO_4 \rightarrow$ Possible products: $CrPO_4$ and $NaNO_3$. $CrPO_4$ is insoluble. Compounds containing PO_4^{3-} are normally insoluble and Cr^{3+} is not an exception. $NaNO_3$ is soluble. Compounds containing Na^+ are always soluble, no exceptions. $Cr(NO_3)_3(aq) + Na_3PO_4(aq) \rightarrow CrPO_4(s)$ and 3 $NaNO_3(aq)$

71. a) $H^+(aq) + \cancel{Cl^-}(aq) + \cancel{Li^+}(aq) + OH^-(aq) \rightarrow H_2O(l) + \cancel{Li^+}(aq) + \cancel{Cl^-}(aq)$
$H^+(aq) + OH^-(aq) \rightarrow H_2O(l)$

b) $\cancel{Mg^{2+}}(aq) + S^{2-}(aq) + Cu^{2+}(aq) + 2\cancel{Cl^-}(aq) \rightarrow CuS(s) + \cancel{Mg^{2+}}(aq) + 2\cancel{Cl^-}(aq)$
$Cu^{2+}(aq) + S^{2-}(aq) \rightarrow CuS(s)$

c) $\cancel{K^+}(aq) + OH^-(aq) + H^+(aq) + \cancel{NO_3^-}(aq) \rightarrow H_2O(l) + \cancel{K^+}(aq) + \cancel{NO_3^-}(aq)$
$H^+(aq) + OH^-(aq) + \rightarrow H_2O(l)$

d) $6\cancel{Na^+}(aq) + 2 PO_4^{3-}(aq) + 3 Ni^{2+}(aq) + 6\cancel{Cl^-}(aq) \rightarrow Ni_3(PO_4)_2(s) + 6\cancel{Na^+}(aq) + 6\cancel{Cl^-}(aq)$
$3 Ni^{2+}(aq) + 2 PO_4^{3-}(aq) + \rightarrow Ni_3(PO_4)_2(s)$

72. a) $2\cancel{K^+}(aq) + SO_4^{2-}(aq) + Ca^{2+}(aq) + 2\cancel{I^-}(aq) \rightarrow CaSO_4(s) + 2\cancel{K^+}(aq) + 2\cancel{I^-}(aq)$
$Ca^{2+}(aq) + SO_4^{2-}(aq) \rightarrow CaSO_4(s)$

b) $NH_4^+(aq) + \cancel{Cl^-}(aq) + \cancel{Na^+}(aq) + OH^-(aq) \rightarrow H_2O(l) + NH_3(g) + \cancel{Na^+}(aq) + \cancel{Cl^-}(aq)$
$NH_4^+(aq) + OH^-(aq) \rightarrow H_2O(l) + NH_3(g)$

c) $Ag^+(aq) + \cancel{NO_3^-}(aq) + \cancel{Na^+}(aq) + Cl^-(aq) \rightarrow AgCl(s) + \cancel{Na^+}(aq) + \cancel{NO_3^-}(aq)$
$Ag^+(aq) + Cl^-(aq) \rightarrow AgCl(s)$

d) $H^+(aq) + \cancel{C_2H_3O_2^-}(aq) + \cancel{K^+}(aq) + CO_3^{2-}(aq) \rightarrow H_2O(l) + CO_2(g) + \cancel{K^+}(aq) + \cancel{C_2H_3O_2^-}(aq)$
$H^+(aq) + CO_3^{2-}(aq) \rightarrow H_2O(l) + CO_2(g)$

73. $Hg_2^{2+}(aq) + \cancel{NO_3^-}(aq) + \cancel{Na^+}(aq) + 2 Cl^-(aq) \rightarrow Hg_2Cl_2(s) + \cancel{Na^+}(aq) + \cancel{NO_3^-}(aq)$
$Hg_2^{2+}(aq) + 2 Cl^-(aq) \rightarrow Hg_2Cl_2(s)$

74. $Pb^{2+}(aq) + \cancel{NO_3^-}(aq) + \cancel{K^+}(aq) + SO_4^{2-}(aq) \rightarrow PbSO_4(s) + \cancel{K^+}(aq) + \cancel{NO_3^-}(aq)$
$Pb^{2+}(aq) + SO_4^{2-}(aq) \rightarrow PbSO_4(s)$

75. Skeletal reaction: $HBr(aq) + KOH(aq) \rightarrow H_2O(l) + KBr(aq)$
                      acid   base   water   salt
Net Ionic Equation: $H^+(aq) + OH^-(aq) \rightarrow H_2O(l)$

76. Skeletal reaction: $HNO_3(aq) + Ca(OH)_2(aq) \rightarrow H_2O(l) + Ca(NO_3)_2(aq)$
                      acid   base   water   salt
Balanced Reaction: $2 HNO_3(aq) + Ca(OH)_2(aq) \rightarrow 2 H_2O(l) + Ca(NO_3)_2(aq)$
Net Ionic Equation: $H^+(aq) + OH^-(aq) \rightarrow H_2O(l)$

77. a) Skeletal reaction: $H_2SO_4(aq) + Ca(OH)_2(aq) \rightarrow H_2O(l) + CaSO_4(s)$
                              acid   base   water   salt
Balanced Reaction: $H_2SO_4(aq) + Ca(OH)_2(aq) \rightarrow 2 H_2O(l) + CaSO_4(s)$

b) Skeletal reaction: $HClO_4(aq) + KOH(aq) \rightarrow H_2O(l) + KClO_4(aq)$
                              acid   base   water   salt
Balanced Reaction: $HClO_4(aq) + KOH(aq) \rightarrow H_2O(l) + KClO_4(aq)$

c) Skeletal reaction: $H_2SO_4(aq) + NaOH(aq) \rightarrow H_2O(l) + Na_2SO_4(aq)$

| | | acid | base | water | salt |

Balanced Reaction: $H_2SO_4(aq) + 2\ NaOH(aq) \rightarrow H_2O(l) + Na_2SO_4(aq)$

78. a) Skeletal reaction: $HI(aq) + LiOH(aq) \rightarrow H_2O(l) + LiI(aq)$

    acid   base   water   salt

    Balanced Reaction: $HI(aq) + LiOH(aq) \rightarrow H_2O(l) + LiI(aq)$

  b) Skeletal reaction: $HC_2H_3O_2(aq) + Ca(OH)_2(aq) \rightarrow H_2O(l) + Ca(C_2H_3O_2)_2(aq)$

    acid   base   water   salt

    Balanced Reaction: $2\ HC_2H_3O_2(aq) + Ca(OH)_2(aq) \rightarrow 2\ H_2O(l) + Ca(C_2H_3O_2)_2(aq)$

  c) Skeletal reaction: $HCl(aq) + Ba(OH)_2(aq) \rightarrow H_2O(l) + BaCl_2(aq)$

    acid   base   water   salt

    Balanced Reaction: $2\ HCl(aq) + Ba(OH)_2(aq) \rightarrow 2\ H_2O(l) + BaCl_2(aq)$

79. **Given:** 25.3 mL, 0.200 M NaOH solution; 15.0 mL $HClO_4$ solution   **Find:** M $HClO_4$ solution

    Conceptual Plan: mL NaOH $\rightarrow$ L NaOH $\rightarrow$ mol NaOH $\rightarrow$ mol $HClO_4$

$$\frac{1\ L}{1000\ mL} \qquad \frac{0.200\ mol\ NaOH}{L\ NaOH} \qquad \frac{1\ mol\ HClO_4}{1\ mol\ NaOH}$$

    mol $HClO_4$, volume $HClO_4$ solution $\rightarrow$ M

$$M = \frac{1\ mol\ HClO_4}{L\ HClO_4\ solution}$$

$$25.3\ mL\ NaOH \times \frac{1\ L}{1000\ mL} \times \frac{0.200\ mol\ NaOH}{L\ NaOH} \times \frac{1\ mol\ HClO_4}{1\ mol\ NaOH} = 0.005060\ mol\ HClO_4$$

    Solution:

$$\frac{0.005060\ mol\ HClO_4}{15.0\ mL\ HClO_4} \times \frac{1000\ mL}{1\ L} = 0.337\ M\ HClO_4$$

    Check: The units of the answer, M $HClO_4$, are correct. The magnitude of the answer is reasonable since it is greater than the M of NaOH.

80. **Given:** 18.45 mL, 0.100 M NaOH solution; 20.0 mL H_3PO_4 solution   **Find:** M H_3PO_4 solution

    Conceptual Plan: mL NaOH $\rightarrow$ L NaOH $\rightarrow$ mol NaOH $\rightarrow$ mol H_3PO_4

$$\frac{1\ L}{1000\ mL} \qquad \frac{0.100\ mol\ NaOH}{L\ NaOH} \qquad \frac{1\ mol\ H_3PO_4}{3\ mol\ NaOH}$$

    mol H_3PO_4, volume H_3PO_4 solution $\rightarrow$ M

$$M = \frac{1\ mol\ H_3PO_4}{L\ H_3PO_4\ solution}$$

    Solution:

$$18.45\ mL\ NaOH \times \frac{1\ L}{1000\ mL} \times \frac{0.100\ mol\ NaOH}{L\ NaOH} \times \frac{1\ mol\ H_3PO_4}{3\ mol\ NaOH} = 0.0006150\ mol\ H_3PO_4$$

$$\frac{0.0006150\ mol\ H_3PO_4}{20.0\ mL\ H_3PO_4} \times \frac{1000\ mL}{1\ L} = 0.0308\ M\ H_3PO_4$$

    Check: The units of the answer, M H_3PO_4, are correct. The magnitude of the answer is reasonable since it is less than the concentration of the NaOH.

81. a) Skeletal Reaction: $HBr(aq) + NiS(aq) \rightarrow NiBr_2(aq) + H_2S(g)$

                                                          gas

    Balanced Reaction: $2\ HBr(aq) + NiS(aq) \rightarrow NiBr_2(aq) + H_2S(g)$

  b) Skeletal Reaction: $NH_4I(aq) + NaOH(aq) \rightarrow NH_4OH(aq) + NaI(aq) \rightarrow H_2O(l) + NH_3(g) + NaI(aq)$

                                        decomposes   gas

    Balanced Reaction: $NH_4I(aq) + NaOH(aq) \rightarrow H_2O(l) + NH_3(g) + NaI(aq)$

  c) Skeletal Reaction: $HBr(aq) + Na_2S(aq) \rightarrow NaBr(aq) + H_2S(g)$

                                                      gas

    Balanced Reaction: $2\ HBr(aq) + Na_2S(aq) \rightarrow 2\ NaBr(aq) + H_2S(g)$

d) Skeletal Reaction:
$HClO_4(aq) + Li_2CO_3(aq) \rightarrow H_2CO_3(aq) + LiClO_4(aq) \rightarrow H_2O(l) + CO_2(g) + LiClO_4(aq)$
                                       decomposes   gas
Balanced Reaction: $2\ HClO_4(aq) + Li_2CO_3(aq) \rightarrow H_2O(l) + CO_2(g) + 2\ LiClO_4(aq)$

82. a) Skeletal Reaction:
$HNO_3(aq) + Na_2SO_3(aq) \rightarrow H_2SO_3(aq) + NaNO_3(aq) \rightarrow H_2O(l) + SO_2(g) + NaNO_3(aq)$
                                        decomposes   gas
Balanced Reaction: $2\ HNO_3(aq) + Na_2SO_3(aq) \rightarrow H_2O(l) + SO_2(g) + 2\ NaNO_3(aq)$

b) Skeletal Reaction: $HCl(aq) + KHCO_3(aq) \rightarrow H_2CO_3(aq) + KCl(aq) \rightarrow H_2O(l) + CO_2(g) + KCl(aq)$
                                        decomposes   gas
Balanced Reaction: $HCl(aq) + KHCO_3(aq) \rightarrow H_2O(l) + CO_2(g) + KCl(aq)$

c) Skeletal Reaction:
$HC_2H_3O_2(aq) + NaHSO_3(aq) \rightarrow NaC_2H_3O_2(aq) + H_2SO_3(aq) \rightarrow H_2O(l) + SO_2(g) + NaC_2H_3O_2(aq)$
                                                decomposes   gas
Balanced Reaction: $HC_2H_3O_2(aq) + NaHSO_3(aq) \rightarrow H_2O(l) + SO_2(g) + NaC_2H_3O_2(aq)$

d) Skeletal Reaction:
$(NH_4)_2SO_4(aq) + Ca(OH)_2(aq) \rightarrow NH_4OH(aq) + CaSO_4(s) \rightarrow H_2O(l) + NH_3(g) + CaSO_4(s)$
                                        decomposes   gas
Balanced Reaction: $(NH_4)_2SO_4(aq) + Ca(OH)_2(aq) \rightarrow 2H_2O(l) + 2NH_3(g) + CaSO_4(s)$

83. a) Ag. The oxidation state of Ag = 0. The oxidation state of an atom in a free element is 0.

b) Ag^+. The oxidation state of Ag^+ = +1. The oxidation state of a monatomic ion is equal to its charge.

c) CaF_2. The oxidation state of Ca = +2, the oxidation state of F = – 1. The oxidation state of a Group 2A metal always has an oxidation state of +2, the oxidation of F is – 1 since the sum of the oxidation states in a neutral formula unit = 0.

d) H_2S. The oxidation state of H = + 1, the oxidation state of S = – 2. The oxidation state of H when listed first is +1, the oxidation state of S is – 2 since S is in group 6A and the sum of the oxidation states in a neutral molecular unit = 0.

e) $CO_3{}^{2-}$. The oxidation state of C = +4, the oxidation state of O = – 2. The oxidation state of O is normally – 2, the oxidation state of C is deduced from the formula since the sum of the oxidation states must equal the charge on the ion. (C ox state) + 4(O ox state) = – 2: (C ox state) + 2(– 2) = – 2, so C ox state = + 4.

f) $CrO_4{}^{2-}$. The oxidation state of Cr = +6, the oxidation state of O = – 2. The oxidation state of O is normally – 2, the oxidation state of Cr is deduced from the formula since the sum of the oxidation states must equal the charge on the ion. (Cr ox state) + 4(O ox state) = – 2; (Cr ox state) + 2(– 2) = – 2, so Cr ox state = + 6.

84. a) Cl_2. The oxidation of both Cl atoms = 0. Since Cl_2 is a free element, the oxidation state of Cl = 0.

b) Fe^{3+}. The oxidation of Fe = +3. The oxidation state of a monatomic ion is equal to its charge.

c) $CuCl_2$. The oxidation state of Cu = +2, the oxidation state of each Cl = – 1. The oxidation state of group 7A atoms is normally – 1, the oxidation state of Cu is deduced from the formula since the sum of the oxidation states in a neutral formula unit = 0

d) CH_4. The oxidation state of C = – 4, the oxidation state of H = +1. The oxidation state of H is normally +1, the oxidation state of C is deduced for the formula since the sum of the oxidation states in a neutral molecular unit = 0. (C ox state) + 4(H ox state) = 0; (C ox state) + 4(+ 1) = 0, so C ox state = – 4.

e) $Cr_2O_7{}^{2-}$. The oxidation state of Cr = +6, the oxidation state of O = − 2. The oxidation state of O is normally − 2, the oxidation state of Cr is deduced from the formula since the sum of the oxidation states must equal the charge of the ion. 2(Cr ox state) + 4(O ox state) = − 2; 2(Cr ox state) + 4(− 2) = − 2, so Cr ox state = +6

f) $HSO_4{}^-$. The oxidation state of H = +1, the oxidation state of S = +6, the oxidation state of O = − 2. The oxidation state of H is normally +1, the oxidation state of O is normally − 2, the oxidation state of S is deduced from the formula since the sum of the oxidation states must equal the charge of the ion. (H ox state) + (S ox state) + 4(O ox state) = − 1;
(+1) + (S ox state) + 4(− 2) = − 1, so S ox state = +6.

85. a) CrO. The oxidation state of Cr = +2, the oxidation state of O = − 2. The oxidation state of O is normally − 2, the oxidation state of Cr is deduced from the formula since the sum of the oxidation states must = 0.
(Cr ox state) + (O ox state) = 0; (Cr ox state) + (− 2) = 0, so Cr = +2.

b) CrO_3. The oxidation state of Cr = +6, the oxidation state of O = − 2. The oxidation state of O is normally − 2, the oxidation state of Cr is deduced from the formula since the sum of the oxidation states must = 0.
(Cr ox state) + 3(O ox state) = 0; (Cr ox state) +3 (− 2) = 0, so Cr = +6.

c) Cr_2O_3. The oxidation state of Cr = +3, the oxidation state of O = − 2. The oxidation state of O is normally − 2, the oxidation state of Cr is deduced from the formula since the sum of the oxidation states must = 0.
2(Cr ox state) +3 (O ox state) = 0; 2(Cr ox state) + 3(− 2) = 0, so Cr = +3.

86. a) ClO^-. The oxidation state of Cl = +1, the oxidation state of O = − 2. The oxidation state of O is normally − 2, the oxidation state of Cl is deduced from the formula since the sum of the oxidation states must equal the charge of the ion. (Cl ox state) + (O ox state) = − 1; (Cl ox state) + (− 2) = − 1, so Cl = +1.

b) $ClO_2{}^-$. The oxidation state of Cl = +3, the oxidation state of O = − 2. The oxidation state of O is normally − 2, the oxidation state of Cl is deduced from the formula since the sum of the oxidation states must equal the charge of the ion. (Cl ox state) + 2(O ox state) = − 1; (Cl ox state) +2 (− 2) = − 1, so Cl = +3.

c) $ClO_3{}^-$. The oxidation state of Cl = +5, the oxidation state of O = − 2. The oxidation state of O is normally − 2, the oxidation state of Cl is deduced from the formula since the sum of the oxidation states must equal the charge of the ion. (Cl ox state) + 3(O ox state) = − 1; (Cl ox state) + 3(− 2) = − 1, so Cl = +5.

d) $ClO_4{}^-$. The oxidation state of Cl = +7, the oxidation state of O = − 2. The oxidation state of O is normally − 2, the oxidation state of Cl is deduced from the formula since the sum of the oxidation states must equal the charge of the ion. (Cl ox state) + 4(O ox state) = − 1; (Cl ox state) + 4(− 2) = − 1, so Cl = +7.

87. a) $4 Li(s) + O_2(g) \rightarrow 2 Li_2O(s)$
oxidation states;   0   0   +1   − 2
This is a redox reaction since Li increases in oxidation number (oxidation) and O decreases in number (reduction). O_2 is the oxidizing agent, Li is the reducing agent.

b) $Mg(s) + Fe^{2+}(aq) \rightarrow Mg^{2+}(aq) + Fe(s)$
oxidation states;   0   +2   +2   0
This is a redox reaction since Mg increases in oxidation number (oxidation) and Fe decreases in number (reduction). Fe^{2+} is the oxidizing agent, Mg is the reducing agent.

c) $Pb(NO_3)_2(aq) + Na_2SO_4(aq) \rightarrow PbSO_4(s) + 2 NaNO_3(aq)$
oxidation states;   +2 +5 − 2   +1   +6 − 2   +2 +6 −2   +1 +5 −2
This is a not a redox reaction since none of the atoms undergoes a change in oxidation number.

d) $HBr(aq) + KOH(aq) \rightarrow H_2O(l) + KBr(aq)$

oxidation states;   +1 - 1   +1 – 2 +1   +1 -2   +1 -2

This is a not a redox reaction since none of the atoms undergoes a change in oxidation number.

88. a) $Al(s) + 3\ Ag^+(aq) \rightarrow Al^{3+}(aq) + 3\ Ag(s)$

oxidation states;   o   +1   +3   0

This is a redox reaction since Al increases in oxidation number (oxidation) and Ag decreases in number (reduction). Ag^+ is the oxidizing agent, Al is the reducing agent.

b) $SO_3(g) + H_2O(l) \rightarrow H_2SO_4(aq)$

oxidation states;   +6 -2   +1 – 2   +1 +6 -2

This is a not a redox reaction since none of the atoms undergoes a change in oxidation number.

c) $Ba(s) + Cl_2(g) \rightarrow BaCl_2(s)$

oxidation states;   o   0   +2 -1

This is a redox reaction since Ba increases in oxidation number (oxidation) and Cl decreases in number (reduction). Ba is the oxidizing agent, Cl_2 is the reducing agent.

d) $Mg(s) + Br_2(l) \rightarrow MgBr_2(s)$

oxidation states;   o   0   +2 -1

This is a redox reaction since Mg increases in oxidation number (oxidation) and Br decreases in number (reduction). Mg is the oxidizing agent, Br_2 is the reducing agent.

89. a) Skeletal reaction: $S(s) + O_2(g) \rightarrow SO_2(g)$
         Balanced reaction: $S(s) + O_2(g) \rightarrow SO_2(g)$

b) Skeletal reaction: $C_3H_6(g) + O_2(g) \rightarrow CO_2(g) + H_2O(g)$
    Balance C: $C_3H_6(g) + O_2(g) \rightarrow 3CO_2(g) + H_2O(g)$
    Balance H: $C_3H_6(g) + O_2(g) \rightarrow 3CO_2(g) + 3H_2O(g)$
    Balance O: $C_3H_6(g) + 9/2\ O_2(g) \rightarrow 3CO_2(g) + 3H_2O(g)$
    Clear fraction: $2C_3H_6(g) + 9O_2(g) \rightarrow 6CO_2(g) + 6H_2O(g)$

c) Skeletal reaction: $Ca(s) + O_2(g) \rightarrow CaO$
    Balance O: $Ca(s) + O_2(g) \rightarrow 2CaO$
    Balance Ca: $2Ca(s) + O_2(g) \rightarrow 2CaO$

d) Skeletal reaction: $C_5H_{12}S(l) + O_2(g) \rightarrow CO_2(g) + H_2O(g) + SO_2(g)$
    Balance C: $C_5H_{12}S(l) + O_2(g) \rightarrow 5CO_2(g) + H_2O(g) + SO_2(g)$
    Balance H: $C_5H_{12}S(l) + O_2(g) \rightarrow 5CO_2(g) + 6H_2O(g) + SO_2(g)$
    Balance S: $C_5H_{12}S(l) + O_2(g) \rightarrow 5CO_2(g) + 6H_2O(g) + SO_2(g)$
    Balance O: $C_5H_{12}S(l) + 9O_2(g) \rightarrow 5CO_2(g) + 6H_2O(g) + SO_2(g)$

90. a) Skeletal reaction: $C_4H_6(g) + O_2(g) \rightarrow CO_2(g) + H_2O(g)$
         Balance C: $C_4H_6(g) + O_2(g) \rightarrow 4CO_2(g) + H_2O(g)$
         Balance H: $C_4H_6(g) + O_2(g) \rightarrow 4CO_2(g) + 3H_2O(g)$
         Balance O: $C_4H_6(g) + 11/2\ O_2(g) \rightarrow 4CO_2(g) + 3H_2O(g)$
         Clear fraction: $2C_4H_6(g) + 11\ O_2(g) \rightarrow 8CO_2(g) + 6H_2O(g)$

b) Skeletal reaction: $C(s) + O_2(g) \rightarrow CO_2(g)$
    Balanced reaction: $C(s) + O_2(g) \rightarrow CO_2(g)$

c) Skeletal reaction: $CS_2(s) + O_2(g) \rightarrow CO_2(g) + SO_2(g)$
    Balance C: $CS_2(s) + O_2(g) \rightarrow CO_2(g) + SO_2(g)$
    Balance S: $CS_2(s) + O_2(g) \rightarrow CO_2(g) + 2SO_2(g)$
    Balance O: $CS_2(s) + 3O_2(g) \rightarrow CO_2(g) + 2SO_2(g)$

d) Skeletal reaction: $C_3H_8O(l) + O_2(g) \rightarrow CO_2(g) + H_2O(g)$
    Balance C: $C_3H_8O(l) + O_2(g) \rightarrow 3CO_2(g) + H_2O(g)$
    Balance H: $C_3H_8O(l) + O_2(g) \rightarrow 3CO_2(g) + 4H_2O(g)$
    Balance O: $C_3H_8O(l) + 9/5\ O_2(g) \rightarrow 3CO_2(g) + 4H_2O(g)$
    Clear fraction: $2C_3H_8O(l) + 9O_2(g) \rightarrow 6CO_2(g) + 8H_2O(g)$

91. **Given:** In 100 g solution, 20.0 g $C_2H_6O_2$; density of solution = 1.03 g/mL   **Find:** M of solution
    Conceptual Plan: g $C_2H_6O_2 \rightarrow$ mol $C_2H_6O_2$ and g solution $\rightarrow$ mL solution $\rightarrow$ L solution

$$\frac{1 \text{ mol } C_2H_6O_2}{62.06 \text{ g } C_2H_6O_2} \qquad \frac{1.00 \text{ mL}}{1.03 \text{ g}} \qquad \frac{1 \text{ L}}{1000 \text{ mL}}$$

then M $C_2H_6O_2$

$$M = \frac{\text{mol } C_2H_6O_2}{\text{L solution}}$$

Solution:

$$20.0 \text{ g } C_2H_6O_2 \times \frac{1 \text{ mol } C_2H_6O_2}{62.06 \text{ g } C_2H_6O_2} = 0.3222 \text{ mol } C_2H_6O_2$$

$$100.0 \text{ g solution} \times \frac{1.00 \text{ mL solution}}{1.03 \text{ g solution}} \times \frac{1 \text{ L}}{1000 \text{ mL}} = 0.09708 \text{ L}$$

$$M = \frac{0.3222 \text{ mol } C_2H_6O_2}{0.09708 \text{ L}} = 3.32 \text{ M}$$

Check: The units of the answer, M $C_2H_6O_2$, are correct. The magnitude of the answer is reasonable since the concentration of solutions is usually between 0 and 18 M.

92. **Given:** 1.35 M NaCl; density of solution = 1.05 g/mL   **Find:** % NaCl by mass
    Conceptual Plan: mol NaCl $\rightarrow$ g NaCl and L solution $\rightarrow$ mL solution $\rightarrow$ g solution then % NaCl

$$\frac{58.45 \text{ g NaCl}}{1 \text{ mol NaCl}} \qquad \frac{1000 \text{ mL}}{1 \text{ L}} \qquad \frac{1.05 \text{ g}}{1.00 \text{ mL}} \qquad \frac{\text{g NaCl}}{\text{g solution}} \times 100$$

Solution: $1.35 \text{ M} = \dfrac{1.35 \text{ mol NaCl}}{1 \text{ L solution}}$

$$1.35 \text{ mol NaCl} \times \frac{58.45 \text{ g NaCl}}{1 \text{ mol NaCl}} = 78.91 \text{ g NaCl} \qquad 1 \text{ L solution} \times \frac{1000 \text{ mL}}{L} \times \frac{1.05 \text{ g solution}}{\text{mL solution}} = 1050 \text{ g solution}$$

$$\frac{78.91 \text{ g NaCl}}{1050 \text{ g solution}} \times 100 = 7.52 \text{ % NaCl}$$

Check: The units of the answer, % NaCl, are correct. The magnitude of the answer is reasonable for the concentration of the solution.

93. **Given:** 2.5 g $NaHCO_3$ **Find:** g HCl
    Conceptual Plan: g $NaHCO_3 \rightarrow$ mol $NaHCO_3 \rightarrow$ mol HCl $\rightarrow$ g HCl

$$\frac{1 \text{ mol } NaHCO_3}{84.02 \text{ g } NaHCO_3} \qquad \frac{1 \text{ mol HCl}}{1 \text{ mol } NaHCO_3} \qquad \frac{36.46 \text{ g HCl}}{1 \text{ mol HCl}}$$

Solution: $HCl(aq) + NaHCO_3(aq) \rightarrow H_2O(l) + CO_2(g) + NaCl(aq)$

$$2.5 \text{ g } NaHCO_3 \times \frac{1 \text{ mol } NaHCO_3}{84.02 \text{ g } NaHCO_3} \times \frac{1 \text{ mol HCl}}{1 \text{ mol } NaHCO_3} \times \frac{36.46 \text{ g HCl}}{1 \text{ mol HCl}} = 1.1 \text{ g HCl}$$

Check: The units of the answer, g HCl, are correct. The magnitude of the answer is reasonable since the molar mass of HCl is less than the molar mass of $NaHCO_3$.

94. **Given:** 3.8 g HCl   **Find:** g $CaCO_3$
    Conceptual Plan: g HCl $\rightarrow$ mol HCl $\rightarrow$ mol $CaCO_3 \rightarrow$ g $CaCO_3$

$$\frac{1 \text{ mol HCl}}{36.46 \text{ g HCl}} \qquad \frac{1 \text{ mol } CaCO_3}{2 \text{ mol HCl}} \qquad \frac{100.09 \text{ g } CaCO_3}{1 \text{ mol } CaCO_3}$$

Solution: $2 HCl(aq) + CaCO_3(s) \rightarrow H_2O(l) + CO_2(g) + CaCl_2(aq)$

$$3.8 \text{ g HCl} \times \frac{\text{mol HCl}}{36.46 \text{ g HCl}} \times \frac{1 \text{ mol } CaCO_3}{2 \text{ mol HCl}} \times \frac{100.09 \text{ g } CaCO_3}{\text{mol } CaCO_3} = 5.2 \text{ g } CaCO_3$$

Check: Units of the answer, g $CaCO_3$, are correct. The magnitude of the answer is reasonable since the molar mass of $CaCO_3$ is greater than the molar mass of HCl.

95. **Given:** 1.0 kg C_8H_{18} **Find:** kg CO_2
    Conceptual Plan: kg $C_8H_{18} \rightarrow$ g $C_8H_{18} \rightarrow$ mol $C_8H_{18} \rightarrow$ mol $CO_2 \rightarrow$ g $CO_2 \rightarrow$ kg CO_2

Solution: $2\ C_8H_{18}(g) + 25\ O_2(g) \rightarrow 16\ CO_2(g) + 18\ H_2O(g)$

$$1.0\ \text{kg}\ C_8H_{18} \times \frac{1000\ \text{g}}{\text{kg}} \times \frac{1\ \text{mol}\ C_8H_{18}}{114.22\ \text{g}\ C_8H_{18}} \times \frac{16\ \text{mol}\ CO_2}{2\ \text{mol}\ C_8H_{18}} \times \frac{44.01\ \text{g}\ CO_2}{1\ \text{mol}\ CO_2} \times \frac{\text{kg}}{1000\ \text{g}} = 3.1\ \text{kg}\ CO_2$$

Check: The units of the answer, kg CO_2, are correct. The magnitude of the answer is reasonable since the ratio of CO_2 to C_8H_{18} is 8:1.

96. **Given:** 18.9 L C_3H_8, d = 0.621 g/ mL   **Find:** kg CO_2
Conceptual Plan: L C_3H_8 → mL C_3H_8 → g C_3H_8 → mol C_3H_8 → mol CO_2 → g CO_2 → kg CO_2

Solution: $C_3H_8(g) + 5\ O_2(g) \rightarrow 3\ CO_2(g) + 4\ H_2O(g)$

$$18.9\ \text{L}\ C_3H_8 \times \frac{1000\ \text{mL}}{\text{L}} \times \frac{0.621\ \text{g}}{\text{mL}} \times \frac{1\ \text{mol}\ C_3H_8}{44.09\ \text{g}\ C_3H_8} \times \frac{3\ \text{mol}\ CO_2}{1\ \text{mol}\ C_3H_8} \times \frac{44.01\ \text{g}\ CO_2}{\text{mol}\ CO_2} \times \frac{\text{kg}}{1000\ \text{g}} = 35.1\ \text{kg}\ CO_2$$

Check: The units of the answer, kg CO_2, are correct. The magnitude of the answer is reasonable since the molar mass of CO_2 and C_3H_8 are close and there is a mole ratio of 1:3.

97. **Given:** 3.00 mL $C_4H_6O_3$, d = 1.08 g/mL; 1.25 g $C_7H_6O_3$; 1.22 g $C_9H_8O_4$ **Find:** limiting reactant, theoretical yield $C_9H_8O_4$ and % yield $C_9H_8O_4$
Conceptual Plan: mL $C_4H_6O_3$ → g $C_4H_6O_3$ → mol $C_4H_6O_3$ → mol $C_9H_8O_4$

$$\frac{1.08\ \text{g}\ C_4H_6O_3}{1.00\ \text{mL}\ C_4H_6O_3} \quad \frac{1\ \text{mol}\ C_4H_6O_3}{102.09\ \text{g}\ C_4H_6O_3} \quad \frac{1\ \text{mol}\ C_9H_8O_4}{1\ \text{mol}\ C_4H_6O_3}$$

→ smallest amount determines limiting reactant

g $C_7H_6O_3$ → mol $C_7H_6O_3$ → mol $C_9H_8O_4$

$$\frac{1\ \text{mol}\ C_7H_6O_3}{138.12\ \text{g}\ C_7H_6O_3} \quad \frac{1\ \text{mol}\ C_9H_8O_4}{1\ \text{mol}\ C_7H_6O_3}$$

then: mol $C_9H_8O_4$ → g $C_9H_8O_4$ **then: determine % yield**

$$\frac{180.1\ \text{g}\ C_9H_8O_4}{\text{mol}\ C_9H_8O_4} \qquad\qquad \frac{\text{actual yield g}\ C_9H_8O_4}{\text{theoretical yield g}\ C_9H_8O_4} \times 100$$

Solution:

$$3.00\ \text{mL}\ C_4H_6O_3 \times \frac{1.08\ \text{g}\ C_4H_6O_3}{\text{mL}\ C_4H_6O_3} \times \frac{1\ \text{mol}\ C_4H_6O_3}{102.09\ \text{g}\ C_4H_6O_3} \times \frac{1\ \text{mol}\ C_9H_8O_4}{1\ \text{mol}\ C_4H_6O_3} = 0.031\underline{7}4\ \text{mol}\ C_9H_8O_4$$

$$1.25\ \text{g}\ C_7H_6O_3 \times \frac{1\ \text{mol}\ C_7H_6O_3}{138.12\ \text{g}\ C_7H_6O_3} \times \frac{1\ \text{mol}\ C_9H_8O_4}{1\ \text{mol}\ C_7H_6O_3} = 0.0090\underline{5}0\ \text{mol}\ C_9H_8O_4$$

$$0.0090\underline{5}0\ \text{mol}\ C_9H_8O_4 \times \frac{180.1\ \text{g}\ C_9H_8O_4}{1\ \text{mol}\ C_9H_8O_4} = 1.6\underline{3}0\ \text{g}\ C_9H_8O_4$$

$$\frac{1.22\ \text{g}\ C_9H_8O_4}{1.6\underline{3}0\ \text{g}\ C_9H_8O_4} \times 100 = 74.8\%$$

Check: The theoretical yield has the correct units, g $C_9H_8O_4$, and has a reasonable magnitude compared to the mass of $C_7H_6O_3$, the limiting reactant. The % yield is reasonable, under 100%.

98. **Given:** 4.62 mL C_2H_5OH, d = 0.789 g/mL; 15.55 g O_2; 3.72 mL H_2O, d = 1.00g/mL

Find: limiting reactant, theoretical yield H_2O and % yield H_2O

Conceptual Plan: mL C_2H_5OH → g C_2H_5OH → mol C_2H_5OH → mol H_2O

$$\frac{0.789 \text{ g } C_2H_5OH}{1.00 \text{ mL } C_2H_5OH} \qquad \frac{1 \text{ mol } C_2H_5OH}{46.07 \text{ g } C_2H_5OH} \qquad \frac{3 \text{ mol } H_2O}{1 \text{ mol } C_2H_5OH}$$

→ **smallest amount determines limiting reactant**

g O_2 → mol O_2 → mol H_2O

$$\frac{1 \text{ mol } O_2}{32.00 \text{ g } O_2} \qquad \frac{3 \text{ mol } H_2O}{3 \text{ mol } O_2}$$

then: mol H_2O → g H_2O then: determine % yield

$$\frac{18.02 \text{ g } H_2O}{\text{mol } H_2O} \qquad \qquad \frac{\text{actual yield g } H_2O}{\text{theoretical yield g } H_2O} \times 100$$

Solution:

$$C_2H_5OH(l) + 3 \, O_2(g) \rightarrow 2 \, CO_2(g) + 3 \, H_2O(l)$$

$$4.62 \text{ mL } C_2H_5OH \times \frac{0.789 \text{ g } C_2H_5OH}{\text{mL } C_2H_5OH} \times \frac{1 \text{ mol } C_2H_5OH}{46.07 \text{ g } C_2H_5OH} \times \frac{3 \text{ mol } H_2O}{1 \text{ mol } C_2H_5OH} = 0.237\underline{4} \text{ mol } H_2O$$

$$15.55 \text{ g } O_2 \times \frac{1 \text{ mol } O_2}{31.998 \text{ g } O_2} \times \frac{1 \text{ mol } H_2O}{1 \text{ mol } O_2} = 0.4859\underline{7} \text{ mol } H_2O$$

$$0.237\underline{4} \text{ mol } O_2 \times \frac{18.02 \text{ g } H_2O}{1 \text{ mol } O_2} = 4.2\underline{7}8 \text{ g } H_2O$$

$$\frac{3.72 \text{ g } H_2O}{4.2\underline{7}8 \text{ g } H_2O} \times 100 = 87.0\%$$

Check: The theoretical yield has the correct units, g H_2O, and has a reasonable magnitude compared to the mass of C_2H_5OH, the limiting reactant. The % yield is reasonable, under 100%.

99. **Given:** (a) 11 molecules H_2, 2 molecules O_2; (b) 8 molecules H_2, 4 molecules O_2; (c) 4 molecules H_2, 5 molecules O_2; (d) 3 molecules H_2, 6 molecules O_2 **Find:** loudest explosion based on equation
Conceptual Plan: loudest explosion will occur in the balloon with the mol ratio closest to the balanced equation and that contains the most H_2
Solution: $2H_2(g) + O_2(g) \rightarrow H_2O(l)$

     Balloon (a) has enough O_2 to react with 4 molecules H_2; balloon (b) has enough O_2 to react with 8 molecules H_2; balloon (c) has enough O_2 to react with 10 molecules H_2; and balloon (d) has enough O_2 for 3 molecules of H_2 to react. Therefore, balloon (b) will have the loudest explosion because it has the most H_2 that will react.
Check: Answer seems correct since it has the most H_2 with enough O_2 in the balloon to completely react.

100. **Given:** Beaker contain 4 ions H^+, 4 ions Cl^-. **Find:** which NaOH beaker will just neutralize HCl beaker
Conceptual Plan: molecules H^+ → molecules OH^- then compare to 4 beakers.

$$\frac{1 \text{ ion } OH^-}{1 \text{ ion } H^+}$$

Solution: $HCl(aq) + NaOH(aq) \rightarrow NaCl(aq) + H_2O(l)$
     Net Ionic: $H^+(aq) + OH^-(aq) \rightarrow H_2O(l)$

$$4 \text{ ions } H^+ \times \frac{1 \text{ ion } OH^-}{1 \text{ ion } H^+} = 4 \text{ ions } OH^-$$

     Beaker (b) contains 2 ions OH^-; Beaker (c) contains 4 ions OH^-;
     Beaker (d) contains 5 ions OH^-; Beaker (e) contains 8 ions OH^-.
     Beaker (c) will completely neutralize beaker (a) with no excess.
Check: The answer is correct because it will completely neutralize the H^+ with no excess OH^-.

101.a)   Skeletal Reaction: $HCl(aq) + Hg_2(NO_3)_2(aq) \rightarrow Hg_2Cl_2(s) + HNO_3(aq)$
        Balance Cl: $2HCl(aq) + Hg_2(NO_3)_2(aq) \rightarrow Hg_2Cl_2(s) + 2HNO_3(aq)$

    b)   Skeletal Reaction: $KHSO_3(aq) + HNO_3(aq) \rightarrow H_2O(l) + SO_2(g) + KNO_3(aq)$
        Balanced Reaction: $KHSO_3(aq) + HNO_3(aq) \rightarrow H_2O(l) + SO_2(g) + KNO_3(aq)$

c) Skeletal Reaction: $NH_4Cl(aq) + Pb(NO_3)_2(aq) \rightarrow PbCl_2(s) + NH_4NO_3(aq)$
   Balance Cl: $2NH_4Cl(aq) + Pb(NO_3)_2(aq) \rightarrow PbCl_2(s) + NH_4NO_3(aq)$
   Balance N: $2NH_4Cl(aq) + Pb(NO_3)_2(aq) \rightarrow PbCl_2(s) + 2NH_4NO_3(aq)$

d) Skeletal Reaction: $NH_4Cl(aq) + Ca(OH)_2(aq) \rightarrow NH_3(g) + H_2O(l) + CaCl_2(aq)$
   Balance Cl: $2NH_4Cl(aq) + Ca(OH)_2(aq) \rightarrow NH_3(g) + H_2O(l) + CaCl_2(aq)$
   Balance N: $2NH_4Cl(aq) + Ca(OH)_2(aq) \rightarrow 2NH_3(g) + H_2O(l) + CaCl_2(aq)$
   Balance H: $2NH_4Cl(aq) + Ca(OH)_2(aq) \rightarrow 2NH_3(g) + 2H_2O(l) + CaCl_2(aq)$

102.a) Skeletal Reaction: $H_2SO_4(aq) + HNO_3(aq) \rightarrow$ No Reaction

b) Skeletal Reaction: $Cr(NO_3)_3(aq) + LiOH(aq) \rightarrow Cr(OH)_3(s) + LiNO_3(aq)$
   Balance OH: $Cr(NO_3)_3(aq) + 3LiOH(aq) \rightarrow Cr(OH)_3(s) + LiNO_3(aq)$
   Balance Li: $Cr(NO_3)_3(aq) + 3LiOH(aq) \rightarrow Cr(OH)_3(s) + 3LiNO_3(aq)$

c) Skeletal Reaction: $C_5H_{12}O(l) + O_2(g) \rightarrow CO_2(g) + H_2O(g)$
   Balance C: $C_5H_{12}O(l) + O_2(g) \rightarrow 5CO_2(g) + H_2O(g)$
   Balance H: $C_5H_{12}O(l) + O_2(g) \rightarrow 5CO_2(g) + 6H_2O(g)$
   Balance O: $C_5H_{12}O(l) + 15/2\ O_2(g) \rightarrow 5CO_2(g) + 6H_2O(g)$
   Clear fraction: $2C_5H_{12}O(l) + 15O_2(g) \rightarrow 10CO_2(g) + 12H_2O(g)$

d) Skeletal Reaction: $SrS(aq) + CuSO_4(aq) \rightarrow SrSO_4(aq) + CuS(s)$
   Balanced Reaction: $SrS(aq) + CuSO_4(aq) \rightarrow SrSO_4(aq) + CuS(s)$

103. **Given:** 1.5 L solution, 0.050 M $CaCl_2$, 0.085 M $Mg(NO_3)_2$ **Find:** g Na_3PO_4
Conceptual Plan: V,M $CaCl_2$ → mol $CaCl_2$ and V,M $Mg(NO_3)_2$ → mol $Mg(NO_3)_2$

$$V \times M = mol \qquad\qquad V \times M = mol$$

then (mol $CaCl_2$ + mol $Mg(NO_3)_2$ → Na_3PO_4 → g Na_3PO_4

$$\frac{2\ mol\ Na_3PO_4}{3\ mol\ (CaCl_2 + Mg(NO_3)_2)} \triangleleft \frac{163.97\ g\ Na_3PO_4}{1\ mol\ Na_3PO_4}$$

Solution: $3CaCl_2(aq) + 2Na_3PO_4(aq) \rightarrow Ca_3(PO_4)_2(s) + 6NaCl(aq)$
   $3\ Mg(NO_3)_2(aq) + 2Na_3PO_4(aq) \rightarrow Mg_3(PO_4)_2(s) + 6\ NaCl(aq)$

   $1.5\ L \times 0.050\ M\ CaCl_2 = 0.07\underline{5}\ mol\ CaCl_2$

   $1.5\ L \times 0.085\ M\ Mg(NO_3)_2 = 0.1\underline{2}75\ mol\ Mg(NO_3)_2$

$$0.2\underline{0}25 \ \cancel{mol\ CaCl_2\ and\ Mg(NO_3)_2} \times \frac{2\ \cancel{mol\ Na_2PO_4}}{3\ \cancel{mol\ CaCl_2\ and\ Mg(NO_3)_2}} \times \frac{163.97\ g\ mol\ Na_2PO_4}{\cancel{mol\ Na_2PO_4}} = 22\ g\ mol\ Na_2PO_4$$

Check: The units of the answer, g Na_3PO_4, are correct. The magnitude of the answer is reasonable since it is needed to remove both the Ca and Mg ions.

104. **Given:** 500.0 mL 0.100 M HCl and 0.200 M H_2SO_4; 0.150 M KOH   **Find:**   volume   KOH   to neutralize the acid
Conceptual Plan:
   mL → L, then VM(HCl) → mol HCl → mol H^+ and VM(H_2SO_4) → mol H_2SO_4 → mol H^+

$$\frac{1\ L}{1000\ mL} \qquad V \times M = mol \qquad \frac{mol\ H^+}{mol\ HCl} \qquad\qquad V \times M = mol \qquad \frac{2\ mol\ H^+}{mol\ H_2SO_4}$$

Total mol H^+ → mol OH^- → mol KOH → volume KOH

$$\frac{mol\ OH^-}{mol\ H^+} \quad \frac{mol\ KOH}{mol\ OH^-}$$

Solution: $500.0\ \cancel{mL} \times \dfrac{1\ \cancel{L}}{1000\ \cancel{mL}} \times \dfrac{0.100\ \cancel{mol\ HCl}}{1\ \cancel{L}} \times \dfrac{1\ mol\ H^+}{1\ \cancel{mol\ HCl}} = 0.0500\underline{0}\ mol\ H^+$

$500.0\ \cancel{mL} \times \dfrac{1\ \cancel{L}}{1000\ \cancel{mL}} \times \dfrac{0.200\ \cancel{mol\ H_2SO_4}}{1\ \cancel{L}} \times \dfrac{2\ mol\ H^+}{1\ \cancel{mol\ H_2SO_4}} = 0.200\underline{0}\ mol\ H^+$

$(0.200\underline{0} + 0.0500\underline{0})\ mol\ H^+ \times \dfrac{1\ \cancel{mol\ OH^-}}{1\ \cancel{mol\ H^+}} \times \dfrac{1\ \cancel{mol\ KOH}}{1\ \cancel{mol\ OH^-}} \times \dfrac{1\ L\ solution}{0.150\ \cancel{mol\ KOH}} = 1.67\ L\ KOH\ solution$

Check: The units of the answer, L KOH, are correct. The magnitude of the answer is reasonable because the average concentration of acid is greater than the concentration of base.

105. **Given:** 1.0 L, 0.10 M OH⁻   **Find:** g Ba

     Conceptual Plan: VM → mol OH⁻ → mol Ba(OH)₂ → mol BaO → mol Ba → g Ba

$$V \times M = mol \quad \frac{1 \text{ mol Ba(OH)}_2}{2 \text{ mol OH}^-} \quad \frac{1 \text{ mol BaO}}{1 \text{ mol Ba(OH)}_2} \quad \frac{1 \text{ mol Ba}}{1 \text{ mol BaO}} \quad \frac{137.3 \text{ g Ba}}{1 \text{ mol Ba}}$$

     Solution: $BaO(s) + H_2O(l) \rightarrow Ba(OH)_2(aq)$

$$1.0 \text{ L} \times \frac{0.10 \text{ mol OH}^-}{\text{L}} \times \frac{1 \text{ mol Ba(OH)}_2}{2 \text{ mol OH}^-} \times \frac{1 \text{ mol BaO}}{1 \text{ mol Ba(OH)}_2} \times \frac{1 \text{ mol Ba}}{1 \text{ mol BaO}} \times \frac{137.3 \text{ g Ba}}{1 \text{ mol Ba}} = 6.9 \text{ g Ba}$$

     Check: The units of the answer, g Ba, are correct. The magnitude is reasonable since the molar mass of Ba is large and there are 2 moles hydroxide per mole Ba.

106. **Given:** 1.00 L, 1.51 M NaF; 49.6 g sample; mixture Cr^{3+} and Mg^{2+} **Find:** g Cr^{3+}

     Conceptual Plan: V,M NaF → mol NaF → mol F⁻ and let x = mol CrF₃ and y = mol MgF₂ → mol F

$$V \times M = mol \quad \frac{1 \text{ mol F}^-}{1 \text{ mol NaF}} \qquad \frac{3 \text{ mol F}}{\text{mol CrF}_3} \quad \frac{2 \text{ mol F}}{\text{mol Mg}_2}$$

     and → g sample then solve for x = mol CrF₃ → mol Cr³⁺ → g Cr³⁺

$$x \text{ (molar mass CrF}_3) = g \text{ CrF}_3 \quad y \text{ (molar mass MgF}_2) = g \text{ MgF}_2 \quad \frac{1 \text{ mol Cr}^{3+}}{1 \text{ mol CrF}_3} \quad \frac{52.00 \text{ g Cr}^{3+}}{1 \text{ mol Cr}^{3+}}$$

     Solution: $1.00 \text{ L} \times \dfrac{1.51 \text{ mol NaF}}{\text{L}} \times \dfrac{1 \text{ mol F}^-}{1 \text{ mol NaF}} = 1.51 \text{ mol F}^-$

$$x \text{ mol CrF}_3 \times \frac{109.00 \text{ g CrF}_3}{\text{mol CrF}_3} = g \text{ CrF}_3$$

     Let x = mol CrF₃ and y = mol MgF₂ ;

     3x = mol F⁻ from CrF₃ ; 2y = mol F⁻ from MgF₂ $y \text{ mol MgF}_2 \times \dfrac{62.30 \text{ g MgF}_2}{\text{mol MgF}_2} = g \text{ MgF}_2$

     3x + 2 y = 1.51 mol F⁻

                        x(109.00) + y(62.30) = 49.6 g sample

     Solve simultaneous equations: x = 0.16$\underline{4}$8 = mol CrF₃

$$0.16\underline{4}8 \text{ mol CrF}_3 \times \frac{1 \text{ mol Cr}^{3+}}{1 \text{ mol CrF}_3} \times \frac{52.00 \text{ g Cr}^{3+}}{1 \text{ mol Cr}^{3+}} = 8.57 \text{ g Cr}^{3+}$$

Check: Units of answer, g Cr³⁺, are correct. The magnitude of the answer is reasonable since it is less than the mass of the sample.

107. **Given:** 30.0% NaNO₃, $9.00/ 100 lb; 20.0 % (NH₄)₂SO₄, $8.10/ 100 lb   **Find:** cost / lb N

     Conceptual Plan: **mass fertilizer → mass NaNO₃ → mass N → cost/lb N**
                          and: mass fertilizer → mass (NH₄)₂SO₄ → mass N → cost/lb N

     Solution:

$$100 \text{ lb fertilizer} \times \frac{30.0 \text{ lb NaNO}_3}{100 \text{ lb fertilizer}} \times \frac{16.48 \text{ lb N}}{100 \text{ lb NaNO}_3} = 4.9\underline{4}4 \text{ lb N}$$

$$\frac{\$9.00}{100 \text{ lb fertilizer}} \times \frac{100 \text{ lb fertilizer}}{4.9\underline{4}4 \text{ lb N}} = \$1.82/ \text{ lb N}$$

$$100 \text{ lb fertilizer} \times \frac{20.0 \text{ lb (NH}_4)_2\text{SO}_4}{100 \text{ lb fertilizer}} \times \frac{21.2 \text{ lb N}}{100 \text{ lb (NH}_4)_2\text{SO}_4} = 4.2\underline{4}0 \text{ lb N}$$

$$\frac{\$8.10}{100 \text{ lb fertilizer}} \times \frac{100 \text{ lb fertilizer}}{4.2\underline{4} \text{ lb N}} = \$1.91/ \text{ lb N}$$

The more economical fertilizer is the NaNO₃ because it costs less/ lb N.

Check: The units of the cost, $/lb N, are correct. The answer is reasonable because you compare the cost/lb N directly.

108. **Given:** 0.110 M HCl; 1.52 g Al(OH)₃   **Find:** volume HCl needed to neutralize

Conceptual Plan: g Al(OH)$_3$ → mol Al(OH)$_3$ → mol HCl → vol HCL

$$\frac{\text{mol Al(OH)}_3}{78.00\text{ g Al(OH)}_3} \qquad \frac{3\text{ mol HCl}}{1\text{ mol Al(OH)}_3} \qquad \frac{\text{mol HCl}}{\text{M HCl}}$$

Solution: 3 HCl(aq) + Al(OH)$_3$(aq) → 3 H$_2$O(l) + AlCl$_3$(aq)

$$1.52\text{ g Al(OH)}_3 \times \frac{1\text{ mol Al(OH)}_3}{78.00\text{ g Al(OH)}_3} \times \frac{3\text{ mol HCl}}{1\text{ mol Al(OH)}_3} \times \frac{1\text{ L}}{0.110\text{ mol HCl}} = 0.531\text{ L HCl}$$

Check: Units of the answer, L HCl, are correct. The magnitude of the answer is reasonable since the mole ratio of HCl to Al(OH)$_3$ is 3:1.

109. **Given:** 24.5 g Au, 24.5 g BrF$_3$, 24.5 g KF   **Find:** g KAuF$_4$

     Conceptual Plan: g Au → mol Au → mol KAuF$_4$

$$\frac{1\text{ mol Au}}{196.97\text{ g Au}} \qquad \frac{2\text{ mol KAuF}_4}{2\text{ mol Au}}$$

   g BrF$_3$ → mol BrF$_3$ → mol KAuF$_4$ → **smallest mol amount determines limiting reactant**

$$\frac{1\text{ mol BrF}_3}{136.9\text{ g BrF}_3} \qquad \frac{2\text{ mol KAuF}_4}{2\text{ mol BrF}_3}$$

   g KF → mol KF → mol KAuF$_4$

$$\frac{1\text{ mol KF}}{58.10\text{ g KF}} \qquad \frac{2\text{ mol KAuF}_4}{2\text{ mol KF}}$$

   then: mol KAuF$_4$ → g KAuF$_4$

$$\frac{312.07\text{ g KAuF}_4}{\text{mol KAuF}_4}$$

   2 Au(s) + 2BrF$_3$(l) + 2KF(s) → Br$_2$(l) + 2KAuF$_4$(s)

   oxidation states;   o   + 3 – 1   +1 – 1   0   +1 +3 – 1

   This is a redox reaction since Au increases in oxidation number (oxidation) and Br decreases in number (reduction).   BrF$_3$ is the oxidizing agent, Au is the reducing agent.

   Solution:

$$24.5\text{ g Au} \times \frac{1\text{ mol Au}}{196.97\text{ g Au}} \times \frac{2\text{ mol KAuF}_4}{2\text{ mol Au}} = 0.12\underline{4}4\text{ mol KAuF}_4$$

$$24.5\text{ g BrF}_3 \times \frac{1\text{ mol BrF}_3}{196.97\text{ g BrF}_3} \times \frac{2\text{ mol KAuF}_4}{2\text{ mol BrF}_3} = 0.17\underline{9}0\text{ mol KAuF}$$

$$24.5\text{ g KF} \times \frac{1\text{ mol KF}}{196.97\text{ g KF}} \times \frac{2\text{ mol KAuF}_4}{2\text{ mol KF}} = 0.42\underline{1}7\text{ mol KAuF}_4$$

$$0.12\underline{4}4\text{ mol KAuF}_4 \times \frac{312.07\text{ g KAuF}_4}{1\text{ mol KAuF}_4} = 38.8\text{ g KAuF}_4$$

Check: Units of the answer, g KAuF$_4$, are correct. The magnitude of the answer is reasonable compared to the mass of the limiting reactant Au.

110. **Given:** 0.10 L, 0.12 M NaCl; 0.23 L, 0.18 M MgCl$_2$; 0.20 M AgNO$_3$ **Find:** volume AgNO$_3$ to precipitate all the Cl$^-$.

     Conceptual Plan: VM(NaCl) → mol NaCl → mol Cl$^-$ and VM(MgCl$_2$) → mol MgCl$_2$ → mol Cl$^-$

$$\text{vol} \times \text{M} = \text{mol} \qquad \frac{1\text{ mol Cl}^-}{1\text{ mol NaCl}} \qquad\qquad \text{vol} \times \text{M} = \text{mol} \qquad \frac{2\text{ mol Cl}^-}{1\text{ mol MgCl}_2}$$

   Then: total mol Cl$^-$ → mol Ag$^+$ → mol AgNO$_3$ → vol AgNO$_3$

$$\frac{1\text{ mol Ag}^+}{1\text{ mol Cl}^-} \qquad \frac{1\text{ mol AgNO}_3}{1\text{ mol Ag}^+} \qquad \frac{1\text{ L AgNO}_3}{0.20\text{ mol AgNO}_3}$$

Solution:

$$0.10 \ \cancel{\text{L NaCl}} \times \frac{0.12 \ \cancel{\text{mol NaCl}}}{\cancel{\text{L NaCl}}} \times \frac{1 \ \text{mol Cl}^-}{1 \ \cancel{\text{mol NaCl}}} = 0.01\underline{2} \ \text{mol Cl}^-$$

$$0.23 \ \cancel{\text{L NaCl}} \times \frac{0.18 \ \cancel{\text{mol NaCl}}}{\cancel{\text{L NaCl}}} \times \frac{2 \ \text{mol Cl}^-}{1 \ \cancel{\text{mol NaCl}}} = 0.1\underline{2}4 \ \text{mol Cl}^-$$

$$0.1\underline{3}6 \ \cancel{\text{mol Cl}^-} \times \frac{1 \ \cancel{\text{mol Ag}^+}}{1 \ \cancel{\text{mol Cl}^-}} \times \frac{1 \ \cancel{\text{mol AgNO}_3}}{1 \ \cancel{\text{mol Ag}^+}} \times \frac{\text{L AgNO}_3}{0.20 \ \cancel{\text{mol AgNO}_3}} = 0.68 \ \text{L AgNO}_3$$

Check; Units of the answer, L AgNO$_3$, are correct. The magnitude of the answer is reasonable since the Cl$^-$ comes from two sources.

111. **Given:** solution may contain Ag$^+$, Ca^{2+}, and Cu^{2+} **Find:** determine which ions are present.
Conceptual Plan: test the solution sequentially with NaCl, Na$_2$SO$_4$ and Na$_2$CO$_3$ and see if precipitates form.
Solution: original solution + NaCl yields no reaction: Ag$^+$ not present: since Cl is normally soluble but Ag$^+$ is an exception.
Original solution with Na$_2$SO$_4$ yields a precipitate and solution 2. The precipitate is CaSO$_4$, so Ca^{2+} is present. SO^{2-} are normally soluble but Ca^{2+} is an exception.
Solution 2 with Na$_2$CO$_3$ yields a precipitate. The precipitate is CuCO$_3$, so Cu^{2+} is present. All CO$_3^{2-}$ are insoluble.
NET IONIC EQUATIONS:
$$\text{Ca}^{2+}(\text{aq}) + \text{SO}_4^{2-}(\text{aq}) \rightarrow \text{CaSO}_4(\text{s})$$
$$\text{Cu}^{2+}(\text{aq}) + \text{CO}_3^{2-}(\text{aq}) \rightarrow \text{CuCO}_3(\text{s})$$
Check: the answer is reasonable since two different precipitates formed and all the Ca^{2+} was removed before the carbonate was added.

112. **Given:** solution may contain Hg$_2^{2+}$, Ba^{2+}, and Fe^{2+} **Find:** determine which ions are present.
Conceptual Plan: test the solution sequentially with KCl, K$_2$SO$_4$ and K$_2$CO$_3$ and see if precipitates form.
Solution: original solution + KCl yields a precipitate and solution 2: The precipitate is Hg$_2$Cl$_2$ so Hg$_2^{2+}$ is present. Cl is normally soluble but Hg$_2^{2+}$ is an exception.
Solution 2 with K$_2$SO$_4$ yields no precipitate. So Ba^{2+} is not present. SO$_4^{2-}$ are normally soluble but Ba^{2+} is an exception.
Solution 2 with K$_2$CO$_3$ yields a precipitate. The precipitate is FeCO$_3$, so Fe^{2+} is present. All CO$_3^{2-}$ are insoluble.
NET IONIC EQUATIONS:
$$\text{Hg}_2^{2+}(\text{aq}) + 2\text{Cl}^-(\text{aq}) \rightarrow \text{Hg}_2\text{Cl}_2(\text{s})$$
$$\text{Fe}^{2+}(\text{aq}) + \text{CO}_3^{2-}(\text{aq}) \rightarrow \text{FeCO}_3(\text{s})$$
Check: the answer is reasonable since two different precipitates formed and all the Hg$_2^{2+}$ was removed before the carbonate was added.

113 **Given:** 15.2 billion L lake water, 1.8 x 10^{-5} M H$_2$SO$_4$, 8.7 x 10^{-6} M HNO$_3$ **Find:** kg CaCO$_3$ needed to neutralize
Conceptual Plan: Vol lake → mol H$_2$SO$_4$ → mol H$^+$ and vol lake → mol HNO$_3$ → mol H$^+$

$$\text{vol} \times M = \text{mol} \qquad \frac{2 \ \text{mol H}^+}{1 \ \text{mol H}_2\text{SO}_4} \qquad \text{vol} \times M = \text{mol} \qquad \frac{1 \ \text{mol H}^+}{1 \ \text{mol HNO}_3}$$

Then: total mol H$^+$ → mol CO$_3^{2-}$ → mol CaCO$_3$ → g CaCO$_3$ → kg CaCO$_3$

$$\frac{1 \ \text{mol CO}_3^{2-}}{1 \ \text{mol H}^+} \qquad \frac{1 \ \text{mol CaCO}_3}{1 \ \text{mol CO}_3^{2-}} \qquad \frac{100.09 \ \text{g CaCO}_3}{1 \ \text{mol CaCO}_3} \qquad \frac{\text{kg}}{1000 \ \text{g}}$$

Solution: $2\text{H}^+(\text{aq}) + \text{CO}_3^{2-}(\text{aq}) \rightarrow \text{H}_2\text{O}(\text{l}) + \text{CO}_2(\text{g})$

$$15.2 \times 10^9 \ \cancel{\text{L}} \times \frac{1.8 \times 10^{-5} \ \cancel{\text{mol H}_2\text{SO}_4}}{\cancel{\text{L soln}}} \times \frac{2 \ \text{mol H}^+}{\cancel{\text{mol H}_2\text{SO}_4}} = 547200 \ \text{mol H}^+$$

$$15.2 \times 10^9 \ \cancel{\text{L}} \times \frac{8.7 \times 10^{-6} \ \cancel{\text{mol HNO}_3}}{\cancel{\text{L soln}}} \times \frac{1 \ \text{mol H}^+}{\cancel{\text{mol HNO}_3}} = 13\underline{2}240 \ \text{mol H}^+$$

$$679440 \; \cancel{\text{mol H}^+} \times \frac{1 \; \cancel{\text{mol CO}_3^{2-}}}{\cancel{\text{mol H}^+}} \times \frac{1 \; \cancel{\text{mol CaCO}_3}}{\cancel{\text{mol CO}_3^{2-}}} \times \frac{100.09 \; \text{g} \; \cancel{\text{CaCO}_3}}{1 \; \cancel{\text{mol CaCO}_3}} \times \frac{\text{kg}}{1000 \; \cancel{\text{g}}} = 3.4 \times 10^4 \; \text{kg CaCO}_3$$

Check: Units of the answer, kg $CaCO_3$, are correct. The magnitude of the answer is reasonable based on the size of the lake.

114. **Given:** 3.5×10^{-3} M Ca^{2+}. 1.1×10^{-3} M Mg^{2+}, 19,5 gal H$_2$O; 0.65 kg detergent/load   **Find:** % by mass Na$_2$CO$_3$

Conceptual Plan: gal H$_2$O $\rightarrow$ L H$_2$O then VM $\rightarrow$ mol Ca^{2+} and VM $\rightarrow$ mol Mg^{2+}

$$\frac{3.785 \; \text{L}}{1 \; \text{gal}} \qquad\qquad \text{vol} \times \text{M} = \text{mol} \qquad\qquad \text{vol} \times \text{M} = \text{mol}$$

Then total moles ions $\rightarrow$ mol CO$_3^{2-}$ $\rightarrow$ mol CaCO$_3$ $\rightarrow$ g CaCO$_3$ $\rightarrow$ kg CaCO$_3$ $\rightarrow$ % CaCO$_3$

$$\frac{1 \; \text{mol CO}_3^{2-}}{1 \; \text{mol ion}} \qquad \frac{1 \; \text{mol CaCO}_3}{1 \; \text{mol CO}_3^{2-}} \qquad \frac{100.09 \; \text{g CaCO}_3}{1 \; \text{mol CaCO}_3} \qquad \frac{\text{kg}}{1000 \; \text{g}} \qquad \frac{\text{kg CaCO}_3}{\text{kg detergent} \times 100}$$

Solution:

$$19.5 \; \cancel{\text{gal}} \times \frac{3.785 \; \cancel{\text{L}}}{1 \; \cancel{\text{gal}}} \times \frac{3.5 \times 10^{-3} \; \text{mol Ca}^{2+}}{\cancel{\text{L}}} = 0.258 \; \text{mol Ca}^{2+}$$

$$19.5 \; \cancel{\text{gal}} \times \frac{3.785 \; \cancel{\text{L}}}{1 \; \cancel{\text{gal}}} \times \frac{1.1 \times 10^{-3} \; \text{mol Mg}^{2+}}{\cancel{\text{L}}} = 0.08118 \; \text{mol Mg}^{2+}$$

$$0.3395 \; \cancel{\text{mol ions}} \times \frac{1 \; \cancel{\text{mol CO}_3^{2-}}}{\cancel{\text{mol ions}}} \times \frac{1 \; \cancel{\text{mol Na}_2\text{CO}_3}}{\cancel{\text{mol CO}_3^{2-}}} \times \frac{106.01 \; \text{g} \; \cancel{\text{CaCO}_3}}{1 \; \cancel{\text{mol CaCO}_3}} \times \frac{\text{kg CaCO}_3}{1000 \; \text{g} \; \cancel{\text{CaCO}_3}} = 0.03599 \; \text{kg Na}_2\text{CO}_3$$

$$\frac{0.03599 \; \cancel{\text{kg Na}_2\text{CO}_3}}{0.65 \; \cancel{\text{kg detergent}}} \times 100 = 5.5 \; \% \; \text{Na}_2\text{CO}_3$$

Check: Units of the answer, % Na$_2$CO$_3$, are correct. The magnitude of the answer is reasonable. % is less than 100 %.

115. **Given:** 45 µg Pb/dL blood, Vol = 5.0 L, 1 mol succimer(C$_4$H$_6$O$_4$S$_2$) = 1 mol Pb   **Find:** mass C$_4$H$_6$O$_4$S$_2$ in mg

Conceptual Plan: Volume blood L $\rightarrow$ Volume blood dL $\rightarrow$ µg Pb $\rightarrow$ g Pb $\rightarrow$ mol Pb $\rightarrow$

$$\frac{10 \; \text{dL}}{\text{L}} \qquad\qquad \frac{45 \; \text{µg}}{\text{dL}} \quad \frac{10^6 \; \text{µg}}{\text{g}} \quad \frac{\text{mol Pb}}{207.2 \; \text{g Pb}} \quad \frac{1 \; \text{mol succimer}}{1 \; \text{mol Pb}}$$

mol succimer $\rightarrow$ g succimer $\rightarrow$ mg succimer

$$\frac{182.23 \; \text{g succimer}}{1 \; \text{mol succimer}} \qquad \frac{1000 \; \text{mg succimer}}{1 \; \text{g succimer}}$$

Solution:

$$5.0 \; \cancel{\text{L blood}} \times \frac{10 \; \cancel{\text{dL}}}{\cancel{\text{L}}} \times \frac{45 \; \cancel{\text{µg}}}{\cancel{\text{dL}}} \times \frac{1 \; \cancel{\text{g}}}{10^6 \; \cancel{\text{µg}}} \times \frac{1 \; \cancel{\text{mol Pb}}}{207.2 \; \cancel{\text{g}}} \times \frac{1 \; \cancel{\text{mol succimer}}}{1 \; \cancel{\text{mol Pb}}} \times \frac{182\,23 \; \cancel{\text{g succimer}}}{1 \; \cancel{\text{mol succimer}}} \times \frac{1000 \; \text{mg}}{\cancel{\text{g}}} = 2.0 \; \text{mg succimer}$$

Check: The units of the answer, mg succimer, are correct. The magnitude is reasonable for the volume of blood and the concentration.

116. In designing the unit you would need to consider the theoretical yield and % yield of the reaction, how changing the limiting reactant would affect the reaction, the stoichiometry between KO$_2$ and O$_2$ to determine the mass of KO$_2$ required to produce enough O$_2$ for 10 minutes. You might also consider the speed of the reaction and whether or not the reaction produced heat. Additionally, because your body does not use 100% of the oxygen taken in with each breath, the apparatus would only need to replenish the oxygen used. The percentage of oxygen in air is about 20% and the percentage in exhaled air is about 16%, so we will assume that 4% of the air would need to be replenished with oxygen. (NOTE: The problem can also be solved by finding the amount of KO$_2$ that would be required to react with all of the exhaled CO$_2$).

Given: air = 4% O$_2$, volume = 5 – 8 L/ min   , 1 mol gas = 22.4 L gas **Find:** O$_2$ for 10 min breathing time

Conceptual Plan: 10 min $\rightarrow$ vol air $\rightarrow$ vol O$_2$ $\rightarrow$ mol O$_2$ $\rightarrow$ mol KO$_2$ $\rightarrow$ g KO$_2$

$$\frac{8 \; \text{L air}}{1 \; \text{min}} \qquad \frac{4 \; \text{L O}_2}{100 \; \text{L air}} \qquad \frac{1 \; \text{mol O}_2}{22.4 \; \text{L O}_2} \qquad \frac{4 \; \text{mol KO}_2}{3 \; \text{mol O}_2} \qquad \frac{71.10 \; \text{g KO}_2}{1 \; \text{mol KO}_2}$$

Solution: $10 \ \cancel{\text{min}}. \ \times \ \dfrac{8 \ \cancel{\text{L air}}}{\cancel{\text{min}}} \ \times \ \dfrac{4 \ \cancel{\text{L O}_2}}{100 \ \cancel{\text{L air}}} \ \times \ \dfrac{1 \ \cancel{\text{mol O}_2}}{22.4 \ \cancel{\text{L O}_2}} \ \times \ \dfrac{4 \ \cancel{\text{mol KO}_2}}{3 \ \cancel{\text{mol O}_2}} \ \times \ \dfrac{71.10 \ \text{g KO}_2}{1 \ \cancel{\text{mol KO}_2}} = 14 \ \text{g KO}_2$

Check: The units of the answer, g KO_2, are correct. The magnitude of the answer is reasonable since it is an amount that could be carried in a portable device.

117. **Given:** 250 g sample, 67.2 mol % Al   **Find:** Theoretical yield in g of Mn
    Conceptual Plan: mol % Al → g Al and mol % MnO_2 → g MnO_2, then mass % Al

$$\dfrac{26.98 \ \text{g Al}}{\text{mol Al}} \qquad\qquad \dfrac{86.94 \ \text{g MnO}_2}{\text{mol MnO}_2} \quad \dfrac{\text{g Al}}{\text{total g}} \ \times 100$$

then: sample → g Al → mol Al → mol Mn

$$\dfrac{38.86 \ \text{g Al}}{100 \ \text{g sample}} \quad \dfrac{\text{mol Al}}{26.98 \ \text{g Al}} \quad \dfrac{3 \ \text{mol Mn}}{4 \ \text{mol Al}} \qquad \textbf{→ smallest mol amount determines limiting reactant}$$

sample → g MnO_2 → mol MnO_2 → mol Mn

$$\dfrac{61.14 \ \text{g MnO}_2}{100 \ \text{g sample}} \quad \dfrac{\text{mol MnO}_2}{86.94 \ \text{g MnO}_2} \quad \dfrac{3 \ \text{mol Mn}}{\text{mol MnO}_2}$$

then mol Mn → g Mn

$$\dfrac{54.94 \ \text{g Mn}}{\text{mol Mn}}$$

Solution: $4\text{Al}(s) + 3 \ \text{MnO}_2(s) → 3\text{Mn} + 2\text{Al}_2\text{O}_3(s)$

Assume 1 mole: $0.672 \ \text{mol Al} \times \dfrac{26.98 \ \text{g Al}}{\text{mol Al}} = 18.13 \ \text{g Al}$ $0.328 \ \text{mol MnO}_2 \times \dfrac{26.98 \ \text{g MnO}_2}{\text{mol MnO}_2} = 28.52 \ \text{g MnO}_2$

$$\dfrac{18.13 \ \text{g Al}}{(18.13 \ \text{g Al} + 28 \ 52 \ \text{g MnO}_2)} \ \times 100 = 38.86 \ \% \ \text{Al} \qquad\qquad \text{So: } 61.14 \ \% \ \text{MnO}_2$$

$$250 \ \cancel{\text{g sample}} \times \dfrac{38.86 \ \cancel{\text{g Al}}}{100 \ \cancel{\text{g sample}}} \times \dfrac{\cancel{\text{mol Al}}}{26.98 \ \cancel{\text{g Al}}} \times \dfrac{3 \ \text{mol Mn}}{4 \ \cancel{\text{mol Al}}} = 1.7\underline{5}8 \ \text{mol Mn}$$

$$250 \ \cancel{\text{g sample}} \times \dfrac{61.14 \ \cancel{\text{g MnO}_2}}{100 \ \cancel{\text{g sample}}} \times \dfrac{\cancel{\text{mol MnO}_2}}{26.98 \ \cancel{\text{g MnO}_2}} \times \dfrac{3 \ \text{mol Mn}}{4 \ \cancel{\text{mol MnO}_2}} = 3.6\underline{0} \ \text{mol Mn}$$

$$1.7\underline{5}8 \ \cancel{\text{mol Mn}} \times \dfrac{54.94 \ \text{g Mn}}{1 \ \cancel{\text{mol Mn}}} = 96.6 \ \text{g Mn}$$

Check: the units of the answer, g Mn, are correct. The magnitude of the answer is reasonable based on the amount of the limiting reactant, Al.

118. **Given:** 151 g $Na_2B_4O_7$ **Find:** g B_5H_9
    Conceptual Plan: g $Na_2B_4O_7$ → mol $Na_2B_4O_7$ → mol B_5H_9 → g B_5H_9

$$\dfrac{\text{mol Na}_2\text{B}_4\text{O}_7}{201.22 \ \text{g Na}_2\text{B}_4\text{O}_7} \quad \dfrac{4 \ \text{mol B}_5\text{H}_9}{5 \ \text{mol Na}_2\text{B}_4\text{O}_7} \quad \dfrac{63.13 \ \text{g B}_5\text{H}_9}{\text{mol B}_5\text{H}_9}$$

Solution: All the B in B_5H_9 goes to the $Na_2B_4O_7$ so the mole ratio between the two can be used.

$$151 \ \cancel{\text{g Na}_2\text{B}_4\text{O}_7} \times \dfrac{1 \ \cancel{\text{mol Na}_2\text{B}_4\text{O}_7}}{201.22 \ \cancel{\text{g Na}_2\text{B}_4\text{O}_7}} \times \dfrac{4 \ \cancel{\text{mol B}_5\text{H}_9}}{5 \ \cancel{\text{mol Na}_2\text{B}_4\text{O}_7}} \times \dfrac{63.13 \ \text{g B}_5\text{H}_9}{1 \ \cancel{\text{mol B}_5\text{H}_9}} = 37.9 \ \text{g B}_5\text{H}_9$$

Check: The units of the answer, g B_5H_9, are correct. The magnitude of the answer is reasonable since the molar mass of B_5H_9 is less than the molar mass of $Na_2B_4O_7$.

119. The correct answer is d. The molar mass of K and O_2 are comparable. Since the stoichiometry has a ratio of 4 mol K to 1 mol O_2, K will be the limiting reactant when mass of K is less than 4 times the mass of O_2.

120. **Given:** 5 mol NO, 10 mol H_2 **Find: conditions of product mixture**
    Conceptual Plan: mol H_2 → mol NO and mol H_2 → mol NH_3 and mol H_2 → mol H_2O
    Solution: The correct answer is a. Since the mol ratio of H_2 to NO is 5:2, the 10 mol of H_2 will require 4 mol NO and H_2 is the limiting reactant. This eliminates answers b and c. Since there is excess NO, this eliminates d, leaving answer a.

121. **Given:** 1 M solution contains 8 particles   **Find:** amount of solute or solvent needed to obtain new concentration

Conceptual Plan: determine amount of solute particles in each new solution, then determine if solute (if the number is greater), or solvent (if the number is less) needs to be added to obtain the new concentration.

Solution: Solution (a) contains 12 particles solute. Concentration is greater than the original, so solute needs

to be added. $12 \text{ particles} \times \dfrac{1 \text{ mol}}{8 \text{ particles}} = 1.5 \text{ mol}$ $(1.5 \text{ mol} - 1.0 \text{ mol}) = 0.5 \text{ mol solute added.}$

$0.5 \text{ mol solute} \times \dfrac{8 \text{ particles}}{1 \text{ mol solute}} = 4 \text{ solute particles added}$

Solution (a) is obtained by adding 4 particles solute to 1 L of original solution

Solution (b) contains 4 particles. Concentration is less than the original so solvent needs to be added.

$4 \text{ particles} \times \dfrac{1 \text{ mol}}{8 \text{ particles}} = 0.5 \text{ mol solute}$ So, 1 L solution contains 0.5 mol = 0.5M

$(1 \text{ M})(1 \text{ L}) = (0.5 \text{ M})(x)$ $x = 2 \text{ L}$

Solution (b) is obtained by diluting 1 L of the original solution to 2 L

Solution (c) contains 6 particles. Concentration is less than the original so solvent needs to be added.

$6 \text{ particles} \times \dfrac{1 \text{ mol}}{8 \text{ particles}} = 0.75 \text{ mol solute}$ So, 1 L solution contains 0.75 mol = 0.75M

$(1 \text{ M})(1 \text{ L}) = (0.75 \text{ M})(x)$ $x = 2 \text{ L}$

Solution (c) is obtained by diluting 1 L of the original solution to 1.3 L

122. **Given:** 6 molecules N_2H_4; 4 molecules N_2O_4 ; (a) contains: 9 molecules N_2. 12 molecules H_2O, and 1 molecule N_2O_4: solution (b) contains: 12 molecules N_2. 16 molecules H_2O , and 2 molecules N_2O_4; solution (c) contains: 9 molecules N_2. 12 molecules H_2O **Find:** theoretical yield N_2, H_2O

Conceptual Plan: **molecules N_2H_4 → molecules N_2**

$\dfrac{3 \text{ molecules } N_2}{2 \text{ molecules } N_2H_4}$ → **smallest molecules amount determines limiting reactant**

molecules N_2O_4 → molecules N_2

$\dfrac{3 \text{ molecules } N_2}{1 \text{ molecules } N_2O_4}$

molecules N_2H_4 → molecules H_2O

$\dfrac{4 \text{ molecules } H_2O}{2 \text{ molecules } N_2H_4}$

molecules N_2H_4 → molecules N_2O_4

$\dfrac{1 \text{ molecules } N_2O_4}{2 \text{ molecules } N_2H_4}$

Solution:

$6 \text{ molecules } N_2H_4 \times \dfrac{3 \text{ molecules } N_2}{2 \text{ molecules } N_2H_4} = 9 \text{ molecules } N_2$

$6 \text{ molecules } N_2O_4 \times \dfrac{3 \text{ molecules } N_2}{1 \text{ molecules } N_2O_4} = 18 \text{ molecules } N_2$

Limiting reactant = N_2H_4 because it produced the least molecules of N_2

$6 \text{ molecules } N_2H_4 \times \dfrac{4 \text{ molecules } H_2O}{2 \text{ molecules } N_2H_4} = 12 \text{ molecules } H_2O$

$6 \text{ molecules } N_2H_4 \times \dfrac{1 \text{ molecules } N_2O_4}{2 \text{ molecules } N_2H_4} = 3 \text{ molecules } N_2O_4 \text{ used}$

Reaction mixture should contain: 9 molecules N_2, 12 molecules H_2O, and 1 molecule N_2O_4, this is best represented by (a)

Chapter 5
Gases

1. Pressure is the force exerted per unit area by gas molecules as they strike the surfaces around them. Pressure is caused by collisions of gas molecules with any surface or other gas molecule.

2. In a shallow well, a pipe runs from a pump at the surface of the ground to the water below. The pump creates a partial vacuum in the pipe, much as your mouth creates a partial vacuum in a straw when you sip a beverage. The result is a pressure difference between the inside and the outside of the pipe. When the pump is attached to the pipe and turned on, however, it removes some of the air molecules from inside the pipe, lowering the pressure there. The pressure pushing down on the surface of the water outside the pipe, however, remains the same. The result is a pressure differential—the pressure outside the pipe is now greater than the pressure inside the pipe. This greater external pressure pushes the water up the pipe to ground level and eventually to the tap where the water is used.

3. In the shallow well, atmospheric pressure does the work of pushing the water up the pipe. The pump acts to reduce the pressure inside the pipe, allowing atmospheric pressure to drive the water to the surface, against the force of gravity. The maximum depth of the well, therefore, depends on the total atmospheric pressure. Even if the pump could create a perfect vacuum (zero pressure) within the pipe, normal atmospheric pressure can only push the water to a total height of about 10.3 m because a 10.3-meter column of water exerts the same pressure—101,325 newtons per square meter or 14.7 pounds per square inch—as the gas molecules in our atmosphere.

4. $101,325 \text{ Pa} = 760 \text{ torr} = 760 \text{ mmHg} = 29.92 \text{ in Hg} = 14.7 \text{ psi} = 1 \text{ atm}$

5. A manometer is a U-shaped tube containing a dense liquid, usually mercury. In an open-ended manometer, one end of the tube is open to atmospheric pressure and the other is attached to a flask containing the gas sample. If the pressure of the gas sample is exactly equal to atmospheric pressure, then the mercury levels on both sides of the tube are the same. If the pressure of the sample is greater than atmospheric pressure, the mercury level on the sample side of the tube is lower than on the side open to the atmosphere. If the pressure of the sample is less than atmospheric pressure, the mercury level on the sample side is higher than on the side open to the atmosphere. This type of manometer always measures the pressure of the gas sample relative to atmospheric pressure. The difference in height between the two levels is equal to the pressure difference from atmospheric pressure.

6. Boyle's law states that the volume of the gas varies inversely to the pressure on the gas, while temperature and number of moles are kept constant ($P_1 V_1 = P_2 V_2$). Charles' law states that the volume of a gas is directly proportional to the temperature of the gas, while pressure and number of moles are kept constant ($V_1 / T_1 = V_2 / T_2$). All temperatures must be in degree Kelvin when used in math calculations. Avagadro's Law states that the volume of a gas is directly proportional to the number of moles of the gas, while pressure and temperature are kept constant ($V_1 / n_1 = V_2 / n_2$).

7. This pain is caused by air-containing cavities within your ear. When you ascend a mountain, the external pressure (the pressure that surrounds you) drops, while the pressure within your ear cavities (the internal pressure) remains the same. This creates an imbalance—the greater internal pressure forces your eardrum to bulge outward, causing pain. With time, and the help of a yawn or two, the excess air within your ear's cavities escapes, equalizing the internal and external pressure and relieving the pain.

8. For every 10 m of depth that a diver descends in water, she experiences an additional 1 atm of pressure due to the weight of the water above her. The pressure regulator used in scuba diving delivers air at a pressure that matches the external pressure; otherwise the diver could not inhale the air. For example, when a diver is at a depth of 20 m below the surface, the regulator delivers air at a pressure of 3 atm to match the 3 atm of pressure around the diver (1 atm due to normal atmospheric pressure and 2 additional atmospheres due to the weight of the water at 20 m). Suppose that a diver inhaled a lungful of air at a pressure of 3 atm and swam quickly to the surface (where the pressure drops to 1 atm) while holding her breath. What would happen to the volume of air in her lungs? Since the pressure decreases by a factor of 3, the volume of the air in her lungs would increase by a factor of 3, severely damaging her lungs and possibly killing her.

9. When we breathe, we expand the volume of our chest cavity, reducing the pressure on the outer surface of the lungs to less than 1 atm (Boyle's law). Because of this pressure differential, the lungs expand, the

pressure in them falls, and air from outside our lungs then flows into them. Extra-long snorkels do not work because of the pressure exerted by water at an increased depth. A diver at 10 m experiences an external pressure of 2 atm. This is more than the muscles of the chest cavity can overcome—the chest cavity and lungs are compressed, resulting in an air pressure within them of more than 1 atm. If the diver had a snorkel that went to the surface—where the air pressure is 1 atm—air would flow out of his lungs, not into them. It would be impossible to breathe.

10. Charles's law explains why a hot-air balloon can take flight. The gas that fills a hot air balloon is warmed with a burner increasing its volume and lowering its density, and causing it to float in the colder, denser surrounding air. Charles's law also explains why the second floor of a house is usually a bit warmer than the ground floor because, when air is heated, its volume increases, resulting in a lower density. The warm, less dense air tends to rise in a room filled with colder, denser air.

11. The ideal gas law (PV = nRT) combines all of the relationships between the four variables (pressure, volume, number of moles and temperature (in Kelvins)) discussed in one simple expression.

12. We know that: $V \propto 1/P$ (Boyle's law) $V \propto T$ (Charles's law) $V \propto n$ (Avogadro's law) Combining these three expressions we get: $V \propto nT/P$. Replace the proportional sign with an equal sign by incorporating R (the ideal gas constant): $V = RnT/P$ Rearranging, we get: $PV = nRT$

13. The molar volume of an ideal gas is the volume occupied by one mole of gas at T = 0 °C (273 K) and P = 1.00 atm. Substituting these values into the ideal gas law, one can calculate that this value as 22.414 L.

14. Since $d = \frac{P\mathfrak{M}}{RT}$ this means that the density will decrease as temperature increases. It will increase as pressure increases or as the molar mass of the gas increases.

15. The pressure due to any individual component in a gas mixture is called the partial pressure (P_n) of that component and can be calculated from the ideal gas law by assuming that each gas component acts independently. The sum of the partial pressures of the components in a gas mixture must equal the total pressure: $P_{total} = P_a + P_b + P_c + \ldots$ where P_{total} is the total pressure and P_a, P_b, P_c... are the partial pressures of the components.

16. Too much oxygen can also cause physiological problems. Scuba divers breathe pressurized air. At 30 m, a scuba diver breathes air at a total pressure of 4.0 atm, making P_{O2} about 0.84 atm. This elevated partial pressure of oxygen raises the density of oxygen molecules in the lungs , resulting in a higher concentration of oxygen in body tissues. When P_{O2} increases beyond 1.4 atm, the increased oxygen concentration in body tissues causes a condition called oxygen toxicity, which results in muscle twitching, tunnel vision, and convulsions.

17. No, when collecting a gas over water, it will contain some water molecules. The vapor pressure of water can be gotten from Table 5.4. Therefore, $P_{Gas} = P_{total} - P_{H2O}$.

18. In Chapter 4, we learned how the coefficients in chemical equations can be used as conversion factors between number of moles of reactants and number of moles of products in a chemical reaction; and that the molar mass can be used to convert the number of moles to the mass. At STP, each mole of gas occupies 22.414 L. The mass of the product will be

    Volume of limiting reagent (L) x $\dfrac{1\,\text{mol limiting reagent}}{22.414\ \text{L}}$ x $\dfrac{c\ \text{mol product}}{a\ \text{mol limiting reagent}}$ x $\dfrac{g\ \text{product}}{1\ \text{mol product}}$ for the reaction:

    a A + b B → c C + d D, where A is the limiting reagent and C is the product of interest.

19. The basic postulates of kinetic molecular theory are: (1) The size of a particle is negligibly small. (2) The average kinetic energy of a particle is proportional to the temperature in kelvins. and (3) The collision of one particle with another (or with the walls) is completely elastic. Pressure is defined as force divided by area.   According to kinetic molecular theory, a gas is a collection of particles in constant motion. The motion results in collisions between the particles and the surfaces around them. As each particle collides with a surface, it exerts a force upon that surface. The result of many particles in a gas sample exerting forces on the surfaces around them is a constant pressure.

20. Boyle's law states that, for a constant number of particles at constant temperature, the volume of a gas is inversely proportional to its pressure. If you decrease the volume of a gas, you force the gas particles to

occupy a smaller space. It follows from kinetic molecular theory that, as long the temperature remains the same, the result is a greater number of collisions with the surrounding surfaces and therefore a greater pressure.

Charles's law states that, for a constant number of particles at constant pressure, the volume of a gas is proportional to its temperature. According to kinetic molecular theory, when you increase the temperature of a gas, the average speed, and thus the average kinetic energy, of the particles increases. Since this greater kinetic energy results in more frequent collisions and more force per collision, the pressure of the gas would increase if its volume were held constant (Gay-Lussac's law). The only way for the pressure to remain constant is for the volume to increase. The greater volume spreads the collisions out over a greater area, so that the pressure (defined as force per unit area) is unchanged.

Avogadro's law states that, at constant temperature and pressure, the volume of a gas is proportional to the number of particles. According to kinetic molecular theory, when you increase the number of particles in a gas sample, the number of collisions with the surrounding surfaces increases. Since the greater number of collisions would result in a greater overall force on surrounding surfaces, the only way for the pressure to remain constant is for the volume to increase so that the number of particles per unit volume (and thus the number of collisions) remains constant.

Dalton's law states that the total pressure of a gas mixture is the sum of the partial pressures of its components. In other words, according to Dalton's law, the components in a gas mixture act identically to, and independently of, one another. According to kinetic molecular theory, the particles have negligible size and they do not interact. Consequently, the only property that would distinguish one type of particle from another is its mass. However, even particles of different masses have the same average kinetic energy at a given temperature, so they exert the same force upon a collision with a surface. Consequently, adding components to a gas mixture—even different *kinds* of gases—has the same effect as simply adding more particles. The partial pressures of all the components sum to the overall pressure.

21. Postulate 2 of kinetic molecular theory states that the average kinetic energy is proportional to the temperature in kelvins. The root mean square velocity of a collection of gas particles is inversely proportional to the square root of the molar mass of the particles in kilograms per mole.

22. Gaseous particles travel at tremendous speeds along very haphazard paths. To a perfume molecule, the path from the perfume bottle in the bathroom to your nose 2 m away is much like the path through a busy shopping mall during a clearance sale. The molecule travels only a short distance before it collides with another molecule, changes direction, only to collide again, and so on. The average distance that a molecule travels between collisions is called its mean free path.

23. The process by which gas molecules spread out in response to a concentration gradient is called diffusion. Effusion, the process by which a gas escapes from a container into a vacuum through a small hole. The rate of effusion is inversely proportional to the square root of the molar mass of the gas.

24. Gases behave ideally when both of the following are true: a) the volume of the gas particles is small compared to the space between them; and b) the forces between the gas particles are not significant. At high pressures the number of molecules increases, so the volume of the gas particles becomes larger and since the spacing between the particles is smaller, the interactions become more significant. At low temperatures, the molecules are not moving as fast as at higher temperatures, so the when they collide the have a greater opportunity to interact.

25. Sulfur Oxides (SO_x) – Sulfur oxides include SO_2 and SO_3, which are produced chiefly during coal-fired electricity generation and industrial metal refining. Carbon Monoxide (CO) – Carbon monoxide is formed by the incomplete combustion of fossil fuels (petroleum, natural gas, and coal). It is emitted mainly by motor vehicles. Nitrogen Oxides (NO_x) – Nitrogen oxides include NO and NO_2, which are emitted by motor vehicles, by fossil-fuel based electricity generation plants, and by any high temperature combustion process that occurs in air. Ozone (O_3) – Ozone is produced when some of the products of fossil-fuel combustion, especially nitrogen oxides and unburned volatile organic compounds (VOCs), react in the presence of sunlight. The levels of all of these pollutants are decreasing over U.S. cities.

26. Ground-level ozone (in the lower atmospheres) is an eye and lung irritant and prolonged exposure has been shown to cause permanent lung damage. Stratospheric ozone (in the upper atmosphere) is a natural part of

our environment that protects the Earth from harmful ultraviolet light. Stratospheric ozone does not harm us because we are not directly exposed to it.

27. Chlorofluorocarbons (CFCs) are blamed for destroying stratospheric ozone. When CFCs reach the stratosphere, UV light (which is less abundant below the ozone layer because the ozone absorbs it) breaks a carbon-chlorine bond in the CFC, generating a very reactive chlorine atom. This chlorine atom then reacts with ozone in a cyclic reaction that destroys two ozone molecules and regenerates itself to repeat the process. In this way, a single chlorine atom can destroy hundreds of ozone molecules. Legislation has been passed in many nations calling for a complete ban on CFC production beginning in 1996.

28. When the sun rises in the Antarctic spring (October), sunlight breaks the relatively weak Cl-Cl bond, releasing chlorine atoms into the stratosphere. The chlorine atoms then deplete ozone through a catalytic cycle. Normally the chlorine that enters our atmosphere from chlorofluorocarbons is neutralized in atmospheric chemical reservoirs. Conditions at the South Pole in the month of October happen to be just right for releasing that chlorine from its reservoirs, allowing it to continue to destroy ozone.

29. a) **Given:** 24.9 in Hg   **Find:** atm
   Conceptual plan: in Hg → atm
   $$\frac{1\,atm}{29.92\,in\,Hg}$$

   Solution: $24.9\ in\,Hg \times \dfrac{1\,atm}{29.92\,in\,Hg} = 0.832\,atm$

   Check: The units (atm) are correct. The magnitude of the answer (<1) makes physical sense because we started with less than 29.92 in Hg.

   b) **Given:** 24.9 in Hg   **Find:** mm Hg
   Conceptual plan: Use answer from part a) then convert   atm → mm Hg
   $$\frac{760\,mm\,Hg}{1\,atm}$$

   Solution: $0.832\,atm \times \dfrac{760\,mm\,Hg}{1\,atm} = 632\ mm\ Hg$

   Check: The units (mm Hg) are correct. The magnitude of the answer (< 760 mm Hg) makes physical sense because we started with less than 1 atm.

   c) **Given:** 24.9 in Hg   **Find:** psi
   Conceptual plan: Use answer from part a) then convert   atm → psi
   $$\frac{14.7\,psi}{1\,atm}$$

   Solution: $0.832\,atm \times \dfrac{14.7\,psi}{1\,atm} = 12.2\ psi$

   Check: The units (psi) are correct. The magnitude of the answer (< 14.7 psi) makes physical sense because we started with less than 1 atm.

   d) **Given:** 24.9 in Hg   **Find:** Pa
   Conceptual plan: Use answer from part a) then convert   atm → Pa
   $$\frac{101,325\,Pa}{1\,atm}$$

   Solution: $0.832\,atm \times \dfrac{101,325\,Pa}{1\,atm} = 8.43 \times 10^4\ Pa$

   Check: The units (mm Hg) are correct. The magnitude of the answer (< 760 mm Hg) makes physical sense because we started with less than 1 atm.

30. a) **Given:** 235 mm Hg   **Find:** torr
   Conceptual plan: mm Hg → torr
   $$\frac{1\,torr}{1\,mm\,Hg}$$

   Solution: $235\ mm\,Hg \times \dfrac{1\,torr}{1\,mm\,Hg} = 235\,torr$

   Check: The units (torr) are correct. The magnitude of the answer (235) makes physical sense because both units are of the same size.

b) **Given:** 235 mm Hg **Find:** psi
   Conceptual plan: mm Hg → atm → psi
   $$\frac{760\,\text{mm Hg}}{1\,\text{atm}} \qquad \frac{14.7\,\text{psi}}{1\,\text{atm}}$$

   Solution: $235\,\cancel{\text{mm Hg}} \times \dfrac{1\,\cancel{\text{atm}}}{760\,\cancel{\text{mm Hg}}} \times \dfrac{14.7\,\text{psi}}{1\,\cancel{\text{atm}}} = 4.54\,\text{psi}$

   Check: The units (psi) are correct. The magnitude of the answer (< 14.7 psi) makes physical sense because we started with less than 760 mm Hg = 1 atm.

c) **Given:** 235 mm Hg **Find:** in Hg
   Conceptual plan: mm Hg → in Hg
   $$\frac{1\,\text{in Hg}}{25.4\,\text{mm Hg}}$$

   Solution: $235\,\cancel{\text{mm Hg}} \times \dfrac{1\,\text{in Hg}}{25.4\,\cancel{\text{mm Hg}}} = 9.25\,\text{in Hg}$

   Check: The units (in Hg) are correct. The magnitude of the answer (9) makes physical sense because inches are larger than mm.

d) **Given:** 235 mm Hg **Find:** atm
   Conceptual plan: mm Hg → atm
   $$\frac{760\,\text{mm Hg}}{1\,\text{atm}}$$

   Solution: $235\,\cancel{\text{mm Hg}} \times \dfrac{1\,\text{atm}}{760\,\cancel{\text{mm Hg}}} = 0.309\,\text{atm}$

   Check: The units (atm) are correct. The magnitude of the answer (< 1) makes physical sense because we started with less than 760 mm Hg.

31. a) **Given:** 31.85 in Hg **Find:** mm Hg
   Conceptual plan: in Hg → mm Hg
   $$\frac{25.4\,\text{mm Hg}}{1\,\text{in Hg}}$$

   Solution: $31.85\,\cancel{\text{in Hg}} \times \dfrac{25.4\,\text{mm Hg}}{1\,\cancel{\text{in Hg}}} = 809.0\,\text{mm Hg}$

   Check: The units (mm Hg) are correct. The magnitude of the answer (809) makes physical sense because inches are larger than mm.

b) **Given:** 31.85 in Hg **Find:** atm
   Conceptual plan: Use answer from part a) then convert mm Hg → atm
   $$\frac{1\,\text{atm}}{760\,\text{mm Hg}}$$

   Solution: $809.0\,\cancel{\text{mm Hg}} \times \dfrac{1\,\text{atm}}{760\,\cancel{\text{mm Hg}}} = 1.064\,\text{atm}$

   Check: The units (atm) are correct. The magnitude of the answer (>1) makes physical sense because we started with more than 760 mm Hg.

c) **Given:** 31.85 in Hg **Find:** torr
   Conceptual plan: Use answer from part a) then convert mm Hg → torr
   $$\frac{1\,\text{torr}}{760\,\text{mm Hg}}$$

   Solution: $809.0\,\cancel{\text{mm Hg}} \times \dfrac{1\,\text{torr}}{760\,\cancel{\text{mm Hg}}} = 809.0\,\text{torr}$

   Check: The units (torr) are correct. The magnitude of the answer (809) makes physical sense because both units are of the same size.

d) **Given:** 31.85 in Hg **Find:** kPa
   Conceptual plan: Use answer from part b) then convert atm → Pa → kPa
   $$\frac{101,325\,\text{Pa}}{1\,\text{atm}} \qquad \frac{1\,\text{kPa}}{1000\,\text{Pa}}$$

   Solution: $1.064\,\cancel{\text{atm}} \times \dfrac{101,325\,\cancel{\text{Pa}}}{1\,\cancel{\text{atm}}} \times \dfrac{1\,\text{kPa}}{1000\,\cancel{\text{Pa}}} = 107.9\,\text{kPa}$

Check: The units (kPa) are correct. The magnitude of the answer (108) makes physical sense because we started with more than 1 atm and there are ~101 kPa in an atm.

32. a) **Given:** 652.5 mm Hg   **Find:** torr
    Conceptual plan: mm Hg → torr

$$\frac{1\,torr}{1\,mm\,Hg}$$

Solution: $652.5\,\cancel{mm\,Hg} \times \dfrac{1\,torr}{1\,mm\,Hg} = 652.5\,torr$

Check: The units (torr) are correct. The magnitude of the answer (653) makes physical sense because both units are of the same size.

b) **Given:** 652.5 mm Hg   **Find:** atm
   Conceptual plan: mm Hg → atm

$$\frac{760\,mm\,Hg}{1\,atm}$$

Solution: $652.5\,\cancel{mm\,Hg} \times \dfrac{1\,atm}{760\,\cancel{mm\,Hg}} = 0.8586\,atm$

Check: The units (psi) are correct. The magnitude of the answer (< 14.7 psi) makes physical sense because we started with less than 760 mm Hg = 1 atm.

c) **Given:** 652.5 mm Hg   **Find:** in Hg
   Conceptual plan: mm Hg → in Hg

$$\frac{1\,in\,Hg}{25.4\,mm\,Hg}$$

Solution: $652.5\,\cancel{mm\,Hg} \times \dfrac{1\,in\,Hg}{25.4\,\cancel{mm\,Hg}} = 25.7\,in\,Hg$

Check: The units (in Hg) are correct. The magnitude of the answer (26) makes physical sense because inches are larger than mm.

d) **Given:** 652.5 mm Hg   **Find:** psi
   Conceptual plan: Use answer from part b) then convert   atm → psi

$$\frac{14.7\,psi}{1\,atm}$$

Solution: $0.8586\,\cancel{atm} \times \dfrac{14.7\,psi}{1\,\cancel{atm}} = 12.6\,psi$

Check: The units (psi) are correct. The magnitude of the answer (< 14.7 psi) makes physical sense because we started with less than 1 atm.

33. a) **Given:** P_{bar} = 755.3 mm Hg and figure   **Find:** P_{gas}
    Conceptual plan: Measure height difference then convert   cm Hg → mm Hg → mm Hg

$$\frac{10\,mm\,Hg}{1\,cm\,Hg} \qquad P_{gas} = h + P_{bar}$$

Solution:

$h = 7.2\,\cancel{cm\,Hg} \times \dfrac{10\,mm\,Hg}{1\,\cancel{cm\,Hg}} = 72\,mm\,Hg \qquad P_{gas} = 72\,mm\,Hg + 755.3\,mm\,Hg = 827\,mm\,Hg$

Check: The units (mm Hg) are correct. The magnitude of the answer (827 mm Hg) makes physical sense because mercury column is higher on the right, indicating that the pressure is above barometric pressure. No significant figures to the right of the decimal point can be reported since the mercury height is known only to the 1's place.

b) **Given:** P_{bar} = 755.3 mm Hg and figure   **Find:** P_{gas}
   Conceptual plan: Measure height difference then convert   cm Hg → mm Hg → mm Hg

$$\frac{10\,mm\,Hg}{1\,cm\,Hg} \qquad P_{gas} = h + P_{bar}$$

Solution:

$h = -4.4\,\cancel{cm\,Hg} \times \dfrac{10\,mm\,Hg}{1\,\cancel{cm\,Hg}} = -44\,mm\,Hg \qquad P_{gas} = -44\,mm\,Hg + 755.3\,mm\,Hg = 711\,mm\,Hg$

Check: The units (mm Hg) are correct. The magnitude of the answer (711 mm Hg) makes physical sense because mercury column is higher on the left, indicating that the pressure is below barometric pressure. No significant figures to the right of the decimal point can be reported since the mercury height is known only to the 1's place.

34. a) **Given:** $P_{bar} = 748.2$ mm Hg and figure   **Find:** P_{gas}
    Conceptual plan: **Measure height difference then convert**   **cm Hg → mm Hg → mm Hg**

    $$\frac{10\,mm\,Hg}{1\,cm\,Hg} \qquad P_{gas} = h + P_{bar}$$

    Solution:

    $$h = -2.2\;\cancel{cm\,Hg}\;\times\;\frac{10\,mm\,Hg}{1\;\cancel{cm\,Hg}} = -22\;mm\,Hg \qquad P_{gas} = -22\;mm\,Hg + 748.2\;mm\,Hg = 726\;mm\,Hg$$

    Check: The units (mm Hg) are correct. The magnitude of the answer (726 mm Hg) makes physical sense because mercury column is higher on the left, indicating that the pressure is below barometric pressure. No significant figures to the right of the decimal point can be reported since the mercury height is known only to the 1's place.

   b) **Given:** $P_{bar} = 748.2$ mm Hg and figure   **Find:** P_{gas}
    Conceptual plan: **Measure height difference then convert**   **cm Hg → mm Hg → mm Hg**

    $$\frac{10\,mm\,Hg}{1\,cm\,Hg} \qquad P_{gas} = h + P_{bar}$$

    Solution:

    $$h = 6.8\;\cancel{cm\,Hg}\;\times\;\frac{10\,mm\,Hg}{1\;\cancel{cm\,Hg}} = 68\;mm\,Hg \qquad P_{gas} = 68\;mm\,Hg + 748.2\;mm\,Hg = 816\;mm\,Hg$$

    Check: The units (mm Hg) are correct. The magnitude of the answer (816 mm Hg) makes physical sense because mercury column is higher on the right, indicating that the pressure is above barometric pressure. No significant figures to the right of the decimal point can be reported since the mercury height is known only to the 1's place.

35. **Given:** $V_1 = 2.8$ L, $P_1 = 755$ mm Hg and $V_2 = 3.7$ L   **Find:** P_2
    Conceptual plan: $V_1, P_1, V_2 → P_2$
    $$P_1 V_1 = P_2 V_2$$

    Solution:

    $$P_1 V_1 = P_2 V_2 \text{ Rearrange to solve for } P_2. \; P_2 = P_1 \frac{V_1}{V_2} = 755\;mm\,Hg \times \frac{2.8\;\cancel{L}}{3.7\;\cancel{L}} = 570\;mm\,Hg = 5.7 \times 10^2\;mm\,Hg$$

    Check: The units (mm Hg) are correct. The magnitude of the answer (570 mm Hg) makes physical sense because Boyle's Law indicates that as the volume increases, the pressure decreases.

36. **Given:** $V_1 = 32.6$ L, $P_1 = 1.3$ atm and $V_2 = 13.8$ L   **Find:** P_2
    Conceptual plan: $V_1, P_1, V_2 → P_2$
    $$P_1 V_1 = P_2 V_2$$

    Solution: $P_1 V_1 = P_2 V_2$ Rearrange to solve for P_2. $P_2 = P_1 \frac{V_1}{V_2} = 1.3\,atm \times \frac{32.6\;\cancel{L}}{13.8\;\cancel{L}} = 3.1\,atm$

    Check: The units (atm) are correct. The magnitude of the answer (3 atm) makes physical sense because Boyle's Law indicates that as the volume decreases, the pressure increases.

37. **Given:** $V_1 = 48.3$ mL, $T_1 = 22$ °C and $T_2 = 87$ °C   **Find:** V_2
    Conceptual plan: °C → K   then $V_1, T_1, T_2 → V_2$
    $$K = °C + 273.15 \qquad\qquad \frac{V_1}{T_1} = \frac{V_2}{T_2}$$

    Solution: $T_1 = 22\,°C + 273.15 = 295$ K and $T_2 = 87\,°C + 273.15 = 360.$ K
    $$\frac{V_1}{T_1} = \frac{V_2}{T_2} \text{ Rearrange to solve for } V_2. \; V_2 = V_1 \frac{T_2}{T_1} = 48.3\;mL \times \frac{360\;K}{295\;K} = 58.9\;mL$$

    Check: The units (mL) are correct. The magnitude of the answer (59 mL) makes physical sense because Charles' Law indicates that as the volume increases, the temperature increases.

38. **Given:** $V_1 = 1.55$ mL, $T_1 = 95.3$ °C and $T_2 = 0.0$ °C   **Find:** V_2
    Conceptual plan: °C → K   then $V_1, T_1, T_2 → V_2$
    $$K = °C + 273.15 \qquad\qquad \frac{V_1}{T_1} = \frac{V_2}{T_2}$$

    Solution: $T_1 = 95.3\,°C + 273.15 = 368.5$ K   and $T_2 = 0.0\,°C + 273.15 = 273.2$ K

$\frac{V_1}{T_1} = \frac{V_2}{T_2}$ Rearrange to solve for V_2. $V_2 = V_1 \frac{T_2}{T_1} = 1.55\ mL \times \frac{273.2\ K}{368.5\ K} = 1.15\ mL$

Check: The units (mL) are correct. The magnitude of the answer (1.15 mL) makes physical sense because Charles' Law indicates that as the volume decreases, the temperature decreases.

39. **Given**: $V_1 = 2.76\ L$, $n_1 = 0.128\ mol$ and $\Delta n = 0.073\ mol$ **Find**: V_2
     Conceptual plan: $n_1 \rightarrow n_2$ then $V_1, n_1, n_2 \rightarrow V_2$

$$n_1 + \Delta n = n_2 \qquad \frac{V_1}{n_1} = \frac{V_2}{n_2}$$

Solution: $n_2 = 0.128\ mol + 0.073\ mol = 0.201\ mol$

$\frac{V_1}{n_1} = \frac{V_2}{n_2}$ Rearrange to solve for V_2. $V_2 = V_1 \frac{n_2}{n_1} = 2.76\ L \times \frac{0.201\ mol}{0.128\ mol} = 4.33\ L$

Check: The units (L) are correct. The magnitude of the answer (4.33 L) makes physical sense because Avogadro's Law indicates that as the number of moles increases, the volume increases.

40. **Given**: $V_1 = 334\ mL$, $n_1 = 0.87\ mol$ and $\Delta n = 0.22\ mol$ **Find**: V_2
     Conceptual plan: $n_1 \rightarrow n_2$ then $V_1, n_1, n_2 \rightarrow V_2$

$$n_1 + \Delta n = n_2 \qquad \frac{V_1}{n_1} = \frac{V_2}{n_2}$$

Solution: $n_2 = 0.87\ mol + 0.22\ mol = 1.09\ mol$

$\frac{V_1}{n_1} = \frac{V_2}{n_2}$ Rearrange to solve for V_2. $V_2 = V_1 \frac{n_2}{n_1} = 334\ mL \times \frac{1.09\ mol}{0.87\ mol} = 420\ mL = 4.2 \times 10^2\ mL$

Check: The units (mL) are correct. The magnitude of the answer (420 L) makes physical sense because Avogadro's Law indicates that as the number of moles increases, the volume increases.

41. **Given**: $n = 0.118\ mol$, $P = 0.97\ atm$ and $T = 305\ K$ **Find**: V
     Conceptual plan: $n, P, T \rightarrow V$

$$PV = nRT$$

Solution: $PV = nRT$ Rearrange to solve for V. $V = \frac{nRT}{P} = \frac{0.118\ mol \times 0.08206\ \frac{L \cdot atm}{mol \cdot K} \times 305\ K}{0.97\ atm} = 3.0\ L$

Check: The units (L) are correct. The magnitude of the answer (3 L) makes sense because, as you will see in the next section, one mole of an ideal gas under standard conditions (273 K and 1 atm) occupies 22.4 L. Although these are not standard conditions, they are close enough for a ballpark check of the answer. Since this gas sample contains 0.118 moles, a volume of 3 L is reasonable.

42. **Given**: $V = 10.0\ L$, $n = 0.448\ mol$, and $T = 315\ K$ **Find**: P
     Conceptual plan: $n, V, T \rightarrow P$

$$PV = nRT$$

Solution:

$PV = nRT$ Rearrange to solve for P. $P = \frac{nRT}{V} = \frac{0.448\ mol \times 0.08206\ \frac{L \cdot atm}{mol \cdot K} \times 315\ K}{10.0\ L} = 1.16\ atm$

Check: The units (atm) are correct. The magnitude of the answer ($\sim$1 L) makes sense because, as you will see in the next section, one mole of an ideal gas under standard conditions (273 K and 1 atm) occupies 22.4 L. Although these are not standard conditions, they are close enough for a ballpark check of the answer. Since this gas sample contains 0.448 moles in a volume of 10 L, a pressure of 1 atm is reasonable.

43. **Given**: $V = 28.5\ L$, $P = 1.8\ atm$, and $T = 298\ K$ **Find**: n
     Conceptual plan: $V, P, T \rightarrow n$

$$PV = nRT$$

Solution: $PV = nRT$ Rearrange to solve for n. $n = \frac{PV}{RT} = \frac{1.8\ atm \times 28.5\ L}{0.08206\ \frac{L \cdot atm}{mol \cdot K} \times 298\ K} = 2.1\ mol$

Check: The units (mol) are correct. The magnitude of the answer (2 mol) makes sense because, as you will see in the next section, one mole of an ideal gas under standard conditions (273 K and 1 atm) occupies 22.4 L. Although these are not standard conditions, they are close enough for a ballpark check of the answer. Since this gas sample has a volume of 28.5 L, and a pressure of 1.8 atm, $\sim$ 2 mol is reasonable.

44. **Given**: $V = 11.1\ L$, $P = 1.3\ atm$, and $n = 0.52\ mol$ **Find**: T

Conceptual plan: $\quad$ V, P, n $\rightarrow$ T
$$PV = nRT$$

Solution: $\quad PV = nRT$ Rearrange to solve for T. $\quad T = \dfrac{PV}{nT} = \dfrac{1.3\ \text{atm} \times 11.8\ \text{L}}{0.52\ \text{mol} \times 0.08206\ \frac{\text{L}\cdot\text{atm}}{\text{mol}\cdot\text{K}}} = 360\ \text{K}$

Check: The units (T) are correct. The magnitude of the answer (360 K) makes sense because, as you will see in the next section, one mole of an ideal gas under standard conditions (273 K and 1 atm) occupies 22.4 L. Although these are not standard conditions, they are close enough for a ballpark check of the answer. Since this gas sample has 0.52 mol, a volume of 11.8 L, and a pressure of 1.3 atm, 360 K is reasonable.

45. **Given:** $P_1 = 36.0$ psi (gauge P), $V_1 = 11.8$ L, $T_1 = 12.0\ °C$, $V_2 = 12.2$ L and $T_2 = 65.0\ °C$
    Find: P_2 and compare to $P_{max} = 38.0$ psi (gauge P)
    Conceptual plan: $\quad °C \rightarrow K \quad$ and gauge P $\rightarrow$ psi $\rightarrow$ atm then $P_1, V_1, T_1, V_2, T_2 \rightarrow P_2$

$$K = °C + 273.15 \qquad\qquad \text{psi} = \text{gauge P} + 14.7 \quad \dfrac{1\ \text{atm}}{14.7\ \text{psi}} \qquad\qquad \dfrac{P_1 V_1}{T_1} = \dfrac{P_2 V_2}{T_2}$$

Solution: $\quad T_1 = 12.0\ °C + 273.15 = 285.2\ K$ and $T_2 = 65.0\ °C + 273.15 = 338.2\ K$

$P_1 = 36.0$ psi (gauge P) $+ 14.7 = 50.7\ \text{psi} \times \dfrac{1\ \text{atm}}{14.7\ \text{psi}} = 3.44898\ \text{atm}$

$P_{max} = 38.0$ psi (gauge P) $+ 14.7 = 52.7\ \text{psi} \times \dfrac{1\ \text{atm}}{14.7\ \text{psi}} = 3.59\ \text{atm}$

$\dfrac{P_1 V_1}{T_1} = \dfrac{P_2 V_2}{T_2}$ Rearrange to solve for P_2. $\quad P_2 = P_1 \dfrac{V_1}{V_2}\dfrac{T_2}{T_1} = 3.44898\ \text{atm} \times \dfrac{11.8\ \text{L}}{12.2\ \text{L}} \times \dfrac{338.2\ \text{K}}{285.2\ \text{K}} = 3.95\ \text{atm}$

This exceeds the maximum tire rating of 3.59 atm or 38.0 psi (gauge P).
Check: The units (atm) are correct. The magnitude of the answer (3.95 atm) makes physical sense because the relative increase in T is greater than the relative increase in V, so P should increase.

46. **Given:** $P_1 = 748$ mm Hg, $V_1 = 28.5$ L, $T_1 = 28.0\ °C$, $P_2 = 385$ mm Hg, and $T_2 = -15.0\ °C$ **Find:** V_2
    Conceptual plan: $\quad °C \rightarrow K \quad$ and mm Hg $\rightarrow$ atm $\quad$ then $\quad P_1, V_1, T_1, V_2, T_2 \rightarrow P_2$

$$K = °C + 273.15 \qquad\qquad \dfrac{1\ \text{atm}}{760\ \text{mm Hg}} \qquad\qquad \dfrac{P_1 V_1}{T_1} = \dfrac{P_2 V_2}{T_2}$$

Solution: $\quad T_1 = 28.0\ °C + 273.15 = 301.2\ K$ and $T_2 = -15.0\ °C + 273.15 = 258.2\ K$

$P_1 = 748\ \text{mm Hg} \times \dfrac{1\ \text{atm}}{760\ \text{mm Hg}} = 0.984211\ \text{atm} \quad P_2 = 385\ \text{mm Hg} \times \dfrac{1\ \text{atm}}{760\ \text{mm Hg}} = 0.506579\ \text{atm}$

$\dfrac{P_1 V_1}{T_1} = \dfrac{P_2 V_2}{T_2}$ Rearrange to solve for V_2. $\quad V_2 = V_1 \dfrac{P_1}{P_2}\dfrac{T_2}{T_1} = 28.5\ \text{L} \times \dfrac{0.984211\ \text{atm}}{0.506579\ \text{atm}} \times \dfrac{258.2\ \text{K}}{301.2\ \text{K}} = 47.4\ \text{L}$

Check: The units (L) are correct. The magnitude of the answer (47 L) makes physical sense because the relative decrease in P is greater than the relative decrease in T, so V should increase.

47. **Given:** $m\ (CO_2) = 28.8$ g, $P = 742$ mm Hg and $T = 22\ °C$ $\qquad$ **Find:** V
    Conceptual plan: $°C \rightarrow K \quad$ and mm Hg $\rightarrow$ atm and g $\rightarrow$ mol $\quad$ then $\quad$ n, P, T $\rightarrow$ V

$$K = °C + 273.15 \qquad \dfrac{1\ \text{atm}}{760\ \text{mm Hg}} \qquad \dfrac{1\ \text{mol}}{44.01\ \text{g}} \qquad\qquad PV = nRT$$

Solution: $T_1 = 22\ °C + 273.15 = 295\ K, \quad P = 742\ \text{mm Hg} \times \dfrac{1\ \text{atm}}{760\ \text{mm Hg}} = 0.976316\ \text{atm}$,

$n = 28.8\ \text{g} \times \dfrac{1\ \text{mol}}{44.01\ \text{g}} = 0.654397\ \text{mol} \qquad\qquad PV = nRT \qquad$ Rearrange to solve for V.

$V = \dfrac{nRT}{P} = \dfrac{0.654397\ \text{mol} \times 0.08206\ \frac{\text{L}\cdot\text{atm}}{\text{mol}\cdot\text{K}} \times 295\ \text{K}}{0.976316\ \text{atm}} = 16.2\ \text{L}$

Check: The units (L) are correct. The magnitude of the answer (16 L) makes sense because, one mole of an ideal gas under standard conditions (273 K and 1 atm) occupies 22.4 L. Although these are not standard conditions, they are close enough for a ballpark check of the answer. Since this gas sample contains 0.65 moles, a volume of 16 L is reasonable.

48. **Given:** 1.0 L of liquid N_2 w/ d = 0.807 g/mL, T = 25.0 °C, P = 1.0 atm, and closet is 1.0 m x 1.0 m x 2.0 m
    Find: V% of closet displaced by evaporated liquid
    Conceptual plan: $°C \rightarrow K \quad$ and L $\rightarrow$ mL $\rightarrow$ g $\rightarrow$ mol $\quad$ then $\quad$ n, P, T $\rightarrow V_{evap}$

$$K = °C + 273.15 \qquad \dfrac{1000\ \text{mL}}{1\ \text{L}} \quad d = m/V \quad \dfrac{1\ \text{mol}}{28.02\ \text{g}} \qquad\qquad PV = nRT$$

then l, w, h → V_{closet} m³ → cm³ → L   finally V_{evap}, V_{closet} → % V displaced

$$V = l \times w \times h$$ $$\frac{(100 \text{ cm})^3}{(1 \text{ m})^3}$$ $$\frac{1 \text{ L}}{1000 \text{ mL}}$$ $$\%V \text{ displaced} = \frac{V_{evap}}{V_{closet}} \times 100\%$$

Solution: $T_1 = 25.0 \text{ °C} + 273.15 = 298.2 \text{ K}$, $1.0 \text{ L} \times \frac{1000 \text{ mL}}{1 \text{ L}} = 1.0 \times 10^3 \text{ mL}$, $d = m/V$ Rearrange to solve

for m. $m = d \times V = 0.807 \frac{g}{mL} \times 1.0 \times 10^3 \text{ mL} = 8.1 \times 10^2 \text{ g} \times \frac{1 \text{ mol}}{28.02 \text{ g}} = 28.908 \text{ mol}$ $PV = nRT$

Rearrange to solve for V.

$$V_{evap} = \frac{nRT}{P} = \frac{28.908 \text{ mol} \times 0.08206 \frac{\text{L} \cdot \text{atm}}{\text{mol} \cdot \text{K}} \times 298.2 \text{ K}}{1.0 \text{ atm}} = 7.0739 \times 10^2 \text{ L}$$

$V_{closet} = l \times w \times h = 1.0 \text{ m} \times 1.0 \text{ m} \times 2.0 \text{ m} = 2.0 \text{ m}^3$ $V_{closet} = 2.0 \text{ m}^3 \times \frac{(100 \text{ cm})^3}{(1 \text{ m})^3} \times \frac{1 \text{ L}}{1000 \text{ cm}^3} = 2.0 \times 10^3 \text{ L}$

$\%V \text{ displaced} = \frac{V_{evap}}{V_{closet}} \times 100\% = \frac{7.0739 \times 10^2 \text{ L}}{2.0 \times 10^3 \text{ L}} \times 100\% = 35 \%$

Check: The units (%) are correct.   The magnitude of the answer (35 %) makes sense because, should be between 0 and 100 %. Looking at the two volumes, when a liquid evaporates the volume increases by several orders of magnitude; when converting from cubic meters to L there is an increase of 3 orders of magnitude.

49. **Given:** sample a = 5 gas particles, sample b = 10 gas particles, and sample c = 8 gas particles, with all temperatures and volumes the same   **Find:** sample with largest P
    Conceptual plan: n, V, T → P
    $$PV = nRT$$
    Solution: $PV = nRT$ Since V and T are constant this means that P α n. The sample with the largest number of gas particles will have the highest P. $P_b > P_c > P_a$.

50. **Given:** $P_1 = 1 \text{ atm}$, $V_1 = 1 \text{ L}$, $T_1 = 25 \text{ °C}$, $V_2 = 0.5 \text{ L}$, and $T_2 = 250. \text{ °C}$ **Find:** Draw picture and P_2
    Conceptual plan: °C → K   then P_1, V_1, T_1, V_2, T_2 → P_2
    $$K = \text{°C} + 273.15$$ $$\frac{P_1 V_1}{T_1} = \frac{P_2 V_2}{T_2}$$
    Solution: $T_1 = 25 \text{ °C} + 273.15 = 298 \text{ K}$ and $T_2 = 250. \text{ °C} + 273.15 = 520. \text{ K}$
    $\frac{P_1 V_1}{T_1} = \frac{P_2 V_2}{T_2}$ Rearrange to solve for P_2. $P_2 = P_1 \frac{V_1}{V_2} \frac{T_2}{T_1} = 1 \text{ atm} \times \frac{1 \text{ L}}{0.5 \text{ L}} \times \frac{520. \text{ K}}{298 \text{ K}} = 3 \text{ atm}$
    Insert a drawing that looks like the one in the original problem, with the following changes: (1) decrease the volume by a factor of 2, and (2) lengthen the tails on the gas particles to indicate that they are moving faster. Keep the same number of particles.
    Check: The units (atm) are correct.   The magnitude of the answer (3 atm) makes physical sense because there is an increase in T and a decrease in V, both of which increase P.

51. **Given:** $P_1 = 755 \text{ mm Hg}$, $T_1 = 25 \text{ °C}$, and $T_2 = 1155 \text{ °C}$ **Find:** P_2
    Conceptual plan: °C → K and mm Hg → atm   then P_1, T_1, T_2 → P_2
    $$K = \text{°C} + 273.15$$ $$\frac{1 \text{ atm}}{760 \text{ mm Hg}}$$ $$\frac{P_1}{T_1} = \frac{P_2}{T_2}$$
    Solution: $T_1 = 25 \text{ °C} + 273.15 = 298 \text{ K}$ and $T_2 = 1155 \text{ °C} + 273.15 = 1428 \text{ K}$
    $P = 755 \text{ mm Hg} \times \frac{1 \text{ atm}}{760 \text{ mm Hg}} = 0.993421 \text{ atm}$ $\frac{P_1}{T_1} = \frac{P_2}{T_2}$ Rearrange to solve for P_2.
    $P_2 = P_1 \frac{T_2}{T_1} = 0.993421 \text{ atm} \times \frac{1428 \text{ K}}{298 \text{ K}} = 4.76 \text{ atm}$
    Check: The units (atm) are correct.   The magnitude of the answer (5 atm) makes physical sense because there is a significant increase in T, which will increase P significantly.

52. **Given:** $V_1 = 1.75 \text{ L}$, $P_1 = 1.35 \text{ atm}$, $T_1 = 25 \text{ °C}$, $V_2 = 1.75 \text{ L}$, and $T_2 = 355 \text{ °C}$ **Find:** P_2
    Conceptual plan: °C → K   then P_1, T_1, T_2 → P_2
    $$K = \text{°C} + 273.15$$ $$\frac{P_1}{T_1} = \frac{P_2}{T_2}$$
    Solution: $T_1 = 25 \text{ °C} + 273.15 = 298 \text{ K}$ and $T_2 = 355 \text{ °C} + 273.15 = 628 \text{ K}$

$\frac{P_1}{T_1} = \frac{P_2}{T_2}$ Rearrange to solve for P_2. $P_2 = P_1 \frac{T_2}{T_1} = 1.35 \text{ atm} \times \frac{628 \text{ K}}{298 \text{ K}} = 2.84 \text{ atm}$

Check: The units (atm) are correct. The magnitude of the answer (3 atm) makes physical sense because there is a significant increase in T, which will increase P significantly.

53. **Given:** STP and m (Ne) = 10.0 g   **Find:** V

Conceptual plan: g → mol → V

$$\frac{1 \text{ mol}}{20.18 \text{ g}} \qquad \frac{22.414 \text{ L}}{1 \text{ mol}}$$

Solution: $10.0 \text{ g} \times \frac{1 \text{ mol}}{20.18 \text{ g}} \times \frac{22.414 \text{ L}}{1 \text{ mol}} = 11.1 \text{ L}$

Check: The units (L) are correct. The magnitude of the answer (11 L) makes sense because, one mole of an ideal gas under standard conditions (273 K and 1 atm) occupies 22.4 L and we have about 0.5 mol.

54. **Given:** STP and CO_2 **Find:** d

Conceptual plan: mol → g then   m,V → d

$$\frac{44.01 \text{ g}}{1 \text{ mol}} \qquad\qquad d = \frac{m}{V}$$

Solution: $1 \text{ mol} \times \frac{44.01 \text{ g}}{1 \text{ mol}} = 44.01 \text{ g} = m$ at STP $V = 22.414 \text{ L}$ $d = \frac{m}{V} = \frac{44.01 \text{ g}}{22.414 \text{ L}} = 1.964 \text{ g/L}$

Check: The units (g/L) are correct. The magnitude of the answer (2 g/L) is reasonable for a gas density.

55. **Given:** H_2, P = 1655 psi, and T = 20.0 °C   **Find:** d

Conceptual plan: °C → K and psi → atm   then   P, T, $\mathfrak{M}$ → d

$$K = °C + 273.15 \qquad \frac{1 \text{ atm}}{14.7 \text{ psi}} \qquad\qquad d = \frac{P\mathfrak{M}}{RT}$$

Solution: T = 20.0 °C + 273.15 = 293.2 K   P = $1655 \text{ psi} \times \frac{1 \text{ atm}}{14.7 \text{ psi}} = 112.585 \text{ atm}$

$$d = \frac{P\mathfrak{M}}{RT} = \frac{112.585 \text{ atm} \times 2.016 \frac{\text{g}}{\text{mol}}}{0.08206 \frac{\text{L atm}}{\text{K mol}} \times 293.2 \text{ K}} = 9.43 \frac{\text{g}}{\text{L}}$$

Check: The units (g/L) are correct. The magnitude of the answer (9 g/L) makes physical sense because this is a high pressure, so the gas density will be on the high side.

56. **Given:** N_2O, d = 2.85 g/L, and T = 298 K   **Find:** P (mm Hg)

Conceptual plan: d, T, $\mathfrak{M}$ → d   then atm → mm Hg

$$d = \frac{P\mathfrak{M}}{RT} \qquad\qquad \frac{760 \text{ mm Hg}}{1 \text{ atm}}$$

Solution: $d = \frac{P\mathfrak{M}}{RT}$ Rearrange to solve for P. $P = \frac{dRT}{\mathfrak{M}} = \frac{2.85 \frac{\text{g}}{\text{L}} \times 0.08206 \frac{\text{L atm}}{\text{K mol}} \times 298 \text{ K}}{44.02 \frac{\text{g}}{\text{mol}}} = 1.58322 \text{ atm}$

$$P = 1.58322 \text{ atm} \times \frac{760 \text{ mm Hg}}{1 \text{ atm}} = 1.20 \times 10^3 \text{ mm Hg}$$

Check: The units (mm Hg) are correct. The magnitude of the answer (1200 mm Hg) makes physical sense because the gas density is reasonable and so we expect a P ~1 atm.

57. **Given:** V = 248 mL, m = 0.433 g, P = 745 mm Hg, and T = 28 °C   **Find:** $\mathfrak{M}$

Conceptual plan: °C → K mm Hg → atm mL → L then V, m → d then d, P, T → $\mathfrak{M}$

$$K = °C + 273.15 \qquad \frac{1 \text{ atm}}{760 \text{ mm Hg}} \qquad \frac{1 \text{ L}}{1000 \text{ mL}} \qquad d = \frac{m}{V} \qquad d = \frac{P\mathfrak{M}}{RT}$$

Solution: T = 28 °C + 273.15 = 301 K   P = $745 \text{ mm Hg} \times \frac{1 \text{ atm}}{760 \text{ mm Hg}} = 0.980263 \text{ atm}$

$V = 248 \text{ mL} \times \frac{1 \text{ L}}{1000 \text{ mL}} = 0.248 \text{ L}$ $d = \frac{m}{V} = \frac{0.433 \text{ g}}{0.248 \text{ L}} = 1.74597 \text{ g/L}$ $d = \frac{P\mathfrak{M}}{RT}$ Rearrange to solve for $\mathfrak{M}$.

$$\mathfrak{M} = \frac{dRT}{P} = \frac{1.74597 \frac{\text{g}}{\text{L}} \times 0.08206 \frac{\text{L atm}}{\text{K mol}} \times 301 \text{ K}}{0.980263 \text{ atm}} = 44.0 \text{ g/mol}$$

144

Check: The units (g/mol) are correct.   The magnitude of the answer (44 g/mol) makes physical sense because this is a reasonable number for a molecular weight of a gas.

58. **Given**: V = 113 mL, m = 0.171 g, P = 721 mm Hg, and T = 32 °C   **Find**: $\mathfrak{M}$

    Conceptual plan: °C $\rightarrow$ K   mm Hg $\rightarrow$ atm   mL $\rightarrow$ L then V, m $\rightarrow$ d then d, P, T $\rightarrow$ $\mathfrak{M}$

$$K = °C + 273.15 \qquad \frac{1\ atm}{760\ mm\ Hg} \qquad \frac{1\ L}{1000\ mL} \qquad d = \frac{m}{V} \qquad d = \frac{P\mathfrak{M}}{RT}$$

    Solution: T = 32 °C + 273.15 = 305 K   P = 721 mm Hg $\times \dfrac{1\ atm}{760\ mm\ Hg}$ = 0.948684 atm

$$V = 113\ mL \times \frac{1\ L}{1000\ mL} = 0.113\ L \qquad d = \frac{m}{V} = \frac{0.171\ g}{0.113\ L} = 1.51327\ g/L \qquad d = \frac{P\mathfrak{M}}{RT} \text{ Rearrange to solve for } \mathfrak{M}.$$

$$\mathfrak{M} = \frac{dRT}{P} = \frac{1.51327\ \frac{g}{L} \times 0.08206\ \frac{L\ atm}{K\ mol} \times 305\ K}{0.948684\ atm} = 39.8\ g/mol$$

    Check: The units (g/mol) are correct.   The magnitude of the answer (40 g/mol) makes physical sense because this is a reasonable number for a molecular weight of a gas.

59. **Given**: m = 38.8 mg, V = 224 mL, T = 55 °C, and P = 886 torr   **Find**: $\mathfrak{M}$

    Conceptual plan: mg $\rightarrow$ g mL $\rightarrow$ L   °C $\rightarrow$ K   torr $\rightarrow$ atm then V, m $\rightarrow$ d then d, P, T $\rightarrow$ $\mathfrak{M}$

$$\frac{1\ g}{1000\ mg} \qquad \frac{1\ L}{1000\ mL} \qquad K = °C + 273.15 \qquad \frac{1\ atm}{760\ torr} \qquad d = \frac{m}{V} \qquad d = \frac{P\mathfrak{M}}{RT}$$

    Solution: m = 38.8 mg $\times \dfrac{1\ g}{1000\ mg}$ = 0.0388 g   V = 224 mL $\times \dfrac{1\ L}{1000\ mL}$ = 0.224 L T = 55 °C + 273.15 = 328 K

$$P = 886\ torr \times \frac{1\ atm}{760\ torr} = 1.165789\ atm \qquad d = \frac{m}{V} = \frac{0.0388\ g}{0.224\ L} = 0.173214\ g/L \qquad d = \frac{P\mathfrak{M}}{RT}$$

    Rearrange to solve for $\mathfrak{M}$. $\mathfrak{M} = \dfrac{dRT}{P} = \dfrac{0.173214\ \frac{g}{L} \times 0.08206\ \frac{L\ atm}{K\ mol} \times 328\ K}{1.165789\ atm} = 4.00\ g/mol$

    Check: The units (g/mol) are correct.   The magnitude of the answer (4 g/mol) makes physical sense because this is a reasonable number for a molecular weight of a gas, especially since the density is on the low side.

60. **Given**: m = 0.555 g, V = 117 mL, T = 85 °C, and P = 753 mm Hg   **Find**: $\mathfrak{M}$

    Conceptual plan: mL $\rightarrow$ L   °C $\rightarrow$ K   mm Hg $\rightarrow$ atm   then V, m $\rightarrow$ d then d, P, T $\rightarrow$ $\mathfrak{M}$

$$\frac{1\ L}{1000\ mL} \qquad K = °C + 273.15 \qquad \frac{1\ atm}{760\ mm\ Hg} \qquad d = \frac{m}{V} \qquad d = \frac{P\mathfrak{M}}{RT}$$

    Solution: V = 117 mL $\times \dfrac{1\ L}{1000\ mL}$ = 0.117 L   T = 85 °C + 273.15 = 358 K

$$P = 753\ mm\ Hg \times \frac{1\ atm}{760\ mm\ Hg} = 0.9907895\ atm \qquad d = \frac{m}{V} = \frac{0.555\ g}{0.117\ L} = 4.74359\ g/L \qquad d = \frac{P\mathfrak{M}}{RT}$$

    Rearrange to solve for $\mathfrak{M}$. $\mathfrak{M} = \dfrac{dRT}{P} = \dfrac{4.74359\ \frac{g}{L} \times 0.08206\ \frac{L\ atm}{K\ mol} \times 358\ K}{0.9907895\ atm} = 141\ g/mol$

    Check: The units (g/mol) are correct.   The magnitude of the answer (141 g/mol) makes physical sense because this is a reasonable number for a molecular weight of a gas, especially since the density is on the high side.

61. **Given**: P_{N2} = 325 torr, P_{O2} = 124 torr, P_{He} = 209 torr, V = 1.05 L, and T = 25.0 °C

    Find: m_{N2}, m_{O2}, m_{He}

    Conceptual plan: °C $\rightarrow$ K   and torr $\rightarrow$ atm and   P, V, T $\rightarrow$ n then   mol $\rightarrow$ g

$$K = °C + 273.15 \qquad \frac{1\ atm}{760\ torr} \qquad PV = nRT \qquad \mathfrak{M}$$

    and P_{N2}, P_{O2}, P_{He} $\rightarrow$ P_{Total}
    $$P_{Total} = P_{N2} + P_{O2} + P_{He}$$

    Solution: T_1 = 25.0 °C + 273.15 = 298.2 K,   PV = nRT   Rearrange to solve for n.

$$n = \frac{PV}{RT} \quad P_{N2} = 325\ torr \times \frac{1\ atm}{760\ torr} = 0.427632\ atm$$

145

$$n_{N2} = \frac{0.427632 \text{ atm} \times 1.05 \text{ L}}{0.08206 \frac{\text{L} \cdot \text{atm}}{\text{mol} \cdot \text{K}} \times 298.2 \text{ K}} = 0.0183493 \text{ mol} \qquad 0.0183493 \text{ mol} \times \frac{28.02 \text{ mol}}{1 \text{ mol}} = 0.514 \text{ g N}_2$$

$$P_{O2} = 124 \text{ torr} \times \frac{1 \text{ atm}}{760 \text{ torr}} = 0.163158 \text{ atm} \qquad n_{o2} = \frac{0.163158 \text{ atm} \times 1.05 \text{ L}}{0.08206 \frac{\text{L} \cdot \text{atm}}{\text{mol} \cdot \text{K}} \times 298.2 \text{ K}} = 0.00700097 \text{ mol}$$

$$0.00700097 \text{ mol} \times \frac{32.00 \text{ mol}}{1 \text{ mol}} = 0.224 \text{ g O}_2$$

$$P_{He} = 209 \text{ torr} \times \frac{1 \text{ atm}}{760 \text{ torr}} = 0.275 \text{ atm} \qquad n_{He} = \frac{0.275 \text{ atm} \times 1.05 \text{ L}}{0.08206 \frac{\text{L} \cdot \text{atm}}{\text{mol} \cdot \text{K}} \times 298.2 \text{ K}} = 0.0118000 \text{ mol}$$

$$0.0118000 \text{ mol} \times \frac{4.003 \text{ mol}}{1 \text{ mol}} = 0.0472 \text{ g He} \quad \text{and}$$

$P_{Total} = P_{N2} + P_{O2} + P_{He} = 0.428 \text{ atm} + 0.163 \text{ atm} + 0.275 \text{ atm} = 0.866 \text{ atm}$

Check: The units (g and atm) are correct. The magnitude of the answer (1 g) makes sense because, gases are not very dense and these pressures are < 1 atm. Since all of the pressures are small, the total is < 1 atm.

62. **Given:** $P_{Total} = 755$ mm Hg, $P_{CO2} = 255$ mm Hg, $P_{Ar} = 124$ mm Hg, $P_{O2} = 167$ mm Hg, V = 10.0 L, and T = 273 K   **Find:** P_{He} and m_{He}

Conceptual plan: $P_{Total}, P_{CO2}, P_{Ar}, P_{O2} \rightarrow P_{He}$ then mm Hg $\rightarrow$ atm   then   P, V, T $\rightarrow$ n   then

$$P_{Total} = P_{CO2} + P_{Ar} + P_{O2} + P_{He} \qquad \frac{1 \text{ atm}}{760 \text{ torr}} \qquad P V = nRT$$

mol $\rightarrow$ g

$$\frac{4.003 \text{ g}}{1 \text{ mol}}$$

Solution: $P_{Total} = P_{CO2} + P_{Ar} + P_{O2} + P_{He}$ Rearrange to solve for P_{He}.

$P_{He} = P_{Total} - P_{CO2} + P_{Ar} + P_{O2} = 755$ mm Hg – 255 mm Hg – 124 mm Hg – 167 mm Hg = 209 mm Hg

$$P_{He} = 209 \text{ torr} \times \frac{1 \text{ atm}}{760 \text{ torr}} = 0.275 \text{ atm} \qquad P V = nRT \qquad \text{Rearrange to solve for n.} \quad n = \frac{PV}{RT}$$

$$n_{He} = \frac{0.275 \text{ atm} \times 10.0 \text{ L}}{0.08206 \frac{\text{L} \cdot \text{atm}}{\text{mol} \cdot \text{K}} \times 273 \text{ K}} = 0.1227548 \text{ mol} \qquad 0.1227548 \text{ mol} \times \frac{4.003 \text{ g}}{1 \text{ mol}} = 0.491 \text{ g He}$$

Check: The units (g) are correct. The magnitude of the answer (1 g) makes sense because, gases are not very dense and these pressures are < 1 atm.

63. **Given:** m (CO_2) = 1.20 g, V = 755 mL, P_{N2} = 725 mm Hg, and T = 25.0 °C   **Find:** P_{Total}

Conceptual plan: mL $\rightarrow$ L and °C $\rightarrow$ K and g $\rightarrow$ mol and n, P, T $\rightarrow$ V   then   atm $\rightarrow$ mm Hg

$$\frac{1 \text{ L}}{1000 \text{ mL}} \qquad K = °C + 273.15 \qquad \frac{1 \text{ mol}}{44.01 \text{ g}} \qquad P V = nRT \qquad \frac{760 \text{ mm Hg}}{1 \text{ atm}}$$

finally $P_{CO2}, P_{N2} \rightarrow P_{Total}$

$$P_{Total} = P_{CO2} + P_{N2}$$

Solution: , V = 755 mL $\times \frac{1 \text{ L}}{1000 \text{ mL}} = 0.755$ L   T = 25.0 °C + 273.15 = 298.2 K,

n = 1.20 g $\times \frac{1 \text{ mol}}{44.01 \text{ g}} = 0.0272665$ mol , $P V = nRT$ Rearrange to solve for P.

$$P = \frac{nRT}{V} = \frac{0.0272665 \text{ mol} \times 0.08206 \frac{\text{L} \cdot \text{atm}}{\text{mol} \cdot \text{K}} \times 298.2 \text{ K}}{0.755 \text{ L}} = 0.883735 \text{ atm}$$

$$P_{CO2} = 0.883735 \text{ atm} \times \frac{760 \text{ mm Hg}}{1 \text{ atm}} = 672 \text{ mm Hg}$$

$P_{Total} = P_{CO2} + P_{N2} = 672$ mm Hg + 725 mm Hg = 1397 mm Hg

Check: The units (mm Hg) are correct. The magnitude of the answer (1400 mm Hg) makes sense because, it must be greater than 725 mm Hg.

64. **Given:** $V_{1He} = 275$ mL, $P_{1He} = 752$ torr, $V_{1Ar} = 475$ mL, and $P_{1Ar} = 722$ torr   **Find:** P_{2He}, P_{2Ar} and P_{Total}

Conceptual plan: $V_{1He}, V_{1Ar} \rightarrow V_2$ $V_1, P_1, V_2 \rightarrow P_2$ then $P_{2He}, P_{2Ar} \rightarrow P_{Total}$

$$V_{1He} + V_{1Ar} = V_2 \qquad P_1 V_1 = P_2 V_2 \qquad P_{Total} = P_{2He} + P_{2Ar}$$

Solution: $V_{1He} + V_{1Ar} = V_2 = 275$ mL + 475 mL = 750. mL, $P_1 V_1 = P_2 V_2$ Rearrange to solve for P_2.

$$P_2 = P_1 \frac{V_1}{V_2} \quad P_{2He} = P_{1He} \frac{V_{1He}}{V_2} = 752 \text{ torr} \times \frac{275 \text{ mL}}{750. \text{ mL}} = 275.733 \text{ torr}$$

$$P_{2Ar} = P_{1Ar} \frac{V_{1Ar}}{V_2} = 722 \text{ torr} \times \frac{475 \text{ mL}}{750. \text{ mL}} = 457.267 \text{ torr}$$

$P_{Total} = P_{2He} + P_{2Ar} = 275.733 \text{ torr} + 457.267 \text{ torr} = 733 \text{ torr}$

Check: The units (torr) are correct. The magnitude of the answers makes physical sense because Boyle's Law indicates that as the volume increases, the pressure decrease. Since both initial pressures are ~700 torr, the final total pressure should be about the same pressure.

65. **Given:** m (N_2) = 1.25 g, m (O_2) = 0.85 g, V = 1.55 L, and T = 18 °C   **Find:** χ_{N2}, χ_{O2}, P_{N2}, P_{O2}
    Conceptual plan: g → mol then n_{N2}, n_{O2} → χ_{N2} and n_{N2}, n_{O2} → χ_{O2} °C → K

$$\mathfrak{M} \qquad \chi_{N2} = \frac{n_{N2}}{n_{N2} + n_{O2}} \qquad \chi_{O2} = \frac{n_{O2}}{n_{N2} + n_{O2}} \qquad K = °C + 273.15$$

then n, V, T → P
    $PV = nRT$

Solution: $n_{N2} = 1.25 \text{ g} \times \frac{1 \text{ mol}}{28.02 \text{ g}} = 0.0446110 \text{ mol}$, $n_{O2} = 0.85 \text{ g} \times \frac{1 \text{ mol}}{32.00 \text{ g}} = 0.026563 \text{ mol}$,

T = 18 °C + 273.15 = 291 K, $\chi_{N2} = \frac{n_{N2}}{n_{N2} + n_{O2}} = \frac{0.0446110 \text{ mol}}{0.0446110 \text{ mol} + 0.026563 \text{ mol}} = 0.626792 = 0.627$,

$\chi_{O2} = \frac{n_{O2}}{n_{N2} + n_{O2}} = \frac{0.026563 \text{ mol}}{0.0446110 \text{ mol} + 0.026563 \text{ mol}} = 0.38$ We can also calculate this as

$\chi_{O2} = 1 - \chi_{N2} = 1 - 0.626792 = 0.373208 = 0.373$ $PV = nRT$

Rearrange to solve for P. $P = \frac{nRT}{V}$

$$P_{N2} = \frac{0.044611 \text{ mol} \times 0.08206 \frac{\text{L} \cdot \text{atm}}{\text{mol} \cdot \text{K}} \times 291 \text{ K}}{1.55 \text{ L}} = 0.687 \text{ atm}$$

$$P_{O2} = \frac{0.026563 \text{ mol} \times 0.08206 \frac{\text{L} \cdot \text{atm}}{\text{mol} \cdot \text{K}} \times 291 \text{ K}}{1.55 \text{ L}} = 0.409 \text{ atm}$$

Check: The units (none and atm) are correct. The magnitude of the answers makes sense because, the mole fractions should total 1 and since the weight of N_2 is greater than O_2, its mole fraction is larger. The number of moles is <<1, so we expect the pressures to be <1 atm, given the V (1.55 L).

66. **Given:** Table 5.3, m (O_2) = 10.0 g , T = 273 K and P = 1.00 atm   **Find:** χ_{O2} and V_{air}
    Conceptual plan: %V → χ_{O2} and   g → mol → V_{O2} → V_{air}

$$\frac{1}{100 \%} \qquad \frac{1 \text{ mol}}{32.00 \text{ g}} \quad \frac{22.414 \text{ L}}{1 \text{ mol}} \qquad \frac{100 \text{ L air}}{21 \text{ L } O_2}$$

Solution: from Table 5.3 %V_{O2} = 21 % $21 \% \times \frac{1}{100 \%} = 0.21 = \chi_{O2}$

$10.0 \text{ g} \times \frac{1 \text{ mol}}{32.00 \text{ g}} \times \frac{22.414 \text{ L}}{1 \text{ mol}} = 7.00 \text{ L} = V_{O2}$ finally $7.00 \text{ L } O_2 \times \frac{100 \text{ L air}}{21 \text{ L } O_2} = 33.3 \text{ L air}$

Check: The units (none and L) are correct. The magnitude of the answer (0.21) makes sense because most of air is nitrogen. The magnitude of the answer (33 L) makes sense because one mole of an ideal gas under standard conditions (273 K and 1 atm) occupies 22.4 L and we have about 1/3 mol of O_2 and so over a mole of air.

67. **Given:** T = 30.0 °C, P_{Total} = 732 mm Hg, and V = 722 mL   **Find:** P_{H2} and m_{H2}
    Conceptual plan: T → P_{H2O} then P_{Total}, P_{H2O} → P_{H2} then   mm Hg → atm   and   mL → L
    Table 5.4 $P_{Total} = P_{H2O} + P_{H2}$ $\frac{1 \text{ atm}}{760 \text{ torr}}$ $\frac{1 \text{ L}}{1000 \text{ mL}}$

and °C → K   P, V, T → n   then   mol → g
    $K = °C + 273.15$ $PV = nRT$ $\frac{2.016 \text{ g}}{1 \text{ mol}}$

Solution: Table 5.4 states that P_{H2O} = 31.86 mm Hg $P_{Total} = P_{H2O} + P_{H2}$

147

Rearrange to solve for P_{H2}. $P_{H2} = P_{Total} - P_{H2O} = 732$ mm Hg $- 31.86$ mm Hg $= 700.$ mm Hg

$P_{He} = 700.$ torr $\times \dfrac{1\,atm}{760\,torr} = 0.921052$ atm $\quad V = 722$ mL $\times \dfrac{1\,L}{1000\,mL} = 0.722$ L , $T = 30.0\,°C + 273.15 = 303.2$ K,

$PV = nRT$ $\quad$ Rearrange to solve for n. $\quad n = \dfrac{PV}{RT}$

$n_{H2} = \dfrac{0.921052\,atm \times 0.722\,L}{0.08206\,\dfrac{L \cdot atm}{mol \cdot K} \times 303.2\,K} = 0.0267277$ mol $\quad 0.0267277$ mol $\times \dfrac{2.016\,g}{1\,mol} = 0.0539$ g H_2

Check: The units (g) are correct. The magnitude of the answer ($<<$ 1 g) makes sense because, gases are not very dense, hydrogen is light, the volume is small and the pressure is ~1 atm.

68. **Given:** T = 25 °C, V = 5.45 L, and $P_{Total} = 745$ mm Hg $\qquad$ **Find:** n
    Conceptual plan: $\mathbf{T \rightarrow P_{H2O}}$ then $\mathbf{P_{Total}, P_{H2O} \rightarrow P_{air}}$ then $\quad$ mm Hg $\rightarrow$ atm $\quad$ and °C $\rightarrow$ K
    $\qquad\qquad\qquad$ *Table 5.4* $\qquad\qquad\qquad P_{Total} = P_{H2O} + P_{air}$ $\qquad\qquad \dfrac{1\,atm}{760\,torr}$ $\qquad K = °C + 273.15$

    P, V, T $\rightarrow$ n
    $\quad PV = nRT$

    Solution: Table 5.4 states that $P_{H2O} = 23.78$ mm Hg $\quad P_{Total} = P_{H2O} + P_{air}$ $\quad$ Rearrange to solve for P_{air}. $\quad P_{air} = P_{Total} - P_{H2O} = 745$ mm Hg $- 23.78$ mm Hg $= 721$ mm Hg

    $P_{air} = 721$ torr $\times \dfrac{1\,atm}{760\,torr} = 0.948684$ atm $\quad T = 25\,°C + 273.15 = 298$ K, $\quad PV = nRT$

    Rearrange to solve for n. $\quad n = \dfrac{PV}{RT} = \dfrac{0.948684\,atm \times 5.45\,L}{0.08206\,\dfrac{L \cdot atm}{mol \cdot K} \times 298\,K} = 0.211$ mol

    Check: The units (mol) are correct. The magnitude of the answer (0.2 mol) makes sense because; 22.4 L of a gas at STP contains 1 mol. We have only 5.45 L, so the answer makes sense.

69. **Given:** T = 25 °C, $P_{Total} = 748$ mm Hg, and V = 0.951 L $\qquad$ **Find:** P_{H2} and m_{H2}
    Conceptual plan: $\mathbf{T \rightarrow P_{H2O}}$ then $\mathbf{P_{Total}, P_{H2O} \rightarrow P_{H2}}$ then $\quad$ mm Hg $\rightarrow$ atm $\quad$ and mL $\rightarrow$ L
    $\qquad\qquad\qquad$ *Table 5.4* $\qquad\qquad\qquad P_{Total} = P_{H2O} + P_{H2}$ $\qquad\qquad \dfrac{1\,atm}{760\,torr}$ $\qquad \dfrac{1\,L}{1000\,mL}$

    and °C $\rightarrow$ K $\quad$ P, V, T $\rightarrow$ n $\quad$ then $\quad$ mol $\rightarrow$ g
    $\quad K = °C + 273.15$ $\qquad PV = nRT$ $\qquad\qquad \dfrac{2.016\,g}{1\,mol}$

    Solution: Table 5.4 states that $P_{H2O} = 23.78$ mm Hg $\quad P_{Total} = P_{H2O} + P_{H2}$
    Rearrange to solve for P_{H2}. $\quad P_{H2} = P_{Total} - P_{H2O} = 748$ mm Hg $- 23.78$ mm Hg $= 724$ mm Hg

    $P_{H2} = 724$ torr $\times \dfrac{1\,atm}{760\,torr} = 0.952632$ atm $\quad T = 25\,°C + 273.15 = 298$ K, $\qquad\qquad PV = nRT$

    Rearrange to solve for n. $\quad n_{H2} = \dfrac{PV}{RT} = \dfrac{0.952632\,atm \times 0.951\,L}{0.08206\,\dfrac{L \cdot atm}{mol \cdot K} \times 298\,K} = 0.0370474$ mol

    0.0370474 mol $\times \dfrac{2.016\,g}{1\,mol} = 0.0747$ g H_2

    Check: The units (g) are correct. The magnitude of the answer ($<<$ 1 g) makes sense because, gases are not very dense, hydrogen is light, the volume is small and the pressure is ~1 atm.

70. **Given:** m (O_2) = 2.0 g, m (He) = 98.0 g, $P_{Total} = 8.5$ atm $\qquad$ **Find:** P_{O2}
    Conceptual plan: g $\rightarrow$ mol then $n_{O2}, n_{He} \rightarrow \chi_{O2}$ $\qquad$ then $\qquad$ $\chi_{O2}, P_{Total} \rightarrow P_{O2}$
    $\qquad\qquad\qquad\qquad$ $\mathfrak{M}$ $\qquad\qquad \chi_{O2} = \dfrac{n_{O2}}{n_{O2} + n_{He}}$ $\qquad\qquad P_{O2} = \chi_{O2}P_{Total}$

    Solution: $n_{N2} = 2.0$ g $\times \dfrac{1\,mol}{32.00\,g} = 0.0625$ mol , $\quad n_{O2} = 98.0$ g $\times \dfrac{1\,mol}{4.003\,g} = 24.4816$ mol ,

    $\chi_{O2} = \dfrac{n_{O2}}{n_{O2} + n_{He}} = \dfrac{0.0625\,mol}{0.0625\,mol + 24.4816\,mol} = 0.0025464$,

    $P_{O2} = \chi_{O2}P_{Total} = 0.0025464 \times 8.5$ atm $= 0.022$ atm

    Check: The units (atm) are correct. The magnitude of the answer (0.22 atm) makes sense because, at these depths high oxygen pressures can cause toxicity.

71. **Given:** m (C) = 15.7 g, P = 1.0 atm, and T = 355 K   **Find:** V

Conceptual plan: g C → mol C → mol H$_2$ then   n (mol H$_2$), P, T → V

$$\frac{1\ mol}{12.01\ g\ C} \qquad \frac{1\ mol\ H_2}{1\ mol\ C} \qquad\qquad PV = nRT$$

Solution: 15.7 g C × $\frac{1\ mol\ C}{12.01\ g\ C}$ × $\frac{1\ mol\ H_2}{1\ mol\ C}$ = 1.30724 mol H$_2$, $PV = nRT$ Rearrange to solve for V.

$$V = \frac{nRT}{P} = \frac{1.30724\ mol \times 0.08206\ \frac{L \cdot atm}{mol \cdot K} \times 355\ K}{1.0\ atm} = 38\ L$$

Check: The units (L) are correct. The magnitude of the answer (38 L) makes sense because, we have more than one mole of gas and so we expect more than 22 L.

72. **Given:** V$_{O2}$ = 1.4 L, T = 315 K, P$_{O2}$ = 0.957 atm   **Find:** g H$_2$O

Conceptual plan: P(mol O$_2$), V(mol O$_2$), T → n(mol O$_2$)   then   mol O$_2$ → mol H$_2$O → g H$_2$O

$$PV = nRT \qquad\qquad \frac{2\ mol\ H_2O}{1\ mol\ O_2} \qquad \frac{18.02\ g\ H_2O}{1\ mol\ H_2O}$$

Solution: $PV = nRT$ Rearrange to solve for n. $n = \frac{PV}{RT} = \frac{0.957\ atm \times 1.4\ L}{0.08206\ \frac{L \cdot atm}{mol \cdot K} \times 315\ K} = 0.051832\ mol\ O_2$

0.051832 mol O$_2$ × $\frac{2\ mol\ H_2O}{1\ mol\ O_2}$ × $\frac{18.02\ g\ H_2O}{1\ mol\ H_2O}$ = 1.9 g H$_2$O

Check: The units (g) are correct. The magnitude of the answer (2 g) makes sense because, we have much less than a mole of oxygen.

73. **Given:** P = 748 mm Hg, T = 86 °C, and m (CH$_3$OH) = 25.8 g, and **Find:** V$_{H2}$ and V$_{CO}$

Conceptual plan: g CH$_3$OH → mol CH$_3$OH → mol H$_2$ and   mm Hg → atm   and °C → K

$$\frac{1\ mol\ CH_3OH}{32.04\ g\ CH_3OH} \qquad \frac{2\ mol\ H_2}{1\ mol\ CH_3OH} \qquad \frac{1\ atm}{760\ torr} \qquad K = °C + 273.15$$

then   n (mol H$_2$), P, T → V   and   mol H$_2$ → mol CO   then   n (mol CO), P, T → V

$$PV = nRT \qquad\qquad \frac{1\ mol\ CO}{2\ mol\ H_2} \qquad\qquad PV = nRT$$

Solution: 25.8 g CH$_3$OH × $\frac{1\ mol\ CH_3OH}{32.04\ g\ CH_3OH}$ × $\frac{2\ mol\ H_2}{1\ mol\ CH_3OH}$ = 1.61049 mol H$_2$,

P$_{H2}$ = 748 torr × $\frac{1\ atm}{760\ torr}$ = 0.984211 atm , T = 86 °C + 273.15 = 359 K, $PV = nRT$ Rearrange to solve for V.

$$V = \frac{nRT}{P} \quad V_{H2} = \frac{1.61049\ mol \times 0.08206\ \frac{L \cdot atm}{mol \cdot K} \times 359\ K}{0.984211\ atm} = 48.2\ L\ H_2$$

1.61049 mol H$_2$ × $\frac{1\ mol\ CO}{2\ mol\ H_2}$ = 0.80525 mol CO , $V_{co} = \frac{0.80525\ mol \times 0.08206\ \frac{L \cdot atm}{mol \cdot K} \times 359\ K}{0.984211\ atm}$ = 24.1 L CO

Check: The units (L) are correct. The magnitude of the answer (48 L & 24 L) makes sense because, we have more than one mole of hydrogen gas and half that of CO and so we expect significantly more than 22L for hydrogen and half that for CO.

74. **Given:** P = 782 mm Hg, T = 25 °C, and m (Al) = 53.2 g, and **Find:** V$_{O2}$

Conceptual plan: g Al → mol Al → mol O$_2$ and   mm Hg → atm   and °C → K   then

$$\frac{1\ mol\ Al}{26.98\ g\ Al} \qquad \frac{3\ mol\ O_2}{4\ mol\ Al} \qquad\qquad \frac{1\ atm}{760\ torr} \qquad K = °C + 273.15$$

n (mol O$_2$), P, T → V

$$PV = nRT$$

Solution: 53.2 g Al × $\frac{1\ mol\ Al}{26.98\ g\ O_2}$ × $\frac{3\ mol\ O_2}{4\ mol\ Al}$ = 1.478873 mol O$_2$,

P$_{O2}$ = 782 torr × $\frac{1\ atm}{760\ torr}$ = 1.028947 atm , T = 25 °C + 273.15 = 298 K, $PV = nRT$ Rearrange to solve for V.

$$V_{O_2} = \frac{nRT}{P} = \frac{1.478873 \text{ mol} \times 0.08206 \frac{L \cdot atm}{mol \cdot K} \times 298 \text{ K}}{1.028947 \text{ atm}} = 35.1 \text{ L O}_2$$

Check: The units (L) are correct.   The magnitude of the answer (35 L) makes sense because, we have more than one mole of oxygen gas and more than 1 atm, so we expect significantly more than 22L.

75. **Given:** V = 11.8 L, and STP   **Find:** m (NaN$_3$)

Conceptual plan: V_{N2} → mol N$_2$ → mol NaN$_3$ → g NaN$_3$

$$\frac{1 \text{ mol N}_2}{22.414 \text{ L N}_2} \qquad \frac{2 \text{ mol NaN}_3}{3 \text{ mol N}_2} \qquad \frac{65.01 \text{ g NaN}_3}{1 \text{ mol NaN}_3}$$

Solution: $11.8 \text{ L N}_2 \times \frac{1 \text{ mol N}_2}{22.414 \text{ L N}_2} \times \frac{2 \text{ mol NaN}_3}{3 \text{ mol N}_2} \times \frac{65.01 \text{ g NaN}_3}{1 \text{ mol NaN}_3} = 22.8 \text{ g NaN}_3$,

Check: The units (g) are correct.   The magnitude of the answer (23 g) makes sense because, we have about a half a mole of nitrogen gas, which translates to even fewer moles of NaN$_3$ and so we expect significantly less than 65 g.

76. **Given:** V = 58.5 mL, and STP   **Find:** m (Li)

Conceptual plan: mL$_{N2}$ → L$_{N2}$ → mol N$_2$ → mol Li → g Li

$$\frac{1 \text{ L}}{1000 \text{ mL}} \qquad \frac{1 \text{ mol N}_2}{22.414 \text{ L N}_2} \qquad \frac{6 \text{ mol Li}}{1 \text{ mol N}_2} \qquad \frac{6.941 \text{ g Li}}{1 \text{ mol Li}}$$

Solution: $58.5 \text{ mL N}_2 \times \frac{1 \text{ L N}_2}{1000 \text{ mL N}_2} \times \frac{1 \text{ mol N}_2}{22.414 \text{ L N}_2} \times \frac{6 \text{ mol Li}}{1 \text{ mol N}_2} \times \frac{6.941 \text{ g Li}}{1 \text{ mol Li}} = 0.109 \text{ g Li}$,

Check: The units (g) are correct.   The magnitude of the answer (0.1 g) makes sense because, we have such a small volume, which translates to a small fraction of a mole of Li and so we expect significantly less than 6.9 g.

77. **Given:** V_{CH4} = 25.5 L, P_{CH4} = 732 torr, and T = 25 °C; mixed with V_{H2O} = 22.8 L, P_{H2O} = 702 torr, and T = 125 °C; forms P_{H2} = 26.2 L at STP   **Find:** % Yield

Conceptual plan: CH$_4$: torr → atm   and   °C → K   and P, V, T → n_{CH4} → n_{H2}

$$\frac{1 \text{ atm}}{760 \text{ torr}} \qquad K = °C + 273.15 \qquad PV = nRT \qquad \frac{3 \text{ mol H}_2}{1 \text{ mol CH}_4}$$

H$_2$O: torr → atm   and   °C → K   and P, V, T → n_{H2O} → n_{H2}

$$\frac{1 \text{ atm}}{760 \text{ torr}} \qquad K = °C + 273.15 \qquad PV = nRT \qquad \frac{3 \text{ mol H}_2}{1 \text{ mol H}_2O}$$

Select smaller n_{H2} as theoretical yield.
then   L$_{H2}$ →   mol H$_2$ (actual yield)   finally   actual yield, theoretical yield → % Yield

$$\frac{1 \text{ mol H}_2}{22.414 \text{ L H}_2} \qquad\qquad \% \text{ Yield} = \frac{actual \ yield}{theoretical \ yield} \times 100 \%$$

Solution: CH$_4$: $P_{N2} = 732 \text{ torr} \times \frac{1 \text{ atm}}{760 \text{ torr}} = 0.963158 \text{ atm}$, T = 25 °C + 273.15 = 298 K, $PV = nRT$

Rearrange to solve for n. $n = \frac{PV}{RT}$ $n_{CH4} = \frac{0.963158 \text{ atm} \times 25.5 \text{ L}}{0.08206 \frac{L \cdot atm}{mol \cdot K} \times 298 \text{ K}} = 1.00436 \text{ mol CH}_4$

$$1.00436 \text{ mol CH}_4 \times \frac{3 \text{ mol H}_2}{1 \text{ mol CH}_4} = 3.01308 \text{ mol H}_2$$

H$_2$O: $P_{N2} = 702 \text{ torr} \times \frac{1 \text{ atm}}{760 \text{ torr}} = 0.923684 \text{ atm}$, T = 125 °C + 273.15 = 398 K, $n = \frac{PV}{RT}$

$n_{H2O} = \frac{0.923684 \text{ atm} \times 22.8 \text{ L}}{0.08206 \frac{L \cdot atm}{mol \cdot K} \times 398 \text{ K}} = 0.644828 \text{ mol H}_2O$ $0.644828 \text{ mol H}_2O \times \frac{3 \text{ mol H}_2}{1 \text{ mol H}_2O} = 1.93448 \text{ mol H}_2$

Water is the limiting reagent since the moles of hydrogen generated is lower.

Theoretical yield = 1.93448 mol H$_2$. $26.2 \text{ L H}_2 \times \frac{1 \text{ mol H}_2}{22.414 \text{ L H}_2} = 1.16891 \text{ mol H}_2$ = actual yield ,

$$\% \text{ Yield} = \frac{actual \ yield}{theoretical \ yield} \times 100 \% = \frac{1.16891 \text{ mol H}_2}{1.93448 \text{ mol H}_2} \times 100 \% = 60.4 \%$$

Check: The units (%) are correct. The magnitude of the answer (60 %) makes sense because; it is between 0 and 100 %.

78. **Given:** P = 25.0 mm Hg, T = 225 K, and m (CF$_3$Cl) = 15.0 g, and 10 cycles   **Find:** V$_{O3}$
    Conceptual plan: g CF$_3$Cl → mol CF$_3$Cl → mol O$_3$ → mol O$_3$ and mm Hg → atm then

$$\frac{1 \text{ mol CF}_3\text{Cl}}{104.46 \text{ g CF}_3\text{Cl}} \qquad \frac{2 \text{ mol O}_3/\text{cycle}}{1 \text{ mol CF}_3\text{Cl}} \qquad 10 \text{ cycles} \qquad \frac{1 \text{ atm}}{760 \text{ torr}}$$

    n, P, T → V
    $$PV = nRT$$

Solution: $15.0 \text{ g CF}_3\text{Cl} \times \dfrac{1 \text{ mol CF}_3\text{Cl}}{104.46 \text{ g CF}_3\text{Cl}} \times \dfrac{2 \text{ mol O}_3/\text{cycle}}{1 \text{ mol CF}_3\text{Cl}} \times 10 \text{ cycles} = 2.871913 \text{ mol O}_3$,

$P_{H2} = 25.0 \text{ torr} \times \dfrac{1 \text{ atm}}{760 \text{ torr}} = 0.0328947 \text{ atm}$, $PV = nRT$ Rearrange to solve for V. $V = \dfrac{nRT}{P}$

$$V_{O3} = \frac{2.871913 \text{ mol} \times 0.08206 \dfrac{\text{L} \cdot \text{atm}}{\text{mol} \cdot \text{K}} \times 225 \text{ K}}{0.0328947 \text{ atm}} = 1.61 \times 10^3 \text{ L O}_3$$

Check: The units (L) are correct. The magnitude of the answer (1600 L) makes sense because, we have ~ 3 moles of ozone gas and the pressure is so low (0.03 atm), so we expect a large volume.

79. a) Yes, since the average kinetic energy of a particle is proportional to the temperature in kelvins and the two gases are at the same temperature, they have the same average kinetic energy.

    b) No, since the helium atoms are lighter, they must move faster to have the same kinetic energy as argon atoms.

    c) No, since the Ar atoms are moving slower to compensate for their larger mass, they will exert the same pressure on the walls of the container.

    d) Since He is lighter, it will have the faster rate of effusion.

80. a) Since both gases have a mole fraction of 0.5, they will have the same partial pressure.

    b) The nitrogen molecules will have a greater velocity since they are lighter than Xe atoms.

    c) Since the average kinetic energy of a particle is proportional to the temperature in kelvins and the two gases are at the same temperature, they have the same average kinetic energy.

    d) Since nitrogen is lighter, it will have the faster rate of effusion.

81. **Given:** F$_2$, Cl$_2$, Br$_2$, and T = 298 K   **Find:** u_{rms} KE$_{avg}$ for each gas and relative rates of effusion
    Conceptual plan: $\mathfrak{M}$, T → u_{rms} → KE$_{avg}$

$$u_{rms} = \sqrt{\frac{3RT}{\mathfrak{M}}} \qquad KE_{avg} = \frac{1}{2}N_A m u_{rms}^2 = \frac{3}{2}RT$$

Solution: F$_2$: $\mathfrak{M} = \dfrac{38.00 \text{ g}}{1 \text{ mol}} \times \dfrac{1 \text{ kg}}{1000 \text{ g}} = 0.03800 \text{ kg/mol}$, $u_{rms} = \sqrt{\dfrac{3RT}{\mathfrak{M}}} = \sqrt{\dfrac{3 \times 8.314 \dfrac{\text{J}}{\text{K} \times \text{mol}} \times 298 \text{ K}}{0.03800 \dfrac{\text{kg}}{\text{mol}}}} = 442 \text{ m/s}$

Cl$_2$: $\mathfrak{M} = \dfrac{70.90 \text{ g}}{1 \text{ mol}} \times \dfrac{1 \text{ kg}}{1000 \text{ g}} = 0.07090 \text{ kg/mol}$, $u_{rms} = \sqrt{\dfrac{3RT}{\mathfrak{M}}} = \sqrt{\dfrac{3 \times 8.314 \dfrac{\text{J}}{\text{K} \times \text{mol}} \times 298 \text{ K}}{0.07090 \dfrac{\text{kg}}{\text{mol}}}} = 324 \text{ m/s}$

Br$_2$: $\mathfrak{M} = \dfrac{159.80 \text{ g}}{1 \text{ mol}} \times \dfrac{1 \text{ kg}}{1000 \text{ g}} = 0.15980 \text{ kg/mol}$, $u_{rms} = \sqrt{\dfrac{3RT}{\mathfrak{M}}} = \sqrt{\dfrac{3 \times 8.314 \dfrac{\text{J}}{\text{K} \times \text{mol}} \times 298 \text{ K}}{0.15980 \dfrac{\text{kg}}{\text{mol}}}} = 216 \text{ m/s}$

All molecules have the same kinetic energy:
$$KE_{avg} = \frac{3}{2}RT = \frac{3}{2} \times 8.314 \frac{\text{J}}{\text{K} \times \text{mol}} \times 298 \text{ K} = 3.72 \times 10^3 \text{ J/mol}$$

151

Since rate of effusion is proportional to $\sqrt{\frac{1}{\mathfrak{M}}}$, F_2 will have the fastest rate and Br_2 will have the slowest rate.

Check: The units (m/s) are correct. The magnitude of the answer (200 – 450 m/s) makes sense because, they are consistent with what was seen in the text and the heavier the molecule, the slower the molecule.

82. **Given**: CO, CO_2, SO_3, and T = 298 K   **Find**: u_{rms} KE_{avg} for each gas, and rate greatest u_{rms} KE_{avg} and rates of effusion

Conceptual plan: $\mathfrak{M}$, T $\rightarrow$ u_{rms} $\rightarrow$ KE_{avg}

$$u_{rms} = \sqrt{\frac{3RT}{\mathfrak{M}}} \qquad KE_{avg} = \frac{1}{2}N_A m u_{rms}^2 = \frac{3}{2}RT$$

Solution: CO: $\mathfrak{M} = \frac{28.01\text{ g}}{1\text{ mol}} \times \frac{1\text{ kg}}{1000\text{ g}} = 0.02801\text{ kg/mol}$, $u_{rms} = \sqrt{\frac{3RT}{\mathfrak{M}}} = \sqrt{\frac{3 \times 8.314\frac{J}{K \times mol} \times 298\text{ K}}{0.02801\frac{kg}{mol}}} = 515.1\text{ m/s}$

CO_2: $\mathfrak{M} = \frac{44.01\text{ g}}{1\text{ mol}} \times \frac{1\text{ kg}}{1000\text{ g}} = 0.04401\text{ kg/mol}$, $u_{rms} = \sqrt{\frac{3RT}{\mathfrak{M}}} = \sqrt{\frac{3 \times 8.314\frac{J}{K \times mol} \times 298\text{ K}}{0.04401\frac{kg}{mol}}} = 411.0\text{ m/s}$

SO_3: $\mathfrak{M} = \frac{80.07\text{ g}}{1\text{ mol}} \times \frac{1\text{ kg}}{1000\text{ g}} = 0.08007\text{ kg/mol}$, $u_{rms} = \sqrt{\frac{3RT}{\mathfrak{M}}} = \sqrt{\frac{3 \times 8.314\frac{J}{K \times mol} \times 298\text{ K}}{0.08007\frac{kg}{mol}}} = 304.7\text{ m/s}$

All molecules have the same kinetic energy:

$$KE_{avg} = \frac{3}{2}RT = \frac{3}{2} \times 8.314\frac{J}{K \times mol} \times 298\text{ K} = 3.72 \times 10^3\text{ J/mol}$$ CO has the fastest speed; all molecules have

the same kinetic energy; and since rate of effusion is proportional to $1/\sqrt{\mathfrak{M}}$, CO will have the fastest rate.

Check: The units (m/s) are correct. The magnitude of the answer (300 – 520 m/s) makes sense because, they are consistent with what was seen in the text and the heavier the molecule, the slower the molecule.

83. **Given**: $^{238}UF_6$ and $^{235}UF_6$ U-235 = 235.054 amu, U-238 = 238.051 amu   **Find**: ratio of effusion rates $^{238}UF_6$ / $^{235}UF_6$

Conceptual plan: $\mathfrak{M}$ ($^{238}UF_6$) , $\mathfrak{M}$ ($^{235}UF_6$) $\rightarrow$ Rate ($^{238}UF_6$) / Rate ($^{235}UF_6$)

$$\frac{Rate(^{238}UF_6)}{Rate(^{235}UF_6)} = \sqrt{\frac{\mathfrak{M}(^{235}UF_6)}{\mathfrak{M}(^{238}UF_6)}}$$

Solution: $^{238}UF_6$: $\mathfrak{M} = \frac{352.05\text{ g}}{1\text{ mol}} \times \frac{1\text{ kg}}{1000\text{ g}} = 0.35205\text{ kg/mol}$, $^{235}UF_6$: $\mathfrak{M} = \frac{349.05\text{ g}}{1\text{ mol}} \times \frac{1\text{ kg}}{1000\text{ g}} = 0.34905\text{ kg/mol}$,

$$\frac{Rate(^{238}UF_6)}{Rate(^{235}UF_6)} = \sqrt{\frac{\mathfrak{M}(^{235}UF_6)}{\mathfrak{M}(^{238}UF_6)}} = \sqrt{\frac{0.34905\text{ kg / mol}}{0.35205\text{ kg / mol}}} = 0.99574$$

Check: The units (none) are correct. The magnitude of the answer (<1) makes sense because, they the heavier molecule has the lower effusion rate because it moves slower.

84. **Given**: Ar and Kr   **Find**: ratio of effusion rates Ar / Kr

Conceptual plan: $\mathfrak{M}$ (Ar) , $\mathfrak{M}$ (Kr) $\rightarrow$ Rate (Ar) / Rate (Kr)

$$\frac{Rate(Ar)}{Rate(Kr)} = \sqrt{\frac{\mathfrak{M}(Kr)}{\mathfrak{M}(Ar)}}$$

Solution: Ar: $\mathfrak{M} = \frac{39.95\text{ g}}{1\text{ mol}} \times \frac{1\text{ kg}}{1000\text{ g}} = 0.03995\text{ kg/mol}$, Kr: $\mathfrak{M} = \frac{83.80\text{ g}}{1\text{ mol}} \times \frac{1\text{ kg}}{1000\text{ g}} = 0.08380\text{ kg/mol}$,

$$\frac{Rate(Ar)}{Rate(Kr)} = \sqrt{\frac{\mathfrak{M}(Kr)}{\mathfrak{M}(Ar)}} = \sqrt{\frac{0.08380\text{ kg / mol}}{0.03995\text{ kg / mol}}} = 1.448$$

Check: The units (none) are correct. The magnitude of the answer (>1) makes sense because, they the lighter molecule the higher effusion rate because it moves faster.

85. **Given**: Ne and unknown gas; and Ne effusion in 76 s and unknown in 155 s
Find: identify unknown gas

Conceptual plan: $\mathfrak{M}$ (Ne), Rate (Ne), Rate (U) → $\mathfrak{M}$ (Kr)

$$\frac{Rate(Ne)}{Rate(U)} = \sqrt{\frac{\mathfrak{M}(U)}{\mathfrak{M}(Ne)}}$$

Solution: Ne: $\mathfrak{M} = \frac{20.18 \text{ g}}{1 \text{ mol}} \times \frac{1 \text{ kg}}{1000 \text{ g}} = 0.02018 \text{ kg/mol}$, $\frac{Rate(Ne)}{Rate(U)} = \sqrt{\frac{\mathfrak{M}(U)}{\mathfrak{M}(Ne)}}$ Rearrange to solve for $\mathfrak{M}(U)$.

$$\mathfrak{M}(U) = \mathfrak{M}(Ne)\left(\frac{Rate(Ne)}{Rate(U)}\right)^2 \qquad \text{Since Rate } \alpha \text{ 1/(effusion time)}$$

$$\mathfrak{M}(U) = \mathfrak{M}(Ne)\left(\frac{Time(U)}{Time(Ne)}\right)^2 = 0.02018 \frac{\text{kg}}{\text{mol}} \times \left(\frac{155 \text{ s}}{76 \text{ s}}\right)^2 = 0.084 \frac{\text{kg}}{\text{mol}} \times \frac{1000 \text{ g}}{1 \text{ kg}} = 84 \text{ g/mol or Kr.}$$

Check: The units (g/mol) are correct. The magnitude of the answer (>Ne) makes sense because, Ne effused faster and so must be lighter.

86. **Given:** NO_2 and I_2 gas; and NO_2 effusion in 42 s   **Find:** effusion time for I_2 gas
    Conceptual plan: $\mathfrak{M}$ (NO$_2$), $\mathfrak{M}$ (Kr), Rate (NO$_2$), → Rate (U)

$$\frac{Rate(N_2O)}{Rate(I_2)} = \sqrt{\frac{\mathfrak{M}(I_2)}{\mathfrak{M}(N_2O)}}$$

Solution: N_2O: $\mathfrak{M} = \frac{44.02 \text{ g}}{1 \text{ mol}} \times \frac{1 \text{ kg}}{1000 \text{ g}} = 0.04402 \text{ kg/mol}$, I_2: $\mathfrak{M} = \frac{253.8 \text{ g}}{1 \text{ mol}} \times \frac{1 \text{ kg}}{1000 \text{ g}} = 0.2538 \text{ kg/mol}$,

$\frac{Rate(N_2O)}{Rate(I_2)} = \sqrt{\frac{\mathfrak{M}(I_2)}{\mathfrak{M}(N_2O)}}$ Since Rate α 1/(effusion time) $\frac{Time(I_2)}{Time(N_2O)} = \sqrt{\frac{\mathfrak{M}(I_2)}{\mathfrak{M}(N_2O)}}$ Rearrange to solve for

Time (I_2). $Time(I_2) = Time(N_2O) \times \sqrt{\frac{\mathfrak{M}(I_2)}{\mathfrak{M}(N_2O)}} = 42 \text{ s} \times \sqrt{\frac{0.2538 \text{ kg / mol}}{0.04402 \text{ kg / mol}}} = 1.0 \times 10^2 \text{ s}$

Check: The units (s) are correct. The magnitude of the answer (100 s) makes sense because, the mass ratio of I_2 to N_2O is ~6, so the time should be over twice as long.

87. Gas A has the higher molar mass, since it has the slower velocity. Gas B will have the higher effusion rate, since it has the higher velocity.

88. T_2 is the higher temperature, since it has the higher average velocity.

89. The postulate that the volume of the gas particles is small compared to the space between them breaks down at high pressure. At high pressures the number of molecules increases, so the volume of the gas particles becomes larger and since the spacing between the particles is smaller, the molecules themselves occupy a significant portion of the volume.

90. The postulate that the forces between the gas particles are not significant breaks down at low temperatures. At low temperatures, the molecules are not moving as fast as at higher temperatures, so the when they collide the have a greater opportunity to interact.

91. **Given:** Ne, n = 1.000 mol, P = 500.0 atm and T = 355.0 K   **Find:** V(ideal) and V(van der Waals)
    Conceptual plan: n, P, T → V   and   n, P, T → V

$$PV = nRT \qquad\qquad \left(P + \frac{an^2}{V^2}\right)(V - nb) = nRT$$

Solution: $PV = nRT$ Rearrange to solve for V. $V = \frac{nRT}{P} = \frac{1.000 \text{ mol} \times 0.08206 \frac{\text{L} \cdot \text{atm}}{\text{mol} \cdot \text{K}} \times 355.0 \text{ K}}{500.0 \text{ atm}} = 0.05826 \text{ L}$

$\left(P + \frac{an^2}{V^2}\right)(V - nb) = nRT$ Rearrange to solve to: $V = \frac{nRT}{\left(P + \frac{an^2}{V^2}\right)} + nb$

Using a = 0.211 L^2 atm/mol^2 and b = 0.0171 L/mol from Table 5.5, and the V from the ideal gas law above, solve for V by successive approximations.

$$V = \frac{1.000 \text{ mol} \times 0.08206 \frac{\text{L} \cdot \text{atm}}{\text{mol} \cdot \text{K}} \times 355.0 \text{ K}}{500.0 \text{ atm} + \frac{0.211 \frac{\text{L}^2 \cdot \text{atm}}{\text{mol}^2} \times (1.000 \text{ mol})^2}{(0.05826 \text{ L})^2}} + \left(1.000 \text{ mol} \times 0.0171 \frac{\text{L}}{\text{mol}}\right) = 0.068915 \text{ L Plug in this new value.}$$

$$V = \cfrac{1.000 \text{ mol} \times 0.08206 \cfrac{L \cdot atm}{mol \cdot K} \times 355.0 \text{ K}}{500.0 \text{ atm} + \cfrac{0.211 \cfrac{L^2 \cdot atm}{mol^2} \times (1.000 \text{ mol})^2}{(0.068915 \text{ L})^2}} + \left(1.000 \text{ mol} \times 0.0171 \cfrac{L}{mol}\right) = 0.070609 \text{ L} \quad \text{Plug in this new value.}$$

$$V = \cfrac{1.000 \text{ mol} \times 0.08206 \cfrac{L \cdot atm}{mol \cdot K} \times 355.0 \text{ K}}{500.0 \text{ atm} + \cfrac{0.211 \cfrac{L^2 \cdot atm}{mol^2} \times (1.000 \text{ mol})^2}{(0.070609 \text{ L})^2}} + \left(1.000 \text{ mol} \times 0.0171 \cfrac{L}{mol}\right) = 0.070817 \text{ L} \quad \text{Plug in this new value.}$$

$$V = \cfrac{1.000 \text{ mol} \times 0.08206 \cfrac{L \cdot atm}{mol \cdot K} \times 355.0 \text{ K}}{500.0 \text{ atm} + \cfrac{0.211 \cfrac{L^2 \cdot atm}{mol^2} \times (1.000 \text{ mol})^2}{(0.070817 \text{ L})^2}} + \left(1.000 \text{ mol} \times 0.0171 \cfrac{L}{mol}\right) = 0.070842 \text{ L} = 0.0708 \text{ L}$$

The two values are different because we are at very high pressures. The pressure is corrected from 500.0 atm to 542.1 atm and the final volume correction is 0.0171 L.

Check: The units (L) are correct. The magnitude of the answer (~0.06 L) makes sense because, we are at such a high pressure and have, one mole of gas.

92. **Given:** Cl_2, n = 1.000 mol, L = 5.000 L and T = 273.0 K   **Find:** P(ideal) and P(van der Waals)
    Conceptual plan: **n, V, T $\rightarrow$ P**   and   **n, V, T $\rightarrow$ P**

$$P V = nRT \qquad\qquad \left(P + \cfrac{an^2}{V^2}\right)(V - nb) = nRT$$

Solution: $P V = nRT$ Rearrange to solve for P. $P = \cfrac{nRT}{V} = \cfrac{1.000 \text{ mol} \times 0.08206 \cfrac{L \cdot atm}{mol \cdot K} \times 273.0 \text{ K}}{5.000 \text{ L}} = 4.480 \text{ atm}$

$\left(P + \cfrac{an^2}{V^2}\right)(V - nb) = nRT$ Rearrange to solve for P. $P = \cfrac{nRT}{(V - nb)} - \cfrac{an^2}{V^2}$ Using a = 6.49 L^2 atm/mol^2 and b = 0.1383 L/mol from Table 5.5:

$$P = \cfrac{1.000 \text{ mol} \times 0.08206 \cfrac{L \cdot atm}{mol \cdot K} \times 273.0 \text{ K}}{5.000 \text{ L} - \left(1.000 \text{ mol} \times 0.1383 \cfrac{L}{mol}\right)} - \cfrac{6.49 \cfrac{L^2 \cdot atm}{mol^2} \times (1.000 \text{ mol})^2}{(5.000 \text{ L})^2} = 2.66 \text{ atm}$$

The pressure values differ because the pressure is high, the temperature is moderate and chlorine is not the smallest gas molecule, all of these contribute to non-ideal behavior.

Check: The units (atm) are correct. The magnitude of the answer (4 atm & 3 atm) makes sense because, we are at such a low temperature and small volume with one mole of gas – we expect a P >1 atm.

93. **Given:** m (penny) = 2.482 g, T = 25 °C, V = 0.899 L, and P_{Total} = 791 mm Hg
    Find: % Zn in penny
    Conceptual plan: T $\rightarrow$ P_{H2O} then P_{Total}, P_{H2O} $\rightarrow$ P_{H2} then   mm Hg $\rightarrow$ atm   and °C $\rightarrow$ K

$$\text{Table 5.4} \qquad\qquad P_{Total} = P_{H2O} + P_{H2} \qquad\qquad \cfrac{1 \text{ atm}}{760 \text{ torr}} \qquad K = °C + 273.15$$

and P, V, T $\rightarrow$ n_{H2} $\rightarrow$ n_{Zn} $\rightarrow$ g_{Zn} $\rightarrow$ % Zn

$$\cdot P V = nRT \qquad \cfrac{1 \text{ mol Zn}}{1 \text{ mol } H_2} \qquad \cfrac{65.39 \text{ g Zn}}{1 \text{ mol Zn}} \qquad \% \, Zn = \cfrac{g_{Zn}}{g_{penny}} \times 100 \, \%$$

Solution: Table 5.4 states that P_{H2O} = 23.78 mm Hg $P_{Total} = P_{H2O} + P_{H2}$ Rearrange to solve for P_{H2}.

$P_{H2} = P_{Total} - P_{H2O} = 791$ mm Hg $- 23.78$ mm Hg $= 767$ mm Hg $P_{H2} = 767 \text{ torr} \times \cfrac{1 \text{ atm}}{760 \text{ torr}} = 1.0095 \text{ atm}$

T = 25 °C + 273.15 = 298 K, $P V = nRT$ Rearrange to solve for n.

$$n_{H2} = \cfrac{PV}{RT} = \cfrac{1.0095 \text{ atm} \times 0.899 \text{ L}}{0.08206 \cfrac{L \cdot atm}{mol \cdot K} \times 298 \text{ K}} = 0.0371123 \text{ mol}$$

$$0.0371123 \text{ mol } H_2 \times \cfrac{1 \text{ mol Zn}}{1 \text{ mol } H_2} \times \cfrac{65.39 \text{ g Zn}}{1 \text{ mol Zn}} = 2.42677 \text{ g Zn}$$

$$\% \, Zn = \frac{g_{Zn}}{g_{penny}} \, x \, 100 \, \% = \frac{2.42677 \text{ g}}{2.482 \text{ g}} \, x \, 100 \, \% = 97.8 \, \% \, Zn$$

Check: The units (% Zn) are correct. The magnitude of the answer (98 %) makes sense because, it should be between 0 and 100 %. We expect about 1/22 a mole of gas, since our conditions are close to STP and we have ~ 1 L of gas.

94. **Given:** m (CFC) = 2.85 g, V = 564 mL, P = 752 mm Hg, and T = 25 °C **Find:** % Cl in CFC

Conceptual plan: mm Hg → atm and mL → L and °C → K and P, V, T → n_{Cl_2} → g_{Cl}

$$\frac{1 \text{ atm}}{760 \text{ torr}} \qquad \frac{1 \text{ L}}{1000 \text{ mL}} \qquad K = {}^\circ C + 273.15 \qquad PV = nRT \qquad \frac{70.90 \text{ g Cl}}{1 \text{ mol Cl}_2}$$

then g_{Cl}, g_{CFC} **→ % Cl**

$$\% \, Cl = \frac{g_{Cl}}{g_{CFC}} \, x \, 100 \, \%$$

Solution: $P_{Cl_2} = 752 \text{ torr } x \dfrac{1 \text{ atm}}{760 \text{ torr}} = 0.98947 \text{ atm}$, $V_{Cl_2} = 564 \text{ mL } x \dfrac{1 \text{ L}}{1000 \text{ mL}} = 0.564 \text{ L}$,

T = 25 °C + 273.15 = 298 K, $PV = nRT$ Rearrange to solve for n.

$$n_{Cl_2} = \frac{PV}{RT} = \frac{0.98947 \text{ atm x } 0.564 \text{ L}}{0.08206 \dfrac{\text{L} \cdot \text{atm}}{\text{mol} \cdot \text{K}} x \, 298 \text{ K}} = 0.022810 \text{ mol Cl}_2 \quad 0.022810 \text{ mol Cl}_2 \, x \, \frac{70.90 \text{ g Cl}}{1 \text{ mol Cl}_2} = 1.6180 \text{ g Cl}$$,

$$\% \, Cl = \frac{g_{Cl}}{g_{CFC}} \, x \, 100 \, \% = \frac{1.6180 \text{ g}}{2.85 \text{ g}} \, x \, 100 \, \% = 56.7 \, \% \, Cl$$

Check: The units (% Cl) are correct. The magnitude of the answer (57 %) makes sense because; it should be between 0 and 100 %. Since there will be carbon in the compound, we do not expect it to be extremely close to 100 %.

95. **Given:** V = 255 mL, m (flask) = 143.187 g, m (flask + gas) = 143.289 g, P = 267 torr, and T = 25 °C **Find:** $\mathfrak{M}$

Conceptual plan: °C → K torr → atm mL → L m (flask), m (flask + gas) → m (gas)

$$K = {}^\circ C + 273.15 \qquad \frac{1 \text{ atm}}{760 \text{ torr}} \qquad \frac{1 \text{ L}}{1000 \text{ mL}} \qquad m \, (gas) = m \, (flask + gas) - m \, (flask)$$

then V, m → d then d, P, T, → $\mathfrak{M}$

$$d = \frac{m}{V} \qquad d = \frac{P\mathfrak{M}}{RT}$$

Solution: T = 25 °C + 273.15 = 298 K, $\quad$ P = 267 torr $x \dfrac{1 \text{ atm}}{760 \text{ torr}} = 0.351216 \text{ atm}$,

$V = 255 \text{ mL } x \dfrac{1 \text{ L}}{1000 \text{ mL}} = 0.255 \text{ L}$, $\quad m \, (gas) = m \, (flask + gas) - m \, (flask) = 143.289 \text{ g} - 143.187 \text{ g} = 0.102 \text{ g}$,

$d = \dfrac{m}{V} = \dfrac{0.102 \text{ g}}{0.255 \text{ L}} = 0.400 \text{ g/L}$, $\qquad d = \dfrac{P\mathfrak{M}}{RT}$ $\qquad$ Rearrange to solve for $\mathfrak{M}$.

$$\mathfrak{M} = \frac{dRT}{P} = \frac{0.400 \dfrac{\text{g}}{\text{L}} x \, 0.08206 \dfrac{\text{L} \cdot \text{atm}}{\text{K} \cdot \text{mol}} x \, 298 \text{ K}}{0.351216 \text{ atm}} = 27.9 \text{ g/mol}$$

Check: The units (g/mol) are correct. The magnitude of the answer (28 g/mol) makes physical sense because this is a reasonable number for a molecular weight of a gas.

96. **Given:** V = 118 mL, m (flask) = 97.129 g, m (flask + gas) = 97.171 g, P = 768 torr, and T = 35 °C **Find:** Is gas pure?

Conceptual plan: °C → K torr → atm mL → L m (flask), m (flask + gas) → m (gas)

$$K = {}^\circ C + 273.15 \qquad \frac{1 \text{ atm}}{760 \text{ torr}} \qquad \frac{1 \text{ L}}{1000 \text{ mL}} \qquad m \, (gas) = m \, (flask + gas) - m \, (flask)$$

then V, m → d then d, P, T, → $\mathfrak{M}$

$$d = \frac{m}{V} \qquad d = \frac{P\mathfrak{M}}{RT}$$

Solution: T = 35 °C + 273.15 = 308 K, $\quad$ P = 768 torr $x \dfrac{1 \text{ atm}}{760 \text{ torr}} = 1.01053 \text{ atm}$,

$V = 118 \text{ mL } x \dfrac{1 \text{ L}}{1000 \text{ mL}} = 0.118 \text{ L}$, $\quad m \, (gas) = m \, (flask + gas) - m \, (flask) = 97.171 \text{ g} - 97.129 \text{ g} = 0.042 \text{ g}$,

$d = \dfrac{m}{V} = \dfrac{0.042 \text{ g}}{0.118 \text{ L}} = 0.35593 \text{ g/L}$, $\qquad d = \dfrac{P\mathfrak{M}}{RT}$ $\qquad$ Rearrange to solve for $\mathfrak{M}$.

$$\mathfrak{M} = \frac{dRT}{P} = \frac{0.35593 \frac{g}{L} \times 0.08206 \frac{L \cdot atm}{K \cdot mol} \times 308 \text{ K}}{1.01053 \text{ atm}} = 8.7 \text{ g/mol}$$ The gas is not pure He, since the molar mass

is not 4.003 g/ml.

Check: The units (g/mol) are correct. The magnitude of the answer (9 g/mol) makes physical sense because this is a reasonable number for a molecular weight of a gas.

97. **Given**: V = 158 mL, m (gas) = 0.275 g,, P = 556 mm Hg, T = 25 °C, gas = 82.666 % C and 17.34 % H.
   Find: $\mathfrak{M}$
   Conceptual plan: °C → K   mm Hg → atm   mL → L   then   V, m → d

$$K = °C + 273.15 \qquad \frac{1 \text{ atm}}{760 \text{ mm Hg}} \qquad \frac{1 \text{ L}}{1000 \text{ mL}} \qquad d = \frac{m}{V}$$

   then d, P, T, → $\mathfrak{M}$ then % C, % H, $\mathfrak{M}$ → formula

$$d = \frac{P\mathfrak{M}}{RT} \qquad \#C = \frac{\mathfrak{M}\, 0.8266\, g\, C}{12.01 \frac{g\, C}{mol\, C}} \qquad \#H = \frac{\mathfrak{M}\, 0.1734\, g\, H}{1.008 \frac{g\, H}{mol\, H}}$$

   Solution: $T = 25 °C + 273.15 = 298 \text{ K}$, $\qquad P = 556 \text{ torr} \times \frac{1 \text{ atm}}{760 \text{ torr}} = 0.731579 \text{ atm}$,

$$V = 158 \text{ mL} \times \frac{1 \text{ L}}{1000 \text{ mL}} = 0.158 \text{ L}, \quad d = \frac{m}{V} = \frac{0.275 \text{ g}}{0.158 \text{ L}} = 1.74051 \text{ g/L}, \qquad d = \frac{P\mathfrak{M}}{RT} \quad \text{Rearrange to solve for } \mathfrak{M}.$$

$$\mathfrak{M} = \frac{dRT}{P} = \frac{1.74051 \frac{g}{L} \times 0.08206 \frac{L \cdot atm}{K \cdot mol} \times 298 \text{ K}}{0.731579 \text{ atm}} = 58.2 \text{ g/mol} ,$$

$$\#C = \frac{\mathfrak{M} \times 0.8266\, g\, C}{12.01 \frac{g\, C}{mol\, C}} = \frac{58.2 \frac{g\, HC}{mol\, HC} \times \frac{0.8266\, g\, C}{1\, g\, HC}}{12.01 \frac{g\, C}{mol\, C}} = 4.00 \frac{mol\, C}{mol\, HC}$$

$$\#H = \frac{\mathfrak{M} \times 0.1734\, g\, H}{1.008 \frac{g\, H}{mol\, H}} = \frac{58.2 \frac{g\, HC}{mol\, HC} \times \frac{0.1734\, g\, H}{1\, g\, HC}}{1.008 \frac{g\, H}{mol\, H}} = 10.0 \frac{mol\, H}{mol\, HC} \quad \text{Formula is } C_4H_{10} \text{ or butane.}$$

Check: The answer came up with integer number of C and H atoms in the formula and a molecular weight (58 g/mol) that is reasonable for a gas.

98. **Given**: STP, V = 258 mL, m (gas) = 0.646 g, gas = 85.63 % C and 14.37 % H.   **Find**: $\mathfrak{M}$
   Conceptual plan: mL → L then V, m → d then d, P, T, → $\mathfrak{M}$

$$\frac{1 \text{ L}}{1000 \text{ mL}} \qquad d = \frac{m}{V} \qquad d = \frac{P\mathfrak{M}}{RT}$$

   then % C, % H, $\mathfrak{M}$ → formula

$$\#C = \frac{\mathfrak{M}\, 0.8563\, g\, C}{12.01 \frac{g\, C}{mol\, C}} \qquad \#H = \frac{\mathfrak{M}\, 0.1437\, g\, H}{1.008 \frac{g\, H}{mol\, H}}$$

   Solution: $V = 258 \text{ mL} \times \frac{1 \text{ L}}{1000 \text{ mL}} = 0.258 \text{ L}, \quad d = \frac{m}{V} = \frac{0.646 \text{ g}}{0.258 \text{ L}} = 2.50388 \text{ g/L}, \quad d = \frac{P\mathfrak{M}}{RT} \quad \text{Rearrange to solve for}$

$$\mathfrak{M}. \quad \mathfrak{M} = \frac{dRT}{P} = \frac{2.50388 \frac{g}{L} \times 0.08206 \frac{L \cdot atm}{K \cdot mol} \times 273.15 \text{ K}}{1 \text{ atm}} = 56.12 \text{ g/mol} ,$$

$$\#C = \frac{\mathfrak{M} \times 0.8563\, g\, C}{12.01 \frac{g\, C}{mol\, C}} = \frac{56.12 \frac{g\, HC}{mol\, HC} \times \frac{0.8565\, g\, C}{1\, g\, HC}}{12.01 \frac{g\, C}{mol\, C}} = 4.00 \frac{mol\, C}{mol\, HC}$$

$$\#H = \frac{\mathfrak{M} \times 0.1437\, g\, H}{1.008 \frac{g\, H}{mol\, H}} = \frac{56.12 \frac{g\, HC}{mol\, HC} \times \frac{0.1437\, g\, H}{1\, g\, HC}}{1.008 \frac{g\, H}{mol\, H}} = 8.00 \frac{mol\, H}{mol\, HC} \quad \text{Formula is } C_4H_8 \text{ or butene.}$$

Check: The answer came up with integer number of C and H atoms in the formula and a molecular weight (56 g/mol) that is reasonable for a gas.

99. **Given**: m (NiO) = 24.78 g, T = 40.0 °C, and P_{Total} = 745 mm Hg   **Find**: V_{O2}

Conceptual plan: $T \rightarrow P_{H2O}$ then $P_{Total}, P_{H2O} \rightarrow P_{O2}$ then $mm\ Hg \rightarrow atm$ and $°C \rightarrow K$

Table 5.4 $\qquad$ $P_{Total} = P_{H2O} + P_{O2}$ $\qquad$ $\dfrac{1\ atm}{760\ torr}$ $\qquad$ $K = °C + 273.15$

and $g_{NiO} \rightarrow n_{NiO} \rightarrow n_{O2}$ then $P, V, T \rightarrow n_{O2}$

$\dfrac{1\ mol\ NiO}{74.69\ g\ NiO}$ $\qquad$ $\dfrac{1\ mol\ O_2}{2\ mol\ NiO}$ $\qquad$ $PV = nRT$

Solution: Table 5.4 states that $P_{H2O} = 55.40\ mm\ Hg$ $\quad$ $P_{Total} = P_{H2O} + P_{O2}$ $\quad$ Rearrange to solve for P_{O2}.
$P_{O2} = P_{Total} - P_{H2O} = 745\ mm\ Hg - 55.40\ mm\ Hg = 689.\underline{6}\ mm\ Hg$

$P_{O2} = 689.\underline{6}\ torr \times \dfrac{1\ atm}{760\ torr} = 0.907368\ atm$ $\qquad$ $T = 40.0\ °C + 273.15 = 313.2\ K,$

$24.78\ g\ NiO \times \dfrac{1\ mol\ NiO}{74.69\ mol\ NiO} \times \dfrac{1\ mol\ O_2}{2\ mol\ NiO} = 0.165\underline{8}857\ mol\ O_2$ $\qquad$ $PV = nRT$

Rearrange to solve for V. $\quad V_{O2} = \dfrac{nRT}{P} = \dfrac{0.165\underline{8}857\ mol \times 0.08206\ \dfrac{L \cdot atm}{mol \cdot K} \times 313.2\ K}{0.907368\ atm} = 4.70\ L$

Check: The units (L) are correct. The magnitude of the answer (5 L) makes sense because, we have much less than 0.5 mole of NiO, so we get less than a mole of oxygen. Thus we expect a volume much less than 22 L.

100. **Given:** $m\ (Ag) = 15.8\ g$, $T = 25\ °C$, and $P_{Total} = 752\ mm\ Hg$ $\qquad$ **Find:** V_{O2}

Conceptual plan: $T \rightarrow P_{H2O}$ then $P_{Total}, P_{H2O} \rightarrow P_{O2}$ then $mm\ Hg \rightarrow atm$ and $°C \rightarrow K$

Table 5.4 $\qquad$ $P_{Total} = P_{H2O} + P_{O2}$ $\qquad$ $\dfrac{1\ atm}{760\ torr}$ $\qquad$ $K = °C + 273.15$

and $g_{Ag} \rightarrow n_{Ag} \rightarrow n_{O2}$ then $P, V, T \rightarrow n_{O2}$

$\dfrac{1\ mol\ Ag}{107.9\ g\ Ag}$ $\qquad$ $\dfrac{1\ mol\ O_2}{4\ mol\ Ag}$ $\qquad$ $PV = nRT$

Solution: Table 5.4 states that $P_{H2O} = 23.78\ mm\ Hg$ $\quad$ $P_{Total} = P_{H2O} + P_{O2}$ $\quad$ Rearrange to solve for P_{O2}.
$P_{O2} = P_{Total} - P_{H2O} = 752\ mm\ Hg - 23.78\ mm\ Hg = 728.\underline{2}2\ mm\ Hg$

$P_{O2} = 728.\underline{2}2\ torr \times \dfrac{1\ atm}{760\ torr} = 0.95\underline{8}184\ atm$ $\quad T = 40.0\ °C + 273.15 = 313.2\ K,$

$15.8\ g\ Ag \times \dfrac{1\ mol\ Ag}{107.9\ mol\ Ag} \times \dfrac{1\ mol\ O_2}{4\ mol\ Ag} = 0.036\underline{6}0780\ mol\ O_2$ $\qquad PV = nRT$ $\quad$ Rearrange to solve for V.

$V_{O2} = \dfrac{nRT}{P} = \dfrac{0.036\underline{6}0780\ mol \times 0.08206\ \dfrac{L \cdot atm}{mol \cdot K} \times 298\ K}{0.95\underline{8}184\ atm} = 0.934\ L$

Check: The units (L) are correct. The magnitude of the answer (1 L) makes sense because, we have ~ 0.1 mole of Ag, so we get less than 0.5 mol of oxygen. Thus we expect a volume much, much less than 22 L.

101. **Given:** HCl, K_2S to H_2S, $V_{H2S} = 42.9\ mL$, $P_{H2S} = 752\ mm\ Hg$, and $T = 25.8\ °C$ $\qquad$ **Find:** $m(K_2S)$

Conceptual plan: read description of reaction and convert words to equation then $°C \rightarrow K$

$\qquad\qquad\qquad\qquad\qquad\qquad\qquad\qquad\qquad\qquad\qquad\qquad\qquad\qquad\qquad\qquad K = °C + 273.15$

and $mm\ Hg \rightarrow atm$ **and** $mL \rightarrow L$ then $P, V, T \rightarrow n_{H2S} \rightarrow n_{K2S} \rightarrow g_{K2S}$

$\dfrac{1\ atm}{760\ torr}$ $\qquad$ $\dfrac{1\ L}{1000\ mL}$ $\qquad$ $PV = nRT$ $\quad$ $\dfrac{1\ mol\ K_2S}{1\ mol\ H_2S}$ $\quad$ $\dfrac{1\ mol\ K_2S}{110.27\ g\ K_2S}$

Solution: $2\ HCl\ (aq) + K_2S\ (s) \rightarrow H_2S\ (g) + 2\ KCl\ (aq)$

$T = 25.8\ °C + 273.15 = 299.0\ K,\ P_{H2S} = 752\ torr \times \dfrac{1\ atm}{760\ torr} = 0.98\underline{9}474\ atm$,

$V_{H2S} = 42.9\ mL \times \dfrac{1\ L}{1000\ mL} = 0.0429\ L$ $\quad PV = nRT$ $\quad$ Rearrange to solve for n_{H2S}.

$n_{H2S} = \dfrac{PV}{RT} = \dfrac{0.98\underline{9}474\ atm \times 0.0429\ L}{0.08206\ \dfrac{L \cdot atm}{mol \cdot K} \times 299.0\ K} = 0.0017\underline{3}003\ mol$

$0.0017\underline{3}003\ mol\ H_2S \times \dfrac{1\ mol\ K_2S}{1\ mol\ H_2S} \times \dfrac{110.27\ g\ K_2S}{1\ mol\ K_2S} = 0.191\ g\ K_2S$

Check: The units (g) are correct. The magnitude of the answer (0.1 g) makes sense because, we have such a small volume of gas generated.

102.a) **Given:** $T = 315\ K$, $P = 50.0\ mm\ Hg$, $V_{SO2} = 285.5\ mL$, $V_{O2} = 158.9\ mL$

Find: limiting reagent and theoretical yield

Conceptual plan: mm Hg $\rightarrow$ atm and $mL_{SO2} \rightarrow L_{SO2}$ then P, V_{SO2}, T $\rightarrow n_{SO2} \rightarrow n_{SO3}$

$$\frac{1\ atm}{760\ mm\ Hg} \qquad \frac{1\ L}{1000\ mL} \qquad PV = nRT \qquad \frac{2\ mol\ SO_3}{2\ mol\ SO_2}$$

and $mL_{O2} \rightarrow L_{O2}$ then P, V_{SO2}, T $\rightarrow n_{O2} \rightarrow n_{SO3}$

$$\frac{1\ L}{1000\ mL} \qquad PV = nRT \qquad \frac{2\ mol\ SO_3}{1\ mol\ O_2}$$

Solution: $50.0\ mm\ Hg \times \dfrac{1\ atm}{760\ mm\ Hg} = 0.065\underline{7}895\ atm$ and $285.5\ mL\ SO_2 \times \dfrac{1\ L\ SO_2}{1000\ mL\ SO_2} = 0.2855\ L$ then

$PV = nRT$ Rearrange to solve for n.

$$n_{SO2} = \frac{PV}{RT} = \frac{0.065\underline{7}895\ atm \times 0.2855\ L}{0.08206\ \dfrac{L \cdot atm}{mol \cdot K} \times 315\ K} = 7.2\underline{6}642 \times 10^{-4}\ mol\ SO_2$$

$$7.2\underline{6}642 \times 10^{-4}\ mol\ SO_2 \times \frac{2\ mol\ SO_3}{2\ mol\ SO_2} = 7.2\underline{6}642 \times 10^{-4}\ mol\ SO_3$$

then $158.9\ mL\ O_2 \times \dfrac{1\ L\ O_2}{1000\ mL\ O_2} = 0.1589\ L\ O_2$ then $PV = nRT$ Rearrange to solve for n.

$$n_{O2} = \frac{PV}{RT} = \frac{0.065\underline{7}895\ atm \times 0.1589\ L}{0.08206\ \dfrac{L \cdot atm}{mol \cdot K} \times 315\ K} = 4.0\underline{4}425 \times 10^{-4}\ mol\ O_2 \quad \text{then}$$

$$4.0\underline{4}425 \times 10^{-4}\ mol\ O_2 \times \frac{2\ mol\ SO_3}{1\ mol\ O_2} = 8.0\underline{8}851 \times 10^{-4}\ mol\ SO_3 \quad \text{Since the amount generated from the } SO_2 \text{ is}$$

less, it is the limiting reagent and the theoretical yield is $7.27 \times 10^{-4}\ mol\ SO_3$.

Check: The units (mol) are correct. The magnitude of the answer (0.0007 mol) makes sense because, we have small volumes of gas involved (compared to 22 L).

b)   **Given:** above info and, $V_{SO3} = 187.2\ mL$ T = 315 K, P = 50.0 mm Hg,   **Find:** % Yield

      Conceptual plan: mm Hg $\rightarrow$ atm and $mL_{SO3} \rightarrow L_{SO3}$ then P, V_{SO2}, T $\rightarrow n_{SO2} \rightarrow n_{SO3}$

$$\frac{1\ atm}{760\ mm\ Hg} \qquad \frac{1\ L}{1000\ mL} \qquad PV = nRT$$

then   actual yield, theoretical yield $\rightarrow$ % yield

$$\%\ Yield = \frac{actual\ yield}{theoretical\ yield} \times 100\ \%$$

Solution: $50.0\ mm\ Hg \times \dfrac{1\ atm}{760\ mm\ Hg} = 0.065\underline{7}895\ atm$ and $187.2\ mL\ SO_3 \times \dfrac{1\ L\ SO_3}{1000\ mL\ SO_3} = 0.1872\ L\ SO_3$

then $PV = nRT$ Rearrange to solve for n. $n_{SO3} = \dfrac{PV}{RT} = \dfrac{0.065\underline{7}895\ atm \times 0.1872\ L}{0.08206\ \dfrac{L \cdot atm}{mol \cdot K} \times 315\ K} = 4.7\underline{6}453 \times 10^{-4}\ mol\ SO_3$

then $\%\ Yield = \dfrac{actual\ yield}{theoretical\ yield} \times 100\ \% = \dfrac{4.7\underline{6}453 \times 10^{-4}\ mol\ SO_3}{7.2\underline{6}642 \times 10^{-4}\ mol\ SO_3} \times 100\ \% = 65.57\ \%$

Check: The units (%) are correct. The magnitude of the answer (66 %) makes sense because it should be between 0 and 100 %. The volume of product is a bit over half of the volume of the limiting reagent and since they and a 2:2 mole ratio, we expect a number a bit over 50 %.

103. **Given:** T = 22 °C, P = 1.02 atm, and m = 11.82 g   **Find:** V_{Total}

      Conceptual plan: °C $\rightarrow$ K and $g_{(NH4)2CO3} \rightarrow n_{(NH4)2CO3} \rightarrow n_{Gas}$ then P, n, T $\rightarrow$ V

$$K = °C + 273.15 \qquad \frac{1\ mol\ (NH_4)_2CO_3}{96.09\ g\ (NH_4)_2CO_3} \qquad \frac{(2 + 1 + 1 = 4)\ mol\ gas}{1\ mol\ NH_4CO_3} \qquad PV = nRT$$

Solution: T = 22 °C + 273.15 = 295 K,

$$11.83\ g\ NH_4CO_3 \times \frac{1\ mol\ (NH_4)_2CO_3}{96.09\ g\ (NH_4)_2CO_3} \times \frac{4\ mol\ gas}{1\ mol\ (NH_4)_2CO_3} = 0.49\underline{2}434\ mol\ gas$$

$PV = nRT$ Rearrange to solve for V_{gas}. $V_{gas} = \dfrac{nRT}{P} = \dfrac{0.49\underline{2}434\ mol\ gas \times 0.08206\ \dfrac{L \cdot atm}{mol \cdot K} \times 295\ K}{1.02\ atm} = 11.7\ L$

Check: The units (L) are correct. The magnitude of the answer (12 L) makes sense because, we have about a half a mole of gas generated.

104. **Given:** $T = 125\ °C$, $P = 748$ mm Hg, and $m = 1.55$ kg **Find:** V_{Total}
   Conceptual plan: $°C \rightarrow K$ and mm Hg $\rightarrow$ atm and kg $_{NH4NO3} \rightarrow$ g $_{NH4NO3} \rightarrow$ n $_{NH4NO3} \rightarrow$ n $_{Gas}$

$$K = °C + 273.15 \qquad \frac{1\ atm}{760\ mm\ Hg} \qquad \frac{1000\ g}{1\ kg} \quad \frac{1\ mol\ NH_4NO_3}{80.05\ g\ NH_4NO_3} \quad \frac{(2+1+4=7)\ mol\ gas}{2\ mol\ NH_4NO_3}$$

then $P, n, T \rightarrow V$
$$PV = nRT$$

Solution: $T = 125\ °C + 273.15 = 398$ $P_{o2} = 748\ mm\ Hg \times \dfrac{1\ atm}{760\ torr} = 0.984211\ atm$ K,

$$1.55\ kg\ NH_4NO_3 \times \frac{1000\ g\ NH_4NO_3}{1\ kg\ NH_4NO_3} \times \frac{1\ mol\ NH_4NO_3}{80.05\ g\ NH_4NO_3} \times \frac{7\ mol\ gas}{2\ mol\ NH_4NO_3} = 67.7701\ mol\ gas \qquad PV = nRT$$

Rearrange to solve for V_{gas}. $V_{gas} = \dfrac{nRT}{P} = \dfrac{67.7701\ mol\ gas \times 0.08206\ \frac{L \cdot atm}{mol \cdot K} \times 398\ K}{0.984211\ atm} = 2250\ L$

Check: The units (L) are correct. The magnitude of the answer (2250 L) makes sense because, we have about a 67 moles of gas generated, so we expect a volume a bit above 67x22 L.

105. **Given:** He and air; $V = 855$ mL, $P = 125$ psi, $T = 25\ °C$, $\mathfrak{M}\ (air) = 28.8$ g/mol **Find:** $\Delta = m(air) - m(He)$
   Conceptual Plan: mL $\rightarrow$ L and psi $\rightarrow$ atm and $°C \rightarrow K$ then $P, T, \mathfrak{M} \rightarrow d$

$$\frac{1\ L}{1000\ mL} \qquad \frac{1\ atm}{14.7\ psi} \qquad K = °C + 273.15 \qquad d = \frac{P\mathfrak{M}}{RT}$$

then $d, V \rightarrow m$ $m(air), m(He) \rightarrow \Delta$
$$d = \frac{m}{V} \qquad \Delta = m(air) - m(He)$$

Solution: $V = 855\ mL \times \dfrac{1\ L}{1000\ mL} = 0.855\ L$, $P = 125\ psi \times \dfrac{1\ atm}{14.7\ psi} = 8.50340\ atm$, $T = 25\ °C + 273.15 = 298K$,

$$d_{air} = \frac{P\mathfrak{M}}{RT} = \frac{8.50340\ atm \times 28.8\ \frac{g\ air}{mol\ air}}{0.08206\ \frac{L \times atm}{K \times mol} \times 298\ K} = 10.0147\ \frac{g\ air}{L}, \quad d = \frac{m}{V} \text{ Rearrange to solve for } m. \quad m = dV$$

$$m_{air} = 10.0147\ \frac{g\ air}{L} \times 0.8554\ L = 8.56257\ g\ air ,$$

$$d_{He} = \frac{P\mathfrak{M}}{RT} = \frac{8.50340\ atm \times 4.03\ \frac{g\ He}{mol\ He}}{0.08206\ \frac{L \times atm}{K \times mol} \times 298\ K} = 1.40136\ \frac{g\ He}{L},$$

$$m_{air} = 1.40136\ \frac{g\ He}{L} \times 0.855\ L = 1.19816\ g\ He, \quad \Delta = m(air) - m(He) = 8.56257\ g\ air - 1.19816\ g\ He = 7.36\ g$$

Check: The units (g) are correct. We expect the difference to be less than the difference in the molecular weights since we have less than a mole of gas.

106. **Given:** $V_1 = 2.95$ L, $P = 0.998$ atm, $T_1 = 25.0\ °C$, $T_2 = -196\ °C$, **Find:** V_2 an compare to 0.61 L
   Conceptual Plan: $°C \rightarrow K$ then $V_1, T_1, T_2 \rightarrow V_2$ and then compare to 0.61 L

$$K = °C + 273.15 \qquad \frac{V_1}{T_1} = \frac{V_2}{T_2}$$

Solution: $T_1 = 25\ °C + 273.15 = 298K$, $T_2 = -196\ °C + 273.15 = 77\ K$, $\dfrac{V_1}{T_1} = \dfrac{V_2}{T_2}$ Rearrange to solve for

V_2. $V_2 = V_1 \times \dfrac{T_2}{T_1} = 2.95\ L \times \dfrac{77\ K}{298\ K} = 0.76\ L$ This is 25 % larger than the measured volume. We expect gases to behave non-ideally as the temperature drops. We are at the boiling point of the material, so the velocity has dramatically decreases and some nitrogen will be condensing.
   Check: The units (L) are correct. We expect the volume to dramatically decrease since the temperature has dropped significantly.

107. **Given:** $Flow_{NO} = 335$ L/s, $P_{NO} = 22.4$ torr, $T_{NO} = 955$ K, $P_{NH3} = 755$ torr, and $T_{NO} = 298$ K, and NH_3 purity = 65.2 % **Find:** $Flow_{NH3}$

Conceptual plan: torr $\rightarrow$ atm   then $P_{NO}, V_{NO}/s, T_{NO} \rightarrow n_{NO}/s \rightarrow n_{NH3}/s$ (pure)

$$\frac{1\,atm}{760\,torr} \qquad\qquad PV = nRT \qquad \frac{4\,mol\,NH_3}{4\,mol\,NO}$$

then n_{NH3}/s (pure) $\rightarrow$ n_{NH3}/s (impure)   then n_{NH3}/s (impure), $P_{NH3}, T_{NH3} \rightarrow$ V_{NH3}/s

$$\frac{100\,mol\,NH_3\,impure}{65.2\,mol\,NH_3\,pure} \qquad\qquad\qquad\qquad PV = nRT$$

Solution: $P_{NO} = 22.4\ \text{torr} \times \dfrac{1\,atm}{760\,torr} = 0.0294737\,atm$, $P_{NH3} = 755\ \text{torr} \times \dfrac{1\,atm}{760\,torr} = 0.993421\,atm$

$PV = nRT$ Rearrange to solve for n_{NO}. Note that we can substitute V/s for V and get n/s as a result.

$$\frac{n_{NO}}{s} = \frac{PV}{RT} = \frac{0.0294737\ \text{atm} \times 335\ \text{L}\ /s}{0.08206\ \frac{\text{L} \cdot \text{atm}}{mol \cdot K} \times 955\ K} = 0.125992\ \frac{mol\,NO}{s}$$

$0.125992\ \dfrac{mol\,NO}{s} \times \dfrac{4\ mol\,NH_3}{4\ mol\,NO} \times \dfrac{100\ mol\,NH_3\,impure}{65.2\ mol\,NH_3\,pure} = 0.193240\ \dfrac{mol\,NH_3\,impure}{s}$ $PV = nRT$

Rearrange to solve for V_{NH3}. Note that we can substitute n/s for n and get V/s as a result.

$$\frac{V_{NH3}}{s} = \frac{nRT}{P} = \frac{0.193240\ \frac{mol\,NH_3\,impure}{s} \times 0.08206\ \frac{\text{L} \cdot \text{atm}}{mol \cdot K} \times 298\ K}{0.993421\ \text{atm}} = 4.76\ \frac{L}{s}\ \text{impure}\ NH_3$$

Check: The units (L) are correct. The magnitude of the answer (5 L/s) makes sense because, we expect it to be less than for the NO. The NO is at a very low concentration and a high temperature, when this converts to a much higher pressure and lower temperature this will go down significantly, even though the ammonia is impure. From a practical standpoint, you would like a low flow rate to make it economical.

108. **Given:** $Flow_{NO} = 2.55$ L/s, $P_{NO} = 12.4$ torr, $T_{NO} = 655$ K, and 8.0 hours   **Find:** m (urea)

Conceptual plan: torr $\rightarrow$ atm   and   hr $\rightarrow$ min $\rightarrow$ s   then $P_{NO}, V_{NO}/s, T_{NO} \rightarrow$ n_{NO}/s

$$\frac{1\,atm}{760\,torr} \qquad\qquad \frac{60\,s}{1\,min} \quad \frac{60\,min}{1\,hr} \qquad\qquad PV = nRT$$

$n_{NO}/s \rightarrow$ n_{urea}/s then   s $\rightarrow n_{urea} \rightarrow$ g_{urea}

$$\frac{2\,mol\,urea}{4\,mol\,NO} \qquad n_{urea} = (n_{urea}/s)(s) \qquad \frac{60.06\,g\,urea}{1\,mol\,urea}$$

Solution: $P_{NO} = 12.4\ \text{torr} \times \dfrac{1\,atm}{760\,torr} = 0.0163579\,atm$, $8.0\ \text{hr} \times \dfrac{60\ \text{min}}{1\ \text{hr}} \times \dfrac{60s}{1\ \text{min}} = 28800\ s$

$PV = nRT$ Rearrange to solve for n_{NO}. Note that we can substitute V/s for V and get n/s as a result.

$$\frac{n_{NO}}{s} = \frac{PV}{RT} = \frac{0.0163579\ atm\ \text{atm} \times 2.55\ \text{L}\ /s}{0.08206\ \frac{\text{L} \cdot \text{atm}}{mol \cdot K} \times 655\ K} = 0.000776059\ \frac{mol\,NO}{s}\ ,$$

$0.000776059\ \dfrac{mol\,NO}{s} \times \dfrac{2\ mol\,urea}{4\ mol\,NO} = 0.000388030\ \dfrac{mol\,urea}{s}\ ,$

$28800\ \text{s} \times 0.000388030\ \dfrac{mol\,urea}{s} \times \dfrac{60.06\ g\,urea}{1\ mol\,urea} = 670\ g\,urea$

Check: The units (g) are correct. The magnitude of the answer (670 g) is not unreasonable mass to add to a car because many more grams of gasoline are burned in 8 hours of driving.

109. **Given:** l = 30.0 cm, w = 20.0 cm, h = 15.0 cm, 14.7 psi   **Find:** Force (lbs)

Conceptual plan: l, w, h $\rightarrow$ Surface Area(cm^2) $\rightarrow$ Surface Area(in^2) $\rightarrow$ Force

$$SA = 2(lxh) + 2(wxh) + 2(lxw) \qquad \frac{(1\,in)^2}{(2.54\,cm)^2} \qquad \frac{14.7\,lbs}{1\,in^2}$$

Solution:

$SA = 2(lxh) + 2(wxh) + 2(lxw) = 2(30.0\ cm \times 15.0\ cm) + 2(20.0\ cm \times 15.0\ cm) + 2(30.0\ cm \times 20.0\ cm) = 2700\ cm^3$

$2700\ cm^2 \times \dfrac{(1\,in)^2}{(2.54\,cm)^2} = 418.50\ in^2$, $418.50\ in^2 \times \dfrac{14.7\,lbs}{1\,in^2} = 6150\ lbs$ The can would be crushed.

Check: The units (lbs) are correct. The magnitude of the answer (6150 lbs) is not unreasonable since there is a large surface area.

110. **Given:** l = 20.0 cm, r = 10.0 cm, 25 mL with d = 0.807 g/ml, $P_1 = 760.0$ mm Hg = 1.000 atm

Find: Force (lbs)

Conceptual plan: $mL \rightarrow g \rightarrow mol$ then $l, r \rightarrow V(cm^3) \rightarrow V(L)$ then $V, n, T \rightarrow P_{N2}$ then

$$d = \frac{m}{V} \quad \frac{1\ mol}{28.02\ g} \qquad\qquad V = \pi r^2 l \qquad \frac{1\ L}{1000\ cm^3} \qquad\qquad PV = nRT$$

$P_{N2}, P_{atm} \rightarrow P_{Total}$ then $atm \rightarrow psi$ $l, r \rightarrow$ **Surface Area(cm^2)** $\rightarrow$ **Surface Area(in^2)** $\rightarrow$ **Force**

$$P_{Total} = P_{atm} + P_{N2} \qquad \frac{14.7\ psi}{1\ atm} \qquad SA = 2\pi r l + 2\pi r^2 \qquad \frac{(1\ in)^2}{(2.54\ cm)^2} \qquad P = \frac{F}{A}$$

Solution: $d = \frac{m}{V}$ Rearrange to solve for m. $m = dV = 0.807\ \frac{g}{mL} \times 25\ mL = 20.175\ g$,

$20.175\ g \times \frac{1\ mol}{28.02\ g} = 0.72002\ mol$, $V = \pi r^2 l = \pi \times (10.0\ cm)^2 \times 20.0\ cm = 6283.19\ cm^3$,

$6283.19\ cm^3 \times \frac{1\ L}{1000\ cm^3} = 6.28319\ L$, $PV = nRT$ Rearrange to solve for P.

$$P_{N2} = \frac{nRT}{V} = \frac{0.72002\ mol \times 0.08206\ \frac{L \cdot atm}{mol \cdot K} \times 298\ K}{6.28319\ L} = 2.80229\ atm\ ,$$

$P_{Total} = P_{atm} + P_{N2} = 1.000\ atm + 2.80229\ atm = 3.80229\ atm$, $3.80229\ atm \times \frac{14.7\ psi}{1\ atm} = 55.894\ psi$

$SA = 2\pi r l + 2\pi r^2 = (2 \times \pi \times 10.0\ cm \times 20.0\ cm) + (2 \times \pi \times (10.0\ cm)^2) = 1884.956\ cm^2$,

$1884.956\ cm^2 \times \frac{(1\ in)^2}{(2.54\ cm)^2} = 292.119\ in^2$, $P = \frac{F}{A}$

Rearrange to solve for F. $292.119\ in^2 \times \frac{55.894\ lbs}{1\ in^2} = 1.6 \times 10^4\ lbs$

Check: The units (lbs) are correct. The magnitude of the answer (16,000 lbs) is not unreasonable since there is a large surface area and this is a high pressure.

111. **Given:** $V_1 = 160.0\ L$, $P_1 = 1855\ psi$, 3.5 L/balloon, $P_2 = 1.0\ atm = 14.7\ psi$ and T = 298 K

Find: # balloons

Conceptual plan: $V_1, P_1, P_2 \rightarrow V_2$ then $L \rightarrow$ # balloons

$$P_1 V_1 = P_2 V_2 \qquad\qquad \frac{1\ balloon}{3.5\ L}$$

Solution: $P_1 V_1 = P_2 V_2$ Rearrange to solve for V_2. $V_2 = \frac{P_1}{P_2} V_1 = \frac{1855\ psi}{14.7\ psi} \times 160.0\ L = 20190.5\ L$,

$20190.5\ L \times \frac{1\ balloon}{3.5\ L} = 5800\ balloons$

Check: The units (balloons) are correct. The magnitude of the answer (5800) is reasonable since a store does not want to buy a new helium tank very often.

112. **Given:** 11.5 mL with d = 0.573 g/ml, T = 28.5 °C, P = 892 torr   **Find:** V

Conceptual plan: $mL \rightarrow g \rightarrow mol$ and $°C \rightarrow K$ and $torr \rightarrow atm$ then $P, n, T \rightarrow V$

$$d = \frac{m}{V} \quad \frac{1\ mol}{58.12\ g} \qquad K = °C + 273.15 \qquad \frac{1\ atm}{760\ torr} \qquad PV = nRT$$

Solution: $d = \frac{m}{V}$ Rearrange to solve for m. $m = dV = 0.573\ \frac{g}{mL} \times 11.5\ mL = 6.5895\ g$,

$6.5895\ g \times \frac{1\ mol}{58.12\ g} = 0.113377\ mol$, T = 28.5C + 273.15 = 301.7 K, $892\ torr \times \frac{1\ atm}{760\ torr} = 1.17368\ atm$

$PV = nRT$ Rearrange to solve for V. $V = \frac{nRT}{P} = \frac{0.113377\ mol \times 0.08206\ \frac{L \cdot atm}{mol \cdot K} \times 301.7\ K}{1.17368\ atm} = 2.39\ L$

Check: The units (L) are correct. The magnitude of the answer (l L) is reasonable since there is a lot less than one mole of butane.

113. **Given:** $r_1 = 2.5\ cm$, $P_1 = 4.00\ atm$. T = 298 K, $P_2 = 1.00\ atm$ **Find:** r_2

Conceptual plan: $r_1 \rightarrow V_1$ $V_1, P_1, P_2 \rightarrow V_2$ then $V_2 \rightarrow r_2$

$$V = \frac{4}{3}\pi r^3 \qquad P_1 V_1 = P_2 V_2 \qquad V = \frac{4}{3}\pi r^3$$

Solution: $V = \frac{4}{3}\pi r^3 = \frac{4}{3} \times \pi \times (2.5\ cm)^3 = 65.450\ cm^3$ $P_1 V_1 = P_2 V_2$ Rearrange to solve for V_2.

161

$V_2 = \dfrac{P_1}{P_2} V_1 = \dfrac{4.00 \text{ atm}}{1.00 \text{ atm}} \times 65.450 \text{ cm}^3 = 261.80 \text{ cm}^3 , \qquad V = \dfrac{4}{3}\pi r^3$

Rearrange to solve for r. $\quad r = \sqrt[3]{\dfrac{3V}{4\pi}} = \sqrt[3]{\dfrac{3 \times 261.80 \text{ cm}^3}{4 \times \pi}} = 4.0 \text{ cm}$

Check: The units (cm) are correct. The magnitude of the answer (4 cm) is reasonable since the bubble will expand as the pressure is decreased.

114. **Given:** max SA = 1257 cm^2, V_1 = 3.0 L, P_1 = 755 torr, T_1 = 298 K, T_2 = 273 K

Find: P_2 to burst balloon

Conceptual plan: torr → atm and A → r → V (cm³) → V (L) then

$$\dfrac{1 \text{ atm}}{760 \text{ torr}} \qquad SA = 4\pi r^2 \quad V = \dfrac{4}{3}\pi r^3 \qquad \dfrac{1 \text{ L}}{1000 \text{ cm}^3}$$

$P_1, V_1, P_2, T_1, V_2, T_2$ → P_2

$$\dfrac{P_1 V_1}{T_1} = \dfrac{P_2 V_2}{T_2}$$

Solution: $P_1 = 755 \text{ torr} \times \dfrac{1 \text{ atm}}{760 \text{ torr}} = 0.993421 \text{ atm} , \qquad SA = 4\pi r^2 \qquad$ Rearrange to solve for r.

$r = \sqrt{\dfrac{SA}{4\pi}} = \sqrt{\dfrac{1257 \text{cm}^2}{4\pi}} = 10.00144 \text{ cm} , \quad V = \dfrac{4}{3}\pi r^3 = \dfrac{4}{3} \times \pi \times (10.00144 \text{ cm})^3 = 4190.600 \text{ cm}^3$

$4190.600 \text{ cm}^3 \times \dfrac{1 \text{ L}}{1000 \text{ cm}^3} = 4.190600 \text{ L} \qquad \dfrac{P_1 V_1}{T_1} = \dfrac{P_2 V_2}{T_2} \quad$ Rearrange to solve for P_2.

$P_2 = P_1 \dfrac{V_1}{V_2} \dfrac{T_2}{T_1} = 0.993421 \text{ atm} \times \dfrac{3.00 \text{ L}}{4.190600 \text{ L}} \times \dfrac{273 \text{ K}}{298 \text{ K}} = 0.652 \text{ atm}$

Check: The units (atm) are correct. The magnitude of the answer (0.65 atm) is reasonable since the pressure must decrease in order for the balloon to expand.

115. **Given:** 2.0 mol CO : 1.0 mol O_2, V = 2.45 L, P_1 = 745 torr, P_2 = 552 torr, and T = 5552 °C

Find: % reacted

Conceptual plan: from PV = nRT we know that P α n, looking at the chemical reaction we see that 2 + 1 = 3 moles of gas gets converted to 2 moles of gas. If all the gas reacts, P_2 = 2/3 P_1. Calculate –ΔP for 100 % reacted and for actual case. Then calculate % reacted.

$$-\Delta P \; 100\% \text{ reacted} = P_1 - \dfrac{2}{3} P_1 \qquad -\Delta P \text{ actual} = P_1 - P_2 \qquad \% \text{ reacted} = \dfrac{\Delta P \text{ actual}}{\Delta P \; 100\% \text{ reacted}} \times 100\%$$

Solution: $-\Delta P \; 100\% \text{ reacted} = P_1 - \dfrac{2}{3} P_1 = 745 \text{ torr} - \dfrac{2}{3} \; 745 \text{ torr} = 248.333 \text{ torr} ,$

$-\Delta P \text{ actual} = P_1 - P_2 = 745 \text{ torr} - 552 \text{ torr} = 193 \text{ torr} ,$

$\% \text{ reacted} = \dfrac{\Delta P \text{ actual}}{\Delta P \; 100\% \text{ reacted}} \times 100\% = \dfrac{193 \text{ torr}}{248.333 \text{ torr}} \times 100\% = 77.7\%$

Check: The units (%) are correct. The magnitude of the answer (78 %) makes sense because; the pressure dropped most of the way to the pressure if all of the reactants had reacted. Note: There are many ways to solve this problem, including calculating the moles of reactants and products using PV = nRT.

116. **Given:** N_2, V_1 = 1.0 L, P_1 = 1.0 atm, T_1 = 300. K, V_1 = 1.0 L, **Find:** d_2

Conceptual plan: $\mathfrak{M}$, V_1, P_1, T_1 → d_1 → d_2

$$d = \dfrac{P\mathfrak{M}}{RT} \quad d = \dfrac{m}{V}$$

Solution: $d_1 = \dfrac{P\mathfrak{M}}{RT} = \dfrac{1.0 \text{ atm} \times 28.02 \; \dfrac{\text{g}}{\text{mol}}}{0.08206 \dfrac{\text{L atm}}{\text{K mol}} \times 300. \text{ K}} = 1.13819 \dfrac{\text{g}}{\text{L}} , \quad d = \dfrac{m}{V}$

Since we have a sealed container $m_1 = m_2$. Rearrange to solve for m. $\quad m = dV$, or $\quad m = d_1 V_1 = d_2 V_2$

Rearrange to solve for d_2. $\quad d_2 = d_1 \dfrac{V_1}{V_2} = 1.13819 \dfrac{\text{g}}{\text{L}} \times \dfrac{1.0 \text{ L}}{3.0 \text{ L}} = 0.379 \dfrac{\text{g}}{\text{L}}$

Check: The units (g/L) are correct. The magnitude of the answer (0.4 g/L) is a typical gas density. The density dropped as the volume went up.

117. **Given:** $P(Total)_1 = 2.2$ atm $= CO + O_2$, $P(Total)_2 = 1.9$ atm $= CO + O_2 + CO_2$, $V = 1.0$ L, $T = 1.0 \times 10^3$ K
Find: CO_2 made
Conceptual plan: $P(Total)_1 = 2.2$ atm $= P(CO)_1 + P(O_2)_1$, $P(Total)_2 = 1.9$ atm $= P(CO)_2 + P(O_2)_2 + P(CO_2)_2$. Let x = amount of $P(O_2)$ reacted. From stoichiometry: $P(CO)_2 = P(CO)_1 - 2x$, $P(O_2)_2 = P(O_2)_1 - x$, $P(CO_2)_2 = 2x$. Thus $P(Total)_2 = 1.9$ atm $= P(CO)_1 - 2x + P(O_2)_1 - x + 2x = P(Total)_1 - x$. Using the initial conditions: 1.9 atm = 2.2 atm $-$ x. So x = 0.3 atm and since $2x = P(CO_2)_2 = 0.6$ atm then P, V, T $\rightarrow$ n

$$PV = nRT$$

Solution: $PV = nRT$ Rearrange to solve for n. $n = \dfrac{PV}{RT} = \dfrac{0.6 \text{ atm} \times 1.0 \text{ L}}{0.08206 \dfrac{\text{L} \cdot \text{atm}}{\text{mol} \cdot \text{K}} \times 1000 \text{ K}} = 0.007$ mol

Check: The units (mol) are correct. The magnitude of the answer (0.007 mol) makes sense because, we have such a small volume, at a very high temperature and such a small pressure. All of these lead us to expect a very small number of moles.

118. **Given:** $r = 1.3 \times 10^{-8}$ cm, V = 100. mL, P = 1.0 atm, $T_1 = 273$ K
Find: V fraction occupied by Xe atoms
Conceptual plan: mL $\rightarrow$ L then   V $\rightarrow$ n $\rightarrow$ atoms   then   r $\rightarrow$ V (cm^3)/atom

$$\dfrac{1 \text{ L}}{1000 \text{ mL}} \qquad \dfrac{1 \text{ mol}}{22.414 \text{ L}} \text{ at STP} \quad 6.022 \times 10^{23} \text{ atoms/mol} \qquad V = \dfrac{4}{3}\pi r^3$$

then   atoms, V (cm^3)/atom $\rightarrow$ V(Xe)   then   V(Xe), V(container) $\rightarrow$ Fraction Xe

$$V(Xe) = (V/atom)(atoms) \qquad\qquad \% V(Xe) = \dfrac{V(Xe)}{V(container)} \times 100 \%$$

Solution: $100 \text{ mL} \times \dfrac{1 \text{ L}}{1000 \text{ mL}} = 0.100 \text{ L}$,

$0.100 \text{ L} \times \dfrac{1 \text{ mol}}{22.414 \text{ L}} = 0.00446149 \text{ mol} \times 6.022 \times 10^{23} \dfrac{\text{atoms}}{\text{mol}} = 2.68671 \times 10^{21}$ atoms

$V = \dfrac{4}{3}\pi r^3 = \dfrac{4}{3} \times \pi \times (1.3 \times 10^{-8} \text{ cm})^3 = 9.2028 \times 10^{-24} \text{ cm}^3 / \text{atom}$,

$V(Xe) = (V/atom)(atoms) = \dfrac{9.2028 \times 10^{-24} \text{cm}^3}{\text{atom}} \times 2.68671 \times 10^{21} \text{ atoms} = 0.024725 \text{ cm}^3$

$\% V(Xe) = \dfrac{V(Xe)}{V(container)} \times 100 \% = \dfrac{0.024725 \text{ cm}^3}{100 \text{ cm}^3} \times 100 \% = 0.025 \% V$

Check: The units (%V) are correct. The magnitude of the answer (0.025 %V) is reasonable since we expect the molecules to take up very little of the volume of a container of a gas.

119. **Given:** $h_1 = 22.6$ m, $T_1 = 22$ °C, and $h_2 = 23.8$ m   **Find:** T_2
Conceptual Plan: °C $\rightarrow$ K since $V_{cylinder} \propto h$ we do not need to know r to use $V_1, T_1, T_2 \rightarrow V_2$

$$K = \text{°C} + 273.15 \qquad\qquad V = \pi r^2 h \qquad\qquad\qquad \dfrac{V_1}{T_1} = \dfrac{V_2}{T_2}$$

Solution: $T_1 = 22$ °C $+ 273.15 = 295$ K, $\dfrac{V_1}{T_1} = \dfrac{V_2}{T_2}$ Rearrange to solve for T_2.

$T_2 = T_1 \times \dfrac{V_2}{V_1} = T_1 \times \dfrac{\pi r^2 l_2}{\pi r^2 l_1} = 295 \text{ K} \times \dfrac{23.8 \text{ m}}{22.6 \text{ m}} = 311 \text{ K}$

Check: The units (K) are correct. We expect the temperature to increase since the volume increased.

120. **Given:** m (CH_4) = 8.0 g, m (Xe) = 8.0 g, $P_{Total} = 0.44$ atm   **Find:** P_{CH4}
Conceptual plan: g $\rightarrow$ mol   then $n_{CH4}, n_{Xe} \rightarrow \chi_{CH4}$ then $\chi_{CH4}, P_{Total} \rightarrow P_{CH4}$

$$\mathfrak{M} \qquad\qquad \chi_{CH4} = \dfrac{n_{CH4}}{n_{CH4} + n_{Xe}} \qquad\qquad P_{CH4} = \chi_{CH4} P_{Total}$$

Solution: $n_{CH4} = 8.0 \text{ g} \times \dfrac{1 \text{ mol}}{16.04 \text{ g}} = 0.49869 \text{ mol}$, $n_{Xe} = 8.0 \text{ g} \times \dfrac{1 \text{ mol}}{131.3 \text{ g}} = 0.060929 \text{ mol}$,

$\chi_{CH4} = \dfrac{n_{CH4}}{n_{CH4} + n_{Xe}} = \dfrac{0.49869 \text{ mol}}{0.49869 \text{ mol} + 0.060929 \text{ mol}} = 0.89112$,

$P_{CH4} = \chi_{CH4} P_{Total} = 0.89112 \times 0.44 \text{ atm} = 0.39 \text{ atm}$

Check: The units (atm) are correct. The magnitude of the answer (0.22 atm) makes sense because, the molecular weight of methane is so much lighter than xenon, so we have so many more moles of methane. The partial pressure of methane is almost as large as the total pressure.

121. **Given:** He, V = 0.35 L, P_{max} = 88 atm, and T = 298 K   **Find:** m_{He}
    Conceptual plan: **P, V, T** $\rightarrow$ **n**   **then**   **mol** $\rightarrow$ **g**
    $$\underset{PV=nRT}{} \qquad \underset{\mathfrak{M}}{}$$

    Solution: $PV = nRT$ Rearrange to solve for n.

    $$n_{He} = \frac{PV}{RT} = \frac{88 \text{ atm} \times 0.35 \text{ L}}{0.08206 \frac{\text{L} \cdot \text{atm}}{\text{mol} \cdot \text{K}} \times 298 \text{ K}} = 1.2595 \text{ mol} \qquad 1.2595 \text{ mol} \times \frac{4.003 \text{ g}}{1 \text{ mol}} = 5.0 \text{ g He}$$

    Check: The units (g) are correct. The magnitude of the answer (5 g) makes sense because, the high pressure and the low volume cancel out (remember 22 L / mol at STP) and so we expect ~ 1 mol and so ~ 4 g.

122. **Given:** NaH + water, V = 0.490 L, P_{Total} = 758 mm Hg, and T = 35 °C   **Find:** m_{H2} and m_{NaH}
    Other: P_{H2}= 42.23 mm Hg at 35 °C
    Conceptual plan: °C $\rightarrow$ K and P_{Total}(mm Hg) $\rightarrow$ P_{H2}(mm Hg) $\rightarrow$ P_{H2}(atm) then
    $$K = °C + 273.15 \qquad\qquad P_{Total} = P_{H2O} + P_{H2} \qquad \frac{1 \text{ atm}}{760 \text{ mm Hg}}$$

    Write balanced reaction
    NaH *(s)* + H_2O *(l)* $\rightarrow$ NaOH *(aq)* + H_2 *(g)*
    P, V, T $\rightarrow$ **n_{H2}** **then** **mol $_{H2}$** $\rightarrow$ **g_{H2}** **then mol $_{H2}$** $\rightarrow$ **mol $_{NaH}$** $\rightarrow$ **g $_{NaH}$**
    $$\underset{PV=nRT}{} \qquad \frac{2.016 \text{ g}}{1 \text{ mol}} \qquad \frac{1 \text{ mol NaH}}{1 \text{ mol H}} \qquad \frac{24.0 \text{ g}}{1 \text{ mol}}$$

    Solution: T = 35°C + 273.15 = 308 K, $P_{Total} = P_{H2O} + P_{H2}$ Rearrange to solve for P_{H2}.

    P_{H2} = 758 mm Hg – 42.23 mm Hg = 715.77 mm Hg, $715.77 \text{ mm Hg} \times \frac{1 \text{ atm}}{760 \text{ mm Hg}} = 0.941803$ atm

    $PV = nRT$ Rearrange to solve for n. $n_{H2} = \frac{PV}{RT} = \frac{0.941803 \text{ atm} \times 0.490 \text{ L}}{0.08206 \frac{\text{L} \cdot \text{atm}}{\text{mol} \cdot \text{K}} \times 308 \text{ K}} = 0.0182589$ mol ,

    $0.0182589 \text{ mol} \times \frac{2.016 \text{ g}}{1 \text{ mol}} = 0.0368 \text{ g H}_2$ and $0.0182589 \text{ mol H}_2 \times \frac{1 \text{ mol NaH}}{1 \text{ mol H}_2} = 0.0182589$ mol NaH ,

    $0.0182589 \text{ mol NaH} \times \frac{24.0 \text{ g}}{1 \text{ mol}} = 0.438$ g NaH

    Check: The units (g) are correct. The magnitude of the answer (0.04g and 0.4 g) makes sense because, we have much less than a mole of each material (remember 22 L / mol at STP) and so we expect < 2 g gas and < 24 g solid.

123. **Given:** 15.0 mL HBr in 1.0 min; and 20.3 mL unknown hydrocarbon gas in 1.0 min
    Find: formula of unknown gas
    Conceptual plan: Since these are gases under the same conditions V α n, V, time → Rate then
    $$Rate = \frac{V}{time}$$

    $\mathfrak{M}$ (HBr), Rate (HBr), Rate (U) $\rightarrow$ **$\mathfrak{M}$ (U)**
    $$\frac{Rate(HBr)}{Rate(U)} = \sqrt{\frac{\mathfrak{M}(U)}{\mathfrak{M}(HBr)}}$$

    Solution: $Rate(HBr) = \frac{V}{time} = \frac{15.0 \text{ mL}}{1.0 \text{ min}} = 15.0 \frac{\text{mL}}{\text{min}}$ $Rate(U) = \frac{V}{time} = \frac{20.3 \text{ mL}}{1.0 \text{ min}} = 20.3 \frac{\text{mL}}{\text{min}}$,

    $\frac{Rate(HBr)}{Rate(U)} = \sqrt{\frac{\mathfrak{M}(U)}{\mathfrak{M}(HBr)}}$ Rearrange to solve for $\mathfrak{M}(U)$.

    $$\mathfrak{M}(U) = \mathfrak{M}(HBr)\left(\frac{Rate(HBr)}{Rate(U)}\right)^2 = 80.91 \frac{\text{g}}{\text{mol}} \times \left(\frac{15.0 \frac{\text{mL}}{\text{min}}}{20.3 \frac{\text{mL}}{\text{min}}}\right)^2 = 44.2 \frac{\text{g}}{\text{mol}} \text{ , formula is } C_3H_8 \text{, propane}$$

    Check: The units (g/mol) are correct. The magnitude of the answer (< HBr) makes sense because, the unknown diffused faster and so must be lighter.

124. Given: 9.0×10^{12} kg/yr octane; atm = 387 ppm CO_2 by volume; atm thickness = 15 km; r_{Earth} = 6371 km, P_{atm} = 381 torr; T_{atm} = 275 K **Find:** $m(CO_2)$ and % increase in CO_2

Conceptual plan: Write a balanced chemical reaction $kg_{C3H8} \rightarrow g_{C3H8} \rightarrow mol_{C3H8} \rightarrow mol_{CO2}$

$$2\ C_3H_8\ (g) + 25\ O_2\ (g) \rightarrow 16\ CO_2\ (g) + 18\ H_2O\ (l) \qquad \frac{1000\ g}{1\ kg} \qquad \frac{1\ mol}{114.22\ g} \qquad \frac{16\ mol\ CO_2}{2\ mol\ C_3H_8}$$

then $mol_{CO2} \rightarrow g_{CO2}$ and $ppm_{CO2} \rightarrow \chi_{CO2} \rightarrow P_{CO2}$ torr $\rightarrow$ atm then $r_{Earth} \rightarrow V_{Earth}$ and

$$\frac{44.01\ g}{1\ mol} \qquad\qquad \frac{1\ part}{10^6\ parts} \quad P_{CO2} = \chi_{CO2}P_{atm} \quad \frac{1\ atm}{760\ torr} \qquad V = \frac{4}{3}\pi r^3$$

r_{Earth} , atm thickness $\rightarrow r_{Earth+atm}$ then $r_{Earth+atm} \rightarrow V_{Earth+atm}$ $\quad V_{Earth+atm}, V_{Earth} \rightarrow V_{atm}$ then

$$r_{Earth+atm} = r_{Earth} + r_{atm} \qquad\qquad V = \frac{4}{3}\pi r^3 \qquad\qquad V_{atm} = V_{Earth+atm} - V_{Earth}$$

$km^3 \rightarrow m^3 \rightarrow cm^3 \rightarrow$ L then $V_{atm}, P_{CO2}, T_{atm} \rightarrow n_{CO2} \rightarrow g_{CO2}$ and

$$\left(\frac{1000\ m}{1\ km}\right)^3 \left(\frac{100\ cm}{1\ m}\right)^3 \frac{1\ L}{1000\ cm^3} \qquad\qquad PV = nRT \qquad \frac{44.01\ g}{1\ mol}$$

$g_{CO2added}, g_{CO2initially} \rightarrow$ % increase$_{CO2}$

$$\% \text{ increase} = \frac{added}{initial} \times 100\ \%$$

Solution: $9.0 \times 10^{12}\ \cancel{kg} \times \frac{1000\ \cancel{g}}{1\ \cancel{kg}} \times \frac{1\ \cancel{mol}}{114.22\ \cancel{g}} \times \frac{16\ \cancel{mol\ CO_2}}{2\ \cancel{mol\ C_3H_8}} \times \frac{44.01\ g}{1\ \cancel{mol}} = 2.7736 \times 10^{16}\ g\ CO_2$ added ,

$387\ parts\ CO_2\ \frac{1\ part}{10^6\ parts} = 3.87 \times 10^{-4} = \chi_{CO2}$, $\qquad\qquad P_{CO2} = \chi_{CO2}P_{atm} = 3.87 \times 10^{-4} \times 381\ torr = 0.147447\ torr$,

$0.147447\ \cancel{torr} \times \frac{1\ atm}{760\ \cancel{torr}} = 0.00019401\ atm$, $\quad V_{Earth} = \frac{4}{3}\pi r^3 = \frac{4}{3} \times \pi \times (6371\ km)^3 = 1.08321 \times 10^{12}\ km^3$,

$r_{Earth+atm} = r_{Earth} + r_{atm} = 6371\ km + 15\ km = 6386\ km$

$V_{Earth+atm} = \frac{4}{3}\pi r^3 = \frac{4}{3} \times \pi \times (6386\ km)^3 = 1.09086 \times 10^{12}\ km^3$,

$V_{atm} = V_{Earth+atm} - V_{Earth} = 1.09086 \times 10^{12}\ km^3 - 1.08321 \times 10^{12}\ km^3 = 7.666 \times 10^9\ km^3$,

$7.666 \times 10^9\ \cancel{km^3} \times \left(\frac{1000\ \cancel{m}}{1\ \cancel{km}}\right)^3 \times \left(\frac{100\ \cancel{cm}}{1\ \cancel{m}}\right)^3 \times \frac{1\ L}{1000\ \cancel{cm^3}} = 7.666 \times 10^{21}\ L$, $\qquad PV = nRT$

Rearrange to solve for n. $\quad n_{CO2\ initial} = \frac{PV}{RT} = \frac{0.00019401\ \cancel{atm} \times 7.666 \times 10^{21}\ L\ \cancel{L}}{0.08206\ \frac{\cancel{L}\cdot\cancel{atm}}{mol \cdot \cancel{K}} \times 275\ \cancel{K}} = 6.591 \times 10^{16}\ mol$,

$6.591 \times 10^{16}\ \cancel{mol} \times \frac{44.01\ g}{1\ \cancel{mol}} = 2.9005 \times 10^{18}\ g\ CO_2$

$\% \text{ increase} = \frac{added}{initial} \times 100\ \% = \frac{2.7736 \times 10^{16}\ g\ CO_2}{2.9005 \times 10^{18}\ g\ CO_2} \times 100\ \% = 1\ \%$ increase

Check: The units (g and %) are correct. The magnitude of the answer (10^{16} g) is reasonable since we started with so much octane and the mass of CO_2 will be larger than the original octane weight since there is so much added oxygen. The % increase is reasonable since the volume of the atmosphere is so large.

125. Given: CH_4: V = 155 mL at STP; O_2: V = 885 mL at STP; NO: V = 55.5 mL at STP; mixed is a flask: V = 2.0 L, T = 275 K, and 90.0 % of limiting reagent used. **Find:** P's of all components and P_{Total}.

Conceptual plan: CH_4: mL $\rightarrow$ L $\rightarrow mol_{CH4} \rightarrow mol_{CO2}$ and

$$\frac{1\ L}{1000\ mL} \qquad \frac{1\ mol}{22.414\ L} \qquad \frac{1\ mol\ CO_2}{5\ mol\ NO}$$

O_2: mL $\rightarrow$ L $\rightarrow mol_{O2} \rightarrow mol_{CO2}$ and NO: mL $\rightarrow$ L $\rightarrow mol_{NO} \rightarrow mol_{CO2}$

$$\frac{1\ L}{1000\ mL} \quad \frac{1\ mol}{22.414\ L} \quad \frac{1\ mol\ CO_2}{5\ mol\ O_2} \qquad\qquad \frac{1\ L}{1000\ mL} \quad \frac{1\ mol}{22.414\ L} \quad \frac{1\ mol\ CO_2}{5\ mol\ NO}$$

the smallest yield to determines the limiting reagent then initial $mol_{NO} \rightarrow$ reacted $mol_{NO} \rightarrow$ final mol_{NO}

NO is the limiting reagent $\qquad\qquad$ 90.0 % $\qquad\qquad$ 0.100 x initial mol_{no}

reacted $mol_{NO} \rightarrow$ reacted mol_{CH4} then initial mol_{CH4}, reacted $mol_{CH4} \rightarrow$ final mol_{CH4} then

$$\frac{1\ mol\ CH_4}{5\ mol\ NO} \qquad\qquad\qquad \text{initial}\ mol_{CH4} - \text{reacted}\ mol_{CH4} = \text{final}\ mol_{CH4}$$

final mol_{CH4}, V, T $\rightarrow$ final P_{CH4} and $\qquad\qquad$ reacted $mol_{NO} \rightarrow$ reacted mol_{O2} then

$$PV = nRT \qquad\qquad\qquad\qquad\qquad \frac{5\ mol\ O_2}{5\ mol\ NO}$$

165

initial mol$_{O2}$, reacted mol$_{O2}$ → final mol$_{O2}$ then final mol$_{O2}$, V, T → final P$_{O2}$ and

initial mol$_{O2}$ − reacted mol$_{O2}$ = final mol$_{O2}$ $PV = nRT$

final mol$_{NO}$, V, T → final P$_{NO}$ and   theoretical mol$_{CO2}$ from NO →   final mol$_{CO2}$

$PV = nRT$ 90.0 %

final mol$_{CO2}$, V, T → P$_{CO2}$ then   final mol$_{CO2}$ → mol$_{H2O}$ then   mol$_{H2O}$, V, T → P$_{H2O}$ and

$PV = nRT$ $\dfrac{1 \text{ mol H}_2\text{O}}{1 \text{ mol CO}_2}$ $PV = nRT$

final mol$_{CO2}$ → mol$_{NO2}$ then   mol$_{NO2}$, V, T → P$_{NO2}$ and final mol$_{CO2}$ → mol$_{OH}$ then

$\dfrac{1 \text{ mol NO}_2}{1 \text{ mol CO}_2}$ $PV = nRT$ $\dfrac{2 \text{ mol OH}}{1 \text{ mol CO}_2}$

mol$_{OH}$, V, T → P$_{OH}$ finally   P$_{CH4}$, P$_{O2}$, P$_{NO}$, P$_{CO2}$, P$_{H2O}$, P$_{NO2}$, P$_{OH}$ → P$_{Ttoal}$

$PV = nRT$ $P_{Total} = \sum P$

Solution: CH$_4$: 155 mL x $\dfrac{1 \text{ L}}{1000 \text{ mL}}$ x $\dfrac{1 \text{ mol CH}_4}{22.414 \text{ L}}$ x $\dfrac{1 \text{ mol CO}_2}{1 \text{ mol CH}_4}$ = 0.00691532 mol CO$_2$,

O$_2$: 885 mL x $\dfrac{1 \text{ L}}{1000 \text{ mL}}$ x $\dfrac{1 \text{ mol O}_2}{22.414 \text{ L}}$ = 0.0394842 mol O$_2$ x $\dfrac{1 \text{ mol CO}_2}{5 \text{ mol O}_2}$ = 0.00789685 mol CO$_2$

NO: 55.5 mL x $\dfrac{1 \text{ L}}{1000 \text{ mL}}$ x $\dfrac{1 \text{ mol NO}}{22.414 \text{ L}}$ x $\dfrac{1 \text{ mol CO}_2}{5 \text{ mol NO}}$ = 0.000495226 mol CO$_2$.

0.000495226 mol CO$_2$ is the smallest yield, so NO is the limiting reagent.

55.5 mL x $\dfrac{1 \text{ L}}{1000 \text{ mL}}$ x $\dfrac{1 \text{ mol NO}}{22.414 \text{ L}}$ = 0.00247613 mol NO

reacted mol NO = 0.900 x mol NO = 0.900 x 0.00247613 mol NO = 0.00222852 mol NO ,

unreacted mol NO = 0.100 x mol NO = 0.100 x 0.00247613 mol NO = 0.000247613 mol NO ,

0.00222852 mol NO x $\dfrac{1 \text{ mol CH}_4}{5 \text{ mol NO}}$ = 0.000445704 mol CH$_4$ reacted ,

0.00691532 mol CH$_4$ − 0.000445704 mol CH$_4$ reacted = 0.00646962 mol CH$_4$ then   *PV = nRT*

Rearrange to solve for P. $P = \dfrac{nRT}{V} = \dfrac{0.00646962 \text{ mol} \times 0.08206 \frac{\text{L} \cdot \text{atm}}{\text{mol} \cdot \text{K}} \times 275 \text{ K}}{2.0 \text{ L}}$ = 0.0730 atm CH$_4$

0.00222852 mol NO x $\dfrac{5 \text{ mol O}_2}{5 \text{ mol NO}}$ = 0.00222852 mol O$_2$ reacted ,

0.0394842 mol O$_2$ − 0.00222852 mol O$_2$ reacted = 0.0372557 mol O$_2$

$P = \dfrac{nRT}{V} = \dfrac{0.0372557 \text{ mol} \times 0.08206 \frac{\text{L} \cdot \text{atm}}{\text{mol} \cdot \text{K}} \times 275 \text{ K}}{2.0 \text{ L}}$ = 0.420 atm O$_2$

$P = \dfrac{nRT}{V} = \dfrac{0.000247613 \text{ mol} \times 0.08206 \frac{\text{L} \cdot \text{atm}}{\text{mol} \cdot \text{K}} \times 275 \text{ K}}{2.0 \text{ L}}$ = 0.00279 atm NO ,

0.00222852 mol NO x $\dfrac{1 \text{ mol CO}_2}{5 \text{ mol NO}}$ = 0.000445704 mol CO$_2$

$P = \dfrac{nRT}{V} = \dfrac{0.000445704 \text{ mol} \times 0.08206 \frac{\text{L} \cdot \text{atm}}{\text{mol} \cdot \text{K}} \times 275 \text{ K}}{2.0 \text{ L}}$ = 0.00503 atm CO$_2$

0.00222852 mol NO x $\dfrac{1 \text{ mol H}_2\text{O}}{5 \text{ mol NO}}$ = 0.000445704 mol H$_2$O

$P = \dfrac{nRT}{V} = \dfrac{0.000445704 \text{ mol} \times 0.08206 \frac{\text{L} \cdot \text{atm}}{\text{mol} \cdot \text{K}} \times 275 \text{ K}}{2.0 \text{ L}}$ = 0.00503 atm H$_2$O

0.00222852 mol NO x $\dfrac{5 \text{ mol NO}_2}{5 \text{ mol NO}}$ = 0.00222852 mol NO$_2$

$P = \dfrac{nRT}{V} = \dfrac{0.00222852 \text{ mol} \times 0.08206 \frac{\text{L} \cdot \text{atm}}{\text{mol} \cdot \text{K}} \times 275 \text{ K}}{2.0 \text{ L}}$ = 0.0251 atm NO$_2$

$$0.00222852 \; \text{mol NO} \; \times \frac{2 \; \text{mol OH}}{5 \; \text{mol NO}} = 0.000891408 \; \text{mol OH}$$

$$P = \frac{nRT}{V} = \frac{0.000891408 \; \text{mol} \times 0.08206 \; \frac{\text{L} \cdot \text{atm}}{\text{mol} \cdot \text{K}} \times 275 \; \text{K}}{2.0 \; \text{L}} = 0.0101 \; \text{atm OH}$$

$$P_{Total} = \sum P = 0.0730 \; \text{atm} + 0.420 \; \text{atm} + 0.00279 \; \text{atm} + 0.00503 \; \text{atm} + 0.00503 \; \text{atm} + 0.0251 \; \text{atm} + 0.0101 \; \text{atm}$$
$$= 0.533 \; \text{atm}$$

Check: The units (atm) are correct. The magnitude of the answers is reasonable. The limiting reagent has the lowest pressure. The product pressures are in line with the ratios of the stoichiometric coefficients.

126. **Given:** He and air **Find:** % He diffused through balloon wall

Conceptual plan: $\mathfrak{M}\,(N_2)$, $\mathfrak{M}\,(O_2) \rightarrow \mathfrak{M}\,(\text{air})$ **then** $\mathfrak{M}\,(\text{air})$, $\mathfrak{M}\,(\text{He})$, **% air diffused** $\rightarrow$ **% He diffused**

$$\mathfrak{M}(air) = \chi(N_2)\mathfrak{M}(N_2) + \chi(O_2)\mathfrak{M}(O_2) \qquad \frac{Rate(He)}{Rate(air)} = \sqrt{\frac{\mathfrak{M}(air)}{\mathfrak{M}(He)}}$$

Solution: $\mathfrak{M}(air) = \chi(N_2)\mathfrak{M}(N_2) + \chi(O_2)\mathfrak{M}(O_2) = \left(\frac{4}{5} \times 28.02 \; \text{g/mol}\right) + \left(\frac{1}{5} \times 32.00 \; \text{g/mol}\right) = 28.82 \; \text{g/mol}$,

$\dfrac{Rate(He)}{Rate(air)} = \sqrt{\dfrac{\mathfrak{M}(air)}{\mathfrak{M}(He)}}$ Since Rate α % diffused, substitute % diffused for rate and rearrange to solve for % He

diffused. $\% \; He \; diffused = \% \; air \; diffused \sqrt{\dfrac{\mathfrak{M}(air)}{\mathfrak{M}(He)}} = 5.0 \% \sqrt{\dfrac{28.82 \; \text{g} / \text{mol}}{4.003 \; \text{g} / \text{mol}}} = 13 \%$

Check: The units (%) are correct. The magnitude of the answer (>5%) makes sense because, He is lighter and so has the higher diffusion rate.

127. **Given:** $P_{CH4} + P_{C2H6} = 0.53 \; \text{atm}$, $P_{CO2} + P_{H2O} = 2.2 \; \text{atm}$ **Find:** χ_{CH4}

Conceptual plan: Write balanced reactions to determine change in moles of gas for CH_4 and C_2H_6.

$2 \; CH_4 \, (g) + 4 \; O_2 \, (g) \rightarrow 4 \; H_2O \, (g) + 2 \; CO_2 \, (g)$ and $2 \; C_2H_6 \, (g) + 5 \; O_2 \, (g) \rightarrow 6 \; H_2O \, (g) + 4 \; CO_2 \, (g)$ thus $\dfrac{6 \; \text{mol gases}}{2 \; \text{mol } CH_4} \quad \dfrac{10 \; \text{mol gases}}{2 \; \text{mol } C_2H_6}$

write expression for final pressure, substituting in data given $\rightarrow \; \chi_{CH4}$

$$\chi_{CH4} = \frac{n_{CH4}}{n_{CH4} + n_{C2H6}} \; \text{and} \; \chi_{C2H6} = 1 - \chi_{CH4}$$

$$P_{CH4} = \chi_{CH4}P_{Total} \quad P_{C2H6} = \chi_{C2H6}P_{Total} \quad P_{Final} = \left(\chi_{CH4}P_{Total} \times \frac{6 \; \text{mol gases}}{1 \; \text{mol } CH_4}\right) + \left((1 - \chi_{CH4})P_{Total} \times \frac{10 \; \text{mol gases}}{1 \; \text{mol } C_2H_6}\right)$$

Solution: $P_{Final} = \left(\chi_{CH4} \times 0.53 \; \text{atm} \times \dfrac{6 \; \text{mol gases}}{2 \; \text{mol } CH_4}\right) + \left((1 - \chi_{CH4}) \times 0.53 \; \text{atm} \times \dfrac{10 \; \text{mol gases}}{2 \; \text{mol } C_2H_6}\right) = 2.2 \; \text{atm}$

Rearrange to solve for $\chi_{CH4} = 0.42$.

Check: The units (none) are correct. The magnitude of the answer (0.42) makes sense because, if it were all methane the final pressure would have been 1.59 atm and if it were all ethane the final pressure would have been 2.65 atm. Since we are closer to the latter pressure we expect the mole fraction of methane to be less than 0.5.

128. **Given:** $P_{C2H2} = 7.8 \; \text{kPa}$ initially, $P_{C2H2} + P_{C6H6} = 3.9 \; \text{kPa}$ **Find:** fraction of C_2H_2 reacted

Conceptual plan: Write balanced reaction to determine change in moles of gas.

$3C_2H_2 \, (g) \rightarrow C_6H_6 \, (g)$ thus $\dfrac{1 \; \text{mol } C_6H_6}{3 \; \text{mol } C_2H_2 \; reacted}$ Since P_{C2H2} α n_{C2H2}, the pressure will drop 2 kPa for every 3 kPa of ethylene that reacts.

$\mathbf{P_{initial}, P_{final} \rightarrow P_{drop}}$ **write expression for reacted P_{C2H2},** **then**

$$P_{drop} = P_{initial} - P_{final} \qquad \text{reacted} \; P_{C2H2} = \Delta P \frac{3 \; \text{kPa} \; C_2H_2 \; reacted}{2 \; \text{kPa} \; pressure \; drop}$$

reacted P_{C2H2}, initial P_{C2H2} $\rightarrow$ % C_2H_2 reacted

$$\% \; C_2H_2 \; reacted = \frac{\text{reacted} \; P_{C_2H_2}}{\text{initial} \; P_{C_2H_2}} \times 100 \%$$

Solution: $P_{drop} = P_{initial} - P_{final} = 7.8 \; \text{kPa} - 3.9 \; \text{kPa} = 3.9 \; \text{kPa}$,

reacted $P_{C2H2} = \Delta P \dfrac{3 \; \text{kPa} \; C_2H_2 \; reacted}{2 \; \text{kPa} \; pressure \; drop} = 3.9 \; kPa \times \dfrac{3 \; \text{kPa} \; C_2H_2 \; reacted}{2 \; \text{kPa} \; pressure \; drop} = 5.85 \; \text{kPa}$

$$\% \ C_2H_2 \ reacted = \frac{reacted \ P_{C_2H_2}}{initial \ P_{C_2H_2}} \ x \ 100 \ \% = \frac{5.85 \ kPa}{7.8 \ kPa} \ x \ 100 \ \% = 75 \ \%$$

Check: The units (%) are correct. The magnitude of the answer (75 %) makes sense because, if all the ethylene reacted the final pressure would have been 2.6 kPa. Since we are most of the way to that, we expect the amount reacted to be higher than 50 %.

129. Since the passengers have more mass than the balloon they have more momentum than the balloon. The passengers will continue to travel in their original direction longer. The car is slowing so the relative position of the passengers is to move forward and the balloons to move backwards. The opposite happens upon acceleration.

130. If the liquid is 10 times denser, then the force needed to move it will be 10 times greater per unit volume. This means that the straw will be 1/10 the length or (10.3 m x 1/10) = 1.3 m

131. B is the limiting reactant (2.0 L of B requires 1.0 L A to completely react). The final container will have 0.5 L A and 2.0 L C, so the final volume will be 2.5 L. The change will be 100 % - ((2.5 L/3.5 L) x 100 %) = -29 %.

132. Since each gas will occupy 22.414 L / mole at STP and we have 2 moles of gas, we will have a volume of 44.828 L.

133. a) False – all gases have the same average kinetic energy at the same temperature.

   b) False – the gases will have the same partial pressures since we have the same number of moles of each.

   c) False – the average velocity of the B molecules will be less than that of the A molecules since the B's are heavier.

   d) True – since B molecules are heavier they will contribute more to the density (d = m/V)

134. Br_2 would deviate the most from ideal behavior since it is the largest of the three.

Chapter 6
Thermochemistry

1. Thermochemistry is the study of the relationships between chemistry and energy. It is so important because energy and its uses are so critical to our society. It is important to understand how much energy is required or released in a process.

2. Energy is the capacity to do work. Work is the result of a force acting through a distance. Examples of energy are kinetic energy, heat energy, electrical energy, chemical energy and light or radiant energy. Examples of work are moving an object, expansion of a cylinder and running a marathon.

3. Kinetic energy is energy associated with the motion of an object. Potential energy is energy associated with the position or composition of an object. Examples of kinetic energy are a moving billiard ball, gas molecules and a raging river. Examples of potential energy are a billiard ball raised above the surface of a billiard table, a compressed spring and molecules.

4. The law of conservation of energy states that energy can neither be created nor destroyed. Energy can be transferred from one object to another, and it can assume different forms. In an energy exchange, energy is transferred between the system and the surroundings. If the system loses energy, the surroundings gain energy, and vice versa.

5. The SI unit of energy is $kg \dfrac{m^2}{s^2}$, defined as the joule (J), named after the English scientist James Joule. Other units of energy are the kilojoule (kJ), the calorie (cal) the Calorie (Cal) and the kilowatt-hour (kWh).

6. The first law of thermodynamics is the law of energy conservation, stated as follows: The total energy of the universe is constant. In other words, because energy is neither created nor destroyed, and the universe does not exchange energy with anything else, its energy content does not change. The first law has many implications, the most important of which is that with energy, you do not get something for nothing. The best we can do with energy is break even—there is no free lunch.

7. According to the first law, a device that would continually produce energy with no energy input, sometimes known as a perpetual motion machine, cannot exist because the best we can do with energy is break even.

8. A state function is a function whose value depends only on the state of the system, not on how the system arrived at that state. Examples are the pressure, volume and the internal energy.

9. The internal energy (E) of a system is the sum of the kinetic and potential energies of all of the particles that compose the system.

10. If energy is flowing out of the system it is like a withdrawal from a checking account, and, therefore, carries a negative sign.

11. If the reactants have a lower internal energy than the products, ΔE_{sys} is positive and energy flows into the system from the surroundings.

12. Heat is the flow of thermal energy caused by a temperature difference. Thermal energy is actually a type of kinetic energy because it arises from the motions of atoms or molecules within a substance. The higher the temperature, the greater the motion of atoms and molecules. Heat is measured in units of energy – joules, calories, kilowatt-hours, …. Temperature is measured in units of Kelvins, degrees Celcius, …..

13. The internal energy (E) of a system is the sum of the kinetic and potential energies of all of the particles that compose the system. The change in the internal energy of the system (ΔE) must be the sum of the heat transferred (q) and the work done (w): $\Delta E = q + w$.

14. According to the first law of thermodynamics, the change in the internal energy of the system (ΔE) must be the sum of the heat transferred (q) and the work done (w): $\Delta E = q + w$. The total change in internal energy (ΔE) is the difference between its initial energy and its final energy. The amount of work done and the

amount of heat transferred is dependant on the details of the path. In one path more energy may be transferred through conversion to heat energy (if, for example there is more friction). In another path more energy may be transferred through work. Work and heat are not state functions, but their sum (ΔE) is constant.

15. The heat capacity of a system is usually defined as the quantity of heat required to change its temperature by 1 °C. Heat capacity (C) is a measure of the system's ability to hold thermal energy without undergoing a large change in temperature. Since water has such a high heat capacity, it can moderate temperature changes, keeping inland temperatures more constant.

16. The work caused by an expansion of volume is simply the negative of the pressure that the volume expands against multiplied by the change in volume that occurs during the expansion: $w = - P \cdot \Delta V$.

17. In calorimetry, the thermal energy exchanged between the reaction (defined as the system) and the surroundings is measured by observing the change in temperature of the surroundings. A bomb calorimeter is used to measure the ΔE_{rxn} for combustion reactions. The calorimeter includes a tight fitting, sealed container forces the reaction to occur at constant volume. A coffee-cup calorimeter is used to measure ΔH_{rxn} for many aqueous reactions. The calorimeter consists of two Styrofoam coffee cups, one inserted into the other, to provide insulation from the laboratory environment. Since the reaction happens under conditions of constant pressure (open to the atmosphere), $q_{rxn} = q_p = \Delta H_{rxn}$.

18. ΔH is of only the heat exchanged with the surroundings under conditions of constant pressure. ΔH is equal to q_p, the heat at constant pressure. Conceptually (and often numerically), ΔH and ΔE are similar: they both represent changes in a state function for the system. However, ΔE, is a measure of all of the energy (heat and work) exchanged with the surroundings. $\Delta H = \Delta E + P\Delta V$

19. An endothermic reaction has a positive ΔH and absorbs heat from the surroundings. An endothermic reaction feels cold to the touch. An exothermic reaction has a negative ΔH and gives off heat to the surroundings. An exothermic reaction feels warm to the touch.

20. The internal energy of a chemical system is the sum of its kinetic energy and its potential energy. It is this potential energy that is the energy source in an exothermic chemical reaction. Under normal circumstances, chemical potential energy (or simply chemical energy) arises primarily from the electrostatic forces between the protons and electrons that compose the atoms and molecules within the system. In an exothermic reaction, some bonds break and new ones form, and the protons and electrons go from an arrangement of higher potential energy to one of lower potential energy. As they rearrange, their potential energy is converted into kinetic energy, the heat emitted in the reaction.

21. The internal energy of a chemical system is the sum of its kinetic energy and its potential energy. It is this potential energy that absorbs the energy in an endothermic chemical reaction. In an endothermic reaction, as some bonds break and others form, the protons and electrons go from an arrangement of lower potential energy to one of higher potential energy, absorbing thermal energy in the process.

22. ΔH_{rxn} is an extensive property; therefore it depends on the quantity of reactants undergoing reaction. ΔH_{rxn} is usually reported for a reaction involving stoichiometric amounts of reactants and is dependant on the specific chemical reaction. For example, for a reaction A + 2 B → C, ΔH_{rxn} is usually reported as the amount of heat emitted or absorbed when 1 mole A reacts with 2 mole B to form 1 mole C.

23. a) If a reaction is multiplied by a factor, the ΔH is multiplied by the same factor.

b) If a reaction is reversed, the sign of ΔH is reversed.

The relationships hold because H is a state function. Twice as much energy is contained in twice as much reactants or products. If the reaction is reversed, the final and initial states have been switched and the direction of heat flow is reversed.

24. Hess's law states that if a chemical equation can be expressed as the sum of a series of steps, then ΔH_{rxn} for the overall equation is the sum of the heats of reactions for each step. This makes it possible to determine ΔH for a reaction without directly measuring it in the laboratory. If you can find related reactions (with known ΔH's) that sum to the reaction of interest, you can find ΔH for the reaction of interest.

25. The standard state is defined as : for a gas –the pure gas at a pressure of exactly 1 atmosphere; for a liquid or solid –the pure substance in its most stable form at a pressure of 1 atm and the temperature of interest (often taken to be 25 °C); and for a substance in solution – a concentration of exactly 1 M. The standard enthalpy change ($\Delta H°$) is the change in enthalpy for a process when all reactants and products are in their standard states. The superscript degree sign indicates standard states.

26. The standard enthalpy of formation ($\Delta H_f°$) for a pure compound is the change in enthalpy when 1 mole of the compound forms from its constituent elements in their standard states. For a pure element in its standard state $\Delta H_f° = 0$.

27. To calculate $\Delta H_{rxn}°$, subtract the heats of formations of the reactants multiplied by their stoichiometric coefficients from the heats of formation of the products multiplied by their stoichiometric coefficients. In the form of an equation:

$$\Delta H^o_{rxn} = \sum n_p \Delta H_f{}^\circ (\text{products}) - \sum n_r \Delta H_f{}^\circ (\text{reactants})$$

28. Most of U.S. energy comes from the combustion of fossil fuels, which include petroleum, natural gas, and coal.

29. One of the main problems associated with the burning of fossil fuels is that, even though they are abundant in the Earth's crust, they are a finite and non-renewable energy source. The other major problems associated with fossil fuel use are related to the products of combustion. Three major environmental problems associated with the emissions of fossil fuel combustion are air pollution, acid rain, and global warming. One of the main products of fossil fuel combustion is carbon dioxide (CO_2), which is a greenhouse gas.

30. One of the main products of fossil fuel combustion is carbon dioxide (CO_2). Carbon dioxide is a greenhouse gas, meaning that it allows visible light from the sun to enter Earth's atmosphere, but prevents heat (in the form of infrared light) from escaping. The result is that carbon dioxide acts as a blanket, keeping Earth warm. However, because of fossil-fuel combustion, carbon dioxide levels in the atmosphere have been steadily increasing. This increase is expected to raise Earth's average temperature. Current observations suggest that Earth has already warmed by about 0.6 °C in the last century, due to an increase of about 25 percent in atmospheric carbon dioxide. Computer models suggest that the warming could worsen if carbon dioxide emissions are not curbed. The possible effects of this warming include heightened storm severity, increasing numbers of floods and droughts, major shifts in agricultural zones, rising sea levels and coastal flooding, and profound changes in habitats that could result in the extinction of some plant and animal species.

31. a) **Given:** 3.55×10^4 J **Find:** cal
Conceptual plan: J → cal
$$\frac{1\,cal}{4.184\,J}$$

Solution: $3.55 \times 10^4 \, \cancel{J} \times \dfrac{1\,cal}{4.814\,\cancel{J}} = 8.48 \times 10^3 \, cal$

Check: The units (cal) are correct. The magnitude of the answer (8000) makes physical sense because a calorie is larger than a Joule, so the answer decreases.

b) **Given:** 1025 Cal **Find:** J
Conceptual plan: Cal → J
$$\frac{4184\,J}{1\,Cal}$$

Solution: $1025 \, \cancel{Cal} \times \dfrac{4184 \, J}{1 \, \cancel{Cal}} = 4.289 \times 10^6 \, J$

Check: The units (J) are correct. The magnitude of the answer (10^6) makes physical sense because a Calorie is much larger than a Joule, so the answer increases.

c) **Given:** 355 kJ **Find:** cal

171

Conceptual plan: kJ → J → cal

$$\frac{1000\,J}{1\,kJ} \qquad \frac{1\,cal}{4.184\,J}$$

Solution: $355\ \cancel{kJ}\ \times\ \dfrac{1000\ \cancel{J}}{1\ \cancel{kJ}}\ \times\ \dfrac{1\,cal}{4.814\ \cancel{J}}\ =\ 8.48\times10^4\ cal$

Check: The units (cal) are correct. The magnitude of the answer (10^4) makes physical sense because a calorie is much smaller than a kJ, so the answer increases.

d) **Given:** 125 kWh   **Find:** J
   Conceptual plan: kWh → J

$$\frac{3.60\times10^6\,J}{1\,kWh}$$

Solution: $125\ \cancel{kWh}\ \times\ \dfrac{3.60\times10^6\,J}{1\ \cancel{kWh}} = 4.50\times10^8\ J$

Check: The units (J) are correct. The magnitude of the answer (10^8) makes physical sense because a kWh is much larger than a Joule, so the answer increases.

32. a) **Given:** 1.58×10^3 kJ   **Find:** kcal
   Conceptual plan: kJ → J → cal → kcal

$$\frac{1000\,J}{1\,kJ} \qquad \frac{1\,cal}{4.184\,J} \qquad \frac{1\,kcal}{1000\,cal}$$

Solution: $1.58\times10^3\ \cancel{kJ}\ \times\ \dfrac{1000\ \cancel{J}}{1\ \cancel{kJ}}\ \times\ \dfrac{1\ \cancel{cal}}{4.184\ \cancel{J}}\ \times\ \dfrac{1\,kcal}{1000\ \cancel{cal}} = 378\ kcal$

Check: The units (kcal) are correct. The magnitude of the answer (400) makes physical sense because a kcal is larger than a kJ, so the answer decreases.

b) **Given:** 865 cal   **Find:** kJ
   Conceptual plan: cal → J → kJ

$$\frac{4.184\,J}{1\,cal} \qquad \frac{1\,kJ}{1000\,J}$$

Solution: $865\ \cancel{cal}\ \times\ \dfrac{4.184\ \cancel{J}}{1\ \cancel{cal}}\ \times\ \dfrac{1\,kJ}{1000\ \cancel{J}} = 3.62\ kJ$

Check: The units (kJ) are correct. The magnitude of the answer (4) makes physical sense because a kJ is much larger than a cal, so the answer decreases.

c) **Given:** 1.93×10^4 J   **Find:** Cal
   Conceptual plan: J → Cal

$$\frac{1\,Cal}{4184\,J}$$

Solution: $1.93\times10^4\ \cancel{J}\ \times\ \dfrac{1\,Cal}{4814\ \cancel{J}} = 4.61\ Cal$

Check: The units (Cal) are correct. The magnitude of the answer (5) makes physical sense because a J is much smaller than a Cal, so the answer increases.

d) **Given:** 1.8×10^4 kJ   **Find:** kWh
   Conceptual plan: kJ → J → kWh

$$\frac{1000\,J}{1\,kJ} \qquad \frac{1\,kWh}{3.60\times10^6\,J}$$

Solution: $1.8\times10^8\ \cancel{kJ}\ \times\ \dfrac{1000\ \cancel{J}}{1\ \cancel{kJ}}\ \times\ \dfrac{1\,kWh}{3.60\times10^6\ \cancel{J}} = 5.0\ kWh$

Check: The units (kWh) are correct. The magnitude of the answer (5) makes physical sense because a kWh is much larger than a Joule, so the answer decreases.

33. a) **Given:** 2155 Cal   **Find:** J

Conceptual plan: $\quad$ Cal $\rightarrow$ J

$$\frac{4184\,J}{1\,Cal}$$

Solution: $\quad$ 2155 $\cancel{Cal}$ x $\dfrac{4184\ J}{1\ \cancel{Cal}}$ = 9.017 x 10^6 J

Check: The units (J) are correct. The magnitude of the answer (10^6) makes physical sense because a Calorie is much larger than a Joule, so the answer increases.

b) **Given:** 2155 Cal $\quad$ **Find:** kJ

$\quad$ **Conceptual plan:** $\quad$ Cal $\rightarrow$ J $\rightarrow$ kWh

$$\frac{4184\,J}{1\,Cal} \quad \frac{1\,kJ}{1000\,J}$$

Solution: $\quad$ 2155 $\cancel{Cal}$ x $\dfrac{4184\ \cancel{J}}{1\ \cancel{Cal}}$ x $\dfrac{1\ kJ}{1000\ \cancel{J}}$ = 3.62 kJ= 9.017 x 10^3 kJ

Check: The units (kJ) are correct. The magnitude of the answer (10^3) makes physical sense because a Calorie is larger than a kJ, so the answer increases.

c) **Given:** 2155 Cal $\quad$ **Find:** kWh

$\quad$ **Conceptual plan:** $\quad$ Cal $\rightarrow$ J $\rightarrow$ kWh

$$\frac{4184\,J}{1\,Cal} \quad \frac{1\,kWh}{3.60\,x\,10^6\,J}$$

Solution: $\quad$ 2155 $\cancel{Cal}$ x $\dfrac{4184\ \cancel{J}}{1\ \cancel{Cal}}$ x $\dfrac{1\ kWh}{3.60\ x\,10^6\ \cancel{J}}$ = 2.50 kWh

Check: The units (kWh) are correct. The magnitude of the answer (3) makes physical sense because a Calorie is much smaller than a kWh, so the answer decreases.

34. a) **Given:** 655 kWh $\quad$ **Find:** J

$\quad$ **Conceptual plan:** $\quad$ kWh $\rightarrow$ J

$$\frac{3.60\,x\,10^6\,J}{1\,kWh}$$

Solution: $\quad$ 655 $\cancel{kWh}$ x $\dfrac{3.60\ x\,10^6\ J}{1\ \cancel{kWh}}$ = 2.36x10^9 J

Check: The units (J) are correct. The magnitude of the answer (10^8) makes physical sense because a kWh is much larger than a Joule, so the answer increases.

b) **Given:** 655 kWh $\quad$ **Find:** kJ

$\quad$ **Conceptual plan:** $\quad$ kWh $\rightarrow$ J $\rightarrow$ kJ

$$\frac{3.60\,x\,10^6\,J}{1\,kWh} \quad \frac{1\,kJ}{1000\,J}$$

Solution: $\quad$ 655 $\cancel{kWh}$ x $\dfrac{3.60\ x\,10^6\ \cancel{J}}{1\ \cancel{kWh}}$ x $\dfrac{1\ kJ}{1000\ \cancel{J}}$ = 2.36x10^6 J

Check: The units (J) are correct. The magnitude of the answer (10^8) makes physical sense because a kWh is much larger than a Joule, so the answer increases.

c) **Given:** 655 kWh $\quad$ **Find:** Cal

$\quad$ **Conceptual plan:** $\quad$ kWh $\rightarrow$ J $\rightarrow$ Cal

$$\frac{3.60\,x\,10^6\,J}{1\,kWh} \quad \frac{1\,Cal}{4184\,J}$$

Solution: $\quad$ 655 $\cancel{kWh}$ x $\dfrac{3.60\ x\,10^6\ \cancel{J}}{1\ \cancel{kWh}}$ x $\dfrac{1\ Cal}{4814\ \cancel{J}}$ = 5.64x10^5 Cal

Check: The units (Cal) are correct. The magnitude of the answer (10^5) makes physical sense because a kWh is much larger than a Cal, so the answer increases.

35. d) $\quad \Delta E_{sys} = - \Delta E_{surr}$

36. The sign is positive since the energy is being taken in or deposited into the system.

37. a) The energy exchange is primarily heat since the skin (part of the surroundings) is cooled. There is a small expansion (work) since water is being converted from a liquid to a gas. The sign of ΔE_{sys} is positive since the surroundings cool.

    b) The energy exchange is primarily work. The sign of ΔE_{sys} is negative since the system is expanding (doing work on the surroundings).

    c) The energy exchange is primarily heat. The sign of ΔE_{sys} is positive since the system is being heated by the flame.

38. a) The energy exchange is primarily work since there is a lot of motion. There is a small amount of heat transferred since there is some friction as the balls roll. The sign of ΔE_{sys} is negative since the kinetic energy if the first ball is transferred to the second ball.

    b) The energy exchange is primarily work. The sign of ΔE_{sys} is negative since the potential energy of the book is decreased as it falls.

    c) The energy exchange is primarily work. The sign of ΔE_{sys} is positive since the father is doing work to move the girl and the swing.

39. **Given:** 415 kJ heat released; 125 kJ work done on surroundings   **Find:** ΔE_{sys}
    Conceptual plan: interpret language to determine the sign of the two terms   then $\mathbf{q, w} \rightarrow \Delta\mathbf{E_{sys}}$
    $$\Delta E = q + w$$

    Solution: since heat is released from the system to the surroundings, $q = -$ 415 kJ; since the system is doing work on the surroundings, $w = -$ 125 kJ. $\Delta E = q + w = -$ 415 kJ - 125 kJ $= -$ 540. kJ $= -$ 5.40 x 10^2 kJ
    Check: The units (kJ) are correct. The magnitude of the answer (-540) makes physical sense because both terms are negative.

40. **Given:** 214 kJ heat absorbed; surroundings do 110 kJ work   **Find:** ΔE_{sys}
    Conceptual plan: interpret language to determine the sign of the two terms   then $\mathbf{q, w} \rightarrow \Delta\mathbf{E_{sys}}$
    $$\Delta E = q + w$$

    Solution: since heat is absorbed by the system, $q = +$ 214 kJ; since the surroundings is doing work on the system, $w = +$ 110 kJ. $\Delta E = q + w =$ 214 kJ + 110 J = 3$\underline{2}$4 kJ = 320 kJ
    Check: The units (kJ) are correct. The magnitude of the answer (+300) makes physical sense because both terms are positive.

41. **Given:** 655 J heat absorbed; 344 J work done on surroundings   **Find:** ΔE_{sys}
    Conceptual plan:
    interpret language to determine the sign of the two terms   then $\mathbf{q, w} \rightarrow \Delta\mathbf{E_{sys}}$
    $$\Delta E = q + w$$

    Solution: since heat is absorbed by the system, $q = +$ 655 J; since the system is doing work on the surroundings, $w = -$ 344 J. $\Delta E = q + w =$ 655 J - 344 J = 311 J
    Check: The units (J) are correct. The magnitude of the answer (+300) makes physical sense because heat term dominates over the work term.

42. **Given:** 155 J heat absorbed; 77 kJ work done on surroundings   **Find:** ΔE_{sys}

    Conceptual plan:
    interpret language to determine the sign of the two terms   J $\rightarrow$ kJ   then $\mathbf{q, w} \rightarrow \Delta\mathbf{E_{sys}}$
    $$\frac{1\,kJ}{1000\,J} \qquad\qquad \Delta E = q + w$$

    Solution: since heat is absorbed by the system, $q = +$ 155 J; since the system is doing work on the surroundings,
    $w = -$ 77 kJ. Thus -77 kJ x $\frac{1000\,J}{1\,kJ} = -$ 7$\underline{7}$000 J   and $\Delta E = q + w =$ 155 J - 7$\underline{7}$000 J $= -$ 7$\underline{7}$000 J $= -$ 77 kJ

    Check: The units (kJ) are correct. The magnitude of the answer (- 77 kJ) makes physical sense because work term dominates over the heat term. In fact the heat term is negligible compared to the work term.

43. Cooler A had more ice after 3 hours because most of the ice in cooler B was melted in order to cool the soft drinks that started at room temperature. In cooler A the drinks were already cold and so the ice only needed to maintain this cool temperature.

44. Since the specific heat capacity of water is much larger than the specific heat capacity of aluminum, much more heat needs to be released by the water, than the aluminum, for each 1 °C of temperature drop. This means that more heat is stored in each kg of water than aluminum.

45. **Given:** 1.50 L water, $T_i = 25.0\ °C$, $T_f = 100.0\ °C$, $d = 1.0\ g/mL$ **Find:** q
   Conceptual plan:
   $L\ \rightarrow\ mL\ \rightarrow\ g$ and   pull C_s from table   and $T_i, T_f\ \rightarrow\ \Delta T$ then $m, C_s, \Delta T\ \rightarrow\ q$

   $\dfrac{1000\,mL}{1\,L}$ $\dfrac{1.0\,g}{1.0\,mL}$ $4.18\ \dfrac{J}{g\cdot °C}$ $\Delta T = T_f - T_i$ $q = m\,C_s\,\Delta T$

   Solution: $1.50\ L \times \dfrac{1000\ mL}{1\ L} \times \dfrac{1.0\ g}{1.0\ mL} = 1500\ g$ and $\Delta T = T_f - T_i = 100.0\ °C - 25.0\ °C = 75.0\ °C$ then

   $q = m\,C_s\,\Delta T = 1500\ g \times 4.18\ \dfrac{J}{g\cdot °C} \times 75.0\ °C = 4.7 \times 10^5\ J$

   Check: The units (J) are correct.   The magnitude of the answer (10^6) makes physical sense because there is such a large mass, a significant temperature change and a high specific heat capacity material.

46. **Given:** 1.50 kg sand, $T_i = 25.0\ °C$, $T_f = 100.0\ °C$ **Find:** q
   Conceptual plan: $kg\ \rightarrow\ g$ and   pull C_s from table   and $T_i, T_f\ \rightarrow\ \Delta T$ then $m, C_s, \Delta T\ \rightarrow\ q$

   $\dfrac{1000\,g}{1\,g}$ $0.84\ \dfrac{J}{g\cdot °C}$ $\Delta T = T_f - T_i$ $q = m\,C_s\,\Delta T$

   Solution: $1.50\ kg \times \dfrac{1000\ g}{1\ kg} = 1500\ g$ and $\Delta T = T_f - T_i = 100.0\ °C - 25.0\ °C = 75.0\ °C$ then

   $q = m\,C_s\,\Delta T = 1500\ g \times 0.84\ \dfrac{J}{g\cdot °C} \times 75.0\ °C = 9.45 \times 10^5\ J$

   Check: The units (J) are correct.   The magnitude of the answer (~10^6) makes physical sense because there is such a large mass, and a significant temperature change.

47. a)   **Given:** 25 g gold, $T_i = 27.0\ °C$, $q = 2.35\ kJ$ **Find:** T_f
      Conceptual plan:
      $kJ\ \rightarrow\ J$ and   pull C_s from table   then $m, C_s, q\ \rightarrow\ \Delta T$ then $T_i, \Delta T\ \rightarrow\ T_f$

      $\dfrac{1000\,g}{1\,g}$ $0.128\ \dfrac{J}{g\cdot °C}$ $q = m\,C_s\,\Delta T$ $\Delta T = T_f - T_i$

      Solution: $2.35\ kJ \times \dfrac{1000\ J}{1\ kJ} = 2350\ J$ then $q = m\,C_s\,\Delta T$ Rearrange to solve for ΔT.

      $\Delta T = \dfrac{q}{m\,C_s} = \dfrac{2350\ J}{25\ g \times 0.128\ \dfrac{J}{g \times °C}} = 734.375\ °C$ finally $\Delta T = T_f - T_i$ Rearrange to solve for T_f.

      $T_f = \Delta T + T_i = 734.375\ °C + 27.0\ °C = 760\ °C$

      Check: The units (°C) are correct.   The magnitude of the answer (760) makes physical sense because there is such a large heat absorbed, such a small mass, and specific heat capacity. The temperature change should be very large.

   b)   **Given:** 25 g silver, $T_i = 27.0\ °C$, $q = 2.35\ kJ$ **Find:** T_f
      Conceptual plan:
      $kJ\ \rightarrow\ J$ and   pull C_s from table   then $m, C_s, q\ \rightarrow\ \Delta T$ then $T_i, \Delta T\ \rightarrow\ T_f$

      $\dfrac{1000\,g}{1\,g}$ $0.235\ \dfrac{J}{g\cdot °C}$ $q = m\,C_s\,\Delta T$ $\Delta T = T_f - T_i$

      Solution: $2.35\ kJ \times \dfrac{1000\ J}{1\ kJ} = 2350\ J$ then $q = m\,C_s\,\Delta T$ Rearrange to solve for ΔT.

$\Delta T = \dfrac{q}{m\,C_s} = \dfrac{2350\ \text{J}}{25\ \text{g} \times 0.235\,\dfrac{\text{J}}{\text{g}\times{}^\circ\text{C}}} = 4\underline{0}0\ {}^\circ\text{C}$ finally $\Delta T = T_f - T_i$ Rearrange to solve for T_f.

$T_f = \Delta T + T_i = 4\underline{0}0\ {}^\circ\text{C} + 27.0\ {}^\circ\text{C} = 430\ {}^\circ\text{C}$

Check: The units (°C) are correct. The magnitude of the answer (430) makes physical sense because there is such a large heat absorbed, such a small mass, and specific heat capacity. The temperature change should be very large. The temperature change should be less than that of the gold because the specific heat capacity is greater.

c) **Given:** 25 g aluminum, $T_i = 27.0\ {}^\circ\text{C}$, $q = 2.35$ kJ   **Find:** T_f
Conceptual plan:
kJ → J and pull C_s from table   then m, C_s, q → ΔT then $T_i, \Delta T$ → T_f
$\dfrac{1000\,\text{g}}{1\,\text{g}}$ $0.903\,\dfrac{\text{J}}{\text{g}\cdot{}^\circ\text{C}}$ $q = m\,C_s\,\Delta T$ $\Delta T = T_f - T_i$

Solution: $2.35\ \text{kJ} \times \dfrac{1000\ \text{J}}{1\ \text{kJ}} = 23\underline{5}0\ \text{J}$ then $q = m\,C_s\,\Delta T$ Rearrange to solve for ΔT.

$\Delta T = \dfrac{q}{m\,C_s} = \dfrac{23\underline{5}0\ \text{J}}{25\ \text{g} \times 0.903\,\dfrac{\text{J}}{\text{g}\times{}^\circ\text{C}}} = 1\underline{0}4.10\ {}^\circ\text{C}$ finally $\Delta T = T_f - T_i$ Rearrange to solve for T_f.

$T_f = \Delta T + T_i = 1\underline{0}4.10\ {}^\circ\text{C} + 27.0\ {}^\circ\text{C} = 130\ {}^\circ\text{C}$

Check: The units (°C) are correct. The magnitude of the answer (130) makes physical sense because there is such a large heat absorbed, and such a small mass. The temperature change should be less than that of the silver because the specific heat capacity is greater.

d) **Given:** 25 g water, $T_i = 27.0\ {}^\circ\text{C}$, $q = 2.35$ kJ   **Find:** T_f
Conceptual plan:
kJ → J and pull C_s from table   then m, C_s, q → ΔT then $T_i, \Delta T$ → T_f
$\dfrac{1000\,\text{g}}{1\,\text{g}}$ $4.18\,\dfrac{\text{J}}{\text{g}\cdot{}^\circ\text{C}}$ $q = m\,C_s\,\Delta T$ $\Delta T = T_f - T_i$

Solution: $2.35\ \text{kJ} \times \dfrac{1000\ \text{J}}{1\ \text{kJ}} = 23\underline{5}0\ \text{J}$ then $q = m\,C_s\,\Delta T$ Rearrange to solve for ΔT.

$\Delta T = \dfrac{q}{m\,C_s} = \dfrac{23\underline{5}0\ \text{J}}{25\ \text{g} \times 4.18\,\dfrac{\text{J}}{\text{g}\times{}^\circ\text{C}}} = 2\underline{2}.491\ {}^\circ\text{C}$ finally $\Delta T = T_f - T_i$ Rearrange to solve for T_f.

$T_f = \Delta T + T_i = 2\underline{2}.491\ {}^\circ\text{C} + 27.0\ {}^\circ\text{C} = 49\ {}^\circ\text{C}$

Check: The units (°C) are correct. The magnitude of the answer (130) makes physical sense because there is such a large heat absorbed, and such a small mass. The temperature change should be less than that of the aluminum because the specific heat capacity is greater.

48. a) **Given:** Pyrex glass, $q = 1.95 \times 10^3$ J, $T_i = 23.0\ {}^\circ\text{C}$, $T_f = 55.4\ {}^\circ\text{C}$ **Find:**   m

Conceptual plan: pull C_s from table   and T_i, T_f → ΔT then $\Delta T, C_s, q$ → m
$0.75\,\dfrac{\text{J}}{\text{g}\cdot{}^\circ\text{C}}$ $\Delta T = T_f - T_i$ $q = m\,C_s\,\Delta T$

Solution: $\Delta T = T_f - T_i = 55.4\ {}^\circ\text{C} - 23.0\ {}^\circ\text{C} = 32.4\ {}^\circ\text{C}$ then $q = m\,C_s\,\Delta T$ Rearrange to solve for m.

$m = \dfrac{q}{C_s\,\Delta T} = \dfrac{1.95 \times 10^3\ \text{J}}{0.75\,\dfrac{\text{J}}{\text{g}\times{}^\circ\text{C}} \times 32.4\ {}^\circ\text{C}} = 80.\ \text{g or } 8.0 \times 10^1\ \text{g}$

Check: The units (g) are correct. The magnitude of the answer (80) makes physical sense because there is such a large heat absorbed and a moderate temperature rise and specific heat capacity.

b) **Given:** sand, q = 1.95×10^3 J, T_i = 23.0 °C, T_f = 62.1 °C   **Find:**   m
   Conceptual plan: pull C_s from table   and T_i, T_f → ΔT then   ΔT, C_s, q → m

$$0.84 \frac{J}{g \cdot °C} \qquad\qquad \Delta T = T_f - T_i \qquad\qquad q = m\, C_s\, \Delta T$$

Solution: $\Delta T = T_f - T_i = $ 62.1 °C − 23.0 °C = 39.1 °C   then $q = m\, C_s\, \Delta T$ Rearrange to solve for m.

$$m = \frac{q}{C_s\,\Delta T} = \frac{1.95 \times 10^3\,\cancel{J}}{0.84 \dfrac{\cancel{J}}{g \times \cancel{°C}} \times 39.1\,\cancel{°C}} = 59\ g$$

Check: The units (g) are correct.   The magnitude of the answer (60) makes physical sense because there is such a large heat absorbed and a moderate temperature rise and specific heat capacity.

c) **Given:** ethanol, q = 1.95×10^3 J, T_i = 23.0 °C, T_f = 44.2 °C   **Find:** m
   Conceptual plan: pull C_s from table   and T_i, T_f → ΔT then   ΔT, C_s, q → m

$$2.42 \frac{J}{g \cdot °C} \qquad\qquad \Delta T = T_f - T_i \qquad\qquad q = m\, C_s\, \Delta T$$

Solution: $\Delta T = T_f - T_i = $ 44.2 °C − 23.0 °C = 21.2 °C   then $q = m\, C_s\, \Delta T$ Rearrange to solve for m.

$$m = \frac{q}{C_s\,\Delta T} = \frac{1.95 \times 10^3\,\cancel{J}}{2.42 \dfrac{\cancel{J}}{g \times \cancel{°C}} \times 21.2\,\cancel{°C}} = 38.0\ g$$

Check: The units (g) are correct.   The magnitude of the answer (40) makes physical sense because there is such a large heat absorbed and small temperature rise and specific high capacity.

d) **Given:** water, q = 1.95×10^3 J, T_i = 23.0 °C, T_f = 32.4 °C   **Find:**   m
   Conceptual plan: pull C_s from table   and T_i, T_f → ΔT then   ΔT, C_s, q → m

$$4.18 \frac{J}{g \cdot °C} \qquad\qquad \Delta T = T_f - T_i \qquad\qquad q = m\, C_s\, \Delta T$$

Solution: $\Delta T = T_f - T_i = $ 32.4 °C − 23.0 °C = 9.4 °C   then $q = m\, C_s\, \Delta T$ Rearrange to solve for m.

$$m = \frac{q}{C_s\,\Delta T} = \frac{1.95 \times 10^3\,\cancel{J}}{4.18 \dfrac{\cancel{J}}{g \times \cancel{°C}} \times 9.4\,\cancel{°C}} = 50.\ g\ or\ 5.0 \times 10^1\ g$$

Check: The units (g) are correct.   The magnitude of the answer (50) makes physical sense because there is such a large heat absorbed and small temperature rise and very specific high capacity.

49. **Given:** V_i = 0.0 L, V_f = 2.5 L, P = 1.1 atm   **Find:** w (J)
    Conceptual plan: V_i, V_f → ΔV then   then   P, ΔV → w (L atm) → w (J)

$$\Delta V = V_f - V_i \qquad\qquad w = -P\,\Delta V \qquad \frac{101.3\ J}{1\ L\ atm}$$

Solution: $\Delta V = V_f - V_i = $ 2.5 L − 0.0 L = 2.5 L   then $w = -P\,\Delta V = -1.1\ \cancel{atm} \times 2.5\ \cancel{L} \times \dfrac{101.3\ J}{1\ \cancel{L}\ \cancel{atm}} = -280\ J$

Check: The units (J) are correct.   The magnitude of the answer (−280) makes physical sense because this is an expansion (negative work) and we have ~ atmospheric pressure and a small volume of expansion.

50. **Given:** ΔV = 0.50 L, P = 1.0 atm   **Find:** w (J)
    Conceptual plan: P, ΔV → w (L atm) → w (J)

$$w = -P\,\Delta V \qquad \frac{101.3\ J}{1\ L\ atm}$$

Solution: $w = -P\,\Delta V = -1.0\ \cancel{atm} \times 0.50\ \cancel{L} \times \dfrac{101.3\ J}{1\ \cancel{L}\ \cancel{atm}} = -51\ J$

Check: The units (J) are correct.   The magnitude of the answer (−51) makes physical sense because this is a small expansion (negative work) and we do not expect breathing to take much energy.

51. **Given:** $q = 565$ J absorbed, $V_i = 0.10$ L, $V_f = 0.85$ L, $P = 1.0$ atm   **Find:** ΔE_{sys}

Conceptual plan: $V_i, V_f \rightarrow \Delta V$ and interpret language to determine the sign of the heat   then
$$\Delta V = V_f - V_i \qquad\qquad\qquad\qquad q = +565 \text{ J}$$

then $P, \Delta V \rightarrow w \text{ (L atm)} \rightarrow w \text{ (J)}$ finally $q, w \rightarrow \Delta E_{sys}$
$$w = -P\,\Delta V \qquad \frac{101.3 \text{ J}}{1 \text{ L atm}} \qquad\qquad \Delta E = q + w$$

Solution: $\Delta V = V_f - V_i = 0.85$ L $- 0.10$ L $= 0.75$ L then $w = -P\,\Delta V = -1.0 \text{ atm} \times 0.75 \text{ L} \times \dfrac{101.3 \text{ J}}{1 \text{ L atm}} = -7\underline{5}.975$ J

$\Delta E = q + w = +565$ J $- 7\underline{5}.975$ J $= 489$ J

Check: The units (J) are correct. The magnitude of the answer (500) makes physical sense because the heat absorbed dominated the small expansion work (negative work).

52. **Given:** $q = 124$ J released, $V_i = 5.55$ L, $V_f = 1.22$ L, $P = 1.00$ atm   **Find:** ΔE_{sys}

Conceptual plan: $V_i, V_f \rightarrow \Delta V$ and interpret language to determine the sign of the heat then
$$\Delta V = V_f - V_i \qquad\qquad\qquad\qquad q = -124 \text{ J}$$

then $P, \Delta V \rightarrow w \text{ (L atm)} \rightarrow w \text{ (J)}$ finally $q, w \rightarrow \Delta E_{sys}$
$$w = -P\,\Delta V \qquad \frac{101.3 \text{ J}}{1 \text{ L atm}} \qquad\qquad \Delta E = q + w$$

Solution: $\Delta V = V_f - V_i = 1.22$ L $- 5.55$ L $= -4.33$ L then

$w = -P\,\Delta V = -1.00 \text{ atm} \times (-4.33 \text{ L}) \times \dfrac{101.3 \text{ J}}{1 \text{ L atm}} = +43\underline{8}.629$ J then $\Delta E = q + w = -124$ J $+ 43\underline{8}.629$ J $= 315$ J

Check: The units (J) are correct. The magnitude of the answer (300) makes physical sense because the compression work dominated the small heat released.

53. **Given:** 1 mol fuel, 3452 kJ heat produced; 11 kJ work done on surroundings   **Find:** ΔE_{sys}, ΔH
Conceptual plan:
interpret language to determine the sign of the two terms   then $q \rightarrow \Delta H$ and $q, w \rightarrow \Delta E_{sys}$
$$\Delta H = q_P \qquad\qquad \Delta E = q + w$$

Solution: since heat is produced by the system to the surroundings, $q = -3452$ kJ; since the system is doing work on the surroundings, $w = -11$ kJ. $\Delta H = q_P = -3452$ kJ and

$\Delta E = q + w = -3452$ kJ $- 11$ kJ $= -3463$ kJ

Check: The units (kJ) are correct. The magnitude of the answer (-3500) makes physical sense because both terms are negative. We expect significant amounts of energy from fuels.

54. **Given:** 1 mol octane, $P = 1.0$ atm, $\Delta E_{sys} = 5084.3$ kJ; $\Delta H = 5074.1$ kJ   **Find:** w
Conceptual plan:
interpret language to determine the sign of the two terms   then $q \rightarrow \Delta H$ and $q, \Delta E_{sys} \rightarrow w$
$$\Delta E_{sys} = -5084.3 \text{ kJ}; \Delta H = -5074.1 \text{ kJ} \qquad\qquad \Delta H = q_P \qquad\qquad \Delta E = q + w$$

Solution: since heat is produced by the system to the surroundings, $\Delta H = q_P = -5074.1$ kJ ; pistons are used to produce energy so $\Delta E_{sys} = -5084.3$ kJ $\Delta E = q + w$ Rearrange to solve for w.

$w = \Delta E - q = -5084.3$ kJ $- -5074.1$ kJ $= -10.2$ kJ

Check: The units (kJ) are correct. The magnitude of the answer (-10) makes physical sense because the work should be negative in an expansion. We expect more heat than work in an engine.

55. a)   combustion is an exothermic process, ΔH is negative

   b)   evaporation requires an input of energy and so it is endothermic, ΔH is positive

   c)   condensation is the reverse of evaporation, so it is exothermic, ΔH is negative

56. a)   sublimation requires an input of energy and so it is endothermic, ΔH is positive

    b)   combustion is an exothermic process, ΔH is negative

    c)   since the temperature drops this is an endothermic process, ΔH is positive

57. **Given:** 177 mL acetone (C_3H_6O), $\Delta H°_{rxn} = -1790$ kJ; d = 0.788 g/mL   **Find:** q
    Conceptual plan: mL acetone → g acetone → mol acetone → q

$$\frac{0.788 \text{ g}}{1 \text{ mL}} \qquad \frac{1 \text{ mol}}{58.08 \text{ g}} \qquad \frac{-1790 \text{ kJ}}{1 \text{ mol}}$$

    Solution: $177 \text{ mL} \times \dfrac{0.788 \text{ g}}{1 \text{ mL}} \times \dfrac{1 \text{ mol}}{58.08 \text{ g}} \times \dfrac{-1790 \text{ kJ}}{1 \text{ mol}} = -4.30 \times 10^3$ kJ or 4.30×10^3 kJ released

    Check: The units (kJ) are correct. The magnitude of the answer (-10^3) makes physical sense because the enthalpy change is negative and we have more than a mole of acetone. We expect more than 1790 kJ to be released.

58. **Given:** natural gas (CH_4), $\Delta H°_{rxn} = -802.3$ kJ; q = 267 kJ   **Find:** m
    Conceptual plan: q → mol natural gas → g natural gas

$$\frac{1 \text{ mol}}{-802.3 \text{ kJ}} \qquad \frac{16.04 \text{ g}}{1 \text{ mol}}$$

    Solution: $267 \text{ kJ} \times \dfrac{1 \text{ mol}}{-802.3 \text{ kJ}} \times \dfrac{16.04 \text{ g}}{1 \text{ mol}} = 5.35$ g

    Check: The units (g) are correct. The magnitude of the answer (5) makes physical sense because the enthalpy change per mole is so large and we need to burn less than a mole.

59. **Given:** pork roast, $\Delta H°_{rxn} = -2217$ kJ; q used = 1.6×10^3 kJ, 10 % efficiency   **Find:** $m(CO_2)$
    Conceptual plan: q used → q generated → mol CO_2 → g CO_2

$$\frac{100 \text{ kJ generated}}{10 \text{ kJ used}} \qquad \frac{3 \text{ mol}}{2217 \text{ kJ}} \qquad \frac{44.01 \text{ g}}{1 \text{ mol}}$$

    Solution: $1.6 \times 10^3 \text{ kJ} \times \dfrac{100 \text{ kJ generated}}{10 \text{ kJ used}} \times \dfrac{3 \text{ mol } CO_2}{2217 \text{ kJ}} \times \dfrac{44.01 \text{ g } CO_2}{1 \text{ mol } CO_2} = 950$ g CO_2

    Check: The units (g) are correct. The magnitude of the answer (~1000) makes physical sense because the process is not very efficient and a lot of energy is needed.

60. **Given:** carbon, $\Delta H°_{rxn} = -393.5$ kJ; q needed = 5.00×10^2 kJ   **Find:** $m(CO_2)$
    Conceptual plan: q needed → mol CO_2 → g CO_2

$$\frac{1 \text{ mol}}{393.5 \text{ kJ}} \qquad \frac{44.01 \text{ g}}{1 \text{ mol}}$$

    Solution: $5.00 \times 10^2 \text{ kJ} \times \dfrac{1 \text{ mol } CO_2}{393.5 \text{ kJ}} \times \dfrac{44.01 \text{ g } CO_2}{1 \text{ mol } CO_2} = 55.9$ g CO_2

    Check: The units (g) are correct. The magnitude of the answer (~1000) makes physical sense because the process is not very efficient and a lot of energy is needed.

61. $\Delta H_{rxn} = q_P$ and $\Delta E_{rxn} = q_V = \Delta H - P \Delta V$. Since combustions always involve expansions; expansions do work and so have a negative value. Combustions are always exothermic and so have a negative value. This means that ΔE_{rxn} is more negative than $\Delta H°_{rxn}$ and so A (-25.9 kJ) is the constant volume process and B (-23.3 kJ) is the constant pressure process.

62. Constant volume conditions should be used because at constant P $\Delta H_{rxn} = q_P$ and at constant V $\Delta E_{rxn} = q_V = \Delta H - P \Delta V$. Since combustions always involve expansions; expansions do work and so have a negative value. Combustions are always exothermic and so have a negative value. This means that ΔE_{rxn} is more negative than $\Delta H°_{rxn}$ and so more heat will be generated in a constant V process.

63. **Given:** 0.514 g biphenyl ($C_{12}H_{10}$), bomb calorimeter, $T_i = 25.8$ °C, $T_f = 29.4$ °C, $C_{cal} = 5.86$ kJ/°C
Find: ΔE_{rxn}
Conceptual plan:
$T_i, T_f \rightarrow \Delta T$ then $\Delta T, C_{cal} \rightarrow q_{cal} \rightarrow q_{rxn}$ then g $C_{12}H_{10} \rightarrow$ mol $C_{12}H_{10}$

$$\Delta T = T_f - T_i \qquad q_{cal} = C_{cal}\,\Delta T \quad q_{cal} = -\,q_{rxn} \qquad \frac{1\,mol}{154.20\,g}$$

then q_{rxn}, mol $C_{12}H_{10} \rightarrow \Delta E_{rxn}$

$$\Delta E_{rxn} = \frac{q_V}{mol\ C_{12}H_{10}}$$

Solution: $\Delta T = T_f - T_i = 29.4\ °C - 25.8\ °C = 3.6\ °C$ then $q_{cal} = C_{cal}\,\Delta T = 5.86\,\frac{kJ}{°C}$ x $3.6\ °C = 21.096$ kJ then

$q_{cal} = -\,q_{rxn} = -21.096$ kJ and $0.514\ g\ C_{12}H_{10}$ x $\dfrac{1\,mol\ C_{12}H_{10}}{154.20\ g\ C_{12}H_{10}} = 0.00333333$ mol $C_{12}H_{10}$ then

$\Delta E_{rxn} = \dfrac{q_V}{mol\ C_{12}H_{10}} = \dfrac{-21.096\ kJ}{0.00333333\ mol\ C_{12}H_{10}} = -6.3$ x 10^3 kJ/mol

Check: The units (kJ/mol) are correct. The magnitude of the answer (-6000) makes physical sense because there is such a large heat generated from a very small amount of biphenyl.

64. **Given:** 1.025 g naphthalene ($C_{10}H_8$), bomb calorimeter, $T_i = 24.25$°C, $T_f = 32.33$ °C, $C_{cal} = 5.11$ kJ/°C
Find: ΔE_{rxn}
Conceptual plan:
$T_i, T_f \rightarrow \Delta T$ then $\Delta T, C_{cal} \rightarrow q_{cal} \rightarrow q_{rxn}$ then g $C_{10}H_8 \rightarrow$ mol $C_{10}H_8$

$$\Delta T = T_f - T_i \qquad q_{cal} = C_{cal}\,\Delta T \quad q_{cal} = -\,q_{rxn} \qquad \frac{1\,mol}{128.16\,g}$$

then q_{rxn}, mol $C_{10}H_8 \rightarrow \Delta E_{rxn}$

$$\Delta E_{rxn} = \frac{q_V}{mol\ C_{10}H_8}$$

Solution: $\Delta T = T_f - T_i = 32.33\ °C - 24.25\ °C = 8.08\ °C$ then $q_{cal} = C_{cal}\,\Delta T = 5.11\,\frac{kJ}{°C}$ x $8.08\ °C = 41.2888$ kJ

then $q_{cal} = -\,q_{rxn} = -41.2888$ kJ and $1.025\ g\ C_{10}H_8$ x $\dfrac{1\,mol\ C_{10}H_8}{128.16\ g\ C_{10}H_8} = 0.007997815$ mol $C_{10}H_8$ then

$\Delta E_{rxn} = \dfrac{q_V}{mol\ C_{10}H_8} = \dfrac{-41.2888\ kJ}{0.007997815\ mol\ C_{10}H_8} = -5.16$ x 10^3 kJ/mol

Check: The units (kJ/mol) are correct. The magnitude of the answer (-5000) makes physical sense because there is such a large heat generated from a very small amount of naphthalene.

65. **Given:** 0.103 g zinc, coffee-cup calorimeter, $T_i = 22.5$°C, $T_f = 23.7$ °C, 50.0 mL solution, d (solution) = 1.0 g/mL, $C_{sol'n} = 4.18$ kJ/g °C   **Find:** ΔH_{rxn}
Conceptual plan:
$T_i, T_f \rightarrow \Delta T$ and mL sol'n $\rightarrow$ g sol'n then $\Delta T, C_{cal} \rightarrow q_{cal} \rightarrow q_{rxn}$ then

$$\Delta T = T_f - T_i \qquad \frac{1.0\,g}{1.0\,mL} \qquad q_{cal} = m\,C_{sol'n}\,\Delta T \quad q_{sol'n} = -\,q_{rxn}$$

g Zn $\rightarrow$ mol Zn then q_{rxn}, mol Zn $\rightarrow \Delta H_{rxn}$

$$\frac{1\,mol}{65.37\,g} \qquad \Delta H_{rxn} = \frac{q_P}{mol\ Zn}$$

Solution: $\Delta T = T_f - T_i = 23.7\ °C - 22.5\ °C = 1.2\ °C$ and $50.0\ mL$ x $\dfrac{1.0\,g}{1.0\,mL} = 50.0$ g then

$q_{sol'n} = m\,C_{sol'n}\,\Delta T = 50.0\ g$ x $4.18\,\dfrac{J}{g\,°C}$ x $1.2\ °C = 250.8$ J then $q_{sol'n} = -\,q_{rxn} = -250.8$ J and

$0.103\ g\ Zn$ x $\dfrac{1\,mol\ Zn}{65.37\ g\ Zn} = 0.00157565$ mol Zn then

$$\Delta H_{rxn} = \frac{q_P}{mol\ Zn} = \frac{-250.8\ J}{0.00157565\ mol\ Zn} = -1.6 \times 10^5\ J/mol = -1.6 \times 10^2\ kJ/mol$$

Check: The units (kJ/mol) are correct. The magnitude of the answer (-160) makes physical sense because there is such a large heat generated from a very small amount of zinc.

66. **Given**: 1.25 g NH_4NO_3, coffee-cup calorimeter, $T_i = 25.8°C$, $T_f = 21.9\ °C$, 25.0 mL solution, d (solution) = 1.0 g/mL, $C_{sol'n} = 4.18$ kJ/g °C   **Find**: ΔH_{rxn}
    Conceptual plan:

    T_i, T_f → ΔT and mL sol'n → g sol'n   then $\Delta T, C_{cal}$ → q_{cal} → q_{rxn} then

    $\Delta T = T_f - T_i$ $\dfrac{1.0\ g}{1.0\ mL}$ $q_{cal} = m\ C_{sol'n} \Delta T$ $q_{sol'n} = -q_{rxn}$

    g NH_4NO_3 → mol NH_4NO_3 then q_{rxn}, mol NH_4NO_3 → ΔH_{rxn}

    $\dfrac{1\ mol}{80.05\ g}$ $\Delta H_{rxn} = \dfrac{q_P}{mol\ NH_4NO_3}$

    Solution: $\Delta T = T_f - T_i = 21.9\ °C - 25.8\ °C = -3.9\ °C$ and $25.0\ mL \times \dfrac{1.0\ g}{1.0\ mL} = 25.0\ g$ then

    $q_{sol'n} = m\ C_{sol'n} \Delta T = 25.0\ g \times 4.18\ \dfrac{J}{g\ °C} \times (-3.9\ °C) = -407.55\ J$ then $q_{sol'n} = -q_{rxn} = 407.55\ J$ and

    $1.25\ g\ NH_4NO_3 \times \dfrac{1\ mol\ NH_4NO_3}{80.05\ g\ NH_4NO_3} = 0.0156152\ mol\ NH_4NO_3$ then

    $\Delta H_{rxn} = \dfrac{q_P}{mol\ NH_4NO_3} = \dfrac{407.55\ J}{0.0156152\ mol\ NH_4NO_3} = 2.6 \times 10^4\ J/mol = 26\ kJ/mol$

    Check: The units (kJ/mol) are correct. The magnitude of the answer (26) makes physical sense because there is such a small amount of heat absorbed.

67. a) Since A + B → 2 C has ΔH_1 then 2 C → A + B will have a $\Delta H_2 = -\Delta H_1$. When the reaction direction is reversed it changes from exothermic to endothermic (or vice versa), so the sign of ΔH changes.

    b) Since A + ½ B → C has ΔH_1 then 2 A + B → 2 C will have a $\Delta H_2 = 2\ \Delta H_1$. When the reaction amount doubles, the amount of heat (or ΔH) doubles.

    c) Since A → B + 2 C has ΔH_1 then ½ A → ½ B + C will have a $\Delta H_{1'} = \frac{1}{2}\ \Delta H_1$. When the reaction amount is cut in half the amount of heat (or ΔH) is cut in half. Then ½ B + C → ½ A will have a $\Delta H_2 = -\Delta H_{1'} = -\frac{1}{2}\ \Delta H_1$. When the reaction direction is reversed it changes from exothermic to endothermic (or vice versa), so the sign of ΔH changes.

68. a) Since A + 2 B → C + 3 D has $\Delta H = 155$ kJ then 3A + 6 B → 3 C + 9 D will have a $\Delta H' = 3\ \Delta H = 3\ (155\ kJ) = 465\ kJ$. When the reaction amount triples, the amount of heat (or ΔH) triples.

    b) Since A + 2 B → C + 3 D has $\Delta H = 155$ kJ then C + 3 D → 3A + 6 B will have a $\Delta H' = -\Delta H = -155\ kJ$. When the reaction direction is reversed it changes from endothermic to exothermic, so the sign of ΔH changes.

    c) Since A + 2 B → C + 3 D has $\Delta H = 155$ kJ then ½ A + B → ½ C + 3/2 D will have a $\Delta H' = \frac{1}{2}\ \Delta H = \frac{1}{2}\ (155\ kJ) = 77.5\ kJ$. When the reaction amount is cut in half the amount of heat (or ΔH) is cut in half. Then ½ C + 3/2 D → ½ A + B will have a $\Delta H'' = -\Delta H' = -77.5\ kJ$. When the reaction direction the sign of is reversed it changes from endothermic to exothermic, so the sign of ΔH changes.

69. Since the first reaction has Fe_2O_3 as a product and the reaction of interest has it as a product, we need to reverse the first reaction. When the reaction direction is reversed ΔH changes.
    $Fe_2O_3\ (s) \rightarrow 2\ Fe\ (s) + 3/2\ O_2\ (g)$ $\Delta H = +824.2\ kJ$

    Since the second reaction has 1 mole CO as a reactant and the reaction of interest has 3 moles of CO as a reactant, we need to multiply the second reaction and the ΔH by 3.
    $3\ [CO\ (g) + 1/2\ O_2\ (g) \rightarrow CO_2\ (g)]$ $\Delta H = 3(-282.7\ kJ) = -848.1\ kJ$

    181

Hess' Law states the ΔH of the net reaction is the sum of the ΔH of the steps.
The rewritten reactions are:

Fe_2O_3 (s) → 2 Fe (s) + ~~3/2 O_2 (g)~~   ΔH = + 824.2 kJ

3 CO (g) + ~~3/2 O_2 (g)~~ → 3 CO_2 (g)   ΔH = − 848.1 kJ
_____

Fe_2O_3 (s) + 3 CO (g) → 2 Fe (s) + 3 CO_2 (g) $ΔH_{rxn}$ = − 23.9 kJ

70. Since the first reaction has $CaCO_3$ as a product and the reaction of interest has it as a product, we simply write the first reaction and the ΔH unchanged.

Ca (s) + CO_2 (g) + 1/2 O_2 (g) → $CaCO_3$ (s)   ΔH = − 812.8 kJ

Since the second reaction has 2 moles CaO as a product and the reaction of interest has 1 mole of CaO as a reactant, we need reverse the direction of the reaction of the second reaction and multiply it by ½. The sign of the ΔH the second reaction is changed and is multiplied by ½.

1/2[2 CaO (s) → 2 Ca (s) + O_2 (g)]   ΔH = −1/2(− 1269.8 kJ) = + 634.9 k

Hess' Law states the ΔH of the net reaction is the sum of the ΔH of the steps.
The rewritten reactions are:

~~Ca (s)~~ + CO_2 (g) + ~~1/2 O_2 (g)~~ → $CaCO_3$ (s)   ΔH = − 812.8 kJ

CaO (s) → ~~Ca (s)~~ + ~~1/2 O_2 (g)~~   ΔH = + 634.9 kJ
_____

CaO (s) + CO_2 (g) → $CaCO_3$ (s) $ΔH_{rxn}$ = −177.9 kJ

71. Since the first reaction has C_5H_{12} as a reactant and the reaction of interest has it as a product, we need to reverse the first reaction. When the reaction direction is reversed ΔH changes.

5 CO_2 (g) + 6 H_2O (g) → C_5H_{12} (l) + 8 O_2 (g)   ΔH = + 3505.8 kJ

Since the second reaction has 1 mole C as a reactant and the reaction of interest has 5 moles of C as a reactant, we need to multiply the second reaction and the ΔH by 5.

5 [C (s) + O_2 (g) → CO_2 (g)]   ΔH = 5(−393.5 kJ) = −1967.5 kJ

Since the third reaction has 2 moles H_2 as a reactant and the reaction of interest has 6 moles of H_2 as a reactant, we need to multiply the third reaction and the ΔH by 3.

3[2 H_2 (g) + O_2 (g) → 2 H_2O (g)]   ΔH = 3(− 483.5 kJ) = − 1450.5 kJ

Hess' Law states the ΔH of the net reaction is the sum of the ΔH of the steps.
The rewritten reactions are:

~~5 CO_2 (g)~~ + ~~6 H_2O (g)~~ → C_5H_{12} (l) + ~~8 O_2 (g)~~   ΔH = + 3505.8 kJ

5 C (s) + ~~5 O_2 (g)~~ → ~~5 CO_2 (g)~~   ΔH = −1967.5 kJ

6 H_2 (g) + ~~3 O_2 (g)~~ → ~~6 H_2O (g)~~   ΔH = − 1450.5 kJ
_____

5 C (s) + 6 H_2 (g) → C_5H_{12} (l) $ΔH_{rxn}$ = + 87.8 kJ

72. Since the first reaction has CH_4 as a product and the reaction of interest has it as a reactant, we need to reverse the first reaction. When the reaction direction is reversed ΔH changes.

CH_4 (g) → C (s) + 2 H_2 (g)   ΔH = + 74.6 kJ

Since the first reaction has CCl_4 as a product and the reaction of interest has it as a product, we simply write the first reaction and the ΔH unchanged.

C (s) + 2 Cl_2 (g) → CCl_4 (g)   ΔH = −95.7 kJ

Since the third reaction has 2 moles HCl as a product and the reaction of interest has 4 moles of HCl as a product, we need to multiply the third reaction and the ΔH by 2.

2[H_2 (g) + Cl_2 (g) → 2 HCl (g)]   ΔH = 2(− 92.3 kJ) = − 184.6 k

Hess' Law states the ΔH of the net reaction is the sum of the ΔH of the steps.
The rewritten reactions are:

CH_4 (g) → ~~C (s)~~ + ~~2 H_2 (g)~~   ΔH = + 74.6 kJ

~~C (s)~~ + 2 Cl_2 (g) → CCl_4 (g)   ΔH = − 95.7 kJ

~~2 H_2 (g)~~ + 2 Cl_2 (g) → 4 HCl (g)   ΔH = − 184.6 kJ
_____

CH_4 (g) + 4 Cl_2 (g) → CCl_4 (g) + 4 HCl (g) $ΔH_{rxn}$ = − 205.7 kJ

73. a) $\frac{1}{2} N_2 (g) + 3/2 H_2 (g) \rightarrow NH_3 (g)$ $\quad\quad\quad\quad$ $\Delta H°_f = -45.9$ kJ/mol

b) $C (s) + O_2 (g) \rightarrow CO_2 (g)$ $\quad\quad\quad\quad\quad\quad$ $\Delta H°_f = -393.5$ kJ/mol

c) $Fe (s) + 3/2 O_2 (g) \rightarrow Fe_2O_3 (g)$ $\quad\quad\quad$ $\Delta H°_f = -824.2$ kJ/mol

d) $C (s) + 2 H_2 (g) \rightarrow CH_4 (g)$ $\quad\quad\quad\quad$ $\Delta H°_f = -74.6$ kJ/mol

74. a) $\frac{1}{2} N_2 (g) + O_2 (g) \rightarrow NO_2 (g)$ $\quad\quad\quad\quad$ $\Delta H°_f = 33.2$ kJ/mol

b) $Mg (s) + C (s) + 3/2 O_2 (g) \rightarrow MgCO_3 (s)$ $\quad$ $\Delta H°_f = -1095.8$ kJ/mol

c) $2 C (s) + 2 H_2 (g) \rightarrow C_2H_4 (g)$ $\quad\quad\quad$ $\Delta H°_f = 52.4$ kJ/mol

d) $C (s) + 2 H_2 (g) + \frac{1}{2} O_2 (g) \rightarrow CH_3OH (l)$ $\quad$ $\Delta H°_f = -238.6$ kJ/mol

75. **Given:** $N_2H_4 (l) + N_2O_4 (g) \rightarrow 2 N_2O (g) + 2 H_2O (g)$ $\quad\quad$ **Find:** $\Delta H°_{rxn}$

Conceptual plan: $\quad$ $\Delta H_{rxn}^0 = \sum n_P \Delta H_f^0 (products) - \sum n_R \Delta H_f^0 (reactants)$

Solution:

Reactant/Product	ΔH_f^0(kJ/mol from Appendix IIB)
$N_2H_4 (l)$	50.6
$N_2O_4 (g)$	11.1
$N_2O (g)$	81.6
$H_2O (g)$	-241.8

Be sure to pull data for the correct formula and phase.

$\Delta H_{rxn}^0 = \sum n_P \Delta H_f^0 (products) - \sum n_R \Delta H_f^0 (reactants)$

$\quad = [2(\Delta H_f^0(N_2O (g)) + 2(\Delta H_f^0(H_2O (g))] - [1(\Delta H_f^0(N_2H_4 (l)) + 1(\Delta H_f^0(N_2O_4 (g))]$

$\quad = [2(81.6 \text{ kJ}) + 2(-241.8 \text{ kJ})] - [1(50.6 \text{ kJ}) + 1(11.1 \text{ kJ})]$

$\quad = [-320.4 \text{ kJ}] - [61.7 \text{ kJ}]$

$\quad = -382.1 \text{ kJ}$

Check: The units (kJ) are correct. The answer is negative, which means that the reaction is exothermic. The answer is dominated by the negative heat of formation of water.

76. **Given:** $C_5H_{12} (l) + 8 O_2 (g) \rightarrow 5 CO_2 (g) + 6 H_2O (g)$ $\quad\quad$ **Find:** $\Delta H°_{rxn}$

Conceptual plan: $\quad$ $\Delta H_{rxn}^0 = \sum n_P \Delta H_f^0 (products) - \sum n_R \Delta H_f^0 (reactants)$

Solution:

Reactant/Product	ΔH_f^0(kJ/mol from Appendix IIB)
$C_5H_{12} (l)$	-146.8
$O_2 (g)$	0.0
$CO_2 (g)$	-393.5
$H_2O (g)$	-241.8

Be sure to pull data for the correct formula and phase.

$\Delta H_{rxn}^0 = \sum n_P \Delta H_f^0 (products) - \sum n_R \Delta H_f^0 (reactants)$

$\quad = [5(\Delta H_f^0(CO_2 (g)) + 6(\Delta H_f^0(H_2O (g))] - [1(\Delta H_f^0(C_5H_{12} (l)) + 8(\Delta H_f^0(O_2 (g))]$

$\quad = [5(-393.5 \text{ kJ}) + 6(-241.8 \text{ kJ})] - [1(-146.8 \text{ kJ}) + 2(0.0 \text{ kJ})]$

$\quad = [-3418.3 \text{ kJ}] - [-146.8 \text{ kJ}]$

$\quad = -3271.5 \text{ kJ}$

Check: The units (kJ) are correct. The answer is negative, which means that the reaction is exothermic, which is typical for combustion reactions.

77. a) **Given:** C_2H_4 (g) + H_2 (g) → C_2H_6 (g) **Find:** $\Delta H°_{rxn}$

Conceptual plan: $\Delta H^0_{rxn} = \sum n_P \Delta H^0_f (products) - \sum n_R \Delta H^0_f (reactants)$

Solution:

Reactant/Product	ΔH^0_f (kJ/mol from Appendix IIB)
C_2H_4 (g)	52.4
H_2 (g)	0.0
C_2H_6 (g)	-84.68

Be sure to pull data for the correct formula and phase.

$\Delta H^0_{rxn} = \sum n_P \Delta H^0_f (products) - \sum n_R \Delta H^0_f (reactants)$

$\quad = [1(\Delta H^0_f(C_2H_6\ (g))] - [1(\Delta H^0_f(C_2H_4\ (g)) + 1(\Delta H^0_f(H_2\ (g))]$

$\quad = [1(-84.68\ kJ)] - [1(52.4\ kJ) + 1(0.0\ kJ)]$

$\quad = [-84.68\ kJ] - [52.4\ kJ]$

$\quad = -137.1\ kJ$

Check: The units (kJ) are correct.   The answer is negative, which means that the reaction is exothermic. Both hydrocarbon terms are negative, so the final answer is negative.

b) **Given:** CO (g) + H_2O (g) → H_2 (g) + CO_2 (g) **Find:** $\Delta H°_{rxn}$

Conceptual plan: $\Delta H^0_{rxn} = \sum n_P \Delta H^0_f (products) - \sum n_R \Delta H^0_f (reactants)$

Solution:

Reactant/Product	ΔH^0_f (kJ/mol from Appendix IIB)
CO (g)	-110.5
H_2O (g)	-241.8
H_2 (g)	0.0
CO_2 (g)	-393.5

Be sure to pull data for the correct formula and phase.

$\Delta H^0_{rxn} = \sum n_P \Delta H^0_f (products) - \sum n_R \Delta H^0_f (reactants)$

$\quad = [1(\Delta H^0_f(H_2\ (g)) + 1(\Delta H^0_f(CO_2\ (g))] - [1(\Delta H^0_f(CO\ (g)) + 1(\Delta H^0_f(H_2O\ (g))]$

$\quad = [1(0.0\ kJ) + 1(-393.5\ kJ)] - [1(-110.5\ kJ) + 1(-241.8\ kJ)]$

$\quad = [-393.5\ kJ] - [-352.3\ kJ]$

$\quad = -41.2\ kJ$

Check: The units (kJ) are correct.   The answer is negative, which means that the reaction is exothermic.

c) **Given:** 3 NO_2 (g) + H_2O (l) → 2 HNO_3 (aq) + NO (g) **Find:** $\Delta H°_{rxn}$

Conceptual plan: $\Delta H^0_{rxn} = \sum n_P \Delta H^0_f (products) - \sum n_R \Delta H^0_f (reactants)$

Solution:

Reactant/Product	ΔH^0_f (kJ/mol from Appendix IIB)
NO_2 (g)	33.2
H_2O (l)	-285.8
HNO_3 (aq)	-207
NO (g)	91.3

Be sure to pull data for the correct formula and phase.

$\Delta H^0_{rxn} = \sum n_P \Delta H^0_f (products) - \sum n_R \Delta H^0_f (reactants)$

$\quad = [2(\Delta H^0_f(HNO_3\ (aq)) + 1(\Delta H^0_f(NO\ (g))] - [3(\Delta H^0_f(NO_2\ (g)) + 1(\Delta H^0_f(H_2O\ (l))]$

$\quad = [2(-207\ kJ) + 1(91.3\ kJ)] - [3(33.2\ kJ) + 1(-285.8\ kJ)]$

$\quad = [-322.7\ kJ] - [-186.2\ kJ]$

$\quad = -137\ kJ$

Check: The units (kJ) are correct. The answer is negative, which means that the reaction is exothermic.

d) **Given**: Cr_2O_3 (s) + 3 CO (g) → 2 Cr (s) + 3 CO_2 (g)   **Find**: $\Delta H°_{rxn}$

Conceptual plan: $\Delta H^0_{rxn} = \sum n_P \Delta H^0_f (products) - \sum n_R \Delta H^0_f (reactants)$

Solution:

Reactant/Product	ΔH^0_f (kJ/mol from Appendix IIB)
Cr_2O_3 (s)	−1139.7
CO (g)	−110.5
Cr (s)	0.0
CO_2 (g)	−393.5

Be sure to pull data for the correct formula and phase.

$\Delta H^0_{rxn} = \sum n_P \Delta H^0_f (products) - \sum n_R \Delta H^0_f (reactants)$

$= [2(\Delta H^0_f (Cr\ (s)) + 3(\Delta H^0_f (CO_2\ (g))] - [1(\Delta H^0_f (Cr_2O_3\ (s)) + 3(\Delta H^0_f (CO\ (g))]$

$= [2(0.0\ kJ) + 3(-393.5\ kJ)] - [1(-1139.7\ kJ) + 3(-110.5\ kJ)]$

$= [-1180.5\ kJ] - [-1471.2\ kJ]$

$= -290.7\ kJ$

Check: The units (kJ) are correct. The answer is negative, which means that the reaction is exothermic.

78. a) **Given**: 2 H_2S (g) + 3 O_2 (g) → 2 H_2O (l) + 2 SO_2 (g)   **Find**: $\Delta H°_{rxn}$

Conceptual plan: $\Delta H^0_{rxn} = \sum n_P \Delta H^0_f (products) - \sum n_R \Delta H^0_f (reactants)$

Solution:

Reactant/Product	ΔH^0_f (kJ/mol from Appendix IIB)
H_2S (g)	−20.6
O_2 (g)	0.0
H_2O (l)	−285.8
SO_2 (g)	−296.8

Be sure to pull data for the correct formula and phase.

$\Delta H^0_{rxn} = \sum n_P \Delta H^0_f (products) - \sum n_R \Delta H^0_f (reactants)$

$= [2(\Delta H^0_f (H_2O\ (l)) + 2(\Delta H^0_f (SO_2\ (g))] - [2(\Delta H^0_f (H_2S\ (g)) + 3(\Delta H^0_f (O_2\ (g))]$

$= [2(-285.8\ kJ) + 2(-296.8\ kJ)] - [2(-20.6\ kJ) + 3(0.0\ kJ)]$

$= [-1165.2\ kJ] - [-41.2\ kJ]$

$= -1124.0\ kJ$

Check: The units (kJ) are correct. The answer is negative, which means that the reaction is exothermic.

b) **Given**: SO_2 (g) + 1/2 O_2 (g) → SO_3 (g)   **Find**: $\Delta H°_{rxn}$

Conceptual plan: $\Delta H^0_{rxn} = \sum n_P \Delta H^0_f (products) - \sum n_R \Delta H^0_f (reactants)$

Solution:

Reactant/Product	ΔH^0_f (kJ/mol from Appendix IIB)
SO_2 (g)	−296.8
O_2 (g)	0.0
SO_3 (g)	−395.7

Be sure to pull data for the correct formula and phase.

$$\Delta H^0_{rxn} = \sum n_P \Delta H^0_f (products) - \sum n_R \Delta H^0_f (reactants)$$

$$= [1(\Delta H^0_f (SO_3 (g)))] - [1(\Delta H^0_f (SO_2 (g)) + 1/2(\Delta H^0_f (O_2 (g)))]$$

$$= [1(-395.7 \text{ kJ})] - [1(-296.8 \text{ kJ}) + 1/2(0.0 \text{ kJ})]$$

$$= [-395.7 \text{ kJ}] - [-296.8 \text{ kJ}]$$

$$= -98.9 \text{ kJ}$$

Check: The units (kJ) are correct. The answer is negative, which means that the reaction is exothermic. The SO_3 has a lower heat of formation than SO_2, so we expect an exothermic reaction.

c) **Given:** $C\ (s) + H_2O\ (g) \rightarrow CO_2\ (g) + H_2\ (g)$ **Find:** $\Delta H°_{rxn}$

Conceptual plan: $\Delta H^0_{rxn} = \sum n_P \Delta H^0_f (products) - \sum n_R \Delta H^0_f (reactants)$

Solution:

Reactant/Product	ΔH^0_f(kJ/mol from Appendix IIB)
$C\ (s)$	0.0
$H_2O\ (g)$	-241.8
$CO_2\ (g)$	-393.5
$H_2\ (g)$	0.0

Be sure to pull data for the correct formula and phase.

$$\Delta H^0_{rxn} = \sum n_P \Delta H^0_f (products) - \sum n_R \Delta H^0_f (reactants)$$

$$= [1(\Delta H^0_f (CO_2 (g)) + 1(\Delta H^0_f (H_2 (g))] - [1(\Delta H^0_f (C (s)) + 1(\Delta H^0_f (H_2O (g))]$$

$$= [1(-393.5 \text{ kJ}) + 1(0.0 \text{ kJ})] - [1(0.0 \text{ kJ}) + 1(-241.8 \text{ kJ})]$$

$$= [-393.5 \text{ kJ}] - [-241.8 \text{ kJ}]$$

$$= -151.7 \text{ kJ}$$

Check: The units (kJ) are correct. The answer is negative, which means that the reaction is exothermic. The CO_2 has a lower heat of formation than H_2O, so we expect an exothermic reaction.

d) **Given:** $N_2O_4\ (g) + 4\ H_2\ (g) \rightarrow N_2\ (g) + 4\ H_2O\ (g)$ **Find:** $\Delta H°_{rxn}$

Conceptual plan: $\Delta H^0_{rxn} = \sum n_P \Delta H^0_f (products) - \sum n_R \Delta H^0_f (reactants)$

Solution:

Reactant/Product	ΔH^0_f(kJ/mol from Appendix IIB)
$N_2O_4\ (g)$	11.1
$H_2\ (g)$	0.0
$N_2\ (g)$	0.0
$H_2O\ (g)$	-241.8

Be sure to pull data for the correct formula and phase.

$$\Delta H^0_{rxn} = \sum n_P \Delta H^0_f (products) - \sum n_R \Delta H^0_f (reactants)$$

$$= [1(\Delta H^0_f (N_2 (g)) + 4(\Delta H^0_f (H_2O (g))] - [1(\Delta H^0_f (N_2O_4 (g)) + 4(\Delta H^0_f (H_2 (g))]$$

$$= [1(0.0 \text{kJ}) + 4(-241.8 \text{ kJ})] - [1(11.1 \text{ kJ}) + 4(0.0 \text{ kJ})]$$

$$= [-967.2 \text{ kJ}] - [11.1 \text{ kJ}]$$

$$= -978.3 \text{ kJ}$$

Check: The units (kJ) are correct. The answer is negative, which means that the reaction is exothermic. The H_2O has a lower heat of formation than N_2O_4, so we expect an exothermic reaction.

79. **Given:** form glucose ($C_6H_{12}O_6$) and oxygen from sunlight, carbon dioxide and water **Find:** $\Delta H°_{rxn}$

Conceptual plan: write balanced reaction then $\Delta H^0_{rxn} = \sum n_P \Delta H^0_f (products) - \sum n_R \Delta H^0_f (reactants)$

Solution: $6\ CO_2\ (g) + 6\ H_2O\ (l) \rightarrow C_6H_{12}O_6\ (s) + 6\ O_2\ (g)$

Reactant/Product	ΔH_f^0 (kJ/mol from Appendix IIB)
$CO_2\ (g)$	-393.5
$H_2O\ (l)$	-285.8
$C_6H_{12}O\ (s)$	-1273.3
$O_2\ (g)$	0.0

Be sure to pull data for the correct formula and phase.

$\Delta H_{rxn}^0 = \sum n_P \Delta H_f^0 (products) - \sum n_R \Delta H_f^0 (reactants)$

$= [1(\Delta H_f^0(C_6H_{12}O\ (s)) + 6(\Delta H_f^0(O_2\ (g))\ ] - [6(\Delta H_f^0(CO_2\ (g)) + 6(\Delta H_f^0(H_2O\ (l))]$

$= [1(-1273.3\ kJ) + 6(0.0\ kJ)] - [6(-393.5\ kJ) + 6(-285.8\ kJ)]$

$= [-1273.3\ kJ] - [-4076\ kJ]$

$= +2803\ kJ$

Check: The units (kJ) are correct. The answer is positive, which means that the reaction is endothermic. The reaction requires the input of light energy, so we expect that this will be an endothermic reaction.

---

80. **Given:** ethanol (C_2H_5OH) combustion **Find:** $\Delta H°_{rxn}$

Conceptual plan: write balanced reaction then $\Delta H_{rxn}^0 = \sum n_P \Delta H_f^0 (products) - \sum n_R \Delta H_f^0 (reactants)$

Solution: combustion is combination with oxygen to form carbon dioxide and water

$C_2H_5OH\ (l) + 1/2\ O_2\ (g) \rightarrow 2\ CO_2\ (g) + 3\ H_2O\ (g)$

Reactant/Product	ΔH_f^0 (kJ/mol from Appendix IIB)
$C_2H_5OH\ (l)$	-277.6
$O_2\ (g)$	0.0
$CO_2\ (g)$	-393.5
$H_2O\ (g)$	-241.8

Be sure to pull data for the correct formula and phase.

$\Delta H_{rxn}^0 = \sum n_P \Delta H_f^0 (products) - \sum n_R \Delta H_f^0 (reactants)$

$= [2(\Delta H_f^0(CO_2\ (g)) + 3(\Delta H_f^0(H_2O\ (g))] - [1(\Delta H_f^0(C_2H_5OH\ (l)) + 1/2(\Delta H_f^0(O_2\ (g))]$

$= [2(-393.5\ kJ) + 3(-241.8\ kJ)] - [1(-277.6\ kJ) + 1/2(0.0\ kJ)]$

$= [-1512.4\ kJ] - [-277.6\ kJ]$

$= -1234.8\ kJ$

Check: The units (kJ) are correct. The answer is negative, which means that the reaction is exothermic, which is typical for combustion reactions.

---

81. **Given:** $2\ CH_3NO_2\ (l) + 3/2\ O_2\ (g) \rightarrow 2\ CO_2\ (g) + 3\ H_2O\ (g) + N_2\ (g)$ and $\Delta H°_{rxn} = -709.2$ kJ/mol
Find: $\Delta H°_f\ (CH_3NO_2\ (l))$

Conceptual plan: fill known values into $\Delta H_{rxn}^0 = \sum n_P \Delta H_f^0 (products) - \sum n_R \Delta H_f^0 (reactants)$ **and**

rearrange to solve for $\Delta H°_f\ (CH_3NO_2\ (l))$
Solution:

Reactant/Product	ΔH_f^0 (kJ/mol from Appendix IIB)
$O_2\ (g)$	0.0
$CO_2\ (g)$	-393.5
$H_2O\ (g)$	-241.8
$N_2\ (g)$	0.0

Be sure to pull data for the correct formula and phase.

$H_{rxn}^0 = \sum n_P \Delta H_f^0 (products) - \sum n_R \Delta H_f^0 (reactants)$

$= [2(\Delta H_f^0(CO_2\ (g)) + 3(\Delta H_f^0(H_2O\ (g)) + 1(\Delta H_f^0(N_2\ (g))] - [2(\Delta H_f^0(CH_3NO_2\ (l)) + 3/2(\Delta H_f^0(O_2\ (g))]$

$-709.2\ kJ = [2(-393.5\ kJ) + 3(-241.8\ kJ) + 1(0.0\ kJ)] - [2(\Delta H_f^0(CH_3NO_2\ (l)) + 3/2(0.0\ kJ)]$

$-709.2\ kJ = [-1512.4\ kJ] - [2(\Delta H_f^0(CH_3NO_2\ (l))]$

$\Delta H_f^0(CH_3NO_2\ (l)) = -401.6\ kJ/mol$

Check: The units (kJ/mol) are correct. The answer is negative, which means that the reaction is exothermic, which is typical for combustion reactions.

82. **Given**: $4 C_3H_5N_3O_9 (l) \rightarrow 12 CO_2 (g) + 10 H_2O (g) + 6 N_2 (g) + O_2 (g)$ and $\Delta H^\circ_{rxn} = -5678$ kJ/mol
    Find: $\Delta H^\circ_f (C_3H_5N_3O_9 (l))$

    Conceptual plan: **fill known values into** $\Delta H^0_{rxn} = \sum n_P \Delta H^0_f (products) - \sum n_R \Delta H^0_f (reactants)$ **and rearrange to solve for** $\Delta H^\circ_f (C_3H_5N_3O_9 (l))$
    Solution:

Reactant/Product	ΔH^0_f (kJ/mol from Appendix IIB)
$CO_2 (g)$	-393.5
$H_2O (g)$	-241.8
$N_2 (g)$	0.0
$O_2 (g)$	0.0

Be sure to pull data for the correct formula and phase.

$$H^0_{rxn} = \sum n_P \Delta H^0_f (products) - \sum n_R \Delta H^0_f (reactants)$$

$$= [12(\Delta H^0_f (CO_2 (g)) + 10(\Delta H^0_f (H_2O (g)) + 6(\Delta H^0_f (N_2 (g)) + 1(\Delta H^0_f (O_2 (g))] - [2(\Delta H^0_f (C_3H_5N_3O_9 (l))]$$

$$-5678 \text{ kJ} = [12(-393.5 \text{ kJ}) + 10(-241.8 \text{ kJ}) + 6(0.0 \text{ kJ}) + 1(0.0 \text{ kJ})] - [4(\Delta H^0_f (C_3H_5N_3O_9 (l))]$$

$$-5678 \text{ kJ} = [-7140. \text{ kJ}] - [4(\Delta H^0_f (C_3H_5N_3O_9 (l))]$$

$$\Delta H^0_f (CH_3NO_2 (l)) = -365.5 \text{ kJ/mol}$$

Check: The units (kJ/mol) are correct. The answer is negative, which is not surprising since this is a combustion reaction.

83. a) **Given**: methane, $\Delta H^\circ_{rxn} = -802.3$ kJ; $q = 1.00 \times 10^2$ kJ   **Find**: $m(CO_2)$
    Conceptual plan: $q \rightarrow mol\ CO_2 \rightarrow g\ CO_2$

$$\frac{1 \text{ mol}}{-802.3 \text{ kJ}} \qquad \frac{44.01 \text{ g}}{1 \text{ mol}}$$

Solution: $-1.00 \times 10^2 \text{ kJ} \times \dfrac{1 \text{ mol } CO_2}{-802.3 \text{ kJ}} \times \dfrac{44.01 \text{ g } CO2}{1 \text{ mol } CO2} = 5.49 \text{ g } CO_2$

Check: The units (g) are correct. The magnitude of the answer (~5) makes physical sense because less than a mole of fuel is used.

b) **Given**: propane, $\Delta H^\circ_{rxn} = -2217$ kJ; $q = 1.00 \times 10^2$ kJ   **Find**: $m(CO_2)$
    Conceptual plan: $q \rightarrow mol\ CO_2 \rightarrow g\ CO_2$

$$\frac{3 \text{ mol}}{-2217 \text{ kJ}} \qquad \frac{44.01 \text{ g}}{1 \text{ mol}}$$

Solution: $-1.00 \times 10^2 \text{ kJ} \times \dfrac{3 \text{ mol } CO_2}{-2217 \text{ kJ}} \times \dfrac{44.01 \text{ g } CO2}{1 \text{ mol } CO2} = 5.96 \text{ g } CO_2$

Check: The units (g) are correct. The magnitude of the answer (~6) makes physical sense because less than a mole of fuel is used.

c) **Given**: octane, $\Delta H^\circ_{rxn} = -5074.1$ kJ; $q = 1.00 \times 10^2$ kJ   **Find**: $m(CO_2)$
    Conceptual plan: $q \rightarrow mol\ CO_2 \rightarrow g\ CO_2$

$$\frac{8 \text{ mol}}{-5074.1 \text{ kJ}} \qquad \frac{44.01 \text{ g}}{1 \text{ mol}}$$

Solution: $-1.00 \times 10^2 \text{ kJ} \times \dfrac{8 \text{ mol } CO_2}{-5074.1 \text{ kJ}} \times \dfrac{44.01 \text{ g } CO2}{1 \text{ mol } CO2} = 6.94 \text{ g } CO_2$

Check: The units (g) are correct. The magnitude of the answer (~7) makes physical sense because less than a mole of fuel is used.

The methane generated the least carbon dioxide for the given amount of heat, while the octane generated the most carbon dioxide for the given amount of heat.

84. **Given:** methanol (CH_3OH) combustion   **Find:** $\Delta H°_{rxn}$, $m(CO_2)$/kJ for methane and octane (using #83)

Conceptual plan: write balanced reaction then $\Delta H^0_{rxn} = \sum n_P \Delta H^0_f (products) - \sum n_R \Delta H^0_f (reactants)$

then $q \rightarrow$ **mol** $CO_2 \rightarrow$ **g** CO_2 **then for octane** $m(CO_2)/$ 1.00×10^2 **kJ** $\rightarrow m(CO_2)/$ **kJ**

$$\frac{1 \, mol}{\Delta H^0_{rxn} \, (kJ)} \qquad \frac{44.01 \, g}{1 \, mol} \qquad\qquad \div 100$$

Solution: combustion is combination with oxygen to form carbon dioxide and water

$CH_3OH \, (l) \; + \; O_2 \, (g) \; \rightarrow \; CO_2 \, (g) \; + \; 2 \, H_2O \, (g)$

Reactant/Product	ΔH^0_f (kJ/mol from Appendix IIB)
$CH_3OH \, (l)$	-238.6
$O_2 \, (g)$	0.0
$CO_2 \, (g)$	-393.5
$H_2O \, (g)$	-241.8

Be sure to pull data for the correct formula and phase.

$\Delta H^0_{rxn} = \sum n_P \Delta H^0_f (products) - \sum n_R \Delta H^0_f (reactants)$

$= [1(\Delta H^0_f (CO_2 \, (g)) + 2(\Delta H^0_f (H_2O \, (g))] - [1(\Delta H^0_f (CH_3OH \, (l)) + 1(\Delta H^0_f (O_2 \, (g))]$

$= [1(- 393.5 \, kJ) + 2(- 241.8 \, kJ)] - [1(-238.6 \, kJ) + 1(0.0 \, kJ)]$

$= [- 877.1 \, kJ] - [- 238.6 \, kJ]$

$= - 638.5 \, kJ$

$-1 \, kJ \; \times \; \dfrac{1 \, mol \, CO_2}{- 638.5 \, kJ} \; \times \; \dfrac{44.01 \, g \, CO_2}{1 \, mol \, CO_2} = 0.06893 \, g \, CO_2$ for methanol and

$\dfrac{6.94 \, g \, CO_2}{-1.00 \times 10^2 \, kJ} \; \times \; -1 \, kJ = 0.0694 \, g \, CO_2$ for octane

Methanol contributes less CO_2 / kJ than octane, contributing less to global warming.

Check: The units (g) are correct.   The magnitude of the answer (~7) makes physical sense because less than a mole of fuel is used.

85. **Given:** 7×10^{12} kg/yr octane (C_8H_{18}), $\Delta H°_{rxn} = - 5074.1$ kJ (using #83), 3×10^{15} kg CO_2 in atmosphere, **Find:** $m(CO_2)$ in kg and time to double atmospheric CO_2

Conceptual plan: use reaction from #83 $C_8H_{18} \, (l) \; + \; 25/2 \, O_2 \, (g) \; \rightarrow \; 8 \, CO_2 \, (g) \; + \; 9 \, H_2O \, (g)$

kg $(C_8H_{18}) \rightarrow$ **g** $(C_8H_{18}) \rightarrow$ **mol** $(C_8H_{18}) \rightarrow$ **mol** $CO_2 \rightarrow$ **g** $CO_2 \rightarrow$ **kg** CO_2 **produced**

$$\frac{1000 \, g}{1 \, kg} \qquad \frac{1 \, mol \, C_8H_{18}}{114.22 \, g} \qquad \frac{8 \, mol \, CO_2}{1 \, mol \, C_8H_{18}} \qquad \frac{44.01 \, g}{1 \, mol} \qquad \frac{1 \, kg}{1000 \, g}$$

then   **kg** $CO_2 \rightarrow$ **yr**

$$\frac{3 \times 10^{15} \, kg \, CO_2}{\left(\dfrac{kg \, CO_2 \, produced}{yr}\right)}$$

Solution:

$7 \times 10^{12} \, kg \; \times \; \dfrac{1000 \, g}{1 \, kg} \; \times \; \dfrac{1 \, mol \, C_8H_{18}}{114.22 \, g} \; \times \; \dfrac{8 \, mol \, CO_2}{1 \, mol \, C_8H_{18}} \; \times \; \dfrac{44.01 \, g \, CO_2}{1 \, mol \, CO_2} \; \times \; \dfrac{1 \, kg}{1000 \, g} = 2.158 \times 10^{13} \, kg \, CO_2$

$= 2 \times 10^{13} \, kg \, CO_2$ per year

$\dfrac{3 \times 10^{15} \, kg \, CO_2}{\left(\dfrac{2.158 \times 10^{13} \, kg \, CO_2 \, produced}{yr}\right)} = 139 \, yr = 100 \, yr$

Check: The units (kg and yr) are correct.   The magnitude of the answer (10^{13} kg) makes physical sense because the mass of CO_2 is larger than the hydrocarbon mass in a combustion (since O is much heavier than H).   The time is consistent with Chapter 5 problems where ~1 % of the atmospheric carbon monoxide is generated each year.

86. **Given:** sunlight power density = 1 kW/m², solar cell efficiency = 15 %, home usage = 385 kWh/month
Find: m² solar cells needed
Conceptual plan:

power density available → power density generated → kWh/ m²·24 hr → kWh/m²day

$$\frac{15\ kW\ generated}{100\ kW\ available} \qquad \frac{8\ hr\ power\ generation}{24\ hr} \qquad \frac{24\ hr}{1\ day}$$

then kWh/ m²day → kWh/ m²month generated then power needed/month → m² needed

$$\frac{30\ days}{1\ month} \qquad\qquad\qquad \div kWh/\ m^2\ month\ generated$$

Solution:
$$\frac{1\ kW\ available}{1 m^2} \times \frac{15\ kW\ generated}{100\ kW\ available} \times \frac{8\ hr\ power\ generation}{24\ hr} \times \frac{24\ hr}{1\ day} \times \frac{30\ day}{1\ month} = 36\ \frac{kWh\ generated}{m^2\ month}$$

$$\frac{385\ \dfrac{kWh\ needed}{month}}{\left(36\ \dfrac{kWh\ generated}{m^2\ month}\right)} = 10.694\ m^2 = 10\ m^2$$

Check: The units (m²) are correct. The magnitude of the answer (10) makes physical sense because this could fit on the roof of a house.

87. **Given:** billiard ball$_A$ = system: m_A = 0.17 kg, v_{A1} = 4.5 m/s slows to v_{A2} = 3.8 m/s and v_{A3} = 0; ball$_B$: m_B = 0.17 kg, v_{B1} = 0 and v_{B2} = 3.8 m/s and $KE = \frac{1}{2}mv^2$ **Find:** w, q, ΔE_{sys}
Conceptual plan:

m, v → KE then KE_{A3}, KE_{A1} → ΔE_{sys} and KE_{A2}, KE_{A1} → q and KE_{B2}, KE_{B1} → w_B
$$KE = \frac{1}{2}mv^2 \qquad \Delta E_{sys} = KE_{A3} - KE_{A1} \qquad q = KE_{A2} - KE_{A1} \qquad w_B = KE_{B2} - KE_{B1}$$

ΔE_{sys}, q → w_A verify that $w_A = -w_B$ so that no heat is transferred to ball$_B$
$$\Delta E = q + w$$

Solution: $KE = \frac{1}{2}mv^2$ since m is in kg and v is in m/s, KE will be in kgm²/s² which is joule.

$$KE_{A1} = \frac{1}{2}\,(0.17\ kg)\left(4.5\frac{m}{s}\right)^2 = 1.\underline{7}213\ \frac{kg\ m^2}{s^2} = 1.\underline{7}213\ J\ ,$$

$$KE_{A2} = \frac{1}{2}\,(0.17\ kg)\left(3.8\frac{m}{s}\right)^2 = 1.\underline{2}274\ \frac{kg\ m^2}{s^2} = 1.\underline{2}274\ J\ ,$$

$$KE_{A3} = \frac{1}{2}\,(0.17\ kg)\left(0\frac{m}{s}\right)^2 = 0\ \frac{kg\ m^2}{s^2} = 0\ J,\quad KE_{B1} = \frac{1}{2}\,(0.17\ kg)\left(0\frac{m}{s}\right)^2 = 0\ \frac{kg\ m^2}{s^2} = 0\ J\ and$$

$$KE_{B2} = \frac{1}{2}\,(0.17\ kg)\left(3.8\frac{m}{s}\right)^2 = 1.\underline{2}274\ \frac{kg\ m^2}{s^2} = 1.\underline{2}274\ J\ .$$

$\Delta E_{sys} = KE_{A3} - KE_{A1} = 0\ J - 1.\underline{7}213\ J = -1.\underline{7}213\ J = -1.7\ J\ ,$

$q = KE_{A2} - KE_{A1} = 1.\underline{2}274\ J - 1.\underline{7}213\ J = -0.\underline{4}939\ J = -0.5\ J\ ,$

$w_B = KE_{B2} - KE_{B1} = 1.\underline{2}274\ J - 0\ J = 1.\underline{2}274\ J$ and $w = \Delta E - q = -1.\underline{7}213\ J - -0.\underline{4}939\ J = -1.\underline{2}274\ J = -1.2\ J\ .$

Since $w_A = -w_B$ so that no heat is transferred to ball$_B$.
Check: The units (kJ) are correct. Since the ball is initially moving and is stopped at the end, it has lost energy (negative ΔE_{sys}). As the ball slows due to friction it is releasing heat (negative q). The kinetic energy is transferred to a second ball, so it does work (w negative).

88. **Given:** 100-W lightbulb in a piston; bulb on for 0.015 hr, V_i = 0.85 L, V_f = 5.88 L, P = 1.0 atm **Find:** w, q, ΔE_{sys}

Conceptual plan:
bulb wattage, time $\rightarrow$ ΔE_{sys}(Wh) $\rightarrow$ ΔE_{sys}(Wh) $\rightarrow$ ΔE_{sys}(J)   and $V_i, V_f \rightarrow \Delta V$ then

$$\Delta E = (wattage)(time) \quad \frac{1\ kW}{1000\ W} \quad \frac{3.60 \times 10^6\ J}{1kWh} \qquad \Delta V = V_f - V_i$$

P, ΔV $\rightarrow$ w (L atm) $\rightarrow$ w (J)   finally $\Delta E_{sys}, w \rightarrow q$

$$w = -P\ \Delta V \quad \frac{101.3\ J}{1\ L\ atm} \qquad \Delta E = q + w$$

Solution: $\Delta E = (wattage)(time) = (100\ W)(0.015\ hr) = 1.5\ Wh \times \frac{1\ kW}{1000\ W} \times \frac{3.60 \times 10^6\ J}{1\ kWh} = 5400\ J$ and

$\Delta V = V_f - V_i = 5.88\ L - 0.85\ L = 5.03\ L$ then

$w = -P\ \Delta V = -1.0\ atm \times 5.03\ L \times \frac{101.3\ J}{1\ L\ atm} = -509.539\ J = -5.0 \times 10^2\ J$ $\Delta E = q + w$

Rearrange to solve for q. $q = \Delta E_{sys} - w = +5400\ J - -509.539\ J = 5900\ J$

Check: The units (J) are correct.   Electricity is added so energy is added (positive ΔE_{sys}). The piston expands and so does work (negative work). In order for the lightbulb to generate light it must be heated or absorb energy (positive q).

89. **Given:** H_2O *(l)* $\rightarrow$ H_2O *(g)* $\Delta H°_{rxn} = +44.01$ kJ/mol; $\Delta T_{body} = -0.50$ °C, $m_{body} = 95$ kg, $C_{body} = 4.0$ J/g °C
   Find: m_{H2O}
   Conceptual plan:
   kg $\rightarrow$ g   then $m_{body}, \Delta T, C_{body}$ $\rightarrow$ q_{body} $\rightarrow$ q_{rxn} (J) $\rightarrow$ q_{rxn} (kJ) $\rightarrow$ mol H_2O $\rightarrow$ g H_2O

$$\frac{1000\ g}{1\ kg} \qquad q_{body} = m_{body}\ C_{body}\ \Delta T_{body} \quad q_{rxn} = -q_{body} \quad \frac{1\ kJ}{1000\ J} \quad \frac{1\ mol}{44.01\ kJ} \quad \frac{18.01\ g}{1\ mol}$$

Solution: $95\ kg \times \frac{1000\ g}{1\ kg} = 95000\ g$ then

$q_{body} = m_{body}\ C_{body}\ \Delta T_{body} = 95000\ g \times 4.0\ \frac{J}{g\ °C} \times (-0.50\ °C) = -190000\ J$ then

$q_{rxn} = -q_{body} = 190000\ J \times \frac{1\ kJ}{1000\ J} \times \frac{1\ mol}{44.01\ kJ} \times \frac{18.01\ g}{1\ mol} = 78\ g\ H_2O$

Check: The units (g) are correct.   The magnitude of the answer (78) makes physical sense because a person can sweat this much on a hot day.

90. **Given:** LP gas combustion, $\Delta H°_{rxn} = -2044$ kJ; 1.5 L water, $T_{H2Oi} = 25.0$ °C, $T_{H2Of} = 100.0$ °C, 15 % efficiency   **Find:** $m_{LP\ gas}$
   Conceptual plan:
   L $\rightarrow$ mL $\rightarrow$ g and T_i, T_f $\rightarrow$ ΔT then $m_{H2O}, \Delta T_{H2O}, C_{H2O}$ $\rightarrow$ q_{H2O} $\rightarrow$ q_{rxn}

$$\frac{1000\ mL}{1\ L} \quad \frac{1.0\ g}{1.0\ mL} \qquad \Delta T = T_f - T_i \qquad q_{H2O} = m_{H2O}\ C_{H2O}\ \Delta T_{H2O} \quad q_{rxn} = -q_{H2O}$$

then q_{rxn} needed $\rightarrow$ q_{rxn} generated (J) $\rightarrow$ q_{rxn} (kJ) $\rightarrow$ mol LP gas $\rightarrow$ g LP gas

$$\frac{100\ J\ generated}{15\ J\ needed} \quad \frac{1\ kJ}{1000\ J} \quad \frac{1\ mol}{-2044\ kJ} \quad \frac{44.09\ g}{1\ mol}$$

Solution: $1.5\ L \times \frac{1000\ mL}{1\ L} \times \frac{1.0\ g}{1.0\ mL} = 1500\ g$ and $\Delta T = T_f - T_i = 100.0\ °C - 25.0\ °C = 75.0\ °C$ then

$q_{H2O} = m_{H2O}\ C_{H2O}\ \Delta T_{H2O} = 1500\ g \times 4.184\ \frac{J}{g\ °C} \times (75.0\ °C) = 470700\ J$ then

$q_{rxn} = -q_{H2O} = -470700\ J\ needed \times \frac{100\ J\ generated}{15\ J\ needed} \times \frac{1\ kJ}{1000\ J} \times \frac{1\ mol}{-2044\ kJ} \times \frac{44.09\ g}{1\ mol} = 68\ g\ LP\ gas$

Check: The units (g) are correct.   The magnitude of the answer (68) makes physical sense because a tank of LP gas contains many orders of magnitude more than this amount.

91. **Given:** H_2O *(s)* $\rightarrow$ H_2O *(l)* $\Delta H°_f$ (H_2O *(s)*) = -291.8 kJ/mol; 355 mL beverage $T_{Bevi} = 25.0$ °C, $T_{Bevf} = 0.0$ °C, $C_{Bev} = 4.184$ J/g °C, $d_{Bev} = 1.0$ g/mL   **Find:** $\Delta H°_{rxn}$ (ice melting) and m_{ice}

Conceptual plan: $\Delta H^0_{rxn} = \sum n_p \Delta H^0_f (products) - \sum n_R \Delta H^0_f (reactants)$ mL $\rightarrow$ g and $T_i, T_f \rightarrow \Delta T$ then

$$\frac{1.0\ g}{1.0\ mL}$$ $$\Delta T = T_f - T_i$$

$m_{H2O}, \Delta T_{H2O}, C_{H2O} \rightarrow q_{H2O} \rightarrow q_{rxn}\ (J) \rightarrow q_{rxn}\ (kJ) \rightarrow$ mol ice $\rightarrow$ g ice

$q_{Bev} = m_{Bev}\ C_{Bev}\ \Delta T_{Bev}$ $q_{rxn} = - q_{Bev}$ $\dfrac{1\ kJ}{1000\ J}$ $\dfrac{1\ mol}{\Delta H^0_{rxn}}$ $\dfrac{18.01\ g}{1\ mol}$

Solution:

Reactant/Product	ΔH^0_f (kJ/mol from Appendix IIB)
H_2O (s)	$- 291.8$
H_2O (l)	$- 285.8$

Be sure to pull data for the correct formula and phase.

$\Delta H^0_{rxn} = \sum n_p \Delta H^0_f (products) - \sum n_R \Delta H^0_f (reactants)$

$= [1(\Delta H^0_f (H_2O\ (l)))] - [1(\Delta H^0_f (H_2O\ (s)))]$

$= [1(-285.8\ kJ)] - [1(-291.8\ kJ)]$

$= + 6.0\ kJ$

355 mL x $\dfrac{1.0\ g}{1.0\ mL}$ = 355 g and $\Delta T = T_f - T_i = 0.0\ °C - 25.0\ °C = -25.0\ °C$ then

$q_{Bev} = m_{Bev}\ C_{Bev}\ \Delta T_{Bev}$ = 355 g x 4.184 $\dfrac{J}{g\ °C}$ x (- 25.0 °C) = 37133 J then

$q_{rxn} = -q_{Bev} = - 37133$ J x $\dfrac{1\ kJ}{1000\ J}$ x $\dfrac{1\ mol}{-6.0\ kJ}$ x $\dfrac{18.01\ g}{1\ mol}$ = 110 g ice

Check: The units (kJ and g) are correct.   The answer is positive, which means that the reaction is endothermic. We expect an endothermic reaction because we know that heat must be added to melt ice. The magnitude of the answer (110 g) makes physical sense because it is much smaller than the weight of the beverage and it would fit in a glass with the beverage.

92. **Given:** CO_2 (s) $\rightarrow CO_2$ (g) $\Delta H°_f (CO_2\ (s)) = - 427.4$ kJ/mol; 15 L water $T_{H2Oi} = 85\ °C$, $T_{H2Of} = 25\ °C$
    Find: $\Delta H°_{rxn}$ (dry ice sublimation) and m_{dryice}
    Conceptual plan:

$\Delta H^0_{rxn} = \sum n_p \Delta H^0_f (products) - \sum n_R \Delta H^0_f (reactants)$ L $\rightarrow$ mL $\rightarrow$ g and $T_i, T_f \rightarrow \Delta T$ then

$$\frac{1000\ mL}{1\ L}\qquad \frac{1.0\ g}{1.0\ mL}\qquad \Delta T = T_f - T_i$$

$m_{H2O}, \Delta T_{H2O}, C_{H2O} \rightarrow q_{H2O} \rightarrow q_{rxn}\ (J) \rightarrow q_{rxn}\ (kJ) \rightarrow$ mol ice $\rightarrow$ g ice

$q_{H2O} = m_{H2O}\ C_{H2O}\ \Delta T_{H2O}$ $q_{rxn} = - q_{H2O}$ $\dfrac{1\ kJ}{1000\ J}$ $\dfrac{1\ mol}{\Delta H^0_{rxn}}$ $\dfrac{44.01\ g}{1\ mol}$

Solution:

Reactant/Product	ΔH^0_f (kJ/mol from Appendix IIB)
CO_2 (s)	$- 427.4$
CO_2 (g)	$- 393.5$

Be sure to pull data for the correct formula and phase.

$\Delta H^0_{rxn} = \sum n_p \Delta H^0_f (products) - \sum n_R \Delta H^0_f (reactants)$

$= [1(\Delta H^0_f (CO_2\ (g)))] - [1(\Delta H^0_f (CO_2\ (s)))]$

$= [1(-393.5\ kJ)] - [1(-427.4\ kJ)]$

$= + 33.9\ kJ$

15 L x $\dfrac{1000\ mL}{1\ L}$ x $\dfrac{1.0\ g}{1.0\ mL}$ = 15000 g and $\Delta T = T_f - T_i = 25\ °C - 85\ °C = -60.\ °C$ then

$q_{H2O} = m_{H2O}\ C_{H2O}\ \Delta T_{H2O}$ = 15000 g x 4.184 $\dfrac{J}{g\ °C}$ x (- 60. °C) = - 3765600 J then

$$q_{rxn} = -q_{H2O} = 3765600 \text{ J} \times \frac{1 \text{ kJ}}{1000 \text{ J}} \times \frac{1 \text{ mol}}{33.9 \text{ kJ}} \times \frac{44.01 \text{ g}}{1 \text{ mol}} = 4900 \text{ g dry ice}$$

Check: The units (kJ and g) are correct. The answer is positive, which means that the reaction is endothermic. We expect an endothermic reaction because we know that heat must be added to sublime dry ice. The magnitude of the answer (4900 g) makes physical sense because the temperature change of the water is fairly large, and the volume of water is large. It is a reasonable amount to put in a cooler.

93. **Given:** 25.5 g aluminum, $T_{Ali} = 65.4\ °C$, 55.2 g water, $T_{H2Oi} = 22.2\ °C$, **Find:** T_f

    Conceptual plan: **pull C_s values from table**   **then**   **m, C_s, T_i → T_f**

        Al: $0.903\ \dfrac{\text{J}}{\text{g}\cdot°\text{C}}$ H_2O: $4.18\ \dfrac{\text{J}}{\text{g}\cdot°\text{C}}$ $q = m\,C_s\left(T_f - T_i\right)$ then set $q_{Al} = -q_{H2O}$

    Solution: $q = m\,C_s\left(T_f - T_i\right)$ substitute in values and set $q_{Al} = -q_{H2O}$.

$$q_{Al} = m_{Al}\,C_{Al}\left(T_f - T_{Ali}\right) = 25.5\ \text{g} \times 0.903\ \frac{\text{J}}{\text{g}\times°\text{C}} \times \left(T_f - 65.4\ °\text{C}\right) =$$

$$-q_{H2O} = -m_{H2O}\,C_{H2O}\left(T_f - T_{H2Oi}\right) = -55.2\ \text{g} \times 4.18\ \frac{\text{J}}{\text{g}\times°\text{C}} \times \left(T_f - 22.2°\text{C}\right)$$

Rearrange to solve for T_f.

$$23.0265\ \frac{\text{J}}{°\text{C}} \times \left(T_f - 65.4\ °\text{C}\right) = -230.736\ \frac{\text{J}}{°\text{C}} \times \left(T_f - 22.2°\text{C}\right) \rightarrow$$

$$23.0265\ \frac{\text{J}}{°\text{C}}\,T_f - 1505.93\ \text{J} = -230.736\ \frac{\text{J}}{°\text{C}}\,T_f + 5168.49\ \text{J} \rightarrow$$

$$-5168.49\ \text{J} - 1505.93\ \text{J} = -230.736\ \frac{\text{J}}{°\text{C}}\,T_f - 23.0265\ \frac{\text{J}}{°\text{C}}\,T_f \rightarrow 6674.42\ \text{J} = 253.7625\ \frac{\text{J}}{°\text{C}}\,T_f \rightarrow$$

$$T_f = \frac{6674.42\ \text{J}}{253.7625\ \frac{\text{J}}{°\text{C}}} = 26.3\ °\text{C}$$

Check: The units (°C) are correct. The magnitude of the answer (26) makes physical sense because the heat transfer is dominated by the water (larger mass and larger specific heat capacity). The final temperature should be closer to the initial temperature of water than of aluminum.

94. **Given:** ethanol: 50.0 mL; d = 0.789 g/mL, $T_{EtOHi} = 7.0\ °C$, water: 50.0 mL; d = 1.0 g/mL $T_{H2Oi} = 28.4\ °C$, **Find:** T_f

    Conceptual plan: **pull C_s values from table**   **mL → g**   **then**   **m, C_s, T_i → T_f**

      EtOH: $2.42\ \dfrac{\text{J}}{\text{g}\cdot°\text{C}}$ H_2O: $4.18\ \dfrac{\text{J}}{\text{g}\cdot°\text{C}}$ EtOH: $\dfrac{0.789\ \text{g}}{1.0\ \text{mL}}$ H_2O: $\dfrac{1.0\ \text{g}}{1.0\ \text{mL}}$ $q = m\,C_s\left(T_f - T_i\right)$ then set $q_{Al} = -q_{H2O}$

    Solution: $50.0\ \text{mL} \times \dfrac{0.789\ \text{g}}{1.0\ \text{mL}} = 39.45\ \text{g EtOH}$ and $50.0\ \text{mL} \times \dfrac{1.0\ \text{g}}{1.0\ \text{mL}} = 50.0\ \text{g}\ H_2O$ then

$$q = m\,C_s\left(T_f - T_i\right) \text{ substitute in values and set } q_{EtOH} = -q_{H2O}.$$

$$q_{EtOH} = m_{EtOH}\,C_{EtOH}\left(T_f - T_{EtOHi}\right) = 39.45\ \text{g} \times 2.42\ \frac{\text{J}}{\text{g}\times°\text{C}} \times \left(T_f - 7.0\ °\text{C}\right) =$$

Rearrange to solve for T_f.

$$-q_{H2O} = -m_{H2O}\,C_{H2O}\left(T_f - T_{H2Oi}\right) = -50.0\ \text{g} \times 4.18\ \frac{\text{J}}{\text{g}\times°\text{C}} \times \left(T_f - 28.4°\text{C}\right)$$

$$95.469\ \frac{\text{J}}{°\text{C}} \times \left(T_f - 7.0\ °\text{C}\right) = -209.2\ \frac{\text{J}}{°\text{C}} \times \left(T_f - 28.4°\text{C}\right) \rightarrow 95.469\ \frac{\text{J}}{°\text{C}}\,T_f - 668.283\ \text{J} = -209.2\ \frac{\text{J}}{°\text{C}}\,T_f + 5941.28\ \text{J}$$

$$\rightarrow -668.283\ \text{J} - 5941.28\ \text{J} = -209.2\ \frac{\text{J}}{°\text{C}}\,T_f - 95.469\ \frac{\text{J}}{°\text{C}}\,T_f \rightarrow 6609.563\ \text{J} = 304.669\ \frac{\text{J}}{°\text{C}}\,T_f \rightarrow$$

$$T_f = \frac{6609.563\ \text{J}}{304.669\ \frac{\text{J}}{°\text{C}}} = 21.7\ °\text{C}$$

Check: The units (°C) are correct. The magnitude of the answer (22) makes physical sense because the heat transfer is dominated by the water (larger mass and larger specific heat capacity). The final temperature should be closer to the initial temperature of water than of ethanol.

95. **Given:** palmitic acid ($C_{16}H_{32}O_2$) combustion ΔH°_f ($C_{16}H_{32}O_2$ (s)) = $-$ 208 kJ/mol; sucrose ($C_{12}H_{22}O_{11}$) combustion ΔH°_f ($C_{12}H_{22}O_{11}$ (s)) = $-$2222 kJ/mol   **Find:** ΔH°_{rxn} in kJ/mol and Cal/g

Conceptual plan: write balanced reaction then $\Delta H^0_{rxn} = \sum n_p \Delta H^0_f (products) - \sum n_R \Delta H^0_f (reactants)$ **then**

kJ/mol → J/mol →   Cal/mol   → Cal/g

$$\frac{1000\ J}{1\ kJ} \qquad \frac{1\ Cal}{4184\ J} \qquad PA: \frac{1\ mol}{256.42\ g} \qquad S: \frac{1\ mol}{342.30\ g}$$

Solution: combustion is combination with oxygen to form carbon dioxide and water (l)

$C_{16}H_{32}O_2$ (s) + 23 O_2 (g) → 16 CO_2 (g) + 16 H_2O (l)

Reactant/Product	ΔH^0_f (kJ/mol from Appendix IIB)
$C_{16}H_{32}O_2$ (s)	$-$ 208
O_2 (g)	0.0
CO_2 (g)	$-$ 393.5
H_2O (g)	$-$ 285.8

Be sure to pull data for the correct formula and phase.

$\Delta H^0_{rxn} = \sum n_P \Delta H^0_f (products) - \sum n_R \Delta H^0_f (reactants)$

$= [16(\Delta H^0_f (CO_2\ (g)) + 16(\Delta H^0_f (H_2O\ (l))] - [1(\Delta H^0_f (C_{16}H_{32}O_2\ (s)) + 23(\Delta H^0_f (O_2\ (g))]$

$= [16(-393.5\ kJ) + 16(-285.8\ kJ)] - [1(-208\ kJ) + 23(0.0\ kJ)]$

$= [-10868.8\ kJ] - [-208\ kJ]$

$= -10,660.8\ kJ/mol = -10,661\ kJ/mol$

$$-10,660.8\ \frac{kJ}{mol} \times \frac{1000\ J}{1\ kJ} \times \frac{1\ Cal}{4184\ J} \times \frac{1\ mol}{256.42\ g} = 9.9378\ Cal/g$$

$C_{12}H_{22}O_{11}$ (s) + 12 O_2 (g) → 12 CO_2 (g) + 11 H_2O (l)

Reactant/Product	ΔH^0_f (kJ/mol from Appendix IIB)
$C_{12}H_{22}O_{11}$ (s)	$-$ 2226.1
O_2 (g)	0.0
CO_2 (g)	$-$ 393.5
H_2O (g)	$-$ 285.8

Be sure to pull data for the correct formula and phase.

$\Delta H^0_{rxn} = \sum n_P \Delta H^0_f (products) - \sum n_R \Delta H^0_f (reactants)$

$= [12(\Delta H^0_f (CO_2\ (g)) + 11(\Delta H^0_f (H_2O\ (l))] - [1(\Delta H^0_f (C_{12}H_{22}O_{11}\ (s)) + 12(\Delta H^0_f (O_2\ (g))]$

$= [12(-393.5\ kJ) + 11(-285.8\ kJ)] - [1(-2226.1\ kJ) + 12(0.0\ kJ)]$

$= [-7865.8\ kJ] - [-2226.1\ kJ]$

$= -5639.7\ kJ/mol$

$$-5639.7\ \frac{kJ}{mol} \times \frac{1000\ J}{1\ kJ} \times \frac{1\ Cal}{4184\ J} \times \frac{1\ mol}{342.30\ g} = -3.938\ Cal/g$$

Check: The units (kJ/mol and Cal/g) are correct. The magnitude of the answers are consistent with the food labels we see everyday.

96. **Given:** hydrogen, methanol (CH_3OH) and octane combustion   **Find:** q released in kJ/kg

Conceptual plan: write balanced reaction then $\Delta H^0_{rxn} = \sum n_P \Delta H^0_f (products) - \sum n_R \Delta H^0_f (reactants)$

then kJ/mol →   kJ/g   →   kJ/kg

$$H_2: \frac{1\ mol}{2.016\ g} \qquad MeOH: \frac{1\ mol}{32.04\ g} \qquad O: \frac{1\ mol}{114.22\ g} \qquad \frac{1000\ g}{1\ kg}$$

Solution: combustion is combination with oxygen to form carbon dioxide and water

H_2 (g) + ½ O_2 (g) → H_2O (g)   This reaction is the heat of formation of gaseous water so

$\Delta H^0_{rxn} = -241.8\ kJ/mol$.

$$-241.8\ \frac{kJ}{mol} \times \frac{1\ mol}{2.016\ g} \times \frac{1000\ g}{1\ kg} = -1.199 \times 10^5\ kJ/g\ H_2 \quad \text{and}$$

CH_3OH (l) + O_2 (g) → CO_2 (g) + 2 H_2O (g)

Reactant/Product	ΔH_f^0 (kJ/mol from Appendix IIB)
$CH_3OH\ (l)$	-238.6
$O_2\ (g)$	0.0
$CO_2\ (g)$	-393.5
$H_2O\ (g)$	-241.8

Be sure to pull data for the correct formula and phase.

$$\Delta H_{rxn}^0 = \sum n_P \Delta H_f^0 (products) - \sum n_R \Delta H_f^0 (reactants)$$
$$= [1(\Delta H_f^0 (CO_2\ (g)) + 2(\Delta H_f^0 (H_2O\ (g))] - [1(\Delta H_f^0 (CH_3OH\ (l)) + 1(\Delta H_f^0 (O_2\ (g))]$$
$$= [1(-393.5\ kJ) + 2(-241.8\ kJ)] - [1(-238.6\ kJ) + 1(0.0\ kJ)]$$
$$= [-877.1\ kJ] - [-238.6\ kJ]$$
$$= -638.5\ kJ$$

$$-638.5\ \frac{kJ}{mol} \times \frac{1\ mol}{32.04\ g} \times \frac{1000\ g}{1\ kg} = -1.993 \times 10^4\ kJ/kg\ CH_3OH \quad \text{and}$$

$$-5074.1\ \frac{kJ}{mol} \times \frac{1\ mol}{114.22\ g} \times \frac{1000\ g}{1\ kg} = -4.4424 \times 10^4\ kJ/kg\ C_8H_{18}$$

Hydrogen delivers the most energy per weight of fuel. This is not surprising since hydrogen is so light.
Check: The units (kJ/kg fuel) are correct. The magnitude of the answers (10^4 - 10^5) makes physical sense because there are many moles of fuel in a kg and the heat of reactions are high.

97. At constant P $\Delta H_{rxn} = q_P$ and at constant V $\Delta E_{rxn} = q_V = \Delta H_{rxn} - P\Delta V$. $PV = nRT$ at constant P, and a constant number of moles of gas as we change the T the only variable that can change is V, so $P\Delta V = nR\Delta T$. Substituting into the equation for ΔE_{rxn} we get $\Delta E_{rxn} = \Delta H_{rxn} - nR\Delta T$ or $\Delta H_{rxn} = \Delta E_{rxn} + nR\Delta T$.

98. **Given:** $SO_2\ (g) + 1/2\ O_2\ (g) \rightarrow SO_3\ (g)$, $\Delta H_{rxn} = +89.5\ kJ$, and $\Delta H_f (SO_3\ (g)) = -204.2\ kJ$
Find: $\Delta H_{rxn}(SO_2\ (g))$
Conceptual plan: fill known values into $\Delta H_{rxn}^0 = \sum n_P \Delta H_f^0 (products) - \sum n_R \Delta H_f^0 (reactants)$ **and rearrange to solve for** $\Delta H_f^\circ ((SO_2\ (g))$
Solution:

Reactant/Product	ΔH_f^0 (kJ/mol)
$O_2\ (g)$	0.0
$SO_3\ (g)$	-204.2

$$\Delta H_{rxn}^0 = \sum n_P \Delta H_f^0 (products) - \sum n_R \Delta H_f^0 (reactants)$$
$$= [1(\Delta H_f^0 (SO_3\ (g))] - [1(\Delta H_f^0 (SO_2\ (g)) + 1/2(\Delta H_f^0 (O_2\ (g))]$$
$$= [1(-204.2\ kJ)] - [1(\Delta H_f^0 (SO_2\ (g)) + 1/2(0.0\ kJ)]$$

$$+89.5\ kJ = [-204.2\ kJ] - [\Delta H_f^0 (SO_2\ (g)]$$

$$\Delta H_f^0 (SO_2\ (g)) = -293.7\ kJ$$

Check: The units (kJ) are correct. The answer is more negative than $\Delta H_f (SO_3\ (g))$ which makes sense since the reaction is endothermic.

99. **Given:** 16 g peanut butter, bomb calorimeter, $T_i = 22.2\ °C$, $T_f = 25.4\ °C$, $C_{cal} = 120.0\ kJ/°C$
Find: calories in peanut butter
Conceptual plan:

$T_i, T_f \rightarrow \Delta T$ then $\quad \Delta T, C_{cal} \rightarrow q_{cal} \rightarrow q_{rxn}\ (kJ) \rightarrow q_{rxn}\ (kJ) \rightarrow q_{rxn}\ (Cal)$

$$\Delta T = T_f - T_i \qquad q_{cal} = C_{cal}\Delta T \qquad q_{rxn} = -q_{cal} \qquad \frac{1000\ J}{1\ kJ} \qquad \frac{1\ Cal}{4184\ J}$$

then $q_{rxn}\ (Cal) \rightarrow Cal/g$
$\div 16$ g peanut butter

Solution: $\Delta T = T_f - T_i = 25.4\ °C - 22.2\ °C = 3.2\ °C$ then $q_{cal} = C_{cal}\Delta T = 120.0\ \frac{kJ}{°C} \times 3.2\ °C = 384\ kJ$ then

$$q_{rxn} = -q_{cal} = -3\underline{8}4 \text{ kJ} \times \frac{1000 \text{ J}}{1 \text{ kJ}} \times \frac{1 \text{Cal}}{4184 \text{ J}} = 9\underline{1}.778 \text{ Cal} \quad \text{then} \quad \frac{91.778 \text{ Cal}}{16 \text{ g}} = 5.7 \text{ Cal/g}$$

Check: The units (Cal/g) are correct. The magnitude of the answer (6) makes physical sense because there is a significant percentage of fat and sugar in peanut butter. The answer is in line with the answers in #93.

100. **Given:** 2.0 mol H_2 (g) + 1.0 mol O_2 (g) at 25°C   **Find:** temperature of water

Conceptual plan: write balanced reaction   then $\Delta H_{rxn}^{\circ} = \sum n_p \Delta H_f^{\circ}(products) - \sum n_R \Delta H_f^{\circ}(reactants)$

then   kJ/mol $\rightarrow$ q(kJ) $\rightarrow$ q(J)   then   2.0 mol H_2 + 1.0 mol O_2 $\rightarrow$ mol H_2O $\rightarrow$ g H_2O then

x mol of limiting reagent $\dfrac{1000 \text{ J}}{1 \text{ kJ}}$ $\dfrac{1 \text{ mol } H_2O}{1 \text{ mol } H_2}$ $\dfrac{18.01 \text{ g}}{1 \text{ mol}}$

$q_{rxn} \rightarrow$ q_{H2O} then   pull C_s for H_2O (l)   then   q, m, C_s, $T_i \rightarrow$ T_f

$q_{rxn} = -q_{H2O}$ $4.18 \dfrac{\text{J}}{\text{g} \cdot {}^{\circ}\text{C}}$ $q = m C_s \left(T_f - T_i\right)$

Solution: combustion is combination with oxygen to form water, choose liquid water because T = 25°C.
H_2 (g) + ½ O_2 (g) $\rightarrow$ H_2O (l)   This reaction is the heat of formation of gaseous water so
$\Delta H_{rxn}^{0} = -285.8$ kJ/mol   The two reactants are in the stoichiometric ratio, so either amount can be used.

$-285.8 \dfrac{\text{kJ}}{1 \text{ mol } H_2} \times 2.0 \text{ mol } H_2 \times \dfrac{1000 \text{ J}}{1 \text{ kJ}} = -5\underline{7}1600 \text{ J}$ and $q_{H2O} = -q_{rxn} = 5\underline{7}1600 \text{ J}$

$2.0 \text{ mol } H_2 \times \dfrac{1 \text{ mol } H_2O}{1 \text{ mol } H_2} \times \dfrac{18.01 \text{ g}}{1 \text{ mol } H_2O} = 36.02 \text{ g } H_2O$ then $q = m C_s \left(T_f - T_i\right)$ Rearrange to solve for T_f.

$$T_f = \frac{m C_s T_i + q}{m C_s} = \frac{\left(36.02 \text{ g} \times 4.18 \dfrac{\text{J}}{\text{g} \times {}^{\circ}\text{C}} \times 25 \, {}^{\circ}\text{C}\right) + 5\underline{7}1600 \text{ J}}{36.02 \text{ g} \times 4.18 \dfrac{\text{J}}{\text{g} \times {}^{\circ}\text{C}}} = 3821{}^{\circ}\text{C}$$ Since this is higher than the

boiling point of water. The heat needed to raise the water to 100 °C is

$q = m C_s \left(T_f - T_i\right) = 36.02 \text{ g} \times 4.18 \dfrac{\text{J}}{\text{g} \times {}^{\circ}\text{C}} \times (100 \, {}^{\circ}\text{C} - 25 \, {}^{\circ}\text{C}) = 1\underline{1}292 \text{ J}$ so $5\underline{7}1600 \text{ J} - 1\underline{1}292 \text{ J} = 5\underline{6}0308 \text{ J}$ is

still available. 2.0 moles H_2O utilizes 88,000 J (= 44 kJ/mol) so 4\underline{7}2308 J (= 5\underline{6}0308 J – 88000 J) is
available to heat steam.
Note: C_s (steam) = 2.04 J/g · °C.

Using equation from above $T_f = \dfrac{m C_s T_i + q}{m C_s} = \dfrac{\left(36.02 \text{ g} \times 2.04 \dfrac{\text{J}}{\text{g} \times {}^{\circ}\text{C}} \times 100. \, {}^{\circ}\text{C}\right) + 4\underline{7}2308 \text{ J}}{36.02 \text{ g} \times 2.04 \dfrac{\text{J}}{\text{g} \times {}^{\circ}\text{C}}} = 6500{}^{\circ}\text{C}$

Check: The units (°C) are correct. The temperature is extremely high. A large amount of heat is liberated and only a relatively small amount of mass absorbs it.

101. **Given:** V_1 = 20.0 L at P_1 = 3.0 atm; P_2 = 1.5 atm let expand at constant T.   **Find:** w, q, ΔE_{sys}

Conceptual plan: $V_1, P_1, P_2 \rightarrow V_2$ then $V_1, V_2 \rightarrow$ ΔV then $P, \Delta V \rightarrow$ w (L atm) $\rightarrow$ w (J)

$P_1 V_1 = P_2 V_2$ $\Delta V = V_2 - V_1$ $w = -P \Delta V$ $\dfrac{101.3 \text{ J}}{1 \text{ L atm}}$

for an ideal gas $\Delta E_{sys} \, \alpha$ T, so since this is a constant temperature process $\Delta E_{sys} = 0$ finally
ΔE_{sys}, w $\rightarrow$ q
$\Delta E = q + w$

Solution: $P_1 V_1 = P_2 V_2$ Rearrange to solve for V_2. $V_2 = V_1 \dfrac{P_1}{P_2} = (20.0 \text{ L}) \times \dfrac{3.0 \text{ atm}}{1.5 \text{ atm}} = 40. \text{ L}$ and

$\Delta V = V_2 - V_1 = 40. \text{ L} - 20.0 \text{ L} = 20. \text{ L}$ then

$w = -P \Delta V = -1.5 \text{ atm} \times 20. \text{ L} \times \dfrac{101.3 \text{ J}}{1 \text{ L atm}} = -3\underline{0}39 \text{ J} = -3.0 \times 10^3 \text{ J}$ $\Delta E = q + w$ Rearrange to solve for q.

$q = \Delta E_{sys} - w = +0 \text{ J} - -3\underline{0}39 \text{ J} = 3.0 \times 10^3 \text{ J}$

Check: The units (J) are correct. Since there is no temperature change, we expect no energy change (ΔE_{sys} = 0). The piston expands and so does work (negative work) and so heat is absorbed (positive q).

102. **Given:** 10.0 g P_4 (s) + O_2 (g) to form P_4O_{10} (s); q released heats 2950 g water from T_i = 18.0 °C to T_f = 38.0 °C   **Find:** $\Delta H°_f (P_4O_{10}$ (s))

Conceptual plan: write balanced reaction   then $\Delta H^0_{rxn} = \sum n_P \Delta H^0_f (products) - \sum n_R \Delta H^0_f (reactants)$ **then**

m, C_s, T_i, T_f → **q_{H2O}** → **q_{rxn} (J)** → **q(kJ)**   **then** **g (P_4)** → **mol (P_4)**   **finally**

$q = m \, C_s \left(T_f - T_i \right)$ $q_{rxn} = - q_{H2O}$ $\dfrac{1 \text{ kJ}}{1000 \text{ J}}$ $\dfrac{123.90 \text{ g}}{1 \text{ mol}}$

q(kJ), mol (P_4) → **$\Delta H°_f (P_4O_{10}$ (s))**

$\Delta H^0_f (P_4O_{10}$ (s)) $= \dfrac{q}{\text{mol } P_4}$

Solution: P_4 (s) + 5 O_2 (g) → P_4O_{10} (s) This reaction is the heat of formation of P_4O_{10} (s) so

$\Delta H^0_{rxn} = \Delta H^0_f (P_4O_{10}$ (s)) then $q = m \, C_s \left(T_f - T_i \right)$ = 2950 g x 4.18 $\dfrac{\text{J}}{\text{g} \times °\text{C}}$ x (38.0 °C - 18.0 °C) = 246620 J

$q_{rxn} = - q_{H2O}$ = -246620 J x $\dfrac{1 \text{ kJ}}{1000 \text{ J}}$ = - 246.620 kJ then 10.0 g P_4 x $\dfrac{1 \text{ mol } P_4}{123.90 \text{ g } P_4}$ = 0.080710 mol P_4 then

$\Delta H^0_f (P_4O_{10}$ (s)) $= \dfrac{q}{\text{mol } P_4} = \dfrac{- 246.620 \text{ kJ}}{0.080710 \text{ mol}}$ = - 3060 kJ/mol

Check: The units (kJ/mol) are correct. The negative sign is consistent with the fact that there was heat released to heat a large amount of water. The magnitude (3000) is not surprising since a small amount of phosphorous heated a lot of water (a high heat capacity material).

103. **Given:** 655 kWh/yr, coal is 3.2 % S, remainder is C, S emitted as SO_2 (g) and gets converted to H_2SO_4 when reacting with water   **Find:** m (H_2SO_4)/yr

Conceptual plan: write balanced reaction   then $\Delta H^0_{rxn} = \sum n_P \Delta H^0_f (products) - \sum n_R \Delta H^0_f (reactants)$

(since the form of sulfur is not given, assume all heat is from combustion of only carbon)   then
kWh → **J** → **kJ** → **mol (C)** → **g (C)** → **g (S)** → **mol (H_2SO_4)** → **mol (H_2SO_4)** → **g (H_2SO_4)**

$\dfrac{3.60 \times 10^6 \text{ J}}{1 \text{kWh}}$ $\dfrac{1 \text{ kJ}}{1000 \text{ J}}$ $\dfrac{\text{mol C}}{\Delta H^0_f (CO_2 (g))}$ $\dfrac{12.01 \text{ g}}{1 \text{ mol}}$ $\dfrac{3.2 \text{ g S}}{(100.0 - 3.2) \text{ g C}}$ $\dfrac{1 \text{ mol}}{32.06 \text{ g}}$ $\dfrac{1 \text{ mol } H_2SO_4}{1 \text{ mol S}}$ $\dfrac{98.09 \text{ g}}{1 \text{ mol}}$

Solution: C (s) + O_2 (g) → CO_2 (g) This reaction is the heat of formation of CO_2 (g) so
$\Delta H^0_{rxn} = \Delta H^0_f (CO_2 (g))$ = - 393.5 kJ/mol then

655 kWh x $\dfrac{3.60 \times 10^6 \text{ J}}{1 \text{ kWh}}$ x $\dfrac{1 \text{ kJ}}{1000 \text{ J}}$ x $\dfrac{\text{mol C}}{393.5 \text{ kJ}}$ x $\dfrac{12.01 \text{ g C}}{1 \text{ mol C}}$ x $\dfrac{3.2 \text{ g S}}{(100.0 - 3.2) \text{ g C}}$ x $\dfrac{1 \text{ mol S}}{32.06 \text{ g S}}$ x

x $\dfrac{1 \text{ mol } H_2SO_4}{1 \text{ mol S}}$ x $\dfrac{98.09 \text{ g } H_2SO_4}{1 \text{ mol } H_2SO_4}$ = 7.3 x 10^3 g H_2SO_4

Check: The units (g) are correct. The magnitude (7300) is reasonable, considering this is just 1 home.

104. **Given:** 2.5 x 10^3 kg SUV, v_1 = 0.0 mph, v_2 = 65.0 mph, octane combustion, 30 % efficiency
Find: m (CO_2)

Conceptual plan: **mi/hr** → **m/hr** → **m/min** → **m/s**   then   **m, v** → **KE** then

$\dfrac{1000 \text{ m}}{0.6214 \text{ mi}}$ $\dfrac{1 \text{ hr}}{60 \text{ min}}$ $\dfrac{1 \text{ min}}{60 \text{ sec}}$ $KE = \frac{1}{2} mv^2$

KE_1, KE_2 → **ΔE used** → **ΔE generated**

$\Delta E_{sys} = KE_2 - KE_1$ $\dfrac{100 \text{ J generated}}{30 \text{ J used}}$

use reaction from #83 C_8H_{18} (l) + 25/2 O_2 (g) → 8 CO_2 (g) + 9 H_2O (g)
with $\Delta H°_{rxn}$ = - 5074.1 kJ

ΔE generated (J) → **kJ** → **mol (C_8H_{18})** → **mol CO_2** → **g CO_2**

$\dfrac{1 \text{ kJ}}{1000 \text{ J}}$ $\dfrac{1 \text{ mol } C_8H_{18}}{5074.1 \text{ kJ}}$ $\dfrac{8 \text{ mol } CO_2}{1 \text{ mol } C_8H_{18}}$ $\dfrac{44.01 \text{ g}}{1 \text{ mol}}$

Solution: $v_1 = 0.0$ m/s, $65.0 \dfrac{\cancel{mi}}{\cancel{hr}} \times \dfrac{1000 \text{ m}}{0.6214 \cancel{mi}} \times \dfrac{1 \cancel{hr}}{60 \cancel{min}} \times \dfrac{1 \cancel{min}}{60 \text{ sec}} = 29.\underline{0}563 \dfrac{m}{s}$ then $KE = \tfrac{1}{2} mv^2$

$KE_1 = \tfrac{1}{2}(2.5 \times 10^3 \ kg)(0)^2 = 0$ $KE_2 = \tfrac{1}{2}(2.5 \times 10^3 \ kg)\left(29.\underline{0}563 \dfrac{m}{s}\right)^2 = 1.\underline{0}5533 \times 10^6 \dfrac{kg \ m^2}{s^2} = 1.\underline{0}5533 \times 10^6 \text{ J}$

$\Delta E_{sys} = KE_2 - KE_1 = 1.\underline{0}5533 \times 10^6 \text{ J} - 0 \text{ J} = 1.\underline{0}5533 \times 10^6 \ \cancel{\text{J used}} \times \dfrac{100 \text{ J generated}}{30 \ \cancel{\text{J used}}} =$

$= 3.\underline{5}1777 \times 10^6 \text{ J generated}$

$3.\underline{5}1777 \times 10^6 \ \cancel{\text{J generated}} \times \dfrac{1 \ \cancel{kJ}}{1000 \ \cancel{J}} \times \dfrac{1 \ \cancel{mol \ C_8H_{18}}}{5074.1 \ \cancel{kJ}} \times \dfrac{8 \ \cancel{mol \ CO_2}}{1 \ \cancel{mol \ C_8H_{18}}} \times \dfrac{44.01 \text{ g } CO_2}{1 \ \cancel{mol \ CO_2}} = 240 \text{ g } CO_2$

Check: The units (g) are correct.   The magnitude (240) is reasonable, considering the vehicle is so heavy and we generate 8 moles of CO_2 for each mole of octane.

105. **Given:** methane combustion, 100 % efficiency, $\Delta T = 10.0$ °C, house = 30.0 m x 30.0 m x 3.0 m, C_s (air) = 30 J/K · mol, 1.00 mol air = 22.4 L   **Find:** m (CH_4)
Conceptual plan:
l, w, h → V(m^3) → V(cm^3) → V(L) → mol (air)   then   m, C_s, ΔT → q_{air} (J)

$V = l \times w \times h$ $\dfrac{(100 \text{ cm})^3}{(1 \text{ m})^3}$ $\dfrac{1 \text{ L}}{1000 \text{ cm}^3}$ $\dfrac{1 \text{ mol air}}{22.4 \text{ L}}$ $q = m \ C_s \ \Delta T$

then q_{air} (J) → q_{rxn} (J) → q(kJ) →   mol (CH_4) → g (CH_4)

$q_{rxn} = - \ q_{air}$ $\dfrac{1 \text{ kJ}}{1000 \text{ J}}$ $\dfrac{1 \text{ mol } CH_4}{-802.3 \text{ kJ}}$ from #83 $\dfrac{16.04 \text{ g}}{1 \text{ mol}}$

Solution: $V = l \times w \times h = 30.0 \text{ m} \times 30.0 \text{ m} \times 3.0 \text{ m} = 2\underline{7}00 \ m^3$ then

$2\underline{7}00 \ \cancel{m^3} \times \dfrac{(100 \ \cancel{cm})^3}{(1 \ \cancel{m})^3} \times \dfrac{1 \ \cancel{L}}{1000 \ \cancel{cm^3}} \times \dfrac{1 \text{ mol air}}{22.4 \ \cancel{L}} = 1.\underline{2}0536 \times 10^5 \text{ mol air}$ then

$q = m \ C_s \ \Delta T = 1.\underline{2}0536 \times 10^5 \ \cancel{mol} \times 30 \ \dfrac{J}{\cancel{mol} \times \cancel{°C}} \times 10.0 \ \cancel{°C} = 3.\underline{6}161 \times 10^7 \text{ J}$

$q_{rxn} = -q_{air} = -3.\underline{6}161 \times 10^7 \ \cancel{J} \times \dfrac{1 \ \cancel{kJ}}{1000 \ \cancel{J}} \times \dfrac{1 \ \cancel{mol \ CH_4}}{-802.3 \ \cancel{kJ}} \times \dfrac{16.04 \text{ g } CH_4}{1 \ \cancel{mol \ CH_4}} = 7\underline{2}2.9 \text{ g } CH_4 = 700 \text{ g } CH_4$

Check: The units (g) are correct.   The magnitude (700) is not surprising since the volume of a house is large.

106. **Given: water:** $V = 35$ L, $T_i = 25.0$ °C, $T_f = 100.0$ °C; fuel = C_7H_{16} , 15 % efficiency, d = 0.78 g/ml
Find: V (fuel)
Conceptual plan: write balanced reaction then $\Delta H^0_{rxn} = \sum n_P \Delta H^0_f (products) - \sum n_R \Delta H^0_f (reactants)$ **then**
L → mL → g then T_i, T_f → ΔT then   m, C_s, ΔT → q_{H2O} (J) → q_{H2O} (kJ) → q_{rxn} (kJ)

$\dfrac{1000 \text{ mL}}{1 \text{ L}}$ $\dfrac{1.0 \text{ g}}{1.0 \text{ mL}}$ $\Delta T = T_f - T_i$ $q_{H2O} = m_{H2O} C_{H2O} \Delta T_{H2O}$ $\dfrac{1 \text{ kJ}}{1000 \text{ J}}$ $q_{rxn} = - \ q_{H2O}$

then q_{rxn} generated (J) → q_{rxn} used (kJ) → mol C_7H_{16} → g C_7H_{16} → mL C_7H_{16}

$\dfrac{100 \text{ J generated}}{15 \text{ J needed}}$ $\dfrac{1 \text{ mol } C_7H_{16}}{\Delta H^0_{rxn}}$ $\dfrac{100.21 \text{ g}}{1 \text{ mol}}$ $\dfrac{1.0 \text{ mL}}{0.78 \text{ g}}$

Solution: combustion is combination with oxygen to form carbon dioxide and water
$C_7H_{16} \ (l) \ + \ 11 \ O_2 \ (g) \ \rightarrow \ 7 \ CO_2 \ (g) \ + \ 8 \ H_2O \ (g)$

Reactant/Product	ΔH^0_f (kJ/mol from Appendix IIB)
$C_7H_{16} \ (l)$	-224.4
$O_2 \ (g)$	0.0
$CO_2 \ (g)$	-393.5
$H_2O \ (g)$	-241.8

Be sure to pull data for the correct formula and phase.

$$\Delta H^0_{rxn} = \sum n_P \Delta H^0_f(products) - \sum n_R \Delta H^0_f(reactants)$$

$$= [7(\Delta H^0_f(CO_2\ (g)) + 8(\Delta H^0_f(H_2O\ (g))] - [1(\Delta H^0_f(C_7H_{16}\ (l)) + 11(\Delta H^0_f(O_2\ (g))]$$

$$= [7(-393.5\ kJ) + 8(-241.8\ kJ)] - [1(-224.4\ kJ) + 11(0.0\ kJ)]$$

$$= [-4691.7\ kJ] - [-224.4\ kJ]$$

$$= -4467.3\ kJ$$

$$35\ \cancel{L} \times \frac{1000\ \cancel{mL}}{1\ \cancel{L}} \times \frac{1.0\ g}{1.0\ \cancel{mL}} = 35000\ g \quad \text{then}\quad \Delta T = T_f - T_i = 100.0\,°C - 25.0\,°C = 75.0\,°C \quad \text{then}$$

$$q_{H2O} = m_{H2O}\, C_{H2O} \Delta T_{H2O} = 35000\ \cancel{g} \times 4.18\ \frac{J}{\cancel{g} \times \cancel{°C}} \times 75.0\ \cancel{°C} = 1.09725 \times 10^7\ \cancel{J} \times \frac{1\,kJ}{1000\ \cancel{J}} = 1.09725 \times 10^4\ kJ$$

$$q_{rxn} = -q_{H2O} = -1.09725 \times 10^4\ \cancel{kJ} \times \frac{100\ \cancel{kJ\ generated}}{15\ \cancel{kJ\ used}} \times \frac{1\ \cancel{mol\ C_7H_{16}}}{-4467.3\ \cancel{kJ}} \times \frac{100.21\ \cancel{g\ C_7H_{16}}}{1\ \cancel{mol\ C_7H_{16}}} \times \frac{1.0\ mL\ C_7H_{16}}{0.78\ \cancel{g\ C_7H_{16}}} =$$

$$= 2.1\ L\ C_7H_{16}$$

Check: The units (mL) are correct. The magnitude (2 L) is a reasonable volume to have to take on a backpacking trip.

107. **Given:** m (ice) = 9.0 g; Coffee: $T_1 = 90.0\ °C$, m = 120.0 g, $C_s = C_{H2O}$, $\Delta H°_{fus} = 6.0$ kJ/mol

Find: T_f of coffee

Conceptual plan: $q_{ice} = -q_{coffee}$ so g (ice) → mol (ice) → $q_{fus}(kJ)$ → q_{fus} (J) → q_{coffee} (J) **then**

$$\frac{1\ mol}{18.01\,g} \qquad \frac{6.0\ kJ}{1\ mol} \qquad \frac{1000\ J}{1\ kJ} \qquad q_{coffee} = -q_{ice}$$

q, m, C_s → ΔT then T_i, ΔT → T_2 now we have slightly cooled coffee in contact with 0.0 °C water

$$q = mC_S\Delta T \qquad \Delta T = T_2 - T_i$$

so $q_{ice} = -q_{coffee}$ with m, C_s, T_i → T_f

$$q = mC_S\left(T_f - T_i\right) \quad \text{then set}\ q_{Al} = -q_{H2O}$$

Solution: $9.0\ \cancel{g} \times \frac{1\ \cancel{mol}}{18.01\ \cancel{g}} \times \frac{6.0\ \cancel{kJ}}{1\ mol} \times \frac{1000\ J}{1\ \cancel{kJ}} = 2.9982 \times 10^3\ J$, $\quad q_{coffee} = -q_{ice} = -2.9982 \times 10^3\ J$

$q = mC_S\Delta T$ Rearrange to solve for ΔT. $\Delta T = \dfrac{q}{mC_S} = \dfrac{-2.9982 \times 10^3\ \cancel{J}}{120.0\ \cancel{g} \times 4.18\ \frac{\cancel{J}}{\cancel{g} \times °C}} = -5.977\ °C$ then $\Delta T = T_2 - T_i$.

Rearrange to solve for T_2. $T_2 = \Delta T + T_i = -5.977\ °C + 90.0\ °C = 84.0225\ °C$ $\quad q = mC_s\left(T_f - T_i\right)$ substitute in values and set $q_{H2O} = -q_{coffee}$.

$$q_{H2O} = m_{H2O}\, C_{H2O}\left(T_f - T_{H2Oi}\right) = 9.0\ g \times 4.18\ \frac{J}{\cancel{g} \times °C} \times \left(T_f - 0.0\ °C\right) =$$

$$-q_{coffee} = -m_{coffee}\, C_{coffee}\left(T_f - T_{coffee2}\right) = -120.0\ g \times 4.18\ \frac{J}{\cancel{g} \times °C} \times \left(T_f - 84.0225\,°C\right)$$

Rearrange to solve for T_f.

$$9.0\ g\ T_f = -120.0\ g\left(T_f - 84.0225\,°C\right) \quad\Rightarrow\quad 9.0\ g\ T_f = -120.0\ g\ T_f + 10082.7\ g \quad\Rightarrow$$

$$-10082.7\ g = -129.0\ \frac{g}{°C} T_f \Rightarrow T_f = \frac{-10082.7\ \cancel{g}}{-129.0\ \frac{\cancel{g}}{°C}} = 78.2\ °C$$

Check: The units (°C) are correct. The temperature is closer to the original coffee temperature since the mass of coffee is so much larger than the ice mass.

108. **Given:** liquid water at −10.0 °C, Cs (ice) = 2.04 J/g · °C; $\Delta H°_{fus} = -322$ J/g (@ 0.0 °C)

Find: ΔH, ΔE, q and w for freezing at -10.0 °C

Conceptual Plan: Assume exactly 1 g H_2O for all calculations (report answers as J/g) and constant P = 1 atm.

Construct the following path: According to Hess' Law $\Delta H_1 + \Delta H_2 + \Delta H_3 = \Delta H_4$

$$= \Delta H°_{fus}\ @\ \textbf{-10.0 °C}$$

#2
Liquid @ 0.0 °C   →   solid @ 0.0 °C
↑ #1   ↓ #3   at constant P, $\Delta H = q$
Liquid @ -10.0 °C   →   solid @ -10.0 °C   for steps #1 and #3 $q = mC_s\Delta T$
#4

Look up the density of liquid and solid water at 0.0 °C (Assume the density of each phase does not change significantly at – 10.0 °C.)
$d_L = 0.9998$ g/mL and $d_S = 0.917$ g/mL

g → mL → L then V_L, V_S → ΔV then P, ΔV → w (L atm) → w (J) then q, w → ΔE

L: $\dfrac{1 \text{ mL}}{0.9998 \text{ g}}$ S: $\dfrac{1 \text{ mL}}{0.917 \text{ g}}$ $\dfrac{1 \text{ L}}{1000 \text{ mL}}$ $\Delta V = V_S - V_L$ $w = -P\,\Delta V$ $\dfrac{101.3 \text{ J}}{1 \text{ L atm}}$ $\Delta E = q + w$

Solution: $\Delta H_1 = q_1 = mC_S\Delta T = 1 \text{ g} \times 4.18 \dfrac{\text{J}}{\text{g} \times °\text{C}} \times (0.00\,°\text{C} - -10.0\,°\text{C}) = +41.8 \text{ J}$,

$\Delta H_2 = q_2 = m\,\Delta H = 1 \text{ g} \times -332 \dfrac{\text{J}}{\text{g}} = -332 \text{ J}$,

$\Delta H_3 = q_3 = mC_S\Delta T = 1 \text{ g} \times 2.04 \dfrac{\text{J}}{\text{g} \times °\text{C}} \times (-10.00\,°\text{C} - 0.0\,°\text{C}) = -20.4 \text{ J}$ so

$\Delta H_4 = q_4 = \Delta H_1 + \Delta H_2 + \Delta H_3 = +41.8 \text{ J} -332 \text{ J} - 20.4 \text{ J} = -310.6 \text{ J} = -311 \text{ J/g}$.

$V_L = 1 \text{ g} \times \dfrac{1 \text{ mL}}{0.9998 \text{ g}} \times \dfrac{1 \text{ L}}{1000 \text{ mL}} = 0.00100020004 \text{ L}$ and $V_S = 1 \text{ g} \times \dfrac{1 \text{ mL}}{0.917 \text{ g}} \times \dfrac{1 \text{ L}}{1000 \text{ mL}} = 0.0010905 \text{ L}$

then $\Delta V = V_S - V_L = 0.0010905 \text{ L} - 0.00100020004 \text{ L} = 9.02999 \times 10^{-5} \text{ L}$

then, $w = -P\,\Delta V = -1 \text{ atm} \times 9.02999 \times 10^{-5} \text{ L} \times \dfrac{101.3 \text{ J}}{1 \text{ L atm}} = -0.009147 \text{ J} = -0.009 \text{ J/g}$

and $\Delta E = q + w = -310.6 \text{ J} - 0.009147 \text{ J} = -311 \text{ J/g}$

Check: The units (J/g) are correct. We expect freezing to release less energy at -10 °C because we are below the normal freezing point. The work is negligible since the volume change is so small.

109. $KE = \frac{1}{2}mv^2$, for an ideal gas $v = u_{rms} = \sqrt{\dfrac{3RT}{\mathfrak{M}}}$ and so $KE_{avg} = \frac{1}{2}N_A m u_{rms}^2 = \frac{3}{2}RT$ then

$\Delta E_{sys} = KE_2 - KE_1 = \frac{3}{2}RT_2 - \frac{3}{2}RT_1 = \frac{3}{2}R\Delta T$. At constant V $\Delta E_{sys} = C_V\Delta T$ so $C_V = \frac{3}{2}R$. At constant P,

$\Delta E_{sys} = q + w = q_P - P\Delta V = \Delta H - P\Delta V$ but since $PV = nRT$, for one mole of an ideal gas at constant

P $P\Delta V = R\Delta T$ so $\Delta E_{sys} = q + w = q_P - P\Delta V = \Delta H - P\Delta V = \Delta H - R\Delta T$ then $\frac{3}{2}R\Delta T = \Delta H - R\Delta T$

or $\Delta H = \frac{5}{2}R\Delta T = C_P\Delta T$ so $C_P = \frac{5}{2}R$.

110. **Given:** fixed amount of an ideal gas; Step #1: $V_1 = 12.0$ L to $V_2 = 24.0$ L at constant P = 1.0 atm; Step #2: gas cooled at constant V = 24.0 L to original T; Step #3: $V_2 = 24.0$ L to $V_1 = 12.0$ L   **Find:** q for entire process
Solution: For the expansion: $w_1 = -(24.0 \text{ L} -12.0 \text{ L})(1.0 \text{ atm}) = -12.0$ L atm
For the contraction: $w_2 = -(12.0 \text{ L} - 24.0 \text{ L})(0.5 \text{ atm}) = 6.0$ L atm

$w_{total} = -6.0 \text{ L atm} \times \dfrac{101 \text{ J}}{\text{L atm}} = -606 \text{ J}$

Since the system ends where it started $\Delta E = 0$ and therefore $q = -w = 606$ J
Check: The units (J) are correct. The total energy change over the entire cycle is 0 since we end where we started, but this does not mean that q has to be 0.

111. d)   only one answer is possible. $\Delta E_{sys} = -\Delta E_{surr}$

112. a)   False. An isothermal process has $\Delta E_{sys} = 0$.

   b)   False. w < 0 for expansions

200

c) True. If $\Delta E_{sys} = 0$ and $\Delta E_{sys} = q + w$ and $w < 0$ then $q > 0$.

d) False. An isothermal process has $\Delta E_{sys} = 0$.

113. a) At constant P, $\Delta E_{sys} = q + w = q_P + w = \Delta H + w$ so $\Delta E_{sys} - w = \Delta H$

114. Since the mass of B is greater, it will work harder on day 1 to cool it down. On day 2 the water will stabilize the temperature with the loss of heat from the water (a high heat capacity material).

115. The aluminum cylinder will be cooler after one hour because it has a lower heat capacity than water (less heat needs to be pulled out for every °C temperature change).

116. **Given:** 2418 J heat produced; 5 kJ work done on surroundings at constant P
Find: ΔE, ΔH, q and w
Conceptual plan: interpret language to determine the sign of the two terms then q, w $\rightarrow$ ΔE_{sys}
$$\Delta E = q + w$$

Solution: since heat is released from the system to the surroundings, $q = - 2418\ J = -2.418\ kJ$; since the system is doing work on the surroundings, $w = -5\ kJ$. At constant P, $\Delta H = q = -2.418\ kJ$; $\Delta E = q + w = -2.418\ kJ - 5\ kJ = -7\ kJ$

Check: The units (kJ) are correct. The magnitude of the answer (-7) makes physical sense because both terms are negative and small.

117. The internal energy of a chemical system is the sum of its kinetic energy and its potential energy. It is this potential energy that is the energy source in an exothermic chemical reaction. Under normal circumstances, chemical potential energy (or simply chemical energy) arises primarily from the electrostatic forces between the protons and electrons that compose the atoms and molecules within the system. In an exothermic reaction, some bonds break and new ones form, and the protons and electrons go from an arrangement of higher potential energy to one of lower potential energy. As they rearrange, their potential energy is converted into kinetic energy, the heat emitted in the reaction and so it feels hot to the touch.

118. b) If ΔV is positive the $w = - P \Delta V < 0$. Since $\Delta E_{sys} = q + w = q_P + w = \Delta H + w$ if w is negative then $\Delta H > \Delta E_{sys}$.

Chapter 7
The Quantum – Mechanical Model of an Atom

1. When a particle is absolutely small it means that you cannot observe it without disturbing it. When you observe the particle, it behaves differently than when you do not observe it. Electrons fit this description.

2. You can measure the position of a baseball by observing the light that strikes the ball, bounces off it, and enters your eye. The baseball is so large in comparison to the disturbance caused by the light that it is virtually unaffected by your observation. By contrast, if you attempt to measure the position an electron using light, the light itself disturbs the electron. The interaction of the light with the electron actually changes its position.

3. The quantum – mechanical model of the atom is important because it explains how electrons exist in atoms and how those electrons determine the chemical and physical properties of elements.

4. Light is electromagnetic radiation, a type of energy embodied in oscillating electric and magnetic fields. Light in a vacuum travels at 3.00×10^8 m/s.

5. The wavelength (λ) of the wave is the distance in space between adjacent crests and is measured in units of distance. The amplitude of the wave is the vertical height of a crest. The more closely spaced the waves, that is, the shorter the wavelength, the more energy there is. The amplitude of the electric and magnetic field wave in light determines the intensity or brightness of the light. The higher the amplitude, the more energy the wave has.

6. The frequency, (v), is the number of cycles (or wave crests) that pass through a stationary point in a given period of time. The units of frequency are cycles per second. The frequency is inversely proportional to the wavelength (λ). Frequency and wavelength are related by the equation: $v = \dfrac{c}{\lambda}$

7. For visible light, wavelength determines the color. Red light has a wavelength of 750 nm, the longest wavelength of visible light, and blue has a wavelength of 500 nm.

8. The presence of a variety of wavelengths in white light is responsible for the way we perceive colors in objects. When a substance absorbs some colors while reflecting others, it appears colored. Grass appears green because it reflects primarily the wavelength associated with green light and absorbs the others.

9. a) gamma rays(γ) – the wavelength range is 10^{-11} to 10^{-15} m. Gamma rays are produced by the sun, other stars, and certain unstable atomic nuclei of Earth. Human exposure to gamma rays is dangerous because the high energy of gamma rays can damage biological molecules.

    b) X – rays – the wavelength range is 10^{-8} to 10^{-11} m. X – rays are used in medicine. X – rays pass through many substances that block visible light and are therefore used to image bones and internal organs. X – rays are sufficiently energetic to damage biological molecules so, while several yearly exposures to X – rays are harmless, excessive exposure increases cancer risk.

    c) ultraviolet radiation (UV) – the wavelength range is 0.4×10^{-6} to 10^{-8} m. Ultraviolet radiation is most familiar as the component of sunlight that produces a sunburn or suntan. While not as energetic as gamma rays or X – rays, ultraviolet light still carries enough energy to damage biological molecules. Excessive exposure to ultraviolet light increases the risk of skin cancer and cataracts and causes premature wrinkling of the skin.

    d) visible light – the wavelength range is 0.75×10^{-6} to 0.4×10^{-6} m (750 nm to 400 nm). Visible light – as long as the intensity is not too high – does not carry enough energy to damage biological molecules. It does, however, cause certain molecules in our eyes to change their shape, sending a signal to brains that results in vision.

    e) infrared radiation (IR) – the wavelength range is 0.75×10^{-6} to 10^{-3} m. The heat you feel when you place your hand near a hot object is infrared radiation. All warm objects, including human bodies, emit infrared light. Although infrared light is invisible to our eyes, infrared sensors can detect it and are often used in night vision technology to "see" in the dark.

f) microwave radiation – the wavelength range is 10^{-3} to 10^{-1} m. Microwave radiation is used in radar and in microwave ovens. Microwave radiation is efficiently absorbed by water and can therefore heat substance that contain water.

g) radio waves – the wavelength range is 10^{-1} to 10^5 m. Radio waves are used to transmit the signals responsible for AM and FM radio, cellular telephones, television, and other forms of communication.

10. Waves interact with each other in a characteristic way called interference: they can cancel each other out or build each other up, depending on their alignment upon interaction. Constructive interference occurs if waves of equal amplitude from two sources are in phase – they align with overlapping crests – and a wave with twice the amplitude results. Destructive interference occurs if the waves are completely out of phase – they align so that the crest from one sounce overlaps the trough form the other source – and the waves cancel each other.

11. Diffraction occurs when a wave encounters an obstacle or a slit that is comparable in size to its wavelength. The wave bends around the slit. The diffraction of light through two slits separated by a distance comparable to the wavelength of the light results in an interference pattern. Each slit acts as a new wave source, and the two new waves interfere with each other. Which result in a pattern of bright and dark lines.

Interference From Two Slits

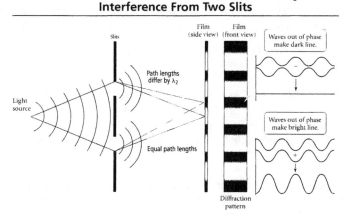

12. The photoelectric effect was the observation that many metals emit electrons when light shines upon then. Classical electromagnetic theory attributed this effect to the transfer of energy from the light to an electron in the metal, dislodging the electron. In this description, changing either the wavelength (color) or the amplitude (intensity) of the light should affect the emission of electrons. So, the rate at which electrons were emitted from a metal due to the photoelectric effect could be increased by using either light of shorter wavelength of light of higher intensity. With dim light there should be a lag time between the initial shining of the light and the emission of an electron. This time would be needed for the transfer of sufficient energy to the electron to dislodge. However, experiments showed that the light used to dislodge electrons had a threshold frequency, below which no electrons were emitted from the metal, no matter how long the light shone on the metal. Low – frequency light would not eject electrons from a metal regardless of its intensity or duration. But, high – frequency light would eject electrons even at low intensity and there was no lag time.

13. Because of the results of the experiments with the photoelectric effect, Einstein proposed that light energy must come in packets. The amount of energy in a light packet depends on its frequency (wavelength). The emission of electrons depends on whether or not a single photon has sufficient energy to dislodge a single electron.

14. A photon is a packet of light. The energy of the photon can be expressed in terms of wavelength as $E = \dfrac{hc}{\lambda}$

or, in terms of frequency as $E = h\nu$.

15. An emission spectrum occurs when an atom absorbs energy and reemits that energy as light. The light emitted contains distinct wavelengths for each element. The emission spectrum of a particular element is

always the same and can be used to identify the element. A white light spectrum is continuous, meaning that there are no sudden interruptions in the intensity of the light as a function of wavelengths. It consists of all wavelengths. Emission spectra are not continuous. They consist of bright lines at specific wavelengths, with complete darkness in between.

16. In the Bohr model electrons travel around the nucleus in circular orbits. Bohr's orbits could exist only at specific, fixed distances form the nucleus. The energy of each orbit was also fixed, or quantized. Bohr called these orbits stationary states and suggested that, although they obeyed the laws of classical mechanics, they also possessed "a peculiar, mechanically unexplainable, stability." Bohr further proposed that, in contradiction to classical electromagnetic theory, no radiation was emitted by an electron orbiting the nucleus in a stationary state. It was only when an electron jumped, or made a transition, from one stationary state to another that radiation was emitted or absorbed. The emission spectrum of an atom consisted of discrete lines because the stationary states existed only at specific, fixed energies. The energy of the photon created when an electron made a transition from one stationary state to another was simple the energy difference between the two stationary states.

17. Electron diffraction occurs when an electron beam is aimed at two closely spaced slits, and a series of detectors is arranged to detect the electrons after they pass through the slits. An interference pattern similar to that observed for light is recorded behind the slits. Electron diffraction was evidence of the wave nature of electrons.

18. The de Broglie wavelength is the wavelength associated with an electron traveling through space. It is related to its kinetic energy. The wavelength, λ, associated with an electron of mass, m, moving at velocity, v, is given by the de Broglie relation: $\lambda = \dfrac{h}{mv}$.

19. Complementary properties are those that exclude one another. The more you know about one, the less you know about the other. Which of two complementary properties you observe depends on the experiment you perform. In electron diffraction, when you try to observe which hole the electron goes through (particle nature) you lose the interference pattern (wave nature). When you try to observe the interference pattern, you cannot determine which hole the electron goes through.

20. Heisenberg's uncertainty principle states that the product of Δx and $m\Delta v$ must be greater than or equal to a finite number. In other words, the more accurately you know the position of an electron (the smaller Δx) the less accurately you can know its velocity (the bigger Δv) and vice versa. The complementarity of the wave nature and particle nature of the electron results in the complementarity of velocity and position. Heisenberg solved the contradiction of an object as both a particle and a wave by introducing complementarity – an electron is observed as either a particle or a wave, but never both at once.

21. A trajectory is a path that is determined by the particle's velocity (the speed and direction of travel), its position, and the forces acting on it. Both position and velocity are required to predict a trajectory.

22. Because the uncertainty principle says that you cannot know both the position and velocity of the electron simultaneously, you cannot predict the trajectory.

23. Deterministic means that the present determines the future. That means that under identical condition, identical results will occur.

24. The indeterminate behavior of an electron means that under identical conditions, the electron does not have the same trajectory and does not "land" in the same spot each time.

25. A probability distribution map is a statistical map that shows where an electron is likely to be found under a given set of conditions.

26. Using the Schrödinger equation we describe the probability distribution maps for electron states. In these the electron has well – defined energy, but not well – defined position. In other words, for each state, we can specify the energy of the electron precisely, but not its location at a given instant. The electron's position is described in terms of an orbital.

27. An orbital is a probability distribution map showing where the electron is likely to be found.

28. The mathematical derivation of energies and orbitals for electrons in atoms comes from solving the Schrödinger equation. The general form of the Schrödinger equation is: $\mathcal{H}\psi = E\psi$. The symbol $\mathcal{H}$ stands for the Hamiltionian operator, a set of mathematical operations that represent the total energy (kinetic and potential) of the electron within the atom. The symbol E is the actual energy of the electron. The symbol ψ is the wave function, a mathematical function that describes the wavelike nature of the electron. A plot of the wave function squared (ψ^2) represents an orbital, a position probability distribution map of the electron.

29. The principal quantum number (n) is an integer and has possible values of 1,2,3,... The principal quantum number determines the overall size and energy of an orbital.

30. The angular momentum quantum number (l) is an integer and has possible values of 0,1,2,3... The angular momentum quantum number determines the shape of the orbital.

31. The magnetic quantum number (m_l) is an integer ranging from $-l$ to $+l$. For example, if $l = 1$, $m_l = -1, 0, +1$. The magnetic quantum number specifies the orientation of the orbital.

32. a) $n = 1, l = 0, m_l = 0$

    b) $n = 2, l = 0, m_l = 0$; $n = 2, l = 1, m_l = -1$; $n = 2, l = 1, m_l = 0$; $n = 2, l = 1, m_l = +1$

    c) $n = 3, l = 0, m_l = =$; $n = 3, l = 1, m_l = -1$; $n = 3, l = 1, m_l = 0$; $n = 3, l = 1, m_l = +1$; $n = 3, l = 2, m_l = -2$; $n = 3, l = 2, m_l = -1$; $n = 3, l = 2, m_l = 0$; $n = 3, l = 2, m_l = +1$; $n = 3, l = 2, m_l = +2$

    d) $n = 4, l = 0, m_l = 0$; $n = 4, l = 1, m_l = -1$; $n = 4, l = 1, m_l = 0$; $n = 4, l = 1, m_l = +1$; $n = 4, l = 2, m_l = -2$; $n = 4, l = 2, m_l = -1$; $n = 4, l = 2, m_l = 0$; $n = 4, l = 2, m_l = +1$; $n = 4, l = 2, m_l = +2$; $n = 4, l = 3, m_l = -3$; $n = 4, l = 3, m_l = -2$; $n = 4, l = 3, m_l = -1$; $n = 4, l = 3, m_l = 0$; $n = 4, l = 3, m_l = +1$; $n = 4, l = 3, m_l = +2$; $n = 4, l = 3, m_l = +3$

33. The probability density is the probability per unit volume of finding the electron at a point in space. The radial distribution function represents the total probability of finding the electron within a thin spherical shell at a distance r from the nucleus. In contrast to probability density, which has a maximum at the nucleus for an s orbital, the radial distribution function has a value of zero at the nucleus. It increases to a maximum and then decreases again with increasing r.

34.

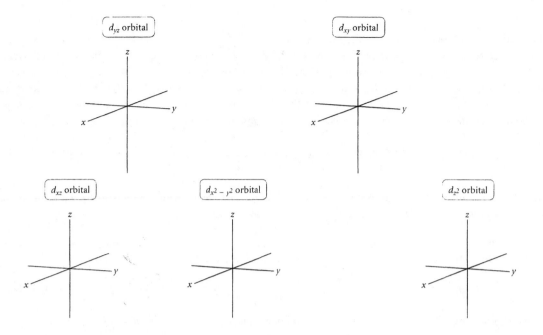

35. The sublevels are s (l=0) which can hold a maximum of 2 electrons; p (l = 1) which can hold a maximum of 6 electrons, d (l = 2), which can hold a maximum of 10 electrons; and f (l = 3) which can hold a maximum of 14 electrons.

36. Atoms are usually drawn as spheres because most atoms contain many electrons occupying a number of different orbitals. Therefore, the shape of an atom is obtained by superimposing all of its orbitals. If we superimpose the s, p, and d orbitals we get a spherical shape.

37. **Given:** distance to sun = 1.496×10^8 km   **Find:** time for light to travel from sun to Earth
Conceptual Plan: distance km → distance m → time

$$\frac{1000\,m}{km} \qquad time = \frac{distance}{3.00 \times 10^8 \text{ m/s}}$$

Solution: $1.496 \times 10^8 \text{ km} \times \dfrac{1000 \text{ m}}{km} \times \dfrac{s}{3.00 \times 10^8 \text{ m}} = 499\,s$

Check: The units of the answer, seconds, is correct. The magnitude of the answer is reasonable, since it corresponds to about 8 min.

38. **Given:** 4.3 light years to star   **Find:** distance in km
Conceptual Plan: light years → days → hours → seconds → m → km

$$\frac{365\,days}{yr} \quad \frac{24\,hr}{day} \quad \frac{3600\,s}{hr} \quad \frac{3.00 \times 10^8\,m}{s} \quad \frac{km}{1000\,m}$$

Solution: $4.3 \text{ light yr} \times \dfrac{365 \text{ days}}{yr} \times \dfrac{24 \text{ hrs}}{day} \times \dfrac{3600 \text{ s}}{hr} \times \dfrac{3.00 \times 10^8 \text{ m}}{s} \times \dfrac{km}{1000 \text{ m}} = 4.1 \times 10^{13}$ km

Check: The units of the answer, km, are correct. The magnitude of the answer is reasonable since it takes much longer for the light to reach Earth from Proxima Centauri than from the sun, the distance should be much greater.

39. i)   by increasing wavelength the order is: d) ultraviolet < c) infrared < b) microwave < a) radio waves

     ii)   by increasing energy the order is: a) radio waves < b) microwaves < c) infrared < d) ultraviolet

40. i)   by increasing frequency the order is: b) radio waves < c) microwaves < d) visible light < a) gamma rays

     ii)   by decreasing energy the order is: a) gamma rays > d) visible light > c) microwaves > b) radio waves

41. a) **Given:** $\lambda = 632.8$ nm **Find:** frequency (ν)
   Conceptual Plan: nm → m → ν

   $$\frac{m}{10^9 \text{ nm}} \qquad \nu = \frac{c}{\lambda}$$

   Solution: $632.8 \text{ nm} \times \dfrac{m}{10^9 \text{ nm}} = 6.328 \times 10^{-7} \text{ m}$ $\qquad \nu = \dfrac{3.00 \times 10^8 \frac{m}{s}}{} \times \dfrac{1}{6.328 \times 10^{-7} \text{ m}} = 4.74 \times 10^{14} \text{ s}^{-1}$

   Check: The units of the answer, s^{-1}, are correct. The magnitude of the answer seems reasonable since wavelength and frequency are inversely proportional.

   b) **Given:** $\lambda = 503$ nm **Find:** frequency (ν)
   Conceptual Plan: nm → m → ν

   $$\frac{m}{10^9 \text{ nm}} \qquad \nu = \frac{c}{\lambda}$$

   Solution: $503 \text{ nm} \times \dfrac{m}{10^9 \text{ nm}} = 5.03 \times 10^{-7} \text{ m}$ $\qquad \nu = \dfrac{3.00 \times 10^8 \frac{m}{s}}{} \times \dfrac{1}{5.03 \times 10^{-7} \text{ m}} = 5.96 \times 10^{14} \text{ s}^{-1}$

   Check: The units of the answer, s^{-1}, are correct. The magnitude of the answer seems reasonable since wavelength and frequency are inversely proportional.

   c) **Given:** $\lambda = 0.052$ nm **Find:** frequency (ν)
   Conceptual Plan: nm → m → ν

   $$\frac{m}{10^9 \text{ nm}} \qquad \nu = \frac{c}{\lambda}$$

   Solution: $0.052 \text{ nm} \times \dfrac{m}{10^9 \text{ nm}} = 5.2 \times 10^{-9} \text{ m}$ $\qquad \nu = \dfrac{3.00 \times 10^8 \frac{m}{s}}{} \times \dfrac{1}{5.2 \times 10^{-9} \text{ m}} = 5.8 \times 10^{18} \text{ s}^{-1}$

   Check: The units of the answer, s^{-1}, are correct. The magnitude of the answer seems reasonable since wavelength and frequency are inversely proportional.

42. a) **Given:** $\nu = 100.2$ MHz **Find:** wavelength (λ)
   Conceptual Plan: MHz → Hz → s^{-1} → λ

   $$\frac{10^6 \text{ Hz}}{\text{MHz}} \qquad 1 \text{ Hz} = 1 s^{-1} \qquad \lambda = \frac{c}{\nu}$$

   Solution:

   $100.2 \text{ MHz} \times \dfrac{10^6 \text{ Hz}}{\text{MHz}} \times \dfrac{s^{-1}}{\text{Hz}} = 1.002 \times 10^8 \text{ s}^{-1}$ $\qquad \lambda = \dfrac{3.00 \times 10^8 \text{ m}}{s} \times \dfrac{s}{1.002 \times 10^8} = 2.99 \text{ m}$

   Check: The units of the answer, m, are correct. The magnitude of the answer is reasonable because FM wavelengths are generally in the 3 – 8 m range.

   b) **Given:** $\nu = 1070$ kHz **Find:** wavelength (λ)
   Conceptual Plan: kHz → Hz → s^{-1} → λ

   $$\frac{10^3 \text{ Hz}}{\text{kHz}} \qquad 1 \text{ Hz} = 1 s^{-1} \qquad \lambda = \frac{c}{\nu}$$

   Solution:

   $1070 \text{ kHz} \times \dfrac{10^3 \text{ Hz}}{\text{kHz}} \times \dfrac{s^{-1}}{\text{Hz}} = 1.070 \times 10^6 \text{ s}^{-1}$ $\qquad \lambda = \dfrac{3.00 \times 10^8 \text{ m}}{s} \times \dfrac{s}{1.070 \times 10^6} = 280. \text{ m}$

   Check: The units of the answer, m, are correct. The magnitude of the answer is reasonable because AM wavelengths are generally in the 100 – 1000 m range.

   c) **Given:** $\nu = 835.6$ MHz **Find:** wavelength (λ)

Conceptual Plan: MHz → Hz → s^{-1} → λ

$$\frac{10^6 \text{ Hz}}{\text{MHz}} \qquad 1\,\text{Hz} = 1\,\text{s}^{-1} \qquad \lambda = \frac{c}{\nu}$$

Solution:

$$835.6 \text{ MHz} \times \frac{10^6 \text{ Hz}}{\text{MHz}} \times \frac{\text{s}^{-1}}{\text{Hz}} = 8.356 \times 10^8 \text{ s}^{-1} \qquad \lambda = \frac{3.00 \times 10^8 \text{ m}}{\text{s}} \times \frac{\text{s}}{8.356 \times 10^8} = 3.59 \times 10^{-1} \text{ m}$$

Check: The units of the answer, m, are correct. The magnitude of the answer is reasonable because cell phone wavelengths are generally in the 0.1 – 0.5 m range.

43. a) **Given:** frequency (ν) from 41 a. = $4.74 \times 10^{14} \text{ s}^{-1}$ **Find:** Energy

    Conceptual Plan: ν → E

$$E = h\nu \qquad h = 6.626 \times 10^{-34} \text{ J s}$$

    Solution: $6.626 \times 10^{-34} \text{ J s} \times \dfrac{4.74 \times 10^{14}}{\text{s}} = 3.14 \times 10^{-19} \text{ J}$

    Check: The units of the answer, J, are correct. The magnitude of the answer is reasonable since we are talking about the energy of one photon.

    b) **Given:** frequency (ν) from 41 b. = $5.96 \times 10^{14} \text{ s}^{-1}$ **Find:** Energy

    Conceptual Plan: ν → E

$$E = h\nu \qquad h = 6.626 \times 10^{-34} \text{ J s}$$

    Solution: $6.626 \times 10^{-34} \text{ J s} \times \dfrac{5.96 \times 10^{14}}{\text{s}} = 3.95 \times 10^{-19} \text{ J}$

    Check: The units of the answer, J, are correct. The magnitude of the answer is reasonable since we are talking about the energy of one photon.

    c) **Given:** frequency (ν) from 41 c. = $5.8 \times 10^{18} \text{ s}^{-1}$ **Find:** Energy

    Conceptual Plan: ν → E

$$E = h\nu \qquad h = 6.626 \times 10^{-34} \text{ J s}$$

    Solution: $6.626 \times 10^{-34} \text{ J s} \times \dfrac{5.8 \times 10^{18}}{\text{s}} = 3.8 \times 10^{-15} \text{ J}$

    Check: The units of the answer, J, are correct. The magnitude of the answer is reasonable since we are talking about the energy of one photon.

44. a) **Given:** frequency (ν) from 42 a. = 100.2 MHz   **Find:** Energy

    Conceptual Plan: MHz → Hz → s^{-1} → E

$$\frac{10^6 \text{ Hz}}{\text{MHz}} \qquad 1\,\text{Hz} = 1\,\text{s}^{-1} \qquad E = h\nu \; ; \; h = 6.626 \times 10^{-34} \text{ J s}$$

    Solution:

$$100.2 \text{ MHz} \times \frac{10^6 \text{ Hz}}{\text{MHz}} \times \frac{\text{s}^{-1}}{\text{Hz}} = 1.002 \times 10^8 \text{ s}^{-1} \qquad 6.626 \times 10^{-34} \text{ J s} \times \frac{1.002 \times 10^8}{\text{s}} = 6.639 \times 10^{-26} \text{ J}$$

    Check: The units of the answer, J, are correct. The magnitude of the answer is reasonable since we are talking about the energy of one photon and have a relatively long wavelength.

    b) **Given:** ν = 1070 kHz   **Find:** Energy

    Conceptual Plan: kHz → Hz → s^{-1} → E

$$\frac{10^3 \text{ Hz}}{\text{kHz}} \qquad 1\,\text{Hz} = 1\,\text{s}^{-1} \qquad E = h\nu \; ; \; h = 6.626 \times 10^{-34} \text{ J s}$$

    Solution:

$$1070 \text{ kHz} \times \frac{10^3 \text{ Hz}}{\text{kHz}} \times \frac{\text{s}^{-1}}{\text{Hz}} = 1.070 \times 10^6 \text{ s}^{-1} \qquad 6.626 \times 10^{-34} \text{ J s} \times \frac{1.070 \times 10^6}{\text{s}} = 7.090 \times 10^{-28} \text{ J}$$

Check: The units of the answer, J, are correct. The magnitude of the answer is reasonable since we are talking about the energy of one photon and have a relatively long wavelength.

c) **Given:** $\nu = 835.6$ MHz   **Find:** Energy
   Conceptual Plan: MHz → Hz → s^{-1} → E

$$\frac{10^6 \text{ Hz}}{\text{MHz}} \quad 1\,\text{Hz} = 1\,\text{s}^{-1} \quad E = h\nu \; ; h = 6.626 \times 10^{-34} \text{ J s}$$

Solution:

$$835.6 \text{ MHz} \times \frac{10^6 \text{ Hz}}{\text{MHz}} \times \frac{\text{s}^{-1}}{\text{Hz}} = 8.356 \times 10^8 \text{ s}^{-1} \qquad 6.626 \times 10^{-34} \text{ J s} \times \frac{8.356 \times 10^8}{\text{s}} = 5.537 \times 10^{-25} \text{ J}$$

Check: The units of the answer, J, are correct. The magnitude of the answer is reasonable since we are talking about the energy of one photon and have a relatively long wavelength.

45. **Given:** $\lambda = 532$ nm and $E_{pulse} = 4.67$ mJ   **Find:** number of photons
    Conceptual Plan: nm → m → E_{photon} → number of photons

$$\frac{m}{10^9 \text{ nm}} \quad E = \frac{hc}{\lambda} ; h = 6.626 \times 10^{-34} \text{ J s} \quad \frac{E_{pulse}}{E_{photon}}$$

Solution:

$$532 \text{ nm} \times \frac{m}{10^9 \text{ nm}} = 5.32 \times 10^{-7} \text{ m} \qquad E = \frac{6.626 \times 10^{-34} \text{ J s} \times \dfrac{3.00 \times 10^8 \text{ m}}{\text{s}}}{5.32 \times 10^{-7} \text{ m}} = 3.7364 \times 10^{-19} \text{ J / photon}$$

$$4.67 \text{ mJ} \times \frac{\text{J}}{1000 \text{ mJ}} \times \frac{1 \text{ photon}}{3.7364 \times 10^{-19} \text{ J}} = 1.25 \times 10^{16} \text{ photons}$$

Check: The units of the answer, number of photons, is correct. The magnitude of the answer is reasonable for the amount of energy involved.

46. **Given:** $\lambda = 6.5$ µm; power = 25.5 watts   **Find:** photons/second
    Conceptual Plan: µm → m → E_{photon} and then watts → J/s → number of photons

$$\frac{m}{10^6 \,\mu\text{m}} \quad E = \frac{hc}{\lambda} ; h = 6.626 \times 10^{-34} \text{ J s} \qquad \frac{\text{J / sec}}{\text{watt}} \quad \frac{\text{J / sec}}{\text{J / photon}}$$

Solution:

$$6.5 \,\mu\text{m} \times \frac{m}{10^6 \,\mu\text{m}} = 6.5 \times 10^{-6} \text{ m} \qquad E = \frac{6.626 \times 10^{-34} \text{ J s} \times \dfrac{3.00 \times 10^8 \text{ m}}{\text{s}}}{6.5 \times 10^{-6} \text{ m}} = 3.058 \times 10^{-20} \text{ J / photon}$$

$$25.5 \text{ watts} \times \frac{\text{J / s}}{1 \text{ watt}} \times \frac{1 \text{ photon}}{3.058 \times 10^{-20} \text{ J}} = 8.3 \times 10^{20} \text{ photons / s}$$

Check: The units of the answer, photons/s, are correct. The magnitude of the answer is reasonable for the amount of energy involved.

47. a) **Given:** $\lambda = 1500$ nm   **Find:** E for 1 mol photons
     Conceptual Plan: nm → m → E_{photon} → $E(J)_{mol}$ → $E(kJ)_{mol}$

$$\frac{m}{10^9 \text{ nm}} \quad E = \frac{hc}{\lambda} \quad \frac{\text{mol}}{6.022 \times 10^{23} \text{ photons}} \quad \frac{kJ}{1000 \text{ J}}$$

Solution:

$$1500 \text{ nm} \times \frac{m}{10^9 \text{ nm}} = 1.500 \times 10^{-6} \text{ m} \qquad E = \frac{6.626 \times 10^{-34} \text{ J s} \times \dfrac{3.00 \times 10^8 \text{ m}}{\text{s}}}{1.500 \times 10^{-6} \text{ m}} = 1.3252 \times 10^{-19} \text{ J / photon}$$

$$\frac{1.3252 \times 10^{-19} \text{ J}}{\text{photon}} \times \frac{6.022 \times 10^{23} \text{ photons}}{\text{mol}} \times \frac{kJ}{1000 \text{ J}} = 79.8 \text{ kJ / mol}$$

Check: The units of the answer, kJ/mol, are correct. The magnitude of the answer is reasonable for a wavelength in the infrared region.

b) **Given:** $\lambda = 500$ nm   **Find:** E for 1 mol photons

Conceptual Plan: nm $\rightarrow$ m $\rightarrow$ E$_{photon}$ $\rightarrow$ E$_{mol}$ $\rightarrow$ E(kJ)$_{mol}$

$$\frac{m}{10^9 \text{ nm}} \qquad E = \frac{hc}{\lambda} \qquad \frac{mol}{6.022 \times 10^{23} \text{ photons}} \qquad \frac{kJ}{1000 \text{ J}}$$

Solution:

$$500 \text{ nm} \times \frac{m}{10^9 \text{ nm}} = 5.00 \times 10^{-7} \text{ m} \qquad E = \frac{6.626 \times 10^{-34} \text{ J s} \times \dfrac{3.00 \times 10^8 \text{ m}}{\text{s}}}{5.00 \times 10^{-7} \text{ m}} = 3.9756 \times 10^{-19} \text{ J / photon}$$

$$\frac{3.9756 \times 10^{-19} \text{ J}}{\text{photon}} \times \frac{6.022 \times 10^{23} \text{ photons}}{\text{mol}} \times \frac{kJ}{1000 \text{ J}} = 239 \text{ kJ / mol}$$

Check: The units of the answer, kJ/mol, are correct. The magnitude of the answer is reasonable for a wavelength in the visible region.

c) **Given:** $\lambda = 150$ nm   **Find:** E for 1 mol photons

Conceptual Plan: nm $\rightarrow$ m $\rightarrow$ E$_{photon}$ $\rightarrow$ E$_{mol}$ $\rightarrow$ E(kJ)$_{mol}$

$$\frac{m}{10^9 \text{ nm}} \qquad E = \frac{hc}{\lambda} \qquad \frac{mol}{6.022 \times 10^{23} \text{ photons}} \qquad \frac{kJ}{1000 \text{ J}}$$

Solution:

$$1.50 \text{ nm} \times \frac{m}{10^9 \text{ nm}} = 1.50 \times 10^{-7} \text{ m} \qquad E = \frac{6.626 \times 10^{-34} \text{ J s} \times \dfrac{3.00 \times 10^8 \text{ m}}{\text{s}}}{1.50 \times 10^{-7} \text{ m}} = 1.3252 \times 10^{-18} \text{ J / photon}$$

$$\frac{1.3252 \times 10^{-18} \text{ J}}{\text{photon}} \times \frac{6.022 \times 10^{23} \text{ photons}}{\text{mol}} \times \frac{kJ}{1000 \text{ J}} = 798 \text{ kJ / mol}$$

Check: The units of the answer, kJ/mol, are correct. The magnitude of the answer is reasonable for a wavelength in the ultraviolet region. Note: the energy increases from the IR to the Vis to the UV as expected.

48. a) **Given:** $\lambda = 0.155$ nm   **Find:** E for 1 mol photons

Conceptual Plan: nm $\rightarrow$ m $\rightarrow$ E$_{photon}$ $\rightarrow$ E$_{mol}$ $\rightarrow$ E(kJ)$_{mol}$

$$\frac{m}{10^9 \text{ nm}} \qquad E = \frac{hc}{\lambda} \qquad \frac{mol}{6.022 \times 10^{23} \text{ photons}} \qquad \frac{kJ}{1000 \text{ J}}$$

Solution:

$$0.155 \text{ nm} \times \frac{m}{10^9 \text{ nm}} = 1.55 \times 10^{-10} \text{ m} \qquad E = \frac{6.626 \times 10^{-34} \text{ J s} \times \dfrac{3.00 \times 10^8 \text{ m}}{\text{s}}}{1.55 \times 10^{-10} \text{ m}} = 1.2824 \times 10^{-15} \text{ J / photon}$$

$$\frac{1.2824 \times 10^{-15} \text{ J}}{\text{photon}} \times \frac{6.022 \times 10^{23} \text{ photons}}{\text{mol}} \times \frac{kJ}{1000 \text{ J}} = 7.72 \times 10^5 \text{ kJ / mol}$$

Check: The units of the answer, kJ/mol, are correct. The magnitude of the answer is reasonable for a wavelength in the X - Ray region.

b) **Given:** $\lambda = 2.55 \times 10^{-5}$ nm **Find:** E for 1 mol photons

Conceptual Plan: $\text{nm} \rightarrow \text{m} \rightarrow E_{photon} \rightarrow E_{mol} \rightarrow E(kJ)_{mol}$

$$\frac{m}{10^9 \, nm} \qquad E = \frac{hc}{\lambda} \qquad \frac{mol}{6.022 \times 10^{23} \, photons} \qquad \frac{kJ}{1000 \, J}$$

Solution:

$$2.55 \times 10^{55} \, \cancel{nm} \times \frac{m}{10^9 \, \cancel{nm}} = 2.55 \times 10^{-14} \, m \qquad E = \frac{6.626 \times 10^{-34} \, J \cdot \cancel{s} \times \frac{3.00 \times 10^8 \, \cancel{m}}{\cancel{s}}}{2.55 \times 10^{-14} \, \cancel{m}} = 7.7953 \times 10^{-12} \, J / photon$$

$$\frac{7.7953 \times 10^{-12} \, \cancel{J}}{\cancel{photon}} \times \frac{6.022 \times 10^{23} \, \cancel{photons}}{mol} \times \frac{kJ}{1000 \, \cancel{J}} = 4.69 \times 10^9 \, kJ / mol$$

Check: The units of the answer, kJ/mol, are correct. The magnitude of the answer is reasonable for a wavelength in the gamma ray region.

49. The interference pattern would be a series of light and dark lines.

50. Since the interference pattern is caused by single electrons interfering with themselves, the pattern remains the same even when the rate of the electrons passing through the slits is one electron per hour. It will simply take longer for the full pattern to develop. When a laser is placed behind the slits to determine which hole the electron passes through, the laser flashes to indicate which hole the electron passed through, but the interference pattern is now absent. With the laser on the electrons hit positions directly behind each slit, as if they were ordinary particles.

51. **Given:** $v = 1.15 \times 10^5$ m/s **Find:** λ

Conceptual Plan: $v \rightarrow \lambda$

$$\lambda = \frac{h}{mv}$$

Solution:

$$\dfrac{6.626 \times 10^{-34}\ \dfrac{\text{kg} \cdot \text{m}^2}{\text{s}^2} \cdot \text{s}}{(9.11 \times 10^{-31}\ \text{kg})(1.15 \times 10^5\ \dfrac{\text{m}}{\text{s}})} = 6.32 \times 10^{-9}\ \text{m}$$

Check: The units of the answer, m, are correct. The magnitude of the answer is very small, as expected for the wavelength of an electron.

52. **Given:** $\lambda = 225$ nm   **Find:** v

    Conceptual Plan: $\lambda \rightarrow v$

$$v = \dfrac{h}{m\lambda}$$

    Solution:

$$\dfrac{6.626 \times 10^{-34}\ \dfrac{\text{kg} \cdot \text{m}^2}{\text{s}^2} \cdot \text{s}}{(9.11 \times 10^{-31}\ \text{kg})(225\ \text{nm})\left(\dfrac{\text{m}}{10^9\ \text{nm}}\right)} = 3.23 \times 10^3\ \text{m/s}$$

    Check: The units of the answer, m/s, are correct. The magnitude of the answer is large, as expected for the speed of an electron.

53. **Given:** m = 143 g; v = 95 mph   **Find:** λ

    Conceptual Plan: m,v $\rightarrow \lambda$

$$\lambda = \dfrac{h}{mv}$$

    Solution:

$$\dfrac{6.626 \times 10^{-34}\ \dfrac{\text{kg} \cdot \text{m}^2}{\text{s}^2} \cdot \text{s}}{(143\ \text{g})\left(\dfrac{\text{kg}}{1000\ \text{g}}\right)\left(\dfrac{95\ \text{mi}}{\text{hr}}\right)\left(\dfrac{1.609\ \text{km}}{\text{mi}}\right)\left(\dfrac{1000\ \text{m}}{\text{km}}\right)\left(\dfrac{\text{hr}}{3600\ \text{s}}\right)} = 1.1 \times 10^{-34}\ \text{m}$$

    The value of the wavelength, 1.1×10^{-34} m, is so small it will not have an effect on the trajectory of the baseball.

    Check: The units of the answer, m, are correct. The magnitude of the answer is very small as would be expected for the de Broglie wavelength of a baseball.

54. **Given:** m = 27 g; v = 765 m/s   **Find:** λ

    Conceptual Plan: m,v $\rightarrow \lambda$

$$\lambda = \dfrac{h}{mv}$$

    Solution:

$$\dfrac{6.626 \times 10^{-34}\ \dfrac{\text{kg} \cdot \text{m}^2}{\text{s}^2} \cdot \text{s}}{(27\ \text{g})\left(\dfrac{\text{kg}}{1000\ \text{g}}\right)\left(\dfrac{765\ \text{m}}{\text{s}}\right)} = 3.2 \times 10^{-35}\ \text{m}$$

    The value of the wavelength, 3.2×10^{-35} m, is so small it will not have an effect on the trajectory of the bullet.

    Check: The units of the answer, m, are correct. The magnitude of the answer is very small as would be expected for the de Broglie wavelength of a bullet.

55. Since the size of the orbital is determined by the n quantum, with the size increasing with increasing n, an electron in a 2s orbital is closer, on average, to the nucleus than an electron in a 3s orbital.

56. Since the size of the orbital is determined by the n quantum, with the size increasing with increasing n, an electron in a 4p orbital is further away, on average, from the nucleus than an electron in a 3p orbital.

57. The value of l is an integer that lies between 0 and $n - 1$.

a) When $n = 1$, l can only be: $l = 0$.

b) When $n = 2$, l can be: $l = 0$ or $l = 1$.

c) When $n = 3$, l can be: $l = 0$, $l = 1$, or $l = 2$.

d) When $n = 4$, l can be: $l = 0$, $l = 1$, $l = 2$, or $l = 3$.

58. The value of m_l is an integer that lies between $-l$ and $+l$.
   a) When $l = 0$; m_l can only be: $m_l = 0$.

   b) When $l = 1$, m_l can be: $m_l = -1$, $m_l = 0$, $m_l = +1$.

   c) When $l = 2$, m_l can be: $m_l = -2$, $m_l = -1$; $m_l = 0$, $m_l = +1$, $m_l = +2$.

   d) When $l = 3$, m_l can be: $m_l = -3$, $m_l = -2$, $m_l = -1$, $m_l = 0$, $m_l = +1$, $m_l = +2$, $m_l = +3$.

59. The quantum number is set c cannot occur together to specify an orbital. l must lie between 0 and $n - 1$, so for $n = 3$, l can only be as high as 2.

60. a) 1s is a real orbital, $n = 1$, $l = 0$.

   b) 2p is a real orbital, $n = 2$, $l = 1$.

   c) 4s is a real orbital, $n = 4$, $l = 0$.

   d) 2d in an impossible representation. $n = 2$, $l = 2$ is not allowed. l must lie between 0 and $n - 1$, so for $n = 2$ l can only be as high as 1(p).

61. The 2s orbital would be the same shape as the 1s orbital but would be larger in size and the 3p orbitals would have the same shape as the 2p orbitals but would be larger in size. Also, the 2s and 3p orbitals would have more nodes.

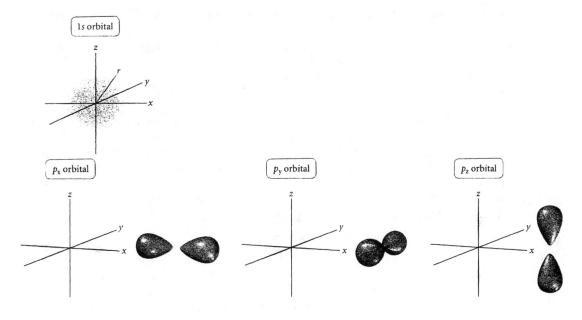

213

62. The 4d orbitals would be the same shape as the 3d orbitals but would be larger in size and the 4d orbital would have more nodes.

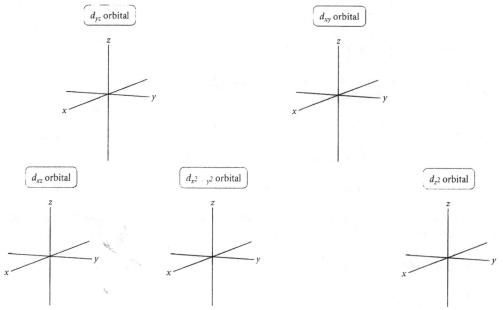

63. When the atom emits a photon of energy, the photon has the same energy as the energy absorbed to move the electron to the excited state. Therefore, the electron has to be in n = 1 following the emission of the photon.

64. a) from n = 3 → n = 1, the electron is moving to a lower energy therefore, there is an emission of energy.

   b) from n = 2 → n = 4, the electron is moving to a higher energy, therefore, there is an absorption of energy.

   c) from n = 4 → n = 3, the electron is moving to a lower energy, therefore, there is an emission of energy.

65. According to the quantum – mechanical model, the higher the n level the higher the energy. So, the transition from 3p → 1s would be a greater energy difference than a transition from 2p → 1s. The lower energy transition would have the longer wavelength. Therefore, the 2p → 1s transition would produce a longer wavelength.

66. According to the quantum – mechanical model, the higher the n level the higher the energy and the higher in energy, the closer the levels are to each other. So, the transition from 3p → 2s would be a greater energy difference than the transition from 4p → 3p. The lower energy transition would have the longer wavelength. Therefore, the 4p → 3p transition would produce a longer wavelength.

67. a) **Given:** n = 2 → n = 1   **Find:** λ
   Conceptual Plan: n =1, n = 2 → ΔE_{atom} → ΔE_{photon} → λ

   $$\Delta E_{atom} = E_1 - E_2 \qquad \Delta E_{atom} \rightarrow - \Delta E_{photon} \qquad E = \frac{hc}{\lambda}$$

   Solution:

   $$\Delta E = E_1 - E_2$$

   $$-2.18 \times 10^{-18} \, J \left(\frac{1}{1^2}\right) - \left[-2.18 \times 10^{-18}\left(\frac{1}{2^2}\right)\right] = -2.18 \times 10^{-18} \, J \left[\left(\frac{1}{1^2}\right) - \left(\frac{1}{2^2}\right)\right] = -1.635 \times 10^{-18} \, J$$

   $$\Delta E_{photon} = -\Delta E_{atom} = 1.635 \times 10^{-18} \, J \qquad \lambda = \frac{hc}{E} = \frac{(6.626 \times 10^{-34} \, J\cdot s)(3.00 \times 10^8 \, m/s)}{1.635 \times 10^{-18} \, J} = 1.22 \times 10^{-7} \, m$$

   This transition would produce a wavelength in the UV region.
   Check: The units of the answer, m, are correct. The magnitude of the answer is reasonable since it is in the region of UV radiation.

214

b) **Given:** $n = 3 \rightarrow n = 1$ **Find:** λ

Conceptual Plan: $n = 1, n = 3 \rightarrow \Delta E_{atom} \rightarrow \Delta E_{photon} \rightarrow \lambda$

$$\Delta E_{atom} = E_1 - E_3 \qquad \Delta E_{atom} \rightarrow -\Delta E_{photon} \qquad E = \frac{hc}{\lambda}$$

Solution:

$\Delta E = E_1 - E_3$

$$\text{✗✗✗} \quad -2.18 \times 10^{-18}\,J\left(\frac{1}{1^2}\right) - \left[-2.18 \times 10^{-18}\left(\frac{1}{3^2}\right)\right] = -2.18 \times 10^{-18}\,J\left[\left(\frac{1}{1^2}\right) - \left(\frac{1}{3^2}\right)\right] = -1.9\underline{3}8 \times 10^{-18}\,J$$

$$\Delta E_{photon} = -\Delta E_{atom} = 1.9\underline{3}8 \times 10^{-18}\,J \qquad \lambda = \frac{hc}{E} = \frac{(6.626 \times 10^{-34}\,\text{✗J✗s})(3.00 \times 10^8\,m/\text{✗s✗})}{1.9\underline{3}8 \times 10^{-18}\,\text{✗J✗}} = 1.03 \times 10^{-7}\,m$$

This transition would produce a wavelength in the UV region.
Check: The units of the answer, m, are correct. The magnitude of the answer is reasonable since it is in the region of UV radiation.

c) **Given:** $n = 4 \rightarrow n = 2$ **Find:** λ

Conceptual Plan: $n = 2, n = 4 \rightarrow \Delta E_{atom} \rightarrow \Delta E_{photon} \rightarrow \lambda$

$$\Delta E_{atom} = E_2 - E_4 \qquad \Delta E_{atom} \rightarrow -\Delta E_{photon} \qquad E = \frac{hc}{\lambda}$$

Solution:

$\Delta E = E_2 - E_4$

$$\text{✗✗✗} \quad -2.18 \times 10^{-18}\,J\left(\frac{1}{2^2}\right) - \left[-2.18 \times 10^{-18}\left(\frac{1}{4^2}\right)\right] = -2.18 \times 10^{-18}\,J\left[\left(\frac{1}{2^2}\right) - \left(\frac{1}{4^2}\right)\right] = -4.0\underline{8}7 \times 10^{-18}\,J$$

$$\Delta E_{photon} = -\Delta E_{atom} = 4.0\underline{8}7 \times 10^{-19}\,J \qquad \lambda = \frac{hc}{E} = \frac{(6.626 \times 10^{-34}\,\text{✗J✗s})(3.00 \times 10^8\,m/\text{✗s✗})}{4.0\underline{8}7 \times 10^{-18}\,\text{✗J✗}} = 4.86 \times 10^{-7}\,m$$

This transition would produce a wavelength in the Visible region.
Check: The units of the answer, m, are correct. The magnitude of the answer is reasonable since it is in the region of Visible light.

d) **Given:** $n = 5 \rightarrow n = 2$ **Find:** λ

Conceptual Plan: $n = 2, n = 5 \rightarrow \Delta E_{atom} \rightarrow \Delta E_{photon} \rightarrow \lambda$

$$\Delta E_{atom} = E_2 - E_5 \qquad \Delta E_{atom} \rightarrow -\Delta E_{photon} \qquad E = \frac{hc}{\lambda}$$

Solution:

$\Delta E = E_2 - E_5$

$$\text{✗✗✗} \quad -2.18 \times 10^{-18}\,J\left(\frac{1}{2^2}\right) - \left[-2.18 \times 10^{-18}\left(\frac{1}{5^2}\right)\right] = -2.18 \times 10^{-18}\,J\left[\left(\frac{1}{2^2}\right) - \left(\frac{1}{5^2}\right)\right] = -4.5\underline{7}8 \times 10^{-19}\,J$$

$$\Delta E_{photon} = -\Delta E_{atom} = 4.5\underline{7}8 \times 10^{-18}\,J \qquad \lambda = \frac{hc}{E} = \frac{(6.626 \times 10^{-34}\,\text{✗J✗s})(3.00 \times 10^8\,m/\text{✗s✗})}{4.5\underline{7}8 \times 10^{-18}\,\text{✗J✗}} = 4.34 \times 10^{-7}\,m$$

This transition would produce a wavelength in the Visible region.
Check: The units of the answer, m, are correct. The magnitude of the answer is reasonable since it is in the region of Visible light.

68. a) **Given:** $n = 4 \rightarrow n = 3$ **Find:** ν

Conceptual Plan: $n = 3, n = 4 \rightarrow \Delta E_{atom} \rightarrow \Delta E_{photon} \rightarrow \nu$

$$\Delta E_{atom} = E_3 - E_4 \qquad \Delta E_{atom} \rightarrow -\Delta E_{photon} \qquad E = h\nu$$

Solution:

$\Delta E = E_3 - E_4$

$$\text{✗✗✗} \quad -2.18 \times 10^{-18}\,J\left(\frac{1}{3^2}\right) - \left[-2.18 \times 10^{-18}\left(\frac{1}{4^2}\right)\right] = -2.18 \times 10^{-18}\,J\left[\left(\frac{1}{3^2}\right) - \left(\frac{1}{4^2}\right)\right] = -1.0\underline{6}0 \times 10^{-19}\,J$$

$$\Delta E_{photon} = -\Delta E_{atom} = 1.0\underline{6}0 \times 10^{-19} \text{ J} \qquad \nu = \frac{E}{h} = \frac{(1.0\underline{6}0 \times 10^{-19} \text{ J})}{6.626 \times 10^{-34} \text{ J(s)}} = 1.60 \times 10^{14} \text{ s}^{-1}$$

Check: The units of the answer, s^{-1}, are correct. The magnitude of the answer is reasonable since it is a transition between two close levels and the levels become closer as the n value increases. Therefore, the energy difference is smaller and the frequency is smaller.

b) **Given:** n = 5 → n = 1 **Find:** ν

  Conceptual Plan: **n =1, n = 5 → ΔE_{atom} → ΔE_{photon} → ν**

  $$\Delta E_{atom} = E_1 - E_5 \qquad \Delta E_{atom} \rightarrow -\Delta E_{photon} \qquad E = h\nu$$

  Solution:

  $$\Delta E = E_1 - E_5$$

  $$= -2.18 \times 10^{-18} \text{ J}\left(\frac{1}{1^2}\right) - \left[-2.18 \times 10^{-18}\left(\frac{1}{5^2}\right)\right] = -2.18 \times 10^{-18} \text{ J}\left[\left(\frac{1}{1^2}\right) - \left(\frac{1}{5^2}\right)\right] = -2.0\underline{9}3 \times 10^{-18} \text{ J}$$

  $$\Delta E_{photon} = -\Delta E_{atom} = 2.0\underline{9}3 \times 10^{-18} \text{ J} \qquad \nu = \frac{E}{h} = \frac{2.0\underline{9}3 \times 10^{-18} \text{ J}}{6.626 \times 10^{-34} \text{ J(s)}} = 3.16 \times 10^{15} \text{ s}^{-1}$$

  Check: The units of the answer, s^{-1}, are correct. The magnitude of the answer is reasonable since it is a transition that will produce a wavelength in the UV region and the frequency is correct for the UV region.

c) **Given:** n = 5 → n = 4 **Find:** ν

  Conceptual Plan: **n =4, n = 5 → ΔE_{atom} → ΔE_{photon} → ν**

  $$\Delta E_{atom} = E_4 - E_5 \qquad \Delta E_{atom} \rightarrow -\Delta E_{photon} \qquad E = h\nu$$

  Solution:

  $$\Delta E = E_4 - E_5$$

  $$= -2.18 \times 10^{-18} \text{ J}\left(\frac{1}{4^2}\right) - \left[-2.18 \times 10^{-18}\left(\frac{1}{5^2}\right)\right] = -2.18 \times 10^{-18} \text{ J}\left[\left(\frac{1}{4^2}\right) - \left(\frac{1}{5^2}\right)\right] = -4.9\underline{0}5 \times 10^{-20} \text{ J}$$

  $$\Delta E_{photon} = -\Delta E_{atom} = 4.9\underline{0}5 \times 10^{-20} \text{ J} \qquad \nu = \frac{E}{h} = \frac{4.9\underline{0}5 \times 10^{-20} \text{ J}}{6.626 \times 10^{-34} \text{ J(s)}} = 7.40 \times 10^{13} \text{ s}^{-1}$$

  Check: The units of the answer, s^{-1}, are correct. The magnitude of the answer is reasonable since it is a transition between two close levels and the levels become closer as the n value increases. Therefore, the energy difference is smaller and the frequency is smaller.

d) **Given:** n = 6 → n = 5 **Find:** ν

  Conceptual Plan: **n =5, n = 6 → ΔE_{atom} → ΔE_{photon} → ν**

  $$\Delta E_{atom} = E_5 - E_6 \qquad \Delta E_{atom} \rightarrow -\Delta E_{photon} \qquad E = h\nu$$

  Solution:

  $$\Delta E = E_5 - E_6$$

  $$= -2.18 \times 10^{-18} \text{ J}\left(\frac{1}{5^2}\right) - \left[-2.18 \times 10^{-18}\left(\frac{1}{6^2}\right)\right] = -2.18 \times 10^{-18} \text{ J}\left[\left(\frac{1}{5^2}\right) - \left(\frac{1}{6^2}\right)\right] = -2.6\underline{6}4 \times 10^{-13} \text{ J}$$

  $$\Delta E_{photon} = -\Delta E_{atom} = 2.6\underline{6}4 \times 10^{-13} \text{ J} \qquad \nu = \frac{E}{h} = \frac{2.6\underline{6}4 \times 10^{-13} \text{ J}}{6.626 \times 10^{-34} \text{ J(s)}} = 4.02 \times 10^{13} \text{ s}^{-1}$$

  Check: The units of the answer, s^{-1}, are correct. The magnitude of the answer is reasonable since it is a transition between two close levels and the levels become closer as the n value increases. Therefore, the energy difference is smaller and the frequency is smaller.

69. **Given:** n(initial) = 7 λ = 397 nm **Find:** n(final)

  Conceptual Plan: λ → ΔE_{photon} → ΔE_{atom} → n = x, n = 7

  $$E = \frac{hc}{\lambda} \quad \Delta E_{photon} \rightarrow -\Delta E_{atom} \qquad \Delta E_{atom} = E_x - E_7$$

Solution: $E = \dfrac{hc}{\lambda} = \dfrac{(6.626 \times 10^{-34} \text{ Jgs})(3.00 \times 10^8 \text{ m}/\text{s})}{(397 \text{ nm})\left(\dfrac{\text{m}}{10^9 \text{ nm}}\right)} = 5.0\underline{0}7 \times 10^{-19} \text{ J}$

$\Delta E_{atom} = -\Delta E_{photon} = -5.0\underline{0}7 \times 10^{-19} \text{ J}$

$\Delta E = E_x - E_7 = -5.0\underline{0}7 \times 10^{-19} = -2.18 \times 10^{-18} \text{ J}\left(\dfrac{1}{x^2}\right) - \left[-2.18 \times 10^{-18}\left(\dfrac{1}{7^2}\right)\right] = -2.18 \times 10^{-18} \text{ J}\left[\left(\dfrac{1}{x^2}\right) - \left(\dfrac{1}{7^2}\right)\right]$

$0.2297 = \left(\dfrac{1}{x^2}\right) - \left(\dfrac{1}{7^2}\right) \qquad 0.25229 = \left(\dfrac{1}{x^2}\right) \qquad x^2 = 3.998 \qquad x = 2$

Check: The answer is reasonable since it is an integer less than the initial value of 7.

70. **Given:** n(final) = 4, ν = 11.4 THz **Find:** n(initial)
 Conceptual Plan: $\nu \rightarrow \Delta E_{photon} \rightarrow \Delta E_{atom} \rightarrow n = 4, n = x$

$\qquad\qquad\qquad E = h\nu \qquad \Delta E_{photon} \rightarrow -\Delta E_{atom} \qquad \Delta E_{atom} = E_4 - E_x$

 Solution: $E = h\nu = (6.626 \times 10^{-34} \text{ Jgs})(114 \text{ THz})\left(\dfrac{10^{12} \text{ Hz}}{\text{T}}\right)\left(\dfrac{\text{s}^{-1}}{\text{Hz}}\right) = 7.5\underline{5}3 \times 10^{-20} \text{ J}$

$\Delta E_{atom} = -\Delta E_{photon} = -7.5\underline{5}3 \times 10^{-20} \text{ J}$

$\Delta E = E_4 - E_x = -7.5\underline{5}3 \times 10^{-20} \text{ J} = -2.18 \times 10^{-18} \text{ J}\left(\dfrac{1}{4^2}\right) - \left[-2.18 \times 10^{-18}\left(\dfrac{1}{x^2}\right)\right] = -2.18 \times 10^{-18} \text{ J}\left[\left(\dfrac{1}{4^2}\right) - \left(\dfrac{1}{x^2}\right)\right]$

$0.03465 = \left(\dfrac{1}{4^2}\right) - \left(\dfrac{1}{x^2}\right) \qquad 0.02785 = \left(\dfrac{1}{x^2}\right) \qquad x^2 = 35.9\underline{2}36 \qquad x = 6$

Check: The answer is reasonable since it is an integer greater than the final value of 4.

71. **Given:** 348 kJ/mol **Find:** λ
 Conceptual Plan: kJ/mol $\rightarrow$ kJ/molec $\rightarrow$ J/molec $\rightarrow$ λ

$\qquad\qquad\qquad \dfrac{6.022 \times 10^{23} \text{ molec}}{\text{mol}} \quad \dfrac{1000 \text{ J}}{\text{kJ}} \quad E = \dfrac{hc}{\lambda}$

 Solution: $\dfrac{348 \text{ kJ}}{\text{mol}} \times \dfrac{\text{mol}}{6.022 \times 10^{23} \text{ molecules}} \times \dfrac{1000 \text{ J}}{\text{kJ}} = 5.7\underline{7}9 \times 10^{-19} \text{ J}$

$\lambda = \dfrac{(6.626 \times 10^{-34} \text{ Jgs})(3.00 \times 10^8 \text{ m}/\text{s})}{5.7\underline{7}9 \times 10^{-19} \text{ J}} = 3.44 \times 10^{-7} \text{ m} = 344 \text{ nm}$

Check: The units of the answer, m or nm, is correct. The magnitude of the answer is reasonable since this wavelength is in the UV region.

72. **Given:** 164 kJ/mol **Find:** λ
 Conceptual Plan: kJ/mol $\rightarrow$ kJ/molec $\rightarrow$ J/molec $\rightarrow$ λ

$\qquad\qquad\qquad \dfrac{6.022 \times 10^{23} \text{ molec}}{\text{mol}} \quad \dfrac{1000 \text{ J}}{\text{kJ}} \quad E = \dfrac{hc}{\lambda}$

 Solution: $\dfrac{164 \text{ kJ}}{\text{mol}} \times \dfrac{\text{mol}}{6.022 \times 10^{23} \text{ molecules}} \times \dfrac{1000 \text{ J}}{\text{kJ}} = 2.7\underline{2}3 \times 10^{-19} \text{ J}$

$\lambda = \dfrac{(6.626 \times 10^{-34} \text{ Jgs})(3.00 \times 10^8 \text{ m}/\text{s})}{2.7\underline{2}3 \times 10^{-19} \text{ J}} = 7.30 \times 10^{-7} \text{ m} = 730 \text{ nm}$

Check: The units of the answer, m or nm, is correct. The magnitude of the answer is reasonable since this wavelength is in the red region of visible light.

73. **Given:** E_{pulse} = 5.0 watts; d = 5.5 mm; hole = 1.2 mm; λ = 532 nm **Find:** photons/s

Conceptual Plan: fraction of beam through hole → fraction of power and then E_{photon} → number photons/s

$$\frac{\text{area hole}}{\text{area beam}} \qquad\qquad \text{fraction x power} \qquad\qquad E = \frac{hc}{\lambda}\ \frac{\text{power}/s}{E/\text{photon}}$$

Solution: $A = \pi r^2 \qquad \dfrac{\pi(0.60mm)^2}{\pi(2.75mm)^2} = 0.0476 \qquad 0.0476 \times 5.0\,\text{watts} \times \dfrac{J/s}{\text{watt}} = 0.238\,J/s$

$$E_{photon} = \frac{(6.626 \times 10^{-34}\,Jgs)(3.00 \times 10^8\,m/s)}{(532\,nm)\left(\dfrac{m}{10^9\,nm}\right)} = 3.736 \times 10^{-19}\ J/\text{photon}$$

$$\frac{0.238\,J/s}{3.736 \times 10^{-19}\ J/\text{photon}} = 6.4 \times 10^{17}\ \text{photons}/s$$

Check: The units of the answer, number of photons /s, is correct. The magnitude of the answer is reasonable.

74. **Given:** $A_{leaf} = 2.50\ cm^2$; $E_{rad} = 1000\ W/m^2$; $\lambda = 504\ nm$ **Find:** photons/s
    Conceptual Plan: E_{rad}/s → E_{leaf}/s and then E_{photon} → number photons/s

$$E_{Rad} \times A_{leaf} \qquad\qquad E = \frac{hc}{\lambda}\ \frac{E_{leaf}/s}{E/\text{photon}}$$

Solution: $E_{rad} = 2.50\ cm^2 \times \dfrac{1000\,W}{m^2} \times \dfrac{m^2}{(100\,cm)^2} \times \dfrac{J/s}{W} = 0.250\,J/s$

$$E_{photon} = \frac{hc}{\lambda} = \frac{(6.626 \times 10^{-34}\,Jgs)(3.00 \times 10^8\,m/s)}{(504\,nm)\left(\dfrac{m}{10^9\,nm}\right)} = 3.944 \times 10^{-19}\ J/\text{photon}$$

$$\frac{E_{rad}}{E_{photon}} = \frac{0.250\,J/s}{3.944 \times 10^{-19}\ J/\text{photon}} = 6.34 \times 10^{17}\ \text{photons}/s$$

Check: The units of the answer, photons/s, are correct. The magnitude of the answer is reasonable compared to the radiation from the sun.

75. **Given:** $KE = 506\ eV$ **Find:** λ
    Conceptual Plan: KE_{ev} → KE_J → v → λ

$$\frac{1.602 \times 10^{-19}\ J}{eV} \qquad KE = 1/2\,mv^2 \qquad \lambda = \frac{h}{mv}$$

Solution:

$$506\,eV\left(\frac{1.602 \times 10^{-19}\ J}{eV}\right)\left(\frac{kggm^2}{s^2}\right) = \frac{1}{2}\left(9.11 \times 10^{-31}\,kg\right)v^2 \qquad v^2 = \frac{506\,eV\left(\dfrac{1.602 \times 10^{-19}\ J}{eV}\right)\left(\dfrac{kg\,gm^2}{s^2}\right)}{\dfrac{1}{2}\left(9.11 \times 10^{-31}\,kg\right)} = 1.7796 \times 10^{14}\ \frac{m^2}{s^2}$$

$$v = 1.33 \times 10^7\,m/s \qquad \lambda = \frac{h}{mv} = \frac{6.626 \times 10^{-34}\ \dfrac{kg\,gm^2}{s}\,gs}{(9.11 \times 10^{-31}\,kg)(1.33 \times 10^7\,m/s)} = 5.47 \times 10^{-11}\ m = 0.0547\ nm$$

Check: The units of the answer, m or nm, are correct. The magnitude of the answer is reasonable because a deBroglie wavelength is usually a very small number.

76. **Given:** $\lambda = 0.989\ nm$; $KE = 969\ eV$ **Find:** BE/ mol
    Conceptual Plan: λ → E_{photon} → BE_{photon} → BE_{mol}

$$E = \frac{hc}{\lambda} \qquad BE_{photon} = E_{photon} - KE \qquad \frac{\text{mol}}{6.022 \times 10^{23}\ \text{photons}}$$

218

Solution: $E_{photon} = \dfrac{hc}{\lambda} = \dfrac{(6.626 \times 10^{-34} \text{ J g s})(3.00 \times 10^8 \text{ m / s})}{(0.989 \text{ nm})\left(\dfrac{\text{m}}{10^9 \text{ nm}}\right)} = 2.0\underline{1}0 \times 10^{-16}$ J / photon

$$BE_{photon} = 2.0\underline{1}0 \times 10^{-16} \text{ J / photon} - \left[(969 \text{ eV})\left(\dfrac{1.602 \times 10^{-19} \text{ J}}{\text{eV}}\right)\right] = 4.5\underline{7}6 \times 10^{-17} \text{ J / photon}$$

$$\dfrac{4.5\underline{7}6 \times 10^{-17} \text{ J}}{\text{photon}} \text{ x } \dfrac{6.022 \times 10^{23} \text{ photons}}{\text{mol}} \text{ x } \dfrac{\text{kJ}}{1000 \text{ J}} = 2.76 \times 10^4 \text{ kJ / mol}$$

Check: The units of the answer, kJ/mol, are correct. The magnitude of the answer is reasonable since it should require a large amount of energy to remove an electron from a metal surface.

77. **Given:** n = 1 → n = ∞   **Find:** E; λ

Conceptual Plan: $\mathbf{n = \infty, \ n = 1 \rightarrow \Delta E_{atom} \rightarrow \Delta E_{photon} \rightarrow \lambda}$

$$\Delta E_{atom} = E_\infty - E_1 \qquad \Delta E_{atom} \rightarrow \Delta E_{photon} \qquad E = \dfrac{hc}{\lambda}$$

Solution: $\Delta E = E_\infty - E_1 \ = \ 0 - \left[-2.18 \times 10^{-18}\left(\dfrac{1}{1^2}\right)\right] = +2.18 \times 10^{-18}$ J

$$\Delta E_{photon} = -\Delta E_{atom} = +2.18 \times 10^{-18} \text{ J}$$

$$\lambda = \dfrac{hc}{E} = \dfrac{(6.626 \times 10^{-34} \text{ J g s})(3.00 \times 10^8 \text{ m / s})}{2.18 \times 10^{-18} \text{ J}} = 9.12 \times 10^{-8} \text{ m} = 91.2 \text{ nm}$$

Check: The units of the answers, J for E and m or nm for part 1, are correct. The magnitude of the answer is reasonable because it would require more energy to completely remove the electron than just moving it to a higher n level. This results in a shorter wavelength.

78. **Given:** E = 496 kJ/mol   **Find:** ν

Conceptual Plan: **kJ/mol → kJ/molecule → J/molecule → ν**

$$\dfrac{6.022 \times 10^{23} \text{ molecules}}{\text{mol}} \qquad \dfrac{1000 \text{ J}}{\text{kJ}} \qquad E = h\nu$$

Solution: $\nu = \dfrac{E}{h} = \dfrac{\left(\dfrac{496 \text{ kJ}}{\text{mol}}\right)\left(\dfrac{\text{mol}}{6.022 \times 10^{23} \text{ atom}}\right)\left(\dfrac{1000 \text{ J}}{\text{kJ}}\right)}{6.626 \times 10^{-34} \text{ J g s}} = 1.24 \times 10^{15} \text{ s}^{-1}$

Check: The units of the answer, s^{-1}, are correct. The magnitude of the answer is reasonable because the frequency is slightly higher than the visible region of the spectrum and this is expected because the excitation of sodium produces a line in the visible region.

79. a) **Given:** n = 1   **Find:** number of orbitals if $l = 0 \rightarrow$ n

Conceptual Plan: **value n → values l → values m_l → number of orbitals**

$$l = 0 \rightarrow n \qquad m_l = -l \rightarrow +l \text{ total } m_l$$

Solution:
n =	1		
l =	0	1	
m_l =	0	-1, 0, +1	

total 4 orbitals

Check: The total orbitals will be equal to the number of l sublevels^2

b) **Given:** n = 2   **Find:** number of orbitals if $l = 0 \rightarrow$ n

Conceptual Plan: **value n → values l → values m_l → number of orbitals**

$$l = 0 \rightarrow n \qquad m_l = -l \rightarrow +l \text{ total } m_l$$

Solution:
n =	2		
l =	0	1	2
m_l =	0	-1, 0, +1	-2, -1, 0, 1, 2

total 9 orbitals

Check: The total orbitals will be equal to the number of l sublevels^2

c) **Given:** n = 3   **Find:** number of orbitals if $l = 0 \rightarrow$ n
    Conceptual Plan: value n $\rightarrow$ values l $\rightarrow$ values m_l $\rightarrow$ number of orbitals
                             $l = 0 \rightarrow$ n $m_l = -1 \rightarrow +1$ total m_l
    Solution: n =   3

$l =$	0	1	2	3
$m_l =$	0	-1, 0, +1	-2,-1,0,1,2	-3,-2,-1,0,1,2,3

               total 16 orbitals
    Check: The total orbitals will be equal to the number of l sublevels[2]

80. a) **Given:** s sublevel   **Find:** number of orbital if $m_l = -l-1 \rightarrow l+1$
    Conceptual Plan: values l $\rightarrow$ values m_l $\rightarrow$ number of orbitals
                      $m_l = -l-1 \rightarrow +l+1$ total m_l
    Solution: sublevel s $\rightarrow l = 0$
               $m_l = -1, 0, +1$
               total 3 orbitals

b) **Given:** p sublevel   **Find:** number of orbital if $m_l = -l-1 \rightarrow l+1$
    Conceptual Plan: values l $\rightarrow$ values m_l $\rightarrow$ number of orbitals
                      $m_l = -l-1 \rightarrow +l+1$ total m_l
    Solution: sublevel p $\rightarrow l = 1$
               $m_l = -2,-1, 0, +1,+2$
               total 5 orbitals

c) **Given:** d sublevel   **Find:** number of orbital if $m_l = -l-1 \rightarrow l+1$
    Conceptual Plan: values l $\rightarrow$ values m_l $\rightarrow$ number of orbitals
                      $m_l = -l-1 \rightarrow +l+1$ total m_l
    Solution: sublevel d $\rightarrow l = 2$
               $m_l = -3,-2,-1, 0, +1,+2,+3$
               total 7 orbitals

81. **Given:** $\lambda = 1875$ nm; 1282 nm; 1093 nm   **Find:** equivalent transitions
    Conceptual Plan: $\lambda \rightarrow E_{photon} \rightarrow E_{atom} \rightarrow$ n

$$E = \frac{hc}{\lambda} \qquad E_{photon} = -E_{atom} \qquad E = -2.18 \times 10^{-18}\,J\left(\frac{1}{n_f^2} - \frac{1}{n_i^2}\right)$$

Solution: Since the wavelength of the transitions are longer wavelengths than those obtained in the visual region, the electron must relax to a higher n level. Therefore, we can assume that the electron returns to the n = 3 level.

For $\lambda = 1875$ nm: $E = \dfrac{(6.626 \times 10^{-34}\,J\cdot s)(3.00 \times 10^8\,m/s)}{1875\,nm\left(\dfrac{m}{10^9\,nm}\right)} = 1.060 \times 10^{-19}\,J$ $1.060 \times 10^{-19}\,J = -1.060 \times 10^{-19}\,J$

$$-1.060 \times 10^{-19}\,J = -2.18 \times 10^{-18}\left(\frac{1}{3^2} - \frac{1}{n^2}\right); \quad n = 4$$

For $\lambda = 1282$ nm: $E = \dfrac{(6.626 \times 10^{-34}\,J\cdot s)(3.00 \times 10^8\,m/s)}{1282\,nm\left(\dfrac{m}{10^9\,nm}\right)} = 1.551 \times 10^{-19}\,J$ $1.551 \times 10^{-19}\,J = -1.551 \times 10^{-19}\,J$

$$-1.551 \times 10^{-19} = -2.18 \times 10^{-18}\left(\frac{1}{3^2} - \frac{1}{n^2}\right); \quad n = 5$$

For $\lambda = 1093$ nm: $E = \dfrac{(6.626 \times 10^{-34}\,J\cdot s)(3.00 \times 10^8\,m/s)}{1093\,nm\left(\dfrac{m}{10^9\,nm}\right)} = 1.819 \times 10^{-19}\,J$ $1.819 \times 10^{-19}\,J = -1.819 \times 10^{-19}\,J$

$$-1.819 \times 10^{-19}\,J = -2.18 \times 10^{-18}\left(\frac{1}{3^2} - \frac{1}{n^2}\right); \quad n = 6$$

Check: The values obtained are all integers, which is correct. The values of n; 4,5,6, are reasonable. The values of n increase as the wavelength decreases because the two n levels involved are further apart and more energy is released as the electron relaxes to the n = 3 level.

82. **Given:** $\lambda = 121.5$ nm; 102.6 nm; 97.23 nm $\qquad$ **Find:** equivalent transitions

Conceptual Plan: $\lambda \rightarrow E_{photon} \rightarrow E_{atom} \rightarrow n$

$$E = \frac{hc}{\lambda} \qquad E_{photon} = -E_{atom} \qquad E = -2.18 \times 10^{-18} J \left(\frac{1}{n_f^2} - \frac{1}{n_i^2} \right)$$

Solution: Since the wavelength of the transitions are shorter wavelengths than those obtained in the visual region, the electron must relax to a lower n level. Therefore, we can assume that the electron returns to the n = 1 level.

For $\lambda = 121.5$ nm: $E = \dfrac{(6.626 \times 10^{-34} Js)(3.00 \times 10^8 m/s)}{121.5 nm \left(\dfrac{m}{10^9 nm} \right)} = 1.636 \times 10^{-18} J \qquad 1.636 \times 10^{-18} J = -1.636 \times 10^{-18} J$

$$-1.636 \times 10^{-18} J = -2.18 \times 10^{-18} \left(\frac{1}{1^2} - \frac{1}{n^2} \right) ; \ n = 2$$

For $\lambda = 102.6$ nm: $E = \dfrac{(6.626 \times 10^{-34} Js)(3.00 \times 10^8 m/s)}{102.6 nm \left(\dfrac{m}{10^9 nm} \right)} = 1.937 \times 10^{-18} J \qquad 1.937 \times 10^{-18} J = -1.937 \times 10^{-18} J$

$$-1.937 \times 10^{-18} J = -2.18 \times 10^{-18} \left(\frac{1}{1^2} - \frac{1}{n^2} \right) ; \ n = 3$$

For $\lambda = 97.23$ nm: $E = \dfrac{(6.626 \times 10^{-34} Js)(3.00 \times 10^8 m/s)}{97.23 nm \left(\dfrac{m}{10^9 nm} \right)} = 2.044 \times 10^{-18} J \qquad 2.044 \times 10^{-18} J = -2.044 \times 10^{-18} J$

$$-2.044 \times 10^{-18} J = -2.18 \times 10^{-18} \left(\frac{1}{1^2} - \frac{1}{n^2} \right) ; \ n = 4$$

Check: The values obtained are all integers, which is correct. The values of n; 2,3,4, are reasonable. The values of n increase as the wavelength decreases because the two n levels involved are further apart and more energy is released as the electron relaxes to the n = 1 level.

83. **Given:** $\Phi = 193$ kJ/mol $\qquad$ **Find:** threshold frequency(ν)

Conceptual Plan: Φ kJ/ mol $\rightarrow$ Φ kJ/ atom $\rightarrow \Phi$ J/ atom $\rightarrow$ ν

$$\frac{6.022 \times 10^{23} \text{ molecules}}{mol} \qquad \frac{1000 J}{kJ} \qquad \Phi = h\nu$$

Solution: $\nu = \dfrac{\Phi}{h} = \dfrac{\left(\dfrac{193 \text{ kJ}}{mol} \right) \left(\dfrac{mol}{6.022 \times 10^{23} \text{ atoms}} \right) \left(\dfrac{1000 J}{kJ} \right)}{6.626 \times 10^{-34} Js} = 4.84 \times 10^{14} s^{-1}$

Check: The units of the answer, s^{-1}, are correct. The magnitude of the answer puts the frequency in the infrared range and is a reasonable answer.

84. **Given:** m = 2 amu; v = 1 x 10^6 m/s $\qquad$ **Find:** λ

Conceptual Plan: m(amu) $\rightarrow$ m(g) $\rightarrow$ m(kg) and then m,v $\rightarrow$ λ

$$\lambda = \frac{h}{mv}$$

Solution: $\dfrac{6.626 \times 10^{-34} \dfrac{kg \ m^2}{s}}{(2 \ amu) \left(\dfrac{1.661 \times 10^{-24} \ g}{amu} \right) \left(\dfrac{kg}{1000 \ g} \right) \left(1 \times 10^6 \ m/s \right)} = 2 \times 10^{-13} \text{ m}$

Check: The units of the answer, m, are correct. The magnitude of the answer is reasonable since it is a smaller wavelength than for an electron and a deuteron has a much larger mass than an electron.

85. **Given:** $\nu_{low} = 30s^{-1}$ $\nu_{hi} = 1.5 \times 10^4\ s^{-1}$; speed = 344 m/s   **Find:** λ_{low} - λ_{hi}

    Conceptual Plan: $\nu_{low} \rightarrow \lambda_{low}$ and $\nu_{hi} = \lambda_{hi}$ then λ_{low} - λ_{hi}

    $$\lambda\nu = \text{speed}$$

    Solution: $\lambda = \dfrac{\text{speed}}{\nu}$ $\lambda_{low} = \dfrac{344\,m/s}{30\ s^{-1}} = 11\,m$ $\lambda_{hi} = \dfrac{344\,m/s}{1.5 \times 10^4\ s^{-1}} = 0.023\,m$ $11\,m - 0.023\,m = 11\,m$

    Check: The units of the answer, m, are correct. The magnitude is reasonable since the value is only determined by the low frequency value because of significant figures.

86. **Given:** $d = 1.5 \times 10^8$ km, $\nu = 1.0 \times 10^{14}\ s^{-1}$ **Find:** number of wave crests

    Conceptual Plan: $\nu \rightarrow \lambda$ and then $d(km) \rightarrow d(m) \rightarrow$ number of waves $\rightarrow$ number of crests

    $$\nu = \frac{c}{\lambda} \qquad\qquad \frac{1000\,m}{km} \quad \frac{d}{\lambda}$$

    Solution: $\dfrac{3.00 \times 10^8\,m/s}{1.0 \times 10^{14}\,s^{-1}} = 3.0 \times 10^{-6}\,m$ $\dfrac{1.5 \times 10^8\,km \times \dfrac{1000\,m}{km}}{3.0 \times 10^{-6}\,m} = 5.0 \times 10^{16}$ waves

    Since wavelength is measured crest to crest, the number of wave crests would be $5.0 \times 10^{13} + 1$

    Check: The answer is reasonable since the wavelength is small and the distance traveled is large.

87. a. **Given:** $n = 1$, $n = 2$, $n = 3$, $L = 155$ pm   **Find:** E_1, E_2, E_3

    Conceptual Plan: $n \rightarrow E$

    $$E_n = \frac{n^2 h^2}{8mL^2}$$

    Solution:

    $$E_1 = \frac{1^2(6.626 \times 10^{-34}\,Js)^2}{8(9.11 \times 10^{-31}kg)(155\,pm)^2\left(\dfrac{m}{10^{12}\,pm}\right)^2} = \frac{1(6.626 \times 10^{-34})^2 J^2 s^2}{8(9.11 \times 10^{-31}kg)(155 \times 10^{-12})^2 m^2} = \frac{1(6.626 \times 10^{-34})^2\left(\dfrac{kg\,gm^2}{s^2}\right)Js^2}{8(9.11 \times 10^{-31}\,kg)(155 \times 10^{-12})^2\,m^2} = 2.51 \times 10^{-18}\,J$$

    $$E_2 = \frac{2^2(6.626 \times 10^{-34}\,Js)^2}{8(9.11 \times 10^{-31}kg)(155\,pm)^2\left(\dfrac{m}{10^{12}\,pm}\right)^2} = \frac{4(6.626 \times 10^{-34})^2 J^2 s^2}{8(9.11 \times 10^{-31}kg)(155 \times 10^{-12})^2 m^2} = \frac{4(6.626 \times 10^{-34})^2\left(\dfrac{kg\,gm^2}{s^2}\right)Js^2}{8(9.11 \times 10^{-31}\,kg)(155 \times 10^{-12})^2\,m^2} = 1.00 \times 10^{-17}\,J$$

    $$E_3 = \frac{3^2(6.626 \times 10^{-34}\,Js)^2}{8(9.11 \times 10^{-31}kg)(155\,pm)^2\left(\dfrac{m}{10^{12}\,pm}\right)^2} = \frac{9(6.626 \times 10^{-34})^2 J^2 s^2}{8(9.11 \times 10^{-31}kg)(155 \times 10^{-12})^2 m^2} = \frac{9(6.626 \times 10^{-34})^2\left(\dfrac{kg\,gm^2}{s^2}\right)Js^2}{8(9.11 \times 10^{-31}\,kg)(155 \times 10^{-12})^2\,m^2} = 2.26 \times 10^{-17}\,J$$

    Check: The units of the answers, J, are correct. The answers seem reasonable since the energy is increasing with increasing n level.

    b. **Given:** $n = 1 \rightarrow n = 2$ and $n = 2 \rightarrow n = 3$ **Find:** λ

    Conceptual Plan: $n = 1, n = 2 \rightarrow \Delta E_{atom} \rightarrow \Delta E_{photon} \rightarrow \lambda$

    $$\Delta E_{atom} = E_2 - E_1 \qquad \Delta E_{atom} \rightarrow -\Delta E_{photon} \qquad E = \frac{hc}{\lambda}$$

    Solution: Using the energies calculated in part a:

    $$E_2 - E_1 = (1.00 \times 10^{-17}\,J - 2.51 \times 10^{-18}\,J) = 7.49 \times 10^{-18}\,J$$

    $$\lambda = \frac{(6.626 \times 10^{-34}\,Js)(3.00 \times 10^8\,m/s)}{7.49 \times 10^{-18}\,J} = 2.65 \times 10^{-8}\,m = 26.5\,nm$$

$$E_3 - E_2 = (2.26 \times 10^{-17}\,J - 1.00 \times 10^{-17}\,J) = 1.26 \times 10^{-17}\,J$$

$$\lambda = \frac{(6.626 \times 10^{-34}\,J\cdot s)(3.00 \times 10^8\,m/s)}{1.26 \times 10^{-17}\,J} = 1.58 \times 10^{-8}\,m = 15.8\,nm$$

These wavelengths would lie in the UV region.

Check: The units of the answers, m, are correct. The magnitude of the answers is reasonable based on the energies obtained for the levels.

88. **Given:** $n = 1$, $\nu = 8.85 \times 10^{13}\,s^{-1}$ **Find:** E, λ

    Conceptual Plan: n,ν → E → λ

$$E = (n + \tfrac{1}{2})h\nu \quad E = \frac{hc}{\lambda}$$

Solution:

$$E = (1 + \tfrac{1}{2})(6.626 \times 10^{-34}\,J\cdot s)(8.85 \times 10^{13}\,s^{-1}) = 8.80 \times 10^{-20}\,J \qquad \lambda = \frac{hc}{E} = \frac{(6.626 \times 10^{-34}\,J\cdot s)(3.00 \times 10^8\,m/s)}{8.80 \times 10^{-20}\,J} = 2.26 \times 10^{-6}\,m$$

Check: The units of the answer, J and m, are correct. The magnitude of the answer puts the vibrational frequency in the infrared region which is reasonable.

89. For the 1s orbital: In the excel spread sheet, call column A: r; and column B: ψ(1s). Make the values for r column A: 0 – 200. In the column B put the equation for the wavefunction written as: =(POWER(1/3.1415,1/2))*(1/POWER(53,3/2))*(EXP((-A2/53))). Go to make chart, chose xy scatter.

    e.g. sample values

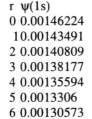

r	ψ(1s)
0	0.00146224
1	0.00143491
2	0.00140809
3	0.00138177
4	0.00135594
5	0.0013306
6	0.00130573

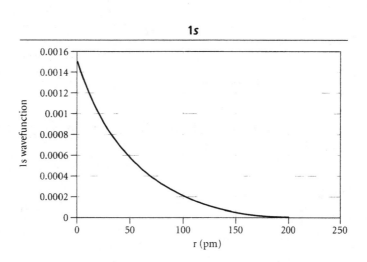

For the 2s orbital: In the same excel spread sheet, call column A: r; and column C: ψ(2s). Use the same values for r in column A: 0 – 200. In the column C put the equation for the wavefunction written as: =(POWER(1/((32)*(3.1415)),1/2))*(1/POWER(53,3/2))*(2-(A2/53))*(EXP((-A2/53))). Go to make chart, chose xy scatter.

e.g.sample values

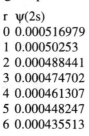

r	$\psi(2s)$
0	0.000516979
1	0.00050253
2	0.000488441
3	0.000474702
4	0.000461307
5	0.000448247
6	0.000435513

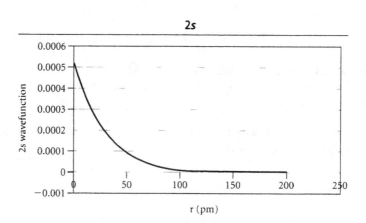

Note: The plot for the 2s orbital extends below the x axis. The x – intercept represents the radial node of the orbital.

90. **Given:** $\Delta E = E_m - E_n = -2.18 \times 10^{-18}(1/m^2) - [-2.18 \times 10^{-18}(1/n^2)]$; $E = hc/\lambda$ **Find:** $1/\lambda = R(1/m^2 - 1/n^2)$

Conceptual Plan: $\Delta E_{atom} \rightarrow E_{photon} \rightarrow 1/\lambda$

$$\Delta E_{atom} = E_m - E_n \qquad \Delta E_{atom} \rightarrow -\Delta E_{photon} \qquad E = \frac{hc}{\lambda}$$

Solution: $\Delta E = E_m - E_n = -2.18 \times 10^{-18}\left(\frac{1}{m^2}\right) \check{S} \left[-2.18 \times 10^{-18}\left(\frac{1}{n^2}\right)\right] = -2.18 \times 10^{-18}\left(\frac{1}{m^2} - \frac{1}{n^2}\right)$

$$E_{photon} = -\left(-2.18 \times 10^{-18}\left(\frac{1}{m^2} - \frac{1}{n^2}\right)\right) = \frac{hc}{\lambda} \qquad \frac{1}{\lambda} = \frac{2.18 \times 10^{-18}}{hc}\left(\frac{1}{m^2} - \frac{1}{n^2}\right) = 1.1 \times 10^7\left(\frac{1}{m^2} - \frac{1}{n^2}\right)$$

$$\frac{1}{\lambda} = R\left(\frac{1}{m^2} - \frac{1}{n^2}\right)$$

91. **Given:** threshold frequency = $2.25 \times 10^{14} s^{-1}$; $\lambda = 5.00 \times 10^{-7}$ m   **Find:** v of electron

Conceptual Plan: $\nu \rightarrow \Phi$ **and then** $\lambda \rightarrow E$ **and then** $\rightarrow KE \rightarrow v$

$$\Phi = h\nu \qquad E = \frac{hc}{\lambda} \qquad KE = E - \Phi \qquad KE = 1/2\, mv^2$$

Solution:

$$\Phi = (6.626 \times 10^{-34}\, J\!\cancel{s})(2.25 \times 10^{14}\, \cancel{s^{-1}}) = 1.491 \times 10^{-19}\, J \qquad E = \frac{(6.626 \times 10^{-34}\, J\!\cancel{s})(3.00 \times 10^8\, \cancel{m}/\cancel{s})}{5.00 \times 10^{-7}\, \cancel{m}} = 3.976 \times 10^{-19}\, J$$

$$KE = 3.976 \times 10^{-19}\, J - 1.491 \times 10^{-19}\, J = 2.485 \times 10^{-19}\, J \qquad v^2 = \frac{2.485 \times 10^{-19}\, \frac{kg\, m^2}{s^2}}{\frac{1}{2}(9.11 \times 10^{-31}\, \cancel{kg})} = 5.455 \times 10^{11}\, \frac{m^2}{s^2}$$

$v = 7.39 \times 10^5$ m/s

Check: The units of the answer, m/s, are correct. The magnitude of the answer is reasonable for the speed of an electron.

92. **Given:** $\lambda = 2.8 \times 10^{-4}$ cm; m = 2.0 g; $\Delta T = 2.0$ K   **Find:** number of photons

Conceptual Plan: $\lambda(cm) \rightarrow \lambda(m) \rightarrow E_{photon}$ **and** $m, \Delta T \rightarrow q_{water}$ **and then** $\rightarrow$ **number photons**

$$\frac{m}{100\, cm} \qquad E = \frac{hc}{\lambda} \qquad q = mC_s\Delta T \qquad \frac{q_{water}}{E_{photon}}$$

Solution: $E_{photon} = \dfrac{(6.626 \times 10^{-34} \, J\cancel{s})(3.00 \times 10^8 \, \cancel{m}/\cancel{s})}{(2.8 \times 10^{-4} \, \cancel{cm})\left(\dfrac{\cancel{m}}{100 \, \cancel{cm}}\right)} = 7.1 \times 10^{-20} \, J/photon$

$q = (2.0 \, g)\left(4.18 \dfrac{J}{\cancel{g}g^\circ C}\right)\left(\dfrac{^\circ C}{K}\right)(2.0 \, K) = \underline{1}6.7 \, J$ 　　　 number of photons $= \dfrac{16.7 \, J}{7.1 \times 10^{-20} \, J/photon} = 2.4 \times 10^{20}$ photons

Check: The units of the answer, photons, is correct. The magnitude of the answer seems reasonable because of large amount of heat energy in needed to raise the temperature of the water.

93. In the Bohr model of the atom, the electron travels in a circular orbit around the nucleus. It is a 2 – dimensional model. The electron is constrained to move only from one orbit to another orbit. But, the electron is treated as a particle that behaves according to the laws of classical physics. The quantum – mechanical model of the atom is 3 – dimensional. In this model, we treat the electron, an absolutely small particle, differently than we treat particles with classical physics. The electron is in an orbital, which gives us the probability of finding the electron within a volume of space.
Because the electron in the Bohr model is constrained to a circular orbit, it would theoretically be possible to know both the position and the velocity of the electron simultaneously. This contradicts the Heisenberg uncertainty principle which states that position and velocity are complementary terms which can not both be known with precision.

94. The transition from n = 3 → n = 2 would cause the photoelectric effect while the transition from n = 4 → n = 3 would not. Because the n levels get closer together as n increases, the energy difference between the 4 and 3 level would be less than the energy difference between the 3 and 2 levels. Therefore, the energy of the photon emitted when the electron moves from 4 to 3 would not be above the threshold energy for the metal. the energy of the photon emitted when the electron makes the transition from n = 3 to n = 2 is larger and surpasses the threshold energy thus causing the photoelectric effect.

95. a) Since the interference pattern is caused by single electrons interfering with themselves, the pattern remains the same even when the rate of the electrons passing through the slits is one electron per minute. It will simply take longer for the full pattern to develop.

   b) When a light is placed behind the slits to determine which hole the electron passes through, the light flashes to indicate which hole the electron passed through, but the interference pattern is now absent. With the laser on the electrons hit positions directly behind each slit, as if they were ordinary particles.

   c) Diffraction occurs when a wave encounter an obstacle of a slit that is comparable in size to its wavelength. The wave bends around the slit. The diffraction of light through two slits separated by a distance comparable to the wavelength of the light results in an interference pattern. Each slit acts as a new wave source, and the two new waves interfere with each other. Which result in a pattern of bright and dark lines.

   d) Since the mass of the bullets and their particle size, are not absolutely small, the bullets will not produce an interference pattern when they pass through the slits. The de Broglie wavelength produced by the bullets will not be sufficiently large enough to interfere with the bullet trajectory and no interference pattern will be observed.

Chapter 8
Periodic Properties of the Elements

1. A periodic property is one that is predictable based on the element's position within the periodic table.

2. The size of the ion is important to nerve signal transmission. The pumps and channels within cell membranes are so sensitive that they can distinguish between the sizes of these two ions and selectively allow only one or the other to pass. The movement of ions is the basis for the transmission of nerve signals in the brain and throughout the body.

3. The first attempt to organize the elements according to similarities in their properties was bade by the German chemist Johann Dobereiner. He grouped elements into triads; three elements with similar properties. A more complex approach was attempted by the English chemist John Newlands. He organized elements into octaves, in analogy to musical notes. When arranged this way, the properties of every eighth element were similar.

4. The modern periodic table is credited primarily to the Russian chemist Dmitri Mendeleev. Mendeleev's table is based on the periodic law, which states that when elements are arranged in order of increasing mass, their properties recur periodically. Mendeleev arranged the elements in a table in which mass increased from left to right and elements with similar properties fell in the same columns.

5. Meyer proposed an organization of the known elements based on some periodic properties. Moseley listed elements according to the atomic number rather than atomic mass. This resolved the problems in Mendeleev's table where an increase in atomic mass did not correlate with similar properties.

6. The periodic law was based on the observations that the properties of elements recur and certain elements have similar properties. The theory that explains the existence of the periodic law is quantum – mechanical theory.

7. Electron spin is a fundamental property of electrons. It is more correctly expressed as saying the electron has inherent angular momentum. The value m_s is the spin quantum number. An electron with $m_s = +1/2$ has a spin opposite of an electron with $m_s = -1/2$.

8. In the Stern – Gerlach experiment a beam of silver atom is split into two separate trajectories by a magnet. The spin of the electrons within the atoms creates a tiny magnetic field that interacts with the external field. One spin orientation causes the deflection of the beam in one direction, while the other orientation causes a deflection in the opposite direction. Since there were only two trajectories, the spin of the electron is quantized, that is, it can have one of two values and nothing in between.

9. An electron configuration shows the particular orbitals that are occupied by electrons in an atom. Some examples are: $H = 1s^1$; $He = 1s^2$; $Li = 1s^2 2s^1$

10. Shielding or screening occurs when one electron is blocked from the full effects of the nuclear charge so that the electron experiences only a part of the nuclear charge. Penetration occurs when an electron penetrates the electron cloud of the 1s orbital and now experiences the full effect of the nuclear charge.

11. The sublevels within a principle level split in multielectron atoms because of penetration of the outer electrons into the region of the core electrons. The sublevels in hydrogen are not split because they are empty in the ground state.

12. An orbital diagram is a different way to show the electron configuration of an atom. It symbolizes the electron as an arrow in a box that represents the orbital.
    The orbital diagram for hydrogen ⊞ atom: H
    1s

13. The Pauli exclusion principle states: No two electrons in an atom can have the same four quantum numbers. Since two electrons occupying the same orbital have three identical quantum numbers (n, l, m_l), they must have different spin quantum numbers. The Pauli exclusion principle implies that each orbital can have a maximum of only two electrons, with opposing spins.

14. Degenerate orbitals are orbitals of the same energy. In a multielectron atom, the orbitals in a sublevel are degenerate. Hund's rule states that when filling degenerate orbitals, electrons fill them singly first, with parallel spins. This is a result of an atom's tendency to find the lowest energy state possible.

15. In order of increasing energy the orbitals are: 1s < 2s < 2p < 3s < 3p < 4s < 3d < 4p < 5s. The 4s orbital fills before the 3d and the 5s fills before the 4d because they are lower in energy because of greater penetration of the 4s and 5s orbitals.

16. Valence electrons are those that are important in chemical bonding. For main – group elements, the valence electrons are those in the outermost principal energy level. For transition elements, we also count the outermost d electrons among the valence even though they are not in the outermost principal energy level. The chemical properties of an element depend on its valence electrons, which are important in bonding because they are held most loosely. This is why the elements in a column of the periodic table have similar chemical properties, they have the same number of valence electrons.

17.

Orbital Blocks of the Periodic Table

18. The number of columns in a block corresponds to the maximum number of electrons that can occupy the particular sublevel of that block. The s block has 2 columns corresponding to one s orbital holding a maximum of 2 electrons. The p block has 6 columns corresponding to the three p orbitals with 2 electrons each.

19. The rows in the periodic table grow progressively longer because you are adding sublevels as the n level increases.

20. The group number of a main – group element is equal to the number of valence electrons for that element.

21. The row number of a main – group element is equal to the highest principal quantum number of that element. However, the principal quantum number of the d orbital being filled across each row in the transition series is equal to the row number minus one. For the inner transition elements, the principal quantum number of the f orbital being filled across each row is the row number minus two.

22. In the first transition series of the d block, Cr and Cu have anomalous electron configurations. Cr would be expected to be $[Ar]4s^23d^4$ but it is found to be $[Ar]4s^13d^5$ and Cu is expected to be $[Ar]4s^23d^9$ but is found to be $[Ar]4s^13d^{10}$.

23. To use the periodic table to write the electron configuration: find the noble gas that precedes the element. The element has the inner electron configuration of that noble gas. Place the symbol for the noble gas in [ ]. Obtain the outer electron configuration by tracing the element across the period and assigning electrons in the appropriate orbitals.

24. The chemical properties of elements are largely determined by the number of valence electrons they contain. Their properties are periodic because the number of valence electrons is periodic. Since elements within a column in the periodic table have the same number of valence electrons, they also have similar chemical properties.

25. a) The alkali metals (group 1A) have 1 valence electron and are among the most reactive metals because their outer electron configuration (ns^1) is one electron beyond a noble gas configuration. They react to

227

lose the ns^1 electron, obtaining a noble gas configuration. This is why the group 1A metals tend to form 1+ cations.

b) The alkaline earth metals (group 2A) have 2 valence electrons and have an outer electron configuration of ns^2 and also tend to be reactive metals. They lose their ns^2 electrons to form 2+ cations.

c) The halogens (group 7A) have 7 valence electrons and have an outer electron configuration of ns^{2}np^5. They are among the most reactive non – metals. They are only one electron short of a noble gas configuration and tend to react to gain that one electron, forming 1– anions.

d) The oxygen family (group 6A) has 6 valence electrons and have an outer electron configuration of ns^{2}np^4. They are 2 electrons short of a noble gas configuration and tend to react to gain those two electrons, forming 2– anions.

26. One way to define atomic radii is to consider the distance between nonbinding atoms in molecules or atoms that are touching each other but are not bonded together. An atomic radius determined in this way is called the nonbonding atomic radius or the van der Waals radius. The van der Waals radius represents the radius of an atom when it is not bonded to another atom.
Another way to define the size of an atom, called bonding atomic radius or covalent radius, is defined differently for nonmetals and metals as follows:
    Nonmetals: one – half the distance between two of the atoms bonded together
    Metal: one – half the distance between two of the atoms next to each other in a crystal of the metal
A more general term, the atomic radius, refers to a set of average bonding radii determined from measurements on a large number of elements and compounds. The atomic radius represents the radius of an atom when it is bonded to another atom and is always smaller than the van der Waals radius.

a) As you move to the right across a period in the periodic table, atomic radius decreases.

b) As you move down a column in the periodic table, atomic radius increases.

27. The effective nuclear charge (Z$_{eff}$) is the average or net charge from the nucleus experienced by the electrons in the outermost levels. Shielding is the blocking of nuclear charge from the outermost electrons. The shielding is primarily due to the inner (core) electrons although there is some interaction and shielding from the electron repulsions of the outer electrons with each other.

28. As you move across a row in the periodic table, the n level stays the same. However, the nuclear charge increases and the amount of shielding stays about the same since the number on inner electrons stays the same. So, the effective nuclear charge experienced by the electrons in the outermost principal energy level increases, resulting is a stronger attraction between the outermost electrons and the nucleus and therefore, smaller atomic radii.

29. a) The radii of transition elements stay roughly constant across each row instead of decreasing in size as in the main group elements. The difference is that, across a row of transition elements, the number of electrons in the outermost principal energy level is nearly constant. As another proton is added to the nucleus with each successive element, another electron is added as well, but the electron goes into an n$_{highest}$ – 1 orbital. The number of outermost electrons stays constant and they experience a roughly constant effective nuclear charge, keeping the radius approximately constant.

b) As you go down the first two rows of a column within the transition metals, the elements follow the same general trend in atomic radii and the main – group elements, i.e., the radii get larger because you are adding outermost electrons into higher n levels.

30. The electron configuration of a main – group monatomic ion can be deduced from the electron configuration of the neutral atom and the charge of the ion. For anions, we simply add the number of electrons required by the magnitude of the charge of the anion. The electron configuration of cations is obtained by subtracting the number of electrons required by the magnitude of the charge.

31. An important exception to simply subtracting the number of electrons occurs for transition metal cations. When writing the electron configuration of a transition metal cation, remove the electrons in the highest n – value orbitals first, even if this does not correspond to the reverse order of filling. Normally, even though the d orbital electrons add after the s orbital electrons, the s orbital electrons are lost first. This is because;

1) the ns and (n − 1)d orbitals are extremely close in energy and depending on the exact configuration can vary in relative energy ordering and 2) as the (n − 1)d orbitals begin to fill in the first transition series, the increasing nuclear charge stabilizes the (n − 1)d orbitals relative to the ns orbitals. This happens because the (n − 1)d orbitals are not outermost orbitals and are therefore not effectively shielded from the increasing nuclear charge by the ns orbitals.

32. a) In general, cations are much smaller than their corresponding parent. This is because the outermost electrons are shielded from the nuclear charge in the atom and contribute greatly to the size of the atom. When these electrons are removed to form the cation, the same nuclear charge is now acting only on the core electrons.

   b) In general, anions are much larger than their corresponding atoms. This is because the extra electron are added to the outermost electrons but no additional proton to increase the nuclear charge. The extra electrons increase the repulsions among the outermost electrons resulting in an anion that is large than the atom.

33. The ionization energy (IE) of an atom or ion is the energy required to remove an electron from the atom or ion in the gaseous state. The ionization energy is always positive because removing an electron always takes energy. The energy required to remove the first electron is called the first ionization energy (IE_1). The energy required to remove the second electron is called the second ionization energy (IE_2).

34. Ionization energy generally decreases as you move down a column in the periodic table because electrons in the outermost principal level become farther away from the positively charged nucleus and are therefore held less tightly.
   Ionization energy generally increases as you move to the right across a period in the periodic table because electrons in the outermost principal energy level generally experience a greater effective nuclear charge.

35. Exceptions occur with elements Be, Mg and Ca in group 2A having a higher first ionization energy than elements B, Al, and Ga group 3A. This exception is caused by the change in going form the s block to the p block. The result is that the electrons in the s orbital shield the electron in the p orbital from nuclear charge making it easier to remove.
   Another exception occurs with N, P, and As in group 5A having a higher first ionization energy than O, S, and Se in group 6A. This exception is caused by the repulsion between electrons when they must occupy the same orbital. Group 5A has 3 p electrons while group 6A has 4 p electrons. In the group 5A elements the p orbitals are half – filled which makes the configuration particularly stable. The 4th group 6A electron must pair with another electron making it easier to remove.

36. The second ionization energy of Mg involves removing the second outermost electron leading to an ion with a noble gas configuration for the core electrons. The third ionization energy requires removing a core electron from an ion with a noble gas configuration. This requires a tremendous amount of energy making IE_3 very high.
   For Al, IE_3 involves removing the third outermost electron for Al, leaving the ion with a noble gas configuration of the core electrons. IE_4 then requires removing a core electron from an ion with a noble gas configuration. This requires a tremendous amount of energy and makes IE_4 very high.
   You can predict where the IE energy is going to by very high by looking for the ionization that requires removing a core electron.

37. The electron affinity (EA) of an atom or ion is the energy change associated with the gaining of an electron by the atom in the gaseous state. The electron affinity is usually – though not always – negative because an atom or ion usually releases energy when it gains an electron. The trends in electron affinity are not as regular as trends in other properties. For main – group elements, electron affinity generally becomes more negative as you move to the right across a row in the periodic table. There is not a corresponding trend in electron affinity going down a column.

38. Metals are good conductors of heat and electricity, they can be pounded into flat sheets (malleability), they can be drawn into wires (ductility), they are often shiny, and they tend to lose electrons in chemical reactions. As you move to the right across a period in the periodic table, metallic character decreases. As you move down a column in the periodic table, metallic character increases.

39. a) The reactions of the alkali metals with halogens results in the formation of metal halides
   $2 M(s) + X_2 \rightarrow 2 MX(s)$

b) Alkali metals react with water to form the dissolved alkali metal ion, the hydroxide ion and hydrogen gas.

$$2 \, M(s) + 2 \, H_2O(l) \rightarrow 2 \, M^+(aq) + 2 \, OH^-(aq) + H_2(g)$$

40. All of the halogens are powerful oxidizing agents.

   a) The halogens react with metals to form metal halides.

   $$2 \, M(s) + n \, X_2 \rightarrow 2 \, MX_n(s)$$

   b) The halogens react with hydrogen to form hydrogen halides.

   $$H_2(g) + X_2 \rightarrow 2 \, HX(g)$$

   c) The halogens react with each other to form interhalogen compounds.

   e.g. $Br_2(l) + F_2(g) \rightarrow 2 \, BrF(g)$

41. a) P   Phosphorus has 15 electrons. Distribute two of these into the 1s orbital, two into the 2s orbital, six into the 2p orbital, two into the 3s orbital, and three into the 3p orbital. $1s^2 2s^2 2p^6 3s^2 3p^3$

   b) C   Carbon has 6 electrons. Distribute two of these into the 1s orbital, two into the 2s orbital, and two into the 2p orbital. $1s^2 2s^2 2p^2$

   c) Na   Sodium has 11 electrons. Distribute two of these into the 1s orbital, two into the 2s orbital, six into the 2p orbital and one into the 3s orbital. $1s^2 2s^2 2p^6 3s^1$

   d) Ar   Argon has 18 electrons. Distribute two of these into the 1s orbital, two into the 2s orbital, six into the 2p orbital, two into the 3s orbital, and six into the 3p orbital. $1s^2 2s^2 2p^6 3s^2 3p^6$

42. a) O   Oxygen has 8 electrons. Distribute two of these into the 1s orbital, two into the 2s orbital, and 4 into the 2p orbital. $1s^2 2s^2 2p^4$

   b) Si   Silicon has 14 electrons. Distribute two of these into the 1s orbital, two into the 2s orbital, six into the 2p orbital, two into the 3s orbital, and two into the 3p orbital. $1s^2 2s^2 2p^6 3s^2 3p^2$

   c) Ne   Neon has 10 electrons. Distribute two of these into the 1s orbital, two into the 2s orbital, and six into the 2p orbital. $1s^2 2s^2 2p^6$

   d) K   Potassium has 19 electrons. Distribute two of these into the 1s orbital, two into the 2s orbital, six into the 2p orbital, two into the 3s orbital, six into the 3p orbital and one into the 4s orbital. $1s^2 2s^2 2p^6 3s^2 3p^6 4s^1$

43. a) N   Nitrogen has 7 electrons and has the electron configuration: $1s^2 2s^2 2p^3$. Draw a box for each orbital putting the lowest energy orbital (1s) on the far left and proceeding to orbitals of higher energy to the right. Distribute the 7 electrons into the boxes representing the orbitals, allowing a maximum of two electrons per orbital and remembering Hund's rule. You can see from the diagram that nitrogen has 3 unpaired electrons.

   $$\boxed{\uparrow\downarrow} \quad \boxed{\uparrow\downarrow} \quad \boxed{\uparrow \mid \uparrow \mid \uparrow}$$
   1s   2s   2p

   b) F   Fluorine has 9 electrons and has the electron configuration: $1s^2 2s^2 2p^5$. Draw a box for each orbital putting the lowest energy orbital (1s) on the far left and proceeding to orbitals of higher energy to the right. Distribute the 9 electrons into the boxes representing the orbitals, allowing a maximum of two electrons per orbital and remembering Hund's rule. You can see from the diagram that fluorine has 1 unpaired electrons.

$$\boxed{\uparrow\downarrow}\quad\boxed{\uparrow\downarrow}\quad\boxed{\uparrow\downarrow\,|\,\uparrow\downarrow\,|\,\uparrow}$$
1s 2s 2p

c) Mg   Magnesium has 12 electrons and has the electron configuration: $1s^2 2s^2 2p^6 3s^2$. Draw a box for each orbital putting the lowest energy orbital (1s) on the far left and proceeding to orbitals of higher energy to the right. Distribute the 12 electrons into the boxes representing the orbitals, allowing a maximum of two electrons per orbital and remembering Hund's rule. You can see from the diagram that magnesium has no unpaired electrons.

$$\boxed{\uparrow\downarrow}\quad\boxed{\uparrow\downarrow}\quad\boxed{\uparrow\downarrow\,|\,\uparrow\downarrow\,|\,\uparrow\downarrow}\quad\boxed{\uparrow\downarrow}$$
1s 2s 2p 3s

d) Al   Aluminum has 13 electrons and has the electron configuration: $1s^2 2s^2 2p^6 3s^2 3p^1$. Draw a box for each orbital putting the lowest energy orbital (1s) on the far left and proceeding to orbitals of higher energy to the right. Distribute the 13 electrons into the boxes representing the orbitals, allowing a maximum of two electrons per orbital and remembering Hund's rule. You can see from the diagram that aluminum has 1 unpaired electron.

$$\boxed{\uparrow\downarrow}\quad\boxed{\uparrow\downarrow}\quad\boxed{\uparrow\downarrow\,|\,\uparrow\downarrow\,|\,\uparrow\downarrow}\quad\boxed{\uparrow\downarrow}\quad\boxed{\uparrow\,|\,\,|\,}$$
1s 2s 2p 3s 3p

44. a) S   Sulfur has 16 electrons and has the electron configuration: $1s^2 2s^2 2p^6 3s^2 3p^4$. Draw a box for each orbital putting the lowest energy orbital (1s) on the far left and proceeding to orbitals of higher energy to the right. Distribute the 16 electrons into the boxes representing the orbitals, allowing a maximum of two electrons per orbital and remembering Hund's rule. You can see from the diagram that sulfur has 2 unpaired electrons.

$$\boxed{\uparrow\downarrow}\quad\boxed{\uparrow\downarrow}\quad\boxed{\uparrow\downarrow\,|\,\uparrow\downarrow\,|\,\uparrow\downarrow}\quad\boxed{\uparrow\downarrow}\quad\boxed{\uparrow\downarrow\,|\,\uparrow\,|\,\uparrow}$$
1s 2s 2p 3s 3p

b) Ca   Calcium has 20 electrons and has the electron configuration: $1s^2 2s^2 2p^6 3s^2 3p^6 4s^2$. Draw a box for each orbital putting the lowest energy orbital (1s) on the far left and proceeding to orbitals of higher energy to the right. Distribute the 20 electrons into the boxes representing the orbitals, allowing a maximum of two electrons per orbital and remembering Hund's rule. You can see from the diagram that nitrogen has no unpaired electrons.

$$\boxed{\uparrow\downarrow}\quad\boxed{\uparrow\downarrow}\quad\boxed{\uparrow\downarrow\,|\,\uparrow\downarrow\,|\,\uparrow\downarrow}\quad\boxed{\uparrow\downarrow}\quad\boxed{\uparrow\downarrow\,|\,\uparrow\downarrow\,|\,\uparrow\downarrow}\quad\boxed{\uparrow\downarrow}$$
1s 2s 2p 3s 3p 4s

c) Ne   Neon has 10 electrons and has the electron configuration: $1s^2 2s^2 2p^6$. Draw a box for each orbital putting the lowest energy orbital (1s) on the far left and proceeding to orbitals of higher energy to the right. Distribute the 10 electrons into the boxes representing the orbitals, allowing a maximum of two electrons per orbital and remembering Hund's rule. You can see from the diagram that neon has no unpaired electrons.

$$\boxed{\uparrow\downarrow}\quad\boxed{\uparrow\downarrow}\quad\boxed{\uparrow\downarrow\,|\,\uparrow\downarrow\,|\,\uparrow\downarrow}$$
1s 2s 2p

d) He   Helium has 2 electrons and has the electron configuration: $1s^2$. Draw a box for each orbital putting the lowest energy orbital (1s) on the far left and proceeding to orbitals of higher energy to the right. Distribute the 2 electrons into the boxes representing the orbitals, allowing a maximum of two electrons per orbital and remembering Hund's rule. You can see from the diagram that helium has 0 unpaired electrons.

$$\boxed{\uparrow\downarrow}$$
1s

45. a) P   The atomic number of P is 15. The noble gas that precedes P in the periodic table is neon, so the inner electron configuration is [Ne]. Obtain the outer electron configuration by tracing the elements between Ne and P and assigning electrons to the appropriate orbitals. Begin with [Ne]. Because P is in row 3, add two 3s electrons.

Next add three 3p electrons as you trace across the p block to P which is in the third column of the p block.

P $[Ne]3s^23p^3$

b) Ge

The atomic number of Ge is 32. The noble gas that precedes Ge in the periodic table is argon, so the inner electron configuration is [Ar]. Obtain the outer electron configuration by tracing the elements between Ar and Ge and assigning electrons to the appropriate orbitals. Begin with [Ar]. Because Ge is in row 4, add two 4s electrons. Next, add ten 3d electrons as you trace across the d block. Finally add two 4p electrons as you trace across the p block to Ge which is in the second column of the p block.

Ge $[Ar]4s^23d^{10}4p^2$

c) Zr

The atomic number of Zr is 40. The noble gas that precedes Zr in the periodic table is krypton, so the inner electron configuration is [Kr]. Obtain the outer electron configuration by tracing the elements between Kr and Zr and assigning electrons to the appropriate orbitals. Begin with [Kr]. Because Zr is in row 5, add two 5s electrons. Next, add two 4d electrons as you trace across the d block to Zr which is in the second column.

Zr $[Kr]5s^24d^2$

d) I

The atomic number of I is 53. The noble gas that precedes I in the periodic table is Krypton, so the inner electron configuration is [Kr]. Obtain the outer electron configuration by tracing the elements between Kr and I and assigning electrons to the appropriate orbitals. Begin with [Kr]. Because I is in row 5, add two 5s electrons. Next, add ten 4d electrons as you trace across the d block. Finally add five 5p electrons as you trace across the p block to I which is in the fifth column of the p block.

I $[Kr]5s^24d^{10}5p^5$

46. a) $[Ar] 4s^23d^{10}4p^6$ To determine the element corresponding to the electron configuration, begin with Ar then trace across the 4s block, the 3d block and then the 4p block until you come to the sixth column. The element is Kr.

b) $[Ar] 4s^23d^2$ To determine the element corresponding to the electron configuration, begin with Ar then trace across the 4s block, and then 3d block until you come to the second column. The element is Ti.

c) $[Kr] 5s^24d^{10}5p^2$ To determine the element corresponding to the electron configuration, begin with Kr then trace across the 5s block, the 4d block and then the 5p block until you come to the second column. The element is Sn.

d) $[Kr] 5s^2$ To determine the element corresponding to the electron configuration, begin with Kr then trace across the 5s block to the second column. The element is Sr.

47. a) Li is in period 2, and the first column in the s block so Li has one 2s electon.

b) Cu is in period 4, and the ninth column in the d block (n – 1) so Cu should have nine 3d electrons, however, it is one of our exceptions so it has ten 3d electrons.

c) Br is in period 4, and the fifth column of the p block, so Br has five 4p electrons.

d) Zr is in period 5, and the second column of the d block (n – 1), so Zr has two 4d electrons.

48. a) Mg is in period 3, and the second column of the s block, so Mg has two 3s electrons.

b) Cr is in period 4, and the fourth column of the d block (n – 1) so Cr should have four 3d electrons, however, Cr in one of our exceptions so it has five 3d electrons.

c) Y is in period 5, and the first column of the d block (n – 1) so Y has one 4d electron.

d) Pb is in period 6, and the second column of the p block, so Pb has two 6p electrons.

49. a) In period 4, an element with five valence electrons could be V or As.

b) In period 4, an element with four 4p electrons would be in the fourth column of the p block and is Se.

c) In period 4, an element with three 3d electrons would be in the third column of the d block (n – 1) and is V.

d) In period 4, an element with a complete outer shell would be in the sixth column of the p block and is Kr.

50. a) In period 3, an element with three valence electrons would be in the first column of the p block and is Al.

b) In period 3, an element with four 3p electrons would be in the fourth column of the p block and is S.

c) In period 3, an element with six 3p electrons would be in the sixth column of the p block and is Ar.

d) In period 3, an element with two 3s electrons and no 3p electrons would be in the second column of the s block and is Mg.

51. a) Ba is in column 2A, so it has two valence electrons.

b) Cs is in column 1A, so it has one valence electron.

c) Ni is in column 8 of the d block, so it has 10 valence electrons (8 from the d block and 2 from the s block)

d) S is in column 6A, so it has six valence electrons.

52. a) Al is in column 3A, so it has three valence electrons. Al is a metal and will tend to lose the three valence electrons to achieve the noble gas configuration of Ne.

b) Sn in in column 4A, so it has four valence electrons. Sn is a metal and will tend to lose the valence electrons to obtain a completely filled n = 3 level.

c) Br is in column 7A, so it has seven valence electrons. Br is a nonmetal and will tend to gain an electron to achieve the noble gas configuration of Kr.

d) Se is in column 6A, so it has six valence electrons. Se is a nonmetal and will tend to gain electrons to achieve the noble gas configuration of Kr.

53. a) The outer electron configuration ns^2 would belong to a reactive metal in the alkaline earth family.

b) The outer electron configuration ns^2np^6 would belong to an unreactive nonmetal in the noble gas family.

c) The outer electron configuration ns^2np^5 would belong to a reactive nonmetal in the halogen family.

d) The outer electron configuration ns^2np^2 would belong to an element in the carbon family. If n = 2, the element is a nonmetal, if n = 3 or 4, the element is a metalloid, and if n = 5 or 6, the element is a metal.

54. a) The outer electron configuration ns^2 would belong to a metal in the alkaline earth family.

b) The outer electron configuration ns^2np^6 would belong to a nonmetal in the noble gas family.

c) The outer electron configuration ns^2np^5 would belong to a nonmetal in the halogen family.

d) The outer electron configuration ns^2np^2 would belong to an element in the carbon family. If $n = 2$, the element is a nonmetal, if $n = 3$ or 4, the element is a metalloid, and if $n = 5$ or 6, the element is a metal.

55. The valence electrons in nitrogen would experience a greater effective nuclear charge. Be has 4 protons and N has 7 protons. Both atoms have 2 core electrons that predominately contribute to the shielding while the valence electrons will contribute a slight shielding effect. So, Be has an effective nuclear charge of slightly more than 2+ and N has an effective nuclear charge of slightly more than 5+.

56. $S(16) = [Ne]3s^23p^4$ $\quad$ $Mg(12) = [Ne]3s^2Al(13) = [Ne]3s^23p^1$ $\quad$ $Si(14) = [Ne]3s^23p^2$
All four atoms have the same number of core electrons that contribute to shielding. So, the effective nuclear charge will decrease with decreasing number of protons. $\quad$ $S > Si > Al > Mg$

57. a) $K(19)$ $[Ar]4s^1$ $\qquad$ $Z_{eff} = Z - \text{core electrons} = 19 - 18 = 1+$

b) $Ca(20)$ $[Ar]4s^2$ $\qquad$ $Z_{eff} = Z - \text{core electrons} = 20 - 18 = 2+$

c) $O(8)$ $[He]2s^22p^4$ $\qquad$ $Z_{eff} = Z - \text{core electrons} = 8 - 2 = 6+$

d) $C(6)$ $[He]2s^22p^2$ $\qquad$ $Z_{eff} = Z - \text{core electrons} = 6 - 2 = 4+$

58. B has an electron configuration of $1s^22s^22p^1$. To estimate the effective nuclear charge experienced by the outer electrons we need to distinguish between two different types of shielding: (1) the shielding of the outermost electrons by the core electrons and (2) the shielding of the outermost electrons by each other. The three outermost electrons in boron experience the 5+ charge of the nucleus through the shield of the two 1s core electrons. We can estimate that the shielding experience by any one of the outermost electrons due to the core electrons is nearly 2. For the 2s electrons the shielding due to the other 2s electron is nearly zero. For the 2p electron however, we would expect that the 2s electrons would contribute some shielding because although the 2p orbital penetrates the 2s orbital to some degree most of the 2p orbital lies outside the 2s orbital. So the effective nuclear charge would be slightly greater than 3+ and the effective nuclear charge felt by the 2s electrons would be greater than the effective nuclear charge felt by the 2p electrons.

59. a) Al or In $\qquad$ In atoms are larger than Al atoms because, as you trace the path between Al and In on the periodic table, you move down a column. Atomic size increases as you move down a column because the outermost electrons occupy orbitals with a higher principal quantum number that are therefore larger, resulting in a larger atom.

b) Si or N $\qquad$ Si atoms are larger than N atoms because, as you trace the path between N and Si on the periodic table, you move down a column (atomic size increases) and then to the left across a period (atomic size increases). These effects add together for an overall increase.

c) P or Pb $\qquad$ Pb atoms are larger than P atoms because, as you trace the path between P and Pb on the periodic table, you move down a column (atomic size increases) and then to the left across a period (atomic size increases). These effects add together for an overall increase.

d) C or F $\qquad$ C atoms are larger than F atoms because, as you trace the path between C and F on the periodic table, you move to the right within the same period. As you move to the right across a period, the effective nuclear charge experienced by the outermost electrons increase, resulting in a smaller size.

60. a) Sn of Si   Sn atoms are larger than Si atoms because, as you trace the path between Si and Sn on the periodic table, you move down a column. Atomic size increases as you move down a column because the outermost electrons occupy orbitals with a higher principal quantum number that are therefore larger, resulting in a larger atom.

   b) Br or Ga   Ga atoms are larger than Br atoms because, as you trace the path between Ga and Br on the periodic table, you move to the right within the same period. As you move to the right across a period, the effective nuclear charge experienced by the outermost electrons increase, resulting in a smaller size.

   c) Sn or Bi   Based on periodic trends alone, you cannot tell which atom is larger, because as you trace the path between Sn and Bi you go to the right across a period (atomic size decreases) and then down a column (atomic size increases). These effects tend to oppose each other, and it is not easy to tell which will predominate.

   d) Se or Sn   Sn atoms are larger than Se atoms because, as you trace the path between Se and Sn on the periodic table, you move down a column (atomic size increases) and then to the left across a period (atomic size increases). These effects add together for an overall increase.

61. Ca, Rb, S, Si, Ge, F   F is above and to the right of the other elements so we start with F as the smallest atom. As you trace a path from F to S you move to the left (size increases) and down (size increases), then you move to Si to the left (size increases) then down to Ge (size increases) then to the left to Ca (size increases) then to the left and down to Rb (size increases). So, in order of increasing atomic radii; F < S < Si < Ge < Ca < Rb

62. Cs, Sb, S, Pb, Se   Cs is below and to the left of the other elements so we start with Cs as the largest atom. As you trace a path from Cs to Pb you move to the right in the same period (size decreases), then from Pb to Sb you move up a column and then to the right (size decreases) from Sb to Se you move up the column and then to the right (size decreases) and finally from Se to S you move up the column (size decreases). So, in order of decreasing radii:
Cs > Pb > Sb > Se > S

63. a) O^{2-} Begin by writing the electron configuration of the neutral atom.
   O $1s^2 2s^2 2p^4$
   Since this ion has a 2 – charge, add two electrons to write the electron configuration of the ion.
   O^{2-} $1s^2 2s^2 2p^6$ or [Ar]

   b) Br^- Begin by writing the electron configuration of the neutral atom.
   Br $[Ar]4s^2 3d^{10} 4p^5$
   Since this ion has a 1 – charge, add one electrons to write the electron configuration of the ion.
   Br^- $[Ar]4s^2 3d^{10} 4p^6$ or [Kr]

   c) Sr^{2+} Begin by writing the electron configuration of the neutral atom.
   Sr $[Kr]5s^2$
   Since this ion has a 2+ charge, remove two electrons to write the electron configuration of the ion.
   Sr^{2+} [Kr]

   d) Co^{3+} Begin by writing the electron configuration of the neutral atom.
   Co $[Ar]4s^2 3d^7$
   Since this ion has a 3+ charge, remove three electrons to write the electron configuration of the ion. Since it is a transition metal, remove the electrons from the 4s orbital before removing electrons from the 3d orbitals.
   Co^{3+} $[Ar]4s^0 3d^6$

   e) Cu^{2+} Begin by writing the electron configuration of the neutral atom. Remember, Cu is one of our exceptions.
   Cu $[Ar]4s^1 3d^{10}$

Since this ion has a 2+ charge, remove two electrons to write the electron configuration of the ion. Since it is a transition metal, remove the electrons from the 4s orbital before removing electrons from the 3d orbitals.

Cu^{2+} $[Ar]4s^03d^9$

64. a) Cl^- Begin by writing the electron configuration of the neutral atom.

Cl $[Ne]3s^23p^5$

Since this ion has a 1 – charge, add one electrons to write the electron configuration of the ion.

Cl^- $[Ne]3s^23p^6$ or $[Ar]$

b) P^{3-} Begin by writing the electron configuration of the neutral atom.

P $[Ne]3s^23p^3$

Since this ion has a 3 – charge, add three electrons to write the electron configuration of the ion.

P^{3-} $[Ne]3s^23p^6$ or $[Ar]$

c) K^+ Begin by writing the electron configuration of the neutral atom.

K $[Ar]4s^1$

Since this ion has a 2+ charge, remove two electrons to write the electron configuration of the ion.

K^+ $[Ar]$

d) Mo^{3+} Begin by writing the electron configuration of the neutral atom. Remember, Mo is one of our exceptions.

Mo $[Kr]5s^14d^5$

Since this ion has a 3+ charge, remove three electrons to write the electron configuration of the ion. Since it is a transition metal, remove the electrons from the 5s orbital before removing electrons from the 4d orbitals.

Mo^{3+} $[Kr]5s^04d^3$

e) V^{3+} Begin by writing the electron configuration of the neutral atom.

V $[Ar]4s^23d^3$

Since this ion has a 3+ charge, remove three electrons to write the electron configuration of the ion. Since it is a transition metal, remove the electrons from the 4s orbital before removing electrons from the 3d orbitals.

V^{3+} $[Ar]4s^03d^2$

65. a) V^{5+} Begin by writing the electron configuration of the neutral atom.

V $[Ar]4s^23d^3$

Since this ion has a 5+ charge, remove five electrons to write the electron configuration of the ion. Since it is a transition metal, remove the electrons from the 4s orbital before removing electrons from the 3d orbitals.

V^{5+} $[Ar]4s^03d^0$ = $[Ne]3s^23p^6$

        3s   3p

V^{5+} is diamagnetic

b) Cr^{3+} Begin by writing the electron configuration of the neutral atom. Remember, Cr is one of our exceptions.

Cr $[Ar]4s^13d^5$

Since this ion has a 3+ charge, remove three electrons to write the electron configuration of the ion. Since it is a transition metal, remove the electrons from the 4s orbital before removing electrons from the 3d orbitals.

Cr^{3+} $[Ar]4s^03d^3$

[Ar]

$$\text{4s} \qquad \text{3d}$$

Cr^{3+} is paramagnetic

c) Ni^{2+} Begin by writing the electron configuration of the neutral atom.

Ni $[Ar]4s^23d^8$

Since this ion has a 2+ charge, remove two electrons to write the electron configuration of the ion. Since it is a transition metal, remove the electrons from the 4s orbital before removing electrons from the 3d orbitals.

Ni^{2+} $[Ar]4s^03d^8$

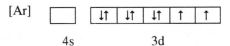

$$\text{[Ar]} \qquad \qquad \text{4s} \qquad \qquad \text{3d}$$

Ni^{2+} is paramagnetic

d) Fe^{3+} Begin by writing the electron configuration of the neutral atom.

Fe $[Ar]4s^23d^6$

Since this ion has a 3+ charge, remove three electrons to write the electron configuration of the ion. Since it is a transition metal, remove the electrons from the 4s orbital before removing electrons from the 3d orbitals.

Fe^{3+} $[Ar]4s^03d^5$

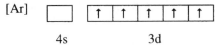

$$\text{[Ar]} \qquad \qquad \text{4s} \qquad \qquad \text{3d}$$

Fe^{3+} is paramagnetic

66. a) Cd^{2+} Begin by writing the electron configuration of the neutral atom.

Cd $[Kr]5s^24d^{10}$

Since this ion has a 2+ charge, remove two electrons to write the electron configuration of the ion. Since it is a transition metal, remove the electrons from the 5s orbital before removing electrons from the 4d orbitals.

Cd^{2+} $[Kr]5s^04d^{10}$

$$\text{[Kr]} \qquad \qquad \text{5s} \qquad \qquad \text{4d}$$

Cd^{2+} is diamagnetic

b) Au^+ Begin by writing the electron configuration of the neutral atom. Remember Au is one of our exceptions.

Au $[Xe]6s^14f^{14}5d^{10}$

Since this ion has a + charge, remove one electrons to write the electron configuration of the ion. Since it is a transition metal, remove the electrons from the 6s orbital before removing electrons from the 5d or 4f orbitals.

Au^+ $[Xe]6s^14f^{14}5d^9$

$$\text{[Xe]} \qquad \qquad \text{6s} \qquad \qquad \text{4f} \qquad \qquad \text{5d}$$

Au^+ is diamagnetic

c) Mo^{3+} Begin by writing the electron configuration of the neutral atom. Remember, Mo is one of our exceptions.

Mo $[Kr]5s^14d^5$

Since this ion has a 3+ charge, remove three electrons to write the electron configuration of the ion. Since it is a transition metal, remove the electrons from the 5s orbital before removing electrons from the 4d orbitals.

Mo^{3+} $[Kr]5s^04d^3$

5s 4d

Mo^{3+} is paramagnetic

d) Zr^{2+} Begin by writing the electron configuration of the neutral atom.
Zr $[Kr]5s^24d^2$
Since this ion has a 2+ charge, remove two electrons to write the electron configuration of the ion. Since it is a transition metal, remove the electrons from the 5s orbital before removing electrons from the 4d orbitals.
Zr^{2+} $[Kr]5s^04d^2$

5s 4d

Zr^{2+} is paramagnetic

67. a) Li or Li^+ A Li atom is larger than Li^+ because cations are smaller than the atoms from which they are formed.

b) I^- or Cs^+ An I^- ion is larger than a Cs^+ ion because, although they are isoelectronic, I^- has two fewer protons than Cs^+ resulting in a lesser pull on the electrons and therefore larger radius.

c) Cr or Cr^{3+} A Cr atom is larger than Cr^{3+} because cations are smaller than the atoms from which they are formed.

d) O or O^{2-} An O^{2-} ion is larger than an O atom because anions are larger than the atoms from which they are formed.

68. a) Sr or Sr^{2+} A Sr atom is larger than Sr^{2+} because cations are smaller than the atoms from which they are formed.

b) N or N^{3-} An N^{3-} ion is larger than an N atom because anions are larger than the atoms from which they are formed.

c) Ni or Ni^{2+} A Ni atom is larger than Ni^{2+} because cations are smaller than the atoms from which they are formed.

d) S^{2-} or Ca^{2+} An S^{2-} ion is larger than a Ca^{2+} ion because, although they are isoelectronic, S^{2-} has four fewer protons than Ca^{2+} resulting in a lesser pull on the electrons and therefore larger radius.

69. Since all the species are isoelectronic, the radius will depend on the number of protons in each species. The fewer the protons the larger the radius.
F: Z = 9; Ne: Z = 10; O: Z = 8; Mg: Z = 12; Na: Z = 11
So: $O^{2-} > F^- > Ne > Na^+ > Mg^{2+}$

70. Since all the species are isoelectronic, the radius will depend on the number of protons in each species. The fewer the protons, the larger the radius.
Se: Z = 34; Kr: Z = 36; Sr: Z = 38; Rb: Z = 37; Br: Z = 35
So: $Sr^{2+} < Rb^+ < Kr < Br^- < Se^{2-}$

71. a) Br or Bi   Br has a higher ionization energy than Bi because, as you trace the path between Br and Bi on the periodic table, you move down a column (ionization energy decreases) and then to the left across a period (ionization energy decreases). Theses effects sum together for an overall decrease.

b) Na or Rb

Na has a higher ionization energy than Rb because, as you trace a path between Na and Rb on the periodic table, you move down a column. Ionization energy decreases as you go down a column because of the increasing size of orbitals with increasing n.

c) As or At

Based on periodic trends alone, it is impossible to tell which has a higher ionization energy because, as trace the path between As and At you go to the right across a period (ionization energy increases) and then down a column (ionization energy decreases). These effects tend to oppose each other, and it is not obvious which will dominate.

d) P or Sn

P has a higher ionization energy than Sn because, as you trace the path between P and Sn on the periodic table, you move down a column (ionization energy decreases) and then to the left across a period (ionization energy decreases). Theses effects sum together for an overall decrease.

72. a) P or I

Based on periodic trends alone, it is impossible to tell which has a higher ionization energy because, as trace the path between P and I you go to the right across a period (ionization energy increases) and then down a column (ionization energy decreases). These effects tend to oppose each other, and it is not obvious which will dominate.

b) Se or Cl

Cl has a higher ionization energy than Se because, as you trace the path between Cl and Se on the periodic table, you move down a column (ionization energy decreases) and then to the left across a period (ionization energy decreases). Theses effects sum together for an overall decrease.

c) P or Sb

P has a higher ionization energy than Sb because, as you trace a path between P and Sb on the periodic table, you move down a column. Ionization energy decreases as you go down a column because of the increasing size of orbitals with increasing n.

d) Ga or Ge

Ge has a higher ionization energy than Ga because, as you trace a path between Ga and Ge on the periodic table, you move to the right within the same period.
Ionization energy increases as you go to the right because of increasing effective nuclear charge.

73. Since ionization energy increases as you move to the right across a period and increases as you move up a column, the element with the smallest first ionization energy would be the element farthest to the left and lowest down on the periodic table. So, In has the smallest ionization energy, as you trace a path to the right and up on the periodic table, the next element reached is Si, continuing up and to the right you reach N and then continuing to the right you reach F. So, in the order of increasing first ionization energy the elements are: In < Si < N < F.

74. Since ionization energy increases as you move to the right across a period and increases as you move up a column, the element with the largest first ionization energy would be the element farthest to the right and highest up on the periodic table. So, Cl has the largest ionization energy, as you trace a path to the left on the periodic table you reach S, as you move down a column and to the left you reach Sn, moving down the column you reach Pb. So, in the order of decreasing first ionization energy the elements are: Cl > S > Sn > Pb.

75. The jump in ionization energy occurs when you change from removing a valence electron to removing a core electron. To determine where this jump occurs you need to look at the electron configuration of the atom.

a) Be $1s^2 2s^2$

The first and second ionization energies involve removing 2s electrons, the third ionization energy removes a core electron, so the jump will occur between the second and third ionization energies.

b) N $1s^2 2s^2 2p^3$

The first five ionization energies involve removing the 2p and 2s electrons, the sixth ionization energy removes a core electron, so the jump will occur between the fifth and sixth ionization energies.

c)	O	$1s^22s^22p^4$	The first six ionization energies involve removing the 2p and 2s electrons, the seventh ionization energy removes a core electron, so the jump will occur between the sixth and seventh ionization energies.
d)	Li	$1s^22s^1$	The first ionization energy involve removing a 2s electrons, the second ionization energy removes a core electron, so the jump will occur between the first and second ionization energies.

76. The jump occurs between IE_3 and IE_4, so removing the first three electrons involves removing valence electrons and the fourth electron is a core electron, so the valence electron configuration would be ns^2np^1; this puts the element in column 3A and would be Al.

77. a) Na or Rb   Na has a more negative electron affinity than Rb. In column 1A electron affinity decreases as you go down the column.

   b) B or S   S has a more negative electron affinity than B. As you trace from B to S in the periodic table, you move to the right which shows the value of the electron affinity becoming more negative. Also, as you move from period 2 to period 3, the value of the electron affinity becomes more negative. Both of these trends sum together for the value of the electron affinity te become more negative.

   c) C or N   C has the more negative electron affinity. As you trace from C to N across the periodic table, you would normally expect N to have the more negative electron affinity. However, N has a half – filled p sublevel which lends it extra stability therefore, it is harder to add an electron.

   d) Li or F   F has the more negative electron affinity. As you trace from Li to F on the periodic table you move to the right in the period. As you go to the right across a period, the value of the electron affinity generally becomes more negative.

78. a) Mg or S   S has the more negative electron affinity. As you trace from Mg to S on the periodic table you move to the right in the period. As you go to the right across a period, the value of the electron affinity generally becomes more negative.

   b) K or Cs   K has the more negative electron affinity. In column 1A as you go down the column the electron affinity becomes less negative.

   c) Si or P   Si has the more negative electron affinity. As you trace from Si to P across the periodic table, you would normally expect P to have the more negative electron affinity. However, P has a half – filled p sublevel which lends extra stability therefore, it is harder to add an electron.

   d) Ga or Br   Br has the more negative electron affinity. As you trace from Ga to Br on the periodic table you move to the right in the period. As you go to the right across a period, the value of the electron affinity generally becomes more negative.

79. a) Sr or Sb   Sr is more metallic than Sb because, as we trace the path between Sr and Sb on the periodic table, we move to the right within the same period. Metallic character decreases as you go to the right.

   b) As or Bi   Bi is more metallic because as we trace a path between As and Bi on the periodic table, we move down a column in the same family (metallic character increases).

   c) Cl or O   Based on periodic trends alone, we cannot tell which is more metallic because as we trace the path between O and Cl, we go to the right across a period (metallic character decreases) and then down a column (metallic character increases). These effects tend to oppose each other, and it is not easy to tell which will predominate.

d) S or As   As is more metallic than S because, as we trace the path between S and As on the periodic table, we move down a column (metallic character increases) and then to the left across a period (metallic character increases). These effects add together for an overall increase.

80. a)   Sb or Pb   Pb is more metallic than Sb because, as we trace the path between Sb and Pb on the periodic table, we move down a column (metallic character increases) and then to the left across a period (metallic character increases). These effects add together for an overall increase.

b)   K or Ge   K is more metallic than Ge because, as we trace the path between K and Ge on the periodic table, we move to the right within the same period. Metallic character decreases as you go to the right.

c)   Ge or Sb   Based on periodic trends alone, we cannot tell which is more metallic because as we trace the path between Ge and Sb, we go to the right across a period (metallic character decreases) and then down a column (metallic character increases). These effects tend to oppose each other, and it is not easy to tell which will predominate.

d)   As or Sn   Sn is more metallic than As because, as we trace the path between As and Sn on the periodic table, we move down a column (metallic character increases) and then to the left across a period (metallic character increases). These effects add together for an overall increase.

81. The order of increasing metallic character is: S < Se < Sb < In < Ba < Fr.
Metallic character decreases as you move left to right across a period and decreases as you move up a column, therefore, the element with the least metallic character will be to the top – right of the periodic table. So, of these elements, S has the least metallic character. As you move down the column, the next element is Se, as you continue down and then to the right, you reach Sb, continuing to the right goes to In, going down the column and then to the right comes to Ba and then down the column and to the right is Fr.

82. The order of decreasing metallic character is: Sr > Ga > Al > Si > P > N.
Metallic character decreases as you move left to right across a period and decreases as you move up a column, therefore, the element with the greatest metallic character will be at the bottom – left of the periodic table. So, of these elements, Sr has the most metallic character. As you trace up the column and then to the right across the period the next element is Ga, trace up the column to Al, then to the right to Si and then P, trace up the column to N.

83. Alkaline earth metals react with halogens to form metal halides. Write the formulas for the reactants and the metal halide product.
$$Sr(s) + I_2(g) \rightarrow SrI_2(s)$$

84. Li would be the alkali metal with the highest ionization energy so it should have the most exothermic reaction with chlorine gas.
$$2\,Li(s) + Cl_2(g) \rightarrow 2\,LiCl(s)$$

85. Alkali metals react with water to form the dissolved metal ion, the hydroxide ion, and hydrogen gas. Write the skeletal equation including each of these and then balance it:
$$Li(s) + H_2O(l) \rightarrow Li^+(aq) + OH^-(aq) + H_2(g)$$
$$2\,Li(s) + 2\,H_2O(l) \rightarrow 2\,Li^+(aq) + 2\,OH^-(aq) + H_2(g)$$

86. Alkali metals react with water to form the dissolved metal ion, the hydroxide ion, and hydrogen gas. Write the skeletal equation including each of these and then balance it:
$$K(s) + H_2O(l) \rightarrow K^+(aq) + OH^-(aq) + H_2(g)$$
$$2\,K(s) + 2\,H_2O(l) \rightarrow 2\,K^+(aq) + 2\,OH^-(aq) + H_2(g)$$

87. The halogens react with hydrogen to form hydrogen halides. Write the skeletal reaction with each of the halogen and hydrogen as the reactants and the hydrogen halide compound as the product and balance the equation.
$$H_2(g) + Br_2(g) \rightarrow HBr(g)$$

$$H_2(g) + Br_2(g) \rightarrow 2 HBr(g)$$

88. Halogens react with each other to form interhalogen compounds. Write the skeletal reaction with each of the halogens as the reactants and the interhalogen compound as the product and balance the equation.
$$Cl_2(g) + F_2(g) \rightarrow ClF(g)$$
$$Cl_2(g) + F_2(g) \rightarrow 2 ClF(g)$$

89. Br: $1s^2 2s^2 2p^6 3s^2 3p^6 4s^2 3d^{10} 4p^5$
Kr: $1s^2 2s^2 2p^6 3s^2 3p^6 4s^2 3d^{10} 4p^6$
Krypton has a completely filled p sublevel giving it chemical stability. Bromine needs one electron to achieve a completely filled p sublevel and therefore has a high electron affinity. It therefore, easily takes on an electron and is reduced to the bromide ion giving it the added stability of the filled p sublevel.

90. K: $1s^2 2s^2 2p^6 3s^2 3p^6 4s^1$
Ar: $1s^2 2s^2 2p^6 3s^2 3p^6$
Argon has a completely filled p sublevel giving it chemical stability. Potassium has one electron in the 4s sublevel and can easily lose this electron so it has a low first ionization energy. It therefore, loses the 4s electron to achieve an argon electron configuration giving it the added stability of the filled p sublevel.

91. Write the electron configuration of vanadium
V: $[Ar] 4s^2 3d^3$
Since this ion has a 3+ charge, remove three electrons to write the electron configuration of the ion. Since it is a transition metal, remove the electrons from the 4s orbital before removing electrons from the 3d orbitals.
V^{3+}: $[Ar] 4s^0 3d^2$
Both vanadium and the V^{3+} ion have unpaired electrons and are paramagnetic.

92. Begin by writing the electron configuration of the neutral atom. Remember, Cu is one of our exceptions.
Cu $[Ar]4s^1 3d^{10}$
Since this ion has a 1+ charge, remove one electron to write the electron configuration of the ion. Since it is a transition metal, remove the electrons from the 4s orbital before removing electrons from the 3d orbitals.
Cu^+ $[Ar]4s^0 3d^{10}$
Cu contains one unpaired electron and is paramagnetic, Cu^+ has all paired electrons and is diamagnetic.

93. Since K^+ has a 1+ charge you would need a cation with a similar size and a 1+ charge. Looking at the ions in the same family, Na^+ would be too small and Rb^+ would be too large. If we then consider Ar^+ and Ca^+ we would have ions of similar size and charge. Between these two Ca^+ would be the easier to achieve because the first ionization energy of Ca is similar to that of K while the first ionization energy of Ar is much larger. However, the second ionization energy of Ca is relatively low making it easy to lose the second electron.

94. Since Na^+ has a 1+ charge you would need a cation with a similar size and a 1+ charge. Looking at the ions in the same family, Li^+ would be too small and K^+ would be too large. If we then consider Ne^+ and Mg^+ we would have ions of similar size and charge. Between these two Mg^+ would be the easier to achieve because the first ionization energy of Mg is similar to that of Na while the first ionization energy of Ne is much larger. However, the second ionization energy of Mg is relatively low making it easy to lose the second electron.

95. C has an outer shell electron configuration of $ns^2 np^2$ based on this you would expect Si and Ge which are in the same family to be most like carbon. Ionization energies for both Si and Ge are similar and tend to be slightly lower than C but all are intermediate in the range of first ionization energies. The electron affinities of Si and Ge are close to that of C.

96. a) Si and Ga   Ga would be larger than Si because as you trace from Si to Ga on the periodic table, you move down a column (radius increases) and then to the left across the period (radius increases). The sum of these to trends would give you a larger radius for Ga.

     b) Si and Ge   Ge would be larger than Si because, as you trace from Si to Ge on the periodic table, you move down a column and the radius increases.

     c) Si and As   As would be most similar to Si in atomic radius because, as you trace from Si to As on the periodic table, you move down the column (radius increase) and then to the right across the period (radius decreases). The sum of these two trends would make As smaller than Ga and Ge and thus closer to the radius of Si.

97. a) N: $[He]2s^22p^3$ Mg: $[Ne]3s^2$ O: $[He]2s^22p^4$
     F: $[He]2s^22p^5$ Al: $[Ne]3s^23p^1$

     b) Mg > Al > N > O > F   Mg and Al would have the largest radius because they are in period n = 3, Al is smaller than Mg because radius decreases as you move to the right across the period. F is smaller than O is smaller than N because as you move to the right across the period, radius decreases.

     c) Al < Mg < O < N < F   (from the table)

     d) The first ionization energy of Al is smaller than the first ionization energy of Mg because Al loses the electron from the 3p orbital which is shielded by the electrons in the 3s orbital, while Mg loses the electron from the filled 3s orbital which has added stability because it is a filled orbital. The first ionization energy of O is lower than the first ionization energy of N because N has a half – filled 2p orbital which adds extra stability thus, making it harder to remove the electron and the fourth electron in the O 2p orbital experiences added electron – electron repulsion from the other electron in its same orbital.

98. a) P: $[Ne]3s^23p^3$ Ca: $[Ar]4s^2$ Si$[Ne]3s^23p^2$
     S: $[Ne]3s^23p^4$ Ga: $[Ar]4s^23d^{10}4p^1$

     b) Ca > Ga > Si > P > S   Ca and Ga would have the largest radius because they are in period n = 4, Ga is smaller than Ca because radius increases as you move to the left across the period. S is smaller than P is smaller than Si because as you move to the right across the period, radius decreases.

     c) Ga < Ca < Si < S < P   (from table)

     d) The first ionization energy of Ga is smaller than the first ionization energy of Ca because Ga loses the electron from the 4p orbital which is shielded by the electrons in the 4s orbital, while Ca loses the electron from the filled 4s orbital which has added stability because it is a filled orbital. The first ionization energy of S is lower than the first ionization energy of P because P has a half – filled 3p orbital which adds extra stability thus, making it harder to remove the electron and the fourth electron in the S 2p orbital experiences added electron – electron repulsion from the other electron in its same orbital.

99. As you move to the right across a row in the periodic table for the main – group elements, the effective nuclear charge (Z_{eff}) experienced by the electrons in the outermost principal energy level increases, resulting in a stronger attraction between the outermost electrons and the nucleus and therefore, smaller atomic radii. Across the row of transition elements, the number of electron in the outermost principal energy level (highest n value) is nearly constant. As another proton is added to the nucleus with each successive element, another electron is added but, that electron goes into an $n_{highest} - 1$ orbital (a core level). The number of outermost electrons stays constant and they experience a roughly constant effective nuclear charge, keeping the radius approximately constant after the first couple of elements in the series.

100. Across the row of transition elements, the number of electron in the outermost principal energy level (highest n value) is nearly constant. As another proton is added to the nucleus with each successive element another electron is added but, the electron goes into an $n_{highest} - 1$ orbital. So, even though the atomic number of Cu is higher than that of V, the outermost electron experience roughly the same effective nuclear charge and thus, the radii of the two elements is nearly the same. Since the radius of the two elements is nearly the same, the volume occupied by the element will be nearly the same, since the mass increases as the atomic number increases, the mass of Cu is greater than the mass of V, density is mass/ volume, so the density of Cu should be greater than the density of V.
We find that the densities are: Cu = 8.96 g/cm^3 V = 5.49 g/cm^3 and our prediction was correct.

101. The noble gases all have a filled outer quantum level, very high first ionization energies, and positive values for the electron affinity and are thus particularly unreactive. The lighter noble gases will not form any

compounds because the ionization energies of He and Ne are both over 2000 kJ/mol. Since ionization energy decreases as you move down a column we find that the heavier noble gases, Ar, Kr, and Xe do form some compounds, they have ionization energies that are close to the ionization energy of H and can thus be forced to lose an electron.

102. The halogens will all add an electron to achieve the stability of the noble gas configuration thus they are all powerful oxidizing agents (they are reduced). F would be the strongest because it adds the electron to the n = 2 level achieving the electron configuration of Ne. Since the n = 2 level lies lower in energy than the outermost level of the other halogens, it is more energetically favorable for F to gain the noble gas configuration than for the other halogens. This combined with the high ionization energy and relatively exothermic electron affinity makes F very reactive. As you move down the column, the n level of the outermost electrons increases, making it less energetically favorable for each of the successive halogens to gain an electron.

103. Group 6A: ns^2np^4 Group 7A: ns^2np^5
The electron affinity of the group 7A elements are more negative than the group 6A elements in the same period because group 7A requires only one electron to achieve the noble gas configuration ns^2np^6 while the group 6A elements require 2 electrons. Adding one electron to the group 6A element will not give them any added stability and leads to extra electron – electron repulsions so the value of the electron affinity is less negative than that for group 7A.

104. Group 5A : ns^2np^3 Group 4A: ns^2np^2
The electron affinity of group 5A elements is more positive than the group 4A elements in the same period because group 5A has a half – filled p sublevel. Adding an electron to this group, adds a fourth electron into the p sublevel and increases the electron – electron repulsions. It also, eliminates the stability of the half – filled sublevel. Adding an electron to a group 4A element however, adds a third electron into the p sublevel, giving it the added stability of the half – filled sublevel.

105. 35 = Br = $[Ar]4s^23d^{10}4p^5$ 53 = I = $[Kr]5s^24d^{10}5p^6$
Br and I are both halogens with an outermost electron configuration of ns^2np^5, the next element with the same outermost electron configuration is 85, At.

106. Begin by writing the electron configuration of the neutral atom. S = $1s^22s^22p^63s^23p^4$

S^+ loses one electron: $1s^22s^22p^63s^23p^3$

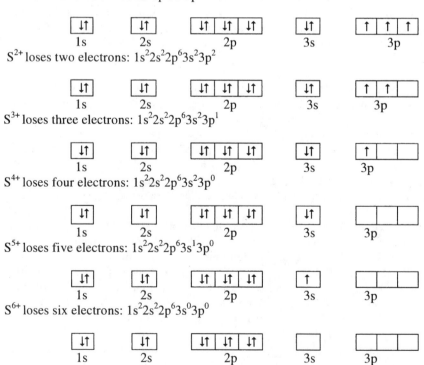

107.a) Using Excel, make a table of radius, atomic number, and density. Using xy scatter, make a chart of radius vs. density. With an exponential trendline, estimate the density of argon and xenon. Also, make a chart or atomic number vs. density. With a linear trendline, estimate the density of argon and xenon.

element	radius(pm)	atomic number	density
	32	2	0.18
Ne	70	10	0.90
Ar	98	18	
Kr	112	36	3.75
Xe	130	54	
Rn		86	9.73
		118	

Radius vs. Density

Atomic Number vs. Density

From the radius vs. density chart: Ar has a density of ~ 2 g/L and Xe has a density of ~ 6.5 g/L. From the atomic number vs. density chart: Ar has a density of ~1.8 g/L and Xe has a density of ~6 g/L.

b) Using the chart of atomic number vs. density, element 118 would be predicted to have a density of ~ 13 g/L.

c) **Given:** Ne: M = 20.18 g/mol; r = 70 pm   **Find:** mass of neon; d neon
   Conceptual Plan: M → m$_{atom}$ and then r → vol$_{atom}$ and then → d

   $$\frac{6.022 \times 10^{23} \text{ atoms}}{\text{mol}} \qquad V = \frac{4}{3}\pi r^3 \qquad d = \frac{\text{mass}}{\text{vol}}$$

   Solution: $\dfrac{20.18 \text{ g}}{\text{mol}} \times \dfrac{\text{mol}}{6.022 \times 10^{23} \text{ atoms}} = 3.35 \times 10^{-23} \text{ g/atom}$

   $$V = \frac{4}{3} \times 3.14 \times (70 \text{ pm})^3 \times \left(\frac{m}{10^{12} \text{ pm}}\right)^3 \times \frac{L}{0.0010 \text{ m}^3} = 1.\underline{4}4 \times 10^{-27} \text{ L}$$

   $$d = \frac{3.35 \times 10^{-23} \text{ g}}{1.\underline{4}4 \times 10^{-27} \text{ L}} = 2.\underline{3}3 \times 10^4 = 2.3 \times 10^4 \text{ g/L}$$

   Check: The units of the answer, g/L, are correct. This density is significantly larger than the actual density of neon gas. This suggests that a L of neon is composed of primarily empty space.

d) **Given:** Ne: M = 20.18 g/ mol, d = 0.90 g/L; Kr: M = 83.30 g/ mol, d = 3.75 g/L; Ar: M = 39.95 g/ mol
   Find: d of argon in g/L

Conceptual Plan: d →mol/L → atoms/L for Kr and Ne and then atoms/L → mol/L →d for Ar

$$mol = \frac{mass}{molar\ mass} \quad \frac{6.022 \times 10^{23}\ atoms}{mol} \quad \frac{mol}{6.022 \times 10^{23}\ atoms} \quad \frac{39.95\ g}{mol}$$

Solution:

for Ne: $\dfrac{0.90\ \cancel{g}}{L} \times \dfrac{\cancel{mol}}{20.18\ \cancel{g}} \times \dfrac{6.022 \times 10^{23}\ atoms}{\cancel{mol}} = 2.69 \times 10^{22}$ atoms/ L

for Kr: $\dfrac{3.75\ \cancel{g}}{L} \times \dfrac{\cancel{mol}}{83.80\ \cancel{g}} \times \dfrac{6.022 \times 10^{23}\ atoms}{\cancel{mol}} = 2.69 \times 10^{22}$ atoms/ L

for Ar: $\dfrac{2.69 \times 10^{22}\ \cancel{atoms}}{L} \times \dfrac{\cancel{mol}}{6.022 \times 10^{23}\ \cancel{atoms}} \times \dfrac{39.95\ g}{\cancel{mol}} = 1.78$ g/ L

Check: The units of the answer, g/L , are correct. The value of the answer agrees with published values.

108. If there were only two p orbitals there would only be 4 p block columns and if there were only three d orbitals there would be only 6 d block columns. So the periodic table would have 12 columns.

H											He
Li	Be							B	C	N	O
F	Ne							Na	Mg	Al	Si
P	S	Cl	Ar	K	Ca	Sc	Ti	V	Cr	Mn	Fe

The noble gas equivalent elements would be: He, O, Si, Fe
The halogen equivalent elements would be: N, Al, Mn
The alkali metal equivalent elements would be: Li, F, P

109. The density increases as you move to the right across the first transition series. For the first transition series, the mass increases as you move to the right across the periodic table. However, the radius of the transition series elements stays nearly constant as you move to the right across the periodic table thus, the volume will remain nearly constant. Since density is mass/ volume the density of the elements increases.

110. If there are 3 possible spin quantum numbers, there will be three s electrons, nine p electrons, and fifteen d electrons.
a) Ne(10 e): $1s^3 2s^3 2p^4$
b) completed n = 2 level: $1s^3 2s^3 2p^9$
c) F(9 e): $1s^3 2s^3 2p^3$ therefore there are 3 unpaired electrons.

111. The longest wavelength would be associated with the lowest energy state next to the ground state of carbon which has 2 unpaired electrons:
Ground state of carbon:

↓↑		↓↑		↑	↑	
1s		2s		2p		

Longest wavelength: one of the p electrons flipped in its orbital which requires the least amount of energy.

↓↑		↓↑		↑	↓	
1s		2s		2p		

The next wavelength would be associated with the pairing of the two p electrons in the same orbital because this requires energy and raises the energy.

↓↑		↓↑		↓↑		
1s		2s		2p		

The next wavelength would be associated with the energy needed to promote one of the s electrons to a p orbital.

↓↑		↑		↑	↑	↑
1s		2s		2p		

112. Element darmstadium (110) would be in the column with Ni, Pd, and Pt so it might be expected to have an electron configuration similar to Ni or Pd or Pt.
Similar to Ni: $[Rn]7s^2 5f^{14} 6d^8$
Similar to Pd: $[Rn]7s^0 5f^{14} 6d^{10}$
Similar to Pt: $[Rn]\ 7s^1 5f^{14} 6d^9$

113. The element that would fill the 8s and 8p orbitals would have atomic number 168. The element is in the noble gas family and would have the properties of noble gases. It would have the electron configuration of $[118]8s^25g^{18}6f^{14}7d^{10}8p^6$. The outer shell electron (highest n level) configuration would be $8s^28p^6$. The element would be relatively inert, have a first ionization energy less than 1037 kJ/mol (the first ionization energy of Rn), and have a positive electron affinity. It would be difficult to form compounds with other elements but would be able to form compounds with fluorine.

114. To determine the second ionization energies look at the electron configuration of the 1+ ions.

First write the electron configuration of the atom:

Li $1s^22s^1$
Be $1s^22s^2$
B $1s^22s^22p^1$
C $1s^22s^22p^2$
N $1s^22s^22p^3$
O $1s^22s^22p^4$
F $1s^22s^22p^5$

Then write the electron configuration of the 1+ ion:

Li^+ $1s^22s^0$
Be^+ $1s^22s^1$
B^+ $1s^22s^2$
C^+ $1s^22s^22p^1$
N^+ $1s^22s^22p^2$
O^+ $1s^22s^22p^3$
F^+ $1s^22s^22p^4$

Based on the electron configuration of the ions, Li^+ should have the largest second ionization energy since the removal of the second electron involves removing a core electron. The lowest second ionization energy should be Be^+ since removing the second electron takes you to the $1s^2$ (stable) configuration.

O would have the highest second ionization energy because the electron configuration of O^+ has a half – filled p orbital which is particularly stable and therefore it would require more energy to remove the second electron. N^+ would have the lowest second ionization energy because the size of N^+ would be larger than the radius of the F^+, so the attraction between the outer electron and the nucleus would be less in N^+ than in F^+ making it easier to remove the elctron.

115. When you move down the column from Al to Ga, the size of the atom actually decreases because not much shielding is contributed by the 3d electrons in the Ga atom while there is a large increase in the nuclear charge, therefore, the effective nuclear charge is greater for Ga than for Al, so the ionization energy does not decrease. As you go from In to Tl, the ionization energy actually increases because the 4f electrons do not contribute to the shielding of the outermost electrons and there is a large increase in the effective nuclear charge.

116. ΔE for the reaction based on the ionization energy and the electron affinity = +147 kJ/ mol

$Na(g) \rightarrow Na^+(g) + e^-$ IE = +496 kJ/mol
$Cl(g) + e^- \rightarrow Cl^-(g)$ EA = - 349 kJ/mol
$Na(g) + Cl(g) \rightarrow Na^+(g) + Cl^-(g)$ ΔE = +147 kJ/mol

117. The second electron is added to an ion with a 1 – charge, so there is a large repulsive force that has to be overcome to add the second electron. Thus, it will require energy to add the second electron and the second electron affinity will have a positive value.

118. The diagonal relationship between some elements could be explained because the atomic size of the atoms on the diagonal would be about the same. Because on the diagonal, the radius would increase as you go down the column but will decrease as you move to the right across the period. Also, the size of the ion formed would be about the same. Therefore, you might expect the elements to have similar behavior.

119. If six electrons rather than eight electrons led to a stable configuration, the electron configuration of the stable configuration would be: ns^2np^4

   a) A noble gas: ns^2np^4
   b) A reactive nonmetal: would have one less electron than the stable configuration: ns^2np^3
   c) A reactive metal: would have one have one more electron than the stable configuration: ns^1

120. a) True: An electron in a 3s orbital is more shielded than an electron in a 2s orbital. This is true since there are more core electrons below a 3s orbital.

   b) True: An electron in a 3s orbital penetrates into the region occupied by the core electrons more than electrons in a 3p orbital. Examine figure 8.5, the radial distribution functions for the 3s, 3p and 3d orbitals. You will see that the 3s electrons penetrate more deeply than the 3p electrons and more than the 3d electrons.

c) False: An electron in an orbital that penetrates closer to the nucleus will experience <u>less</u> shielding than an electron in an orbital that does not penetrate as far.

d) True: An electron in an orbital that penetrates close to the nucleus will tend to experience a higher effective nuclear charge than on that does not. Since the orbital penetrates closer to the nucleus, the electron will experience less shielding and therefore, a higher effective nuclear charge.

121. An electron in a 5p orbital could have any one of the following combinations of quantum numbers.
5,1, -1,+1/2   5,1,-1,-1/2   5,1,0,+1/2   5,1,0,-1/2   5,1,1,+1/2   5,1,1,-1/2
An electron in a 6d orbital could have any one of the following combinations of quantum numbers.
6,2,-2,+1/2   6,2,-2,-1/2   6,2,-1,+1/2   6,2,-1,-1/2   6,2,0,+1/2   6,2,0,-1/2
6,2,1,+1/2   6,2,1,-1/2   6,2,2,+1/2   6,2,2,-1/2

122. The 4s electrons in calcium have relatively low ionization energies (IE_1 = 590 kJ/mol; IE_2 = 1145 kJ/mol) because they are valence electrons. The energetic cost for calcium to lose a third electron is extraordinarily high because the next electron to be lost is a core electron. Similarly, the electron affinity of fluorine to gain one electron (- 328 kJ/mol)is highly exothermic because the added electron completes fluoride's valence shell. The gain of a second electron by the negatively charged fluoride anion would not be favorable. Therefore, we would expect calcium and fluoride to combine in a 1:2 ratio.

Chapter 9
Chemical Bonding I: Lewis Theory

1. Bonding theories are central to chemistry because they explain how atoms bond together to form molecules. Bonding theories explain why some combinations of atoms are stable and others are not.

2. Bonding theories explain why some combinations of atoms are stable and others are not. Bonding theories also predict the shapes of molecules which in turn determine many of their physical and chemical properties. They also predict how many bonds will form between atoms in a compound

3. Chemical bonds form because they lower the potential energy between the charged particles that compose the atom. Bonds involve the attraction and repulsion of charged particles.

4. a)   Potential energy is directly proportional to the magnitude of the charge.

    b)   The potential energy is positive for charges of the same sign, and negative for charges of opposite sign.

    c)   The magnitude of the potential energy is indirectly proportional to the separation between the charged particles.

5. The three types of bonds are: Ionic bonds – which occurs between a metal and nonmetal and is characterized by the transfer of electrons; Covalent bonds – which occurs between a nonmetal and nonmetal and is characterized by the sharing of electrons; and Metallic bonds – which occurs between a metal and a metal and is characterized by the electron being pooled.

6. In a Lewis structure, the valence electrons of main – group elements are represented as dots surrounding the symbol for the element.

7. Bonds are formed when atoms obtain a stable electron configuration since the stable configuration is usually eight electrons in the outermost shell, this is known as the octet rule.

8. In Lewis theory, a chemical bond is the sharing or transfer of electrons to attain stable electron configurations for the bonding atoms. If electrons are transferred the bond is an ionic bond. If the electrons are shared the bond is a covalent bond.

9. In Lewis theory, we represent ionic bonding by moving electron dots from the metal to the nonmetal and then allowing the resultant ions to form a crystalline lattice composed of alternating cations and anions. The cation loses its valence electron(s) and is left with an octet in the previous principal energy level, the anion gains electron(s) to form an octet. The Lewis structure of the anion is usually written within brackets with the charge in the upper right – hand corner, outside the brackets. The positive and negative charges attract one another, resulting in the compound.

10. To use Lewis theory to determine the formula of an ionic compound, determine the number of valence electrons lost by the metal to form the octet, and the number of electrons gained by the nonmetal to form the octet. Consider the ionic compound formed between sodium and sulfur. The Lewis structures for sodium and sulfur are:

$$Na \bullet \qquad {\overset{\bullet\bullet}{\underset{\bullet}{\bullet S}}}{:}$$

Sodium must lose one electron to achieve the octet, while sulfur must gain two electrons to achieve the octet. So the compound requires two sodium atoms for each sulfur atom giving the formula Na_2S.

11. Lattice energy is the energy associated with forming a crystalline lattice of alternating cations and anions from the gaseous ions. Since the cations are positively charged and the anions are negatively charged there is a lowering of potential – as prescribed by Coulomb's law – when the ions come together to form a lattice. That energy is emitted as heat when the lattice forms.

12. The formation of the crystalline NaCl lattice from sodium cations and chloride anions is highly exothermic and more than compensates for the endothermicity of the electron transfer process. In other words, the formation of ionic compounds is not exothermic because sodium "wants" to lose electrons and chlorine

"wants" to gain them; rather, it is exothermic because of the large amount of heat released when sodium and chlorine ions coalesce to form a crystalline lattice.

13. The Born – Haber cycle is a hypothetical series of steps that represents the formation of an ionic compound from its constituent elements. The steps are chosen so that the change in enthalpy of each step is known except for the last one, which is the lattice energy. In terms of the formation of NaCl, the steps are:
Step 1: The formation of gaseous sodium from solid sodium (heat of sublimation of sodium).
Step 2: The formation of a chlorine atom from a chlorine molecule (bond energy of chlorine).
Step 3: The ionization of gaseous sodium (ionization energy of sodium).
Step 4: The addition of an electron to gaseous chlorine (the electron affinity of chlorine).
Step 5: The formation of the crystalline solid from the gaseous ions (the lattice energy)
The overall reaction is the formation of NaCl(s), so we can use Hess' law to determine the lattice energy.

$$\Delta H^{\circ}_f = \Delta H_{step\ 1} + \Delta H_{step\ 2} + \Delta H_{step\ 3} + \Delta H_{step\ 4} + \Delta H_{step\ 5}$$

ΔH°_f = heat of sublimation + ½ bond energy + ionization energy + electron affinity + lattice energy
Since all the terms are know except the lattice energy, we can calculate the lattice energy.

14. As the ionic radii increase as you move down a group, the ions cannot get as close to each other and therefore, do not release as much energy when the lattice forms. Thus, the lattice energy decreases (becomes less negative) as the radius increases.
Since the magnitude of the potential energy of two interacting charges depends not only on the distance between the charges but also on the product of the charges, so, lattice energies become more exothermic with increasing magnitude of ionic charge.

15. We modeled ionic solids as a lattice of individual ions held together by coulombic forces, which are equal in all directions. To melt the solid, these forces must be overcome, which requires a significant amount of heat. Therefore, the model accounts for the high melting points of ionic solids.

16. In the ionic bonding model, electrons are transferred from the metal to the nonmetal, but the transferred electrons remain localized on one atom. The model does not include any free electrons that might conduct electricity, and the ions themselves are fixed in place; therefore, our model accounts for the nonconductivity of ionic solids. When the ionic solid dissolves in water, however, the cations and anions dissociate, forming free ions in solution. Theses ions can move in response to electrical forces, creating an electrical current. Thus, our model predicts that solutions of ionic compounds conduct electricity.

17. A pair of electrons that is shared between two atoms is called a bonding pair, while a pair of electrons that is associated with only one atom – and therefore, not involved in bonding – is called a lone pair.

18. A single bond occurs when one pair of electrons is shared between two atoms. A double bond results when two electron pairs are shared between the same two atoms. Double bonds are shorter and stronger than single bonds. A triple bond results when three electron pairs are shared between the same two atoms. Triple bonds are even shorter and stronger than double bonds.

19. Generally, combinations of atoms that can satisfy the octet rule on each atom are stable, while those combinations that do not satisfy the octet rule are not stable.

20. Lewis theory shows that covalent bonds are highly directional. The attraction between two covalently bonded atoms is due to the sharing of one or more electron pairs. Thus, each bond links just one specific pair of atoms – in contrast to ionic bonds, which are nondirectional and hold together the entire array of ions. The fundamental units of covalently bonded compounds are individual molecules. These molecules can interact with one another in a number of different ways, however, the interaction between molecules are generally much weaker than the bonding interactions within a molecule. When a molecular compound melts or boils, the molecules themselves remain intact. Only the weak interactions between the molecules must be overcome. Consequently, molecular compounds tend to have lower melting and boiling points than ionic compounds.

21. Electronegativity is the ability of an atom to attract electrons to itself in a chemical bond. This results in a polar bond. Electronegativity generally increases across a period in the periodic table. And, electronegativity generally decreases down a column (group) in the periodic table. The most electronegative element is fluorine.

22. If two elements with identical electronegativities form a covalent bond, they share the electrons equally, and the bond is purely covalent or nonpolar.
   If there is an intermediate electronegativity difference between the two elements, such as between two different nonmetals, then the bond is polar covalent.
   If there is a large electronegativity difference between the two elements in a bond, such as normally occurs between a metal and a nonmetal, the electron from the metal is almost completely transferred to the nonmetal, and the bond is ionic.

23. Percent ionic character is defined as the ratio of a bond's actual dipole moment to the dipole moment it would have if the electron were completely transferred from one atom to the other, multiplied by 100.
   A bond in which an electron is completely transferred form one atom to another would have 100% ionic character. However, no bond is 100% ionic. Percent ionic character generally increases as the electronegativity difference increases. In general, bonds with greater than 50% ionic character are referred to as ionic bonds.

24. A dipole moment (μ) occurs anytime there is a separation of positive and negative charge. It is used to quantify the polarity of a bond. The magnitude of the dipole moment created by separating two particles of equal but opposite charges of magnitude (q) by a distance (r) is given by: $\mu = qr$.

25. To calculate the dipole moment we use $\mu = qr$:

   For 100 pm: $\mu = 1.6 \times 10^{-19}\ C \times 100\ pm \times \dfrac{m}{10^{12}\ pm} \times \dfrac{D}{3.34 \times 10^{-30}\ C\cdot m} = 4.8\ D$

   For 200 pm: $\mu = 1.6 \times 10^{-19}\ C \times 200\ pm \times \dfrac{m}{10^{12}\ pm} \times \dfrac{D}{3.34 \times 10^{-30}\ C\cdot m} = 9.6\ D$

26. The steps for writing a Lewis structure are:
   1. Write the correct skeletal structure for the molecule.
   2. Calculate the total number of electrons for the Lewis structure by summing the valence electrons of each atom in the molecule.
   3. Distribute the electrons among the atoms, giving octets (or duets for hydrogen) to as many atoms as possible.
   4. If any atoms lack an octet, form double or triple bonds as necessary to give them octets.

27. The total number of electrons for a Lewis structure of a molecule is the sum of the valence electrons of each atom in the molecule.
   The total number of electrons for the Lewis structure of an ion is found by summing the number of valence electrons for each atom and then subtracting 1 electron for each positive charge or adding 1 electron for each negative charge.

28. Resonance structures result when you can write two or more Lewis structures for the same molecule. A resonance hybrid is then the weighted average of the resonance structures.

29. In some cases we can write resonance structures that are not equivalent.. One possible resonance structure may be somewhat better than another. In such cases the true structure may still be represented as an average of the resonance structures, but with the better resonance structure contributing more to the true structure. Multiple nonequivalent resonance structures may be weighted differently in their contributions to the true overall structure of a molecule.

30. Formal charge is a fictitious charge assigned to each atom in a Lewis structure that helps us to distinguish among competing Lewis structures. The formal charge of an atom in a Lewis structure is the charge it would have if all bonding electrons were shared equally between the bonded atoms. Formal charge can be calculated simply be taking the number of valence electrons in the atom and subtracting the number of electrons that it "owns" in a Lewis structure. An atom in a Lewis structure "owns" all of its lone pair electrons and 1/2 of its bonding electrons.
   Formal charge = number of valence electrons – (number of lone pair electron + 1//2 number of bonding electrons)
   The concept of formal charge is useful because it can help us distinguish between competing skeletal structures or competing resonance structures.

31. The octet rule has some exceptions because not all atoms always have eight electrons surrounding them. The three major categories are: 1) odd – electron species, molecules or ions with an odd number of electron. For example: NO ; 2) incomplete octets, molecules or ions with fewer than eight electrons around an atom. For example: BF_3; and 3) expanded octets, molecules or ions with more than eight electrons around an atom. For example: AsF_5.

32. Elements in the third row of the periodic table and beyond often exhibit expanded octets. Elements in the first or second row of the periodic table can never have expanded octets.

33. The bond energy of a chemical bond is the energy required to break 1 mole of the bond in the gas phase. Since breaking bonds is endothermic and forming bonds is exothermic we can calculate the overall enthalpy change as a sum of the enthalpy changes associated with breaking the required bonds in the reactants and forming the required bonds in the products.

34. A reaction is exothermic when weak bonds break and strong bonds form. A reaction is endothermic when strong bonds break and weak bonds form.

35. When metal atoms bond together to form a solid, each metal atom donates one or more electrons to an electron sea.

36. Metals conduct electricity because the electrons in a metal are free to move. The movement or flow of electrons in response to an electric potential is an electric current. Metals are also excellent conductors of heat because of the highly mobile electrons, which help to disperse thermal energy throughout the metal.
The malleability of metals and the ductility of metals are also accounted for by the electron sea model. Since there are no localized or specific "bonds" in a metal, it can be deformed relatively easily by forcing the metal ions to slide past one another. The electron sea can easily accommodate these deformations by flowing into the new shape.

37. N : $1s^2 2s^2 2p^3$ •N̈•   The electrons included in the Lewis structure are: $2s^2 2p^3$.

38. Ne : $1s^2 2s^2 2p^6$:N̈e: The electrons included in the Lewis structure are: $2s^2 2p^6$.

39. a.) Al: $1s^2 2s^2 2p^6 3s^2 3p^1$

Al :

b) Na^+: $1s^2 2s^2 2p^6$

Na$^+$

c.) Cl: $1s^2 2s^2 2p^6 3s^2 3p^5$

:C̈l•

d) Cl^-: $1s^2 2s^2 2p^6 3s^2 3p^6$

:C̈l:⁻

40. a.) S^{2-} : $1s^2 2s^2 2p^6 3s^2 3p^6$

:S̈:$^{2-}$

b) Mg: $1s^2 2s^2 2p^6 3s^2$

Mg:

c) Mg^{2+}: $1s^2 2s^2 2p^6$

Mg^{2+}

d)   P: $1s^2 2s^2 2p^6 3s^2 3p^3$

•• P •

41. a) NaF: Draw the Lewis structures for Na and F based on their valence electrons. Na: $3s^1$ F: $2s^2 2p^5$

Na •   •• F •

Sodium must lose one electron and be left with the octet from the previous shell, while fluorine needs to gain one electron to get an octet.

Na^+ $\left[\; F \; \right]^-$

b) CaO: Draw the Lewis structures for Ca and O based on their valence electrons. Ca: $4s^2$ O: $2s^2 2p^4$

Ca •   •• O •

Calcium must lose two electrons and be left with the octet from the previous shell, while oxygen needs to gain two electrons to get an octet.

$Ca^{2+} \left[\; O \; \right]^{2-}$

c) $SrBr_2$:   Draw the Lewis structures for Sr and Br based on their valence electrons. Sr: $5s^2$ Br: $4s^2 4p^5$

Sr •   •• Br •

Strontium must lose two electrons and be left with the octet from the previous shell, while bromine needs to gain one electron to get an octet.

$Sr^{2+} \; 2 \left[\; Br \; \right]^-$

d) K_2O: Draw the Lewis structures for K and O based on their valence electrons. K: $4s^1$ O: $2s^2 2p^4$

K •   •• O •

Potassium must lose one electron and be left with the octet from the previous shell, while oxygen needs to gain two electrons to get an octet.

$2K^+ \left[\; O \; \right]^{2-}$

42. a) SrO: Draw the Lewis structures for Sr and O based on their valence electrons. Sr: $5s^2$ O: $2s^2 2p^4$

Sr •   •• O •

Strontium must lose two electrons and be left with the octet from the previous shell, while oxygen needs to gain two electrons to get an octet.

$Sr^{2+} \left[\; O \; \right]^{2-}$

b) Li_2S: Draw the Lewis structures for Li and S based on their valence electrons. Li: $2s^1$ S: $3s^2 3p^4$

Li •   •• S •

Lithium must lose one electron and be left with the octet from the previous shell, while sulfur needs to gain two electrons to get an octet.

$2 \, Li^+ \left[\; S \; \right]^{2-}$

c)   CaI$_2$:   Draw the Lewis structures for Ca and I based on their valence electrons. Ca: $4s^2$ I: $5s^2 5p^5$

Ca$\colon$ $\colon \overset{\bullet\bullet}{\underset{\bullet\bullet}{I}} \bullet$

Calcium must lose two electrons and be left with the octet from the previous shell, while iodine needs to gain one electron to get an octet.

Ca^{2+} $_2$ $\left[\colon \overset{\bullet\bullet}{\underset{\bullet\bullet}{I}} \colon \right]^{-}$

d)   RbF: Draw the Lewis structures for Rb and F based on their valence electrons. Ca: $5s^1$ I: $2s^2 2p^5$

Rb$\bullet$ $\colon \overset{\bullet\bullet}{\underset{\bullet\bullet}{F}} \bullet$

Rubidium must lose one electron and be left with the octet from the previous shell, while fluorine needs to gain one electron to get an octet.

Rb^{+} $\left[\colon \overset{\bullet\bullet}{\underset{\bullet\bullet}{F}} \colon \right]^{-}$

43. a)   Sr and Se: Draw the Lewis structures for Sr and Se based on their valence electrons. Sr: $5s^2$ Se: $4s^2 4p^4$

Sr$\colon$ $\colon \overset{\bullet\bullet}{\underset{\bullet}{Se}} \bullet$

Strontium must lose two electrons and be left with the octet from the previous shell, while selenium needs to gain two electrons to get an octet.

Sr^{2+} $\left[\colon \overset{\bullet\bullet}{\underset{\bullet\bullet}{Se}} \colon \right]^{2-}$

Thus, we need one Sr^{2+} and one Se^{2-}. Write the formula with subscripts (if necessary) to indicate the number of atoms.

SrSe

b)   Ba and Cl   Draw the Lewis structures for Ba and Cl based on their valence electrons. Ba: $6s^2$ Cl: $3s^2 3p^5$

Ba$\colon$ $\colon \overset{\bullet\bullet}{\underset{\bullet\bullet}{Cl}} \bullet$

Barium must lose two electrons and be left with the octet from the previous shell, while chlorine needs to gain one electron to get an octet.

Ba^{2+} $_2$ $\left[\colon \overset{\bullet\bullet}{\underset{\bullet\bullet}{Cl}} \colon \right]^{-}$

Thus, we need one Ba^{2+} and two Cl^{-}. Write the formula with subscripts (if necessary) to indicate the number of atoms.

BaCl$_2$

c)   Na and S   Draw the Lewis structures for Na and S based on their valence electrons. Na: $3s^1$ S: $3s^2 3p^4$

Na$\bullet$ $\colon \overset{\bullet\bullet}{\underset{\bullet}{S}} \bullet$

Sodium must lose one electron and be left with the octet from the previous shell, while sulfur needs to gain two electrons to get an octet.

2 Na^{+} $\left[\colon \overset{\bullet\bullet}{\underset{\bullet\bullet}{S}} \colon \right]^{2-}$

Thus, we need two Na^{+} and one S^{2-}. Write the formula with subscripts (if necessary) to indicate the number of atoms.

Na$_2$S

d) Al and O   Draw the Lewis structures for Al and O based on their valence electrons. Al: $3s^23p^1$ O: $2s^22p^4$

$$\text{Al} \bullet \quad \text{:O} \bullet$$

Aluminum must lose three electrons and be left with the octet from the previous shell, while oxygen needs to gain two electrons to get an octet.

$$2\ \text{Al}^{3+}\ _3\left[:\text{O}:\right]^{2-}$$

Thus, we need two Al^{3+} and three O^{2-} in order to lose and gain the same number of electrons. Write the formula with subscripts (if necessary) to indicate the number of atoms.
    Al_2O_3

44. a) Ca and N   Draw the Lewis structures for Ca and N based on their valence electrons. Ca: $4s^2$ N: $2s^22p^3$

$$\text{Ca:} \quad \bullet \text{N} \bullet$$

Calcium must lose two electrons and be left with the octet from the previous shell, while nitrogen needs to gain three electrons to get an octet.

$$3\ \text{Ca}^{2+}\ _2\left[:\text{N}:\right]^{3-}$$

Thus, we need three Ca^{2+} and two N^{3-} in order to lose and gain the same number of electrons. Write the formula with subscripts (if necessary) to indicate the number of atoms.
    Ca_3N_2

b) Mg and I   Draw the Lewis structures for Mg and I based on their valence electrons. Mg: $3s^2$ I: $5s^25p^5$

$$\text{Mg:} \quad :\text{I} \bullet$$

Magnesium must lose two electrons and be left with the octet from the previous shell, while iodine needs to gain one electron to get an octet.

$$\text{Mg}^{2+}\ _2\left[:\text{I}:\right]^{-}$$

Thus, we need one Mg^{2+} and two I^-. Write the formula with subscripts (if necessary) to indicate the number of atoms.
    MgI_2

c) Ca and S   Draw the Lewis structures for Ca and S based on their valence electrons. Ca: $4s^2$ S: $3s^23p^4$

$$\text{Ca:} \quad :\text{S} \bullet$$

Calcium must lose two electrons and be left with the octet from the previous shell, while sulfur needs to gain two electrons to get an octet.

$$\text{Ca}^{2+}\left[:\text{S}:\right]^{2-}$$

Thus, we need one Ca^{2+} and one S^{2-}. Write the formula with subscripts (if necessary) to indicate the number of atoms.
    CaS

d) Cs and F   Draw the Lewis structures for Cs and F based on their valence electrons. Cs: $6s^{21}$ F: $2s^22p^5$

$$\text{Cs} \bullet \quad :\text{F} \bullet$$

Cesium must lose one electron and be left with the octet from the previous shell, while fluorine needs to gain one electron to get an octet.

Thus, we need one Cs^+ and one F^-. Write the formula with subscripts (if necessary) to indicate the number of atoms.

$$CsF$$

45. As the size of the alkaline metal ions increases down the column, so does the distance between the metal cations and the oxide anion. Therefore, the magnitude of the lattice energy of the oxides decreases making the formation of the oxides less exothermic and the compounds less stable. Since the ions cannot get as close to each other they therefore, do not release as much energy.

46. Rubidium is below potassium on the periodic table and iodine is below bromine on the periodic table. Therefore, both the rubidium ion and the iodide ion are larger than the potassium ion and the bromide ion. So, the rubidium ion and the iodide ion cannot get as close to each other as the potassium ion and the bromide ion, therefore, they do not release as much energy and the lattice energy of potassium bromide is more exothermic.

47. Cesium is slightly larger than barium, but oxygen is slightly larger than fluorine so, we cannot use size to explain the difference in the lattice energy. However, the charge on cesium ion is 1+ and the charge on fluoride ion is 1 −, while the charge on barium ion is 2+ and the charge on oxide ion is 2 −. The coulombic equation states that the magnitude of the potential also depends on the product of the charges. Since the product of the charges for $CsF = 1 −$, and the product of the charges for $BaO = 4 −$, the stabilization for BaO relative to CsF should be about four times greater which is what we see in its much more exothermic lattice energy.

48. $RbBr < KCl < SrO < CaO$. KCl and RbBr both have a product of the charges of 1 −, while SrO and CaO have a product of the charges of 4 −. So, the lattice energies of KCl and RbBr are less than SrO and CaO. Within KCl and RbBr, rubidium ion is larger than potassium ion and bromide ion is larger than chloride ion. Therefore, the rubidium ion and the bromide ion will be farther apart leading to a smaller lattice energy. Between SrO and CaO, the strontium ion is larger than the calcium ion, so the strontium oxide will have a smaller lattice energy.

49. **Given:** $\Delta H_f°KCl = -436.5$ kJ/mol; $IE_1(K) = 419$ kJ/mol; $\Delta H_{sub}(K) = 89.0$ kJ/mol; $Cl_2(g)$ bond energy = 243 kJ/mol; $EA(Cl) = -349$ kJ/mol.
Find: lattice energy
Conceptual Plan:

$$K(s) + 1/2Cl_2(g) \rightarrow K(g) + 1/2Cl_2(g) \rightarrow K^+(g) + 1/2Cl_2(g) \rightarrow K^+(g) + Cl(g) \rightarrow K^+(g) + Cl^-(g) \rightarrow KCl(s)$$

ΔH_{sub} IE_1 Bond energy   EA   lattice energy

$\Delta H_f°$

Solution: $\Delta H_f° = \Delta H_{sub} + IE_1 + 1/2$ **Bond energy** $+$ **EA** $+$ **lattice energy**

$$-436.5\frac{kJ}{mol} = +89.0\frac{kJ}{mol} + 419\frac{kJ}{mol} + \frac{1}{2}(243)\frac{kJ}{mol} + (-349)\frac{kJ}{mol} + \text{lattice energy}$$

lattice energy $= -717$ kJ/mol

50. **Given:** $\Delta H_f°CaO = -634.9$ kJ/mol; $IE_1(Ca) = 590$ kJ/mol; $IE_2(Ca) = 1145$ kJ/mol; $\Delta H_{sub}(Ca) = 178$ kJ/mol; $O_2(g)$ bond energy = 498 kJ/mol; $EA_1(O) = -141$ kJ/mol; $EA_2(O) = 744$ kJ/mol.
Find: lattice energy
Conceptual Plan:

$$Ca(s)+1/2O_2(g) \rightarrow Ca(g)+1/2O_2(g) \rightarrow Ca^+(g)+1/2O_2(g) \rightarrow Ca^{2+}(g)+1/2O_2(g) \rightarrow Ca^{2+}(g)+O(g) \rightarrow Ca^{2+}(g)+O^-(g)$$

ΔH_{sub} IE_1 IE_2 Bond energy EA_1

$$\rightarrow Ca^{2+}(g)+O^{2-}(g) \rightarrow CaBr_2(s)$$

EA_2 lattice energy

$\Delta H_f°$

Solution: $\Delta H_f^\circ = \Delta H_{sub} + IE_1 \quad + IE_2 + 1/2\text{Bond energy} + EA_1 + EA_2 + \text{ lattice energy}$

$$-634.9\,\frac{kJ}{mol} = +178\,\frac{kJ}{mol} + 590\,\frac{kJ}{mol} + 1145\,\frac{kJ}{mol} + \frac{1}{2}(498)\,\frac{kJ}{mol} + (-141)\,\frac{kJ}{mol} + 744\,\frac{kJ}{mol} + \text{lattice energy}$$

lattice energy = -3400 kJ/mol

51. a) Hydrogen: Write the Lewis structure of each atom based on the number of valence electrons.

   H•   •H

   When the two hydrogen atoms share their electrons, they each get a duet, which is a stable configuration for hydrogen

   H —— H

   b) The halogens: Write the Lewis structure of each atom based on the number of valence electrons.

   :X• •X:

   If the two halogens pair together they can each achieve an octet, which is a stable configuration. So, the halogens are predicted to exist as diatomic molecules.

   :X — X:

   c.) Oxygen: Write the Lewis structure of each atom based on the number of valence electrons.

   :O• •O:

   In order to achieve a stable octet on each oxygen, the oxygen atoms will need to share two electron pairs. So, oxygen is predicted to exist as a diatomic molecule with a double bond.

   :O = O:

   d) Nitrogen: Write the Lewis structure of each atom based on the number of valence electrons.

   •N•   •N•

   In order to achieve a stable octet on each nitrogen, the nitrogen atoms will need to share three electron pairs. So, nitrogen is predicted to exist as a diatomic molecule with a triple bond.

   N ≡ N

52. Write the Lewis structure for N and H based on the number of valence electrons.

   If nitrogen combines with three hydrogen atoms, the nitrogen will achieve a stable octet and each hydrogen will have a duet of electrons which is a stable configuration. If the nitrogen were to combine with only two hydrogen atoms, the nitrogen could only achieve a seven electron configuration, which is not stable. Also, if the nitrogen were to combine with four hydrogen atoms, the nitrogen would have a nine electron configuration which is not stable. So, Lewis theory predicts that nitrogen will combine with three hydrogen atoms.

53. a) PH_3: Write the Lewis structure for each atom based on the valence electron.

   •P•   •H

   The phosphorus will share an electron pair with each hydrogen in order to achieve a stable octet.

   b) SCl_2: Write the Lewis structure for each atom based on the valence electron.

257

:S· :Cl·

The sulfur will share an electron pair with each chlorine in order to achieve a stable octet.

:S—Cl:
|
:Cl:

c) HI: Write the Lewis structure for each atom based on the valence electron.

H·   ·I:

The iodine will share an electron pair with hydrogen in order to achieve a stable octet.

H—I:

d) CH$_4$:   Write the Lewis structure for each atom based on the valence electron.

·C·   H·

The carbon will share an electron pair with each hydrogen in order to achieve a stable octet.

```
      H
      |
H —— C —— H
      |
      H
```

54. a) NF$_3$:   Write the Lewis structure for each atom based on the valence electron.

·N·   ·F:

The nitrogen will share an electron pair with each fluorine in order to achieve a stable octet.

:F—N—F:
|
:F:

b) HBr: Write the Lewis structure for each atom based on the valence electron.

H·   ·Br:

The bromine will share an electron pair with hydrogen in order to achieve a stable octet.

H—Br:

c) SBr$_2$:   Write the Lewis structure for each atom based on the valence electron.

:S·   :Br·

The sulfur will share an electron pair with each bromine in order to achieve a stable octet.

:S—Br:
|
:Br:

d) CCl$_4$:   Write the Lewis structure for each atom based on the valence electron.

·C·   :Cl·

258

The carbon will share an electron pair with each chlorine in order to achieve a stable octet.

55. a) Br and Br: pure covalent   From figure 9.10 we find the electronegativity of Br is 2.5. Since both atoms are the same, the electronegativity difference (ΔEN) = 0, and using table 9.1 we classify this bond as pure covalent.

b) C and Cl: polar covalent   From figure 9.10 we find the electronegativity of C is 2.5 and Cl is 3.0. The electronegativity difference (ΔEN) is $\Delta EN = 3.0 - 2.5 = 0.5$. Using table 9.1 we classify this bond as polar covalent.

c) C and S: pure covalent   From figure 9.10 we find the electronegativity of C is 2.5 and S is 2.5. The electronegativity difference (ΔEN) is $\Delta EN = 2.5 - 2.5 = 0$. Using table 9.1 we classify this bond as pure covalent.

d) Sr and O: ionic   From figure 9.10 we find the electronegativity of Sr is 1.0 and O is 3.5. The electronegativity difference (ΔEN) is $\Delta EN = 3.5 - 1.0 = 2.5$. Using table 9.1 we classify this bond as ionic.

56. a) C and N: polar covalent   From figure 9.10 we find the electronegativity of C is 2.5 and N is 3.0. The electronegativity difference (ΔEN) is $\Delta EN = 3.0 - 2.5 = 0.5$. Using table 9.1 we classify this bond as polar covalent.

b) N and S: polar covalent   From figure 9.10 we find the electronegativity of S is 2.5 and N is 3.0. The electronegativity difference (ΔEN) is $\Delta EN = 3.0 - 2.5 = 0.5$. Using table 9.1 we classify this bond as polar covalent.

c) K and F: ionic   From figure 9.10 we find the electronegativity of K is 0.8 and F is 4.0. The electronegativity difference (ΔEN) is $\Delta EN = 4.0 - 0.8 = 3.2$. Using table 9.1 we classify this bond as ionic.

d) N and N: pure covalent   From figure 9.10 we find the electronegativity of N is 3.0. Since both atoms are the same, the electronegativity difference (ΔEN) = 0, and using table 9.1 we classify this bond as pure covalent.

57. CO: Write the Lewis structure for each atom based on the valence electron.

The carbon will share three electron pair with oxygen in order to achieve a stable octet.
The oxygen atom is more electronegative than the carbon atom, so the oxygen will have a partial negative charge and the carbon will have a partial positive charge.

To estimate the percent ionic character, determine the difference in electronegativity between carbon and oxygen.
From figure 9.10 we find the electronegativity of C is 2.5 and O is 3.5. The electronegativity difference (ΔEN) is $\Delta EN = 3.5 - 2.5 = 1.0$.
From figure 9.12, we can estimate a percent ionic character of 25%

58. BrF: Write the Lewis structure for each atom based on the valence electron.

The bromine and fluorine will share an electron pair to achieve a stable octet.
The fluorine atom is more electronegative than the bromine atom, so the fluorine will have a partial negative charge and the bromine will have a partial positive charge.

$$\overset{\longrightarrow}{\underset{}{}}$$

$$:\!\overset{\bullet\bullet}{\underset{\bullet\bullet}{Br}}\!\!-\!\!\overset{\bullet\bullet}{\underset{\bullet\bullet}{F}}\!:$$

To estimate the percent ionic character, determine the difference in electronegativity between bromine and fluorine.
From figure 9.10 we find the electronegativity of Br = 2.0 and F = 4.0. The electronegativity difference (ΔEN) is $\Delta EN = 4.0 - 2.0 = 2.0$.
From figure 9.12, we can estimate a percent ionic character of 70%

59. a.) CI_4:   Write the correct skeletal structure for the molecule.

$$I\!-\!\overset{\displaystyle |}{\underset{\displaystyle |}{C}}\!-\!I$$

Calculate the total number of electrons for the Lewis structure by summing the valence electron of each atom in the molecule.

(number of valence e⁻ for C) + 4(number of valence e⁻ for I) = 4 + 4(7) = 32

Distribute the electrons among the atoms, giving octets (or duets for H) to as many atoms as possible. Begin with the bonding electrons, and then proceed to lone pairs on terminal atoms and finally to lone pairs of the central atom.

All 32 valence electrons are used
If any atom lacks an octet, form double or triple bonds as necessary to give them octets.
All atoms have octets, duets for H, structure is complete.

b) N_2O: Write the correct skeletal structure for the molecule
     N is the less electronegative, so it is central
     N— N —O

Calculate the total number of electrons for the Lewis structure by summing the valence electron of each atom in the molecule

2(number of valence e⁻ for N) + (number of valence e⁻ for O) = 2(5) + 6 = 16

Distribute the electrons among the atoms, giving octets (or duets for H) to as many atoms as possible. Begin with the bonding electrons, and then proceed to lone pairs on terminal atoms and finally to lone pairs of the central atom.

$$:\!\overset{\bullet\bullet}{\underset{\bullet\bullet}{N}}\!\!-\!\!N\!\!-\!\!\overset{\bullet\bullet}{\underset{\bullet\bullet}{O}}\!:$$

All 16 valence electrons are used
If any atom lacks an octet, form double or triple bonds as necessary to give them octets.

$$:\!N\!\!\equiv\!\!N\!-\!\overset{\bullet\bullet}{\underset{\bullet\bullet}{O}}\!:$$

All atoms have octets, duets for H, structure is complete

c) SiH_4:   Write the correct skeletal structure for the molecule
     H is always terminal so Si is the central atom

$$H\!-\!\overset{\displaystyle H}{\underset{\displaystyle H}{Si}}\!-\!H$$

Calculate the total number of electrons for the Lewis structure by summing the valence electrons of each atom in the molecule

(number of valence e⁻ for Si) + 4(number of valence e⁻ for H) = 4 + 4(1) = 8

Distribute the electrons among the atoms, giving octets (or duets for H) to as many atoms as possible. Begin with the bonding electrons, and then proceed to lone pairs on terminal atoms and finally to lone pairs of the central atom.

```
        H
        |
H ── Si ── H
        |
        H
```

All 8 valence electrons are used.

If any atom lacks an octet, form double or triple bonds as necessary to give them octets.

All atoms have octets, duets for H, structure is complete.

d) Cl_2CO: Write the correct skeletal structure for the molecule

C is the least electronegative, so it is the central atom

```
          O
          |
Cl ── C ── Cl
```

Calculate the total number of electrons for the Lewis structure by summing the valence electrons of each atom in the molecule

(number of valence e^- for C) + 2(number of valence e^- for Cl) + (number of valence e^- for O) = $4 + 2(7) + 6 = 24$

Distribute the electrons among the atoms, giving octets (or duets for H) to as many atoms as possible. Begin with the bonding electrons, and then proceed to lone pairs on terminal atoms and finally to lone pairs of the central atom.

```
         ••
       : O :
          |
  ••      |      ••
: Cl ── C ── Cl :
  ••            ••
```

All 24 valence electrons are used.

If any atom lacks an octet, form double or triple bonds as necessary to give them octets.

```
       : O :
          ‖
  ••             ••
: Cl ── C ── Cl :
  ••             ••
```

All atoms have octets, duets for H, structure is complete.

e) H_3COH: Write the correct skeletal structure for the molecule

C is less electronegative and H is terminal

```
          O ── H
          |
H ── C ── H
          |
          H
```

Calculate the total number of electrons for the Lewis structure by summing the valence electrons of each atom in the molecule

(number of valence e^- for C) + 4(number of valence e^- for H) + (number of valence e^- for O) = $4 + 4(1) + 6 = 14$

Distribute the electrons among the atoms, giving octets (or duets for H) to as many atoms as possible. Begin with the bonding electrons, and then proceed to lone pairs on terminal atoms and finally to lone pairs of the central atom.

```
         ••
       : O ── H
          |
H ── C ── H
          |
          H
```

All 14 valence electrons are used.

If any atom lacks an octet, form double or triple bonds as necessary to give them octets.

All atoms have octets, duets for H, structure is complete.

f) OH^-: Write the correct skeletal structure for the ion

```
O ── H
```

Calculate the total number of electrons for the Lewis structure by summing the valence electrons of each atom in the ion and adding 1 for the 1 – charge.

(number of valence e⁻ for O) + (number of valence e⁻ for H) + 1 = 6 + 1 + 1 = 8

Distribute the electrons among the atoms, giving octets (or duets for H) to as many atoms as possible. Begin with the bonding electrons, and then proceed to lone pairs on terminal atoms and finally to lone pairs of the central atom.

$$\overset{\bullet\bullet}{\underset{\bullet\bullet}{\;\;\mathrm{O}}} \text{—— H}$$

All 8 valence electrons are used.

If any atom lacks an octet, form double or triple bonds as necessary to give them octets.

Lastly, write the Lewis structure in brackets with the charge of the ion in the upper right – hand corner.

$$\left[\overset{\bullet\bullet}{\underset{\bullet\bullet}{\;\;\mathrm{O}}} \text{—— H} \right]^{-}$$

g) BrO⁻: Write the correct skeletal structure for the ion

Br —— O

Calculate the total number of electrons for the Lewis structure by summing the valence electrons of each atom in the ion and adding 1 for the 1 – charge.

(number of valence e⁻ for O) + (number of valence e⁻ for Br) + 1 = 6 + 7 + 1 = 14

Distribute the electrons among the atoms, giving octets (or duets for H) to as many atoms as possible. Begin with the bonding electrons, and then proceed to lone pairs on terminal atoms and finally to lone pairs of the central atom.

$$\mathrm{Br} \text{——} \mathrm{O}$$

All 14 valence electrons are used.

If any atom lacks an octet, form double or triple bonds as necessary to give them octets.

Lastly, write the Lewis structure in brackets with the charge of the ion in the upper right – hand corner.

$$\left[\mathrm{Br} \text{——} \mathrm{O} \right]^{-}$$

60. a) N_2H_2: Write the correct skeletal structure for the molecule

H —— N —— N —— H

Calculate the total number of electrons for the Lewis structure by summing the valence electrons of each atom in the molecule

2(number of valence e⁻ for N) + 2(number of valence e⁻ for H) = 2(5) + 2(1) = 12

Distribute the electrons among the atoms, giving octets (or duets for H) to as many atoms as possible. Begin with the bonding electrons, and then proceed to lone pairs on terminal atoms and finally to lone pairs of the central atom.

H —— N —— N —— H

All 12 valence electrons are used.

If any atom lacks an octet, form double or triple bonds as necessary to give them octets.

H —— N ＝ N —— H

All atoms have octets, duets for H, structure is complete.

b) N_2H_4: Write the correct skeletal structure for the molecule

H   H
  \   /
   N —— N
  /   \
H   H

Calculate the total number of electrons for the Lewis structure by summing the valence electrons of each atom in the molecule

2(number of valence e⁻ for N) + 4(number of valence e⁻ for H) = 2(5) + 4(1) = 14

Distribute the electrons among the atoms, giving octets (or duets for H) to as many atoms as possible. Begin with the bonding electrons, and then proceed to lone pairs on terminal atoms and finally to lone pairs of the central atom.

All 14 valence electrons are used.

If any atom lacks an octet, form double or triple bonds as necessary to give them octets.

All atoms have octets, duets for H, structure is complete.

c) C₂H₂: Write the correct skeletal structure for the molecule

H —— C —— C —— H

Calculate the total number of electrons for the Lewis structure by summing the valence electrons of each atom in the molecule

2(number of valence e⁻ for C) + 2(number of valence e⁻ for H) = 2(4) + 2(1) = 10

Distribute the electrons among the atoms, giving octets (or duets for H) to as many atoms as possible. Begin with the bonding electrons, and then proceed to lone pairs on terminal atoms and finally to lone pairs of the central atom.

H —— C —— C̈ —— H

All 10 valence electrons are used.

If any atom lacks an octet, form double or triple bonds as necessary to give them octets.

H —— C ≡≡≡ C —— H

All atoms have octets, duets for H, structure is complete.

d) C₂H₄: Write the correct skeletal structure for the molecule

Calculate the total number of electrons for the Lewis structure by summing the valence electrons of each atom in the molecule

2(number of valence e⁻ for C) + 4(number of valence e⁻ for H) = 2(4) + 4(1) = 12

Distribute the electrons among the atoms, giving octets (or duets for H) to as many atoms as possible. Begin with the bonding electrons, and then proceed to lone pairs on terminal atoms and finally to lone pairs of the central atom.

All 12 valence electrons are used.

If any atom lacks an octet, form double or triple bonds as necessary to give them octets.

All atoms have octets, duets for H, structure is complete.

e) H₃COCH₃:Write the correct skeletal structure for the molecule

Calculate the total number of electrons for the Lewis structure by summing the valence electrons of each atom in the molecule

2(number of valence e⁻ for C) + (number of valence e⁻ for O) + 6(number of valence e⁻ for H) = 2(4) + 6 + 6(1) = 20

Distribute the electrons among the atoms, giving octets (or duets for H) to as many atoms as possible. Begin with the bonding electrons, and then proceed to lone pairs on terminal atoms and finally to lone pairs of the central atom.

$$H - \underset{\underset{H}{|}}{\overset{\overset{H}{|}}{C}} - \overset{\bullet\bullet}{\underset{\bullet\bullet}{O}} - \underset{\underset{H}{|}}{\overset{\overset{H}{|}}{C}} - H$$

All 20 valence electrons are used.

If any atom lacks an octet, form double or triple bonds as necessary to give them octets.

All atoms have octets, duets for H, structure is complete.

f) CN⁻: Write the correct skeletal structure for the ion

C — N

Calculate the total number of electrons for the Lewis structure by summing the valence electrons of each atom in the ion and adding 1 for the 1 – charge.

(number of valence e⁻ for C) + (number of valence e⁻ for N) + 1 = 4 + 5 + 1 = 10

Distribute the electrons among the atoms, giving octets (or duets for H) to as many atoms as possible. Begin with the bonding electrons, and then proceed to lone pairs on terminal atoms and finally to lone pairs of the central atom.

$$\overset{\bullet\bullet}{C} - \overset{\bullet\bullet}{\underset{\bullet\bullet}{N}}\,\bullet\bullet$$

All 10 valence electrons are used.

If any atom lacks an octet, form double or triple bonds as necessary to give them octets.

$$\bullet\bullet\,C \equiv N\,\bullet\bullet$$

Lastly, write the Lewis structure in brackets with the charge of the ion in the upper right – hand corner.

$$\left[\bullet\bullet\,C \equiv N\,\bullet\bullet\right]^{-}$$

g) NO₂⁻: Write the correct skeletal structure for the ion

O — N — O

Calculate the total number of electrons for the Lewis structure by summing the valence electrons of each atom in the ion and adding 1 for the 1 – charge.

2(number of valence e⁻ for O) + (number of valence e⁻ for N) + 1 = 2(6) + 5 + 1 = 18

Distribute the electrons among the atoms, giving octets (or duets for H) to as many atoms as possible. Begin with the bonding electrons, and then proceed to lone pairs on terminal atoms and finally to lone pairs of the central atom.

$$\bullet\bullet\,\overset{\bullet\bullet}{\underset{\bullet\bullet}{O}} - \overset{\bullet\bullet}{N} - \overset{\bullet\bullet}{\underset{\bullet\bullet}{O}}\,\bullet\bullet$$

All 18 valence electrons are used.

If any atom lacks an octet, form double or triple bonds as necessary to give them octets.

$$\bullet\bullet\,\overset{\bullet\bullet}{\underset{\bullet\bullet}{O}} - \overset{\bullet\bullet}{N} = \overset{\bullet\bullet}{O}\,\bullet\bullet$$

Lastly, write the Lewis structure in brackets with the charge of the ion in the upper right – hand corner.

$$\left[\bullet\bullet\,\overset{\bullet\bullet}{\underset{\bullet\bullet}{O}} - \overset{\bullet\bullet}{N} = \overset{\bullet\bullet}{O}\,\bullet\bullet\right]^{-}$$

61. a) SeO₂: Write the correct skeletal structure for the molecule
Se is the less electronegative, so it is central

O — Se — O

Calculate the total number of electrons for the Lewis structure by summing the valence electrons of each atom in the molecule (number of valence e⁻ for Se) + 2(number of valence e⁻ for O) = 6 +2(6) = 18

Distribute the electrons among the atoms, giving octets (or duets for H) to as many atoms as possible. Begin with the bonding electrons, and then proceed to lone pairs on terminal atoms and finally to lone pairs of the central atom.

$$:\ddot{O}—Se—\ddot{O}:$$

All 18 valence electrons are used.

If any atom lacks an octet, form double or triple bonds as necessary to give them octets.

$$:\ddot{O}—Se{=}\ddot{O}:$$

All atoms have octets, duets for H, structure is complete. However, the double bond can form from either oxygen atom, so there are two resonance forms.

$$:\ddot{O}—Se{=}\ddot{O}: \longleftrightarrow :\ddot{O}{=}Se—\ddot{O}:$$

Calculate the formal charge on each atom by finding the number of valence electrons and subtracting the number of lone pair electrons and one – half the number of bonding electrons.

$$:\ddot{O}—Se{=}\ddot{O}: \longleftrightarrow :\ddot{O}{=}Se—\ddot{O}:$$

number of valence electrons	6	6	6	6	6	6
- number of lone pair electrons	6	2	4	4	2	6
- 1/2(number of bonding electrons)	1	3	2	2	3	1
Formal charge	–1	+1	0	0	+1	–1

b) CO_3^{2-}: Write the correct skeletal structure for the ion

Calculate the total number of electrons for the Lewis structure by summing the valence electrons of each atom in the ion and adding 2 for the 2 – charge.

3(number of valence e⁻ for O) + (number of valence e⁻ for C) + 2 = 3(6) + 4 + 2 = 24

Distribute the electrons among the atoms, giving octets (or duets for H) to as many atoms as possible. Begin with the bonding electrons, and then proceed to lone pairs on terminal atoms and finally to lone pairs of the central atom.

$$:\overset{\bullet\bullet}{O}:$$
$$:\ddot{O}—C—\ddot{O}:$$

All 24 valence electrons are used.

If any atom lacks an octet, form double or triple bonds as necessary to give them octets.

$$:\overset{\bullet\bullet}{O}:$$
$$:\ddot{O}—C{=}\ddot{O}:$$

Lastly, write the Lewis structure in brackets with the charge of the ion in the upper right – hand corner.

$$\left[\begin{array}{c} :\overset{\bullet\bullet}{O}: \\ :\ddot{O}—C{=}\ddot{O}: \end{array} \right]^{2-}$$

All atoms have octets, duets for H, structure is complete. However, the double bond can form from any oxygen atom, so there are three resonance forms.

Calculate the formal charge on each atom by finding the number of valence electrons and subtracting the number of lone pair electrons and one – half the number of bonding electrons.

	O_{left}	O_{top}	O_{right}	C
number of valence electrons	6	6	6	4
- number of lone pair electrons	6	6	4	0
- 1/2(number of bonding electrons)	1	1	2	4
Formal charge	−1	−1	0	0

The sum of the formal charges is – 2 which is the overall charge of the ion. The other resonance forms would be the same.

c) ClO⁻: Write the correct skeletal structure for the ion

Cl —— O

Calculate the total number of electrons for the Lewis structure by summing the valence electrons of each atom in the ion and adding 1 for the 1 – charge.

(number of valence e⁻ for O) + (number of valence e⁻ for Cl) + 1 = 6 + 7 + 1 = 14

Distribute the electrons among the atoms, giving octets (or duets for H) to as many atoms as possible. Begin with the bonding electrons, and then proceed to lone pairs on terminal atoms and finally to lone pairs of the central atom.

All 14 valence electrons are used.

If any atom lacks an octet, form double or triple bonds as necessary to give them octets.
Lastly, write the Lewis structure in brackets with the charge of the ion in the upper right – hand corner.

All atoms have octets, duets for H, structure is complete.

Calculate the formal charge on each atom by finding the number of valence electrons and subtracting the number of lone pair electrons and one – half the number of bonding electrons.

	Cl	O
number of valence electrons	7	6
- number of lone pair electrons	6	6
- 1/2(number of bonding electrons)	1	1
Formal charge	0	−1

The sum of the formal charges is – 1 which is the overall charge of the ion.

d. NO₂⁻: Write the correct skeletal structure for the ion

O —— N —— O

Calculate the total number of electrons for the Lewis structure by summing the valence electrons of each atom in the ion and adding 1 for the 1 – charge.

2(number of valence e⁻ for O) + (number of valence e⁻ for N) + 1 = 2(6) + 5 + 1 = 18

Distribute the electrons among the atoms, giving octets (or duets for H) to as many atoms as possible. Begin with the bonding electrons, and then proceed to lone pairs on terminal atoms and finally to lone pairs of the central atom.

$$\ddot{\text{O}} - \text{N} - \ddot{\text{O}}\text{:}$$

All 14 valence electrons are used.
If any atom lacks an octet, form double or triple bonds as necessary to give them octets.

$$\text{:}\ddot{\text{O}} = \text{N} - \ddot{\text{O}}\text{:}$$

Lastly, write the Lewis structure in brackets with the charge of the ion in the upper right – hand corner.

$$\left[\text{:}\ddot{\text{O}} = \text{N} - \ddot{\text{O}}\text{:}\right]^{-}$$

All atoms have octets, duets for H, structure is complete. However, the double bond can form from either oxygen atom, so there are two resonance forms.

$$\left[\text{:}\ddot{\text{O}} = \text{N} - \ddot{\text{O}}\text{:}\right]^{-} \longleftrightarrow \left[\text{:}\ddot{\text{O}} - \text{N} = \ddot{\text{O}}\text{:}\right]^{-}$$

Calculate the formal charge on each atom by finding the number of valence electrons and subtracting the number of lone pair electrons and one – half the number of bonding electrons. Using the left side structure:

	O	N	O
number of valence electrons	6	5	6
- number of lone pair electrons	4	2	6
- 1/2(number of bonding electrons)	2	3	1
Formal charge	0	0	– 1

The sum of the formal charges is – 1 which is the overall charge of the ion.

62. a) ClO_3^-: Write the correct skeletal structure for the ion

$$\text{O} - \underset{\underset{\text{O}}{|}}{\text{Cl}} - \text{O}$$

Calculate the total number of electrons for the Lewis structure by summing the valence electrons of each atom in the ion and adding 1 for the 1 – charge.

3(number of valence e^- for O) + (number of valence e^- for Cl) + 1 = 3(6) + 7 + 1 = 26

Distribute the electrons among the atoms, giving octets (or duets for H) to as many atoms as possible. Begin with the bonding electrons, and then proceed to lone pairs on terminal atoms and finally to lone pairs of the central atom.

$$\text{:}\ddot{\text{O}} - \underset{\underset{\ddot{\text{O}}}{|}}{\text{Cl}} - \ddot{\text{O}}\text{:}$$

All 26 valence electrons are used.
If any atom lacks an octet, form double or triple bonds as necessary to give them octets.
Lastly, write the Lewis structure in brackets with the charge of the ion in the upper right – hand corner.

$$\left[\text{:}\ddot{\text{O}} - \underset{\underset{\ddot{\text{O}}}{|}}{\text{Cl}} - \ddot{\text{O}}\text{:}\right]^{-}$$

All atoms have octets, duets for H, structure is complete.
Calculate the formal charge on each atom by finding the number of valence electrons and subtracting the number of lone pair electrons and one – half the number of bonding electrons.

	O_{left}	O_{top}	O_{right}	Cl
number of valence electrons	6	6	6	7
- number of lone pair electrons	6	6	6	2
- 1/2(number of bonding electrons)	1	1	1	3
Formal charge	−1	−1	−1	+2

The sum of the formal charges is − 1 which is the overall charge of the ion.

b) ClO_4^-: Write the correct skeletal structure for the ion

Calculate the total number of electrons for the Lewis structure by summing the valence electrons of each atom in the ion and adding 1 for the 1 – charge.

4(number of valence e⁻ for O) + (number of valence e⁻ for Cl) + 1 = 4(6) + 7 + 1 = 32

Distribute the electrons among the atoms, giving octets (or duets for H) to as many atoms as possible. Begin with the bonding electrons, and then proceed to lone pairs on terminal atoms and finally to lone pairs of the central atom.

All 26 valence electrons are used.

If any atom lacks an octet, form double or triple bonds as necessary to give them octets.

Lastly, write the Lewis structure in brackets with the charge of the ion in the upper right – hand corner.

All atoms have octets, duets for H, structure is complete.

Calculate the formal charge on each atom be finding the number of valence electrons and subtracting the number of lone pair electrons and one – half the number of bonding electrons. Using the left side structure:

	O_{left}	O_{top}	O_{right}	O_{bottom}	Cl
number of valence electrons	6	6	6	6	7
- number of lone pair electrons	6	6	6	6	0
- 1/2(number of bonding electrons)	1	1	1	1	4
Formal charge	−1	−1	−1	−1	+3

The sum of the formal charges is − 1 which is the overall charge of the ion.

c) NO_3^-: Write the correct skeletal structure for the ion

Calculate the total number of electrons for the Lewis structure by summing the valence electrons of each atom in the ion and adding 1 for the 1 – charge.

3(number of valence e⁻ for O) + (number of valence e⁻ for N) + 1 = 3(6) + 5 + 1 = 24

Distribute the electrons among the atoms, giving octets (or duets for H) to as many atoms as possible. Begin with the bonding electrons, and then proceed to lone pairs on terminal atoms and finally to lone pairs of the central atom.

All 24 valence electrons are used.
If any atom lacks an octet, form double or triple bonds as necessary to give them octets.

Lastly, write the Lewis structure in brackets with the charge of the ion in the upper right – hand corner.

All atoms have octets, duets for H, structure is complete. However, the double bond can form from any oxygen atom, so there are three resonance forms.

Calculate the formal charge on each atom be finding the number of valence electrons and subtracting the number of lone pair electrons and one – half the number of bonding electrons. Using the left hand structure

	O_{left}	O_{top}	O_{right}	N
number of valence electronss	6	6	6	5
- number of lone pair electrons	6	6	4	0
- 1/2(number of bonding electrons)	1	1	2	4
Formal charge	−1	−1	0	+1

The sum of the formal charges is – 1 which is the overall charge of the ion. The other resonance forms would be the same.

d) NH_4^+:   Write the correct skeletal structure for the ion

Calculate the total number of electrons for the Lewis structure by summing the valence electrons of each atom in the ion and subtracting 1 for the 1+ charge.

4(number of valence e^- for H) + (number of valence e^- for N) – 1 = 4(1) + 5 – 1 = 8

Distribute the electrons among the atoms, giving octets (or duets for H) to as many atoms as possible. Begin with the bonding electrons, and then proceed to lone pairs on terminal atoms and finally to lone pairs of the central atom.

269

All 8 valence electrons are used.

If any atom lacks an octet, form double or triple bonds as necessary to give them octets.

Lastly, write the Lewis structure in brackets with the charge of the ion in the upper right – hand corner.

$$\left[\begin{array}{c} H \\ | \\ H - N - H \\ | \\ H \end{array} \right]^{+}$$

All atoms have octets, duets for H, structure is complete.

Calculate the formal charge on each atom be finding the number of valence electrons and subtracting the number of lone pair electrons and one – half the number of bonding electrons.

	H_{left}	H_{top}	H_{right}	H_{bottom}	N
number of valence electrons	1	1	1	1	5
- number of lone pair electrons	0	0	0	0	0
- 1/2(number of bonding electrons)	1	1	1	1	4
Formal charge	0	0	0	0	+1

The sum of the formal charges is + 1 which is the overall charge of the ion.

63.

$$\begin{array}{cc} \underset{I}{\overset{H}{\underset{|}{H - C = S}}} & \underset{II}{\overset{H}{\underset{|}{H - S = C}}} \end{array}$$

Calculate the formal charge on each atom in structure I by finding the number of valence electrons and subtracting the number of lone pair electrons and one – half the number of bonding electrons.

	H_{left}	H_{top}	C	S
number of valence electrons	1	1	4	6
- number of lone pair electrons	0	0	0	4
- 1/2(number of bonding electrons)	1	1	4	2
Formal charge	0	0	0	0

The sum of the formal charges is 0 which is the overall charge of the molecule.

Calculate the formal charge on each atom in structure II by finding the number of valence electrons and subtracting the number of lone pair electrons and one – half the number of bonding electrons

	H_{left}	H_{top}	S	C
number of valence electrons	1	1	6	4
- number of lone pair electrons	0	0	0	4
- 1/2(number of bonding electrons)	1	1	4	2
Formal charge	0	0	+2	- 2

The sum of the formal charges is 0 which is the overall charge of the molecule.

Structure I is the better Lewis structure because it has the least amount of formal charge on each atom.

64.

I   II

Calculate the formal charge on each atom in structure I by finding the number of valence electrons and subtracting the number of lone pair electrons and one – half the number of bonding electrons.

	H_{left}	H_{top}	H_{right}	H_{bottom}	S	C
number of valence electrons	1	1	1	1	6	4
- number of lone pair electrons	0	0	0	0	0	4
- 1/2(number of bonding electrons)	1	1	1	1	4	2
Formal charge	0	0	0	0	+2	- 2

The sum of the formal charges is 0 which is the overall charge of the molecule.
Calculate the formal charge on each atom in structure by finding the number of valence electrons and subtracting the number of lone pair electrons and one – half the number of bonding electrons.

	H_{left}	H_{top}	H_{right}	H_{bottom}	C	S
number of valence electrons	1	1	1	1	4	6
- number of lone pair electrons	0	0	0	0	0	4
- 1/2(number of bonding electrons)	1	1	1	1	4	2
Formal charge	0	0	0	0	0	0

The sum of the formal charges is 0 which is the overall charge of the molecule.
Structure II is the better Lewis structure because it has the least amount of formal charge on each atom.

65. :O≡C–Ö: does not provide a significant contribution to the resonance hybrid as it has a +1 formal charge on a very electronegative oxygen.

	O_{left}	O_{right}	C
number of valence electrons	6	6	4
- number of lone pair electrons	2	6	0
- 1/2(number of bonding electrons)	3	1	4
Formal charge	+1	−1	0

66. Compare the two forms of each molecule with O as a central atom and a terminal atom. Determine the formal charge on the central atom for all the structures.

:Ö=N=N: :N=O=N: :F—O—F: :O—F—F:

I   II   III   IV

	I	II	III	IV
	N	O	O	F
number of valence electrons	5	6	6	7
- number of lone pair electrons	0	0	4	4
- 1/2(number of bonding electrons)	3	4	4	2
Formal charge	+1	+2	0	+1

We can see from the formal charge on the central atom, O has to be terminal for the N_2O molecule. When O is the central atom is has a +2 formal charge and it is the more electronegative atom. So, this would not be a good structure. For the OF_2 molecule, O has to be the central atom. When O is central it has a formal charge of 0, when the F is central it has a formal charge of +1. This puts a positive formal charge on the most electronegative atom which is not acceptable.

67. a) BCl_3: Write the correct skeletal structure for the molecule.

B is the less electronegative, so it is central

Calculate the total number of electrons for the Lewis structure by summing the valence electrons of each atom in the molecule

(number of valence e⁻ for B) + 3(number of valence e⁻ for Cl) = 3 +3(7) = 24

Distribute the electrons among the atoms, giving octets (or duets for H) to as many atoms as possible. Begin with the bonding electrons, and then proceed to lone pairs on terminal atoms and finally to lone pairs of the central atom.

All 24 valence electrons are used.

B has an incomplete octet. If we complete the octet, there is a formal charge of – 1 on the B which is less electronegative than Cl.

b) NO_2: Write the correct skeletal structure for the molecule.

N is the less electronegative, so it is central

O —— N —— O

Calculate the total number of electrons for the Lewis structure by summing the valence electrons of each atom in the molecule

(number of valence e⁻ for N) + 2(number of valence e⁻ for O) = 5 +2(6) = 17

Distribute the electrons among the atoms, giving octets (or duets for H) to as many atoms as possible. Begin with the bonding electrons, and then proceed to lone pairs on terminal atoms and finally to lone pairs of the central atom.

All 17 valence electrons are used.

N has an incomplete octet. It has 7 electrons because we have an odd number of valence electrons.

c) BH_3: Write the correct skeletal structure for the molecule.

B is the less electronegative, so it is central

H
|
H —— B —— H

Calculate the total number of electrons for the Lewis structure by summing the valence electrons of each atom in the molecule

(number of valence e⁻ for B) + 3(number of valence e⁻ for H) = 3 +3(1) = 6

Distribute the electrons among the atoms, giving octets (or duets for H) to as many atoms as possible. Begin with the bonding electrons, and then proceed to lone pairs on terminal atoms and finally to lone pairs of the central atom.

H
|
H —— B —— H

All 6 valence electrons are used.

B has an incomplete octet. H cannot double bond, so it is not possible to complete the octet on B with a double bond.

68. a) BBr_3: Write the correct skeletal structure for the molecule.

B is the less electronegative, so it is central

Calculate the total number of electrons for the Lewis structure by summing the valence electrons of each atom in the molecule

272

(number of valence e⁻ for B) + 3(number of valence e⁻ for Br) = 3 +3(7) = 24

Distribute the electrons among the atoms, giving octets (or duets for H) to as many atoms as possible. Begin with the bonding electrons, and then proceed to lone pairs on terminal atoms and finally to lone pairs of the central atom.

$$\overset{\overset{\displaystyle\cdot\cdot}{\underset{|}{\cdot\,Br\,\cdot}}}{{:\!Br\!-\!B\!-\!Br:}}$$

All 24 valence electrons are used.

B has an incomplete octet. If we complete the octet, there is a formal charge of – 1 on the B which is less electronegative than Br.

b) NO: Write the correct skeletal structure for the molecule.

N——O

Calculate the total number of electrons for the Lewis structure by summing the valence electrons of each atom in the molecule

(number of valence e⁻ for N) + (number of valence e⁻ for O) = 5 +6 = 11

Distribute the electrons among the atoms, giving octets (or duets for H) to as many atoms as possible. Begin with the bonding electrons, and then proceed to lone pairs on terminal atoms and finally to lone pairs of the central atom.

$$\overset{\displaystyle\cdot}{\underset{\displaystyle\cdot\cdot}{N}}\!=\!\!\overset{\displaystyle\cdot\cdot}{O}:$$

All 11 valence electrons are used.

N has an incomplete octet. It has 7 electrons because we have an odd number of valence electrons.

c) ClO₂: Write the correct skeletal structure for the molecule.

Cl is less electronegative so it is central

O —— Cl —— O

Calculate the total number of electrons for the Lewis structure by summing the valence electrons of each atom in the molecule

(number of valence e⁻ for Cl) + 2(number of valence e⁻ for O) = 5 +2(6) = 17

Distribute the electrons among the atoms, giving octets (or duets for H) to as many atoms as possible. Begin with the bonding electrons, and then proceed to lone pairs on terminal atoms and finally to lone pairs of the central atom.

$$\overset{\displaystyle\cdot\cdot}{\underset{\displaystyle\cdot\cdot}{O}}\!=\!\overset{\displaystyle\cdot}{Cl}\!-\!\overset{\displaystyle\cdot\cdot}{\underset{\displaystyle\cdot\cdot}{O}}:$$

All 17 valence electrons are used.

Cl has an incomplete octet. It has 7 electrons because we have an odd number of valence electrons.

69. a) PO₄³⁻: Write the correct skeletal structure for the ion.

Calculate the total number of electrons for the Lewis structure by summing the valence electrons of each atom in the ion and adding 3 for the 3 – charge.

4(number of valence e⁻ for O) + (number of valence e⁻ for P) + 3 = 4(6) + 5 + 3 = 32

Distribute the electrons among the atoms, giving octets (or duets for H) to as many atoms as possible. Begin with the bonding electrons, and then proceed to lone pairs on terminal atoms and finally to lone pairs of the central atom.

All 32 valence electrons are used.

Lastly, write the Lewis structure in brackets with the charge of the ion in the upper right – hand corner.

All atoms have octets, duets for H, structure is complete.

Calculate the formal charge on each atom by finding the number of valence electrons and subtracting the number of lone pair electrons and one – half the number of bonding electrons.

	O_{left}	O_{top}	O_{right}	O_{bottom}	P
number of valence electrons	6	6	6	6	5
- number of lone pair electrons	6	6	6	6	0
- 1/2(number of bonding electrons)	1	1	1	1	4
Formal charge	−1	−1	−1	−1	+1

The sum of the formal charges is 3−which is the overall charge of the ion. However, we can write a resonance structure with a double bond to an oxygen because P can expand its octet. This leads to lower formal charges on P and O

Using the leftmost structure calculate the formal charge on each atom by finding the number of valence electrons and subtracting the number of lone pair electrons and one – half the number of bonding electrons.

	O_{left}	O_{top}	O_{right}	O_{bottom}	P
number of valence electrons	6	6	6	6	5
- number of lone pair electrons	4	6	6	6	0
- 1/2(number of bonding electrons)	2	1	1	1	5
Formal charge	0	−1	−1	−1	0

The sum of the formal charges is 3−which is the overall charge of the ion. These resonance forms would all have the lower formal charges associated with the double bonded O and P.

b) CN⁻: Write the correct skeletal structure for the ion.

$$C \text{——} N$$

Calculate the total number of electrons for the Lewis structure by summing the valence electrons of each atom in the ion and adding 1 for the 1 – charge.

(number of valence e⁻ for C) + (number of valence e⁻ for N) + 1 = 4 + 5 + 1 = 10

Distribute the electrons among the atoms, giving octets (or duets for H) to as many atoms as possible. Begin with the bonding electrons, and then proceed to lone pairs on terminal atoms and finally to lone pairs of the central atom.

$$:C \text{——} N:$$

All 10 valence electrons are used.

If any atom lacks an octet, form double or triple bonds as necessary to give them octets.

$$:C \equiv N:$$

Lastly, write the Lewis structure in brackets with the charge of the ion in the upper right – hand corner.

$$\left[:C \equiv N: \right]^{-}$$

All atoms have octets, duets for H, structure is complete.

Calculate the formal charge on each atom be finding the number of valence electrons and subtracting the number of lone pair electrons and one – half the number of bonding electrons.

$$\left[:C \equiv N: \right]^{-}$$

	C	N
number of valence electrons	4	5
- number of lone pair electrons	2	2
- 1/2(number of bonding electrons)	3	3
Formal charge	–1	0

The sum of the formal charges is – 1 which is the overall charge of the ion

c) SO_3^{2-}: Write the correct skeletal structure for the ion.

$$\begin{array}{c} O \\ | \\ O \text{——} S \text{——} O \end{array}$$

Calculate the total number of electrons for the Lewis structure by summing the valence electrons of each atom in the ion and adding 2 for the 2 – charge.

3(number of valence e⁻ for O) + (number of valence e⁻ for S) + 2 = 3(6) + 6 + 2 = 26

Distribute the electrons among the atoms, giving octets (or duets for H) to as many atoms as possible. Begin with the bonding electrons, and then proceed to lone pairs on terminal atoms and finally to lone pairs of the central atom.

All 26 valence electrons are used.

Lastly, write the Lewis structure in brackets with the charge of the ion in the upper right – hand corner.

Calculate the formal charge on each atom be finding the number of valence electrons and subtracting the number of lone pair electrons and one – half the number of bonding electrons.

$$\left[\begin{array}{c} \overset{\displaystyle \cdots}{\underset{\cdots}{O}} \\ | \\ \overset{\cdots}{O}-S-\overset{\cdots}{O} \end{array}\right]^{2-}$$

	O_{left}	O_{top}	O_{right}	S
number of valence electrons	6	6	6	6
- number of lone pair electrons	6	6	6	2
- 1/2(number of bonding electrons)	1	1	1	3
Formal charge	−1	−1	−1	+1

The sum of the formal charges is − 1 which is the overall charge of the ion. However, we can write a resonance structure with a double bond to an oxygen because S can expand its octet. This leads to a lower formal charge

$$\left[\begin{array}{c} \overset{\cdots}{O} \\ | \\ O=S-\overset{\cdots}{O} \end{array}\right]^{2-} \longleftrightarrow \left[\begin{array}{c} \overset{\cdots}{O} \\ \| \\ \overset{\cdots}{O}-S-\overset{\cdots}{O} \end{array}\right]^{2-} \longleftrightarrow \left[\begin{array}{c} \overset{\cdots}{O} \\ | \\ \overset{\cdots}{O}-S=O \end{array}\right]^{2-}$$

Using the leftmost resonance form: Calculate the formal charge on each atom be finding the number of valence electrons and subtracting the number of lone pair electrons and one – half the number of bonding electrons.

	O_{left}	O_{top}	O_{right}	S
number of valence electrons	6	6	6	6
- number of lone pair electrons	4	6	6	2
- 1/2(number of bonding electrons)	2	1	1	4
Formal charge	0	−1	−1	0

The sum of the formal charges is 2–which is the overall charge of the ion. These resonance forms would all have the lower formal charge on the double bonded O and S.

d) ClO_2^- : Write the correct skeletal structure for the ion.

$$O \text{——} Cl \text{——} O$$

Calculate the total number of electrons for the Lewis structure by summing the valence electrons of each atom in the ion and adding 1 for the 1 – charge.

$$2(\text{number of valence } e^- \text{ for O}) + (\text{number of valence } e^- \text{ for Cl}) + 1 = 2(6) + 7 + 1 = 20$$

Distribute the electrons among the atoms, giving octets (or duets for H) to as many atoms as possible. Begin with the bonding electrons, and then proceed to lone pairs on terminal atoms and finally to lone pairs of the central atom.

$$\overset{\cdots}{\underset{\cdots}{O}} \text{——} \overset{\cdots}{Cl} \text{——} \overset{\cdots}{\underset{\cdots}{O}}$$

All 20 valence electrons are used.

Lastly, write the Lewis structure in brackets with the charge of the ion in the upper right – hand corner.

$$\left[\overset{\cdots}{\underset{\cdots}{O}} \text{——} \overset{\cdots}{Cl} \text{——} \overset{\cdots}{\underset{\cdots}{O}}\right]^-$$

All atoms have octets, duets for H, structure is complete.
Calculate the formal charge on each atom be finding the number of valence electrons and subtracting the number of lone pair electrons and one – half the number of bonding electrons.

$$\left[\overset{\cdots}{\underset{\cdots}{O}} \text{——} \overset{\cdots}{Cl} \text{——} \overset{\cdots}{\underset{\cdots}{O}}\right]^-$$

	O_{left}	O_{right}	Cl
number of valence electrons	6	6	7
- number of lone pair electrons	6	6	4
- 1/2(number of bonding electrons)	1	1	2
Formal charge	-1	-1	$+1$

The sum of the formal charges is -1 which is the overall charge of the ion. However, we can write a resonance structure with a double bond to an oxygen because Cl can expand its octet. This leads to a lower formal charge

Using the leftmost resonance form: Calculate the formal charge on each atom be finding the number of valence electrons and subtracting the number of lone pair electrons and one – half the number of bonding electrons.

	O_{left}	O_{right}	Cl
number of valence electrons	6	6	7
- number of lone pair electrons	4	6	4
- 1/2(number of bonding electrons)	2	1	3
Formal charge	0	-1	0

The sum of the formal charges is 1–which is the overall charge of the ion. These resonance forms would all have the lower formal charge on the double bonded O and Cl.

70. a) SO_4^{2-}: Write the correct skeletal structure for the ion.

```
        O
        |
   O — S — O
        |
        O
```

Calculate the total number of electrons for the Lewis structure by summing the valence electrons of each atom in the molecule and adding 2 for the 2 – charge.

4(number of valence e⁻ for O) + (number of valence e⁻ for S) + 2 = 4(6) + 6 + 2 = 32

Distribute the electrons among the atoms, giving octets (or duets for H) to as many atoms as possible. Begin with the bonding electrons, and then proceed to lone pairs on terminal atoms and finally to lone pairs of the central atom.

All 32 valence electrons are used.

Lastly, write the Lewis structure in brackets with the charge of the ion in the upper right – hand corner.

All atoms have octets, duets for H, structure is complete.
Calculate the formal charge on each atom be finding the number of valence electrons and subtracting the number of lone pair electrons and one – half the number of bonding electrons.

$$
\left[
\begin{array}{ccccc}
 & & \ddot{\overset{\displaystyle\cdots}{O}} & & \\
 & & | & & \\
\ddot{\overset{\displaystyle\cdots}{O}} & \!\!\!-\!\!\! & S & \!\!\!-\!\!\! & \ddot{\overset{\displaystyle\cdots}{O}} \\
 & & | & & \\
 & & \ddot{\overset{\displaystyle\cdots}{O}} & &
\end{array}
\right]^{2-}
$$

	O_{left}	O_{top}	O_{right}	O_{bottom}	S
number of valence electrons	6	6	6	6	6
- number of lone pair electrons	6	6	6	6	0
- 1/2(number of bonding electrons)	1	1	1	1	4
Formal charge	−1	−1	−1	−1	+2

The sum of the formal charges is − 2 which is the overall charge of the ion. However, we can write a resonance structure with double bonds to two oxygen atoms because S can expand its octet. This leads to lower formal charges.

Using the leftmost resonance form: Calculate the formal charge on each atom be finding the number of valence electrons and subtracting the number of lone pair electrons and one – half the number of bonding electrons.

	O_{left}	O_{top}	O_{right}	O_{bottom}	S
number of valence electrons	6	6	6	6	6
- number of lone pair electrons	4	4	6	6	0
- 1/2(number of bonding electrons)	2	2	1	1	6
Formal charge	0	0	− 1	− 1	0

The sum of the formal charges is 2− which is the overall charge of the ion. These resonance forms would all have the lower formal charges on the double bonded O and S.

b) HSO_4^- : Write the correct skeletal structure for the ion

$$
\begin{array}{ccccc}
 & & O & & \\
 & & | & & \\
O & \!\!-\!\! & S & \!\!-\!\! & O \!\!-\!\! H \\
 & & | & & \\
 & & O & &
\end{array}
$$

Calculate the total number of electrons for the Lewis structure by summing the valence electrons of each atom in the ion and adding 1 for the 1 – charge.
    4(number of valence e^- for O) + (number of valence e^- for S) + (number of valence e^- for H) + 1 =   4(6) + 6 + 1 +1 = 32
Distribute the electrons among the atoms, giving octets (or duets for H) to as many atoms as possible. Begin with the bonding electrons, and then proceed to lone pairs on terminal atoms and finally to lone pairs of the central atom.

278

All 32 valence electrons are used.

Lastly, write the Lewis structure in brackets with the charge of the ion in the upper right – hand corner.

All atoms have octets, duets for H, structure is complete.

Calculate the formal charge on each atom be finding the number of valence electrons and subtracting the number of lone pair electrons and one – half the number of bonding electrons.

	O_{left}	O_{top}	O_{right}	O_{bottom}	S	H
number of valence electrons	6	6	6	6	6	1
- number of lone pair electrons	6	6	4	6	0	0
- 1/2(number of bonding electrons)	1	1	2	2	4	1
Formal charge	–1	–1	0	–1	+2	0

The sum of the formal charges is – 1 which is the overall charge of the ion. However, we can write a resonance structure with double bonds to two oxygen atoms because S can expand its octet. This leads to a lower formal charges.

Using the leftmost resonance form: Calculate the formal charge on each atom by finding the number of valence electrons and subtracting the number of lone pair electrons and one – half the number of bonding electrons.

	O_{left}	O_{top}	O_{right}	O_{bottom}	S	H
number of valence electrons	6	6	6	6	6	1
- number of lone pair electrons	4	4	4	6	0	0
- 1/2(number of bonding electrons)	2	2	2	2	6	1
Formal charge	0	0	0	–1	0	0

The sum of the formal charges is 1– which is the overall charge of the ion. Each of these resonance forms would all have lower formal charges on O and S.

c) SO₃: Write the correct skeletal structure for the molecule

Calculate the total number of electrons for the Lewis structure by summing the valence electrons of each atom in the molecule.

3(number of valence e⁻ for O) + (number of valence e⁻ for S) = 3(6) + 6 = 24

Distribute the electrons among the atoms, giving octets (or duets for H) to as many atoms as possible. Begin with the bonding electrons, and then proceed to lone pairs on terminal atoms and finally to lone pairs of the central atom.

All 24 valence electrons are used.

If any atom lacks an octet, form double or triple bonds as necessary to give them octets.

All atoms have octets, duets for H, structure is complete.

Calculate the formal charge on each atom be finding the number of valence electrons and subtracting the number of lone pair electrons and one – half the number of bonding electrons.

	O_left	O_top	O_right	S
number of valence electrons	6	6	6	6
- number of lone pair electrons	6	6	4	0
- 1/2(number of bonding electrons)	1	1	2	4
Formal charge	−1	−1	0	+2

The sum of the formal charges is 0 which is the overall charge of the molecule. However, we can write a resonance structure with a double bond to all oxygen atoms because S can expand its octet. This leads to lower formal charges.

Calculate the formal charge on each atom be finding the number of valence electrons and subtracting the number of lone pair electrons and one – half the number of bonding electrons.

	O_left	O_top	O_right	S
number of valence electrons	6	6	6	6
- number of lone pair electrons	4	4	4	0
- 1/2(number of bonding electrons)	2	2	2	6
Formal charge	0	0	0	0

The sum of the formal charges is 0 which is the overall charge of the molecule. This resonance form would have the lower formal charges on each atom.

d) BrO₂⁻:   Write the correct skeletal structure for the ion

O ——— Br ——— O

Calculate the total number of electrons for the Lewis structure by summing the valence electrons of each atom in the molecule and adding 1 for the 1 – charge.

2(number of valence e⁻ for O) + (number of valence e⁻ for Br) + 1 = 2(6) + 7 + 1 = 20

Distribute the electrons among the atoms, giving octets (or duets for H) to as many atoms as possible. Begin with the bonding electrons, and then proceed to lone pairs on terminal atoms and finally to lone pairs of the central atom.

$$\ddot{:}\overset{\displaystyle ..}{\underset{\displaystyle ..}{O}} - \overset{\displaystyle ..}{Br} - \overset{\displaystyle ..}{\underset{\displaystyle ..}{O}}\ddot{:}$$

All 20 valence electrons are used.

Lastly, write the Lewis structure in brackets with the charge of the ion in the upper right – hand corner.

$$\left[:\overset{..}{\underset{..}{O}} - \overset{..}{Br} - \overset{..}{\underset{..}{O}}: \right]^{-}$$

All atoms have octets, duets for H, structure is complete.

Calculate the formal charge on each atom be finding the number of valence electrons and subtracting the number of lone pair electrons and one – half the number of bonding electrons.

$$\left[:\overset{..}{\underset{..}{O}} - \overset{..}{Br} - \overset{..}{\underset{..}{O}}: \right]^{-}$$

	O_{left}	O_{right}	Br
number of valence electrons	6	6	7
- number of lone pair electrons	6	6	4
- 1/2(number of bonding electrons)	1	1	2
Formal charge	−1	−1	+1

The sum of the formal charges is – 1 which is the overall charge of the ion. However, we can write a resonance structure with a double bond to an oxygen because Br can expand its octet. This leads to a lower formal charge

$$\left[\overset{..}{\underset{..}{O}} = \overset{..}{Br} - \overset{..}{\underset{..}{O}}: \right]^{-} \longleftrightarrow \left[:\overset{..}{\underset{..}{O}} - \overset{..}{Br} = \overset{..}{O} \right]^{-}$$

Using the leftmost resonance form: Calculate the formal charge on each atom be finding the number of valence electrons and subtracting the number of lone pair electrons and one – half the number of bonding electrons.

	O_{left}	O_{right}	Br
number of valence electron	6	6	7
- number of lone pair electrons	4	6	4
- 1/2(number of bonding electrons)	2	1	3
Formal charge	0	−1	0

The sum of the formal charges is 1–which is the overall charge of the ion. These resonance forms would both have the lower formal charges on the double bonded O and Br.

71. a) PF_5: Write the correct skeletal structure for the molecule

Calculate the total number of electrons for the Lewis structure by summing the valence electrons of each atom in the molecule

(number of valence e^- for P) + 5(number of valence e^- for F) = 5 +5(7) = 40

Distribute the electrons among the atoms, giving octets (or duets for H) to as many atoms as possible. Begin with the bonding electrons, and then proceed to lone pairs on terminal atoms and finally to lone pairs of the central atom. Arrange additional electrons around the central atom, giving it an expanded octet of up to 12 electrons.

281

b) I_3^- :   Write the correct skeletal structure for the ion

I — I — I

Calculate the total number of electrons for the Lewis structure by summing the valence electrons of each atom in the ion and adding 1 for the 1 – charge.

3(number of valence e^- for I) + 1 = 3(7) + 1 = 22

Distribute the electrons among the atoms, giving octets (or duets for H) to as many atoms as possible. Begin with the bonding electrons, and then proceed to lone pairs on terminal atoms and finally to lone pairs of the central atom. Arrange additional electrons around the central atom, giving it an expanded octet of up to 12 electrons.

Lastly, write the Lewis structure in brackets with the charge of the ion in the upper right – hand corner.

c) SF_4:   Write the correct skeletal structure for the molecule

Calculate the total number of electrons for the Lewis structure by summing the valence electrons of each atom in the molecule

(number of valence e^- for S) + 4(number of valence e^- for F) = 6 + 4(7) = 34

Distribute the electrons among the atoms, giving octets (or duets for H) to as many atoms as possible. Begin with the bonding electrons, and then proceed to lone pairs on terminal atoms and finally to lone pairs of the central atom. Arrange additional electrons around the central atom, giving it an expanded octet of up to 12 electrons.

d) GeF_4 :   Write the correct skeletal structure for the molecule

Calculate the total number of electrons for the Lewis structure by summing the valence electrons of each atom in the molecule

(number of valence e^- for Ge) + 4(number of valence e^- for F) = 4 + 4(7) = 32

Distribute the electrons among the atoms, giving octets (or duets for H) to as many atoms as possible. Begin with the bonding electrons, and then proceed to lone pairs on terminal atoms and finally to lone pairs of the central atom. Arrange additional electrons around the central atom, giving it an expanded octet of up to 12 electrons.

72. a) ClF_5 :   Write the correct skeletal structure for the molecule

Calculate the total number of electrons for the Lewis structure by summing the valence electrons of each atom in the molecule

(number of valence e⁻ for Cl) + 5(number of valence e⁻ for F) = 7 +5(7) = 40

Distribute the electrons among the atoms, giving octets (or duets for H) to as many atoms as possible. Begin with the bonding electrons, and then proceed to lone pairs on terminal atoms and finally to lone pairs of the central atom. Arrange additional electrons around the central atom, giving it an expanded octet of up to 12 electrons.

b) AsF_6^- :   Write the correct skeletal structure for the ion.

Calculate the total number of electrons for the Lewis structure by summing the valence electrons of each atom in the ion and adding one for the 1 – charge.

(number of valence e⁻ for As) + 6(number of valence e⁻ for F) + 1 = 5 +6(7) + 1 = 48

Distribute the electrons among the atoms, giving octets (or duets for H) to as many atoms as possible. Begin with the bonding electrons, and then proceed to lone pairs on terminal atoms and finally to lone pairs of the central atom. Arrange additional electrons around the central atom, giving it an expanded octet of up to 12 electrons.

Lastly, write the Lewis structure in brackets with the charge of the ion in the upper right – hand corner.

c) Cl_3PO: Write the correct skeletal structure for the molecule.

Calculate the total number of electrons for the Lewis structure by summing the valence electron of each atom in the molecule

(number of valence e⁻ for N) + (number of valence e⁻ for O) = 5 +6 = 11

Distribute the electrons among the atoms, giving octets (or duets for H) to as many atoms as possible. Begin with the bonding electrons, and then proceed to lone pairs on terminal atoms and finally to lone pairs of the central atom. Arrange additional electrons around the central atom, giving it an expanded octet of up to 12 electrons.

d) IF₅ :   Write the correct skeletal structure for the molecule

Calculate the total number of electrons for the Lewis structure by summing the valence electrons of each atom in the molecule

(number of valence e⁻ for I) + 5(number of valence e⁻ for F) = 7 +5(7) = 42

Distribute the electrons among the atoms, giving octets (or duets for H) to as many atoms as possible. Begin with the bonding electrons, and then proceed to lone pairs on terminal atoms and finally to lone pairs of the central atom. Arrange additional electrons around the central atom, giving it an expanded octet of up to 12 electrons.

73. Bond strength: $H_3CCH_3 < H_2CCH_2 < HCCH$
    Bond length: $H_3CCH_3 > H_2CCH_2 > HCCH$
    Write the Lewis structures for the three compounds. Compare the C – C bonds. Triple bonds are stronger than double bonds which are stronger than single bonds. Also, single bonds are longer than double bonds are longer than triple bonds.

    HCCH (10 e⁻) H_2CCH_2 (12 e⁻) H_3CCH_3(14 e⁻)

74. Strongest bond: HNNH   Shortest bond: HNNH
    Write the Lewis structures for the three compounds. Compare the N – N bonds. Triple bonds are stronger than double bonds which are stronger than single bonds. Also, single bonds are longer than double bonds are longer than triple bonds.

    H_2NNH_2(14 e⁻)   HNNH(12 e⁻)

75. Rewrite the reaction using the Lewis structures of the molecules involved.

Determine which bonds are broken in the reaction and sum the bond energies of these

$\Sigma(\Delta H$'s bonds broken)
$= 4(C - H) + (C = C) + (H - H)$
$= 4(414 \text{ kJ/mol}) + (611 \text{ kJ/mol}) + (436 \text{ kJ/mol})$
$= 2703 \text{ kJ/mol}$

Determine which bonds are formed in the reaction and sum the negatives of the bond energies of these

$\Sigma(-\Delta H$'s of bonds formed)
$= -6(C - H) - (C - C)$
$= -6(414 \text{ kJ/mol}) - (347 \text{ kJ/mol})$
$= -2831 \text{ kJ/mol}$

Find ΔH_{rxn} by summing the results of the two steps.

ΔH_{rxn} $= \Sigma(\Delta H$'s bonds broken$) + \Sigma(-\Delta H$'s of bonds formed$)$
$= 2703 \text{ kJ/mol} - 2831 \text{ kJ/mol}$
$= -128 \text{ kJ/mol}$

76. Rewrite the reaction using the Lewis structures of the molecules involved.

Determine which bonds are broken in the reaction and sum the bond energies of these

$\Sigma(\Delta H$'s bonds broken)
$= 5(C - H) + (C - C) + (C - O) + (O - H) + 3(O = O)$
$= 5(414 \text{ kJ/mol}) + (347 \text{ kJ/mol}) + (350 \text{ kJ/mol}) + (464 \text{ kJ/mol}) + 3(498)$
$= 4735 \text{ kJ/mol}$

Determine which bonds are formed in the reaction and sum the negatives of the bond energies of these

$\Sigma(-\Delta H$'s of bonds formed)
$= -4(C = O) - 6(O - H)$
$= -4(799 \text{ kJ/mol}) - 6(464 \text{ kJ/mol})$
$= -5980 \text{ kJ/mol}$

Find ΔH_{rxn} by summing the results of the two steps.

ΔH_{rxn} $= \Sigma(\Delta H$'s bonds broken$) + \Sigma(-\Delta H$'s of bonds formed$)$
$= 4735 \text{ kJ/mol} - 5980 \text{ kJ/mol}$
$= -1245 \text{ kJ/mol}$

77. Rewrite the reaction using the Lewis structures of the molecules involved.

Determine which bonds are broken in the reaction and sum the bond energies of these

$\Sigma(\Delta H$'s bonds broken)
$= 4(O - H)$
$= 4(464 \text{ kJ/mol})$
$= 1856 \text{ kJ/mol}$

Determine which bonds are formed in the reaction and sum the negatives of the bond energies of these

$\Sigma(-\Delta H$'s of bonds formed)
$= -2(C = O) - 2(H - H)$
$= -2(799 \text{ kJ/mol}) - 2(436 \text{ kJ/mol})$
$= -2470 \text{ kJ/mol}$

Find ΔH_{rxn} by summing the results of the two steps.

ΔH_{rxn} $= \Sigma(\Delta H$'s bonds broken$) + \Sigma(-\Delta H$'s of bonds formed$)$
$= 1856 \text{ kJ/mol} - 2470 \text{ kJ/mol}$
$= -614 \text{ kJ/mol}$

78. Rewrite the reaction using the Lewis structures of the molecules involved.

Determine which bonds are broken in the reaction and sum the bond energies of these

Σ(ΔH's bonds broken)
= (O – H) + 2(C – F) + 2(C – Cl)
= (464 kJ/mol) + 2(552 kJ/mol) + 2(339 kJ/mol)
= 2246 kJ/mol

Determine which bonds are formed in the reaction and sum the negatives of the bond energies of theses

Σ(-ΔH's of bonds formed)
= – (O – H) – (O – F) – (C – F) – 2(C – Cl)
= – (464 kJ/mol) – (190 kJ/mol) – (552 kJ/mol) – 2(339 kJ/mol)
= –1884 kJ/mol

Find ΔH$_{rxn}$ by summing the results of the two steps.

ΔH$_{rxn}$ = Σ(ΔH's bonds broken) + Σ(-ΔH's of bonds formed)
= 2246 kJ/mol – 1884 kJ/mol
= +362 kJ/mol

From the bond energies we find the ΔH$_{rxn}$ is positive. Therefore, you need to put more energy into the reaction than you get out of the reaction and this makes the reaction less likely to happen.

79. a) BI$_3$: This is a covalent compound between two nonmetals.
Write the correct skeletal structure for the molecule

Calculate the total number of electrons for the Lewis structure by summing the valence electrons of each atom in the molecule

(number of valence e⁻ for B) + (number of valence e⁻ for I) = 3 +3(7) = 24

Distribute the electrons among the atoms, giving octets (or duets for H) to as many atoms as possible. Begin with the bonding electrons, and then proceed to lone pairs on terminal atoms and finally to lone pairs of the central atom.

b) K$_2$S: This is an ionic compound between a metal and nonmetal
Draw the Lewis structures for K and S based on their valence electrons. K: $4s^1$ S: $3s^2 3p^4$

Potassium must lose one electron and be left with the octet from the previous shell, while sulfur needs to gain two electrons to get an octet.

c) HCFO: This is a covalent compound between nonmetals.
Write the correct skeletal structure for the molecule

Calculate the total number of electrons for the Lewis structure by summing the valence electrons of each atom in the molecule (number of valence e⁻ for H)+(number of valence e⁻ for C)+(number of valence e⁻ for F)+(number of valence e⁻ for O) = 1 + 4 + 7 +6 = 18

Distribute the electrons among the atoms, giving octets (or duets for H) to as many atoms as possible. Begin with the bonding electrons, and then proceed to lone pairs on terminal atoms and finally to lone pairs of the central atom.

```
    ··
  : O :
    |       ··
H — C — F :
            ··
```

If any atom lacks an octet, form double or triple bonds as necessary to give them octets.

```
    ··
  : O :
    ‖       ··
H — C — F :
            ··
```

d) PBr₃: This is a covalent compound between two nonmetals.
Write the correct skeletal structure for the molecule

```
      Br
      |
Br — P — Br
```

Calculate the total number of electrons for the Lewis structure by summing the valence electrons of each atom in the molecule

(number of valence e⁻ for P) + 3(number of valence e⁻ for Br) = 5 + 3(7) = 26

Distribute the electrons among the atoms, giving octets (or duets for H) to as many atoms as possible. Begin with the bonding electrons, and then proceed to lone pairs on terminal atoms and finally to lone pairs of the central atom.

```
       ··
     : Br :
       |
 : Br — P — Br :
   ··   ··   ··
```

80. a) Al₂O₃: This is an ionic compound between a metal and nonmetal

Draw the Lewis structures for Al and O based on their valence electrons. Al: $3s^2 3p^1$ O: $2s^2 2p^4$

```
··        ··
Al ·    : O ·
          ·
```

Aluminum must lose three electrons and be left with the octet from the previous shell, while oxygen needs to gain two electrons to get an octet.

```
         3+       ··      2−
  2 Al       3  [ : O : ]
                   ··
```

b) ClF₅: This is a covalent compound between two nonmetals.
Write the correct skeletal structure for the molecule

```
    F
    |   F
F — Cl <
    |   F
    F
```

Calculate the total number of electrons for the Lewis structure by summing the valence electrons of each atom in the molecule

(number of valence e⁻ for Cl) + 5(number of valence e⁻ for F) = 7 +5(7) = 40

Distribute the electrons among the atoms, giving octets (or duets for H) to as many atoms as possible. Begin with the bonding electrons, and then proceed to lone pairs on terminal atoms and finally to lone pairs of the central atom. Arrange additional electrons around the central atom, giving it an expanded octet of up to 12 electrons.

c) MgI$_2$: This is an ionic compound between a metal and nonmetal
Draw the Lewis structures for Mg and I based on their valence electrons. Mg: $3s^2$ I: $5s^25p^5$

Mg $\bullet$ $\bullet$ I $\bullet$

Magnesium must lose two electrons and be left with the octet from the previous shell, while iodine needs to gain one electron to get an octet.

Mg^{2+} 2$\left[\bullet \overset{\bullet\bullet}{\underset{\bullet\bullet}{I}} \bullet \right]^{-}$

d) XeO$_4$: This is a covalent compound between two nonmetals.
Write the correct skeletal structure for the molecule

$$
\begin{array}{c}
O \\
| \\
O - Xe - O \\
| \\
O
\end{array}
$$

Calculate the total number of electrons for the Lewis structure by summing the valence electrons of each atom in the molecule

(number of valence e$^-$ for Xe) + 4(number of valence e$^-$ for O) = 8 + 4(6) = 32

Distribute the electrons among the atoms, giving octets (or duets for H) to as many atoms as possible. Begin with the bonding electrons, and then proceed to lone pairs on terminal atoms and finally to lone pairs of the central atom.

81. a) BaCO$_3$: Ba^{2+}
Determine the cation and anion
Ba^{2+} CO$_3^{2-}$
Write the Lewis structure for the barium cation based on the valence electrons
Ba $5s^2$ Ba^{2+} $5s^0$
Ba $\vdots$ Ba^{2+}

Ba must lose two electrons and be left with the octet from the previous shell
Write the Lewis structure for the covalent anion.
Write the correct skeletal structure for the ion

$$
\begin{array}{c}
O \\
| \\
O - C - O
\end{array}
$$

Calculate the total number of electrons for the Lewis structure by summing the valence electrons of each atom in the ion and adding two for the 2 – charge.

(number of valence e$^-$ for C) + 3(number of valence e$^-$ for O) = 4 + 3(6) + 2 = 24

288

Distribute the electrons among the atoms, giving octets (or duets for H) to as many atoms as possible. Begin with the bonding electrons, and then proceed to lone pairs on terminal atoms and finally to lone pairs of the central atom.

If any atom lacks an octet, form double or triple bonds as necessary to give them octets.

Lastly, write the Lewis structure in brackets with the charge of the ion in the upper right – hand corner.

The double bond can be between the C and any of the oxygen atoms, so there are resonance structures

b) $Ca(OH)_2$: Ca^{2+}

Determine the cation and anion
   Ca^{2+} OH^-

Write the Lewis structure for the calcium cation based on the valence electrons
   $Ca\ 4s^2$ $Ca^{2+}\ 4s^0$

   Ca : Ca^{2+}

Ca must lose two electrons and be left with the octet from the previous shell
Write the Lewis structure for the covalent anion.
Write the correct skeletal structure for the ion
   O—H

Calculate the total number of electrons for the Lewis structure by summing the valence electrons of each atom in the ion and adding one for the 1 – charge.
   (number of valence e^- for H) + (number of valence e^- for O) +1 = 1 + 6 +1 = 8

Distribute the electrons among the atoms, giving octets (or duets for H) to as many atoms as possible. Begin with the bonding electrons, and then proceed to lone pairs on terminal atoms and finally to lone pairs of the central atom.

Lastly, write the Lewis structure in brackets with the charge of the ion in the upper right – hand corner.

c) KNO_3: K^+

Determine the cation and anion

K^+ NO_3^-

Write the Lewis structure for the potassium cation based on the valence electrons

K $4s^1$ K^+ $4s^0$

K •

K$^=$

K must lose one electron and be left with the octet from the previous shell

Write the Lewis structure for the covalent anion.

Write the correct skeletal structure for the ion

Calculate the total number of electrons for the Lewis structure by summing the valence electrons of each atom in the ion and adding one for the 1 – charge.

(number of valence e$^-$ for N) + (number of valence e$^-$ for O) = 5 + 3(6) +1 = 24

Distribute the electrons among the atoms, giving octets (or duets for H) to as many atoms as possible. Begin with the bonding electrons, and then proceed to lone pairs on terminal atoms and finally to lone pairs of the central atom.

If any atom lacks an octet, form double or triple bonds as necessary to give them octets.

Lastly, write the Lewis structure in brackets with the charge of the ion in the upper right – hand corner.

The double bond can be between the N and any of the oxygen atoms, so there are resonance structures

d) $LiIO$: Li^+

Determine the cation and anion

Li^+ IO^-

Write the Lewis structure for the lithium cation based on the valence electrons

Li $2s^1$ Li^+ $2s^0$

Li•

Li^+

Li must lose one electrons and be left with the octet from the previous shell

Write the Lewis structure for the covalent anion.

Write the correct skeletal structure for the ion

I —— O

290

Calculate the total number of electrons for the Lewis structure by summing the valence electrons of each atom in the ion and adding one for the 1 – charge.

(number of valence e⁻ for I) + (number of valence e⁻ for O) = 7 + 6 + 1 = 14

Distribute the electrons among the atoms, giving octets (or duets for H) to as many atoms as possible. Begin with the bonding electrons, and then proceed to lone pairs on terminal atoms and finally to lone pairs of the central atom.

Lastly, write the Lewis structure in brackets with the charge of the ion in the upper right – hand corner.

82. a) RbIO₂: Rb⁺

Determine the cation and anion

Rb⁺   IO₂⁻

Write the Lewis structure for the Rubidium cation based on the valence electrons

Rb $5s^1$ Rb⁺ $5s^0$

Rb•

              Rb⁺

Rb must lose one electrons and be left with the octet from the previous shell

Write the Lewis structure for the covalent anion.

Write the correct skeletal structure for the ion

O —— I —— O

Calculate the total number of electrons for the Lewis structure by summing the valence electrons of each atom in the ion and adding one for the 1 – charge.

(number of valence e⁻ for I) + 2 (number of valence e⁻ for O) = 7 + 2(6) + 1 = 20

Distribute the electrons among the atoms, giving octets (or duets for H) to as many atoms as possible. Begin with the bonding electrons, and then proceed to lone pairs on terminal atoms and finally to lone pairs of the central atom.

Lastly, write the Lewis structure in brackets with the charge of the ion in the upper right – hand corner.

b) NH₄Cl:

Determine the cation and anion

NH₄⁺   Cl⁻

Write the Lewis structure for the covalent cation.

Write the correct skeletal structure for the ion

Calculate the total number of electrons for the Lewis structure by summing the valence electrons of each atom in the ion and subtracting one for the 1 + charge.

(number of valence e⁻ for N) + 4(number of valence e⁻ for H) – 1 = 5 + 4(1) – 1 = 8

Distribute the electrons among the atoms, giving octets (or duets for H) to as many atoms as possible. Begin with the bonding electrons, and then proceed to lone pairs on terminal atoms and finally to lone pairs of the central atom.

$$
\begin{array}{c}
\text{H} \\
| \\
\text{H} - \text{N} - \text{H} \\
| \\
\text{H}
\end{array}
$$

Lastly, write the Lewis structure in brackets with the charge of the ion in the upper right – hand corner.

$$
\left[
\begin{array}{c}
\text{H} \\
| \\
\text{H} - \text{N} - \text{H} \\
| \\
\text{H}
\end{array}
\right]^{+}
$$

Write the Lewis structure for the chlorine anion based on the valence electrons

Cl $3s^2 3p^5$

•• ••
• Cl :
•• ••

Cl must gain one electron to complete its octet.

$$
\left[
\begin{array}{c}
•• \\
: \text{Cl} : \\
••
\end{array}
\right]^{-}
$$

$$
\left[
\begin{array}{c}
•• \\
: \text{O} - \text{H} \\
••
\end{array}
\right]^{-}
$$

c) KOH: K$^+$

Determine the cation and anion

   K$^+$ OH$^-$

Write the Lewis structure for the potassium cation based on the valence electrons

   K $4s^1$ K$^+$ $4s^0$

   K •

      K$^+$

K must lose one electron and be left with the octet from the previous shell
Write the Lewis structure for the covalent anion.
Write the correct skeletal structure for the ion

   O —— H

Calculate the total number of electrons for the Lewis structure by summing the valences electrons of each atom in the ion and adding one for the 1 – charge.

   (number of valence e$^-$ for H) + (number of valence e$^-$ for O) +1 = 1 + 6 +1 = 8

Distribute the electrons among the atoms, giving octets (or duets for H) to as many atoms as possible. Begin with the bonding electrons, and then proceed to lone pairs on terminal atoms and finally to lone pairs of the central atom.

••
: O — H
••

Lastly, write the Lewis structure in brackets with the charge of the ion in the upper right – hand corner.

$$
\left[
\begin{array}{c}
•• \\
: \text{O} - \text{H} \\
••
\end{array}
\right]^{-}
$$

$$
\left[
: \text{C} \equiv \text{N} :
\right]^{-}
$$

d) Sr(CN)$_2$: Sr$^+$

Determine the cation and anion

   Sr$^+$ CN$^-$

Write the Lewis structure for the strontium cation based on the valence electrons

   Sr $5s^1$ Sr$^+$ $5s^0$

   Sr•

        Sr$^+$

Sr must lose one electron and be left with the octet from the previous shell
Write the Lewis structure for the covalent anion.

Write the correct skeletal structure for the ion

$$C \text{---} N$$

Calculate the total number of electrons for the Lewis structure by summing the valence electrons of each atom in the ion and adding one for the 1 − charge.

(number of valence e⁻ for N) + (number of valence e⁻ for C) = 5 + 4 + 1 = 10

Distribute the electrons among the atoms, giving octets (or duets for H) to as many atoms as possible. Begin with the bonding electrons, and then proceed to lone pairs on terminal atoms and finally to lone pairs of the central atom.

$$\vdots C \text{---} N \vdots$$

Complete octets on both atoms by forming a triple bond

$$\vdots C \equiv N \vdots$$

Lastly, write the Lewis structure in brackets with the charge of the ion in the upper right – hand corner.

$$\left[\vdots C \equiv N \vdots \right]^{-}$$

83. a) C_4H_8: Write the correct skeletal structure for the molecule

Calculate the total number of electrons for the Lewis structure by summing the valence electrons of each atom in the molecule.

4 (number of valence e⁻ for C) + 8(number of valence e⁻ for H) = 4(4) + 8(1) = 24

Distribute the electrons among the atoms, giving octets (or duets for H) to as many atoms as possible.

All atoms have octets or duets for H,

b) C_4H_4:   Write the correct skeletal structure for the molecule

Calculate the total number of electrons for the Lewis structure by summing the valence electrons of each atom in the molecule.

4 (number of valence e⁻ for C) + 4(number of valence e⁻ for H) = 4(4) + 4(1) = 20

Distribute the electrons among the atoms, giving octets (or duets for H) to as many atoms as possible.

Complete octets by forming double bonds on alternating carbons, draw resonance structures.

c) C_6H_{12}: Write the correct skeletal structure for the molecule.

Calculate the total number of electrons for the Lewis structure by summing the valence electrons of each atom in the molecule.

6 (number of valence e⁻ for C) + 12(number of valence e⁻ for H) = 6(4) + 12(1) = 36

Distribute the electrons among the atoms, giving octets (or duets for H) to as many atoms as possible. Begin with the bonding electrons, and then proceed to lone pairs on terminal atoms and finally to lone pairs of the central atom.

All 36 electrons are used and all atoms have octets or duets for H.

d) C_6H_6: Write the correct skeletal structure for the molecule.

Calculate the total number of electrons for the Lewis structure by summing the valence electrons of each atom in the molecule.

6 (number of valence e⁻ for C) + 6(number of valence e⁻ for H) = 6(4) + 6(1) = 30

Distribute the electrons among the atoms, giving octets (or duets for H) to as many atoms as possible.

Complete octets by forming double bonds on alternating carbons, draw resonance structures.

294

84. H₂NCH₂COOH
Write the correct skeletal structure for the molecule

Calculate the total number of electrons for the Lewis structure by summing the valence electrons of   each atom in the molecule.

2 (number of valence e⁻ for C) + 2(number of valence e⁻ for O) + (number of valence e⁻ for N) + 5(number of valence e⁻ for H) = 2(4) + 2(6) + 5 + 5(1) = 30

Distribute the electrons among the atoms, giving octets (or duets for H) to as many atoms as possible. Begin with the bonding electrons, and then proceed to lone pairs on terminal atoms and finally to lone pairs of the central atom.

All 30 electrons are used.
Draw a double bond to satisfy the octet on C

85. **Given:** 26.01% C; 4.38 % H; 69.52 % O; molar mass = 46.02 g/mol
   Find: molecular formula and Lewis structure
   Conceptual Plan:
   convert mass to mol of each element → pseudoformula → empirical formula

   $$\frac{1\ mol\ C}{12.01\ g\ C} \qquad \frac{1\ mol\ H}{1.008\ g\ H} \qquad \frac{1\ mol\ O}{16.00\ g\ O} \qquad \text{divide by smallest number}$$

   → molecular formula→Lewis structure
   empirical formula x n

   Solution: $26.01\ \cancel{g\ C} \times \dfrac{1\ mol\ C}{12.01\ \cancel{g\ C}} = 2.166\ mol\ C$

   $4.38\ \cancel{g\ H} \times \dfrac{1\ mol\ H}{1.008\ \cancel{g\ H}} = 4.3\underline{4}5\ mol\ H$

   $69.52\ \cancel{g\ O} \times \dfrac{1\ mol\ O}{16.00\ \cancel{g\ O}} = 4.345\ mol\ O$

   $C_{2.166}H_{4.345}O_{4.345}$

   $C_{\frac{2.166}{2.166}}H_{\frac{4.345}{2.166}}O_{\frac{4.345}{2.166}} \rightarrow CH_2O_2$

   The correct empirical formula is CH_2O_2

   empirical formula mass = (12.01 g/mol) + 2(1.008 g/mol) + 2(16.00 g/mol) = 46.03 g/mol

   $n = \dfrac{\text{molar mass}}{\text{formula molar mass}} = \dfrac{46.02\ g/mol}{46.03\ g/mol} = 1$

   molecular formula   = CH_2O_2 x 1
                            = CH_2O_2

Write the correct skeletal structure for the molecule

Calculate the total number of electrons for the Lewis structure by summing the valence electrons of each atom in the molecule.

(number of valence e⁻ for C) + 2(number of valence e⁻ for O) + 2(number of valence e⁻ for H)
= 4 + 2(6) + 2(1) = 18

Distribute the electrons among the atoms, giving octets (or duets for H) to as many atoms as possible. Begin with the bonding electrons, and then proceed to lone pairs on terminal atoms and finally to lone pairs of the central atom.

$$
\begin{array}{c}
:\overset{\cdot\cdot}{\underset{}{O}}: \\
| \\
H - C - \overset{\cdot\cdot}{\underset{\cdot\cdot}{O}} - H
\end{array}
$$

Complete the octet on C by forming a double bond

$$
\begin{array}{c}
:O: \\
\| \\
H - C - \overset{\cdot\cdot}{\underset{\cdot\cdot}{O}} - H
\end{array}
$$

86. **Given:** 28.57% C; 4.80 % H; 66.64 % N; molar mass = 42.04 g/mol
Find: molecular formula and Lewis structure
Conceptual Plan:
convert mass to mol of each element → pseudoformula → empirical formula

$$\frac{1 \text{ mol C}}{12.01 \text{ g C}} \quad \frac{1 \text{ mol H}}{1.008 \text{ g H}} \quad \frac{1 \text{ mol N}}{14.00 \text{ g N}} \qquad \text{divide by smallest number}$$

→ molecular formula→Lewis structure
    empirical formula x n

Solution: $28.57 \text{ g C} \times \dfrac{1 \text{ mol C}}{12.01 \text{ g C}} = 2.380 \text{ mol C}$

$4.80 \text{ g H} \times \dfrac{1 \text{ mol H}}{1.008 \text{ g H}} = 4.7\underline{6}2 \text{ mol H}$

$66.64 \text{ g N} \times \dfrac{1 \text{ mol N}}{14.00 \text{ g N}} = 4.760 \text{ mol N}$

$C_{2.380}H_{4.762}N_{4.762}$

$C_{\frac{2.380}{2.380}}H_{\frac{4.762}{2.380}}N_{\frac{4.762}{2.380}} \rightarrow CH_2N_2$

The correct empirical formula is CH_2N_2
empirical formula mass = (12.01 g/mol) + 2(1.008 g/mol) + 2(14.00 g/mol) = 42.03 g/mol

$n = \dfrac{\text{molar mass}}{\text{formula molar mass}} = \dfrac{42.04 \text{ g/mol}}{42.03 \text{ g/mol}} = 1$

molecular formula $= CH_2N_2 \text{ x } 1$
                         $= CH_2N_2$

Write the correct skeletal structure for the molecule

$$
\begin{array}{c}
H \\
| \\
H - C - N - N
\end{array}
$$

Calculate the total number of electrons for the Lewis structure by summing the valence electrons of each atom in the molecule.

(number of valence e⁻ for C) + 2(number of valence e⁻ for N) + 2(number of valence e⁻ for H)
= 4 + 2(5) + 2(1) = 16

Distribute the electrons among the atoms, giving octets (or duets for H) to as many atoms as possible. Begin with the bonding electrons, and then proceed to lone pairs on terminal atoms and finally to lone pairs of the central atom.

$$
\begin{array}{c}
H \\
| \\
H - C - \overset{}{\underset{\cdot\cdot}{N}} - \overset{\cdot\cdot}{\underset{\cdot\cdot}{N}}:
\end{array}
$$

Complete the octet on C and N by forming a double bonds

$$
\begin{array}{c}
H \\
| \\
H - C = N = \overset{\cdot\cdot}{\underset{\cdot\cdot}{N}}
\end{array}
$$

Calculate the formal charge on each atom in the structure by finding the number of valence electrons and subtracting the number of lone pair electrons and one – half the number of bonding electrons.

296

	H_{left}	H_{top}	C	N_{left}	N_{right}
number of valence electron	1	1	4	5	5
- number of lone pair electrons	0	0	0	0	4
- 1/2(number of bonding electrons)	1	1	4	4	2
Formal charge	0	0	0	+1	- 1

The diazomethane molecule has nitrogen atoms next to each other with a +1 and a – 1 charge. Nitrogen is more electronegative than C which has a 0 formal charge. The nitrogen with the +1 charge is not a very stable configuration for nitrogen, particularly next to the 0 formal charge C atom.

87. The lattice energy of Al_2O_3 is –15,916 kJ/mol. The thermite reaction is exothermic due to the energy released when the Al_2O_3 lattice forms. The lattice energy of Al_2O_3 is much more negative than the lattice energy of Fe_2O_3.

88. For NaCl, E is proportional to (1+)(1–) = –1. While for XY. E is proportional to (3+)(3–) = –9. So, the relative stabilization for XY relative to NaCl should be roughly nine times greater. $\Delta H_{lattice}$ (XY) = 9 x $\Delta H_{lattice}$ (NaCl)

89. HNO_3 Write the correct skeletal structure for the molecule

Calculate the total number of electrons for the Lewis structure by summing the valence electrons of each atom in the molecule.

3(number of valence e⁻ for O) + (number of valence e⁻ for N) + (number of valence e⁻ for H) = 3(6) + 5 +1 = 24

Distribute the electrons among the atoms, giving octets (or duets for H) to as many atoms as possible. Begin with the bonding electrons, and then proceed to lone pairs on terminal atoms and finally to lone pairs of the central atom.

All 24 valence electrons are used

If any atom lacks an octet, form double or triple bonds as necessary to give them octets. The double bond can be formed to any of the three oxygen atoms, so there are three resonance forms.

All atoms have octets, duets for H, structures is complete.

To determine which resonance hybrid(s) is most important, calculate the formal charge on each atom in each structure by finding the number of valence electrons and subtracting the number of lone pair electrons and one – half the number of bonding electrons.

	Structure I						Structure II				
	O_{left}	O_{top}	O_{right}	N	H		O_{left}	O_{top}	O_{right}	N	H
number of valence electrons	6	6	6	5	1		6	6	6	5	1
- number of lone pair electrons	4	4	6	0	0		4	6	4	0	0
- 1/2(number of bonding electrons)	2	2	1	4	1		2	1	2	4	1
Formal charge	0	0	–1	+1	0		0	–1	0	+1	0

Structure III
O_{left}	O_{top}	O_{right}	N	H

number of valence electrons	6	6	6	5	1
- number of lone pair electrons	2	6	6	0	0
- 1/2(number of bonding electrons)	3	1	1	4	1
Formal charge	+1	−1	−1	+1	0

The sum of the formal charges is 0 for each structure which is the overall charge of the molecule. However, in structures I and II, the individual formal charges are lower and these two forms would contribute equally to the structure of HNO_3 and structure III would be less important since the individual formal charges are higher.

90. Cl_2CO Write the correct skeletal structure for the molecule

Calculate the total number of electrons for the Lewis structure by summing the valence electron of each atom in the molecule.

1(number of valence e^- for O) + (number of valence e^- for C) + 2(number of valence e^- for Cl) = 6 + 4 + 2(7) = 24

Distribute the electrons among the atoms, giving octets (or duets for H) to as many atoms as possible. Begin with the bonding electrons, and then proceed to lone pairs on terminal atoms and finally to lone pairs of the central atom.

All 24 valence electrons are used

If any atom lacks an octet, form double or triple bonds as necessary to give them octets. The double bond can be formed to any of the three terminal atoms, so there are three resonance forms.

All atoms have octets, duets for H, structures is complete.

To determine which resonance hybrids(s) is most important, calculate the formal charge on each atom in each structure by finding the number of valence electrons and subtracting the number of lone pair electrons and one – half the number of bonding electrons.

	Structure I				Structure II			
	Cl_{left}	Cl_{right}	O	C	Cl_{left}	Cl_{right}	O	C
number of valence electrons	7	7	6	4	7	7	6	4
- number of lone pair electrons	6	6	4	0	4	6	6	0
- 1/2(number of bonding electrons)	1	1	2	4	2	1	1	4
Formal charge	0	0	0	0	+1	0	−1	0

	Structure III			
	Cl_{left}	Cl_{right}	O	C
number of valence electrons	7	7	6	4
- number of lone pair electrons	6	4	6	0
- 1/2(number of bonding electrons)	1	2	1	4
Formal charge	0	+1	−1	0

The sum of the formal charges is 0 for each structure, which is the overall charge of the molecule. However, in structures I the individual formal charges are lower and this form would be more important to Cl_2CO than structure II and structure II.

91. CNO⁻   Write the skeletal structure:
                C – N – O
            Determine the number of valence electrons.
                (valence e⁻ from C) + (valence e⁻ from N) + (valence e⁻ from O) +1(from the negative charge)
                $4 + 5 + 6 + 1 = 16$

            Distribute the electrons to complete octets if possible.

Determine the formal charge on each atom for each structure

	Structure I				Structure II		
	C	N	O		C	N	O
number of valence electrons	4	5	6		4	5	6
- number of lone pair electrons	4	0	4		2	0	6
- 1/2(number of bonding electrons)	2	4	2		3	4	1
Formal charge	–2	+1	0		–1	+1	–1

	Structure III		
	C	N	O
number of valence electrons	4	5	6
- number of lone pair electrons	6	0	2
- 1/2(number of bonding electrons)	1	4	3
Formal charge	–3	+1	+1

Structures I,II,and III all follow the octet rule but have varying degrees of negative formal charge on carbon, which is the least electronegative atom. Also the amount of formal charge is very high in all three resonance forms. Therefore, none of these resonance forms contribute to the stability of the fulminate ion and the ion is not very stable.

92. The Lewis structures for the three ions will be similar. So, we can write the Lewis structure for one ion and use it to determine the other two.
    Br₃⁻ : Write the correct skeletal structure for the ion
        Br —— Br —— Br

Calculate the total number of electrons for the Lewis structure by summing the valence electrons of each atom in the ion and adding 1 for the 1 – charge.
    3(number of valence e⁻ for Br) + 1 = 3(7) +1 = 22
Distribute the electrons among the atoms, giving octets to as many atoms as possible. Begin with the bonding electrons, and then proceed to lone pairs on terminal atoms and finally to lone pairs of the central atom. Assign electrons above 8 to the central atom.

Lastly, place the ion in brackets and place the charge in the upper right hand corner.

Since Br, I and F are all in the same family, each of these ions would have 22 electrons and should have the same Lewis structure

$$\left[\ddot{\;}\overset{\cdots}{Br} \!-\! \overset{\cdots}{Br} \!-\! \overset{\cdots}{Br}\ddot{\;} \right]^{-} , \left[\ddot{\;}\overset{\cdots}{I} \!-\! \overset{\cdots}{I} \!-\! \overset{\cdots}{I}\ddot{\;} \right]^{-} , \left[\ddot{\;}\overset{\cdots}{F} \!-\! \overset{\cdots}{F} \!-\! \overset{\cdots}{F}\ddot{\;} \right]^{-}$$

All three ions are written with 5 electron groups around the central atom. Bromine and Iodine can accommodate 10 electrons around the central atom. However, fluorine cannot. Fluorine is in period 2 and can accommodate at most 8 electrons around the central atom because there are no orbitals low enough in energy to hybridize with the 2s and 2p orbitals. Therefore, F_3^- does not exist.

93. $HCSNH_2$: Write the correct skeletal structure for the molecule.

(skeletal structure)

Calculate the total number of electrons for the Lewis structure by summing the valence electrons of each atom in the molecule.

(number of valence e$^-$ for N) + (number of valence e$^-$ for S) + (number of valence e$^-$ for C) + 3(number of valence e$^-$ for H) = 5 + 6 + 4 + 3(1) = 18

Distribute the electrons among the atoms, giving octets (or duets for H) to as many atoms as possible. Begin with the bonding electrons, and then proceed to lone pairs on terminal atoms and finally to lone pairs of the central atom.

(Lewis structure)

Complete the octet on C by forming a double bond.

(Lewis structure with polar/nonpolar labels)

94. H_2NCONH_2 Write the correct skeletal structure for the molecule.

(skeletal structure)

Calculate the total number of electrons for the Lewis structure by summing the valence electron of each atom in the molecule.

2(number of valence e$^-$ for N) + (number of valence e$^-$ for O) + 4(number of valence e$^-$ for H)
= 2(5) + 6 + 2(1) = 24

Distribute the electrons among the atoms, giving octets (or duets for H) to as many atoms as possible. Begin with the bonding electrons, and then proceed to lone pairs on terminal atoms and finally to lone pairs of the central atom.

(Lewis structure)

Complete the octet on C with a double bond.

(Lewis structure with polar labels)

The C – O bond would be the most polar because it has the greater difference in electronegativity.
$$\Delta EN \; C\!-\!O = 1.0 \quad \Delta EN \; C - N = 0.5$$

95. a) O_2^-: Write the correct skeletal structure for the radical

O —— O

Calculate the total number of electrons for the Lewis structure by summing the valence electrons of each atom in the radical and adding 1 for the 1 – charge.

2(number of valence e$^-$ for O) + 1 = 2(6) + 1 = 13

Distribute the electrons among the atoms, giving octets to as many atoms as possible. Begin with the bonding electrons, and then proceed to lone pairs on terminal atoms and finally to lone pairs of the central atom.

$$\left[\overset{\bullet\bullet}{\underset{\bullet\bullet}{\text{O}}}{-}\overset{\bullet\bullet}{\underset{\bullet\bullet}{\text{O}}}\!\!\bullet\bullet \right]^{-}$$

All 13 valence electrons are used.

O has an incomplete octet. It has 7 electrons because we have an odd number of valence electrons.

b) O^-:   Write the Lewis structure based on the valence electrons: $2s^2 2p^5$.

$$\left[\overset{\bullet\bullet}{\underset{\bullet\bullet}{\text{O}}}\!\!\bullet\bullet \right]^{-}$$

c) OH: Write the correct skeletal structure for the molecule

$$\text{H}\text{----}\text{O}$$

Calculate the total number of electrons for the Lewis structure by summing the valence electrons of each atom in the molecule

(number of valence e⁻ for O) + (number of valence e⁻ for H) = 6 + 1 = 7

Distribute the electrons among the atoms, giving octets (or duets for H) to as many atoms as possible. Begin with the bonding electrons, and then proceed to lone pairs on terminal atoms and finally to lone pairs of the central atom.

$$\text{H}\text{----}\overset{\bullet\bullet}{\underset{\bullet\bullet}{\text{O}}}\,\bullet$$

All 7 valence electrons are used.

O has an incomplete octet. It has 7 electrons because we have an odd number of valence electrons.

d) CH_3OO: Write the correct skeletal structure for the radical

C is the less electronegative, so it is central

$$\begin{array}{c}\text{H}\\|\\\text{H}\text{----}\text{C}\text{----}\text{O}\text{----}\text{O}\\|\\\text{H}\end{array}$$

Calculate the total number of electrons for the Lewis structure by summing the valence electrons of each atom in the molecule

3(number of valence e⁻ for H) + (number of valence e⁻ for C) + 2(number of valence e⁻ for O) = 3(1) + 4 + 2(6) = 19

Distribute the electrons among the atoms, giving octets (or duets for H) to as many atoms as possible. Begin with the bonding electrons, and then proceed to lone pairs on terminal atoms and finally to lone pairs of the central atom.

$$\begin{array}{c}\text{H}\\|\\\text{H}\text{----}\text{C}\text{----}\overset{\bullet\bullet}{\underset{\bullet\bullet}{\text{O}}}\text{----}\overset{\bullet\bullet}{\underset{\bullet\bullet}{\text{O}}}\,\bullet\\|\\\text{H}\end{array}$$

All 19 valence electrons are used.

O has an incomplete octet. It has 7 electrons because we have an odd number of valence electrons.

96.

$$\overset{\bullet\bullet}{\underset{\bullet\bullet}{\text{O}}}{=}\text{N}{-}\overset{\bullet\bullet}{\underset{\bullet\bullet}{\text{O}}}\!\!\bullet\bullet \;\longrightarrow\; \text{N}{=}\overset{\bullet\bullet}{\underset{\bullet\bullet}{\text{O}}}\!\!\bullet\bullet \;+\; \overset{\bullet\bullet}{\underset{\bullet}{\text{O}}}\!\!\bullet$$

$$\overset{\bullet\bullet}{\underset{\bullet}{\text{O}}}\!\!\bullet \;+\; \overset{\bullet\bullet}{\underset{\bullet\bullet}{\text{O}}}{=}\overset{\bullet\bullet}{\underset{\bullet\bullet}{\text{O}}} \;\longrightarrow\; \overset{\bullet\bullet}{\underset{\bullet\bullet}{\text{O}}}{=}\text{O}{-}\overset{\bullet\bullet}{\underset{\bullet\bullet}{\text{O}}}\!\!\bullet\bullet$$

Where NO_2 and NO are the free radicals.

97. Rewrite the reaction using the Lewis structures of the molecules involved.

$$H-H \text{ (g) } + 1/2 \overset{\bullet\bullet}{O} = \overset{\bullet\bullet}{O} \text{ (g) } \rightarrow H - \overset{\bullet\bullet}{\underset{\bullet\bullet}{O}} - H$$

Determine which bonds are broken in the reaction and sum the bond energies of these

$\Sigma(\Delta H$'s bonds broken)
$= (H-H) + 1/2(O=O)$
$= (436 \text{ kJ/mol}) + 1/2(498)$
$= 685 \text{ kJ/mol}$

Determine which bonds are formed in the reaction and sum the negatives of the bond energies of these

$\Sigma(-\Delta H$'s of bonds formed)
$= -2(O-H)$
$= -2(464 \text{ kJ/mol})$
$= -928 \text{ kJ/mol}$

Find ΔH_{rxn} by summing the results of the two steps.

$\Delta H_{rxn} = \Sigma(\Delta H$'s bonds broken) $+ \Sigma(-\Delta H$'s of bonds formed)
$\qquad = 685 \text{ kJ/mol} - 928 \text{ kJ/mol}$
$\qquad = -243 \text{ kJ/mol}$

$CH_4(g) + 2O_2(g) \rightarrow CO_2(g) + 2H_2O(g)$

Rewrite the reaction using the Lewis structures of the molecules involved.

Determine which bonds are broken in the reaction and sum the bond energies of these

$\Sigma(\Delta H$'s bonds broken)
$= 4(C-H) + 2(O=O)$
$= (414 \text{ kJ/mol}) + 2(498)$
$= 2652 \text{ kJ/mol}$

Determine which bonds are formed in the reaction and sum the negatives of the bond energies of these

$\Sigma(-\Delta H$'s of bonds formed)
$= -2(C=O) - 4(O-H)$
$= -2(799 \text{ kJ/mol}) - 4(464 \text{ kJ/mol})$
$= -3454 \text{ kJ/mol}$

Find ΔH_{rxn} by summing the results of the two steps.

$\Delta H_{rxn} = \Sigma(\Delta H$'s bonds broken) $+ \Sigma(-\Delta H$'s of bonds formed)
$\qquad = 2653 \text{ kJ/mol} - 3454 \text{ kJ/mol}$
$\qquad = -802 \text{ kJ/mol}$

Compare

	kJ/mol	kJ/g
H_2	−243	−120
CH_4	−802	−50.1

So, methane yields more energy per mole but hydrogen yields more energy per gram.

98. octane $= C_8H_{18}$

$C_8H_{18}(l) + 25/2 O_2(g) \rightarrow 8CO_2(g) + 9H_2O(g)$

Rewrite the reaction using the Lewis structures of the molecules involved.

Determine which bonds are broken in the reaction and sum the bond energies of these

$\Sigma(\Delta H$'s bonds broken)

$= 18(C - H) + 25/2 (O = O) + 7(C - C)$

$= 18(414$ kJ/mol$) + 25/2(498) + 7(347)$

$= 16106$ kJ/mol

Determine which bonds are formed in the reaction and sum the negatives of the bond energies of theses

$\Sigma(-\Delta H$'s of bonds formed)

$= - 16(C = O) - 18(O - H)$

$= - 16(799$ kJ/mol$) - 18(464$ kJ/mol$)$

$= -21136$ kJ/mol

Find ΔH_{rxn} by summing the results of the two steps.

ΔH_{rxn} $= \Sigma(\Delta H$'s bonds broken$) + \Sigma(-\Delta H$'s of bonds formed$)$

$= 16106$ kJ/mol $- 21136$ kJ/mol

$= - 5030$ kJ/mol

$\Delta H_{rxn} = \Sigma(\Delta H_f$(products)$) - \Sigma(\Delta H_f$(reactants)$)$

$= [8\Delta H_f(CO_2(g)) + 9\Delta H_f(H_2O(g))] - [\Delta H_f(C_8H_{18}(l)) + 25/2\Delta H_f(O_2(g))]$

$= [8(- 393.5$ kJ/mol$) + 9(- 241.8$ kJ/mol$)] - [(- 250$ kJ/mol$) + 25/2(0)]$

$= - 5074$ kJ/mol

% difference $= \dfrac{- 5074 \text{ kJ} - (-5030 \text{ kJ})}{-5074 \text{ kJ}}$ x $100 = 0.8671\%$

You would expect the value calculated from the heats of formation to be more accurate. The bond energy values are average values not values for a specific molecule. The heats of formation are for specific compounds.

99. a) Cl_2O_7: Write the correct skeletal structure for the molecule

Calculate the total number of electrons for the Lewis structure by summing the valence electrons of each atom in the molecule

2(number of valence e⁻ for Cl) + 7(number of valence e⁻ for O) = 2(7)5 + 7(6) = 56

Distribute the electrons among the atoms, giving octets (or duets for H) to as many atoms as possible. Begin with the bonding electrons, and then proceed to lone pairs on terminal atoms and finally to lone pairs of the central atom.

Form double bonds to minimize formal charge.

b) H_3PO_3: Write the correct skeletal structure for the molecule

303

```
           O
           |
    H ——— P ——— O ——— H
           |
           O
           |
           H
```

Calculate the total number of electrons for the Lewis structure by summing the valence electrons of each atom in the molecule

(number of valence e⁻ for P) + 3(number of valence e⁻ for O) + 3(number of valence e⁻ for H) = 5 + 3(6) + 3(1) = 26

Distribute the electrons among the atoms, giving octets (or duets for H) to as many atoms as possible. Begin with the bonding electrons, and then proceed to lone pairs on terminal atoms and finally to lone pairs of the central atom.

Form double bond to minimize formal charge.

c) H_3AsO_4: Write the correct skeletal structure for the radical

```
               O
               |
    H ——— O ——— As ——— O ——— H
               |
               O
               |
               H
```

Calculate the total number of electrons for the Lewis structure by summing the valence electrons of each atom in the molecule

(number of valence e⁻ for As) + 4(number of valence e⁻ for O) + 3(number of valence e⁻ for H) = 5 + 4(6) + 3(1) = 32

Distribute the electrons among the atoms, giving octets (or duets for H) to as many atoms as possible. Begin with the bonding electrons, and then proceed to lone pairs on terminal atoms and finally to lone pairs of the central atom.

```
                    ••
                 •• O ••
                    |
          ••        |        ••
    H ——— O ——— As ——— O ——— H
          ••        |        ••
                 •• O ••
                    |
                    H
```

Form double bond to minimize formal charge.

$$
\begin{array}{c}
:\!\overset{\displaystyle ..}{O}\!: \\
\parallel \\
H\!-\!\overset{..}{\underset{..}{O}}\!-\!As\!-\!\overset{..}{\underset{..}{O}}\!-\!H \\
\mid \\
:\!\overset{}{\underset{..}{O}}\!: \\
\mid \\
H
\end{array}
$$

100. N_3^- :   Write the correct skeletal structure for the ion
$$N-N-N$$

Calculate the total number of electrons for the Lewis structure by summing the valence electrons of each atom in the ion and adding 1 for the 1 – charge.

3(number of valence e^- for N) +1 = 3(5) + 1 = 16

Distribute the electrons among the atoms, giving octets to as many atoms as possible. Begin with the bonding electrons, and then proceed to lone pairs on terminal atoms and finally to lone pairs of the central atom.

$$:\overset{..}{N}-N-\overset{..}{\underset{..}{N}}:$$

Complete octets with double or triple bonds.

$$\overset{..}{\underset{..}{N}}=N=\overset{..}{\underset{..}{N}}$$

Lastly write the ion is brackets with the charge in the upper right hand corner.

$$\left[\overset{..}{\underset{..}{N}}=N=\overset{..}{\underset{..}{N}}\right]^-$$

Write the resonance forms.

$$\left[\overset{..}{\underset{..}{N}}=N=\overset{..}{\underset{..}{N}}\right]^- \longleftrightarrow \left[:N\equiv N-\overset{..}{\underset{..}{N}}:\right]^- \longleftrightarrow \left[:\overset{..}{\underset{..}{N}}-N\equiv N:\right]^-$$

101. $Na^+F^- < Na^+O^{2-} < Mg^{2+}F^- < Mg^{2+}O^{2-} < Al^{3+}O^{2-}$

The lattice energy is proportional to the magnitude of the charge and inversely proportional to the distance between the atoms. Na^+F^- would have the smallest lattice energy because the magnitude of the charges on Na and F are the smallest. $Mg^{2+}F^-$ and Na^+O^{2-} both have the same magnitude formal charge, the O^{2-} is larger than F^- in size, Na^+ is larger than Mg^{2+}, so Na^+O^{2-} should be less than $Mg^{2+}F^-$. The magnitude of the charge makes $Mg^{2+}O^{2-} < Al^{3+}O^{2-}$.

102. Rewrite the reaction using the Lewis structures of the molecules involved.

$$H-H \;+\; :\overset{..}{\underset{..}{Br}}-\overset{..}{\underset{..}{Br}}: \;\longrightarrow\; 2\,H-\overset{..}{\underset{..}{Br}}:$$

Determine which bonds are broken in the reaction and sum the bond energies of these

$\Sigma(\Delta H$'s bonds broken)

= (H – H) + (Br – Br)

= (436 kJ/mol) + (193 kJ/mol)

= 629 kJ/mol

Determine which bonds are formed in the reaction and sum the negatives of the bond energies of theses

$\Sigma(-\Delta H$'s of bonds formed)

= – 2(H – Br)

= – 2(364 kJ/mol)

= – 728 kJ/mol

Find ΔH_{rxn} by summing the results of the two steps.

ΔH_{rxn} = $\Sigma(\Delta H$'s bonds broken) + $\Sigma(-\Delta H$'s of bonds formed)

= 629 kJ/mol – 728 kJ/mol

= – 99 kJ/mol

$\Delta H_f^{\,o}$ from the table = –36.3 kJ/mol

The value for $\Delta H_f^{\,o}$ would be expected to be 1/2 the value calculated from the bond energies. Since it is not, we can account for the difference by looking at the types of bonds broken and formed. The H_2 and Br_2

bonds are pure covalent bonds while the HBr bond formed will be polar covalent. The distribution of the electron density will be unequal.

103.

Step 1:
    Bonds broken: $2(S = O) + (H - O) = 2(523) + (464) = 1510$ kJ/mol
    Bonds formed: $-2(S - O) - (S = O) - (O - H) = -2(265) - (523) - (464) = -1517$ kJ/mol

$$\Delta H_{step} = -7 \text{ kJ/mol}$$

Step 2:
    Bonds broken: $2(S - O) + (S = O) + (O - H) + (O = O) = 2(265) + (523) + (464) + (498) = 2015$ kJ/mol
    Bonds formed: $: -2(S - O) - (S = O) - (O - H) - (O - O) = -2(265) - (523) - (464) - (142) = -1659$ kJ/mol

$$\Delta H_{step} = +356 \text{ kJ/mol}$$

Step 3:
    Bonds broken: $2(S - O) + (S = O) + 2(O - H) = 2(265) + (523) + 2(464) = 1981$ kJ/mol
    Bonds formed: $-2(S - O) - 2(S = O) - 2(O - H) = -2(265) + -2(523) + -2(464) = -2504$ kJ/mol

$$\Delta H_{step} = -523 \text{ kJ/mol}$$

Hess's law states that ΔH for the reaction is the sum of ΔH of the steps:
$\Delta H_{rxn} = (-7 \text{ kJ/mol}) + (+356 \text{ kJ/mol}) + (-523 \text{ kJ/mol}) = -174$ kJ/mol

104. **Given:** 0.167 g acid; 27.8 mL 0.100 M NaOH; 40.00% C; 6.41 % H; 53.29 % O
    Find: molar mass, molecular formula, Lewis structure
    Conceptual Plan: mL → L → mol NaOH → mol acid → molar mass and then:

$$\frac{L}{1000 \text{ mL}} \quad \text{mol} = VM \quad \text{mol acid} = \text{mol base} \quad \frac{mass}{mol}$$

convert mass to mol of each element → pseudoformula → empirical formula → molecular formula

$$\frac{1 \text{ mol C}}{12.01 \text{ g C}} \quad \frac{1 \text{ mol H}}{1.008 \text{ g H}} \quad \frac{1 \text{ mol N}}{14.00 \text{ g N}} \qquad \text{divide by smallest number} \quad \text{empirical formula x n}$$

→Lewis structure

Solution: $27.8 \text{ mL} \times \dfrac{1 \text{ L}}{1000 \text{ mL}} \times \dfrac{0.100 \text{ mol NaOH}}{L} \times \dfrac{1 \text{ mol acid}}{1 \text{ mol NaOH}} = 0.00278$ mol acid

$$\frac{0.167 \text{ g acid}}{0.00278 \text{ mol acid}} = 60.1 \text{ g / mol}$$

$$40.00 \text{ g C} \times \frac{1 \text{ mol C}}{12.01 \text{ g C}} = 3.331 \text{ mol C}$$

$$6.41 \text{ g H} \times \frac{1 \text{ mol H}}{1.008 \text{ g H}} = 6.359 \text{ mol H}$$

$$53.29 \text{ g O} \times \frac{1 \text{ mol O}}{16.00 \text{ g O}} = 3.331 \text{ mol O}$$

$$C_{3.331}H_{4.762}O_{3.331}$$

$$C_{\frac{3.331}{3.331}}H_{\frac{6.359}{3.331}}O_{\frac{3.331}{3.331}} \rightarrow CH_2O$$

The correct empirical formula is CH_2O

empirical formula mass = (12.01 g/mol) + 2(1.008 g/mol) + (16.00 g/mol) = 30.03 g/mol

$$n = \frac{\text{molar mass}}{\text{formula molar mass}} = \frac{60.1 \text{ g/mol}}{30.03 \text{ g/mol}} = 2$$

molecular formula $\qquad = CH_2O \times 2$

$\qquad\qquad\qquad\qquad = C_2H_4O_2$

Write the correct skeletal structure for the molecule

Calculate the total number of electrons for the Lewis structure by summing the valence electrons of each atom in the molecule.

2(number of valence e^- for C) + 2(number of valence e^- for O) + 4(number of valence e^- for H) = 2(4) + 2(6) + 4(1) = 24

Distribute the electrons among the atoms, giving octets (or duets for H) to as many atoms as possible. Begin with the bonding electrons, and then proceed to lone pairs on terminal atoms and finally to lone pairs of the central atom.

Complete the octet on C by forming a double bond

105. **Given:** μ = 1.08 D HCl, 20% ionic and μ = 1.82 D HF, 45% ionic **Find:** r

Conceptual Plan: $\mu \rightarrow \mu_{calc} \rightarrow r$

% ionic character = $\dfrac{\mu}{\mu_{calc}}$ $\qquad$ $\mu_{calc} = qr$

Solution: For HCl $\qquad \mu_{calc} = \dfrac{1.08}{0.20} = 5.4 \text{ D}$

$$\dfrac{5.4 \text{ D} \times \dfrac{3.34 \times 10^{-30} \text{ C gm}}{\text{D}} \times \dfrac{10^{12} \text{ pm}}{\text{m}}}{1.6 \times 10^{-19} \text{ C}} = 113 \text{ pm}$$

For HF $\qquad \mu_{calc} = \dfrac{1.82}{0.45} = 4.04 \text{ D}$

$$\dfrac{4.04 \text{ D} \times \dfrac{3.34 \times 10^{-30} \text{ C gm}}{\text{D}} \times \dfrac{10^{12} \text{ pm}}{\text{m}}}{1.6 \times 10^{-19} \text{ C}} = 84 \text{ pm}$$

106. Formation reaction: $6C(s) + 3H_2(g) \rightarrow C_6H_6(g)$ ΔH_f° = 82.9 kJ/mol

Using bond energies we would have the reaction: $6C(g) + 3H_2(g) \rightarrow C_6H_6(g)$ so we have to include in the bond energy calculation the energy needed to convert $C(s) \rightarrow C(g)$ (718.4 kJ/mol)

Rewrite the reaction with the Lewis structures.

$6C(s) \rightarrow 6C(g)$ $\qquad\qquad$ 6(718.4 kJ) $\qquad$ = 4310.4 kJ

$6C(g) + 3 H - H(g) \rightarrow$ (g)

bonds broken: $3 (H - H) = 3 (436 \text{ kJ/mol}) = 1308 \text{ kJ}$

bonds formed: $-3(C = C) - 3(C - C) - 6(C - H) = -3(611) - 3(347) - 6(414) = -5358 \text{ kJ}$

ΔH from bond energies $= +(4310 \text{ kJ}) + (1308 \text{ kJ}) - 5358 \text{ kJ} = +260 \text{ kJ/mol}$

The difference between the value calculated from bond energies (260 kJ/mol) and $\Delta H_f^\circ = 82.9$ kJ/mol for benzene leads us to conclude there is a great deal of stabilization from the two resonance forms and that they contribute much to the formation of benzene.

107. In order for the four P atoms to be equivalent, they must all be in the same electronic environment. That is, they must all see the same number of bonds and lone pair electrons. The only way to achieve this is with a tetrahedral configuration where the P atoms are at the four points of the tetrahedron.

108. **Given:** $\Delta H_f^\circ CaBr_2 = -675$ kJ/mol; $IE_1(Ca) = 590$ kJ/mol; $IE_2(Ca) = 1145$ kJ/mol; $\Delta H_{sub}(Ca) = 178$ kJ/mol; $Br_2(g)$ bond energy = 193 kJ/mol; $\Delta H_{vap}(Br_2(l)) = 31$ kJ/mol; $EA(Br) = -325$ kJ/mol.

Find: lattice energy

Conceptual Plan:

$Ca(s)+Br_2(l) \rightarrow Ca(g)+Br_2(l) \rightarrow Ca^+(g)+Br_2(l) \rightarrow Ca^{2+}(g)+Br_2(l) \rightarrow Ca^{2+}(g)+Br_2(g) \rightarrow Ca^{2+}(g)+2Br(g)$

ΔH_{sub} IE_1 IE_2 ΔH_{vap} Bond   energy

$\rightarrow Ca^{2+}(g)+2Br^-(g) \rightarrow CaBr_2(s)$

EA   lattice energy

ΔH_f°

Solution: $\Delta H_f^\circ = \Delta H_{sub} + IE_1 + IE_2 + \Delta H_{vap} + \text{Bond energy} + 2 \text{ EA} + \text{lattice energy}$

$-675 \dfrac{\text{kJ}}{\text{mol}} = +178 \dfrac{\text{kJ}}{\text{mol}} + 590 \dfrac{\text{kJ}}{\text{mol}} + 1145 \dfrac{\text{kJ}}{\text{mol}} + 31 \dfrac{\text{kJ}}{\text{mol}} + 2(-325) \dfrac{\text{kJ}}{\text{mol}} + \text{lattice energy}$

lattice energy $= -1969$ kJ/mol

109. **Given:** $\Delta H_f^\circ PI_3(s) = -24.7$ kJ/mol; $P - I = 184$ kJ/mol; $I - I = 151$ kJ/mol; $\Delta H_f^\circ P(g) = 334$ kJ/mol; $\Delta H_f^\circ I_2(g) = 62$ kJ/mol

Find: $\Delta H_{sub} PI_3(s)$

Conceptual Plan: $PI_3(s) \rightarrow PI_3(g)$; use Hess's law

Solution:

Reaction		ΔH(kJ/mol)	
$PI_3(s)$	$\rightarrow P(s) + 3/2 \ I_2(s)$	$+ 24.7$	(this is the reverse of the formation reaction)
$P(s)$	$\rightarrow P(g)$	$+334$	(formation of P(g))
$3/2 \ I_2(s)$	$\rightarrow 3/2 \ I_2(g)$	$3/2(62)$	(formation of $I_2(g)$)
$3/2 \ I_2(g)$	$\rightarrow 3 \ I(g)$	$3/2(151)$	(breaking I – I bond)
$P(g) + 3I(g)$	$\rightarrow PI_3(g)$	$- 3(184)$	(forming P – I bond)
$PI_3(s)$	$\rightarrow PI_3(g)$	$+126$	(sublimation of $PI_3(s)$)

110. a) is true: Strong bonds break and weak bonds form. In an endothermic reaction, the energy required to break the bonds is greater than the energy given off when the bonds are formed ($\Delta H > 0$), therefore, in an endothermic reaction the bonds that are breaking are stronger than the bonds that are forming.

111. When we say that a compound is "energy rich" we mean that it gives off a great amount of energy when it reacts. It means that there is a lot of energy stored in the compound. This energy is released when the weak bonds in the compound break and much stronger bonds are formed in the product thereby releasing energy.

112. In solid covalent compounds, the electrons in the bonds are shared directly between the atoms involved in the molecule. Each molecule is a distinct unit. Ionic compounds, on the other hand, are not distinct units. Rather, they are composed of alternating positive and negative ions in a three – dimensional crystalline array.

113. Lewis theory is successful because it allows us to understand and predict many chemical observations. We can use it to determine the formula of ionic compounds, to account for low melting points and boiling points of molecular compounds compared to ionic compounds. Lewis theory allows us to predict what molecules or ions will be stable, which will be more reactive, and which will not exist. Lewis theory, however, does not really tell us anything about how the bonds in the molecules and ions form. It does not give us a way to account for the paramagnetism of oxygen. And, by itself, Lewis theory does not really tell us anything about the shape of the molecule or ion.

Chapter 10
Chemical Bonding II: Molecular Shapes, Valence Bond Theory, and Molecular Orbital Theory

1. The properties of molecules are directly related to their shape. The sensation of taste, immune response, the sense of smell, and many types of drug action all depend on the shape – specific interactions between molecules and proteins.

2. According to VSEPR theory, the repulsion between electron groups on interior atoms of a molecule, therefore, determines the geometry of the molecule.

3. The five basic electron geometries are:
    1) Linear, which has two electron groups
    2) Trigonal planar, which has three electron groups
    3) Tetrahedral, which has four electron groups
    4) Trigonal bypyramid, which has five electron groups
    5) Octahedral, which has six electron groups.
    An electron group is at least one pair of electrons.

4. The electron geometry is the geometrical arrangement of the electron groups around the atom.
    The molecular geometry is the geometrical arrangement of the atoms around the central atom.
    The electron geometry and the molecular geometry are the same when every electron group bonds two atoms together. Therefore, the presence of lone pair electrons gives a different molecular geometry and electron geometry.

5. a) Four electron groups gives tetrahedral electron geometry, while three bonding groups and one lone pair give a trigonal pyramidal molecular geometry.

    b) Four electron groups gives a tetrahedral electron geometry, while two bonding groups and two lone pair give a bent molecular geometry.

    c) Five electron groups gives a trigonal bipyramidal electron geometry, while four bonding groups and one lone pair give a seesaw molecular geometry.

    d) Five electron groups gives a trigonal bipyramidal electron geometry, while three bonding groups and two lone pair give a T – shaped molecular geometry.

    e) Five electron groups gives a trigonal bipyramidal electron geometry, while two bonding groups and three lone pair give a linear geometry.

f) Six electron groups gives an octahedral electron geometry, while five bonding groups and one lone pair give a square pyramidal molecular geometry.

g) Six electron groups gives an octahedral electron geometry, while four bonding groups and two lone pair gives a square planar molecular geometry.

6. Larger molecules may have two or more interior atoms. When predicting the shapes of these molecules, determine the geometry about each interior atom and use them to determine the entire three – dimensional shape of the molecules.

7. To determine if a molecule is polar:
   1. Draw the Lewis structure for the molecule and determine the molecular geometry
   2. Determine whether the molecule contains polar bonds.
   3. Determine whether the polar bonds add together to form a net dipole moment
Polarity is important because polar and nonpolar molecules have different properties. Polar molecules interact strongly with other polar molecules while they do not interact with nonpolar molecules.

8. According to valence bond theory a chemical bond results from the overlap of two half – filled orbitals with spin – pairing of the two valence electrons.

9. According to valence bond theory, the shape of the molecule is determined by the geometry of the overlapping orbitals.

10. In valence bond theory, the interaction energy is usually negative (or stabilizing) when the interacting atomic orbitals contain a total to two electrons that can spin – pair.

11. Hybridization is a mathematical procedure in which the standard atomic orbitals are combined to form new atomic orbitals called hybrid orbitals. Hybrid orbitals are still localized on individual atoms, but they have different shapes and energies from those of standard atomic orbitals. They are necessary in valence bond theory because they correspond more closely to the actual distribution of electron in chemically bonded atoms.

12. Hybrid orbitals minimize the energy of the molecule by maximizing the orbital overlap in a bond.

13. The number of standard atomic orbitals added together always equals the number of hybrid orbitals formed. The total number of orbitals is conserved.

14.

Hybridization Scheme

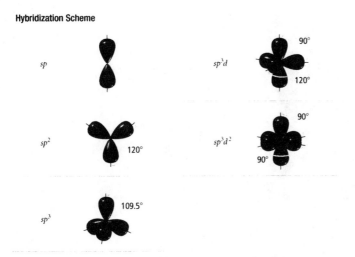

15. The double bond in Lewis theory is simply two pair of electrons between the same two atoms. However, in valence bond theory we see that it is made up of two different kinds of bonds. The double bond in valence bond theory consists of one σ bond and one π bond. Valence bond theory shows us that rotation about a double bond is severely restricted. Because of the side – by – side overlap of the p orbitals, the π bond must essentially break

for rotation to occur. The single bond consists of overlap that results in a σ bond. Since the overlap is linear, rotation is not restricted.

16. a) A linear electron geometry corresponds to sp hybridization.

   b) A trigonal planar electron geometry corresponds to sp^2 hybridization.

   c) A tetrahedral electron geometry corresponds to sp^3 hybridization.

   d) A trigonal bipyramidal electron geometry corresponds to sp^3d hybridization.

   e) An octahedral electron geometry corresponds to sp^3d^2 hybridization.

17. In molecular orbital theory, atoms will bond when the electrons in the atoms can lower their energy by occupying the molecular orbitals of the resultant molecule.

18. In valence bond theory, hybrid orbitals are weighted linear sums of the valence atomic orbitals of a particular atom, and the hybrid orbitals remain localized on that atom. In molecular orbital theory, the molecular orbitals are weighted linear sums of the valence atomic orbitals of all the atoms in a molecule, and many of the molecular orbitals are delocalized over the entire molecule.

19. Constructive interference between two atomic orbitals gives rise to a molecular orbital that is lower in energy than the atomic orbitals. This is the bonding orbital. Destructive interference between two atomic orbitals gives rise to a molecular orbital that is higher in energy than the atomic orbitals. This is the antibonding orbital.

20. The bond order in a diatomic molecule is the number of electrons in bonding MO's minus the number in antibonding MO's divided by two. The higher the bond order, the stronger the bond. A negative or zero bond order indicates that a bond will not form between the atoms.

21. Molecular orbitals can be approximated by a linear combination of atomic orbitals. The total number of MO's formed from a particular set of AO's will always equal the number of AO's used.

22. a) σ_{2s}

   b) σ^*_{2s}

   c) σ_{2p}

   d) σ^*_{2p}

   e) π_{2p}

f) π^{*}_{2p}

23.

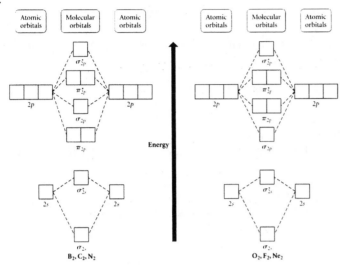

24. The degree of mixing between two orbitals decreases with increasing energy difference between them. Mixing of the 2s and $2p_x$ orbitals is greater in B_2, C_2, and N_2 than in O_2, F_2, and Ne_2, because in B, C, and N the energy levels of the atomic orbitals are more closely spaced than in O, F, and Ne. This mixing produces a change in energy ordering for the π_{2p} and the σ_{2p} molecular orbitals.

25. A paramagnetic species has unpaired electrons in molecular orbitals of equal energy. A paramagnetic species is attracted to a magnetic field. The magnetic property is a direct result of the unpaired electrons. The spin and angular momentum of the electrons generate tiny magnetic fields. A diamagnetic species has all of the electrons paired. The magnetic fields caused by the electron spin and orbital angular momentum tend to cancel each other. A diamagnetic species is not attracted to a magnetic field, and is, in fact, slightly repelled.

26. When two atomic orbitals are different, the weighting of each orbital in forming a molecular orbital may be different. When a molecular orbital is approximated as a linear combination of atomic orbitals of different energies, the lower energy atomic orbital makes a greater contribution to the bonding molecular orbital and the higher energy atomic orbital makes a greater contribution to the antibonding molecular orbital. The shape of the molecular orbital shows a greater electron density at the atom that has the lower atomic orbital energy.

27. Nonbonding orbitals are atomic orbitals not involved in a bond and will remain localized on the atom.

28. In Lewis theory, a chemical bond is the transfer or sharing of electrons represented as dots. Lewis theory allows us to predict the combination of atoms that form stable molecules. Also, we can predict the general shape of a molecule.
Lewis theory is a quick way to predict the stability and shapes of molecules based on the number of valence electrons. However, it does not deal at all with how the bonds that we make are formed. Valence bond theory is a more advanced bonding theory that treats electrons in a quantum – mechanical manner. A quantitative approach is extremely complicated but, a qualitative approach allows an understanding of how the bonds are formed. In valence bond theory, electrons reside in quantum – mechanical orbitals localized on individual atoms. When two atoms approach each other, the electrons and nucleus of one atom interact with the electron and nucleus of the other atom. If the energy of the system is lowered, a chemical bond forms. So, valence bond theory portrays a chemical bond as the overlap of two half – filled atomic orbitals. The shape of the molecule can be predicted from the geometry of the overlapping orbitals. Also, valence bond theory explains the rigidity of the double bond. But, valence bond theory treats the electrons as if they reside in the quantum – mechanical orbitals that we calculate for atoms. This is an oversimplification that is partially compensated for by introducing the concept of hybridization. An even more complex quantum – mechanical model is molecular

orbital theory. In molecular orbital theory, a chemical bond occurs when the electrons in the atoms can lower their energy by occupying the molecular orbitals of the resultant molecule. The chemical bonds in MO theory are not localized between atoms, but spread throughout the entire molecule. Molecular orbital theory uses trial functions to solve the Schrödinger equation for the molecules. In order to determine how well the trial function works, you calculate the energy, trying to minimize the energy. However, no matter how "good" your guess, you can never do better than nature at minimizing energy. These minimum energy calculations for orbitals must be done by computer.

All three of these models have strengths and weaknesses, none is "correct". Depending on what information you need, depends on which approach you use.

29. 4 electron pairs: A trigonal pyramidal molecular geometry has three bonding groups and one lone pair of electrons, so there are four electron pairs on atom A.

30. 3 electron pairs: A trigonal planar molecular geometry has three bonding groups and no lone pair of electrons so there are three electron pairs on atom A.

31. a) 4 total electron groups, 4 bonding groups, 0 lone pair
        A tetrahedral molecular geometry has four bonding groups and no lone pair. So, there are four total electron groups, four bonding groups and no lone pair.

     b) 5 total electron groups, 3 bonding groups, 2 lone pair.
        A T – shaped molecular geometry has three bonding groups and two lone pair. So, there are five total electron groups, three bonding groups and two lone pair.

     c) 6 total electron groups, 5 bonding groups, 1 lone pair.
        A square pyramidal molecular geometry has five bonding groups and one lone pair. So, there are six total electron groups, five bonding groups and one lone pair.

32. a) 6 total electron groups, 6 bonding groups, 0 lone pair.
        An octahedral molecular geometry has six bonding groups and no lone pair. So, there are six total electron groups, six bonding groups and no lone pair.

     b) 6 electron groups, 4 bonding groups, 2 lone pair
        A square planar molecular geometry has four bonding groups and two lone pair. So, there are six total electron groups, four bonding groups and two lone pair.

     c) 5 electron groups, 4 bonding groups, 1 lone pair
        A seesaw molecular geometry has four bonding groups and one lone pair. So, there are five total electron groups, four bonding groups and one lone pair.

33. a) PF_3:   Electron geometry – tetrahedral; molecular geometry – trigonal pyramidal; bond angle = 109.5°
                Because of the lone pair, the bond angle will be less than 109.5°.
                Draw a Lewis structure for the molecule:
                    PF_3 has 26 valence electrons

                Determine the total number of electron groups around the central atom:
                There are 4 electron groups on P

                Determine the number of bonding groups and the number of lone pairs around the central atom:
                There are three bonding groups and one lone pair

                Use Table 10.1 to determine the electron geometry and molecular geometry and bond angles:
                Four electron groups is tetrahedral electron geometry, three bonding groups and one lone pair is trigonal pyramidal molecular geometry, the idealized bond angles for tetrahedral are 109.5°; however, the lone pair will make the bond angle less than idealized.

b) SBr₂: Electron geometry – tetrahedral; molecular geometry – bent; bond angle = 109.5°
Because of the lone pairs, the bond angle will be less than 109.5°.
Draw a Lewis structure for the molecule:

SBr₃ has 20 valence electrons

Determine the total number of electron groups around the central atom:
There are 4 electron groups on S

Determine the number of bonding groups and the number of lone pairs around the central atom:
There are 2 bonding groups and two lone pair

Use Table 10.1 to determine the electron geometry and molecular geometry and bond angles:
Four electron groups is tetrahedral electron geometry, two bonding groups and two lone pair is a bent molecular geometry, the idealized bond angles for tetrahedral are 109.5°; however, the lone pairs will make the bond angle less than idealized.

c) CHCl₃: Electron geometry – tetrahedral; molecular geometry – tetrahedral; bond angle = 109.5°
Because there are no lone pair, the bond angle will be 109.5°.
Draw a Lewis structure for the molecule:
CHCl₃ has 26 valence electrons

Determine the total number of electron groups around the central atom:
There are 4 electron groups on C

Determine the number of bonding groups and the number of lone pairs around the central atom:
There are four bonding groups and no lone pair

Use Table 10.1 to determine the electron geometry and molecular geometry and bond angles:
Four electron groups is tetrahedral electron geometry, four bonding groups and no lone pair is a tetrahedral molecular geometry, the idealized bond angles for tetrahedral are 109.5°;
however, because the attached atoms have different electronegativities the bond angles are less than idealized.

d) CS₂: Electron geometry – linear; molecular geometry – linear; bond angle = 180°
Because there are no lone pair, the bond angle will 180°.
Draw a Lewis structure for the molecule:
CS₂ has 16 valence electrons

Determine the total number of electron groups around the central atom:
There are 2 electron groups on C

Determine the number of bonding groups and the number of lone pairs around the central atom:
There are 2 bonding groups and no lone pair

Use Table 10.1 to determine the electron geometry and molecular geometry and bond angles:
Two electron groups is linear geometry, two bonding groups and no lone pair is linear molecular geometry, the idealized bond angle is 180°

34. a) CF$_4$: Electron geometry – tetrahedral; molecular geometry – tetrahedral; bond angle = 109.5°
Draw a Lewis structure for the molecule:
CF$_4$ has 32 valence electrons

Determine the total number of electron groups around the central atom:
There are 4 electron groups on C

Determine the number of bonding groups and the number of lone pairs around the central atom:
There are four bonding groups and no lone pair

Use Table 10.1 to determine the electron geometry and molecular geometry and bond angles:
Four electron groups is tetrahedral electron geometry, four bonding groups and no lone pair is a
tetrahedral molecular geometry, the idealized bond angles for tetrahedral are 109.5°

b) NF$_3$: Electron geometry – tetrahedral; molecular geometry – trigonal pyramidal; bond angle = 109.5°
Because of the lone pair, the bond angle will be less than 109.5°.
Draw a Lewis structure for the molecule:
NF$_3$ has 26 valence electrons

Determine the total number of electron groups around the central atom:
There are 4 electron groups on N

Determine the number of bonding groups and the number of lone pairs around the central atom:
There are three bonding groups and one lone pair

Use Table 10.1 to determine the electron geometry and molecular geometry and bond angles:
Four electron groups is tetrahedral electron geometry, three bonding groups and one lone pair is a
trigonal pyramidal molecular geometry, the idealized bond angles for tetrahedral are 109.5°;
however, the lone pair will make the bond angle less than idealized.

c) OF$_2$: Electron geometry – tetrahedral; molecular geometry – bent; bond angle = 109.5°
Because of the lone pairs, the bond angle will be less than 109.5°.
Draw a Lewis structure for the molecule:
OF$_2$ has 20 valence electrons

Determine the total number of electron groups around the central atom:
There are 4 electron groups on O

Determine the number of bonding groups and the number of lone pairs around the central atom:
There are two bonding groups and two lone pair

Use Table 10.1 to determine the electron geometry and molecular geometry and bond angles:
Four electron groups is tetrahedral electron geometry, two bonding groups and two lone pair is a
bent molecular geometry, the idealized bond angles for tetrahedral are 109.5°, however, the lone
pairs will make the bond angle less than idealized.

d) H$_2$S: Electron geometry – tetrahedral; molecular geometry – bent; bond angle = 109.5°
Because of the lone pair, the bond angle will be less than 109.5°.

Draw a Lewis structure for the molecule:

H_2S has 8 valence electrons

H —— S —— H

Determine the total number of electron groups around the central atom:

There are 4 electron groups on S

Determine the number of bonding groups and the number of lone pairs around the central atom:

There are two bonding groups and two lone pair

Use Table 10.1 to determine the electron geometry and molecular geometry and bond angles:

Four electron groups is tetrahedral electron geometry, two bonding groups and two lone pair is a bent molecular geometry, the idealized bond angles for tetrahedral are 109.5°; however, the lone pairs will make the bond angle less than idealized.

35. H_2O will have the smaller bond angle because lone pair – lone pair repulsions are greater than lone – pair bonding pair repulsions.

Draw the Lewis structures for both structures:

H_3O^+ has 8 valence electrons H_2O has 8 valence electrons

3 bonding groups and 1 lone pair   2 bonding groups and 2 lone pair

Both have 4 electron groups, but the 2 lone pair in H_2O will cause the bond angle to be smaller because of the lone pair – lone pair repulsions.

36. ClO_3^- will have the smaller bond angle because lone pair – bonding pair repulsions are greater than bonding pair – bonding pair repulsions.

Draw the Lewis structures for both structures:

ClO_3^- has 26 valence electrons ClO_4^- has 32 valence electrons

3 bonding groups and 1 lone pair   4 bonding groups and no lone pair

Both have 4 electron groups, but the lone pair in ClO_3^- will cause the bond angle to be smaller because of the lone pair – bonding pair repulsions.

37. a) SF_4 Draw a Lewis structure for the molecule:

SF_4 has 34 valence electrons

Determine the total number of electron groups around the central atom:

There are 5 electron groups on S

Determine the number of bonding groups and the number of lone pairs around the central atom:

There are four bonding groups and one lone pair

Use Table 10.1 to determine the electron geometry and molecular geometry:

The electron geometry is trigonal bipyramidal so the molecular geometry is seesaw

317

Sketch the molecule:

b) ClF₃   Draw a Lewis structure for the molecule:
           ClF₃ has 28 valence electrons

Determine the total number of electron groups around the central atom:
There are 5 electron groups on Cl

Determine the number of bonding groups and the number of lone pairs around the central atom:
There are three bonding groups and two lone pair

Use Table 10.1 to determine the electron geometry and molecular geometry:
The electron geometry is trigonal bipyramidal so the molecular geometry is T – shape

Sketch the molecule:

```
      F
      |
F —— Cl
      |
      F
```

c) IF₂⁻   Draw a Lewis structure for the ion:
           IF₂⁻ has 22 valence electrons

$$\left[\mathbf{:}\ddot{\underset{..}{F}} — \overset{..}{\underset{..}{I}} — \ddot{\underset{..}{F}}\mathbf{:} \right]^{-}$$

Determine the total number of electron groups around the central atom:
There are 5 electron groups on I

Determine the number of bonding groups and the number of lone pairs around the central atom:
There are two bonding groups and three lone pair

Use Table 10.1 to determine the electron geometry and molecular geometry:
The electron geometry is trigonal bipyramidal so the molecular geometry is linear

Sketch the ion:

$$[F —— I —— F\ ]^{-}$$

d) IBr₄⁻   Draw a Lewis structure for the ion:
            IBr₄⁻ has 36 valence electrons

$$\left[\begin{array}{c} \mathbf{:}\ddot{Br}\mathbf{:} \\ | \\ \mathbf{:}\ddot{Br} — \overset{..}{I} — \ddot{Br}\mathbf{:} \\ | \\ \mathbf{:}\ddot{Br}\mathbf{:} \end{array} \right]^{-}$$

Determine the total number of electron groups around the central atom:

There are 6 electron groups on I

Determine the number of bonding groups and the number of lone pairs around the central atom:
There are four bonding groups and two lone pair

Use Table 10.1 to determine the electron geometry and molecular geometry:
The electron geometry is octahedral so the molecular geometry is square planar

Sketch the ion:

38. a) BrF$_5$ Draw a Lewis structure for the molecule:
BrF$_5$ has 42 valence electrons

Determine the total number of electron groups around the central atom:
There are 6 electron groups on Br

Determine the number of bonding groups and the number of lone pairs around the central atom:
There are five bonding groups and one lone pair

Use Table 10.1 to determine the electron geometry and molecular geometry:
The electron geometry is octahedral so the molecular geometry is square pyramidal

Sketch the molecule:

b) SCl$_6$ Draw a Lewis structure for the molecule:
SCl$_6$ has 48 valence electrons

Determine the total number of electron groups around the central atom:
There are 6 electron groups on S

Determine the number of bonding groups and the number of lone pairs around the central atom:
There are six bonding groups and no lone pair

Use Table 10.1 to determine the electron geometry and molecular geometry:
The electron geometry is octahedral so the molecular geometry is octahedral

Sketch the molecule:

$$Cl - S - Cl$$

(central atom S with six Cl atoms in octahedral arrangement)

c) PF₅   Draw a Lewis structure for the molecule:

PF₅ has 40 valence electrons

(Lewis structure of PF₅ with central P bonded to five F atoms each with three lone pairs)

Determine the total number of electron groups around the central atom:
There are 5 electron groups on P

Determine the number of bonding groups and the number of lone pairs around the central atom:
There are five bonding groups and no lone pair

Use Table 10.1 to determine the electron geometry and molecular geometry:
The electron geometry is trigonal bipyramidal so the molecular geometry is trigonal bipyramidal

Sketch the molecule:

(trigonal bipyramidal sketch of PF₅ with central P bonded to five F atoms)

d) IF₄⁺   Draw a Lewis structure for the ion:

IF₄⁺ has 34 valence electrons

(Lewis structure of IF₄⁺ shown in brackets with a + charge, central I bonded to four F atoms each with three lone pairs)

Determine the total number of electron groups around the central atom:
There are 5 electron groups on I

Determine the number of bonding groups and the number of lone pairs around the central atom:
There are four bonding groups and one lone pair

Use Table 10.1 to determine the electron geometry and molecular geometry:
The electron geometry is trigonal bipyramidal so the molecular geometry is seesaw

Sketch the ion:

39. a) C_2H_2 Draw the Lewis structure:

H — C ≡ C — H

Atom	Number of Electron Groups	Number of Lone Pairs	Molecular Geometry
Left C	2	0	Linear
Right C	2	0	Linear

Sketch the molecule:

H — C ≡ C — H

b) C_2H_4 Draw the Lewis structure:

Atom	Number of Electron Groups	Number of Lone Pairs	Molecular Geometry
Left C	3	0	Trigonal planar
Right C	3	0	Trigonal planar

Sketch the molecule:

c) C_2H_6 Draw the Lewis structure:

Atom	Number of Electron Groups	Number of Lone Pairs	Molecular Geometry
Left C	4	0	Tetrahedral
Right C	4	0	Tetrahedral

Sketch the molecule:

40. a) N₂   Draw the Lewis structure:

:N≡N:

Atom	Number of Electron Groups	Number of Lone Pairs	Molecular Geometry
Left N	2	1	Linear
Right N	2	1	Linear

Sketch the molecule:

N≡N

b) N₂H₂   Draw the Lewis structure:

H — N̈═N̈ — H

Atom	Number of Electron Groups	Number of Lone Pairs	Molecular Geometry
Left N	3	1	Bent
Right N	3	1	Bent

Sketch the molecule:

c) N₂H₄   Draw the Lewis structure:

Atom	Number of Electron Groups	Number of Lone Pairs	Molecular Geometry
Left N	4	1	Trigonal pyramidal
Right C	4	1	Trigonal pyramidal

Sketch the molecule:

41. a) Four pair of electrons gives a tetrahedral electron geometry, the lone pair would cause lone pair – bonded pair repulsions and would have a trigonal pyramidal molecular geometry.

b) Five pair of electrons gives a trigonal bipyramidal electron geometry, the lone pair occupies an equatorial position in order to minimize lone pair – bonded pair repulsions and the molecule would have a seesaw molecular geometry.

c) Six pair of electrons gives an octahedral electron geometry, the two lone pair would occupy opposite position in order to minimize lone pair – lone pair repulsions. The molecular geometry would be square planar

42. a) Four pair of electrons gives a tetrahedral electron geometry, the two lone pair would cause repulsions that would lead to a bent molecular geometry.

b) Five pair of electrons gives a trigonal bipyramidal geometry. The three lone pair would occupy equatorial positions in order to minimize the lone pair – lone pair repulsions. This would give a linear molecular geometry.

c) Six pair of electrons gives an octahedral electron geometry. The lone pair would occupy a position to minimize the lone pair – bonded pair repulsions and gives a square pyramidal molecular geometry.

43. a) CH_3OH Draw the Lewis structure, determine the geometry about each interior atom:

Atom	Number of Electron Groups	Number of Lone Pairs	Molecular Geometry
C	4	0	Tetrahedral
O	4	2	Bent

Sketch the molecule:

b) CH_3OCH_3 Draw the Lewis structure, determine the geometry about each interior atom:

Atom	Number of Electron Groups	Number of Lone Pairs	Molecular Geometry
C	4	0	Tetrahedral
O	4	2	Bent
C	4	0	Tetrahedral

Sketch the molecule:

c) H_2O_2 Draw the Lewis structure, determine the geometry about each interior atom:

Atom	Number of Electron	Number of	Molecular Geometry

323

	Groups	Lone Pairs	
O	4	2	Bent
O	4	2	Bent

Sketch the molecule:

44. a) CH_3NH_2 Draw the Lewis structure, determine the geometry about each interior atom:

Atom	Number of Electron Groups	Number of Lone Pairs	Molecular Geometry
C	4	0	Tetrahedral
N	4	1	Trigonal Pyramidal

Sketch the molecule:

b) $CH_3CO_2CH_3$ Draw the Lewis structure, determine the geometry about each interior atom:

Atom	Number of Electron Groups	Number of Lone Pairs	Molecular Geometry
Left C	4	0	Tetrahedral
Center C	3	O	Trigonal Planar
O	4	2	Bent
Right C	4	0	Tetrahedral

Sketch the molecule:

c) NH_2CO_2H Draw the Lewis structure, determine the geometry about each interior atom

Atom	Number of Electron Groups	Number of Lone Pairs	Molecular Geometry
N	4	1	Trigonal Pyramidal
C	3	0	Trigonal Planar
O	4	2	Bent

Sketch the molecule:

45. Draw the Lewis structure for CO_2 and CCl_4 and determine the molecular geometry.

Number of electron groups on C	2	4
Number of lone pair	0	0
Molecular geometry	linear	tetrahedral

Even though each molecule contains polar bonds, the sum of the bond dipoles gives a net dipole of zero for each molecule.

46. Draw the Lewis structure of CH_3F and determine the molecular geometry.

Number of electron groups on C	4
Number of lone pair	0
Molecular geometry	tetrahedral

The molecule is tetrahedral but is polar because the C – H bond dipole is different than the C – F bond dipole. Because the bond dipoles are different, the sum of the bond dipoles is NOT zero. Therefore, the molecule is polar.

47. a) PF_3 – polar

Draw the Lewis structure and determine the molecular geometry:
The molecular geometry from problem 33 is trigonal pyramidal

Determine if the molecule contains polar bonds:
The electronegativities of P = 2.1 and F = 4. Therefore the bonds are polar.

Determine whether the polar bond add together to form a net dipole:
Because the molecule is trigonal pyramidal the three dipole moments sum to a net dipole moment.
The molecule is polar

b) SBr_2 – polar

Draw the Lewis structure and determine the molecular geometry:
The molecular geometry from problem 33 is bent

Determine if the molecule contains polar bonds:
The electronegativities of S = 2.5 and Br = 2.0. Therefore the bonds are polar

Determine whether the polar bond adds together to form a net dipole:
Because the molecule is bent, the two dipole moments sum to a net dipole moment. The molecule is polar.

c) $CHCl_3$ – polar
Draw the Lewis structure and determine the molecular geometry:
The molecular geometry from problem 33 is tetrahedral

Determine if the molecule contains polar bonds:
The electronegativities of C = 2.5, H = 2.1 and Cl = 3.0. Therefore the bonds are polar.

Determine whether the polar bonds add together to form a net dipole:
Because the bonds have different dipole moments because of the different atoms involved, the four dipole moments sum to a net dipole moment. The molecule is polar.

d) CS_2 – nonpolar
Draw the Lewis structure and determine the molecular geometry:
The molecular geometry from problem 33 is linear

Determine if the molecule contains polar bonds:
The electronegativities of C = 2.5 and S = 2.5. Therefore the bonds are nonpolar. Also, the molecule is linear which would result in a zero net dipole even if the bonds were polar.

The molecule is nonpolar

48. a) CF_4 – nonpolar
Draw the Lewis structure and determine the molecular geometry:
The molecular geometry from problem 34 is tetrahedral

Determine if the molecule contains polar bonds:
The electronegativities of C = 2.5 and F = 4.0. Therefore the bonds are polar.

Determine whether the polar bonds add together to form a net dipole:
Because the molecular geometry is tetrahedral, the four dipole moments sum to a zero net dipole moment. The molecule is nonpolar.

b) NF_3 – polar
Draw the Lewis structure and determine the molecular geometry:
The molecular geometry from problem 34 is trigonal pyramidal

Determine if the molecule contains polar bonds:
The electronegativities of N = 3.0 and F = 4.0. Therefore the bonds are polar.

Determine whether the polar bonds add together to form a net dipole:
Because the molecular geometry is trigonal pyramidal the three dipole moments sum to a net dipole moment. The molecule is polar.

c) OF_2 – polar
Draw the Lewis structure and determine the molecular geometry:
The molecular geometry from problem 34 is bent

Determine if the molecule contains polar bonds:
The electronegativities of O = 3.5 and F = 4.0. Therefore the bonds are polar.

Determine whether the polar bonds add together to form a net dipole:
Because the molecular geometry is bent, the two dipole moments sum to a net dipole moment. The molecule is polar.

d) H_2S – polar

Draw the Lewis structure and determine the molecular geometry:
The molecular geometry from problem 34 is bent

Determine if the molecule contains polar bonds:
The electronegativities of H = 2.1 and S = 2.5. Therefore the bonds are polar.

Determine whether the polar bonds add together to form a net dipole:
Because the molecular geometry is bent, the two dipole moments sum to a net dipole moment. The molecule is polar.

49. a) ClO_3^- – polar

Draw the Lewis structure and determine the molecular geometry:

Four electron pair, with one lone pair gives a trigonal pyramidal molecular geometry

Determine if the molecule contains polar bonds:
The electronegativities of Cl = 3.0 and O = 3.5. Therefore the bonds are polar.

Determine whether the polar bonds add together to form a net dipole:
Because the molecular geometry is trigonal pyramidal, the three dipole moments sum to a net dipole moment. The molecule is polar.

b) SCl_2 – polar

Draw the Lewis structure and determine the molecular geometry:

Four electron pair with two lone pair gives a bent molecular geometry

Determine if the molecule contains polar bonds:
The electronegativities of S = 2.5 and Cl = 3.0. Therefore the bonds are polar.

Determine whether the polar bonds add together to form a net dipole:
Because the molecular geometry is bent, the two dipole moments sum to a net dipole moment. The molecule is polar.

c) SCl_4 – polar

Draw the Lewis structure and determine the molecular geometry:

Five electron pair with one lone pair give a seesaw molecular geometry

Determine if the molecule contains polar bonds:
The electronegativities of S = 2.5 and Cl = 3.0. Therefore the bonds are polar.

Determine whether the polar bonds add together to form a net dipole:
Because the molecular geometry is seesaw, the four dipole moments sum to a net dipole moment. The molecule is polar.

d) $BrCl_5$ – nonpolar

Draw the Lewis structure and determine the molecular geometry:

Six electron pair with one lone pair give square pyramidal molecular geometry

Determine if the molecule contains polar bonds:
The electronegativity of Br = 2.8 and Cl = 3.0. The difference is only 0.2, therefore the bonds are nonpolar. Even though the molecular geometry is square pyramidal, the five bonds are nonpolar so there is no net dipole. The molecule is nonpolar.

50. a) $SiCl_4$ – nonpolar

Draw the Lewis structure and determine the molecular geometry:

Four electron pairs with no lone pairs gives a tetrahedral molecular geometry

Determine if the molecule contains polar bonds:
The electronegativities of Cl = 3.0 and Si = 1.8. Therefore the bonds are polar.

Determine whether the polar bonds add together to form a net dipole:
Because the molecular geometry is tetrahedral, the four dipole moments sum to a zero net dipole moment. The molecule is nonpolar

b) CF_2Cl_2 – polar

Draw the Lewis structure and determine the molecular geometry:

Four electron pair with no lone pair gives a tetrahedral molecular geometry

Determine if the molecule contains polar bonds:
The electronegativities of C = 2.5, F = 4.0 and Cl = 3.0. Therefore the bonds are polar.

Determine whether the polar bond add together to form a net dipole:
Even though the molecular geometry is tetrahedral which normally yields a nonpolar molecule, the four dipole moments sum to a net dipole moment because of the different electronegativities of Cl and F. The molecule is polar.

c) SeF_6 – nonpolar

Draw the Lewis structure and determine the molecular geometry:

Six electron pair with no lone pair gives an octahedral molecular geometry

Determine if the molecule contains polar bonds:
The electronegativities of Se = 3.0 and F = 4.0. Therefore the bonds are polar.

Determine whether the polar bond add together to form a net dipole:
Because the molecular geometry is octahedral, the six dipole moments sum to a zero net dipole moment. The molecule is nonpolar.

d) IF_5 – polar

Draw the Lewis structure and determine the molecular geometry:

Six electron pairs with one lone pair give square pyramidal molecular geometry

Determine if the molecule contains polar bonds:
The electronegativities of I = 2.0 and F = 4.0. Therefore the bonds are polar.

Determine whether the polar bond add together to form a net dipole:
Because the molecular geometry is square pyramidal, the five dipole moments sum to a net dipole moment. The molecule is polar.

51. a) Be $2s^2$ 0 bonds can form. Beryllium contains no unpaired electrons, so no bonds can form without hybridization.

    b) P $3s^2 3p^3$ 3 bonds can form. Phosphorus contains 3 unpaired electrons, so 3 bonds can form without hybridization.

    c) F $2s^2 2p^5$ 1 bond can form. Fluorine contains 1 unpaired electron, so 1 bond can form without hybridization.

52. a) B $2s^2 2p^1$ 1 bond can form. Boron contains 1 unpaired electron, so 1 bond can form without hybridization.

    b) N $2s^2 2p^3$ 3 bonds can form. Nitrogen contains 3 unpaired electrons, so 3 bonds can form without hybridization.

    c) O $2s^2 2p^4$ 2 bonds can form. Oxygen contains 2 unpaired electrons, so w bonds can form without hybridization.

53. PH_3

The unhybridized bond angles should be 90°. So, without hybridization, there is not very good agreement between valence bond theory and the actual bond angle of 93.3°

54. SF$_2$

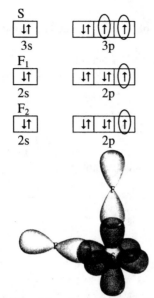

The unhybridized bond angles should be 90°. So, without hybridization, there is not very good agreement between valence bond theory and the actual bond angle of 98.2°

55. C $2s^2 2p^2$

56. C $2s^2 2p^2$

57. sp^2 Only sp^2 hybridization of this set of orbitals has a remaining p orbital to form a π bond.
sp^3 hybridization utilizes all 3 p orbitals
sp^{3}d^2 hybridization utilizes all 3 p orbitals and 2 d orbitals

58. sp^{3}d   sp^{3}d hybridization utilizes an s orbital, 3 p orbitals and d orbital. Since 5 orbitals are used, 5 hybrid orbitals are formed and 5 bonds can form.
sp^3 hybridization utilizes an s orbital and 3 p orbitals. 4 orbitals are used, so 4 hybrid orbitals form and 4 bonds can form.
sp^2 hybridization utilizes an s orbital and 2 p orbitals. 3 orbitals are used, so 3 hybrid orbitals form. This allows 3 σ and 1 π bond to form for a total of 4 bonds formed.

59. a)   CCl$_4$ Write the Lewis structure for the molecule:

Use VSEPR to predict the electron geometry:
Four electron groups around the central atom give tetrahedral electron geometry

Select the correct hybridization for the central atom based on the electron geometry:

Tetrahedral electron geometry has sp³ hybridization

Sketch the molecule and label the bonds:

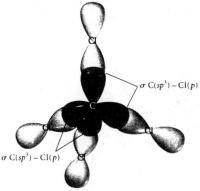

$\sigma\ C(sp^3) - Cl(p)$

$\sigma\ C(sp^3) - Cl(p)$

b) NH₃   Write the Lewis structure for the molecule:

$$H - \overset{\overset{\textstyle H}{|}}{\underset{\bullet\bullet}{N}} - H$$

Use VSEPR to predict the electron geometry:
Four electron groups around the central atom give tetrahedral electron geometry

Select the correct hybridization for the central atom based on the electron geometry:
Tetrahedral electron geometry has sp³ hybridization

Sketch the molecule and label the bonds:

Lone pair in N sp^3

$\sigma\ N(sp^3) - H(s)$

$\sigma\ N(sp^3) - H(s)$

c) OF₂   Write the Lewis structure for the molecule:

$$\overset{\bullet\bullet}{\underset{\bullet\bullet}{F}} - \overset{\bullet\bullet}{\underset{\bullet\bullet}{O}} - \overset{\bullet\bullet}{\underset{\bullet\bullet}{F}}$$

Use VSEPR to predict the electron geometry:
Four electron groups around the central atom give tetrahedral electron geometry

Select the correct hybridization for the central atom based on the electron geometry:
Tetrahedral electron geometry has sp³ hybridization

Sketch the molecule and label the bonds:

Lone pair in O sp^3

$\sigma\ O(sp^3) - F(p)$

d) CO₂   Write the Lewis structure for the molecule:

$$\overset{\bullet\bullet}{\underset{\bullet\bullet}{O}} = C = \overset{\bullet\bullet}{\underset{\bullet\bullet}{O}}$$

Use VSEPR to predict the electron geometry:

Two electron groups around the central atom gives linear electron geometry

Select the correct hybridization for the central atom based on the electron geometry:
Linear electron geometry has sp hybridization

Sketch the molecule and label the bonds:

π C(p_y) – O(p_y) π C(p_z) – O(p_z)

σ C(sp) – O(p)

60. a) CH_2Br_2 Write the Lewis structure for the molecule:

H
|
:Br — C — H
|
:Br:

Use VSEPR to predict the electron geometry:
Four electron groups around the central atom give tetrahedral electron geometry

Select the correct hybridization for the central atom based on the electron geometry:
Tetrahedral electron geometry has sp^3 hybridization

Sketch the molecule and label the bonds:

σ C(sp^3) – H(s)

σ C(sp^3) – Br(p)

b) SO_2 Write the Lewis structure for the molecule:

O === S — O:

Use VSEPR to predict the electron geometry:
Three electron groups around the central atom gives trigonal planar electron geometry

Select the correct hybridization for the central atom based on the electron geometry:
Trigonal planar electron geometry has sp^2 hybridization

Sketch the molecule and label the bonds:

π S(p) – O(p)

Lone pair
in S(sp^2)

σ S(sp^2) – O(p)

c) NF_3 Write the Lewis structure for the molecule:

:F — N — F:
|
:F:

Use VSEPR to predict the electron geometry:
Four electron groups around the central atom give tetrahedral electron geometry

Select the correct hybridization for the central atom based on the electron geometry:
Tetrahedral electron geometry has sp^3 hybridization

Sketch the molecule and label the bonds:

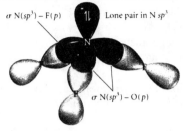

σ N(sp^3) – F(p) $\quad$ Lone pair in N sp^3

σ N(sp^3) – O(p)

d) BF_3 Write the Lewis structure for the molecule:

Use VSEPR to predict the electron geometry:
Three electron groups around the central atom gives trigonal planar electron geometry

Select the correct hybridization for the central atom based on the electron geometry:
Trigonal planar electron geometry has sp^2 hybridization

Sketch the molecule and label the bonds:

Empty p orbital

σ B(sp^2) – F(p)

σ B(sp^2) – F(p)

61. a) $COCl_2$ Write the Lewis structure for the molecule:

Use VSEPR to predict the electron geometry:
Three electron groups around the central atom gives trigonal planar electron geometry

Select the correct hybridization for the central atom based on the electron geometry:
Trigonal planar electron geometry has sp^2 hybridization

Sketch the molecule and label the bonds:

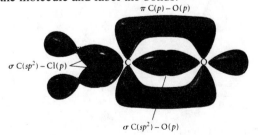

π C(p) – O(p)

σ C(sp^2) – Cl(p)

σ C(sp^2) – O(p)

b) BrF₅ Write the Lewis structure for the molecule:

Use VSEPR to predict the electron geometry:
Six electron pairs around the central atoms gives octahedral electron geometry

Select the correct hybridization for the central atom based on the electron geometry:
Octahedral electron geometry has sp^3d^2 hybridization

Sketch the molecule and label the bonds:

$\sigma\ Br(sp^3d^2) - F(p)$

$\sigma\ Br(sp^3d^2) - F(p)$

Lone pair in $Br(sp^3d^2)$

c) XeF₂ Write the Lewis structure for the molecule:

F —— Xe —— F

Use VSEPR to predict the electron geometry:
Five electron groups around the central atom gives trigonal bipyramidal geometry

Select the correct hybridization for the central atom based on the electron geometry:
Trigonal bipyramidal geometry has sp^3d hybridization
Sketch the molecule and label the bonds:

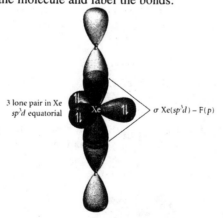

3 lone pair in Xe
sp^3d equatorial

$\sigma\ Xe(sp^3d) - F(p)$

d) I₃⁻ Write the Lewis structure for the molecule:

$$\left[\ddot{\underset{\cdot\cdot}{I}} - \overset{\cdot\cdot}{\underset{\cdot\cdot}{I}} - \ddot{\underset{\cdot\cdot}{I}} \right]^{-}$$

Use VSEPR to predict the electron geometry:
Five electron groups around the central atom gives trigonal bipyramidal geometry

Select the correct hybridization for the central atom based on the electron geometry:

Trigonal bipyramidal geometry has sp³d hybridization

Sketch the molecule and label the bonds:

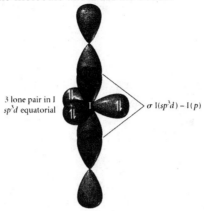

3 lone pair in I
sp³d equatorial

σ I(sp³d) – I(p)

62. a) SO_3^{2-} Write the Lewis structure for the ion:

Use VSEPR to predict the electron geometry:
Four electron groups around the central atom give tetrahedral electron geometry

Select the correct hybridization for the central atom based on the electron geometry:
Tetrahedral electron geometry has sp³ hybridization

Sketch the molecule and label the bonds:

Lone pair

σ S(sp³) – O(p)   σ S(sp³) – O(p)

b) PF_6^- Write the Lewis structure for the ion:

Use VSEPR to predict the electron geometry:
Six electron pairs around the central atoms gives octahedral electron geometry

Select the correct hybridization for the central atom based on the electron geometry:
Octahedral electron geometry has sp³d² hybridization

Sketch the molecule and label the bonds:

$\sigma\ P(sp^3d^2) - F(p)$
All six bonds

c) BrF₃   Write the Lewis structure for the molecule:

Use VSEPR to predict the electron geometry:
Five electron groups around the central atom gives trigonal bipyramidal geometry

Select the correct hybridization for the central atom based on the electron geometry:
Trigonal bipyramidal geometry has sp³d hybridization

Sketch the molecule and label the bonds:

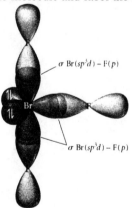

$\sigma\ Br(sp^3d) - F(p)$

$\sigma\ Br(sp^3d) - F(p)$

d) HCN   Write the Lewis structure for the molecule:
H — C ≡ N **

Use VSEPR to predict the electron geometry:
Two electron groups around the central atom gives linear electron geometry

Select the correct hybridization for the central atom based on the electron geometry:
Linear electron geometry has sp hybridization

Sketch the molecule and label the bonds:

63. a) N₂H₂   Write the Lewis structure for the molecule:

$$H \text{---} \overset{\bullet\bullet}{N} = \overset{\bullet\bullet}{N} \text{---} H$$

Use VSEPR to predict the electron geometry:
Three electron groups around each interior atom gives trigonal planar electron geometry

Select the correct hybridization for the central atom based on the electron geometry:
Trigonal planar electron geometry has sp² hybridization

Sketch the molecule and label the bonds:

b) N₂H₄   Write the Lewis structure for the molecule:

Use VSEPR to predict the electron geometry:
Four electron groups around each interior atom gives tetrahedral electron geometry

Select the correct hybridization for the central atom based on the electron geometry:
Tetrahedral electron geometry has sp³ hybridization

Sketch the molecule and label the bonds:

c) CH₃NH₂ Write the Lewis structure for the molecule:

Use VSEPR to predict the electron geometry:
Four electron groups around the C gives tetrahedral electron geometry, four electron groups around the N gives tetrahedral geometry.

Select the correct hybridization for the central atom based on the electron geometry:
Tetrahedral electron geometry has sp³ hybridization of both C and N

Sketch the molecule and label the bonds:

64. a) C_2H_2 Write the Lewis structure for the molecule:

Use VSEPR to predict the electron geometry:
Two electron groups around each interior atom gives linear electron geometry

Select the correct hybridization for the central atom based on the electron geometry:
Linear electron geometry has sp hybridization

Sketch the molecule and label the bonds:

b) C_2H_4 Write the Lewis structure for the molecule:

Use VSEPR to predict the electron geometry:
Three electron groups around each interior atom gives trigonal planar electron geometry

Select the correct hybridization for the central atom based on the electron geometry:
Trigonal planar electron geometry has sp^2 hybridization

Sketch the molecule and label the bonds:

c) C_2H_6 Write the Lewis structure for the molecule:

H   H
| |
H — C — C — H
| |
H   H

Use VSEPR to predict the electron geometry:
Four electron groups around each interior atom gives tetrahedral electron geometry

Select the correct hybridization for the central atom based on the electron geometry:
Tetrahedral electron geometry has sp^3 hybridization

Sketch the molecule and label the bonds:

$\sigma\ C(sp^3) - H(s)$ $\sigma\ C(sp^3) - H(s)$

$\sigma\ C(sp^3) - C(sp^3)$

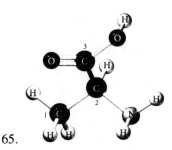

65.

C – 1 and C – 2 each have four electron pairs around the atom, which is tetrahedral electron pair geometry. Tetrahedral electron pair geometry is sp^3 hybridization.

C – 3 has three electron pairs around the atom, which is trigonal planar electron pair geometry. Trigonal planar electron pair geometry is sp^2 hybridization.

O has four electron pairs around the atom, which is tetrahedral electron pair geometry. Tetrahedral electron pair geometry is sp^3 hybridization.

N has four electron pairs around the atom, which is tetrahedral electron pair geometry. Tetrahedral electron pair geometry is sp^3 hybridization.

66.

C – 1 and C – 4 each have three electron pairs around the atom, which is trigonal planar electron pair geometry. Trigonal planar electron pair geometry is sp^2 hybridization.

C – 2 and C – 3 each have four electron pairs around the atom, which is tetrahedral electron pair geometry. Tetrahedral electron pair geometry is sp^3 hybridization.

O – 1 and O – 2 each have four electron pairs around the atom, which is tetrahedral electron pair geometry. Tetrahedral electron pair geometry is sp^3 hybridization.

N has four electron pairs around the atom, which is tetrahedral electron pair geometry. Tetrahedral electron pair geometry is sp^3 hybridization.

67. 1s + 1s constructive interference results in a bonding orbital

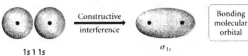

68. 1s – 1s destructive interference results in an antibonding orbital

69. Be_2^+ has 7 electrons

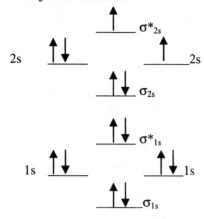

$2s$ σ^*_{2s} $2s$

σ_{2s}

σ^*_{1s}

$1s$ $1s$

σ_{1s}

Bond order $= \dfrac{4-3}{2} = \dfrac{1}{2}$ stable

Be_2^- has 9 electrons

$2p$ $2p$

σ_{2p}

σ^*_{2s}

$2s$ $2s$

σ_{2s}

σ^*_{1s}

$1s$ $1s$

σ_{1s}

Bond order $= \dfrac{5-4}{2} = \dfrac{1}{2}$ stable

70. Li_2^+ has 5 electron

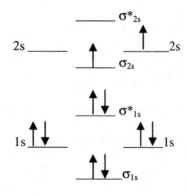

σ^*_{2s}

$2s$ $2s$

σ_{2s}

σ^*_{1s}

$1s$ $1s$

σ_{1s}

Bond order $= \dfrac{3-2}{2} = \dfrac{1}{2}$ stable

Li_2^- has 7 electrons

σ^*_{2s}

$2s$ $2s$

σ_{2s}

σ^*_{1s}

$1s$ $1s$

σ_{1s}

Bond order $= \dfrac{4-3}{2} = \dfrac{1}{2}$ stable

71. The bonding and antibonding molecular orbitals from the combination of p_x and p_x atomic orbitals lie along the internuclear axis.

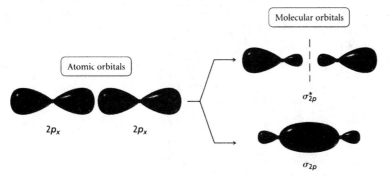

72. The bonding and antibonding molecular orbital from the combination of p_y and p_y atomic orbital lie above and below the internuclear axis.

When the p_z and the p_z orbitals combine, similar bonding and antibonding molecular orbitals form. The only difference between the resulting MOs is a rotation about the internuclear axis. The energies and the names of the bonding and antibonding MOs obtained from the combination of the p_z atomic orbitals are identical to those obtained from the combination of the p_y atomic orbitals which lie in front and back of the internuclear axis.

73.

a) 4 valence electrons

Bond order = $\dfrac{2-2}{2} = 0$

diamagnetic

b) 6 valence electrons

Bond order = $\dfrac{4-2}{2} = 1$

paramagnetic

c) 8 valence electrons

Bond order = $\dfrac{6-2}{2} = 2$

diamagnetic

d) 9 valence electrons

Bond order = $\dfrac{7-2}{2} = 2.5$

paramagnetic

74.

a) 10 valence electrons | b) 12 valence electrons | c) 13 valence electrons | d) 14 valence electrons

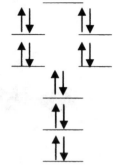

σ^*_{2p}

σ^*_{2p}

π_{2p}

σ_{2p}

σ^*_{2s}

σ_{2s}

Bond order = $\dfrac{8-2}{2} = 3$

diamagnetic

Bond order = $\dfrac{8-4}{2} = 2$

paramagnetic

Bond order = $\dfrac{8-5}{2} = 1.5$

paramagnetic

Bond order = $\dfrac{8-6}{2} = 1$

diamagnetic

75. a) Write an energy level diagram for the molecular orbitals in H_2^{2-}. The ion has 4 valence electrons. Assign the electrons to the molecular orbitals beginning with the lowest energy orbitals and following Hund's rule.

σ^*_{1s}

σ_{1s}

Bond order = $\dfrac{2-2}{2} = 0$ With a bond order of 0, the ion will not exist.

b) Write an energy level diagram for the molecular orbitals in Ne_2. The molecule has 16 valence electrons. Assign the electrons to the molecular orbitals beginning with the lowest energy orbitals and following Hund's rule.

σ^*_{3p}

σ^*_{3p}

π_{3p}

σ_{3p}

σ^*_{3s}

σ_{3s}

Bond order = $\dfrac{8-8}{2} = 0$ With a bond order of 0, the molecule will not exist.

c) Write an energy level diagram for the molecular orbitals in He_2^{2+}. The ion has 2 valence electrons. Assign the electrons to the molecular orbitals beginning with the lowest energy orbitals and following Hund's rule.

σ^*_{1s}

σ_{1s}

Bond order = $\dfrac{2-0}{2} = 1$ With a bond order of 1, the ion will exist.

d) Write an energy level diagram for the molecular orbitals in F_2^{2-}. The molecule has 16 valence electrons.

Assign the electrons to the molecular orbitals beginning with the lowest energy orbitals and following Hund's rule.

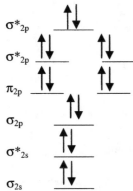

Bond order = $\dfrac{8-8}{2} = 0$ With a bond order of 0, the ion will not exist.

76. a) Write an energy level diagram for the molecular orbitals in C_2^{2+}. The ion has 6 valence electrons.
Assign the electrons to the molecular orbitals beginning with the lowest energy orbitals and following Hund's rule.

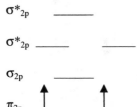

Bond order = $\dfrac{4-2}{2} = 1$ With a bond order of 1, the ion will exist.

b) Write an energy level diagram for the molecular orbitals in Li_2. The ion has 2 valence electrons.
Assign the electrons to the molecular orbitals beginning with the lowest energy orbitals and following Hund's rule.

σ^*_{2s} _____

σ_{2s} ⇅ _____

Bond order = $\dfrac{2-0}{2} = 1$ With a bond order of 1, the molecule will exist.

c) Write an energy level diagram for the molecular orbitals in Be_2^{2+}. The ion has 2 valence electrons.
Assign the electrons to the molecular orbitals beginning with the lowest energy orbitals and following Hund's rule.

σ^*_{2s} _____

σ_{2s} ⇅ _____

Bond order = $\dfrac{2-0}{2} = 1$ With a bond order of 1, the ion will exist.

d) Write an energy level diagram for the molecular orbitals in Li_2^{2-}. The ion has 4 valence electrons. Assign the electrons to the molecular orbitals beginning with the lowest energy orbitals and following Hund's rule.

σ^*_{2s}

σ_{2s}

Bond order $= \dfrac{2-2}{2} = 0$ With a bond order of 0, the ion will not exist.

77. C_2^- has the highest bond order, the highest bond energy and the shortest bond. Write an energy level diagram for the molecular orbitals in C_2. Assign the electrons to the molecular orbitals beginning with the lowest energy orbitals and following Hund's rule.

C_2 (8 valence electrons); C_2^+ (7 valence electrons): C_2^- (9 valence electrons)

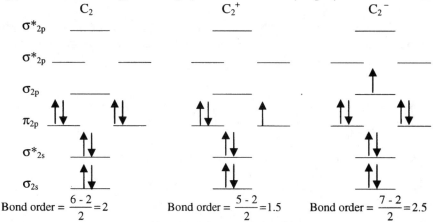

Bond order $= \dfrac{6-2}{2} = 2$ Bond order $= \dfrac{5-2}{2} = 1.5$ Bond order $= \dfrac{7-2}{2} = 2.5$

C_2^- has the highest bond order at 2.5. Bond order is directly related to bond energy, so C_2^- has the largest bond energy and bond order is indirectly related to bond length, so C_2^- has the shortest bond length.

78. O_2 has the highest bond order, the highest bond energy and the shortest bond. Write an energy level diagram for the molecular orbitals in O_2. Assign the electrons to the molecular orbitals beginning with the lowest energy orbitals and following Hund's rule.

O_2 (12 valence electrons); O_2^- (13 valence electrons): O_2^{2-} (14 valence electrons)

O_2 (12 valence electrons) O_2^- (13 valence electrons) O_2^{2-} (14 valence electrons)

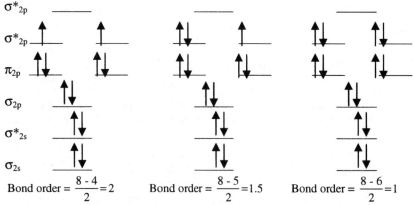

Bond order $= \dfrac{8-4}{2} = 2$ Bond order $= \dfrac{8-5}{2} = 1.5$ Bond order $= \dfrac{8-6}{2} = 1$

O_2 has the highest bond order at 2. Bond order is directly related to bond energy, so O_2 has the largest bond energy and bond order is indirectly related to bond length, so O_2 has the shortest bond length.

79. Write an energy level diagram for the molecular orbitals in CO using O_2 energy ordering. Assign the electrons to the molecular orbitals beginning with the lowest energy orbitals and following Hund's rule.

CO has 10 valence electrons.

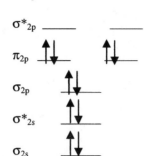

Bond order $= \dfrac{8-2}{2} = 3$

The electron density toward the O atom since it is more electronegative.

80.   HCl(8 valence electrons)

H $1s$ ⬆

σ ⬆⬇

Bond order $= \dfrac{2-0}{2} = 1$

nonbonding
p orbitals on Cl

The electron density will be skewed toward the Cl atom since it is more electronegative.

81. a) COF_2 Write the Lewis structure for the molecule:

Use VSEPR to predict the electron geometry:
Three electron groups around the central atom gives trigonal planar electron geometry. Three bonding pairs of electrons give trigonal planar molecular geometry.

Determine if the molecule contains polar bonds:
The electronegativities of C = 2.5, O = 3.5 and F = 4.0 Therefore the bonds are polar.

Determine whether the polar bond add together to form a net dipole:
Even though a trigonal planar molecular geometry normally is nonpolar, because the bonds have different dipole moments the sum of the dipole moments is not zero. The molecule is polar.

345

Select the correct hybridization for the central atom based on the electron geometry:
Trigonal planar geometry has sp² hybridization.

Sketch the molecule and label the bonds:

b) S₂Cl₂   Write the Lewis structure for the molecule:

Use VSEPR to predict the electron geometry:
Four electron groups around the central atom gives tetrahedral electron geometry. Two bonding pairs and two lone pair of electrons gives bent molecular geometry.

Determine if the molecule contains polar bonds:
The electronegativities of S = 2.5 and Cl = 3.0. Therefore the bonds are polar.

Determine whether the polar bonds add together to form a net dipole:
In a bent molecular geometry the sum of the dipole moments is not zero. The molecule is polar.

Select the correct hybridization for the central atom based on the electron geometry:
Tetrahedral geometry has sp³ hybridization.

Sketch the molecule and label the bonds:

c) SF₄   Write the Lewis structure for the molecule:

Use VSEPR to predict the electron geometry:
Five electron groups around the central atom gives trigonal bipyramidal electron geometry. Four bonding pair and one lone pair of electrons gives seesaw molecular geometry.

Determine if the molecule contains polar bonds:
The electronegativities of S = 2.5 and F = 4.0. Therefore the bonds are polar.

Determine whether the polar bonds add together to form a net dipole:
In a seesaw molecular geometry the sum of the dipole moments is not zero. The molecule is polar.

Select the correct hybridization for the central atom based on the electron geometry:
Trigonal bipyramidal electron geometry has sp³d hybridization.

Sketch the molecule and label the bonds:

$\sigma\ S(sp^3d) - F(p)$
All four bonds

82. a) IF₅   Write the Lewis structure for the molecule:

$$\overset{\displaystyle \cdot\cdot}{\underset{\displaystyle \cdot\cdot}{\vdots F \vdots}}$$

Use VSEPR to predict the electron geometry:
Six electron groups around the central atom gives octahedral electron geometry. Five bonding pairs and one lone pair of electrons gives square pyramidal molecular geometry.

Determine if the molecule contains polar bonds:
The electronegativities of I = 2.5 and F = 4.0 Therefore the bonds are polar.

Determine whether the polar bonds add together to form a net dipole:
In a square pyramidal molecular geometry the sum of the dipole moments is not zero. The molecule is polar.

Select the correct hybridization for the central atom based on the electron geometry:
Octahedral electron geometry has sp^3d^2 hybridization

Sketch the molecule and label the bonds:

$\sigma\ I(sp^3d^2) - F(p)$
All five bonds

b) CH₂CHCH₃
Write the Lewis structure for the molecule:

Use VSEPR to predict the electron geometry:
C – 1 and C – 2 each have three electron groups around the atom, this gives trigonal planar electron geometry. Three bonding pairs of electrons give trigonal planar molecular geometry.
C – 3 has four electron groups around the C atom, four electron groups gives tetrahedral electron geometry. Four bonding groups gives tetrahedral molecular geometry.

Determine if the molecule contains polar bonds:
The electronegativities of C = 2.5, and H = 2.1. Therefore the bonds are slightly polar because the difference in electronegativity is less than 0.5.

Determine whether the polar bond add together to form a net dipole:
The trigonal planar molecular geometry and the tetrahedral molecular geometry give a net dipole moment of zero. The molecule is nonpolar.

Select the correct hybridization for the central atom based on the electron geometry:
Trigonal planar electron geometry has sp^2 hybridization and the tetrahedral electron geometry has sp^3 hybridization.

Sketch the molecule and label the bonds:

c) CH₃SH Write the Lewis structure for the molecule:

Use VSEPR to predict the electron geometry:
Four electron groups around the C atom and the S atom gives tetrahedral electron geometry. Four bonding pairs of electrons around the C gives tetrahedral molecular geometry and two bonding groups and two lone pair around the S gives bent molecular geometry.

Determine if the molecule contains polar bonds:
The electronegativities of C = 2.5, S = 2.5 and H = 2.1 The C – H bonds and the S – H bond will be slightly polar, the C – S bond will be nonpolar.

Determine whether the polar bond add together to form a net dipole:
In both molecular geometries the sum of the dipole moments is not zero. The molecule is polar.

Select the correct hybridization for the central atom based on the electron geometry:
Tetrahedral electron geometry has sp^3 hybridization on both C and S.

Sketch the molecule and label the bonds:

83. a)   serine

$C-1$ and $C-3$ each have four electron pair around the atom. Four electron pair gives tetrahedral electron geometry, tetrahedral electron geometry has sp^3 hybridization. Four bonding pair and zero lone pair gives tetrahedral molecular geometry.

$C-2$ has three electron pair around the atom. Three electron pair gives trigonal planar geometry, trigonal planar geometry has sp^2 hybridization. Three bonding pair and zero lone pair gives trigonal planar molecular geometry.

N has four electron pair around the atom. Four electron pair gives tetrahedral electron geometry, tetrahedral electron geometry has sp^3 hybridization. Three bonding pair and one lone pair gives trigonal pyramidal molecular geometry.

$O-1$ and $O-2$ each has four electron pair around the atom. Four electron pair gives tetrahedral electron geometry, tetrahedral electron geometry has sp^3 hybridization. Two bonding pair and two lone pair gives bent molecular geometry.

b)   asparagine

$C-1$ and $C-3$ each have four electron pair around the atom. Four electron pair gives tetrahedral electron geometry, tetrahedral electron geometry has sp^3 hybridization. Four bonding pair and zero lone pair gives tetrahedral molecular geometry.

$C-2$ and $C-4$ each have three electron pair around the atom. Three electron pair gives trigonal planar geometry, trigonal planar geometry has sp^2 hybridization. Three bonding pair and zero lone pair gives trigonal planar molecular geometry.

$N-1$ and $N-2$ each have four electron pair around the atom. Four electron pair gives tetrahedral electron geometry, tetrahedral electron geometry has sp^3 hybridization. Three bonding pair and one lone pair gives trigonal pyramidal molecular geometry.

O has four electron pair around the atom. Four electron pair gives tetrahedral electron geometry, tetrahedral electron geometry has sp^3 hybridization. Two bonding pair and two lone pair gives bent molecular geometry.

c) cysteine

C – 1 and C – 3 each have four electron pair around the atom. Four electron pair gives tetrahedral electron geometry, tetrahedral electron geometry has sp^3 hybridization. Four bonding pair and zero lone pair gives tetrahedral molecular geometry.

C – 2 has three electron pair around the atom. Three electron pair gives trigonal planar geometry, trigonal planar geometry has sp^2 hybridization. Three bonding pair and zero lone pair gives trigonal planar molecular geometry.

N has four electron pair around the atom. Four electron pair gives tetrahedral electron geometry, tetrahedral electron geometry has sp^3 hybridization. Three bonding pair and one lone pair gives trigonal pyramidal molecular geometry.

O and S have four electron pair around the atom. Four electron pair gives tetrahedral electron geometry, tetrahedral electron geometry has sp^3 hybridization. Two bonding pair and two lone pair gives bent molecular geometry.

84. a) cytosine

N – 1 has 3 bonding pair of electrons and 1 lone pair, 4 electron pair is tetrahedral electron geometry and sp^3 hybridization. 3 bonding pair of electrons gives trigonal pyramidal molecular geometry.

C – 2 has 3 bonding pair of electrons and 0 lone pair, 3 electron pair is trigonal planar geometry and sp^2 hybridization. 3 bonding pair of electrons gives trigonal planar molecular geometry.

N – 3 has 2 bonding pair of electrons and 1 lone pair, 3 electron pair is trigonal planar electron geometry and sp^2 hybridization. 2 bonding pair and 1 lone pair gives bent molecular geometry

C – 4 has 3 bonding pair of electrons and 0 lone pair, 3 electron pair is trigonal planar geometry and sp^2 hybridization. 3 bonding pair of electrons gives trigonal planar molecular geometry.

C – 5 has 3 bonding pair of electrons and 0 lone pair, 3 electron pair is trigonal planar geometry and sp^2 hybridization. 3 bonding pair of electrons gives trigonal planar molecular geometry.

C – 6 has 3 bonding pair of electrons and 0 lone pair, 3 electron pair is trigonal planar geometry and sp^2 hybridization. 3 bonding pair of electrons gives trigonal planar molecular geometry.

N outside the ring has 3 bonding pair of electrons and 1 lone pair, 4 electron pair is tetrahedral electron geometry and sp^3 hybridization. 3 bonding pair of electrons gives trigonal pyramidal molecular geometry.

b) adenine

N – 1 has 2 bonding pair of electrons and 1 lone pair, 3 electron pair is trigonal planar electron geometry and sp^2 hybridization. 2 bonding pair and 1 lone pair gives bent molecular geometry.

C – 2 has 3 bonding pair of electrons and 0 lone pair, 3 electron pair is trigonal planar geometry and sp^2 hybridization. 3 bonding pair of electrons gives trigonal planar molecular geometry.

N – 3 has 2 bonding pair of electrons and 1 lone pair, 3 electron pair is trigonal planar electron geometry and sp^2 hybridization. 2 bonding pair and 1 lone pair gives bent molecular geometry

C – 4 has 3 bonding pair of electrons and 0 lone pair, 3 electron pair is trigonal planar geometry and sp^2 hybridization. 3 bonding pair of electrons gives trigonal planar molecular geometry.

C – 5 has 3 bonding pair of electrons and 0 lone pair, 3 electron pair is trigonal planar geometry and sp^2 hybridization. 3 bonding pair of electrons gives trigonal planar molecular geometry.

C – 6 has 3 bonding pair of electrons and 0 lone pair, 3 electron pair is trigonal planar geometry and sp^2 hybridization. 3 bonding pair of electrons gives trigonal planar molecular geometry.

N – 7 has 2 bonding pair of electrons and 1 lone pair, 3 electron pair is trigonal planar electron geometry and sp^2 hybridization. 2 bonding pair and 1 lone pair gives bent molecular geometry

C – 8 has 3 bonding pair of electrons and 0 lone pair, 3 electron pair is trigonal planar geometry and sp^2 hybridization. 3 bonding pair of electrons gives trigonal planar molecular geometry.

N – 9 has 3 bonding pair of electrons and 1 lone pair, 4 electron pair is tetrahedral electron geometry and sp^3 hybridization. 3 bonding pair of electrons gives trigonal pyramidal molecular geometry.

N outside the ring has 3 bonding pair of electrons and 1 lone pair, 4 electron pair is tetrahedral electron geometry and sp^3 hybridization. 3 bonding pair of electrons gives trigonal pyramidal molecular geometry.

c) thymine

N – 1 has 3 bonding pair of electrons and 1 lone pair, 4 electron pair is tetrahedral electron geometry and sp^3 hybridization. 3 bonding pair of electrons gives trigonal pyramidal molecular geometry.

C – 2 has 3 bonding pair of electrons and 0 lone pair, 3 electron pair is trigonal planar geometry and sp^2 hybridization. 3 bonding pair of electrons gives trigonal planar molecular geometry.

N – 3 has 3 bonding pair of electrons and 1 lone pair, 4 electron pair is tetrahedral electron geometry and sp^3 hybridization. 3 bonding pair and 1 lone pair gives trigonal pyramidal molecular geometry

C – 4 has 3 bonding pair of electrons and 0 lone pair, 3 electron pair is trigonal planar geometry and sp^2 hybridization. 3 bonding pair of electrons gives trigonal planar molecular geometry.

C – 5 has 3 bonding pair of electrons and 0 lone pair, 3 electron pair is trigonal planar geometry and sp^2 hybridization. 3 bonding pair of electrons gives trigonal planar molecular geometry.

C – 6 has 3 bonding pair of electrons and 0 lone pair, 3 electron pair is trigonal planar geometry and sp^2 hybridization. 3 bonding pair of electrons gives trigonal planar molecular geometry.

C outside the ring has 4 bonding pair of electrons and 0 lone pair, 4 electron pair is tetrahedral electron geometry and sp^3 hybridization. 4 bonding pair of electrons gives tetrahedral molecular geometry.

d) guanine

N – 1 has 3 bonding pair of electrons and 1 lone pair, 4 electron pair is tetrahedral electron geometry and sp^3 hybridization. 3 bonding pair of electrons gives trigonal pyramidal molecular geometry.

C – 2 has 3 bonding pair of electrons and 0 lone pair, 3 electron pair is trigonal planar geometry and sp^2 hybridization. 3 bonding pair of electrons gives trigonal planar molecular geometry.

N – 3 has 2 bonding pair of electrons and 1 lone pair, 3 electron pair is trigonal planar electron geometry and sp^2 hybridization. 2 bonding pair and 1 lone pair gives bent molecular geometry

C – 4 has 3 bonding pair of electrons and 0 lone pair, 3 electron pair is trigonal planar geometry and sp^2 hybridization. 3 bonding pair of electrons gives trigonal planar molecular geometry.

C – 5 has 3 bonding pair of electrons and 0 lone pair, 3 electron pair is trigonal planar geometry and sp^2 hybridization. 3 bonding pair of electrons gives trigonal planar molecular geometry.

C – 6 has 3 bonding pair of electrons and 0 lone pair, 3 electron pair is trigonal planar geometry and sp^2 hybridization. 3 bonding pair of electrons gives trigonal planar molecular geometry.

N – 7 has 2 bonding pair of electrons and 1 lone pair, 3 electron pair is trigonal planar electron geometry and sp^2 hybridization. 2 bonding pair and 1 lone pair gives bent molecular geometry

C – 8 has 3 bonding pair of electrons and 0 lone pair, 3 electron pair is trigonal planar geometry and sp^2 hybridization. 3 bonding pair of electrons gives trigonal planar molecular geometry.

N – 9 has 3 bonding pair of electrons and 1 lone pair, 4 electron pair is tetrahedral electron geometry and sp^3 hybridization. 3 bonding pair of electrons gives trigonal pyramidal molecular geometry.

N outside the ring has 3 bonding pair of electrons and 1 lone pair, 4 electron pair is tetrahedral electron geometry and sp^3 hybridization. 3 bonding pair of electrons gives trigonal pyramidal molecular geometry.

85. 4 π bonds; 25 σ bonds; the lone pair on the O's and N – 2 occupy sp^2 orbitals, the lone pairs on N – 1, N – 3 and N – 4 occupy sp^3 orbitals.

86. 5 π bonds; 21 σ bonds;

There is rotation around the bond from C – 1 to the ring and from C – 1 to OH bond. There is rotation around the O – 2 to the ring bond and around the O – 2 to C – 2 bond. There is rotation around the C – 2 to C – 3 bond. The C – 1 to O – 1 bond is rigid, the ring structure is rigid and the C – 2 to O – 3 bond is rigid.

87. a) water soluble – the 4 C – OH bonds, the C = O bond and the C – O bonds in the ring, make the molecule polar. Because of the large electronegativity difference between the C and O, each of the bonds will have a dipole moment. The sum of the dipole moments does NOT give a net zero dipole moment, so the molecule is polar. Since it is polar, it will be water soluble.

b) fat soluble – There is only one C – O bond in the molecule. The dipole moment from this bond is not enough to make the molecule polar because of all of the non polar components of the molecule. The C – H bonds in the structure lead to a net dipole of zero for most of the sites in the molecule. Since the molecule is nonpolar, it is fat soluble.

c) water soluble – the carboxylic acid function (COOH group) along with the N atom in the ring make the molecule polar. Because of the electronegativity difference between the C and O and the C and N atoms, the bonds will have a dipole moment and the net dipole moment of the molecule is NOT zero, so the molecule is polar. Since the molecule is polar, it is water soluble.

d) fat soluble – The two O atoms in the structure contribute a very small amount to the net dipole moment of this molecule. The majority of the molecule is nonpolar because there is no net dipole moment at the interior C atoms. Because the molecule is nonpolar it is fat soluble.

88. The soap molecule has a nonpolar hydrocarbon end and an anionic end when it is dissolved in water. In order to dissolve in water, the sodium stearate congregates to form small spheres (called micelles) with the nonpolar ends on the insides and the anionic ends on the surface. The anionic end interacts with the polar water molecules, while the nonpolar hydrocarbon end can attract and interact with the nonpolar grease. This allows the soapy water to remove the grease.

89. ClF has 14 valence electron. Assign the electrons to the lowest energy MO's first and then follow Hund's rule.

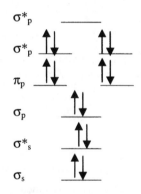

90. CN^+ (8 valence electrons) CN (9 valence electrons) CN^- (10 valence electrons)

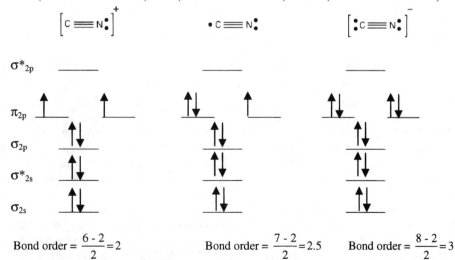

Bond order = $\dfrac{6-2}{2} = 2$ Bond order = $\dfrac{7-2}{2} = 2.5$ Bond order = $\dfrac{8-2}{2} = 3$

According to Lewis theory the CN^- ion would be the most stable because it completes the octet on both atoms, The other two (CN^+ and CN) have an incomplete octet on C.

According to molecular orbital theory, the CN^- ion would be the most stable because it has the highest bond order, 3. The other two species would also exist but would be less stable.

91. BrF (14 valence electrons)

no central atom, no hybridization, no electron structure

BrF_2^- (22 valence electrons)

Five electron pairs on the central atom, electron geometry is trigonal bipyramidal, two bonding pairs and three lone pairs gives a linear molecular geometry. An electron geometry of trigonal bipyramidal has sp^3d hybridization.

BrF_3 (28 valence electrons)

Five electron pairs on the central atom, electron geometry is trigonal bipyramidal, three bonding pairs and two lone pairs gives a T – shaped molecular geometry. An electron geometry of trigonal bipyramidal has sp^3d hybridization.

BrF_4^- (36 valence electrons)

Six electron pairs on the central atom, electron geometry is octahedral, four bonding pairs and two lone pairs gives a square planar molecular geometry. An electron geometry of octahedral has sp^3d^2 hybridization.

BrF_5(42 valence electrons)

Six electron pairs on the central atom, electron geometry is octahedral, five bonding pairs and one lone pair gives a square pyramidal molecular geometry. An electron geometry of octahedral has sp^3d^2 hybridization.

92. Write the Lewis structure:

C – 1 and C – 3 each have 3 pair of electrons and a trigonal planar structure giving sp^2 hybridization on the C with a p orbital left for the π bond. C – 2 has 2 pair of electrons and is linear which gives sp hybridization and 2 p orbitals left for the π bonds. According to valence bond theory, the π bonds are formed by the sideways overlap of p orbitals. Since the remaining p orbitals on C – 2 are perpendicular to each other, the π bonds formed between C – 1 and C – 2 and between C – 2 and C – 3 must also be perpendicular to each other. Therefore, the two trigonal planar structures at C –1 and C – 3 will be perpendicular to each other.

93. According to valence bond theory, CH_4, NH_3, and H_2O are all sp^3 hybridized. This hybridization results in a tetrahedral electron group configuration with a 109.5° bond angle. NH_3 and H_2O deviate from this idealized bond angle because their lone electron pairs exist in their own sp^3 orbitals. The presence of lone pairs lowers the tendency for the central atom's orbitals to hybridize. As a result, as lone pairs are added, the bond angle moves further from the 109.5° hybrid angle to the 90° unhybridized angle.

94. Using the MO diagram for H_2O assign the 8 valence electrons to the molecular orbitals. Start with the lowest energy orbital first and follow Hund's rule.

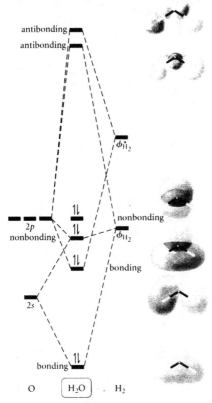

Bond order $= \dfrac{4 - 0}{2} = 2$

With a bond order of 2, the molecule is stable.

95. Using the MO diagram for NH_3 assign the 8 valence electrons to the molecular orbitals. Start with the lowest energy orbital first and follow Hund's rule.

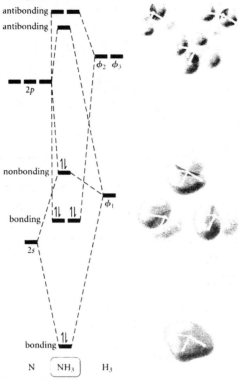

Bond order = $\dfrac{6-0}{2} = 3$

With a bond order of 3 the molecule is stable.

96. a) In the isomerization, you need to break the C – C π bond but not the σ bond. So the energy needed would be the difference between the bond energy of a C = C bond and a C – C bond.

C = C   611 kJ/mol
C – C   347 kJ/mol

Therefore, the energy needed to break the π bond would be 264 kJ/mol = 2.64×10^5 J/mol

$$\frac{264 \text{ kJ}}{\text{mol}} \times \frac{1000 \text{ J}}{\text{kJ}} \times \frac{\text{mol}}{6.022 \times 10^{23} \text{ molecules}} = 4.38 \times 10^{-19} \frac{\text{J}}{\text{molecule}}$$

b) **Given:** 4.38×10^{-19} J/ molecule   **Find:** ν and part of the spectrum
Conceptual Plan: $E \rightarrow \nu$

$$E = h\nu$$

Solution: $\nu = \dfrac{E}{h} = \dfrac{4.38 \times 10^{-19} \text{ J}}{6.62 \times 10^{-34} \text{ Js}} = 6.62 \times 10^{14} \text{ s}^{-1}$

This frequency is right near the border of the ultraviolet – visible region of the electromagnetic spectrum.

97. Write the Lewis structure for :
Determine electron pair geometry around each central atom:
Determine the molecular geometry, determine idealized bond angles and predict actual bond angles:
NO_2

:Ö — N̈ = Ö:

2 bonding pair and a lone electron gives trigonal planar electron geometry, the molecular geometry will be bent. Trigonal planar electron geometry has idealized bond angles of 120°. The bond angle is expected to be slightly less than 120° because of the lone electron occupying the third sp^2 orbital.

NO_2^+

$$\left[\ddot{O} = N = \ddot{O}\right]^+$$

Two bonding pair of electrons and no lone pair gives linear electron geometry and molecular geometry. Linear electron geometry has a bond angle of $180°$.

NO_2^-

$$\left[:\ddot{O} - \ddot{N} = \ddot{O}\right]^-$$

Two bonding pair of electrons and one lone pair gives trigonal planar electron geometry, the molecular geometry will be bent.

Trigonal planar electron geometry has idealized bond angles of $120°$. The bond angle is expected to be less than $120°$ because of the lone pair electrons occupying the third sp^2 orbital. Further, the bond angle should be less than the bond angle in NO_2 because the presence of lone pairs lowers the tendency for the central atom's orbitals to hybridize. As a result, as lone pairs are added, the bond angle moves further from the $120°$ hybrid angle to the $90°$ unhybridized angle and the two electrons will increase this tendency.

98. As you move down the column from F to Cl to Br to I, the atomic radius of the atoms increases. Because of this, the larger atoms cannot be accommodated with the smaller bond angle. The attached atoms themselves would begin to overlap their orbitals. So, as the size of the attached atom increases, the bond angle becomes larger, approaching the hybridized $109.5°$ angle.

99. Statement a is the best statement.
Statement b neglects the lowering of potential energy that arises from the interaction of the lone pair electrons with the bonding electrons.
Statement c neglects the interaction of the electrons altogether. The bonds form to accommodate the electrons, not the other way around.

100. A molecule with four bond groups and one lone pair would need 5 equivalent positions around the central atom. In two dimensions, this could be accommodated with a pentagon shape around the central atom. The idealized bond angles would be $108°$; however, because of the lone pair occupying one of the positions, the bond angles would be less than $108°$

101. In Lewis theory, a covalent bond comes from the sharing of electrons.
A single bond shares 2 electrons (one pair)
A double bond shares 4 electrons (two pair)
A triple bond shares 6 electrons (three pair)

In valence bond theory, a covalent bond forms when orbitals overlap. The orbitals can be unhybridzed or hybridized orbitals.
A single bond forms when a σ bond is formed from the overlap of an s orbital with an s orbital, an s orbital with a p orbital or a p orbital and a p orbital overlapping end to end.
A double bond is a combination of a σ bond and a π bond. The π bond forms from the sideways overlap of a p orbital on each of the atoms involved in the bond. The p orbitals must have the same orientation
A triple bond is a combination of a σ bond and a 2π bonds. The π bonds form from the sideways overlap of a p orbital on each of the atoms involved in the bond. The p orbitals must have the same orientation so each π bond is formed from a different set of p orbitals.

In molecular orbital theory, molecular orbitals form. These are combinations of the atomic orbitals of the atoms involved in the bond. The bonds form when the valence electrons occupy more bonding molecular orbitals than antibonding molecular orbitals. This is calculated by the bond order.
A single bond, has a bond order of 1
A double bond, has a bond order of 2
A triple bond, has a bond order of 3

102. In period 2, the atoms are smaller and they do not have d orbitals available to hybridize, so they cannot accommodate as many atoms around the central atom. In order to complete the octet of electrons multiple bonds must form. In the period 3 and higher atoms, more atoms can surround the central atom and the d orbitals can hybridize with the s and p orbitals. There are now, more orbitals available to overlap, and there is space for them to do so. The central atom, therefore, can attain a stable configuration of eight or more electrons without having to multiple bond.

Chapter 11
Liquids, Solids, and Intermolecular Forces

1. The key to the gecko's sticky feet lies in the millions of microhairs, called setae, that line its toes. Each seta is between 30 and 130 μm long and branches out to end in several hundred flattened tips called spatula. This unique structure allows the gecko's toes to have unusually close contact with the surfaces it climbs. The close contact allows intermolecular forces—which are significant only at short distances—to hold the gecko to the wall.

2. Intermolecular forces are important because they are the forces that hold many liquids and solids—such as water and ice, for example—together. All living organisms depend on intermolecular forces for many physiological processes. Intermolecular forces are responsible for the very existence of the condensed phases.

3. The main properties of liquids are that: liquids have much higher densities in comparison to gases and generally have lower densities in comparison to solids; liquids have an indefinite shape and assume the shape of their container; liquids have a definite volume; and liquids are not easily compressed.

4. The main properties of solids are that: solids have much higher densities in comparison to gases, and usually higher densities than liquids; solids have a definite shape; they do not assume the shape of their container; solids have a definite volume; they are not easily compressed; and solids may be crystalline (ordered) or amorphous (disordered).

5. Solids may be crystalline, in which case the atoms or molecules that compose them are arranged in a well-ordered three-dimensional array, or they may be amorphous, in which case the atoms or molecules that compose them have no long-range order.

6. One phase of matter can be transformed to another by changing the temperature, pressure, or both. A liquid can be converted to a gas by heating; and a gas can be condensed into a liquid by cooling. In general, increases in pressure favor the denser phase, so increasing the pressure of a gas sample results in a transition to the liquid phase. A solid can be converted to a liquid by heating, and a liquid can be converted to a solid by cooling. In general, increases in pressure favor the denser phase (since atoms are pushed closer together), so increasing the pressure of most liquids results in a transition to the solid phase.

7. Since there is the most molecular motion in the gas phase and the least molecular motion in the solid phase (since atoms are pushed closer together), a substance will be converted from a solid then to a liquid and finally to a gas as the temperature increases. The strength of the intermolecular interactions is least in the gas phase, since there are large distances between particles and they are moving very fast. Intermolecular forces are the strongest in liquids and solids, where molecules are "touching" one another. The strength of the interactions in the condensed phases will determine at what temperature the substance will melt and boil.

8. Intermolecular forces originate from the interactions between charges, partial charges, and temporary charges on molecules (or atoms and ions), much as bonding forces originate from interactions between charged particles in atoms.

9. Intermolecular forces, even the strongest ones, are generally much weaker than bonding forces. The reason for the relative weakness of intermolecular forces compared to bonding forces is also related to Coulomb's law $\left(E = \dfrac{1}{4\pi\varepsilon_o} \dfrac{q_1 q_2}{r} \right)$. Bonding forces are the result of large charges (the charges on protons and electrons) interacting at very close distances. Intermolecular forces are the result of smaller charges (as we shall see in the following discussion) interacting at greater distances.

10. Dispersion forces (also called London forces) are the result of fluctuations in the electron distribution within molecules or atoms. Since all atoms and molecules have electrons, they all exhibit dispersion forces. The electrons in an atom or molecule may, at any one instant, be unevenly distributed.

The magnitude of the dispersion force depends on how easily the electrons in the atom or molecule can move or polarize in response to an instantaneous dipole, which in turn depends on the size (or volume) of the electron cloud. A larger electron cloud results in a greater dispersion force because the electrons are held less tightly by the nucleus and can therefore polarize more easily. If all other variables are constant, the dispersion force increases with increasing molar mass because molecules or atoms of higher molar mass generally have more electrons dispersed over a greater volume. The shape of the molecules can also affect the magnitude of the dispersion forces. The larger the area of interaction between two molecules, the larger the dispersion forces.

11. The dipole-dipole force exists in all molecules that are polar. Polar molecules have permanent dipoles that interact with the permanent dipoles of neighboring molecules. The positive end of one permanent dipole is attracted to the negative end of another; this attraction is the dipole-dipole force.

12. Miscibility is the ability to mix without separating into two phases. In general, polar liquids are miscible with other polar liquids, but are not miscible with non-polar liquids. Non-polar liquids are miscible with other non-polar liquids.

13. The hydrogen bond is a sort of super dipole-dipole force. Polar molecules containing hydrogen atoms bonded directly to fluorine, oxygen, or nitrogen exhibit an intermolecular force called hydrogen bonding. The large electronegativity difference between hydrogen and these electronegative elements means that the H atoms will have fairly large partial positive charges (δ+), while the F, O, or N atoms will have fairly large partial negative charges (δ-). In addition, since these atoms are all are quite small, they can approach one another very closely. The result is a strong attraction between the hydrogen in each of these molecules and the F, O, or N on its neighbors, an attraction called a hydrogen bond.

14. The ion-dipole force occurs when an ionic compound is mixed with a polar compound and is especially important in aqueous solutions of ionic compounds. For example, when sodium chloride is mixed with water, the sodium and chloride ions interact with water molecules via ion-dipole forces. Notice that the positive sodium ions interact with the negative poles of water molecules, while the negative chloride ions interact with the positive poles. Ion-dipole forces are the strongest of the types of intermolecular forces discussed here and are responsible for the ability of ionic substances to form solutions with water.

15. Surface tension is the tendency of liquids to minimize their surface area. Molecules at the surface have relatively fewer neighbors with which to interact, because there are no molecules above it. Consequently, molecules at the surface are inherently less stable—they have higher potential energy—than those in the interior. In order to increase the surface area of the liquid, some molecules from the interior have to be moved to the surface, a process requiring energy. The surface tension of a liquid is the energy required to increase the surface area by a unit amount. Surface tension decreases with decreasing intermolecular forces.

16. Viscosity is the resistance of a liquid to flow. Viscosity is measured in a unit called the poise (P), defined as 1 g/cm·s. The centipoise (cP) is a convenient unit because the viscosity of water at room temperature is approximately one centipoise. Viscosity is greater in substances with stronger intermolecular forces because molecules are more strongly attracted to each other, preventing them from flowing around each other as freely. Viscosity also depends on molecular shape, increasing in longer molecules that can interact over a greater area and possibly become entangled. Viscosity increases with increasing molar mass (and therefore increasing magnitude of dispersion forces) and with increasing length (and therefore increasing potential for molecular entanglement). Viscosity also depends on temperature because thermal energy partially overcomes the intermolecular forces, allowing molecules to flow past each other more easily.

17. Capillary action is the ability of a liquid to flow against gravity up a narrow tube. Capillary action results from a combination of two forces: the attraction between molecules in a liquid, called cohesive forces, and the attraction between these molecules and the surface of the tube, called adhesive forces. The adhesive forces cause the liquid to spread out over the surface of the tube, while the cohesive forces cause the liquid to stay together. If the adhesive forces are greater than the cohesive forces (as is the case for water in a glass tube), the attraction to the surface draws the liquid up the tube while the cohesive forces pull along those molecules not in direct contact with the tube walls. The water rises up the tube until the force of gravity balances the capillary action—the thinner the tube, the higher the rise. If the adhesive forces are smaller than the cohesive forces (as is the case for liquid mercury), the liquid does not rise up the tube at all (and in fact will drop to a level below the level of the surrounding liquid).

18. Molecules are in constant motion due to thermal energy. The higher the temperature, the greater the average energy of the collection of molecules. However, at any one time, some molecules will have more thermal energy than the average and some will have less. The molecules with the highest thermal energy have enough energy to break free from the surface—where molecules are held less tightly than in the interior due to fewer neighbor-neighbor interactions—and into the gas phase. This process is called vaporization, the phase transition from liquid to gas. Some of the water molecules in the gas phase, at the low end of the energy distribution curve for the gaseous molecules, can plunge back into the liquid and be captured by intermolecular forces. This process—the opposite of vaporization—is called condensation, the phase transition from gas to liquid.

19. The molecules that leave the liquid are the ones at the high end of the energy curve—the most energetic. If no additional heat enters the liquid, the average energy of the entire collection of molecules goes down—much as the class average on an exam goes down if you eliminate the highest-scoring students. So vaporization is an endothermic process; it takes energy to vaporize the molecules in a liquid. Also, vaporization requires overcoming the intermolecular forces that hold liquids together. Since energy must be absorbed to pull the molecules apart, the process is endothermic. Condensation is the opposite process, so it must be exothermic. Also, gas particles have more energy than those in the liquid. It is the least energetic of these that condense, adding energy to the liquid.

20. The weaker the intermolecular forces, the more molecules to are allowed to evaporate at a given temperature, making the liquid more volatile.

21. The heat of vaporization (ΔH_{vap}) is the amount of heat required to vaporize one mole of a liquid to a gas. The heat of vaporization of a liquid can be used to calculate the amount of heat energy required to vaporize a given mass of the liquid (or the amount of heat given off by the condensation of a given mass of liquid), and to compare the volatility of two substances.

22. Molecules are in constant motion. Molecules leave the liquid for the gas phase and gas phase molecules condense to become a liquid. Dynamic equilibrium has been reached when the rate of condensation and the rate of vaporization become equal. Although condensation and vaporization continue, at equal rates, the concentration of water vapor above the liquid is constant. The pressure of a gas in dynamic equilibrium with its liquid is called its vapor pressure.

23. When a system in dynamic equilibrium is disturbed, the system responds so as to minimize the disturbance and return to a state of equilibrium.

24. The vapor pressure of a liquid increases with increasing temperature. However, the relationship is not linear, but rather, it is exponential. As the temperature of a liquid increases the vapor increases more and more quickly. As the temperature is decreased, the vapor pressure decreases following this same relationship.

25. The boiling point of a liquid is the temperature at which its vapor pressure equals the external pressure. The normal boiling point of a liquid is the temperature at which its vapor pressure equals 1 atm.

26. The Clausius-Clapeyron Equation is the relationship between vapor pressure and temperature. It can be expressed as: $\ln P_{vap} = \dfrac{-\Delta H_{vap}}{R}\left(\dfrac{1}{T}\right) + \ln \beta$. In this expression P_{vap} is the vapor pressure, ß is a constant that depends on the gas, ΔH_{vap} is the heat of vaporization, R is the gas constant (8.314 J/mol K), and T is the temperature in kelvins. The Clausius-Clapeyron equation gives a linear relationship—not between the vapor pressure and the temperature (which have an exponential relationship)—but between the natural log of the vapor pressure and the inverse of temperature. The Clausius-Claperyon equation leads to a convenient way to measure the heat of vaporization in the laboratory; or to calculate the vapor pressure of a liquid at a temperature (if the heat of vaporization and a vapor pressure at one temperature are known).

27. As the temperature rises, more liquid vaporizes and the pressure within the container increases. As more and more gas is forced into the same amount of space, the density of the gas becomes higher and higher. At the same time, the increasing temperature causes the density of the liquid to become lower and lower. At the critical temperature, the meniscus between the liquid and gas disappears and the gas and liquid phases commingle to form a supercritical fluid.

28. Sublimation is the phase transition from solid to gas, without going through a liquid phase. A common example of sublimation is the carbon dioxide, where "dry ice" converts from a solid to a gas, without going through a "wet" (or liquid) phase.

29. Fusion, or melting, is the phase transition from solid to liquid. The term fusion is used for melting because, if you heat several crystals of a solid, they will fuse into a continuous liquid upon melting. Fusion is endothermic because solids have less kinetic energy than liquids, so energy must be added to the solid.

30. The heat of fusion (ΔH_{fus}) is the amount of heat required to melt 1 mol of a solid. The heat of fusion of a solid can be used to calculate the amount of heat energy required to melt a given mass of the solid (or the amount of heat given off by the freezing of a given mass of liquid).

31. There are two horizontal lines (i.e. heat is added, but the temperature stays constant) in the heating curve because there are two endothermic phase changes. The heat that is added is used to change the phase from solid to liquid or liquid to gas.

32. The slopes indicate how much heat is necessary to increase the temperature of the sample. The slope is proportional to $1/C_s$ (the specific heat capacity of the phase). The amount of molecular motion and the amount of intermolecular interactions is different in each phase, and so the specific heat capacity and the slope is different for each phase.

33. A phase diagram is simply a map of the phase of a substance as a function of pressure (on the y-axis) and temperature (on the x-axis).

34. When a line is crossed in a phase diagram it means that a phase transition has occurred.

35. Water has a low molar mass (18.01 g/mol), yet it is a liquid at room temperature. Water's high boiling point for its molar mass can be understood by examining the structure of the water molecule. The bent geometry of the water molecule and the highly polar nature of the O–H bonds result in a molecule with a significant dipole moment. Water's two O–H bonds (hydrogen directly bonded to oxygen) allow a water molecule to form strong hydrogen bonds with four other water molecules, resulting in a relatively high boiling point. Water's high polarity also allows it to dissolve many other polar and ionic compounds, and even a number of nonpolar gases such as oxygen and carbon dioxide (by inducing a dipole moment in their molecules). Water has an exceptionally high specific heat capacity. One significant difference between the phase diagram of water and that of other substances is that the fusion curve for water has a negative slope. The fusion curve within the phase diagrams for most substances has a positive slope because increasing pressure favors the denser phase, which for most substances is the solid phase. This negative slope means that ice is less dense than liquid water and so ice floats. The solids sink in the liquids of most other substances.

36. X-ray crystallography is used to examine the structure of crystalline materials (materials that have an ordered array of atoms). The technique is based on the wave nature of x-rays. Atoms within crystal structures have spacings between them on the order of 10^2 pm,. When light of similar wavelength (which happens to fall in the X-ray region of the electromagnetic spectrum) interacts with a sample the waves are diffracted by the atoms. The waves interact with each other to either constructively (the reinforce each

other) or destructively (they cancel each other) interfere to form interference patterns or diffraction patterns. The exact pattern of diffraction reveals the spacings between planes of atoms. How the waves interact is dependent on the path that the waves take. Consider two planes of atoms within a crystalline lattice separated by a distance d, as shown in Figure 11.42. If two rays of light with wavelength λ that are initially in phase (that is, the crests of one wave are aligned with the crests of the other) diffract from the two layers, the diffracted rays may interfere with each other constructively or destructively, depending on the difference between the path lengths traveled by each ray. If the difference between the two path lengths ($2a$) is an integral number (n) of wavelengths, then the interference will be constructive or $n\lambda=2a$. Using trigonometry, we can see that the angle of reflection (θ) is related to the distance a and the separation between layers (d) by the following relation: $\sin\theta = a/d$. Rearranging and substituting into $n\lambda=2a$, we get: $n\lambda = 2\,d\sin\theta$, known as Bragg's law. For a given wavelength of light incident on atoms arranged in layers, we can then measure the angle that produces constructive interference (which appears as a bright spot on the X-ray diffraction pattern) and then compute d, the distance between the atomic layers.

37. A crystalline lattice is the regular arrangements of atoms within a crystalline solid. The crystalline lattice can be represented by a small collection of atoms, ions, or molecules a fundamental building block called the unit cell. When the unit cell is repeated over and over—like the tiles of a floor or the pattern in a wallpaper design, but in three dimensions—the entire lattice can be reproduced.

38.

Cubic Cell Name   Structure

Simple Cubic

Body-centered Cubic

Face-centered Cubic

39. Atoms in a simple cubic cell structure have a coordination number of 6, an edge length of 2r, and 1 atom in the unit cell. Atoms in a body-centered cubic cell structure have a coordination number of 8, an edge length of $4r/\sqrt{3}$, and 2 atoms in the unit cell. Atoms in a face-centered cubic cell structure have a coordination number of 12, an edge length of $2\sqrt{2}r$, and 4 atoms in the unit cell.

40. In hexagonal closest packing, the third layer of atoms aligns exactly on top of the first. The pattern from one layer to the next is ABAB... with alternating layers aligning exactly on top of one another. The unit cell for this crystal structure is not a cubic unit cell, but a hexagonal one, as shown in Figure 11.48. In cubic closest packing, the third layer of atoms is offset from the first. The pattern from one layer to the next is ABCABC....with every fourth layer aligning with the first. The unit cell for this crystal structure is the face-centered cubic unit cell.

41. The three types of solids are molecular solids, ionic solids and atomic solids. Molecular solids are those solids whose composite units are molecules. The lattice sites in a crystalline molecular solid are therefore occupied by molecules. Ice (solid H_2O) and dry ice (solid CO_2) are examples of molecular solids. Molecular solids are held together by the kinds of intermolecular forces—dispersion forces, dipole-dipole forces, and hydrogen bonding. Ionic solids are those solids whose composite units are ions. Table salt (NaCl) and calcium fluoride (CaF_2) are good examples of ionic solids. Ionic solids are held together by the coulombic interactions that occur between the cations and anions occupying the lattice sites in the crystal. Atomic Solids are those solids whose composite units are individual atoms are called atomic solids. Atomic solids can themselves be divided into three categories—nonbonding atomic solids, metallic atomic solids,

and network covalent atomic solids—each held together by a different kind of force. Nonbonding atomic solids, which include only the noble gases in their solid form, are held together by relatively weak dispersion forces. Metallic atomic solids, such as iron or gold, are held together by metallic bonds, which in the simplest model are represented by the interaction of metal cations with a sea of electrons that surround them. Network covalent atomic solids, such as diamond, graphite, and silicon dioxide, are held together by covalent bonds.

42. The coordination number of the unit cell for an ionic compound represents the number of close cation-anion interactions. Since these interactions lower potential energy, the crystal structure of a particular ionic compound will be the one that maximizes the coordination number, while accommodating both charge neutrality (each unit cell must be charge neutral) and the different sizes of the cations and anions that compose the particular compound. In general, the more similar the radii of the cation and the anion, the higher the possible coordination number.

43. Cesium chloride (CsCl) is a good example of an ionic compound containing cations and anions of similar size (Cs^+ radius = 167 pm; Cl^- radius = 181 pm). In the cesium chloride structure, the chloride ions occupy the lattice sites of a simple cubic cell and one cesium ion lies in the very center of the cell, as shown in Figure 11.51. Notice that the cesium chloride unit cell contains one chloride anion ($8 \times 1/8 = 1$) and one cesium cation (the cesium ion in the middle belongs entirely to the unit cell) for a ratio of Cs to Cl of 1:1, just as in the formula for the compound.

The crystal structure of sodium chloride must accommodate the more disproportionate sizes of Na^+ (radius = 97 pm) and Cl^- (radius = 181 pm). The larger chloride anion could theoretically fit many of the smaller sodium cations around it, but charge neutrality requires that each sodium cation be surrounded by an equal number of chloride anions. The structure that minimizes the energy is shown in Figure 11.52 and has a coordination number of 6 (each chloride anion is surrounded by six sodium cations and vice versa). You can visualize this structure, called the rock salt structure, as chloride anions occupying the lattice sites of a face-centered cubic structure with the smaller sodium cations occupying the holes between the anions. (Alternatively, you can visualize this structure as the sodium cations occupying the lattice sites of a face-centered cubic structure with the larger chloride anions occupying the spaces between the cations.) Each unit cell contains four chloride anions ($[8 \times 1/8] + [6 \times 1/2] = 4$) and four sodium cations ($12 \times 1/4$) resulting in a ratio of 1:1, just as in the formula of the compound.

You can visualize this structure, called the zinc blende structure, as sulfide anions occupying the lattice sites of a face-centered cubic structure with the smaller zinc cations occupying four of the eight tetrahedral holes located directly beneath each corner atom. A tetrahedral hole is the empty space that lies in the center of a tetrahedral arrangement of four atoms, as shown below. Each unit cell contains four sulfide anions ($[8 \times 1/8] + [6 \times 1/2] = 4$) and four zinc cations (each of the four zinc cations is completely contained within the unit cell), resulting in a ratio of 1:1, just as in the formula of the compound.

44. The fluorite (CaF_2) structure shown in Figure 11.54. You can visualize this structure as calcium cations occupying the lattice sites of a face-centered cubic structure with the larger fluoride anions occupying all eight of the tetrahedral holes located directly beneath each corner atom. Each unit cell contains four calcium cations ($[8 \times 1/8] + [6 \times 1/2] = 4$) and eight fluoride anions (each of the eight fluoride anions is completely contained within the unit cell), resulting in a cation to anion ratio of 1:2, just as in the formula of the compound.

45. Atomic Solids can themselves be divided into three categories—nonbonding atomic solids, metallic atomic solids, and network covalent atomic solids. Nonbonding atomic solids, which include only the noble gases in their solid form, are held together by relatively weak dispersion forces. Metallic atomic solids, such as iron or gold, are held together by metallic bonds, which in the simplest model are represented by the interaction of metal cations with a sea of electrons that surround them. Network covalent atomic solids, such as diamond, graphite, and silicon dioxide, are held together by covalent bonds.

46. In band theory, bands are the combination atomic orbitals of the atoms within a solid crystal to form orbitals that are not localized on individual atoms, but delocalized over the entire crystal. In band theory, electrons become mobile when they make a transition from the highest occupied molecular orbital into higher-energy empty molecular orbitals. For this reason, the occupied molecular orbitals are often called the valence band and the unoccupied orbitals are called the conduction band.

47. The band gap is an energy gap that exists between the valence band and conduction band. In metals, the valence band and conduction band are always energetically continuous—the energy difference between the top of the valence band and the bottom of the conduction band is infinitesimally small. In semiconductors, the band gap is small, allowing some electrons to be promoted at ordinary temperatures resulting in limited conductivity. In insulators, the band gap is large, and electrons are not promoted into the conduction band at ordinary temperatures, resulting in no electrical conductivity.

48. Doped semiconductors contain minute amounts of impurities that result in additional electrons in the conduction band or electron "holes" in the valence band. For example, silicon is a group 4A semiconductor. Its valence electrons just fill its valence band. When silicon is doped with phosphorus, a group 5A element with five valence electrons, its conductivity increases. The phosphorus atoms are incorporated into the silicon crystal structure, but each phosphorus atom brings with it one additional electron. Since the valence band is completely full, the additional electrons must go into the conduction band. These electrons are then mobile and can conduct electrical current. This type of semiconductor is called an n-type semiconductor because the charge carriers are negatively charged electrons in the conduction band. Silicon can also be doped with a group 3A element, such as gallium, which has only three valence electrons. When gallium is incorporated into the silicon crystal structure, it results in electron "holes," empty molecular orbitals in the valence band. The presence of holes also allows for the movement of electrical current because electrons in the valence band can move between holes. In this way, the holes move in the opposite direction as the electrons. This type of semiconductor is called p-type semiconductor because the hole acts as a positive charge.

49. a) dispersion forces

    b) dispersion forces and dipole-dipole forces

    c) dispersion forces

    d) dispersion forces, dipole-dipole forces and hydrogen bonding

    e) dispersion forces

    f) dispersion forces, dipole-dipole forces and hydrogen bonding

    g) dispersion forces and dipole-dipole forces

    h) dispersion forces

50. a) dispersion forces and dipole-dipole forces

    b) dispersion forces, dipole-dipole forces and hydrogen bonding

    c) dispersion forces

    d) dispersion forces

    e) dispersion forces and dipole-dipole forces

    f) dispersion forces and dipole-dipole forces

    g) dispersion forces, dipole-dipole forces and hydrogen bonding

    h) dispersion forces

51. a) CH_4 < b) CH_3CH_3 < c) CH_3CH_2Cl < d) CH_3CH_2OH. The first two molecules only exhibit dispersion forces, so the boiling point increases with increasing molar mass. The third molecule also exhibits dipole-dipole forces, which are stronger than dispersion forces. The last molecule exhibits hydrogen bonding. Since these are the strongest intermolecular forces in this group, the last molecule has the highest boiling point.

52. a) H_2S < b) H_2Se < c) H_2O The first two molecules only exhibit dispersion forces and dipole-dipole forces, so the boiling point increases with increasing molar mass. The third molecule also exhibits hydrogen bonding. Since these are the strongest intermolecular forces in this group, the last molecule has the highest boiling point.

53. a) CH_3OH has the higher boiling point since it exhibits hydrogen bonding.

    b) CH_3CH_2OH has the higher boiling point since it exhibits hydrogen bonding.

    c) CH_3CH_3 has the higher boiling point since it has the larger molar mass.

54. a) NH_3 has the higher boiling point since it exhibits hydrogen bonding.

    b) CS_2 has the higher boiling point since it has the larger molar mass.

    c) NO_2 has the higher boiling point since it exhibits dipole-dipole forces.

55. a) Br_2 has the higher vapor pressure since it has the smaller molar mass.

    b) H_2S has the higher vapor pressure since it does not exhibit hydrogen bonding.

    c) PH_3 has the higher vapor pressure since it does not exhibit hydrogen bonding.

56. a) CH_4 has the higher vapor pressure since it has the smaller molar mass and it does not exhibit dipole-dipole forces.
    b) CH_3OH has the higher vapor pressure since it has the smaller molar mass, since both exhibit hydrogen bonding.
    c) H_2CO has the higher vapor pressure since it has the smaller molar mass and it does not exhibit hydrogen bonding.

57. a) This will not form a homogeneous solution, since one is polar and one is nonpolar.

    b) This will form a homogeneous solution. There will be ion-dipole interactions between the K^+ and Cl^- ions and the water molecules. There will also be dispersion forces, dipole-dipole forces and hydrogen bonding between the water molecules.

    c) This will form a homogeneous solution. There will be dispersion forces present.

    d) This will form a homogeneous solution. There will be dispersion forces, dipole-dipole forces and hydrogen bonding.

58. a) This will form a homogeneous solution. There will be dispersion forces present.

    b) This will not form a homogeneous solution, since one is polar and one is nonpolar.

    c) This will form a homogeneous solution. There will be ion-dipole interactions between the Li^+ and NO_3^- ions and the water molecules. There will also be dispersion forces, dipole-dipole forces and hydrogen bonding between the water molecules.

    d) This will not form a homogeneous solution, since one is polar and one is nonpolar.

59. Water will have the higher surface tension since it exhibits hydrogen bonding, a strong intermolecular force. Acetone can not form hydrogen bonds.

60. a) Water "wets" surfaces that are capable of dipole-dipole interactions. The water will form strong adhesive forces with the surface when these dipole-dipole forces are present and so the water will spread to cover as much of the surface as possible. Water does not experience strong intermolecular forces with oil and other nonpolar surfaces. The water will bead up, maximizing the cohesive interactions, which involve strong hydrogen bonds. So water will bead up on surfaces that can only exhibit dispersion forces.

b) Mercury will bead up on surfaces since it is not capable of forming strong intermolecular interactions (only dispersion forces).

61. Compound A will have the higher viscosity since it can interact with other molecules along the entire molecule, not just at a single point. Also the molecule is very flexible and the molecules can get tangled with each other.

62. Multigrade oils contain polymers (long molecules made up of repeating structural units) that coil at low temperatures but unwind at high temperatures. At low temperatures, the coiled polymers—because of their compact shape—do not contribute very much to the viscosity of the oil. As the temperature increases, however, the molecules unwind and their long shape results in intermolecular forces and molecular entanglements that prevent the viscosity from decreasing as much as it would normally. The result is an oil whose viscosity is less temperature-dependent than it would be otherwise, allowing the same oil to be used over a wider range of temperatures.

63. In a clean glass tube the water can generate strong adhesive interactions with the glass (due to the dipoles at the surface of the glass). Water experiences adhesive forces with glass that are stronger than its cohesive forces, causing it to climb the surface of a glass tube. When grease or oil coats the glass this interferes with the formation of these adhesive interactions with the glass, since oils are nonpolar and cannot interact strongly with the dipoles in the water. Without these experiencing these strong intermolecular forces with oil, the water's cohesive forces will be greater and it will be drawn away from the surface of the tube.

64. Water can generate strong adhesive interactions with the glass (due to the dipoles at the surface of the glass), but hexane is nonpolar and cannot interact strongly with the glass surface.

65. The water in the 12 cm diameter beaker will evaporate more quickly because there is more surface area for the molecules to evaporate from. The vapor pressure will be the same in the two containers because the vapor pressure is the pressure of the gas when it is in dynamic equilibrium with the liquid (evaporation rate = condensation rate). The vapor pressure is dependent only on the substance and the temperature. The 12 cm diameter container will reach this dynamic equilibrium faster.

66. The acetone will evaporate more quickly since it is not capable of forming hydrogen bonds, so the intermolecular forces are much weaker. This will also result in a larger vapor pressure at the same temperature as the water.

67. The boiling point and higher heat of vaporizaion of oil is much higher than that of water, so it will not vaporize as quickly as the water. The evaporation of water cools your skin because evaporation is an endothermic process.

68. Water molecules at room temperature have a lower kinetic energy at room temperature than at 100 °C. The heat of vaporization is the energy difference between the molecules in the liquid phase and the gas phase. Since the energy of the liquid is lower at room temperature, then the energy difference that must be overcome to become steam is greater, so the heat of vaporization is greater.

69. **Given:** 955 kJ from candy bar, water d = 1.00 g/ml   **Find:** L(H_2O) vaporized at 100.0 °C

    Other: $\Delta H°_{vap}$ = 40.7 kJ/mol

    Conceptual plan: q → mol H_2O → g H_2O → mL H_2O → L H_2O

$$\frac{1\,mol}{40.7\,kJ} \qquad \frac{18.01\,g}{1\,mol} \qquad \frac{1.00\,mL}{1.00\,g} \qquad \frac{1\,L}{1000\,mL}$$

Solution: $955\,kJ \times \dfrac{1\,mol}{40.7\,kJ} \times \dfrac{18.01\,g}{1\,mol} \times \dfrac{1.00\,mL}{1\,g} \times \dfrac{1\,L}{1000\,mL} = 0.423\,L\,H_2O$

Check: The units (L) are correct. The magnitude of the answer (< 1 L) makes physical sense because we are vaporizing about 20 moles of water.

70. **Given:** 55.0 mL water, d = 1.00 g/ml, heated to 100.0 °C **Find:** heat (kJ) to vaporize at 100.0 °C
    Other: $\Delta H°_{vap}$ = 40.7 kJ/mol
    Conceptual plan: mL H_2O → g H_2O → mol H_2O → q

$$\frac{1.00\ g}{1.00\ mL} \qquad \frac{1\ mol}{18.01\ g} \qquad \frac{40.7\ kJ}{1\ mol}$$

Solution: $55.0\ mL \times \dfrac{1.00\ g}{1.00\ mL} \times \dfrac{1\ mol}{18.01\ g} \times \dfrac{40.7\ kJ}{1\ mol} = 124\ kJ$

Check: The units (kJ) are correct. The magnitude of the answer (124 kJ) makes physical sense because we are vaporizing about 3 moles of water.

71. **Given:** 0.88 g water condenses on iron block 75.0 g at $T_i = 22$ °C **Find:** T_f (iron block)
    Other: $\Delta H°_{vap}$ = 44.0 kJ/mol; C_{Fe} = 0.449 J/g · °C from text
    Conceptual plan: g H_2O → mol H_2O → q_{H2O} (kJ) → q_{H2O} (J) → q_{Fe} then q_{Fe}, m_{Fe}, T_i → T_f

$$\frac{1\ mol}{18.01\ g} \qquad \frac{-44.0\ kJ}{1\ mol} \qquad \frac{1000\ J}{1\ kJ} \qquad -q_{H2O} = q_{Fe} \qquad q = m\ C_s\left(T_f - T_i\right)$$

Solution: $0.88\ g \times \dfrac{1\ mol}{18.01\ g} \times \dfrac{-44.0\ kJ}{1\ mol} \times \dfrac{1000\ J}{1\ kJ} = -2149.92\ J$ then $-q_{H2O} = q_{Fe} = 2149.92\ J$ then

$q = m\ C_s\left(T_f - T_i\right)$ Rearrange to solve for T_f.

$$T_f = \frac{m\ C_s\ T_i + q}{m\ C_s} = \frac{\left(75.0\ g \times 0.449\ \dfrac{J}{g \times °C} \times 22\ °C\right) + 2149.92\ J}{75.0\ g \times 0.449\ \dfrac{J}{g \times °C}} = 86\ °C$$

Check: The units (°C) are correct. The temperature rose, which is consistent with heat being added to the block. The magnitude of the answer (86 °C) makes physical sense because even though we have ~ 1/20 th of a mole, the energy involved in condensation is very large.

72. **Given:** 1.02 g rubbing alcohol (C_3H_8O) evaporated from aluminum block 55.0 g at $T_i = 25$ °C
    Find: T_f (aluminum block)   **Other:** $\Delta H°_{vap}$ = 45.4 kJ/mol; C_{Al} = 0.903 J/g · °C from text
    Conceptual plan:
    g C_3H_8O → mol C_3H_8O → q_{C3H8O} (kJ) → q_{C3H8O} (J) → q_{Al} then q_{Al}, m_{Fe}, T_i → T_f

$$\frac{1\ mol}{60.09\ g} \qquad \frac{-45.4\ kJ}{1\ mol} \qquad \frac{1000\ J}{1\ kJ} \qquad -q_{H2O} = q_{Al} \qquad q = m\ C_s\left(T_f - T_i\right)$$

Solution: $1.02\ g \times \dfrac{1\ mol}{60.09\ g} \times \dfrac{45.4\ kJ}{1\ mol} \times \dfrac{1000\ J}{1\ kJ} = 770.644\ J$ then $-q_{H2O} = q_{Al} = -770.644\ J$ then

$q = m\ C_s\left(T_f - T_i\right)$ Rearrange to solve for T_f.

$$T_f = \frac{m\ C_s\ T_i + q}{m\ C_s} = \frac{\left(55.0\ g \times 0.903\ \dfrac{J}{g \times °C} \times 25\ °C\right) - 770.644\ J}{55.0\ g \times 0.903\ \dfrac{J}{g \times °C}} = 9.5\ °C$$

Check: The units (°C) are correct. The temperature dropped, which is consistent with heat being removed from the block. The magnitude of the answer (9.5 °C) makes physical sense because even though we have only a fraction of a mole, the energy involved in vaporization is very large.

73. **Given:**

Temperature (K)	Vapor Pressure (torr)
200	65.3
210	134.3
220	255.7
230	456.0
235	597.0

Find: $\Delta H°_{vap}$ (NH_3) and normal boiling point

Conceptual Plan: To find the heat of vaporization, use Excel or similar software to make a plot of the natural log of vapor pressure (ln P) as a function of the inverse of the temperature in K (1/T). Then fit the points to a line and determine the slope of the line.   Since the slope = - ΔH_{vap}/R, we find the heat of vaporization as follows:

slope $= -\Delta H_{vap}/R$ → $\Delta H_{vap} = -$ slope $\times R$ then $\;$ J → kJ.

$$\frac{1\text{ kJ}}{1000\text{ J}}$$

For the normal boiling point, use the equation of the best fit line, substitute 760 torr for the pressure and calculate the temperature.

Solution: Data was plotted in Excel.

The slope of the best fitting line is -2969.9 K.

$$\Delta H_{vap} = - slope \; x \; R = -- 2969.9 \text{ K} \; \text{x} \; \frac{8.314 \text{ J}}{\text{K mol}} =$$

$$= \frac{2.46917 \times 10^4 \text{ J}}{\text{mol}} \text{x} \frac{1 \text{ kJ}}{1000 \text{ J}} = 24.7 \frac{\text{kJ}}{\text{mol}}$$

$$\ln P = -2969.9 \text{ K}\left(\frac{1}{T}\right) + 19.036 \;\text{→}$$

$$\ln 760 = -2969.9 \text{ K}\left(\frac{1}{T}\right) + 19.036 \;\text{→}$$

$$2969.9 \text{ K}\left(\frac{1}{T}\right) = 19.036 - 6.63332 \;\text{→}$$

$$T = \frac{2969.9 \text{ K}}{12.40268} = 239 \text{ K}$$

Check: The units (kJ/mol) are correct. The magnitude of the answer (25) is consistent with other values in the text.

74. **Given:**

Temperature (K)	Vapor Pressure (torr)
65	130.5
70	289.5
75	570.8
80	1028
85	1718

Find: $\Delta H°_{vap}$ (N_2) and normal boiling point

Conceptual Plan: To find the heat of vaporization, use Excel or similar software to make a plot of the natural log of vapor pressure (ln P) as a function of the inverse of the temperature in K ($1/T$). Then fit the points to a line and determine the slope of the line. Since the slope $= -\Delta H_{vap}/R$, we find the heat of vaporization as follows:

slope $= -\Delta H_{vap}/R$ → $\Delta H_{vap} = -$ slope $\times R$ then $\;$ J → kJ.

$$\frac{1\text{ kJ}}{1000\text{ J}}$$

For the normal boiling point, use the equation of the best fit line, substitute 760 torr for the pressure and calculate the temperature.

Solution: Data was plotted in Excel.

The slope of the best fitting line is -711.98 K.

$$\Delta H_{vap} = - slope \; x \; R = -- 711.98 \text{ K} \; \text{x} \; \frac{8.314 \text{ J}}{\text{K mol}} =$$

$$= \frac{5.91940 \times 10^3 \text{ J}}{\text{mol}} \text{x} \frac{1 \text{ kJ}}{1000 \text{ J}} = 5.92 \frac{\text{kJ}}{\text{mol}}$$

$$\ln P = -711.98 \text{ K}\left(\frac{1}{T}\right) + 15.833 \;\text{→}$$

$$\ln 760 = -711.98 \text{ K}\left(\frac{1}{T}\right) + 15.833 \;\text{→}$$

$$711.98 \text{ K}\left(\frac{1}{T}\right) = 15.833 - 6.63332 \;\text{→}$$

$$T = \frac{711.98 \text{ K}}{9.19968} = 77.4 \text{ K}$$

Check: The units (kJ/mol) are correct. The magnitude of the answer (6) is lower than other values quoted in the text. This is consistent with the fact that nitrogen boils at such a low temperature.

75. Given: ethanol, $\Delta H^\circ_{vap} = 38.56$ kJ/mol; normal boiling point = 78.4 °C **Find:** $P_{Ethanol}$ at 15 °C

Conceptual plan: °C → K and kJ → J then ΔH°_{vap}, T_1, P_1, T_2 → P_2

$$K = °C + 273.15 \qquad \frac{1000\ J}{1\ kJ} \qquad \ln\frac{P_2}{P_1} = \frac{-\Delta H_{vap}}{R}\left(\frac{1}{T_2} - \frac{1}{T_1}\right)$$

Solution: $T_1 = 78.4\ °C + 273.15 = 351.6$ K; $T_2 = 15\ °C + 273.15 = 288$ K;

$$\frac{38.56\ kJ}{mol} \times \frac{1000\ J}{1\ kJ} = 3.856 \times 10^4\ \frac{J}{mol} \qquad P_1 = 760\ torr \qquad \ln\frac{P_2}{P_1} = \frac{-\Delta H_{vap}}{R}\left(\frac{1}{T_2} - \frac{1}{T_1}\right)$$ Substitute values in

equation. $\ln\dfrac{P_2}{760\ torr} = \dfrac{-3.856 \times 10^4\ \frac{J}{mol}}{8.314\ \frac{J}{K\ mol}}\left(\dfrac{1}{288\ K} - \dfrac{1}{351.6\ K}\right) = -2.9\underline{1}302$ →

$$\frac{P_2}{760\ torr} = e^{-2.91302} = 0.05\underline{4}311 \rightarrow P_2 = 0.054311 \times 760\ torr = 41\ torr$$

Check: The units (torr) are correct. Since 15 °C is significantly below the boiling point, we expect the answer to be much less than 760 torr.

76. Given: benzene, $\Delta H^\circ_{vap} = 30.72$ kJ/mol; normal boiling point = 80.1 °C; $P_2 = 445$ torr **Find:** T_2

Conceptual plan: °C → K and kJ → J then ΔH°_{vap}, T_1, P_1, T_2 → P_2

$$K = °C + 273.15 \qquad \frac{1000\ J}{1\ kJ} \qquad \ln\frac{P_2}{P_1} = \frac{-\Delta H_{vap}}{R}\left(\frac{1}{T_2} - \frac{1}{T_1}\right)$$

Solution: $T_1 = 80.1\ °C + 273.15 = 353.3$ K; $\dfrac{30.72\ kJ}{mol} \times \dfrac{1000\ J}{1\ kJ} = 3.072 \times 10^4\ \dfrac{J}{mol}$; $P_1 = 760$ torr;

$P_2 = 445$ torr $\quad \ln\dfrac{P_2}{P_1} = \dfrac{-\Delta H_{vap}}{R}\left(\dfrac{1}{T_2} - \dfrac{1}{T_1}\right)$ Substitute values in equation.

$$\ln\frac{445\ torr}{760\ torr} = \frac{-3.072 \times 10^4\ \frac{J}{mol}}{8.314\ \frac{J}{K\ mol}}\left(\frac{1}{T_2} - \frac{1}{353.3\ K}\right) \rightarrow -0.53\underline{5}244 = -3.69\underline{4}972 \times 10^3\ K\left(\frac{1}{T_2} - 0.0028\underline{3}0456\right)$$

$$\rightarrow \frac{1.4\underline{4}857 \times 10^{-4}}{K} = \left(\frac{1}{T_2} - \frac{0.0028\underline{3}0456}{K}\right) \rightarrow \frac{1}{T_2} = \frac{2.9\underline{7}531 \times 10^{-3}}{K} \rightarrow T_2 = 336.0\underline{9}90\ K = 63\ °C$$

Check: The units (°C) are correct. Since the pressure is over half of 760 torr we expect a temperature a little lower than the boiling point.

77. Given: 47.5 g water freezes **Find:** energy released **Other:** $\Delta H^\circ_{fus} = 6.02$ kJ/mol from text

Conceptual plan: g H_2O → mol H_2O → q_{H2O} (kJ) → q_{H2O} (J)

$$\frac{1\ mol}{18.01\ g} \qquad \frac{-6.02\ kJ}{1\ mol} \qquad \frac{1000\ J}{1\ kJ}$$

Solution: $47.5\ g \times \dfrac{1\ mol}{18.01\ g} \times \dfrac{-6.02\ kJ}{1\ mol} \times \dfrac{1000\ J}{1\ kJ} = -15900\ J$ or 15900 J released or 15.9 kJ released

Check: The units (J) are correct. The magnitude (15900 J) makes sense since we are freezing about 3 moles of water. Freezing is exothermic, so heat is released.

78. Given: 25.0 g dry ice(CO_2) sublimation **Find:** heat required **Other:** $\Delta H^\circ_{sub} = 32.3$ kJ/mol

Conceptual plan: g dry ice → mol dry ice → $q_{dry\ ice}$ (kJ) → $q_{dry\ ice}$ (J)

$$\frac{1\ mol}{44.01\ g} \qquad \frac{32.3\ kJ}{1\ mol} \qquad \frac{1000\ J}{1\ kJ}$$

Solution: $25.0 \, \cancel{g} \times \dfrac{1 \, \cancel{mol}}{44.01 \, \cancel{g}} \times \dfrac{32.3 \, \cancel{kJ}}{1 \, \cancel{mol}} \times \dfrac{1000 \, J}{1 \, \cancel{kJ}} = 18300 \, J$ required or $18.3 \, kJ$ released

Check: The units (J) are correct. The magnitude (18300 J) makes sense since we are subliming just over 0.5 moles of dry ice. Sublimation is endothermic, so heat is required.

79. **Given:** 8.5 g ice; 255 g water   **Find:** ΔT of water   **Other:** $\Delta H^\circ_{fus} = 6.0 \, kJ/mol$; $C_{H2O} = 4.18 \, J/g \cdot {}^\circ C$ from text

Conceptual plan: $q_{ice} = -q_{water}$ so   g (ice) $\rightarrow$ mol (ice) $\rightarrow$ q_{fus}(kJ) $\rightarrow$ q_{fus} (J) $\rightarrow$ q_{water} (J)   **then**

$$\dfrac{1 \, mol}{18.01 \, g} \qquad \dfrac{6.0 \, kJ}{1 \, mol} \qquad \dfrac{1000 \, J}{1 \, kJ} \qquad q_{water} = -q_{ice}$$

q, m, C$_s$ $\rightarrow$ ΔT_1 now we have slightly cooled water in contact with 0.0 °C water

$$q = m C_S \Delta T_1$$

so $q_{ice} = -q_{water}$ with   m, C$_s$ $\rightarrow$ ΔT_2 with $\Delta T_1 \, \Delta T_2$ $\rightarrow$ ΔT_{Total}

$$q = m C_S \Delta T_2 \quad then \ set \ q_{ice} = -q_{H2O} \qquad \Delta T_{Total} = \Delta T_1 + \Delta T_2$$

Solution: $8.5 \, \cancel{g} \times \dfrac{1 \, \cancel{mol}}{18.01 \, \cancel{g}} \times \dfrac{6.0 \, \cancel{kJ}}{1 \, \cancel{mol}} \times \dfrac{1000 \, J}{1 \, \cancel{kJ}} = 2.\underline{8}3176 \times 10^3 \, J$, $q_{water} = -q_{ice} = -2.\underline{8}3176 \times 10^3 \, J$

$q = m C_S \Delta T$ Rearrange to solve for ΔT. $\Delta T_1 = \dfrac{q}{m C_S} = \dfrac{-2.83176 \times 10^3 \, \cancel{J}}{255 \, \cancel{g} \times 4.18 \dfrac{\cancel{J}}{\cancel{g} \times {}^\circ C}} = -2.\underline{6}567 \, {}^\circ C$.

$q = m C_S \Delta T$ substitute in values and set $q_{ice} = -q_{water}$.

$$q_{ice} = m_{ice} \, C_{ice} \left(T_f - T_{icei} \right) = 8.5 \, \cancel{g} \times 4.18 \dfrac{J}{\cancel{g} \times {}^\circ C} \times \left(T_f - 0.0 \, {}^\circ C \right) = \qquad\qquad\qquad \rightarrow$$

$$-q_{water} = -m_{water} \, C_{water} \, \Delta T_{water2} = -255 \, \cancel{g} \times 4.18 \dfrac{J}{\cancel{g} \times {}^\circ C} \times \Delta T_{water2}$$

$8.5 \, T_f = -255 \, \Delta T_{water2} = -255 \left(T_f - T_{f1} \right)$ Rearrange to solve for T_f. $8.5 \, T_f + 255 \, T_f = 255 \, T_{f1}$ $\rightarrow$

$26\underline{3}.5 \, T_f = 255 \, T_{f1}$ $\rightarrow$ $T_f = 0.967\underline{7}4 \, T_{f1}$ but $\Delta T_1 = \left(T_{f1} - T_{i1} \right) = -2.\underline{6}567 \, {}^\circ C$ which says that

$T_{f1} = T_{i1} - 2.\underline{6}567 \, {}^\circ C$ and $\Delta T_{Total} = \left(T_f - T_{i1} \right)$ so

$\Delta T_{Total} = 0.967\underline{7}4 \, T_{f1} - T_{i1} = 0.967\underline{7}4 \left(T_{i1} - 2.\underline{6}567 \, {}^\circ C \right) - T_{i1} = -2.\underline{6}567 \, {}^\circ C - 0.032\underline{2}6 T_{i1}$. This implies that the larger the initial temperature of the water, the larger the temperature drop. If the initial temperature was 90 °C, the temperature drop would be 5.6 °C. If the initial temperature was 25 °C, the temperature drop would be 3.5°C. If the initial temperature was 5 °C, the temperature drop would be 2.8 °C. This makes physical sense because the lower the initial temperature of the water, the less kinetic energy it initially has and the smaller the heat transfer from the water to the melted ice will be.

Check: The units (°C) are correct. The temperature drop form the melting of the ice is only 2.7 °C because the mass of the water is so much larger than the ice.

80. **Given:** 352 mL water, $T_i = 25 \, {}^\circ C$, $T_f = 5 \, {}^\circ C$, d = 1.0 g/mL; ice $T_i = 0 \, {}^\circ C$, $T_f = 5 \, {}^\circ C$ **Find:** g (ice)
Other: $\Delta H^\circ_{fus} = 6.02 \, kJ/mol$; $C_{H2O} = 4.18 \, J/g \cdot {}^\circ C$ from text
Conceptual plan:
mL $\rightarrow$ g   then   m, C$_s$, T$_i$, T$_f$ $\rightarrow$ q_{water} (J) $\rightarrow$ q_{ice} (J)   then q_{ice}, ΔH°_{fus}, C_{H2O}, T$_i$, T$_f$ $\rightarrow$ g (ice)

$$\dfrac{1.0 \, g}{1.0 \, mL} \qquad\qquad q = m C_S \left(T_f - T_i \right) \quad q_{ice} = -q_{water} \quad q_{ice} = m C_S \left(T_f - T_i \right) + m \dfrac{1 \, mol}{18.01 g} \times \dfrac{6.02 \, kJ}{1 \, mol} \times \dfrac{1000 \, J}{1 \, kJ}$$

Solution: $352 \, \cancel{mL} \times \dfrac{1.0 \, g}{1.0 \, \cancel{mL}} = 3\underline{5}2 \, g$

$q_{water} = m_{water} \, C_{water} \left(T_f - T_i \right) = 3\underline{5}2 \, \cancel{g} \times 4.18 \dfrac{J}{\cancel{g} \times {}^\circ \cancel{C}} \times \left(5 \, {}^\circ \cancel{C} - 25 \, {}^\circ \cancel{C} \right) = -2.\underline{9}4272 \times 10^4 \, J$,

$q_{ice} = -q_{water} = 2.\underline{9}4272 \times 10^4 \, J$ then $q_{ice} = m C_S \left(T_f - T_i \right) + m \dfrac{1 \, \cancel{mol}}{18.01 g} \times \dfrac{6.02 \, \cancel{kJ}}{1 \, \cancel{mol}} \times \dfrac{1000 \, J}{1 \, \cancel{kJ}}$ substitute values.

$2.\underline{9}4272 \times 10^4 \, J = m \times 4.18 \dfrac{J}{g \times {}^\circ \cancel{C}} \times \left(5 \, {}^\circ \cancel{C} - 0 \, {}^\circ \cancel{C} \right) + m \times \dfrac{334.26 \, J}{1 g}$ Rearrange to solve for m.

$$m = \frac{2.94272 \times 10^4 \; \cancel{J}}{\dfrac{355.\underline{1}6 \; \cancel{J}}{1 g}} = 83 \; g$$

Check: The units (g) are correct.   The temperature drop is large and so is the amount of water we want to cool, so the mass seems reasonable.

81. **Given:** 10.0 g ice $T_i = -10.0 \; °C$ to steam at $T_f = 110.0 \; °C$ **Find:** heat required (kJ)
  Other: $\Delta H°_{fus} = 6.02$ kJ/mol; $\Delta H°_{vap} = 40.7$ kJ/mol; $C_{ice} = 2.09$ J/g · °C; $C_{H2O} = 4.18$ J/g · °C; $C_{steam} = 2.01$ J/g · °C
  Conceptual plan: Follow the heating curve in Figure 11.36. $q_{Total} = q_1 + q_2 + q_3 + q_4 + q_5$ where $q_1, q_3,$ and q_5 are heating of a single phase then J → kJ   and q_2 and q_4 are phase transitions.

$$q = m C_S (T_f - T_i) \qquad\qquad \frac{1 \; kJ}{1000 \; J} \qquad\qquad q = m \times \frac{1 \; mol}{18.01 g} \times \frac{\Delta H}{1 \; mol}$$

Solution:

$$q_1 = m_{ice} \, C_{ice} (T_{icef} - T_{icei}) = 10.0 \; \cancel{g} \times 2.09 \frac{J}{\cancel{g} \times \cancel{°C}} \times (0.0 \; \cancel{°C} - -10.0 \; \cancel{°C}) = 209 \; \cancel{J} \times \frac{1 \; kJ}{1000 \; \cancel{J}} = 0.209 \; kJ \; ,$$

$$q_2 = m \times \frac{1 \; \cancel{mol}}{18.01 g} \times \frac{\Delta H_{fus}}{1 \; \cancel{mol}} = 10.0 \; \cancel{g} \times \frac{1 \; \cancel{mol}}{18.01 \cancel{g}} \times \frac{6.02 \; kJ}{1 \; \cancel{mol}} = 3.3\underline{4}3 \; kJ \; ,$$

$$q_3 = m_{water} \, C_{water} (T_{waterf} - T_{wateri}) = 10.0 \; \cancel{g} \times 4.18 \frac{J}{\cancel{g} \times \cancel{°C}} \times (100.0 \; \cancel{°C} - 0.0 \; \cancel{°C}) = 4180 \; \cancel{J} \times \frac{1 \; kJ}{1000 \; \cancel{J}} = 4.18 \; kJ \; ,$$

$$q_4 = m \times \frac{1 \; \cancel{mol}}{18.01 g} \times \frac{\Delta H_{vap}}{1 \; \cancel{mol}} = 10.0 \; \cancel{g} \times \frac{1 \; \cancel{mol}}{18.01 \cancel{g}} \times \frac{40.7 \; kJ}{1 \; \cancel{mol}} = 22.\underline{5}99 \; kJ \; ,$$

$$q_5 = m_{steam} \, C_{steam} (T_{steamf} - T_{steami}) = 10.0 \; \cancel{g} \times 2.01 \frac{J}{\cancel{g} \times \cancel{°C}} \times (110.0 \; \cancel{°C} - 100.0 \; \cancel{°C}) = 201 \; \cancel{J} \times \frac{1 \; kJ}{1000 \; \cancel{J}} = 0.201 \; kJ \; .$$

$$q_{Total} = q_1 + q_2 + q_3 + q_4 + q_5 = 0.209 \; kJ + 3.3\underline{4}3 \; kJ + 4.18 \; kJ + 22.\underline{5}99 \; kJ + 0.201 \; kJ = 30.5 \; kJ$$

Check: The units (kJ) are correct.   The amount of heat is dominated the vaporization step. Since we have less than 1 mole we expect less than 41 kJ.

82. **Given:** 1.00 mole ice $T_i = 145.0 \; °C$ to ice at $T_f = - 50.0 \; °C$ **Find:** heat evolved (kJ) **Other:** $\Delta H°_{fus} = 6.02$ kJ/mol; $\Delta H°_{vap} = 40.7$ kJ/mol; $C_{ice} = 2.09$ J/g · °C; $C_{H2O} = 4.18$ J/g · °C; $C_{steam} = 2.01$ J/g · °C
  Conceptual plan: mol → g   Follow the heating curve in Figure 11.36, only in reverse.

$$\frac{18.01 \; g}{1 \; mol}$$

$q_{Total} = q_1 + q_2 + q_3 + q_4 + q_5$ where $q_1, q_3,$ and q_5 are heating of a single phase then J → kJ

$$q = m C_S (T_f - T_i) \qquad\qquad \frac{1 \; kJ}{1000 \; J}$$

and q_2 and q_4 are phase transitions.

$$q = mol \times \frac{\Delta H}{1 \; mol}$$

Solution: $1.00 \; \cancel{mol} \times \dfrac{18.01 \; g}{1 \; \cancel{mol}} = 18.\underline{0}1 \; g$

$$q_1 = m_{steam} \, C_{steam} (T_{steamf} - T_{steami}) = 18.\underline{0}1 \; \cancel{g} \times 2.01 \frac{J}{\cancel{g} \times \cancel{°C}} \times (100.0 \; \cancel{°C} - 145.0 \; \cancel{°C}) = - 16\underline{2}9.00 \; \cancel{J} \times \frac{1 \; kJ}{1000 \; \cancel{J}}$$

$$= -1.6\underline{2}9 \; kJ$$

$$q_2 = mol \times \frac{-\Delta H_{vap}}{1 mol} = 1.00 \; \cancel{mol} \times \frac{-40.7 \; kJ}{1 \; \cancel{mol}} = - 40.7 \; kJ \; ,$$

$$q_3 = m_{water} \, C_{water} (T_{waterf} - T_{wateri}) = 18.\underline{0}1 \; \cancel{g} \times 4.18 \frac{J}{\cancel{g} \times \cancel{°C}} \times (0.0 \; \cancel{°C} - 100.0 \; \cancel{°C}) = - 75\underline{2}8.2 \; \cancel{J} \times \frac{1 \; kJ}{1000 \; \cancel{J}}$$

$$= - 7.5\underline{2}82 \; kJ$$

$$q_4 = mol \times \frac{-\Delta H_{fus}}{1 mol} = 1.00 \; \cancel{mol} \times \frac{-6.02 \; kJ}{1 \; \cancel{mol}} = - 6.02 \; kJ \; ,$$

$$q_5 = m_{ice}\, C_{ice}\left(T_{icef} - T_{icei}\right) = 18.01\ \text{g} \times 2.09\ \frac{\text{J}}{\text{g} \times {}^{\circ}\text{C}} \times (-50.0\ {}^{\circ}\text{C} - 0.0\ {}^{\circ}\text{C}) = -1882.0\ \text{J} \times \frac{1\ \text{kJ}}{1000\ \text{J}} .$$

$$= -1.8820\ \text{kJ}$$

$q_{Total} = q_1 + q_2 + q_3 + q_4 + q_5 = -1.629\ \text{kJ} - 40.7\ \text{kJ} - 7.5282\ \text{kJ} - 6.02\ \text{kJ} - 1.8820\ \text{kJ} = -57.8\ \text{kJ}$ or 57.8 kJ released

Check: The units (kJ) are correct.   The amount of heat is dominated the vaporization step. Since we have less than 1 mole we expect less than 41 kJ.

83. a) solid

    b) liquid

    c) gas

    d) supercritical fluid

    e) solid/liquid equilibrium

    f) liquid/gas equilibrium

    g) solid/liquid/gas equilibrium

84. a) 184.4 °C

    b) 113.6 °C

    c) solid

    d) gas

85. **Given:** nitrogen, normal boiling point = 77.3 K, normal melting point = 63.1 K, critical temperature = 126.2 K, critical pressure = 2.55×10^4 torr, triple point at 63.1 K and 94.0 torr
   Find: Sketch phase diagram. Does nitrogen have a stable liquid phase at 1 atm?

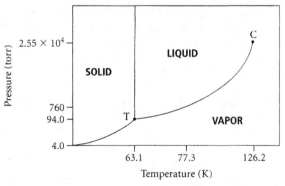

Nitrogen has a stable liquid phase at 1 atm.

86. **Given:** argon, normal boiling point = 87.2 K, normal melting point = 84.1 K, critical temperature = 150.8 K, critical pressure = 48.3 atm, triple point at 83.7 K and 0.68 atm
   Find: Sketch phase diagram. Which has the greater density, solid or liquid argon?

The solid has the higher density because the slope of the solid/liquid equilibrium line is positive. If we start in the liquid and increase the pressure, we will cross into the solid phase, the dense phase.

87. a)   0.027 mmHg, the higher of the two triple points

   b)   The Rhombic phase is denser because if we start in the Monoclinic phase at 100 °C and increase the pressure, we will cross into the Rhombic phase.

88. The triple point marked "O" shows the equilibrium of Ice II, Ice III, and Ice V. Ice II is denser than Ice I because you can generate Ice II from Ice I by increasing the pressure (and pushing the molecules closer together). Ice III would sink in liquid water. Note that the slope of the Ice III/liquid line has the typical positive slope.

89. Water has a low molar mass (18.01 g/mol), yet it is a liquid at room temperature. Water's high boiling point for its molar mass can be understood by examining the structure of the water molecule. The bent geometry of the water molecule and the highly polar nature of the O–H bonds result in a molecule with a significant dipole moment. Water's two O–H bonds (hydrogen directly bonded to oxygen) allow a water molecule to form strong hydrogen bonds with four other water molecules, resulting in a relatively high boiling point.

90. Water's high polarity also allows it to dissolve many other polar and ionic compounds, and even a number of nonpolar gases such as oxygen and carbon dioxide (by inducing a dipole moment in their molecules). Consequently, water is the main solvent within living organisms, transporting nutrients and other important compounds throughout the body. Water is also the main solvent of the environment, allowing aquatic animals, for example, to survive by breathing dissolved oxygen and aquatic plants to survive by using dissolved carbon dioxide for photosynthesis.

91. Water has an exceptionally high specific heat capacity, which has a moderating effect on the climate of coastal cities. Also, its high ΔH_{vap} causes water evaporation and condensation to have a strong effect on temperature. A tremendous amount of heat can be stored in large bodies of water. The heat will be absorbed or released from the large bodies of water preferentially over the land around it. In some cities, such as San Francisco, for example, the daily fluctuation in temperature can be less than 10 °C. This same moderating effect occurs over the entire planet, two-thirds of which is covered by water. In other words, without water, the daily temperature fluctuations on our planet might be more like those on Mars, where temperature fluctuations of 63 °C (113 °F) have been measured between midday and early morning.

92. One significant difference between the phase diagram of water and that of other substances is that the fusion curve for water which has a negative slope. The fusion curve within the phase diagrams for most substances has a positive slope because increasing pressure favors the denser phase, which for most substances is the solid phase. This negative slope means that ice is less dense than liquid water and so ice floats. The solids sink in the liquids of most other substances. The frozen layer of ice at the surface of a winter lake insulates the water in the lake from further freezing. If this ice layer sank, it would kill bottom-dwelling aquatic life and possibly allow the lake to freeze solid, eliminating virtually all life in the lake.

93. **Given:** x-ray with λ = 154 pm, maximum reflection angle of θ = 28.3°; assume n = 1   **Find:** distance between layers   **Conceptual plan:** $\lambda , \theta, n \rightarrow d$
$$n \lambda = 2d \ sin\theta$$

   Solution: $n \lambda = 2d \ sin\theta$ Rearrange to solve for d. $d = \dfrac{n \lambda}{2 \ sin\theta} = \dfrac{1 \times 154 \ pm}{2 \ sin \ 28.3°} = 162 \ pm$

   Check: The units (pm) are correct. The magnitude (164 pm) makes sense since n = 1 and the sin is always < 1. The number is consistent with interatomic distances.

94. **Given:** distance between layers = 286 pm, maximum reflection angle of θ = 7.23°; assume n = 1   **Find:** λ (x-ray) with **Conceptual plan:** $d , \theta, n \rightarrow \lambda$
$$n \lambda = 2d \ sin\theta$$

   Solution: $n \lambda = 2d \ sin\theta$ Rearrange to solve for λ. $\lambda = \dfrac{2d \ sin\theta}{n} = \dfrac{2 \times 286 \ pm \times sin \ 7.23°}{1} = 72.0 \ pm$

   Check: The units (pm) are correct. The magnitude (72 pm) makes sense since n = 1 and the sin is always < 1. The number is consistent with x-ray wavelengths.

95. a)   8 corner atoms x (1/8 atom / unit cell) = 1 atom / unit cell

b) 8 corner atoms x (1/8 atom / unit cell) + 1 atom in center = (1 + 1) atoms / unit cell = 2 atoms / unit cell

c) 8 corner atoms x (1/8 atom / unit cell) + 6 face-centered atoms x (1/2 atom / unit cell) = (1 + 3) atoms / unit cell = 4 atoms / unit cell

96. a) coordination number of 12 since this is a face-centered cubic structure

b) coordination number of 12 since this is a hexagonal closest packed structure

c) coordination number of 8 since this is a body-centered cubic structure

97. **Given:** platinum, face-centered cubic structure, r = 139 pm **Find:** edge length of unit cell and density (g/cm^3) **Conceptual plan:**
$$r \rightarrow l \quad \text{and} \quad l \rightarrow V(pm^3) \rightarrow V(cm^3) \quad \text{and} \quad \mathfrak{M}, \text{FCC structure} \rightarrow m \quad \text{then} \quad m, V \rightarrow d$$

$$l = 2\sqrt{2}\,r \qquad V = l^3 \qquad \frac{(1\ cm)^3}{(10^{10}\ pm)^3} \qquad m = \frac{4\ atoms}{unit\ cell} \times \frac{\mathfrak{M}}{N_A} \qquad d = m/V$$

Solution: $l = 2\sqrt{2}\,r = 2\sqrt{2}$ x 139 pm = 39\underline{3}.151 pm = 393 pm and

$$V = l^3 = (39\underline{3}.151\ \cancel{pm})^3 \times \frac{(1\ cm)^3}{(10^{10}\ \cancel{pm})^3} = 6.0\underline{7}682 \times 10^{-23}\ cm^3 \text{ and}$$

$$m = \frac{4\ atoms}{unit\ cell} \times \frac{\mathfrak{M}}{N_A} = \frac{4\ \cancel{atoms}}{unit\ cell} \times \frac{195.09\ g}{1\ \cancel{mol}} \times \frac{1\ \cancel{mol}}{6.022 \times 10^{23}\ \cancel{atoms}} = 1.29\underline{5}848 \times 10^{-21}\ \frac{g}{unit\ cell} \text{ then}$$

$$d = \frac{m}{V} = \frac{1.29\underline{5}848 \times 10^{-21}\ \dfrac{g}{\cancel{unit\ cell}}}{6.0\underline{7}682 \times 10^{-23}\ \dfrac{cm^3}{\cancel{unit\ cell}}} = 21.3\ \frac{g}{cm^3}$$

Check: The units (pm and g/cm^3) are correct. The magnitude (393 pm) makes sense because it must be larger than the radius of an atom. The magnitude (21 g/ cm^3) is consistent for Pt from chapter 1.

98. **Given:** molybdenum, body-centered cubic structure, r = 136 pm **Find:** edge length of unit cell and density (g/cm^3)
Conceptual plan:
$$r \rightarrow l \quad \text{and} \quad l \rightarrow V(pm^3) \rightarrow V(cm^3) \quad \text{and} \quad \mathfrak{M}, \text{BCC structure} \rightarrow m \quad \text{then} \quad m, V \rightarrow d$$

$$l = \frac{4r}{\sqrt{3}} \qquad V = l^3 \qquad \frac{(1\ cm)^3}{(10^{10}\ pm)^3} \qquad m = \frac{2\ atoms}{unit\ cell} \times \frac{\mathfrak{M}}{N_A} \qquad d = m/V$$

Solution: $l = \dfrac{4r}{\sqrt{3}} = \dfrac{4\ \text{x}\ 136\ pm}{\sqrt{3}} = 31\underline{4}.079\ pm = 314\ pm$ and

$$V = l^3 = (31\underline{4}.079\ \cancel{pm})^3 \times \frac{(1\ cm)^3}{(10^{10}\ \cancel{pm})^3} = 3.0\underline{9}823 \times 10^{-23}\ cm^3 \text{ and}$$

$$m = \frac{2\ atoms}{unit\ cell} \times \frac{\mathfrak{M}}{N_A} = \frac{2\ \cancel{atoms}}{unit\ cell} \times \frac{95.94\ g}{1\ \cancel{mol}} \times \frac{1\ \cancel{mol}}{6.022 \times 10^{23}\ \cancel{atoms}} = 3.18\underline{6}317 \times 10^{-22}\ \frac{g}{unit\ cell} \text{ then}$$

$$d = \frac{m}{V} = \frac{3.18\underline{6}317 \times 10^{-22}\ \dfrac{g}{\cancel{unit\ cell}}}{3.0\underline{9}823 \times 10^{-23}\ \dfrac{cm^3}{\cancel{unit\ cell}}} = 10.3\ \frac{g}{cm^3}$$

Check: The units (pm and g/cm^3) are correct. The magnitude (314 pm) makes sense because it must be larger than the radius of an atom. The magnitude (10 g/ cm^3) is reasonable for a metal density.

99. **Given:** rhodium, face-centered cubic structure, $d = 12.41$ g/cm^3 **Find:** r (Rh)
    Conceptual plan:
    $\mathfrak{M}$, FCC structure $\rightarrow$ m   then   m, V $\rightarrow$ d then V(cm^3) $\rightarrow$ l (cm) $\rightarrow$ l (pm)   then l $\rightarrow$ r

    $$m = \frac{4 \text{ atoms}}{\text{unit cell}} \; x \; \frac{\mathfrak{M}}{N_A} \qquad d = m/V \qquad V = l^3 \qquad \frac{10^{10} \text{ pm}}{1 \text{ cm}} \qquad l = 2\sqrt{2} \; r$$

    Solution: $m = \dfrac{4 \text{ atoms}}{\text{unit cell}} \; x \; \dfrac{\mathfrak{M}}{N_A} = \dfrac{4 \text{ atoms}}{\text{unit cell}} \; x \; \dfrac{102.905 \text{ g}}{1 \text{ mol}} \; x \; \dfrac{1 \text{ mol}}{6.022 \text{ x } 10^{23} \text{ atoms}} = 6.835271 \text{ x } 10^{-22} \; \dfrac{\text{g}}{\text{unit cell}}$ then

    $d = \dfrac{m}{V}$ Rearrange to solve for V. $V = \dfrac{m}{d} = \dfrac{6.835271 \text{ x } 10^{-22} \; \frac{\text{g}}{\text{unit cell}}}{12.41 \; \frac{\text{g}}{\text{cm}^3}} = 5.507873 \text{ x } 10^{-23} \; \dfrac{\text{cm}^3}{\text{unit cell}}$ then $V = l^3$

    Rearrange to solve for l. $l = \sqrt[3]{V} = \sqrt[3]{5.507873 \text{ x } 10^{-23} \text{ cm}^3} = 3.804831 \text{x } 10^{-8} \text{ cm } x \dfrac{10^{10} \text{ pm}}{1 \text{ cm}} = 380.4831 \text{ pm}$ then

    $l = 2\sqrt{2} \; r$ Rearrange to solve for r. $r = \dfrac{l}{2\sqrt{2}} = \dfrac{380.4831 \text{ pm}}{2\sqrt{2}} = 134.5 \text{ pm}$

    Check: The units (pm) are correct. The magnitude (135 pm) is consistent with atom diameters.

100. **Given:** barium, body-centered cubic structure, $d = 3.59$ g/cm^3 **Find:** r (Ba)
    Conceptual plan:
    $\mathfrak{M}$, BCC structure $\rightarrow$ m   then   m, V $\rightarrow$ d then V(cm^3) $\rightarrow$ l (cm) $\rightarrow$ l (pm)   then l $\rightarrow$ r

    $$m = \frac{2 \text{ atoms}}{\text{unit cell}} \; x \; \frac{\mathfrak{M}}{N_A} \qquad d = m/V \qquad V = l^3 \qquad \frac{10^{10} \text{ pm}}{1 \text{ cm}} \qquad l = \frac{4 \; r}{\sqrt{3}}$$

    Solution: $m = \dfrac{2 \text{ atoms}}{\text{unit cell}} \; x \; \dfrac{\mathfrak{M}}{N_A} = \dfrac{2 \text{ atoms}}{\text{unit cell}} \; x \; \dfrac{137.34 \text{ g}}{1 \text{ mol}} \; x \; \dfrac{1 \text{ mol}}{6.022 \text{ x } 10^{23} \text{ atoms}} = 4.561275 \text{ x } 10^{-22} \; \dfrac{\text{g}}{\text{unit cell}}$ then $d = \dfrac{m}{V}$

    Rearrange to solve for V. $V = \dfrac{m}{d} = \dfrac{4.561275 \text{ x } 10^{-22} \; \frac{\text{g}}{\text{unit cell}}}{3.59 \; \frac{\text{g}}{\text{cm}^3}} = 1.270550 \text{ x } 10^{-22} \; \dfrac{\text{cm}^3}{\text{unit cell}}$ then $V = l^3$

    Rearrange to solve for l. $l = \sqrt[3]{V} = \sqrt[3]{1.270550 \text{ x } 10^{-22} \text{ cm}^3} = 5.027336 \text{ x } 10^{-8} \text{ cm } x \dfrac{10^{10} \text{ pm}}{1 \text{ cm}} = 502.7336 \text{ pm}$ then

    $l = \dfrac{4 \; r}{\sqrt{3}}$ Rearrange to solve for r. $r = \dfrac{l\sqrt{3}}{4} = \dfrac{502.7336 \text{ pm } x \sqrt{3}}{4} = 217.7 \text{ pm}$

    Check: The units (pm) are correct. The magnitude (218 pm) is consistent with atom diameters.

101. **Given:** polonium, simple cubic structure, $d = 9.3$ g/cm^3; $r = 167$ pm; $\mathfrak{M} = 209$ g/mol   **Find:** estimate N_A
    Conceptual plan:
    $r \rightarrow l$ and $l \rightarrow$ V(pm^3) $\rightarrow$ V(cm^3) then $d, V \rightarrow m$ then $\mathfrak{M}$, SC structure $\rightarrow$ m

    $$l = 2r \qquad V = l^3 \qquad \frac{(1 \text{ cm})^3}{(10^{10} \text{ pm})^3} \qquad d = m/V \qquad m = \frac{1 \text{ atom}}{\text{unit cell}} \; x \; \frac{\mathfrak{M}}{N_A}$$

    Solution: $l = 2 \; r = 2 \text{ x } 167 \text{ pm} = 334 \text{ pm}$ and $V = l^3 = (334 \text{ pm})^3 \; x \; \dfrac{(1 \text{ cm})^3}{(10^{10} \text{ pm})^3} = 3.72597 \text{ x } 10^{-23} \text{ cm}^3$ then

    $d = \dfrac{m}{V}$ Rearrange to solve for m. $m = d \; V = 9.3 \; \dfrac{\text{g}}{\text{cm}^3} \; x \; \dfrac{3.72597 \text{ x } 10^{-23} \text{ cm}^3}{\text{unit cell}} = 3.46515 \text{ x } 10^{-22} \; \dfrac{\text{g}}{\text{unit cell}}$ then

    $m = \dfrac{1 \text{ atom}}{\text{unit cell}} \; x \; \dfrac{\mathfrak{M}}{N_A}$ Rearrange to solve for N_A.

    $N_A = \dfrac{1 \text{ atom}}{\text{unit cell}} \; x \; \dfrac{\mathfrak{M}}{m} = \dfrac{1 \text{ atom}}{\text{unit cell}} \; x \; \dfrac{209 \text{ g}}{1 \text{ mol}} \; x \; \dfrac{1 \text{ unit cell}}{3.46515 \text{ x } 10^{-22} \text{ g}} = 6.03 \text{ x } 10^{23} \; \dfrac{\text{atom}}{\text{mol}}$

    Check: The units (atoms/mol) are correct. The magnitude (6 x 10^{23}) is consistent with Avogadro's number.

102. **Given:** palladium, face-centered cubic structure, $d = 12.0$ g/cm^3; $r = 138$ pm; $\mathfrak{M} = 106.42$ g/mol

Find: estimate N_A

Conceptual plan:

$r \rightarrow l$ and $l \rightarrow V(\text{pm}^3) \rightarrow V(\text{cm}^3)$ then $d, V \rightarrow m$ then $\mathfrak{M}$, FCC structure $\rightarrow m$

$$l = 2\sqrt{2}\,r \qquad V = l^3 \qquad \frac{(1\text{ cm})^3}{(10^{10}\text{ pm})^3} \qquad d = m/V \qquad m = \frac{4\text{ atoms}}{\text{unit cell}} \times \frac{\mathfrak{M}}{N_A}$$

Solution: $l = 2\sqrt{2}\,r = 2\sqrt{2} \times 138$ pm $= 390.323$ pm and

$$V = l^3 = \left(390.323\text{ pm}\right)^3 \times \frac{(1\text{ cm})^3}{(10^{10}\text{ pm})^3} = 5.94665 \times 10^{-23}\text{ cm}^3 \text{ then } d = \frac{m}{V} \text{ Rearrange to solve for m.}$$

$$m = dV = 12.0\,\frac{\text{g}}{\text{cm}^3} \times \frac{5.94665 \times 10^{-23}\text{ cm}^3}{\text{unit cell}} = 7.13598 \times 10^{-22}\,\frac{\text{g}}{\text{unit cell}} \text{ then } m = \frac{4\text{ atoms}}{\text{unit cell}} \times \frac{\mathfrak{M}}{N_A} \text{ Rearrange to}$$

solve for N_A. $N_A = \frac{4\text{ atoms}}{\text{unit cell}} \times \frac{\mathfrak{M}}{m} = \frac{4\text{ atoms}}{\text{unit cell}} \times \frac{106.42\text{ g}}{1\text{ mol}} \times \frac{1\text{ unit cell}}{7.13598 \times 10^{-22}\text{ g}} = 5.97 \times 10^{23}\,\frac{\text{atom}}{\text{mol}}$

Check: The units (atoms/mol) are correct. The magnitude (6×10^{23}) is consistent with Avogadro's number.

103. a) atomic, since Ar is an atom

b) molecular, since water is a molecule

c) ionic, since K_2O is an ionic solid

d) atomic, since iron is an atom

104. a) ionic, since $CaCl_2$ is an ionic solid

b) molecular, since CO_2 is a molecule

c) atomic, since iron is an atom

d) molecular, since I_2 is a molecule

105. LiCl has the highest melting point since it is the only ionic solid in the group. The other three solids are held together by intermolecular forces while LiCl is held together by stronger coulombic interactions between the cations and anions of the crystal lattice.

106. C (diamond) has the highest melting point (3800 °C). Both covalent network solids and ionic solids have high melting points. NaCl has a melting point of 801 °C. In diamond (Figure 11.57a), each carbon atom forms four covalent bonds to four other carbon atoms in a tetrahedral geometry. This structure extends throughout the entire crystal, so that a diamond crystal can be thought of as a giant molecule, held together by these covalent bonds. Since covalent bonds are very strong, covalent atomic solids have high melting points.

107. a) TiO_2 because it is an ionic solid

b) $SiCl_4$ because it is larger, and therefore, has stronger dispersion forces

c) Xe because it is larger, and therefore, has stronger dispersion forces

d) CaO because the ions have greater charge, stronger dipole-dipole interactions

108. a) Fe because it is an atomic solid held together by metallic bonding

b) KCl because it is an ionic solid

c) Ti because it is an atomic solid held together by metallic bonding

d) H_2O because it is capable of hydrogen bonding

109. The Ti atoms occupy the corner positions and the center of the unit cell - 8 corner atoms x (1/8 atom / unit cell) + 1 atom in center = (1 + 1) Ti atoms / unit cell = 2 Ti atoms / unit cell. The O atoms occupy four positions on the top and bottom faces and two positions inside the unit cell - 4 face-centered atoms x (1/2 atom / unit cell) + 2 atoms in the interior = (2 + 2) O atoms / unit cell = 4 O atoms / unit cell. Therefore there are 2 Ti atoms / unit cell and 4 O atoms / unit cell, so the ratio Ti:O is 2:4 or 1:2. The formula for the compound is TiO_2.

110. The Re atoms occupy the corner positions and the center of the unit cell - 8 corner atoms x (1/8 atom / unit cell) = 1 Re atom / unit cell. The O atoms occupy twelve edge positions - 12 edge atoms x (1/4 atom / unit cell) = 3 O atoms / unit cell. Therefore there are 1 Re atom / unit cell and 3 O atoms / unit cell, so the ratio Re:O is 1:3. The formula for the compound is ReO_3.

111. In CsCl: The Cs atoms occupy the center of the unit cell - 1 atom in center = 1 Cs atom / unit cell. The Cl atoms occupy corner positions of the unit cell - 8 corner atoms x (1/8 atom / unit cell) = 1 Cl atom / unit cell. Therefore there are 1 Cl atom / unit cell and 1 Cl atom / unit cell, so the ratio Cs:Cl is 1:1. The formula for the compound is CsCl, as expected.

In $BaCl_2$: The Ba atoms occupy the corner positions and the face-centered positions of the unit cell - 8 corner atoms x (1/8 atom / unit cell) + 6 face-centered atoms x (1/2 atom / unit cell) = (1 + 3) Ba atoms / unit cell = 4 Ba atoms / unit cell. The Cl atoms occupy eight positions inside the unit cell - 8 Cl atoms / unit cell. Therefore there are 4 Ba atoms / unit cell and 8 Cl atoms / unit cell, so the ratio Ba:Cl is 4:8 or 1:2. The formula for the compound is $BaCl_2$, as expected.

112. In Li_2O: The Li atoms occupy eight positions inside the unit cell - 8 Li atoms / unit cell. The O atoms occupy the corner positions and the face-centered positions of the unit cell - 8 corner atoms x (1/8 atom / unit cell) + 6 face-centered atoms x (1/2 atom / unit cell) = (1 + 3) Li atoms / unit cell = 4 O atoms / unit cell. Therefore there are 4 O atoms / unit cell and 8 Li atoms / unit cell, so the ratio Li:O is 8:4 or 2:1. The formula for the compound is Li_2O, as expected.

In AgI: The Ag atoms occupy four positions inside the unit cell - 4 Ag atoms / unit cell. The I atoms occupy the corner positions and the face-centered positions of the unit cell - 8 corner atoms x (1/8 atom / unit cell) + 6 face-centered atoms x (1/2 atom / unit cell) = (1 + 3) I atoms / unit cell = 4 I atoms / unit cell. Therefore there are 4 I atoms / unit cell and 4 Ag atoms / unit cell, so the ratio Ag:I is 4:4 or 1:1. The formula for the compound is AgI, as expected.

113. a) Zn should have little or no band gap because it is the only metal in the group.

114. **Given:** 5.45 g sodium crystal   **Find:** number of molecular orbitals in the valence band
Conceptual plan:

g $\rightarrow$ mol $\rightarrow$ Na_N $\rightarrow$ **number of valence electrons** $\rightarrow$ **number of molecular orbitals**

$$\frac{1 \text{ mol}}{22.99 \text{ g}} \quad \frac{6.022 \times 10^{23} \text{ atoms}}{1 \text{ mol}} \quad \frac{1 \text{ 3s electron}}{1 \text{ Na atom}} \quad \frac{1 \text{ molecular orbital}}{1 \text{ 3s electron}}$$

Solution:

$$5.45 \text{ g Na} \times \frac{1 \text{ mol Na}}{22.99 \text{ g Na}} \times \frac{6.022 \times 10^{23} \text{ Na atoms}}{1 \text{ mol Na}} \times \frac{1 \text{ 3s electron}}{1 \text{ Na atom}} \times \frac{1 \text{ molecular orbital}}{1 \text{ 3s electron}} = 1.43 \times 10^{23} \text{ molecular orbitals}$$

Check: The units (number of molecular orbitals) are correct. The magnitude (10^{23}) is expected since there are so many orbitals because we have about a ¼ mole of atoms. Metals can conduct electricity because of these large numbers of orbitals.

115. a) p-type semiconductor – Ge is Group 4A and Ga is Group 3A, so the Ga will generate electron "holes".

b) n-type semiconductor – Si is Group 4A and As is Group 5A, so the As will add electrons to the conduction band.

116. a) p-type semiconductor – Si is Group 4A and Ga is Group 3A, so the Ga will generate electron "holes".

b) n-type semiconductor – Ge is Group 4A and Sb is Group 5A, so the Sb will add electrons to the conduction band.

117. The general trend is that melting point increases with increasing mass. This is due to the fact that the electrons of the larger molecules are held more loosely and a stronger dipole moment can be induced more easily. HF is the exception to the rule. It has a relatively high melting point due to hydrogen bonding.

118. The general trend is that boiling point increases with increasing mass. This is due to the fact that the electrons of the larger molecules are held more loosely and a stronger dipole moment can be induced more easily. H_2O is the exception to the rule. It has a relatively high boiling point due to hydrogen bonding.

119. **Given:** $P_{H2O} = 23.76$ torr at 25 °C; 1.25 g water in 1.5 L container   **Find:** m (H_2O) as liquid
Conceptual plan:
°C → K and torr → atm then P, V, T → mol (g) → g (g) then g (g), g $(l)_i$ → g $(l)_f$

$$K = °C + 273.15 \qquad \frac{1\ atm}{760\ torr} \qquad PV = nRT \qquad \frac{18.01\ g}{1\ mol} \qquad g\ (l)_f = g\ (l)_i - g\ (g)$$

Solution: T = 25 °C + 273.15 = 298 K, $23.76\ torr \times \dfrac{1\ atm}{760\ torr} = 0.0312632$ atm then $PV = nRT$

Rearrange to solve for n. $n = \dfrac{PV}{RT} = \dfrac{0.0312632\ atm \times 1.5\ L}{0.08206\ \frac{L\ atm}{K\ mol} \times 298\ K} = 0.00191768$ mol then

$0.00191768\ mol \times \dfrac{18.01\ g}{1\ mol} = 0.0345375$ g in gas phase then

$g\ (l)_f = g\ (l)_i - g\ (g) = 1.25\ g - 0.0345375\ g = 1.22$ g remaining as liquid   Yes, there is 1.22 g of liquid.

Check: The units (g) are correct. The magnitude (1.2 g) is expected since very little material is expected to be in the gas phase.

120. **Given:** $P_{CCl3F} = 856$ torr at 300 K; 11.5 g CCl_3F in 1.0 L container   **Find:** m (CCl_3F) as liquid
Conceptual plan: torr → atm then P, V, T → mol (g) → g (g) then g (g), g $(l)_i$ → g $(l)_f$

$$\frac{1\ atm}{760\ torr} \qquad PV = nRT \qquad \frac{137.36\ g}{1\ mol} \qquad g\ (l)_f = g\ (l)_i - g\ (g)$$

Solution: $856\ torr \times \dfrac{1\ atm}{760\ torr} = 1.12632$ atm   then $PV = nRT$ Rearrange   to   solve   for   n.

$n = \dfrac{PV}{RT} = \dfrac{1.12632\ atm \times 1.0\ L}{0.08206\ \frac{L\ atm}{K\ mol} \times 300\ K} = 0.0457517$ mol   then $0.0457517\ mol \times \dfrac{137.36\ g}{1\ mol} = 6.2845$ g in gas phase

then $g\ (l)_f = g\ (l)_i - g\ (g) = 11.5\ g - 6.2845\ g = 5.2$ g remaining as liquid   Yes, there is 5.2 g of liquid.

Check: The units (g) are correct. The magnitude (5 g) is expected since even at moderate pressures little material is expected to be in the gas phase.

121. gas → liquid → solid

122. The solid is denser than the liquid. Since the triple point temperature is lower than the normal melting point, the slope of the fusion curve must be positive. This means that as you start in the liquid phase and increase the pressure you will eventually cross into the solid phase. As pressure increases, the phases get denser, as the atoms, molecules or ions are pushed closer and closer together.

123. **Given:** Ice: $T_1 = 0$ °C exactly, m = 53.5 g; Water: $T_1 = 75$ °C, m = 115 g   **Find:** T_f

    Other: $\Delta H°_{fus} = 6.0$ kJ/mol; $C_{H2O} = 4.18$ J/g ·°C

    Conceptual plan: $q_{ice} = -\ q_{water}$ so   g (ice) $\rightarrow$ mol (ice) $\rightarrow$ q_{fus}(kJ) $\rightarrow$ q_{fus} (J) $\rightarrow$ q_{water} (J)   **then**

$$\frac{1\ mol}{18.01\ g} \qquad \frac{6.02\ kJ}{1\ mol} \qquad \frac{1000\ J}{1\ kJ} \qquad q_{water} = -\ q_{ice}$$

q, m, C_s $\rightarrow$ **ΔT**   **then**   **T_i , ΔT** $\rightarrow$ **T_2**   now we have slightly cooled water in contact with 0.0 °C water

$$q = mC_S\Delta T \qquad\qquad \Delta T = T_2 - T_i$$

so   **$q_{ice} = -\ q_{water}$**   **with**   **m, C_s, T_i** $\rightarrow$ **T_f**

$$q = m\ C_s\left(T_f - T_i\right) \quad then\ set\ q_{ice} = -\ q_{water}$$

Solution: $53.5\ g \times \dfrac{1\ mol}{18.01\ g} \times \dfrac{6.02\ kJ}{1\ mol} \times \dfrac{1000\ J}{1\ kJ} = 1.7\underline{8}828 \times 10^4$ J , $q_{water} = -\ q_{ice} = -1.7\underline{8}828 \times 10^4$ J

$q = mC_S\Delta T$ Rearrange to solve for ΔT. $\Delta T = \dfrac{q}{mC_S} = \dfrac{-1.7\underline{8}828 \times 10^4\ J}{115\ g \times 4.18\ \frac{J}{g \times °C}} = -37.\underline{2}017$ °C   then $\Delta T = T_2 - T_i$.

Rearrange to solve for T_2. $T_2 = \Delta T + T_i = -37.\underline{2}017$ °C + 75 °C = 37.798 °C $q = m\ C_s\left(T_f - T_i\right)$ substitute in values and set $q_{ice} = -\ q_{water}$.

$$q_{ice} = m_{ice}\ C_{ice}\left(T_f - T_{icei}\right) = 53.5\ g \times 4.18\ \frac{J}{g \times °C} \times \left(T_f - 0.0\ °C\right) =$$

Rearrange to solve for T_f.

$$-q_{water} = -m_{water}\ C_{water}\left(T_f - T_{water\ 2}\right) = -115\ g \times 4.18\ \frac{J}{g \times °C} \times \left(T_f - 37.798°C\right)$$

$53.5\ T_f = -115\left(T_f - 37.798°C\right)$ $\rightarrow$ $53.5\ T_f = -115\ T_f + 4\underline{3}46.8°C$ $\rightarrow$ $-4\underline{3}46.8\ °C = -16\underline{8}.5\ T_f$

$\rightarrow T_f = \dfrac{-4\underline{3}46.8\ °C}{-16\underline{8}.5} = 2\underline{5}.8\ °C = 26\ °C$

Check: The units (°C) are correct. The temperature is between the two initial temperatures. Since the ice mass is about half the water mass, we are not surprised that the temperature is closer to the original ice temperature.

124. **Given:** Steam: $T_1 = 100$ °C, m = 0.552 g; Water: $T_1 = 5.0$ °C, m = 4.25 g   **Find:** T_f

    Other: $\Delta H°_{vap} = 40.7$ kJ/mol; $C_{H2O} = 4.18$ J/g ·°C

    Conceptual plan:

$q_{steam} = -\ q_{water}$ so   **g (steam)** $\rightarrow$ **mol (steam)** $\rightarrow$ **q_{vap}(kJ)** $\rightarrow$ **q_{fvap} (J)** $\rightarrow$ **q_{water} (J)**   **then**

$$\frac{1\ mol}{18.01\ g} \qquad \frac{-40.7\ kJ}{1\ mol} \qquad \frac{1000\ J}{1\ kJ} \qquad q_{steam} = -\ q_{ice}$$

q, m, C_s $\rightarrow$ **ΔT then T_i , ΔT** $\rightarrow$ **T_2**   now we have slightly warmed water in contact with 100.0 °C water

$$q = mC_S\Delta T \qquad\qquad \Delta T = T_2 - T_i$$

so   **$q_{ice} = -\ q_{water}$**   **with**   **m, C_s, T_i** $\rightarrow$ **T_f**

$$q = m\ C_s\left(T_f - T_i\right) \quad then\ set\ q_{steam} = -\ q_{water}$$

Solution: $0.552\ g \times \dfrac{1\ mol}{18.01\ g} \times \dfrac{-40.7\ kJ}{1\ mol} \times \dfrac{1000\ J}{1\ kJ} = 1.2\underline{4}744 \times 10^3$ J , $q_{water} = -\ q_{steam} = --1.2\underline{4}744 \times 10^3$ J

$q = mC_S\Delta T$ Rearrange to solve for ΔT. $\Delta T = \dfrac{q}{mC_S} = \dfrac{1.2\underline{4}744 \times 10^3\ J}{4.25\ g \times 4.18\ \frac{J}{g \times °C}} = 70.\underline{2}190$ °C   then $\Delta T = T_2 - T_i$.

Rearrange to solve for T_2. $T_2 = \Delta T + T_i = 70.\underline{2}190$ °C + 5.0 °C = $75.\underline{2}190$ °C $q = m\ C_s\left(T_f - T_i\right)$ substitute in values and set $q_{steam} = -\ q_{water}$.

$$q_{steam} = m_{steam} \; C_{steam} \left(T_f - T_{steami} \right) = 0.552 \text{ g} \times 4.18 \; \frac{J}{g \times {}^{\circ}C} \times \left(T_f - 100.0 \; {}^{\circ}C \right) =$$

Rearrange to solve for T_f.

$$- q_{water} = - m_{water} \; C_{water} \left(T_f - T_{water2} \right) = - 4.25 \text{ g} \times 4.18 \; \frac{J}{g \times {}^{\circ}C} \times \left(T_f - 75.2190 \; {}^{\circ}C \right)$$

$$0.552 \left(T_f - 100.0 \; {}^{\circ}C \right) = - 4.25 \left(T_f - 75.2190 \; {}^{\circ}C \right) \; \rightarrow \; 0.552 \; T_f - 55.2 \; {}^{\circ}C = - 4.25 \; T_f + 319.681 \; {}^{\circ}C \; \rightarrow$$

$$- 374.881 \; {}^{\circ}C = - 4.802 \; T_f \; \rightarrow \; T_f = \frac{-374.881 \; {}^{\circ}C}{-4.802} = 78.1 \; {}^{\circ}C$$

Check: The units (°C) are correct. The temperature is between the two initial temperatures. Since there is so much heat involved in the vaporization process, we are not surprised that the temperature is closer to the original steam temperature.

125. **Given**: Home: 6.0 m x 10.0 m x 2.2 m; T = 30 °C, P_{H2O} = 85 % of P°_{H2O} **Find**: m (H_2O) removed
    Other: P°_{H2O} = 31.86 mm Hg from text
    Conceptual plan:
l, w, h $\rightarrow$ V (m^3) $\rightarrow$ V (cm^3) $\rightarrow$ V (L)   and P°_{H2O} $\rightarrow$ P_{H2O} (mm Hg) $\rightarrow$ P_{H2O} (atm)   and

$$V = l \times w \times h \qquad \frac{(100 \text{ cm})^3}{(1 \text{ m})^3} \qquad \frac{1 \text{ L}}{1000 \text{ cm}^3} \qquad\qquad P_{H2O} = 0.85 \; P^{\circ}_{H2O} \qquad \frac{1 \text{ atm}}{760 \text{ mm Hg}}$$

°C $\rightarrow$ K   then   P, V, T $\rightarrow$ mol (H_2O) $\rightarrow$ g (H_2O)

$$K = {}^{\circ}C + 273.15 \qquad\qquad\qquad PV = nRT \qquad \frac{18.01 \text{ g}}{1 \text{ mol}}$$

Solution: $V = l \times w \times h = 6.0 \text{ m} \times 10.0 \text{ m} \times 2.2 \text{ m} = 132 \text{ m}^3 \times \dfrac{(100 \text{ cm})^3}{(1 \text{ m})^3} \times \dfrac{1 \text{ L}}{1000 \text{ cm}^3} = 1.32 \times 10^5 \text{ L}$,

$P_{H2O} = 0.85 \; P^0_{H2O} = 0.85 \times 31.86 \text{ mm Hg} \times \dfrac{1 \text{ atm}}{760 \text{ mm Hg}} = 0.035633 \text{ atm}$,   T = 30 °C + 273.15 = 303 K,   then

$PV = nRT$ Rearrange to solve for n. $n = \dfrac{PV}{RT} = \dfrac{0.035633 \text{ atm} \times 1.32 \times 10^5 \text{ L}}{0.08206 \; \frac{\text{L atm}}{\text{K mol}} \times 303 \text{ K}} = 189.17 \text{ mol}$ then

$$189.17 \text{ mol} \times \frac{18.01 \text{ g}}{1 \text{ mol}} = 3400 \text{ g to remove}$$

Check: The units (g) are correct. The magnitude of the answer (3400 g) makes sense since the volume of the house is so large. We are removing almost 200 moles of water.

126. **Given**: Flask with 0.55 g water at T = 28 °C, P°_{H2O} = 28.36 mm Hg
    Find: minimum V of flask for all vapor
    Conceptual plan:
g (H_2O) $\rightarrow$ mol (H_2O) and P°_{H2O} (mm Hg) $\rightarrow$ P_{H2O} (atm)   and   °C $\rightarrow$ K   then   P, n, T $\rightarrow$ V

$$\frac{1 \text{ mol}}{18.01 \text{ g}} \qquad\qquad\qquad \frac{1 \text{ atm}}{760 \text{ mm Hg}} \qquad\qquad K = {}^{\circ}C + 273.15 \qquad\qquad PV = nRT$$

Solution: $0.55 \text{ g} \times \dfrac{1 \text{ mol}}{18.01 \text{ g}} = 0.030539 \text{ mol}$, $P_{H2O} = 28.63 \text{ mm Hg} \times \dfrac{1 \text{ atm}}{760 \text{ mm Hg}} = 0.03767105 \text{ atm}$,

T = 28 °C + 273.15 = 301 K,   then $PV = nRT$ Rearrange to solve for V.

$$V = \frac{nRT}{P} = \frac{0.030539 \text{ mol} \times 0.08206 \; \frac{\text{L atm}}{\text{K mol}} \times 301 \text{ K}}{0.03767105 \text{ atm}} = 20.02 \text{ L} = 2.0 \times 10^1 \text{ L}$$

Check: The units (L) are correct. The magnitude of the answer (20 L) makes sense since we have about 1/30 mole and a pressure of about 1/30 atm and at STP one mole of a gas occupies 22 L.

127. CsCl has a higher melting point than AgI because of its higher coordination number. In CsCl, one anion bonds to 8 cations (and vice versa) while in AgI, one anion bonds only to 4 cations.

128. KCl has a higher melting point than copper iodide because of its higher coordination number. In KCl, one anion bonds to 6 cations (and vice versa) while in copper iodide, one anion bonds only to 4 cations.

129. a) atoms are connected across the face diagonal (c), so $c = 4r$

b) From the Pythagorean Theorem $c^2 = a^2 + b^2$, from part a) $c = 4r$ and for a cubic structure $a = l$, $b = l$ so
$(4r)^2 = l^2 + l^2$ → $16r^2 = 2l^2$ → $8r^2 = l^2$ → $l = \sqrt{8r^2}$ → $l = 2\sqrt{2}\,r$

130. a) atoms are connected across the cube diagonal (c), so $c = 4r$

b) Since b forms the diagonal of the face, where each edge length $a = l$ and combining this with the Pythagorean Theorem $b^2 = l^2 + l^2$ → $b^2 = 2l^2$ → $b = \sqrt{2}\,l$

c) From the Pythagorean Theorem $c^2 = a^2 + b^2$, from part a) $c = 4r$ and from part b) $b = \sqrt{2}\,l$ and for a cubic structure $a = l$ so $(4r)^2 = l^2 + \left(\sqrt{2}\,l\right)^2$ → $16r^2 = l^2 + 2l^2$ → $16r^2 = 3l^2$ → $4r = \sqrt{3}\,l$ → $l = \dfrac{4r}{\sqrt{3}}$

131. **Given:** diamond, V (unit cell) = 0.0454 nm^3; d = 3.52 g/cm^3 **Find:** number of carbon atoms / unit cell
Conceptual plan: $V(nm^3)$ → $V(cm^3)$ then d, V → m → mol → atoms

$$\frac{(1\ cm)^3}{(10^7\ nm)^3} \qquad d = m/V \qquad \frac{1\ mol}{12.01\ g} \quad \frac{6.022 \times 10^{23}\ atoms}{1\ mol}$$

Solution: $0.0454\ nm^3 \times \dfrac{(1\ cm)^3}{(10^7\ nm)^3} = 4.54 \times 10^{-23}\ cm^3$ then $d = \dfrac{m}{V}$ Rearrange to solve for m.

$m = dV = 3.52\ \dfrac{g}{cm^3} \times 4.54 \times 10^{-23}\ cm^3 = 1.59808 \times 10^{-22}\ g$ then

$\dfrac{1.59808 \times 10^{-22}\ g}{unit\ cell} \times \dfrac{1\ mol}{12.01\ g} \times \dfrac{6.022 \times 10^{23}\ atoms}{1\ mol} = 8.01\ \dfrac{C\ atoms}{unit\ cell} = 8\ \dfrac{C\ atoms}{unit\ cell}$

Check: The units (atoms) are correct. The magnitude (8) makes sense because it is a fairly small number and our answer within our calculation error of an integer.

132. **Given:** metal, d = 12.3 g/cm^3; r = 0.134 nm, face-centered cubic lattice   **Find:** $\mathfrak{M}$
Conceptual plan:
r → l → $V(nm^3)$ → $V(cm^3)$ then d, V → m then m, FCC structure → $\mathfrak{M}$

$$l = 2\sqrt{2}\,r \qquad V = l^3 \qquad \frac{(1\ cm)^3}{(10^7\ nm)^3} \qquad d = m/V \qquad m = \frac{4\ atoms}{unit\ cell} \times \frac{\mathfrak{M}}{N_A}$$

Solution: $l = 2\sqrt{2}\,r = 2\sqrt{2} \times 0.134\ nm = 0.379009\ nm$,

$V = l^3 = (0.379009\ nm)^3 = 0.544439\ nm^3 \times \dfrac{(1\ cm)^3}{(10^7\ nm)^3} = 5.44439 \times 10^{-23}\ cm^3$ then $d = \dfrac{m}{V}$ Rearrange to solve

for m. $m = dV = 12.3\ \dfrac{g}{cm^3} \times 5.44439 \times 10^{-23}\ cm^3 = 6.69660 \times 10^{-22}\ g$ then $m = \dfrac{4\ atoms}{unit\ cell} \times \dfrac{\mathfrak{M}}{N_A}$ Rearrange to

solve for $\mathfrak{M}$. $\mathfrak{M} = \dfrac{unit\ cell}{4\ atoms} \times N_A \times m = \dfrac{unit\ cell}{4\ atoms} \times \dfrac{6.022 \times 10^{23}\ atoms}{1\ mol} \times \dfrac{6.69660 \times 10^{-22}\ g}{unit\ cell} = 101\ \dfrac{g}{mol}$

Ruthenium
Check: The units (g/mol) are correct. The magnitude (101) makes sense because it is a reasonable atomic mass for a metal and it is close to Ruthenium.

133. a) $CO_2(s) \rightarrow CO_2(g)$ at 194.7 K

b) $CO_2(s) \rightarrow$ triple point at 216.5 K $\rightarrow CO_2(g)$ just above 216.5 K

c) $CO_2(s) \rightarrow CO_2(l)$ at somewhat above 216 K $\rightarrow CO_2(g)$ at around 250 K

d) CO_2 (s) → CO_2 above the critical point where there is no distinction between liquid and gas. This change occurs at about 300 K.

134. If atmospheric pressure is 2500 mm Hg, water would still be a liquid. At a higher pressure atmospheric pressure, water would remain a liquid to a lower temperature than 0 °C, this could reduce the damage done to organisms that are exposed to cold temperatures. At a higher atmospheric pressure there would be more molecules in the gas phase and the atmosphere would not behave as ideally, water might condense more readily, lowering the vapor pressure of water. This could have an adverse affect on living organisms. At higher atmospheric pressures, cell walls would need to be stronger to withstand higher pressures. This would most likely make the cell walls less permeable and affect many biological systems.

135. **Given:** KCl, rock salt structure **Find:** density (g/cm^3) **Other:** r (K$^+$) = 133 pm; r (Cl$^-$) = 181 pm from Chapter 8
Conceptual plan: Rock salt structure is a face-centered cubic structure with anions at the lattice points and cations in the holes between lattice sites → assume r = r(Cl$^-$), but $\mathfrak{M} = \mathfrak{M}_{(KCl)}$
r(K$^+$), r(Cl$^-$) → l and l → V(pm^3) → V(cm^3) and , FCC structure → m then   m, V → d

from Figure 11.52 $l = 2r(Cl^-) + 2r(K^+)$ $V = l^3$ $\dfrac{(1\ cm)^3}{(10^{10}\ pm)^3}$ $m = \dfrac{4\ formula\ units}{unit\ cell} \times \dfrac{\mathfrak{M}}{N_A}$ $d = m/V$

Solution: $l = 2r(Cl^-) + 2r(K^+) = 2(181\ pm) + 2(133\ pm) = 628\ pm$ and

$V = l^3 = (628\ pm)^3 \times \dfrac{(1\ cm)^3}{(10^{10}\ pm)^3} = 2.4\underline{7}673 \times 10^{-22}\ cm^3$ and

$m = \dfrac{4\ formula\ units}{unit\ cell} \times \dfrac{\mathfrak{M}}{N_A} = \dfrac{4\ formula\ units}{unit\ cell} \times \dfrac{74.55\ g}{1\ mol} \times \dfrac{1\ mol}{6.022 \times 10^{23}\ formula\ units} = 4.95\underline{1}976 \times 10^{-22}\ \dfrac{g}{unit\ cell}$ then

$d = \dfrac{m}{V} = \dfrac{4.95\underline{1}976 \times 10^{-22}\ \dfrac{g}{unit\ cell}}{2.4\underline{7}673 \times 10^{-22}\ \dfrac{cm^3}{unit\ cell}} = 1.9\underline{9}940\ \dfrac{g}{cm^3} = 2.00\ \dfrac{g}{cm^3}$

Check: The units (g/cm^3) are correct. The magnitude (2 g/ cm^3) is reasonable for a salt density. The published value is 1.98 g/cm^3. This method of estimating the density gives a value that is close to the experimentally measured density.

136. **Given:** butane (C_4H_{10}), $\Delta H°_{vap}$ = 22.44 kJ/mol; normal boiling point = − 0.4 °C, 0.55 g; 250 mL flask
Find: amount of butane present as a liquid at − 22 °C, and at 25 °C
Conceptual plan:
at each temperature: °C → K and   kJ → J   then $\Delta H°_{vap}$, T$_1$, P$_1$, T$_2$ → P$_2$

$K = °C + 273.15$ $\dfrac{1000\ J}{1\ kJ}$ $\ln \dfrac{P_2}{P_1} = \dfrac{-\Delta H_{vap}}{R}\left(\dfrac{1}{T_2} - \dfrac{1}{T_1}\right)$

and   mL → L then P$_2$, V , T$_2$ → mol → g (g) → g (l)

$\dfrac{1\ L}{1000\ mL}$ $PV = nRT$ $\dfrac{58.12\ g}{1\ mol}$ $g\ (l) = g_{Total} - g\ (g)$

Solution: T$_1$ = − 0.4 °C + 273.15 = 272.8 K;   T$_2$ = − 22 °C + 273.15 = 251 K;

$\dfrac{22.44\ kJ}{mol} \times \dfrac{1000\ J}{1\ kJ} = 2.244 \times 10^4\ \dfrac{J}{mol}$

P$_1$ = 1 atm $\ln \dfrac{P_2}{P_1} = \dfrac{-\Delta H_{vap}}{R}\left(\dfrac{1}{T_2} - \dfrac{1}{T_1}\right)$ Substitute values in equation.

$\ln \dfrac{P_2}{1\ atm} = \dfrac{-2.244 \times 10^4\ \dfrac{J}{mol}}{8.314\ \dfrac{J}{K\ mol}}\left(\dfrac{1}{251\ K} - \dfrac{1}{272.8\ K}\right) = -0.85\underline{9}312$ → $\dfrac{P_2}{1\ atm} = e^{-0.859312} = 0.42\underline{3}45$ →

P$_2$ = 0.42$\underline{3}$45 x 1 atm = 0.42345 atm and 250 mL x $\dfrac{1\ L}{1000\ mL}$ = 0.25 L then $PV = nRT$

Rearrange to solve for n. $n = \dfrac{PV}{RT} = \dfrac{0.42345 \text{ atm} \times 0.25 \text{ L}}{0.08206 \dfrac{\text{L atm}}{\text{K mol}} \times 251 \text{ K}} = 0.0051397 \text{ mol}$ then

$0.0051397 \text{ mol} \times \dfrac{58.12 \text{ g}}{1 \text{ mol}} = 0.29872 \text{ g in gas phase}$ then

$g(l) = g_{Total} - g(g) = 0.55 \text{ g} - 0.29872 \text{ g} = 0.25 \text{ g as liquid at} -22 \text{ °C}$

$T_1 = -0.4 \text{ °C} + 273.15 = 272.8 \text{ K};$ $T_2 = 25 \text{ °C} + 273.15 = 298 \text{ K};$ $\dfrac{22.44 \text{ kJ}}{\text{mol}} \times \dfrac{1000 \text{ J}}{1 \text{ kJ}} = 2.244 \times 10^4 \dfrac{\text{J}}{\text{mol}}$

$P_1 = 1 \text{ atm}$ $\ln \dfrac{P_2}{P_1} = \dfrac{-\Delta H_{vap}}{R}\left(\dfrac{1}{T_2} - \dfrac{1}{T_1}\right)$ Substitute values in equation.

$\ln\dfrac{P_2}{1 \text{ atm}} = \dfrac{-2.244 \times 10^4 \dfrac{\text{J}}{\text{mol}}}{8.314 \dfrac{\text{J}}{\text{K mol}}}\left(\dfrac{1}{298 \text{ K}} - \dfrac{1}{272.8 \text{ K}}\right) = 0.836667 \rightarrow \dfrac{P_2}{1 \text{ atm}} = e^{0.836667} = 2.30866 \rightarrow$

$P_2 = 2.30866 \times 1 \text{ atm} = 2.30866 \text{ atm}$ and $250 \text{ mL} \times \dfrac{1 \text{ L}}{1000 \text{ mL}} = 0.25 \text{ L}$ then $PV = nRT$

Rearrange to solve for n. $n = \dfrac{PV}{RT} = \dfrac{2.30866 \text{ atm} \times 0.25 \text{ L}}{0.08206 \dfrac{\text{L atm}}{\text{K mol}} \times 298 \text{ K}} = 0.023602 \text{ mol}$ then

$0.023602 \text{ mol} \times \dfrac{58.12 \text{ g}}{1 \text{ mol}} = 1.3718 \text{ g in gas phase}$ since the amount that can be put in the gas phase is greater than the

available amount, there is no liquid present at 25 °C.

Check: The units (g) are correct.   The magnitude of the answers (0.25 g and 0 g) makes sense since we expect less to be in the liquid phase at a higher temperature. The second temperature is over the boiling point, so we expect a lot in the gas phase.

137. Decreasing the pressure will decrease the temperature of liquid nitrogen. Because the nitrogen is boiling, its temperature must be constant at a given pressure. As the pressure decreases, the boiling point decreases, and therefore so does the temperature. Remember that vaporization is an endothermic process, so as the nitrogen vaporizes it will remove heat from the liquid, dropping its temperature. If the pressure drops below the pressure of the triple point, the phase change will shift from vaporization to sublimation and the liquid nitrogen will become solid.

138. **Given:** cubic closest packing structure   **Find:** fraction of empty space to 5 significant figures
Conceptual plan: cubic closest packing is the same as face-centered cubic structure   so
calculate the volume of the atoms and the volume of the unit cell   then $V_{atoms}, V_{unit\ cell} \rightarrow \% V_{empty}$

$\dfrac{4 \text{ atoms}}{\text{unit cell}}$ and $V_{atom} = \dfrac{\frac{4}{3}\pi r^3}{\text{atom}}$ $V_{unit\ cell} = l^3$ and $l = 2\sqrt{2}r$ $\% V_{empty} = \dfrac{V_{unit\ cell} - V_{atoms}}{V_{unit\ cell}} \times 100 \%$

Solution: $V_{atoms} = \dfrac{4 \text{ atoms}}{\text{unit cell}} \times \dfrac{\frac{4}{3}\pi r^3}{\text{atom}} = \dfrac{\frac{16}{3}\pi r^3}{\text{unit cell}}$ and $V_{unit\ cell} = l^3 = \left(2\sqrt{2}r\right)^3$ so $\% V_{empty} = \dfrac{V_{unit\ cell} - V_{atoms}}{V_{unit\ cell}} \times 100 \%$

or $\% V_{empty} = \dfrac{\left(2\sqrt{2}r\right)^3 - \frac{16}{3}\pi r^3}{\left(2\sqrt{2}r\right)^3} \times 100 \% = \dfrac{2^3\,2^{3/2}\,r^3 - \frac{2^4}{3}\pi r^3}{2^3\,2^{3/2}\,r^3} \times 100 \% = \dfrac{\sqrt{2} - \frac{\pi}{3}}{\sqrt{2}} \times 100 \% = 25.952 \%$

Check: The units (%) are correct. The magnitude (26 %) is consistent with what is stated in the text.

139. **Given:** cubic closest packing structure = cube with touching spheres of radius = r on alternating corners of a cube **Find:** body diagonal of cube and radius of tetrahedral hole
Solution: The cell edge length = l and $l^2 + l^2 = (2r)^2$ $\rightarrow$ $2l^2 = 4r^2$ $\rightarrow$ $l^2 = 2r^2$. Since body diagonal = *BD* is the hypotenuse of the right triangle formed by the face diagonal and the cell edge we have

$(BD)^2 = l^2 + (2r)^2 = 2\,r^2 + 4r^2 = 6\,r^2$ ➔ $BD = \sqrt{6}\ r$. The radius of the tetrahedral hole = r_T is the half the body diagonal minus the radius of the sphere or

$$r_T = \frac{BD}{2} - r = \frac{\sqrt{6}\ r}{2} - r = \left(\frac{\sqrt{6}}{2} - 1\right) r = \left(\frac{\sqrt{6} - 2}{2}\right) r = \left(\frac{\sqrt{3}\sqrt{2} - \sqrt{2}\sqrt{2}}{\sqrt{2}\sqrt{2}}\right) r = \left(\frac{\sqrt{3} - \sqrt{2}}{\sqrt{2}}\right) r \approx 0.22474\ r$$

140. **Given:** $\Delta H°_{fus} = -6.02$ kJ/mol @ 0.0 °C; C_s (liquid water) = 75.2 J/mol · K; C_s (ice) = 37.7 J/mol · K
Find: ΔH_{fus} at -10.0 °C
Conceptual Plan: Assume exactly 1 mol H_2O for all calculations (report answer as kJ/mol). Since K = °C =273.13, ΔT (°C) = ΔT (K). Construct the following path:

	#2		
Liquid @ 0.0 °C	→	solid @ 0.0 °C	According to Hess' Law $\Delta H_1 + \Delta H_2 + \Delta H_3 = \Delta H_4$
↑ #1		↓ #3	= $\Delta H°_{fus}$ @ -10.0 °C
Liquid @ -10.0 °C	→	solid @ -10.0 °C	at constant P, $\Delta H = q$
	#4		for steps #1 and #3 $q = nC_s\Delta T$

for steps #1 and #3 **J ➔ kJ**

$$\frac{1\ kJ}{1000\ J}$$

Solution:

$$\Delta H_1 = q_1 = nC_S\Delta T = 1\ \text{mol} \times 75.2\ \frac{J}{\text{mol} \times °C} \times (0.00\ °C\ \text{-}\ \text{-}10.0\ °C) = +752\ J \times \frac{1\ kJ}{1000\ J} = +0.752\ kJ\ ,$$

$$\Delta H_2 = q_2 = n\Delta H = 1\ \text{mol} \times -6.02\ \frac{kJ}{\text{mol}} = -6.02\ kJ\ ,$$

$$\Delta H_3 = q_3 = nC_S\Delta T = 1\ \text{mol} \times 37.7\ \frac{J}{\text{mol} \times °C} \times (-10.00\ °C - 0.0\ °C) = -377\ J \times \frac{1\ kJ}{1000\ J} = -0.377\ kJ\ \text{so}$$

$$\Delta H_4 = \Delta H_1 + \Delta H_2 + \Delta H_3 = 0.752\ kJ - 6.02\ kJ - 0.377\ kJ = -5.65\ kJ$$

Check: The units (kJ/mol) are correct. We expect freezing to release less energy at -10 °C because we are below the normal freezing point.

141. Melting of an ice cube in a glass of water will not raise or lower the level of the liquid in the glass as long as the ice is always floating in the liquid. This is because the ice will displace a volume of water based on its mass. By the same logic, melting floating icebergs will not raise the ocean levels (assuming that the dissolved solids content, and thus the density, will not change when the icebergs melt). Dissolving ice formations that are supported by land will raise the ocean levels, just as pouring more water into the glass will raise the liquid level in the glass.

142. The water a container with a larger surface area will evaporate more quickly because there is more surface area for the molecules to evaporate from. Vapor pressure is the pressure of the gas when it is in dynamic equilibrium with the liquid (evaporation rate = condensation rate). The vapor pressure is dependent only on the substance and the temperature. The larger the surface area the more quickly it will reach this dynamic state.

143. Substance A will have the larger change in vapor pressure with the same temperature change. To understand this consider the Clausius-Clapeyron Equation: $\ln\frac{P_2}{P_1} = \frac{-\Delta H_{vap}}{R}\left(\frac{1}{T_2} - \frac{1}{T_1}\right)$, if we use the same temperatures we see that $\frac{P_2}{P_1}\ \alpha\ e^{-\Delta H_{vap}}$. So the smaller the heat of vaporization the larger the final vapor pressure. We can also consider that the lower the heat of vaporization the easier it is to convert the substance from a liquid to a gas. This again leads to Substance A having the larger change in vapor pressure.

144. The triple point will be at a lower temperature since the fusion equilibrium line has a positive slope. This means that we will be increasing both temperate and pressure as we travel from the triple point to the normal melting point.

145. $\Delta H_{sub} = \Delta H_{fus} + \Delta H_{vap}$ as long as the heats of fusion and vaporization are measured at the same temperatures.

146. The liquid segment will have the least steep slope because it takes the most kJ/mol to raise the temperature of the phase.

147. Water has an exceptionally high specific heat capacity, which has a moderating effect on the temperature of the root cellar. A large amount of heat can be stored in a large vat of water. The heat will be absorbed or released from the large bodies of water preferentially over the area around it. As the temperature of the air drops, the water will release heat keeping the temperature more constant. If the temperature of the cellar falls enough to begin to freeze the water, the heat given off during the freezing will further protect the food in the cellar.

Chapter 12
Solutions

1. As seawater moves through the intestine, it flows past cells that line the digestive tract, which consist of largely fluid interiors surrounded by membranes. Although cellular fluids themselves contain dissolved ions, including sodium and chloride, the fluids are more dilute than seawater. Nature's tendency towards mixing (which tends to produce solutions of uniform concentration), together with the selective permeability of the cell membranes (which allow water to flow in and out, but restrict the flow of dissolved solids) causes a flow of solvent out of the body's cells and into the seawater.

2. A solution, a homogeneous mixture of two or more substances. A solution has at least two components. The majority component is usually called the solvent and the minority component is usually called the solute.

3. A substance is soluble in another substance if they can form a homogeneous mixture. The solubility of a substance is the amount of the substance that will dissolve in a given amount of solvent. Several different units can be used to express the solubility, such as, grams of solute per 100 grams of solvent, grams of solute per liter of solvent, or moles of solute per liter of solution.

4. Ideal gases do not interact with each other in any way (that is, there are no significant forces between their constituent particles). When the two gases mix their potential energy remains unchanged, so this does not drive the mixing. The tendency to mix is related, rather, to a concept called entropy. Entropy is a measure of energy randomization or energy dispersal in a system. Recall that a gas at any temperature above 0 K has kinetic energy due to the motion of its atoms. When the gases are separated, their kinetic energies are also confined to those regions. However, when the gases mix the kinetic energy of each gas becomes spread out or dispersed over a larger volume. Therefore, the mixture of the two gases has greater energy dispersal, or greater entropy, than the separated components. The pervasive tendency for all kinds of energy to spread out, or disperse, whenever it is not restrained from doing so is the reason that two ideal gases mix.

5. Entropy is a measure of energy randomization or energy dispersal in a system. When two substances mix to form a solution there is an increase in randomness, due to the fact that the components are no longer segregated to separate regions.

6. Whether two substances will spontaneously mix to form a homogeneous solution is dependent on a number of different types of intermolecular forces including dispersion forces, dipole-dipole forces, hydrogen bonding, and ion-dipole forces.

7. A solution always forms if the solvent-solute interactions are comparable to, or stronger than, the solvent-solvent interactions and the solute-solute interactions.

8. The statement that "like dissolves like" means that similar kinds of solvents dissolve similar kinds of solutes. Polar solvents, such as water, tend to dissolve many polar or ionic solutes, and non-polar solvents, such as hexane, tend to dissolve many non-polar solutes.

9. Step 1: Separating the solute into its constituent particles. This step is always endothermic (positive ΔH) because energy is required to overcome the forces that hold the solute together.

    Step 2: Separating the solvent particles from each other to make room for the solute particles. This step is also endothermic because energy is required to overcome the intermolecular forces among the solvent particles.

    Step 3: Mixing the solute particles with the solvent particles. This step is exothermic, because energy is released as the solute particles interact with the solvent particles through the various types of intermolecular forces.

10. The heat of hydration is simply the enthalpy change that occurs when 1 mol of the gaseous solute ions are dissolved in water. In aqueous solutions, $\Delta H_{solvent}$ and ΔH_{mix} can be combined into a single term called the heat of hydration ($\Delta H_{hydration}$). Because the ion-dipole interactions that occur between a dissolved ion and the surrounding water molecules are much stronger than the hydrogen bonds in water, $\Delta H_{hydration}$ is always largely negative (exothermic) for ionic compounds. Using the heat of hydration, we can write the enthalpy

of solution as a sum of just two terms, one endothermic and one exothermic: $\Delta H_{soln} = \Delta H_{solute} + \Delta H_{solvent} + \Delta H_{mix} = \Delta H_{solute} + \Delta H_{hydration} =$ endothermic(+) term + exothermic(-) term. For ionic compounds, ΔH_{solute}, the energy required to separate the solute into its constituent particles, is simply the negative of the solute's lattice energy ($\Delta H_{solute} = - \Delta H_{lattice}$), discussed in Section 9.4. For ionic aqueous solutions, then, the overall enthalpy of solution depends on the relative magnitudes of ΔH_{solute} and $\Delta H_{hydration}$, with three possible scenarios (in each case we refer to the magnitude or absolute value of ΔH): (1) if $\Delta H_{solute} < \Delta H_{hydration}$ the amount of energy required to separate the solute into its constituent ions is less than the energy given off when the ions are hydrated. ΔH_{soln} is therefore negative and the solution process is exothermic and the solution feels warm to the touch. (2) if $\Delta H_{solute} > \Delta H_{hydration}$ the amount of energy required to separate the solute into its constituent ions is greater than the energy given off when the ions are hydrated. ΔH_{soln} is therefore positive and the solution process is endothermic (if a solution forms at all) and the resulting solution feels cool to the touch. (3) if $\Delta H_{solute} \approx \Delta H_{hydration}$ the amount of energy required to separate the solute into its constituent ions is about equal to the energy given off when the ions are hydrated. ΔH_{soln} is therefore approximately zero and the solution process is neither appreciably exothermic nor appreciably endothermic and there is no noticeable change in temperature.

11. In any solution formation, the initial rate of dissolution far exceeds the rate of deposition. But as the concentration of dissolved solute increases, the rate of deposition also increases. Eventually the rate of dissolution and deposition become equal—dynamic equilibrium has been reached.

    A saturated solution is a solution in which the dissolved solute is in dynamic equilibrium with the solid (or undissolved) solute is called. If you add additional solute to a saturated solution, it will not dissolve.

    An unsaturated solution is a solution containing less than the equilibrium amount of solute is called. If you add additional solute to an unsaturated solution, it will dissolve.

    A supersaturated solution is a solution containing more than the equilibrium amount of solute. Such solutions are unstable and the excess solute normally precipitates out of the solution. However, in some cases, if left undisturbed, a supersaturated solution can exist for an extended period of time.

12. Although there are several exceptions, the solubility of most solids in water increases with increasing temperature. Recrystallization is a common technique to purify a solid. In this technique, the solid is put into water (or some other solvent) at an elevated temperature. Enough solid is added to the solvent to create a saturated solution at the elevated temperature. As the solution cools, it becomes supersaturated and the excess solid begins to come out of solution. If the solution cools slowly, the solid forms crystals as it comes out of solution. The crystalline structure tends to reject impurities, resulting in a purer solid.

13. The solubility of gases in liquids decreases with increasing temperature. The decreasing solubility of gases with increasing temperature results in a lower oxygen concentration available for fish and other aquatic life in warm waters.

14. The higher the pressure of a gas above a liquid, the more soluble the gas is in the liquid. In a sealed can of soda pop, for example, the carbon dioxide is maintained in solution by a high pressure of carbon dioxide within the can. When the can is opened, this pressure is released and the solubility of carbon dioxide decreases, resulting in bubbling

15. Henry's law quantifies the solubility of gases with increasing pressure as follows: $S_{gas} = k_H P_{gas}$, where S_{gas} is the solubility of the gas, k_H is a constant of proportionality (called the Henry's law constant) that depends on the specific solute and solvent and also on temperature, and P_{gas} is the partial pressure of the gas. The equation simply shows that the solubility of a gas in a liquid is directly proportional to the pressure of the gas above the liquid, so the solubility of a gas is known at a certain temperature; the solubility at another pressure at this temperature can be calculated.

16. The common ways of reporting solution concentration include:

    a) Molarity- $M = \dfrac{\text{amount solute (moles)}}{\text{volume solution (L)}}$,

    b) molality - $m = \dfrac{\text{amount solute (moles)}}{\text{mass solvent (kg)}}$,

c) parts by mass - $\dfrac{\text{mass solute}}{\text{mass solution}} \times$ multiplication factor, where percent by mass (%)factor = 100, parts per million by mass (ppm) factor = 10^6, and parts per billion by mass (ppb) factor = 10^9

d) parts by volume (%, ppm, ppb) - $\dfrac{\text{volume solute}}{\text{volume solution}} \times$ multiplication factor, where the same factors are used,

e) mole fraction - $\chi = \dfrac{\text{amount solute (in moles)}}{\text{total amount of solute and solvent (in moles)}}$, and

f) mole percent χ x 100 % .

17. Parts by mass and parts by volume are ratios of masses and volume, respectively. A parts by mass concentration is the ratio of the mass of the solute to the mass of the solution, all multiplied by a multiplication factor: where percent by mass (%) factor = 100, parts per million by mass (ppm) factor = 10^6, and parts per billion by mass (ppb) factor = 10^9. The size of the multiplication factor depends on the concentration of the solution. For example, in percent by mass, the multiplication factor is 100 %, so

Percent by mass = $\dfrac{\text{mass solute}}{\text{mass solution}} \times 100\,\%$. If a solution with a concentration of 28 % by mass contains 28 g of solute per 100 g of solution.

18. The vapor pressure of the solution is lower than the vapor pressure of the pure solvent. The simplest explanation for the lowering of the vapor pressure of a solution relative to that of the pure solvent is related to the concept of dynamic equilibrium itself. In dynamic equilibrium the rate of vaporization is equal to the rate of condensation. When a non-volatile solute is added, however, the solute particles interfere with the ability of the solvent particles to vaporize, simply because they occupy some of the surface area formerly occupied by the solvent. The rate of vaporization is therefore diminished compared to that of the pure solvent. The change in the rate of vaporization creates an imbalance in the rates; the rate of condensation is now greater than the rate of vaporization. The net effect is that some of the molecules that were in the gas phase condense into the liquid. As they condense, the reduced number of molecules in the gas phase causes the rate of condensation to decrease. Eventually the two rates become equal again, but only after the concentration of molecules in the gas phase has decreased, which means a lower vapor pressure for the solution compared to the pure solvent.

19. Raoult's law quantifies the relationship between the vapor pressure of a solution and its concentration as: $P_{solution} = \chi_{solvent}\, P^o_{solvent}$, where $P_{solution}$ is the vapor pressure of the solution, $\chi_{solvent}$ is the mole fraction of the solvent, and $P^o_{solvent}$ is the vapor pressure of the pure solvent. This equation allows you to calculate the vapor pressure of a solution or to calculate the concentration of a solution, given the vapor pressure of the solution.

20. When calculating the vapor pressure of a solution containing an ionic solute, the number of particles that the ionic solid dissociates into needs to be considered. In calculating the vapor pressure, it is the mole fraction of the total number of particles that is used in the calculation.

21. An ideal solution is a solution that follows Raoult's law at all concentrations for both the solute and the solvent. A nonideal solution will exhibit deviations from Raoult's law in the vapor pressure of a component as mole fraction of this component decreases from 1 (i.e. the pure component). If the solute-solvent interactions are particularly strong (stronger than solvent-solvent interactions), then the solute tends to prevent the solvent from vaporizing as easily as it would otherwise and the vapor pressure of the solution will be less than that predicted by Raoult's law. If the solute-solvent interactions are particularly weak (weaker than solvent-solvent interactions), then the solute tends to allow more vaporization than would occur with just the solvent and the vapor pressure of the solution will be greater than predicted by Raoult's law.

22. A non-volatile solute lowers the vapor pressure of a solution relative to that of the pure solvent. The vapor pressure lowering occurs at all temperatures, which shifts the vaporization curve in the phase diagram. This means that the temperature must be raised above the pure solvent normal boiling point in order for the solution vapor pressures to be raised to 1 atm. This shift also results in a lowering of where the vapor

pressure curve intersects the solid-gas curve. The net effect is that the solution has a lower melting point and a higher boiling point than the pure solvent.

23. Colligative properties are properties that depend on the amount of solute and not the type of solute are called. Examples of collogative properties are vapor pressure lowering, freezing point depression, boiling point elevation and osmotic pressure.

24. Osmosis is defined as the flow of solvent from a solution of lower solute concentration to one of higher solute concentration solution through a semipermeable membrane—a membrane that selectively allows some substances to pass through but not others. The osmotic pressure is the pressure required to stop the osmotic flow and is given by the following equation: $\Pi = MRT$.

25. The van't Hoff factor (i) is the ratio of moles of particles in solution to moles of formula units dissolved: $i = \dfrac{moles\ of\ particles}{moles\ of\ formula\ units\ dissolved}$. The van't Hoff factor corrects for the fact that the ionic solute is not completely dissolved into the expected number of ions, leaving ion pairs in solution. The result is that the number of particles in the solution is not as high as theoretically expected.

26. A colloidal dispersion, or simply a colloid, is a mixture in which a dispersed substance (which is solute-like) is finely divided in a dispersing medium (which is solvent-like). The easiest way to define a colloid is based on the size of the solute-like particles. If the particles are small (for example, individual small molecules), then the mixture is a solution. If the particles have a diameter greater than 1μm (for example, grains of sand), then the mixture is a heterogeneous mixture. If the particles are between 1 nm and 1000 nm in size, the mixture is a colloid. Colloidal particles are small enough to be kept dispersed throughout the dispersing medium by collisions with other molecules or atoms.

27. The Tyndall effect is the scattering of light by a colloidal dispersion. The Tyndall effect is often used as a test to determine whether a mixture is a solution or a colloid, since solutions contain completely dissolved solute molecules that are too small to scatter light.

28. Colloidal suspensions are kept stable by electrostatic repulsions that occur at their surfaces. These electrostatic repulsions are caused by charges or dipoles on the surface of the particles.

29. a) hexane, toluene, or CCl_4; dispersion forces

    b) water, methanol; dispersion, dipole-dipole, hydrogen bonding

    c) hexane, toluene, or CCl_4; dispersion forces

    d) water, acetone, methanol, ethanol; dispersion, ion-dipole

30. a) water, methanol; dispersion, dipole-dipole, hydrogen bonding

    b) water, acetone, methanol, ethanol; dispersion, ion-dipole

    c) hexane, toluene, or CCl_4; dispersion forces

    d) water, acetone, methanol, ethanol; dispersion, ion-dipole

31. $HOCH_2CH_2CH_2OH$ would be more soluble in water because it has –OH groups on both ends of the molecule, so it can hydrogen bond on both ends, not just one end.

32. CH_2Cl_2 would be more soluble in water because it is a polar molecule and can exhibit dipole-dipole interactions with the water molecules. CCl_4 is a nonpolar molecule.

33. a) water; dispersion, dipole-dipole, hydrogen bonding

    b) hexane; dispersion forces

    c) water; dispersion, dipole-dipole

d) water; dispersion, dipole-dipole, hydrogen bonding

34. a) hexane; dispersion forces

    b) water; dispersion, dipole-dipole, hydrogen bonding

    c) hexane; dispersion forces

    d) water; dispersion, dipole-dipole, hydrogen bonding

35. a) endothermic

    b) The lattice energy is greater in magnitude than the heat of hydration

    c)

    d) The solution forms because chemical systems tend towards greater entropy.

36. a) exothermic

    b) The lattice energy is smaller in magnitude than the heat of hydration

c)

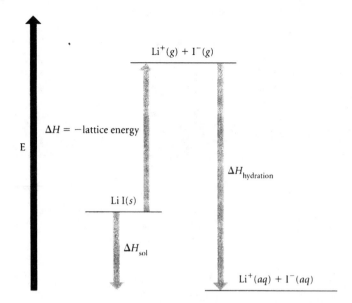

d) The solution forms because chemical systems tend towards lower energy and greater entropy.

37. **Given:** $AgNO_3$: Lattice Energy $= -820.$ kJ/mol, $\Delta H_{soln} = +22.6$ kJ/mol   **Find:** $\Delta H_{hydration}$
Conceptual plan: **Lattice Energy, ΔH_{soln} → $\Delta H_{hydration}$**
$$\Delta H_{soln} = \Delta H_{solute} + \Delta H_{hydration} \text{ where } \Delta H_{solute} = -\Delta H_{lattice}$$
Solution: $\Delta H_{soln} = \Delta H_{solute} + \Delta H_{hydration}$ where $\Delta H_{solute} = -\Delta H_{lattice}$ so $\Delta H_{hydration} = \Delta H_{soln} + \Delta H_{lattice}$
$\Delta H_{hydration} = 22.6$ kJ/mol $- 820.$ kJ/mol $= -797$ kJ/mol

Check: The units (kJ/mol) are correct. The magnitude of the answer (-800) makes physical sense because the lattice energy is so negative and so it dominates the calculation.

38. **Given:** LiCl: Lattice Energy $= -834$ kJ/mol, $\Delta H_{soln} = -37.0$ kJ/mol; NaCl: Lattice Energy $= -769$ kJ/mol, $\Delta H_{soln} = +3.88$ kJ/mol;   **Find:** $\Delta H_{hydration}$ and which has stronger ion-dipole interactions
Conceptual plan: **Lattice Energy, ΔH_{soln} → $\Delta H_{hydration}$ then compare values**
$$\Delta H_{soln} = \Delta H_{solute} + \Delta H_{hydration} \text{ where } \Delta H_{solute} = -\Delta H_{lattice}$$
Solution: $\Delta H_{soln} = \Delta H_{solute} + \Delta H_{hydration}$ where $\Delta H_{solute} = -\Delta H_{lattice}$ so $\Delta H_{hydration} = \Delta H_{soln} + \Delta H_{lattice}$
LiCl: $\Delta H_{hydration} = -37.0$ kJ/mol $- 834$ kJ/mol $= -871$ kJ/mol

NaCl: $\Delta H_{hydration} = +3.88$ kJ/mol $- 769$ kJ/mol $= -765$ kJ/mol

Since $\Delta H_{hydration}$ of LiCl is more negative than for NaCl, LiCl has the stronger ion-dipole interactions
Check: The units (kJ/mol) are correct. The magnitude of the answer (-900 and -800) makes physical sense because the lattice energies are so negative and so they dominate the calculation. We expect stronger interactions with LiCl since the Li^+ ion is smaller than the Na^+ ion and so its charge density is higher and will interact more strongly with the dipoles of the water molecules.

39. **Given:** LiI: Lattice Energy $= -7.3 \times 10^2$ kJ/mol, $\Delta H_{hydration} = -793$ kJ/mol; 15.0 g LiI
Find: ΔH_{soln} and heat evolved
Conceptual plan: **Lattice Energy, $\Delta H_{hydration}$ → ΔH_{soln} and g → mol then mol, ΔH_{soln} → q**
$$\Delta H_{soln} = \Delta H_{solute} + \Delta H_{hydration} \text{ where } \Delta H_{solute} = -\Delta H_{lattice} \qquad \frac{1 \text{ mol}}{133.843 \text{ g}} \qquad q = n\,\Delta H_{soln}$$
Solution: $\Delta H_{soln} = \Delta H_{solute} + \Delta H_{hydration}$ where $\Delta H_{solute} = -\Delta H_{lattice}$ so $\Delta H_{soln} = \Delta H_{hydration} - \Delta H_{lattice}$
$\Delta H_{soln} = -793$ kJ/mol $- -730$ kJ/mol $= -60$ kJ/mol $= -6 \times 10^1$ kJ/mol and

$15.0 \text{ g} \times \dfrac{1 \text{ mol}}{133.843 \text{ g}} = 0.11\underline{2}072 \text{ mol}$ then $q = n\,\Delta H_{soln} = 0.11\underline{2}072 \text{ mol} \times -6 \times 10^1 \dfrac{\text{kJ}}{\text{mol}} = -7$ kJ or 7 kJ released

Check: The units (kJ/mol and kJ) are correct. The magnitude of the answer (-60) makes physical sense because the lattice energy and the heat of hydration are about the same. The magnitude of the heat (7) makes physical sense since 15 g is much less than a mole, and so the amount of heat released is going to be small.

40. **Given:** KNO_3: Lattice Energy $= -163.8$ kcal/mol, $\Delta H_{hydration} = -155.5$ kcal/mol; 1.00×10^2 kJ absorbed
   Find: ΔH_{soln} and m (KNO_3)
   Conceptual plan: Lattice Energy, $\Delta H_{hydration}$ → ΔH_{soln} (kcal) → ΔH_{soln} (kcal)   then

   $$\Delta H_{soln} = \Delta H_{solute} + \Delta H_{hydration} \text{ where } \Delta H_{solute} = -\Delta H_{lattice}$$

   mol, q   → ΔH_{soln} then   mol → g

   $q = n\,\Delta H_{soln}$ $\dfrac{101.11\text{ g}}{1\text{ mol}}$

   Solution: $\Delta H_{soln} = \Delta H_{solute} + \Delta H_{hydration}$ where $\Delta H_{solute} = -\Delta H_{lattice}$ so $\Delta H_{soln} = \Delta H_{hydration} - \Delta H_{lattice}$

   $\Delta H_{soln} = [163.8 \text{ kcal/mol} + (-155.5 \text{ kcal/mol})](4.184 \text{ kJ/kcal}) = 34.7 \text{ kJ/mol}$ then $q = n\,\Delta H_{soln}$ Rearrange to

   solve for n. $n = \dfrac{q}{\Delta H_{soln}} = \dfrac{1.00 \times 10^2 \text{ kJ}}{34.7 \dfrac{\text{kJ}}{\text{mol}}} = 2.8818 \text{ mol}$ then $2.8818 \text{ mol} \times \dfrac{101.11 \text{ g}}{1 \text{ mol}} = 2.9 \times 10^3 \text{ g}$

   Check: The units (kJ/mol and g) are correct. The magnitude of the answer (+ 35) makes physical sense because the lattice energy and the heat of hydration are about the same, with the lattice energy dominating, so the answer is positive. The problem hints at a positive heat of solution by saying that heat is absorbed. The magnitude of the mass (290) makes physical sense since 100 kJ will require over 2 moles of salt.

41. The solution is unsaturated since we are dissolving 25g of NaCl per 100 g of water and the solubility from the figure is ~ 35 g NaCl per 100 g of water.

42. The solution is almost saturated since we are dissolving 32 g of KNO_3 per 100 g of water and the solubility from the figure is ~ 36 g KNO_3 per 100 g of water.

43. At 40 °C the solution has 45 g of KNO_3 per 100 g of water and it can contain up to 63 g of KNO_3 per 100 g of water. At 0 °C the solubility from the figure is ~ 14 g KNO_3 per 100 g of water, so ~ 31 g KNO_3 per 100 g of water will precipitate out of solution.

44. At 60 °C the solution has 42 g of KCl per 100 g of water and it can contain up to 45 g of KCl per 100 g of water. At 0 °C the solubility from the figure is ~ 26 g KCl per 100 g of water, so ~ 16 g KCl per 100 g of water will precipitate out of solution.

45. Since the solubility of gases decrease as the temperature increased, dissolved oxygen will be removed from the solution.

46. Since the solubility of gases decrease as the temperature increased, dissolved oxygen was removed from the solution and so there was no oxygen in the water for the fish to breathe.

47. Henry's Law says that as pressure increases, nitrogen will more easily dissolve in blood. To reverse this process, divers should ascend to lower pressures.

48. Henry's Law says that as pressure increases, oxygen will more easily dissolve in blood. To reverse this process, divers should ascend to lower pressures or breathe special gas mixtures with lower oxygen levels.

49. **Given:** room temperature, 80.0 L aquarium, $P_{Total} = 1.0$ atm; $\chi_{N2} = 0.78$ **Find:** m (N_2)
   Other: $k_H(N_2) = 6.1 \times 10^{-4}$ M/L at 25 °C
   Conceptual plan: P_{Total}, χ_{N2} → P_{N2} then $P_{N2}, k_H(N_2)$ → S_{N2} then   L → mol   → g

   $P_{N2} = \chi_{N2}\,P_{Total}$ $S_{N2} = k_H(N_2)\,P_{N2}$ S_{N2} $\dfrac{28.01 \text{ g}}{1 \text{ mol}}$

   Solution: $P_{N2} = \chi_{N2}\,P_{Total} = 0.78 \times 1.0 \text{ atm} = 0.78 \text{ atm}$ then

   $S_{N2} = k_H(N_2)\,P_{N2} = 6.1 \times 10^{-4} \dfrac{\text{M}}{\text{atm}} \times 0.78 \text{ atm} = 4.758 \times 10^{-4} \text{ M}$ then

   $80.0 \text{ L} \times 4.758 \times 10^{-4} \dfrac{\text{mol}}{\text{L}} \times \dfrac{28.01 \text{ g}}{1 \text{ mol}} = 1.1 \text{ g}$

   Check: The units (g) are correct. The magnitude of the answer (1) seems reasonable since we have 80 L of water and expect much less than a mole of nitrogen.

50. **Given:** Helium, 25 °C, $P_{He} = 1.0$ atm **Find:** S_{He} (M) **Other:** $k_H(He) = 3.7 \times 10^{-4}$ M/L at 25 °C

Conceptual plan: $P_{He}, k_H(He) \rightarrow S_{He}$

$$S'_{He} = k_H(He) P_{He}$$

Solution: $S_{He} = k_H(He) P_{He} = 3.7 \times 10^{-4} \dfrac{M}{\text{atm}} \times 1.0 \text{ atm} = 3.7 \times 10^{-4}$ M

Check: The units (M) are correct. The magnitude of the answer (10^{-4}) seems reasonable since this is the value of k_H.

51. **Given:** NaCl and water; 133 g NaCl in 1.00 L solution **Find:** M, m, and mass percent

Other: d = 1.08 g/mL

Conceptual plan: $g_{NaCl} \rightarrow$ **mol** and $L \rightarrow mL \rightarrow g_{soln}$ and $g_{soln}\ g_{NaCl} \rightarrow g_{H2O} \rightarrow kg_{H2O}$ **then**

$$\dfrac{1 \text{ mol NaCl}}{58.44 \text{ g NaCl}} \qquad \dfrac{1000 \text{ mL}}{1 \text{ L}} \quad \dfrac{1.08 \text{ g}}{1 \text{ mL}} \qquad g_{H2O} = g_{soln} - g_{NaCl} \qquad \dfrac{1 \text{ kg}}{1000 \text{ g}}$$

mol, V $\rightarrow$ M and **mol, kg$_{H2O}$ $\rightarrow m$** and $g_{soln}\ g_{NaCl} \rightarrow$ **mass percent**

$$M = \dfrac{\text{amount solute (moles)}}{\text{volume solution (L)}} \qquad m = \dfrac{\text{amount solute (moles)}}{\text{mass solvent (kg)}} \qquad mass\ percent = \dfrac{\text{mass solute}}{\text{mass solution}} \times 100\%$$

Solution: $133 \text{ g NaCl} \times \dfrac{1 \text{ mol NaCl}}{58.44 \text{ g NaCl}} = 2.27584 \text{ mol NaCl}$ and $1.00 \text{ L} \times \dfrac{1000 \text{ mL}}{1 \text{ L}} \times \dfrac{1.08 \text{ g}}{1 \text{ mL}} = 1080 \text{ g soln}$ and

$g_{H2O} = g_{soln} - g_{NaCl} = 1080 \text{ g} - 133 \text{ g} = 947 \text{ g H}_2\text{O} \times \dfrac{1 \text{ kg}}{1000 \text{ g}} = 0.947 \text{ kg H}_2\text{O}$ then

$$M = \dfrac{\text{amount solute (moles)}}{\text{volume solution (L)}} = \dfrac{2.27584 \text{ mol NaCl}}{1.00 \text{ L soln}} = 2.28 \text{ M}\ \ \text{and}$$

$$m = \dfrac{\text{amount solute (moles)}}{\text{mass solvent (kg)}} = \dfrac{2.27584 \text{ mol NaCl}}{0.947 \text{ kg H}_2\text{O}} = 2.4\ m\ \ \text{and}$$

$$mass\ percent = \dfrac{\text{mass solute}}{\text{mass solution}} \times 100\% = \dfrac{133 \text{ g NaCl}}{1080 \text{ g soln}} \times 100\% = 12.3\ \%\ \text{by mass}.$$

Check: The units (M, m and percent by mass) are correct. The magnitude of the answer (2.28 M) seems reasonable since we have 133 g NaCl, which is a couple of moles and we have 1 L. The magnitude of the answer (2.4 m) seems reasonable since it is a little higher than the molarity, which we expect since we only use the solvent weight in the denominator. The magnitude of the answer (12 %) seems reasonable since we have 133 g NaCl and just over 1000 g of solution.

52. **Given:** KNO$_3$ and water; 88.4 g KNO$_3$ in 1.50 L solution **Find:** M, m, and mass percent

Other: d = 1.05 g/mL

Conceptual plan: $g_{KNO3} \rightarrow$ **mol** and $L \rightarrow mL \rightarrow g_{soln}$ and $g_{soln}\ g_{KNO3} \rightarrow g_{H2O} \rightarrow kg_{H2O}$ **then**

$$\dfrac{1 \text{ mol KNO}_3}{101.11 \text{ g KNO}_3} \qquad \dfrac{1000 \text{ mL}}{1 \text{ L}} \quad \dfrac{1.05 \text{ g}}{1 \text{ mL}} \qquad g_{H2O} = g_{soln} - g_{KNO3} \qquad \dfrac{1 \text{ kg}}{1000 \text{ g}}$$

mol, V $\rightarrow$ M and **mol, kg$_{H2O}$ $\rightarrow m$** and $g_{soln}\ g_{KNO3} \rightarrow$ **mass percent**

$$M = \dfrac{\text{amount solute (moles)}}{\text{volume solution (L)}} \qquad m = \dfrac{\text{amount solute (moles)}}{\text{mass solvent (kg)}} \qquad mass\ percent = \dfrac{\text{mass solute}}{\text{mass solution}} \times 100\%$$

Solution: $88.4 \text{ g NaCl} \times \dfrac{1 \text{ mol KNO}_3}{101.11 \text{ g KNO}_3} = 0.874295 \text{ mol KNO}_3$ and $1.50 \text{ L} \times \dfrac{1000 \text{ mL}}{1 \text{ L}} \times \dfrac{1.05 \text{ g}}{1 \text{ mL}} = 1575 \text{ g soln}$

and $g_{H2O} = g_{soln} - g_{NaCl} = 1575 \text{ g} - 88.4 \text{ g} = 1486.6 \text{ g H}_2\text{O} \times \dfrac{1 \text{ kg}}{1000 \text{ g}} = 1.4866 \text{ kg H}_2\text{O}$ then

$$M = \dfrac{\text{amount solute (moles)}}{\text{volume solution (L)}} = \dfrac{0.874295 \text{ mol KNO}_3}{1.50 \text{ L soln}} = 0.583 \text{ M}\ \ \text{and}$$

$$m = \dfrac{\text{amount solute (moles)}}{\text{mass solvent (kg)}} = \dfrac{0.874295 \text{ mol KNO}_3}{1.4866 \text{ kg H}_2\text{O}} = 0.588\ m\ \ \text{and}$$

$$mass\ percent = \frac{mass\ solute}{mass\ solution} \times 100\% = \frac{88.4\ g\ KNO_3}{1575\ g\ soln} \times 100\% = 5.61\%\ by\ mass\ .$$

Check: The units (M, m and percent by mass) are correct. The magnitude of the answer (0.58 M) seems reasonable since we have 88.4 g KNO_3, which is less than a mole and we have 1.5 L. The magnitude of the answer (0.59 m) seems reasonable since it is a little higher than the molarity, which we expect since we only use the solvent weight in the denominator. The magnitude of the answer (6 %) seems reasonable since we have 88 g KNO_3 and ~ 1500 g of solution.

53. **Given:** initial solution: 50.0 mL of 5.00 M KI; final solution contains: 3.25 g KI in 25.0 mL
    Find: final volume to dilute initial solution to
    Conceptual plan:
    final solution: $g_{KI} \rightarrow mol$ and $mL \rightarrow L$ then mol, V $\rightarrow$ M_2 then $M_1, V_1, M_2 \rightarrow V_2$

    $$\frac{1\ mol\ KI}{166.006\ g\ KI} \qquad \frac{1\ L}{1000\ mL} \qquad M = \frac{amount\ solute\ (moles)}{volume\ solution\ (L)} \qquad M_1\ V_1 = M_2\ V_2$$

    Solution: and $3.25\ \cancel{g\ KI} \times \dfrac{1\ mol\ KI}{166.006\ \cancel{g\ KI}} = 0.0195776\ mol\ KI$ and $25.0\ \cancel{mL} \times \dfrac{1\ L}{1000\ \cancel{mL}} = 0.0250\ mL$

    then $M = \dfrac{amount\ solute\ (moles)}{volume\ solution\ (L)} = \dfrac{0.0195776\ mol\ KI}{0.0250\ L\ soln} = 0.783104\ M$ then $M_1\ V_1 = M_2\ V_2$.

    Rearrange to solve for V_2. $\qquad V_2 = \dfrac{M_1}{M_2}\ x\ V_1 = \dfrac{5.00\ M}{0.783104\ M}\ x\ 50.0\ mL = 319\ mL$ diluted volume

    Check: The units (mL) are correct. The magnitude of the answer (319 mL) seems reasonable since we are starting with a concentration of 5 M and ending with a concentration of less than 1 M.

54. **Given:** initial solution: 125 mL of 8.00 M $CuCl_2$; final solution contains: 5.9 g $CuCl_2$ in 50.0 mL
    Find: final volume to dilute initial solution to
    Conceptual plan:
    final solution: $g_{CuCl2} \rightarrow mol$ and $mL \rightarrow L$ then mol, V $\rightarrow$ M_2 then $M_1, V_1, M_2 \rightarrow V_2$

    $$\frac{1\ mol\ CuCl_2}{134.45\ g\ CuCl_2} \qquad \frac{1\ L}{1000\ mL} \qquad M = \frac{amount\ solute\ (moles)}{volume\ solution\ (L)} \qquad M_1\ V_1 = M_2\ V_2$$

    Solution: and $5.9\ \cancel{g\ CuCl_2} \times \dfrac{1\ mol\ CuCl_2}{134.45\ \cancel{g\ CuCl_2}} = 0.043884\ mol\ CuCl_2$ and $50.0\ \cancel{mL} \times \dfrac{1\ L}{1000\ \cancel{mL}} = 0.0500\ mL$

    then $M = \dfrac{amount\ solute\ (moles)}{volume\ solution\ (L)} = \dfrac{0.043884\ mol\ CuCl_2}{0.0500\ L\ soln} = 0.87768\ M$ then $M_1\ V_1 = M_2\ V_2$. Rearrange to solve

    for V_2. $\qquad V_2 = \dfrac{M_1}{M_2}\ x\ V_1 = \dfrac{8.00\ M}{0.87768\ M}\ x\ 125\ mL = 1100\ mL$ diluted volume

    Check: The units (mL) are correct. The magnitude of the answer (1100 mL) seems reasonable since we are starting with a concentration of 8 M and ending with a concentration of less than 1 M.

55. **Given:** $AgNO_3$ and water; 3.4 % Ag by mass, 4.8 L solution   **Find:** m (Ag)   **Other:** d = 1.01 g/mL
    Conceptual plan: L $\rightarrow$ mL $\rightarrow$ g_{soln} $\rightarrow$ g_{Ag}
    $$\frac{1000\ mL}{1\ L} \qquad \frac{1.01\ g}{1\ mL} \qquad \frac{3.4\ g\ Ag}{100\ g\ soln}$$

    Solution: $4.8\ \cancel{L} \times \dfrac{1000\ \cancel{mL}}{1\ \cancel{L}} \times \dfrac{1.01\ g}{1\ \cancel{mL}} = 4848\ g\ soln$ then $4848\ \cancel{g\ soln} \times \dfrac{3.4\ g\ Ag}{100\ \cancel{g\ soln}} = 160\ g\ Ag = 1.6\ x\ 10^2\ g\ Ag$.

    Check: The units (g) are correct. The magnitude of the answer (160 g) seems reasonable since we have almost 5000 g solution.

56. **Given:** dioxin and water; 0.085 % dioxin by mass, 2.5 L solution   **Find:** m (dioxin)   **Other:** d = 1.00 g/mL
    Conceptual plan: L $\rightarrow$ mL $\rightarrow$ g_{soln} $\rightarrow$ g_{dioxin}
    $$\frac{1000\ mL}{1\ L} \qquad \frac{1.01\ g}{1\ mL} \qquad \frac{0.085\ g\ dioxin}{100\ g\ soln}$$

Solution: $2.5 \, \cancel{L} \times \dfrac{1000 \, \cancel{mL}}{1 \, \cancel{L}} \times \dfrac{1.00 \, g}{1 \, \cancel{mL}} = 2\underline{5}00 \, g$ soln   then $2\underline{5}00 \, \cancel{g\,soln} \times \dfrac{0.085 \, g \, dioxin}{100 \, \cancel{g\,soln}} = 2.1 \, g$ dioxin .

Check: The units (g) are correct.   The magnitude of the answer (2 g) seems reasonable since we have 2500 g solution and a low concentration.

57. **Given:** Ca^{2+} and water; 0.0085 % Ca^{2+} by mass, 1.2 g Ca   **Find:** m (water)
   Conceptual plan: $g_{Ca} \rightarrow g_{soln} \rightarrow g_{H2O}$

$$\dfrac{100 \, g \, soln}{0.0085 \, g \, Ca} \qquad g_{H2O} = g_{soln} - g_{Ca}$$

   Solution: $1.2 \, \cancel{g\,Ca} \times \dfrac{100 \, g \, soln}{0.0085 \, \cancel{g\,Ca}} = 1\underline{4}118 \, g$ soln then $g_{H2O} = g_{soln} - g_{Ca} = 1\underline{4}118 \, g - 1.2 \, g = 1.4 \times 10^4 \, g$ water .

   Check: The units (g) are correct.   The magnitude of the answer (10^4 g) seems reasonable since we have such a low concentration of Ca.

58. **Given:** Pb and water; 0.0011 % Pb by mass, 150 mg Pb   **Find:** V (mL)   **Other:** d = 1.00 g/mL
   Conceptual plan: $mg_{Pb} \rightarrow g_{Pb} \rightarrow g_{soln} \rightarrow mL$

$$\dfrac{1000 \, g}{1 \, mg} \quad \dfrac{100 \, g \, soln}{0.0011 \, g \, Pb} \quad \dfrac{1 \, mL}{1.00 \, g}$$

   Solution: $150 \, \cancel{mg\,Pb} \times \dfrac{1 \, \cancel{g\,Pb}}{1000 \, \cancel{mg\,Pb}} \times \dfrac{100 \, \cancel{g\,soln}}{0.0011 \, \cancel{g\,Pb}} \times \dfrac{1 \, mL}{1.00 \, \cancel{g}} = 1.4 \times 10^4 \, mL$

   Check: The units (mL) are correct.   The magnitude of the answer (10^4 g) seems reasonable since we have such a low concentration of Pb.

59. **Given:** concentrated HNO_3: 70.3 % HNO_3 by mass, d = 1.41 g/mL; final solution: 1.15 L of 0.100 M HNO_3 **Find:** describe final solution preparation
   Conceptual plan:
   $M_2, V_2 \rightarrow mol_{HNO3} \rightarrow g_{HNO3} \rightarrow g_{conc\,acid} \rightarrow mL_{conc\,acid}$ **then describe method**

$$mol = M \, V \qquad \dfrac{63.02 \, g \, HNO_3}{1 \, mol \, HNO_3} \quad \dfrac{100 \, g \, conc \, acid}{70.3 \, g \, HNO_3} \quad \dfrac{1 \, mL}{1.41 \, g}$$

   Solution: $mol = M \, V = 0.100 \, \dfrac{mol \, HNO_3}{1 \, \cancel{L\,soln}} \times 1.15 \, \cancel{L\,soln} = 0.115 \, mol \, HNO_3$ then

$$0.115 \, \cancel{mol\,HNO_3} \times \dfrac{63.02 \, \cancel{g\,HNO_3}}{1 \, \cancel{mol\,HNO_3}} \times \dfrac{100 \, \cancel{g\,conc\,acid}}{70.3 \, \cancel{g\,HNO_3}} \times \dfrac{1 \, mL \, conc \, acid}{1.41 \, \cancel{g\,conc\,acid}} = 7.31 \, mL \, conc \, acid \ .$$

   Prepare the solution by putting 1.00 L of distilled water in a container. Carefully pour in the 7.31 mL of the concentrated acid, mix the solution and allow it to cool. Finally add enough water to generate a total volume of solution (1.15 L). It is important to add acid to water, and not the reverse, since there is such a large amount of heat released upon mixing.
   Check: The units (mL) are correct.   The magnitude of the answer (7 g) seems reasonable since we are starting with such a very concentrated solution and diluting it to a low concentration.

60. **Given:** concentrated HCl: 37.0 % HCl by mass, d = 1.20 g/mL; final solution: 2.85 L of 0.500 M HCl
   Find: describe final solution preparation
   Conceptual plan: $M_2, V_2 \rightarrow mol_{HCl} \rightarrow g_{HCl} \rightarrow g_{conc\,acid} \rightarrow mL_{conc\,acid}$ **then describe method**

$$mol = M \, V \qquad \dfrac{36.46 \, g \, HCl}{1 \, mol \, HCl} \quad \dfrac{100 \, g \, conc \, acid}{37.0 \, g \, HCl} \quad \dfrac{1 \, mL}{1.20 \, g}$$

   Solution: $mol = M \, V = 0.500 \, \dfrac{mol \, HCl}{1 \, \cancel{L\,soln}} \times 2.85 \, \cancel{L\,soln} = 1.4\underline{2}5 \, mol \, HCl$ then

$$1.4\underline{2}5 \, \cancel{mol\,HCl} \times \dfrac{36.46 \, \cancel{g\,HCl}}{1 \, \cancel{mol\,HCl}} \times \dfrac{100 \, \cancel{g\,conc\,acid}}{37.0 \, \cancel{g\,HCl}} \times \dfrac{1 \, mL \, conc \, acid}{1.20 \, \cancel{g\,conc\,acid}} = 117 \, mL \, conc \, acid \ .$$

   Prepare the solution by putting 2.5 L of distilled water in a container. Carefully pour in the 117 mL of the concentrated acid, mix the solution and allow it to cool. Finally add enough water to generate a total volume of solution. It is important to add acid to water, and not the reverse, since there is such a large amount of heat released upon mixing.

Check: The units (mL) are correct. The magnitude of the answer (117 g) seems reasonable since we are starting with such a concentrated solution and diluting it to a low concentration.

61. a) **Given**: 1.00×10^2 mL of 0.500 M KCl   **Find**: describe final solution preparation

   Conceptual plan: $\textbf{mL} \rightarrow \textbf{L}$ then $\textbf{M, V} \rightarrow \textbf{mol}_{KCl} \rightarrow \textbf{g}_{KCl}$ then describe method

$$\frac{1 L}{1000\ mL} \qquad mol = M\ V \qquad \frac{74.56\ g\ KCl}{1\ mol\ KCl}$$

   Solution:

$$1.00 \times 10^2\ \cancel{mL} \times \frac{1 L}{1000\ \cancel{mL}} = 0.100\ L$$

$$mol = M\ V = 0.500\ \frac{mol\ KCl}{1\ \cancel{L\ soln}} \times 0.100\ \cancel{L\ soln} = 0.0500\ mol\ KCl$$

then $0.0500\ \cancel{mol\ KCl} \times \dfrac{74.56\ g\ KCl}{1\ \cancel{mol\ KCl}} = 3.73\ g\ KCl$.

Prepare the solution carefully adding 3.73 g KCl in a 100-mL volumetric flask. Add ~ 75 mL of distilled water and agitate the solution until the salt dissolves completely. Finally add enough water to generate a total volume of solution (add water to the mark on the flask).

Check: The units (g) are correct. The magnitude of the answer (7 g) seems reasonable since we are making a small volume of solution and the formula weight of KCl is ~ 75 g/mol.

   b) **Given**: 1.00×10^2 g of 0.500 m KCl   **Find**: describe final solution preparation

   Conceptual plan:

$m \rightarrow \textbf{mol}_{KCl}/\textbf{1 kg solvent} \rightarrow \textbf{g}_{KCl}/\textbf{1 kg solvent}$ then $\textbf{g}_{KCl}/\textbf{1 kg solvent, g}_{soln} \rightarrow \textbf{g}_{KCl}, \textbf{g}_{H2O}$

$$m = \frac{\text{amount solute (moles)}}{\text{mass solvent (kg)}} \qquad \frac{74.56\ g\ KCl}{1\ mol\ KCl} \qquad\qquad g_{soln} = g_{KCl} + g_{H2O}$$

then describe method

   Solution: $m = \dfrac{\text{amount solute (moles)}}{\text{mass solvent (kg)}}$ so $\ 0.500\ m = \dfrac{0.500\ mol\ KCl}{1\ kg\ H_2O}$ so

$$\frac{0.500\ \cancel{mol\ KCl}}{1\ kg\ H_2O} \times \frac{74.56\ g\ KCl}{1\ \cancel{mol\ KCl}} = \frac{37.28\ g\ KCl}{1000\ g\ H_2O} \quad g_{soln} = g_{KCl} + g_{H2O} \text{ so } g_{soln} - g_{KCl} = g_{H2O}$$

substitute into ratio $\dfrac{0.0372\underline{8}\ g\ KCl}{1\ g\ H_2O} = \dfrac{x\ g\ KCl}{100\ g\ soln - x\ g\ KCl}$ Rearrange and solve for x g KCl

$0.0372\underline{8}\ (100\ g\ soln - x\ g\ KCl) = x\ g\ KCl$ → $3.72\underline{8} - 0.0372\underline{8}\ (x\ g\ KCl) = x\ g\ KCl$ →

$3.72\underline{8} = 1.0372\underline{8}\ (x\ g\ KCl)$ → $\dfrac{3.72\underline{8}}{1.0372\underline{8}} = x\ g\ KCl = 3.59\ g\ KCl$ then

$g_{H2O} = g_{soln} - g_{KCl} = 100.\ g - 3.59\ g = 96.41\ g\ H_2O$.

Prepare the solution carefully adding 3.59 g KCl to a container with 96.41 g of distilled water and agitate the solution until the salt dissolves completely.

Check: The units (g) are correct. The magnitude of the answer (3.6 g) seems reasonable since we are making a small volume of solution and the formula weight of KCl is ~ 75 g/mol.

   c) **Given**: 1.00×10^2 g of 5.0 % KCl by mass   **Find**: describe final solution preparation

   Conceptual plan: $\textbf{g}_{soln} \rightarrow \textbf{g}_{KCl}$ then $\textbf{g}_{KCl}, \textbf{g}_{soln} \rightarrow \textbf{g}_{H2O}$

$$\frac{5.0\ g\ KCl}{100\ g\ soln} \qquad\qquad g_{soln} = g_{KCl} + g_{H2O}$$

then describe method

   Solution: $1.00 \times 10^2\ \cancel{g\ soln} \times \dfrac{5.0\ g\ KCl}{100\ \cancel{g\ soln}} = 5.0\ g\ KCl$ then $g_{soln} = g_{KCl} + g_{H2O}$.

So $g_{H2O} = g_{soln} - g_{KCl} = 100.\ g - 5.0\ g = 95\ g\ H_2O$

Prepare the solution carefully adding 5.0 g KCl to a container with 95 g of distilled water and agitate the solution until the salt dissolves completely.

Check: The units (g) are correct. The magnitude of the answer (5 g) seems reasonable since we are making a small volume of solution and the solution is 5 % by mass KCl.

62. a) **Given:** 125 mL of 0.100 M $NaNO_3$ **Find:** describe final solution preparation
   Conceptual plan: $mL \rightarrow L$ then $M, V \rightarrow mol_{NaNO3} \rightarrow g_{NaNO3}$ then describe method

$$\frac{1L}{1000\ mL} \qquad mol = M\ V \qquad \frac{85.00\ g\ NaNO_3}{1\ mol\ NaNO_3}$$

Solution: $125\ \cancel{mL} \times \dfrac{1L}{1000\ \cancel{mL}} = 0.125\ L$

$mol = M\ V = 0.100\ \dfrac{mol\ NaNO_3}{1\ \cancel{L\ soln}} \times 0.125\ \cancel{L\ soln} = 0.0125\ mol\ NaNO_3$ then

$0.0125\ \cancel{mol\ NaNO_3} \times \dfrac{85.00\ g\ NaNO_3}{1\ \cancel{mol\ NaNO_3}} = 1.06\ g\ NaNO_3$.

Prepare the solution carefully adding 1.06 g $NaNO_3$ to a container. Add ~ 100 mL of distilled water and agitate the solution until the salt dissolves completely. Finally add enough water to generate a total volume of solution (125 mL).
Check: The units (g) are correct. The magnitude of the answer (7 g) seems reasonable since we are making a small volume of solution and the formula weight of KCl is ~ 75 g/mol.

b) **Given:** 125 g of 0.100 m $NaNO_3$ **Find:** describe final solution preparation
   Conceptual plan: $m \rightarrow mol_{NaNO3}/1\ kg\ solvent \rightarrow g_{NaNO3}/1\ kg\ solvent$ then

$$m = \frac{amount\ solute\ (moles)}{mass\ solvent\ (kg)} \qquad \frac{85.00\ g\ NaNO_3}{1\ mol\ NaNO_3}$$

$g_{NaNO3}/1\ kg\ solvent, g_{soln} \rightarrow g_{NaNO3}, g_{H2O}$ then describe method

$$g_{soln} = g_{NaNO3} + g_{H2O}$$

Solution: $m = \dfrac{amount\ solute\ (moles)}{mass\ solvent\ (kg)}$ so $0.100\ m = \dfrac{0.500\ mol\ NaNO_3}{1\ kg\ H_2O}$ so

$\dfrac{0.100\ \cancel{mol\ NaNO_3}}{1\ kg\ H_2O} \times \dfrac{85.00\ g\ NaNO_3}{1\ \cancel{mol\ NaNO_3}} = \dfrac{8.50\ g\ NaNO_3}{1000\ g\ H_2O}$ then $g_{soln} = g_{NaNO3} + g_{H2O}$ so

$g_{soln} - g_{NaNO3} = g_{H2O}$ substitute into ratio $\dfrac{8.50\ g\ NaNO_3}{1\ g\ H_2O} = \dfrac{x\ g\ NaNO_3}{125\ g\ soln - x\ g\ NaNO_3}$

Rearrange and solve for x g $NaNO_3$ $0.00850\ (125\ g\ soln - x\ g\ NaNO_3) = x\ g\ NaNO_3 \rightarrow$

$1.0\underline{6}25 - 0.00850\ (x\ g\ NaNO_3) = x\ g\ NaNO_3 \rightarrow \qquad 1.0\underline{6}25 = 1.00850\ (x\ g\ NaNO_3) \rightarrow$

$\dfrac{3.7\underline{2}8}{1.00850} = x\ g\ NaNO_3 = 1.05\ g\ NaNO_3$ then $g_{H2O} = g_{soln} - g_{KCl} = 125\ g - 1.05\ g = 124\ g\ H_2O$.

Prepare the solution carefully adding 1.05 g $NaNO_3$ to a container with 124 g of distilled water and agitate the solution until the salt dissolves completely.
Check: The units (g) are correct. The magnitude of the answer (1 g) seems reasonable since we are making a small volume of solution and the formula weight of $NaNO_3$ is 85 g/mol.

c) **Given:** 125 g of 1.0 % $NaNO_3$ by mass **Find:** describe final solution preparation
   Conceptual plan: $g_{soln} \rightarrow g_{NaNO3}$ then $g_{NaNO3}, g_{soln} \rightarrow g_{H2O}$

$$\frac{1.0\ g\ NaNO_3}{100\ g\ soln} \qquad\qquad g_{soln} = g_{NaNO3} + g_{H2O}$$

then describe method

Solution: $125\ \cancel{g\ soln} \times \dfrac{1.0\ g\ NaNO_3}{100\ \cancel{g\ soln}} = 1.25\ g\ NaNO_3$ then $g_{soln} = g_{NaNO3} + g_{H2O}$. So

$$g_{H2O} = g_{soln} - g_{KCl} = 125\ g - 1.25\ g = 124\ g\ H_2O$$

Prepare the solution carefully adding 1.3 g $NaNO_3$ to a container with 124 g of distilled water and agitate the solution until the salt dissolves completely.
Check: The units (g) are correct. The magnitude of the answer (1 g) seems reasonable since we are making a small volume of solution and the solution is 1 % by mass $NaNO_3$.

63. a) **Given:** 28.4 g of glucose ($C_6H_{12}O_6$) in 355 g water; final volume = 378 mL   **Find:** molarity

Conceptual plan: mL $\rightarrow$ L and g $_{C6H12O6}$ $\rightarrow$ mol $_{C6H12O6}$ then mol $_{C6H12O6}$, V $\rightarrow$ M

$$\frac{1\,L}{1000\,mL} \qquad \frac{1\,mol\,C_6H_{12}O_6}{180.16\,g\,C_6H_{12}O_6} \qquad M = \frac{amount\ solute\ (moles)}{volume\ solution\ (L)}$$

Solution: $378\ \cancel{mL} \times \dfrac{1\,L}{1000\ \cancel{mL}} = 0.378\ L$ and

$$28.4\ \cancel{g\,C_6H_{12}O_6} \times \frac{1\,mol\,C_6H_{12}O_6}{180.16\ \cancel{g\,C_6H_{12}O_6}} = 0.15\underline{7}638\ mol\,C_6H_{12}O_6$$

$$M = \frac{amount\ solute\ (moles)}{volume\ solution\ (L)} = \frac{0.15\underline{7}638\ mol\,C_6H_{12}O_6}{0.378\ L} = 0.417\ M$$

Check: The units (M) are correct.   The magnitude of the answer (0.4 M) seems reasonable since we have 1/8 mole in about 1/3 L.

b) **Given:** 28.4 g of glucose ($C_6H_{12}O_6$) in 355 g water; final volume = 378 mL   **Find:** molality

Conceptual plan: g $_{H2O}$ $\rightarrow$ kg $_{H2O}$ and g $_{C6H12O6}$ $\rightarrow$ mol $_{C6H12O6}$ then mol $_{C6H12O6}$, kg $_{H2O}$ $\rightarrow$ m

$$\frac{1\,kg}{1000\,g} \qquad \frac{1\,mol\,C_6H_{12}O_6}{180.16\,g\,C_6H_{12}O_6} \qquad m = \frac{amount\ solute\ (moles)}{mass\ solvent\ (kg)}$$

Solution: $355\ \cancel{g} \times \dfrac{1\,kg}{1000\ \cancel{g}} = 0.355\ kg$ and

$$28.4\ \cancel{g\,C_6H_{12}O_6} \times \frac{1\,mol\,C_6H_{12}O_6}{180.16\ \cancel{g\,C_6H_{12}O_6}} = 0.15\underline{7}638\ mol\,C_6H_{12}O_6$$

$$m = \frac{amount\ solute\ (moles)}{mass\ solvent\ (kg)} = \frac{0.15\underline{7}638\ mol\,C_6H_{12}O_6}{0.355\ kg} = 0.444\ m$$

Check: The units (m) are correct.   The magnitude of the answer (0.4 m) seems reasonable since we have 1/8 mole in about 1/3 kg.

c) **Given:** 28.4 g of glucose ($C_6H_{12}O_6$) in 355 g water; final volume = 378 mL   **Find:** percent by mass

Conceptual plan: g $_{C6H12O6}$, g $_{H2O}$ $\rightarrow$ g $_{soln}$ then g $_{C6H12O6}$, g $_{soln}$ $\rightarrow$ **percent by mass**

$$g_{soln} = g_{C6H12O6} + g_{H2O} \qquad mass\ percent = \frac{mass\ solute}{mass\ solution} \times 100\,\%$$

Solution: $g_{soln} = g_{C6H12O6} + g_{H2O} = 28.4\ g + 355\ g = 38\underline{3}.4\ g$ soln then

$$mass\ percent = \frac{mass\ solute}{mass\ solution} \times 100\,\% = \frac{28.4\ g\,C_6H_{12}O_6}{38\underline{3}.4\ g\ soln} \times 100\,\% = 7.41\ percent\ by\ mass$$

Check: The units (percent by mass) are correct.   The magnitude of the answer (7 %) seems reasonable since we are dissolving 28 g in 355 g.

d) **Given:** 28.4 g of glucose ($C_6H_{12}O_6$) in 355 g water; final volume = 378 mL   **Find:** mole fraction

Conceptual plan:

g $_{C6H12O6}$ $\rightarrow$ mol $_{C6H12O6}$ and g $_{H2O}$ $\rightarrow$ mol $_{H2O}$ then mol $_{C6H12O6}$, mol $_{H2O}$ $\rightarrow$ $\chi_{C6H12O6}$

$$\frac{1\,mol\,C_6H_{12}O_6}{180.16\,g\,C_6H_{12}O_6} \qquad \frac{1\,mol\,H_2O}{18.02\,g\,H_2O} \qquad \chi = \frac{amount\ solute\ (in\ moles)}{total\ amount\ of\ solute\ and\ solvent\ (in\ moles)}$$

Solution: $28.4\ \cancel{g\,C_6H_{12}O_6} \times \dfrac{1\,mol\,C_6H_{12}O_6}{180.16\ \cancel{g\,C_6H_{12}O_6}} = 0.15\underline{7}638\ mol\,C_6H_{12}O_6$ and

$$355\ \cancel{g\,H_2O} \times \frac{1\,mol\,H_2O}{18.02\ \cancel{g\,H_2O}} = 19.\underline{7}003\ mol\,H_2O \qquad then$$

$$\chi = \frac{amount\ solute\ (in\ moles)}{total\ amount\ of\ solute\ and\ solvent\ (in\ moles)} = \frac{0.15\underline{7}638\ \cancel{mol}}{0.15\underline{7}638\ \cancel{mol} + 19.\underline{7}003\ \cancel{mol}} = 0.00794$$

Check: The units (none) are correct.   The magnitude of the answer (0.008) seems reasonable since we have many more grams of water and water has a much lower molecular weight.

399

e) **Given:** 28.4 g of glucose ($C_6H_{12}O_6$) in 355 g water; final volume = 378 mL   **Find:** mole percent

Conceptual plan: use answer from part d)   then $\chi_{C6H12O6}$ → mole percent

$$\chi \times 100\%$$

Solution: *mole percent* = $\chi \times 100\% = 0.00794 \times 100\% = 0.794$ mole percent

Check: The units (%) are correct.   The magnitude of the answer (0.8) seems reasonable since we have many more grams of water and water has a much lower molecular weight and we are just increasing the answer from part d) by a factor of 100.

64. a) **Given:** 20.2 mL of methanol (CH_3OH) in 100.0 mL water; final volume = 118 mL   **Find:** molarity

Other: d (CH_3OH) = 0.782 g/mL; d (H_2O) = 1.00 g/mL

Conceptual plan: mL → L and mL_{CH3OH} → g_{CH3OH} → mol_{CH3OH} then mol_{CH3OH}, V → M

$$\frac{1L}{1000\ mL} \qquad \frac{0.782\ g}{1\ mL} \quad \frac{1\ mol\ CH_3OH}{32.04\ g\ CH_3OH} \qquad M = \frac{amount\ solute\ (moles)}{volume\ solution\ (L)}$$

Solution: $118\ \cancel{mL} \times \dfrac{1L}{1000\ \cancel{mL}} = 0.118\ L$ and

$$20.2\ \cancel{mL\ CH_3OH} \times \frac{0.782\ g\ \cancel{CH_3OH}}{1\ \cancel{mL\ CH_3OH}} \times \frac{1\ mol\ CH_3OH}{32.04\ \cancel{g\ CH_3OH}} = 0.492990\ mol\ CH_3OH$$

$$M = \frac{amount\ solute\ (moles)}{volume\ solution\ (L)} = \frac{0.492990\ mol\ CH_3OH}{0.118\ L} = 4.18\ M$$

Check: The units (M) are correct.   The magnitude of the answer (4 M) seems reasonable since we have 1/2 mole in about 1/8 L.

b) **Given:** 20.2 mL of methanol (CH_3OH) in 100.0 mL water; final volume = 118 mL   **Find:** molality

Other: d (CH_3OH) = 0.782 g/mL; d (H_2O) = 1.00 g/mL

Conceptual plan:

mL_{CH3OH} → g_{CH3OH} → mol_{CH3OH} and mL_{H2O} → g_{H2O} → kg_{H2O} then mol_{CH3OH}, kg_{H2O} → *m*

$$\frac{0.782\ g}{1\ mL} \quad \frac{1\ mol\ CH_3OH}{32.04\ g\ CH_3OH} \qquad \frac{1.00\ g}{1\ mL} \quad \frac{1\ kg}{1000\ g} \qquad m = \frac{amount\ solute\ (moles)}{mass\ solvent\ (kg)}$$

Solution: $20.2\ \cancel{mL\ CH_3OH} \times \dfrac{0.782\ g\ \cancel{CH_3OH}}{1\ \cancel{mL\ CH_3OH}} \times \dfrac{1\ mol\ CH_3OH}{32.04\ \cancel{g\ CH_3OH}} = 0.492990\ mol\ CH_3OH$ and

$$100.0\ \cancel{mL} \times \frac{1.00\ \cancel{g}}{1\ \cancel{mL}} \times \frac{1\ kg}{1000\ \cancel{g}} = 0.1000\ kg\ \text{ then}$$

$$m = \frac{amount\ solute\ (moles)}{mass\ solvent\ (kg)} = \frac{0.492990\ mol\ CH_3OH}{0.1000\ kg} = 4.93\ m$$

Check: The units (*m*) are correct.   The magnitude of the answer (5 *m*) seems reasonable since we have 1/2 mole in 1/10 kg.

c) **Given:** 20.2 mL of methanol (CH_3OH) in 100.0 mL water; final volume = 118 mL

Find: percent by mass

Other: d (CH_3OH) = 0.782 g/mL; d (H_2O) = 1.00 g/mL

Conceptual plan: mL_{CH3OH} → g_{CH3OH} and mL_{H2O} → g_{H2O} then g_{CH3OH}, g_{H2O} → g_{soln} then

$$\frac{0.782\ g}{1\ mL} \qquad\qquad \frac{1.00\ g}{1\ mL} \qquad\qquad g_{soln} = g_{C6H12O6} + g_{H2O}$$

g_{CH3OH}, g_{soln} → percent by mass

$$mass\ percent = \frac{mass\ solute}{mass\ solution} \times 100\%$$

Solution: $20.2\ \cancel{mL\ CH_3OH} \times \dfrac{0.782\ g\ CH_3OH}{1\ \cancel{mL\ CH_3OH}} = 15.7964\ g\ CH_3OH$ and

400

$$100.0 \text{ mL} \times \frac{1.00 \text{ g}}{1 \text{ mL}} = 100.0 \text{ g} \quad g_{soln} = g_{CH3OH} + g_{H2O} = 15.\underline{7}964 \text{ g} + 100.0 \text{ g} = 115.\underline{7}964 \text{ g soln then}$$

$$mass \ percent = \frac{mass \ solute}{mass \ solution} \times 100\% = \frac{15.\underline{7}964 \text{ g CH}_3\text{OH}}{115.\underline{7}964 \text{ g soln}} \times 100\% = 13.6 \text{ percent by mass}$$

Check: The units (percent by mass) are correct. The magnitude of the answer (14 %) seems reasonable since we are dissolving 16 g in 100 g.

d) **Given:** 20.2 mL of methanol (CH_3OH) in 100.0 mL water; final volume = 118 mL
Find: mole fraction
Other: d (CH_3OH) = 0.782 g/mL; d (H_2O) = 1.00 g/mL
Conceptual plan: $mL_{CH3OH} \rightarrow g_{CH3OH} \rightarrow mol_{CH3OH}$ and $mL_{H2O} \rightarrow g_{H2O} \rightarrow mol_{H2O}$ **then**

$$\frac{0.782 \text{ g}}{1 \text{ mL}} \quad \frac{1 \text{ mol CH}_3\text{OH}}{32.04 \text{ g CH}_3\text{OH}} \qquad \frac{1.00 \text{ g}}{1 \text{ mL}} \quad \frac{1 \text{ mol H}_2\text{O}}{18.01 \text{ g H}_2\text{O}}$$

$mol_{CH3OH}, mol_{H2O} \rightarrow \chi_{CH3OH}$

$$\chi = \frac{\text{amount solute (in moles)}}{\text{total amount of solute and solvent (in moles)}}$$

Solution: $20.2 \text{ mL CH}_3\text{OH} \times \dfrac{0.782 \text{ g CH}_3\text{OH}}{1 \text{ mL CH}_3\text{OH}} \times \dfrac{1 \text{ mol CH}_3\text{OH}}{32.04 \text{ g CH}_3\text{OH}} = 0.49\underline{2}990 \text{ mol CH}_3\text{OH}$ and

$$100.0 \text{ mL} \times \frac{1.00 \text{ g}}{1 \text{ mL}} \times \frac{1 \text{ mol H}_2\text{O}}{18.01 \text{ g H}_2\text{O}} = 5.55\underline{2}471 \text{ mol H}_2\text{O} \qquad \text{then}$$

$$\chi = \frac{\text{amount solute (in moles)}}{\text{total amount of solute and solvent (in moles)}} = \frac{0.49\underline{2}990 \text{ mol}}{0.49\underline{2}990 \text{ mol} + 5.55\underline{2}471 \text{ mol}} = 0.0815$$

Check: The units (none) are correct. The magnitude of the answer (0.08) seems reasonable since we have many more grams of water and water has a lower molecular weight.

e) **Given:** 20.2 mL of methanol (CH_3OH) in 100.0 mL water; final volume = 118 mL
Find: mole percent
Other: d (CH_3OH) = 0.782 g/mL; d (H_2O) = 1.00 g/mL
Conceptual plan: use answer from part d)   **then** $\chi_{C6H12O6} \rightarrow$ **mole percent**
$\chi \times 100\%$

Solution: *mole percent* = $\chi \times 100\% = 0.0815 \times 100\% = 8.15$ mole percent

Check: The units (%) are correct. The magnitude of the answer (8) seems reasonable since we have many more grams of water and water has a lower molecular weight and we are just increasing the answer from part d) by a factor of 100.

65. The level has decreased more in the beaker filled with pure water. The dissolved salt in the seawater decreases the vapor pressure and subsequently lowers the rate of vaporization.

66. b) Assume that the solutions obey Raoult's Law ($P_{solution} = \chi_{solvent} P^o_{solvent}$). Each of the solutions has the same amount of solvent, so we need to compare the number of moles of particles in the solvent. Without doing any calculations we can see that b) will have the lower number of particles than a) because b) has the higher molecular weight. Potassium acetate will generate ~ 2 moles of particles per mole of the salt, so it will generate more than the other two.

67. **Given:** 28.5 g of glycerin ($C_3H_8O_3$) in 125 mL water at 30 °C; P^o_{H2O} = 31.8 torr   **Find:** P_{H2O}
Other: d (H_2O) = 1.00 g/mL; glycerin is a nonionic solid
Conceptual plan:
$g_{C3H8O3} \rightarrow mol_{C3H8O3}$ and $mL_{H2O} \rightarrow g_{H2O} \rightarrow mol_{H2O}$ then $mol_{C3H8O3}, mol_{H2O} \rightarrow \chi_{H2O}$

$$\frac{1 \text{ mol C}_3\text{H}_8\text{O}_3}{92.09 \text{ g C}_3\text{H}_8\text{O}_3} \qquad \frac{1.00 \text{ g}}{1 \text{ mL}} \quad \frac{1 \text{ mol H}_2\text{O}}{18.01 \text{ g H}_2\text{O}} \qquad \chi = \frac{\text{amount solute (in moles)}}{\text{total amount of solute and solvent (in moles)}}$$

then χ_{H2O}, $P°_{H2O}$ → P_{H2O}

$$P_{solution} = \chi_{solvent} \, P°_{solvent}$$

Solution: $28.5 \text{ g } C_3H_8O_3 \times \dfrac{1 \text{ mol } C_3H_8O_3}{92.09 \text{ g } C_3H_8O_3} = 0.309466 \text{ mol } C_3H_8O_3$ and

$$125 \text{ mL} \times \dfrac{1.00 \text{ g}}{1 \text{ mL}} \times \dfrac{1 \text{ mol } H_2O}{18.01 \text{ g } H_2O} = 6.94059 \text{ mol } H_2O \qquad \text{then}$$

$$\chi = \dfrac{\text{amount solvent (in moles)}}{\text{total amount of solute and solvent (in moles)}} = \dfrac{6.94059 \text{ mol}}{0.309466 \text{ mol} + 6.94059 \text{ mol}} = 0.957316 \text{ then}$$

$$P_{solution} = \chi_{solvent} \, P°_{solvent} = 0.957316 \times 31.8 \text{ torr} = 30.4 \text{ torr}$$

Check: The units (torr) are correct. The magnitude of the answer (30 torr) seems reasonable since it is a drop from the pure vapor pressure. Very few moles of glycerin are added, so the pressure will not drop much.

68. **Given:** 10.85 % naphthalene($C_{10}H_8$) by mass in hexane(C_6H_{14}) at 25 °C; $P°_{C6H14}$ = 151 torr
   Find: P_{C6H14}
   Conceptual plan: % naphthalene($C_{10}H_8$) by mass → g_{C10H8}, g_{C6H14} then g_{C10H8} → mol $_{C10H8}$ and

$$\dfrac{10.85 \text{ g } C_{10}H_8}{100 \text{ g } (C_{10}H_8 + C_6H_{14})} \qquad \qquad \dfrac{1 \text{ mol } C_{10}H_8}{128.16 \text{ g } C_{10}H_8}$$

g_{C6H14} → mol $_{C6H14}$ then mol $_{C10H8}$, mol $_{C6H14}$ → χ_{C6H14} then χ_{C6H14}, $P°_{C6H14}$ → P_{C6H14}

$$\dfrac{1 \text{ mol } C_6H_{14}}{86.17 \text{ g } C_6H_{14}} \qquad \chi = \dfrac{\text{amount solute (in moles)}}{\text{total amount of solute and solvent (in moles)}} \qquad P_{solution} = \chi_{solvent} \, P°_{solvent}$$

Solution: $\dfrac{10.85 \text{ g } C_{10}H_8}{100 \text{ g } (C_{10}H_8 + C_6H_{14})}$ means 10.85 g $C_{10}H_8$ and (100 g - 10.85 g) = 89.15 g C_6H_{14} then

$$10.85 \text{ g } C_{10}H_8 \times \dfrac{1 \text{ mol } C_{10}H_8}{128.16 \text{ g } C_{10}H_8} = 0.08465980 \text{ mol } C_{10}H_8 \text{ and}$$

$$89.15 \text{ g } C_6H_{14} \times \dfrac{1 \text{ mol } C_6H_{14}}{86.17 \text{ g } C_6H_{14}} = 1.034583 \text{ mol } C_6H_{14} \qquad \text{then}$$

$$\chi = \dfrac{\text{amount solvent (in moles)}}{\text{total amount of solute and solvent (in moles)}} = \dfrac{1.034583 \text{ mol}}{0.08465980 \text{ mol} + 1.034583 \text{ mol}} = 0.9243599 \text{ then}$$

$$P_{solution} = \chi_{solvent} \, P°_{solvent} = 0.9243599 \times 151 \text{ torr} = 140. \text{ torr } C_6H_{14}$$

Check: The units (torr) are correct. The magnitude of the answer (140 torr) seems reasonable since it is a drop from the pure vapor pressure. Only a fraction of a mole of naphthalene is added, so the pressure will not drop much.

69. **Given:** 5.50 % NaCl by mass in water at 25 °C;   **Find:** P_{H2O} **Other:** $P°_{H2O}$ = 23.78 torr, i_{NaCl} = 1.9
   Conceptual plan: % NaCl by mass → g_{NaCl}, g_{H2O} then g_{NaCl} → mol $_{NaCl}$ and

$$\dfrac{5.50 \text{ g NaCl}}{100 \text{ g } (NaCl + H_2O)} \qquad \qquad \dfrac{1 \text{ mol NaCl}}{58.44 \text{ g NaCl}}$$

g_{H2O} → mol $_{H2O}$ then mol $_{NaCl}$, mol $_{H2O}$ → χ_{H2O} then χ_{H2O}, $P°_{H2O}$ → P_{H2O}

$$\dfrac{1 \text{ mol } H_2O}{18.01 \text{ g } H_2O} \qquad \chi = \dfrac{\text{amount solute (in moles)}}{\text{total amount of solute and solvent (in moles)}} \qquad P_{solution} = \chi_{solvent} \, P°_{solvent}$$

Solution: $\dfrac{5.50 \text{ g NaCl}}{100 \text{ g } (NaCl + H_2O)}$ means 5.50 g NaCl and (100 g - 5.50 g) = 94.5 g H_2O then

$$5.50 \text{ g NaCl} \times \dfrac{1 \text{ mol NaCl}}{58.44 \text{ g NaCl}} = 0.0941136 \text{ mol NaCl and } 94.5 \text{ g } H_2O \times \dfrac{1 \text{ mol } H_2O}{18.01 \text{ g } H_2O} = 5.24708 \text{ mol } H_2O$$

then $\chi_{solv} = \dfrac{\text{amount solvent (in moles)}}{\text{total amount solute and solvent (in moles)}} = \dfrac{5.24708 \text{ mol}}{5.24708 \text{ mol} + 1.9(0.0941136 \text{ mol})} = 0.96704$ then

$$P_{soln} = \chi_{solv} P°_{solv} = 0.96704 \times 23.78 \text{ torr} = 23.0 \text{ torr}$$

Check: The units (torr) are correct. The magnitude of the answer (23 torr) seems reasonable since it is a drop from the pure vapor pressure. Only a fraction of a mole of NaCl is added, so the pressure will not drop much.

70. **Given**: $CaCl_2$ and water; $P°_{H2O}$ = 92.6 mm Hg, $P°_{H2O}$ = 81.6 mm Hg at 50 °C; **Find**: mass percent $CaCl_2$
Conceptual plan: $P_{H2O}, P°_{H2O} \rightarrow \chi_{H2O}$ then assume 1 mol water, $\chi_{H2O} \rightarrow$ mol $_{CaCl2}$ then

$$P_{solution} = \chi_{solvent} \, P°_{solvent} \qquad\qquad \chi_{H2O} = \frac{\text{mol } H_2O}{\text{mol } H_2O + 3 \text{ x mol } CaCl_2}$$

mol $_{CaCl2} \rightarrow$ g $_{CaCl2}$ and   mol $_{H2O} \rightarrow$ g $_{H2O}$ then   g $_{CaCl2}$, g $_{H2O} \rightarrow$ **percent by mass $CaCl_2$**

$$\frac{110.99 \text{ g } CaCl_2}{1 \text{ mol } CaCl_2} \qquad\qquad \frac{18.01 \text{ g } H_2O}{1 \text{ mol } H_2O} \qquad\qquad mass \; percent = \frac{mass \; solute}{mass \; solution} \times 100 \, \%$$

Solution:

$$P_{solution} = \chi_{solvent} \, P°_{solvent} \qquad \text{Rearrange to solve for } \chi_{H2O}. \quad \chi_{solvent} = \frac{P_{solution}}{P°_{solvent}} = \frac{81.6 \text{ mm Hg}}{92.6 \text{ mm Hg}} = 0.881210$$

then assume 1 mol water $\chi_{H2O} = \dfrac{\text{mol } H_2O}{\text{mol } H_2O + 3 \text{ x mol } CaCl_2}$ so $0.881210 = \dfrac{1 \text{ mol}}{1 \text{ mol} + 3 \text{ x mol } CaCl_2}$

Rearrange to solve for mol $_{CaCl2}$.

$$0.881210 \left(1 \text{ mol} + 3 \text{ x mol } CaCl_2 \right) = 1 \text{ mol} \rightarrow \text{mol } CaCl_2 = \frac{1 \text{ mol} - 0.881210 \text{ mol}}{2.64363} = 0.0449345 \text{ mol } CaCl_2$$

then $\dfrac{5.50 \text{ g NaCl}}{100 \text{ g (NaCl} + H_2O)}$ means 5.50 g NaCl and (100 g - 5.50 g) = 94.5 g H_2O

then $0.0449345 \text{ mol } CaCl_2 \times \dfrac{110.99 \text{ g } CaCl_2}{1 \text{ mol } CaCl_2} = 4.98727 \text{ g } CaCl_2$ and $1 \text{ mol } H_2O = 18.01 \text{ g } H_2O$ then

$$mass \; percent = \frac{mass \; solute}{mass \; solution} \times 100 \, \% = \frac{4.98727 \text{ g } CaCl_2}{4.98727 \text{ g} + 18.01 \text{ g}} \times 100 \, \% = 21.69 \text{ percent by mass } CaCl_2$$

Check: The units (%) are correct. The magnitude of the answer (22 %) seems reasonable since there is a significant drop of the pure vapor pressure and the formula mass of the salt is much larger than water's molar mass.

71. **Given**: 50.0 g of heptane (C_7H_{16}) and 50.0 g of octane (C_8H_{18}) at 25 °C; $P°_{C7H16}$ = 45.8 torr; $P°_{C8H18}$ = 10.9 torr
a) **Find**: P_{C7H16}, P_{C8H18}
Conceptual plan:
g $_{C7H16} \rightarrow$ mol $_{C7H16}$ and g $_{C8H18} \rightarrow$ mol $_{C8H18}$ then   mol $_{C7H16}$, mol $_{C8H18} \rightarrow \chi_{C7H16}, \chi_{C8H18}$

$$\frac{1 \text{ mol } C_7H_{16}}{100.20 \text{ g } C_7H_{16}} \qquad\qquad \frac{1 \text{ mol } C_8H_{18}}{114.22 \text{ g } C_8H_{18}} \qquad \chi_{C7H16} = \frac{\text{amount } C_7H_{16} \text{ (in moles)}}{\text{total amount (in moles)}} \qquad \chi_{C8H18} = 1 - \chi_{C7H16}$$

then $\chi_{C7H16}, P°_{C7H16} \rightarrow P_{C7H16}$ and $\chi_{C8H18}, P°_{C8H18} \rightarrow P_{C8H18}$

$$P_{C7H16} = \chi_{C7H16} \, P°_{C7H16} \qquad\qquad P_{C8H18} = \chi_{C8H18} \, P°_{C8H18}$$

Solution: $50.0 \text{ g } C_7H_{16} \times \dfrac{1 \text{ mol } C_7H_{16}}{100.20 \text{ g } C_7H_{16}} = 0.499002 \text{ mol } C_7H_{16}$ and

$50.0 \text{ g } C_8H_{18} \times \dfrac{1 \text{ mol } C_8H_{18}}{114.22 \text{ g } C_8H_{18}} = 0.437752 \text{ mol } C_8H_{18}$ then

$$\chi_{C7H16} = \frac{\text{amount } C_7H_{16} \text{ (in moles)}}{\text{total amount (in moles)}} = \frac{0.499002 \text{ mol}}{0.499002 \text{ mol} + 0.437752 \text{ mol}} = 0.532693 \text{ and}$$

$\chi_{C8H18} = 1 - \chi_{C7H16} = 1 - 0.532693 = 0.467307$ then

$P_{C7H16} = \chi_{C7H16} \, P°_{C7H16} = 0.532693 \times 45.8 \text{ torr} = 24.4 \text{ torr}$ and

$P_{C8H18} = \chi_{C8H18} \, P°_{C8H18} = 0.467307 \times 10.9 \text{ torr} = 5.09 \text{ torr}$

Check: The units (torr) are correct. The magnitude of the answer (24 and 5 torr) seems reasonable since it we expect a drop in half from the pure vapor pressures since we have roughly a 50:50 mole ratio of the two components.

b) **Find**: P_{Total}

Conceptual plan: $\mathbf{P_{C7H16}, P_{C8H18} \rightarrow P_{Total}}$

$$P_{Total} = P_{C7H16} + P_{C8H18}$$

Solution: $P_{Total} = P_{C7H16} + P_{C8H18} = 24.4 \text{ torr} + 5.09 \text{ torr} = 29.5 \text{ torr}$

Check: The units (torr) are correct. The magnitude of the answer (30 torr) seems reasonable considering the two pressures.

c) **Find**: mass percent composition of the gas phase

Conceptual plan: **since n α P and we are calculating a mass percent, which is a ratio of masses, we can simply convert 1 torr to 1 mole so**

$\mathbf{P_{C7H16}, P_{C8H18} \rightarrow n_{C7H16}, n_{C8H18}}$ **then** $\mathbf{mol_{C7H16} \rightarrow g_{C7H16}}$ **and** $\mathbf{mol_{C8H18} \rightarrow g_{C8H18}}$

$$\frac{100.20 \text{ g } C_7H_{16}}{1 \text{ mol } C_7H_{16}} \qquad \frac{114.22 \text{ g } C_8H_{18}}{1 \text{ mol } C_8H_{18}}$$

then $\mathbf{g_{C7H16}, g_{C8H18} \rightarrow mass\ percents}$

$$mass\ percent = \frac{mass\ solute}{mass\ solution} \times 100\ \%$$

Solution: so nC7H16 = 24.4 mol and nC8H18 = 5.09 mol then

$$24.4 \ \overline{mol\ C_7H_{16}} \ \times \ \frac{100.20 \text{ g } C_7H_{16}}{1 \ \overline{mol\ C_7H_{16}}} = 2444.88 \text{ g } C_7H_{16} \ \text{ and}$$

$$5.09 \ \overline{mol\ C_8H_{18}} \ \times \ \frac{114.22 \text{ g } C_8H_{18}}{1 \ \overline{mol\ C_8H_{18}}} = 581.380 \text{ g } C_8H_{18} \ \text{ then}$$

$$mass\ percent = \frac{mass\ solute}{mass\ solution} \times 100\ \% = \frac{2444.88 \ \overline{\text{g } C_7H_{16}}}{2444.88 \ \overline{\text{g } C_7H_{16}} + 581.380 \ \overline{\text{g } C_8H_{18}}} \times 100\ \% =$$

$= 80.8$ percent by mass C_7H_{16}

then $100\ \% - 80.8\ \% = 19.2$ percent by mass C_8H_{18}

Check: The units (%) are correct. The magnitudes of the answers (81 % and 19 %) seem reasonable considering the two pressures.

d) The two mass percents are different because the vapor is richer in the more volatile component (the lighter molecule).

72. **Given**: **pentane(C_5H_{12}) and hexane(C_6H_{14})** $P_{Total} = 258$ torr; $P°_{C5H12} = 425$ torr; $P°_{C6H14} = 151$ torr at 25°C
Find: $\chi_{C5H12}, \chi_{C6H14}$

Conceptual plan: $P_{Total} = P_{C5H12} + P_{C6H14}$ **where** $P_{C5H12} = \chi_{C5H12} P°_{C5H12}$ **and** $P_{C6H14} = \chi_{C6H14} P°_{C6H14}$ **but**

$\chi_{C6H14} = 1 - \chi_{C5H12}$ **so** $P_{Total} = \chi_{C5H12} P°_{C5H12} + (1 - \chi_{C5H12}) P°_{C6H14}$ **substitute in values and solve for** $\chi_{C5H12}, \chi_{C6H14}$

Solution: $P_{Total} = \chi_{C5H12} P°_{C5H12} + (1 - \chi_{C5H12}) P°_{C6H14}$ so $258 \ \overline{torr} = \chi_{C5H12} 425 \ \overline{torr} + (1 - \chi_{C5H12}) 151 \ \overline{torr} \rightarrow$

$258 - 151 = \chi_{C5H12} (425 - 151) \rightarrow \chi_{C5H12} = \dfrac{107}{274} = 0.391$ and $\chi_{C6H14} = 1 - \chi_{C5H12} = 1 - 0.391 = 0.609$

Check: The units (none) are correct. The magnitudes of the answers (0.4 and 0.6) seems reasonable since it the total vapor pressures is closer to the vapor pressure of hexane, so we expect there to be more hexane in the liquid.

73. **Given:** 4.08 g of chloroform ($CHCl_3$) and 9.29 g of acetone (CH_3COCH_3); at 35 °C $P°_{CHCl3} = 295$ torr; $P°_{CH3COCH3} = 332$ torr; assume ideal behavior; $P_{Total\ measured} = 312$ torr
Find: P_{CHCl3}, $P_{CH3COCH3}$ and P_{Total} then is soln ideal?
Conceptual plan: $g_{CHCl3} \rightarrow mol_{CHCl3}$ and $g_{CH3COCH3} \rightarrow mol_{CH3COCH3}$ **then**

$$\frac{1\ mol\ CHCl_3}{119.38\ g\ CHCl_3} \qquad \frac{1\ mol\ CH_3COCH_3}{58.08\ g\ CH_3COCH_3}$$

mol_{CHCl3}, $mol_{CH3COCH3} \rightarrow \chi_{CHCl3}$, $\chi_{CH3COCH3}$ **then** χ_{CHCl3}, $P°_{CHCl3} \rightarrow P_{CHCl3}$ **and**

$$\chi_{CHCl3} = \frac{amount\ CHCl_3\ (in\ moles)}{total\ amount\ (in\ moles)} \qquad \chi_{CH3COCH3} = 1 - \chi_{CHCl3} \qquad P_{CHCl3} = \chi_{CHCl3}\ P°_{CHCl3}$$

$\chi_{CH3COCH3}$, $P°_{CH3COCH3} \rightarrow P_{CH3COCH3}$ **then** P_{CHCl3}, $P_{CH3COCH3} \rightarrow P_{Total}$ **then compare values**

$$P_{CH3COCH3} = \chi_{CH3COCH3}\ P°_{CH3COCH3} \qquad P_{Total} = P_{CHCl3} + P_{CH3COCH3}$$

Solution:

$$4.08\ \cancel{g\ CHCl_3}\ \times\ \frac{1\ mol\ CHCl_3}{119.38\ \cancel{g\ CHCl_3}} = 0.034\underline{1}766\ mol\ CHCl_3\ and$$

$$9.29\ \cancel{g\ CH_3COCH_3}\ \times\ \frac{1\ mol\ CH_3COCH_3}{58.08\ \cancel{g\ CH_3COCH_3}} = 0.159952\ mol\ CH_3COCH_3\ \ then$$

$$\chi_{CHCl3} = \frac{amount\ CHCl_3\ (in\ moles)}{total\ amount\ (in\ moles)} = \frac{0.034\underline{1}766\ \cancel{mol}}{0.034\underline{1}766\ \cancel{mol} + 0.159952\ \cancel{mol}} = 0.17\underline{6}052\ and$$

$\chi_{CH3COCH3} = 1 - \chi_{CHCl3} = 1 - 0.17\underline{6}052 = 0.82\underline{3}948$ then $P_{CHCl3} = \chi_{CHCl3}\ P°_{CHCl3} = 0.17\underline{6}052 \times 295$ torr $= 51.9$ torr

and $P_{CH3COCH3} = \chi_{CH3COCH3}\ P°_{CH3COCH3} = 0.82\underline{3}948 \times 332$ torr $= 274$ torr then

$P_{Total} = P_{CHCl3} + P_{CH3COCH3} = 51.9$ torr $+ 274$ torr $= 326$ torr .

Since 326 torr $\neq$ 312 torr, the solution is not behaving ideally. The chloroform-acetone interactions are stronger than the chloroform-chloroform and acetone-acetone interactions.
Check: The units (torr) are correct. The magnitude of the answer seems reasonable since each is a fraction of the pure vapor pressures. We are not surprised that the solution is not ideal, since the typed of bonds in the two molecules are very different.

74. **Given:** methanol (CH_3OH) and water; $\chi_{H2O} = 0.312$; at 39.9 °C $P_{Total\ measured} = 211$ torr, $P°_{CH3OH} = 256$ torr; $P°_{H2O} = 55.3$ torr;   **Find:** is soln ideal?
Conceptual plan: $\chi_{H2O} \rightarrow \chi_{CH3OH}$ **then** χ_{H2O}, $P°_{H2O} \rightarrow P_{H2O}$ **and** χ_{CH3OH}, $P°_{CH3OH} \rightarrow P_{CH3OH}$

$$\chi_{CH3OH} = 1 - \chi_{H2O} \qquad P_{H2O} = \chi_{H2O}\ P°_{H2O} \qquad P_{CH3OH} = \chi_{CH3OH}\ P°_{CH3OH}$$

then P_{H2O}, $P_{CH3OH} \rightarrow P_{Total}$ **then compare values**

$$P_{Total} = P_{H2O} + P_{CH3OH}$$

Solution:

$\chi_{CH3OH} = 1 - \chi_{H2O} = 1 - 0.312 = 0.688$ then $P_{H2O} = \chi_{H2O}\ P°_{H2O} = 0.312 \times 55.3$ torr $= 17.\underline{2}536$ torr and

$P_{CH3OH} = \chi_{CH3OH}\ P°_{CH3OH} = 0.688 \times 256$ torr $= 17\underline{6}.128$ torr then

$P_{Total} = P_{H2O} + P_{CH3OH} = 17.\underline{2}536$ torr $+ 17\underline{6}.128$ torr $= 193$ torr

Since 193 torr $\neq$ 211 torr, the solution is not behaving ideally. The methanol-water interactions are weaker than the methanol-methanol and water-water interactions.
Check: The units (torr) are correct. The magnitude of the answer seems reasonable since each is a fraction of the pure vapor pressures. We are not surprised that the solution is not ideal, since the typed of bonds in the two molecules are very different.

75. **Given:** 55.8 g of glucose ($C_6H_{12}O_6$) in 455 g water **Find:** T_f and T_b
Other: $K_f = 1.86$ °C/m; $K_b = 0.512$ °C/m;
Conceptual plan: $g_{H2O} \rightarrow kg_{H2O}$ and $g_{C6H12O6} \rightarrow mol_{C6H12O6}$ **then** $mol_{C6H12O6}$, $kg_{H2O} \rightarrow m$

$$\frac{1\ kg}{1000\ g} \qquad \frac{1\ mol\ C_6H_{12}O_6}{180.16\ g\ C_6H_{12}O_6} \qquad m = \frac{amount\ solute\ (moles)}{mass\ solvent\ (kg)}$$

m, $K_f \rightarrow \Delta T_f \rightarrow T_f$ and m, $K_b \rightarrow \Delta T_b \rightarrow T_b$

$$\Delta T_f = K_f\ m \quad T_f = T°_f - \Delta T_f \qquad \Delta T_b = K_b\ m \quad T_b = T_b - T°_b$$

405

Solution:

$$455 \ \cancel{g} \times \frac{1 \text{kg}}{1000 \ \cancel{g}} = 0.455 \text{ kg} \quad \text{and} \quad 55.8 \ \cancel{g \, C_6 H_{12} O_6} \times \frac{1 \text{ mol} \, C_6 H_{12} O_6}{180.16 \ \cancel{g \, C_6 H_{12} O_6}} = 0.30\underline{9}725 \text{ mol} \, C_6 H_{12} O_6 \quad \text{then}$$

$$m = \frac{\text{amount solute (moles)}}{\text{mass solvent (kg)}} = \frac{0.30\underline{9}725 \text{ mol} \, C_6 H_{12} O_6}{0.455 \text{ kg}} = 0.68\underline{0}714 \ m \quad \text{then}$$

$$\Delta T_f = K_f \, m = 1.86 \frac{{}^\circ C}{\cancel{m}} \times 0.68\underline{0}714 \ \cancel{m} = 1.27 \ {}^\circ C \quad \text{then} \quad T_f = T_f^\circ - \Delta T_f = 0.00 \ {}^\circ C - 1.27 \ {}^\circ C = -1.27 \ {}^\circ C$$

$$\text{and} \qquad \Delta T_b = K_b \, m = 0.512 \frac{{}^\circ C}{\cancel{m}} \times 0.68\underline{0}714 \ \cancel{m} = 0.349 \ {}^\circ C \quad \text{and} \quad \Delta T_b = T_b - T_b^\circ \quad \text{so}$$

$$T_b = T_b^\circ + \Delta T_b = 100.000 \ {}^\circ C + 0.349 \ {}^\circ C = 100.349 \ {}^\circ C$$

Check: The units (°C) are correct. The magnitudes of the answers seem reasonable since the molality is ~ 2/3. The shift in boiling point less than the shift in freezing point because the constant is smaller for freezing.

76. **Given:** 21.2 g of ethylene glycol ($C_2 H_6 O_2$) in 85.4 g water   **Find:** T_f and T_b
    Other: $K_f = 1.86 \ {}^\circ C/m$; $K_b = 0.512 \ {}^\circ C/m$;
    Conceptual plan: $g_{H2O} \rightarrow kg_{H2O}$ and $g_{C2H6O2} \rightarrow mol_{C2H6O2}$ then $mol_{C2H6O2}, kg_{H2O} \rightarrow m$

$$\frac{1 \text{kg}}{1000 \text{ g}} \qquad \frac{1 \text{ mol} \, C_2 H_6 O_2}{62.07 \text{ g} \, C_2 H_6 O_2} \qquad m = \frac{\text{amount solute (moles)}}{\text{mass solvent (kg)}}$$

$m, K_f \rightarrow \Delta T_f \rightarrow T_f$ and $m, K_b \rightarrow \Delta T_b \rightarrow T_b$

$$\Delta T_f = K_f \, m \quad T_f = T_f^\circ - \Delta T_f \qquad \Delta T_b = K_b \, m \quad \Delta T_b = T_b - T_b^\circ$$

Solution:

$$84.5 \ \cancel{g} \times \frac{1 \text{kg}}{1000 \ \cancel{g}} = 0.0845 \text{ kg} \quad \text{and} \quad 21.2 \ \cancel{g \, C_2 H_6 O_2} \times \frac{1 \text{ mol} \, C_2 H_6 O_2}{62.07 \ \cancel{g \, C_2 H_6 O_2}} = 0.34\underline{1}561 \text{ mol} \, C_2 H_6 O_2 \quad \text{then}$$

$$m = \frac{\text{amount solute (moles)}}{\text{mass solvent (kg)}} = \frac{0.34\underline{1}561 \text{ mol} \, C_2 H_6 O_2}{0.0845 \text{ kg}} = 4.0\underline{4}214 \ m \quad \text{then}$$

$$\Delta T_f = K_f \, m = 1.86 \frac{{}^\circ C}{\cancel{m}} \times 4.0\underline{4}214 \ \cancel{m} = 7.52 \ {}^\circ C \quad \text{then} \quad T_f = T_f^\circ - \Delta T_f = 0.00 \ {}^\circ C - 7.52 \ {}^\circ C = -7.52 \ {}^\circ C \quad \text{and}$$

$$\Delta T_b = K_b \, m = 0.512 \frac{{}^\circ C}{\cancel{m}} \times 4.0\underline{4}214 \ \cancel{m} = 2.07 \ {}^\circ C \quad \text{and} \quad \Delta T_b = T_b - T_b^\circ \quad \text{so}$$

$$T_b = T_b^\circ + \Delta T_b = 100.00 \ {}^\circ C + 2.07 \ {}^\circ C = 102.07 \ {}^\circ C$$

Check: The units (°C) are correct. The magnitudes of the answers seem reasonable since the molality is ~ 4. The shift in boiling point less than the shift in freezing point because the constant is smaller for freezing.

77. **Given:** 17.5 g of unknown nonelectrolyte in 100.0 g water, $T_f = -1.8 \ {}^\circ C$ **Find:** $\mathfrak{M}$
    Other: $K_f = 1.86 \ {}^\circ C/m$
    Conceptual plan: $g_{H2O} \rightarrow kg_{H2O}$ and $T_f \rightarrow \Delta T_f$ then $\Delta T_f, K_f \rightarrow m$ then $m, kg_{H2O} \rightarrow mol_{Unk}$

$$\frac{1 \text{kg}}{1000 \text{ g}} \qquad T_f = T_f^\circ - \Delta T_f \qquad \Delta T_f = K_f \, m \qquad m = \frac{\text{amount solute (moles)}}{\text{mass solvent (kg)}}$$

then $g_{Unk}, mol_{Unk} \rightarrow \mathfrak{M}$

$$\mathfrak{M} = \frac{g_{Unk}}{mol_{Unk}}$$

Solution:

$$100.0 \ \cancel{g} \times \frac{1 \text{kg}}{1000 \ \cancel{g}} = 0.1000 \text{ kg} \quad \text{and} \quad T_f = T_f^\circ - \Delta T_f \quad \text{so} \quad \Delta T_f = T_f^\circ - T_f = 0.00 \ {}^\circ C - -1.8 \ {}^\circ C = +1.8 \ {}^\circ C$$

$\Delta T_f = K_f m$ Rearrange to solve for m. $m = \dfrac{\Delta T_f}{K_f} = \dfrac{1.8\ ^\circ\text{C}}{1.86\ \dfrac{^\circ\text{C}}{m}} = 0.96\underline{7}74\ m$ then $m = \dfrac{\text{amount solute (moles)}}{\text{mass solvent (kg)}}$ so

$mol_{Unk} = m_{Unk} \times kg_{H2O} = 0.96\underline{7}74\ \dfrac{\text{mol Unk}}{kg} \times 0.1000\ \text{kg} = 0.096\underline{7}74\ \text{mol Unk}$ then

$\mathfrak{M} = \dfrac{g_{Unk}}{mol_{Unk}} = \dfrac{17.5\ \text{g}}{0.096774\ \text{mol}} = 180\ \dfrac{\text{g}}{\text{mol}} = 1.8 \times 10^2\ \dfrac{\text{g}}{\text{mol}}$

Check: The units (g/mol) are correct. The magnitude of the answer (180 g/mol) seems reasonable since the molality is ~ 0.1 and we have ~18 g. It is a reasonable molecular weight for a solid or liquid.

78. **Given**: 35.9 g of unknown nonelectrolyte in 150.0 g water, $T_f = -1.3\ ^\circ\text{C}$ **Find**: $\mathfrak{M}$
   Other: $K_f = 1.86\ ^\circ\text{C}/m$;
   Conceptual plan:
   $g_{H2O} \rightarrow kg_{H2O}$ **and** $T_f \rightarrow \Delta T_f$ **then** $\Delta T_f, K_f \rightarrow m$ **then** $m, kg_{H2O} \rightarrow mol_{Unk}$

   $\dfrac{1\,kg}{1000\,g}$ $T_f = T_f^o - \Delta T_f$ $\Delta T_f = K_f m$ $m = \dfrac{\text{amount solute (moles)}}{\text{mass solvent (kg)}}$

   then $g_{Unk}, mol_{Unk} \rightarrow \mathfrak{M}$

   $\mathfrak{M} = \dfrac{g_{Unk}}{mol_{Unk}}$

   Solution:
   $150.0\ \text{g} \times \dfrac{1\,kg}{1000\ \text{g}} = 0.1500\ \text{kg}$ and $T_f = T_f^o - \Delta T_f$ so $\Delta T_f = T_f^o - T_f = 0.00\ ^\circ\text{C} - -1.3\ ^\circ\text{C} = +1.3\ ^\circ\text{C}$

   $\Delta T_f = K_f m$ Rearrange to solve for m. $m = \dfrac{\Delta T_f}{K_f} = \dfrac{1.3\ ^\circ\text{C}}{1.86\ \dfrac{^\circ\text{C}}{m}} = 0.69\underline{8}92\ m$ then $m = \dfrac{\text{amount solute (moles)}}{\text{mass solvent (kg)}}$ so

   $mol_{Unk} = m_{Unk} \times kg_{H2O} = 0.69\underline{8}92\ \dfrac{\text{mol Unk}}{kg} \times 0.1500\ \text{kg} = 0.10\underline{4}839\ \text{mol Unk}$ then

   $\mathfrak{M} = \dfrac{g_{Unk}}{mol_{Unk}} = \dfrac{35.9\ \text{g}}{0.104839\ \text{mol}} = 340\ \dfrac{\text{g}}{\text{mol}}$

   Check: The units (g/mol) are correct. The magnitude of the answer (340 g/mol) seems reasonable since the molality is ~ 0.7 and we have ~36 g. It is a reasonable molecular weight for a solid or liquid.

79. **Given**: 24.6 g of glycerin ($C_3H_8O_3$) in 250.0 mL of solution at 298 K   **Find**: Π
   Conceptual plan: $mL_{soln} \rightarrow L_{soln}$ **and** $g_{C3H8O3} \rightarrow mol_{C3H8O3}$ **then** $mol_{C3H8O3}, L_{soln} \rightarrow M$ **then**

   $\dfrac{1L}{1000\ mL}$ $\dfrac{1\ \text{mol}\,C_3H_8O_3}{92.09\ \text{g}\ C_3H_8O_3}$ $M = \dfrac{\text{amount solute (moles)}}{\text{volume solution (L)}}$

   $M, T \rightarrow \Pi$
   $\Pi = M R T$

   Solution:
   $250.0\ \text{mL} \times \dfrac{1L}{1000\ \text{mL}} = 0.2500\ \text{L}$ and $24.6\ \text{g}\,C_3H_8O_3 \times \dfrac{1\ \text{mol}\,C_3H_8O_3}{92.09\ \text{g}\,C_3H_8O_3} = 0.26\underline{7}130\ \text{mol}\,C_3H_8O_3$ then

   $M = \dfrac{\text{amount solute (moles)}}{\text{volume solution (L)}} = \dfrac{0.26\underline{7}130\ \text{mol}\,C_3H_8O_3}{0.2500\ \text{L}} = 1.0\underline{6}852\ M$ then

   $\Pi = M R T = 1.0\underline{6}852\ \dfrac{\text{mol}}{\text{L}} \times 0.08206\ \dfrac{\text{L atm}}{\text{K mol}} \times 298\ \text{K} = 26.1\ \text{atm}$

   Check: The units (atm) are correct. The magnitude of the answer (26 atm) seems reasonable since the molarity is ~ 1.

80. **Given:** sucrose ($C_{12}H_{22}O_{11}$) in 5.00×10^2 g water; $\Pi = 8.55$ atm at 298 K **Find:** m ($C_{12}H_{22}O_{11}$)
Other: d = 1.0 g/mL
Conceptual plan: $\Pi, T \rightarrow M$ then   g $_{H2O}$, d, $\mathfrak{m} \rightarrow$ g $_{C12H22O11}$

$$\Pi = MRT \qquad M = \frac{\text{amount solute (moles)}}{\text{volume solution (L)}} \text{ with } \frac{1L}{1000 \text{ mL}}, \frac{342.30 \text{ g } C_{12}H_{22}O_{11}}{1 \text{ mol } C_{12}H_{22}O_{11}} \text{ and } \frac{1.0 \text{ mL}}{1.0 \text{ g}}$$

Solution:

$$\Pi = MRT \text{ for M.} \quad M = \frac{\Pi}{RT} = \frac{8.55 \text{ atm}}{0.08206 \frac{L \text{ atm}}{K \text{ mol}} \times 298 \text{ K}} = 0.349638 \frac{\text{mol}}{L}$$

Substitute quantities into of definition of M.

$$M = \frac{\text{amount solute (moles)}}{\text{volume solution (L)}} = \frac{\left(x \text{ g } C_{12}H_{22}O_{11} \right)\left(\dfrac{1 \text{ mol } C_{12}H_{22}O_{11}}{342.30 \text{ g } C_{12}H_{22}O_{11}} \right)}{\left(5.00 \times 10^2 \text{ g } H_2O + x \text{ g } C_{12}H_{22}O_{11} \right) \times \dfrac{1.0 \text{ mL}}{1.0 \text{ g}} \times \dfrac{1L}{1000 \text{ mL}}} = 0.349638 \frac{\text{mol}}{L}$$

Rearrange to solve for $x \text{ g } C_{12}H_{22}O_{11}$. $x \text{ g } C_{12}H_{22}O_{11} = 0.119681 x \left(5.00 \times 10^2 \text{ g } H_2O + x \text{ g } C_{12}H_{22}O_{11} \right) \rightarrow$

$$0.880312 x \left(x \text{ g } C_{12}H_{22}O_{11} \right) = 59.8405 \rightarrow x \text{ g } C_{12}H_{22}O_{11} = \frac{59.8405}{0.880312} = 68.0 \text{ g } C_{12}H_{22}O_{11}$$

Check: The units (g) are correct. The magnitude of the answer (68 g) seems reasonable since the molarity is ~ 1/3 and we have 0.5 L of water.

81. **Given:** 27.55 mg unknown protein in 25.0 mL solution; $\Pi = 3.22$ torr at 25 °C **Find:** $\mathfrak{M}$ $_{\text{unknown protein}}$
Conceptual plan:
°C $\rightarrow$ K   and   torr $\rightarrow$ atm   then $\Pi, T \rightarrow M$ then   mL$_{\text{soln}} \rightarrow$ L$_{\text{soln}}$ then

$$K = °C + 273.15 \qquad \frac{1 \text{ atm}}{760 \text{ torr}} \qquad \Pi = MRT \qquad \frac{1L}{1000 \text{ mL}}$$

L$_{\text{soln}}$, M $\rightarrow$ mol $_{\text{unknown protein}}$ and mg $\rightarrow$ g   then   g $_{\text{unknown protein}}$, mol $_{\text{unknown protein}}$ $\rightarrow$ $\mathfrak{M}$ $_{\text{unknown protein}}$

$$M = \frac{\text{amount solute (moles)}}{\text{volume solution (L)}} \qquad \frac{1 \text{ g}}{1000 \text{ mg}} \qquad \mathfrak{M} = \frac{g_{\text{unknown protein}}}{\text{mol}_{\text{unknown protein}}}$$

Solution: 25 °C + 273.15 = 298 K and $3.22 \text{ torr} \times \dfrac{1 \text{ atm}}{760 \text{ torr}} = 0.00423684$ atm $\Pi = MRT$ for M.

$$M = \frac{\Pi}{RT} = \frac{0.00423684 \text{ atm}}{0.08206 \frac{L \text{ atm}}{K \text{ mol}} \times 298 \text{ K}} = 1.73258 \times 10^{-4} \frac{\text{mol}}{L} \quad \text{then} \quad 25.0 \text{ mL} \times \frac{1L}{1000 \text{ mL}} = 0.0250 \text{ L} \quad \text{then}$$

$$M = \frac{\text{amount solute (moles)}}{\text{volume solution (L)}} \quad \text{Rearrange to solve for mol}_{\text{unknown protein}}.$$

$$\text{mol}_{\text{unknown protein}} = M \times L = 1.73258 \times 10^{-4} \frac{\text{mol}}{L} \times 0.0250 \text{ L} = 4.33146 \times 10^{-4} \text{ mol and}$$

$$27.55 \text{ mg} \times \frac{1 \text{ g}}{1000 \text{ mg}} = 0.02755 \text{ g then} \quad \mathfrak{M} = \frac{g_{\text{unknown protein}}}{\text{mol}_{\text{unknown protein}}} = \frac{0.02755 \text{ g}}{4.33146 \times 10^{-4} \text{ mol}} = 6.36 \times 10^3 \frac{g}{\text{mol}}$$

Check: The units (g/mol) are correct. The magnitude of the answer (6400 g/mol) seems reasonable for a large biological molecule. A small amount of material is put into 0.025 L, so the concentration is very small and the molecular weight is large.

82. **Given:** 18.75 mg of hemoglobin in 15.0 mL of solution at 25 °C, $\mathfrak{M}$ $_{\text{hemoglobin}} = 6.5 \times 10^4$ g/mol **Find:** Π
Conceptual plan: mL$_{\text{soln}}$ $\rightarrow$ L$_{\text{soln}}$ and   mg$_H$ $\rightarrow$ g$_H$ $\rightarrow$ mol$_H$ then   mol$_H$, L$_{\text{soln}}$ $\rightarrow$ M   then

$$\frac{1L}{1000 \text{ mL}} \qquad \frac{1 \text{ g}}{1000 \text{ mg}} \qquad \frac{1 \text{ mol H}}{6.5 \times 10^4 \text{ g H}} \qquad M = \frac{\text{amount solute (moles)}}{\text{volume solution (L)}}$$

M, T → Π

$\Pi = M\,RT$

Solution:

$$15.0 \text{ mL} \times \frac{1\text{L}}{1000\text{ mL}} = 0.0150 \text{ L} \quad \text{and} \quad 18.75 \text{ mg H} \times \frac{1\text{ g}}{1000\text{ mg}} \times \frac{1\text{ mol H}}{6.5 \times 10^4 \text{ g H}} = 2.\underline{8}8465 \times 10^{-7} \text{ mol H}$$

then $M = \dfrac{\text{amount solute (moles)}}{\text{volume solution (L)}} = \dfrac{2.\underline{8}8465 \times 10^{-7} \text{ mol H}}{0.0150 \text{ L}} = 1.\underline{9}231 \times 10^{-5} \text{ M}$ then

$$\Pi = M\,RT = 1.\underline{9}231 \times 10^{-5} \frac{\text{mol}}{\text{L}} \times 0.08206 \frac{\text{L atm}}{\text{K mol}} \times 298 \text{ K} = 4.7 \times 10^{-4} \text{ atm} = 0.36 \text{ torr}$$

Check: The units (atm) are correct. The magnitude of the answer (10^{-4} atm) seems reasonable since the molarity is ~ 1.

83. a) **Given:** 0.100 m of K_2S, completely dissociated   **Find:** T_f, T_b
    Other: $K_f = 1.86$ °C/m; $K_b = 0.512$ °C/m;
    Conceptual plan: $m, i, K_f \;\rightarrow\; \Delta T_f$ then $\Delta T_f \rightarrow T_f$ and $m, i, K_b \;\rightarrow\; \Delta T_b$ then $\Delta T_b \rightarrow T_b$

    $$\Delta T_f = K_f\,i\,m \;\; i=3 \qquad T_f = T_f^{\circ} - \Delta T_f \qquad \Delta T_b = K_b\,i\,m \;\; i=3 \qquad T_b = T_b^{\circ} + \Delta T_b$$

    Solution:

    $\Delta T_f = K_f\,i\,m = 1.86 \dfrac{°\text{C}}{m} \times 3 \times 0.100 \; m = 0.558 \text{ °C}$ then

    $T_f = T_f^{\circ} - \Delta T_f = 0.000\,°\text{C} - 0.558 \text{ °C} = -0.558 \text{ °C}$ and

    $\Delta T_b = K_b\,i\,m = 0.512 \dfrac{°\text{C}}{m} \times 3 \times 0.100 \; m = 0.154 \text{ °C}$ then

    $T_b = T_b^{\circ} - \Delta T_b = 100.000\,°\text{C} + 0.154 \text{ °C} = 100.154 \text{ °C}$.

    Check: The units (°C) are correct. The magnitude of the answer (- 0.6 °C and 100.2 °C) seems reasonable since the molality of the particles is 0.3. The shift in boiling point less than the shift in freezing point because the constant is smaller for freezing.

    b) **Given:** 21.5 g $CuCl_2$ in 4.50×10^2 g water, completely dissociated   **Find:** T_f, T_b
    Other: $K_f = 1.86$ °C/m; $K_b = 0.512$ °C/m;
    Conceptual plan: $g_{H2O} \rightarrow kg_{H2O}$ and $g_{CuCl2} \rightarrow mol_{CuCl2}$ then $mol_{CuCl2}, kg_{H2O} \rightarrow m$

    $$\frac{1\text{ kg}}{1000\text{ g}} \qquad\qquad \frac{1\text{ mol }CuCl_2}{134.46 \text{ g }CuCl_2} \qquad\qquad m = \frac{\text{amount solute (moles)}}{\text{mass solvent (kg)}}$$

    $m, i, K_f \;\rightarrow\; \Delta T_f \;\rightarrow\; T_f$ and $m, i, K_b \;\rightarrow\; \Delta T_b \;\rightarrow\; T_b$

    $$\Delta T_f = K_f\,i\,m \; i=3 \quad T_f = T_f^{\circ} - \Delta T_f \qquad \Delta T_b = K_b\,i\,m \; i=3 \quad T_b = T_b^{\circ} + \Delta T_b$$

    Solution:

    $4.5 \times 10^2 \text{ g} \times \dfrac{1\text{ kg}}{1000\text{ g}} = 0.450 \text{ kg}$ and $21.5 \text{ g }CuCl_2 \times \dfrac{1\text{ mol }CuCl_2}{134.46 \text{ g }CuCl_2} = 0.15\underline{9}904 \text{ mol }CuCl_2$ then

    $m = \dfrac{\text{amount solute (moles)}}{\text{mass solvent (kg)}} = \dfrac{0.15\underline{9}904 \text{ mol }CuCl_2}{0.450 \text{ kg}} = 0.35\underline{5}341 \; m$ then

    $\Delta T_f = K_f\,i\,m = 1.86 \dfrac{°\text{C}}{m} \times 3 \times 0.35\underline{5}341 \; m = 1.98 \text{ °C}$ then

    $T_f = T_f^{\circ} - \Delta T_f = 0.000\,°\text{C} - 1.98 \text{ °C} = -1.98 \text{ °C}$ and

    $\Delta T_b = K_b\,i\,m = 0.512 \dfrac{°\text{C}}{m} \times 3 \times 0.35\underline{5}341 \; m = 0.546 \text{ °C}$ then

    $T_b = T_b^{\circ} - \Delta T_b = 100.000\,°\text{C} + 0.546 \text{ °C} = 100.546 \text{ °C}$.

    Check: The units (°C) are correct. The magnitude of the answer (- 2 °C and 100.5 °C) seems reasonable since the molality of the particles is ~ 1. The shift in boiling point less than the shift in freezing point because the constant is smaller for freezing.

c) **Given:** 5.5 % by mass $NaNO_3$, completely dissociated   **Find:** T_f, T_b

    Other: $K_f = 1.86\ °C/m$; $K_b = 0.512\ °C/m$;

    Conceptual plan:

    percent by mass $\rightarrow$ g_{NaNO3}, g_{H2O} **then** g_{H2O} $\rightarrow$ kg_{H2O} **and** g_{NaNO3} $\rightarrow$ mol_{NaNO3} **then**

$$mass\ percent = \frac{mass\ solute}{mass\ solution} \times 100\ \% \qquad \frac{1\ kg}{1000\ g} \qquad \frac{1\ mol\ NaNO_3}{84.99\ g\ NaNO_3}$$

    mol_{NaNO3}, kg_{H2O} $\rightarrow$ m **then** m, i, K_f $\rightarrow$ ΔT_f $\rightarrow$ T_f **and** m, i, K_b $\rightarrow$ ΔT_b $\rightarrow$ T_b

$$m = \frac{amount\ solute\ (moles)}{mass\ solvent\ (kg)} \qquad \Delta T_f = K_f\,i\,m \quad i = 2 \quad T_f = T_f^\circ - \Delta T_f \qquad \Delta T_b = K_b\,i\,m \quad i = 2 \quad T_b = T_b^\circ + \Delta T_b$$

    Solution:

$$mass\ percent = \frac{mass\ solute}{mass\ solution} \times 100\ \% \text{ so } 5.5\ \% \text{ by mass } NaNO_3 \text{ means } 5.5\ g\ NaNO_3 \text{ and } 100.0\ g - 5.5\ g$$

$$= 94.5\ g\ water.\text{ Then } 94.5\ g \times \frac{1\,kg}{1000\ g} = 0.0945\ kg \quad \text{and}$$

$$5.5\ g\,NaNO_3 \times \frac{1\ mol\,NaNO_3}{84.99\ g\,NaNO_3} = 0.064\underline{7}13\ mol\,NaNO_3 \text{ then}$$

$$m = \frac{amount\ solute\ (moles)}{mass\ solvent\ (kg)} = \frac{0.064\underline{7}13\ mol\ NaNO_3}{0.0945\ kg} = 0.6\underline{8}480\ m \text{ then}$$

$$\Delta T_f = K_f\,i\,m = 1.86\,\frac{°C}{m} \times 2 \times 0.6\underline{8}480\ m = 2.5\ °C \text{ then } T_f = T_f^\circ - \Delta T_f = 0.000°C - 2.3\ °C = -2.5\ °C$$

$$\text{and } \Delta T_b = K_b\,i\,m = 0.512\,\frac{°C}{m} \times 2 \times 0.6\underline{8}480\ m = 0.70\ °C \text{ then}$$

$$T_b = T_b^\circ - \Delta T_b = 100.000°C + 0.64\ °C = 100.70\ °C .$$

    Check: The units ($°C$) are correct. The magnitude of the answer (- 2 °C and 100.6 °C) seems reasonable since the molality of the particles is ~ 1. The shift in boiling point less than the shift in freezing point because the constant is smaller for freezing.

84. a)   **Given:** 10.5 g $FeCl_3$ in 1.50×10^2 g water, completely dissociated   **Find:** T_f, T_b

    Other: $K_f = 1.86\ °C/m$; $K_b = 0.512\ °C/m$;

    Conceptual plan: g_{H2O} $\rightarrow$ kg_{H2O} **and** g_{FeCl3} $\rightarrow$ mol_{FeCl3} **then** mol_{FeCl3}, kg_{H2O} $\rightarrow$ m

$$\frac{1\,kg}{1000\ g} \qquad \frac{1\ mol\,FeCl_3}{162.21\ g\,FeCl_3} \qquad m = \frac{amount\ solute\ (moles)}{mass\ solvent\ (kg)}$$

    m, i, K_f $\rightarrow$ ΔT_f $\rightarrow$ T_f **and** m, i, K_b $\rightarrow$ ΔT_b $\rightarrow$ T_b

$$\Delta T_f = K_f\,i\,m \quad i = 4 \quad T_f = T_f^\circ - \Delta T_f \qquad \Delta T_b = K_b\,i\,m \quad i = 4 \quad T_b = T_b^\circ + \Delta T_b$$

    Solution:

$$4.5 \times 10^2\ g \times \frac{1\,kg}{1000\ g} = 0.450\ kg \quad \text{and} \quad 10.5\ g\,FeCl_3 \times \frac{1\ mol\,FeCl_3}{162.21\ g\,FeCl_3} = 0.64\underline{7}325\ mol\,FeCl_3 \text{ then}$$

$$m = \frac{amount\ solute\ (moles)}{mass\ solvent\ (kg)} = \frac{0.64\underline{7}325\ mol\ FeCl_3}{0.150\ kg} = 0.43\underline{1}550\ m \text{ then}$$

$$\Delta T_f = K_f\,i\,m = 1.86\,\frac{°C}{m} \times 4 \times 0.43\underline{1}550\ m = 3.21\ °C \text{ then } T_f = T_f^\circ - \Delta T_f = 0.000°C - 3.21\ °C = -3.21\ °C$$

$$\text{and } \Delta T_b = K_b\,i\,m = 0.512\,\frac{°C}{m} \times 4 \times 0.43\underline{1}550\ m = 0.884\ °C \text{ then}$$

$$T_b = T_b^\circ - \Delta T_b = 100.000°C + 0.884\ °C = 100.884\ °C .$$

    Check: The units ($°C$) are correct. The magnitude of the answer (- 3 °C and 100.9 °C) seems reasonable since the molality of the particles is ~ 2. The shift in boiling point less than the shift in freezing point because the constant is smaller for freezing.

c) **Given:** 3.5 % by mass KCl, completely dissociated   **Find:** T_f, T_b
   Other: $K_f = 1.86\ °C/m$; $K_b = 0.512\ °C/m$;
   Conceptual plan:
   percent by mass $\rightarrow$ g_{KCl}, g_{H2O} **then** g_{H2O} $\rightarrow$ kg_{H2O} **and** g_{KCl} $\rightarrow$ mol_{KCl} **then**

$$mass\ percent = \frac{mass\ solute}{mass\ solution} \times 100\ \% \qquad \frac{1\ kg}{1000\ g} \qquad \frac{1\ mol\ KCl}{74.55\ g\ KCl}$$

   mol $_{NaNO3}$, **kg$_{H2O}$** $\rightarrow m$ **then** m, i, K_f $\rightarrow$ ΔT_f $\rightarrow$ T_f **and** m, i, K_b $\rightarrow$ ΔT_b $\rightarrow$ T_b

$$m = \frac{amount\ solute\ (moles)}{mass\ solvent\ (kg)} \qquad \Delta T_f = K_f\,i\,m \quad i = 2 \quad T_f = T_f^° - \Delta T_f \qquad \Delta T_b = K_b\,i\,m \quad i = 2 \quad T_b = T_b^° + \Delta T_b$$

Solution:

$$mass\ percent = \frac{mass\ solute}{mass\ solution} \times 100\ \%$$ so 3.5 % by mass KCl means 3.5 g KCl and $100.0\ g - 3.5\ g = 96.5$

g water. Then $96.5\ g \times \dfrac{1\ kg}{1000\ g} = 0.0965\ kg$ and $3.5\ g\ KCl \times \dfrac{1\ mol\ KCl}{74.55\ g\ KCl} = 0.046948\ mol\ KCl$ then

$$m = \frac{amount\ solute\ (moles)}{mass\ solvent\ (kg)} = \frac{0.046948\ mol\ KCl}{0.0965\ kg} = 0.48651\ m \quad then$$

$$\Delta T_f = K_f\,i\,m = 1.86\ \frac{°C}{m} \times 2 \times 0.48651\ m = 1.8\ °C \quad then \quad T_f = T_f^° - \Delta T_f = 0.000\ °C - 1.8\ °C = -1.8\ °C$$

and $\Delta T_b = K_b\,i\,m = 0.512\ \dfrac{°C}{m} \times 2 \times 0.48651\ m = 0.50\ °C$ then

$$T_b = T_b^° - \Delta T_b = 100.000\ °C + 0.50\ °C = 100.50\ °C\ .$$

Check: The units (°C) are correct. The magnitude of the answer (- 2 °C and 100.5 °C) seems reasonable since the molality of the particles is ~ 1. The shift in boiling point less than the shift in freezing point because the constant is smaller for freezing.

c) **Given:** 0.150 m of MgF_2, completely dissociated   **Find:** T_f, T_b
   Other: $K_f = 1.86\ °C/m$; $K_b = 0.512\ °C/m$;
   Conceptual plan:
   m, i, K_f $\rightarrow$ ΔT_f **then** ΔT_f $\rightarrow$ T_f **and** m, i, K_b $\rightarrow$ ΔT_b **then** ΔT_b $\rightarrow$ T_b

$$\Delta T_f = K_f\,i\,m \quad i = 3 \qquad T_f = T_f^° - \Delta T_f \qquad \Delta T_b = K_b\,i\,m \quad i = 3 \qquad T_b = T_b^° + \Delta T_b$$

Solution:

$$\Delta T_f = K_f\,i\,m = 1.86\ \frac{°C}{m} \times 3 \times 0.150\ m = 0.837\ °C \quad then$$

$$T_f = T_f^° - \Delta T_f = 0.000\ °C - 0.837\ °C = -0.837\ °C \quad and$$

$$\Delta T_b = K_b\,i\,m = 0.512\ \frac{°C}{m} \times 3 \times 0.150\ m = 0.230\ °C \quad then$$

$$T_b = T_b^° - \Delta T_b = 100.000\ °C + 0.230\ °C = 100.230\ °C\ .$$

Check: The units (°C) are correct. The magnitude of the answer (- 0.8 °C and 100.2 °C) seems reasonable since the molality of the particles is 0.5. The shift in boiling point less than the shift in freezing point because the constant is smaller for freezing.

85. a) **Given:** 0.100 m of $FeCl_3$ **Find:** T_f **Other:** $K_f = 1.86\ °C/m$; $i_{measured} = 3.4$
   Conceptual plan: m, i, K_f $\rightarrow$ ΔT_f **then** ΔT_f $\rightarrow$ T_f

$$\Delta T_f = K_f\,i\,m \qquad T_f = T_f^° - \Delta T_f$$

Solution:

$$\Delta T_f = K_f\,i\,m = 1.86\ \frac{°C}{m} \times 3.4 \times 0.100\ m = 0.632\ °C \quad then$$

$$T_f = T_f^° - \Delta T_f = 0.000\ °C - 0.632\ °C = -0.632\ °C\ .$$

Check: The units (°C) are correct. The magnitude of the answer (- 0.6 °C) seems reasonable since the molality of the particles is 0.3.

b) **Given:** 0.085 M of K_2SO_4 at 298 K   **Find:** Π **Other:** $i_{measured} = 2.6$
Conceptual plan: $M, i, T \rightarrow \Pi$

$$\Pi = i \, M \, RT$$

Solution: $\Pi = i \, M \, RT = 2.6 \times 0.085 \, \dfrac{\text{mol}}{\text{L}} \times 0.08206 \, \dfrac{\text{L atm}}{\text{K mol}} \times 298 \text{ K} = 5.4 \text{ atm}$

Check: The units (atm) are correct. The magnitude of the answer (5 atm) seems reasonable since the molarity is ~ 0.2.

c) **Given:** 1.22 % by mass $MgCl_2$ **Find:** T_b **Other:** $K_b = 0.512 \, °C/m$; $i_{measured} = 2.7$
Conceptual plan:
percent by mass $\rightarrow$ g_{MgCl2}, g_{H2O} **then** $g_{H2O} \rightarrow kg_{H2O}$ **and** $g_{MgCl2} \rightarrow mol_{MgCl2}$ **then**

$$mass \; percent = \frac{mass \; solute}{mass \; solution} \times 100 \, \% \qquad \frac{1 \, \text{kg}}{1000 \, \text{g}} \qquad \frac{1 \, \text{mol} \, MgCl_2}{95.22 \, \text{g} \, MgCl_2}$$

mol_{MgCl2}, kg_{H2O} $\rightarrow m$ **then** m, i, K_b $\rightarrow$ ΔT_b $\rightarrow$ T_b

$$m = \frac{amount \; solute \; (moles)}{mass \; solvent \; (kg)} \qquad \Delta T_b = K_b \, i \, m \qquad T_b = T_b^° + \Delta T_b$$

Solution:

$mass \; percent = \dfrac{mass \; solute}{mass \; solution} \times 100 \%$ so 1.22 % by mass $MgCl_2$ means 1.22 g $MgCl_2$ and

$100.00 \text{ g} - 1.22 \text{ g} = 98.78 \text{ g water.}$ Then $98.78 \text{ g} \times \dfrac{1 \text{kg}}{1000 \text{ g}} = 0.09878 \text{ kg}$ and

$1.22 \text{ g } MgCl_2 \times \dfrac{1 \, \text{mol} \, MgCl_2}{95.22 \text{ g } MgCl_2} = 0.0128124 \text{ mol } MgCl_2$ then

$m = \dfrac{amount \; solute \; (moles)}{mass \; solvent \; (kg)} = \dfrac{0.0128124 \text{ mol } MgCl_2}{0.09878 \text{ kg}} = 0.129706 \; m$ then

$\Delta T_b = K_b \, i \, m = 0.512 \, \dfrac{°C}{m} \times 2.7 \times 0.129706 \; m = 0.18 \, °C$ then

$T_b = T_b^° - \Delta T_b = 100.000 °C + 0.18 \, °C = 100.18 \, °C$.

Check: The units (°C) are correct. The magnitude of the answer (100.2 °C) seems reasonable since the molality of the particles is ~ 1/3.

86. a) **Given:** NaCl; 1.50×10^2 g water and $T_f = -1.0 \, °C$ **Find:** m(NaCl)
Other: $K_f = 1.86 \, °C/m$; $i_{measured} = 1.9$
Conceptual plan:
$T_f \rightarrow \Delta T_f$ **then** $\Delta T_f, i, K_f$ $\rightarrow$ m **then** $g_{H2O} \rightarrow kg_{H2O}$ **then** $m, kg_{H2O} \rightarrow mol_{NaCl}$

$$T_f = T_f^° - \Delta T_f \qquad\qquad \Delta T_f = K_f \, i \, m \qquad\qquad \frac{1 \, \text{kg}}{1000 \, \text{g}} \qquad\qquad m = \frac{amount \; solute \; (moles)}{mass \; solvent \; (kg)}$$

then mol_{NaCl} $\rightarrow$ g_{NaCl}

$$\frac{58.44 \; \text{g NaCl}}{1 \; \text{mol NaCl}}$$

Solution:
$T_f = T_f^° - \Delta T_f$ so $\Delta T_f = T_f^° - T_f = 0.0 °C - 1.0 \, °C = -1.0 \, °C$ then $\Delta T_f = K_f \, i \, m$

Rearrange to solve for m. $m = \dfrac{\Delta T_f}{K_f \, i} = \dfrac{1.0 \, °C}{1.86 \, \frac{°C}{m} \times 1.9} = 0.28297 \, m$ NaCl   then

$1.50 \times 10^2 \text{ g} \times \dfrac{1 \text{kg}}{1000 \text{ g}} = 0.150 \text{ kg}$ then $m = \dfrac{amount \; solute \; (moles)}{mass \; solvent \; (kg)}$ so

$$mol_{NaCl} = m \times kg_{H2O} = 0.28297 \frac{\text{mol NaCl}}{kg_{H2O}} \times 0.150 \ kg_{H2O} = 0.042445 \text{ mol NaCl} \quad \text{then}$$

$$0.042445 \text{ mol NaCl} \times \frac{58.44 \text{ g NaCl}}{1 \text{ mol NaCl}} = 2.5 \text{ NaCl}$$

Check: The units (g) are correct. The magnitude of the answer (2.5 g) seems reasonable since the temperature change is moderate and NaCl has a low formula mass.

b) **Given:** $MgSO_4$; 2.50×10^2 mL solution and $\Pi = 3.82$ atm at 298 K   **Find:** $m(MgSO_4)$
   Other: $i_{measured} = 1.3$
   Conceptual plan:
   $°C \rightarrow K$ then $i, \Pi, T \rightarrow M$ then $mL_{soln} \rightarrow L_{soln}$ then $L_{soln}, M \rightarrow mol_{MgSO4} \rightarrow g_{MgSO4}$

$K = °C + 273.15$	$\Pi = iMRT$	$\dfrac{1L}{1000 \text{ mL}}$	$M = \dfrac{\text{amount solute (moles)}}{\text{volume solution (L)}}$ $\dfrac{120.38 \text{ g MgSO}_4}{1 \text{ mol MgSO}_4}$

   Solution:
   $\Pi = iMRT$ Rearrange to solve for M.

$$M = \frac{\Pi}{iRT} = \frac{3.82 \text{ atm}}{1.3 \times 0.08206 \frac{L \text{ atm}}{K \text{ mol}} \times 298 \text{ K}} = 0.12016 \frac{\text{mol MgSO}_4}{L} \quad \text{then}$$

$$2.50 \times 10^2 \text{ mL} \times \frac{1L}{1000 \text{ mL}} = 0.250 \text{ L} \quad \text{then} \quad M = \frac{\text{amount solute (moles)}}{\text{volume solution (L)}} \quad \text{so}$$

$$mol_{MgSO4} = M \times L_{soln} = 0.12016 \frac{\text{mol MgSO}_4}{L} \times 0.250 \text{ L} = 0.030041 \text{ mol MgSO}_4 \quad \text{finally}$$

$$0.030041 \text{ mol MgSO}_4 \times \frac{120.38 \text{ g MgSO}_4}{1 \text{ mol MgSO}_4} = 3.6 \text{ g MgSO}_4$$

Check: The units (g) are correct. The magnitude of the answer (4 g) seems reasonable since the pressure is moderate and $MgSO_4$ has a low formula mass.

c) **Given:** $FeCl_3$; 2.50×10^2 g water and $T_b = 102 °C$ **Find:** $m(FeCl_3)$
   Other: $K_b = 0.512 °C/m$; $i_{measured} = 3.4$
   Conceptual plan:
   $T_b \rightarrow \Delta T_b$ then $\Delta T_b, i, K_b \rightarrow m$ then $g_{H2O} \rightarrow kg_{H2O}$ then $m, kg_{H2O} \rightarrow mol_{FeCl3}$

$T_b = T_b^° + \Delta T_b$	$\Delta T_b = K_b i m$	$\dfrac{1 kg}{1000 g}$	$m = \dfrac{\text{amount solute (moles)}}{\text{mass solvent (kg)}}$

   then $mol_{FeCl3} \rightarrow g_{FeCl3}$
   $$\frac{162.21 \text{ g FeCl}_3}{1 \text{ mol FeCl}_3}$$

   Solution:
   $T_b = T_b^° + \Delta T_b$ so $\Delta T_b = T_b - T_b^° = 102°C - 100 °C = 2 °C$ then $\Delta T_b = K_b i m$

   Rearrange to solve for m. $m = \dfrac{\Delta T_b}{K_b i} = \dfrac{2 °C}{0.512 \frac{°C}{m} \times 3.4} = 1.149 \ m \ FeCl_3$ then

$$2.50 \times 10^2 \text{ g} \times \frac{1 kg}{1000 \text{ g}} = 0.250 \text{ kg} \quad \text{then} \quad m = \frac{\text{amount solute (moles)}}{\text{mass solvent (kg)}} \quad \text{so}$$

$$mol_{FeCl3} = m \times kg_{H2O} = 1.149 \frac{\text{mol FeCl}_3}{kg_{H2O}} \times 0.250 \ kg_{H2O} = 0.2872 \text{ mol FeCl}_3 \quad \text{then}$$

$$0.2872 \text{ mol FeCl}_3 \times \frac{162.21 \text{ g FeCl}_3}{1 \text{ mol FeCl}_3} = 47 \text{ g FeCl}_3 = 50 \text{ g FeCl}_3$$

Check: The units (g) are correct. The magnitude of the answer (50 g) seems reasonable since the temperature change is significant and we are making 0.25 L of solution.

87. **Given:** 0.100 M of ionic solution, Π = 8.3 atm at 25 °C **Find:** $i_{measured}$

Conceptual plan: °C $\rightarrow$ K then Π, M, T $\rightarrow$ i

$\quad\quad\quad\quad\quad\quad\quad\quad$ $K = °C + 273.15$ $\quad\quad\quad\quad$ $\Pi = iMRT$

Solution: 25 °C + 273.15 = 298 K $\quad$ then $\quad\quad\quad$ $\Pi = iMRT$ $\quad\quad\quad$ Rearrange to solve for i.

$$i = \frac{\Pi}{MRT} = \frac{8.3 \text{ atm}}{0.100 \frac{\text{mol}}{\text{L}} \times 0.08206 \frac{\text{L atm}}{\text{K mol}} \times 298 \text{ K}} = 3.4$$

Check: The units (none) are correct. The magnitude of the answer (3) seems reasonable for an ionic solution with a high osmotic pressure.

88. **Given:** 8.92 g of KBr in 500.0 mL solution, Π = 6.97 atm at 25 °C $\quad\quad\quad$ **Find:** $i_{measured}$

Conceptual plan:

°C $\rightarrow$ K $\quad$ and $\quad$ $mL_{soln} \rightarrow L_{soln}$ $\quad$ and $\quad$ $g_{KBr} \rightarrow mol_{KBr}$ then $\quad$ $mol_{KBr}, L_{soln} \rightarrow$ M $\quad$ then

$\quad$ $K = °C + 273.15$ $\quad\quad\quad\quad$ $\dfrac{1L}{1000\ mL}$ $\quad\quad\quad\quad$ $\dfrac{1\ mol\ KBr}{119.01\ g\ KBr}$ $\quad\quad\quad$ $M = \dfrac{\text{amount solute (moles)}}{\text{volume solution (L)}}$

Π, M, T $\rightarrow$ i

$\quad\quad$ $\Pi = iMRT$

Solution:

25 °C + 273.15 = 298 K $\quad$ and $\quad$ 500.0 mL $\times \dfrac{1L}{1000\ mL}$ = 0.5000 L $\quad$ and

8.92 g KBr $\times \dfrac{1\ mol\ KBr}{119.01\ g\ KBr}$ = 0.0749517 mol KBr $\quad$ then

M = $\dfrac{\text{amount solute (moles)}}{\text{volume solution (L)}}$ = $\dfrac{0.0749517\ mol\ KBr}{0.5000\ L}$ = 0.149903 $\dfrac{mol\ KBr}{L}$ $\quad$ then $\Pi = iMRT$ $\quad$ Rearrange to solve for i.

$$i = \frac{\Pi}{MRT} = \frac{6.97 \text{ atm}}{0.149903 \frac{\text{mol}}{\text{L}} \times 0.08206 \frac{\text{L atm}}{\text{K mol}} \times 298 \text{ K}} = 1.90$$

Check: The units (none) are correct. The magnitude of the answer (1.9) seems reasonable for KBr since we expect i to be 2 if it completely dissociates. Since both ions are large and have only one charge each, we expect i to be close to the theoretical value.

89. Chloroform is polar and has stronger solute-solvent interactions than nonpolar carbon tetrachloride.

90. Each molecule has one –OH group that is capable of hydrogen bonding. Since phenol is a smaller molecule than naphthol, the –OH group has a bigger impact on the overall polarity of the molecule.

91. **Given:** $KClO_4$: Lattice Energy = $-$ 599 kJ/mol, $\Delta H_{hydration}$ = $-$ 548 kJ/mol; 10.0 g $KClO_4$ in 100.00 mL solution **Find:** ΔH_{soln} and ΔT **Other:** C_s = 4.05 J/g °C; d = 1.05 g/mL

Conceptual plan:

Lattice Energy, $\Delta H_{hydration}$ $\rightarrow$ ΔH_{soln} and g $\rightarrow$ mol then mol, ΔH_{soln} $\rightarrow$ q(kJ) $\rightarrow$ q(J)

$\Delta H_{soln} = \Delta H_{solute} + \Delta H_{hydration}$ where $\Delta H_{solute} = - \Delta H_{lattice}$ $\quad$ $\dfrac{1\ mol}{138.56\ g}$ $\quad\quad\quad$ $q = n\ \Delta H_{soln}$ $\quad$ $\dfrac{1000\ J}{1\ kJ}$

then $\quad$ mL_{soln} $\rightarrow$ g_{soln} then $\quad$ q, g_{soln}, C_s $\rightarrow$ ΔT

$\quad\quad\quad\quad$ $\dfrac{1.05\ g}{1\ mL}$ $\quad\quad\quad\quad$ $q = m\ C_s\ \Delta T$

Solution:

$\Delta H_{soln} = \Delta H_{solute} + \Delta H_{hydration}$ where $\Delta H_{solute} = - \Delta H_{lattice}$ so $\Delta H_{soln} = \Delta H_{hydration} - \Delta H_{lattice}$

$\Delta H_{soln} = -$ 548 kJ/mol - - 599 kJ/mol = +51 kJ/mol $\quad$ and $\quad$ 10.0 g $\times \dfrac{1\ mol}{138.56\ g}$ = 0.0721709 mol $\quad$ then

$q = n\ \Delta H_{soln}$ = 0.0721709 mol $\times$ 51 $\dfrac{kJ}{mol}$ = +3.6807 kJ $\times \dfrac{1000\ J}{1\ kJ}$ = +3680.7 J absorbed then

100.0 mL $\times \dfrac{1.05\ g}{1\ mL}$ = 105 g $\quad$ Since heat is absorbed in the when $KClO_4$ dissolves then the temperature will

drop or q = $-$ 3680.7 J and $q = m\ C_s\ \Delta T$ Rearrange to solve for ΔT.

414

$$\Delta T = \frac{q}{m\,C_s} = \frac{-3680.7\ \text{J}}{105\ \text{g} \times 4.05\ \frac{\text{J}}{\text{g}\ ^\circ\text{C}}} = -8.7\ ^\circ\text{C}$$

Check: The units (kJ/mol and °C) are correct. The magnitude of the answer (51 kJ/mol) makes physical sense because the lattice energy is larger than the heat of hydration. The magnitude of the temperature change (- 9 °C) makes physical sense since heat is absorbed and the heat of solution is fairly small.

92. **Given**: NaOH: Lattice Energy = - 887 kJ/mol, $\Delta H_{hydration}$ = - 932 kJ/mol; 25.0 g NaOH in solution, T_i = 25.0 °C; T_f = 100.0 °C **Find**: ΔH_{soln} and m (solution) **Other**: C_s = 4.01 J/g °C; d = 1.05 g/mL
   Conceptual plan:
   Lattice Energy, $\Delta H_{hydration}$ → **ΔH_{soln}** and **g** → **mol** then **mol, ΔH_{soln}** → **q(kJ)** → **q(J)**

   $\Delta H_{soln} = \Delta H_{solute} + \Delta H_{hydration}$ where $\Delta H_{solute} = -\Delta H_{lattice}$ $\dfrac{1\ mol}{40.00\ g}$ $q = n\,\Delta H_{soln}$ $\dfrac{1000\ J}{1\ kJ}$

   and T_i, T_f → **ΔT** then **q, ΔT, C_s** → **g_{soln}** then **g_{soln}** → **mL_{soln}**

   $\Delta T = T_f - T_i$ $q = m\,C_s\,\Delta T$ $\dfrac{1\ mL}{1.05\ g}$

   Solution:
   $\Delta H_{soln} = \Delta H_{solute} + \Delta H_{hydration}$ where $\Delta H_{solute} = -\Delta H_{lattice}$ so $\Delta H_{soln} = \Delta H_{hydration} - \Delta H_{lattice}$

   $\Delta H_{soln} = -932$ kJ/mol $- -887$ kJ/mol $= -45$ kJ/mol and $25.0\ \text{g} \times \dfrac{1\ mol}{40.00\ \text{g}} = 0.625\ mol$ then

   $q = n\,\Delta H_{soln} = 0.625\ \text{mol} \times -45\ \dfrac{kJ}{\text{mol}} = -28.125\ \text{kJ} \times \dfrac{1000\ J}{1\ \text{kJ}} = -28125$ J released then

   $\Delta T = T_f - T_i = 100.0\,^\circ\text{C} - 25.0\,^\circ\text{C} = 75.0\ ^\circ\text{C}$ since heat is released in the when NaOH dissolves then the temperature will rise or q = + 28125 J and $q = m\,C_s\,\Delta T$ Rearrange to solve for m.

   $$m = \frac{q}{C_s\,\Delta T} = \frac{+28125\ \text{J}}{4.01\ \frac{\text{J}}{\text{g}\ ^\circ\text{C}} \times 75.0\ ^\circ\text{C}} = 93.526\ \text{g}_{soln}$$ then $93.526\ \text{g} \times \dfrac{1\ mL}{1.05\ \text{g}} = 89$ mL soln

   Check: The units (kJ/mol and mL) are correct. The magnitude of the answer (- 45 kJ/mol) makes physical sense because the lattice energy is smaller than the heat of hydration. The magnitude of the solution volume (90 mL) makes physical sense since have 2/3 mole of NaOH and large temperature change. NaOH is a strong base and so we expect heat to be released and need to take precautions in the lab.

93. **Given**: Argon, 0.0537 L; 25 °C, P_{Ar} = 1.0 atm to make 1.0 L saturated solution **Find**: k_H(Ar)
   Conceptual plan: **°C → K** and **P_{Ar}, V, T → mol_{He}** then **mol_{He}, V_{soln}, P_{Ar} → k_H(He)**

   $K = \,^\circ C + 273.15$ $PV = nRT$ $S_{Ar} = k_H(Ar)P_{Ar}$ with $S_{Ar} = \dfrac{mol_{Ar}}{L_{soln}}$

   Solution: 25 °C + 273.15 = 298 K and $PV = nRT$ Rearrange to solve for n.

   $$n = \frac{PV}{RT} = \frac{1.0\ \text{atm} \times 0.0537\ \text{L}}{0.08206\ \frac{\text{L atm}}{\text{K mol}} \times 298\ \text{K}} = 0.00219597\ mol$$ then $S_{Ar} = k_H(Ar)P_{Ar}$ with $S_{Ar} = \dfrac{mol_{Ar}}{L_{soln}}$ Substitute

   in values and rearrange to solve for k_H. $k_H(Ar) = \dfrac{mol_{Ar}}{L_{soln}P_{He}} = \dfrac{0.00219597\ mol}{1.0\,L_{soln} \times 1.0\ atm} = 2.2 \times 10^{-3}\ \dfrac{M}{atm}$

   Check: The units (M/atm) are correct. The magnitude of the answer (10^{-3}) seems reasonable since it is consistent with other values in the text.

94. **Given**: gas: 1.65 L; 25 °C, P = 725 torr; and k_H = 0.112 M/atm   **Find**: volume of saturated solution
   Conceptual plan: **°C → K** and **torr → atm** **P, V, T → mol_{gas}** then **mol_{He}, k_H, P → V_{soln}**

   $K = \,^\circ C + 273.15$ $\dfrac{1\ atm}{760\ torr}$ $PV = nRT$ $S_{gas} = k_H(gas)P_{gas}$ with $S_{gas} = \dfrac{mol_{gas}}{L_{soln}}$

   Solution: 25 °C + 273.15 = 298 K and $725\ \text{torr} \times \dfrac{1\ atm}{760\ \text{torr}} = 0.953947$ atm then $PV = nRT$ Rearrange to solve for n. $n = \dfrac{PV}{RT} = \dfrac{0.953947 \text{ atm} \times 1.65 \text{ L}}{0.08206 \dfrac{\text{L atm}}{\text{K mol}} \times 298 \text{ K}} = 0.0643666 \text{ mol}$ then $S_{gas} = k_H(gas)P_{gas}$

with $S_{gas} = \dfrac{mol_{gas}}{L_{soln}}$ Substitute in values and rearrange to solve for V_{soln}.

$L_{soln} = \dfrac{mol_{gas}}{k_H(gas)P_{gas}} = \dfrac{0.0643666 \text{ mol}}{0.112 \dfrac{\text{mol}}{\text{L atm}} \times 0.953947 \text{ atm}} = 0.602 \text{ L soln}$

Check: The units (L) are correct. The magnitude of the answer (0.6 L) seems reasonable since the Henry's Law constant is so large.

95. **Given**: 0.0020 ppm by mass Hg = legal limit; 0.0040 ppm by mass Hg = contaminated water; 50.0 mg Hg ingested   **Find**: volume of contaminated water

    Conceptual plan: $mg_{Hg} \rightarrow g_{Hg} \rightarrow g_{H2O} \rightarrow mL_{H2O} \rightarrow L_{H2O}$

    $$\dfrac{1 \text{ g}}{1000 \text{ mg}} \qquad \dfrac{10^6 \text{ g water}}{0.0040 \text{ g Hg}} \qquad \dfrac{1 \text{ mL}}{1.00 \text{ g}} \qquad \dfrac{1 \text{ L}}{1000 \text{ mL}}$$

    Solution:

    $$50.0 \text{ mg Hg} \times \dfrac{1 \text{ g Hg}}{1000 \text{ mg Hg}} \times \dfrac{10^6 \text{ g water}}{0.0040 \text{ g Hg}} \times \dfrac{1 \text{ mL water}}{1.00 \text{ g water}} \times \dfrac{1 \text{ L water}}{1000 \text{ mL water}} = 1.3 \times 10^4 \text{ L water}$$

    Check: The units (L) are correct. The magnitude of the answer (10^4 L) seems reasonable since the concentration is so low.

96. **Given**: 2.4 g Na ingested / day; 0.050 % Na by mass in water; d = 1.0 g/mL   **Find**: volume of water

    Conceptual plan: $g_{Na} \rightarrow g_{H2O} \rightarrow mL_{H2O} \rightarrow L_{H2O}$

    $$\dfrac{100.000 \text{ g water}}{0.050 \text{ g Na}} \qquad \dfrac{1 \text{ mL}}{1.0 \text{ g}} \qquad \dfrac{1 \text{ L}}{1000 \text{ mL}}$$

    Solution: $2.4 \text{ g Na} \times \dfrac{100.000 \text{ g water}}{0.050 \text{ g Na}} \times \dfrac{1 \text{ mL water}}{1.0 \text{ g water}} \times \dfrac{1 \text{ L water}}{1000 \text{ mL water}} = 4.8 \text{ L water}$

    Check: The units (L) are correct. The magnitude of the answer (5 L) seems reasonable since the concentration is low, but not extremely low.

97. **Given**: 12.5 % NaCl by mass in water at 55 °C; 2.5 L vapor   **Find**: g_{H2O} in vapor
    Other: $P°_{H2O} = 118$ torr, $i_{NaCl} = 1.9$
    Conceptual plan: % NaCl by mass $\rightarrow$ g_{NaCl}, g_{H2O} then $g_{NaCl} \rightarrow mol_{NaCl}$ and

    $$\dfrac{12.5 \text{ g NaCl}}{100 \text{ g (NaCl} + H_2O)} \qquad\qquad \dfrac{1 \text{ mol NaCl}}{58.44 \text{ g NaCl}}$$

    $g_{H2O} \rightarrow mol_{H2O}$ then $mol_{NaCl}, mol_{H2O} \rightarrow \chi_{NaCl} \rightarrow \chi_{H2O}$ then $\chi_{H2O}, P°_{H2O} \rightarrow P_{H2O}$

    $$\dfrac{1 \text{ mol } H_2O}{18.02 \text{ g } H_2O} \qquad \chi = \dfrac{\text{amount solute (in moles)}}{\text{total amount of solute and solvent (in moles)}} \qquad \chi_{H2O} = 1 - i_{NaCl}\chi_{NaCl} \qquad P_{solution} = \chi_{solvent} P^o_{solvent}$$

    then torr $\rightarrow$ atm   and   °C $\rightarrow$ K   P, V, T $\rightarrow$ $mol_{H2O} \rightarrow g_{H2O}$

    $$\dfrac{1 \text{ atm}}{760 \text{ torr}} \qquad K = °C + 273.15 \qquad PV = nRT \qquad \dfrac{18.02 \text{ g } H_2O}{1 \text{ mol } H_2O}$$

    Solution:
    $\dfrac{12.5 \text{ g NaCl}}{100 \text{ g (NaCl} + H_2O)}$ means 12.5 g NaCl and (100 g - 12.5 g) = 87.5 g H_2O then

    $12.5 \text{ g NaCl} \times \dfrac{1 \text{ mol NaCl}}{58.44 \text{ g NaCl}} = 0.213895 \text{ mol NaCl}$ and $87.5 \text{ g } H_2O \times \dfrac{1 \text{ mol } H_2O}{18.02 \text{ g } H_2O} = 4.85572 \text{ mol } H_2O$

    then $\chi = \dfrac{\text{amount solute (in moles)}}{\text{total amount of solute and solvent (in moles)}} = \dfrac{0.213895 \text{ mol}}{0.213895 \text{ mol} + 4.85572 \text{ mol}} = 0.0421916$ then

    $\chi_{H2O} = 1 - i_{NaCl}\chi_{NaCl} = 1 - 1.9 \times 0.0421916 = 0.919836$ then

416

$P_{solution} = \chi_{solvent}\, P^o_{solvent} = 0.919836 \times 118 \text{ torr} = 108.541 \text{ torr } H_2O$ then

$108.541 \text{ torr } H_2O \times \dfrac{1 \text{ atm}}{760 \text{ torr}} = 0.142817 \text{ atm}$

and $55\,°C + 273.15 = 328 \text{ K}$ then $PV = nRT$ Rearrange to solve for n.

$n = \dfrac{PV}{RT} = \dfrac{0.142817 \text{ atm} \times 2.5 \text{ L}}{0.08206 \dfrac{L \cdot atm}{K \cdot mol} \times 328 \text{ K}} = 0.013265 \text{ mol}$ then $0.013265 \text{ mol } H_2O \times \dfrac{18.02 \text{ g } H_2O}{1 \text{ mol } H_2O} = 0.24 \text{ g } H_2O$

Check: The units (g) are correct. The magnitude of the answer (0.2 g) seems reasonable since there is very little mass in a vapor.

98. **Given:** 19.5 mg water in 1 L vapor at 25 °C **Find:** mole percent solute in solution **Other:** P^o_{H2O} = 23.78 torr

Conceptual plan:

$\text{mg}_{H2O} \to \text{g}_{H2O} \to \text{mol}_{H2O}$ and $°C \to K$ then $V, \text{mol}_{H2O}, T \to P_{H2O}$ then

$\dfrac{1 \text{ g}}{1000 \text{ mg}} \quad \dfrac{1 \text{ mol } H_2O}{18.01 \text{ g } H_2O}$ $\qquad K = °C + 273.15$ $\qquad PV = nRT$

then atm $\to$ torr then $P_{H2O}, P^o_{H2O} \to \chi_{H2O} \to \chi_{Solute} \to$ mole percent solute

$\dfrac{760 \text{ torr}}{1 \text{ atm}}$ $\qquad P_{H2O} = \chi_{H2O}\, P^o_{H2O} \quad \chi_{Solute} = 1 - \chi_{H2O} \quad$ mole percent solute $= \chi_{Solute} \times 100\%$

Solution:

$19.5 \text{ mg } H_2O \times \dfrac{1 \text{ g } H_2O}{1000 \text{ mg } H_2O} \times \dfrac{1 \text{ mol } H_2O}{18.01 \text{ g } H_2O} = 0.00108273 \text{ mol } H_2O$ and $55\,°C + 273.15 = 328 \text{ K}$ then

$PV = nRT$ Rearrange to solve for P.

$P = \dfrac{nRT}{V} = \dfrac{0.00108273 \text{ mol} \times 0.08206 \dfrac{L \cdot atm}{K \cdot mol} \times 298 \text{ K}}{1.00 \text{ L}} = 0.0264770 \text{ atm}$

$0.0264770 \text{ atm} \times \dfrac{760 \text{ torr}}{1 \text{ atm}} = 20.1225 \text{ torr}$ and $P_{H2O} = \chi_{H2O}\, P^o_{H2O}$ Rearrange to solve for χ_{H2O}.

$\chi_{H2O} = \dfrac{P_{H2O}}{P^o_{H2O}} = \dfrac{20.1225 \text{ torr}}{23.78 \text{ torr}} = 0.846194$ then $\chi_{Solute} = 1 - \chi_{H2O} = 1 - 0.846194 = 0.153806$ then

mole percent solute $= \chi_{Solute} \times 100\% = 0.153806 \times 100\% = 15.3$ mole percent

Check: The units (mole percent) are correct. The magnitude of the answer (15 mole percent g) seems reasonable since we expect there to be more water than solute.

99. **Given:** $T_b = 106.5\,°C$ aqueous solution **Find:** T_f **Other:** $K_f = 1.86\,°C/m$; $K_b = 0.512\,°C/m$

Conceptual plan: $T_b \to \Delta T_b$ then $\Delta T_b, K_b \to m$ then $m, K_f \to \Delta T_f \to T_f$

$\qquad T_b = T^o_b + \Delta T_b \qquad \Delta T_b = K_b m \qquad \Delta T_f = K_f m \quad T_f = T^o_f - \Delta T_f$

Solution:

$T_b = T^o_b + \Delta T_b$ so $\Delta T_b = T_b - T^o_b = 106.5\,°C - 100.0\,°C = 6.5\,°C$ then $\Delta T_b = K_b m$

Rearrange to solve for m. $m = \dfrac{\Delta T_b}{K_b} = \dfrac{6.5\,°C}{0.512\,\dfrac{°C}{m}} = 12.695\, m$ then

$\Delta T_f = K_f m = 1.86\,\dfrac{°C}{m} \times 12.695\, m = 23.6\,°C$ then $T_f = T^o_f - \Delta T_f = 0.000\,°C - 23.6\,°C = -24\,°C$.

Check: The units (°C) are correct. The magnitude of the answer (- 24 °C) seems reasonable since the shift in boiling point less than the shift in freezing point because the constant is smaller for freezing.

100. **Given:** $P_{H2O} = 20.5$ torr at 25 °C aqueous solution **Find:** T_b **Other:** $P°_{H2O} = 23.78$ torr; $K_b = 0.512$ °C/m
Conceptual plan: $P_{H2O}, P°_{H2O} \rightarrow \chi_{H2O}$ assume 1kg water   kg $_{H2O} \rightarrow$ mol$_{H2O}$ then

$$P_{H_2O} = \chi_{H_2O}\, P°_{H_2O}$$

$$\frac{1\ mol\, H_2O}{18.01\ g\, H_2O}$$

mol$_{H2O}$, $\chi_{H2O} \rightarrow$ mol $_{Solute}$ then mol $_{Solute}$, kg $_{H2O} \rightarrow m_{Solute}$ then m, $K_b \rightarrow \Delta T_b \rightarrow T_b$

$$\chi_{H2O} = \frac{moles\ H_2O}{moles\ H_2O\ +\ moles\ solute}$$

$$m = \frac{amount\ solute\ (moles)}{mass\ solvent\ (kg)}$$

$$\Delta T_b = K_b\, m \quad T_b = T_b^o + \Delta T_b$$

Solution:

$$P_{H2O} = \chi_{H2O}\, P°_{H2O} \quad \text{Rearrange to solve for } \chi_{H2O}.\ \chi_{H2O} = \frac{P_{H2O}}{P°_{H2O}} = \frac{20.5\ \cancel{torr}}{23.78\ \cancel{torr}} = 0.86\underline{2}069 \quad \text{then}$$

$$1000\ \cancel{g\, H_2O} \times \frac{1\ mol\, H_2O}{18.01\ \cancel{g\, H_2O}} = 55.5\underline{2}470\ mol\, H_2O \quad \text{then}$$

$$\chi_{H2O} = \frac{moles\ H_2O}{moles\ H_2O\ +\ moles\ solute} = \frac{55.5\underline{2}470\ \cancel{mol}}{55.5\underline{2}470\ \cancel{mol}\ +\ x\ \cancel{mol}} = 0.86\underline{2}069 \quad \text{Solve for x moles of solute.}$$

$$55.5\underline{2}470\ mol = 0.86\underline{2}069\ (55.5\underline{2}470\ mol\ +\ x\,mol\,) \rightarrow x = \frac{(55.5\underline{2}470 - 47.\underline{8}661)\ mol}{0.86\underline{2}069} = 8.\underline{8}8395\ mol \quad \text{then}$$

$$m = \frac{amount\ solute\ (moles)}{mass\ solvent\ (kg)} = \frac{8.\underline{8}8395\ mol}{1\ kg} = 8.\underline{8}8395\ m \quad \text{then}\quad \Delta T_b = K_b\, m = 0.512\ \frac{°C}{\cancel{m}} \times 8.\underline{8}8395\ \cancel{m} = 4.5\ °C$$

then $T_b = T_b^o + \Delta T_b = 100.0\ °C + 4.5\ °C = 104.5\ °C$.

Check: The units (°C) are correct. The magnitude of the answer (4.5 °C) seems reasonable since there is a significant lowering of the vapor pressure.

101. a) **Given:** 0.90 % NaCl by mass per volume; isotonic aqueous solution at 25 °C; KCl; $i = 1.9$
Find: % KCl by mass per volume
Conceptual plan: Isotonic solutions will have the same number of particles. Since i is the same,

$$\frac{1\ mol\ KCl}{1\ mol\ NaCl}$$

The new % mass per volume will be the mass ratio of the two salts.

$$percent\ by\ mass\ per\ volume = \frac{mass\ solute}{V} \times 100\ \% \quad \frac{1\ mol\ NaCl}{58.44\ g\ NaCl} \quad \text{and} \quad \frac{74.56\ g\ KCl}{1\ mol\ KCl}$$

Solution:

$$percent\ by\ mass\ per\ volume = \frac{mass\ solute}{V} \times 100\ \% =$$

$$= \frac{0.0090\ \cancel{g\ NaCl}}{V} \times \frac{1\ \cancel{mol\ NaCl}}{58.44\ \cancel{g\ NaCl}} \times \frac{1\ \cancel{mol\ KCl}}{1\ \cancel{mol\ NaCl}} \times \frac{74.56\ g\ KCl}{1\ \cancel{mol\ KCl}} \times 100\ \% = 1.1\ \%\ KCl\ \text{by mass per volume}$$

Check: The units (% KCl by mass per volume) are correct. The magnitude of the answer (1.1) seems reasonable since the molar mass of KCl is larger than the molar mass of NaCl.

b) **Given:** 0.90 % NaCl by mass per volume; isotonic aqueous solution at 25 °C; NaBr; $i = 1.9$
Find: % NaBr by mass per volume
Conceptual plan: Isotonic solutions will have the same number of particles. Since i is the same,

$$\frac{1\ mol\ NaBr}{1\ mol\ NaCl}$$

the new % mass per volume will be the mass ratio of the two salts.

$$percent\ by\ mass\ per\ volume = \frac{mass\ solute}{V} \times 100\ \% \quad \frac{1\ mol\ NaCl}{58.44\ g\ NaCl} \quad \text{and} \quad \frac{102.90\ g\ NaBr}{1\ mol\ NaBr}$$

Solution:

$$percent\ by\ mass\ per\ volume = \frac{mass\ solute}{V} \times 100\ \% =$$

$$= \frac{0.0090\ \cancel{g\ NaCl}}{V} \times \frac{1\ \cancel{mol\ NaCl}}{58.44\ \cancel{g\ NaCl}} \times \frac{1\ \cancel{mol\ NaBr}}{1\ \cancel{mol\ NaCl}} \times \frac{102.90\ g\ NaBr}{1\ \cancel{mol\ NaBr}} \times 100\ \% = 1.6\ \%\ NaBr\ \text{by mass per volume}$$

418

Check: The units (% NaBr by mass per volume) are correct. The magnitude of the answer (1.6) seems reasonable since the molar mass of NaBr is larger than the molar mass of NaCl.

c) **Given:** 0.90 % NaCl by mass per volume; isotonic aqueous solution at 25 °C; glucose ($C_6H_{12}O_6$); $i =$ 1.9   **Find:** % glucose by mass per volume

Conceptual plan: Isotonic solutions will have the same number of particles. Since glucose is a nonelectrolyte, the i is not the same, then use the mass ratio of the two compounds.

$$\frac{1.9 \text{ mol } C_6H_{12}O_6}{1 \text{ mol NaCl}} \qquad percent\ by\ mass\ per\ volume = \frac{mass\ solute}{V} \times 100\ \% \qquad \frac{1 \text{ mol NaCl}}{58.44 \text{ g NaCl}} \text{ and } \frac{180.16 \text{ g } C_6H_{12}O_6}{1 \text{ mol } C_6H_{12}O_6}$$

Solution:

$$percent\ by\ mass\ per\ volume = \frac{mass\ solute}{V} \times 100\ \% =$$

$$= \frac{0.0090 \text{ g NaCl}}{V} \times \frac{1 \text{ mol NaCl}}{58.44 \text{ g NaCl}} \times \frac{1.9 \text{ mol } C_6H_{12}O_6}{1 \text{ mol NaCl}} \times \frac{180.16 \text{ g } C_6H_{12}O_6}{1 \text{ mol } C_6H_{12}O_6} \times 100\ \% =$$

$$= 5.3\ \% \ C_6H_{12}O_6 \text{ by mass per volume}$$

Check: The units (% $C_6H_{12}O_6$ by mass per volume) are correct. The magnitude of the answer (1.6) seems reasonable since the molar mass of $C_6H_{12}O_6$ is larger than the molar mass of NaCl and we need more moles of $C_6H_{12}O_6$ since it is a nonelectrolyte.

102. **Given:** 28.5 g of magnesium citrate ($Mg_3(C_6H_5O_3)_2$) in 235 mL of solution at 37 °C, complete dissociation
Find: Π
Conceptual plan:
$$mL_{soln} \rightarrow L_{soln} \quad \text{and} \quad g_{Mg3(C6H5O3)2} \rightarrow mol_{Mg3(C6H5O3)2} \quad \text{then} \quad mol_{Mg3(C6H5O3)2}, L_{soln} \rightarrow M$$

$$\frac{1 L}{1000 \text{ mL}} \qquad \frac{1 \text{ mol } Mg_3(C_6H_5O_3)_2}{323.14 \text{ g } Mg_3(C_6H_5O_3)_2} \qquad M = \frac{amount\ solute\ (moles)}{volume\ solution\ (L)}$$

then $\quad M, i, T \rightarrow Π$
$Π = iMRT \quad$ where $i = 5$

Solution:

$$235 \text{ mL} \times \frac{1 L}{1000 \text{ mL}} = 0.235 \text{ L} \quad \text{and}$$

$$28.5 \text{ g } Mg_3(C_6H_5O_3)_2 \times \frac{1 \text{ mol } Mg_3(C_6H_5O_3)_2}{323.14 \text{ g } Mg_3(C_6H_5O_3)_2} = 0.0881982 \text{ mol } Mg_3(C_6H_5O_3)_2 \text{ then}$$

$$M = \frac{amount\ solute\ (moles)}{volume\ solution\ (L)} = \frac{0.0881982 \text{ mol } Mg_3(C_6H_5O_3)_2}{0.235 \text{ L}} = 0.375311 \text{ M} \text{ then}$$

$$Π = iMRT = 5 \times 0.375311 \frac{mol}{L} \times 0.08206 \frac{L\ atm}{K\ mol} \times 310.\ K = 47.7 \text{ atm}$$

Check: The units (atm) are correct. The magnitude of the answer (48 atm) seems reasonable since the molarity is ~ 1.5.

103. **Given:** 4.5701 g of $MgCl_2$ and 43.238 g water, $P_{soln} = 0.3624$ atm, $P°_{soln} = 0.3804$ atm at 348.0 K
Find: $i_{measured}$
Conceptual plan: $g_{MgCl2} \rightarrow mol_{MgCl2}$ **and** $g_{H2O} \rightarrow mol_{H2O}$ **then** $P_{soln}, P°_{soln}, \rightarrow \chi_{MgCl2}$

$$\frac{1 \text{ mol } MgCl_2}{95.218 \text{ g } MgCl_2} \qquad \frac{1 \text{ mol } H_2O}{18.015 \text{ g } H_2O} \qquad P_{Soln} = (1 - \chi_{MgCl2})\,P°_{H2O}$$

then $\quad mol_{MgCl2}, mol_{H2O}, \chi_{MgCl2} \rightarrow i$

$$\chi_{MgCl2} = \frac{i\left(moles\ MgCl_2\right)}{moles\ H_2O + i\left(moles\ MgCl_2\right)}$$

Solution:

$$4.5701 \text{ g } MgCl_2 \times \frac{1 \text{ mol } MgCl_2}{95.218 \text{ g } MgCl_2} = 0.047996177 \text{ mol } MgCl_2 \quad \text{and}$$

$$43.238 \; \cancel{g\,H_2O} \times \frac{1 \; mol\,H_2O}{18.015 \; \cancel{g\,H_2O}} = 2.400\underline{1}110 \; mol\,H_2O \quad then \quad P_{Soln} = (1 - \chi_{MgCl2})\,P^o_{H2O} \quad so$$

$$\chi_{MgCl2} = 1 - \frac{P_{Soln}}{P^o_{H2O}} = 1 - \frac{0.3624 \; atm}{0.3804 \; atm} = 0.0473\underline{1}861 \qquad then$$

$$\chi_{MgCl2} = \frac{i \left(moles \; MgCl_2 \right)}{moles \; H_2O + i \left(moles \; MgCl_2 \right)} = \frac{i \left(0.04799\underline{6}177 \; mol \right)}{2.400\underline{1}110 \; mol + i \left(0.04799\underline{6}177 \; mol \right)} = 0.0473\underline{1}861$$

Solve for i. $i \, (0.04799\underline{6}177) = 0.0473\underline{1}861 \, (2.400\underline{1}110 + i \, (0.04799\underline{6}177)) \quad \rightarrow$

$$i \, (0.04799\underline{6}177 - 0.002271\underline{1}112) = 0.1135\underline{6}99 \quad \rightarrow \quad i = \frac{0.1135\underline{6}99}{0.0457\underline{2}506} = 2.484 \, .$$

Check: The units (none) are correct. The magnitude of the answer (2.5) seems reasonable for $MgCl_2$ since we expect i to be 3 if it completely dissociates. Since Mg is small and doubly charges, we expect a significant drop from 3.

104. **Given:** 7.050 g of HNO_2 and 1.000 kg of water, $T_f = - 0.2929 \; ^\circ C$ **Find:** fraction dissociated
Other: $K_f = 1.86 \; ^\circ C/m$;
Conceptual plan:

g $_{HNO2}$ $\rightarrow$ mol $_{HNO2}$ **then** mol $_{HNO2}$, kg$_{H2O}$ $\rightarrow$ m **then** $m, \Delta T_{factual}, K_f \rightarrow i_{actual}$ **then**

$$\frac{1 \; mol\,HNO_2}{47.02 \; g\,HNO_2} \qquad\qquad m = \frac{amount \; solute \; (moles)}{mass \; solvent \; (kg)} \qquad\qquad \Delta T_{factual} = i_{actual} m K_f$$

i_{actual} $\rightarrow$ **fraction dissociated**
fraction dissociated = $i_{actual} - 1$

Solution: $7.050 \; \cancel{g\,HNO_2} \times \frac{1 \; mol\,HNO_2}{47.02 \; \cancel{g\,HNO_2}} = 0.1499\underline{4}25 \; mol\,HNO_2$ then

$$m = \frac{amount \; solute \; (moles)}{mass \; solvent \; (kg)} = \frac{0.1499\underline{4}25 \; mol\,HNO_2}{1.000 \; kg} = 0.1499\underline{4}25 \; m \quad then \quad \Delta T_{factual} = i_{actual} m K_f \rightarrow$$

$0.2929 = i \, (0.1499\underline{4}25 \; \cancel{m}) \left(\frac{1.86\,^\circ C}{\cancel{m}} \right) \rightarrow i = 1.05\underline{0}2$ then fraction dissociated = $i_{actual} - 1 = 1.05\underline{0}2 - 1 = 0.050$

Check: The units (none) are correct. The magnitude of the answer (0.05) seems reasonable since weak acids do not fully dissociate.

105. **Given:** $T_b = 375.5 \; K$ aqueous solution **Find:** P_{H2O} **Other:** $P^o_{H2O} = 0.2467 \; atm$; $K_b = 0.512 \; ^\circ C/m$
Conceptual plan: $T_b \rightarrow \Delta T_b$ **then** $\Delta T_b, K_b \rightarrow m$ assume 1kg water kg $_{H2O} \rightarrow$ mol$_{H2O}$ **then**

$$T_b = T_b^o + \Delta T_b \qquad\qquad \Delta T_b = K_b m \qquad\qquad \frac{1 \; mol\,H_2O}{18.02 \; g\,H_2O}$$

$m \rightarrow$ mol $_{Solute}$ **then** mol$_{H2O}$, mol $_{Solute} \rightarrow \chi_{H2O}$ **then** $\chi_{H2O}, P^o_{H2O} \rightarrow P_{H2O}$

$$m = \frac{amount \; solute \; (moles)}{mass \; solvent \; (kg)} \qquad \chi_{H2O} = \frac{moles \; H_2O}{moles \; H_2O + moles \; solute} \qquad P_{H2O} = \chi_{H2O} \, P^o_{H2O}$$

Solution:

$T_b = T_b^o + \Delta T_b$ so $\Delta T_b = T_b - T_b^o = 375.5 \; K - 373.15 \; K = 2.4 \; K = 2.4 \; ^\circ C$ then $\Delta T_b = K_b m$

Rearrange to solve for m. $m = \frac{\Delta T_b}{K_b} = \frac{2.4 \; ^\circ\cancel{C}}{0.512 \; \frac{^\circ\cancel{C}}{m}} = 4.\underline{6}875 \; m$ then

$1000 \; \cancel{g\,H_2O} \times \frac{1 \; mol\,H_2O}{18.02 \; \cancel{g\,H_2O}} = 55.49\underline{3}90 \; mol\,H_2O$ then $m = \frac{amount \; solute \; (moles)}{mass \; solvent \; (kg)} = \frac{x \; mol}{1 \; kg} = 4.\underline{6}875 \; m$ so

$x = 4.\underline{6}875 \; mol$ then $\chi_{H2O} = \frac{moles \; H_2O}{moles \; H_2O + moles \; solute} = \frac{55.49\underline{3}90 \; \cancel{mol}}{55.49\underline{3}90 \; \cancel{mol} + 4.\underline{6}875 \; \cancel{mol}} = 0.922\underline{1}106$

then $P_{H2O} = \chi_{H2O} \, P^o_{H2O} = 0.922\underline{1}106 \times 0.2467 \; atm = 0.227 \; atm$

Check: The units (atm) are correct. The magnitude of the answer (0.227 atm) seems reasonable since the mole fraction is lowered by $\sim$ 8%.

106. **Given:** 0.438 M K_2CrO_4 aqueous solution; $d = 1.063$ g/mL at 298 K; complete dissociation   **Find:** P_{Soln}
Other: $P°_{H2O} = 0.0313$ atm
Conceptual plan:
assume 1 L solution, so we have 0.438 mol_{K2CrO4} → **g $_{K2CrO4}$** **then** mL_{soln} → g_{soln} **then**

$$\frac{194.20 \text{ g } K_2CrO_4}{1 \text{ mol } K_2CrO_4} \qquad \frac{1.063 \text{ g}}{1 \text{ mL}}$$

g $_{K2CrO4}$, g_{soln} → **g_{H2O}** → **mol_{H2O}** **then** **mol_{H2O}, mol $_{Solute}$** → **χ_{H2O}** **then** **χ_{H2O}, $P°_{H2O}$** → **P_{H2O}**

$$g\ H_2O = g\ soln - g\ K_2CrO_4 \quad \frac{1 \text{ mol } H_2O}{18.01 \text{ g } H_2O} \qquad \chi_{H2O} = \frac{\text{moles } H_2O}{\text{moles } H_2O + \text{moles solute}} \qquad P_{Soln} = (1 - i\chi_{K_2CrO_4}) P^o_{H2O} \quad i = 3$$

Solution:

$$0.438 \ \text{mol} K_2CrO_4 \ \times \ \frac{194.20 \text{ g } K_2CrO_4}{1 \ \text{mol} K_2CrO_4} = 85.0596 \text{ g } K_2CrO_4 \quad \text{then} \quad 1000 \ \text{mL} \times \frac{1.063 \text{ g}}{1 \text{ mL}} = 1063 \text{ g soln}$$

then $g\ H_2O = g\ soln - g\ K_2CrO_4 = 1063$ g soln - 85.0596 g K_2CrO_4 = 977.0404 g H_2O then

$$977.0404 \ \text{g } H_2O \times \frac{1 \text{ mol } H_2O}{18.01 \text{ g } H_2O} = 54.2999 \text{ mol } H_2O \text{ then}$$

$$\chi_{K_2CrO_4} = \frac{\text{moles } K_2CrO_4}{\text{moles } H_2O + \text{moles } K_2CrO_4} = \frac{0.438 \ \text{mol}}{54.2999 \ \text{mol} + 0.438 \ \text{mol}} = 0.00800177 \quad \text{then}$$

$$P_{Soln} = (1 - i\chi_{K_2CrO_4}) P^o_{H2O} = (1 - 3 \times 0.00800177)\ 0.0313 \text{ atm} = 0.0305 \text{ atm}$$

Check: The units (atm) are correct.   The magnitude of the answer (0.305 atm) seems reasonable since the mole fraction is lowered by < 1 %.

107. **Given:** equal masses of carbon tetrachloride (CCl_4) and chloroform ($CHCl_3$) at 316 K; $P°_{CCl4} = 0.354$ atm; $P°_{CHCl3} = 0.526$ atm   **Find:** χ_{CCl4}, χ_{CHCl3} in vapor; and P_{CHCl3} in flask of condensed vapor
Conceptual plan: assume 100 grams of each g $_{CCl4}$ → mol $_{CCl4}$ **and** g $_{CHCl3}$ → mol $_{CHCl3}$ **then**

$$\frac{1 \text{ mol } CCl_4}{153.82 \text{ g } CCl_4} \qquad \frac{1 \text{ mol } CHCl_3}{119.38 \text{ g } CHCl_3}$$

mol $_{CCl4}$, mol $_{CHCl3}$ → **χ_{CCl4}, χ_{CHCl3} then** **χ_{CCl4}, $P°_{CCl4}$** → **P_{CCl4} and** **χ_{CHCl3}, $P°_{CHCl3}$** → **P_{CHCl3} then**

$$\chi_{CCl4} = \frac{\text{amount } CCl_4 \text{ (in moles)}}{\text{total amount (in moles)}} \qquad \chi_{CHCl3} = 1 - \chi_{CCl4} \qquad P_{CCl4} = \chi_{CCl4} \ P^o_{CCl4} \qquad P_{CHCl3} = \chi_{CHCl3} \ P^o_{CHCl3}$$

P_{CCl4}, P_{CHCl3} → **P_{Total} then since n α P and we are calculating a mass percent, which is a ratio of masses,**
$$P_{Total} = P_{CCl4} + P_{CHCl3}$$
we can simply convert 1 atm to 1 mole so P_{CCl4}, P_{CHCl3} → **n $_{CCl4}$, n $_{CHCl3}$ then**

$$\chi_{CCl4} = \frac{\text{amount } CCl_4 \text{ (in moles)}}{\text{total amount (in moles)}}$$

mol $_{CCl4}$, mol $_{CHCl3}$ → **χ_{CCl4}, χ_{CHCl3} then for the second vapor** χ_{CHCl3}, $P°_{CHCl3}$ → P_{CHCl3}

$$\chi_{CHCl3} = 1 - \chi_{CCl4} \qquad\qquad P_{CHCl3} = \chi_{CHCl3} \ P^o_{CHCl3}$$

Solution:

$$100.00 \ \text{g } CCl_4 \times \frac{1 \text{ mol } CCl_4}{153.82 \text{ g } CCl_4} = 0.65011051 \text{ mol } CCl_4 \text{ and}$$

$$100.00 \ \text{g } CHCl_3 \times \frac{1 \text{ mol } CHCl_3}{119.38 \text{ g } CHCl_3} = 0.83766125 \text{ mol } CHCl_3 \text{ then}$$

$$\chi_{CCl4} = \frac{\text{amount } CCl_4 \text{ (in moles)}}{\text{total amount (in moles)}} = \frac{0.65011051 \ \text{mol}}{0.65011051 \ \text{mol} + 0.83766125 \ \text{mol}} = 0.43696925 \text{ and}$$

$$\chi_{CHCl3} = 1 - \chi_{CCl4} = 1 - 0.43696925 = 0.56303075 \text{ then}$$

$$P_{CCl4} = \chi_{CCl4} \ P^o_{CCl4} = 0.43696925 \times 0.354 \text{ atm} = 0.154687 \text{ atm} \text{ and}$$

$P_{CHCl3} = \chi_{CHCl3}\, P^{o}_{CHCl3} = 0.56303075 \times 0.526 \text{ atm} = 0.296154 \text{ atm}$ then

$P_{Total} = P_{CCl4} + P_{CHCl3} = 0.154687 \text{ atm} + 0.296154 \text{ atm} = 0.450841 \text{ atm}$ then

$\text{mol}_{CCl4} = 0.154687 \text{ mol}$ and $\text{mol}_{CHCl3} = 0.296154 \text{ mol}$ then

$$\chi_{CCl4} = \frac{\text{amount CCl}_4 \text{ (in moles)}}{\text{total amount (in moles)}} = \frac{0.154687 \text{ mol}}{0.154687 \text{ mol} + 0.296154 \text{ mol}} = 0.343108 = 0.343 \text{ in the first vapor}$$

and $\chi_{CHCl3} = 1 - \chi_{CCl4} = 1 - 0.343108 = 0.656892 = 0.657$ in the first vapor   then in the second vapor

$P_{CHCl3} = \chi_{CHCl3}\, P^{o}_{CHCl3} = 0.656892 \times 0.526 \text{ atm} = 0.345525 \text{ atm} = 0.346 \text{ atm}$

Check: The units (none and atm) are correct. The magnitude of the answers seems reasonable since it we expect the lighter component to be preferentially in the vapor phase. This effect is magnified in the second vapor.

108. In the previous problem we saw that the original liquid has the $\chi_{CHCl3} = 0.563$ when the second vapor is condensed it rose to 0.657. Continue the calculation scheme from above.

$P_{CCl4} = \chi_{CCl4}\, P^{o}_{CCl4} = 0.343108 \times 0.354 \text{ atm} = 0.121460 \text{ atm}$ converting to moles; $\text{mol}_{CCl4} = 0.121460 \text{ mol}$ and $\text{mol}_{CHCl3} = 0.345525 \text{ mol}$ then

$$\chi_{CCl4} = \frac{\text{amount CCl}_4 \text{ (in moles)}}{\text{total amount (in moles)}} = \frac{0.121460 \text{ mol}}{0.121460 \text{ mol} + 0.345525 \text{ mol}} = 0.260094 = 0.260 \text{ in the second vapor}$$

and $\chi_{CHCl3} = 1 - \chi_{CCl4} = 1 - 0.260094 = 0.739906 = 0.740$ in the second vapor   then in the third vapor

$P_{CHCl3} = \chi_{CHCl3}\, P^{o}_{CHCl3} = 0.739906 \times 0.526 \text{ atm} = 0.389191 \text{ atm}$ and

$P_{CCl4} = \chi_{CCl4}\, P^{o}_{CCl4} = 0.260094 \times 0.354 \text{ atm} = 0.0920732 \text{ atm}$ converting to moles

$\text{mol}_{CCl4} = 0.0920732 \text{ mol}$ and $\text{mol}_{CHCl3} = 0.389191 \text{ mol}$ then

$$\chi_{CCl4} = \frac{\text{amount CCl}_4 \text{ (in moles)}}{\text{total amount (in moles)}} = \frac{0.0920732 \text{ mol}}{0.0920732 \text{ mol} + 0.389191 \text{ mol}} = 0.191315 = 0.191 \text{ in the third vapor}$$

and $\chi_{CHCl3} = 1 - \chi_{CCl4} = 1 - 0.191315 = 0.808685 = 0.809$ in the third vapor   then in the fourth vapor

$P_{CHCl3} = \chi_{CHCl3}\, P^{o}_{CHCl3} = 0.808685 \times 0.526 \text{ atm} = 0.425368 \text{ atm}$ and

$P_{CCl4} = \chi_{CCl4}\, P^{o}_{CCl4} = 0.191315 \times 0.354 \text{ atm} = 0.0677255 \text{ atm}$ converting to moles

$\text{mol}_{CCl4} = 0.0677255 \text{ mol}$ and $\text{mol}_{CHCl3} = 0.425368 \text{ mol}$ then

$$\chi_{CCl4} = \frac{\text{amount CCl}_4 \text{ (in moles)}}{\text{total amount (in moles)}} = \frac{0.0677255 \text{ mol}}{0.0677255 \text{ mol} + 0.425368 \text{ mol}} = 0.137348 = 0.137 \text{ in the fourth vapor}$$

and $\chi_{CHCl3} = 1 - \chi_{CCl4} = 1 - 0.137348 = 0.862652 = 0.863$ in the fourth vapor . The concentration of the lighter component in the gas phase, or distillate, increases with each step.

109. **Given**: N_2: $k_H(N_2) = 6.1 \times 10^{-4}$ M/L at 25 °C; 14.6 mg/L at 50 °C and 1.00 atm; $P_{N2} = 0.78$ atm;
O_2: $k_H(O_2) = 1.3 \times 10^{-3}$ M/L at 25 °C; 27.8 mg/L at 50 °C and 1.00 atm; $P_{O2} = 0.21$ atm;   and 1.5 L water
Find: V (N_2) and V (O_2)
Conceptual plan: at 25 °C: P_{Total}, χ_{N2} → P_{N2}   then   **P_{N2}, $k_H(N_2)$ → S_{N2}**   then   **L → mol**

$$P_{N2} = \chi_{N2}\, P_{Total} \qquad\qquad S_{N2} = k_H(N_2)\, P_{N2} \qquad\qquad S_{N2}$$

at 50 °C: L → mL → mg → g → mol   then **$\text{mol}_{25\,°C}$, $\text{mol}_{25\,°C}$ → $\text{mol}_{removed}$**   then   **°C → K**

$$\frac{1000 \text{ mL}}{1 \text{ L}} \quad \frac{14.6 \text{ mg}}{1 \text{ L}} \quad \frac{1 \text{ g}}{1000 \text{ mg}} \quad \frac{1 \text{ mol}}{28.01 \text{ g}} \qquad mol_{removed} = mol_{25°C} - mol_{50°C} \qquad K = °C + 273.15$$

then P, n, T → V

$$PV = nRT$$

at 25 °C: P_{Total}, χ_{O2} → P_{O2}   then   **P_{O2}, $k_H(O_2)$ → S_{O2}**   then   **L → mol**

$$P_{O2} = \chi_{O2}\, P_{Total} \qquad\qquad S_{O2} = k_H(O_2)\, P_{O2} \qquad\qquad S_{O2}$$

at 50 °C: L → mL → mg → g → mol   then   **$\text{mol}_{25\,°C}$, $\text{mol}_{25\,°C}$ → $\text{mol}_{removed}$**   then **°C → K**

$$\frac{1000 \text{ mL}}{1 \text{ L}} \quad \frac{27.8 \text{ mg}}{1 \text{ L}} \quad \frac{1 \text{ g}}{1000 \text{ mg}} \quad \frac{1 \text{ mol}}{32.00 \text{ g}} \qquad mol_{removed} = mol_{25°C} - mol_{50°C} \qquad K = °C + 273.15$$

then P, n, T → V

$$PV = nRT$$

Solution:

at 25 °C: $P_{N2} = \chi_{N2} \, P_{Total} = 0.78 \times 1.0 \text{ atm} = 0.78 \text{ atm}$ then

$$S_{N2} = k_H(N_2)\,P_{N2} = 6.1 \times 10^{-4} \, \frac{M}{atm} \times 0.78 \, atm = 4.\underline{7}58 \times 10^{-4} \, M \quad \text{then}$$

$$1.5 \, L \times 4.\underline{7}58 \times 10^{-4} \, \frac{mol}{L} = 0.0007\underline{1}371 \, mol$$

at 50 °C: $\quad 1.5 \, L \times \dfrac{14.6 \, mg}{1 \, L \, atm} \times 0.78 \, atm \times \dfrac{1 \, g}{1000 \, mg} \times \dfrac{1 \, mol}{28.01 \, g} = 0.00060\underline{9}85 \, mol \quad$ then

$mol_{removed} = mol_{25°C} - mol_{50°C} = 0.0007\underline{1}371 \, mol - 0.00060\underline{9}85 \, mol = 1.\underline{0}39 \times 10^{-4} \, mol$.

then $50 \, °C + 273.15 = 323 \, K$ then $PV = nRT$ Rearrange to solve for V.

$$V = \frac{nRT}{P} = \frac{1.\underline{0}39 \times 10^{-4} \, mol \times 0.08206 \, \frac{L \, atm}{K \, mol} \times 323 \, K}{1.00 \, atm} = 0.002\underline{7}526 \, L$$

at 25 °C: $P_{O2} = \chi_{O2} \, P_{Total} = 0.21 \times 1.0 \text{ atm} = 0.21 \text{ atm}$ then

$$S_{O2} = k_H(O_2)\,P_{O2} = 1.3 \times 10^{-3} \, \frac{M}{atm} \times 0.21 \, atm = 2.\underline{7}3 \times 10^{-4} \, M \quad \text{then} \quad 1.5 \, L \times 2.\underline{7}3 \times 10^{-4} \, \frac{mol}{L} = 0.0004\underline{0}95 \, mol$$

at 50 °C: $\quad 1.5 \, L \times \dfrac{27.8 \, mg}{1 \, L \, atm} \times 0.21 \, atm \times \dfrac{1 \, g}{1000 \, mg} \times \dfrac{1 \, mol}{32.00 \, g} = 0.0002\underline{7}366 \, g \quad$ then

$mol_{removed} = mol_{25°C} - mol_{50°C} = 0.0004\underline{0}95 \, mol - 0.0002\underline{7}366 \, mol = 1.\underline{3}58 \times 10^{-4} \, mol$

then $50 \, °C + 273.15 = 323 \, K$ then $PV = nRT$ Rearrange to solve for V.

$$V = \frac{nRT}{P} = \frac{1.\underline{3}58 \times 10^{-4} \, mol \times 0.08206 \, \frac{L \, atm}{K \, mol} \times 323 \, K}{1.00 \, atm} = 0.003\underline{5}994 \, L \quad \text{finally}$$

$$V_{Total} = V_{N2} + V_{O2} = 0.002\underline{7}526 \, L + 0.003\underline{5}994 \, L = 0.0064 \, L$$

Check: The units (L) are correct. The magnitude of the answer (0.006 L) seems reasonable since we have so little dissolves gas at room temperature and most is still soluble at 50 °C.

---

110. **Given:** pentane (C_5H_{12}) and hexane (C_6H_{14}): 35.5 percent by mass C_5H_{12} in vapor at 25 °C; $P°_{C5H12} = 425$ torr; $P°_{C6H14} = 151$ torr **Find:** percent by mass C_5H_{12} and percent by mass C_6H_{14} in solution

Conceptual plan:

mass percents → g_{C5H12}, g_{C6H14} then **g_{C5H12} → mol C_5H_{12} and g_{C6H14} → mol C_6H_{14}**

$$mass \; percent = \frac{mass \; solute}{mass \; solution} \times 100\%$$

$$\frac{1 \, mol \, C_5H_{12}}{72.15 \, g \, C_5H_{12}} \qquad \frac{1 \, mol \, C_6H_{14}}{86.17 \, g \, C_6H_{14}}$$

then **mol C_5H_{12}, mol C_6H_{14} → $\chi_{C5H12vapor}$** then **$\chi_{C5H12vapor}, P°_{C5H12}, P°_{C6H14}$ → $\chi_{C5H12soln}$** then

$$\chi_{C5H12} = \frac{amount \; C_5H_{12} \; (in \; moles)}{total \; amount \; (in \; moles)}$$

$$\chi_{C5H12vapor} = \frac{P_{C5H12}}{P_{Total}} = \frac{\chi_{C5H12soln} \, P°_{C5H12}}{\chi_{C5H12soln} \, P°_{C5H12} + (1 - \chi_{C5H12soln}) \, P°_{C6H14}}$$

assume

1 total mole of solution → mol C_5H_{12}, mol C_6H_{14} then **mol C_5H_{12} → g_{C5H12} and mol C_6H_{14} → g_{C6H14}**

$$\chi_{C6H14soln} = 1 - \chi_{C5H12soln}$$

$$\frac{72.15 \, g \, C_5H_{12}}{1 \, mol \, C_5H_{12}} \qquad \frac{86.17 \, g \, C_6H_{14}}{1 \, mol \, C_6H_{14}}$$

finally **g_{C5H12}, g_{C6H14} → mass percents**

$$mass \; percent = \frac{mass \; solute}{mass \; solution} \times 100\%$$

Solution:

$$mass \; percent = \frac{mass \; solute}{mass \; solution} \times 100\% \quad \text{means that} \quad 35.5 \, g \; C_5H_{12} \text{ and } 100.0 \, g - 35.5 \, g = 64.5 \, g \, C_6H_{14}$$

423

then $35.5 \text{ g C}_5\text{H}_{12} \times \dfrac{1 \text{ mol C}_5\text{H}_{12}}{72.15 \text{ g C}_5\text{H}_{12}} = 0.49\underline{2}030 \text{ mol C}_5\text{H}_{12}$ and

$64.5 \text{ g C}_6\text{H}_{14} \times \dfrac{1 \text{ mol C}_6\text{H}_{14}}{86.17 \text{ g C}_6\text{H}_{14}} = 0.74\underline{8}520 \text{ mol C}_6\text{H}_{14}$ then

$\chi_{C5H12} = \dfrac{\text{amount C}_5\text{H}_{12} \text{ (in moles)}}{\text{total amount (in moles)}} = \dfrac{0.49\underline{2}030 \text{ mol}}{0.49\underline{2}030 \text{ mol} + 0.74\underline{8}520 \text{ mol}} = 0.39\underline{6}622$ then

$\chi_{C5H12vapor} = \dfrac{P_{C5H12}}{P_{Total}} = \dfrac{\chi_{C5H12soln}\, P^o_{C5H12}}{\chi_{C5H12soln}\, P^o_{C5H12} + (1 - \chi_{C5H12soln})\, P^o_{C6H14}}$ Substitute in values and solve for $\chi_{C5H12soln}$.

$0.39\underline{6}622 = \dfrac{\chi_{C5H12soln} \times 425 \text{ torr}}{\chi_{C5H12soln} \times 425 \text{ torr} + (1 - \chi_{C5H12soln}) \times 151 \text{ torr}} \rightarrow$

$0.39\underline{6}622 \left(425 \chi_{C5H12soln} + 151(1 - \chi_{C5H12soln})\right) = 425 \chi_{C5H12soln} \rightarrow$

$168.564 \chi_{C5H12soln} + 59.\underline{8}900 - 59.\underline{8}900 \chi_{C5H12soln} = 425 \chi_{C5H12soln} \rightarrow 31\underline{6}.326 \chi_{C5H12soln} = 59.\underline{8}900 \rightarrow$

$\chi_{C5H12soln} = \dfrac{59.\underline{8}900}{31\underline{6}.326} = 0.18\underline{9}330$ then $\chi_{C6H14soln} = 1 - \chi_{C5H12soln} = 1 - 0.18\underline{9}330 = 0.81\underline{0}670$ so

mol $_{C5H12} = 0.18\underline{9}330$ mol and mol $_{C6H14} = 0.81\underline{0}670$ mol then

$0.18\underline{9}330 \text{ mol C}_5\text{H}_{12} \times \dfrac{72.15 \text{ g C}_5\text{H}_{12}}{1 \text{ mol C}_5\text{H}_{12}} = 13.\underline{6}602 \text{ g C}_5\text{H}_{12}$ and

$0.81\underline{0}670 \text{ mol C}_6\text{H}_{14} \times \dfrac{86.17 \text{ g C}_6\text{H}_{14}}{1 \text{ mol C}_6\text{H}_{14}} = 69.\underline{8}554 \text{ g C}_6\text{H}_{14}$ finally

$mass\ percent = \dfrac{mass\ solute}{mass\ solution} \times 100\% = \dfrac{13.\underline{6}602 \text{ g C}_5\text{H}_{12}}{13.\underline{6}602 \text{ g C}_5\text{H}_{12} + 69.\underline{8}554 \text{ g C}_6\text{H}_{14}} \times 100\% = 16.4 \text{ percent by mass C}_5\text{H}_{12}$

and $100.0 - 16.4 = 83.6$ mass percent C_6H_{14}

Check: The units (mass percent) are correct. We expect the mass percent of C_6H_{14} to be much higher than the mass percent of C_5H_{12} because the vapor is richer in this component and it is the less volatile phase.

111. **Given:** 1.10 g glucose ($C_6H_{12}O_6$) and sucrose ($C_{12}H_{22}O_{11}$) mixture in 25.0 mL solution and $\Pi = 3.78$ atm at 298 K   **Find:** percent composition of mixture

Conceptual plan: $\Pi, T \rightarrow M$ then $mL_{soln} \rightarrow L_{soln}$ then $L_{soln}, M \rightarrow mol_{mixture}$ then

$$\Pi = M\,RT \qquad\qquad \dfrac{1 \text{ L}}{1000 \text{ mL}} \qquad\qquad M = \dfrac{\text{amount solute (moles)}}{\text{volume solution (L)}}$$

$mol_{mixture}, g_{mixture} \rightarrow mol_{C6H12O6}, mol_{C12H22O11}$ then

$g_{mixture} = mol\ C_6H_{12}O_6 \times \dfrac{180.16 \text{ g } C_6H_{12}O_6}{1 \text{ mol } C_6H_{12}O_6} + mol\ C_{12}H_{22}O_{11} \times \dfrac{342.30 \text{ g } C_{12}H_{22}O_{11}}{1 \text{ mol } C_{12}H_{22}O_{11}}$ with $mol_{mixture} = mol\ C_6H_{12}O_6 + mol\ C_{12}H_{22}O_{11}$

$mol_{C6H12O6} \rightarrow g_{C6H12O6}$ and $mol_{C12H22O11} \rightarrow g_{C12H22O11}$ and $g_{C6H12O6}, g_{C12H22O11} \rightarrow$ **mass percents**

$$\dfrac{180.16 \text{ g } C_6H_{12}O_6}{1 \text{ mol } C_6H_{12}O_6} \qquad \dfrac{342.30 \text{ g } C_{12}H_{22}O_{11}}{1 \text{ mol } C_{12}H_{22}O_{11}} \qquad mass\ percent = \dfrac{mass\ solute}{mass\ solution} \times 100\%$$

Solution:

$\Pi = M\,RT$ Rearrange to solve for M. $M = \dfrac{\Pi}{RT} = \dfrac{3.78 \text{ atm}}{0.08206 \dfrac{\text{L atm}}{\text{K mol}} \times 298 \text{ K}} = 0.15\underline{4}577 \dfrac{\text{mol mixture}}{\text{L}}$ then

$25.0 \text{ mL} \times \dfrac{1 \text{ L}}{1000 \text{ mL}} = 0.0250 \text{ L}$ then $M = \dfrac{\text{amount solute (moles)}}{\text{volume solution (L)}}$ so

$mol_{mixture} = M \times L_{soln} = 0.15\underline{4}577 \dfrac{\text{mol mixture}}{\text{L}} \times 0.0250 \text{ L} = 0.0038\underline{6}442 \text{ mol mixture}$ then

$g_{mixture} = mol\ C_6H_{12}O_6 \times \dfrac{180.16 \text{ g } C_6H_{12}O_6}{1 \text{ mol } C_6H_{12}O_6} + mol\ C_{12}H_{22}O_{11} \times \dfrac{342.30 \text{ g } C_{12}H_{22}O_{11}}{1 \text{ mol } C_{12}H_{22}O_{11}}$ with

$mol_{mixture} = mol\ C_6H_{12}O_6 + mol\ C_{12}H_{22}O_{11}$ so

$$1.10 \text{ g} = \text{mol C}_6\text{H}_{12}\text{O}_6 \text{ x } \frac{180.16 \text{ g C}_6\text{H}_{12}\text{O}_6}{1 \text{ mol C}_6\text{H}_{12}\text{O}_6} + (0.00386442 \text{ mol - mol C}_6\text{H}_{12}\text{O}_6) \text{ x } \frac{342.30 \text{ g C}_{12}\text{H}_{22}\text{O}_{11}}{1 \text{ mol C}_{12}\text{H}_{22}\text{O}_{11}} \rightarrow$$

$$1.10 = 180.16 \text{ x mol C}_6\text{H}_{12}\text{O}_6 + 1.32228 - 342.30 \text{ x mol C}_6\text{H}_{12}\text{O}_6 \rightarrow 162.14 \, x \text{ mol C}_6\text{H}_{12}\text{O}_6 = 0.22228 \rightarrow$$

$$x \text{ mol C}_6\text{H}_{12}\text{O}_6 = \frac{0.22228}{162.14} = 0.00137091 \text{ mol C}_6\text{H}_{12}\text{O}_6 \quad \text{then}$$

$$\text{mol C}_{12}H_{22}O_{11} = \text{mol}_{mixture} - \text{mol C}_6H_{12}O_6 = 0.00386442 \text{ mol - } 0.00137091 \text{ mol} = 0.0024935 \text{ mol C}_{12}H_{22}O_{11} \quad \text{then}$$

$$0.00137091 \text{ mol C}_6\text{H}_{12}\text{O}_6 \text{ x } \frac{180.16 \text{ g C}_6\text{H}_{12}\text{O}_6}{1 \text{ mol C}_6\text{H}_{12}\text{O}_6} = 0.24698 \text{ g C}_6\text{H}_{12}\text{O}_6 \quad \text{and}$$

$$0.0024935 \text{ mol C}_{12}\text{H}_{22}\text{O}_{11} \text{ x } \frac{342.30 \text{ g C}_{12}\text{H}_{22}\text{O}_{11}}{1 \text{ mol C}_{12}\text{H}_{22}\text{O}_{11}} = 0.85353 \text{ g C}_{12}\text{H}_{22}\text{O}_{11} \quad \text{finally}$$

$$mass\ percent = \frac{mass\ solute}{mass\ solution} \times 100\% = \frac{0.24698 \text{ g C}_6\text{H}_{12}\text{O}_6}{0.24698 \text{ g C}_6\text{H}_{12}\text{O}_6 + 0.85353 \text{ g C}_{12}\text{H}_{22}\text{O}_{11}} \times 100\% = 22.44\% \text{ C}_6\text{H}_{12}\text{O}_6 \, by\ mass$$

and $100.00\% - 22.44\% = 77.56\%$ $C_{12}H_{22}O_{11}$ by mass

Check: The units (% by mass) are correct. We expect the percent by $C_6H_{12}O_6$ to be larger than that for $C_{12}H_{22}O_{11}$ since the g $_{mixture}$ /mol $_{mixture}$ = 285 g/mol, which is closer to $C_{12}H_{22}O_{11}$ than $C_6H_{12}O_6$ and the molar mass of $C_{12}H_{22}O_{11}$ is larger than the molar mass of $C_6H_{12}O_6$.

112. **Given:** 631 mL methanol (CH_3OH) and 501 mL water; solution = 14.29 M CH_3OH, d (CH_3OH) = 0.792 g/mL **Find:** volume change on mixing

Conceptual plan: $V_{CH3OH}, V_{H2O} \rightarrow V_{before\ mixing}$ **then** $mL_{CH3OH} \rightarrow g_{CH3OH} \rightarrow mol_{CH3OH}$ **then**

$$V_{before\ mixing} = V_{CH3OH} + V_{H2O} \qquad \frac{0.792 \text{ g}}{1 \text{ mL}} \quad \frac{1 \text{ mol CH}_3\text{OH}}{32.04 \text{ g CH}_3\text{OH}}$$

$mol_{CH3OH}, M \rightarrow L_{soln} \rightarrow mL_{soln}$ **then** $V_{before\ mixing}, L_{soln} \rightarrow \Delta V_{mixing}$

$$M = \frac{amount\ solute\ (moles)}{volume\ solution\ (L)} \quad \frac{1000 \text{ mL}}{1 \text{ L}} \qquad \qquad \Delta V_{mixing} = V_{before\ mixing} - V_{soln}$$

Solution:

$$V_{before\ mixing} = V_{CH3OH} + V_{H2O} = 631 \text{ mL} + 501 \text{ mL} = 1132 \text{ mL} \quad \text{then}$$

$$631 \text{ mL x } \frac{0.792 \text{ g}}{1 \text{ mL}} \text{ x } \frac{1 \text{ mol CH}_3\text{OH}}{32.04 \text{ g CH}_3\text{OH}} = 15.5978 \text{ mol CH}_3\text{OH} \quad \text{then} \quad M = \frac{amount\ solute\ (moles)}{volume\ solution\ (L)} \quad \text{so}$$

$$L_{soln} = \frac{mol_{CH3OH}}{M} = \frac{15.5978 \text{ mol CH}_3\text{OH}}{14.29 \dfrac{\text{mol CH}_3\text{OH}}{\text{L}}} = 1.09152 \text{ L} \quad \text{then} \quad 1.09152 \text{ L x } \frac{1000 \text{ mL}}{1 \text{ L}} = 1091.52 \text{ mL} \quad \text{then}$$

$$\Delta V_{mixing} = V_{before\ mixing} - V_{soln} = 1132 \text{ mL - } 1091.52 \text{ mL} = 40.48 \text{ mL} = 4 \text{ x } 10^1 \text{ mL}$$

Check: The units (mL) are correct. Since the intermolecular forces between a methanol molecule and a water molecule are different that between two water molecules or between two methanol molecules, the spacing between molecules changes and thus the volume changes. The amount of the change (~ 4 %) is reasonable.

113. **Given:** isopropyl alcohol (($CH_3)_2CHOH$) and propyl alcohol ($CH_3CH_2CH_2OH$) at 313 K; solution 2/3 by mass isopropyl alcohol $P_{2/3} = 0.110$ atm; solution 1/3 by mass isopropyl alcohol $P_{1/3} = 0.089$ atm; **Find:** P°_{iso} and P°_{pro} and explain why they are different

Conceptual plan: since these are isomers, they have the same molar mass and so the fraction by mass is the same as the mole fraction so mole fractions, P_{soln}'s $\rightarrow$ P°'s

$$\chi_{iso} = \frac{amount\ iso\ (in\ moles)}{total\ amount\ (in\ moles)} \quad \chi_{pro} = 1 - \chi_{iso} \quad P_{iso} = \chi_{iso} P^\circ_{iso} \quad P_{pro} = \chi_{pro} P^\circ_{pro} \quad \text{and} \quad P_{soln} = P_{iso} + P_{pro}$$

Solution:

Solution 1: $\chi_{iso} = $ 2/3 and $\chi_{iso} = $ 1/3 $P_{soln} = P_{iso} + P_{pro}$ so $0.110 \text{ atm} = 2/3 P^\circ_{iso} + 1/3 P^\circ_{pro}$ and

Solution 2: $\chi_{iso} = $ 1/3 and $\chi_{iso} = $ 2/3 $P_{soln} = P_{iso} + P_{pro}$ so $0.089 \text{ atm} = 1/3 P^\circ_{iso} + 2/3 P^\circ_{pro}$. We now have 2 equations and 2 unknowns and a number of ways to solve this. One way is to rearrange the first equation for

P^o_{iso} and then substitute into the other equation. Thus, $P^o_{iso} = 3/2\,(0.110\ \text{atm} - 1/3 P^o_{pro})$ and

$$0.089\ \text{atm} = \frac{1}{3}\cdot\frac{3}{2}(0.110\ \text{atm} - 1/3 P^o_{pro}) + \frac{2}{3}P^o_{pro} \rightarrow 0.089\ \text{atm} = 0.0550\ \text{atm} - \frac{1}{6}P^o_{pro} + \frac{2}{3}P^o_{pro} \rightarrow$$

$$\frac{1}{2}P^o_{pro} = 0.0340\ \text{atm} \rightarrow P^o_{pro} = 0.0680\ \text{atm} = 0.068\ \text{atm}\ \text{and then}$$

$$P^o_{iso} = 3/2\,(0.110\ \text{atm} - 1/3 P^o_{pro}) = 3/2\,(0.110\ \text{atm} - 1/3(0.0680\ \text{atm})) = 0.131\ \text{atm}$$

The major intermolecular attractions are between the OH groups. The OH group at the end of the chain in propyl alcohol is more accessible than the one in the middle of the chain in isopropyl alcohol. In addition, the molecular shape of propyl alcohol is a straight chain of carbon atoms, while that of isopropyl alcohol has a branched chain and is more like a ball. The contact area between two ball-like objects is smaller than that of two chain-like objects. The smaller contact area in isopropyl alcohol means the molecules don't attract each other as strongly as do those of propyl alcohol. As a result of both of these factors, the vapor pressure of isopropyl alcohol is higher.

Check: The units (atm) are correct. The magnitude of the answers seems reasonable since the solution partial pressures are both ~0.1 atm.

114. **Given:** metal, M, of atomic weight 96 forms MF_x salt; 9.18 g of MF_x completely dissociates in 100.0 g water, $T_b = 374.38\ \text{K}$;   **Find:** x and formula unit   **Other:** $K_b = 0.512\ °C/m$

Conceptual plan:

$g_{H2O} \rightarrow kg_{H2O}$ and $T_b \rightarrow \Delta T_b$ then $\Delta T_b, i, K_f \rightarrow m$ then $m, kg_{H2O} \rightarrow \text{mol}_{Unk}$

$$\frac{1\,\text{kg}}{1000\,\text{g}} \qquad T_b = T_b^o + \Delta T_b \qquad \Delta T_b = K_b i m \quad \text{where } i = 1 + x \qquad m = \frac{\text{amount solute (moles)}}{\text{mass solvent (kg)}}$$

then $g_{MFx}, \text{mol}_{MFx} \rightarrow \mathfrak{M} \rightarrow x$

$$\mathfrak{M} = \frac{g_{MFx}}{mol_{MFx}} \qquad \frac{1\ \text{mol}\ MF_x}{(96 + 19x)\ \text{g}\ MF_x} \qquad \frac{(96 + 19x)\ \text{g}\ MF_x}{1\ \text{mol}\ MF_x}$$

Solution:

$$100.0\ \text{g} \times \frac{1\,\text{kg}}{1000\,\text{g}} = 0.1000\ \text{kg}\quad \text{and}\quad T_b = T_b^o + \Delta T_b\ \text{so}$$

$$\Delta T_b = T_b - T_b^o = 374.38\ \text{K} - 373.15\ \text{K} = +1.23\ \text{K} = +1.23\ °C \quad \text{then}\quad \Delta T_b = K_b i m\quad \text{where}\ i = 1 + x\quad \text{so}$$

$$\Delta T_b = K_b(1 + x)m\quad \text{Rearrange to solve for } m.\quad m = \frac{\Delta T_b}{K_b(1+x)} = \frac{1.23\ °C}{0.512\ \frac{°C}{m}(1+x)} = \frac{2.40234}{(1+x)}\,m \quad \text{then}$$

$$m = \frac{\text{amount solute (moles)}}{\text{mass solvent (kg)}}\quad \text{so}\quad mol_{MFx} = m_{MFx} \times kg_{H2O} = \frac{2.40234}{(1+x)}\frac{\text{mol}\ MF_x}{\text{kg}} \times 0.1000\ \text{kg} = \frac{0.240234}{(1+x)}\ \text{mol}\ MF_x$$

then $\mathfrak{M} = \dfrac{g_{MFx}}{mol_{MFx}} = \dfrac{9.18\ \text{g}}{\dfrac{0.240234}{(1+x)}\ \text{mol}\ MF_x} = \dfrac{1\ \text{mol}\ MF_x}{(96 + 19x)\ \text{g}\ MF_x}$ Rearrange and solve for x.

$$(9.18\ \text{g})(1\ \text{mol}\ MF_x) = (96 + 19x)(\text{g}\ MF_x)\left(\frac{0.240234}{(1+x)}\ \text{mol}\ MF_x\right) \rightarrow 9.18(1 + x) = 0.240234(96 + 19x) \rightarrow$$

$$9.18x - 4.5645x = 23.062 - 9.18 \rightarrow 4.6155x = 13.882 \rightarrow x = \frac{13.882}{4.6155} = 3.0\ \text{so the salt is } MF_3.$$

Since molybdenum has an atomic mass ~ 96 amu, the salt is MoF_3.

Check: The units (none) are correct. The answer (3.0) seems reasonable since it is a small integer.

115. a) The two substances mix because their intermolecular forces between themselves are roughly equal to the forces between each other and there is a pervasive tendency to increase randomness, which happens when the two substances mix.

   b) $\Delta H_{soln} \approx 0$, since the intermolecular forces between themselves are roughly equal to the forces between each other.

   c) ΔH_{solute} and $\Delta H_{solvent}$ are positive, ΔH_{mix} is negative and equals the sum of ΔH_{solute} and $\Delta H_{solvent}$.

116. The warm coolant water should not be put directly into the river without cooling, because it will raise the temperature of the water. When water is warmed, there is less dissolved oxygen in the water and this will be detrimental to aquatic life that depends on this dissolved oxygen.

117. d) More solute particles are found in an ionic solution, since the solute breaks apart into its ions. The vapor pressure is lowered the more solute particle are present.

118. b) NaCl. If all of the substances have the same cost per kilogram, we need to determine which substance will generate the largest number of particles. $HOCH_2CH_2OH$ generates 1 mol particle / 62.07 g; NaCl generates 2 mol particles / 58.44 g; KCl generates 2 mol particles / 74.56 g; $MgCl_2$ generates 3 mol particles / 95.22 g; and $SrCl_2$ generates 3 particles / 158.53 g. So NaCl will generate 1 mole of particles for each 29 g.

119. The balloon not only loses He, it also takes in N_2 and O_2 from the air surrounding the balloon (due to the tendency for mixing), increasing the density of the balloon.

Chapter 13
Chemical Kinetics

1. Unlike mammals, which actively regulate their body temperature through metabolic activity, lizards are ectotherms—their body temperature depends on their surroundings. When splashed with cold water, a lizard's body simply gets colder. The drop in body temperature immobilizes the lizard because its movement depends on chemical reactions that occur within its muscles, and the rates of those reactions—how fast they occur—are highly sensitive to temperature. In other words, when the temperature drops, the reactions that produce movement occur more slowly; therefore the movement itself slows down. Cold reptiles are lethargic, unable to move very quickly. For this reason, reptiles try to maintain their body temperature in a narrow range by moving between sun and shade.

2. The rates of chemical reactions, and especially the ability to control those rates, are important many phenomena in our every day lives. For example, the human body's ability to switch a specific reaction on or off at a specific time is achieved largely by controlling the rate of that reaction through the use of enzymes. Chemical kinetics is important to chemists and engineers. The launching of a rocket depends on controlling the rate at which fuel burns—too quickly and the rocket can explode, too slowly and it will not leave the ground. The rate of nuclear decay in a nuclear power plant must be carefully controlled in order to provide electricity safely and efficiently. Chemists must always consider reaction rates when synthesizing compounds. No matter how stable a compound might be, its synthesis is impossible if the rate at which it forms is too slow. As we have seen with reptiles, reaction rates are important to life.

3. The rate of a chemical reaction is measured as a change in the amounts of reactants or products (usually in terms of concentration) divided by the change in time. Typical units are molarity per second (M/s), molarity per minute (M/min), and molarity per year (M/yr), depending on how fast the reaction proceeds.

4. The reaction rate is defined as the negative of the change in concentration of a reactant divided by the change in time, because reactant concentrations decrease as a reaction proceeds; therefore the change in the concentration of a reactant is negative. The negative sign in the definition thus makes the overall rate positive. In other words, the negative sign is the result of the convention that reaction rates are usually reported as positive quantities. Since the product concentrations are increasing, the concentration of a product divided by the change in time is positive.

5. The average rate of the reaction can be calculated for any time interval as: $\text{Rate} = -\dfrac{1}{a}\dfrac{[A]_{t_2} - [A]_{t_1}}{t_2 - t_1} = -\dfrac{1}{b}\dfrac{[B]_{t_2} - [B]_{t_1}}{t_2 - t_1} = -\dfrac{1}{c}\dfrac{[C]_{t_2} - [C]_{t_1}}{t_2 - t_1} = -\dfrac{1}{d}\dfrac{[D]_{t_2} - [D]_{t_1}}{t_2 - t_1}$ for the chemical reaction: $aA + bB \rightarrow cC + dD$. The instantaneous rate of the reaction is the rate at any one point in time, represented by the instantaneous slope of the curve at that point. We can obtain the instantaneous rate from the slope of the tangent to the curve at the point of interest.

6. For a zero order reaction, $\text{Rate} = k\,[A]^0 = k$, so doubling the concentration of A does nothing to the reaction rate. For a first order reaction, $\text{Rate} = k\,[A]^1 = k\,[A]$, so doubling the concentration of A doubles the reaction rate. For a second order reaction, $\text{Rate} = k\,[A]^2$, so doubling the concentration of A quadruples the reaction rate.

7. The reaction order can not be determined by the stoichiometry of the reaction. It can only be determined by running controlled experiments where the concentrations of the reactants are varied and the reaction rates are measured and analyzed.

8. When multiple reactants are present, $\text{Rate} = k\,[A]^m[B]^n$ where m is the reaction order with respect to A and n is the reaction order with respect to B. The overall order is simply the sum of the exponents $(m + n)$.

9. The rate law shows the relationship between the rate of a reaction and the concentrations of the reactants. The integrated rate law for a chemical reaction is a relationship between the concentration of a reactant and time.

10. For a zero order reaction, $[A]_t = -kt + [A]_0$. For a first order reaction, $ln[A]_t = -kt + ln[A]_0$. For a second order reaction, $\dfrac{1}{[A]_t} = kt + \dfrac{1}{[A]_0}$.

11. The half-life ($t_{1/2}$) of a reaction is the time required for the concentration of a reactant to fall to one-half of its initial value. For a zero order reaction, $t_{1/2} = \dfrac{[A]_0}{2k}$. For a first order reaction, $t_{1/2} = \dfrac{0.693}{k}$. For a second order reaction, $t_{1/2} = \dfrac{1}{k[A]_0}$.

12. The rates of chemical reactions are, in general, highly sensitive to temperature. Reaction rates increase as the temperature increases. The temperature dependence of the reaction rate is contained in the rate constant, k (which is actually a constant only when the temperature remains constant.)

13. The modern form of the Arrhenius equation, which relates the rate constant (k) and the temperature in Kelvin (T), is as follows: $k = A\, e^{-E_a/RT}$, where R is the gas constant (8.314 J/mol K), A is a constant called the frequency factor (or the pre-exponential factor), and E_a is called the activation energy (or activation barrier). The frequency factor is the number of times that the reactants approach the activation barrier per unit time. The exponential factor is the fraction of approaches that are successful in surmounting the activation barrier and forming products. The exponential factor increases with increasing temperature, but decreases with an increasing value for the activation energy. As the temperature increases, the number of collisions increases and the number of molecules having enough thermal energy to surmount the activation barrier increases. At any given temperature, a sample of molecules will have a distribution of energies, as shown in Figure 13.14. Under common circumstances, only a small fraction of the molecules have enough energy to make it over the activation barrier. Because of the shape of the energy distribution curve, however, a small change in temperature results in a large difference in the number of molecules having enough energy to surmount the activation barrier.

14. An Arrhenius Plot is a plot of the natural log of the rate constant ($ln\,k$) versus the inverse of the temperature in Kelvin ($1/T$) yields a straight line with a slope of $-E_a/R$ and a y-intercept of $ln\,A$.

15. In the collision model, a chemical reaction occurs after a sufficiently energetic collision between the two reactant molecules. In collision theory, therefore, each approach to the activation barrier is a collision between the reactant molecules. The value of the frequency factor should simply be the number of collisions that occur per second. In the collision model $k = p\, z\, e^{-E_a/RT}$, where the frequency factor, A, has been separated into two separate parts, where p is called the orientation factor and z is the collision frequency. The collision frequency is simply the number of collisions that occur per unit time. The orientation factor says that if two molecules are to react with each other, they must collide in such a way that allows the necessary bonds to break and form. The small orientation factor indicates that the orientational requirements for this reaction are fairly stringent—the molecules must be aligned in a very specific way for the reaction to occur. When two molecules with sufficient energy and the correct orientation collide, something unique happens. The electrons on one of the atoms or molecules are attracted to the nuclei of the other; some bonds begin to weaken while other bonds begin to form and, if all goes well, the reactants go through the transition state and are transformed into the products and a chemical reaction occurs.

16. When we write a chemical equation to represent a chemical reaction, we usually represent the overall reaction, not the series of individual steps by which the reaction occurs. The overall equation simply shows the substances present at the beginning of the reaction and the substances formed by the reaction—it does not show the intermediate steps that may be involved. A reaction mechanism is a series of individual chemical steps by which an overall chemical reaction occurs.

17. An elementary step is a step in a reaction mechanism. Elementary steps cannot be broken down into simpler steps—they occur as they are written. Elementary steps are characterized by their molecularity, the number of reactant particles involved in the step. The molecularity of the three most common types of elementary steps are as follows: unimolecular - A $\rightarrow$ products and Rate = $k\,[A]$; bimolecular - A + A $\rightarrow$ products and Rate = $k\,[A]^2$; and bimolecular - A + B $\rightarrow$ products and Rate = $k\,[A][B]$. Elementary steps in which three

reactant particles collide, called termolecular steps, are very rare because the probability of three particles simultaneously colliding is small.

18. For a proposed reaction mechanism such as the one above to be valid—mechanisms can only be validated, not proven—two conditions must be met: (1) the elementary steps in the mechanism must sum to the overall reaction; and (2) the rate law predicted by the mechanism must be consistent with the experimentally observed rate law.

19. Reaction intermediates are species that are formed in one step of a mechanism and consumed in another step. An intermediate is not found in the balanced equation for the overall reaction, but plays a key role in the mechanism.

20. A catalyst is a substance that increases the rate of a chemical reaction but is not consumed by the reaction. A catalyst works by providing an alternative mechanism for the reaction—one in which the rate-determining step has a lower activation energy.

21. In homogeneous catalysis, the catalyst exists in the same phase as the reactants. In heterogeneous catalysis, the catalyst exists in a phase different from the reactants.

22. Heterogeneous catalysis occurs by the following four-step process: (1) Adsorption – the reactants are adsorbed onto the metal surface; (2) Diffusion – the reactants diffuse on the surface until they approach each other; (3) Reaction – the reactants react to form the products; and (4) Desorption – the products desorb from the surface into the gas phase.

23. Enzymes are biological catalysts that increase the rates of biochemical reactions. Enzymes are large protein molecules with complex three-dimensional structures. Within that structure is a specific area called the active site. The properties and shape of the active site are just right to bind the reactant molecule, usually called the substrate. The substrate fits into the active site in a manner that is analogous to a key fitting into a lock.

24. The general mechanism by which an enzyme (E) binds a substrate (S) and then reacts to form the products (P) is as follows: (1) $E + S \rightleftharpoons ES$ (fast); and (2) $ES \rightarrow E + P$ (slow, rate-limiting).

25. a) $\text{Rate} = -\dfrac{1}{2}\dfrac{\Delta[HBr]}{\Delta t} = \dfrac{\Delta[H_2]}{\Delta t} = \dfrac{\Delta[Br_2]}{\Delta t}$

b) **Given:** first 15.0 s; 0.500 M to 0.455 M   **Find:** average rate
Conceptual plan: $t_1, t_2, [HBr]_1, [HBr]_2 \rightarrow$ **average rate**

$$\text{Rate} = -\dfrac{1}{2}\dfrac{\Delta[HBr]}{\Delta t}$$

Solution: $\text{Rate} = -\dfrac{1}{2}\dfrac{[HBr]_{t_2} - [HBr]_{t_1}}{t_2 - t_1} = -\dfrac{1}{2}\dfrac{0.455\text{ M} - 0.500\text{ M}}{15.0\text{s} - 0.0\text{ s}} = 1.5 \times 10^{-3}\text{ M s}^{-1}$

Check: The units (M s^{-1}) are correct. The magnitude of the answer (10^{-3}M s^{-1}) makes physical sense because rates are always positive and we are not changing the concentration much in 15 s.

c) **Given:** 0.500 L vessel and part b) data   **Find:** mol$_{Br2}$ formed
Conceptual plan: average rate, $t_1, t_2, \rightarrow \Delta[Br_2]$ then $\Delta[Br_2], L \rightarrow$ mol$_{Br2}$ **formed**

$$\text{Rate} = \dfrac{\Delta[Br_2]}{\Delta t} \qquad\qquad M = \dfrac{mol_{Br2}}{L}$$

Solution:

$\text{Rate} = 1.5 \times 10^{-3}\text{ M s}^{-1} = \dfrac{\Delta[Br_2]}{\Delta t} = \dfrac{\Delta[Br_2]}{15.0\text{s} - 0.0\text{ s}}$ Rearrange to solve for $\Delta[Br_2]$.

$\Delta[Br_2] = 1.5 \times 10^{-3}\dfrac{M}{s} \times 15.0\text{ s} = 0.0225\text{ M}$ then $M = \dfrac{mol_{Br2}}{L}$. Rearrange to solve for mol$_{Br2}$.

$0.0225\dfrac{\text{mol Br}_2}{L} \times 0.500\text{ L} = 0.011\text{ mol Br}_2$.

Check: The units (mol) are correct. The magnitude of the answer (0.01 mol) makes physical sense because the times are the same as in part b) and we need to rates divide by 2 twice because of the stoichiometric coefficient difference and the volume of the vessel.

26. a) $\text{Rate} = -\dfrac{1}{2}\dfrac{\Delta[N_2O]}{\Delta t} = \dfrac{1}{2}\dfrac{\Delta[N_2]}{\Delta t} = \dfrac{\Delta[O_2]}{\Delta t}$

b) **Given**: first 10.0 s; 0.018 mol O_2 in 0.250 L   **Find**: average rate

    Conceptual plan: mol_{O2}, L $\rightarrow$ M   then $t_1, t_2, [O_2]_1, [O_2]_2$ $\rightarrow$ **average rate**

$$M = \frac{mol_{Br2}}{L} \qquad\qquad \text{Rate} = \frac{\Delta[O_2]}{\Delta t}$$

    Solution: at $t_1 = 0$ s we have no O_2. $M = \dfrac{mol_{O2}}{L} = \dfrac{0.018\ mol\,O_2}{0.250\ L} = 0.072$ M then

$$\text{Rate} = \frac{[O_2]_{t_2} - [O_2]_{t_1}}{t_2 - t_1} = \frac{0.072\ M - 0.000\ M}{10.0s - 0.0\ s} = 7.2 \times 10^{-3}\ M\ s^{-1}$$

    Check: The units ($M\ s^{-1}$) are correct. The magnitude of the answer ($10^{-3}\ M\ s^{-1}$) makes physical sense because rates are always positive and we are not changing the concentration much in 10 s.

c) **Given**: part b) data   **Find**: $\dfrac{\Delta[N_2O]}{\Delta t}$

    Conceptual plan: average rate $\rightarrow$ $\dfrac{\Delta[N_2O]}{\Delta t}$

$$\text{Rate} = -\frac{1}{2}\frac{\Delta[N_2O]}{\Delta t} = \frac{\Delta[O_2]}{\Delta t}$$

    Solution: $\text{Rate} = -\dfrac{1}{2}\dfrac{\Delta[N_2O]}{\Delta t} = \dfrac{\Delta[O_2]}{\Delta t}$ Rearrange to solve for $\dfrac{\Delta[N_2O]}{\Delta t}$.

$$\frac{\Delta[N_2O]}{\Delta t} = -2\frac{\Delta[O_2]}{\Delta t} = -2 \times 7.2 \times 10^{-3}\ M\ s^{-1} = -0.014\ M\ s^{-1}$$

    Check: The units ($M\ s^{-1}$) are correct. The magnitude of the answer ($-0.01\ M\ s^{-1}$) makes physical sense because multiply by 2 because of the stoichiometric coefficient difference and the change in concentration with time is negative since this is a reactant.

27. a) $\text{Rate} = -\dfrac{1}{2}\dfrac{\Delta[A]}{\Delta t} = -\dfrac{\Delta[B]}{\Delta t} = \dfrac{1}{3}\dfrac{\Delta[C]}{\Delta t}$

b) **Given**: $\dfrac{\Delta[A]}{\Delta t} = -0.100$ M/s   **Find**: $\dfrac{\Delta[B]}{\Delta t}$, and $\dfrac{\Delta[C]}{\Delta t}$

    Conceptual plan: $\dfrac{\Delta[A]}{\Delta t}$ $\rightarrow$ $\dfrac{\Delta[B]}{\Delta t}$, **and** $\dfrac{\Delta[C]}{\Delta t}$

$$\text{Rate} = -\frac{1}{2}\frac{\Delta[A]}{\Delta t} = -\frac{\Delta[B]}{\Delta t} = \frac{1}{3}\frac{\Delta[C]}{\Delta t}$$

    Solution: $\text{Rate} = -\dfrac{1}{2}\dfrac{\Delta[A]}{\Delta t} = -\dfrac{\Delta[B]}{\Delta t} = \dfrac{1}{3}\dfrac{\Delta[C]}{\Delta t}$ Sustitiute in value and solve for the two desired values.

$$-\frac{1}{2}\frac{-0.100\ M}{s} = -\frac{\Delta[B]}{\Delta t} \text{ so } \frac{\Delta[B]}{\Delta t} = -0.0500\ M\,s^{-1} \text{ and } -\frac{1}{2}\frac{-0.100\ M}{s} = \frac{1}{3}\frac{\Delta[C]}{\Delta t} \text{ so}$$

$$\frac{\Delta[C]}{\Delta t} = 0.150\ M\,s^{-1}$$

    Check: The units ($M\ s^{-1}$) are correct. The magnitude of the answer ($-0.05\ M\ s^{-1}$) makes physical sense because fewer moles of B are reacting for every mole of A and the change in concentration with time is negative since this is a reactant. The magnitude of the answer ($0.15\ M\ s^{-1}$) makes physical sense because more moles of C are being formed for every mole of A reacting and the change in concentration with time is positive since this is a product.

28. a) $\text{Rate} = -\dfrac{\Delta[A]}{\Delta t} = -2\dfrac{\Delta[B]}{\Delta t} = \dfrac{1}{2}\dfrac{\Delta[C]}{\Delta t}$

b) **Given:** $\frac{\Delta[C]}{\Delta t} = 0.025$ M/s **Find:** $\frac{\Delta[B]}{\Delta t}$, and $\frac{\Delta[A]}{\Delta t}$

Conceptual plan: $\frac{\Delta[C]}{\Delta t}$ → $\frac{\Delta[B]}{\Delta t}$, **and** $\frac{\Delta[A]}{\Delta t}$

$$\text{Rate} = -\frac{\Delta[A]}{\Delta t} = -2\frac{\Delta[B]}{\Delta t} = \frac{1}{2}\frac{\Delta[C]}{\Delta t}$$

Solution: $\text{Rate} = -\frac{\Delta[A]}{\Delta t} = -2\frac{\Delta[B]}{\Delta t} = \frac{1}{2}\frac{\Delta[C]}{\Delta t}$ Sustitiue in value and solve for the two desired values.

$-2\frac{\Delta[B]}{\Delta t} = \frac{1}{2}\frac{0.025\ M}{s}$ so $\frac{\Delta[B]}{\Delta t} = -0.0063\ M\,s^{-1}$ and $-\frac{\Delta[A]}{\Delta t} = \frac{1}{2}\frac{0.025\ M}{s}$ so

$\frac{\Delta[A]}{\Delta t} = -0.013\ M\,s^{-1}$

Check: The units ($M\,s^{-1}$) are correct. The magnitude of the answer ($-0.006\ M\,s^{-1}$) makes physical sense because fewer moles of B are reacting for every mole of C being formed and the change in concentration with time is negative since this is a reactant. The magnitude of the answer ($-0.01\ M\,s^{-1}$) makes physical sense because fewer moles of A are reacting for every mole of C being formed and the change in concentration with time is negative since this is a reactant. B has to smallest stoichiometric coefficient and so its rate of change has the smallest magnitude.

29. a) **Given:** $[C_4H_8]$ versus time data **Find:** average rate between 0 and 10 s, and between 40 and 50 s
Conceptual plan: $t_1, t_2, [C_4H_8]_1, [C_4H_8]_2$ → **average rate**

$$\text{Rate} = -\frac{\Delta[C_4H_8]}{\Delta t}$$

Solution: for 0 to 10 s: $\text{Rate} = -\frac{[C_4H_8]_{t_2} - [C_4H_8]_{t_1}}{t_2 - t_1} = -\frac{0.913\ M - 1.000\ M}{10.\ s - 0.\ s} = 8.7 \times 10^{-3}\ M\,s^{-1}$ and

for 40 to 50 s: $\text{Rate} = -\frac{[C_4H_8]_{t_2} - [C_4H_8]_{t_1}}{t_2 - t_1} = -\frac{0.637\ M - 0.697\ M}{50.\ s - 40.\ s} = 6.0 \times 10^{-3}\ M\,s^{-1}$

Check: The units ($M\,s^{-1}$) are correct. The magnitude of the answer ($10^{-3}M\,s^{-1}$) makes physical sense because rates are always positive and we are not changing the concentration much in 10 s. Also reactions slow as they proceed because the concentration of the reactants is decreasing.

b) **Given:** $[C_4H_8]$ versus time data **Find:** $\frac{\Delta[C_2H_4]}{\Delta t}$ between 20 and 30 s

Conceptual plan: $t_1, t_2, [C_4H_8]_1, [C_4H_8]_2$ → $\frac{\Delta[C_2H_4]}{\Delta t}$

$$\text{Rate} = -\frac{\Delta[C_4H_8]}{\Delta t} = \frac{1}{2}\frac{\Delta[C_2H_4]}{\Delta t}$$

Solution: $\text{Rate} = -\frac{[C_4H_8]_{t_2} - [C_4H_8]_{t_1}}{t_2 - t_1} = -\frac{0.763\ M - 0.835\ M}{30.\ s - 20.\ s} = 7.2 \times 10^{-3}\ M\,s^{-1} = \frac{1}{2}\frac{\Delta[C_2H_4]}{\Delta t}$ Rearrange to

solve for $\frac{\Delta[C_2H_4]}{\Delta t}$. So $\frac{\Delta[C_2H_4]}{\Delta t} = 2(7.2 \times 10^{-3}\ M\,s^{-1}) = 1.4 \times 10^{-2}\ M\,s^{-1}$.

Check: The units ($M\,s^{-1}$) are correct. The magnitude of the answer ($10^{-2}M\,s^{-1}$) makes physical sense because rate of product formation is always positive and we are not changing the concentration much in 10 s. The rate of change of the product is faster than the decline of the reactant because of the stoichiometric coefficients.

30. a) **Given:** $[NO_2]$ versus time data **Find:** average rate between 10 and 20 s, and between 50 and 60 s
Conceptual plan: $t_1, t_2, [NO_2]_1, [NO_2]_2$ → **average rate**

$$\text{Rate} = -\frac{\Delta[NO_2]}{\Delta t}$$

Solution: for 10 to 20 s: $\text{Rate} = -\frac{[NO_2]_{t_2} - [NO_2]_{t_1}}{t_2 - t_1} = -\frac{0.904\ M - 0.951\ M}{20.\ s - 10.\ s} = 4.7 \times 10^{-3}\ M\,s^{-1}$ and for 50 to 60 s: Rate $= -\dfrac{[NO_2]_{t_2} - [NO_2]_{t_1}}{t_2 - t_1} = -\dfrac{0.740\ M - 0.778\ M}{60.\ s - 50.\ s} = 3.8 \times 10^{-3}\ M\ s^{-1}$

Check: The units ($M\ s^{-1}$) are correct.   The magnitude of the answer ($10^{-3}M\ s^{-1}$) makes physical sense because rates are always positive and we are not changing the concentration much in 10 s.   Also reactions slow as they proceed because the concentration of the reactants is decreasing.

b)   **Given:** [NO_2] versus time data   **Find:** $\dfrac{\Delta[O_2]}{\Delta t}$ between 50 and 60 s

   Conceptual plan: average rate from part a)   → $\dfrac{\Delta[O_2]}{\Delta t}$

$$\text{Rate} = -\frac{\Delta[NO_2]}{\Delta t} = 2\frac{\Delta[O_2]}{\Delta t}$$

   Solution: Rate $= -\dfrac{\Delta[NO_2]}{\Delta t} = 2\dfrac{\Delta[O_2]}{\Delta t}$ Sustitiute in value and solve for the desired value.

$3.8 \times 10^{-3}\ M\ s^{-1} = 2\dfrac{\Delta[O_2]}{\Delta t}$ so $\dfrac{\Delta[O_2]}{\Delta t} = 1.9 \times 10^{-3}\ M\ s^{-1}$,

   Check: The units ($M\ s^{-1}$) are correct.   The magnitude of the answer ($10^{-3}M\ s^{-1}$) makes physical sense because rate of product formation is always positive and we are not changing the concentration much in 10 s.   The rate of change of the product is slower than the decline of the reactant because of the stoichiometric coefficients.

31. a)   **Given:** [Br_2] versus time plot
   Find: (i) average rate between 0 and 25 s; (ii) instantaneous rate at 25 s; and (iii) instantaneous rate of HBr formation at 50 s
   Conceptual plan: (i) $t_1, t_2, [Br_2]_1, [Br_2]_2$ →   **average rate**   **then**

$$\text{Rate} = -\frac{\Delta[Br_2]}{\Delta t}$$

   (ii) draw tangent at 25 s and determine slope →   **instantaneous rate**   **then**

$$\text{Rate} = -\frac{\Delta[Br_2]}{\Delta t}$$

   (iii) draw tangent at 50 s and determine slope →   **instantaneous rate**   → $\dfrac{\Delta[HBr]}{\Delta t}$

$$\text{Rate} = -\frac{\Delta[Br_2]}{\Delta t} \qquad\qquad \text{Rate} = \frac{1}{2}\frac{\Delta[HBr]}{\Delta t}$$

   Solution:

(i) Rate $= -\dfrac{[Br_2]_{t_2} - [Br_2]_{t_1}}{t_2 - t_1} = -\dfrac{0.75\ M - 1.00\ M}{25\ s - 0.\ s} =$ and

$= 1.0 \times 10^{-2}\ M\ s^{-1}$

(ii) at 25 s:

Slope $= \dfrac{\Delta y}{\Delta x} = \dfrac{0.68\ M - 0.85\ M}{35\ s - 15\ s} = -8.5 \times 10^{-3}\ M\ s^{-1}$

since the slope $= \dfrac{\Delta[Br_2]}{\Delta t}$ and   Rate $= -\dfrac{\Delta[Br_2]}{\Delta t}$,

then Rate $= -(-8.5 \times 10^{-3}\ M\ s^{-1}) = 8.5 \times 10^{-3}\ M\ s^{-1}$

(iii) at 50 s:

Slope $= \dfrac{\Delta y}{\Delta x} = \dfrac{0.53\ M - 0.66\ M}{60.\ s - 40.\ s} = -6.5 \times 10^{-3}\ M\ s^{-1}$

since the slope $= \dfrac{\Delta[Br_2]}{\Delta t}$ and Rate $= -\dfrac{\Delta[Br_2]}{\Delta t} = \dfrac{1}{2}\dfrac{\Delta[HBr]}{\Delta t}$ then

$\dfrac{\Delta[HBr]}{\Delta t} = -2\dfrac{\Delta[Br_2]}{\Delta t} = -2(-6.5 \times 10^{-3}\ M\ s^{-1}) = 1.3 \times 10^{-2}\ M\ s^{-1}$

Check: The units ($M\ s^{-1}$) are correct.   The magnitude of the first answer is larger than the second answer because the rate is slowing down and the first answer includes the initial portion of the data.

The magnitudes of the answers (10^{-3} M s^{-1}) makes physical sense because rates are always positive and we are not changing the concentration much.

b) **Given:** $[Br_2]$ versus time data; and $[HBr]_0 = 0$ M
   Find: plot $[HBr]$ with time

   Conceptual plan: **Since** $Rate = -\dfrac{\Delta[Br_2]}{\Delta t} = \dfrac{1}{2}\dfrac{\Delta[HBr]}{\Delta t}$ **. The rate of change of $[HBr]$ will be twice that of $[Br_2]$. The plot will start at the origin.**

   Check: The units (M versus s) are correct. The plot makes sense because the has the same general shape of the original plot, only we are increasing instead of decreasing and out concentration axis has changed by a factor of two (to account for the difference in stoichiometric coefficients.

32. **Given:** $[H_2O_2]$ versus time plot; and 1.5 L H_2O_2 initially   **Find:** (a) average rate between 10 and 20 s; (b) instantaneous rate at 30 s; (c) instantaneous rate of O_2 formation at 50 s; and (d) mol_{O_2} formed in first 50 s
    Conceptual plan: (a) $t_1, t_2, [H_2O_2]_1, [H_2O_2]_2 \rightarrow$ **average rate**   **then**

    $$Rate = -\frac{1}{2}\frac{\Delta[H_2O_2]}{\Delta t}$$

    (b) **draw tangent at 30 s and determine slope $\rightarrow$ instantaneous rate   then**

    $$Rate = -\frac{1}{2}\frac{\Delta[H_2O_2]}{\Delta t}$$

    (c) **draw tangent at 50 s and determine slope $\rightarrow$ instantaneous rate $\rightarrow$** $\dfrac{\Delta[O_2]}{\Delta t}$

    $$Rate = -\frac{1}{2}\frac{\Delta[H_2O_2]}{\Delta t} \qquad Rate = \frac{\Delta[O_2]}{\Delta t}$$

    (d) $[H_2O_2]_{0\,s},\ [H_2O_2]_{50\,s} \rightarrow \Delta\ [H_2O_2] \rightarrow \Delta\ [O_2]$ **then** $\Delta\ [O_2], V \rightarrow mol_{O_2}$

    $$\Delta[H_2O_2] = [H_2O_2]_{50\,s} - [H_2O_2]_{0\,s} \quad Rate = -\frac{1}{2}\frac{\Delta[H_2O_2]}{\Delta t} = \frac{\Delta[O_2]}{\Delta t} \qquad M = \frac{mol_{O_2}}{L}$$

    Solution:

    (a) $Rate = -\dfrac{[H_2O_2]_{t_2} - [H_2O_2]_{t_1}}{t_2 - t_1} = -\dfrac{0.55\ M - 0.75\ M}{20.\ s - 10.\ s} =$

    $= 2.0 \times 10^{-2}$ M s^{-1} and

    (b) at 30 s:

    $Slope = \dfrac{\Delta y}{\Delta x} = \dfrac{0.28\ M - 0.52\ M}{40.\ s - 20.\ s} = -1.2 \times 10^{-2}$ M s^{-1} since

    the slope $= \dfrac{\Delta[H_2O_2]}{\Delta t}$ and $Rate = -\dfrac{1}{2}\dfrac{\Delta[H_2O_2]}{\Delta t}$, then

    $Rate = (-0.5)(-1.2 \times 10^{-2}$ M s$^{-1}) = 6.0 \times 10^{-3}$ M s^{-1}.

    (c) at 50 s:

    $Slope = \dfrac{\Delta y}{\Delta x} = \dfrac{0.15\ M - 0.28\ M}{60.\ s - 40.\ s} = -6.5 \times 10^{-3}$ M s^{-1} since the slope = $\dfrac{\Delta[H_2O_2]}{\Delta t}$ and   Rate = $-\dfrac{1}{2}\dfrac{\Delta[H_2O_2]}{\Delta t} = \dfrac{\Delta[O_2]}{\Delta t}$ then

$\dfrac{\Delta[O_2]}{\Delta t} = (-0.5)(-6.5 \times 10^{-3} \text{ M s}^{-1}) = 3.3 \times 10^{-3} \text{ M s}^{-1}$

(d) $\Delta[H_2O_2] = [H_2O_2]_{50\,s} - [H_2O_2]_{0\,s} = 0.23 \text{ M} - 1.00 \text{ M} = 0.77 \text{ M}$ since

$\Delta[O_2] = -\dfrac{1}{2}\Delta[H_2O_2] = (-0.5)(0.77 \text{ M}) = 0.3\underline{8}5 \text{ M}$ then $M = \dfrac{mol_{O2}}{L}$ so

$mol_{O2} = M \, L = 0.3\underline{8}5\dfrac{\text{mol O}_2}{\text{L}} \times 1.5 \text{ L} = 0.58 \text{ mol O}_2$

Check: (a) The units (M s^{-1}) are correct. The magnitude of the first answer is reasonable considering the concentrations and times involves (1M / 100 s). (b) The units (M s^{-1}) are correct. We expect the answer in this part to be less than in the first part because the rate is decreasing as the reaction proceeds. (c) The units (M s^{-1}) are correct. We expect the answer in this part to be less than in the first part because the rate is decreasing as the reaction proceeds. (d) The units (mol) are correct. We expect an answer less than 1 mol since the drop in reactant concentration is less than 1 M, we have 1.5 L and only half as much O$_2$ is generated as hydrogen peroxide is consumed.

33. a) **Given:** Rate versus [A] plot   **Find:** reaction order
    Conceptual Plan: Look at shape of plot and match to possibilities.
    Solution: The plot is a linear plot, so Rate α [A] or the reaction is first order.
    Check: The order of the reaction is a common reaction order.

b) **Given:** part a)   **Find:** sketch plot of [A] versus time
    Conceptual plan: Using result from part a), shape plot of [A] versus time should be curved with [A] decreasing. Use 1.0 M as initial concentration.
    Solution:

    Check: The plot has a shape that matches the one in the text for first order plots.

c) **Given: part a)**   **Find:** write a rate law and estimate k
    Conceptual plan: Using result from part a), the slope of the plot is the rate constant.

    Solution: Slope = $\dfrac{\Delta y}{\Delta x} = \dfrac{0.010\,\frac{\text{M}}{\text{s}} - 0.00\,\frac{\text{M}}{\text{s}}}{1.0 \text{ M} - 0.0 \text{ M}} = 0.010 \text{ s}^{-1}$ so Rate = k [A]^1 or Rate = k [A] or

    Rate = 0.010 s^{-1} [A]
    Check: The units (s^{-1}) are correct. The magnitude of the answer (10^{-2} s^{-1}) makes physical sense because rate and concentration data. Remember that concentration is in units of M, so plugging the rate constant into the equation has the units of the rate as M s^{-1}, which is correct.

34. a) **Given:** Rate versus [A] plot   **Find:** reaction order
    Conceptual Plan: Look at shape of plot and match to possibilities.
    Solution: The plot is a linear plot that is horizontal, so Rate is independent of [A] or the reaction is zero order.
    Check: The order of the reaction is a common reaction order.

b) **Given:** part a)   **Find:** sketch plot of [A] versus time

Conceptual plan: Using result from part a), shape plot of [A] versus time should be a straight line with [A] decreasing. Use 1.0 M as initial concentration.

Solution:

Check: The plot has a shape that matches the one in the text for zero order plots.

c) **Given: part a)**   **Find:** write a rate law and estimate k

    Conceptual plan: Using result from part a), the rate is equal to the rate constant.

    Solution: Rate = k [A]^0 or Rate = k or Rate = 0.010 M s^{-1}

    Check: The units (Ms^{-1}) are correct. The magnitude of the answer (10^{-2} Ms^{-1}) makes physical sense because rate and concentration data. Plugging the rate constant into the equation the rate has the units of the rate as M s^{-1}, which is correct.

35. **Given:** reaction order: a) first-order; b) second-order; and c) zero-order   **Find:** units of k

    Conceptual plan: Using rate law, rearrange to solve for k.

$$\text{Rate} = k \text{ [A]}^n, \text{ where n = reaction order}$$

Solution: for all cases Rate has units of M s^{-1} and [A] has units of M

a) Rate = k [A]^1 = k [A] so $k = \dfrac{\text{Rate}}{[A]} = \dfrac{\frac{\cancel{M}}{s}}{\cancel{M}} = s^{-1}$;   b) Rate = k [A]^2 so $k = \dfrac{\text{Rate}}{[A]^2} = \dfrac{\frac{\cancel{M}}{s}}{\cancel{M}M} = M^{-1} s^{-1}$;

c) Rate = k [A]^0 = k = M s^{-1} .

Check: The units (s^{-1}, M^{-1}s^{-1} and Ms^{-1}) are correct. The units for k change with the reaction order so that the units on the rate remain as M s^{-1}.

36. **Given:** k = 0.053/s and [N$_2$O$_5$] = 0.055 M; reaction order: a) first-order; b) second-order and zero-order (change units on k as necessary)   **Find:** rate

    Conceptual plan: Using rate law, substitute in values to solve for Rate.

$$\text{Rate} = k \text{ [N}_2\text{O}_5]^n, \text{ where n = reaction order}$$

Solution: for all cases Rate has units of M s^{-1} and [A] has units of M. Use the results from problem #35 to choose the appropriate units for k.

a)   Rate = k [N$_2$O$_5$]^1 = k [N$_2$O$_5$] = $\dfrac{0.053}{s}$ x 0.055 M = 2.9 x 10^{-3} $\dfrac{M}{s}$;

b)   Rate = k [N$_2$O$_5$]^2 = k [N$_2$O$_5$] = $\dfrac{0.053}{M\,s}$ x (0.055 M)^2 = 1.6 x 10^{-4} $\dfrac{M}{s}$;and   Rate = k [N$_2$O$_5$]^0 = k = 5.3 x 10^{-2} $\dfrac{M}{s}$

Check: The units (Ms^{-1}) are correct. The magnitude of the rate changes as the order of the reaction changes, because we are multiplying by the concentration a different number of times in each case. The higher the order the lower the rate since the concentration is less than 1 M.

37. **Given:** A, B and C react to form products. Reaction is first order in A, second order in B and zero order in C

    Find: a) rate law; b) overall order of reaction; c) factor change in rate if [A] doubled; d) factor change in rate if [B] doubled; e) factor change in rate if [C] doubled; and f) factor change in rate if [A], [B] and [C] doubled.

Conceptual plan:

a) Using general rate law form, substitute in values for orders.

$$\text{Rate} = k\,[A]^m\,[B]^n\,[C]^p \text{, where m, n and p = reaction orders}$$

b) Using rate law in part a) add up all reaction orders.

$$\textit{overall reaction order} = m + n + p$$

c) through f) Using rate law from part a) substitute in concentration changes.

$$\frac{\text{Rate 2}}{\text{Rate 1}} = \frac{k\,[A]_2^1\,[B]_2^2}{k\,[A]_1^1\,[B]_1^2}$$

Solution:

a) $m = 1$, $n = 2$, and $p = 0$ so Rate $= k\,[A]^1[B]^2[C]^0$ or Rate $= k\,[A][B]^2$.

b) *overall reaction order* $= m + n + p = 1 + 2 + 0 = 3$ so it is a third order reaction overall.

c) $\dfrac{\text{Rate 2}}{\text{Rate 1}} = \dfrac{k\,[A]_2^1\,[B]_2^2}{k\,[A]_1^1\,[B]_1^2}$ and $[A]_2 = 2\,[A]_1$, $[B]_2 = [B]_1$, $[C]_2 = [C]_1$, so $\dfrac{\text{Rate 2}}{\text{Rate 1}} = \dfrac{k\,(2\,[A]_1)^1\,[B]_1^2}{k\,[A]_1^1\,[B]_1^2} = 2$ so the

reaction rate doubles (factor of 2).

d) $\dfrac{\text{Rate 2}}{\text{Rate 1}} = \dfrac{k\,[A]_2^1\,[B]_2^2}{k\,[A]_1^1\,[B]_1^2}$ and $[A]_2 = [A]_1$, $[B]_2 = 2\,[B]_1$, $[C]_2 = [C]_1$, so $\dfrac{\text{Rate 2}}{\text{Rate 1}} = \dfrac{k\,[A]_1\,(2\,[B]_1)^2}{k\,[A]_1\,[B]_1^2} = 2^2 = 4$

so the reaction rate quadruples (factor of 4).

e) $\dfrac{\text{Rate 2}}{\text{Rate 1}} = \dfrac{k\,[A]_2^1\,[B]_2^2}{k\,[A]_1^1\,[B]_1^2}$ and $[A]_2 = [A]_1$, $[B]_2 = [B]_1$, $[C]_2 = 2\,[C]_1$, so $\dfrac{\text{Rate 2}}{\text{Rate 1}} = \dfrac{k\,[A]_1\,[B]_1^2}{k\,[A]_1\,[B]_1^2} = 1$ so the

reaction rate is unchanged (factor of 1).

f) $\dfrac{\text{Rate 2}}{\text{Rate 1}} = \dfrac{k\,[A]_2^1\,[B]_2^2}{k\,[A]_1^1\,[B]_1^2}$ and $[A]_2 = 2\,[A]_1$, $[B]_2 = 2\,[B]_1$, $[C]_2 = 2\,[C]_1$, so

$\dfrac{\text{Rate 2}}{\text{Rate 1}} = \dfrac{k\,(2\,[A]_1)^1\,(2\,[B]_1)^2}{k\,[A]_1\,[B]_1^2} = 2 \times 2^2 = 8$ so the reaction rate goes up by a factor of 8.

Check: The units (none) are correct. The rate law is consistent with the orders given and the overall order is larger that any of the individual orders. The factors are consistent with the reaction orders. The larger the order the larger the factor. When all concentrations are changes the rate changes the most. If a reactant is not in the rate law, then changing its concentration has no effect on the reaction rate.

38. **Given:** A, B and C react to form products. reaction is zero order in A, one-half order in B and second order in C **Find:** a) rate law; b) overall order of reaction; c) factor change in rate if [A] doubled; d) factor change in rate if [B] doubled; e) factor change in rate if [C] doubled; and f) factor change in rate if [A], [B] and [C] doubled.

Conceptual plan:

a) Using general rate law form, substitute in values for orders.

$$\text{Rate} = k\,[A]^m\,[B]^n\,[C]^p \text{, where m, n and p = reaction orders}$$

b) Using rate law in part a) add up all reaction orders.

$$\textit{overall reaction order} = m + n + p$$

c) through f) Using rate law from part a) substitute in concentration changes.

$$\frac{\text{Rate 2}}{\text{Rate 1}} = \frac{k\,[B]_2^{1/2}\,[C]_2^2}{k\,[B]_1^{1/2}\,[C]_1^2}$$

Solution:

a) $m = 1$, $n = 2$, and $p = 0$ so Rate $= k\,[A]^0[B]^{1/2}[C]^2$ or Rate $= k\,[B]^{1/2}[C]^2$.

b) *overall reaction order* $= m + n + p = 0 + 1/2 + 2 = 5/2 = 2.5$ so it is a two and a half order reaction overall.

c) $\dfrac{\text{Rate 2}}{\text{Rate 1}} = \dfrac{k\,[B]_2^{1/2}\,[C]_2^2}{k\,[B]_1^{1/2}\,[C]_1^2}$ and $[A]_2 = 2\,[A]_1$, $[B]_2 = [B]_1$, $[C]_2 = [C]_1$, so $\dfrac{\text{Rate 2}}{\text{Rate 1}} = \dfrac{k\,[B]_1^{1/2}\,[C]_1^2}{k\,[B]_1^{1/2}\,[C]_1^2} = 1$ so the

reaction rate is unchanged (factor of 1).

437

d) $\dfrac{\text{Rate 2}}{\text{Rate 1}} = \dfrac{k\,[B]_2^{1/2}\,[C]_2^2}{k\,[B]_1^{1/2}\,[C]_1^2}$ and $[A]_2 = [A]_1$, $[B]_2 = 2\,[B]_1$, $[C]_2 = [C]_1$, so $\dfrac{\text{Rate 2}}{\text{Rate 1}} = \dfrac{\cancel{k}\,(2\,\cancel{[B]_1})^{1/2}\,\cancel{[C]_1^2}}{\cancel{k}\,\cancel{[B]_1^{1/2}}\,\cancel{[C]_1^2}} = 2^{1/2}$

so the reaction rate increases by a factor of $2^{1/2}$.

e) $\dfrac{\text{Rate 2}}{\text{Rate 1}} = \dfrac{k\,[B]_2^{1/2}\,[C]_2^2}{k\,[B]_1^{1/2}\,[C]_1^2}$ and $[A]_2 = [A]_1$, $[B]_2 = [B]_1$, $[C]_2 = 2\,[C]_1$, so $\dfrac{\text{Rate 2}}{\text{Rate 1}} = \dfrac{\cancel{k}\,\cancel{[B]_1^{1/2}}\,(2\,\cancel{[C]_1})^2}{\cancel{k}\,\cancel{[B]_1^{1/2}}\,\cancel{[C]_1^2}} = 2^2 = 4$

so the reaction rate is quadruples (factor of 4).

f) $\dfrac{\text{Rate 2}}{\text{Rate 1}} = \dfrac{k\,[B]_2^{1/2}\,[C]_2^2}{k\,[B]_1^{1/2}\,[C]_1^2}$ and $[A]_2 = 2\,[A]_1$, $[B]_2 = 2\,[B]_1$, $[C]_2 = 2\,[C]_1$, so

$\dfrac{\text{Rate 2}}{\text{Rate 1}} = \dfrac{\cancel{k}\,(2\,\cancel{[B]_1})^{1/2}\,(2\,\cancel{[C]_1})^2}{\cancel{k}\,\cancel{[B]_1^{1/2}}\,\cancel{[C]_1^2}} = 2^{1/2} \times 2^2 = 2^{5/2}$ so the reaction rate goes up by a factor of $2^{5/2}$.

Check: The units (none) are correct. The rate law is consistent with the orders given and the overall order is larger that any of the individual orders. The factors are consistent with the reaction orders. The larger the order the larger the factor. When all concentrations are changes the rate changes the most. If a reactant is not in the rate law, then changing its concentration has no effect on the reaction rate.

39. **Given:** table of [A] versus initial rate   **Find:** rate law and k
    Conceptual plan: **Using general rate law form, compare rate ratios to determine reaction order.**

$$\frac{\text{Rate 2}}{\text{Rate 1}} = \frac{k\,[A]_2^n}{k\,[A]_1^n}$$

Then use one of the concentration/ initial rate pairs to determine k.

$$\text{Rate} = k\,[A]^n$$

Solution:

$\dfrac{\text{Rate 2}}{\text{Rate 1}} = \dfrac{k\,[A]_2^n}{k\,[A]_1^n}$ Comparing the first two sets of data: $\dfrac{0.210\ \cancel{M/s}}{0.053\ \cancel{M/s}} = \dfrac{\cancel{k}\,(0.200\ \cancel{M})^n}{\cancel{k}\,(0.100\ \cancel{M})]^n}$ and $3.\underline{9}623 = 2^n$ so

n = 2. If we compare the first and the last data sets: $\dfrac{0.473\ \cancel{M/s}}{0.053\ \cancel{M/s}} = \dfrac{\cancel{k}\,(0.300\ \cancel{M})^n}{\cancel{k}\,(0.100\ \cancel{M})]^n}$ and $8.\underline{9}245 = 3^n$ so n =

2. This second comparison is not necessary, but it increases our confidence in the reaction order. So Rate $= k\,[A]^2$. Selecting the second data set and rearranging the rate equation

$k = \dfrac{\text{Rate}}{[A]^2} = \dfrac{0.210\,\dfrac{M}{s}}{(0.200\,M)^2} = 5.25\ M^{-1}\,s^{-1}$ so Rate $= 5.25\ M^{-1}\,s^{-1}[A]^2$

Check: The units (none and $M^{-1}\,s^{-1}$) are correct. The rate law is a common form. The rate is changing more rapidly that the concentration, so second order is consistent. The rate constant is consistent with the units necessary to get rate as M/s and the magnitude is reasonable since we have a second order reaction.

40. **Given:** table of [A] versus initial rate   **Find:** rate law and k
    Conceptual plan: **Using general rate law form, compare rate ratios to determine reaction order.**

$$\frac{\text{Rate 2}}{\text{Rate 1}} = \frac{k\,[A]_2^n}{k\,[A]_1^n}$$

Then use one of the concentration/ initial rate pairs to determine k.

$$\text{Rate} = k\,[A]^n$$

Solution:

$\dfrac{\text{Rate 2}}{\text{Rate 1}} = \dfrac{k\,[A]_2^n}{k\,[A]_1^n}$ Comparing the first two sets of data: $\dfrac{0.016\ \cancel{M/s}}{0.008\ \cancel{M/s}} = \dfrac{\cancel{k}\,(0.30\ \cancel{M})^n}{\cancel{k}\,(0.15\ \cancel{M})]^n}$ and $2 = 2^n$ so n = 1. If

we compare the first and the last data sets: $\dfrac{0.032\ \cancel{M/s}}{0.008\ \cancel{M/s}} = \dfrac{\cancel{k}\,(0.032\ \cancel{M})^n}{\cancel{k}\,(0.008\ \cancel{M})]^n}$ and $4 = 4^n$ so n = 1. This second

comparison is not necessary, but it increases our confidence in the reaction order. So Rate $= k\,[A]$.

Selecting the second data set and rearranging the rate equation $k = \dfrac{\text{Rate}}{[A]} = \dfrac{0.016 \dfrac{M}{s}}{0.30\ M} = 5.3 \times 10^{-2}\ s^{-1}$ so

Rate $= 5.3 \times 10^{-2}\ s^{-1} [A]$.

Check: The units (none and s^{-1}) are correct. The rate law is a common form. The rate is changing as rapidly as the concentration is consistent with first order. The rate constant is consistent with the units necessary to get rate as M/s and the magnitude is reasonable since we have a first order reaction.

41. **Given**: table of $[NO_2]$ and $[F_2]$ versus initial rate   **Find**: rate law, k, and overall order
    Conceptual plan: **Using general rate law form, compare rate ratios to determine reaction order of each reactant. Be sure to choose data that changes only one concentration at a time.**

$$\frac{\text{Rate 2}}{\text{Rate 1}} = \frac{k\ [NO_2]_2^m\ [F_2]_2^n}{k\ [NO_2]_1^m\ [F_2]_1^n}$$

Then use one of the concentration/ initial rate pairs to determine k.

$$\text{Rate} = k\ [NO_2]^m\ [F_2]^n$$

Solution:

$\dfrac{\text{Rate 2}}{\text{Rate 1}} = \dfrac{k\ [NO_2]_2^m\ [F_2]_2^n}{k\ [NO_2]_1^m\ [F_2]_1^n}$ Comparing the first two sets of data: $\dfrac{0.051\ M/s}{0.026\ M/s} = \dfrac{k\ (0.200\ M)^m\ (0.100\ M)^n}{k\ (0.100\ M)^m\ (0.100\ M)^n}$ and

$1.915 = 2^m$ so m $= 1$. If we compare the second and the third data sets:

$\dfrac{0.103\ M/s}{0.051\ M/s} = \dfrac{k\ (0.200\ M)^m\ (0.200\ M)^n}{k\ (0.200\ M)^m\ (0.100\ M)^n}$ and $2 = 2^n$ so n $= 1$. Other comparisons can be made, but are not

necessary. They should reinforce these values of the reaction orders. So Rate $= k\ [NO_2][F_2]$. Selecting the

last data set and rearranging the rate equation $k = \dfrac{\text{Rate}}{[NO_2][F_2]} = \dfrac{0.411 \dfrac{M}{s}}{(0.400\ M)\ (0.400\ M)} = 2.57\ M^{-1}s^{-1}$ so

Rate $= 2.57\ M^{-1}s^{-1}[NO_2][F_2]$ and the reactions is second order overall.

Check: The units (none and $M^{-1}s^{-1}$) are correct. The rate law is a common form. The rate is changing as rapidly as the each concentration is consistent with first order in each reactant. The rate constant is consistent with the units necessary to get rate as M/s and the magnitude is reasonable since we have a second order reaction.

42. **Given**: table of $[CH_3Cl]$ and $[Cl_2]$ versus initial rate   **Find**: rate law, k, and overall order
    Conceptual plan: **Using general rate law form, compare rate ratios to determine reaction order of each reactant. Be sure to choose data that changes only one concentration at a time.**

$$\frac{\text{Rate 2}}{\text{Rate 1}} = \frac{k\ [CH_3Cl]_2^m\ [Cl_2]_2^n}{k\ [CH_3Cl]_1^m\ [Cl_2]_1^n}$$

Then use one of the concentration/ initial rate pairs to determine k.

$$\text{Rate} = k\ [CH_3Cl]^m\ [Cl_2]^n$$

Solution:

$\dfrac{\text{Rate 2}}{\text{Rate 1}} = \dfrac{k\ [CH_3Cl]_2^m\ [Cl_2]_2^n}{k\ [CH_3Cl]_1^m\ [Cl_2]_1^n}$ Comparing the first two sets of data:

$\dfrac{0.029\ M/s}{0.014\ M/s} = \dfrac{k\ (0.100\ M)^m\ (0.050\ M)^n}{k\ (0.050\ M)^m\ (0.050\ M)^n}$ and $2.0714 = 2^m$ so m $= 1$. If we compare the second and the

third data sets: $\dfrac{0.041\ M/s}{0.029\ M/s} = \dfrac{k\ (0.100\ M)^m\ (0.100\ M)^n}{k\ (0.100\ M)^m\ (0.050\ M)^n}$ and $1.414 = 2^n$ so n $= 1/2$. Other comparisons can

be made, but are not necessary. They should reinforce these values of the reaction orders. So

Rate $= k\ [CH_3Cl]\ [Cl_2]^{1/2}$. Selecting the last data set and rearranging the rate equation

$$k = \frac{\text{Rate}}{[CH_3Cl][Cl_2]^{1/2}} = \frac{0.115\frac{M}{s}}{(0.200\ M)(0.200\ M)^{1/2}} = 1.29\ M^{-1/2}\ s^{-1}\ so\quad \text{Rate} = 1.29\ M^{-1/2}\ s^{-1}[CH_3Cl][Cl_2]^{1/2}\quad \text{and the}$$

reactions is one and a half order overall.

Check: The units (none and $M^{-1/2}s^{-1}$) are correct. The rate law is not as common as others, but is reasonable. The rate is changing as rapidly as the CH_3Cl concentration is consistent with first order in this reactant. The rate is changing a bit more slowly than the Cl_2 concentration, which is consistent with half order in this reactant. The rate constant is consistent with the units necessary to get rate as M/s and the magnitude is reasonable since we have a one an a half order reaction.

43. a) The reaction is zero order. Since the slope of the plot is independent of the concentration, there is no dependence of the concentration of the reactant in the rate law.

b) The reaction is first order. The expression for the half life of a first order reaction is $t_{1/2} = \frac{0.693}{k}$, which is independent of the reactant concentration.

c) The reaction is second order. The integrated rate expression for the a second order reaction is $\frac{1}{[A]_t} = kt + \frac{1}{[A]_0}$, which is linear when the inverse of the concentration is plotted versus time.

44. a) The reaction is second order. The expression for the half life of a second order reaction, $t_{1/2} = \frac{1}{k[A]_0}$, which shows that the half life decreases as concentration increases.

b) The reaction is first order. The integrated rate expression for a first order reaction is $ln[A]_t = -kt + ln[A]_0$ which is linear when the natural log of the concentration is plotted versus time.

c) The reaction is zero order. The expression for the half life of a zero order reaction, $t_{1/2} = \frac{[A]_0}{2k}$, which shows that the half life increases as concentration increases.

45. **Given**: table of [AB] versus time   **Find**: reaction order, k, and [AB] at 25 s
Conceptual plan: **Look at the data and see if any common reaction orders can be eliminated. If the data does not show an equal concentration drop with time, then zero order can be eliminated. Look for changes in the half life (compare time for concentration to drop to one half of any value). If the half life is not constant, then the first order can be eliminated. If the half life is getting longer as the concentration drops, this might suggest second order. Plot the data as indicated by the appropriate rate law. Determine k from the slope of the plot. Finally calculate the [AB] at 25 s by using the appropriate integrated rate expression.**
Solution: By the above logic, we can eliminate both the zero order and the first order reactions. (alternatively, you could make all three plots and only one should be linear.) This suggests that we should have a second order reaction. Plot 1/[AB] versus

time. Since $\frac{1}{[AB]_t} = kt + \frac{1}{[AB]_0}$, the slope will be

the rate constant. The slope can be determined by measuring $\Delta y/\Delta x$ on the plot or by using functions, such as "add trendline" in Excel. Thus the rate constant is 0.0225 $M^{-1}\ s^{-1}$ and the rate law is Rate = 0.0225 $M^{-1}s^{-1}[AB]^2$.

Finally, use $\frac{1}{[AB]_t} = kt + \frac{1}{[AB]_0}$, substitute in the

values of $[AB]_0$, 25 s and k and rearrange to

solve for [AB] at 25 s. $[AB]_t = \dfrac{1}{kt + \dfrac{1}{[AB]_0}} = \dfrac{1}{(0.0225\ M^{-1}\ s^{-1})(25\ s) + \left(\dfrac{1}{0.950\ M}\right)} = 0.619\ M$

Check: The units (none, $M^{-1}s^{-1}$, and M) are correct. The rate law is a common form. The plot was extremely linear, confirming second order kinetics. The rate constant is consistent with the units necessary to get rate as M/s and the magnitude is reasonable since we have a second order reaction. The [AB] at 25 s is in between the values at 0 s and 50 s.

46. **Given:** table of $[N_2O_5]$ versus time   **Find:** reaction order, k, and $[N_2O_5]$ at 250 s

    Conceptual plan: **Look at the data and see if any common reaction orders can be eliminated. If the data does not show an equal concentration drop with time, then zero order can be eliminated. Look for changes in the half life (compare time for concentration to drop to one half of any value). If the half life is not constant, then the first order can be eliminated. If the half life is getting longer as the concentration drops, this might suggest second order. Plot the data as indicated by the appropriate rate law. Determine k from the slope of the plot. Finally calculate the $[N_2O_5]$ at 250 s by using the appropriate integrated rate expression.**

    Solution: By the above logic, we can see that the reaction is most likely first order. It takes just under 75 s for the concentration to be cut in half for any concentration. Plot $\ln [N_2O_5]$ versus time. Since $ln[A]_t = -kt + ln[A]_0$, the negative of the slope will be the rate constant. The slope can be determined by measuring $\Delta y/\Delta x$ on the plot or by using functions, such as "add trendline" in Excel.

Thus the rate constant is $0.00780\ s^{-1}$ and the rate law is Rate = $0.00780\ s^{-1}[N_2O_5]$.

    Finally, use $ln[N_2O_5]_t = -kt + ln[N_2O_5]_0$, substitute in the values of $[N_2O_5]_0$, 250 s and k and rearrange to solve for $[N_2O_5]$ at 250 s. $ln[N_2O_5]_{250\,s} = -(0.00780\ s^{-1})(250\ s) + ln[1.000]_0$ then $[N_2O_5]_{250\,s} = e^{-1.95} = 0.142\ M$.

    Check: The units (none, s^{-1}, and M) are correct. The rate law is a common form. The plot was extremely linear, confirming first order kinetics. The rate constant is consistent with the units necessary to get rate as M/s and the magnitude is reasonable since we have a first order reaction. The $[N_2O_5]$ at 250 s is less than the value at 200 s.

47. **Given:** table of $[C_4H_8]$ versus time   **Find:** reaction order, k, and reaction rate when $[C_4H_8] = 0.25$ M

    Conceptual plan: **Look at the data and see if any common reaction orders can be eliminated. If the data does not show an equal concentration drop with time, then zero order can be eliminated. Look for changes in half life (compare time for concentration to drop to one half of any value). If the half life is not constant, then the first order can be eliminated. If the half life is getting longer as the concentration drops, this might suggest second order. Plot the data as indicated by the appropriate rate law. Determine k from the slope of the plot. Finally calculate the reaction rate when $[C_4H_8] = 0.25$ M by using the rate law.**

    Solution: By the above logic, we can see that the reaction is most likely first order. It takes about 60 s for the concentration to be cut in half for any concentration. Plot $\ln [C_4H_8]$ versus time. Since $ln[A]_t = -kt + ln[A]_0$, the negative of the slope will be the rate constant. The slope can be determined by measuring $\Delta y/\Delta x$ on the plot or by using functions, such as "add trendline" in Excel. Thus the rate constant is $0.0112\ s^{-1}$ and the rate law is Rate = $0.0112\ s^{-1}[C_4H_8]$.

    Finally, use Rate = $0.0112\ s^{-1}[C_4H_8]$, substitute in the values of $[C_4H_8]$. Rate = $0.0112\ s^{-1}[0.25\ M] = 2.8 \times 10^{-3}\ M\ s^{-1}$.

    Check: The units (none, s^{-1}, and $M\ s^{-1}$) are correct. The rate law is a common form. The plot was extremely linear, confirming first order kinetics. The rate constant is consistent with the units necessary to get rate as M/s and the magnitude is reasonable since we have a first order reaction. The rate when $[C_4H_8] = 0.25$ M s is consistent with the average rate using 90 s and 100 s.

441

48. **Given:** table of [A] versus time   **Find:** reaction order, k, and reaction rate when [A] = 0.10 M

Conceptual plan: **Look at the data and see if any common reaction orders can be eliminated. If the data does not show an equal concentration drop with time, then zero order can be eliminated. Look for changes in half life (compare time for concentration to drop to one half of any value). If the half life is not constant, then the first order can be eliminated. If the half life is getting longer as the concentration drops, this might suggest second order. Plot the data as indicated by the appropriate rate law. Determine k from the slope of the plot. Finally calculate the reaction rate when [A] = 0.10 M by using the rate law.**

Solution: By the above logic, we can see that the reaction is most likely zero order. There is a difference of about 0.085 M between each data point, so the rate is independent of the [A]. Plot [A] versus time. Since $[A]_t = -kt + [A]_0$, the negative of the slope will be the rate constant. The slope can be determined by measuring $\Delta y/\Delta x$ on the plot or by using functions, such as "add trendline" in Excel. Thus the rate constant is 3.41 x 10^{-3} M s^{-1} and the rate law is Rate = 3.41×10^{-3} M s^{-1}. Finally, since the rate is independent of concentration,

Rate = 3.41×10^{-3} M s^{-1} at 0.10 M and all other concentrations.

$y = -0.00341x + 0.99960$

NOTE: A plot is not necessary since the kinetics are so simple.

Check: The units (none, M s^{-1}, and M s^{-1}) are correct. The rate law is a common form. The plot was extremely linear, confirming zero order kinetics. The rate constant is consistent with the units necessary to get rate as M/s and the magnitude is reasonable since we have a zero order reaction. The rate is the same as any average rate that can be calculated using the data.

49. **Given:** plot of ln [A] versus time has slope = - 0.0045/s; $[A]_0$ = 0.250 M

  Find: a) k; b) rate law; c) $t_{1/2}$; and d) [A] after 225 s

Conceptual plan:

a) **A plot of ln [A] versus time is linear for a first order reaction. Using $ln[A]_t = -kt + ln[A]_0$, the rate constant is the negative of the slope.**

b) **Rate law is first order. Add rate constant from part a).**

c) **For a first order reaction, $t_{1/2} = \dfrac{0.693}{k}$. Substitute in k from part a).**

d) **Use the integrated rate law, $ln[A]_t = -kt + ln[A]_0$, and substitute in k and the initial concentration.**

Solution:

a) Since the rate constant is the negative of the slope, $k = 4.5 \times 10^{-3}$ s^{-1}.

b) Since the reaction is first order, Rate = 4.5×10^{-3} s^{-1} [A].

c) $t_{1/2} = \dfrac{0.693}{k} = \dfrac{0.693}{0.0045/s} = 1.5 \times 10^2$ s.

d) $ln[A]_t = -kt + ln[A]_0$, and substitute in k and the initial concentration. So

$ln[A]_t = -(0.0045/s)\,(225\ s) + ln\ 0.250\ M = -\ 2.39879$ and $[A]_{250s} = e^{-2.39879} = 0.0908$ M

Check: The units (s^{-1}, none, s, and M) are correct. The rate law is a common form. The rate constant is consistent with value of the slope. The half life is consistent with a small value of k. The concentration at 225 s is consistent with being between one and two half lives.

50. **Given:** plot of 1/[AB] versus time has slope = 0.055/M s; $[A]_0$ = 0.250 M

  Find: a) k; b) rate law; c) $t_{1/2}$ when $[AB]_0$ = 0.55 M; and d) [A] and [B] after 75 s

Conceptual plan:

a) **A plot of 1/[AB] versus time is linear for a second order reaction. Using $\dfrac{1}{[AB]_t} = kt + \dfrac{1}{[AB]_0}$, the rate constant is the slope.**

b) **Rate law is second order. Add rate constant from part a).**

c) **For a second order reaction, $t_{1/2} = \dfrac{1}{k[AB]_0}$. Substitute in k from part a).**

442

d) Use the integrated rate law, $\dfrac{1}{[AB]_t} = kt + \dfrac{1}{[AB]_0}$, and substitute in k, t and the initial concentration

to get the [AB]. then $[AB]_0, [AB] \rightarrow [A], [B]$.

$$\Delta[AB] = [AB]_{0s} - [AB]_{75s} \quad \text{with} \quad \frac{1 \text{ mol A}}{1 \text{ mol AB}} \quad \text{and} \quad \frac{1 \text{ mol B}}{1 \text{ mol AB}}$$

Solution:

a) Since the rate constant is the slope, $k = 5.5 \times 10^{-2} \text{ M}^{-1} \text{ s}^{-1}$.

b) Since the reaction is second order, Rate $= 5.5 \times 10^{-2} \text{ M}^{-1} \text{ s}^{-1} [AB]^2$.

c) $t_{1/2} = \dfrac{1}{k[AB]_0}$ so $t_{1/2} = \dfrac{1}{(5.5 \times 10^{-2} \cancel{\text{M}^{-1}} \cancel{\text{s}^{-1}}) (0.550 \cancel{\text{M}})} = 33$ s .

d) $\dfrac{1}{[AB]_t} = kt + \dfrac{1}{[AB]_0}$ so $[AB]_t = \dfrac{1}{kt + \dfrac{1}{[AB]_0}} = \dfrac{1}{(5.5 \times 10^{-2} \text{ M}^{-1} \cancel{\text{s}^{-1}}) (75 \cancel{\text{s}}) + \left(\dfrac{1}{0.250 \text{ M}}\right)} = 0.1\underline{2}308$ M then

$\Delta[AB] = [AB]_{0s} - [AB]_{75s} = 0.250$ M $- 0.1\underline{2}308$ M $= 0.1\underline{2}692$ M AB so

$0.1\underline{2}692 \, \dfrac{\cancel{\text{mol AB}}}{\text{L}} \times \dfrac{1 \text{ mol A}}{1 \cancel{\text{ mol AB}}} = 0.13$ M A and $0.1\underline{2}692 \, \dfrac{\cancel{\text{mol AB}}}{\text{L}} \times \dfrac{1 \text{ mol B}}{1 \cancel{\text{ mol AB}}} = 0.13$ M B .

Check: The units ($\text{M}^{-1} \text{ s}^{-1}$, none, s, and M) are correct. The rate law is a common form. The rate constant is consistent with value of the slope. The half life is consistent with a small value of k. The concentration at 75 s is consistent with being about one half life.

51. **Given:** decomposition of SO_2Cl_2, first order; $k = 1.4 \times 10^{-4} \text{ s}^{-1}$
    Find: a) $t_{1/2}$; b) t to decrease to 25 % of $[SO_2Cl_2]_0$; c) t to 0.78 M when $[SO_2Cl_2]_0 = 1.00$ M; and d) $[SO_2Cl_2]$
    after 2.00×10^2 s and 5.00×10^2 s when $[SO_2Cl_2]_0 = 0.150$ M
    Conceptual plan:
    a) $k \rightarrow t_{1/2}$
    $$t_{1/2} = \frac{0.693}{k}$$
    b) $[SO_2Cl_2]_0$, 25 % of $[SO_2Cl_2]_0$, $k \rightarrow$ t
    $$ln[A]_t = -kt + ln[A]_0$$
    c) $[SO_2Cl_2]_0$, $[SO_2Cl_2]_t$, $k \rightarrow$ t
    $$ln[A]_t = -kt + ln[A]_0$$
    d) $[SO_2Cl_2]_0$, t, $k \rightarrow [SO_2Cl_2]_t$
    $$ln[A]_t = -kt + ln[A]_0$$

Solution:

a) $t_{1/2} = \dfrac{0.693}{k} = \dfrac{0.693}{1.42 \times 10^{-4} \text{ s}^{-1}} = 4.88 \times 10^3$ s

b) $[SO_2Cl_2]_t = 0.25 \, [SO_2Cl_2]_0$. Since $ln[SO_2Cl_2]_t = -kt + ln[SO_2Cl_2]_0$ rearrange to solve for t

$t = -\dfrac{1}{k} \ln\dfrac{[SO_2Cl_2]_t}{[SO_2Cl_2]_0} = -\dfrac{1}{1.42 \times 10^{-4} \text{ s}^{-1}} \ln\dfrac{0.25 \, \cancel{[SO_2Cl_2]_0}}{\cancel{[SO_2Cl_2]_0}} = 9.8 \times 10^3$ s

c) $[SO_2Cl_2]_t = 0.78$ M; $[SO_2Cl_2]_0 = 1.00$ M. Since $ln[SO_2Cl_2]_t = -kt + ln[SO_2Cl_2]_0$ rearrange to solve

for t $\quad t = -\dfrac{1}{k} \ln\dfrac{[SO_2Cl_2]_t}{[SO_2Cl_2]_0} = -\dfrac{1}{1.42 \times 10^{-4} \text{ s}^{-1}} \ln\dfrac{0.78 \, \cancel{\text{M}}}{1.00 \, \cancel{\text{M}}} = 1.8 \times 10^3$ s

d) $[SO_2Cl_2]_0 = 0.150$ M and 2.00×10^2 s in

$ln[SO_2Cl_2]_t = -\left(1.42 \times 10^{-4} \cancel{\text{s}^{-1}}\right)\left(2.00 \times 10^2 \cancel{\text{s}}\right) + \ln 0.150$ M $= -1.9\underline{2}552 \rightarrow$

$[SO_2Cl_2]_t = e^{-1.92552} = 0.146$ M and $[SO_2Cl_2]_0 = 0.150$ M and 5.00×10^2 s in

$ln[SO_2Cl_2]_t = -\left(1.42 \times 10^{-4}\ s^{-1}\right)\left(5.00 \times 10^2\ s\right) + \ln 0.150\ M = -1.9\underline{6}812$ → $[SO_2Cl_2]_t = e^{-1.96812} = 0.140\ M$

Check: The units (s, s, s, and M) are correct. The rate law is a common form. The half life is consistent with a small value of k. The time to 25% is consistent with two half lives. The time to 0.78 M is consistent with being less than one half life. The final concentrations are consistent with the time being less than one half life.

52. **Given:** decomposition of XY, second order in XY; $k = 7.02 \times 10^{-3}\ M^{-1} s^{-1}$
Find: a) $t_{1/2}$ when $[XY]_0 = 0.100\ M$; b) t to decrease to 12.5 % of $[XY]_0 = 0.100\ M$ and 0.200 M; c) t to 0.062 M when $[XY]_0 = 0.150\ M$; and d) $[XY]$ after 5.0×10^1 s and 5.50×10^2 s when $[XY]_0 = 0.050\ M$
Conceptual plan:
a) $[XY]_0, k$ → $t_{1/2}$

$$t_{1/2} = \frac{1}{k[A]_0}$$

b) $[XY]_0$, 12.5 % of $[XY]_0, k$ → t

$$\frac{1}{[A]_t} = kt + \frac{1}{[A]_0}$$

c) $[XY]_0, [XY]_t, k$ → t

$$\frac{1}{[A]_t} = kt + \frac{1}{[A]_0}$$

d) $[XY]_0, t, k$ → $[XY]_t$

$$\frac{1}{[A]_t} = kt + \frac{1}{[A]_0}$$

Solution:

a) $t_{1/2} = \dfrac{1}{k[XY]_0} = \dfrac{1}{(7.02 \times 10^{-3}\ M^{-1} s^{-1})(0.100\ M)} = 1.42 \times 10^3\ s$

b) $[XY]_t = 0.125\ [XY]_0 = 0.125 \times 0.100\ M = 0.0125\ M$. Since $\dfrac{1}{[XY]_t} = kt + \dfrac{1}{[XY]_0}$ rearrange to solve for t

$t = \dfrac{1}{k}\left(\dfrac{1}{[XY]_t} - \dfrac{1}{[XY]_0}\right) = \dfrac{1}{(7.02 \times 10^{-3}\ M^{-1} s^{-1})}\left(\dfrac{1}{0.0125\ M} - \dfrac{1}{0.100\ M}\right) = 9.97 \times 10^3\ s$ and

$[XY]_t = 0.125\ [XY]_0 = 0.125 \times 0.200\ M = 0.0250\ M$. Since $\dfrac{1}{[XY]_t} = kt + \dfrac{1}{[XY]_0}$ rearrange to solve for t

$t = \dfrac{1}{k}\left(\dfrac{1}{[XY]_t} - \dfrac{1}{[XY]_0}\right) = \dfrac{1}{(7.02 \times 10^{-3}\ M^{-1} s^{-1})}\left(\dfrac{1}{0.0250\ M} - \dfrac{1}{0.200\ M}\right) = 4.99 \times 10^3\ s$

c) $[XY]_t = 0.062$; $[XY]_0 = 0.150\ M$. Since $\dfrac{1}{[XY]_t} = kt + \dfrac{1}{[XY]_0}$ rearrange to solve for t

$t = \dfrac{1}{k}\left(\dfrac{1}{[XY]_t} - \dfrac{1}{[XY]_0}\right) = \dfrac{1}{(7.02 \times 10^{-3}\ M^{-1} s^{-1})}\left(\dfrac{1}{0.062\ M} - \dfrac{1}{0.150\ M}\right) = 1.3 \times 10^3\ s$

c) $[XY]_0 = 0.050\ M$ and 5.0×10^1 s in $\dfrac{1}{[XY]_t} = kt + \dfrac{1}{[XY]_0}$ →

$\dfrac{1}{[XY]_t} = (7.02 \times 10^{-3}\ M^{-1} s^{-1})(5.0 \times 10^1\ s) + \dfrac{1}{0.050\ M} = \dfrac{20.351}{M}$ so $[XY] = 0.049\ M$ and

$[XY]_0 = 0.050\ M$ and 5.50×10^2 s in $\dfrac{1}{[XY]_t} = (7.02 \times 10^{-3}\ M^{-1} s^{-1})(5.50 \times 10^2\ s) + \dfrac{1}{0.050\ M} = \dfrac{23.\underline{8}61}{M}$

so $[XY] = 0.042\ M$.

Check: The units (s, s, s, s, M and M) are correct. The rate law is a common form. The half life is consistent with a small value of k. The time to 12.5 % is consistent with three half lives, where the half life time is increasing. The next time (5000 s) is shorter because the initial concentration is higher. The last time is the shortest because it is less than a half life with an intermediate concentration. The final concentrations are consistent with the time being much less than one half life.

53. **Given:** $t_{1/2}$ for radioactive decay of U-238 = 4.5 billion years and independent of $[U\text{-}238]_0$ **Find:** t to decrease by 10 %; number U-238 atoms today, when 1.5×10^{18} atoms formed 13.8 billion years ago
    Conceptual plan: $t_{1/2}$ independent of concentration implies first order kinetics, $t_{1/2} \rightarrow k$ then

$$t_{1/2} = \frac{0.693}{k}$$

90 % of $[U\text{-}238]_0, k \rightarrow t$ and $[U\text{-}238]_0, t, k \rightarrow$ $[U\text{-}238]_t$
  $ln[A]_t = -kt + ln[A]_0$ $ln[A]_t = -kt + ln[A]_0$

Solution: $t_{1/2} = \dfrac{0.693}{k}$ rearrange to solve for k. $k = \dfrac{0.693}{t_{1/2}} = \dfrac{0.693}{4.5 \times 10^9 \text{ yr}} = 1.\underline{5}4 \times 10^{-10} \text{ yr}^{-1}$ then

$[U\text{-}238]_t = 0.10 \, [U\text{-}238]_0$. Since $ln[U\text{-}238]_t = -kt + ln[U\text{-}238]_0$ rearrange to solve for t

$t = -\dfrac{1}{k} \, ln\dfrac{[U\text{-}238]_t}{[U\text{-}238]_0} = -\dfrac{1}{1.\underline{5}4 \times 10^{-10} \text{ yr}^{-1}} \, ln\dfrac{0.90 \; \cancel{[U\text{-}238]_0}}{\cancel{[U\text{-}238]_0}} = 6.8 \times 10^8 \text{ yr}$ and $[U\text{-}238]_0 = 1.5 \times 10^{18}$ atoms;

$t = 13.8 \times 10^9$ yr in

$ln[U\text{-}238]_t = -kt + ln[U\text{-}238]_0 = -(1.\underline{5}4 \times 10^{-10} \; \cancel{\text{yr}^{-1}})(13.8 \times 10^9 \; \cancel{\text{yr}}) + ln\left(1.5 \times 10^{18} \text{ atoms}\right) = 39.7\underline{2}6797$ $\rightarrow$

$[U\text{-}238]_t = e^{39.726797} = 1.8 \times 10^{17}$ atoms

Check: The units (yr and atoms) are correct. The time to 10 % decay is consistent with less than one half life. The final concentration is consistent with the time being about three half lives.

54. **Given:** $t_{1/2}$ for radioactive decay of C-14 = 5730 years
    Find: t to decrease by 25 %; mmol C-14 atoms left, after 2255 yr in sample initially contains 1.5 mmol C-14
    Conceptual plan: radioactive decay implies first order kinetics, $t_{1/2} \rightarrow k$ then

$$t_{1/2} = \frac{0.693}{k}$$

75 % of $[C\text{-}14]_0, k \rightarrow t$ and $[C\text{-}14]_0, t, k \rightarrow$ $[C\text{-}14]_t$
  $ln[A]_t = -kt + ln[A]_0$ $ln[A]_t = -kt + ln[A]_0$

Solution: $t_{1/2} = \dfrac{0.693}{k}$ rearrange to solve for k. $k = \dfrac{0.693}{t_{1/2}} = \dfrac{0.693}{5730 \text{ yr}} = 1.2\underline{0}942 \times 10^{-4} \text{ yr}^{-1}$ then

$[C\text{-}14]_t = 0.75 \, [C\text{-}14]_0$. Since $ln[C\text{-}14]_t = -kt + ln[C\text{-}14]_0$ rearrange to solve for t

$t = -\dfrac{1}{k} \, ln\dfrac{[C\text{-}14]_t}{[C\text{-}14]_0} = -\dfrac{1}{1.2\underline{0}942 \times 10^{-4} \text{ yr}^{-1}} \, ln\dfrac{0.75 \; \cancel{[C\text{-}14]_0}}{\cancel{[C\text{-}14]_0}} = 2.4 \times 10^3 \text{ yr}$ and $[C\text{-}14]_0 = 1.5$ mmol;

$t = 2255$ yr in $ln[C\text{-}14]_t = -kt + ln[C\text{-}14]_0 = -(1.2\underline{0}942 \times 10^{-4} \; \cancel{\text{yr}^{-1}})(2255 \; \cancel{\text{yr}}) + ln\left(1.5 \text{ mmol}\right) = 0.13\underline{2}741$ $\rightarrow$

$[C\text{-}14]_t = e^{0.132741} = 1.1$ mmol

Check: The units (yr and mmol) are correct. The time to 25 % decay is consistent with less than one half life. The final concentration is consistent with the time being less than one half life.

55.

56.

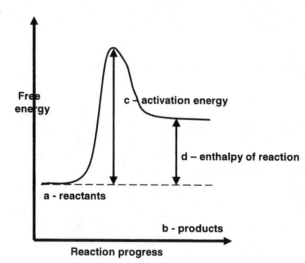

57. **Given:** activation energy = 56.8 kJ/mol, frequency factor = 1.5×10^{11} /s, 25 °C   **Find:** rate constant

Conceptual plan: °C $\rightarrow$ K   and   kJ/mol $\rightarrow$ J/mol   then $E_a, T, A \rightarrow k$

$$K = °C + 273.15 \qquad \frac{1000\ J}{1\ kJ} \qquad k = A\ e^{-E_a/RT}$$

Solution: $T = 25°C + 273.15 = 298$ K and $\dfrac{56.8\ \cancel{kJ}}{mol} \times \dfrac{1000\ J}{1\ \cancel{kJ}} = 5.68 \times 10^4\ \dfrac{J}{mol}$ then

$$k = A\ e^{-E_a/RT} = (1.5 \times 10^{11}\ s^{-1})\ e^{\left(\frac{-5.68\,\times\,10^4\ \frac{\cancel{J}}{\cancel{mol}}}{8.314\,\frac{\cancel{J}}{K\,\cancel{mol}}\,298\,\cancel{K}}\right)} = 17\ s^{-1}$$

Check: The units (s^{-1}) are correct.   The rate constant is consistent with a large activation energy and a large frequency factor.

58. **Given:** 32 °C, rate constant = 0.055/s, and frequency factor = 1.2×10^{13} /s   **Find:** activation energy

Conceptual plan: °C $\rightarrow$ K   then $E_a, T, A \rightarrow k$ then   J/mol $\rightarrow$ kJ/mol

$$K = °C + 273.15 \qquad\qquad k = A\ e^{-E_a/RT} \qquad\qquad \frac{1\ kJ}{1000\ J}$$

Solution: $T = 32°C + 273.15 = 305$ K then $k = A\ e^{-E_a/RT}$ Rearrange to solve for E_a.

$$E_a = -RT \ln\left(\frac{k}{A}\right) = -8.314\,\frac{J}{K\,mol} \times 305\,\cancel{K} \times \ln\left(\frac{0.055\ \cancel{s^{-1}}}{1.2 \times 10^{13}\ \cancel{s^{-1}}}\right) = 8.37 \times 10^4\ \frac{\cancel{J}}{mol} \times \frac{1\ kJ}{1000\ \cancel{J}} = 83.7\ \frac{kJ}{mol}\ .$$

446

Check: The units (kJ/mol) are correct. The activation energy is consistent with a modest rate constant and a large frequency factor.

59. **Given:** table of rate constant versus T   **Find:** E_a, and A

Conceptual plan: Since $\ln k = \dfrac{-E_a}{R}\left(\dfrac{1}{T}\right) + \ln A$ **a plot of ln k versus 1/T will have a slope = -E_a/R and an intercept = ln A.**

Solution: The slope can be determined by measuring $\Delta y/\Delta x$ on the plot or by using functions, such as "add trendline" in Excel. Since the slope = - 30189 K = -E_a/R then

$E_a = -(slope)R =$

$-(-30189 \text{ K})\left(8.314 \dfrac{\text{J}}{\text{K mol}}\right)\left(\dfrac{1 \text{ kJ}}{1000 \text{ J}}\right) =$

$= 251 \dfrac{\text{kJ}}{\text{mol}}$

and intercept = 27.399 = ln A then
$A = e^{intercept} = e^{27.399} = 7.93 \times 10^{11} \text{ s}^{-1}$.

Check: The units (kJ/mol and s^{-1}) are correct. The plot was extremely linear, confirming Arrhenius behavior. The activation and frequency factor are typical form many reactions.

60. **Given:** table of rate constant versus T   **Find:** E_a, and A

Conceptual plan: Since $\ln k = \dfrac{-E_a}{R}\left(\dfrac{1}{T}\right) + \ln A$ **a plot of ln k versus 1/T will have a slope = -E_a/R and an intercept = ln A.**

Solution: The slope can be determined by measuring $\Delta y/\Delta x$ on the plot or by using functions, such as "add trendline" in Excel. Since the slope = - 10283 K = -E_a/R then

$E_a = -(slope)R =$

$= -(-10283 \text{ K})\left(8.314 \dfrac{\text{J}}{\text{K mol}}\right)\left(\dfrac{1 \text{ kJ}}{1000 \text{ J}}\right)$

$= 85.5 \dfrac{\text{kJ}}{\text{mol}}$

and intercept = 29.967 = ln A then
$A = e^{intercept} = e^{29.967} = 1.03 \times 10^{13} \text{ s}^{-1}$.

Check: The units (kJ/mol and s^{-1}) are correct. The plot was extremely linear, confirming Arrhenius behavior. The activation and frequency factor are typical form many reactions.

61. **Given:** table of rate constant versus T   **Find:** E_a, and A

Conceptual plan: Since $\ln k = \dfrac{-E_a}{R}\left(\dfrac{1}{T}\right) + \ln A$ **a plot of ln k versus 1/T will have a slope = -E_a/R and an intercept = ln A.**

Solution: The slope can be determined by measuring $\Delta y/\Delta x$ on the plot or by using functions, such as "add trendline" in Excel. Since the slope = - 2767.2 K = -E_a/R then

$E_a = -(slope)R =$

$= -(-2767.2 \text{ K})\left(8.314 \dfrac{\text{J}}{\text{K mol}}\right)\left(\dfrac{1 \text{ kJ}}{1000 \text{ J}}\right) =$

$= 23.0 \dfrac{\text{kJ}}{\text{mol}}$

and intercept = 25.112 = ln A then

$A = e^{\text{int}ercept} = e^{25.112} = 8.05 \times 10^{10} \text{ s}^{-1}$.

Check: The units (kJ/mol and s^{-1}) are correct. The plot was extremely linear, confirming Arrhenius behavior. The activation and frequency factor are typical form many reactions.

62. **Given**: table of rate constant versus T **Find**: E_a, and A

Conceptual plan: Since $\ln k = \dfrac{-E_a}{R}\left(\dfrac{1}{T}\right) + \ln A$ **a plot of ln k versus 1/T will have a slope = -E$_a$/R and an intercept = ln A.**

Solution: The slope can be determined by measuring $\Delta y/\Delta x$ on the plot or by using functions, such as "add trendline" in Excel. Since the slope = - 11$\underline{6}$24 K = -E$_a$/R then
$E_a = -(slope)R =$

$y = -11624x + 32.055$

$= - (-11\underline{6}24 \text{ K})\left(8.314 \dfrac{\text{J}}{\text{K mol}}\right)\left(\dfrac{1 \text{ kJ}}{1000 \text{ J}}\right)$

$= 96.6 \dfrac{\text{kJ}}{\text{mol}}$

and intercept = 32.0$\underline{5}$5 = ln A then
$A = e^{\text{int}ercept} = e^{32.0\underline{5}5} = 8.34 \times 10^{13} \text{ s}^{-1}$.

Check: The units (kJ/mol and s^{-1}) are correct. The plot was extremely linear, confirming Arrhenius behavior. The activation and frequency factor are typical form many reactions.

63. **Given**: rate constant = 0.0117/s at 400. K, and 0.689/s at 450. K **Find**: a) E$_a$ and b) rate constant at 425 K

Conceptual plan: a) k_1, T$_1$, k_2, T$_2$ → E$_a$ then J/mol → kJ/mol b) E$_a$, k_1, T$_1$, T$_2$ → k_2

$\ln\left(\dfrac{k_2}{k_1}\right) = \dfrac{E_a}{R}\left(\dfrac{1}{T_1} - \dfrac{1}{T_2}\right)$ $\dfrac{1 \text{ kJ}}{1000 \text{ J}}$ $\ln\left(\dfrac{k_2}{k_1}\right) = \dfrac{E_a}{R}\left(\dfrac{1}{T_1} - \dfrac{1}{T_2}\right)$

Solution: $\ln\left(\dfrac{k_2}{k_1}\right) = \dfrac{E_a}{R}\left(\dfrac{1}{T_1} - \dfrac{1}{T_2}\right)$ Rearrange to solve for E$_a$.

$E_a = \dfrac{R \ln\left(\dfrac{k_2}{k_1}\right)}{\left(\dfrac{1}{T_1} - \dfrac{1}{T_2}\right)} = \dfrac{8.314 \dfrac{\text{J}}{\text{K mol}} \ln\left(\dfrac{0.689 \text{ s}^{-1}}{0.0117 \text{ s}^{-1}}\right)}{\left(\dfrac{1}{400. \text{ K}} - \dfrac{1}{450. \text{ K}}\right)} = 1.22 \times 10^5 \dfrac{\text{J}}{\text{mol}} \times \dfrac{1 \text{ kJ}}{1000 \text{ J}} = 122 \dfrac{\text{kJ}}{\text{mol}}$ and

$\ln\left(\dfrac{k_2}{k_1}\right) = \dfrac{E_a}{R}\left(\dfrac{1}{T_1} - \dfrac{1}{T_2}\right)$ with k_1, = 0.0117/s, T$_1$ = 400. K, T$_2$ = 425 K Rearrange to solve for k_2.

$\ln k_2 = \dfrac{E_a}{R}\left(\dfrac{1}{T_1} - \dfrac{1}{T_2}\right) + \ln k_1 = \dfrac{1.22 \times 10^5 \dfrac{\text{J}}{\text{mol}}}{8.314 \dfrac{\text{J}}{\text{K mol}}}\left(\dfrac{1}{400. \text{ K}} - \dfrac{1}{425 \text{ K}}\right) + \ln 0.0117 \text{ s}^{-1} = -2.29\underline{0}2$ →

$k_2 = e^{-2.29\underline{0}2} = 0.101 \text{ s}^{-1}$

Check: The units (kJ/mol and s^{-1}) are correct. The activation energy is typical for a reaction. The rate constant at 425 K is in between the values given at 400 K and 450 K.

64. **Given**: rate constant = 0.000122/s at 27 °C, and 0.228/s at 77 °C **Find**: a) E$_a$ and b) rate constant at 17 °C

Conceptual plan:
a) °C → K then k_1, T$_1$, k_2, T$_2$ → E$_a$ then J/mol → kJ/mol;

$K = °C + 273.15$ $\ln\left(\dfrac{k_2}{k_1}\right) = \dfrac{E_a}{R}\left(\dfrac{1}{T_1} - \dfrac{1}{T_2}\right)$ $\dfrac{1 \text{ kJ}}{1000 \text{ J}}$

b) °C → K then E$_a$, k_1, T$_1$, T$_2$ → k_2

$K = °C + 273.15$ $\ln\left(\dfrac{k_2}{k_1}\right) = \dfrac{E_a}{R}\left(\dfrac{1}{T_1} - \dfrac{1}{T_2}\right)$

Solution: $T_1 = 27°C + 273.15 = 300.$ K and $T_2 = 77°C + 273.15 = 350.$ K then $\ln\left(\dfrac{k_2}{k_1}\right) = \dfrac{E_a}{R}\left(\dfrac{1}{T_1} - \dfrac{1}{T_2}\right)$

Rearrange to solve for E_a.

$$E_a = \frac{R\ln\left(\dfrac{k_2}{k_1}\right)}{\left(\dfrac{1}{T_1} - \dfrac{1}{T_2}\right)} = \frac{8.314\ \dfrac{\text{J}}{\text{K mol}}\ \ln\left(\dfrac{0.228\ \cancel{\text{s}^{-1}}}{0.000122\ \cancel{\text{s}^{-1}}}\right)}{\left(\dfrac{1}{300.\ \cancel{\text{K}}} - \dfrac{1}{350.\ \cancel{\text{K}}}\right)} = 1.32 \times 10^5\ \frac{\cancel{\text{J}}}{\text{mol}} \times \frac{1\ \text{kJ}}{1000\ \cancel{\text{J}}} = 132\ \frac{\text{kJ}}{\text{mol}}\ \text{ and}$$

$\ln\left(\dfrac{k_2}{k_1}\right) = \dfrac{E_a}{R}\left(\dfrac{1}{T_1} - \dfrac{1}{T_2}\right)$ with $k_1 = 0.000122/\text{s}$, $T_1 = 300.$ K, $T_2 = 17°C + 273.15 = 290.$ K

Rearrange to solve for k_2.

$$\ln k_2 = \frac{E_a}{R}\left(\frac{1}{T_1} - \frac{1}{T_2}\right) + \ln k_1 = \frac{1.32 \times 10^5\ \dfrac{\cancel{\text{J}}}{\text{mol}}}{8.314\ \dfrac{\text{J}}{\text{K mol}}}\left(\frac{1}{300.\ \cancel{\text{K}}} - \frac{1}{290.\ \cancel{\text{K}}}\right) + \ln 0.000122\ s^{-1} = -1.08\underline{2}98 \quad \rightarrow$$

$k_2 = e^{-1.08\underline{2}98} = 0.0000198\ s^{-1} = 1.98 \times 10^{-5}\ s^{-1}$

Check: The units (kJ/mol and s^{-1}) are correct. The activation energy is typical for a reaction. The rate constant at 17 °C is smaller than the values given at 27°C.

65. **Given:** rate constant doubles from at 10.0 °C to 20.0 °C   **Find:** E_a
Conceptual plan: °C $\rightarrow$ K   then $k_1, T_1, k_2, T_2 \rightarrow E_a$ then   J/mol $\rightarrow$ kJ/mol;
$$K = °C + 273.15 \qquad \ln\left(\frac{k_2}{k_1}\right) = \frac{E_a}{R}\left(\frac{1}{T_1} - \frac{1}{T_2}\right) \qquad \frac{1\ \text{kJ}}{1000\ \text{J}}$$
Solution: $T_1 = 10.0\ °C + 273.15 = 283.2$ K and $T_2 = 20.0\ °C + 273.15 = 293.2$ K and $k_2 = 2\ k_1$ then

$\ln\left(\dfrac{k_2}{k_1}\right) = \dfrac{E_a}{R}\left(\dfrac{1}{T_1} - \dfrac{1}{T_2}\right)$ Rearrange to solve for E_a.

$$E_a = \frac{R\ln\left(\dfrac{k_2}{k_1}\right)}{\left(\dfrac{1}{T_1} - \dfrac{1}{T_2}\right)} = \frac{8.314\ \dfrac{\text{J}}{\text{K mol}}\ \ln\left(\dfrac{2\ \cancel{k_1}}{\cancel{k_1}}\right)}{\left(\dfrac{1}{283.2\ \cancel{\text{K}}} - \dfrac{1}{293.2\ \cancel{\text{K}}}\right)} = 4.785 \times 10^4\ \frac{\cancel{\text{J}}}{\text{mol}} \times \frac{1\ \text{kJ}}{1000\ \cancel{\text{J}}} = 47.85\ \frac{\text{kJ}}{\text{mol}}$$

Check: The units (kJ/mol) are correct. The activation energy is typical for a reaction.

66. **Given:** rate constant triples from at 20.0 °C to 35.0 °C   **Find:** E_a
Conceptual plan: °C $\rightarrow$ K   then $k_1, T_1, k_2, T_2 \rightarrow E_a$ then   J/mol $\rightarrow$ kJ/mol;
$$K = °C + 273.15 \qquad \ln\left(\frac{k_2}{k_1}\right) = \frac{E_a}{R}\left(\frac{1}{T_1} - \frac{1}{T_2}\right) \qquad \frac{1\ \text{kJ}}{1000\ \text{J}}$$
Solution: $T_1 = 20.0\ °C + 273.15 = 293.2$ K and $T_2 = 35.0\ °C + 273.15 = 808.2$ K and $k_2 = 3\ k_1$ then

$\ln\left(\dfrac{k_2}{k_1}\right) = \dfrac{E_a}{R}\left(\dfrac{1}{T_1} - \dfrac{1}{T_2}\right)$ Rearrange to solve for E_a.

$$E_a = \frac{R\ln\left(\dfrac{k_2}{k_1}\right)}{\left(\dfrac{1}{T_1} - \dfrac{1}{T_2}\right)} = \frac{8.314\ \dfrac{\text{J}}{\text{K mol}}\ \ln\left(\dfrac{3\ \cancel{k_1}}{\cancel{k_1}}\right)}{\left(\dfrac{1}{293.2\ \cancel{\text{K}}} - \dfrac{1}{308.2\ \cancel{\text{K}}}\right)} = 5.502 \times 10^4\ \frac{\cancel{\text{J}}}{\text{mol}} \times \frac{1\ \text{kJ}}{1000\ \cancel{\text{J}}} = 55.02\ \frac{\text{kJ}}{\text{mol}}$$

Check: The units (kJ/mol) are correct. The activation energy is typical for a reaction.

67. Reaction would have the faster rate because the orientation factor, p, would be larger for this reaction since the reactants are symmetrical.

68. Reaction b would have the smaller orientation factor, because we area reacting an asymmetric molecule with a homonuclear diatomic molecule (symmetrical) and so the orientation is important. In reaction a both reacting species are symmetrical and so orientation is unimportant.

69. Since the first reaction is the slow step, it is the rate determining step. Using this first step to determine the rate law, Rate $= k_1$ $[AB]^2$. Since this is the observed rate law, this mechanism is consistent with the experimental data.

70. a) The reaction can not occur in a single step where in which X and Y collide, because the rate law would be Rate $= k$ $[X]$ $[Y]$. This is not consistent with the stated rate law of Rate $= k$ $[X]^2$ $[Y]$.

    b) Since the second step is the rate determining step, Rate $= k_3$ $[X_2]$ $[Y]$. X_2 is an intermediate, so its concentration can not appear in the rate law. Using the fast equilibrium in the first step, we see that $k_1[X]^2 = k_2$ $[X_2]$ or $[X_2] = \dfrac{k_1}{k_2}[X]^2$. Substituting this into the first rate expression we get that Rate $= \dfrac{k_3 k_1}{k_2}$ $[X]^2$ $[Y]$. Simplifying this expression we see Rate $= k$ $[X]^2$ $[Y]$, which is consistent with the experimentally derived rate law.

71. a) The overall reaction is the sum of the steps in the mechanism:

$$Cl_2 (g) \underset{k_2}{\overset{k_1}{\rightleftharpoons}} 2\,\cancel{Cl(g)}$$
$$\cancel{Cl(g)} + CHCl_3 (g) \xrightarrow{k_3} HCl (g) + \cancel{CCl_3 (g)}$$
$$\cancel{Cl(g)} + \cancel{CCl_3 (g)} \xrightarrow{k_4} CCl_4 (g)$$

$$Cl_2 (g) + CHCl_3 (g) \rightarrow HCl (g) + CCl_4 (g)$$

    b) The intermediates are the species that are generated by one step and consumed by other steps. These are a Cl (g) and CCl_3 (g).

    c) Since the second step is the rate determining step, Rate $= k_3$ $[Cl]$ $[CHCl_3]$. Since Cl is an intermediate, its concentration can not appear in the rate law. Using the fast equilibrium in the first step, we see that $k_1[Cl_2] = k_2$ $[Cl]^2$ or $[Cl] = \sqrt{\dfrac{k_1}{k_2}[Cl_2]}$. Substituting this into the first rate expression we get that Rate $= k_3 \sqrt{\dfrac{k_1}{k_2}}[Cl_2]^{1/2}[CHCl_3]$. Simplifying this expression we see Rate $= k$ $[Cl_2]^{1/2}$ $[CHCl_3]$.

72. a) The overall reaction is the sum of the steps in the mechanism:

$$NO_2 (g) + Cl_2 (g) \xrightarrow{k_1} ClNO_2 (g) + \cancel{Cl(g)}$$
$$NO_2 (g) + \cancel{Cl(g)} \xrightarrow{k_2} ClNO_2 (g)$$

$$2\,NO_2 (g) + Cl_2 (g) \rightarrow 2\,ClNO_2 (g)$$

    b) The intermediates are the species that are generated by one step and consumed by other steps. This is Cl (g).

    c) Since the first step is the rate determining step, Rate $= k_1$ $[NO_2]$ $[Cl_2]$. Since both of these species are reactants, this is the predicted rate law.

73. Heterogeneous catalysts require a large surface area because catalysis can only happen at the active sites on the surface. A greater surface area means greater opportunity for the substrate to react which results in a speedier reaction.

74.

The initial and final energies (reactants and products) remain the same. The activation energy drops. There are usually more steps in the reaction progress diagram.

75. Assume Rate ratio α k ratio (since concentration terms will cancel each other) and $k = A\,e^{-E_a/RT}$.
T = 25 °C + 273.15 = 298 K $E_{a1} = 1.25 \times 10^5$ J/mol and $E_{a2} = 5.5 \times 10^4$ J/mol. Ratio of rates will be

$$\frac{k_2}{k_1} = \frac{\cancel{A}\,e^{-E_{a2}/RT}}{\cancel{A}\,e^{-E_{a1}/RT}} = \frac{e^{\frac{-5.5\times10^4\frac{\cancel{J}}{\cancel{mol}}}{\left(8.314\frac{\cancel{J}}{K\,\cancel{mol}}\right)298\,\cancel{K}}}}{e^{\frac{-1.25\times10^5\frac{\cancel{J}}{\cancel{mol}}}{\left(8.314\frac{\cancel{J}}{K\,\cancel{mol}}\right)298\,\cancel{K}}}} = \frac{e^{-22.199}}{e^{-50.453}} = 10^{12}.$$

76. Assume Rate ratio α k ratio (since concentration terms will cancel each other) and $k = A\,e^{-E_a/RT}$.
T = 25 °C + 273.15 = 298 K. $E_{a1} = 1.25 \times 10^5$ J/mol and $E_{a2} = 5.5 \times 10^{54}$ J/mol. Ratio of rates will be

$$\frac{k_2}{k_1} = 10^6 = \frac{\cancel{A}\,e^{-E_{a2}/RT}}{\cancel{A}\,e^{-E_{a1}/RT}} = \frac{e^{\frac{-E_{a2}}{\left(8.314\frac{J}{K\,mol}\right)298\,\cancel{K}}}}{e^{\frac{-1.08\times10^5\frac{\cancel{J}}{\cancel{mol}}}{\left(8.314\frac{\cancel{J}}{K\,\cancel{mol}}\right)298\,\cancel{K}}}} = \frac{e^{\frac{-E_{a2}}{2.47756\times10^3\frac{J}{mol}}}}{1.17\times10^{-19}} \;\rightarrow\; e^{\frac{-E_{a2}}{2.4\underline{7}756\times10^3\frac{J}{mol}}} = 1.17\times10^{-13} \;\rightarrow$$

$$\frac{-E_{a2}}{2.4\underline{7}756\times10^3\frac{J}{mol}} = \ln(1.17\times10^{-13}) = -29.\underline{7}766 \;\rightarrow\; E_{a2} = 7.38\times10^4\frac{J}{mol} = 73.8\frac{J}{mol}.$$

77. **Given:** table of [CH$_3$CN] versus time **Find:** a) reaction order, k; b) $t_{1/2}$; and t for 90 % conversion
Conceptual plan: a and b) **Look at the data and see if any common reaction orders can be eliminated. If the data does not show an equal concentration drop with time, then zero order can be eliminated. Look for changes in the half life (compare time for concentration to drop to one half of any value). If the half life is not constant, then the first order can be eliminated. If the half life is getting longer as the concentration drops, this might suggest second order. Plot the data as indicated by the appropriate rate law or if it is first order and there is an obvious half life in the date, a plot is not necessary. Determine k from the slope of the plot (or using half life equation for first order). c) Finally calculate the time to 90 % conversion using the appropriate integrated rate equation.**
Solution: a and b) By the above logic, we can see that the reaction is first order. It takes 15.0 hr for the concentration to be cut in half for any concentration (1.000 M to 0.501 M; 0.794 M to 0.398 M; and 0.631

M to 0.316 M), so $t_{1/2}$ = 15.0 hr. Then use $t_{1/2} = \dfrac{0.693}{k}$ and rearrange to solve for k.

$$k = \frac{0.693}{t_{1/2}} = \frac{0.693}{15.0 \text{ hr}} = 0.0462 \text{ hr}^{-1}.$$

c) $[CH_3CN]_t = 0.10 \; [CH_3CN]_0$. Since $ln[CH_3CN]_t = -kt + ln[CH_3CN]_0$ rearrange to solve for t

$$t = -\frac{1}{k} \ln\frac{[CH_3CN]_t}{[CH_3CN]_0} = -\frac{1}{0.0462 \text{ hr}^{-1}} \ln\frac{0.10 \; [CH_3CN]_0}{[CH_3CN]_0} = 49.8 \text{ hr} .$$

Check: The units (none, hr^{-1}, hr, and hr) are correct. The rate law is a common form. The data showed a constant half life very clearly. The rate constant is consistent with the units necessary to get rate as M/s and the magnitude is reasonable since we have a first order reaction. The time to 90 % conversion is consistent with a time between three and four half lives.

78. **Given:** table of $[X_2Y]$ versus time
   Find: a) reaction order, k; b) $t_{1/2}$ at initial concentration; and [X] at 10.0 hr
   Conceptual plan: **a) Look at the data and see if any common reaction orders can be eliminated. If the data does not show an equal concentration drop with time, then zero order can be eliminated. Look for changes in the half life (compare time for concentration to drop to one half of any value). If the half life is not constant, then the first order can be eliminated. If the half life is getting longer as the concentration drops, this might suggest second order. Plot the data as indicated by the appropriate rate law. Determine k from the slope of the plot. b) Calculate the half life with the appropriate equation. c) Finally calculate the $[X_2Y]$ at 10.0 hr using the appropriate integrated rate expression and then convert this to a change in $[X_2Y]$ and then to [X] using the reaction stoichiometry.**
   Solution:
   a)   By the above logic, we can eliminate
        both the zero order and the first order
        reactions. (alternatively, you could
        make all three plots and only one should
        be linear.) This suggests that we
        should have a second order reaction.
        Plot $1/[X_2Y]$ versus time. Since

$$\frac{1}{[X_2Y]_t} = kt + \frac{1}{[X_2Y]_0}$$, the slope will be the

rate constant. The slope can be determined
by measuring $\Delta y/\Delta x$ on the plot or by using functions, such as "add trendline" in Excel. Thus the rate
constant is $1.6827 \text{ M}^{-1} \text{ hr}^{-1}$ and the rate law is Rate = $1.68 \text{ M}^{-1} \text{ hr}^{-1} [X_2Y]^2$.

b) $t_{1/2} = \dfrac{1}{k[X_2Y]_0}$ so $t_{1/2} = \dfrac{1}{(1.6827 \text{ M}^{-1} \text{ hr}^{-1})(0.100 \text{ M})} = 5.94 \text{ hr}$.

d)   Finally, use $\dfrac{1}{[X_2Y]_t} = kt + \dfrac{1}{[X_2Y]_0}$, substitute in the values of $[X_2Y]_0$, 10.0 hr and k and rearrange to
       solve for $[X_2Y]$ at 10.0 hr.

$$[X_2Y]_t = \frac{1}{kt + \dfrac{1}{[X_2Y]_0}} = \frac{1}{(1.6827 \text{ M}^{-1} \text{ hr}^{-1})(10.0 \text{ hr}) + \left(\dfrac{1}{0.100 \text{ M}}\right)} = 0.037\underline{2}759 \text{ M} \quad \text{then}$$

$\Delta [X_2Y] = [X_2Y]_0 - [X_2Y]_{10.0 \text{ hr}} = 0.100 \, M - 0.037\underline{2}759 \text{ M} = 0.06\underline{2}724 \text{ M}$ then

$$\frac{0.06\underline{2}724 \text{ mol } X_2Y}{L} \times \frac{2 \text{ mol } X}{1 \text{ mol } X_2Y} = 0.13 \text{ M } X .$$

Check: The units (none, M^{-1}hr^{-1}, hr, and M) are correct. The rate law is a common form. The plot was extremely linear, confirming second order kinetics. The rate constant is consistent with the units necessary to get rate as M/s and the magnitude is reasonable since we have a second order reaction.

The half life is consistent with the data table, which indicates that the half life is a little over 5 hr. The [X] at 10 hr s is consistent with the changes that we see in the data table through 5 hr.

79. **Given:** Rate $= k \dfrac{[A][C]^2}{[B]^{1/2}} = 0.0115$ M/s at certain initial concentrations of A, B and C; double A and C concentration and triple B concentration **Find:** reaction rate

Conceptual plan: $[A]_1, [B]_1, [C]_1, \text{Rate 1}, [A]_2, [B]_2, [C]_2 \rightarrow \text{Rate 2}$

$$\frac{\text{Rate 2}}{\text{Rate 1}} = \frac{k \dfrac{[A]_2 [C]_2^2}{[B]_2^{1/2}}}{k \dfrac{[A]_1 [C]_1^2}{[B]_1^{1/2}}}$$

Solution:

$$\frac{\text{Rate 2}}{\text{Rate 1}} = \frac{k \dfrac{[A]_2 [C]_2^2}{[B]_2^{1/2}}}{k \dfrac{[A]_1 [C]_1^2}{[B]_1^{1/2}}}$$ Rearrange to solve for Rate 2. $\text{Rate 2} = \dfrac{k \dfrac{[A]_2 [C]_2^2}{[B]_2^{1/2}}}{k \dfrac{[A]_1 [C]_1^2}{[B]_1^{1/2}}} \text{Rate 1}$ $[A]_2 = 2[A]_1, [B]_2 = 3[B]_1,$

$[C]_2 = 2[C]_1$ and Rate 1 = 0.0115 M/s so

$$\text{Rate 2} = \frac{\cancel{k} \dfrac{2[A]_1 (2[C]_1)^2}{(3[B]_1)^{1/2}}}{\cancel{k} \dfrac{[A]_1 [C]_1^2}{[B]_1^{1/2}}} 0.0115 \frac{M}{s} = \frac{2^3}{3^{1/2}} 0.0115 \frac{M}{s} = 0.0531 \frac{M}{s}$$

Check: The units (M s^{-1}) are correct. The should increase because we have a factor of 8 (2^3) divided by the square root of three.

80. **Given:** Rate $= k \dfrac{[O_3]^2}{[O_2]}$ initially 1.0 mol O_3, and 1.0 mol O_2, in 1.0 L

Find: fraction O_3 reacted when reaction rate cuts in half

Conceptual plan:

mol, L $\rightarrow$ M then $[O_3]_1, [O_2]_1, \text{Rate 1, Rate 2} \rightarrow [O_3]_2$ then $[O_3]_1, [O_3]_2 \rightarrow O_3$ fraction reacted

$$M = \frac{mol}{L} \qquad\qquad \frac{\text{Rate 2}}{\text{Rate 1}} = \frac{k \dfrac{[O_3]_2^2}{[O_2]_2}}{k \dfrac{[O_3]_1^2}{[O_2]_1}} \qquad O_3 \text{ fraction reacted} = \frac{[O_3]_1 - [O_3]_2}{[O_3]_1}$$

Solution: $M = \dfrac{mol}{L}$ so $[O_3]_1 = \dfrac{1.0 \text{ mol}}{1.0 \text{ L}} = 1.0$ M and $[O_2]_1 = \dfrac{1.0 \text{ mol}}{1.0 \text{ L}} = 1.0$ M. Rate 1 = 2 Rate 2. Let x = $\Delta[O_3]$

so $[O_3]_2 = [O_3]_1 - x$ and $[O_2]_2 = [O_2]_1 + 3/2$ x. Substitute values into $\dfrac{\text{Rate 2}}{\text{Rate 1}} = \dfrac{k \dfrac{[O_3]_2^2}{[O_2]_2}}{k \dfrac{[O_3]_1^2}{[O_2]_1}}$ and rearrange to

solve for x. $\dfrac{\text{Rate 2}}{2 \text{ Rate 2}} = \dfrac{\cancel{k} \dfrac{(1.0 \text{ M} - x)^2}{(1.0 \text{ M} + 3/2 \text{ x})}}{\cancel{k} \dfrac{(1.0 \text{ M})^2}{(1.0 \text{ M})}} \rightarrow 0.50 \text{ M} (1.0 \text{ M} + 3/2 \text{ x}) = (1.0 \text{ M} - x)^2 \rightarrow$

$0.50 + 0.75 \text{ x} = 1.0 - 2.0x + x^2 \rightarrow 0 = x^2 - 2.75x + 0.50$ solve with quadratic equation

$\left(x = \dfrac{-b \pm \sqrt{b^2 - 4ac}}{2a} \right)$. So

$$x = \frac{2.75 \pm \sqrt{(-2.75)^2 - (4)(1.0)(0.50)}}{2(1.0)} = \frac{2.75 \pm \sqrt{5.5625}}{2.0} = \frac{2.75 \pm 2.3585}{2.0} = 0.19575 \text{ M or } 2.55 \text{ M}$$ The answer

must be 0.19575 M because the other answer is larger than our initial concentration (and is, therefore,

impossible). O_3 *fraction reacted* $= \dfrac{[O_3]_1 - [O_3]_2}{[O_3]_1} = \dfrac{x}{[O_3]_1} = \dfrac{0.19575 \text{ M}}{1.0 \text{ M}} = 0.2$

Check: The units (M) are correct. The concentration is reasonable since there are two forces slowing down the reaction – 1) the decrease in the reactant and 2) the increase of the product (which appears in the rate law). The calculation can be double checked by substituting in the value of x and the resulting rate $= 0.5\,k$.

81. **Given:** N_2O_5 decomposes to NO_2 and O_2, first order in $[N_2O_5]$; $t_{1/2} = 2.81$ hr at 25 °C; $V = 1.5$ L, $P°_{N2O5} = 745$ torr **Find:** P_{O2} after 215 minutes

Conceptual plan:

Write a balanced reaction. then $t_{1/2} \rightarrow k$ **then** $°C \rightarrow K$ **and** **torr** $\rightarrow$ **atm then**

$\qquad N_2O_5 \rightarrow 2\,NO_2 + \frac{1}{2}\,O_2 \qquad t_{1/2} = \dfrac{0.693}{k} \qquad K = °C + 273.15 \qquad \dfrac{1 \text{ atm}}{760 \text{ torr}}$

$P°_{N2O5}$ **, V, T** $\rightarrow$ **n/V then min** $\rightarrow$ **hr** $[N_2O_5]_0, t, k \rightarrow [N_2O_5]_t$ **then** $[N_2O_5]_0, [N_2O_5]_t \rightarrow [O_2]_t$

$\qquad PV = nRT \qquad \dfrac{1 \text{ hr}}{60 \text{ min}} \qquad ln[A]_t = -kt + ln[A]_0 \qquad [O_2]_t = ([N_2O_5]_0 - [N_2O_5]_t) \times \dfrac{1/2 \text{ mol } O_2}{1 \text{ mol } N_2O_5}$

then $[O_2]_t$ **, V, T** $\rightarrow P°_{O2}$ **then finally** **atm** $\rightarrow$ **torr**

$\qquad PV = nRT \qquad \dfrac{760 \text{ torr}}{1 \text{ atm}}$

Solution: $t_{1/2} = \dfrac{0.693}{k}$ and rearrange to solve for k. $k = \dfrac{0.693}{t_{1/2}} = \dfrac{0.693}{2.81 \text{ hr}} = 0.246619 \text{ hr}^{-1}$. then

$T = 25$ °C $+ 273.15 = 298$ K. $745 \text{ torr} \times \dfrac{1 \text{ atm}}{760 \text{ torr}} = 0.980263$ atm then $PV = nRT$ Rearrange to solve

for n/V. $\dfrac{n}{V} = \dfrac{P}{RT} = \dfrac{0.980263 \text{ atm}}{0.08206 \dfrac{L \cdot atm}{K \cdot mol} \times 298 \text{ K}} = 0.0400862$ M then $215 \text{ min} \times \dfrac{1 \text{ hr}}{60 \text{ min}} = 3.58333$ hr .

Since $ln[N_2O_5]_t = -kt + ln[N_2O_5]_0 = -(0.246619 \text{ hr}^{-1})(3.58333 \text{ hr}) + ln(0.0400862 \text{ M}) = -4.10044 \rightarrow$

$[N_2O_5]_t = e^{-4.10044} = 0.0165653$ M then

$[O_2]_t = ([N_2O_5]_0 - [N_2O_5]_t) \times \dfrac{1/2 \text{ mol } O_2}{1 \text{ mol } N_2O_5} = (0.0400862\,\dfrac{\text{mol } N_2O_5}{L} - 0.0165653\,\dfrac{\text{mol } N_2O_5}{L}) \times \dfrac{1/2 \text{ mol } O_2}{1 \text{ mol } N_2O_5} =$

$= 0.0117605$ M O_2

then finally $PV = nRT$ rearrange to solve for P.

$P = \dfrac{n}{V}RT = 0.0117605\,\dfrac{\text{mol}}{L} \times 0.08206\,\dfrac{L \cdot atm}{K \cdot mol} \times 298 \text{ K} = 0.287589 \text{ atm} \times \dfrac{760 \text{ torr}}{1 \text{ atm}} = 219$ torr

Check: The units (torr) are correct. The pressure is reasonable because it must be less than one half of the original pressure.

82. **Given:** Cyclopropane (C_3H_6) reacts, first order in $[C_3H_6]$; $k = 5.87 \times 10^{-4}$ /s at 485 °C; $V = 2.5$ L, $P°_{C3H6} = 722$ torr **Find:** t to $P_{C3H6} = 100.0$ torr

Conceptual plan: **Since P α M we do not need to convert P to M.** $P°_{C3H6}, P_{C3H6}, k \rightarrow t$

$\qquad\qquad\qquad\qquad\qquad\qquad\qquad\qquad\qquad\qquad\qquad\qquad ln[A]_t = -kt + ln[A]_0$

Solution: $ln[C_3H_6]_t = -kt + ln[C_3H_6]_0$ rearrange to solve for t

$t = -\dfrac{1}{k}\,ln\dfrac{[C_3H_6]_t}{[C_3H_6]_0} = -\dfrac{1}{k}\,ln\dfrac{P_{C3H6}}{P°_{C3H60}} = -\dfrac{1}{5.87 \times 10^{-4}\text{ s}^{-1}}\,ln\dfrac{100.\text{ torr}}{722 \text{ torr}} = 3.37 \times 10^3 \text{ s} = 56.1$ min

Check: The units (s or min) are correct. The time is reasonable because it is about three half lives (pressure dropped to 14 % of original pressure).

83. **Given:** I_2 formation from I atoms, second order in I; $k = 1.5 \times 10^{10}$ M^{-1}s^{-1}, $[I]_0 = 0.0100$ M

454

Find: t to decrease by 95 %

Conceptual plan: $[I]_0, [I]_t, k \rightarrow t$

$$\frac{1}{[A]_t} = kt + \frac{1}{[A]_0}$$

Solution: $[I]_t = 0.05\,[I]_0 = 0.05 \times 0.0100\,M = 0.0005\,M$. Since $\frac{1}{[I]_t} = kt + \frac{1}{[I]_0}$ rearrange to solve for t

$$t = \frac{1}{k}\left(\frac{1}{[I]_t} - \frac{1}{[I]_0}\right) = \frac{1}{(1.5 \times 10^{10}\,M^{-1}s^{-1})}\left(\frac{1}{0.0005\,M} - \frac{1}{0.0100\,M}\right) = 1.267 \times 10^{-7}\,s = 1 \times 10^{-7}\,s\;.$$

Check: The units (s) are correct. We expect the time to be extremely small because the rate constant is so large.

84. **Given:** sucrose hydrolysis, first order in $[C_{12}H_{22}O_{11}]$; $k = 1.8 \times 10^{-4}\,s^{-1}$ at 25 °C; V = 2.55 L, $[C_{12}H_{22}O_{11}]_0 =$ 0.150 M, and 195 min **Find:** $m(C_{12}H_{22}O_{11})$ hydrolyzed

Conceptual plan: $min \rightarrow s$ then $[C_{12}H_{22}O_{11}]_0, t, k \rightarrow [C_{12}H_{22}O_{11}]_t$ then

$$\frac{60\,s}{1\,min} \qquad\qquad ln[A]_t = -kt + ln[A]_0$$

V, $[C_{12}H_{22}O_{11}]_0, [C_{12}H_{22}O_{11}]_t \rightarrow$ **mol** $C_{12}H_{22}O_{11}$ **hydrolyzed** $\rightarrow$ **g** $C_{12}H_{22}O_{11}$ **hydrolyzed**

$$mol\ C_{12}H_{22}O_{11} = ([C_{12}H_{22}O_{11}]_0 - [C_{12}H_{22}O_{11}]_t) \times V \qquad \frac{342.30\ g\ C_{12}H_{22}O_{11}}{1\ mol\ C_{12}H_{22}O_{11}}$$

Solution: $195\ min \times \dfrac{60\ sec}{1\ min} = 11700\ s$. Since

$$ln[C_{12}H_{22}O_{11}]_t = -kt + ln[C_{12}H_{22}O_{11}]_0 = -(1.8 \times 10^{-4}\,s^{-1})(11700\,s) + ln\,(0.150\,M) = -4.00312 \rightarrow$$

$$[C_{12}H_{22}O_{11}]_t = e^{-4.00312} = 0.0182585\,M \quad then$$

$$mol\ C_{12}H_{22}O_{11} = ([C_{12}H_{22}O_{11}]_0 - [C_{12}H_{22}O_{11}]_t) \times V = \left(0.150\ \frac{mol\ C_{12}H_{22}O_{11}}{L} - 0.0182585\ \frac{mol\ C_{12}H_{22}O_{11}}{L}\right) \times 2.55\ L =$$

$$= 0.335941\ mol\ C_{12}H_{22}O_{11}$$

$$0.335941\ mol\ C_{12}H_{22}O_{11} \times \frac{342.30\ g\ C_{12}H_{22}O_{11}}{1\ mol\ C_{12}H_{22}O_{11}} = 115\ g\ C_{12}H_{22}O_{11}\;.$$

Check: The units (g) are correct. The mass is reasonable because it must be less than the original amount in solution (131 g). The amount is close to the original amount in solution because the final sucrose concentration is so low, because we have gone over three half lives.

85. a) There are two elementary steps in the reaction mechanism because there are two peaks in the reaction progress diagram.

   b)

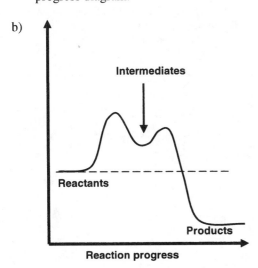

   c) The first step is the rate limiting step because it has the higher activation energy.

d) The overall reaction is exothermic because the products are at a lower energy than the reactants.

86. a) The first step is the rate limiting step because it has the higher activation energy.

b) Since the first step is the rate determining step, Rate = k_1 [HCl] [$H_2C=CH_2$]. The reaction will be second order overall.

c) The overall reaction is exothermic because the products are at a lower energy than the reactants.

87. **Given:** n-butane desorption from single crystal aluminum oxide, first order; $k = 0.128$ s^{-1} at 150 K; initially completely covered
Find: a) $t_{1/2}$; b) t for 25 % and for 50 % to desorb; c) fraction remaining after 10 s and 20 s
Conceptual plan: a) $k \rightarrow t_{1/2}$ b) $[C_4H_{10}]_0, [C_4H_{10}]_t, k \rightarrow t$ c) $[C_4H_{10}]_0, t, k \rightarrow [C_4H_{10}]_t$

$$t_{1/2} = \frac{0.693}{k}$$ $$ln[A]_t = -kt + ln[A]_0$$ $$ln[A]_t = -kt + ln[A]_0$$

Solution:

a) $t_{1/2} = \dfrac{0.693}{k} = \dfrac{0.693}{0.128 \text{ s}^{-1}} = 5.41 \text{ s}$.

b) $ln[C_4H_{10}]_t = -kt + ln[C_4H_{10}]_0$ rearrange to solve for t. For 25 % desorbed $[C_4H_{10}]_0 = 0.75 \, [C_4H_{10}]_t$

and $t = -\dfrac{1}{k} \ln \dfrac{[C_4H_{10}]_t}{[C_4H_{10}]_0} = -\dfrac{1}{0.128 \text{ s}^{-1}} \ln \dfrac{0.75 \, [C_4H_{10}]_0}{[C_4H_{10}]_0} = 2.2 \text{ s}$. For 50 % desorbed

$[C_4H_{10}]_0 = 0.50 \, [C_4H_{10}]_t$ and $t = -\dfrac{1}{k} \ln \dfrac{[C_4H_{10}]_t}{[C_4H_{10}]_0} = -\dfrac{1}{0.128 \text{ s}^{-1}} \ln \dfrac{0.50 \, [C_4H_{10}]_0}{[C_4H_{10}]_0} = 5.4 \text{ s}$.

c) For 10 s $ln[C_4H_{10}]_t = -kt + ln[C_4H_{10}]_0 = -(0.128 \text{ s}^{-1}) (10 \text{ s}) + \ln(1.00) = -1.28 \rightarrow$

$[C_4H_{10}]_t = e^{-1.28} = 0.28 = $ fraction covered   and for 20 s

$ln[C_4H_{10}]_t = -kt + ln[C_4H_{10}]_0 = -(0.128 \text{ s}^{-1}) (20 \text{ s}) + \ln(1.00) = -2.56 \rightarrow$

$[C_4H_{10}]_t = e^{-2.56} = 0.077 = $ fraction covered .

Check: The units (s, s, s, none, and none) are correct.   The half life is reasonable considering the size of the rate constant. The time to 25 % desorbed is less than one half life. The time to 50 % desorbed is the half life. The fraction at 10 s is consistent with about two half lives. The fraction covered at 20 s is consistent with about four half lives.

88. **Given:** 120 nm film n-pentane evaporation from single crystal aluminum oxide, zero order; $k = 1.92 \times 10^{13}$ molecules / cm^2 s at 120 K; initially coverage $= 8.9 \times 10^{16}$ molecules / cm^2
Find: a) $t_{1/2}$; b) fraction remaining after 10 s
Conceptual plan:
a) $[C_5H_{12}]_0, k \rightarrow t_{1/2}$

$$t_{1/2} = \frac{[A]_0}{2k}$$

b) $[C_5H_{12}]_0, t, k \rightarrow [C_5H_{12}]_t$ then $[C_5H_{12}]_0, [C_5H_{12}]_t \rightarrow$ **fraction remaining**

$$[A]_t = -kt + [A]_0$$ $$fraction \ remaining = \frac{[C_5H_{12}]_t}{[C_5H_{12}]_0}$$

Solution:

a) $t_{1/2} = \dfrac{[C_5H_{12}]_0}{2k} = \dfrac{8.9 \times 10^{16} \, \frac{\text{molecules}}{\text{cm}^2}}{2 \times 1.92 \times 10^{13} \, \frac{\text{molecules}}{\text{cm}^2 \text{ s}}} = 2.3 \times 10^3 \text{ s}$

b)

$$[C_5H_{12}]_t = -kt + [C_5H_{12}]_0 = -\left(1.92 \times 10^{13} \frac{molecules}{cm^2 \ s}\right)(10 \ s) + 8.9 \times 10^{16} \frac{molecules}{cm^2} = 8.\underline{8}808 \times 10^{16} \frac{molecules}{cm^2}$$

$$fraction \ remaining = \frac{[C_5H_{12}]_t}{[C_5H_{12}]_0} = \frac{8.\underline{8}808 \times 10^{16} \dfrac{molecules}{cm^2}}{8.9 \times 10^{16} \dfrac{molecules}{cm^2}} = 0.99\underline{7}84 = 1.0 \ \text{so within experimental error, all}$$

are remaining on the surface.

Check: The units (s and none) are correct. The half life is reasonable considering the size of the rate constant. The fraction at 10 s is the fact that the time is very, very small compared to the half life.

89. a) **Given:** table of rate constant versus T **Find:** E_a, and A

Conceptual plan: First convert temperature data into Kelvins (°C + 273.15 = K). Since $\ln k = \dfrac{-E_a}{R}\left(\dfrac{1}{T}\right) + \ln A$ **a plot of ln k versus 1/T will have a slope = -E_a/R and an intercept = ln A.**

Solution: The slope can be determined by measuring $\Delta y/\Delta x$ on the plot or by using functions, such as "add trendline" in Excel. Since the slope = $- 10\underline{7}59$ K $= - E_a$/R then

$$E_a = -(slope)R =$$

$$= -(-10\underline{7}59 \ K)\left(8.314 \frac{J}{K \ mol}\right)\left(\frac{1 \ kJ}{1000 \ J}\right)$$

$$= 89.5 \ \frac{kJ}{mol}$$

and intercept = $26.7\underline{6}9$ = ln A then

$$A = e^{int \ ercept} = e^{26.7\underline{6}9} = 4.22 \times 10^{11} \ s^{-1}.$$

Check: The units (kJ/mol and s^{-1}) are correct. The plot was extremely linear, confirming Arrhenius behavior. The activation and frequency factor are typical form many reactions.

b) **Given:** part a) results **Find:** k at 15 °C

Conceptual plan: °C → K then T, E_a, A → k

$$°C + 273.15 = K \qquad \ln k = \frac{-E_a}{R}\left(\frac{1}{T}\right) + \ln A$$

Solution: 15 °C + 273.15 = 288 K then

$$\ln k = \frac{-E_a}{R}\left(\frac{1}{T}\right) + \ln A = \frac{- 89.5 \frac{kJ}{mol} \times \frac{1000 \ J}{1 \ kJ} E_a}{8.314 \frac{J}{K \ mol}}\left(\frac{1}{288 \ K}\right) + \ln (4.22 \times 10^{11} \ s^{-1}) = -1\underline{0}.610 \ \rightarrow$$

$$k = e^{-1\underline{0}.610} = 2.5 \times 10^{-5} \ M^{-1} s^{-1}.$$

Check: The units (M^{-1} s^{-1}) are correct. The value of the rate constant is less than the value at 25 °C.

c) **Given:** part a) results, 0.155 M C_2H_5Br and 0.250 M OH$^-$ at 75 °C **Find:** initial reaction rate

Conceptual plan:
°C → K then T, E_a, A → k then k, [C_2H_5Br], [OH$^-$] → initial reaction rate

$$°C + 273.15 = K \qquad \ln k = \frac{-E_a}{R}\left(\frac{1}{T}\right) + \ln A \qquad \text{Rate} = k \ [C_2H_5Br] \ [OH^-]$$

Solution: 75 °C + 273.15 = 348 K then

$$\ln k = \frac{-E_a}{R}\left(\frac{1}{T}\right) + \ln A = \frac{- 89.5 \frac{kJ}{mol} \times \frac{1000 \ J}{1 \ kJ} E_a}{8.314 \frac{J}{K \ mol}}\left(\frac{1}{348 \ K}\right) + \ln (4.22 \times 10^{11} \ s^{-1}) = -4.\underline{1}656 \ \rightarrow$$

$$k = e^{-4.\underline{1}656} = 1.\underline{5}521 \times 10^{-2} \ M^{-1} s^{-1}.$$

Rate $= k$ [C_2H_5Br] [OH^-] = (1.5521 x 10^{-2} M^{-1} s^{-1}) (0.155 M) (0.250 M) = 6.0 x 10^{-4} M s^{-1}

Check: The units (M s^{-1}) are correct.   The value of the rate is reasonable considering the value of the rate constant (larger than in the table) and the fact that the concentrations are less than 1 M.

90. **Given:** $k = 2.35$ x 10^{-4} s^{-1} at 293 K and $k = 9.15$ x 10^{-4} s^{-1} at 303 K   **Find:** A
    Conceptual plan: °C $\rightarrow$ K   then k_1, T_1, k_2, T_2 $\rightarrow$ E_a then k_2, T_2, E_a $\rightarrow$ A

$$K = °C + 273.15 \qquad \ln k = \frac{-E_a}{R}\left(\frac{1}{T}\right) + \ln A \qquad k = A e^{-E_a/RT}$$

Solution: $T_1 = 293$ K, $k_1 = 2.35$ x 10^{-4} s^{-1}; and $T_2 = 303$ K   and $k_2 = 9.15$ x 10^{-4} s^{-1} then

$\ln\left(\dfrac{k_2}{k_1}\right) = \dfrac{E_a}{R}\left(\dfrac{1}{T_1} - \dfrac{1}{T_2}\right)$ Rearrange to solve for E_a.

$$E_a = \frac{R \ln\left(\dfrac{k_2}{k_1}\right)}{\left(\dfrac{1}{T_1} - \dfrac{1}{T_2}\right)} = \frac{8.314 \dfrac{J}{K\ mol} \ln\left(\dfrac{9.15 \times 10^{-4} s^{-1}}{2.35 \times 10^{-4} s^{-1}}\right)}{\left(\dfrac{1}{293 K} - \dfrac{1}{303 K}\right)} = 1.00334 \times 10^5 \frac{J}{mol}$$. Since $k = A e^{-E_a/RT}$ rearrange to

solve for A. $A = k e^{E_a/RT} = 9.15 \times 10^{-4} s^{-1}\ e^{\left(\frac{1.00334 \times 10^5 \frac{J}{mol}}{\left(8.314 \frac{J}{K\ mol}\right)303\ K}\right)} = 1.8 \times 10^{14}\ s^{-1}$.

Check: The units (s^{-1}) are correct.   The frequency factor is typical for a reaction.

91. a)   No, because the activation energy is zero. This means that the rate constant ($k = A e^{-E_a/RT}$) will be independent of temperature.

    b)   No bond is broken and the two radicals attract to each other.

    d)   Formation of diatomic gases from atomic gases.

92. a)   Nitrogen has a triple bond, so it will take more energy to break the N≡N bond than the H–H bond.

    b)   **Given:** $E_a = 315$ kJ/mol for reaction 1 and $E_a = 23$ kJ/mol for reaction 2; frequency factor similar; and 25 °C
       Find: ratio of rate constants
       Conceptual Plan: °C $\rightarrow$ K   then   T, E_a's, A $\rightarrow$ k_1/k_2

$$°C + 273.15 = K \qquad \frac{k_1}{k_2} = \frac{A e^{-E_{a1}/RT}}{A e^{-E_{a2}/RT}}$$

Solution: T = 25 °C + 273.15 = 298 K. E_{a1} = 315 kJ/mol and E_{a2} = 23 kJ/mol. Ratio of rate constants

will be $\dfrac{k_1}{k_2} = \dfrac{A e^{-E_{a1}/RT}}{A e^{-E_{a2}/RT}} = \dfrac{e^{\left(\frac{-315 \frac{kJ}{mol} \times \frac{1000 J}{1 kJ}}{8.314 \frac{J}{K\ mol} 298\ K}\right)}}{e^{\left(\frac{-23 \frac{kJ}{mol} \times \frac{1000 J}{1 kJ}}{8.314 \frac{J}{K\ mol} 298\ K}\right)}} = 6.5 \times 10^{-52}$.

    Check: The units (none) are correct. Since there is a large difference between the activations energies, we expect a large difference in the rate constants.

93. **Given:** $t_{1/2}$ for radioactive decay of C-14 = 5730 years; bone has 19.5 % C-14 in living bone
    Find: age of bone
    Conceptual plan:
    radioactive decay implies first order kinetics, $t_{1/2}$ $\rightarrow$ k then   19.5 % of [C-14]$_0$, k $\rightarrow$ t

$$t_{1/2} = \frac{0.693}{k} \qquad\qquad ln[A]_t = -kt + ln[A]_0$$

Solution: $t_{1/2} = \dfrac{0.693}{k}$ rearrange to solve for k. $k = \dfrac{0.693}{t_{1/2}} = \dfrac{0.693}{5730 \text{ yr}} = 1.20942 \times 10^{-4} \text{ yr}^{-1}$ then

$[\text{C-14}]_t = 0.195 \, [\text{C-14}]_0$. Since $ln[\text{C-14}]_t = -kt + ln[\text{C-14}]_0$ rearrange to solve for t

$t = -\dfrac{1}{k} \, ln\dfrac{[\text{C-14}]_t}{[\text{C-14}]_0} = -\dfrac{1}{1.20942 \times 10^{-4} \text{ yr}^{-1}} \, ln\dfrac{0.195 \, [\text{C-14}]_0}{[\text{C-14}]_0} = 1.35 \times 10^4 \text{ yr}$.

Check: The units (yr) are correct. The time to 19.5 % decay is consistent with the time being between two and three half lives.

94. **Given:** $t_{1/2}$ for radioactive decay of U-238 = 4.5 billion years; rock has 83.2 % of original U-238
Find: age of rock
Conceptual plan:
radioactive decay implies first order kinetics, $t_{1/2} \rightarrow k$ then   82.3 % of [U-238]$_0$, $k \rightarrow t$

$$t_{1/2} = \dfrac{0.693}{k} \qquad\qquad\qquad ln[\text{A}]_t = -kt + ln[\text{A}]_0$$

Solution: $t_{1/2} = \dfrac{0.693}{k}$ rearrange to solve for k. $k = \dfrac{0.693}{t_{1/2}} = \dfrac{0.693}{4.5 \times 10^9 \text{ yr}} = 1.54 \times 10^{-10} \text{ yr}^{-1}$ then

$[\text{U-238}]_t = 0.823 \, [\text{U-238}]_0$. Since $ln[\text{U-238}]_t = -kt + ln[\text{U-238}]_0$ rearrange to solve for t

$t = -\dfrac{1}{k} \, ln\dfrac{[\text{U-238}]_t}{[\text{U-238}]_0} = -\dfrac{1}{1.54 \times 10^{-10} \text{ yr}^{-1}} \, ln\dfrac{0.832 \, [\text{U-238}]_0}{[\text{U-238}]_0} = 1.19 \times 10^9 \text{ yr}$.

Check: The units (yr) are correct. The time to 82.3 % decay is consistent with the time being less than one half life.

95. a) For each, check that all steps sum to overall reaction and that the predicted rate law is consistent with experimental data (Rate = $k\,[\text{H}_2]\,[\text{I}_2]$).
For the first mechanism, the single step is the overall reaction. The rate law is determined by the stoichiometry, so Rate = $k\,[\text{H}_2]\,[\text{I}_2]$ and the mechanism is valid.
For the second mechanism, the overall reaction is the sum of the steps in the mechanism:

$$\text{I}_2\,(g) \underset{k_2}{\overset{k_1}{\rightleftharpoons}} 2\,\text{I}\,(g)$$

$$\text{H}_2\,(g) + 2\,\text{I}\,(g) \xrightarrow{k_3} 2\,\text{HI}\,(g)$$ So the sum matches the overall reaction.

$$\overline{\text{H}_2\,(g) + \text{I}_2\,(g) \rightarrow 2\,\text{HI}\,(g)}$$

Since the second step is the rate determining step, Rate = $k_3\,[\text{H}_2]\,[\text{I}]^2$. Since I is an intermediate, its concentration can not appear in the rate law. Using the fast equilibrium in the first step, we see that

$k_1[\text{I}_2] = k_2\,[\text{I}]^2$ or $[\text{I}]^2 = \dfrac{k_1}{k_2}\,[\text{I}_2]$. Substituting this into the first rate expression we get that

Rate = $k_3\dfrac{k_1}{k_2}\,[\text{H}_2]\,[\text{I}_2]$ and the mechanism is valid.

For the third mechanism, the overall reaction is the sum of the steps in the mechanism:

$$\text{I}_2\,(g) \underset{k_2}{\overset{k_1}{\rightleftharpoons}} 2\,\text{I}\,(g)$$

$$\text{H}_2\,(g) + \text{I}\,(g) \underset{k_4}{\overset{k_3}{\rightleftharpoons}} \text{H}_2\text{I}\,(g)$$ So the sum matches the overall reaction.

$$\overline{\text{H}_2\text{I}\,(g) + \text{I}\,(g) \xrightarrow{k_5} 2\,\text{HI}\,(g)}$$

$$\overline{\text{H}_2\,(g) + \text{I}_2\,(g) \rightarrow 2\,\text{HI}\,(g)}$$

Since the third step is the rate determining step, Rate = $k_5\,[\text{H}_2\text{I}]\,[\text{I}]$. Since H_2I and I are intermediates, their concentrations can not appear in the rate law. Using the fast equilibrium in the first step, we see that $k_1[\text{I}_2] = k_2\,[\text{I}]^2$ or $[\text{I}] = \sqrt{\dfrac{k_1}{k_2}[\text{I}_2]}$. Using the fast equilibrium in the second step, we see that $k_3[\text{H}_2]\,[\text{I}]$

$= k_4 [H_2I]$ or $[H_2I] = \dfrac{k_3}{k_4}[H_2][I]$. Substituting the both of these expressions for the intermediates into

the first rate expression we get that Rate $= k_5[H_2I][I] = k_5 \dfrac{k_3}{k_4}[H_2][I]\sqrt{\dfrac{k_1}{k_2}[I_2]}$. Substituting again for

[I] we get Rate $= k_5 \dfrac{k_3}{k_4}[H_2]\sqrt{\dfrac{k_1}{k_2}[I_2]}\sqrt{\dfrac{k_1}{k_2}[I_2]}$. Simplifying this expression we see

Rate $= k_5 \dfrac{k_3}{k_4}\dfrac{k_1}{k_2}[H_2][I_2]$ and the mechanism is valid.

b) To distinguish between mechanisms, you could look for the buildup of $I(g)$ and/or $H_2I(g)$, the intermediates.

96. a) The overall reaction is the sum of the steps in the mechanism:

$NH_3\ (aq) + OCl^-\ (aq) \underset{k_2}{\overset{k_1}{\rightleftharpoons}} \cancel{NH_2Cl(aq)} + \cancel{OH^-(aq)}$

$\cancel{NH_2Cl(aq)} + NH_3\ (aq) \xrightarrow{k_3} \cancel{N_2H_5^+(aq)} + Cl^-\ (aq)$

$\cancel{N_2H_5^+(aq)} + \cancel{OH^-(aq)} \xrightarrow{k_4} N_2H_4\ (aq) + H_2O\ (l)$ So the sum matches the overall reaction.

$\overline{2\,NH_3\ (aq) + OCl^-\ (aq) \rightarrow N_2H_4\ (aq) + H_2O\ (l) + Cl^-\ (aq)}$

b) Since the second step is the rate determining step, Rate $= k_3[NH_2Cl][NH_3]$. Since NH_2Cl is an intermediate, its concentration can not appear in the rate law. Using the fast equilibrium in the first step, we see that $k_1[NH_3][OCl^-] = k_2[NH_2Cl][OH^-]$ or $[NH_2Cl] = \dfrac{k_1}{k_2}\dfrac{[NH_3][OCl^-]}{[OH^-]}$. Substituting this

into the first rate expression we get that Rate $= k_3\dfrac{k_1}{k_2}\dfrac{[NH_3][OCl^-]}{[OH^-]}[NH_3]$ or Rate $= k_3\dfrac{k_1}{k_2}\dfrac{[NH_3]^2[OCl^-]}{[OH^-]}$.

97. a) For a zero order reaction, the rate is independent of the concentration. If the first half goes in the first 100 s, the second half will go in the second 100 s. This means that there will be none or 0 % left at 200 s.

b) For a first order reaction, the half life is independent of concentration. This means that if half of the reactant decomposes in the first 100 s, then half of this (or another 25 % of the original amount) will decompose in the second 100 s. This means that at 200 s 50 % + 25 % = 75 % has decomposed or 25 % remains.

c) For a second order reaction, $t_{1/2} = \dfrac{1}{k[A]_0} = 100$ s and the integrated rate expression is $\dfrac{1}{[A]_t} = kt + \dfrac{1}{[A]_0}$.

We can rearrange the first expression to solve for k as $k = \dfrac{1}{100\ \text{s}[A]_0}$. Substituting this and 200 s into

the integrated rate expression we get $\dfrac{1}{[A]_t} = \dfrac{200\ \cancel{s}}{100\ \cancel{s}[A]_0} + \dfrac{1}{[A]_0} \rightarrow \dfrac{1}{[A]_t} = \dfrac{3}{[A]_0} \rightarrow \dfrac{[A]_t}{[A]_0} = \dfrac{1}{3}$ or 33 % remains.

98. **Given:** $t_{1/2}$ for radioactive decay of Pu-239 $= 24{,}000$ years; 1 mole initially to 1 atom   **Find:** t
Conceptual plan:
radioactive decay implies first order kinetics, $t_{1/2} \rightarrow k$ then   [Pu-239]$_0$, [Pu-239]$_t$, $k \rightarrow t$

$$t_{1/2} = \dfrac{0.693}{k} \qquad\qquad ln[A]_t = -kt + ln[A]_0$$

Solution: $t_{1/2} = \dfrac{0.693}{k}$ rearrange to solve for k. $k = \dfrac{0.693}{t_{1/2}} = \dfrac{0.693}{24000\ \text{yr}} = 2.\underline{8}875 \times 10^{-5}\ \text{yr}^{-1}$ then

$[\text{Pu-}239]_t = 1$ and $[\text{Pu-}239]_0 = 6.022 \times 10^{23}$. Since $ln[\text{Pu-}239]_t = -kt + ln[\text{Pu-}239]_0$ rearrange to solve for

t, $t = -\dfrac{1}{k} \, ln\dfrac{[\text{Pu-}239]_t}{[\text{Pu-}239]_0} = -\dfrac{1}{2.8875 \times 10^{-5}\ \text{yr}^{-1}} \, ln\dfrac{1\ \text{atom Pu-239}}{6.022 \times 10^{23}\ \text{atom Pu-239}} = 1.9 \times 10^6\ \text{yr}$.

Check: The units (yr) are correct. The time to decay 1 atom is consistent with the time being 79 half lives, which makes sense since $2^{-79} = 6.09 \times 10^{23}$.

99. Using the energy diagram show and using Hess' Law, we can see that the activation energy for the decomposition is equal to the activation energy for the formation reaction plus the heat of formation of 2 moles of HI or

$E_{aformation} = E_{adecomposition} + 2\,\Delta H_f^0\,(\text{HI})$. So

$E_{aformation} = 185\ \text{kJ} + 2\,\text{mol}(-5.65\ \text{kJ/mol}) = 174\ \text{kJ}$.

Check: Since the reaction is endothermic, we expect the activation energy in the reverse direction to be less in the reverse direction.

Note: energy axis is not to scale.

100. **Given:** first order reaction, $E_a = 249$ kJ/mol, $A = 1.6 \times 10^{14}$ s^{-1}, and 710 K
Find: k, fraction decomposed in 15 min and T for double the reaction rate
Conceptual plan:
T, A, E$_a$ → k then   min → s then k, t → fraction decomposed   then k_2/k_1, T$_1$, E$_a$ → T$_2$

$k = Ae^{-E_a/RT}$ $\qquad \dfrac{60\ \text{s}}{1\ \text{min}} \qquad ln[A]_t = -kt + ln[A]_0 \qquad\qquad ln\left(\dfrac{k_2}{k_1}\right) = \dfrac{E_a}{R}\left(\dfrac{1}{T_1} - \dfrac{1}{T_2}\right)$

Solution: Since $k = Ae^{-E_a/RT} = 1.6 \times 10^{14}\ \text{s}^{-1}\ e^{\left(\dfrac{-249\frac{\text{kJ}}{\text{mol}} \times \frac{1000\ \text{J}}{1\ \text{kJ}}}{8.314\frac{\text{J}}{\text{K mol}}\,710\ \text{K}}\right)} = 7.6657 \times 10^{-5}\ \text{s}^{-1} = 7.7 \times 10^{-5}\ \text{s}^{-1}$ then

$15\ \text{min} \times \dfrac{60\ \text{s}}{1\ \text{min}} = 900\ \text{s}$ in $ln[\text{C}_2\text{H}_5\text{Cl}]_t = -kt + ln[\text{C}_2\text{H}_5\text{Cl}]_0$ Rearrange to solve for fraction remaining

$\rightarrow \dfrac{[\text{C}_2\text{H}_5\text{Cl}]_t}{[\text{C}_2\text{H}_5\text{Cl}]_0} = e^{-kt} = e^{-(7.6657 \times 10^{-5}\ \text{s}^{-1})(900\ \text{s})} = 0.93333$ thus fraction decomposed $= 1 - 0.93333 = 0.06667 =$

0.07. $T_1 = 710$ K, $k_2/k_1 = 2$ and $ln\left(\dfrac{k_2}{k_1}\right) = \dfrac{E_a}{R}\left(\dfrac{1}{T_1} - \dfrac{1}{T_2}\right)$ Rearrange to solve for T$_2$.

$T_2 = \dfrac{\dfrac{E_a}{R}}{\dfrac{E_a}{RT_1} - ln\left(\dfrac{k_2}{k_1}\right)} = \dfrac{\dfrac{249\frac{\text{kJ}}{\text{mol}} \times \frac{1000\ \text{J}}{1\ \text{kJ}}}{8.314\frac{\text{J}}{\text{K mol}}}}{\left(\dfrac{249\frac{\text{kJ}}{\text{mol}} \times \frac{1000\ \text{J}}{1\ \text{kJ}}}{8.314\frac{\text{J}}{\text{K mol}} \times 710\ \text{K}}\right) - ln\,(2)} = 721.86\ \text{K} = 720\ \text{K}$.

Check: The units (s^{-1}, none and K) are correct. The reaction rate is reasonable considering the frequency facto, activation energy and T. The fraction decomposed is reasonable since 900 s is a small fraction of the half life. The temperature is reasonable since many reactions double their rate with an increase in temp of 10 K.

461

101. a) Since the rate determining step involves the collision of two molecules, the expected reaction order would be second order.

b) The proposed mechanism is:

$$CH_3NC + \cancel{CH_3NC} \underset{k_2}{\overset{k_1}{\rightleftharpoons}} CH_3NC^* + \cancel{CH_3NC} \qquad \text{(fast)}$$

$$\underline{\cancel{CH_3NC^*} \xrightarrow{k_3} CH_3CN \qquad\qquad \text{(slow) So the sum matches the overall reaction.}}$$

$$CH_3NC \rightarrow CH_3CN$$

Since the second step is the rate determining step, Rate $= k_3[CH_3NC^*]$. Since CH_3NC^* is an intermediate, its concentration can not appear in the rate law. Using the fast equilibrium in the first step, we see that $k_1[CH_3NC]^2 = k_2[CH_3NC^*][CH_3NC]$ or $[CH_3NC^*] = \dfrac{k_1}{k_2}[CH_3NC]$. Substituting this into the first rate expression we get that Rate $= k_3\dfrac{k_1}{k_2}[CH_3NC]$, which simplifies to Rate $= k\,[CH_3NC]$.

This matches the experimental observation of first order and the mechanism is valid.

102. a) Rate $= k\,[A]^{1/2}$ and Rate $= -\dfrac{d\,[A]}{d\,t}$ so $\dfrac{d\,[A]}{d\,t} = -k\,[A]^{1/2}$ moving the A terms to the left and the t and constants to the right we have $\dfrac{d\,[A]}{[A]^{1/2}} = -k\,dt$. Integrating we get $\displaystyle\int_{[A]_0}^{[A]} \dfrac{d\,[A]}{[A]^{1/2}} = -\int_0^t k\,dt$. When we evaluate this integral

$2[A]^{1/2}\Big|_{[A]_0}^{[A]} = -k\,t\Big|_0^t$ ➜ $2[A]_t^{1/2} - 2[A]_0^{1/2} = -k\,t$ ➜ $2[A]_t^{1/2} = -k\,t + 2[A]_0^{1/2}$ the integrated rate law.

b) To derive the half life, set $[A]_t = 1/2[A]_0$. Substituting this into $2[A]_t^{1/2} = -k\,t + 2[A]_0^{1/2}$ we get

$2\left(1/2[A]_0\right)^{1/2} = -k\,t_{1/2} + 2[A]_0^{1/2}$ ➜ $t_{1/2} = \dfrac{2[A]_0^{1/2} - 2\left(1/2[A]_0\right)^{1/2}}{k}$ ➜ $t_{1/2} = \dfrac{\left(2-\sqrt{2}\right)[A]_0^{1/2}}{k}$.

103. a) **Given:** N_2O_5 decomposes to NO_2 and O_2, first order in $[N_2O_5]$; $k = 7.48 \times 10^{-3}$ s^{-1}; $P^\circ_{N2O5} = 0.100$ atm
Find: t to $P_{Total} = 0.145$ atm
Conceptual plan:
Write a balanced reaction. Then Write expression for P_{Total} in terms of amount reacted
$$N_2O_5 \rightarrow 2\,NO_2 + \tfrac{1}{2}\,O_2 \qquad\qquad \text{let x} = P_{N2O5reacted} \quad P_{Total} = P_{N2O5} + P_{NO2} + P_{O2}$$
x, P°_{N2O5}, k $\rightarrow$ t
$$ln\,[A]_t = -k\,t + ln\,[A]_0$$
Solution: $P_{Total} = P_{N2O5} + P_{NO2} + P_{O2} = (0.100\,\text{atm} - x) + (2x) + (1/2\,x) = 0.100\,\text{atm} + 1.5\,x$ Set

$P_{Total} = 0.145\,\text{atm} = 0.100\,\text{atm} + 1.5\,x$ and solve for x. $x = \dfrac{0.145\,\text{atm} - 0.100\,\text{atm}}{1.5} = 0.030\,\text{atm}$ then

$P_{N2O5} = 0.100\,\text{atm} - x = 0.100\,\text{atm} - 0.030\,\text{atm} = 0.070\,\text{atm}$. Since P α n/V or M

$ln\,[N_2O_5]_t = -k\,t + ln\,[N_2O_5]_0$ rearrange to solve for t.

$$t = -\dfrac{ln\dfrac{[N_2O_5]_t}{[N_2O_5]_0}}{k} = -\dfrac{ln\left(\dfrac{0.070\,\cancel{atm}}{0.100\,\cancel{atm}}\right)}{7.48 \times 10^{-3}\,\text{s}^{-1}} = 4\underline{7}.684\,\text{s} = 48\,\text{s}$$

Check: The units (s) are correct. The time is reasonable because it is less than one half life and the amount decomposing is less that 50 %.

b) **Given:** N_2O_5 decomposes to NO_2 and O_2, first order in $[N_2O_5]$; $k = 7.48 \times 10^{-3}$ s^{-1}; $P^\circ_{N2O5} = 0.100$ atm
Find: t to $P_{Total} = 0.200$ atm
Conceptual plan:
Write a balanced reaction. then Write expression for P_{Total} in terms of amount reacted
$$N_2O_5 \rightarrow 2\,NO_2 + \tfrac{1}{2}\,O_2 \qquad\qquad \text{let x} = P_{N2O5reacted} \quad P_{Total} = P_{N2O5} + P_{NO2} + P_{O2}$$
x, P°_{N2O5}, k $\rightarrow$ t
$$ln\,[A]_t = -k\,t + ln\,[A]_0$$

Solution: $P_{Total} = P_{N2O5} + P_{NO2} + P_{O2} = (0.100\,\text{atm} - x) + (2x) + (1/2\,x) = 0.100\,\text{atm} + 1.5\,x$ Set

$P_{Total} = 0.200\,\text{atm} = 0.100\,\text{atm} + 1.5\,x$ and solve for x. $x = \dfrac{0.200\,\text{atm} - 0.100\,\text{atm}}{1.5} = 0.066667\,\text{atm}$ then

$P_{N2O5} = 0.100\,\text{atm} - x = 0.100\,\text{atm} - 0.066667\,\text{atm} = 0.033333\,\text{atm}$. Since $P \propto n/V$ or M

$ln[N_2O_5]_t = -kt + ln[N_2O_5]_0$ rearrange to solve for t.

$$t = -\dfrac{ln\dfrac{[N_2O_5]_t}{[N_2O_5]_0}}{k} = -\dfrac{ln\left(\dfrac{0.033333\,\text{atm}}{0.100\,\text{atm}}\right)}{7.48 \times 10^{-3}\,\text{s}^{-1}} = 146.873\,\text{s} = 150\,\text{s} = 1.5 \times 10^2\,\text{s}\ .$$

Check: The units (s) are correct. The time is reasonable because it is between one and two half lives and the amount decomposing is 67 %.

c) **Given:** N_2O_5 decomposes to NO_2 and O_2, first order in $[N_2O_5]$; $k = 7.48 \times 10^{-3}\,\text{s}^{-1}$; $P^\circ_{N2O5} = 0.100$ atm
   Find: P_{Total} after 100 s
   Conceptual plan:

$P^\circ_{N2O5}, k, t \ \rightarrow P_{N2O5}$ then Write a balanced reaction. then $P^\circ_{N2O5}, P_{N2O5} \ \rightarrow \ x$ then

$\quad ln[A]_t = -kt + ln[A]_0 \qquad\qquad N_2O_5 \rightarrow 2\,NO_2 + \tfrac{1}{2}\,O_2 \qquad x = P^0_{N2O5} - P_{N2O5}$

Write expression for P_{Total} in terms of amount reacted.

$\quad$ let $x = P_{N2O5\,reacted}$ $P_{Total} = P_{N2O5} + P_{NO2} + P_{O2}$

Solution: Since $P \propto n/V$ or M

$ln[N_2O_5]_t = -kt + ln[N_2O_5]_0 = -\left(7.48 \times 10^{-3}\,\text{s}^{-1}\right)(100\,s) + ln\,(0.100\,atm) = -3.05059$

$P_{N2O5} = e^{-3.05059} = 0.0473312\,\text{atm}$ so $x = P^0_{N2O5} - P_{N2O5} = 0.100\,\text{atm} - 0.0473312\,\text{atm} = 0.052669\,\text{atm}$
finally
$P_{Total} = P_{N2O5} + P_{NO2} + P_{O2} = (0.100\,\text{atm} - x) + (2x) + (1/2\,x) =$
$= 0.100\,\text{atm} + 1.5\,x = 0.100\,\text{atm} + 1.5(0.052669\,\text{atm}) = 0.179\,\text{atm}$

Check: The units (atm) are correct. The pressure is reasonable because the time is between those for parts a and b.

104. For this mechanism, the overall reaction is the sum of the steps in the mechanism:

$$Cl_2\,(g) \underset{k_2}{\overset{k_1}{\rightleftharpoons}} 2\,Cl\,(g)$$

$$\cancel{Cl(g)} + CO\,(g) \underset{k_4}{\overset{k_3}{\rightleftharpoons}} \cancel{ClCO\,(g)}$$

$$\underline{\cancel{ClCO\,(g)} + Cl_2\,(g) \overset{k_5}{\longrightarrow} Cl_2CO\,(g) + \cancel{Cl(g)}}$$

$$CO\,(g) + 2\,Cl_2\,(g) \rightarrow Cl_2CO\,(g) + 2\,Cl\,(g)$$

There is no overall reaction given.
Since the third step is the rate determining step, Rate $= k_5\,[ClCO]\,[Cl_2]$. Since ClCO is an intermediate, its concentration can not appear in the rate law. Using the fast equilibrium in the second step, we see that

$k_3[Cl]\,[CO] = k_4\,[ClCO]$ or $[ClCO] = \dfrac{k_3}{k_4}\,[Cl]\,[CO]$. Substituting this expression into the first rate expression

we get Rate $= k_5\,\dfrac{k_3}{k_4}\,[Cl]\,[CO]\,[Cl_2]$. Since Cl is an intermediate, its concentration can not appear in the rate

law. Using the fast equilibrium in the first step, we see that $k_1[Cl_2] = k_2\,[Cl]^2$ or $[Cl] = \sqrt{\dfrac{k_1}{k_2}[Cl_2]}$.

Substituting this expression into last first rate expression we get that Rate $= k_5\,\dfrac{k_3}{k_4}\,\sqrt{\dfrac{k_1}{k_2}[Cl_2]}\,[CO]\,[Cl_2] =$

$= k_5\,\dfrac{k_3}{k_4}\,\sqrt{\dfrac{k_1}{k_2}}\,[CO]\,[Cl_2]^{3/2}$. Simplifying this expression we see Rate $= k\,[CO]\,[Cl_2]^{3/2}$.

105. **Given:** N_2O_3 decomposes to NO_2 and NO, first order in $[N_2O_3]$, table of $[NO_2]$ versus time, at 50,000 s $=$
   $[N_2O_3] = 0$ $\qquad\qquad$ **Find:** k
   Conceptual plan: Write a balanced reaction. then Write expression for P_{NO2} in terms P_{N2O3} then
   $\qquad\qquad\qquad N_2O_3 \rightarrow NO_2 + NO \qquad\qquad\qquad P_{N2O3} = 0.784\,\text{atm} - P_{NO2}$

Plot ln P_{N2O3} versus time (this will have the same slope as ln $[N_2O_3]$ versus time). **Since** $ln[A]_t = -kt + ln[A]_0$ **, the negative of the slope will be the rate constant.**

Solution: $P_{N2O3} = 0.784$ atm $- P_{NO2}$ Plot ln P_{N2O3} versus time (this will have the same slope as ln $[N_2O_3]$ versus time). Since $ln[A]_t = -kt + ln[A]_0$, the negative of the slope will be the rate constant. The slope can be determined by measuring $\Delta y / \Delta x$ on the plot or by using functions, such as "add trendline" in Excel. The last point (50,000 s) can not be plotted because the concentration is 0 and the ln 0 is undefined, Thus the rate constant is 3.20×10^{-4} s^{-1} and the rate law is Rate = $3.20\,10^{-4}$ s^{-1}$[N_2O_3]$.

$y = -0.000320x - 0.243428$

Check: The units (s^{-1}) are correct. The rate constant is typical for a reaction.

106. Since Rate = k [CHCl$_3$] [Cl$_2$]$^{1/2}$, Rate a = k (3) (2)$^{1/2}$ = 5.2 k, Rate b = k (4) (2)$^{1/2}$ = 5.7 k, and Rate b = k (2) (4)$^{1/2}$ = 4 k. So b has the fastest rate.

107. Reaction A is second order. A plot of 1/[A] versus time will be liner $\left(\dfrac{1}{[A]_t} = kt + \dfrac{1}{[A]_0} \right)$. Reaction B is first order. A plot of ln [A] versus time will be linear ($ln[A]_t = -kt + ln[A]_0$). Reactant concentrations drop more quickly for first order reactions than for second order reactions.

108. A reaction that slows down as the reaction proceeds and has a half life that is dependent on the concentration is a second order reaction. Statement (a) will be false because this describes a first order reaction. Statement (b) is true because it describes a second order reaction. Statements (c) and (d) are false because they describe a zero order reaction.

Chapter 14
Chemical Equilibrium

1. Like adult hemoglobin, fetal hemoglobin is in equilibrium with oxygen. However, the equilibrium constant for fetal hemoglobin is larger than the equilibrium constant for adult hemoglobin, meaning that the reaction tends to go farther in the direction of the product. Consequently, fetal hemoglobin loads oxygen at a lower oxygen concentration than adult hemoglobin. In the placenta, fetal blood flows in close proximity to maternal blood, without the two ever mixing. Because of the different equilibrium constants, the maternal hemoglobin unloads oxygen which the fetal hemoglobin then binds and carries into its own circulatory system. Nature has thus evolved a chemical system through which the mother's hemoglobin can in effect hand off oxygen to the hemoglobin of the fetus.

2. Dynamic equilibrium in a chemical reaction, is the condition in which the rate of the forward reaction equals the rate of the reverse reaction. Dynamic equilibrium is called dynamic because the forward and reverse reactions are still occurring, however, they are occurring at the same rate.

3. The general expression of the equilibrium constant is: $K = \dfrac{[C]^c [D]^d}{[A]^a [B]^b}$

4. The equilibrium constant for a reaction is defined as the ration – at equilibrium – of the concentrations of the products raised to their stoichiometric coefficients divided by the concentrations of the reactants raised to their stoichiometric coefficients. If the equilibrium constant for a reaction is large, the equilibrium point of the reaction lies far to the right – the concentration of products is large and the concentration of reactants is small. If the equilibrium constant for a reaction is small, the equilibrium point of the reaction lies far to the left – the concentration of products is small and the concentration of reactants is large.

5. If you reverse the equation, invert the equilibrium constant. $K_{reverse} = \dfrac{1}{K_{forward}}$

    If you multiply the coefficients in the equation by a factor, raise the equilibrium constant to the same factor. That is, if you multiply the reaction by n, raise the equilibrium constant K to the n. $K' = K^n$

6. If you add two or more individual chemical equations to obtain an overall equation, multiply the corresponding equilibrium constants by each other to obtain the overall equilibrium constant. So, for two reactions with equilibrium constants of K_1 and K_2 the equilibrium constant for the combined reaction $K_3 = K_1 K_2$.

7. K_c is the equilibrium constant with respect to concentration in molarity. K_p is the equilibrium constant with respect to partial pressures in atmospheres. The two can be related: $K_p = K_c (RT)^{\Delta n}$

8. For the equilibrium constant, concentrations are expressed in terms of molarity and partial pressures are expressed in terms of atmospheres. The equilibrium constant usually is written with no units. Formally, the values of concentration or partial pressures that we substitute into the equilibrium constant expressions are ratios of the concentration or pressure to a reference concentration or reference pressure. So, as long as concentration units are expressed in molarity or atmospheres, we simply enter the quantities directly into the equilibrium expression, dropping their corresponding units.

9. The concentration of a solid does not change because a solid does not expand to fill its container. Its concentration, therefore, depends only on its density, which is constant as long as some solid is present. Consequently, solids are not included in the equilibrium expression. Similarly, the concentration of a pure liquid does not change, so, liquids are also excluded from the equilibrium expression.

10. For any reaction, the equilibrium concentrations of the reactants and products will depend on the initial concentration. However, the equilibrium constant will always be the same at a given temperature, regardless of the initial concentrations.

11. When we know the initial concentrations of the reactants and products and the equilibrium concentration of one reactant or product, the other equilibrium concentrations can be deduced from the stoichiometry of the

reaction. From the initial and equilibrium concentration of the one reactant, we can find the change in concentration for that reactant. Using the stoichiometry of the reaction, we can determine the equilibrium concentrations of the other reactants and products. We generally use an ICE table to keep track of the changes.

12. The definition of the reaction quotient takes the same form as the definition of the equilibrium constant, except that the reaction need not be at equilibrium. So the reaction quotient (Q_c) is the ratio – at any point in the reaction – of the concentrations of the products raise their stoichiometric coefficients divided by the concentration of the reactants raised to their stoichiometric coefficients. The value of Q relative to K is a measure of the progress of the reaction toward equilibrium. At equilibrium, the reaction quotient is equal to the equilibrium constant.

13. Standard states are defined as 1 M concentration, or 1 atm pressure. So the value of K_c and K_p when the reactants and products are in their standard states is 1.

14. a) When $Q < K$ the reaction goes to the right (toward products).
    b) When $Q > K$ the reaction goes to the left (toward reactants).
    c) When $Q = K$ the reaction is at equilibrium.

15. To solve a problem given initial concentrations and the equilibrium constant you would: Prepare an ICE table; and then calculate Q; compare Q and K_c and predict the direction of the reaction; represent the change with x; sum the table and determine the equilibrium values; put the equilibrium values in the equilibrium expression and solve for x. Determine the reactant and product concentration.

16. When adding a small value of x, we can often ignore x because of significant figures. In addition and subtraction, the number of significant figures depends on the number with the fewest decimal places. Therefore, a small value of x would not be significant. In multiplication and division, the number of significant figures depends on the fraction with the fewest significant figures, therefore, we cannot ignore x in this case.

17. According to LeChatelier's principle, when a chemical system at equilibrium is disturbed, the system shifts in a direction that minimizes the disturbance.

18. If a system is at equilibrium:
    Increasing the concentration of one or more of the reactants causes the reaction to shift to the right
    Increasing the concentration of one or more of the products causes the reaction to shift to the left.
    Decreasing the concentration of one or more of the reactants causes the reaction to shift to the left.
    Decreasing the concentration of one or more of the products causes the reaction to shift to the right.

19. If a chemical system is at equilibrium:
    Decreasing the volume causes the reaction to shift in the direction that has the fewer moles of gas particles.
    Increasing the volume causes the reaction to shift in the direction that has the greater number of moles of gas particles.
    If a reaction has an equal number of moles of gas on both sides of the chemical equation, then a change in volume produces no effect on the equilibrium.
    Adding an inert gas to the mixture at a fixed volume has no effect on the equilibrium.

20. If the temperature of a system at equilibrium is changed, the system shifts in a direction to counter that change. So, if the temperature is increases, the reaction shifts in the direction that tends to decrease the temperature and vice versa.
    In an exothermic chemical reaction:
    Increasing the temperature causes the reaction to shift left and the value of the equilibrium constant decreases.
    Decreasing the temperature causes the reaction to shift right and the value of the equilibrium constant increases.
    In an endothermic chemical reactant:
    Increasing the temperature causes the reaction to shift right and the equilibrium constant increases.
    Decreasing the temperature causes the reaction to shift left and the equilibrium constant decreases.

21. The equilibrium constant is defined as the concentrations of the products raised to their stoichiometric coefficients divided by the concentrations of the reactants raised to their stoichiometric coefficients.

a) $K = \dfrac{[SbCl_3][Cl_2]}{[SbCl_5]}$

b) $K = \dfrac{[NO]^2[Br_2]}{[BrNO]^2}$

c) $K = \dfrac{[CS_2][H_2]^4}{[CH_4][H_2S]^2}$

d) $K = \dfrac{[CO_2]^2}{[CO]^2[O_2]}$

22. a) The equilibrium constant is defined as the concentrations of the products **raised to their stoichiometric coefficients** divided by the concentrations of the reactants **raised to their stoichiometric coefficients**.

$K = \dfrac{[H_2]^2[S_2]}{[H_2S]^2}$

b) The equilibrium constant is defined as the **concentrations of the products** raised to their stoichiometric coefficients **divided by the concentrations of the reactants** raised to their stoichiometric coefficients.

$K = \dfrac{[COCl_2]}{[CO][Cl_2]}$

23. With an equilibrium constant of 1.4×10^{-5}, the value of the equilibrium constant is small, therefore, the concentration of reactants will be greater than the concentration of reactants. This is independent of the initial concentration of the reactants and products.

24. Figure a at equilibrium has 8 $C_2H_4Cl_2$; 2 Cl_2; and 2 C_2H_4.
Figure b at equilibrium has 6 $C_2H_4Br_2$; 4 Br_2; and 4 C_2H_4.
Figure c at equilibrium has 3 $C_2H_4I_2$; 7 I_2; and 7 C_2H_4.
Since the equilibrium constant is concentration of products/ concentration of reactants, the equilibrium situation which has the largest concentration of products will have the largest equilibrium constant. Therefore, $K_{Cl2} > K_{Br2} > K_{I2}$.

25. (i) has 10 H_2 and 10 I_2
(ii) has 7 H_2 and 7 I_2 and 6 HI
(iii) has 5 H_2 and 5 I_2 and 10 HI
(iv) has 4 H_2 and 4 I_2 and 12 HI
(v) has 3 H_2 and 3 I_2 and 14 HI
(vi) has 3 H_2 and 3 I_2 and 14 HI
a) Concentration of (v) and (vi) are the same so the system reached equilibrium at (v).

b) If a catalyst was added to the system, the system would reach the conditions at (v) sooner, since a catalyst speeds up the reaction but does not change the equilibrium conditions.

c) The final figure (vi)would have the same amount of reactants and products since a catalyst speeds up the reaction, but does not change the equilibrium concentrations.

26. The equilibrium constant gives us the ratio of products to reactants at equilibrium, it does not say how long it takes to reach equilibrium. So, after 15 minutes, if the smaller equilibrium constant has more products, than the kinetics of that reaction are faster.

27. a) If you reverse the reaction, invert the equilibrium constant. So, $K' = \dfrac{1}{K_p} = \dfrac{1}{2.26x10^4} = 4.42 \times 10^{-5}$. The reactants will be favored.

b) If you multiply the coefficients in the equation by a factor, raise the equilibrium constant to the same factor.

So, $K' = (K_p)^{1/2} = (2.26 \times 10^4)^{1/2} = 1.50 \times 10^2$. The products will be favored.

c) Begin with the reverse of the reaction and invert the equilibrium constant.

$$K_{reverse} = \frac{1}{K_p} = \frac{1}{2.26 \times 10^4} = 4.42 \times 10^{-5}$$

Then, multiply the reaction by 2 and raise the value of K_{revere} to the 2 power.

$K' = (K_{reverse})^2 = (4.42 \times 10^{-5})^2 = 1.96 \times 10^{-9}$. The reactants will be favored.

28. a) The reaction is multiplied by 1/2 so raise the value of the equilibrium constant to 1/2.

$K' = (K_p)^{1/2} = (2.2 \times 10^6)^{1/2} = 1.5 \times 10^3$. The products will be favored.

b) The reaction is multiplied by 3, so raise the value of the equilibrium constant to 3.

$K' = (K_p)^3 = (2.2 \times 10^6)^3 = 1.1 \times 10^{19}$. The products will be favored.

c) Begin with the reverse of the reaction and invert the equilibrium constant.

$$K_{reverse} = \frac{1}{K_p} = \frac{1}{2.2 \times 10^6} = 4.5 \times 10^{-7}$$

Then, multiply the reaction by 2 and raise the value of K_{revere} to the 2 power.

$K' = (K_{reverse})^2 = (4.5 \times 10^{-7})^2 = 2.1 \times 10^{-13}$. The reactants will be favored.

29. To find the equilibrium constant for reaction 3, you need to combine reactions 1 and 2 to get reaction 3. Begin by reversing reaction 2, then multiply reaction 1 by 2 and add the two new reactions. When you add reactions you multiply the values of K.

$N_2(g) + O_2(g) \rightleftharpoons 2NO(g) \qquad K_1 = \frac{1}{K_p} = \frac{1}{2.1 \times 10^{30}} = 4.\underline{7}6 \times 10^{-31}$

$2NO(g) + Br_2(g) \rightleftharpoons 2NOBr(g) \qquad K_2 = (K_p)^2 = (5.3)^2 = 28.\underline{0}9$

$N_2(g) + O_2(g) + Br_2(g) \rightleftharpoons 2NOBr(g) \qquad K_3 = K_1 K_2 = (4.\underline{7}6 \times 10^{-31})(28.\underline{0}9) = 1.3 \times 10^{-29}$

30. To find the equilibrium constant for reaction 3, you need to combine reactions 1 and 2 to get reaction 3. Begin by multiplying reaction 1 by 2 and then reverse reaction 2 and add the two new reactions. When you add reactions you multiply the values of K.

$2A(s) \rightleftharpoons B(g) + 2C(g) \qquad K_1 = (K_p)^2 = (0.0334)^2 = 1.1 \times 10^{-3}$

$B(g) + 2C(g) \rightleftharpoons 3D(g) \qquad K_2 = \frac{1}{K_p} = \frac{1}{2.35} = 0.425$

$2A(s) \rightleftharpoons 3D(g) \qquad K' = K_1 K_2 = (1.1 \times 10^{-3})(0.425) = 4.68 \times 10^{-4}$

31. a) **Given:** $K_p = 6.26 \times 10^{-22}$ **Find:** K_c
Conceptual Plan: $K_p \rightarrow K_c$
$$K_p = K_c (RT)^{\Delta n}$$

Solution: $\Delta n = $ mol product gas – mol reactant gas $= 2 - 1 = 1$

$$K_c = \frac{K_p}{(RT)^{\Delta n}} = \frac{6.26 \times 10^{-22}}{(0.08206 \frac{L \cdot atm}{mol \cdot K} \times 298 \ K)^1} = 2.56 \times 10^{-23}$$

Check: Substitute into the equation and confirm that you get the original value of K_p.

$$K_p = K_c (RT)^{\Delta n} = (2.56 \times 10^{-23})(0.08206 \frac{L \cdot atm}{mol \cdot K} \times 298)^1 = 6.26 \times 10^{-22}$$

b) **Given:** $K_p = 7.7 \times 10^{24}$ **Find:** K_c

Conceptual Plan: $K_p \rightarrow K_c$

$$K_p = K_c(RT)^{\Delta n}$$

Solution: Δn = mol product gas − mol reactant gas = 4 − 2 = 2

$$K_c = \frac{K_p}{(RT)^{\Delta n}} = \frac{7.7 \times 10^{24}}{(0.08206 \frac{L \cdot atm}{mol \cdot K} \times 298 \ K)^2} = 1.3 \times 10^{22}$$

Check: Substitute into the equation and confirm that you get the original value of K_p.

$$K_p = K_c(RT)^{\Delta n} = (1.3 \times 10^{22})(0.08206 \frac{L \cdot atm}{mol \cdot K} \times 298)^2 = 7.7 \times 10^{24}$$

c) **Given:** $K_p = 81.9$ **Find:** K_c

Conceptual Plan: $K_p \rightarrow K_c$

$$K_p = K_c(RT)^{\Delta n}$$

Solution: Δn = mol product gas − mol reactant gas = 2 − 2 = 0

$$K_c = \frac{K_p}{(RT)^{\Delta n}} = \frac{81.9}{(0.08206 \frac{L \cdot atm}{mol \cdot K} \times 298 \ K)^0} = 81.9$$

Check: Substitute into the equation and confirm that you get the original value of K_p.

$$K_p = K_c(RT)^{\Delta n} = (81.9)(0.08206 \frac{L \cdot atm}{mol \cdot K} \times 298)^0 = 81.9$$

32. a) **Given:** $K_c = 5.9 \times 10^{-3}$ **Find:** K_p

Conceptual Plan: $K_p \rightarrow K_c$

$$K_p = K_c(RT)^{\Delta n}$$

Solution: Δn = mol product gas − mol reactant gas = 2 − 1 = 1

$$K_p = K_c(RT)^{\Delta n} = 5.9 \times 10^{-3}(0.08206 \frac{L \cdot atm}{mol \cdot K} \times 298 \ K)^1 = 1.4 \times 10^{-1}$$

Check: Substitute into the equation and confirm that you get the original value of K_p.

$$K_c = \frac{K_p}{(RT)^{\Delta n}} = \frac{1.4 \times 10^{-1}}{(0.08206 \frac{L \cdot atm}{mol \cdot K} \times 298 \ K)^1} = 0.0059$$

b) **Given:** $K_c = 3.7 \times 10^8$ **Find:** K_p

Conceptual Plan: $K_p \rightarrow K_c$

$$K_p = K_c(RT)^{\Delta n}$$

Solution: Δn = mol product gas − mol reactant gas = 2 − 4 = − 2

$$K_p = K_c(RT)^{\Delta n} = 3.7 \times 10^8 (0.08206 \frac{L \cdot atm}{mol \cdot K} \times 298 \ K)^{-2} = 6.2 \times 10^5$$

Check: Substitute into the equation and confirm that you get the original value of K_p.

$$K_c = \frac{K_p}{(RT)^{\Delta n}} = \frac{6.2 \times 10^5}{(0.08206 \frac{L \cdot atm}{mol \cdot K} \times 298 \ K)^{-2}} = 3.7 \times 10^8$$

c) **Given:** $K_c = 4.10 \times 10^{-31}$ **Find:** K_p

Conceptual Plan: $K_p \rightarrow K_c$

$$K_p = K_c(RT)^{\Delta n}$$

Solution: Δn = mol product gas − mol reactant gas = 2 − 2 = 0

$$K_p = K_c(RT)^{\Delta n} = 4.10 \times 10^{-31} (0.08206 \frac{L \cdot atm}{mol \cdot K} \times 298 \ K)^0 = 4.10 \times 10^{-31}$$

Check: Substitute into the equation and confirm that you get the original value of K_p.

$$K_c = \frac{K_p}{(RT)^{\Delta n}} = \frac{4.10 \times 10^{-31}}{(0.08206 \frac{L \cdot atm}{mol \cdot K} \times 298 \ K)^0} = 4.10 \times 10^{-31}$$

33. a) Since H_2O is a liquid, it is omitted from the equilibrium expression. $K_{eq} = \dfrac{[HCO_3^-][OH^-]}{[CO_3^{2-}]}$

b) Since $KClO_3$ and KCl are both solids they are omitted from the equilibrium expression. $K_{eq} = [O_2]^3$

c) Since H_2O is a liquid, it is omitted from the equilibrium expression. $K_{eq} = \dfrac{[H_3O^+][F^-]}{[HF]}$

d) Since H_2O is a liquid, it is omitted from the equilibrium expression. $K_{eq} = \dfrac{[NH_4^+][OH^-]}{[NH_3]}$

34. Since PCl_3 is a liquid it is omitted from the equilibrium expression. $K_{eq} = \dfrac{[Cl_2]}{[PCl_5]}$

35. **Given:** At equilibrium: [CO] = 0.105M, [H_2] = 0.114M, [CH_3OH] = 0.185M   **Find:** K_c
Conceptual Plan: Balanced reaction → equilibrium expression → K_c
Solution: $K_c = \dfrac{[CH_3OH]}{[CO][H_2]^2} = \dfrac{(0.185)}{(0.105)(0.114)^2} = 136$
Check: The answer is reasonable since the concentration of products is greater than the concentration of reactants and the equilibrium constant should be greater than 1.

36. **Given:** At equilibrium: [NH_3] = 0.278M, [H_2S] = 0.355M   **Find:** K_c
Conceptual Plan: Balanced reaction → equilibrium expression → K_c
Solution: Since NH_4HS is a solid it is omitted from the equilibrium expression:
$K_c = [NH_3][H_2S] = (0.278)(0.355) = 0.0987$
Check: The answer is reasonable since the concentration of products is less than 1M, the equilibrium constant is less than 1.

37. At 500K: **Given:** At equilibrium: [N_2] = 0.115M, [H_2] = 0.105M, and [NH_3] = 0.439   **Find:** K_c
Conceptual Plan: Balanced reaction → equilibrium expression → K_c
Solution: $K_c = \dfrac{[NH_3]^2}{[N_2][H_2]^3} = \dfrac{(0.439)^2}{(0.115)(0.105)^3} = 1.45 \times 10^3$
Check: The value is reasonable since the concentration of products is greater than the concentration of reactants.

At 575K: **Given:** At equilibrium: [N_2] = 0.110M, [NH_3] = 0.128, K_c = 9.6   **Find:** [H_2]
Conceptual Plan: Balanced reaction → equilibrium expression → [H_2]
Solution: $K_c = \dfrac{[NH_3]^2}{[N_2][H_2]^3}$ $9.6 = \dfrac{(0.128)^2}{(0.110)(x)^3}$ $x = 0.249$
Check: Plug the value for x back into the equilibrium expression, and check the value.
$9.6 = \dfrac{(0.128)^2}{(0.110)(0.249)^3}$

At 775K: **Given:** At equilibrium: [N_2] = 0.120M, [H_2] = 0.140, K_c = 0.0584   **Find:** [NH_3]
Conceptual Plan: Balanced reaction → equilibrium expression → [NH_3]
Solution: $K_c = \dfrac{[NH_3]^2}{[N_2][H_2]^3}$ $0.0584 = \dfrac{(x)^2}{(0.120)(0.140)^3}$ $x = 0.00439$
Check: Plug the value for x back into the equilibrium expression, and check the value.
$0.0584 = \dfrac{(0.00439)^2}{(0.120)(0.140)^3}$

38. At 25°C : **Given:** At equilibrium: [H_2] = 0.0355M, [I_2] = 0.0388M, and [HI] = 0.922   **Find:** K_c
Conceptual Plan: Balanced reaction → equilibrium expression → K_c

Solution: $K_c = \dfrac{[HI]^2}{[H_2][I_2]} = \dfrac{(0.922)^2}{(0.0355)(0.0388)} = 617$

Check: The value is reasonable since the concentration of products is greater than the concentration of reactants.

At 340°C: **Given:** At equilibrium: $[I_2] = 0.0455$, and $[HI] = 0.387$, $K_c = 9.6$ **Find:** $[H_2]$
Conceptual Plan: Balanced reaction → equilibrium expression → [H$_2$]
Solution: $K_c = \dfrac{[HI]^2}{[H_2][I_2]}$ $9.6 = \dfrac{(0.387)^2}{(x)(0.0455)}$ $x = 0.343$
Check: Plug the value for x back into the equilibrium expression, and check the value.
$9.6 = \dfrac{(0.387)^2}{(0.343)(0.0455)}$

At 445°C: **Given:** At equilibrium: $[H_2] = 0.0485$M, $[I_2] = 0.0468$, $K_c = 50.2$ **Find:** [HI]
Conceptual Plan: Balanced reaction → equilibrium expression → [HI]
Solution: $K_c = \dfrac{[HI]^2}{[H_2][I_2]}$ $50.2 = \dfrac{(x)^2}{(0.0485)(0.0468)}$ $x = 0.338$
Check: Plug the value for x back into the equilibrium expression, and check the value.
$50.2 = \dfrac{(0.338)^2}{(0.0485)(0.0468)}$

39. **Given:** $P(NO) = 118$ torr; $P(Br_2) = 176$ torr, $K_p = 28.4$ **Find:** $P(NOBr)$
Conceptual Plan: **torr → atm and then balanced reation → equilibrium expression → P(NOBr)**

$$\dfrac{1\ atm}{760\ torr}$$

Solution: $P_{NO} = 118$ torr x $\dfrac{1\ atm}{760\ torr} = 0.15\underline{5}3$ atm $P_{Br_2} = 176$ torr x $\dfrac{1\ atm}{760\ torr} = 0.23\underline{1}6$

$K_p = \dfrac{P_{NOBr}^2}{P_{NO}^2 P_{Br_2}}$ $28.4 = \dfrac{x^2}{(0.15\underline{5}3)^2(0.23\underline{1}6)}$ $x = 0.398$ atm $= 303$ torr

Check: Plug the value for x back into the equilibrium expression, and check the value.
$28.4 = \dfrac{(0.398)^2}{(0.15\underline{5}3)^2(0.23\underline{1}6)}$

40. **Given:** $P(SO_2) = 117$ torr; $P(Cl_2) = 255$ torr, $K_p = 2.91$ x 10^3 **Find:** $P(SO_2Cl_2)$
Conceptual Plan: **torr → atm and then balanced reation → equilibrium expression → P(SO$_2$Cl$_2$)**

$$\dfrac{1\ atm}{760\ torr}$$

Solution: $P_{SO_2} = 117$ torr x $\dfrac{1\ atm}{760\ torr} = 0.15\underline{3}9$ atm $P_{Cl_2} = 255$ torr x $\dfrac{1\ atm}{760\ torr} = 0.33\underline{5}5$

$K_p = \dfrac{P_{SO_2} P_{Cl_2}}{P_{SO_2Cl_2}}$ 2.91 x $10^3 = \dfrac{(0.15\underline{3}9)(0.33\underline{5}5)}{(x)}$ $x = 1.77$ x 10^{-5} atm $= 0.0135$ torr

Check: Plug the value for x back into the equilibrium expression, and check the value. 2.91 x $10^3 = \dfrac{(0.15\underline{3}9)(0.33\underline{5}5)}{(1.77 \text{ x } 10^{-5})}$

41. **Given:** $[Fe^{3+}]_{initial} = 1.0$ x 10^{-3} M; $[SCN^-]_{initial} = 8.0$ x 10^{-4} M; $[FeSCN^{2+}]_{eq} = 1.7$ x 10^{-4} M **Find:** K_c
Conceptual Plan: 1. **Prepare ICE table**
2. **Calculate concentration change for known value**
3. **Calculate concentration changes for other reactants/products**
4. **Determine equilibrium concentration**
5. **Write the equilibrium expression and determine K_c**
Solution: $Fe^{3+}(aq) + SCN^-(aq) \leftrightarrows FeSCN^{3+}(aq)$

	$[Fe^{3+}]$	$[SCN^-]$	$[FeSCN^{3+}]$
I	1.0×10^{-3}	8.0×10^{-4}	0.00
C	-1.7×10^{-4}	-1.7×10^{-4}	$+1.7 \times 10^{-4}$
E	8.3×10^{-4}	6.3×10^{-4}	1.7×10^{-4}

$$K_c = \frac{[\text{FeSCN}^{2+}]}{[\text{Fe}^{3+}][\text{SCN}^-]} = \frac{(1.7 \times 10^{-4})}{(8.3 \times 10^{-4})(6.3 \times 10^{-4})} = 3.3 \times 10^2$$

42. Given: $[\text{SO}_2\text{Cl}_2]_{\text{initial}} = 0.020$ M; $[\text{Cl}_2]_{\text{eq}} = 1.2 \times 10^{-2}$M   **Find:** K_c

Conceptual Plan: 1. **Prepare ICE table**
     2. **Calculate concentration change for known value**
     3. **Calculate concentration changes for other reactants/products**
     4. **Determine equilibrium concentration**
     5. **Write the equilibrium expression and determine K_c**

Solution: $\text{SO}_2\text{Cl}_2(g) \rightleftharpoons \text{SO}_2(g) + \text{Cl}_2(g)$

	$[\text{SO}_2\text{Cl}_2]$	$[\text{SO}_2]$	$[\text{Cl}_2]$
I	0.020	0.00	0.00
C	-1.2×10^{-2}	$+1.2 \times 10^{-2}$	$+1.2 \times 10^{-2}$
E	0.0080	1.2×10^{-2}	1.2×10^{-2}

$$K_c = \frac{[\text{SO}_2][\text{Cl}_2]}{[\text{SO}_2\text{Cl}_2]} = \frac{(1.2 \times 10^{-2})(1.2 \times 10^{-2})}{(0.0080)} = 0.018$$

43. Given: 3.67 L flask; 0.763 g H_2 initial; 96.9 g I_2 initial; 90.4 g HI equilibrium   **Find:** K_c

Conceptual Plan: g → mol → M and then

$$n = \frac{g}{\text{molar mass}} \quad M = \frac{n}{V}$$

     1. **Prepare ICE table**
     2. **Calculate concentration change for known value**
     3. **Calculate concentration changes for other reactants/products**
     4. **Determine equilibrium concentration**
     5. **Write the equilibrium expression and determine K_c**

Solution: $0.763 \text{ g } H_2 \times \dfrac{1 \text{ mol } H_2}{2.016 \text{ g } H_2} = 0.37\underline{8}5 \text{ mol } H_2 \qquad \dfrac{0.37\underline{8}5 \text{ mol } H_2}{3.67 \text{ L}} = 0.103 \text{ M}$

$96.9 \text{ g } I_2 \times \dfrac{1 \text{ mol } I_2}{253.8 \text{ g } I_2} = 0.38\underline{1}8 \text{ mol } I_2 \qquad \dfrac{0.38\underline{1}8 \text{ mol } I_2}{3.67 \text{ L}} = 0.104 \text{ M}$

$90.4 \text{ g HI} \times \dfrac{1 \text{ mol HI}}{127.9 \text{ g } I_2} = 0.70\underline{6}8 \text{ mol HI} \qquad \dfrac{0.70\underline{6}8 \text{ mol HI}}{3.67 \text{ L}} = 0.193 \text{ M}$

	$H_2(g) +$	$I_2(g)$	$\rightleftharpoons$	$2HI(g)$
	$[H_2]$	$[I_2]$		$[HI]$
I	0.103	0.104		0.00
C	-0.0965	-0.0965		$+0.193$
E	0.0065	0.0075		0.193

$$K_c = \frac{[\text{HI}]^2}{[H_2][I_2]} = \frac{(0.193)^2}{(0.0065)(0.0075)} = 764$$

44. Given: 5.19 L flask; 26.9 g CO initial; 2.34 g H_2 initial; 8.65 g CH_3OH equilibrium   **Find:** K_c

Conceptual Plan: g → mol → M and then

$$n = \frac{g}{\text{molar mass}} \quad M = \frac{n}{V}$$

     1. **Prepare ICE table**
     2. **Calculate concentration change for known value**
     3. **Calculate concentration changes for other reactants/products**
     4. **Determine equilibrium concentration**
     5. **Write the equilibrium expression and determine K_c**

Solution: $26.9 \text{ g CO}_2 \times \dfrac{1 \text{ mol CO}}{28.01 \text{ g CO}} = 0.96\underline{0}4 \text{ mol CO} \qquad \dfrac{0.96\underline{0}4 \text{ mol CO}}{5.19 \text{ L}} = 0.185 \text{ M}$

$2.34 \text{ g } H_2 \times \dfrac{1 \text{ mol } H_2}{2.016 \text{ g } H_2} = 1.1\underline{6}1 \text{ mol } H_2 \qquad \dfrac{1.1\underline{6}1 \text{ mol } H_2}{5.19 \text{ L}} = 0.224 \text{ M}$

$8.65 \text{ g } CH_3OH \times \dfrac{1 \text{ mol } CH_3OH}{32.04 \text{ g } CH_3OH} = 0.27\underline{0}0 \text{ mol } CH_3OH \qquad \dfrac{0.27\underline{0}0 \text{ mol } CH_3OH}{5.19 \text{ L}} = 0.0520 \text{ M}$

$$
\begin{array}{ccccc}
& CO(g) & + 2H_2(g) & \leftrightharpoons & CH_3OH(g) \\
& [CO] & [H_2] & & [CH_3OH] \\
I & 0.185 & 0.224 & & 0.00 \\
C & -0.0520 & -0.104 & & +0.0520 \\
E & 0.133 & 0.120 & & 0.0520
\end{array}
$$

$$
K_c = \frac{[CH_3OH]}{[CO][H_2]} = \frac{(0.0520)}{(0.133)(0.120)} = 27.2
$$

45. **Given:** $K_c = 8.5 \times 10^{-3}$; $[NH_3] = 0.166$; $[H_2S] = 0.166$ **Find:** Will solid form or decompose?
   Conceptual Plan: Calculate Q → compare Q and K_c
   Solution: $Q = [NH_3][H_2S] = (0.166)(0.166) = 0.0276$
   $Q = 0.0276$ and $K_c = 8.5 \times 10^{-3}$ so $Q > K_c$ and the reaction will shift to the left, so more solid will form.

46. **Given:** $K_p = 2.4 \times 10^{-4}$; $P_{H2} = 0.112$; $P_{S2} = 0.055$; $P_{H2S} = 0.445$ **Find:** Is the reaction at equilibrium?
   Conceptual Plan: Calculate Q → compare Q and K_p

   Solution: $Q = \dfrac{P_{H_2}^2 P_{S_2}}{P_{H_2S}^2} = \dfrac{(0.112)^2(0.055)}{(0.445)^2} = 3.48 \times 10^{-3}$ $Q = 3.48 \times 10^{-3}$ and $K_p = 2.4 \times 10^{-4}$

   so $Q > K_p$ and the system is not at equilibrium and the reaction will shift to the left to reach equilibrium.

47. **Given:** 6.55 g Ag_2SO_4, 1.5 L solution, $K_c = 1.1 \times 10^{-5}$ **Find:** will more solid dissolve
   Conceptual Plan:
   g Ag_2SO_4 → mol Ag_2SO_4 → $[Ag_2SO_4]$ → $[Ag^+],[SO_4^{-2}]$ → calculate Q and compare to K_c.

   $$\frac{1\ mol\ Ag_2SO_4}{311.81\ g} \quad \frac{mol\ Ag_2SO_4}{vol\ solution} \qquad Q = [Ag^+]^2[SO_4^{2-}]$$

   Solution: $6.55\ g\ Ag_2SO_4 \left(\dfrac{1\ mol\ Ag_2SO_4}{311.81\ g\ Ag_2SO_4} \right) = 0.0140\ mol\ Ag_2SO_4$

   $\dfrac{0.0210\ mol\ Ag_2SO_4}{1.5\ L\ solution} = 0.0140\ M\ Ag_2SO_4$

   $[Ag^+] = 2[Ag_2SO_4] = 2(0.0140\ M) = 0.0280\ M\ [SO_4^{2-}] = [Ag_2SO_4] = 0.0140\ M$

   $Q = [Ag^+]^2[SO_4^{2-}] = (0.0280)^2(0.0140) = 1.1 \times 10^{-5}$

   $Q = K_c$ so the system is at equilibrium and is a saturated solution. Therefore, if more solid is added it will not dissolve.

48. **Given:** $K_p = 6.7$ at 298 K; 2.25 L flask; $NO_2 = 0.055$ mol; $N_2O_4 = 0.082$ mol   **Find:** Is the reaction at equilibrium?
   Conceptual Plan: K_p → K_c and mol → M and then calculate Q and compare to K_c.

   $$K_p = K_c(RT)^{\Delta n} \qquad M = \frac{mol}{V}$$

   Solution: $K_c = \dfrac{K_p}{(RT)^{\Delta n}} = \dfrac{(6.7)}{[(.0821\frac{L \cdot atm}{mol \cdot K})(298K)]^{-1}} = 164$

   $Q = \dfrac{[N_2O_4]}{[NO]^2} = \dfrac{\left(\dfrac{0.082\ mol}{2.25\ L}\right)}{\left(\dfrac{0.055\ mol}{2.25\ L}\right)^2} = 61$

   $Q < K_c$, the reaction is not at equilibrium and will shift to the right.

49. a)   **Given:** $[A] = 1.0$ M, $[B] = 0.0$ $K_c = 2.0$; $a = 1$, $b = 1$ **Find:** $[A]$, $[B]$ at equilibrium
   Conceptual Plan: Prepare an ICE table; and then calculate Q; compare Q and K_c and predict the direction of the reaction; represent the change with x; sum the table and determine the equilibrium values; put the equilibrium values in the equilibrium expression and solve for x. Determine $[A]$ and $[B]$.
   Solution:

$$A(g) \leftrightarrows B(g)$$

	[A]	[B]
I	1.0	0.00
C	- x	x
E	1 – x	x

$$Q = \frac{[B]}{[A]} = \frac{0}{1} = 0 \qquad\qquad Q < K \text{ therefore, the reaction will proceed to the right by } x$$

$$K_c = \frac{[B]}{[A]} = \frac{(x)}{(1 - x)} = 2.0 \qquad x = 0.67$$

$$[A] = 1 - 0.67 = 0.33 \qquad [B] = 0.67$$

Check: Plug the values into the equilibrium expression: $K_c = \dfrac{0.67}{0.33} = 2.0$

b) **Given:** [A] = 1.0 M, [B] = 0.0 K_c = 2.0; a = 2, b = 2 **Find:** [A], [B] at equilibrium
Conceptual Plan: Prepare an ICE table; and then calculate Q; compare Q and K_c and predict the direction of the reaction; represent the change with x; sum the table and determine the equilibrium values; put the equilibrium values in the equilibrium expression and solve for x. Determine [A] and [B].
Solution:

$$2A(g) \leftrightarrows 2B(g)$$

	[A]	[B]
I	1.0	0.00
C	- 2x	2x
E	1 – 2x	2x

$$Q = \frac{[B]^2}{[A]^2} = \frac{0}{1} = 0 \qquad\qquad Q < K \text{ therefore, the reaction will proceed to the right by } x$$

$$K_c = \frac{[B]^2}{[A]^2} = \frac{(2x)^2}{(1 - 2x)^2} = 2.0 \qquad x = 0.29\underline{3}$$

$$[A] = 1 - 2(0.29\underline{3}) = 0.414 = 0.41 \qquad [B] = 2(0.29\underline{3}) = 0.586 = 0.59$$

Check: Plug the values into the equilibrium expression: $K_c = \dfrac{(0.59)^2}{(0.41)^2} = 2.0$

c) **Given:** [A] = 1.0 M, [B] = 0.0 K_c = 2.0; a = 1, b = 2 **Find:** [A], [B] at equilibrium
Conceptual Plan: Prepare an ICE table; and then calculate Q; compare Q and K_c and predict the direction of the reaction; represent the change with x; sum the table and determine the equilibrium values; put the equilibrium values in the equilibrium expression and solve for x. Determine [A] and [B].
Solution:

$$A(g) \leftrightarrows 2B(g)$$

	[A]	[B]
I	1.0	0.00
C	- x	2x
E	1 – x	2x

$$Q = \frac{[B]^2}{[A]} = \frac{0}{1} = 0 \qquad\qquad Q < K \text{ therefore, the reaction will proceed to the right by } x$$

$$K_c = \frac{[B]^2}{[A]} = \frac{(2x)^2}{(1 - x)} = 2.0 \qquad 4x^2 + 2x - 2 = 0$$

$$(4x - 2)(x + 1) = 0 \; ; \; x = - 1 \text{ or } x = 0.5, \text{ therefore, } x = 0.5$$

$$[A] = 1 - 0.50 = 0.50M \qquad [B] = 2x = 2(0.50) = 1.0M$$

Check: Plug the values into the equilibrium expression: $K_c = \dfrac{(1.0)^2}{0.50} = 2.0$

50. a) **Given:** [A] = 1.0 M, [B] = 1.0, [C] = 0.0 K_c = 4.0; a = 1, b = 1, c = 2 **Find:** [A],[B],[C] at equilibrium
Conceptual Plan: Prepare an ICE table; and then calculate Q; compare Q and K_c and predict the direction of the reaction; represent the change with x; sum the table and determine the equilibrium values; put the equilibrium values in the equilibrium expression and solve for x. Determine [A], [B]. and [C].

Solution:

	A(g)	+ B(g)	$\leftrightarrows$	2C(g)
	[A]	[B]		[C]
I	1.0	1.0		0.0
C	- x	-x		2x
E	1 – x	1 – x		2x

$Q = \dfrac{[C]^2}{[A][B]} = \dfrac{0}{(1)(1)} = 0$ $Q < K$ therefore, the reaction will proceed to the right by x

$K_c = \dfrac{[C]^2}{[A][B]} = \dfrac{(2x)^2}{(1 - x)(1 - x)} = 4.0$ x = 0.50

[A] = [B] = 1 - 0.50 = 0.50 M   [C] = 2x = 1.0M

Check: Plug the values into the equilibrium expression: $K_c = \dfrac{(1.0)^2}{(0.50)(0.50)} = 4.0$

b) **Given:** [A] = 1.0 M, [B] = 1.0, [C] = 0.0 K_c = 4.0; a = 1, b = 1, c = 1   **Find:** [A],[B],[C] at equilibrium
Conceptual Plan: Prepare an ICE table; and then calculate Q; compare Q and K_c and predict the direction of the reaction; represent the change with x; sum the table and determine the equilibrium values; put the equilibrium values in the equilibrium expression and solve for x. Determine [A], [B]. and [C].
Solution:

	A(g)	+ B(g)	$\leftrightarrows$	C(g)
	[A]	[B]		[C]
I	1.0	1.0		0.0
C	- x	-x		x
E	1 – x	1 – x		x

$Q = \dfrac{[C]}{[A][B]} = \dfrac{0}{(1)(1)} = 0$ $Q < K$ therefore, the reaction will proceed to the right by x

$K_c = \dfrac{[C]}{[A][B]} = \dfrac{(x)}{(1 - x)(1 - x)} = 4.0$ $4x^2 - 9x + 4 = 0$

x = 1.64 or x = 0.61, therefore, x = 0.61

[A] = [B] = 1 - 0.61 = 0.39 M   [C] = x = 0.61M

Check: Plug the values into the equilibrium expression: $K_c = \dfrac{(0.61)}{(0.39)(0.39)} = 4.0$

c) **Given:** [A] = 1.0 M, [B] = 1.0, [C] = 0.0 K_c = 4.0; a = 2, b = 1, c = 1   **Find:** [A],[B],[C] at equilibrium
Conceptual Plan: Prepare an ICE table; and then calculate Q; compare Q and K_c and predict the direction of the reaction; represent the change with x; sum the table and determine the equilibrium values; put the equilibrium values in the equilibrium expression and solve for x. Determine [A], [B]. and [C].
Solution:

	2A(g)	+ B(g)	$\leftrightarrows$	C(g)
	[A]	[B]		[C]
I	1.0	1.0		0.0
C	- 2x	-x		x
E	1 – 2x	1 – x		x

$Q = \dfrac{[C]}{[A]^2[B]} = \dfrac{0}{(1)(1)} = 0$ $Q < K$ therefore, the reaction will proceed to the right by x

$K_c = \dfrac{[C]}{[A]^2[B]} = \dfrac{(x)}{(1 - 2x)^2(1 - x)} = 4.0$

$- 16x^3 + 32x^2 - 20x + 4.0 = 0$

x = 0.326

[A] = 1 – 2x = 0.348; [B] = 1 – x = 0.674; [C] = x = 0.326

Check: Plug the values into the equilibrium expression: $K_c = \dfrac{(0.326)}{(0.348)^2(0.674)} = 4.0$

51. **Given:** [N_2O_4] = 0.0500 M, [NO_2] = 0.0 K_c = 0.513   **Find:** [N_2O_4], [NO_2] at equilibrium

Conceptual Plan: Prepare an ICE table; and then calculate Q; compare Q and K_c and predict the direction of the reaction; represent the change with x; sum the table and determine the equilibrium values; put the equilibrium values in the equilibrium expression and solve for x. Determine $[N_2O_4]$ and $[NO_2]$.

Solution:

$$N_2O_4\ (g) \leftrightarrows 2\ NO_2(g)$$

	$[N_2O_4]$	$[NO_2]$
I	0.0500	0.00
C	- x	2x
E	0.0500 – x	2x

$$Q = \frac{[NO_2]^2}{[N_2O_4]} = \frac{0}{0.0500} = 0 \qquad\qquad Q < K \text{ therefore, the reaction will proceed to the right by x}$$

$$K_c = \frac{[NO_2]^2}{[N_2O_4]} = \frac{(2x)^2}{(0.0500 - x)} = 0.513 \qquad 4x^2 + 0.513x - 0.02565 = 0$$

$$\frac{-b \pm \sqrt{b^2 - 4ac}}{2a} = \frac{-0.513 \pm \sqrt{(0.513)^2 - 4(4)(-0.02565)}}{2(4)} = \frac{-0.513 \pm \sqrt{0.6735}}{2(4)}$$

x = - 0.1667 or x = 0.0385, therefore, x = 0.0385

[A] = 0.0500 - 0.03850 = 0.0115M   [B] = 2x = 2(0.03850) = 0.0770M

Check: Plug the values into the equilibrium expression: $K_c = \frac{(0.0770)^2}{0.0115} = 0.515$

52. **Given:** [CO] = 0.1500 M, $[Cl_2]$ = 0.175, $[COCl_2]$ = 0.0 K_c = 255   **Find:** [CO], $[Cl_2]$, $[COCl_2]$ at equilibrium
   Conceptual Plan: Prepare an ICE table; and then calculate Q; compare Q and K_c and predict the direction of the reaction; represent the change with x; sum the table and determine the equilibrium values; put the equilibrium values in the equilibrium expression and solve for x. Determine [CO], $[Cl_2]$. and $[COCl_2]$.
   Solution:

$$CO\ (g)\ +Cl_2\ (g) \leftrightarrows COCl_2\ (g)$$

	[CO]	$[Cl_2]$	$[COCl_2]$
I	0.1500	0.175	0.0
C	- x	-x	x
E	0.1500–x	0.175 – x	x

$$Q = \frac{[COCl_2]}{[CO][Cl_2]} = \frac{0}{(0.1500)(0.175)} = 0 \qquad\qquad Q < K \text{ therefore, the reaction will proceed to the right by x}$$

$$K_c = \frac{[COCl_2]}{[CO][Cl_2]} = \frac{x}{(0.1500 - x)(0.175 - x)} = 255 \qquad 255x^2 - 83.875x + 6.69375 = 0$$

$$\frac{-b \pm \sqrt{b^2 - 4ac}}{2a} = \frac{-(-83.875) \pm \sqrt{(-83.875)^2 - 4(255)(6.69375)}}{2(255)}$$

x = 0.1927 or x = 0.1362, therefore, x = 0.1362

[CO] = 0.1500 - 0.1362 = 0.01377

$[Cl_2]$ = 0.175 - 0.1362 = 0.03878

$[COCl_2]$ = x = 0.1362M

Check: Plug the values into the equilibrium expression: $K_c = \frac{(0.1362)}{(0.01377)(0.03878)} = 255$

53. **Given:** [CO] = 0.10 M, $[CO_2]$ = 0.0 K_c = 4.0 x 10^3 **Find:** $[CO_2]$ at equilibrium
   Conceptual Plan: Prepare an ICE table; and then calculate Q; compare Q and K_c and predict the direction of the reaction; represent the change with x; sum the table and determine the equilibrium values; put the equilibrium values in the equilibrium expression and solve for x. Determine [CO], $[Cl_2]$. and $[COCl_2]$.
   Solution:

$$NiO(s) + CO(g) \rightleftharpoons Ni(s) + CO_2(g)$$

	[CO]	[CO$_2$]
I	0.10	0.0
C	- x	x
E	0.10 – x	x

$$Q = \frac{[CO_2]}{[CO]} = \frac{0}{(0.10)} = 0 \qquad Q < K \text{ therefore, the reaction will proceed to the right by x}$$

$$K_c = \frac{[CO_2]}{[CO]} = \frac{x}{(0.10 - x)} = 4.0 \times 10^3 \qquad 4.0 \times 10^3(0.10 - x) = x$$

$$x = 0.10$$

$$[CO_2] = 0.10 \text{ M}$$

Check: since the equilibrium constant is so large, the reaction goes essentially to completion, therefore, it is reasonable that the concentration of product is 0.10 M

54. **Given:** [CO] = 0.125M M, [H$_2$O] = 0.125M [CO$_2$] = 0.0, [H$_2$] = 0.0 K_c = 102
    Find: [CO], [H$_2$O], [CO$_2$], [H$_2$] at equilibrium
    Conceptual Plan: Prepare an ICE table; and then calculate Q; compare Q and K_c and predict the direction of the reaction; represent the change with x; sum the table and determine the equilibrium values; put the equilibrium values in the equilibrium expression and solve for x. Determine [CO], [Cl$_2$]. and [COCl$_2$].
    Solution:

$$CO(g) + H_2O(g) \rightleftharpoons CO_2(g) + H_2(g)$$

	[CO]	[H$_2$O]	[CO$_2$]	[H$_2$]
I	0.125	0.125	0.0	0.0
C	- x	-x	x	x
E	0.125–x	0.125 – x	x	x

$$Q = \frac{[CO_2][H_2]}{[CO][H_2O]} = \frac{0}{(0.125)(0.125)} = 0 \qquad Q < K \text{ therefore, the reaction will proceed to the right by x}$$

$$K_c = \frac{[CO_2][H_2]}{[CO][H_2O]} = \frac{(x)(x)}{(0.125 - x)(0.125 - x)} = 102$$

$$\sqrt{\frac{(x)(x)}{(0.125 - x)(0.125 - x)}} = \sqrt{102}$$

$$\frac{x}{0.125 - x} = \pm10.0995$$

$$\pm10.0995(0.125 - x) = x$$

$$x = 0.11373 \text{ or } x = - 0.1387, \text{ therefore, } x = 0.1137$$

$$[CO] = [H_2O] = 0.125 - 0.1137 = 0.0113$$

$$[H_2] = [CO_2] = x = 0.11373 = 0.114$$

Check: Plug the values into the equilibrium expression: $K_c = \dfrac{(0.114)(0.114)}{(0.0113)(0.0113)} = 101.7 = 102$

55. **Given:** [HC$_2$H$_3$O$_2$] = 0.210M M, [H$_3$O$^+$] = 0.0, [C$_2$H$_3$O$_2^-$] = 0.0, K_c = 1.8 × 10^{-5}
    Find: [HC$_2$H$_3$O2], [H$_2$O$^+$], [C$_2$H$_3$O$_2^-$] at equilibrium
    Conceptual Plan: Prepare an ICE table; and then calculate Q; compare Q and K_c and predict the direction of the reaction; represent the change with x; sum the table and determine the equilibrium values; put the equilibrium values in the equilibrium expression and solve for x. Determine [CO], [Cl$_2$]. and [COCl$_2$].

    Solution:

$$HC_2H_3O_2(aq) + H_2O(l) \rightleftharpoons H_3O^+(aq) + C_2H_3O_2^-(aq)$$

	[HC$_2$H$_3$O$_2$]	[H$_2$O]	[H$_3$O$^+$]	[C$_2$H$_3$O$_2^-$]
I	0.210		0.0	0.0
C	- x		x	x
E	0.210–x		x	x

477

$$Q = \frac{[H_3O^+][C_2H_3O_2^-]}{[HC_2H_3O_2]} = \frac{0}{(0.210)} = 0 \qquad Q < K \text{ therefore, the reaction will proceed to the right by x}$$

$$K_c = \frac{[H_3O^+][C_2H_3O_2^-]}{[HC_2H_3O_2]} = \frac{(x)(x)}{(0.210 - x)} = 1.8 \times 10^{-5}$$

assume x is small compared to 0.210

$$x^2 = 0.210(1.8 \times 10^{-5})$$

$$x = 0.00194 \qquad\qquad \text{check assumption: } \frac{0.00194}{0.210} \times 100 = 0.92\text{ \%; assumption valid}$$

$$[H_3O^+] = [C_2H_3O_2^-] = 0.00194M$$

$$[HC_2H_3O_2] = 0.210 - 0.00194 = 0.200\underline{7} = 0.210M$$

Check: Plug the values into the equilibrium expression: $K_c = \frac{(0.00194)(0.00194)}{(0.210)} = 1.79 \times 10^{-5}$; within 1

significant figure of true value, answers are valid.

56. **Given:** $[SO_2Cl_2] = 0.175M$ M, $[SO_2] = 0.0$, $[Cl_2] = 0.0$ $K_c = 2.99 \times 10^{-7}$
Find: $[SO_2Cl_2]$, $[SO_2]$, $[Cl_2]$ at equilibrium
Conceptual Plan: Prepare an ICE table; and then calculate Q; compare Q and K_c and predict the direction of the reaction; represent the change with x; sum the table and determine the equilibrium values; put the equilibrium values in the equilibrium expression and solve for x. Determine $[SO_2Cl_2]$, $[SO_2]$, and $[Cl_2]$.
Solution:

	SO_2Cl_2 (g)	$\leftrightarrows$	SO_2 (g)	+ Cl_2(g)
	$[SO_2Cl_2]$		$[SO_2]$	$[Cl_2]$
I	0.175		0.0	0.0
C	- x		x	x
E	0.175–x		x	x

$$Q = \frac{[SO_2][Cl_2]}{[SO_2Cl_2]} = \frac{0}{(0.175)} = 0 \qquad Q < K \text{ therefore, the reaction will proceed to the right by x}$$

$$K_c = \frac{[SO_2][Cl_2]}{[SO_2Cl_2]} = \frac{(x)(x)}{(0.175 - x)} = 2.99 \times 10^{-7}$$

assume x is small compared to 0.175

$$x^2 = 2.99 \times 10^{-7}(0.175)$$

$$x = 2.2\underline{8}7 \times 10^{-4} \qquad\qquad \text{check assumption: } \frac{2.2\underline{8}7 \times 10^{-4}}{0.175} \times 100 = 0.13\%\text{; assumption valid.}$$

$$[SO_2] = [Cl_2] = x = 2.2\underline{8}7 \times 10^{-4} = 2.29 \times 10^{-4}$$

$$[SO_2Cl_2] = 0.175 - 2.2\underline{8}7 \times 10^{-4} = 0.174\underline{7} = 0.175$$

Check: Plug the values into the equilibrium expression:

$$K_c = \frac{(0.2.2\underline{8}7 \times 10^{-4})(2.2\underline{8}7 \times 10^{-4})}{(0.175)} = 2.996 \times 10^{-7} = 3.00 \times 10^{-7};$$

within 1 significant figure of the true value, therefore, answers are valid.

57. **Given:** $P_{Br2} = 755$ torr, $P_{Cl2} = 735$ torr, $P_{BrCl} = 0.0$, $K_p = 1.11 \times 10^{-4}$ **Find:** P_{BrCl} at equilibrium
Conceptual Plan: Torr $\rightarrow$ atm and then:Prepare an ICE table; and then calculate Q; compare Q and K_c and predict the direction of the reaction; represent the change with x; sum the table and determine the equilibrium values; put the equilibrium values in the equilibrium expression and solve for x. Determine P_{BrCl}
Solution:

$$P_{Br_2} = 755 \text{ torr x } \frac{1 \text{ atm}}{760 \text{ torr}} = 0.993\underline{4} \text{ atm} \qquad P_{Cl_2} = 735 \text{ torr x } \frac{1 \text{ atm}}{760 \text{ torr}} = 0.967\underline{1} \text{ atm}$$

	Br_2 (g)	+ Cl_2(g)	$\leftrightarrows$	$2BrCl$ (g)
	P_{Br2}	P_{Cl2}		P_{BrCl}

I	0.9934	0.9671	0.0
C	- x	-x	2x
E	0.9934–x	0.9671– x	2x

$$Q = \frac{P_{BrCl}^2}{P_{Br_2} P_{Cl_2}} = \frac{0}{(0.9934)(0.9671)} = 0$$ $Q < K$ therefore, the reaction will proceed to the right by x

$$K_c = \frac{P_{BrCl}^2}{P_{Br_2} P_{Cl_2}} = \frac{(2x)^2}{(0.9934 - x)(0.9671 - x)} = 1.11 \times 10^{-4}$$

asusme x is small compared ot 0.9934 and 0.9671

$$\frac{(2x)^2}{(0.9934)(0.9671)} = 1.11 \times 10^{-4}$$ $4x^2 = 1.066 \times 10^{-4}$

$x = 0.00516 = 3.92$ torr

$P_{BrCl} = 2x = 2(3.92 \text{ torr}) = 7.84$ torr

Check: Plug the values into the equilibrium expression:

$$K_c = \frac{(2(0.00516))^2}{(0.9934 - 0.00516)(0.99671 - 0.00516)} = 1.065 \times 10^{-4} = 1.12 \times 10^{-4};$$

within 1 significant figure of the true value, therefore, answers are valid.

58. **Given:** $P_{CO} = 1344$ torr, $P_{H2O} = 1766$ torr, $P_{CO2} = 0.0$, $P_{H2} = 0.0$, $K_p = 0.0611$ **Find:** P_{CO2}, P_{H2} at equilibrium
Conceptual Plan: Torr → atm and then:Prepare an ICE table; and then calculate Q; compare Q and K_c and predict the direction of the reaction; represent the change with x; sum the table and determine the equilibrium values; put the equilibrium values in the equilibrium expression and solve for x. Determine P_{CO2} and P_{H2}

Solution: $P_{CO} = 1344$ torr $\times \dfrac{1 \text{ atm}}{760 \text{ torr}} = 1.76\underline{8}4$ atm $P_{H_2O} = 1766$ torr $\times \dfrac{1 \text{ atm}}{760 \text{ torr}} = 2.32\underline{3}7$ atm

	CO (g)	+H$_2$O(g)	⇆CO$_2$ (g) +	H$_2$(g)
	P$_{CO}$	P$_{H2O}$	P$_{CO2}$	P$_{H2}$
I	1.76$\underline{8}$4	2.32$\underline{3}$7	0.0	0.0
C	- x	-x	x	x
E	1.7684–x	2.3237 – x	x	x

$$Q = \frac{P_{CO_2} P_{H_2}}{P_{CO} P_{H_2O}} = \frac{0}{(1.7684)(2.3237)} = 0$$ $Q < K$ therefore, the reaction will proceed to the right by x

$$K_c = \frac{P_{CO_2} P_{H_2}}{P_{CO} P_{H_2O}} = \frac{(x)(x)}{(1.7684 - x)(2.3237 - x)} = 0.0611$$

$x^2 = (0.0611)(4.1092 - 4.0921x + x^2)$

$x^2 = (0.25107 - 0.2500x + 0.0611x^2)$

$0.9389x^2 + 0.2500\ x - 0.25107 = 0$

$$\frac{-b \pm \sqrt{b^2 - 4ac}}{2a} = \frac{-0.2500 \pm \sqrt{(0.2500)^2 - 4(0.9389)(-0.25107)}}{2(0.9389)}$$

$x = 0.4008$ or - 0.6671 so: $x = 0.4008$

$P_{CO_2} = P_{H_2} = x = 0.4008$ atm = 305 torr

Check: Plug the values into the equilibrium expression:

$$K_c = \frac{(0.4008)^2}{(1.7684 - 0.4008)(2.3237 - 0.4008)} = 0.06108 = 0.061;$$

within 1 significant figure of the true value, therefore, answers are valid.

59. a) **Given:** [A] = 1.0 M, [B] = [C] = 0.0, $K_c = 1.0$ **Find:** [A], [B], [C] at equilibrium
Conceptual Plan: Prepare an ICE table; and then calculate Q; compare Q and K_c and predict the direction of the reaction; represent the change with x; sum the table and determine the equilibrium values; put the equilibrium values in the equilibrium expression and solve for x. Determine [A], [B]. and [C].
Solution:

$$
\begin{array}{lccc}
 & A\ (g) & \rightleftharpoons & B\ (g) + C(g) \\
 & [A] & & [B]\quad [C] \\
I & 1.0 & & 0.0\quad 0.0 \\
C & -x & & x\quad\ \ x \\
E & 1.0-x & & x\quad\ \ x
\end{array}
$$

$$Q = \frac{[B][C]}{[A]} = \frac{0}{(1.0)} = 0 \qquad\qquad Q < K \text{ therefore, the reaction will proceed to the right by x}$$

$$K_c = \frac{[B][C]}{[A]} = \frac{(x)(x)}{(1.0-x)} = 1.0$$

$$x^2 = 1.0(1.0-x)$$

$$x^2 + x - 1 = 0$$

$$\frac{-b \pm \sqrt{b^2 - 4ac}}{2a} \qquad \frac{-1 \pm \sqrt{1^2 - 4(1)(-1)}}{2(1)}$$

x = 0.6$\underline{1}$5 or x = - 1.615, therefore, x = 0.6$\underline{1}$5

[B] = [C] = x = 0.6$\underline{1}$5 = 0.62

[A] = 1.0 - 0.6$\underline{1}$5 = 0.385 = 0.38

Check: Plug   the   values   into   the   equilibrium

expression: $K_c = \dfrac{(0.62)(0.62)}{(0.38)} = 1.01 = 1.0;$ which is the equilibrium constant so the values are correct.

b) **Given:** [A] = 1.0 M, [B] = [C] = 0.0, $K_c = 0.010$ **Find:** [A], [B], [C] at equilibrium
Conceptual Plan: Prepare an ICE table; and then calculate Q; compare Q and K_c and predict the direction of the reaction; represent the change with x; sum the table and determine the equilibrium values; put the equilibrium values in the equilibrium expression and solve for x. Determine [A], [B]. and [C].
Solution:

$$
\begin{array}{lccc}
 & A\ (g) & \rightleftharpoons & B\ (g) + C(g) \\
 & [A] & & [B]\quad [C] \\
I & 1.0 & & 0.0\quad 0.0 \\
C & -x & & x\quad\ \ x \\
E & 1.0-x & & x\quad\ \ x
\end{array}
$$

$$Q = \frac{[B][C]}{[A]} = \frac{0}{(1.0)} = 0 \qquad\qquad Q < K \text{ therefore, the reaction will proceed to the right by x}$$

$$K_c = \frac{[B][C]}{[A]} = \frac{(x)(x)}{(1.0-x)} = 0.010$$

$$x^2 = 0.010(1.0-x)$$

$$x^2 + 0.010x - 0.010 = 0$$

$$\frac{-b \pm \sqrt{b^2 - 4ac}}{2a} \qquad \frac{-(0.010) \pm \sqrt{(0.010)^2 - 4(1)(-0.010)}}{2(1)}$$

x = 0.09$\underline{5}$12 or x = - 0.1005, therefore, x = 0.09$\underline{5}$12

[B] = [C] = x = 0.09$\underline{5}$12 = 0.095

[A] = 1.0 - 0.09$\underline{5}$12 = 0.90488 = 0.90

Check: Plug   the   values   into   the   equilibrium

expression: $K_c = \dfrac{(0.095)(0.095)}{(0.90)} = 0.01002 = 0.010;$

which is the equilibrium constant so the values are correct.

c) **Given:** [A] = 1.0 M, [B] = [C] = 0.0, $K_c = 1.0 \times 10^{-5}$ **Find:** [A], [B], [C] at equilibrium
Conceptual Plan: Prepare an ICE table; and then calculate Q; compare Q and K_c and predict the direction of the reaction; represent the change with x; sum the table and determine the equilibrium values; put the equilibrium values in the equilibrium expression and solve for x. Determine [A], [B]. and [C].
Solution:

$$
\begin{array}{cccc}
& A\ (g) & \rightleftarrows & B\ (g) + C(g) \\
& [A] & & [B] \quad [C] \\
I & 1.0 & & 0.0 \quad 0.0 \\
C & -x & & x \quad\ \ x \\
E & 1.0\text{--}x & & x \quad\ \ x
\end{array}
$$

$Q = \dfrac{[B][C]}{[A]} = \dfrac{0}{(1.0)} = 0$ $Q < K$ therefore, the reaction will proceed to the right by x

$K_c = \dfrac{[B][C]}{[A]} = \dfrac{(x)(x)}{(1.0 - x)} = 1.0 \times 10^{-5}$

assume x is small compared to 1.0

$x^2 = 1.0(1.0 \times 10^{-5})$

$x = 0.003\underline{1}6$ check assumption: $\dfrac{0.003\underline{1}6}{1.0} \times 100 = 0.32\%$, assumption valid

$[B] = [C] = x = 0.003\underline{1}6 = 0.0032$

$[A] = 1.0 - 0.003\underline{1}6 = 0.9968 = 1.0$

Check: Plug the values into the equilibrium expression:

$K_c = \dfrac{(0.0032)(0.0032)}{(1.0)} = 1.024 \times 10^{-5} = 1.0 \times 10^{-5}$;

which is the equilibrium constant so the values are correct.

60. a)   **Given:** $P_B = 1.0$ atm, $P_A = 00$ atm, $P_{BrCl} = 0.0$, $K_p = 1.0$ **Find:** P_B, P_A at equilibrium

     Conceptual Plan: Prepare an ICE table; and then calculate Q; compare Q and K_p and predict the direction of the reaction; represent the change with x; sum the table and determine the equilibrium values; put the equilibrium values in the equilibrium expression and solve for x. Determine P_A, P_B

     Solution:

$$
\begin{array}{cccc}
& A\ (g) & \rightleftarrows & 2B\ (g) \\
& P_A & & P_B \\
I & 0.0 & & 1.0 \\
C & x & & -2x \\
E & x & & 1.0 - 2x
\end{array}
$$

$Q = \dfrac{P_B^2}{P_A} =$ since there is no A, the reaction shifts to the right

$K_p = \dfrac{P_B^2}{P_A} = \dfrac{(1.0 - 2x)^2}{(x)} = 1.0$

$1.0 - 4x + 4x^2 = 1.0x$

$4x^2 - 5x + 1.0 = 0$

$\dfrac{-b \pm \sqrt{b^2 - 4ac}}{2a} \quad\quad \dfrac{-(-5) \pm \sqrt{(-5)^2 - 4(4)(1)}}{2(4)}$

$x = 0.25$ or $x = 1.0$, therefore, $x = 0.25$

$P_A = x = 0.25$; $P_B = 1.0 - 2x = 1.0 - 0.50 = 0.50$

     Check: Plug   the   values   into   the   equilibrium   expression:

$K_p = \dfrac{(0.50)^2}{(0.25)} = 1.0$; which is the equilibrium constant

   b)   **Given:** $P_B = 1.0$ atm, $P_A = 00$ atm, $P_{BrCl} = 0.0$, $K_p = 1.0 \times 10^{-4}$ **Find:** P_B, P_A at equilibrium

     Conceptual Plan: Prepare an ICE table; and then calculate Q; compare Q and K_p and predict the direction of the reaction; represent the change with x; sum the table and determine the equilibrium values; put the equilibrium values in the equilibrium expression and solve for x. Determine P_A, P_B

     Solution:

$$
\begin{array}{cccc}
& A\ (g) & \rightleftarrows & 2B\ (g) \\
& P_A & & P_B \\
I & 0.0 & & 1.0
\end{array}
$$

C   x   -2x

E   x   1.0 - 2x

$Q = \dfrac{P_B^2}{P_A}$ = since there is no A, the reaction shifts to the right

$K_p = \dfrac{P_B^2}{P_A} = \dfrac{(1.0 - 2x)^2}{(x)} = 1.0 \times 10^{-4}$

$1.0 - 4x + 4x^2 = (1.0 \times 10^{-4})x$

$4x^2 - 4.0001x + 1.0 = 0$

$\dfrac{-b \pm \sqrt{b^2 - 4ac}}{2a} = \dfrac{-(-4.0001) \pm \sqrt{(-4.0001)^2 - 4(4)(1)}}{2(4)} = \dfrac{-(-4.0001) \pm \sqrt{8.0 \times 10^{-4}}}{2(4)}$

x = 0.5035 or x = 0.4965, therefore, x = 0.4965

$P_A = x = 0.4965 = 0.50$; $P_B = 1.0 - 2x = 1.0 - 2(0.4965) = 0.007$

Check: Plug   the   values   into   the   equilibrium   expression:

$K_p = \dfrac{(0.007)^2}{(0.4965)} = 9.867 \times 10^{-5} = 1.0 \times 10^{-4}$; which is the equilibrium constant

c) **Given:** $P_B = 1.0$ atm, $P_A = 00$ atm, $P_{BrCl} = 0.0$, $K_p = 1.0 \times 10^5$ **Find:** P_B , P_A at equilibrium
Conceptual Plan: Prepare an ICE table; and then calculate Q; compare Q and K_p and predict the direction of the reaction; represent the change with x; sum the table and determine the equilibrium values; put the equilibrium values in the equilibrium expression and solve for x. Determine P_A, P_B.
Solution:

	A (g) ⇆	2B (g)
	P_A	P_B
I	0.0	1.0
C	x	-2x
E	x	1.0 - 2x

$Q = \dfrac{P_B^2}{P_A}$ = since there is no A, the reaction shifts to the right

$K_p = \dfrac{P_B^2}{P_A} = \dfrac{(1.0 - 2x)^2}{(x)} = 1.0 \times 10^5$

assume x is small compared to 1.0

$\dfrac{1.0}{x} = 1.0 \times 10^5$

$x = 1.0 \times 10^{-5}$ check assumption: $\dfrac{1.0 \times 10^{-5}}{1.0} \times 100 = 0.001$ %; assumption valid

$P_A = x = 1.0 \times 10^{-5}$ atm; $P_B = 1.0 - 2x = 1.0 - 2(1.0 \times 10^{-5}) = 0.99998$ atm

Check: Plug   the   values   into   the   equilibrium   expression:

$K_p = \dfrac{(0.99998)^2}{(1.0 \times 10^{-5})} = 9.9996 \times 10^4 = 1.0 \times 10^5$; which is the equilibrium constant

61. **Given:** $CO(g) + Cl_2(g) \rightleftharpoons COCl_2(g)$ at equilibrium   **Find:** what is the effect of each of the following
a) $COCl_2$ is added to the reaction mixture: Adding $COCl_2$ increases the concentration of $COCl_2$ and causes the reaction to shift to the left.

b) Cl_2 is added to the reaction mixture: Adding Cl_2 increases the concentration of Cl_2 and causes the reaction to shift to the right.

c) $COCl_2$ is removed from the reaction mixture: removing the $COCl_2$ decreases the concentration of $COCl_2$ and causes the reaction to shift to the right.

62. **Given:** $2BrNO(g) \rightleftharpoons 2NO(g) + Br_2(g)$ at equilibrium   **Find:** what is the effect of each of the following

a) NO is added to the reaction mixture: Adding NO increases the concentration of NO and causes the reaction to shift to the left.

b) BrNO is added to the reaction mixture: Adding BrNO increases the concentration of BrNO and causes the reaction to shift to the right.

c) Br_2 is removed from the reaction mixture: Removing Br_2 decreases the concentration of Br_2 and causes the reaction to shift to the right.

63. **Given:** $2KClO_3(s) \leftrightarrows 2KCl(s) + 3O_2(g)$ at equilibrium   **Find:** what is the effect of each of the following
    a) O_2 is removed from the reaction mixture: Removing the O_2 decreases the concentration of O_2 and causes the reaction to shift to the right.

    b) KCl is added to the reaction mixture: Adding KCl does not cause any change in the reaction. KCl is a solid and the concentration remains constant so the addition of more solid does not change the equilibrium concentration.

    c) $KClO_3$ is added to the reaction mixture: Adding $KClO_3$ does not cause any change in the reaction. $KClO_3$ is a solid and the concentration remains constant so the addition of more solid does not change the equilibrium concentration.

    d) O_2 is added to the reaction mixture: Adding O_2 increases the concentration of O_2 and causes the reaction to shift to the left.

64. **Given:** $C(s) + H_2O(g) \leftrightarrows CO(g) + H_2(g)$ **Find:** what is the effect of each of the following
    a) C is added to the reaction mixture: Adding C does not cause any change in the reaction. C is a solid and the concentration remains constant so the addition of more solid does not change the equilibrium concentration.

    b) H_2O is condensed and removed from the reaction mixture: Removing the H_2O decreases the concentration of H_2O and causes the reaction to shift to the left.

    c) CO is added to the reaction mixture: Adding CO increases the concentration of CO and causes the reaction to shift to the left.

    d) H_2 is removed from the reaction mixture: Removing the H_2 decreases the concentration of H_2 and causes the reaction to shift to the right.

65. a) **Given:** $I_2(g) \leftrightarrows 2I(g)$ at equilibrium   **Find:** the effect of increasing the volume
    The chemical equation has 2 moles of gas on the right and 1 mole of gas on the left. Increasing the volume of the reaction mixture decreases the pressure and causes the reaction to shift to the right (toward the side with more moles of gas particles).

    b) **Given:** $2H_2S(g) \leftrightarrows 2H_2(g) + S_2(g)$ **Find:** the effect of decreasing the volume
    The chemical equation has 3 moles of gas on the right and 2 mole of gas on the left. Decreasing the volume of the reaction mixture increases the pressure and causes the reaction to shift to the left (toward the side with fewer moles of gas particles).

    c) **Given:** $I_2(g) + Cl_2(g) \leftrightarrows 2ICl(g)$ **Find:** the effect of decreasing the volume
    The chemical equation has 2 moles of gas on the right and 2 mole of gas on the left. Decreasing the volume of the reaction mixture increases the pressure but causes no shift in the reaction because the moles are equal on both sides.

66. a) **Given:** $CO(g) + H_2O(g) \leftrightarrows CO_2(g) + H_2(g)$ **Find:** the effect of decreasing the volume
    The chemical equation has 2 moles of gas on the right and 2 mole of gas on the left. Decreasing the volume of the reaction mixture increases the pressure but causes no shift in the reaction because the moles are equal on both sides

    b) **Given:** $PCl_3(g) + Cl_2(g) \leftrightarrows PCl_5(g)$ **Find:** the effect of increasing the volume

The chemical equation has 2 moles of gas on the left and 1 mole of gas on the right. Increasing the volume of the reaction mixture decreases the pressure and causes the reaction to shift to the left (toward the side with more moles of gas particles).

c) **Given:** $CaCO_3(s) \leftrightarrows CaO(s) + CO_2(g)$ **Find:** the effect of increasing the volume
The chemical equation has 1 moles of gas on the right and 0 mole of gas on the left. Increasing the volume of the reaction mixture decreases the pressure and causes the reaction to shift to the right (toward the side with more moles of gas particles).

67. **Given:** $C(s) + CO_2(g) \leftrightarrows 2CO(g)$ is endothermic **Find:** the effect of increasing the temperature
Since the reaction is endothermic we can think of the heat as a reactant, increasing the temperature is equivalent to adding a reactant causing the reaction to shift to the right. This will cause an increase in the concentration of products and a decrease in the concentration of reactant, therefore, the value of K will increase.
Find: the effect of decreasing the temperature
Since the reaction is endothermic we can think of the heat as a reactant, decreasing the temperature is equivalent to removing a reactant causing the reaction to shift to the left. This will cause a decrease in the concentration of products and an increase in the concentration of reactants, therefore, the value of K will decrease.

68. **Given:** $C_6H_{12}O_6(s) + 6\ O_2(g) \leftrightarrows 6CO_2(g) + 6\ H_2O(g)$ is exothermic
Find: the effect of increasing the temperature
Since the reaction is exothermic we can think of the heat as a product, increasing the temperature is equivalent to adding a product causing the reaction to shift to the left. This will cause a decrease in the concentration of products and an increase in the concentration of reactant, therefore, the value of K will decrease.
Find: the effect of decreasing the temperature
Since the reaction is exothermic we can think of the heat as a product, decreasing the temperature is equivalent to removing a product causing the reaction to shift to the right. This will cause an increase in the concentration of products and a decrease in the concentration of reactants, therefore, the value of K will increase.

69. **Given:** $C(s) + 2H_2(g) \leftrightarrows CH_4(g)$ is exothermic   **Find:** determine which will favor CH_4
a) adding more C to the reaction mixture: does NOT favor CH_4. Adding C does not cause any change in the reaction. C is a solid and the concentration remains constant so the addition of more solid does not change the equilibrium concentration.

b) adding more H_2 to the reaction mixture: favors CH_4. Adding H_2 increases the concentration of H_2 causing the reaction to shift to the right.

c) raising the temperature of the reaction mixture: does NOT favor CH_4. Since the reaction is exothermic we can think of heat as a product, raising the temperature is equivalent to adding a product causing the reaction to shift to the left.

d) lowering the volume of the reaction mixture: favors CH_4. The chemical equation has 1 moles of gas on the right and 2 mole of gas on the left. Decreasing the volume of the reaction mixture increases the pressure and causes the reaction to shift to the right (toward the side with fewer moles of gas particles).

e) adding a catalyst to the reaction mixture: does NOT favor CH_4. A catalyst added to the reaction mixture only speeds up the reaction, it does not change the equilibrium concentration.

f) adding neon gas to the reaction mixture: does NOT favor CH_4. Adding an inert gas to a reaction mixture at a fixed volume has no effect on the equilibrium

70. **Given:** $C(s) + H_2O(g) \leftrightarrows CO(g) + H_2(g)$ is endothermic   **Find:** Determine which will favor H_2
a) adding more C to the reaction mixture: does NOT favor H_2. Adding C does not cause any change in the reaction. C is a solid and the concentration remains constant so the addition of more solid does not change the equilibrium concentration.

b) adding more H_2O to the reaction mixture: favors H_2. Adding H_2O increases the concentration and causes the reaction to shift to the right.

c) raising the temperature of the reaction mixture: favors H_2. Since the reaction is endothermic we can think of heat as a reactant, raising the temperature is equivalent to adding a reactant causing the reaction to shift to the right.

d) increasing the volume of the reaction mixture: favors H_2. The chemical equation has 2 moles of gas on the right and 1 mole of gas on the left. Increasing the volume of the reaction mixture decreases the pressure and causes the reaction to shift to the right (toward the side with more moles of gas particles).

e) adding a catalyst to the reaction mixture: does NOT favor H_2. A catalyst added to the reaction mixture only speeds up the reaction, it does not change the equilibrium concentration.

f) adding an inert gas to the reaction mixture: does NOT favor H_2. Adding an inert gas to a reaction mixture at a fixed volume has no effect on the equilibrium.

71. a) To find the value of K for the new equation, combine the two given equation to yield the new equation. Reverse equation 1, and use $1/K_1$ and then add to equation 2. To find K for equation 3 use $(1/K_1)(K_2)$.

$$
\begin{array}{lll}
HBO_2(aq) & \rightleftharpoons & \cancel{Hb(aq)} + O_2(aq) & K_1 = 1/1.8 \\
\cancel{Hb(aq)} + CO(aq) \rightleftharpoons & HbCO(aq) & K_2 = 306 \\
\hline
HBO_2(aq) + CO(aq) \rightleftharpoons & HbCO(aq) + O_2(aq) & K_3 = K_1 K_2 = (1/1.8)(306) = 170
\end{array}
$$

b) **Given:** $O_2 = 20\%$, $CO = 0.10\%$ **Find:** The ratio $\dfrac{[HbCO]}{[HbO_2]}$

Conceptual Plan: Determine the equilibrium expression and then determine $\dfrac{[HbCO]}{[HbO_2]}$

Solution: $K = \dfrac{[HbCO][O_2]}{[HbO_2][CO]}$ $170 = \dfrac{[HbCO](20.0)}{[HbO_2](0.10)}$ $\dfrac{[HbCO]}{[HbO_2]} = 170\left(\dfrac{0.10}{20.0}\right) = \dfrac{0.85}{1.0}$

Since the ratio is almost 1:1, 0.10% CO will replace about 50% of the O_2 in the blood. The CO blocks the uptake of O_2 by the blood and is therefore, highly toxic.

72. **Given:** $P = 1$ atm, $T = 298$ K, $N_2 = 78\%$, $O_2 = 21\%$, $K_p = 4.1 \times 10^{-31}$ **Find:** [NO] in molecules/cm^3
Conceptual Plan:
%vol → n → M and then K_p → K_c and then: **Prepare an ICE table; represent the change with**

$$PV = nRT \qquad \dfrac{n}{1 \text{ L air}} \qquad K_p = K_c(RT)^{\Delta n}$$

x; sum the table and determine the equilibrium values; put the equilibrium values in the equilibrium expression and solve for x. Determine [NO] in mol/L → molecules/cm^3

$$\dfrac{6.022 \times 10^{23} \text{ molecules}}{\text{mole}} \qquad \dfrac{1 \text{ L}}{1000 \text{ mL}} \qquad \dfrac{\text{mL}}{cm^3}$$

Solution: Assume 1 L of air.

$$n_{N_2} = \dfrac{(1 \text{ atm})(0.78 \text{ L})}{\left(0.0821\dfrac{L \cdot atm}{mol \cdot K}\right)(298 \text{ K})} = 0.03\underline{1}88 \text{ mol} \qquad n_{O_2} = \dfrac{(1 \text{ atm})(0.21 \text{ L})}{\left(0.0821\dfrac{L \cdot atm}{mol \cdot K}\right)(298 \text{ K})} = 0.008\underline{5}8 \text{ mol}$$

$[N_2] = 0.03\underline{1}88 \text{ mol/L}$ $[O_2] = 0.008\underline{5}8 \text{ mol/L}$

$$K_p = K_c(RT)^{\Delta n} \qquad K_c = \dfrac{K_p}{(RT)^{\Delta n}} = \dfrac{4.1 \times 10^{-31}}{\left((0.0821\dfrac{L \cdot atm}{mol \cdot K})(298K)\right)^0} = 4.1 \times 10^{-31}$$

$$
\begin{array}{lcccc}
& N_2 \text{ (g)} & +O_2 \text{ (g)} & \rightleftharpoons & 2 \text{ NO (g)} \\
& [N_2] & [O_2] & & [NO] \\
I & 0.03\underline{1}9 & 0.008\underline{5}8 & & 0.0 \\
C & -x & -x & & x \\
E & 0.03\underline{1}9{-}x & 0.008\underline{5}8{-}x & & x
\end{array}
$$

The reaction will proceed to the right by x

$$K_c = \frac{[NO]^2}{[N_2][O_2]} = \frac{(2x)^2}{(0.0319 - x)(0.00858 - x)} = 4.1 \times 10^{-31}$$

Assume x is small compared to 0.00858

$x = 5.\underline{2}9 \times 10^{-18}$ check assumption: $\dfrac{5.\underline{2}9 \times 10^{-18}}{0.00858} \times 100 = 6.2 \times 10^{-14}\%$

$[NO] = 2x = 2(5.\underline{2}9 \times 10^{-18}) = 1.\underline{0}6 \times 10^{-17} M$

$$1.\underline{0}6 \times 10^{-17} \frac{mol}{L} \times \frac{6.022 \times 10^{23} \text{ molecules}}{mol} \times \frac{L}{1000 \ mL} \times \frac{mL}{cm^3} = 6.38 \times 10^4 \frac{\text{molecules}}{cm^3}$$

$$= 6.4 \times 10^4 \frac{\text{molecules}}{cm^3}$$

Check: The answer is reasonable since the reaction has a small equilibrium constant so you would not expect to produce much product.
The reaction to produce NO is endothermic, so we can think of heat as a reactant. So, raising the temperature (as in an automobile engine) shifts the reaction to the right, producing more NO.

73. **Given:** $C_2H_4(g) + Cl_2(g) \leftrightarrows C_2H_4Cl_2(g)$ is exothermic
    Find: Which of the following will maximize $C_2H_4Cl_2$
    a) increasing the reaction volume. Will not maximize $C_2H_4Cl_2$. The chemical equation has 1 mole of gas on the right and 2 moles of gas on the left. Increasing the volume of the reaction mixture decreases the pressure and causes the reaction to shift to the left (toward the side with more moles of gas particles).

    b) removing $C_2H_4Cl_2$ as it forms. Will maximize $C_2H_4Cl_2$. Removing the $C_2H_4Cl_2$ will decrease the concentration of $C_2H_4Cl_2$ and will cause the reaction to shift to the right, producing more $C_2H_4Cl_2$.

    c) lowering the reaction temperature. Will maximize $C_2H_4Cl_2$. The reaction is exothermic so we can think of heat as a product. Lowering the temperature will cause the reaction to shift to the right, producing more $C_2H_4Cl_2$.

    d. adding Cl_2. Will maximize $C_2H_4Cl_2$. Adding Cl_2 increases the concentration of Cl_2 so the reaction shifts to the right which will produce more $C_2H_4Cl_2$.

74. **Given:** $C_2H_4(g) + I_2(g) \leftrightarrows C_2H_4I_2(g)$ is endothermic
    Find: Which of the following will maximize $C_2H_4I_2$
    a) decreasing the reaction volume: Will maximize $C_2H_4I_2$. The chemical equation has 1 mole of gas on the right and 2 moles of gas on the left. Decreasing the volume of the reaction mixture increases the pressure and causes the reaction to shift to the right (toward the side with less moles of gas particles).

    b) removing I_2 from the reaction mixture. Will not maximize $C_2H_4I_2$. Removing I_2 decreases the concentration of I_2 and the reaction will shift to the left to produce more I_2.

    c) raising the temperature of the reaction. Will maximize $C_2H_4I_2$. The reaction is endothermic so we can think of heat as a reactant. Raising the temperature will cause the reaction to shift to the right, producing more $C_2H_4I_2$.

    d) adding C_2H_4 to the reaction mixture. Will maximize $C_2H_4I_2$. Adding C_2H_4 will increase the concentration of C_2H_4 and cause the reaction to shift to the right to produce more $C_2H_4I_2$.

75. **Given:** Reaction 1 at equilibrium: $P_{H2} = 0.958$ atm; $P_{I2} = 0.877$ atm; $P_{HI} = 0.0200$ atm: reaction 2: $P_{H2} = P_{I2} = 0.621$ atm; $P_{HI} = 0.101$ atm **Find:** Is reaction 2 at equilibrium, if not, what is the P_{HI} at equilibrium.
    Conceptual Plan: Use equilibrium Partial Pressures to determine K_p. Use K_p to determine if reaction 2 is at equilibrium. Prepare an ICE table; and then calculate Q; compare Q and K_p and predict the direction of the reaction; represent the change with x; sum the table and determine the equilibrium values; put the equilibrium values in the equilibrium expression and solve for x. Determine P_{HI}.

    Solution: $H_2(g) + I_2(g) \leftrightarrows 2HI(g)$

$$\begin{array}{cccc} & P_{H2} & P_{I2} & P_{HI} \\ \text{Reaction 1:} & 0.958 & 0.877 & 0.020 \end{array}$$

$$K_p = \frac{P_{HI}^2}{P_{H_2}P_{I_2}} = \frac{(0.020)^2}{(0.958)(0.877)} = 4.7\underline{6}10 \times 10^{-4}$$

$$\begin{array}{cccc} & H_2(g) + & I_2(g) \leftrightarrows & 2HI(g) \\ \text{Reaction 2:} & P_{H2} & P_{I2} & P_{HI} \\ I & 0.621 & 0.621 & 0.101 \\ C & x & x & -2x \\ E & 0.621+x & 0.621+x & 0.101 -2x \end{array}$$

$$Q = \frac{P_{HI}^2}{P_{H_2}P_{I_2}} = \frac{0.101^2}{(0.621)(0.621)} = 0.0264: \quad Q > K \text{ so the reaction shifts to the left}$$

$$K_p = \frac{P_{HI}^2}{P_{H_2}P_{I_2}} = \frac{(0.101 - x)^2}{(0.621+x)(0.621+x)} = 4.7\underline{6}10 \times 10^{-4}$$

$$\sqrt{\frac{(0.101 - 2x)^2}{(0.621+x)(0.621+x)}} = \sqrt{4.7\underline{6}10 \times 10^{-4}}$$

$$\frac{(0.101 - 2x)}{(0.621+x)} = 2.1\underline{8}2 \times 10^{-2}$$

x = 0.04325 = 0.0433

$$P_{H_2} = P_{I_2} = 0.621+x = 0.621 + 0.0433 = 0.664 \text{ atm}; \quad P_{HI} = 0.101 - 2x = 0.101 - 2(0.0433) = 0.0144 \text{ atm}$$

Check: Plug the values into the equilibrium expression:

$$K_p = \frac{(0.0144)^2}{(0.664)} = 4.703 \times 10^{-4} = 4.70 \times 10^{-4} \text{ ; this value is close to the original equilbirium constant}$$

76. **Given:** Reaction 1 initial: $H_2S = 0.500$ M; $SO_2 = 0.500$M; H_2O at equilibrium = 0.0011 M: reaction 2: H_2S = 0.250 M; $SO_2 = 0.325$M; **Find:** $[H_2O]$ at equilibrium in reaction 2.
Conceptual Plan: Prepare an ICE table. Determine the equilibrium concentrations in reaction 1 and determine K_c. Use K_c to determine the equilibrium concentrations for reaction 2. Prepare an ICE table; and then calculate Q; compare Q and K_c and predict the direction of the reaction; represent the change with x; sum the table and determine the equilibrium values; put the equilibrium values in the equilibrium expression and solve for x. Determine $[H_2O]$.
Solution: $2H_2S(g) + SO_2(g) \leftrightarrows 3S(s) + 2H_2O(g)$

$$\begin{array}{ccccc} & [H_2S] & [SO_2] & [S] & [H_2O] \\ \text{Reaction 1:} & & & & \\ I & 0.500 & 0.500 & \text{constant} & \\ C & -2x & -x & & 2x \\ E & 0.500-x & 0.500-x & & 0.0011 \end{array}$$

2x = 0.0011, x = 5.5 × 10^{-4}

$[H_2S] = 0.500 - 0.0011 = 0.4989 \quad [SO_2] = 0.500 - 5.5 \times 10^{-4} = 0.49945$

$$K_c = \frac{[H_2O]^2}{[H_2S]^2[SO_2]} = \frac{(0.0011)^2}{(0.4989)^2(0.49945)} = 9.6\underline{9}8 \times 10^{-6}$$

$$2H_2S(g) + SO_2(g) \leftrightarrows 3S(s) + 2H_2O(g)$$

$$\begin{array}{ccccc} & [H_2S] & [SO_2] & [S] & [H_2O] \\ \text{Reaction 2:} & & & & \\ I & 0.250 & 0.325 & \text{constant} & \\ C & -2x & -x & & 2x \\ E & 0.250-x & 0.325-x & & 2x \end{array}$$

Reaction shifts to the right

$$K_c = \frac{[H_2O]^2}{[H_2S]^2[SO_2]} = \frac{(2x)^2}{(0.250-x)^2(0.325-x)} = 9.698 \times 10^{-6}$$

Assume x is small compared to 0.250 and 0.325

$$4x^2 = 1.9699 \times 10^{-7}$$
$$x^2 = 4.9248 \times 10^{-8}$$

$x = 2.22 \times 10^{-4}$ check assumption: $\frac{2.22 \times 10^{-4}}{0.250} = 8.9 \times 10^{-4} \times 100\% = 0.089\%$; assumption valid

$[H_2O] = 2x = 2(2.22 \times 10^{-4}) = 4.44 \times 10^{-4} M$

$[H_2S] = 0.250 - 2(2.22 \times 10^{-4}) = 0.250M$

$[SO_2] = 0.325 - 2.22 \times 10^{-4} = 0.325M$

Check: Plug the values into the equilibrium expression:

$K_c = \frac{(4.44 \times 10^{-4})^2}{(0.250)^2(0.325)} = 9.71 \times 10^{-6}$; this value is close to the original equilibrium constant

77. **Given:** 200.0 L container; 1.27 kg N_2; 0.310 kg H_2; 725K; $K_p = 5.3 \times 10^{-5}$
    Find: mass in g of NH_3 and % yield
    Conceptual Plan:

$K_p \rightarrow K_c$ and then kg $\rightarrow$ g $\rightarrow$ mol $\rightarrow$ M and then Prepare an ICE table; represent the change

$K_p = K_c(RT)^{\Delta n}$ $\frac{1000\ g}{kg}$ $\frac{g}{molar\ mass}$ $\frac{mol}{vol}$

with x; sum the table and determine the equilibrium values; put the equilibrium values in the equilibrium expression and solve for x. Determine [NH₃]. Then M $\rightarrow$ mol $\rightarrow$ g and then determine

M x vol   mol x molar mass

theoretical yield NH₃ $\rightarrow$ % yield

determine limiting reactant $\frac{actual\ yield}{theoretical\ yield}$

Solution:

$K_p = K_c(RT)^{\Delta n}$ $K_c = \frac{K_p}{(RT)^{\Delta n}} = \frac{5.3 \times 10^{-5}}{\left((0.0821 \frac{L \cdot atm}{mol \cdot K})(725K)\right)^{-2}} = 0.1877$

$n_{N_2} = 1.27\ kg\ N_2 \times \frac{1000\ g}{kg} \times \frac{1\ mol\ N_2}{28.00\ g\ N_2} = 45.357\ mol\ N_2$ $n_{H_2} = 0.310\ kg\ H_2 \times \frac{1000\ g}{kg} \times \frac{1\ mol\ H_2}{28.00\ g\ H_2} = 153.77\ mol\ H_2$

$$N_2(g) + 3H_2(g) \rightleftharpoons 2NH_3(g)$$

Reaction 1: $[N_2]$ $[H_2]$ $[NH_3]$
    I   0.2268   0.7689   0.0
    C   -x   -3x   2x
    E   0.2268-x 0.7689-3x 2x

Reaction shifts to the right

$$K_c = \frac{[NH_3]^2}{[N_2][H_2]^3} = \frac{(2x)^2}{(0.2268-x)(0.7689-3x)^3} = 0.1877$$

Assume x is small compared to 0.2268 and 0.7689

$\frac{(2x)^2}{(0.2268)(0.7689)^3} = 0.1877$ $x = 0.06956$ check assumption: $\frac{0.06956}{0.2268} \times 100 = 30.7$ not valid

Use method of successive substitution to solve for x.

$x = 0.0461$

$[NH_3] = 2x = 2(0.0461) = 0.0922M$

Check: Plug   the   values   into   the   equilibrium   expression:

$K_c = \frac{(0.0922)^2}{(0.2268 - 0.0461)(0.7689 - 3(0.0461))^3} = 0.1876$;

this value is close to the original equilbirium constant

488

Determine grams NH_3: $0.0922 \dfrac{\text{mol NH}_3}{\text{L}} \times \overline{200.0 \text{ L}} \times \dfrac{17.02 \text{ g NH}_3}{\text{mol NH}_3} = 313.8 \text{ g} = 3.1 \times 10^2 \text{ g}$

Determine the theoretical yield: Determine the limiting reactant:

$1.27 \text{ kg N}_2 \times \dfrac{1000 \text{ g}}{\text{kg}} \times \dfrac{1 \text{ mol N}_2}{28.0 \text{ g N}_2} \times \dfrac{2 \text{ mol NH}_3}{1 \text{ mol N}_2} \times \dfrac{17.02 \text{ g NH}_3}{\text{mol NH}_3} = 1544 \text{ g NH}_3$

$0.310 \text{ kg H}_2 \times \dfrac{1000 \text{ g}}{\text{kg}} \times \dfrac{1 \text{ mol H}_2}{2.016 \text{ g H}_2} \times \dfrac{2 \text{ mol NH}_3}{3 \text{ mol H}_2} \times \dfrac{17.02 \text{ g NH}_3}{\text{mol NH}_3} = 1745 \text{ g NH}_3$

N_2 produces the least amount of NH_3 therefore, it is the limiting reactant and the theoretical yield is 1.54×10^3 g NH_3.

% yield $= \dfrac{3.1 \times 10^2 \text{ g}}{1.54 \times 10^3 \text{ g}} \times 100 = 20.\%$

78. **Given:** $V = 85.0$ L, 22.3 kg CH_4, 55.4 kg CO_2 T = 825 K, $K_p = 4.5 \times 10^2$ **Find:** g H_2 at equilibrium
Conceptual Plan: kg → g → mol → P and then prepare an ICE table; represent the change

$$\dfrac{1000 \text{ g}}{\text{kg}} \quad \dfrac{\text{g}}{\text{molar mass}} \quad PV = nRT$$

with x; sum the table and determine the equilibrium values; put the equilibrium values in the equilibrium expression and solve for x. Determine $P(H_2)$. Then P → mol → g and then determine

$$PV = nRT \quad \text{mol x molar mass}$$

theoretical yield H_2 → %

determine limiting reactant

$\dfrac{\text{actual yield}}{\text{theoretical yield}}$

Solution:

$n_{CH_4} = 23.3 \text{ kg} \times \dfrac{1000 \text{ g}}{\text{kg}} \times \dfrac{1 \text{ mol}}{16.0 \text{ g}} = 1456.2 \text{ mol}$ $\quad P_{CH_4} = \dfrac{nRT}{V} = \dfrac{(1456 \text{ mol})(0.0821 \frac{\text{L} \cdot \text{atm}}{\text{mol} \cdot \text{K}})(825 \text{ K})}{85.0 \text{ L}} = 1160 \text{ atm}$

$n_{CO_2} = 55.4 \text{ kg} \times \dfrac{1000 \text{ g}}{\text{kg}} \times \dfrac{1 \text{ mol}}{44.0 \text{ g}} = 1259 \text{ mol}$ $\quad P_{CO_2} = \dfrac{nRT}{V} = \dfrac{(1259 \text{ mol})(0.0821 \frac{\text{L} \cdot \text{atm}}{\text{mol} \cdot \text{K}})(825 \text{ K})}{85.0 \text{ L}} = 1003 \text{ atm}$

$$CH_4(g) + CO_2(g) \rightleftharpoons 2CO(g) + 2H_2(g)$$

	P_{CH4}	P_{CO2}	P_{CO}	P_{H2}
I	1160	1003	0.00	0.00
C	-x	-x	2x	2x
E	1160-x	1003-x	2x	2x

$K_p = \dfrac{P_{CO}^2 P_{H_2}^2}{P_{CH_4} P_{CO_2}} = \dfrac{(2x)^2 (2x)^2}{(1160 - x)(1003 - x)} = 4.5 \times 10^2$

Assume x is small compared to 1003 and 1160

$x^4 = 3.27 \times 10^7$ $\quad x = 75.6$ $\quad$ check assumption: $\dfrac{75.6}{1003} \times 100 = 7.54\%$ assumption not valid

Use method of successive substitutions

$x = 73.0$

Check:

Plug into equilibrium expression: $K_p = \dfrac{P_{CO}^2 P_{H_2}^2}{P_{CH_4} P_{CO_2}} = \dfrac{(2(73.0))^2 (2(73.0))^2}{(1160 - 73.0)(1003 - 73.0)} = 4.49 \times 10^2 = 4.5 \times 10^2$;

which is the equilibrium constant
Determine the grams of H_2.

$P_{H_2} = 2(73.0) = 146 \text{ atm}$ $\quad n_{H_2} = \dfrac{PV}{RT} = \dfrac{(146 \text{ atm})(85.0 \text{ L})}{(0.0821 \frac{\text{L} \cdot \text{atm}}{\text{mol} \cdot \text{K}})(825 \text{ K})} = 183.3 \text{ mol}$

$183.3 \text{ mol} \times \dfrac{2.016 \text{ g H}_2}{\text{mol}} = 369.3 \text{ g} = 369 \text{ g H}_2$

Determine % yield

$$1456 \text{ mol CH}_4 \times \frac{2 \text{ mol H}_2}{\text{mol CH}_4} = 2912 \text{ mol H}_2$$

$$1259 \text{ mol CO}_2 \times \frac{2 \text{ mol H}_2}{\text{mol CO}_2} = 2518 \text{ mol H}_2$$

CO_2 is limiting reactant

$$\frac{183.2 \text{ mol H}_2}{2518 \text{ mol H}_2} \times 100 = 7.28\% \text{ yield}$$

79. **Given:** At equilibrium: $P_{CO} = 0.30$ atm; $P_{Cl2} = 0.10$ atm; $P_{COCl2} = 0.60$ atm, add 0.40 atm Cl_2
   Find: P_{CO} when system returns to equilibrium.
   Conceptual Plan: Use equilibrium Partial Pressures to determine K_p. For the new conditions: prepare an ICE table; represent the change with x; sum the table and determine the equilibrium values; put the equilibrium values in the equilibrium expression and solve for x. Determine P_{CO}.
   Solution: $CO(g) + Cl_2(g) \leftrightarrows COCl_2(g)$

   Condition 1: P_{CO} $\quad P_{Cl2}$ $\quad P_{COCl2}$
   $\qquad\qquad\quad$ 0.30 $\quad$ 0.10 $\quad$ 0.60

   $$K_p = \frac{P_{COCl_2}}{P_{CO}P_{Cl_2}} = \frac{(0.60)}{(0.30)(0.10)} = 20.$$

   $CO(g) + Cl_2(g) \leftrightarrows COCl_2(g)$

Condition 2:	P_{CO}	P_{Cl2}	P_{COCl2}
I	0.30	0.10+0.40	0.60
C	-x	-x	+x
E	0.30-x	0.50-x	0.60 + x

   Reaction shifts to the right because the concentration of Cl_2 was increased

   $$K_p = \frac{P_{COCl_2}}{P_{CO}P_{Cl_2}} = \frac{(0.60+x)}{(0.30-x)(0.50-x)} = 20$$

   $$20x^2 - 17x + 2.4 = 0$$

   $$\frac{-b \pm \sqrt{b^2 - 4ac}}{2a} = \frac{-(-17) \pm \sqrt{(-17)^2 - 4(20)(2.4)}}{2(20)}$$

   x = 0.67 or 0.18 So, x = 0.18

   $P_{CO} = 0.30 - 0.18 = 0.12$ atm; $P_{Cl_2} = 0.50 - 0.18 = 0.32$; $P_{COCl_2} = 0.60 + 0.18 = 0.78$ atm

   Check: Plug the values into the equilibrium expression:

   $$K_p = \frac{(0.78)}{(0.12)(0.32)} = 20.3 = 20. \text{ ; this is the same as the original equilbrium constant.}$$

80. **Given:** SO_2 P = 3.00 atm; O_2 P = 1.00 atm; at equilibrium, $P_{total} = 3.75$ atm; T = 27°C**Find:** K_c
   Conceptual Plan: Prepare an ICE table; represent the change with x; sum the table and determine the equilibrium values; use the total pressure and solve for x. Determine partial pressure of each at equilibrium. Determine $K_p \rightarrow K_c$.

   $$K_p = K_c(RT)^{\Delta n}$$

   Solution: $2SO_2(g) + O_2(g) \leftrightarrows 2SO_3(g)$

	P_{SO2}	P_{O2}	P_{SO3}
I	3.00	1.00	0.00
C	-2x	-x	+2x
E	3.00-2x	1.00-x	2x

$$P_{Total} = P_{SO_2} + P_{O_2} + P_{SO_3} \qquad 3.75 = 3.00 - 2x + (1.00 - x) + 2x$$

$$x = 0.25 \qquad P_{SO_2} = (3.00 - 2(0.25)) = 2.50 \text{ atm}; \quad P_{O_2} = (1.00 - 0.25) = 0.75 \text{ atm}; \quad P_{SO_3} = 2(0.25) = 0.50 \text{ atm}$$

$$K_p = \frac{P_{SO_3}^2}{P_{SO_2}^2 P_{O_2}} = \frac{(0.50)^2}{(2.50)^2 (0.75)} = 0.05\underline{3}3 = 0.053$$

Check: The value of the pressure of SO_3 is small compared to the pressures of SO_2 and O_2, therefore, you would expect K_p to be less than 1.

$$K_p = K_c (RT)^{\Delta n} \qquad 0.05\underline{3}3 = K_c ((0.0821 \frac{L \cdot atm}{mol \cdot K})(27 + 273K))^{-1}$$

$$K_c = 1.\underline{3}12 = 1.3$$

81. **Given:** $K_p = 0.76$; P_{total} at equilibrium = 1.00 **Find:** $P_{initial}$ CCl_4
Conceptual Plan: Prepare an ICE table; represent the P(CCl₄) with A and the change with x; sum the table and determine the equilibrium values; use the total pressure and solve for A in terms of x. Determine partial pressure of each at equilibrium use the equilibrium expression to determine x and then determine A

Solution: $CCl_4(g) \rightleftharpoons C(s) + 2Cl_2(g)$

	P_{CCl4}	P_C	P_{Cl2}
I	A	constant	0.00
C	-x		+2x
E	A-x		2x

$$P_{Total} = P_{CCl_4} + P_{Cl_2} \qquad 1.0 = A - x + 2x \qquad A = 1 - x$$

$$P_{CCl_4} = (A - x) = (1-x) - x = 1 - 2x; \quad P_{Cl_2} = (2x)$$

$$K_p = \frac{P_{Cl_2}^2}{P_{CCl_4}} = \frac{(2x)^2}{(1-2x)} = 0.76$$

$$4x^2 + 1.52x - 0.76 = 0 \qquad x = 0.285 \text{ or } -0.665 \text{ so } x = 0.2\underline{8}5$$

$$A = 1 - x = 1.0 - 0.285 = 0.715 = 0.72 \text{ atm}$$

Check: Plug values into equilibrium expression:

$$K_p = \frac{P_{Cl_2}^2}{P_{CCl_4}} = \frac{(2x)^2}{(A-x)} = \frac{(2(0.285))^2}{(0.715-0.285)} = 0.755 = 0.76; \text{ the original equilibrium constant}$$

82. **Given:** $K = 3.0$; $SO_2 = 2.4$ mol initial; $SO_3 = 1.2$ mol equilibrium **Find:** mol NO_2 initial
Conceptual Plan: Assume 1.0 L, prepare ICE table; represent the change with x; sum the table and determine the equilibrium values; determine initial values.
Solution: $SO_2(g) + NO_2(g) \rightleftharpoons SO_3(g) + NO(g)$

	$[SO_2]$	$[NO_2]$	$[SO_3]$	$[NO]$
I	2.4	y	0.0	0.0
C	-x	-x	x	x
E	1.2	y-1.2	1.2	1.2

$x = 1.2$, fill in table

$$K = \frac{[SO_3][NO]}{[SO_2][NO_2]} \qquad 3.0 = \frac{(1.2)(1.2)}{(1.2)(y - 1.2)} \qquad y = 1.6$$

mol NO_2 initial = 1.6 mol

83. **Given:** vol = 0.654 L, T = 1000 K, $K_p = 3.9 \times 10^{-2}$ **Find:** mass CaO as equilibrium
Conceptual Plan: $K_p \rightarrow P_{CO2} \rightarrow n(CO_2) \rightarrow n(CaO) \rightarrow g$
    PV = nRT   stoichiometry   g = n(molar mass)

Solution: Since $CaCO_3$ and CaO are solids, they are not included in the equilibrium expression.

$$K_p = P_{CO_2} = 3.9 \times 10^{-2} \qquad n = \frac{PV}{RT} = \frac{(3.9 \times 10^{-2} \text{ atm})(0.654 \text{ L})}{(0.0821 \frac{\text{L} \cdot \text{atm}}{\text{mol} \cdot \text{K}})(1000 \text{ K})} = 3.\underline{1}06 \times 10^{-4} \text{ mol } CO_2$$

$$3.\underline{1}06 \times 10^{-4} \text{ mol } CO_2 \times \frac{1 \text{ mol } CaO}{1 \text{ mol } CO_2} \times \frac{56.1 \text{ g } CaO}{1 \text{ mol } CaO} = 0.0174 \text{ g} = 0.017 \text{ g } CaO$$

Check: The small value of K would give a small amount of products, so we would not expect to have a large mass of CaO formed.

84. **Given:** at equilibrium: N_2O_4, P = 0.28 atm; NO_2, P = 1.1 atm; T = 350 K   **Find:** equilibrium pressures when volume doubles.

Conceptual Plan: $P(N_2O_4)$, $P(NO_2)$ → K_p and then P when volume doubles and then prepare ICE table; represent the change with x; sum the table and determine the equilibrium values.

Solution: $K_p = \dfrac{P_{NO_2}^2}{P_{N_2O_4}} = \dfrac{(1.1)^2}{0.28} = 4.\underline{3}21$

When the volume is doubled, the partial pressure of each gas will decrease by half.

$$N_2O_2(g) \leftrightharpoons 2NO_2(g)$$

	P_{N2O4}	P^2_{NO2}
I	0.28/2	1.1/2
C	-x	+2x
E	0.14-x	0.55+2x

Reaction shifts to the side with more moles, to the right

$$K_p = \frac{P_{NO_2}^2}{P_{N_2O_4}} = \frac{(0.55 + 2x)^2}{(0.14 - x)} = 4.\underline{3}21$$

$$4x^2 + 6.521x - 0.3024 = 0$$

$$\frac{-b \pm \sqrt{b^2 - 4ac}}{2a} = \frac{-(6.521) \pm \sqrt{(6.521)^2 - 4(4)(0.3024)}}{2(4)}$$

$x = 0.0451$ or -1.675 So, x = 0.0451

$P_{N_2O_4} = 0.14 - 0.0451 = 0.0949 \text{ atm} = 0.095 \text{ atm}$; $P_{NO_2} = 0.55 + 2(0.0451) = 0.6402 = 0.64 \text{ atm}$

Check: Plug the values into the equilibrium expression:

$$K_p = \frac{(0.6402)^2}{(0.0949)} = 4.31 = 4.3.\text{ ; this is the same as the original equilibrium constant.}$$

85. a) **Given:** NO (P = 522 torr), O_2 (P = 421 torr); at equilibrium, P_{total} = 748 torr   **Find:** K_p

Conceptual Plan: Prepare an ICE table; represent the change with x; sum the table and determine the equilibrium values; use the total pressure and solve for x. torr → atm → K_p

Solution: $2NO(g) + O_2(g) \leftrightharpoons 2NO_2(g)$

	P_{NO}	P_{O2}	P_{NO2}
I	522 torr	421 torr	0.00
C	-2x	-x	+2x
E	522-2x	421-x	2x

$P_{Total} = P_{NO} + P_{O_2} + P_{NO_2}$ $748 = 522 - 2x + (421 - x) + 2x$

$x = 195 \text{ torr}$ $P_{NO} = (522 - 2(195) = 132 \text{ torr}$; $P_{O_2} = (421 - 195) = 226 \text{ torr}$; $P_{NO_2} = 2(195) = 390 \text{ torr}$

$P_{NO} = 132 \text{ torr} \times \dfrac{1 \text{ atm}}{760 \text{ torr}} = 0.17\underline{3}7 \text{ atm}$; $P_{O_2} = 226 \text{ torr} \times \dfrac{1 \text{ atm}}{760 \text{ torr}} = 0.29\underline{7}4 \text{ atm}$; $P_{NO_2} = 390 \text{ torr} \times \dfrac{1 \text{ atm}}{760 \text{ torr}} = 0.51\underline{3}2 \text{ atm}$

$$K_p = \frac{P_{NO_2}^2}{P_{NO}^2 P_{O_2}} = \frac{(0.51\underline{3}2)^2}{(0.17\underline{3}7)^2 (0.29\underline{7}4)} = 29.34 = 29.3$$

b) **Given:** NO (P = 255 torr), O_2 (P = 185 torr), K_p = 29.3   **Find:** equilibrium P N_2O_4

Conceptual Plan:

torr → atm and then prepare an ICE table; represent the change with x; sum the table and

$$\frac{atm}{760 \text{ torr}}$$

determine the equilibrium values; put the equilibrium values in the equilibrium expression and solve for x. Determine P N_2O_4.

Solution: $P_{NO} = 255 \text{ torr} \times \dfrac{1 \text{ atm}}{760 \text{ torr}} = 0.33\underline{5}5 \text{ atm}$ $P_{O_2} = 185 \text{ torr} \times \dfrac{1 \text{ atm}}{760 \text{ torr}} = 0.24\underline{3}4 \text{ atm}$

$$2NO(g) + O_2(g) \rightleftarrows 2NO_2(g)$$

	P_{NO}	P_{O2}	P_{NO2}
I	0.3355	0.2434	0.00
C	-2x	-x	+2x
E	0.3355-2x	0.2434-x	2x

$$K_p = \frac{P_{NO_2}^2}{P_{NO}^2 P_{O_2}} = \frac{(2x)^2}{(0.3355 - 2x)^2 (0.2434-x)} = 29.3$$

$$x = 0.11\underline{1}25 \qquad P_{NO_2} = 2x = 2(0.11\underline{1}25) = 0.22\underline{2}5 \text{ atm}$$

$$0.22\underline{2}5 \text{ atm} \times \frac{760 \text{ torr}}{1 \text{ atm}} = 169.1 \text{ torr} = 169 \text{ torr}$$

Check: Plug the values into the equilibrium expression:

$$K_p = \frac{(0.22\underline{2}5)^2}{(0.1130)^2 (0.1322)} = 29.327 = 29.3 \text{ ; this is the same as the original equilibrium constant.}$$

86. **Given:** 2.75 L, 950 K, 0.100 mol SO_2, 0.100 mol O_2; K_p =0.355   **Find:** P_{total} at equilibrium
    Conceptual Plan:

       n → P and then prepare an ICE table; represent the change with x; sum the table and
       PV = nRT

determine the equilibrium values; put the equilibrium values in the equilibrium expression and solve
for x and then determine P for each reactant and product → P_{total}

$$P_{total} = P_{SO_2} + P_{O_2} + P_{SO_3}$$

Solution: $P = \dfrac{nRT}{V}$ $P_{O_2} = P_{SO_2} = \dfrac{(0.100 \text{ mol})(0.0821 \frac{L \cdot atm}{mol \cdot K})(950 \text{ K})}{2.75 \text{ L}} = 2.8\underline{3}6 \text{ atm}$

$$2SO_2(g) + O_2(g) \rightleftarrows 2SO_3(g)$$

	P_{SO2}	P_{O2}	P_{SO3}
I	2.836	2.836	0.00
C	-2x	-x	+2x
E	2.836-2x	2.836-x	2x

$$K_p = \frac{P_{SO_3}^2}{P_{SO_2}^2 P_{O_2}} = \frac{(2x)^2}{(2.836 - 2x)^2 (2.836 - x)} = 0.355$$

$$-1.42x^3 + 8.054x^2 - 14.275x + 8.096 = 0$$

$$x = 0.6629 = 0.663$$

$$P_{SO_3} = 2x = 2(0.663) = 1.3\underline{2}6 = 1.33 \text{ atm}$$

$$P_{SO_2} = (2.836 - 2x) = (2.836 - 2(0.663)) = 1.5\underline{1}0 = 1.51 \text{ atm}$$

$$P_{O_2} = (2.836 - x) = (2.836 - 0.663) = 2.1\underline{7}3 = 2.17 \text{ atm}$$

$$P_{Total} = 1.33 + 1.51 + 2.17 = 5.01 \text{ atm}$$

Check: Plug the values into the equilibrium expression:

$$K_p = \frac{P_{SO_3}^2}{P_{SO_2}^2 P_{O_2}} = \frac{(1.33)^2}{(1.51)^2 (2.17)} = 3.575;$$

this is within 3 significant figures of the original equilibrium constant.

87. **Given:** P(NOCl) at equilibrium = 115 torr; K_p = 0.27, T = 700 K,   **Find:** initial pressure NO, Cl_2
    Conceptual Plan:

       torr → atm and then prepare an ICE table; represent the change with x; sum the table and
       $\dfrac{atm}{760 \text{ torr}}$

determine the equilibrium values; put the equilibrium values in the equilibrium expression and
determine initial pressure.

Solution: $115 \text{ torr} \times \dfrac{1 \text{ atm}}{760 \text{ torr}} = 0.15\underline{1}3 \text{ atm}$

$$2NO(g) + Cl_2(g) \rightleftharpoons 2NOCl(g)$$

	P_{NO}	P_{Cl2}	P_{NOCl}
I	A	A	0.00
C	-2x	-x	+2x
E	A-2x	A-x	0.151
	A-0.151	A-0.0756	

Let A = initial pressure of NO and Cl_2

2x = 0.151, so, x = 0.0756

$$K_p = \frac{P_{NOCL}^2}{P_{NO}^2 P_{Cl_2}} = \frac{(0.151)^2}{(A - 0.151)^2 (A - 0.0756)} = 0.27$$

$$0.27A^3 - 0.1019A^2 + 0.01231A - 0.022336 = 0$$

$$A = 0.565$$

$$P_{NO} = P_{Cl_2} = A = 0.565 \text{atm} = 429 \text{ torr}$$

Check: Plug the values into the equilibrium expression:

$$K_p = \frac{P_{NOCL}^2}{P_{NO}^2 P_{Cl_2}} = \frac{(0.151)^2}{(0.565 - 0.151)^2 (0.565 - 0.0756)}\ 0.2\underline{7}2\ ;$$

this is within 1 significant figure of the original equilbrium constant.

88. **Given:** $P(N_2O_4) = 1$ atm, K_p reaction $1 = 1 \times 10^4$, K_p reaction $2 = 0.10$ **Find:** which component will have P > 0.2atm

Conceptual Plan: Use reaction 2 to determine $P(NO_2)$. Then, prepare an ICE table; represent the change with x; sum the table and determine the equilibrium values; put the equilibrium values in the equilibrium expression and solve for x

Solution:
$$2NO(g) \rightleftharpoons N_2O_4(g)$$

	P_{NO}	P_{N2O4}
I	0.00	1.00
C	+2x	-x
E	+2x	1.00 - x

$$K_p = \frac{P_{N_2O_4}}{P_{NO}^2} = \frac{(1.00 - x)}{(2x)^2} = 0.10$$

$$0.40x^2 + x - 1.00 = 0$$

$$\frac{-b \pm \sqrt{b^2 - 4ac}}{2a} = \frac{-1 \pm \sqrt{1^2 - 4(0.40)(-1.00)}}{2(0.40)}$$

$$x = 0.7655 = 0.77$$

$$P_{NO_2} = 2x = 1.54$$

Because K_p for reaction 1 is so large, essentially all of the material is products, so the P(NO) and P(O_2) will be negligible.

89. **Given:** P = 0.750 atm, density = 0.520 g/L, T = 337°C **Find:** K_c

Conceptual Plan: Prepare an ICE table; represent the P(CCl_4) with A and the change with x; sum the table and determine the equilibrium values; use the total pressure and solve for A in terms of x. Determine partial pressure of each at equilibrium in terms of x and then use the density to determine

$$d = \frac{PM}{RT}$$

the apparent molar mass and then use the mole fraction (in terms of P) and the molar mass of each

$$\chi_A = \frac{P_A}{P_{Total}}$$

gas, to determine x.

Solution:
$$2NO_2(g) \rightleftharpoons 2NO(g) + O_2(g)$$

	P_{NO2}	P_{NO}	P_{O2}
I	A	0.00	0.00
C	-2x	+2x	+x
E	A-2x	2x	x

$$P_{Total} = P_{NO_2} + P_{NO} + P_{O_2} \qquad 0.750 = A - 2x + 2x + x \qquad A = 0.750 - x$$

$$P_{NO_2} = (A - 2x) = (0.750 - x) - 2x = (0.750 - 3x); \quad P_{NO} = (2x); \quad P_{O_2} = x$$

$$d = \frac{PM}{RT} \qquad M = \frac{dRT}{P} = \frac{(0.520\,\frac{g}{\cancel{L}})(0.0821\frac{\cancel{L}\cdot atm}{mol\cdot \cancel{K}})(610\,\cancel{K})}{0.750\,\cancel{atm}} = 34.72\ g/mol$$

$$M = \chi_{NO_2}M_{NO_2} + \chi_{NO}M_{NO} + \chi_{O_2}M_{O_2} = \frac{P_{NO_2}}{P_{total}}M_{NO_2} + \frac{P_{NO}}{P_{total}}M_{NO} + \frac{P_{O_2}}{P_{total}}M_{O_2}$$

$$P_{Total}M = P_{NO_2}M_{NO_2} + P_{NO}M_{NO} + P_{O_2}M_{O_2}$$

$$(0.750)(34.7) = (0.750 - 3x)(46.0) + 2x(30.0) + x(32.0)$$

$$x = 0.184$$

$$K_p = \frac{P_{NO}^2 P_{O_2}}{P_{NO_2}^2} = \frac{(2x)^2(x)}{(0.750\text{-}3x)} = \frac{(2(0.184))^2(0.184)}{(0.750\text{-}3(0.184))^2} = 0.63\underline{5}6$$

$$K_p = K_c(RT)^{\Delta n} \qquad 0.63\underline{5}6 = K_c((0.0821\frac{L\cdot atm}{mol\cdot K})(610K))^1$$

$$K_c = 1.27 \times 10^{-2}$$

90. **Given:** Reaction 1 $K_c = 7.75$, Reaction 2 $K_c = 4.00$, $[N_2O_5]_{initial} = 4.00M$, $[O_2]_{equil} = 4.50M$
Find: concentration of other species at equilibrium
Conceptual Plan: **Combine reaction 1 and reaction 2 to get the overall reaction and then prepare an ICE table; represent the change with x; sum the table and determine the equilibrium values; use the total pressure and solve for x, use x to determine equilibrium concentration.**
Solution:

$$N_2O_5\,(g) \leftrightharpoons N_2O_3(g) + O_2(g) \qquad K_1 = 7.75$$
$$\cancel{N_2O_3}(g) \leftrightharpoons N_2O(g) + O_2(g) \qquad K_2 = 4.00$$
$$\overline{N_2O_5(g) \leftrightharpoons N_2O(g) + 2O_2(g)} \qquad K = K_1K_2 = 31.0$$

I	4.00	0.00	0.00
C	-x	x	2x
E	4.00 – x	x	4.50

$$K_c = \frac{[N_2O][O_2]^2}{[N_2O_5]} = 31.0 = \frac{(x)(4.50)^2}{(4.00 - x)}$$

$$x = 2.42$$

$$[N_2O_5] = 4.00 - x = 4.00 - 2.42 = 1.58M$$

$$[N_2O] = x = 2.42M$$

$$[O_2] = 4.50M$$

Use either reaction 1 or reaction 2 and solve for $[N_2O_3]$

$$K_c = \frac{[N_2O_3][O_2]}{[N_2O_5]} = 7.75 = \frac{(y)(4.50)}{(1.58)}$$

$$y = 2.72$$

$$[N_2O_3] = y = 2.72M$$

Check: Plug the values into the equilibrium expression into any of the equilibrium expressions:
e.g. For the overall reaction:

$$K_c = \frac{[N_2O][O_2]^2}{[N_2O_5]} = \frac{(2.42)(4.50)^2}{(1.58)} = 31.0;\ \text{the equilibrium constant}$$

e.g. For reaction 2:

$$K_c = \frac{[N_2O][O_2]}{[N_2O_3]} = \frac{(2.42)(4.50)}{(2.72)} = 4.00$$

91. Yes, the direction will depend on the volume. If the initial moles of A and B are equal, the initial concentration of A and B are equal regardless of the volume. Since $K_c = \frac{[B]^2}{[A]} = 1$, if the volume is such that the $[A] = [B] < 1.0$, than $Q < K$ and the reaction goes right to reach equilibrium, but, if the volume is such that the $[A] = [B] > 1.0$, than $Q > K$ and the reaction goes left to reach equilibrium.

92. $K_p = 0.50$ means that P(products) < P(reactants). If the reactants and products are in their standard states, than P of each reactant and product = 1.0. So $Q > K$ and to reach equilibrium the reaction will have to shift left.

93. An examination of the data shows when $P_A = 1.0$ then $P_B = 1.0$, therefore, $K_p = \dfrac{P_B^b}{P_A^a} = \dfrac{(1.0)^b}{(1.0)^a} = 1.0$.

Therefore, the value of the numerator and denominator must be equal. We see from the data that $P_B = \sqrt{P_A}$, so $P_B^2 = P_A$. Since, the stoichiometric coefficients become exponents in the equilibrium expression, $a = 1$ and $b = 2$.

Chapter 15
Acids and Bases

1. The pain of heartburn is caused by hydrochloric acid which is excreted in the stomach to kill microorganisms and activate enzymes that break down food. The hydrochloric acid can sometimes back up out of the stomach and into the esophagus, a phenomenon known as acid reflux. When hydrochloric acid comes in contact with the lining of the esophagus, the H^+ ions irritate the esophageal tissues, resulting the burning sensation. The simplest way to relieve mild heartburn is to swallow repeatedly. Saliva contains bicarbonate ion (HCO_3^-) that acts as a base and, when swallowed, neutralizes some of the acid in the esophagus. Heartburn can also be treated with antacids such as Tums, milk of magnesia, or Mylanta. These over – the – counter medications contain more base than does saliva and therefore, do a better job of neutralizing the esophageal acid.

2. Acids have the following general properties: a sour taste, the ability to dissolve many metals, the ability to turn blue litmus paper red, and the ability to neutralize bases.
   Bases have the following general properties: a bitter taste, a slippery feel, the ability to turn red litmus paper blue, and the ability to neutralize acids.

3. A carboxylic acid contains the following group of atoms: H——O——C—— (with =O above the C). Carboxylic acids are often found in substances derived from living organisms. Examples are citric acid, malic acid, acetic acid.

4. An Arrhenius acid is a substance that produces H^+ in aqueous solution.
   An Arrhenius base is a substance that produces OH^- in aqueous solution.

5. The hydronium ion is H_3O^+. In water, H^+ ions always associate with H_2O molecules to form hydronium ions and other associated species with the general formula $H(H_2O)_n^+$.

6. A Bronsted – Lowry acid is a proton (H^+) donor.
   A Bronsted – Lowry base is a proton (H^+) acceptor.

7. According to Huheey: " The differences between the various acid – base concepts are not concerned with which is right, but which is most convenient to use in a particular situation." There is no single correct definition, we use the definition that is best for a particular situation.

8. Amphoteric substances are those that can act as acids or bases depending on the circumstances. Some amphoteric substances are H_2O and NH_3.

9. A conjugate acid – base pair are two substances related to each other by the transfer of a proton. In the reaction:
   $NH_3(aq) + H_2O(l) \leftrightarrows NH_4^+(aq)$ and $OH^-(aq)$, the conjugate pairs are: NH_3/NH_4^+ and H_2O/OH^-.

10. A strong acid completely ionizes in solution. An example is HCl.
    A weak acid only partially ionizes in solution. An example is HF.

11. A diprotic acid is one that contains two ionizable protons. An example is H_2SO_4.
    A triprotic acid is one that contains three ionizable protons. An example is H_3PO_4.

12. An acid ionization constant (K_a) is the equilibrium constant for the ionization reaction of a weak acid. The smaller the acid ionization constant, the weaker the acid.

13. The autoionization of water is: $H_2O(l) + H_2O(l) \leftrightarrows H_3O^+(aq) + OH^-(aq)$
    and has the ion product of water: $K_w = [H_3O^+][OH^-]$.
    It can also be written: $H_2O(l) \leftrightarrows H^+(aq) + OH^-(aq)$ and the ion product of water is: $K_w = [H^+][OH^-]$.
    At 25 $^\circ$C, $K_w = 1.0 \times 10^{-14}$.

14. Since $K_w = 1.0 \times 10^{-14}$, the concentration of H_3O^+ time the concentration of OH^- is always 1.0×10^{-14}, therefore, if $[H_3O^+]$ increases, then $[OH^-]$ decreases and if the $[H_3O^+]$ decreases, then $[OH^-]$ increases.

15. We define pH as: $pH = -\log[H_3O^+]$. An acidic solution has a pH < 7, a basic solution has a pH > 7 and a neutral solution has a pH = 7.

16. We define pH as: $pOH = -\log[OH^-]$. An acidic solution has pOH > 7, a basic solution has pOH < 7, and a neutral solution has pOH = 7.

17. We can neglect the contribution of the autoionization of water to the H_3O^+ concentration in a solution of a strong or weak acid because it is negligible compared to the concentration from the acid itself. Even the weakest of the weak acids has an ionization constant that is four orders of magnitude larger than that of water.

18. The x is small approximation is used when the equilibrium constant is relatively small and the initial concentration is relatively large. We make the assumption that x is small compared to the initial concentration. If the assumption is valid, x is < 5% of the initial concentration.

19. The percent ionization is defined as: $\text{percent ionization} = \dfrac{\text{concentraion of ionized acid}}{\text{initial concentraion of acid}} \times 100$. The percent ionization of a weak acid decreases with the increasing concentration of the acid.

20. The complete ionization of the strong acid produces a significant concentration of H_3O^+ and suppresses the formation of additional H_3O^+ by the ionization of the weak acid. Because of Le Chatelier's principle, the formation of H_3O^+ by the strong acid causes the weak acid to ionize even less than it would in the absence of the strong acid.

21. $B(aq) + H_2O(l) \leftrightarrows BH^+(aq) + OH^-(aq)$

22. An anion that is the conjugate base of a weak acid is itself a weak base. An anion that is the conjugate base of a strong acid is pH – neutral. $A^-(aq) + H_2O(l) \leftrightarrows HA(aq) + OH^-(aq)$

23. At 25 °C, the product of K_a for and acid and K_b for its conjugate base is $K_w = 1.0 \times 10^{-14}$.

24. A cation that is the conjugate acid of a weak base such as NH_4^+ is a weak acid. Small highly charged metal cations such as Al^{3+} and Fe^{3+} form weakly acidic solutions.

25. For most polyprotic acids, K_{a1} is much larger than K_{a2}. Therefore, the amount of H_3O^+ contributed by the first ionization step is much larger than that contributed by the second or third ionization step. In addition, the production of H_3O^+ by the first step inhibits additional production of H_3O^+ by the second step because of Le Chatelier's principle.

26. For a weak diprotic acid, $[X^{2-}] = K_{a2}$. This result is general for all diprotic acids in which the x is small approximation is valid.

27. For an H – Y binary acid, the factors affecting the ease with which this hydrogen will be donated are the polarity of the bond and the strength of the bond.

28. The factors affecting the ease with which the hydrogen will be donated (and therefore acidic) are the electronegativity of the element Y and the number of oxygen atoms attached tot he element Y.

29. A Lewis acid is an electron pair acceptor. A Lewis base is an electron pair donor.

30. A Lewis acid has an empty orbital (or can rearrange electrons to create an empty orbital) that can accept an electron pair. A Lewis base has a lone pair of electrons it can donate to the Lewis acid.

31. The combustion of fossil fuels produces oxides of sulfur and nitrogen, which react with oxygen and water to form sulfuric and nitric acids. These acids then combine with rain to form acid rain. Acid rain is a significant problem in the northeastern United States.

32. Acid rain corrodes man – made structures and also damages aquatic environments and forests. Environmental legislation has helped stabilize the amount of acid rain being produced.

33. a) acid $HNO_3(aq) \rightarrow H^+(aq) + NO_3^-(aq)$

b) acid $NH_4^+(aq) \rightarrow H^+(aq) + NH_3(aq)$

c) base $KOH(aq) \rightarrow K^+(aq) + OH^-(aq)$

d) acid $HC_2H_3O_2(aq) \rightarrow H^+(aq) + C_2H_3O_2^-(aq)$

34. a) base $NaOH(aq) \rightarrow Na^+(aq) + OH^-(aq)$

     b) acid $H_2SO_4(aq) \rightarrow 2H^+(aq) + SO_4^{2-}(aq)$

     c) acid $HBr(aq) \rightarrow H^+(aq) + Br^-(aq)$

     d) base $Sr(OH)_2 \rightarrow Sr^{2+}(aq) + 2OH^-(aq)$

35. a) Since H_2CO_3 donates a proton to H_2O it is the acid. After H_2CO_3 donates the proton it becomes HCO_3^-, the conjugate base. Since H_2O accepts a proton, it is the base. After H_2O accepts the proton it becomes H_3O^+ the conjugate acid.

     b) Since H_2O donates a proton to NH_3 it is the acid. After H_2O donates the proton it becomes OH^-, the conjugate base. Since NH_3 accepts a proton, it is the base. After NH_3 accepts the proton it becomes NH_4^+ the conjugate acid.

     c) Since HNO_3 donates a proton to H_2O it is the acid. After HNO_3 donates the proton it becomes NO_3^-, the conjugate base. Since H_2O accepts a proton, it is the base. After H_2O accepts the proton it becomes H_3O^+ the conjugate acid.

     d) Since H_2O donates a proton to C_5H_5N it is the acid. After H_2O donates the proton it becomes OH^-, the conjugate base. Since C_5H_5N accepts a proton, it is the base. After C_5H_5N accepts the proton it becomes $C_5H_5NH^+$ the conjugate acid.

36. a) Since HI donates a proton to H_2O it is the acid. After HI donates the proton it becomes I^-, the conjugate base. Since H_2O accepts a proton, it is the base. After H_2O accepts the proton it becomes H_3O^+ the conjugate acid.

     b) Since H_2O donates a proton to CH_3NH_2 it is the acid. After H_2O donates the proton it becomes OH^-, the conjugate base. Since CH_3NH_2 accepts a proton, it is the base. After CH_3NH_2 accepts the proton it becomes $CH_3NH_3^+$ the conjugate acid.

     c) Since H_2O donates a proton to CO_3^{2-} it is the acid. After H_2O donates the proton it becomes OH^-, the conjugate base. Since CO_3^{2-} accepts a proton, it is the base. After CO_3^{2-} accepts the proton it becomes HCO_3^- the conjugate acid.

     d) Since HBr donates a proton to H_2O it is the acid. After HBr donates the proton it becomes Br^-, the conjugate base. Since H_2O accepts a proton, it is the base. After H_2O accepts the proton it becomes H_3O^+ the conjugate acid.

37. a) Cl^- $HCl(aq) + H_2O(l) \rightarrow H_3O^+(aq) + Cl^-(aq)$

     b) HSO_3^- $H_2SO_3(aq) + H_2O(l) \rightleftarrows H_3O^+(aq) + HSO_3^-(aq)$

     c) CHO_2^- $HCHO_2(aq) + H_2O(l) \rightleftarrows H_3O^+(aq) + CHO_2^-(aq)$

     d) F^- $HF(aq) + H_2O(l) \rightleftarrows H_3O^+(aq) + F^-(aq)$

38. a) NH_4^+ $NH_3(aq) + H_2O(l) \rightleftarrows NH_4^+(aq) + OH^-(aq)$

     b) $HClO_4$ $HClO_4(aq) + H_2O(l) \rightarrow H_3O^+(aq) + ClO_4^-(aq)$

c) H_2SO_4 $H_2SO_4(aq) + H_2O(l) \rightarrow H_3O^+(aq) + HSO_4^-(aq)$

d) HCO_3^- $HCO_3^-(aq) + H_2O(l) \leftrightarrows H_2CO_3(aq) + OH^-(aq)$

39. $H_2PO_4^- + H_2O(l) \leftrightarrows H_3O^+(aq) + HPO_4^{2-}(aq)$
$H_2PO_4^- + H_2O(l) \leftrightarrows H_3PO_4(aq) + OH^-(aq)$

40. $HCO_3^-(aq) + H_2O(l) \leftrightarrows H_3O^+(aq) + CO_3^{2-}(aq)$
$HCO_3^-(aq) + H_2O(l) \leftrightarrows H_2CO_3(aq) + OH^-(aq)$

41. a) HNO_3 is a strong acid

b) HCl is a strong acid

c) HBr is a strong acid

d) H_2SO_3 is a weak acid $H_2SO_3(aq) + H_2O(l) \leftrightarrows H_3O^+(aq) + HSO_3^-(aq)$
$$K_a = \frac{[H_3O^+][HSO_3^-]}{[H_2SO_3]}$$

42. a) HF is a weak acid $HF(aq) + H_2O(l) \leftrightarrows H_3O^+(aq) + F^-(aq)$
$$K_a = \frac{[H_3O^+][F^-]}{[HF]}$$

b) $HCHO_2$ is a weak acid $HCHO_2(aq) + H_2O(l) \leftrightarrows H_3O^+(aq) + CHO_2^-(aq)$
$$K_a = \frac{[H_3O^+][CHO_2^-]}{[HCHO_2]}$$

c) H_2SO_4 is a strong acid

d) H_2CO_3 is a weak acid $H_2CO_3(aq) + H_2O(l) \leftrightarrows H_3O^+(aq) + HCO_3^-(aq)$
$$K_{a_1} = \frac{[H_3O^+][HCO_3^-]}{[H_2CO_3]}$$

43. a) contains no HA, 10 H^+, and 10 A^-

b) contains 3 HA, 3 H^+, and 7 A^-

c) contains 9 HA, 1 H^+, and 1 A^-
So, solution a > solution b > solution c

44. HCl is a strong acid, $K_a(HF) = 3.5 \times 10^{-4}$, $K_a(HClO) = 2.9 \times 10^{-8}$, $K_a(HC_6H_5O) = 1.3 \times 10^{-10}$
The larger the value of K_a the stronger the acid and the greater the $[H_3O^+]$.
The order of decreasing $[H_3O^+]$ is HCl > HF > HClO > HC_6H_5O

45. a) F^- is a stronger base than Cl^-.
F^- is the conjugate base of HF(a weak acid), Cl^- is the conjugate base of HCl(a strong acid), the weaker the acid, the stronger the conjugate base.

b) NO_2^- is a stronger base than NO_3^-.
NO_2^- is the conjugate base of HNO_2(a weak acid), NO_3^- is the conjugate base of HNO_3(a strong acid), the weaker the acid, the stronger the conjugate base.

c) ClO^- is a stronger base than F^-.
F^- is the conjugate base of HF ($K_a = 3.5 \times 10^{-4}$), ClO^- is the conjugate base of HClO($K_a = 2.9 \times 10^{-8}$)
HClO is the weaker acid, the weaker the acid, the stronger the conjugate base.

46. a) ClO_2^- is a stronger base than ClO_4^-.

500

ClO_2^- is the conjugate base of $HClO_2$(a weak acid), ClO_4^- is the conjugate base of $HClO_4$(a strong acid), the weaker the acid, the stronger the conjugate base.

b) H_2O is a stronger base than Cl^-.
   H_2O is the conjugate base of H_3O^+, Cl^- is the conjugate base of HCl(a strong acid), the weaker the acid, the stronger the conjugate base.

c) CN^- is stronger base than ClO^-.
   CN^- is the conjugate base of HCN($K_a = 4.9$ x 10^{-10}), ClO^- is the conjugate base of HClO ($K_a = 2.9$ x 10^{-8}), the weaker the acid, the stronger the conjugate base.

47. a) **Given:** $K_w = 1.0$ x 10^{-14},$[H_3O^+] = 9.7$ x 10^{-9} M   **Find:** [OH$^-$]
      Conceptual Plan: [H$_3$O$^+$] → [OH$^-$]
      $$K_w = 1 \text{ x } 10^{-14} = [H_3O^+][OH^-]$$
      Solution:
      $K_w = 1 \text{ x } 10^{-14} = (9.7 \text{ x } 10^{-9})[OH^-]$

      $[OH^-] = 1.0 \text{ x } 10^{-6}$M

      $[OH^-] > [H_3O^+]$ so the solution is basic

   b) **Given:** $K_w = 1.0$ x 10^{-14},$[H_3O^+] = 2.2$ x 10^{-6} M   **Find:** [OH$^-$]
      Conceptual Plan: [H$_3$O$^+$] → [OH$^-$]
      $$K_w = 1 \text{ x } 10^{-14} = [H_3O^+][OH^-]$$
      Solution:
      $K_w = 1 \text{ x } 10^{-14} = (2.2 \text{ x } 10^{-6})[OH^-]$

      $[OH^-] = 4.5 \text{ x } 10^{-9}$M

      $[H_3O^+] > [OH^-]$ so the solution is acidic

   c) **Given:** $K_w = 1.0$ x 10^{-14},$[H_3O^+] = 1.2$ x 10^{-9}M   **Find:** [OH$^-$]
      Conceptual Plan: [H$_3$O$^+$] → [OH$^-$]
      $$K_w = 1 \text{ x } 10^{-14} = [H_3O^+][OH^-]$$
      Solution:
      $K_w = 1 \text{ x } 10^{-14} = (1.2 \text{ x } 10^{-9})[OH^-]$

      $[OH^-] = 8.3 \text{ x } 10^{-6}$M

      $[OH^-] > [H_3O^+]$ so the solution is basic

48. a) **Given:** $K_w = 1.0$ x 10^{-14}, $[OH^-] = 5.1$ x 10^{-4}M   **Find:** [H$_3$O$^+$]
      Conceptual Plan: [OH$^-$] → [H$_3$O$^+$]
      $$K_w = 1 \text{ x } 10^{-14} = [H_3O^+][OH^-]$$
      Solution:
      $K_w = 1 \text{ x } 10^{-14} = [H_3O^+](5.1 \text{ x } 10^{-4})$

      $[H_3O^+] = 2.0 \text{ x } 10^{-11}$M

      $[OH^-] > [H_3O^+]$ so the solution is basic

   b) **Given:** $K_w = 1.0$ x 10^{-14}, $[OH^-] = 1.7$ x 10^{-12} M   **Find:** [H$_3$O$^+$]
      Conceptual Plan: [OH$^-$] → [H$_3$O$^+$]
      $$K_w = 1 \text{ x } 10^{-14} = [H_3O^+][OH^-]$$
      Solution:
      $K_w = 1 \text{ x } 10^{-14} = [H_3O^+](1.7 \text{ x } 10^{-12})$

      $[H_3O^+] = 5.9 \text{ x } 10^{-3}$M

      $[H_3O^+] > [OH^-]$ so the solution is acidic

   c) **Given:** $K_w = 1.0$ x 10^{-14}, $[OH^-] = 2.8$ x 10^{-2}M   **Find:** [H$_3$O$^+$]
      Conceptual Plan: [OH$^-$] → [H$_3$O$^+$]
      $$K_w = 1 \text{ x } 10^{-14} = [H_3O^+][OH^-]$$

Solution:

$K_w = 1 \times 10^{-14} = [H_3O^+](2.8 \times 10^{-2})$

$[H_3O^+] = 3.6 \times 10^{-13} M$

$[OH^-] > [H_3O^+]$ so the solution is basic

49. a) **Given:** $[H_3O^+] = 1.7 \times 10^{-8} M$ **Find:** pH and pOH

    Conceptual Plan: $[H_3O^+] \rightarrow$ **pH** $\rightarrow$ **pOH**

                     $pH = -\log[H_3O^+]$ $pH + pOH = 14$

    Solution: $pH = -\log(1.7 \times 10^{-8}) = 7.77$ $pOH = 14.00 - 7.77 = 6.23$

    $pH > 7$ so the solution is basic.

    b) **Given:** $[H_3O^+] = 1. \times 10^{-7} M$ **Find:** pH and pOH

    Conceptual Plan: $[H_3O^+] \rightarrow$ **pH** $\rightarrow$ **pOH**

                     $pH = -\log[H_3O^+]$ $pH + pOH = 14$

    Solution: $pH = -\log(1.0 \times 10^{-7}) = 7.00$ $pOH = 14.00 - 7.00 = 7.00$

    $pH = 7$ so the solution is neutral.

    c) **Given:** $[H_3O^+] = 2.2 \times 10^{-6} M$ **Find:** pH and pOH

    Conceptual Plan: $[H_3O^+] \rightarrow$ **pH** $\rightarrow$ **pOH**

                     $pH = -\log[H_3O^+]$ $pH + pOH = 14$

    Solution: $pH = -\log(2.2 \times 10^{-6}) = 5.66$ $pOH = 14.00 - 5.66 = 8.34$

    $pH < 7$ so the solution is acidic.

50. a) **Given:** $pH = 8.55$ **Find:** $[H_3O^+], [OH^-]$

    Conceptual Plan: pH $\rightarrow [H_3O^+] \rightarrow [OH^-]$

                    $pH = -\log[H_3O^+]$ $K_w = 1 \times 10^{-14} = [H_3O^+][OH^-]$

    Solution: $pH = -\log[H_3O^+]$ $8.55 = -\log[H_3O^+]$

            $-8.55 = \log[H_3O^+]$ $10^{-8.55} = 10^{\log[H_3O^+]}$

            $10^{-8.55} = [H_3O^+]$ $[H_3O^+] = 2.8 \times 10^{-9}$

            $K_w = 1 \times 10^{-14} = (2.8 \times 10^{-9})[OH^-]$

            $[OH^-] = 3.6 \times 10^{-6} M$

    b) **Given:** $pH = 11.23$ **Find:** $[H_3O^+], [OH^-]$

    Conceptual Plan: pH $\rightarrow [H_3O^+] \rightarrow [OH^-]$

                    $pH = -\log[H_3O^+]$ $K_w = 1 \times 10^{-14} = [H_3O^+][OH^-]$

    Solution: $pH = -\log[H_3O^+]$ $11.23 = -\log[H_3O^+]$

           $-11.23 = \log[H_3O^+]$ $10^{-11.23} = 10^{\log[H_3O^+]}$

          $10^{-11.23} = [H_3O^+]$ $[H_3O^+] = 5.9 \times 10^{-12}$

            $K_w = 1 \times 10^{-14} = (5.9 \times 10^{-12})[OH^-]$

            $[OH^-] = 1.7 \times 10^{-3} M$

    c) **Given:** $pH = 2.87$ **Find:** $[H_3O^+], [OH^-]$

    Conceptual Plan: pH $\rightarrow [H_3O^+] \rightarrow [OH^-]$

                    $pH = -\log[H_3O^+]$ $K_w = 1 \times 10^{-14} = [H_3O^+][OH^-]$

    Solution: $pH = -\log[H_3O^+]$ $2.87 = -\log[H_3O^+]$

           $-2.87 = \log[H_3O^+]$ $10^{-2.87} = 10^{\log[H_3O^+]}$

          $10^{-2.87} = [H_3O^+]$ $[H_3O^+] = 1.3 \times 10^{-3}$

            $K_w = 1 \times 10^{-14} = (1.3 \times 10^{-3})[OH^-]$

            $[OH^-] = 7.4 \times 10^{-12} M$

51. $pH = -\log[H_3O^+]$ $K_w = 1 \times 10^{-14} = [H_3O^+][OH^-]$

$[H_3O^+]$	$[OH^-]$	pH	Acidic or basic
7.1×10^{-4}	1.4×10^{-11}	**3.15**	acidic
3.7×10^{-9}	2.7×10^{-6}	8.43	basic
8×10^{-12}	1×10^{-3}	**11.1**	basic
6.2×10^{-4}	**1.6×10^{-11}**	3.20	acidic

$[H_3O^+] = 10^{-3.15} = 7.1 \times 10^{-4}$ $[OH^-] = \dfrac{1 \times 10^{-14}}{7.1 \times 10^{-4}} = 1.4 \times 10^{-11}$

$[OH^-] = \dfrac{1 \times 10^{-14}}{3.7 \times 10^{-9}} = 2.7 \times 10^{-6}$ $pH = -\log(3.7 \times 10^{-9}) = 8.43$

$[H_3O^+] = 10^{-11.1} = 8 \times 10^{-12}$ $[OH^-] = \dfrac{1 \times 10^{-14}}{8 \times 10^{-12}} = 1 \times 10^{-3}$

$[H_3O^+] = \dfrac{1 \times 10^{-14}}{1.6 \times 10^{-11}} = 6.2 \times 10^{-4}$ $pH = -\log(6.2 \times 10^{-4}) = 3.20$

52. $pH = -\log[H_3O^+]$ $K_w = 1 \times 10^{-14} = [H_3O^+][OH^-]$

$[H_3O^+]$	$[OH^-]$	pH	Acidic or basic
3.5×10^{-3}	2.9×10^{-12}	2.46	acidic
2.6×10^{-8}	**3.8×10^{-7}**	7.58	basic
1.8×10^{-9}	5.6×10^{-6}	8.74	basic
7.1×10^{-8}	1.4×10^{-7}	**7.15**	basic

$[OH^-] = \dfrac{1 \times 10^{-14}}{3.5 \times 10^{-3}} = 2.9 \times 10^{-12}$ $pH = -\log(3.5 \times 10^{-3}) = 2.46$

$[H_3O^+] = \dfrac{1 \times 10^{-14}}{3.8 \times 10^{-7}} = 2.6 \times 10^{-8}$ $pH = -\log(2.6 \times 10^{-8}) = 7.58$

$[OH^-] = \dfrac{1 \times 10^{-14}}{1.8 \times 10^{-9}} = 5.6 \times 10^{-6}$ $pH = -\log(1.8 \times 10^{-9}) = 8.74$

$[H_3O^+] = 10^{-7.15} = 7.1 \times 10^{-8}$ $[OH^-] = \dfrac{1 \times 10^{-14}}{7.1 \times 10^{-8}} = 1.4 \times 10^{-7}$

53. **Given:** $K_w = 2.4 \times 10^{-14}$ at 37°C   **Find:** $[H_3O^+]$, pH
   Conceptual Plan: $K_w \rightarrow [H_3O^+] \rightarrow pH$
   $$K_w = [H_3O^+][OH^-] \quad pH = -\log[H_3O^+]$$
   Solution: $H_2O(l) + H_2O(l) \rightleftharpoons H_3O^+(aq) + OH^-(aq)$
   $K_w = [H_3O^+][OH^-]$
   $[H_3O^+] = [OH^-] = \sqrt{K_w} = \sqrt{2.4 \times 10^{-14}} = 1.5 \times 10^{-7}$
   $pH = -\log[H_3O^+] = -\log(1.6 \times 10^{-7}) = 6.82$
   Check: The value of K_w increased indicating more products formed, so the $[H_3O^+]$ increases and the pH decreases from the values at 25°C

54. The increasing value of K_w indicates more products are formed as the temperature increases. According to Le Chatelier, this means the heat is a reactant. Therefore, the autoionization of water is endothermic.

55. a) **Given:** 0.15M HCl   (strong acid)   **Find:** $[H_3O^+]$, $[OH^-]$, pH
   Conceptual Plan: [HCl] $\rightarrow$ $[H_3O^+]$ $\rightarrow$ pH and then $[H_3O^+]$ $\rightarrow$ $[OH^-]$
   $$[HCl] \rightarrow [H_3O^+] \quad pH = -\log[H_3O^+] \qquad [H_3O^+][OH^-] = 1 \times 10^{-14}$$
   Solution: 0.15 M HCl = 0.15 M H_3O^+ $pH = -\log(0.15) = 0.82$
   $[OH^-] = 1 \times 10^{-14} / 0.15 \text{ M} = 6.67 \times 10^{-14}$
   Check: HCl is a strong acid with a relatively high concentration, so we expect the pH to be low and the $[OH^-]$ to be small.

   b) **Given:** 0.025M HNO_3 (strong acid)   **Find:** $[H_3O^+]$, $[OH^-]$, pH
   Conceptual Plan: [HNO_3] $\rightarrow$ $[H_3O^+]$ $\rightarrow$ pH and then $[H_3O^+]$ $\rightarrow$ $[OH^-]$
   $$[HNO_3] \rightarrow [H_3O^+] \qquad pH = -\log[H_3O^+] \quad [H_3O^+][OH^-] = 1 \times 10^{-14}$$
   Solution: 0.025 M HNO_3 = 0.025 M H_3O^+ $pH = -\log(0.025) = 1.60$
   $[OH^-] = 1.0 \times 10^{-14} / 0.025 \text{ M} = 4.0 \times 10^{-13}$
   Check: HNO_3 is a strong acid, so we expect the pH to be low and the $[OH^-]$ to be small.

c) **Given:** 0.072M HBr and 0.015M HNO$_3$ (strong acids)   **Find:** [H$_3$O$^+$],[OH$^-$], pH

Conceptual Plan:[HBr]+ [HNO$_3$] → [H$_3$O$^+$] → pH and then [H$_3$O$^+$] → [OH$^-$]

         [HBr] + [HNO$_3$] → [H$_3$O$^+$]   pH = -log[H$_3$O$^+$]   [H$_3$O$^+$][OH$^-$] = 1 x 10^{-14}

Solution: 0.072 M HBr = 0.072 M H$_3$O$^+$ and 0.015M HNO$_3$ = 0.015M H$_3$O$^+$

Total H$_3$O$^+$ = 0.072M + 0.015M = 0.087M   pH = −log(0.100) = 1.06

         [OH$^-$] = 1.0 x 10^{-14} / 0.087 M = 1.1 x 10^{-13}

Check: HBr and HNO$_3$ are both strong acids and completely dissociate, this gives a relatively high concentration, so we expect the pH to be low and the [OH$^-$] to be small.

d) **Given:** HNO$_3$ = 0.855% by mass, d$_{solution}$ = 1.01 g/mL   **Find:** [H$_3$O$^+$],[OH$^-$], pH

Conceptual Plan:

     % mass HNO$_3$ → g HNO$_3$ → mol HNO$_3$ and then g soln → mL soln → L soln→ M HNO$_3$

       $\dfrac{\%}{100}$ $\dfrac{\text{mol HNO}_3}{63.018 \text{ g HNO}_3}$ $\dfrac{1.01 \text{ g soln}}{\text{mL soln}}$ $\dfrac{1000 \text{ mL soln}}{\text{L soln}}$

→M H$_3$O$^+$ → pH and then [H$_3$O$^+$] → [OH$^-$]

[HNO$_3$] → [H$_3$O$^+$]   pH = -log[H$_3$O$^+$] [H$_3$O$^+$][OH$^-$] = 1 x 10^{-14}

Solution: $\dfrac{0.855 \text{ g HNO}_3}{100 \text{ g soln}}$ x $\dfrac{1 \text{ mol HNO}_3}{63.018 \text{ g HNO}_3}$ x $\dfrac{1.01 \text{ g soln}}{\text{mL soln}}$ x $\dfrac{1000 \text{ mL soln}}{\text{L soln}}$ = 0.137 M HNO$_3$

0.137 M HNO$_3$ = 0.137 M H$_3$O$^+$ pH = −log(0.137) = 0.863

         [OH$^-$] = 1.00 x 10^{-14} / 0.137 M = 7.30 x 10^{-14}

Check: HNO$_3$ is a strong acids and completely dissociates, this gives a relatively high concentration, so we expect the pH to be low and the [OH$^-$] to be small.

56. a) **Given:** 0.028M HI   (strong acid)   **Find:** [H$_3$O$^+$],[OH$^-$], pH

Conceptual Plan:[HI] → [H$_3$O$^+$] → pH and then [H$_3$O$^+$] → [OH$^-$]

         [HI] → [H$_3$O$^+$]   pH = -log[H$_3$O$^+$]   [H$_3$O$^+$][OH$^-$] = 1 x 10^{-14}

Solution: 0.028 M HI = 0.028 M H$_3$O$^+$ pH = −log(0.028) = 1.55

         [OH$^-$] = 1.0 x 10^{-14} / 0.028 M = 3.6 x 10^{-13}

Check: HI is a strong acid with a relatively high concentration, so we expect the pH to be low and the [OH$^-$] to be small.

b) **Given:** 0.115M HClO$_4$ (strong acid)   **Find:** [H$_3$O$^+$],[OH$^-$], pH

Conceptual Plan:[HClO$_4$] → [H$_3$O$^+$] → pH and then [H$_3$O$^+$] → [OH$^-$]

         [HClO$_4$] → [H$_3$O$^+$]   pH = -log[H$_3$O$^+$] [H$_3$O$^+$][OH$^-$] = 1 x 10^{-14}

Solution: 0.115 M HClO$_4$ = 0.115 M H$_3$O$^+$ pH = −log(0.115) = 0.939

         [OH$^-$] = 1.0 x 10^{-14} / 0.115 M = 8.7 x 10^{-14}

Check: HClO$_4$ is a strong acid, so we expect the pH to be low and the [OH$^-$] to be small.

c) **Given:** 0.055M HClO$_4$ and 0.028M HCl (strong acids)   **Find:** [H$_3$O$^+$],[OH$^-$], pH

Conceptual Plan:[HCl] + [HClO$_4$] → [H$_3$O$^+$] → pH and then [H$_3$O$^+$] → [OH$^-$]

         [HCl] + [HClO$_4$] → [H$_3$O$^+$]   pH = -log[H$_3$O$^+$] [H$_3$O$^+$][OH$^-$] = 1 x 10^{-14}

Solution: 0.055 M HClO$_4$ = 0.055 M H$_3$O$^+$ and 0.028M HNO$_3$ = 0.028M H$_3$O$^+$

       Total H$_3$O$^+$ = 0.055M + 0.028M = 0.083M   pH = −log(0.083) = 1.08

       [OH$^-$] = 1.0 x 10^{-14} / 0.083 M = 1.2 x 10^{-13}

Check: HClO$_4$ and HNO$_3$ are both strong acids and completely dissociate, this gives a relatively high concentration, so we expect the pH to be low and the [OH$^-$] to be small.

d) **Given:** HCl = 1.85% by mass, d$_{solution}$ = 1.01 g/mL   **Find:** [H$_3$O$^+$],[OH$^-$], pH

Conceptual Plan:

     % mass HCl→ g HCl → mol HCl and then g soln → mL soln → L soln→ M HCl

       $\dfrac{\%}{100}$ $\dfrac{\text{mol HCl}}{35.458 \text{ g HCl}}$ $\dfrac{1.01 \text{ g soln}}{\text{mL soln}}$ $\dfrac{1000 \text{ mL soln}}{\text{L soln}}$

→M H$_3$O$^+$ → pH and then [H$_3$O$^+$] → [OH$^-$]

[HCl] → [H$_3$O$^+$]   pH = -log[H$_3$O$^+$][H$_3$O$^+$][OH$^-$] = 1 x 10^{-14}

Solution: $\dfrac{1.85 \text{ g HCl}}{100 \text{ g soln}}$ x $\dfrac{1 \text{ mol HCl}}{35.458 \text{ g HCl}}$ x $\dfrac{1.01 \text{ g soln}}{\text{mL soln}}$ x $\dfrac{1000 \text{ mL soln}}{\text{L soln}}$ = 0.527 M HCl

$$0.527 \text{ M HCl} = 0.527 \text{ M H}_3\text{O}^+ \qquad \text{pH} = -\log(0.137) = 0.278$$
$$[\text{OH}^-] = 1.0 \times 10^{-14} / 0.527 \text{ M} = 1.9 \times 10^{-14}$$

Check: HCl is a strong acids and completely dissociates, this gives a relatively high concentration, so we expect the pH to be low and the $[\text{OH}^-]$ to be small.

57. a) **Given:** pH = 1.25, 0.250 L **Find:** g HI
  Conceptual Plan: pH $\rightarrow$ $[\text{H}_3\text{O}^+]$ $\rightarrow$[HI] $\rightarrow$ mol HI $\rightarrow$ g HI
     pH = -log$[\text{H}_3\text{O}^+]$ $[\text{H}_3\text{O}^+]$$\rightarrow$ [HI]   mol = MV   g = mol(127.9 g/mol)

  Solution: $[\text{H}_3\text{O}^+] = 10^{-1.25} = 0.056\text{M} = [\text{HI}]$
$$\frac{0.056 \text{ mol HI}}{\text{L}} \times 0.250 \text{ L} \times \frac{127.90 \text{ g HI}}{\text{mol HI}} = 1.8 \text{ g HI}$$

 b) **Given:** pH = 1.75, 0.250 L **Find:** g HI
  Conceptual Plan: pH $\rightarrow$ $[\text{H}_3\text{O}^+]$ $\rightarrow$[HI] $\rightarrow$ mol HI $\rightarrow$ g HI
     pH = -log$[\text{H}_3\text{O}^+]$ $[\text{H}_3\text{O}^+]$$\rightarrow$ [HI]   mol = MV   g = mol(127.9 g/mol)

  Solution: $[\text{H}_3\text{O}^+] = 10^{-1.75} = 0.017\underline{8}\text{M} = [\text{HI}]$
$$\frac{0.017\underline{8} \text{ mol HI}}{\text{L}} \times 0.250 \text{ L} \times \frac{127.90 \text{ g HI}}{\text{mol HI}} = 0.57 \text{ g HI}$$

 c) **Given:** pH = 2.85, 0.250 L **Find:** g HI
  Conceptual Plan: pH $\rightarrow$ $[\text{H}_3\text{O}^+]$ $\rightarrow$[HI] $\rightarrow$ mol HI $\rightarrow$ g HI
     pH = -log$[\text{H}_3\text{O}^+]$ $[\text{H}_3\text{O}^+]$$\rightarrow$ [HI]   mol = MV   g = mol(127.9 g/mol)

  Solution: $[\text{H}_3\text{O}^+] = 10^{-2.85} = 0.0014\text{M} = [\text{HI}]$
$$\frac{0.0014 \text{ mol HI}}{\text{L}} \times 0.250 \text{ L} \times \frac{127.90 \text{ g HI}}{\text{mol HI}} = 0.045 \text{ g HI}$$

58. a) **Given:** pH = 2.50, 0.500 L **Find:** g HClO_4
  Conceptual Plan: pH $\rightarrow$ $[\text{H}_3\text{O}^+]$ $\rightarrow$[HClO_4] $\rightarrow$ mol HClO_4 $\rightarrow$ g HClO_4
     pH = -log$[\text{H}_3\text{O}^+]$ $[\text{H}_3\text{O}^+]$$\rightarrow$ [HClO_4]   mol = MV   g = mol(100.46 g/mol)

  Solution:

$[\text{H}_3\text{O}^+] = 10^{-2.50} = 0.003\underline{1}6\text{M} = [\text{HClO}_4]$ $\dfrac{0.003\underline{1}6 \text{ mol HClO}_4}{\text{L}} \times 0.500 \text{ L} \times \dfrac{100.46 \text{ g HClO}_4}{\text{mol HClO}_4} = 0.16 \text{ g HClO}_4$

 b) **Given:** pH = 1.50, 0.500 L **Find:** g HClO_4
  Conceptual Plan: pH $\rightarrow$ $[\text{H}_3\text{O}^+]$ $\rightarrow$[HClO_4] $\rightarrow$ mol HClO_4 $\rightarrow$ g HClO_4
     pH = -log$[\text{H}_3\text{O}^+]$ $[\text{H}_3\text{O}^+]$$\rightarrow$ [HClO_4]   mol = MV   g = mol(100.46 g/mol)

  Solution:

$[\text{H}_3\text{O}^+] = 10^{-1.50} = 0.03\underline{1}6\text{M} = [\text{HClO}_4]$ $\dfrac{0.03\underline{1}6 \text{ mol HClO}_4}{\text{L}} \times 0.500 \text{ L} \times \dfrac{100.46 \text{ g HClO}_4}{\text{mol HClO}_4} = 1.6 \text{ g HClO}_4$

 c) **Given:** pH = 0.50, 0.500 L **Find:** g HClO_4
  Conceptual Plan: pH $\rightarrow$ $[\text{H}_3\text{O}^+]$ $\rightarrow$[HClO_4] $\rightarrow$ mol HClO_4 $\rightarrow$ g HClO_4
     pH = -log$[\text{H}_3\text{O}^+]$ $[\text{H}_3\text{O}^+]$$\rightarrow$ [HClO_4]   mol = MV   g = mol(100.46 g/mol)

  Solution:

$[\text{H}_3\text{O}^+] = 10^{-0.50} = 0.3\underline{1}6\text{M} = [\text{HClO}_4]$ $\dfrac{0.3\underline{1}6 \text{ mol HClO}_4}{\text{L}} \times 0.500 \text{ L} \times \dfrac{100.46 \text{ g HClO}_4}{\text{mol HClO}_4} = 16 \text{ g HClO}_4$

59. **Given:** 0.100M benzoic acid. $K_a = 6.5 \times 10^{-5}$ **Find:** $[\text{H}_3\text{O}^+]$, pH
Conceptual Plan: Write a balanced reaction. Prepare an ICE table; represent the change with x; sum the table and determine the equilibrium values; put the equilibrium values in the equilibrium expression and solve for x. Determine $[\text{H}_3\text{O}^+]$ and pH
Solution: $\text{HC}_7\text{H}_5\text{O}_2(aq) + \text{H}_2\text{O}(l) \rightleftharpoons \text{H}_3\text{O}^+(aq) + \text{C}_7\text{H}_5\text{O}_2{}^-(aq)$

I	0.100M	0.0	0.0
C	- x	x	x
E	0.100 – x	x	x

$$K_a = \frac{[H_3O^+][C_7H_5O_2^-]}{[HC_7H_5O_2]} = \frac{(x)(x)}{(0.100 - x)} = 6.5 \times 10^{-5}$$

Assume x is small compared to 0.100

$$x^2 = (6.5 \times 10^{-5})(0.100) \qquad x = 2.5 \times 10^{-3} \text{ M} = [H_3O^+]$$

$$pH = -\log(2.5 \times 10^{-3}) = 2.60$$

60. **Given:** 0.200M formic acid. $K_a = 1.8 \times 10^{-4}$ **Find:** $[H_3O^+]$, pH
    Conceptual Plan: Write a balanced reaction. Prepare an ICE table; represent the change with x; sum the table and determine the equilibrium values; put the equilibrium values in the equilibrium expression and solve for x. Determine $[H_3O^+]$ and pH
    Solution: $HCH_2O(aq) + H_2O(l) \leftrightarrows H_3O^+(aq) + CH_2O^-(aq)$

I	0.200M	0.0	0.0
C	- x	x	x
E	0.200 – x	x	x

$$K_a = \frac{[H_3O^+][CH_2O^-]}{[HCH_2O]} = \frac{(x)(x)}{(0.200 - x)} = 1.8 \times 10^{-4}$$

Assume x is small compared to 0.200

$$x^2 = (1.8 \times 10^{-4})(0.200) \qquad x = 6.0 \times 10^{-3} \text{ M} = [H_3O^+]$$

$$pH = -\log(6.0 \times 10^{-3}) = 2.22$$

61. a) **Given:** 0.500M HNO_2. $K_a = 4.6 \times 10^{-4}$ **Find:** $[HNO_2]$, pH
    Conceptual Plan: Write a balanced reaction. Prepare an ICE table; represent the change with x; sum the table and determine the equilibrium values; put the equilibrium values in the equilibrium expression and solve for x. Determine $[H_3O^+]$ and pH
    Solution: $HNO_2(aq) + H_2O(l) \leftrightarrows H_3O^+(aq) + NO_2^-(aq)$

I	0.500M	0.0	0.0
C	- x	x	x
E	0.500 – x	x	x

$$K_a = \frac{[H_3O^+][NO_2^-]}{[HNO_2]} = \frac{(x)(x)}{(0.500 - x)} = 4.6 \times 10^{-4}$$

Assume x is small compared to 0.500

$$x^2 = (4.6 \times 10^{-4})(0.500) \qquad x = 0.015M = [H_3O^+]$$

Check assumption: $\dfrac{0.015}{0.500} \times 100 = 3.0\%$ assumption valid

$[HNO_2] = 0.500 - 0.015 = 0.485M$ $\qquad\qquad\qquad$ $pH = -\log(0.015) = 1.82$

b) **Given:** 0.100M HNO_2. $K_a = 4.6 \times 10^{-4}$ **Find:** $[HNO_2]$, pH
    Conceptual Plan: Write a balanced reaction. Prepare an ICE table; represent the change with x; sum the table and determine the equilibrium values; put the equilibrium values in the equilibrium expression and solve for x. Determine $[H_3O^+]$ and pH
    Solution: $HNO_2(aq) + H_2O(l) \leftrightarrows H_3O^+(aq) + NO_2^-(aq)$

I	0.100M	0.0	0.0
C	- x	x	x
E	0.100 – x	x	x

$$K_a = \frac{[H_3O^+][NO_2^-]}{[HNO_2]} = \frac{(x)(x)}{(0.100 - x)} = 4.6 \times 10^{-4}$$

Assume x is small compared to 0.100

$$x^2 = (4.6 \times 10^{-4})(0.100) \qquad x = 0.0068M = [H_3O^+]$$

Check assumption: $\dfrac{0.0068}{0.100} \times 100 = 6.8\%$ assumption not valid

$$x^2 = (4.6 \times 10^{-4})(0.100 - x) \qquad x^2 + 4.6 \times 10^{-4}x - 4.6 \times 10^{-5} = 0$$

$$x = 0.00656$$

$$[HNO_2] = 0.100 - 0.00656 = 0.093M$$

$$pH = -\log(0.00656) = 2.18$$

c) **Given:** 0.100M HNO_2. $K_a = 4.6 \times 10^{-4}$ **Find:** $[HNO_2]$, pH

Conceptual Plan: Write a balanced reaction. Prepare an ICE table; represent the change with x; sum the table and determine the equilibrium values; put the equilibrium values in the equilibrium expression and solve for x. Determine $[H_3O^+]$ and pH

Solution: $HNO_2(aq) + H_2O(l) \leftrightarrows H_3O^+(aq) + NO_2^-(aq)$

I	0.0100M	0.0	0.0
C	- x	x	x
E	0.0100 – x	x	x

$$K_a = \frac{[H_3O^+][NO_2^-]}{[HNO_2]} = \frac{(x)(x)}{(0.0100 - x)} = 4.6 \times 10^{-4}$$

Assume x is small compared to 0.100

$x^2 = (4.6 \times 10^{-4})(0.0100)$ $x = 0.0021M = [H_3O^+]$

Check assumption: $\frac{0.0021}{0.0100} \times 100 = 21\%$ assumption not valid

$x^2 = (4.6 \times 10^{-4})(0.0100 - x)$ $x^2 + 4.6 \times 10^{-4}x - 4.6 \times 10^{-6} = 0$

$x = 0.0019$

$pH = -\log(0.0019) = 2.72$

62. a) **Given:** 0.250 M HF $K_a = 3.5 \times 10^{-4}$ **Find:** pH

Conceptual Plan: Write a balanced reaction. Prepare an ICE table; represent the change with x; sum the table and determine the equilibrium values; put the equilibrium values in the equilibrium expression and solve for x. Determine $[H_3O^+]$ and pH

Solution: $HF(aq) + H_2O(l) \leftrightarrows H_3O^+(aq) + F^-(aq)$

I	0.250M	0.0	0.0
C	- x	x	x
E	0.250 – x	x	x

$$K_a = \frac{[H_3O^+][F^-]}{[HF]} = \frac{(x)(x)}{(0.250 - x)} = 3.5 \times 10^{-4}$$

Assume x is small compared to 0.250

$x^2 = (3.5 \times 10^{-4})(0.250)$ $x = 0.00935M = [H_3O^+]$

Check assumption: $\frac{0.00935}{0.250} \times 100 = 3.7\%$ assumption valid

$pH = -\log(0.00935) = 2.03$

b) **Given:** 0.0500 M HF $K_a = 3.5 \times 10^{-4}$ **Find:** pH

Conceptual Plan: Write a balanced reaction. Prepare an ICE table; represent the change with x; sum the table and determine the equilibrium values; put the equilibrium values in the equilibrium expression and solve for x. Determine $[H_3O^+]$ and pH

Solution: $HF(aq) + H_2O(l) \leftrightarrows H_3O^+(aq) + F^-(aq)$

I	0.0500M	0.0	0.0
C	- x	x	x
E	0.0500 – x	x	x

$$K_a = \frac{[H_3O^+][F^-]}{[HF]} = \frac{(x)(x)}{(0.0500 - x)} = 3.5 \times 10^{-4}$$

Assume x is small compared to 0.0500

$x^2 = (3.5 \times 10^{-4})(0.0500)$ $x = 0.00418M = [H_3O^+]$

Check assumption: $\frac{0.00418}{0.050} \times 100 = 8.3\%$ assumption not valid

$x^2 + 3.5 \times 10^{-4} x - 1.75 \times 10^{-5} = 0$ $x = 0.0040 = [H_3O^+]$

$pH = -\log(0.0040) = 2.40$

c) **Given:** 0.0250 M HF $K_a = 3.5 \times 10^{-4}$ **Find:** pH

Conceptual Plan: Write a balanced reaction. Prepare an ICE table; represent the change with x; sum the table and determine the equilibrium values; put the equilibrium values in the equilibrium expression and solve for x. Determine $[H_3O^+]$ and pH

Solution: $HF(aq) + H_2O(l) \leftrightharpoons H_3O^+(aq) + F^-(aq)$

I	0.0250M	0.0	0.0
C	- x	x	x
E	0.0250 – x	x	x

$$K_a = \frac{[H_3O^+][F^-]}{[HF]} = \frac{(x)(x)}{(0.0250 - x)} = 3.5 \times 10^{-4}$$

Assume x is small compared to 0.0250

$x^2 = (3.5 \times 10^{-4})(0.0250)$ $\qquad$ $x = 0.00295M = [H_3O^+]$

Check assumption: $\dfrac{0.00295}{0.0250} \times 100 = 11.8\%$ assumption not valid

$x^2 + 3.5 \times 10^{-4} \, x - 8.75 \times 10^{-6} = 0$ $\qquad$ $x = 0.00279 = [H_3O^+]$

$pH = -\log(0.00279) = 2.55$

63. **Given:** 15.0 mL glacial acetic, d = 1.05 g/mL, dilute to 1.50 L, $K_a = 1.8 \times 10^{-5}$ $\qquad$ **Find:** pH
Conceptual Plan:

mL acetic acid $\rightarrow$ g acetic acid $\rightarrow$ mol acetic acid $\rightarrow$ M and then write a balanced reaction.

$\dfrac{1.05 \text{ g}}{\text{mL}}$ $\qquad$ $\dfrac{\text{mol acetic acid}}{60.05 \text{ g}}$ $\qquad$ $M = \dfrac{\text{mol}}{L}$

Prepare an ICE table; represent the change with x; sum the table and determine the equilibrium values; put the equilibrium values in the equilibrium expression and solve for x. Determine $[H_3O^+]$ and pH

Solution: $15.0 \text{ mL} \times \dfrac{1.05 \text{ g}}{\text{mL}} \times \dfrac{1 \text{ mol}}{60.05 \text{ g}} \times \dfrac{1}{1.50 \text{ L}} = 0.1748 \text{ M}$

$HC_2H_3O_2(aq) + H_2O(l) \leftrightharpoons H_3O^+(aq) + C_2H_3O_2^-(aq)$

I	0.1748M	0.0	0.0
C	- x	x	x
E	0.1748 – x	x	x

$$K_a = \frac{[H_3O^+][C_2H_3O_2^-]}{[HC_2H_3O_2]} = \frac{(x)(x)}{(0.1748 - x)} = 1.8 \times 10^{-5}$$

Assume x is small compared to 0.1748

$x^2 = (1.8 \times 10^{-5})(0.1748)$ $\qquad$ $x = 0.00179M = [H_3O^+]$

Check assumption: $\dfrac{0.00179}{0.1748} \times 100 = 1.0\%$ assumption valid

$pH = -\log(0.00179) = 2.75$

64. **Given:** 1.35% formic acid, d = 1.01 g/mL, $K_a = 1.8 \times 10^{-4}$ $\qquad$ **Find:** pH
Conceptual Plan: **% formic acid $\rightarrow$ g formic acid $\rightarrow$ mol and g soln $\rightarrow$ mL soln $\rightarrow$ L soln and then M**

$\dfrac{1.01 \text{ g soln}}{\text{mL soln}}$ $\quad$ $\dfrac{\text{mol}}{46.03 \text{ g}}$ $\qquad$ $\dfrac{1000 \text{ mL soln}}{\text{L soln}}$

Write a balanced reaction. Prepare an ICE table; represent the change with x; sum the table and determine the equilibrium values; put the equilibrium values in the equilibrium expression and solve for x. Determine $[H_3O^+]$ and pH

Solution: $\dfrac{1.35 \text{ g } \cancel{\text{HCHO}}}{100 \text{ g } \cancel{\text{soln}}} \times \dfrac{\text{mol HCHO}}{46.03 \cancel{\text{ g}}} \times \dfrac{1.01 \cancel{\text{ g soln}}}{\cancel{\text{mL soln}}} \times \dfrac{1000 \cancel{\text{ mL soln}}}{\text{L soln}} = 0.2962M$

$HCHO_2(aq) + H_2O(l) \leftrightharpoons H_3O^+(aq) + CHO_2^-(aq)$

I	0.2962M	0.0	0.0
C	- x	x	x
E	0.1748 – x	x	x

$$K_a = \frac{[H_3O^+][CHO_2^-]}{[HCHO_2]} = \frac{(x)(x)}{(0.2962 - x)} = 1.8 \times 10^{-4}$$

Assume x is small compared to 0.2962

$x^2 = (1.8 \times 10^{-4})(0.2962)$ $\qquad$ $x = 0.00730M = [H_3O^+]$

Check assumption: $\dfrac{0.00730}{0.2962} \times 100 = 2.5\%$ assumption valid

$pH = -\log(0.00730) = 2.14$

65. **Given:** 0.185 M HA, pH = 2.95   **Find:** K_a

Conceptual Plan: pH → [H₃O⁺] and then write a balanced reaction, prepare and ICE table, calculate equilibrium concentrations, and then plug into the equilibrium expression to solve for K_a.

Solution: $[H_3O^+] = 10^{-2.95} = 0.0012 \text{ M} = [A^-]$

	$HA(aq) + H_2O(l) \rightleftharpoons$	$H_3O^+(aq) +$	$A^-(aq)$
I	0.185M	0.0	0.0
C	- x	x	x
E	0.185 – 0.0012	0.0012	0.0012

$$K_a = \frac{[H_3O^+][A^-]}{[HA]} = \frac{(0.0012)(0.0012)}{(0.185 - 0.0012)} = 6.8 \times 10^{-6}$$

66. **Given:** 0.115 M HA, pH = 3.29   **Find:** K_a

Conceptual Plan: pH → [H₃O⁺] and then write a balanced reaction, prepare and ICE table, calculate equilibrium concentrations, and then plug into the equilibrium expression to solve for K_a.

Solution: $[H_3O^+] = 10^{-3.29} = 5.13 \times 10^{-4} \text{ M} = [A^-]$

	$HA(aq) + H_2O(l) \rightleftharpoons$	$H_3O^+(aq) +$	$A^-(aq)$
I	0.185M	0.0	0.0
C	- x	x	x
E	$0.115 - 5.13 \times 10^{-4}$	5.13×10^{-4}	5.13×10^{-4}

$$K_a = \frac{[H_3O^+][A^-]}{[HA]} = \frac{(5.13 \times 10^{-4})(5.13 \times 10^{-4})}{(0.115 - 5.13 \times 10^{-4})} = 2.3 \times 10^{-6}$$

67. **Given:** 0.125 HCN $K_a = 4.9 \times 10^{-10}$ **Find:** % ionization

Conceptual Plan: Write a balanced reaction. Prepare an ICE table; represent the change with x; sum the table and determine the equilibrium values; put the equilibrium values in the equilibrium expression and solve for x and then x → % ionization

$$\% \text{ ionization} = \frac{x}{[HCN]_{original}} \times 100$$

Solution:

	$HCN(aq) + H_2O(l) \rightleftharpoons$	$H_3O^+(aq) +$	$CN^-(aq)$
I	0.125M	0.0	0.0
C	- x	x	x
E	0.125 – x	x	x

$$K_a = \frac{[H_3O^+][CN^-]}{[HCN]} = \frac{(x)(x)}{(0.125 - x)} = 4.9 \times 10^{-10}$$

Assume x is small compared to 0.125

$$x^2 = (4.9 \times 10^{-10})(0.125) \qquad x = 7.83 \times 10^{-6}$$

$$\% \text{ ionization} = \frac{7.83 \times 10^{-6}}{0.125} \times 100 = 0.0063\% \text{ ionized}$$

68. **Given:** 0.225 $HC_7H_5O_2$ $K_a = 6.5 \times 10^{-5}$ **Find:** % ionization

Conceptual Plan: Write a balanced reaction. Prepare an ICE table; represent the change with x; sum the table and determine the equilibrium values; put the equilibrium values in the equilibrium expression and solve for x and then x → % ionization

$$\% \text{ ionization} = \frac{x}{[HC_7H_5O_2]_{original}} \times 100$$

Solution:

	$HC_7H_5O_2(aq) + H_2O(l) \rightleftharpoons H_3O^+(aq) +$		$C_7H_5O_2^-(aq)$
I	0.125M	0.0	0.0
C	- x	x	x
E	0.125 – x	x	x

$$K_a = \frac{[H_3O^+][C_7H_5O_2^-]}{[HC_7H_5O_2]} = \frac{(x)(x)}{(0.225 - x)} = 6.5 \times 10^{-5}$$

Assume x is small compared to 0.225

$$x^2 = (6.5 \times 10^{-5})(0.1225) \qquad x = 0.00382$$

$$\% \text{ ionization} = \frac{0.00382}{0.225} \times 100 = 1.7\% \text{ ionized}$$

69. a) **Given:** 1.00M $HC_2H_3O_2$ $K_a = 1.8 \times 10^{-5}$ **Find:** % ionization
Conceptual Plan: Write a balanced reaction. Prepare an ICE table; represent the change with x; sum the table and determine the equilibrium values; put the equilibrium values in the equilibrium expression and solve for x and then x → % ionization

$$\% \text{ ionization} = \frac{x}{[HC_2H_3O_2]_{original}} \times 100$$

Solution: $HC_2H_3O_2 \text{ (aq)} + H_2O(l) \leftrightarrows H_3O^+(aq) + C_2H_3O_2^- \text{ (aq)}$

I	1.0 M	0.0	0.0
C	- x	x	x
E	1.00 – x	x	x

$$K_a = \frac{[H_3O^+][C_2H_3O_2^-]}{[HC_2H_3O_2]} = \frac{(x)(x)}{(1.00 - x)} = 1.8 \times 10^{-5}$$

Assume x is small compared to 1.00

$$x^2 = (1.8 \times 10^{-5})(1.00) \qquad x = 0.004\underline{2}4$$

$$\% \text{ ionization} = \frac{0.004\underline{2}4}{1.00} \times 100 = 0.42\% \text{ ionized}$$

b) **Given:** 0.500 M $HC_2H_3O_2$ $K_a = 1.8 \times 10^{-5}$ **Find:** % ionization
Conceptual Plan: Write a balanced reaction. Prepare an ICE table; represent the change with x; sum the table and determine the equilibrium values; put the equilibrium values in the equilibrium expression and solve for x and then x → % ionization

$$\% \text{ ionization} = \frac{x}{[HC_2H_3O_2]_{original}} \times 100$$

Solution: $HC_2H_3O_2 \text{ (aq)} + H_2O(l) \leftrightarrows H_3O^+(aq) + C_2H_3O_2^- \text{ (aq)}$

I	0.500 M	0.0	0.0
C	- x	x	x
E	0.500 – x	x	x

$$K_a = \frac{[H_3O^+][C_2H_3O_2^-]}{[HC_2H_3O_2]} = \frac{(x)(x)}{(0.500 - x)} = 1.8 \times 10^{-5}$$

Assume x is small compared to 0.500

$$x^2 = (1.8 \times 10^{-5})(0.500) \qquad x = 0.003\underline{0}0$$

$$\% \text{ ionization} = \frac{0.003\underline{0}0}{0.500} \times 100 = 0.60\% \text{ ionized}$$

c) **Given:** 0.100M $HC_2H_3O_2$ $K_a = 1.8 \times 10^{-5}$ **Find:** % ionization
Conceptual Plan: Write a balanced reaction. Prepare an ICE table; represent the change with x; sum the table and determine the equilibrium values; put the equilibrium values in the equilibrium expression and solve for x and then x → % ionization

$$\% \text{ ionization} = \frac{x}{[HC_2H_3O_2]_{original}} \times 100$$

Solution: $HC_2H_3O_2 \text{ (aq)} + H_2O(l) \leftrightarrows H_3O^+(aq) + C_2H_3O_2^- \text{ (aq)}$

I	0.100 M	0.0	0.0
C	- x	x	x
E	0.100 – x	x	x

$$K_a = \frac{[H_3O^+][C_2H_3O_2^-]}{[HC_2H_3O_2]} = \frac{(x)(x)}{(0.100 - x)} = 1.8 \times 10^{-5}$$

Assume x is small compared to 1.00

$$x^2 = (1.8 \times 10^{-5})(0.100) \qquad x = 0.001\underline{3}4$$

$$\% \text{ ionization} = \frac{0.001\underline{3}4}{0.100} \times 100 = 1.3\% \text{ ionized}$$

d) **Given:** 0.0500M $HC_2H_3O_2$ $K_a = 1.8 \times 10^{-5}$ **Find:** % ionization
Conceptual Plan: Write a balanced reaction. Prepare an ICE table; represent the change with x; sum the table and determine the equilibrium values; put the equilibrium values in the equilibrium expression and solve for x and then x → % ionization

$$\% \text{ ionization} = \frac{x}{[HC_2H_3O_2]_{original}} \times 100$$

Solution:

	$HC_2H_3O_2 \text{ (aq)} + H_2O\text{(l)} \leftrightarrows$	$H_3O^+\text{(aq)} +$	$C_2H_3O_2^-\text{ (aq)}$
I	0.0500 M	0.0	0.0
C	- x	x	x
E	0.0500 – x	x	x

$$K_a = \frac{[H_3O^+][C_2H_3O_2^-]}{[HC_2H_3O_2]} = \frac{(x)(x)}{(0.0500 - x)} = 1.8 \times 10^{-5}$$

Assume x is small compared to 0.0500

$$x^2 = (1.8 \times 10^{-5})(0.0500) \qquad x = 9.\underline{4}9 \times 10^{-4}$$

$$\% \text{ ionization} = \frac{9.\underline{4}9 \times 10^{-4}}{0.0500} \times 100 = 1.9\% \text{ ionized}$$

70. a) **Given:** 1.00M $HCHO_2$ $K_a = 1.8 \times 10^{-4}$ **Find:** % ionization

Conceptual Plan: Write a balanced reaction. Prepare an ICE table; represent the change with x; sum the table and determine the equilibrium values; put the equilibrium values in the equilibrium expression and solve for x and then x → % ionization

$$\% \text{ ionization} = \frac{x}{[HCHO_2]_{original}} \times 100$$

Solution:

	$HCHO_2 \text{ (aq)} + H_2O\text{(l)} \leftrightarrows H_3O^+\text{(aq)} + CHO_2^-\text{ (aq)}$		
I	1.0 M	0.0	0.0
C	- x	x	x
E	1.00 – x	x	x

$$K_a = \frac{[H_3O^+][CHO_2^-]}{[HCHO_2]} = \frac{(x)(x)}{(1.00 - x)} = 1.8 \times 10^{-4}$$

Assume x is small compared to1.00

$$x^2 = (1.8 \times 10^{-4})(1.00) \qquad x = 0.01\underline{3}4$$

$$\% \text{ ionization} = \frac{0.01\underline{3}4}{1.00} \times 100 = 1.3\% \text{ ionized}$$

b) **Given:** 0.500 M $HCHO_2$ $K_a = 1.8 \times 10^{-4}$ **Find:** % ionization

Conceptual Plan: Write a balanced reaction. Prepare an ICE table; represent the change with x; sum the table and determine the equilibrium values; put the equilibrium values in the equilibrium expression and solve for x and then x → % ionization

$$\% \text{ ionization} = \frac{x}{[HCHO_2]_{original}} \times 100$$

Solution:

	$HCHO_2 \text{ (aq)} + H_2O\text{(l)} \leftrightarrows$	$H_3O^+\text{(aq)} +$	$CHO_2^-\text{ (aq)}$
I	0.500 M	0.0	0.0
C	- x	x	x
E	0.500 – x	x	x

$$K_a = \frac{[H_3O^+][CHO_2^-]}{[HCHO_2]} = \frac{(x)(x)}{(0.500 - x)} = 1.8 \times 10^{-4}$$

Assume x is small compared to1.00

$$x^2 = (1.8 \times 10^{-4})(0.500) \qquad x = 0.009\underline{4}9$$

$$\% \text{ ionization} = \frac{0.009\underline{4}9}{0.500} \times 100 = 1.9\% \text{ ionized}$$

c) **Given:** 0.100M $HCHO_2$ $K_a = 1.8 \times 10^{-4}$ **Find:** % ionization

Conceptual Plan: Write a balanced reaction. Prepare an ICE table; represent the change with x; sum the table and determine the equilibrium values; put the equilibrium values in the equilibrium expression and solve for x and then x → % ionization

$$\% \text{ ionization} = \frac{x}{[HCHO_2]_{original}} \times 100$$

Solution: $HCHO_2 (aq) + H_2O(l) \rightleftharpoons H_3O^+(aq) + CHO_2^- (aq)$

I	0.100 M	0.0	0.0
C	- x	x	x
E	0.100 – x	x	x

$$K_a = \frac{[H_3O^+][CHO_2^-]}{[HCHO_2]} = \frac{(x)(x)}{(0.100 - x)} = 1.8 \times 10^{-4}$$

Assume x is small compared to 0.100

$$x^2 = (1.8 \times 10^{-4})(0.100) \qquad x = 0.00424$$

$$\% \text{ ionization} = \frac{0.00424}{0.100} \times 100 = 4.2\% \text{ ionized}$$

d) **Given:** 0.0500 M $HCHO_2$ $K_a = 1.8 \times 10^{-4}$ **Find:** % ionization

Conceptual Plan: Write a balanced reaction. Prepare an ICE table; represent the change with x; sum the table and determine the equilibrium values; put the equilibrium values in the equilibrium expression and solve for x and then x → % ionization

$$\% \text{ ionization} = \frac{x}{[HCHO_2]_{original}} \times 100$$

Solution: $HCHO_2 (aq) + H_2O(l) \rightleftharpoons H_3O^+(aq) + CHO_2^- (aq)$

I	0.0500 M	0.0	0.0
C	- x	x	x
E	0.0500 – x	x	x

$$K_a = \frac{[H_3O^+][CHO_2^-]}{[HCHO_2]} = \frac{(x)(x)}{(0.0500 - x)} = 1.8 \times 10^{-4}$$

Assume x is small compared to 0.0500

$$x^2 = (1.8 \times 10^{-4})(0.0500) \qquad x = 0.00303$$

$$\% \text{ ionization} = \frac{0.00303}{0.0500} \times 100 = 6.1\% \text{ ionized}$$

71. **Given:** 0.148 M HA 1.55% dissociation **Find:** K_a

Conceptual Plan: M → $[H_3O^+]$ → K_a and then write a balanced reaction, determine equilibrium concentration and plug into the equilibrium expression.

Solution: (0.148 M HA)(0.0155) = 0.002294 $[H_3O^+] = [A^-]$

	$HA(aq) + H_2O(l) \rightleftharpoons$	$H_3O^+(aq) + A^- (aq)$	
I	0. 148M	0.0	0.0
C	- x	x	x
E	0.148 – 0.002294	0.002294	0.002294

$$K_a = \frac{[H_3O^+][A^-]}{[HA]} = \frac{(0.002294)(0.002294)}{(0.148 - 0.002294)} = 3.61 \times 10^{-5}$$

72. **Given:** 0.085 M HA 0.59% dissociation **Find:** K_a

Conceptual Plan: M → $[H_3O^+]$ → K_a and then write a balanced reaction, determine equilibrium concentration and plug into the equilibrium expression.

Solution: (0.085 M HA)(0.0059) = 3.25×10^{-4} $[H_3O^+] = [A^-]$

	$HA(aq) + H_2O(l) \rightleftharpoons$	$H_3O^+(aq) + A^- (aq)$	
I	0. 085M	0.0	0.0
C	- x	x	x
E	$0.085 - 3.25 \times 10^{-4}$	3.25×10^{-4}	3.25×10^{-4}

$$K_a = \frac{[H_3O^+][A^-]}{[HA]} = \frac{(3.25 \times 10^{-4})(3.25 \times 10^{-4})}{(0.085 - 3.25 \times 10^{-4})} = 1.9 \times 10^{-6}$$

73. a) **Given:** 0.250 M HF $K_a = 3.5 \times 10^{-4}$ **Find:** pH, % dissociation

Conceptual Plan: Write a balanced reaction. Prepare an ICE table; represent the change with x; sum the table and determine the equilibrium values; put the equilibrium values in the equilibrium expression and solve for x and then x → % ionization

$$\% \text{ ionization} = \frac{x}{[HF]_{original}} \times 100$$

Solution: $HF(aq) + H_2O(l) \leftrightarrows H_3O^+(aq) + F^-(aq)$

I	0.250M	0.0	0.0
C	- x	x	x
E	0.250 – x	x	x

$$K_a = \frac{[H_3O^+][F^-]}{[HF]} = \frac{(x)(x)}{(0.250 - x)} = 3.5 \times 10^{-4}$$

Assume x is small compared to 0.250

$$x^2 = (3.5 \times 10^{-4})(0.250) \qquad x = 0.009\underline{3}5M = [H_3O^+]$$

$$\frac{0.009\underline{3}5}{0.250} \times 100 = 3.7\%$$

$$pH = -\log(0.009\underline{3}5) = 2.03$$

b) **Given:** 0.100 M HF $\quad K_a = 3.5 \times 10^{-4}$ **Find:** pH, % dissociation
Conceptual Plan: Write a balanced reaction. Prepare an ICE table; represent the change with x; sum the table and determine the equilibrium values; put the equilibrium values in the equilibrium expression and solve for x and then x → % ionization

$$\% \text{ ionization} = \frac{x}{[HF]_{original}} \times 100$$

Solution: $HF(aq) + H_2O(l) \leftrightarrows H_3O^+(aq) + F^-(aq)$

I	0.1000M	0.0	0.0
C	- x	x	x
E	0.100 – x	x	x

$$K_a = \frac{[H_3O^+][F^-]}{[HF]} = \frac{(x)(x)}{(0.100 - x)} = 3.5 \times 10^{-4}$$

Assume x is small compared to 0.100

$$x^2 = (3.5 \times 10^{-4})(0.100) \qquad x = 0.005\underline{9}2M = [H_3O^+]$$

$$\frac{0.005\underline{9}2}{0.100} \times 100 = 5.9\%$$

x > 5.0 % therefore, assumption invalid

$$x^2 + 3.5 \times 10^{-4}x - 3.5 \times 10^{-5} = 0$$

$$x = 0.005\underline{7}4 \text{ or } -0.00609$$

$$pH = -\log(0.005\underline{7}4) = 2.24$$

$$\% \text{ dissociation} = \frac{0.005\underline{7}4}{0.100} \times 100 = 5.7\%$$

c) **Given:** 0.050 M HF $\quad K_a = 3.5 \times 10^{-4}$ **Find:** pH, % dissociation
Conceptual Plan: Write a balanced reaction. Prepare an ICE table; represent the change with x; sum the table and determine the equilibrium values; put the equilibrium values in the equilibrium expression and solve for x and then x → % ionization

$$\% \text{ ionization} = \frac{x}{[HF]_{original}} \times 100$$

Solution: $HF(aq) + H_2O(l) \leftrightarrows H_3O^+(aq) + F^-(aq)$

I	0.050M	0.0	0.0
C	- x	x	x
E	0.050 – x	x	x

$$K_a = \frac{[H_3O^+][F^-]}{[HF]} = \frac{(x)(x)}{(0.050 - x)} = 3.5 \times 10^{-4}$$

Assume x is small compared to 0.250

$$x^2 = (3.5 \times 10^{-4})(0.050) \qquad x = 0.00418M = [H_3O^+]$$

$$\frac{0.00418}{0.050} \times 100 = 8.4\%$$

Assumption invalid.

$$x^2 + 3.5 \times 10^{-4}x - 1.75 \times 10^{-5} = 0$$

$$x = 0.00401 \text{ or } -0.00436$$

$$pH = -\log(0.00401) = 2.40$$

$$\% \text{ dissociation} = \frac{0.00401}{0.050} \times 100 = 8.0\%$$

74. a) **Given:** 0.100 M HA, $K_a = 1.0 \times 10^{-5}$ **Find:** pH, % dissociation
Conceptual Plan: Write a balanced reaction. Prepare an ICE table; represent the change with x; sum the table and determine the equilibrium values; put the equilibrium values in the equilibrium expression and solve for x and then x → % ionization

$$\% \text{ ionization} = \frac{x}{[HA]_{original}} \times 100$$

Solution: HA(aq) + H_2O(l) ⇆ H_3O^+(aq) + A^-(aq)

	HA	H_3O^+	A^-
I	0.100M	0.0	0.0
C	- x	x	x
E	0.100 – x	x	x

$$K_a = \frac{[H_3O^+][A^-]}{[HA]} = \frac{(x)(x)}{(0.100 - x)} = 1.0 \times 10^{-5}$$

Assume x is small compared to 0.100

$$x^2 = (1.0 \times 10^{-5})(0.100) \qquad x = 0.00100M = [H_3O^+]$$

$$\frac{0.00100}{0.100} \times 100 = 1.0\%$$

$$pH = -\log(0.00100) = 3.00$$

b) **Given:** 0.100 M HA, $K_a = 1.0 \times 10^{-3}$ **Find:** pH, % dissociation
Conceptual Plan: Write a balanced reaction. Prepare an ICE table; represent the change with x; sum the table and determine the equilibrium values; put the equilibrium values in the equilibrium expression and solve for x and then x → % ionization

$$\% \text{ ionization} = \frac{x}{[HA]_{original}} \times 100$$

Solution: HA(aq) + H_2O(l) ⇆ H_3O^+(aq) + A^-(aq)

	HA	H_3O^+	A^-
I	0.100M	0.0	0.0
C	- x	x	x
E	0.100 – x	x	x

$$K_a = \frac{[H_3O^+][A^-]}{[HA]} = \frac{(x)(x)}{(0.100 - x)} = 1.0 \times 10^{-3}$$

$$x^2 = (1.0 \times 10^{-3} - x)(0.100) \qquad x^2 + 1 \times 10^{-3}x - 1 \times 10^{-4} = 0$$

$$x = 0.0095 = [H_3O^+]$$

$$\frac{0.0095}{0.100} \times 100 = 9.5\%$$

$$pH = -\log(0.0095) = 2.02$$

c) **Given:** 0.100 M HA, $K_a = 1.0 \times 10^{-1}$ **Find:** pH, % dissociation
Conceptual Plan: Write a balanced reaction. Prepare an ICE table; represent the change with x; sum the table and determine the equilibrium values; put the equilibrium values in the equilibrium expression and solve for x and then x → % ionization

$$\% \text{ ionization} = \frac{x}{[HA]_{original}} \times 100$$

Solution: $HA(aq) + H_2O(l) \rightleftharpoons H_3O^+(aq) + \quad A^-(aq)$

I	0.100M	0.0	0.0
C	- x	x	x
E	0.100 – x	x	x

$$K_a = \frac{[H_3O^+][A^-]}{[HA]} = \frac{(x)(x)}{(0.100 - x)} = 1.0 \times 10^{-1}$$

$$x^2 = (1.0 \times 10^{-1} - x)(0.100) \qquad x^2 + 0.10x - 0.01 = 0$$

$$x = 0.0616 = [H_3O^+]$$

$$\frac{0.0616}{0.100} \times 100 = 61.8\%$$

$$pH = -\log(0.0095) = 1.21$$

75. a) **Given:** 0.115 HBr (strong acid), 0.125 $HCHO_2$ (weak acid) **Find:** pH
   Conceptual Plan: Since mixture is a strong acid, weak acid, the strong acid will dominate. Use the concentration of the strong acid to determine $[H_3O^+]$ and then pH
   Solution: 0.115 M HBr = 0.115 M $[H_3O^+]$ pH = $- \log(0.115) = 0.939$

   b) **Given:** 0.150 M HNO_2 (weak acid), 0.085 M HNO_3 (strong acid) **Find:** pH
   Conceptual Plan: Since mixture is a strong acid, weak acid, the strong acid will dominate. Use the concentration of the strong acid to determine $[H_3O^+]$ and then pH
   Solution: 0.085 M HNO_3 = 0.085 M $[H_3O^+]$ pH = $- \log(0.085) = 1.07$

   c) **Given:** 0.185M $HCHO_2$, $K_a = 1.8 \times 10^{-4}$; 0.225 M $HC_2H_3O_2$, $K_a = 1.8 \times 10^{-5}$ **Find:** pH
   Conceptual Plan: Since the mixture is a weak acid, weak acid and the K values are only 10^1 apart, you need to find $[H_3O^+]$ from each reaction. Write a balanced reaction. Prepare an ICE table; represent the change with x; sum the table and determine the equilibrium values; put the equilibrium values in the equilibrium expression and solve for x
   Solution: $HCHO_2 (aq) + H_2O(l) \rightleftharpoons H_3O^+(aq) + CHO_2^- (aq)$

I	0.185 M	0.0	0.0
C	- x	x	x
E	0.185 – x	x	x

$$K_a = \frac{[H_3O^+][CHO_2^-]}{[HCHO_2]} = \frac{(x)(x)}{(0.185 - x)} = 1.8 \times 10^{-4}$$

Assume x is small compared to 0.100

$$x^2 = (1.8 \times 10^{-4})(0.185) \qquad x = 0.00577$$

$HC_2H_3O_2 (aq) + H_2O(l) \rightleftharpoons H_3O^+(aq) + C_2H_3O_2^- (aq)$

I	0.225 M	0.00577	0.0
C	- x	x	x
E	0.225 – x	x	x

$$K_a = \frac{[H_3O^+][C_2H_3O_2^-]}{[HC_2H_3O_2]} = \frac{(0.00577 + x)(x)}{(0.225 - x)} = 1.8 \times 10^{-5}$$

Assume x is small compared to 0.0.225

$$x^2 + 0.00602x - 4.05 \times 10^{-6} = 0 \qquad x = 0.00062$$

$$[H_3O^+] = 0.00577 + x = 0.00577 + 0.00062 = 0.006389 \text{ M}$$

$$pH = - \log(0.006389) = 2.19$$

   d) **Given:** 0.050 M $HC_2H_3O_2$, $K_a = 1.8 \times 10^{-5}$; 0.050 M HCN, $K_a = 4.9 \times 10^{-10}$ **Find:** pH
   Conceptual Plan: Since the values of K are more than 10^1 apart, the acid with the larger K will dominate the reaction. Write a balanced reaction. Prepare an ICE table; represent the change with x; sum the table and determine the equilibrium values; put the equilibrium values in the equilibrium expression and solve for x
   Solution: $HC_2H_3O_2 (aq) + H_2O(l) \rightleftharpoons H_3O^+(aq) + C_2H_3O_2^- (aq)$

I	0.0500 M	0.0	0.0
C	- x	x	x
E	0.0500 – x	x	x

$$K_a = \frac{[H_3O^+][C_2H_3O_2^-]}{[HC_2H_3O_2]} = \frac{(x)(x)}{(0.0500 - x)} = 1.8 \times 10^{-5}$$

Assume x is small compared to 0.0500

$x^2 = (1.8 \times 10^{-5})(0.0500)$ $\qquad$ $x = 9.\underline{4}9 \times 10^{-4}$

$pH = -\log(9.\underline{4}9 \times 10^{-4}) = 3.02$

76. a) **Given:** 0.075 HNO_3 (strong acid), 0.175 $HC_7H_5O_2$ (weak acid) $\qquad$ **Find:** pH
Conceptual Plan: Since mixture is a strong acid, weak acid, the strong acid will dominate. Use the concentration of the strong acid to determine $[H_3O^+]$ and then pH
Solution: 0.075 M H NO_3 = 0.075 M $[H_3O^+]$ $\quad$ pH = $-\log(0.075)$ = 1.12

b) **Given:** 0.020 M HBr (strong acid), 0.015 $HClO_4$ M HNO_3 (strong acid) **Find:** pH
Conceptual Plan: Since mixture is a strong acid and strong acid, $[H_3O^+]$ is the sum of the concentration of both acids, and then determine pH
Solution: 0.020 M HBr = 0.020 $[H_3O^+]$, 0.015 M $HClO_4$ = 0.015 M $[H_3O^+]$
$[H_3O^+]$ = 0.020 + 0.015 = 0.035M $\quad$ pH = $-\log(0.035)$ = 1.46

c) **Given:** 0.095M HF, $K_a = 3.5 \times 10^{-4}$; 0.225 M $HC_6H_5O_2$, $K_a = 1.3 \times 10^{-10}$ $\qquad$ **Find:** pH
Conceptual Plan: Since the values of K are more than 10^1 apart, the acid with the larger K will dominate the reaction. Write a balanced reaction. Prepare an ICE table; represent the change with x; sum the table and determine the equilibrium values; put the equilibrium values in the equilibrium expression and solve for x
Solution: $HF(aq) + H_2O(l) \rightleftarrows H_3O^+(aq) + F^-(aq)$

I	0.095M	0.0	0.0
C	- x	x	x
E	0.095 – x	x	x

$$K_a = \frac{[H_3O^+][F^-]}{[HF]} = \frac{(x)(x)}{(0.095 - x)} = 3.5 \times 10^{-4}$$

$x^2 = (3.5 \times 10^{-4})(0.095)$ $\qquad$ $x = 0.005\underline{7}7M = [H_3O^+]$

$pH = -\log(0.005\underline{7}7) = 2.24$

d) **Given:** 0.100 M $HCHO_2$, $K_a = 1.8 \times 10^{-4}$; 0.050 M HClO, $K_a = 2.9 \times 10^{-8}$ $\qquad$ **Find:** pH
Conceptual Plan: Since the values of K are more than 10^1 apart, the acid with the larger K will dominate the reaction. Write a balanced reaction. Prepare an ICE table; represent the change with x; sum the table and determine the equilibrium values; put the equilibrium values in the equilibrium expression and solve for x
Solution: $HCHO_2 (aq) + H_2O(l) \rightleftarrows H_3O^+(aq) + C_2H_3O_2^-(aq)$

I	0.100 M	0.0	0.0
C	- x	x	x
E	0.100 – x	x	x

$$K_a = \frac{[H_3O^+][CHO_2^-]}{[HCHO_2]} = \frac{(x)(x)}{(0.100 - x)} = 1.8 \times 10^{-4}$$

Assume x is small compared to 0.0500

$x^2 = (1.8 \times 10^{-4})(0.100)$ $\qquad$ $x = 0.004\underline{2}4$

$pH = -\log(0.004\underline{2}4) = 2.37$

77. a) **Given:** 0.15 M NaOH $\qquad$ **Find:** $[OH^-]$, $[H_3O^+]$, pH, pOH
Conceptual Plan: [NaOH] $\rightarrow$ $[OH^-]$ $\rightarrow$ $[H_3O^+]$ $\rightarrow$ pH $\rightarrow$ pOH
$\qquad\qquad$ $K_w = [H_3O^+][OH^-]$ $\quad$ pH = $-\log[H_3O^+]$ $\quad$ pH + pOH =14
Solution: $[OH^-]$ = [NaOH] = 0.15M

$$[H_3O^+] = \frac{K_w}{[OH^-]} = \frac{1 \times 10^{-14}}{0.15 \text{ M}} = 6.7 \times 10^{-14} M$$

$pH = -\log(6.7 \times 10^{-14}) = 13.18$

$pOH = 14.00 - 13.18 = 0.82$

b) **Given:** 1.5×10^{-3} M $Ca(OH)_2$ **Find:** $[OH^-]$, $[H_3O^+]$, pH, pOH
Conceptual Plan: $[Ca(OH)_2] \rightarrow [OH^-] \rightarrow [H_3O^+] \rightarrow pH \rightarrow pOH$
$$K_w = [H_3O^+][OH^-] \quad pH = -\log[H_3O^+] \quad pH + pOH = 14$$
Solution: $[OH^-] = 2[Ca(OH)_2] = 2(1.5 \times 10^{-3}) = 0.0030$ M

$$[H_3O^+] = \frac{K_w}{[OH^-]} = \frac{1 \times 10^{-14}}{0.0030 \text{ M}} = 3.\underline{3}3 \times 10^{-12} \text{M}$$

$pH = -\log(3.\underline{3}3 \times 10^{-12}) = 11.48$

$pOH = 14.00 - 11.48 = 2.52$

c) **Given:** 4.8×10^{-4} M $Sr(OH)_2$ **Find:** $[OH^-]$, $[H_3O^+]$, pH, pOH
Conceptual Plan: $[Sr(OH)_2] \rightarrow [OH^-] \rightarrow [H_3O^+] \rightarrow pH \rightarrow pOH$
$$K_w = [H_3O^+][OH^-] \quad pH = -\log[H_3O^+] \quad pH + pOH = 14$$
Solution: $[OH^-] = [Sr(OH)_2] = 2(4.8 \times 10^{-4}) = 9.6 \times 10^{-4}$ M

$$[H_3O^+] = \frac{K_w}{[OH^-]} = \frac{1 \times 10^{-14}}{9.6 \times 10^{-4} \text{ M}} = 1.\underline{0}4 \times 10^{-11} \text{M}$$

$pH = -\log(1.\underline{0}4 \times 10^{-11}) = 10.98$

$pOH = 14.00 - 10.98 = 3.02$

d) **Given:** 8.7×10^{-5} M KOH **Find:** $[OH^-]$, $[H_3O^+]$, pH, pOH
Conceptual Plan: $[KOH] \rightarrow [OH^-] \rightarrow [H_3O^+] \rightarrow pH \rightarrow pOH$
$$K_w = [H_3O^+][OH^-] \quad pH = -\log[H_3O^+] \quad pH + pOH = 14$$
Solution: $[OH^-] = [KOH] = 8.7 \times 10^{-5}$ M

$$[H_3O^+] = \frac{K_w}{[OH^-]} = \frac{1 \times 10^{-14}}{8.7 \times 10^{-5} \text{M}} = 1.\underline{1} \times 10^{-10} \text{M}$$

$pH = -\log(1.\underline{1} \times 10^{-10}) = 9.94$

$pOH = 14.00 - 9.94 = 4.06$

78. a) **Given:** 8.77×10^{-3} M LiOH **Find:** $[OH^-]$, $[H_3O^+]$, pH, pOH
Conceptual Plan: $[LiOH] \rightarrow [OH^-] \rightarrow [H_3O^+] \rightarrow pH \rightarrow pOH$
$$K_w = [H_3O^+][OH^-] \quad pH = -\log[H_3O^+] \quad pH + pOH = 14$$
Solution: $[OH^-] = [LiOH] = 8.77 \times 10^{-3}$ M

$$[H_3O^+] = \frac{K_w}{[OH^-]} = \frac{1 \times 10^{-14}}{8.77 \times 10^{-3} \text{M}} = 1.1\underline{4}0 \times 10^{-12} \text{M}$$

$pH = -\log(1.1\underline{4}0 \times 10^{-12}) = 11.943$

$pOH = 14.00 - 11.943 = 2.057$

b) **Given:** 0.0112 M $Ba(OH)_2$ **Find:** $[OH^-]$, $[H_3O^+]$, pH, pOH
Conceptual Plan: $[Ba(OH)_2] \rightarrow [OH^-] \rightarrow [H_3O^+] \rightarrow pH \rightarrow pOH$
$$K_w = [H_3O^+][OH^-] \quad pH = -\log[H_3O^+] \quad pH + pOH = 14$$
Solution: $[OH^-] = 2[Ba(OH)_2] = 2(0.0112) = 0.0224$ M

$$[H_3O^+] = \frac{K_w}{[OH^-]} = \frac{1 \times 10^{-14}}{0.0224 \text{ M}} = 4.6\underline{4}4 \times 10^{-13} \text{M}$$

$pH = -\log(4.6\underline{4}4 \times 10^{-13}) = 12.350$

$pOH = 14.000 - 12.350 = 1.650$

c) **Given:** 1.9×10^{-4} M KOH **Find:** $[OH^-]$, $[H_3O^+]$, pH, pOH
Conceptual Plan: $[KOH] \rightarrow [OH^-] \rightarrow [H_3O^+] \rightarrow pH \rightarrow pOH$
$$K_w = [H_3O^+][OH^-] \quad pH = -\log[H_3O^+] \quad pH + pOH = 14$$
Solution: $[OH^-] = [KOH] = 1.9 \times 10^{-4}$ M

$$[H_3O^+] = \frac{K_w}{[OH^-]} = \frac{1 \times 10^{-14}}{1.9 \times 10^{-4} \text{ M}} = 5.\underline{2}6 \times 10^{-11} \text{M}$$

$pH = -\log(5.\underline{2}6 \times 10^{-11}) = 10.28$

$pOH = 14.00 - 10.28 = 3.72$

d) **Given:** 5.0×10^{-4} M $Ca(OH)_2$ **Find:** $[OH^-]$, $[H_3O^+]$, pH, pOH

    Conceptual Plan: $[Ca(OH)_2] \rightarrow [OH^-] \rightarrow [H_3O^+] \rightarrow pH \rightarrow pOH$

$$K_w = [H_3O^+][OH^-] \quad pH = -\log[H_3O^+] \quad pH + pOH = 14$$

    Solution: $[OH^-] = [Ca(OH)_2] = 2(5.0 \times 10^{-4}) = 0.0010$ M

$$[H_3O^+] = \frac{K_w}{[OH^-]} = \frac{1 \times 10^{-14}}{0.0010 \text{ M}} = 1.\underline{0}0 \times 10^{-11} \text{M}$$

$$pH = -\log(1.\underline{0}0 \times 10^{-11}) = 11.00$$

$$pOH = 14.00 - 10.90 = 3.00$$

79. **Given:** 3.85% KOH by mass, d = 1.01 g/mL   **Find:** pH

    Conceptual Plan:

       % mass $\rightarrow$ g KOH $\rightarrow$ mol KOH and mass soln $\rightarrow$ mL soln $\rightarrow$ L soln $\rightarrow$ M KOH $\rightarrow$ $[OH^{-1}]$

                 $\dfrac{1 \text{ mol KOH}}{56.01 \text{ g KOH}}$ $\dfrac{1.01 \text{ g soln}}{\text{mL soln}}$ $\dfrac{1000 \text{ mL soln}}{\text{L soln}}$

    $\rightarrow$ pOH $\rightarrow$ pH

    pOH = -log$[OH^-]$ pH + pOH = 14

    Solution: $\dfrac{3.85 \text{ g KOH}}{100.0 \text{ g soln}} \times \dfrac{1 \text{ mol KOH}}{56.01 \text{ g KOH}} \times \dfrac{1.01 \text{ g soln}}{\text{mL soln}} \times \dfrac{1000 \text{ mL soln}}{\text{L soln}} = 0.694\underline{2}$ M KOH

    $[OH^-] = [KOH] = 0.694\underline{2}$ M   pOH = -log(0.694\underline{2}) = 0.159   pH = 14.000 - 0.159 = 13.841

80. **Given:** 1.55% NaOH by mass, d = 1.01 g/mL   **Find:** pH

    Conceptual Plan:

       % mass $\rightarrow$ g NaOH $\rightarrow$ mol NaOH and mass soln $\rightarrow$ mL soln $\rightarrow$ L soln $\rightarrow$ MNaOH $\rightarrow$ $[OH^{-1}]$

                 $\dfrac{1 \text{ mol NaOH}}{40.01 \text{ g KOH}}$ $\dfrac{1.01 \text{ g soln}}{\text{mL soln}}$ $\dfrac{1000 \text{ mL soln}}{\text{L soln}}$

    $\rightarrow$ pOH $\rightarrow$ pH

    pOH = -log$[OH^-]$ pH + pOH = 14

    Solution: $\dfrac{1.55 \text{ g NaOH}}{100.0 \text{ g soln}} \times \dfrac{1 \text{ mol NaOH}}{40.01 \text{ g KOH}} \times \dfrac{1.01 \text{ g soln}}{\text{mL soln}} \times \dfrac{1000 \text{ mL soln}}{\text{L soln}} = 0.391\underline{4}$ M KOH

    $[OH^-] = [NaOH] = 0.391\underline{4}$ M   pOH = -log(0.391\underline{4}) = 0.407   pH = 14.000 - 0.407 = 13.593

81. a) $NH_3(aq) + H_2O(l) \rightleftharpoons NH_4^+(aq) + OH^-(aq)$ $K_b = \dfrac{[NH_4^+][OH^-]}{[NH_3]}$

    b) $HCO_3^-(aq) + H_2O(l) \rightleftharpoons H_2CO_3(aq) + OH^-(aq)$ $K_b = \dfrac{[H_2CO_3][OH^-]}{[HCO_3^-]}$

    c) $CH_3NH_2(aq) + H_2O(l) \rightleftharpoons CH_3NH_3^+(aq) + OH^-(aq)$ $K_b = \dfrac{[CH_3NH_3^+][OH^-]}{[CH_3NH_2]}$

82. a) $CO_3^{2-} + H_2O(l) \rightleftharpoons HCO_3^-aq) + OH^-(aq)$ $K_b = \dfrac{[HCO_3^-][OH^-]}{[CO_3^{2-}]}$

    b) $C_6H_5NH_2 + H_2O(l) \rightleftharpoons C_6H_5NH_3^+(aq) + OH^-(aq)$ $K_b = \dfrac{[C_6H_5NH_3^+][OH^-]}{[C_6H_5NH_2]}$

    c) $C_2H_5NH_2 + H_2O(l) \rightleftharpoons C_2H_5NH_3^+(aq) + OH^-(aq)$ $K_b = \dfrac{[C_2H_5NH_3^+][OH^+]}{[C_2H_5NH_2]}$

83. **Given:** 0.15M NH_3 $K_b = 1.76 \times 10^{-5}$ **Find:** $[OH^-]$, pH, pOH

    Conceptual Plan: Write a balanced reaction. Prepare an ICE table; represent the change with x; sum the table and determine the equilibrium values; put the equilibrium values in the equilibrium expression and solve for x.

    x = $[OH^-]$ $\rightarrow$ pOH $\rightarrow$ pH

      pOH = -log$[OH^-]$ pH + pOH = 14

Solution: $NH_3(aq) + H_2O(l) \leftrightarrows NH_4^+(aq) + OH^-(aq)$

I	0.15	0.0	0.0
C	-x	x	x
E	0.15 – x	x	x

$$K_b = \frac{[NH_4^+][OH^-]}{[NH_3]} = \frac{(x)(x)}{(0.15 - x)} = 1.76 \times 10^{-5}$$

Assume x is small

$x^2 = (1.76 \times 10^{-5})(0.15)$ $x = [OH^-] = 0.00162$ M

$pOH = -\log(0.00162) = 2.79$

$pH = 14.00 - 2.80 = 11.21$

84. **Given:** $0.125M\ CO_3^{2-}$ $K_b = 1.8 \times 10^{-4}$ **Find:** $[OH^-]$,pH, pOH
Conceptual Plan: Write a balanced reaction. Prepare an ICE table; represent the change with x; sum the table and determine the equilibrium values; put the equilibrium values in the equilibrium expression and solve for x.
$x = [OH^-] \rightarrow pOH \rightarrow pH$
   $pOH = -\log[OH^-]$ $pH + pOH = 14$
Solution: $CO_3^{2-} + H_2O(l) \leftrightarrows HCO_3^-(aq) + OH^-(aq)$

I	0.125	0.0	0.0
C	-x	x	x
E	0.125 – x	x	x

$$K_b = \frac{[HCO_3^-][OH^-]}{[CO_3^-]} = \frac{(x)(x)}{(0.15 - x)} = 1.8 \times 10^{-5}$$

Assume x is small

$x^2 = (1.8 \times 10^{-4})(0.125)$ $x = [OH^-] = 0.00474$ M

$pOH = -\log(0.00474) = 2.32$

$pH = 14.00 - 2.32 = 11.68$

85. **Given:** $pK_b = 10.4$, 455 mg/L caffeine   **Find:** pH
Conceptual Plan: $pK_b \rightarrow K_b$ and then mg/L $\rightarrow$ g/L $\rightarrow$ mol/L and then Write a balanced reaction. Prepare an ICE table; represent the change with x; sum the table and determine the equilibrium values; put the equilibrium values in the equilibrium expression and solve for x.
$x = [OH^-] \rightarrow pOH \rightarrow pH$
   $pOH = -\log[OH^-]$ $pH + pOH = 14$
Solution: $K_b = 10^{-10.4} = 3.98 \times 10^{-11}$

$$\frac{455\ \text{mg caffeine}}{\text{L soln}} \times \frac{\text{g caffeine}}{1000\ \text{mg caffeine}} \times \frac{1\ \text{mol caffeine}}{194.19\ \text{g}} = 0.002342\ \text{M caffeine}$$

$C_8H_{10}N_4O_2(aq) + H_2O(l) \leftrightarrows HC_8H_{10}N_4O_2^+(aq) + OH^-(aq)$

I	0.002342	0.0	0.0
C	-x	x	x
E	0.002342– x	x	x

$$K_b = \frac{[HC_8H_{10}N_4O_2^+][OH^-]}{[C_8H_{10}N_4O_2]} = \frac{(x)(x)}{(0.002342 - x)} = 3.98 \times 10^{-11}$$

Assume x is small

$x^2 = (3.98 \times 10^{-11})(0.002342)$ $x = [OH^-] = 3.05 \times 10^{-7}$ M

$pOH = -\log(3.05 \times 10^{-7}) = 6.5$

$pH = 14.00 - 6.5 = 7.5$

86. **Given:** $pK_b = 4.2$, 225 mg/L amphetamine   **Find:** pH
Conceptual Plan: $pK_b \rightarrow K_b$ and then mg/L $\rightarrow$ g/L $\rightarrow$ mol/L and then Write a balanced reaction. Prepare an ICE table; represent the change with x; sum the table and determine the equilibrium values; put the equilibrium values in the equilibrium expression and solve for x.
$x = [OH^-] \rightarrow pOH \rightarrow pH$
   $pOH = -\log[OH^-]$ $pH + pOH = 14$

Solution: $K_b = 10^{-4.2} = \underline{6}.31 \times 10^{-5}$

$$\frac{225 \text{ mg amphetamine}}{\text{L soln}} \times \frac{\text{g amphetamine}}{1000 \text{ mg amphetamine}} \times \frac{1 \text{ mol amphetamine}}{135.21 \text{ g}} = 0.00166\underline{4} \text{ M caffeine}$$

	$C_9H_{13}N(aq)$ + $H_2O(l)$ ⇌	$C_9H_{13}NH^+(aq)$ +	$OH^-(aq)$
I	0.00166\underline{4}	0.0	0.0
C	-x	x	x
E	0.00166\underline{4} - x	x	x

$$K_b = \frac{[C_9H_{13}NH^+][OH^-]}{[C_9H_{13}N]} = \frac{(x)(x)}{(0.00166\underline{4} - x)} = \underline{6}.31 \times 10^{-5}$$

Assume x is small

$$x^2 = (\underline{6}.31 \times 10^{-5})(0.00166\underline{4}) \qquad x = [OH^-] = \underline{3}.16 \times 10^{-4} \text{ M}$$

$$pOH = -\log(\underline{3}.16 \times 10^{-4}) = 3.5$$

$$pH = 14.00 - 3.5 = 10.5$$

87. **Given:** 0.150 M morphine, pH = 10.5 **Find:** K_b
    Conceptual Plan:
      pH → pOH → [OH⁻] and then write a balanced equation, prepare and ICE table, determine
          pH = pOH = 14   pOH = -log[OH⁻]
    equilibrium concentrations → K_b
    Solution: pOH = 14.0 - 10.5 = 3.5 $[OH^-] = 10^{-3.5} = \underline{3}.16 \times 10^{-4} = [\text{Hmorphine}^+]$

	morphine(aq) + $H_2O(l)$ ⇌	$\text{Hmorphine}^+(aq)$ +	$OH^-(aq)$
I	0.150	0.0	0.0
C	-x	x	x
E	0.150 - x	3.16×10^{-4}	3.16×10^{-4}

$$K_b = \frac{[\text{Hmorphine}^+][OH^-]}{[\text{morphine}]} = \frac{(3.16 \times 10^{-4})(3.16 \times 10^{-4})}{(0.150 - 3.16 \times 10^{-4})} = \underline{6}.68 \times 10^{-7} = 7 \times 10^{-7}$$

88. **Given:** 0.135 M base, pH = 11.23 **Find:** K_b
    Conceptual Plan:
      pH → pOH → [OH⁻] and then write a balanced equation, prepare and ICE table, determine
          pH = pOH = 14   pOH = -log[OH⁻]
    equilibrium concentrations → K_b
    Solution: pOH = 14.00 - 11.23 = 2.77 $[OH^-] = 10^{-2.77} = 1.\underline{6}98 \times 10^{-3} = [HB^+]$

	B(aq) + $H_2O(l)$ ⇌	$HB^+(aq)$ +	$OH^-(aq)$
I	0.135	0.0	0.0
C	-x	x	x
E	0.135 - x	$1.\underline{6}98 \times 10^{-3}$	$1.\underline{6}98 \times 10^{-3}$

$$K_b = \frac{[HB^+][OH^-]}{[B]} = \frac{(1.\underline{6}98 \times 10^{-3})(1.\underline{6}98 \times 10^{-3})}{(0.150 - 1.\underline{6}98 \times 10^{-3})} = 2.\underline{1}6 \times 10^{-5} = 2.2 \times 10^{-5}$$

89. a) pH neutral: Br^- is the conjugate base of a strong acid, therefore, it is pH neutral.

    b) weak base: ClO^- is the conjugate base of a weak acid, therefore, it is a weak base.
                        $ClO^-(aq) + H_2O(l) ⇌ HClO(aq) + OH^-(aq)$

    c) weak base: CN^- is the conjugate base of a weak acid, therefore, it is a weak base.
                        $CN^-(aq) + H_2O(l) ⇌ HCN(aq) + OH^-(aq)$

    d) pH neutral: Cl^- is the conjugate base of a strong acid, therefore, it is pH neutral.

90. a) weak base: $C_7H_5O_2^-$ is the conjugate base of a weak acid, therefore, it is a weak base.
                        $C_7H_5O_2^-(aq) + H_2O(l) ⇌ H C_7H_5O_2(aq) + OH^-(aq)$

    b) pH neutral: I^- is the conjugate base of a strong acid, therefore, it is pH neutral.

    c) pH neutral: NO_3^- is the conjugate base of a strong acid, therefore, it is pH neutral.

d) weak base: F^- is the conjugate base of a weak acid, therefore, it is a weak base.

$$F^-(aq) + H_2O(l) \rightleftarrows HF(aq) + OH^-(aq)$$

91. **Given:** $[F^-] = 0.140$ M, $K_a(HF) = 3.5 \times 10^{-4}$ **Find:** $[OH^-]$, pOH

    Conceptual Plan:

    Determine K_b. Write a balanced reaction. Prepare an ICE table; represent the change with x;

    $$K_b = \frac{K_w}{K_a}$$

    sum the table and determine the equilibrium values; put the equilibrium values in the equilibrium expression and solve for x. Determine $[OH^-] \rightarrow$ **pOH** $\rightarrow$ **pH**

    $$pOH = -log[OH^-] \quad pH + pOH = 14$$

    Solution: $F^-(aq) + H_2O(l) \rightleftarrows HF(aq) + OH^-(aq)$

I	0.140	0.0	0.0
C	-x	x	x
E	0.140– x	x	x

    $$K_b = \frac{K_w}{K_a} = \frac{1 \times 10^{-14}}{3.5 \times 10^{-4}} = \frac{(x)(x)}{(0.140 - x)}$$

    Assume x is small

    $$x = 2.0 \times 10^{-6} = [OH^-] \qquad pOH = -log(2.0 \times 10^{-6}) = 5.70$$

    $$pH = 14.00 - 5.70 = 8.30$$

92. **Given:** $[HCO_3^-] = 0.250$ M, $K_a(H_2CO_3) = 4.3 \times 10^{-7}$ **Find:** $[OH^-]$, pOH

    Conceptual Plan:

    Determine K_b. Write a balanced reaction. Prepare an ICE table; represent the change with x;

    $$K_b = \frac{K_w}{K_a}$$

    sum the table and determine the equilibrium values; put the equilibrium values in the equilibrium expression and solve for x. Determine $[OH^-] \rightarrow$ **pOH** $\rightarrow$ **pH**

    $$pOH = -log[OH^-] \quad pH + pOH = 14$$

    Solution: $HCO_3^-(aq) + H_2O(l) \rightleftarrows H_2CO_3(aq) + OH^-(aq)$

I	0.250	0.0	0.0
C	-x	x	x
E	0.250– x	x	x

    $$K_b = \frac{K_w}{K_a} = \frac{1 \times 10^{-14}}{4.3 \times 10^{-7}} = \frac{(x)(x)}{(0.250 - x)}$$

    Assume x is small

    $$x = 7.6 \times 10^{-5} = [OH^-] \qquad pOH = -log(7.6 \times 10^{-5}) = 4.12$$

    $$pH = 14.00 - 4.12 = 9.88$$

93. a) weak acid: NH_4^+ is the conjugate acid of a weak base, therefore, it is a weak acid.

    $$NH_4^+(aq) + H_2O(l) \rightleftarrows H_3O^+(aq) + NH_3(aq)$$

    b) pH neutral: Na^+ is the counterion of a strong base, therefore, it is pH neutral.

    c) weak acid: The Co^{3+} cation is a small, highly charged metal cation, therefore, it is a weak acid.

    $$Co(H_2O)_6^{3+}(aq) + H_2O(l) \rightleftarrows Co(H_2O)_5(OH)^{2+}(aq) + H_3O^+(aq)$$

    d) weak acid: $CH_2NH_3^+$ is the conjugate acid of a weak base, therefore, it is a weak acid.

    $$CH_2NH_3^+(aq) + H_2O(l) \rightleftarrows H_3O^+(aq) + CH_2NH_2(aq)$$

94. a) pH neutral: Sr^{2+} is the counterion of a strong base, therefore, it is pH neutral.

    b) weak acid: The Mn^{3+} cation is a small, highly charged metal cation, therefore, it is a weak acid.

    $$Mn(H_2O)_6^{3+}(aq) + H_2O(l) \rightleftarrows Mn(H_2O)_5(OH)^{2+}(aq) + H_3O^+(aq)$$

    c) weak acid: $C_5H_5NH^+$ is the conjugate acid of a weak base, therefore, it is a weak acid.

    $$C_5H_5NH^+(aq) + H_2O(l) \rightleftarrows H_3O^+(aq) + C_5H_5NH(aq)$$

d)   pH neutral: Li^+ is the counterion of a strong base, therefore, it is pH neutral.

95. a)   acidic: $FeCl_3$ Fe^{3+} is a small, highly charged metal cation and is therefore, acidic. Cl^- is the conjugate base of a strong acid, therefore, it is pH neutral.

   b)   basic: NaF Na^+ is the counterion of a strong base, therefore, it is pH neutral. F^- is the conjugate base of a weak acid, therefore, it is basic.

   c)   pH neutral: $CaBr_2$ Ca^{2+} is the counterion of a strong base, therefore, it is pH neutral. Br^- is the conjugate base of a strong acid, therefore, it is pH neutral.

   d)   acidic: NH_4Br NH_4^+ is the conjugate acid of a weak base, therefore, it is acidic. Br^- is the conjugate base of a strong acid, therefore, it is pH neutral.

   e)   acidic: $C_6H_5NH_3NO_2$ $C_6H_5NH_3^+$ is the conjugate acid of a weak base, therefore, it is a weak acid. NO_2^- is the conjugate base of a weak acid, therefore, it is a weak base. To determine pH, compare K values.

   $$K_a\,(C_6H_5NH_3^+) = \frac{1 \times 10^{-14}}{3.9 \times 10^{-10}} = 2.6 \times 10^{-5} \qquad K_b\,(NO_2^-) = \frac{1 \times 10^{-14}}{4.6 \times 10^{-4}} = 2.2 \times 10^{-11}$$

   $K_a > K_b$ therefore, the solution is acidic.

96. a)   acidic: $Al(NO_3)_3$ Al^{3+} is a small, highly charged metal cation and is therefore, acidic. NO_3^- is the conjugate base of a strong acid, therefore, it is pH neutral.

   b)   acidic: $C_2H_5NH_3NO_3$ $C_2H_5NH_3^+$ is the conjugate acid of a weak base, therefore, it is acidic. NO_3^- is the conjugate base of a strong acid, therefore, it is pH neutral.

   c)   basic: K_2CO_3 K^+ is the counterion of a strong base, therefore, it is pH neutral. CO_3^{2-} is the conjugate base of a weak acid, therefore, it is basic.

   d)   pH neutral: RbI Rb^+ is the counterion of a strong base, therefore, it is pH neutral. I^- is the conjugate base of a strong acid, therefore, it is pH neutral.

   e)   basic NH_4ClO NH_4^+ is the conjugate acid of a weak base, therefore, it is a weak acid. ClO^- is the conjugate base of a weak acid, therefore, it is a weak base. To determine pH, compare K values.

   $$K_a\,(NH_4^+) = \frac{1 \times 10^{-14}}{1.8 \times 10^{-5}} = 5.6 \times 10^{-10} \qquad K_b\,(ClO^-) = \frac{1 \times 10^{-14}}{2.9 \times 10^{-8}} = 3.4 \times 10^{-7}$$

   $K_b > K_a$ therefore, the solution is basic.

97. Identify each species and determine acid, base, neutral.
   NaCl pH neutral: Na^+ is the counterion of a strong base, therefore, it is pH neutral. Cl^- is the conjugate base of a strong acid, therefore, it is pH neutral.
   NH_4Cl acidic: NH_4^+ is the conjugate acid of a weak base, therefore, it is acidic. Cl^- is the conjugate base of a strong acid, therefore, it is pH neutral.
   $NaHCO_3$ basic: Na^+ is the counterion of a strong base, therefore, it is pH neutral. HCO_3^- is the conjugate base of a weak acid, therefore, it is basic.
   NH_4ClO_2 acidic: NH_4ClO_2 NH_4^+ is the conjugate acid of a weak base, therefore, it is a weak acid. ClO_2^- is the conjugate base of a weak acid, therefore, it is a weak base. $K_a(NH_4^+) = 5.6 \times 10^{-10}$ $K_b(ClO_2^-) = 9.1 \times 10^{-13}$
   NaOH strong base
       Increasing acidity: $NaOH < NaHCO_3 < NaCl < NH_4ClO_2 < NH_4Cl$

98. Identify each species and determine acid, base, neutral.
   CH_3NH_3Br acidic: $CH_3NH_3^+$ is the conjugate acid of a weak base, therefore, it is acidic. Br^- is the conjugate base of a strong acid, therefore, it is pH neutral.
   KOH strong base
   KBr pH neutral: K^+ is the counterion of a strong base, therefore, it is pH neutral. Br^- is the conjugate base of a strong acid, therefore, it is pH neutral.

KCN basic: K^+ is the counterion of a strong base, therefore, it is pH neutral. CN^- is the conjugate base of a weak acid, therefore, it is basic.

$C_5H_5NHNO_2$ acidic: $C_5H_5NH^+$ is the conjugate acid of a weak base, therefore, it is acidic. NO_2^- is the conjugate base of a weak acid, therefore, it is basic. $K_a(C_5H_5NH^+) = 5.9 \times 10^{-6}$; $K_b(NO_2^-) = 2.2 \times 10^{-11}$

Increasing basicity: $CH_3NH_3Br < C_5H_5NHNO_2 < KBr < KCN < KOH$

99. a) **Given:** 0.10 M NH_4Cl **Find:** pH
Conceptual Plan: Identify each species and determine which will contribute to pH. Write a balanced reaction. Prepare an ICE table; represent the change with x; sum the table and determine the equilibrium values; put the equilibrium values in the equilibrium expression and solve for x. Determine $[H_3O^+] \rightarrow$ pH
Solution: NH_4^+ is the conjugate acid of a weak base, therefore, it is acidic. Cl^- is the conjugate base of a strong acid, therefore, it is pH neutral.

$$NH_4^+ (aq) + H_2O(l) \leftrightharpoons NH_3 (aq) + H_3O^+ (aq)$$

I	0.10	0.0	0.0
C	-x	x	x
E	0.10– x	x	x

$$K_a = \frac{K_w}{K_b} = \frac{1 \times 10^{-14}}{1.8 \times 10^{-5}} = 5.\underline{5}6 \times 10^{-10} = \frac{(x)(x)}{(0.10 - x)}$$

Assume x is small

$x = 7.\underline{4}5 \times 10^{-6} = [H_3O^+]$ $pH = -\log(7.\underline{4}5 \times 10^{-6}) = 5.13$

b) **Given:** 0.10 M $NaC_2H_3O_2$ **Find:** pH
Conceptual Plan: Identify each species and determine which will contribute to pH. Write a balanced reaction. Prepare an ICE table; represent the change with x; sum the table and determine the equilibrium values; put the equilibrium values in the equilibrium expression and solve for x. Determine $[OH^-] \rightarrow$ pOH $\rightarrow$ pH

$$pOH = -\log[OH^-] \quad pH + pOH = 14$$

Solution: Na^+ is the counterion of a strong base, therefore, is pH neutral. $C_2H_3O_2^-$ is the conjugate base of a weak acid, therefore, it is basic.

$$C_2H_3O_2^- (aq) + H_2O(l) \leftrightharpoons H C_2H_3O_2 (aq) + OH^- (aq)$$

I	0.10	0.0	0.0
C	-x	x	x
E	0.10– x	x	x

$$K_b = \frac{K_w}{K_a} = \frac{1 \times 10^{-14}}{1.8 \times 10^{-5}} = 5.\underline{5}6 \times 10^{-10} = \frac{(x)(x)}{(0.10 - x)}$$

Assume x is small

$x = 7.\underline{4}5 \times 10^{-6} = [OH^-]$ $pOH = -\log(7.\underline{4}5 \times 10^{-6}) = 5.13$

$pH = 14.00 - 5.13 = 8.87$

c) **Given:** 0.10 M NaCl   **Find:** pH
Conceptual Plan: Identify each species and determine which will contribute to pH.
Solution: Na^+ is the counterion of a strong base, therefore, it is pH neutral. Cl^- is the conjugate base of a strong acid, therefore, it is pH neutral.
pH = **7.0**

100. a) **Given:** 0.20 M $NaCHO_2$ **Find:** pH
Conceptual Plan: Identify each species and determine which will contribute to pH. Write a balanced reaction. Prepare an ICE table; represent the change with x; sum the table and determine the equilibrium values; put the equilibrium values in the equilibrium expression and solve for x. Determine $[OH^-] \rightarrow$ pOH $\rightarrow$ pH

$$pOH = -\log[OH^-] \quad pH + pOH = 14$$

Solution: Na^+ is the counterion of a strong base, therefore, is pH neutral. CHO_2^- is the conjugate base of a weak acid, therefore, it is basic.

$$CHO_2^- \text{ (aq) } + H_2O(l) \leftrightarrows \qquad HCHO_2 \text{ (aq)} + OH^- \text{ (aq)}$$

	CHO_2^-	$HCHO_2$	OH^-
I	0.20	0.0	0.0
C	-x	x	x
E	0.20- x	x	x

$$K_b = \frac{K_w}{K_a} = \frac{1 \times 10^{-14}}{1.8 \times 10^{-4}} = 5.\underline{5}6 \times 10^{-11} = \frac{(x)(x)}{(0.20 - x)}$$

Assume x is small

$x = 3.\underline{3}3 \times 10^{-6} = [OH^-] \qquad pOH = -log(3.\underline{3}3 \times 10^{-6}) = 5.48$

$pH = 14.00 - 5.48 = 8.52$

b) **Given:** 0.20 M CH_3NH_3I **Find:** pH

Conceptual Plan: **Identify each species and determine which will contribute to pH. Write a balanced reaction. Prepare an ICE table; represent the change with x; sum the table and determine the equilibrium values; put the equilibrium values in the equilibrium expression and solve for x. Determine $[H_3O^+] \rightarrow pH$**

Solution: $CH_3NH_4^+$ is the conjugate acid of a weak base, therefore, it is acidic. Cl^- is the conjugate base of a strong acid, therefore, it is pH neutral.

$$CH_3NH_3^+ \text{ (aq) } + H_2O(l) \leftrightarrows \quad CH_3NH_2 \text{ (aq) } + H_3O^+ \text{ (aq)}$$

	$CH_3NH_3^+$	CH_3NH_2	H_3O^+
I	0.20	0.0	0.0
C	-x	x	x
E	0.20- x	x	x

$$K_a = \frac{K_w}{K_b} = \frac{1 \times 10^{-14}}{4.4 \times 10^{-4}} = 2.\underline{2}7 \times 10^{-11} = \frac{(x)(x)}{(0.20 - x)}$$

Assume x is small

$x = 2.\underline{1}3 \times 10^{-6} = [H_3O^+] \qquad pH = -log(2.\underline{1}3 \times 10^{-6}) = 5.67$

c) **Given:** 0.20 M KI **Find:** pH

Conceptual Plan: Identify each species and determine which will contribute to pH.

Solution: K^+ is the counterion of a strong base, therefore, it is pH neutral. I^- is the conjugate base of a strong acid, therefore, it is pH neutral.

pH = 7.0

101. **Given:** 0.15 M KF **Find:** concentration of all species

Conceptual Plan: Identify each species and determine which will contribute to pH. Write a balanced reaction. Prepare an ICE table; represent the change with x; sum the table and determine the equilibrium values; put the equilibrium values in the equilibrium expression and solve for x. And then, determine $[OH^-] \rightarrow [H_3O^+]$

$$K_w = [H_3O^+][OH^-]$$

Solution: K^+ is the counterion of a strong base, therefore, is pH neutral. F^- is the conjugate base of a weak acid, therefore, it is basic.

$$F^- \text{ (aq) } + H_2O(l) \leftrightarrows HF \text{ (aq)} + OH^- \text{ (aq)}$$

	F^-	HF	OH^-
I	0.15	0.0	0.0
C	-x	x	x
E	0.15- x	x	x

$$K_b = \frac{K_w}{K_a} = \frac{1 \times 10^{-14}}{3.5 \times 10^{-4}} = \frac{(x)(x)}{(0.15 - x)}$$

Assume x is small

$x = 2.1 \times 10^{-6} = [OH^-] = [HF] \qquad [H_3O^+] = \frac{K_w}{[OH^-]} = \frac{1 \times 10^{-14}}{2.1 \times 10^{-6}} = 4.8 \times 10^{-9}$

$[K^+] = 0.15$ M

$[F^-] = (0.15 - 2.1 \times 10^{-6}) = 0.15$ M

$[HF] = 2.1 \times 10^{-6}$

$[OH^-] = 2.1 \times 10^{-6}$

$[H_3O^+] = 4.8 \times 10^{-9}$

102. **Given:** 0.225 M $C_6H_5NH_3Cl$ **Find:** concentration of all species

Conceptual Plan: Identify each species and determine which will contribute to pH. Write a balanced reaction. Prepare an ICE table; represent the change with x; sum the table and determine the equilibrium values; put the equilibrium values in the equilibrium expression and solve for x. And then, determine $[H_3O^+] \rightarrow [OH^-]$

$$K_w = [H_3O^+][OH^-]$$

Solution: $C_6H_5NH_3^+$ is the conjugate acid of a weak base, therefore, it is a weak acid. Cl^- is the conjugate base of a strong acid, therefore, it is pH neutral.

	$C_6H_5NH_3^+$ (aq) $+$ H_2O(l) $\leftrightarrows$	$C_6H_5NH_2$ (aq) $+$	H_3O^+ (aq)
I	0.225	0.0	0.0
C	-x	x	x
E	0.225- x	x	x

$$K_a = \frac{K_w}{K_b} = \frac{1 \times 10^{-14}}{3.9 \times 10^{-10}} = 2.5\underline{6} \times 10^{-5} = \frac{(x)(x)}{(0.225 - x)}$$

Assume x is small

$$x = 0.0024 = [H_3O^+] = [CH_5NH_2] \qquad [OH^-] = \frac{K_w}{[H_3O^+]} = \frac{1 \times 10^{-14}}{0.0024} = 4.2 \times 10^{-12}$$

$[C_6H_5NH_3^+] = 0.225 - 0.0024 = 0.223$ M
$[Cl^-] = 0.225$ M
$[C_6H_5NH_2] = 0.0024$ M
$[H_3O^+] = 0.0024$ M
$[OH^-] = 4.2 \times 10^{-12}$ M

103. H_3PO_4(aq) $+ H_2O$(l) $\leftrightarrows H_3O^+$(aq) $+ H_2PO_4^-$ (aq) $K_{a1} = \dfrac{[H_3O^+][H_2PO_4^-]}{[H_3PO_4]}$

       $H_2PO_4^-$ (aq) $+ H_2O$(l) $\leftrightarrows H_3O^+$(aq) $+ HPO_4^{2-}$ (aq) $K_{a2} = \dfrac{[H_3O^+][HPO_4^{2-}]}{[H_2PO_4^-]}$

       HPO_4^{2-} (aq) $+ H_2O$(l) $\leftrightarrows H_3O^+$(aq) $+ PO_4^{3-}$ (aq) $K_{a3} = \dfrac{[H_3O^+][PO_4^{3-}]}{[HPO_4^{2-}]}$

104. H_2CO_3(aq) $+ H_2O$(l) $\leftrightarrows H_3O^+$(aq) $+ HCO_3^-$ (aq) $K_{a1} = \dfrac{[H_3O^+][HCO_3^-]}{[H_2CO_3]}$

       HCO_3^- (aq) $+ H_2O$(l) $\leftrightarrows H_3O^+$(aq) $+ CO_3^{2-}$ (aq) $K_{a2} = \dfrac{[H_3O^+][CO_3^{2-}]}{[HCO_3^-]}$

105.a)   **Given:** 0.350 M H_3PO_4 $K_{a1} = 7.5 \times 10^{-3}$, $K_{a2} = 6.2 \times 10^{-8}$ **Find:** $[H_3O^+]$, pH

Conceptual Plan: K_{a1} much larger than K_{a2} so, use K_{a1} to calculate $[H_3O^+]$. Write a balanced reaction. Prepare an ICE table; represent the change with x; sum the table and determine the equilibrium values; put the equilibrium values in the equilibrium expression and solve for x.

Solution: H_3PO_4(aq) $+ H_2O$(l) $\leftrightarrows H_3O^+$(aq) $+ H_2PO_4^-$ (aq)

I	0.350M	0.0	0.0
C	- x	x	x
E	0.350 – x	x	x

$$K_a = \frac{[H_3O^+][H_2PO_4^-]}{[H_3PO_4]} = \frac{(x)(x)}{(0.350 - x)} = 7.3 \times 10^{-3}$$

Assume x is small compared to 0.350

$$x^2 = (7.3 \times 10^{-3})(0.350) \qquad x = 0.0512M = [H_3O^+]$$

Check assumption: $\dfrac{0.0512}{0.350} \times 100 = 14.6\%$ assumption not valid

$$x^2 + 7.5 \times 10^{-3} \, x - 0.002625 = 0 \qquad x = 0.04\underline{7}62 = [H_3O^+]$$

$$pH = - \log(0.04\underline{7}62) = 1.32$$

b)   **Given:** 0.350 M $H_2C_2O_4$ $K_{a1} = 6.0 \times 10^{-2}$, $K_{a2} = 6.0 \times 10^{-5}$ **Find:** $[H_3O^+]$, pH

Conceptual Plan: K_{a1} much larger than K_{a2} so, use K_{a1} to calculate $[H_3O^+]$. Write a balanced reaction. Prepare an ICE table; represent the change with x; sum the table and determine the equilibrium values; put the equilibrium values in the equilibrium expression and solve for x.

Solution: $H_2C_2O_4(aq) + H_2O(l) \leftrightarrows H_3O^+(aq) + HC_2O_4^-(aq)$

I	0.350M	0.0	0.0
C	- x	x	x
E	0.350 – x	x	x

$K_a = \dfrac{[H_3O^+][HC_2O_4^-]}{[H_2C_2O_4]} = \dfrac{(x)(x)}{(0.350 - x)} = 6.0 \times 10^{-2}$

$x^2 + 6.0 \times 10^{-2} x - 0.021 = 0$ $\qquad$ $x = 0.1\underline{1}79 = 0.12$ M $[H_3O^+]$

$pH = -\log(0.1\underline{1}79) = 0.92$

106 a) **Given:** 0.125 M H_2CO_3 $\quad$ $K_{a1} = 4.3 \times 10^{-7}$, $K_{a2} = 5.6 \times 10^{-11}$ $\qquad$ **Find:** $[H_3O^+]$, pH

Conceptual Plan: K_{a1} much larger than K_{a2} so, use K_{a1} to calculate $[H_3O^+]$. Write a balanced reaction. Prepare an ICE table; represent the change with x; sum the table and determine the equilibrium values; put the equilibrium values in the equilibrium expression and solve for x.

Solution: $H_2CO_3(aq) + H_2O(l) \leftrightarrows H_3O^+(aq) + HCO_3^-(aq)$

I	0.125M	0.0	0.0
C	- x	x	x
E	0.125 – x	x	x

$K_a = \dfrac{[H_3O^+][HCO_3^-]}{[H_2CO_3]} = \dfrac{(x)(x)}{(0.125 - x)} = 4.3 \times 10^{-7}$

Assume x is small

$x^2 = (4.3 \times 10^{-7})(0.125)$ $\qquad$ $x = 2.\underline{3}2 \times 10^{-4} = [H_3O^+]$

$pH = -\log(2.\underline{3}2 \times 10^{-4}) = 3.63$

b) **Given:** 0.125 M $H_3C_6H_5O_3$ $\qquad$ $K_{a1} = 7.4 \times 10^{-4}$, $K_{a2} = 1.7 \times 10^{-5}$, $K_{a3} = 4.0 \times 10^{-7}$

Find: $[H_3O^+]$, pH

Conceptual Plan: K_{a1} and K_{a2} are only 10^{-1} apart so, use consider both to calculate $[H_3O^+]$. Write a balanced reaction. Prepare an ICE table; represent the change with x; sum the table and determine the equilibrium values; put the equilibrium values in the equilibrium expression and solve for x.

Solution: $H_3C_6H_5O_3(aq) + H_2O(l) \leftrightarrows H_3O^+(aq) + H_2C_6H_5O_3^-(aq)$

I	0.125M	0.0	0.0
C	- x	x	x
E	0.125 – x	x	x

$K_{a_1} = \dfrac{[H_3O^+][H_2C_6H_5O_3^-]}{[H_3C_6H_5O_3]} = \dfrac{(x)(x)}{(0.125 - x)} = 7.4 \times 10^{-4}$

$x^2 + 7.4 \times 10^{-4} x - 9.25 \times 10^{-5} = 0$ $\qquad$ $x = 0.009\underline{2}55 = [H_3O^+] = [H_2C_6H_5O_3^-]$

and then:

$\qquad H_2C_6H_5O_3^-(aq) + H_2O(l) \leftrightarrows H_3O^+(aq) + HC_6H_5O_3^{2-}(aq)$

I	0.009255M	0.009255	0.0
C	- y	y	y
E	0.009255 – y	0.009255 + y	y

$K_a = \dfrac{[H_3O^+][HC_6H_5O_3^{2-}]}{[H_2C_6H_5O_3^-]} = \dfrac{(0.009255 + y)(y)}{(0.009255 - y)} = 1.7 \times 10^{-5}$

Assume y is small $\qquad$ Then, $y = 1.7 \times 10^{-5}$

$[H_3O^+] = 1.7 \times 10^{-5}$ (from second ionization)

$[H_3O^+] = 0.009\underline{2}55 + 1.7 \times 10^{-5} = 0.009\underline{2}7$ M $\qquad\qquad$ $pH = -\log(0.009\underline{2}7) = 2.03$

107. **Given:** 0.500 M H_2SO_3 $\quad$ $K_{a1} = 1.6 \times 10^{-2}$, $K_{a2} = 6.4 \times 10^{-8}$ $\qquad$ **Find:** concentration all species

Conceptual Plan: Conceptual Plan: K_{a1} much larger than K_{a2} so, use K_{a1} to calculate $[H_3O^+]$. Write a balanced reaction. Prepare an ICE table; represent the change with x; sum the table and determine the equilibrium values; put the equilibrium values in the equilibrium expression and solve for x.

Solution: $H_2SO_3(aq) + H_2O(l) \leftrightarrows H_3O^+(aq) + HSO_3^-(aq)$

I	0.500M	0.0	0.0
C	- x	x	x
E	0.500 – x	x	x

$$K_a = \frac{[H_3O^+][HSO_3^-]}{[H_2SO_3]} = \frac{(x)(x)}{(0.500 - x)} = 1.6 \times 10^{-2}$$

$$x^2 + 1.6 \times 10^{-2} \, x - 0.0080 = 0 \qquad x = 0.08\underline{1}8 = 0.082 \text{ M } [H_3O^+] = [HSO_3^-]$$

Use the values from reaction 1 in reaction 2

$$HSO_3^-\,(aq) + H_2O(l) \leftrightarrows H_3O^+(aq) + SO_3^{2-}\,(aq)$$

I	0.0818M	0.0818	0.0
C	- y	y	y
E	0.0818 – y	0.0818+y	y

$$K_a = \frac{[H_3O^+][SO_3^{2-}]}{[HSO_3^-]} = \frac{(0.0818 + y)(y)}{(0.0818 - y)} = 6.4 \times 10^{-8}$$

Assume y is small $\qquad y = 6.4 \times 10^{-8}$

$[H_2SO_3] = 0.500 - 0.08\underline{1}8 = 0.418$ M

$[HSO_3^-] = x = 0.08\underline{1}8 = 0.082$ M

$[SO_3^{2-}] = y = 6.4 \times 10^{-8}$ M

$[H_3O^+] = x + y = 0.08\underline{1}8 = 0.082$ M

$$[OH^-] = \frac{K_w}{[H_3O^+]} = \frac{1 \times 10^{-14}}{0.0818} = 1.2 \times 10^{-13} \text{ M}$$

108. **Given:** 0.155 M H_2CO_3 $\quad K_{a1} = 4.3 \times 10^{-7}, K_{a2} = 5.6 \times 10^{-11}$ **Find:** concentration all species
Conceptual Plan: Conceptual Plan: K_{a1} **much larger than** K_{a2} **so, use** K_{a1} **to calculate** $[H_3O^+]$ **and** $[HCO_3^-]$, **use** K_{a2} **to find** $[CO_3^-]$. **Write a balanced reaction. Prepare an ICE table; represent the change with x; sum the table and determine the equilibrium values; put the equilibrium values in the equilibrium expression and solve for x.**
Solution: $H_2CO_3(aq) + H_2O(l) \leftrightarrows \quad H_3O^+(aq) + HCO_3^-\,(aq)$

I	0.125M	0.0	0.0
C	- x	x	x
E	0.125 – x	x	x

$$K_a = \frac{[H_3O^+][HCO_3^-]}{[H_2CO_3]} = \frac{(x)(x)}{(0.155 - x)} = 4.3 \times 10^{-7}$$

Assume x is small

$$x^2 = (4.3 \times 10^{-7})(0.155) \qquad x = 2.58 \times 10^{-4} \text{ M} = [H_3O^+] = [HCO_3^-]$$

Reaction 2

$$HCO_3^-\,(aq) + H_2O(l) \leftrightarrows H_3O^+(aq) + CO_3^{2-}\,(aq)$$

Since K_{a2} is small, $[CO_3^{2-}] = K_{a2}$

$[H_2CO_3] = 0.155 - 2.\underline{5}8 \times 10^{-4} = 0.1547 = 0.155$ M M

$[HCO_3^-] = x = 2.\underline{5}8 \times 10^{-4} = 2.6 \times 10^{-4}$ M

$[SO_3^{2-}] = y = 6.4 \times 10^{-8}$ M

$[H_3O^+] = x = 2.\underline{5}8 \times 10^{-4} = 2.6 \times 10^{-4}$ M

$$[OH^-] = \frac{K_w}{[H_3O^+]} = \frac{1 \times 10^{-14}}{2.\underline{5}8 \times 10^{-4}} = 3.88 \times 10^{-11} \text{ M} = 3.9 \times 10^{-11}\text{M}$$

109.a) **Given:** $[H_2SO_4] = 0.50$ M $K_{a2} = 0.012$ **Find:** $[H_3O^+]$,pH
Conceptual Plan: first ionization step is strong, use K_{a2} **and reaction 2. Write a balanced reaction. Prepare an ICE table; represent the change with x; sum the table and determine the equilibrium values; put the equilibrium values in the equilibrium expression and solve for x.**
Solution: $H_2SO_4(aq) + H_2O(l) \rightarrow H_3O^+(aq) + HSO_4^-\,(aq)$ strong

0.50 M

$[H_3O^+] = [HSO_4^-] = 0.50$ M

$HSO_4^-\,(aq) + H_2O(l) \leftrightarrows H_3O^+(aq) + SO_4^{2-}\,(aq)$

I	0.500M	0.500	0.0
C	- x	x	x
E	0.500 – x	x	x

$$K_a = \frac{[H_3O^+][SO_4^{2-}]}{[HSO_4^-]} = \frac{(x)(x)}{(0.500 - x)} = 0.012$$

$$x^2 + 0.512 \, x - 0.006 = 0 \qquad x = 0.01\underline{1}5 = [H_3O^+] \text{ from second ionization step}$$

$[H_3O^+] = 0.50 + 0.011 = 0.51$M

$$pH = - \log(0.51) = 0.29$$

b) **Given:** $[H_2SO_4] = 0.10$ M $K_{a2} = 0.012$ **Find:** $[H_3O^+]$,pH

Conceptual Plan: first ionization step is strong, use K_{a2} and reaction 2. Write a balanced reaction. Prepare an ICE table; represent the change with x; sum the table and determine the equilibrium values; put the equilibrium values in the equilibrium expression and solve for x.

Solution: $H_2SO_4(aq) + H_2O(l) \rightarrow H_3O^+(aq) + HSO_4^-(aq)$ strong

       0.10 M

       $[H_3O^+] = [HSO_4^-] = 0.10$ M

       $HSO_4^-(aq) + H_2O(l) \leftrightarrows H_3O^+(aq) + SO_4^{2-}(aq)$

I	0.10M	0.10	0.0
C	- x	x	x
E	0.10 – x	x	x

$$K_a = \frac{[H_3O^+][SO_4^{2-}]}{[HSO_4^-]} = \frac{(x)(x)}{(0.10 - x)} = 0.012$$

$$x^2 + 0.112\,x - 0.0012 = 0 \qquad x = 0.009\underline{8}48$$

$$\frac{0.009\underline{8}48}{0.10} \times 100 = 9.8\% \text{ contribution of second ionizations step not negligible}$$

$[H_3O^+] = 0.10 + 0.0085 = 0.1085 = 0.11M$

$pH = - \log(0.11) = 0.96$

c) **Given:** $[H_2SO_4] = 0.050$ M $K_{a2} = 0.012$ **Find:** $[H_3O^+]$,pH

Conceptual Plan: first ionization step is strong, use K_{a2} and reaction 2. Write a balanced reaction. Prepare an ICE table; represent the change with x; sum the table and determine the equilibrium values; put the equilibrium values in the equilibrium expression and solve for x.

Solution: $H_2SO_4(aq) + H_2O(l) \rightarrow H_3O^+(aq) + HSO_4^-(aq)$ strong

       0.050 M

       $[H_3O^+] = [HSO_4^-] = 0.050$ M

       $HSO_4^-(aq) + H_2O(l) \leftrightarrows H_3O^+(aq) + SO_4^{2-}(aq)$

I	0.050M	0.10	0.0
C	- x	x	x
E	0.050 – x	x	x

$$K_a = \frac{[H_3O^+][SO_4^{2-}]}{[HSO_4^-]} = \frac{(x)(x)}{(0.050 - x)} = 0.012$$

$$x^2 + 0.062\,x - 0.006 = 0 \qquad x = 0.008\underline{5}09$$

$$\frac{0.008\underline{5}09}{0.05} \times 100 = 17\% \text{ contribution of second ionizations step not negligible}$$

$[H_3O^+] = 0.050 + 0.0085 = 0.0585 = 0.059M$

$pH = - \log(0.059) = 1.23$

110.a) **Given:** 0.10 M H_2A, $K_{a1} = 1.0 \times 10^{-4}$, $K_{a2} = 5.0 \times 10^{-5}$ **Find:** is second ionization negligible?

Conceptual Plan: Write a balanced reaction for both ionization steps. Prepare an ICE table; represent the change with x; sum the table and determine the equilibrium values; put the equilibrium values in the equilibrium expression and solve for x.

       $H_2A(aq) + H_2O(l) \rightarrow H_3O^+(aq) + HA^-(aq)$

I	0.10M	0.0	0.0
C	- x	x	x
E	0.10 – x	x	x

$$K_a = \frac{[H_3O^+][HA^-]}{[H_2A]} = \frac{(x)(x)}{(0.10 - x)} = 1.0 \times 10^{-4}$$

$$x^2 + 1.0 \times 10^{-4}\,x - 1.0 \times 10^{-5} = 0 \qquad x = 0.003\underline{1}1$$

       $HA^-(aq) + H_2O(l) \leftrightarrows H_3O^+(aq) + A^{2-}(aq)$

I	0.003\underline{1}1	0.003\underline{1}1	0.0
C	- y	y	y
E	0.003\underline{1}1– y	y	y

$$K_{a2} = \frac{[H_3O^+][A^{2-}]}{[HA^-]} = \frac{(y)(y)}{(0.003\underline{1}1 - y)} = 5.0 \times 10^{-5}$$

$$y^2 + 0.00311\,y - 1.55 \times 10^{-7} = 0 \qquad y = 4.\underline{8}3 \times 10^{-5}$$

$$\frac{4.\underline{8}3 \times 10^{-5}}{0.00311} \times 100 = 1.5\% \text{ contribution of second ionizations step negligible}$$

$[H_3O^+] = 0.003\underline{1}1 \qquad pH = -\log(0.003\underline{1}1) = 2.5$

b) **Given:** 0.10 M H_2A, $K_{a1} = 1.0 \times 10^{-4}$, $K_{a2} = 1.0 \times 10^{-6}$ **Find:** is second ionization negligible?
Conceptual Plan: Write a balanced reaction for both ionization steps. Prepare an ICE table; represent the change with x; sum the table and determine the equilibrium values; put the equilibrium values in the equilibrium expression and solve for x.

    $H_2A(aq) + H_2O(l) \rightarrow \quad H_3O^+(aq) + HA^-(aq)$

I	0.10M	0.0	0.0
C	- x	x	x
E	0.10 – x	x	x

$$K_a = \frac{[H_3O^+][HA^-]}{[H_2A]} = \frac{(x)(x)}{(0.10 - x)} = 1.0 \times 10^{-4}$$

$$x^2 + 1.0 \times 10^{-4}\,x - 1.0 \times 10^{-5} = 0 \qquad x = 0.003\underline{1}1$$

    $HA^-(aq) + H_2O(l) \leftrightarrows \quad H_3O^+(aq) + A^{2-}(aq)$

I	0.003\underline{1}1	0.003\underline{1}1	0.0
C	- y	y	y
E	0.003\underline{1}1– y	y	y

$$K_{a2} = \frac{[H_3O^+][A^{2-}]}{[HA^-]} = \frac{(y)(y)}{(0.003\underline{1}1 - y)} = 1.0 \times 10^{-6}$$

$$y^2 + 0.00311\,y - 3.11 \times 10^{-9} = 0 \qquad y = 9.\underline{9}8 \times 10^{-7}$$

$$\frac{9.\underline{9}8 \times 10^{-7}}{0.00311} \times 100 = 0.032\% \text{ contribution of second ionizations step negligible}$$

$[H_3O^+] = 0.003\underline{1}1 \qquad pH = -\log(0.003\underline{1}1) = 2.5$

c) **Given:** 0.10 M H_2A, $K_{a1} = 1.0 \times 10^{-4}$, $K_{a2} = 1.0 \times 10^{-5}$ **Find:** is second ionization negligible?
Conceptual Plan: Write a balanced reaction for both ionization steps. Prepare an ICE table; represent the change with x; sum the table and determine the equilibrium values; put the equilibrium values in the equilibrium expression and solve for x.

    $H_2A(aq) + H_2O(l) \rightarrow \quad H_3O^+(aq) + HA^-(aq)$

I	0.10M	0.0	0.0
C	- x	x	x
E	0.10 – x	x	x

$$K_a = \frac{[H_3O^+][HA^-]}{[H_2A]} = \frac{(x)(x)}{(0.10 - x)} = 1.0 \times 10^{-4}$$

$$x^2 + 1.0 \times 10^{-4}\,x - 1.0 \times 10^{-5} = 0 \qquad x = 0.003\underline{1}1$$

    $HA^-(aq) + H_2O(l) \leftrightarrows \quad H_3O^+(aq) + A^{2-}(aq)$

I	0.003\underline{1}1	0.003\underline{1}1	0.0
C	- y	y	y
E	0.003\underline{1}1– y	y	y

$$K_{a2} = \frac{[H_3O^+][A^{2-}]}{[HA^-]} = \frac{(y)(y)}{(0.003\underline{1}1 - y)} = 1.0 \times 10^{-5}$$

$$y^2 + 0.00311\,y - 3.11 \times 10^{-8} = 0 \qquad y = 9.\underline{9}3 \times 10^{-6}$$

$$\frac{9.\underline{9}3 \times 10^{-6}}{0.00311} \times 100 = 0.32\% \text{ contribution of second ionizations step negligible}$$

$[H_3O^+] = 0.003\underline{1}1 \qquad pH = -\log(0.003\underline{1}1) = 2.5$

111.a)   HCl is the stronger acid. HCl is the weaker bond, therefore, it is more acidic.

b)   HF is the stronger acid. F is more electronegative than O, so the bond is more polar and more acidic.

c) H_2Se is the stronger acid. The H – Se bond is weaker, therefore, it is more acidic.

112. Increasing acid strength: $NaH < H_2S < H_2Te < HI$
H_2Te is a stronger acid than H_2S because the H – Te bond is weaker. HI is a stronger acid than H_2Te because I is more electronegative than Te. NaH is not acidic because H is more electronegative than Na.

113. a) H_2SO_4 is the stronger acid because it has more oxygen atoms.

b) $HClO_2$ is the stronger acid because it has more oxygen atoms.

c) HClO is the stronger acid because Cl is more electronegative than Br.

d) CCl_3COOH is the stronger acid because Cl is more electronegative than H.

114. Increasing acid strength: $HIO_3 < HBrO_3 < HClO_3$.
Cl is more electronegative than Br which is more electronegative than I.

115. S^{2-} is the stronger base. Base strength is determined from the corresponding acid. The weaker the acid, the stronger the base. H_2S is the weaker acid because it has a stronger bond.

116. AsO_4^{3-} is the stronger base. Base strength is determined from the corresponding acid. The weaker the acid, the stonger the base. H_3AsO_4 is the weaker acid because P is more electronegative than As.

117. a) Lewis acid: Fe^{3+} has empty d orbital and can accept lone pair electrons.

b) Lewis acid: BH_3 has an empty p orbital to accept a lone pair of electrons.

c) Lewis base: NH_3 has a lone pair of electrons to donate.

d) Lewis base: F^- has lone pair electrons to donate.

118. a) Lewis acid: $BeCl_2$ has empty p orbitals to accept lone pair electrons.

b) Lewis base: OH^- has lone pair electrons to donate.

c) Lewis acid: $B(OH)_3$ has an empty p orbital to accept a lone pair of electrons.

d) Lewis base: CN^- has lone pair electrons to donate.

119. a) Fe^{3+} accepts electron pair from H_2O, so Fe^{3+} is the Lewis acid and H_2O is the Lewis base.

b) Zn^{2+} accepts electron pair from NH_3, so Zn^{2+} is the Lewis acid and NH_3 is the Lewis base.

c) The empty p orbital on B accepts an electron pair from $(CH_3)_3N$, so BF_3 is the Lewis acid and $(CH_3)_3N$ is the Lewis base.

120. a) Ag^+ accepts electron pair from NH_3, so Ag^+ is the Lewis acid and NH_3 is the Lewis base.

b) The empty p orbital on Al accepts electron pair from NH_3, $AlBr_3$ is the Lewis acid and NH_3 is the Lewis base.

c) The empty p orbital on B accepts electron pair from F^-, so BF_3 is the Lewis acid and F^- is the Lewis base.

121. a) weak acid. The beaker contains 10 HF molecule, $2H_3O^+$ ions and $2F^-$ ions. Since both the molecule and the ions exist in solution, the acid is a weak acid.

b) strong acid. The beaker contains $12H_3O^+$ ions and $2OH^-$ ions. Since the molecule is completely ionized in solution, the acid is a strong acid.

c) weak acid. The beaker contains 10 $HCHO_2$ molecules, $2H_3O^+$ ions and $2CHO_2^-$ ions. Since both the molecule and the ions exist in solution, the acid is a weak acid.

d) strong acid. The beaker contains $12H_3O^+$ ions and $2NO_3^-$ ions. Since the molecule is completely ionized in solution, the acid is a strong acid.

122.a) weak base. The beaker contains 11 NH_3 molecules, 2 NH_4^+ ions and $2OH^-$ ions. Since both the molecule and the ions exist in solution, the acid is a weak acid.

b) strong base. The beaker contains 12 Na^+ ions and $12OH^-$ ions. Since the molecule is completely ionized in solution, it is a strong base.

c) weak base. The beaker contains 12 Na^+, 10 H_2CO_3 molecules, $2HCO_3^-$ ions, and $2OH^-$ ions. The beaker contains the HCO_3^- ion from the $NaHCO_3$ and H_2CO_3 molecules from the reaction of the salt.

d) strong base. The beaker contains 12 Sr^{2+} ions and 24 OH^- ions. Since the molecule is completely ionized in solution, it is a strong base.

123. $HbH^+(aq) + O_2(aq) \leftrightarrows HbO_2(aq) + H^+(aq)$

Using LeChatlier's Principle, if the $[H^+]$ increases, the reaction will shift left, if the $[H^+]$ decreases, the reaction will shift right. So, if the pH of blood is too acidic (low pH; $[H^+]$ increased), the reaction will shift to the left. This will cause less of the HbO_2 in the blood and decrease the oxygen – carrying capacity of the hemoglobin in the blood.

124. $CO_2(g) + H_2O(l) \leftrightarrows H_2CO_3(aq)$

$H_2CO_3(aq) + H_2O(l) \leftrightarrows HCO_3^-(aq) + H_3O^+(aq)$

As the concentration of CO_2 in the atmosphere increases, more will dissolve in H_2O and form H_2CO_3. The H_2CO_3 will then act as a weak acid with H_2O and form HCO_3^- and H_3O^+ causing the water(oceans) to be more acidic. If the pH of the oceans decreases, the added H_3O^+ will react with the CO_3^{2-} ion in the $CaCO_3$ in the limestone structures and decompose the $CaCO_3$.

$2H_3O^+(aq) + CaCO_3(s) \rightarrow Ca^{2+}(aq) + H_2CO_3(aq) + 2H_2O \rightarrow H_2O(l) + CO_2(g)$

125. **Given:** 4.00×10^2 mg $Mg(OH)_2$, 2.00×10^2 mL HCl solution, pH = 1.3

Find: volume neutralized, % neutralized.

Conceptual Plan:

mg $Mg(OH)_2$ → g $Mg(OH)_2$ → mol $Mg(OH)_2$ and then pH → $[H_3O^+]$ and then mol $Mg(OH)_2$

$$\frac{g\ Mg(OH)_2}{1000\ mg} \qquad \frac{mol\ Mg(OH)_2}{58.326\ g} \qquad pH = -\log [H_3O^+]$$

mol OH^- → mol H_3O^+ → vol H_3O^+ → % neutralized.

$$\frac{2\ OH^-}{Mg(OH)_2} \qquad \frac{H_3O^+}{OH^-} \qquad \frac{mol\ H_3O^+}{M(H_3O^+)} \qquad \frac{vol\ HCl\ neutralized}{total\ vol\ HCl} \times 100$$

Solution: $[H_3O^+] = 10^{-1.3} = 0.05011\ M = 0.05\ M$

$$4.00 \times 10^2\ \overline{mg\ Mg(OH)_2} \times \frac{\overline{g\ Mg(OH)_2}}{1000\ \overline{mg\ Mg(OH)_2}} \times \frac{1\ \overline{mol\ Mg(OH)_2}}{58.326\ \overline{g\ Mg(OH)_2}} \times \frac{2\ \overline{mol\ OH^-}}{1\ \overline{mol\ Mg(OH)_2}}$$

$$\times \frac{1\ \overline{mol\ H_3O^+}}{1\ \overline{mol\ OH^-}} \times \frac{1\ \overline{L}}{0.0501\ \overline{mol\ H_3O^+}} \times \frac{1000\ mL}{\overline{L}} = 273.7\ mL = 274\ mL\ neutralized$$

Stomach contains 2.00×10^2 mL HCl at pH = 1.3 and 4.00×10^2 mg will neutralize 274 mL of pH 1.3 HCl, so all of the stomach acid will be neutralized.

126. **Given:** 4.3 billion L, pH = 5.5   **Find:** mass in kg $CaCO_3$

Conceptual Plan:

pH → $[H_3O^+]$ and then vol lake → mol $[H_3O^+]$ → mol $CaCO_3$ → g $CaCO_3$ → kg $CaCO_3$

$$pH = -\log[H_3O^+] \qquad mol = vol \times M \qquad \frac{mol\ CaCO_3}{2\ mol\ H_3O^+} \quad \frac{100.09\ g\ CaCO_3}{mol\ CaCO_3} \quad \frac{kg\ CaCO_3}{1000\ g\ CaCO_3}$$

Solution: $[H_3O^+] = 10^{-5.5} = 3.16 \times 10^{-6}$ M

$$4.3 \times 10^9 \; \cancel{L} \times \frac{3.16 \times 10^{-6} \; \cancel{\text{mol } H_3O^+}}{\cancel{L}} \times \frac{1 \; \cancel{\text{mol } CaCO_3}}{2 \; \cancel{\text{mol } H_3O^+}} \times \frac{100.09 \text{ g } \cancel{CaCO_3}}{\cancel{\text{mol } CaCO_3}} \times \frac{1 \text{ kg}}{1000 \; \cancel{g}} = 680.01 \text{ kg} = 6.8 \times 10^2 \text{ kg } CaCO_3$$

127. **Given:** pH of Great Lakes acid rain = 4.5, West Coast = 5.4
Find: $[H_3O^+]$ and ratio of Great Lakes/ West Coast
Conceptual Plan: pH → $[H_3O^+]$, and then ratio of $[H_3O^+]$ Great Lakes to West Coast.
$$\text{pH} = -\log[H_3O^+]$$
Solution: Great Lakes: $[H_3O^+] = 10^{-4.5} = 3.16 \times 10^{-5}$ M   West Coast: $[H_3O^+] = 10^{-5.4} = 3.98 \times 10^{-6}$ M

$$\frac{\text{Great Lakes}}{\text{West Coast}} = \frac{3.16 \times 10^{-5} \text{ M}}{3.98 \times 10^{-6} \text{ M}} = 7.94 = 8 \text{ times more acidic}$$

128. **Given:** pH of Sauvignon Blanc = 3.23, Cabernet Sauvignon = 3.64
Find: $[H_3O^+]$ and ratio of Sauvignon Blanc to Cabernet Sauvignon
Conceptual Plan: pH → $[H_3O^+]$, and then ratio of $[H_3O^+]$ Sauvignon Blanc to Cabernet Sauvignon.
$$\text{pH} = -\log[H_3O^+]$$
Solution:

Sauvignon Blanc: $[H_3O^+] = 10^{-3.23} = 5.888 \times 10^{-4}$ M   Cabernet Sauvignon: $[H_3O^+] = 10^{-3.64} = 2.291 \times 10^{-4}$ M

$$\frac{\text{Sauvignon Blanc}}{\text{Cabernet Sauvignon}} = \frac{5.888 \times 10^{-4} \text{ M}}{2.291 \times 10^{-4} \text{ M}} = 2.570 = 2.57 \text{ times more acidic}$$

129. **Given:** 6.5×10^2 mg aspirin, 8 ounces water, $pK_a = 3.5$ **Find:** pH of solution
Conceptual Plan:

mg aspirin → g aspirin → mol aspirin and ounces → quart → L and then [aspirin] and pK_a
$$\frac{\text{g aspirin}}{1000 \text{ mg}} \qquad \frac{\text{mol aspirin}}{180.16 \text{ g}} \qquad \frac{1 \text{ qt}}{32 \text{ ounces}} \qquad \frac{1 \text{ L}}{1.0567 \text{ qt}} \qquad \frac{\text{mol aspirin}}{\text{L soln}} \qquad pK_a = -\log K_a$$

→K_a and then: Write a balanced reaction. Prepare an ICE table; represent the change with x; sum the table and determine the equilibrium values; put the equilibrium values in the equilibrium expression and solve for x. Determine $[H_3O^+]$ → pH
$$\text{pH} = -\log[H_3O^+]$$

Solution: $\dfrac{6.5 \times 10^2 \; \cancel{\text{mg aspirin}}}{8 \; \cancel{\text{ounces}}} \times \dfrac{1 \; \cancel{\text{gram aspirin}}}{1000 \; \cancel{\text{mg aspirin}}} \times \dfrac{\text{mol aspirin}}{180.16 \; \cancel{g}} \times \dfrac{32 \; \cancel{\text{ounces}}}{\cancel{qt}} \times \dfrac{1.0567 \; \cancel{qt}}{1 \text{ L}} = 0.0152$ M

$K_a = 10^{-3.5} = 3.16 \times 10^{-4}$

$\text{aspirin(aq)} + H_2O(l) \rightleftharpoons H_3O^+(aq) + \text{aspirin}^-(aq)$

I	0.0152M	0.0	0.0
C	- x	x	x
E	0.0152– x	x	x

$K_a = \dfrac{[H_3O^+][\text{aspirin}^-]}{[\text{aspirin}]} = \dfrac{(x)(x)}{(0.0152 - x)} = 3.16 \times 10^{-4}$

$x^2 + 3.16 \times 10^{-4}x - 4.80 \times 10^{-6} = 0$ 　　　　$x = 2.04 \times 10^{-3}$ M $= [H_3O^+]$

$\text{pH} = -\log(2.04 \times 10^{-3}) = 2.69 = 2.7$

130. **Given:** 565 mg/L ddC, $pK_b = 9.8$ **Find:** % protonated
Conceptual Plan: mg → g → mol → M and then pK_b → K_b and then: Write a balanced reaction. Prepare an ICE table; represent the change with x; sum the table and determine the equilibrium values; put the equilibrium values in the equilibrium expression and solve for x.

Solution: $\dfrac{565 \; \cancel{\text{mg ddC}}}{L} \times \dfrac{\cancel{\text{g ddC}}}{1000 \; \cancel{\text{mg ddC}}} \times \dfrac{\text{mol ddC}}{224.22 \; \cancel{\text{g ddC}}} = 0.0025199$ M

$K_b = 10^{-9.8} = 1.585 \times 10^{-10}$

$\text{ddC(aq)} + H_2O(l) \rightleftharpoons HddC^+(aq) + OH^-(aq)$

I	0.0025199	0.0	0.0
C	-x	x	x
E	0.0025199– x	x	x

$$K_b = \frac{[HddC^+][OH^-]}{[ddC]} = \frac{(x)(x)}{(0.0025\underline{1}99 - x)} = 1.585 \times 10^{-10}$$

Assume x is small

$$x^2 = (1.585 \times 10^{-10})(0.0025\underline{1}99) \qquad x = [OH^-] = [HddC^+] = 6.32 \times 10^{-7}\ M$$

$$\%\ \text{protonated} = \frac{[HddC^+]_{equilibrium}}{[ddC]_{original}} \times 100 = 0.025\ \%$$

131.a) **Given: 0.0100M HClO$_4$**   **Find: pH**

Conceptual Plan:[HClO$_4$] → [H$_3$O$^+$] → pH

[HClO$_4$] → [H$_3$O$^+$]   pH = -log[H$_3$O$^+$]

Solution: 0.0100 M HClO$_4$ = 0.0100 M H$_3$O$^+$ pH = $-\log(0.0100) = 2.000$

b) **Given: 0.115M HClO$_2$,K_a =   1.1 x 10^{-2}**   **Find: pH**

Conceptual Plan: Write a balanced reaction. Prepare an ICE table; represent the change with x; sum the table and determine the equilibrium values; put the equilibrium values in the equilibrium expression and solve for x. Determine [H$_3$O$^+$] and pH

Solution: HClO$_2$ (aq) + H$_2$O(l) ⇌ H$_3$O$^+$(aq) + ClO$_2^-$ (aq)

I	0.115M	0.0	0.0
C	- x	x	x
E	0.115 – x	x	x

$$K_a = \frac{[H_3O^+][ClO_2^-]}{[HClO_2]} = \frac{(x)(x)}{(0.115 - x)} = 1.1 \times 10^{-2}$$

Assume x is small compared to 0.115

$$x^2 = (1.1 \times 10^{-2})(0.115) \qquad x = 0.03\underline{5}6M = [H_3O^+]$$

Check assumption: $\dfrac{0.03\underline{5}6}{0.115}$ x 100 =30.9% assumption not valid

$$x^2 + 1.1 \times 10^{-2}x - 0.001265 = 0$$

$$x = 0.03\underline{0}49\ \text{or}\ -0.0415$$

$$pH = -\log(0.03\underline{0}49) = 1.52$$

c) **Given: 0.045M Sr(OH)$_2$**   **Find: pH**

Conceptual Plan: [Sr(OH)$_2$] → [OH$^-$] → [H$_3$O$^+$] → pH

$$K_w = [H_3O^+][OH^-] \quad pH = -\log[H_3O^+] \quad pH + pOH = 14$$

Solution: [OH$^-$] = [Sr(OH)$_2$] = 2(0.045) = 0.090 M

$$[H_3O^+] = \frac{K_w}{[OH^-]} = \frac{1 \times 10^{-14}}{0.090\ M} = 1.\underline{1}1 \times 10^{-13}M$$

$$pH = -\log(1.\underline{1}1 \times 10^{-13}) = 12.95$$

d) **Given: 0.0852 KC$_6$H$_5$O, K_a (HC$_6$H$_5$O)= 4.9 x 10^{-10}**   **Find: pH**

Conceptual Plan: Identify each species and determine which will contribute to pH. Write a balanced reaction. Prepare an ICE table; represent the change with x; sum the table and determine the equilibrium values; put the equilibrium values in the equilibrium expression and solve for x. Determine [OH$^-$] → pOH → pH

$$pOH = -\log[OH^-] \quad pH + pOH = 14$$

Solution: K$^+$ is the counterion of a strong base, therefore, is pH neutral. CN$^-$ is the conjugate base of a weak acid, therefore, it is basic.

CN$^-$ (aq) + H$_2$O(l) ⇌ HCN (aq)+ OH$^-$ (aq)

I	0.0852	0.0	0.0
C	-x	x	x
E	0.0852 – x	x	x

$$K_b = \frac{K_w}{K_a} = \frac{1 \times 10^{-14}}{4.9 \times 10^{-10}} = 2.\underline{0}4 \times 10^{-5} = \frac{(x)(x)}{(0.0852 - x)}$$

Assume x is small

$$x = 1.\underline{3}2 \times 10^{-3} = [OH^-] \qquad pOH = -\log(1.\underline{3}2 \times 10^{-3}) = 2.88$$

$$pH = 14.00 - 2.88 = 11.12$$

e) **Given:** 0.155 NH_4Cl, K_b (NH_3)= 1.8 x 10^{-5} **Find:** pH

Conceptual Plan: Identify each species and determine which will contribute to pH. Write a balanced reaction. Prepare an ICE table; represent the change with x; sum the table and determine the equilibrium values; put the equilibrium values in the equilibrium expression and solve for x. Determine [H_3O^+] → pH

Solution: NH_4^+ is the conjugate acid of a weak base, therefore, it is acidic. Cl^- is the conjugate base of a strong acid, therefore, it is pH neutral.

	NH_4^+ (aq) + H_2O(l) $\leftrightarrows$ NH_3 (aq) + H_3O^+(aq)		
I	0.155	0.0	0.0
C	-x	x	x
E	0.155– x	x	x

$$K_a = \frac{K_w}{K_b} = \frac{1 \times 10^{-14}}{1.8 \times 10^{-5}} = 5.\underline{5}6 \times 10^{-10} = \frac{(x)(x)}{(0.155 - x)}$$

Assume x is small

$$x = 9.\underline{2}8 \times 10^{-6} = [H_3O^+] \qquad pH = -\log(9.\underline{2}8 \times 10^{-6}) = 5.03$$

132.a) **Given:** 0.0650M HNO_3 **Find:** pH

Conceptual Plan:[HNO_3] → [H_3O^+] → pH
   [HNO_3] → [H_3O^+]   pH = -log[H_3O^+]

Solution: 0.0650M HNO_3= 0.0650M H_3O^+ pH = $-\log(0.0650)$ = 1.187

b) **Given:** 0.150M HNO_2,K_a = 4.6 x 10^{-4} **Find:** pH

Conceptual Plan: Write a balanced reaction. Prepare an ICE table; represent the change with x; sum the table and determine the equilibrium values; put the equilibrium values in the equilibrium expression and solve for x. Determine [H_3O^+] and pH

Solution: HNO_2 (aq) + H_2O(l) $\leftrightarrows$ H_3O^+(aq) + NO_2^- (aq)

I	0.150M	0.0	0.0
C	- x	x	x
E	0.150 – x	x	x

$$K_a = \frac{[H_3O^+][NO_2^-]}{[HNO_2]} = \frac{(x)(x)}{(0.150 - x)} = 4.6 \times 10^{-4}$$

Assume x is small compared to 0.150

$$x^2 = (4.6 \times 10^{-4})(0.150) \qquad x = 0.007\underline{2}7M = [H_3O^+]$$

Check assumption: $\dfrac{0.007\underline{2}7}{0.150}$ x 100 =4.85% assumption valid

$$pH = -\log(0.007\underline{2}7) = 2.14$$

c) **Given:** 0.0195M KOH **Find:** pH

Conceptual Plan: [KOH] → [OH^-] → [H_3O^+] → pH
   $K_w = [H_3O^+][OH^-]$ pH = -log[H_3O^+]   pH + pOH =14

Solution: [OH^-] = [KOH] = (0.0195) = 0.0195 M

$$[H_3O^+] = \frac{K_w}{[OH^-]} = \frac{1 \times 10^{-14}}{0.0195 \text{ M}} = 5.1\underline{2}8 \times 10^{-13}M$$

$$pH = -\log(5.1\underline{2}8 \times 10^{-13}) = 12.290$$

d. **Given:** 0.245 CH_3NH_3I, K_b (CH_3NH_3)= 4.4 x 10^{-4} **Find:** pH

Conceptual Plan: Identify each species and determine which will contribute to pH. Write a balanced reaction. Prepare an ICE table; represent the change with x; sum the table and determine the equilibrium values; put the equilibrium values in the equilibrium expression and solve for x. Determine [H_3O^+] → pH

Solution: $CH_3NH_3^+$ is the conjugate acid of a weak base, therefore, it is acidic. I^- is the conjugate base of a strong acid, therefore, it is pH neutral.

	$CH_3NH_4^+$ (aq) + H_2O(l) $\leftrightarrows$ CH_3NH_2 (aq) + H_3O^+(aq)		
I	0.245	0.0	0.0
C	-x	x	x
E	0.245– x	x	x

$$K_a = \frac{K_w}{K_b} = \frac{1 \times 10^{-14}}{4.4 \times 10^{-4}} = 2.\underline{2}72 \times 10^{-11} = \frac{(x)(x)}{(0.245 - x)}$$

Assume x is small

$x = 2.\underline{3}6 \times 10^{-6} = [H_3O^+]$ $pH = -\log(2.\underline{3}6 \times 10^{-6}) = 5.63$

e) **Given:** 0.312 KC_6H_5O, K_a (HC_6H_5O)= 1.3 x 10^{-10} **Find:** pH
    Conceptual Plan: Identify each species and determine which will contribute to pH. Write a balanced reaction. Prepare an ICE table; represent the change with x; sum the table and determine the equilibrium values; put the equilibrium values in the equilibrium expression and solve for x. Determine [OH⁻] → pOH → pH
    $$pOH = -\log[OH^-] \quad pH + pOH = 14$$
    Solution: K^+ is the counterion of a strong base, therefore, is pH neutral. $C_6H_5O^-$ is the conjugate base of a weak acid, therefore, it is basic.

	$C_6H_5O^-$ (aq) + H_2O(l) $\leftrightarrows$ HC_6H_5O (aq) +		OH^-(aq)
I	0. 312	0.0	0.0
C	-x	x	x
E	0. 312– x	x	x

$$K_b = \frac{K_w}{K_a} = \frac{1 \times 10^{-14}}{1.3 \times 10^{-10}} = 7.\underline{6}9 \times 10^{-5} = \frac{(x)(x)}{(0.312 - x)}$$

Assume x is small

$x = 4.\underline{9}0 \times 10^{-3} = [OH^-]$ $pOH = -\log(4.\underline{9}0 \times 10^{-3}) = 2.31$

$pH = 14.00 - 2.31 = 11.69$

133.a) **Given:** 0.0550M HI (strong acid), 0.00850M HF (weak acid)   **Find:** pH
    Conceptual Plan: Since mixture is a strong acid, weak acid, the strong acid will dominate. Use the concentration of the strong acid to determine [H₃O⁺] and then pH
    Solution: 0.0550M HI = 0.0550 M $[H_3O^+]$ pH = - log(0.0550) = 1.260

b) **Given:** 0.112 M NaCl (salt), 0.0953 M KF (salt)   **Find:** pH
    Conceptual Plan: Identify each species and determine which will contribute to pH. Write a balanced reaction. Prepare an ICE table; represent the change with x; sum the table and determine the equilibrium values; put the equilibrium values in the equilibrium expression and solve for x. Determine [H₃O⁺] → pH
    Solution: Na^+ is the counterion of a strong base, therefore, it is pH neutral. Cl^- is the conjugate base of a strong acid, therefore, it is pH neutral. K^+ is the counterion of a strong base, therefore, it is pH neutral. F^- is the conjugate base of a weak acid. Therefore, it will produce a basic solution.

	F^- (aq) + H_2O(l) $\leftrightarrows$ HF(aq)+		OH^-(aq)
I	0.0953	0.0	0.0
C	-x	x	x
E	0.0953– x	x	x

$$K_b = \frac{K_w}{K_a} = \frac{1 \times 10^{-14}}{3.5 \times 10^{-4}} = \frac{(x)(x)}{(0.0953 - x)}$$

Assume x is small

$x = 1.\underline{6}50 \times 10^{-6} = [OH^-]$ $pOH = -\log(1.\underline{6}50 \times 10^{-6}) = 5.78$

$pH = 14.00 - 5.78 = 8.22$

c) **Given:** 0.132 M NH_4Cl (salt), 0.150 M HNO_3 (strong acid)   **Find:** pH
    Conceptual Plan: Since the mixture is a strong acid and a salt, the strong acid will dominate. Use the concentration of the strong acid to determine [H₃O⁺] and then pH.
    Solution: 0. 150M HNO_3 = 0.150 M $[H_3O^+]$ pH = - log(0.150) = 0.824

d) **Given:** 0.0887M $NaC_7H_5O_2$ (salt) 0.225 M KBr(salt)
    Conceptual Plan: Identify each species and determine which will contribute to pH. Write a balanced reaction. Prepare an ICE table; represent the change with x; sum the table and determine the equilibrium values; put the equilibrium values in the equilibrium expression and solve for x. Determine [H₃O⁺] → pH

Solution: Na^+ is the counterion of a strong base, therefore, it is pH neutral. $C_7H_5O_2^-$ is the conjugate base of a weak acid. Therefore, it will produce a basic solution. K^+ is the counterion of a strong base, therefore, it is pH neutral. Cl^- is the conjugate base of a strong acid, therefore, it is pH neutral.

	$C_7H_5O_2^-$ (aq) + H_2O(l) $\leftrightarows$	$H\,C_7H_5O_2$ (aq)+	OH^- (aq)
I	0.0887	0.0	0.0
C	-x	x	x
E	0.0887– x	x	x

$$K_b = \frac{K_w}{K_a} = \frac{1 \times 10^{-14}}{6.5 \times 10^{-5}} = \frac{(x)(x)}{(0.0887 - x)}$$

Assume x is small

$x = 3.\underline{6}94 \times 10^{-6} = [OH^-]$ $\quad$ $pOH = -\log(3.\underline{6}94 \times 10^{-6}) = 5.43$

$pH = 14.00 - 5.43 = 8.57$

e) **Given:** 0.0450 M HCl (strong acid), 0.0225 M HNO_3 (strong acid) **Find:** pH
Conceptual Plan: Since mixture is a strong acid and strong acid, $[H_3O^+]$ is the sum of the concentration of both acids, and then determine pH
Solution: 0.0450 M HCl = 0.020 $[H_3O^+]$, 0. 0225 M HNO_3 = 0.0225 M $[H_3O^+]$
$[H_3O^+] = 0.0450 + 0.0225 = 0.0675M$ $pH = -\log(0.0675) = 1.171$

134.a) **Given:** 0.050 M KOH (strong base), 0.015 M $Ba(OH)_2$ (strong base) **Find:** pH
Conceptual Plan: Since mixture is a strong base and strong base, $[OH^-]$ is the sum of the concentration of both acids, and then determine pOH and then pH
Solution: 0.050 M KOH = 0.050 $[OH^-]$, 0.015 M $Ba(OH)_2$ = 2(0.015 M) $[OH^-]$
$[OH^-] = 0.050 + 0.030 = 0.080M$ $pOH = -\log(0.080) = 1.10$, $pH = 14.00 - 1.10 = 12.90$

b) **Given:** 0.265 M NH_4NO_3 (salt), 0.102 M HCN(weak acid) **Find:** pH
Conceptual Plan: Identify each species and determine which will contribute to pH. Write a balanced reaction. Prepare an ICE table; represent the change with x; sum the table and determine the equilibrium values; put the equilibrium values in the equilibrium expression and solve for x. Determine $[H_3O^+]$ $\rightarrow$ pH
Solution: NH_4^+ is the conjugate acid of a weak base, therefore, it is basic. NO_3^- is the conjugate base of a strong acid, therefore, it is pH neutral. HCN is a weak acid and will produce an acidic solution.

$$K_a (NH_4^+) = \frac{1 \times 10^{-14}}{1.8 \times 10^{-5}} = 5.56 \times 10^{-10} \qquad K_a (HCN) = 4.9 \times 10^{-10}$$

Solution:

	NH_4^+ (aq) + H_2O(l) $\leftrightarows$ NH_3 (aq) +	H_3O^+ (aq)	
I	0.265	0.0	0.0
C	-x	x	x
E	0. 265– x	x	x

$$K_a = \frac{K_w}{K_b} = \frac{1 \times 10^{-14}}{1.8 \times 10^{-5}} = 5.\underline{5}6 \times 10^{-10} = \frac{(x)(x)}{(0.265 - x)}$$

Assume x is small

$x = 1.\underline{2}1 \times 10^{-5} = [H_3O^+]$

	HCN(aq) + H_2O(l) $\leftrightarows$	H_3O^+(aq)	+	CN^- (aq)
I	0.102	1.21×10^{-5}		0.0
C	- x	x		x
E	0.102 – x	$1.21 \times 10^{-5} + x$		x

$$K_a = \frac{[H_3O^+][CN^-]}{[HCN]} = \frac{(1.21\times10^{-5} + x)(x)}{(0.102 - x)} = 4.9\times10^{-10}$$

Assume x is small compared to 0.102.

$$\frac{(1.21\times10^{-5})x + x^2}{0.102} = 4.9\times10^{-10}$$

$$(1.21\times10^{-5})x + x^2 = 4.\underline{9}98\times10^{-11}$$

$$x^2 + (1.21\times10^{-5})x - 4.\underline{9}98\times10^{-11} = 0$$

$$x = \frac{-1.21\times10^{-5} \pm \sqrt{(1.21\times10^{-5})^2 - 4(1)(-4.\underline{9}98\times10^{-11})}}{2(1)}$$

$x = 3.\underline{2}55\times10^{-6}$ or -1.536×10^{-5} \qquad Concentration cannot be negative.

$[H_3O^+] = 1.\underline{2}1\times10^{-5} + 3.\underline{2}6\times10^{-6} = 1.\underline{5}36\times10^{-5}$

$pH = -\log(1.\underline{5}36\times10^{-5}) = 4.81$

c) **Given:** 0.075 RbOH (strong base), 0.100 M NaHCO₃ (salt)
Conceptual Plan: Since the mixture is a strong base and a salt, the strong base will dominate. Use the concentration of the strong base to determine [OH⁻] and then pOH → pH
Solution: 0.075 M RbOH = 0.075 [OH⁻] pOH = - log(0.075) = 1.12   pH = 14.00 – 1.12 = 12.88

d) **Given:** 0.088 HClO₄ (strong acid), 0.022 KOH (strong base) **Find:** pH
Conceptual Plan: Strong acid and strong base with neutralize each other, strong acid is in excess and is used to determine the pH.
Solution: $HClO_4(aq) + KOH(aq) \rightarrow H_2O(l) + KClO_4(aq)$

0.088	0.022	
- 0.022	- 0.022	
0.066 M		

$[H_3O^+] = 0.066$ \qquad pH = -log(0.066) = 1.18

e) **Given:** 0.115 M NaClO (salt), 0.0500 KI (salt) \qquad\qquad **Find:** pH
Conceptual Plan: Identify each species and determine which will contribute to pH. Write a balanced reaction. Prepare an ICE table; represent the change with x; sum the table and determine the equilibrium values; put the equilibrium values in the equilibrium expression and solve for x. Determine [H₃O⁺] → pH
Solution: Na^+ is the counterion of a strong base, therefore, it is pH neutral. ClO^- is the conjugate base of a weak acid. Therefore, it will produce a basic solution. K^+ is the counterion of a strong base, therefore, it is pH neutral. I^- is the conjugate base of a strong acid, therefore, it is pH neutral.

	ClO^- (aq) $+$ H₂O(l) $\leftrightharpoons$	HClO (aq)$+$	OH$^-$(aq)
I	0.115	0.0	0.0
C	-x	x	x
E	0.115– x	x	x

$$K_b = \frac{K_w}{K_a} = \frac{1 \times 10^{-14}}{2.9 \times 10^{-8}} = \frac{(x)(x)}{(0.115 - x)}$$

Assume x is small

$x = 1.\underline{9}9 \times 10^{-4} = [OH^-]$ \qquad pOH = -log(1.\underline{9}9 x 10^{-4}) = 3.70

pH = 14.00 - 3.70 = 10.30

135.a) \quad sodium cyanide = NaCN \qquad\qquad nitric acid = HNO₃
\qquad\qquad $H^+(aq) + CN^-(aq) \leftrightharpoons HCN(aq)$

b) \quad ammonium chloride = NH₄Cl \quad sodium hydroxide = NaOH
\qquad\qquad $NH_4^+(aq) + OH^-(aq) \leftrightharpoons NH_3(aq) + H_2O(l)$

c) \quad sodium cyanide = NaCN \qquad\qquad ammonium bromide = NH₄Br
\qquad\qquad $NH_4^+(aq) + CN^-(aq) \leftrightharpoons NH_3(aq) + HCN(aq)$

d) \quad potassium hydrogen sulfate = KHSO₄ lithium acetate = LiC₂H₃O₂
\qquad\qquad $HSO_4^-(aq) + C_2H_3O_2^-(aq) \leftrightharpoons SO_4^{2-}(aq) + HC_2H_3O_2 (aq)$

e) sodium hypochlorite = NaClO   ammonia = NH_3
No reaction, both are bases

136. **Given:** 0.682 g opium, 8.92 mL of 0.0166 M H_2SO_4,   **Find:** % morphine
Conceptual Plan:

vol H_2SO_4 → mol H_2SO_4 → mol H_3O^+ → mol morphine → g morphine → % morphine

$$mol = VM \qquad \frac{mol\ H_3O^+}{H_2SO_4} \qquad \frac{mol\ morphine}{mol\ H_3O^+} \qquad \frac{285.4\ g\ morphine}{mol\ morphine} \qquad \frac{g\ morphine}{g\ opium}\ x\ 100$$

Solution:

$$8.92\ \overline{mL\ H_2SO_4}\ x\ \frac{1\ \overline{L}}{1000\ \overline{mL}}\ x\ \frac{0.0116\ \overline{mol\ H_2SO_4}}{\overline{L}}\ x\ \frac{2\ \overline{mol\ H_3O^+}}{\overline{mol\ H_2SO_4}}\ x\ \frac{\overline{mol\ morphine}}{\overline{mol\ H_3O^+}}\ x\ \frac{285.4\ g\ morphine}{\overline{mol\ morphine}}\ = 0.05906\ g\ morphi$$

$$\frac{0.05906\ g\ morphine}{0.682\ g\ opium}\ x\ 100 = 8.66\ \%$$

137. **Given:** 1.0M urea, pH = 7.050   **Find:** K_a Hurea$^+$
Conceptual Plan: pH → pOH → [OH$^-$] → K_b(urea) → K_a(Hurea$^+$). Write a balanced reaction.
$$pH + pOH = 14 \qquad pOH = -log[OH^-]$$
Prepare an ICE table; represent the change with x; sum the table and determine the equilibrium values; put the equilibrium values in the equilibrium expression and determine K_b.
Solution: pOH = 14.000 − 7.050 = 6.950 $[OH^{-1}] = 10^{-6.950} = 1.122\ x\ 10^{-7}$M

	urea (aq) + H_2O(l) $\rightleftharpoons$	Hurea$^+$(aq)+	OH$^-$(aq)
I	1.0	0.0	0.0
C	-x	x	x
E	1.0− 1.122 x 10^{-7}	1.122 x 10^{-7}	1.122 x 10^{-7}

$$K_b = \frac{[Hurea^+][OH^-]}{[urea]} = \frac{(1.122\ x\ 10^{-7})(1.122\ x\ 10^{-7})}{(1.0 - 1.122\ x\ 10^{-7})} = 1.2589\ x\ 10^{-14}$$

$$K_a = \frac{K_w}{K_b} = \frac{1.00\ x\ 10^{-14}}{1.2589\ x\ 10^{-14}} = 0.7943 = 0.794$$

138. **Given:** 0.1 M $HC_2H_3O_2$, $K_a = 1.8\ x\ 10^{-5}$; 0.10 M NH_4Cl, $K_b = 1.8\ x\ 10^{-5}$ **Find:** [NH_3]
Conceptual Plan: Use $HC_2H_3O_2$ to determine [H_3O^+], then use NH_4Cl to determine [NH_3], Write a balanced reaction. Prepare an ICE table; represent the change with x; sum the table and determine the equilibrium values.
Solution: $HC_2H_3O_2$ (aq) + H_2O(l) $\rightleftharpoons$ H_3O^+(aq) + $C_2H_3O_2^-$ (aq)

I	0.10 M	0.0	0.0
C	- x	x	x
E	0.10− x	x	x

$$K_a = \frac{[H_3O^+][C_2H_3O_2^-]}{[HC_2H_3O_2]} = \frac{(x)(x)}{(0.10 - x)} = 1.8\ x\ 10^{-5}$$

Assume x is small compared to 0.10

$$x^2 = (1.8\ x\ 10^{-5})(0.10)$$

$$x = [H_3O^+] = 0.00134\ M$$

	NH_4^+ (aq) + H_2O(l) $\rightleftharpoons$	NH_3 (aq) +	H_3O^+ (aq)
I	0.10 M	0.0	0.00134
C	-y	y	y
E	0.10 − y	y	0.00134+ y

$$K_a = \frac{K_w}{K_b} = \frac{1\ x\ 10^{-14}}{1.8\ x\ 10^{-5}} = 5.56\ x\ 10^{-10} = \frac{(x)(0.00134 + y)}{(0.10 - y)}$$

Assume y is small compared to 0.10

$$y^2 + 0.00134\ y - 5.56\ x\ 10^{-11} \qquad y = [NH_3] = 4.1\ x\ 10^{-8}M$$

139. The calculation is incorrect because it neglects the contribution from the autoionization of water.

HI is a strong acid, so $[H_3O^+]$ from HI $= 1.0 \times 10^{-7}$

$$H_2O(l) + H_2O(l) \rightleftharpoons H_3O^+(aq) + OH^-(aq)$$

I		1×10^{-7}	0.0
C	$-x$	x	x
E		$1 \times 10^{-7} + x$	x

$K_w = [H_3O^+][OH^-] = 1.0 \times 10^{-14}$

$(1 \times 10^{-7} + x)(x) = 1.0 \times 10^{-14}$ $\qquad$ $x^2 + 1 \times 10^{-7}\, x - 1.0 \times 10^{-14} = 0$

$x = 6.18 \times 10^{-8}$

$[H_3O^+] = (1 \times 10^{-7} + x) = (1 \times 10^{-7} + 6.18 \times 10^{-8}) = 1.618 \times 10^{-7}$

$pH = -\log(1.618 \times 10^{-7}) = 6.79$

140. **Given:** 2.55 g HA, molar mass = 85.0 g/mol, 250.0 g H_2O, FP = $-0.257\ ^\circ C$ **Find:** K_a

Conceptual Plan:

g HA $\rightarrow$ mol HA $\rightarrow$ m HA $\rightarrow$ i $\rightarrow$ % ionization and then mol HA $\rightarrow$ M HA and then: write a

$$\text{mol HA} = \frac{\text{g HA}}{\text{molar mass}} \quad \frac{\text{mol HA}}{\text{kg } H_2O} \quad \frac{\text{mol HA}}{\text{kg } H_2O} \quad \Delta T = iK_f m$$

balanced reaction, prepare an ICE table, calculate equilibrium concentrations, and then plug into the equilibrium expression to solve for K_a.

Solution:

$$2.55\,\text{g HA} \times \frac{1\,\text{mol}}{85.0\,\text{g HA}} = 0.0300\,\text{mol HA} \qquad \frac{0.0300\,\text{mol HA}}{\left(250.0\,\text{g } H_2O \times \dfrac{\text{kg}}{1000\,\text{g}}\right)} = 0.120\,m$$

$$\Delta T = iK_f m \qquad (0.257\ ^\circ C) = i\left(1.86\,\frac{^\circ C}{m}\right)(0.120\,m) \qquad i = 1.151 = \text{moles of particles in solution/mol HA}$$

$$HA(aq) + H_2O(l) \rightleftharpoons H_3O^+(aq) + A^-(aq)$$
$$1 - y \qquad\qquad y \qquad\quad y$$

So: $(1 - y) + y + y = 1.151$ $\qquad\qquad$ $y = 0.151 = $ fraction of HA dissociated

$$M\,HA = \frac{0.0300\,\text{mol HA}}{(250.0\,\text{g} + 2.55\,\text{g})\left(\dfrac{1.00\,\text{mL}}{1.00\,\text{g}}\right)\left(\dfrac{L}{1000\,\text{mL}}\right)} = 0.1188\,M$$

$(0.1188\,M)(0.151) = 0.01794\,M = [H_3O^+] = [A^-]$ at equilibrium

$$HA(aq) + H_2O(l) \rightleftharpoons H_3O^+(aq) + A^-(aq)$$

I	0.1188M	0.0	0.0
C	$-x$	x	x
E	$0.1188 - 0.01794$	0.01794	0.01794

$$K_a = \frac{[H_3O^+][A^-]}{[HA]} = \frac{(0.01794)(0.01794)}{(0.1188 - 0.01794)} = 0.0036997 = 3.7 \times 10^{-3}$$

141. **Given:** 0.00115M HCl, 0.01000M $HClO_2$ $K_a = 1.1 \times 10^{-2}$ $\qquad$ **Find:** pH

Conceptual Plan: Use HCl to determine $[H_3O^+]$, use $[H_3O^+]$ and $HClO_2$ to determine dissociation of $HClO_2$. Write a balanced reaction, prepare and ICE table, calculate equilibrium concentrations, and then plug into the equilibrium expression.

Solution: 0.00115M HCl = 0.00115M H_3O^+

$$HClO_2(aq) + H_2O(l) \rightleftharpoons H_3O^+(aq) + ClO_2^-(aq)$$

I	0.0100M	0.00115	0.0
C	$-x$	x	x
E	$0.01000 - x$	$0.00115 + x$	x

$$K_a = \frac{[H_3O^+][ClO_2^-]}{[HClO_2]} = \frac{(0.00115 + x)(x)}{(0.0100 - x)} = 1.1 \times 10^{-2}$$

$x^2 + 0.01215x - 1.1 \times 10^{-4} = 0$ $\qquad\qquad$ $x = 0.006045$

$[H_3O^+] = 0.00115 + 0.006045 = 0.00719$

$pH = -\log(0.00719) = 2.14$

142. Volume should be increased to 4 L.

$$HA(aq) + H_2O(l) \rightleftharpoons H_3O^+(aq) + A^-(aq)$$

Initial equilibrium conditions: [HA] = A, [H$_3$O$^+$] = [A$^-$] = x

$$K_a = \frac{[H_3O^+][A^-]}{[HA]} = \frac{(x)(x)}{(A)}$$

Second equilibrium conditions: [HA] = A/y, [H$_3$O$^+$] = [A$^-$] = x/2

$$K_a = \frac{[H_3O^+][A^-]}{[HA]} = \frac{(x)(x)}{(A)} = \frac{\left(\frac{x}{2}\right)\left(\frac{x}{2}\right)}{\left(\frac{A}{y}\right)}$$

$$\frac{x^2A}{y} = \frac{x^2A}{4} \qquad y = 4, \text{ so for the concentration of [H}^+\text{] to be halved,}$$

the [A] needs to decrease to 1/4 th the original concentration.

So, the volume has to increase to 4 L

143. **Given:** 1.0M HA, $K_a = 1.0 \times 10^{-8}$ $K = 4.0$ for reaction 2 **Find:** [H$^+$], [A$^-$], [HA$_2^-$]
   Conceptual Plan: Combine reaction 1 and reaction 2 and determine equilibrium expression and the value of K. Prepare an ICE table, calculate equilibrium concentrations, and then plug into the equilibrium expression
   Solution:

	HA(aq)	$\rightleftharpoons$	H$^+$(aq) +	A$^-$(aq)	$K = 1.0 \times 10^{-8}$
	HA(aq) + A$^-$(aq)	$\rightleftharpoons$	HA$_2^+$(aq)		$K = 4.0$
	2HA(aq)	$\rightleftharpoons$	H$^+$(aq) +	HA$_2^+$(aq)	$K = 4.0 \times 10^{-8}$
I	1.0		0.0	0.0	
C	- 2x		x	x	
E	1.0 – 2x		x	x	

$$K = \frac{[H^+][HA_2^-]}{[HA]^2} = 4.0 \times 10^{-8} = \frac{(x)(x)}{(1.0 - 2x)^2}$$

$$x^2 + 16 \times 10^{-8}x - 4 \times 10^{-8} = 0 \qquad x = 1.9992 \times 10^{-4}$$

	HA(aq)	$\rightleftharpoons$	H$^+$(aq) +	A$^-$(aq)	$K = 1.0 \times 10^{-8}$
I	1.0		1.9992×10^{-4}	0.0	
C	- 2y		y	y	
E	1.0 – 2y		1.9992×10^{-4} +y	y	

$$K = \frac{[H^+][A^-]}{[HA]} = 1.0 \times 10^{-8} = \frac{(1.9992 \times 10^{-4} +y)(y)}{(1.0 - y)}$$

$$y^2 + 1.9992 \times 10^{-4}x - 1 \times 10^{-8} = 0 \qquad y = 4.29 \times 10^{-5}$$

[H$^+$] = x + y = 1.9992 $\times 10^{-4}$ + 4.29 $\times 10^{-5}$ = 2.4 $\times 10^{-4}$

[A$^-$] = y = 4.29 $\times 10^{-5}$

[HA$_2^-$] = x = 2.0 $\times 10^{-4}$

144. In the gas phase, (CH$_3$)$_3$N is a stronger Lewis base than CH$_3$NH$_2$ because the polar C – H bond repels the H$^+$ that needs to be added. In the liquid phase, the steric hindrance from the size of the CH$_3$ groups becomes more pronounced therefore, it is harder to add the H$^+$ ion.

145. Solution b would be most acidic.

   a) 0.0100 M HCl (strong acid) and 0.0100 M KOH(strong base), since the concentrations are equal , the acid and base will completely neutralize each other and the resulting solution will be pH neutral.

   b) 0.0100 M HF (weak acid) and 0.0100 KBr (salt). K_a (HF) = 3.5 $\times 10^{-4}$. The weak acid will produce and acidic solution. K$^+$ is the counterion of a strong base and is pH neutral. Br$^-$ is the conjugate base of a strong acid and is pH neutral.

   c) 0.0100 M NH$_4$Cl (salt) and 0.100 M CH$_3$NH$_3$Br. K_b(NH$_3$) = 1.8 $\times 10^{-5}$, K_b(CH$_3$NH$_2$) = 4.4 $\times 10^{-4}$. NH$_4^+$ is the conjugate acid of a weak base and CH$_3$NH$_3^+$ is the conjugate acid of a weak base. Cl$^-$ and Br$^-$ are the conjugate base of a strong acid and will be pH neutral. The solution will be acidic, however, K_a for the conjugate acids is much smaller K_a for HF, so the solution will be acidic, but not as acidic as HF.

d) 0.100 M NaCN (salt) and 0.100 M CaCl$_2$. Na$^+$ and Ca^{2+} ion are the counterion of a strong base, therefore, they are pH neutral. Cl$^-$ is the conjugate base of a strong acid and is pH neutral. CN$^-$ is the conjugate base of a weak acid and will produce a basic solution.

146. Solution a would be most basic.

a) 0.100 M NaClO(salt) and 0.100 M NaF(salt). Na$^+$ is the counterion of a strong base and is pH neutral. ClO$^-$ is the conjugate base of a weak acid (HClO, $K_a = 2.9$ x 10^{-8}) F$^-$ is the conjugate base of a weak acid (HF, $K_a = 3.5$ x 10^{-4}), the solution will be basic and ClO$^-$ is a stronger base than F$^-$.

b) 0.0100 M KCl(salt) and 0.0100 M KClO$_2$(salt). K$^+$ is the counterion of a strong base and is pH neutral. Cl$^-$ is the conjugate base of a strong acid and is pH neutral. ClO$_2$$^-$ is the conjugate base of a weak acid (HClO$_2$, $K_a = 1.1$ x 10^{-2}) and will produce a basic solution, however, ClO$_2$$^-$ is a weaker base than ClO$^-$

c) 0.0100 M HNO$_3$ (strong acid) and 0.0100 M NaOH(strong base), since the concentration are equal, the acid and base will completely neutralize each other and the resulting solution will be pH neutral.

d) 0.0100 M NH$_4$Cl(salt) and 0.0100 M HCN(weak acid). NH$_4$$^+$ is the conjugate acid of a weak base and will be acidic. HCN is a weak acid and will be acidic. Cl$^-$ is the conjugate base of a strong acid and is pH neutral.

147. CH$_3$COOH < CH$_2$ClCOOH < CHCl$_2$COOH < CCl$_3$COOH
Since Cl is more electronegative than H, as you add Cl you increase the amount of electronegativity and pull elctron density away from the O – H bond making it more acidic.

Chapter 16
Aqueous Ionic Equilibrium

1. The pH range of human blood is held between 7.36 and 7.42. This nearly constant blood pH is maintained by buffers, which is a chemical system that resists pH changes, neutralizing added acid or base. An important buffer system in blood is a mixture of carbonic acid (H_2CO_3) and bicarbonate ion (HCO_3^-).

2. A buffer is a chemical system that resists pH changes. The buffer works by neutralizing added acid or base. Most buffers contain significant amounts of both a weak acid and its conjugate base (or a weak base and its conjugate acid). When additional base is added to a buffer, the weak acid reacts with the base, neutralizing it (generating more of the buffer system conjugate base). When additional acid is added to buffer, the conjugate base reacts with the acid, neutralizing it (generating more of the buffer system conjugate acid). In this way, a buffer can maintain a nearly constant pH.

3. The common ion effect occurs when a solution contains two substances ($HC_2H_3O_2$ and $NaC_2H_3O_2$) that share a common ion ($C_2H_3O_2^-$). The presence of the $C_2H_3O_2^-$(aq) ion causes the acid to ionize even less than it normally would, resulting in a less acidic solution (higher pH). This effect is an example of Le Châtelier's principle shifting an equilibrium, because of the addition (or removal) of the common ion from the solution.

4. The Henderson-Hasselbalch equation $\left(pH = pK_a + \log \dfrac{[base]}{[acid]} \right)$, allows easy calculation of the pH of a buffer solution from the initial concentrations of the buffer components as long as the "x is small" approximation is valid.

5. When the concentration of the conjugate acid and base components of a buffer system are equal the pH is equal to the pK_a of the weak acid of the buffer system. When more of the acid component is present the pH becomes more acidic (pH drops). When more of the base component is present the pH becomes more basic (pH rises). The pH in both cases can be calculates with the Henderson-Hasselbalch equation.

6. When the concentration of the conjugate acid and base components of a buffer system are equal the pH is equal to the pK_a of the weak acid of the buffer system. When a small amount of a strong acid is added, it will react with the conjugate base of the buffer system, converting it to the weak acid of the buffer system. Thus the weak acid concentration increases and the conjugate base concentration decreases, and the pH drops slightly at most. When a small amount of a strong base is added, it will react with the weak acid of the buffer system, converting it to the conjugate base of the buffer system. Thus the weak acid concentration decreases and the conjugate base concentration increases, and the pH rises slightly at most.

7. To find the pH of this solution, determine which component is the acid and which component is the base and substitute their concentrations into the Henderson-Hasselbalch equation to compute pH. The pK_a is the negative of the log of the equilibrium constant of the acid dissociation reaction where the weak acid component and water are the reactants, and the conjugate base and H_3O^+ are the products. At the end, confirm that the "x is small" approximation is valid by calculating the $[H_3O^+]$ from the pH. Since H_3O^+ is formed by ionization of the acid, the calculated $[H_3O^+]$ has to be less than 0.05 (or 5%) of the initial concentration of the acid in order for the "x is small" approximation to be valid.

8. The factors that influence the effectiveness of a buffer are: the relative amounts of the acid and conjugate base (the closer they are to each other the more effective the buffer) and the absolute concentrations of the acid and conjugate base (the higher the absolute concentrations the more effective the buffer).

9. The relative concentrations of acid and conjugate base should not differ by more than a factor of 10 in order for a buffer to be reasonably effective. Using the Henderson-Hasselbalch equation, this means that the pH should be with in one pH unit of the weak acid's pK_a.

10. In an acid-base titration, a basic (or acidic) solution of unknown concentration is reacted with an acidic (or basic) solution of known concentration. The known solution is slowly added to the unknown one while the pH is monitored with either a pH meter or an indicator (a substance whose color depends on the pH). As the acid and base combine, they neutralize each other. At the equivalence point — the point in the titration when the number of moles of base is stoichiometrically equal to the number of moles of acid—the titration

is complete. When this point is reached, neither reactant is in excess and the number of moles of the reactants are related by the reaction stoichiometry.

11. The titration of weak acid by a strong base will always have a basic equivalence point because, at the equivalence point, all of the acid has been converted into its conjugate base, resulting in a weakly basic solution.

12. The volume required to get to the equivalence point is only dependent on the concentration and volume of acid or base to be titrated and the base or acid used to do the titration, because the equivalence point is dependent on the stoichiometry of the balanced reaction of the acid and base. The stoichiometry only considers the number of moles involved, not the strength of the reactants involved.

13. a) The initial pH of the solution is simply the pH of the strong acid. Since strong acids completely dissociate, the concentration of H_3O^+ is the concentration of the strong acid and $pH = -\log [H_3O^+]$.

    b) Before the equivalence point, H_3O^+ is in excess. Calculate the $[H_3O^+]$ by subtracting the number of moles of added OH^- from the initial number of moles of H_3O^+ and dividing by the *total* volume. Then convert to pH using $-\log [H_3O^+]$.

    c) At the equivalence point, neither reactant is in excess and the $pH = 7.00$.

    d) Beyond the equivalence point, OH^- is in excess. Calculate the $[OH^-]$ by subtracting the initial number of moles of H_3O^+ from the number of moles of added OH^- and dividing by the *total* volume. Then convert to pH using $-\log [H_3O^+]$.

14. a) The initial pH is that of the weak acid solution to be titrated. Calculate the pH by working an equilibrium problem (similar to Examples 15.5 and 15.6) using the concentration of the weak acid as the initial concentration.

    b) Between the initial pH and the equivalence point, the solution becomes a buffer. Use the reaction stoichiometry to compute the amounts of each buffer component and then use the Henderson-Hasselbalch equation to compute the pH (as in Example 16.3).

    c) Half-way to the equivalence point, the buffer components are exactly equal and $pH = pK_a$.

    d) At the equivalence point, the acid has all been converted into its conjugate base. Calculate the pH by working an equilibrium problem for the ionization of water by the ion acting as a weak base (similar to Example 15.14). (Compute the concentration of the ion acting as a weak base by dividing the number of moles of the ion by the total volume at the equivalence point.)

    e) Beyond the equivalence point, OH^- is in excess. You can ignore the weak base and calculate the $[OH^-]$ by subtracting the initial number of moles of H_3O^+ from the number of moles of added OH^- and dividing by the total volume.

15. When a polyprotic acid is titrated with a strong base, and if K_{a1} and K_{a2} are sufficiently different, the pH curve will have two equivalence points because the two acidic protons will be titrated sequentially. The titration of the first acidic proton will be completed before the titration of the second acidic proton.

16. The volume required to get to the first equivalence point is identical to the volume between the first and second equivalence points, because the equivalence point is dependent on the stoichiometry of the balanced reaction of the acid and base. The stoichiometry only considers the number of moles involved, not the strength of the reactants involved. There are the same number of moles of the first acidic proton and the second acidic proton.

17. The endpoint is the point when the indicator changes color in an acid-base titration. The equivalence point is when stoichiometrically equivalent amounts of acid and base have reacted. With the correct indicator, the endpoint of the titration will occur at the equivalence point.

18. An indicator (HIn) is itself a weak organic acid that has a different color than its conjugate base (In⁻). The color of a solution containing an indicator depends on the relative concentrations of HIn and In⁻. As the

[H_3O^+] changes during the titration, the above relative concentrations of HIn and In$^-$ change accordingly. At low pH, the [H_3O^+] is high and the equilibrium favors the acid species and the color is that of the acid species. As the titration proceeds, the [H_3O^+] decreases, shifting towards higher concentrations of the conjugate base, and the color changes. Because the color of an indicator is intense, only a small amount is required—an amount that will not affect the pH of the solution or the equivalence point of the neutralization reaction.

19. The solubility product constant (K_{sp}) is the equilibrium expression for a chemical equation representing the dissolution of an ionic compound. The expression of the solubility product constant of A_mX_n is: $K_{sp} = [A^{n+}]^m [X^{m-}]^n$.

20. The molar solubility, S, is simply the solubility in units of moles per liter (mol/L). The molar solubility of a compound, A_mX_n, can be computed directly from K_{sp} by solving for S in the expression: $K_{sp} = (mS)^m (nS)^n = m^m n^n S^{m+n}$.

21. In accordance with Le Châtelier's principle, the presence of a common ion in solution causes the equilibrium to shift to the left (compared to its position with pure water as the solvent), which means that less of the ionic compound dissolves. Thus, the solubility of an ionic compound is lower in a solution containing a common ion than in pure water. The exact value of the solubility can be calculated by working an equilibrium problem in which the concentration of the common ion is accounted for in the initial conditions. The molar solubility of a compound, A_mX_n, in a solution with an initial concentration of $A^{n+} = [A^{n+}]_0$ and an initial concentration of $X^{m-} = [X^{m-}]_0$ can be computed directly from K_{sp} by solving for S in the expression: $K_{sp} = ([A^{n+}]_0 + mS)^m ([X^{m-}]_0 + nS)^n$.

22. In general, the solubility of an ionic compound with a strongly basic or weakly basic anion increases with increasing acidity (decreasing pH). If the anion is neutralized by reaction with H$^+$, to form the conjugate acid of the basic anion, Le Châtelier's principle says that the solubility equilibrium will shift to the right, allowing more solid to dissolve. Remember that the K_{sp} expression only has the terms of the cation and the anion concentrations. If the anion is converted to a different species (such as the conjugate acid), the concentration of the anion drops, allowing more solid to dissolve.

23. Q is the reaction quotient, the product of the concentrations of the ionic components raised to their stoichiometric coefficients, and K is the product of the concentrations of the ionic components raised to their stoichiometric coefficients at equilibrium. For a solution containing an ionic compound: If $Q < K_{sp}$, the solution is unsaturated. More of the solid ionic compound can dissolve in the solution; If $Q = K_{sp}$, the solution is saturated and the solution is holding the equilibrium amount of the dissolved ions and additional solid will not dissolve in the solution; and If $Q > K_{sp}$, the solution is supersaturated and under most circumstances, the excess solid will precipitate out of a supersaturated solution.

24. Selective precipitation, a process for separating metal cations from a solution containing several different dissolved metal cations. In the process, a metal cation can often be separated by the addition of a reagent that forms a precipitate with one of the dissolved cations but not the others. The appropriate reagent must form compounds with both metal cations with sufficiently different K_{sp} values (a difference of a factor of at least 10^3), so that one compound will remains dissolved while the other compound significantly precipitates.

25. Qualitative analysis is a systematic way to determine the metal ions present in an unknown solution by the selective precipitation of the ions. The word qualitative means involving quality or kind. So qualitative analysis involves finding the kind of ions present in the solution. Quantitative analysis is concerned with quantity, or the amounts of substances in a solution or mixture.

26. A general qualitative analysis scheme is involves separating a mixture of the common ions into five groups by sequentially adding five different precipitating agents. After each precipitating agent is added, the mixture is put into a centrifuge to separate the solid from the liquid. The liquid is decanted for the next step, and the solid is set aside for subsequent analysis. Group I remove insoluble chlorides by treating the solution with dilute HCl. Since most chlorides are soluble, the chloride ions do not form a precipitate with the majority of the cations in mixture. However, Ag$^+$, Pb^{2+}, and Hg$_2^{2+}$ do form insoluble chlorides and will precipitate out. The absence of a precipitate constitutes a negative test for Ag$^+$, Pb^{2+}, and Hg$_2^{2+}$. After the solid is separated from the liquid, the solution is ready for the next step, where Group II, acid-insoluble sulfides are removed. This is accomplished by taking the aqueous mixture containing the remaining metal cations and treating it with H_2S, a weak diprotic acid that dissociates to form sulfide ions, S^{2-}. Since the

solution is acidic from the first treatment, only the acid-insoluble sulfide metals will precipitate out. These include Hg^{2+}, Cd^{2+}, Bi^{3+}, Cu^{2+}, Sn^{4+}, As^{3+}, and Sb^{3+}. If any of these metal cations are present, they precipitate out as sulfides. After the solid is separated from the liquid, the solution is ready for the next step. In the third step, Group III, the base-insoluble sulfides and hydroxides, are removed by taking the acidic aqueous mixture containing the remaining metal cations is treating it with a base and additional H_2S. The added base reacts with acid, shifting the H_2S ionization equilibria to the right and creating a higher S^{2-} concentration. This causes the precipitation of those sulfides that were too soluble to precipitate out in the previous step, but not soluble enough to prevent precipitation with the higher sulfide ion concentration. The ions that precipitate as sulfides at this point (if they are present) are Co^{2+}, Zn^{2+}, Mn^{2+}, Ni^{2+}, Fe^{2+}. In addition, the basic solution causes Cr^{3+} and Al^{3+} to precipitate as hydroxides. After the solid is separated from the liquid, the solution is ready for the next step, removing the Group IV, insoluble carbonate, metal ions. At this stage, all of the cations have been precipitated except those belonging to the alkali metal family (group 1A in the periodic table) and the alkaline earth metal family (group 2A in the periodic table). The alkaline earth metal cations can be precipitated by adding sodium carbonate to the solution. The carbonate ion precipitates Mg^{2+}, Ca^{2+}, and Ba^{2+} as metal carbonates, which are separated from the liquid. The only dissolved ions belong to Group V, the alkali metals and NH_4^+. The liquid decanted from the previous step can now contain are Na^+, K^+, and NH_4^+. These cations do not form insoluble compounds with any anions and cannot be precipitated from the solution. Their presence can be tested, however, by other means. Sodium and potassium ions, for example, are usually identified through flame tests. The sodium ion produces a yellow-orange flame and the potassium ion produces a violet flame. By applying the above procedure, nearly two dozen metal cations can be separated from a solution initially containing all of them. Each of the groups can then be further analyzed to determine the specific ions present from that group.

27. The only solution that HNO_2 will ionize less in is d) 0.10 M $NaNO_2$. It is the only solution that generates a common ion NO_2^- with nitrous acid.

28. Formic acid is $HCHO_2$ which dissociates to H+ and CHO_2^-. The only solution that generates a common ion (CHO_2^-) with formic acid is c) $NaCHO_2$.

29. a) **Given:** 0.15 M $HCHO_2$ and 0.10 M $NaCHO_2$ **Find:** pH **Other:** K_a $(HCHO_2) = 1.8 \times 10^{-4}$
Conceptual Plan:
M $NaCHO_2$ $\rightarrow$ M CHO_2^- then M $HCHO_2$, M CHO_2^- $\rightarrow$ $[H_3O^+]$ $\rightarrow$ pH

$NaCHO_2\ (aq) \rightarrow Na^+\ (aq) + CHO_2^-\ (aq)$ ICE Chart $pH = -\log [H_3O^+]$

Solution: Since 1 CHO_2^- ion is generated for each $NaCHO_2$, $[CHO_2^-] = 0.10$ M CHO_2^-.

$$HCHO_2\ (aq) + H_2O\ (l) \rightleftharpoons H_3O^+\ (aq) + CHO_2^{2-}\ (aq)$$

	$[HCHO_2]$	$[H_3O^+]$	$[CHO_2^{2-}]$
Initial	0.15	≈ 0.00	0.10
Change	$-x$	$+x$	$+x$
Equil	$0.15 - x$	$+x$	$0.10 + x$

$K_a = \dfrac{[H_3O^+][CHO_2^-]}{[HCHO_2]} = 1.8 \times 10^{-4} = \dfrac{x(0.10 + x)}{0.15 - x}$ Assume x is small (x << 0.10 < 0.15) so

$\dfrac{x(0.10 + x)}{0.15 - x} = 1.8 \times 10^{-4} = \dfrac{x(0.10)}{0.15}$ and $x = 2.7 \times 10^{-4} = [H_3O^+]$. Confirm that assumption is valid

$\dfrac{2.7 \times 10^{-4}}{0.10} \times 100\% = 0.27\%$ so assumption is valid. Finally,

$pH = -\log [H_3O^+] = -\log (2.7 \times 10^{-4}) = 3.57$

Check: The units (none) are correct. The magnitude of the answer makes physical sense because pH should be greater than $-\log (0.15) = 0.82$ because this is a weak acid and there is a common ion effect.

b) **Given:** 0.12 M NH_3 and 0.18 M NH_4Cl **Find:** pH **Other:** K_b $(NH_3) = 1.79 \times 10^{-5}$
Conceptual Plan:
M NH_4Cl $\rightarrow$ M NH_4^+ then M NH_3, M NH_4^+ $\rightarrow$ $[OH^-]$ $\rightarrow$ $[H_3O^+]$ $\rightarrow$ pH

$NH_4Cl\ (aq) \rightarrow NH_4^+\ (aq) + Cl^-\ (aq)$ ICE Chart $K_w = [H_3O^+][OH^-]$ $pH = -\log [H_3O^+]$

Solution: Since 1 NH_4^+ ion is generated for each NH_4Cl, $[NH_4^+] = 0.18$ M NH_4^+.

$$NH_3\,(aq) + H_2O\,(l) \rightleftharpoons NH_4^+\,(aq) + OH^-\,(aq)$$

	$[NH_3]$	$[NH_4^+]$	$[OH^-]$
Initial	0.12	0.18	≈ 0.00
Change	$-x$	$+x$	$+x$
Equil	$0.12 - x$	$0.18 + x$	$+x$

$$K_b = \frac{[NH_4^+]\,[OH^-]}{[NH_3]} = 1.79 \times 10^{-5} = \frac{(0.18 + x)x}{0.12 - x}$$

Assume x is small ($x \ll 0.12 < 0.18$) so $\dfrac{(0.18 + x)x}{0.12 - x} = 1.79 \times 10^{-5} = \dfrac{(0.18)x}{0.12}$ and x = $1.\underline{1}9333 \times 10^{-5}$ =

$[OH^-]$. Confirm that assumption is valid $\dfrac{1.\underline{1}9333 \times 10^{-5}}{0.12} \times 100\,\% = 9.9 \times 10^{-3}\,\%$ so assumption is valid.

$K_w = [H_3O^+][OH^-]$ so $[H_3O^+] = \dfrac{K_w}{[OH^-]} = \dfrac{1.0 \times 10^{-14}}{1.\underline{1}9333 \times 10^{-5}} = 8.\underline{3}799 \times 10^{-10}\,M$.   Finally,

$pH = -\log [H_3O^+] = -\log (8.\underline{3}799 \times 10^{-10}) = 9.08$

Check: The units (none) are correct. The magnitude of the answer makes physical sense because pH should be less than $14 + \log (0.12) = 13.1$ because this is a weak base and there is a common ion effect.

30. a) **Given:** 0.175 M $HC_2H_3O_2$ and 0.110 M $KC_2H_3O_2$ **Find:** pH
   Other: $K_a\,(HC_2H_3O_2) = 1.8 \times 10^{-5}$
   Conceptual Plan:
   M $KC_2H_3O_2$ $\rightarrow$ M $C_2H_3O_2^-$ then   M $HC_2H_3O_2$, M $C_2H_3O_2^-$ $\rightarrow$ $[H_3O^+]$ $\rightarrow$ pH
   $KC_2H_3O_2\,(aq) \rightarrow K^+\,(aq) + C_2H_3O_2^-\,(aq)$ ICE Chart $pH = -\log [H_3O^+]$
   Solution: Since 1 $C_2H_3O_2^-$ ion is generated for each $KC_2H_3O_2$, $[C_2H_3O_2^-] = 0.110$ M $C_2H_3O_2^-$.

$$HC_2H_3O_2\,(aq) + H_2O\,(l) \rightleftharpoons H_3O^+\,(aq) + C_2H_3O_2^{2-}\,(aq)$$

	$[HC_2H_3O_2]$	$[H_3O^+]$	$[C_2H_3O_2^{2-}]$
Initial	0.175	≈ 0.00	0.110
Change	$-x$	$+x$	$+x$
Equil	$0.175 - x$	$+x$	$0.110 + x$

$K_a = \dfrac{[H_3O^+]\,[HC_2H_3O_2^-]}{[HC_2H_3O_2]} = 1.8 \times 10^{-5} = \dfrac{x(0.110 + x)}{0.175 - x}$ Assume x is small ($x \ll 0.110 < 0.175$) so

$\dfrac{x(0.110 + x)}{0.175 - x} = 1.8 \times 10^{-5} = \dfrac{x(0.110)}{0.175}$ and x = $2.\underline{8}636 \times 10^{-5} = [H_3O^+]$. Confirm that assumption is valid

$\dfrac{2.\underline{8}636 \times 10^{-5}}{0.110} \times 100\,\% = 0.026\,\%$ so assumption is valid. Finally,

$pH = -\log [H_3O^+] = -\log (2.\underline{8}636 \times 10^{-5}) = 4.54$

Check: The units (none) are correct. The magnitude of the answer makes physical sense because pH should be greater than $-\log (0.110) = 0.96$ because this is a weak acid and there is a common ion effect.

b) **Given:** 0.195 M CH_3NH_2 and 0.105 M CH_3NH_3Br **Find:** pH
   Other: $K_b\,(CH_3NH_2) = 4.4 \times 10^{-4}$
   Conceptual Plan: M CH_3NH_3Br $\rightarrow$ M $CH_3NH_3^+$ then
   $CH_3NH_3Br\,(aq) \rightarrow CH_3NH_3^+\,(aq) + Br^-\,(aq)$
   M CH_3NH_3, M $CH_3NH_3^+$ $\rightarrow$ $[OH^-]$ $\rightarrow$ $[H_3O^+]$ $\rightarrow$ pH
   ICE Chart $K_w = [H_3O^+][OH^-]$ $pH = -\log [H_3O^+]$
   Solution: Since 1 $CH_3NH_3^+$ ion is generated for each CH_3NH_3Br, $[CH_3NH_3^+] = 0.105$ M $CH_3NH_3^+$.

$$CH_3NH_2\,(aq) + H_2O\,(l) \rightleftharpoons CH_3NH_3^+\,(aq) + OH^-\,(aq)$$

	$[CH_3NH_2]$	$[CH_3NH_3^+]$	$[OH^-]$
Initial	0.195	0.105	≈ 0.00
Change	$-x$	$+x$	$+x$
Equil	$0.195 - x$	$0.105 + x$	$+x$

$$K_b = \frac{[CH_3NH_3^+][OH^-]}{[CH_3NH_2]} = 4.4 \times 10^{-4} = \frac{(0.105 + x)x}{0.195 - x}$$

Assume x is small (x << 0.105 < 0.195) so $\frac{(0.105 + x)x}{0.195 - x} = 4.4 \times 10^{-4} = \frac{(0.105)x}{0.195}$ and x = 8.17143 × 10⁻⁴

= [OH⁻]. Confirm that assumption is valid $\frac{8.17143 \times 10^{-4}}{0.105} \times 100\% = 0.78\%$ so assumption is valid.

$K_w = [H_3O^+][OH^-]$ so $[H_3O^+] = \frac{K_w}{[OH^-]} = \frac{1.0 \times 10^{-14}}{8.17143 \times 10^{-4}} = 1.22378 \times 10^{-11}$ M .

Finally, $pH = -\log[H_3O^+] = -\log(1.22378 \times 10^{-11}) = 10.91$.

Check: The units (none) are correct. The magnitude of the answer makes physical sense because pH should be less than 14 + log (0.195) = 13.3 because this is a weak base and there is a common ion effect.

31. **Given**: 0.15 M $HC_7H_5O_2$ in pure water and in 0.10 M $NaC_7H_5O_2$
 Find: % ionization in both solutions **Other**: K_a ($HC_7H_5O_2$) = 6.5 × 10⁻⁵
 Conceptual Plan:
 pure water: M $HC_7H_5O_2$ → [H_3O^+] → % ionization then in $NaC_7H_5O_2$ solution:

$$ICE\ Chart \qquad \%\ ionization = \frac{[H_3O^+]_{equil}}{[HC_7H_5O_2]_0} \times 100\%$$

M $NaC_7H_5O_2$ → M $C_7H_5O_2^-$ then M H $C_7H_5O_2$, M $C_7H_5O_2^-$ → [H_3O^+] → % ionization

$$NaC_7H_5O_2\ (aq) \to Na^+\ (aq) + C_7H_5O_2^-\ (aq) \qquad\qquad ICE\ Chart \quad \%\ ionization = \frac{[H_3O^+]_{equil}}{[HC_7H_5O_2]_0} \times 100\%$$

Solution: in pure water:

$$HC_7H_5O_2\ (aq) + H_2O\ (l) \rightleftharpoons H_3O^+\ (aq) + C_7H_5O_2^{2-}\ (aq)$$

	[$HC_7H_5O_2$]	[H_3O^+]	[$C_7H_5O_2^{2-}$]
Initial	0.15	≈ 0.00	0.00
Change	−x	+ x	+ x
Equil	0.15 − x	+ x	+ x

$$K_a = \frac{[H_3O^+][C_7H_5O_2^-]}{[HC_7H_5O_2]} = 6.5 \times 10^{-5} = \frac{x^2}{0.15 - x}$$

Assume x is small (x << 0.10) so $\frac{x^2}{0.15 - x} = 6.5 \times 10^{-5} = \frac{x^2}{0.15}$ and x = 3.1225 × 10⁻³ = [H_3O^+]. then

$\%\ ionization = \frac{[H_3O^+]_{equil}}{[HC_7H_5O_2]_0} \times 100\% = \frac{3.1225 \times 10^{-3}}{0.15} \times 100\% = 2.1\%$, which also confirms that the assumption is valid (since it is less than 5 %). In $NaC_7H_5O_2$ solution: Since 1 $C_7H_5O_2^-$ ion is generated for each $NaC_7H_5O_2$, [$C_7H_5O_2^-$] = 0.10 M $C_7H_5O_2^-$.

$$HC_7H_5O_2\ (aq) + H_2O\ (l) \rightleftharpoons H_3O^+\ (aq) + C_7H_5O_2^{2-}\ (aq)$$

	[$HC_7H_5O_2$]	[H_3O^+]	[$C_7H_5O_2^{2-}$]
Initial	0.15	≈ 0.00	0.10
Change	−x	+ x	+ x
Equil	0.15 − x	+ x	0.10 + x

$K_a = \frac{[H_3O^+][C_7H_5O_2^-]}{[HC_7H_5O_2]} = 6.5 \times 10^{-5} = \frac{x(0.10 + x)}{0.15 - x}$ Assume x is small (x << 0.10 < 0.15) so

$\frac{x(0.10 + x)}{0.15 - x} = 6.5 \times 10^{-5} = \frac{x(0.10)}{0.15}$ and x = 9.75 × 10⁻⁵ = [H_3O^+]. then $\%\ ionization = \frac{[H_3O^+]_{equil}}{[HC_7H_5O_2]_0} \times 100\% =$

$\frac{9.75 \times 10^{-5}}{0.15} \times 100\% = 0.065\%$, which also confirms that the assumption is valid (since it is less than 5 %).

The percent ionization in the sodium benzoate solution is less than is pure water because of the common ion effect. An increase in one of the products (benzoate ion) shifts the equilibrium to the left, so less acid dissociates.

Check: The units (%) are correct. The magnitude of the answer makes physical sense because the acid is weak and so the percent ionization is low. With a common ion present, the percent ionization decreases.

32. **Given:** 0.13 M HCHO$_2$ in pure water and in 0.11 M KCHO$_2$ **Find:** % ionization in both solutions **Other:** K$_a$ (HCHO$_2$) = 1.8 x 10^{-4}

Conceptual Plan: pure water: M HCHO$_2$ → [H$_3$O$^+$] → % ionization then in KCHO$_2$ solution:

$$\text{ICE Chart} \qquad \% \ ionization = \frac{[\text{H}_3\text{O}^+]_{equil}}{[\text{HC}_7\text{H}_5\text{O}_2]_0} \ x \ 100 \ \%$$

M KCHO$_2$ → M CHO$_2^-$ then M HCHO$_2$, M CHO$_2^-$ → [H$_3$O$^+$] → % ionization

KCHO$_2$ (aq) → K$^+$ (aq) + CHO$_2^-$ (aq) $\qquad$ ICE Chart $\qquad \% \ ionization = \frac{[\text{H}_3\text{O}^+]_{equil}}{[\text{HC}_7\text{H}_5\text{O}_2]_0} \ x \ 100 \ \%$

Solution: in pure water:

HCHO$_2$ (aq) + H$_2$O (l) ⇌ H$_3$O$^+$ (aq) + CHO$_2^{2-}$ (aq)

	[HCHO$_2$]	[H$_3$O$^+$]	[CHO$_2^{2-}$]
Initial	0.13	≈ 0.00	0.00
Change	−x	+ x	+ x
Equil	0.13 − x	+ x	+ x

$K_a = \dfrac{[\text{H}_3\text{O}^+][\text{CHO}_2^-]}{[\text{HCHO}_2]} = 1.8 \ x \ 10^{-4} = \dfrac{x^2}{0.13 - x}$

Assume x is small (x << 0.10) so $\dfrac{x^2}{0.13 - x} = 1.8 \ x \ 10^{-4} = \dfrac{x^2}{0.13}$ and x = 4.8374 x 10^{-3} = [H$_3$O$^+$]. then

$\% \ ionization = \dfrac{[\text{H}_3\text{O}^+]_{equil}}{[\text{HCHO}_2]_0} \ x \ 100 \ \% = \dfrac{4.8374 \ x \ 10^{-3}}{0.13} \ x \ 100 \ \% = 3.7 \ \%$, which also confirms that the assumption is valid (since it is less than 5 %).

In KCHO$_2$ solution: Since 1 CHO$_2^-$ ion is generated for each KCHO$_2$, [CHO$_2^-$] = 0.11 M CHO$_2^-$.

HCHO$_2$ (aq) + H$_2$O (l) ⇌ H$_3$O$^+$ (aq) + CHO$_2^{2-}$ (aq)

	[HCHO$_2$]	[H$_3$O$^+$]	[CHO$_2^{2-}$]
Initial	0.13	≈ 0.00	0.10
Change	−x	+ x	+ x
Equil	0.13 − x	+ x	0.10 + x

$K_a = \dfrac{[\text{H}_3\text{O}^+][\text{CHO}_2^-]}{[\text{HCHO}_2]} = 1.8 \ x \ 10^{-4} = \dfrac{x(0.11 + x)}{0.13 - x}$

Assume x is small (x << 0.11 < 0.13) so $\dfrac{x(0.11 + x)}{0.13 - x} = 1.8 \ x \ 10^{-4} = \dfrac{x(0.11)}{0.13}$ and x = 2.1273 x 10^{-4} = [H$_3$O$^+$].

then $\% \ ionization = \dfrac{[\text{H}_3\text{O}^+]_{equil}}{[\text{HCHO}_2]_0} \ x \ 100 \ \% = \dfrac{2.1273 \ x \ 10^{-4}}{0.13} \ x \ 100 \ \% = 0.16 \ \%$, which also confirms that the assumption is valid (since it is less than 5 %). The percent ionization in the potassium formate solution is less than is pure water because of the common ion effect. An increase in one of the products (formate ion) shifts the equilibrium to the left, so less acid dissociates.

Check: The units (%) are correct. The magnitude of the answer makes physical sense because the acid is weak and so the percent ionization is low. With a common ion present, the percent ionization decreases.

33. a) **Given:** 0.15 M HF **Find:** pH **Other:** K$_a$ (HF) = 3.5 x 10^{-4}

Conceptual Plan: M HF → [H$_3$O$^+$] → pH

$$\text{ICE Chart} \qquad pH = - \log [\text{H}_3\text{O}^+]$$

Solution:

HF (aq) + H$_2$O (l) ⇌ H$_3$O$^+$ (aq) + F$^-$ (aq)

	[HF]	[H$_3$O$^+$]	[F$^-$]
Initial	0.15	≈ 0.00	0.00
Change	−x	+ x	+ x
Equil	0.15 − x	+ x	+ x

$K_a = \dfrac{[\text{H}_3\text{O}^+][\text{F}^-]}{[\text{HF}]} = 3.5 \ x \ 10^{-4} = \dfrac{x^2}{0.15 - x}$ Assume x is

small (x << 0.15) so $\dfrac{x^2}{0.15 - x} = 3.5 \ x \ 10^{-4} = \dfrac{x^2}{0.15}$ and x = 7.2457 x 10^{-3} = [H$_3$O$^+$]. Confirm that

assumption is valid $\dfrac{7.2457 \ x \ 10^{-3}}{0.15} \ x \ 100 \ \% = 4.8 \ \% \ < 5 \ \%$ so assumption is valid.

Finally, $pH = - \log [\text{H}_3\text{O}^+] = - \log (7.2457 \ x \ 10^{-3}) = 2.14$.

Check: The units (none) are correct. The magnitude of the answer makes physical sense because pH should be greater than − log (0.15) = 0.82 because this is a weak acid.

b) **Given:** 0.15 M NaF   **Find:** pH   **Other:** K_a (HF) $= 3.5 \times 10^{-4}$

Conceptual Plan:

$$\text{M NaF} \rightarrow \text{M F}^- \quad \text{and} \quad K_a \rightarrow K_b \quad \text{then} \quad \text{M F}^- \rightarrow [\text{OH}^-] \rightarrow [\text{H}_3\text{O}^+] \rightarrow \text{pH}$$

$\text{NaF}\,(aq) \rightarrow \text{Na}^+\,(aq) + \text{F}^-\,(aq)$ $K_w = K_a\,K_b$ ICE Chart $K_w = [\text{H}_3\text{O}^+][\text{OH}^-]$ $pH = -\log[\text{H}_3\text{O}^+]$

Solution: Since 1 F$^-$ ion is generated for each NaF, [F$^-$] = 0.15 M F$^-$. Since $K_w = K_a\,K_b$, rearrange to

solve for K_b. $K_b = \dfrac{K_w}{K_a} = \dfrac{1.00 \times 10^{-14}}{3.5 \times 10^{-4}} = 2.\underline{8}571 \times 10^{-11}$

$$\text{F}^-\,(aq) + \text{H}_2\text{O}(l) \rightleftharpoons \text{HF}(aq) + \text{OH}^-\,(aq)$$

	[F$^-$]	[HF]	[OH$^-$]
Initial	0.15	0.00	≈ 0.00
Change	$-x$	$+x$	$+x$
Equil	$0.15 - x$	$+x$	$+x$

$K_b = \dfrac{[\text{HF}][\text{OH}^-]}{[\text{F}^-]} = 2.\underline{8}571 \times 10^{-11} = \dfrac{x^2}{0.15 - x}$

Assume x is small (x << 0.15) so $\dfrac{x^2}{0.15 - x} = 2.\underline{8}571 \times 10^{-11} = \dfrac{x^2}{0.15}$ and x = $2.\underline{0}702 \times 10^{-6}$ = [OH$^-$].

Confirm that assumption is valid $\dfrac{2.\underline{0}702 \times 10^{-6}}{0.15} \times 100\,\% = 0.0014\,\% < 5\,\%$ so assumption is valid.

$K_w = [\text{H}_3\text{O}^+][\text{OH}^-]$ so $[\text{H}_3\text{O}^+] = \dfrac{K_w}{[\text{OH}^-]} = \dfrac{1.0 \times 10^{-14}}{2.\underline{0}702 \times 10^{-6}} = 4.\underline{8}305 \times 10^{-9}$ M. Finally,

$pH = -\log[\text{H}_3\text{O}^+] = -\log(4.\underline{8}305 \times 10^{-9}) = 8.32$.

Check: The units (none) are correct. The magnitude of the answer makes physical sense because pH should be slightly basic, since the fluoride ion is a very weak base.

c) **Given:** 0.15 M HF and 0.15 M NaF   **Find:** pH   **Other:** K_a (HF) $= 3.5 \times 10^{-4}$

Conceptual Plan: $\text{M NaF} \rightarrow \text{M F}^- \quad \text{then} \quad \text{M HF, M F}^- \rightarrow [\text{H}_3\text{O}^+] \rightarrow \text{pH}$

$\text{NaF}\,(aq) \rightarrow \text{Na}^+\,(aq) + \text{F}^-\,(aq)$ ICE Chart $pH = -\log[\text{H}_3\text{O}^+]$

Solution: : Since 1 F$^-$ ion is generated for each NaF, [F$^-$] = 0.15 M F$^-$.

$$\text{HF}(aq) + \text{H}_2\text{O}(l) \rightleftharpoons \text{H}_3\text{O}^+\,(aq) + \text{F}^-\,(aq)$$

	[HF]	[H$_3$O$^+$]	[F$^-$]
Initial	0.15	≈ 0.00	0.15
Change	$-x$	$+x$	$+x$
Equil	$0.15 - x$	$+x$	$0.15 + x$

$K_a = \dfrac{[\text{H}_3\text{O}^+][\text{F}^-]}{[\text{HF}]} = 3.5 \times 10^{-4} = \dfrac{x(0.15 + x)}{0.15 - x}$

Assume x is small (x << 0.15) so $\dfrac{x(0.15 + x)}{0.15 - x} = 3.5 \times 10^{-4} = \dfrac{x(0.15)}{0.15}$ and x = 3.5×10^{-4} = [H$_3$O$^+$].

Confirm that assumption is valid $\dfrac{3.5 \times 10^{-4}}{0.15} \times 100\,\% = 0.23\,\% < 5\,\%$ so assumption is valid.

Finally, $pH = -\log[\text{H}_3\text{O}^+] = -\log(3.5 \times 10^{-4}) = 3.46$.

Check: The units (none) are correct. The magnitude of the answer makes physical sense because pH should be greater than in part a (2.14) because of the common ion effect suppressing the dissociation of the weak acid.

34. a) **Given:** 0.18 M CH$_3$NH$_2$ **Find:** pH   **Other:** K_b (CH$_3$NH$_2$) $= 4.4 \times 10^{-4}$

Conceptual Plan: $\text{M CH}_3\text{NH}_3 \rightarrow [\text{OH}^-] \rightarrow [\text{H}_3\text{O}^+] \rightarrow \text{pH}$

ICE Chart $K_w = [\text{H}_3\text{O}^+][\text{OH}^-]$ $pH = -\log[\text{H}_3\text{O}^+]$

Solution:

$$\text{CH}_3\text{NH}_2\,(aq) + \text{H}_2\text{O}(l) \rightleftharpoons \text{CH}_3\text{NH}_3^+\,(aq) + \text{OH}^-\,(aq)$$

	[CH$_3$NH$_2$]	[CH$_3$NH$_3^+$]	[OH$^-$]
Initial	0.18	0.00	≈ 0.00
Change	$-x$	$+x$	$+x$
Equil	$0.18 - x$	$+x$	$+x$

$K_b = \dfrac{[\text{CH}_3\text{NH}_3^+][\text{OH}^-]}{[\text{CH}_3\text{NH}_2]} = 4.4 \times 10^{-4} = \dfrac{x^2}{0.18 - x}$

Assume x is small (x << 0.18) so $\dfrac{x^2}{0.18 - x} = 4.4 \times 10^{-4} = \dfrac{x^2}{0.18}$ and x = $8.\underline{8}994 \times 10^{-3}$ = [OH$^-$].

Confirm that assumption is valid $\dfrac{8.\underline{8}994 \times 10^{-3}}{0.18} \times 100\,\% = 4.9\,\% < 5\,\%$ so assumption is valid.

$K_w = [H_3O^+][OH^-]$ so $[H_3O^+] = \dfrac{K_w}{[OH^-]} = \dfrac{1.0 \times 10^{-14}}{8.\underline{8}994 \times 10^{-3}} = 1.\underline{1}237 \times 10^{-12}$ M .

Finally, $pH = -\log [H_3O^+] = -\log (1.\underline{1}237 \times 10^{-12}) = 11.95$.

Check: The units (none) are correct. The magnitude of the answer makes physical sense because pH should be less than $14 + \log (0.18) = 13.3$ because this is a weak base.

b) **Given:** 0.18 M CH_3NH_3Cl **Find:** pH   **Other:** K_b (CH_3NH_2) $= 4.4 \times 10^{-4}$
   Conceptual Plan:
   M CH_3NH_3Cl → M $CH_3NH_3^+$ **and** K_b → K_a **then**   M $CH_3NH_3^+$ → $[H_3O^+]$ →   **pH**
   $CH_3NH_3Cl\ (aq) \rightarrow CH_3NH_3^+\ (aq) + Cl^-\ (aq)$ $K_w = K_a\ K_b$ ICE Chart $pH = -\log [H_3O^+]$
   Solution: Since 1 $CH_3NH_3^+$ ion is generated for each CH_3NH_3Cl, $[CH_3NH_3^+] = 0.18$ M $CH_3NH_3^+$.

   Since $K_w = K_a\ K_b$, rearrange to solve for K_b. $K_b = \dfrac{K_w}{K_a} = \dfrac{1.00 \times 10^{-14}}{4.4 \times 10^{-4}} = 2.\underline{2}727 \times 10^{-11}$

   $CH_3NH_3^+\ (aq) + H_2O(l) \rightleftharpoons H_3O^+\ (aq) + CH_3NH_2(aq)$

	$[CH_3NH_3^+]$	$[H_3O^+]$	$[CH_3NH_2]$
Initial	0.18	≈ 0.00	0.00
Change	$-x$	$+x$	$+x$
Equil	$0.18 - x$	$+x$	$+x$

   $K_b = \dfrac{[H_3O^+]\,[CH_3NH_2]}{[CH_3NH_3^+]} = 2.\underline{2}727 \times 10^{-11} = \dfrac{x^2}{0.18 - x}$

   Assume x is small (x << 0.18) so $\dfrac{x^2}{0.18 - \cancel{x}} = 2.\underline{2}727 \times 10^{-11} = \dfrac{x^2}{0.18}$ and $x = 2.\underline{0}226 \times 10^{-6} = [H_3O^+]$.

   Confirm that assumption is valid $\dfrac{2.\underline{0}226 \times 10^{-6}}{0.18} \times 100\,\% = 0.0012\,\% < 5\,\%$ so assumption is valid.

   Finally, $pH = -\log [H_3O^+] = -\log (2.\underline{0}226 \times 10^{-6}) = 5.69$.

   Check: The units (none) are correct. The magnitude of the answer makes physical sense because pH should be slightly acidic, since the methylammonium cation is a very weak acid.

c) **Given:** 0.18 M CH_3NH_2 and 0.18 M CH_3NH_3Cl **Find:** pH   **Other:** K_b (CH_3NH_2) $= 4.4 \times 10^{-4}$
   Conceptual Plan: M CH_3NH_3Cl →   M $CH_3NH_3^+$ **then**
               $CH_3NH_3Cl\ (aq) \rightarrow CH_3NH_3^+\ (aq) + Cl^-\ (aq)$
   M CH_3NH_2, M $CH_3NH_3^+$ → $[OH^-]$ → $[H_3O^+]$ →   **pH**
               ICE Chart $K_w = [H_3O^+][OH^-]$ $pH = -\log [H_3O^+]$
   Solution: Since 1 $CH_3NH_3^+$ ion is generated for each CH_3NH_3Cl, $[CH_3NH_3^+] = 0.105$ M $CH_3NH_3^+$.
       $CH_3NH_2\ (aq) + H_2O(l) \rightleftharpoons CH_3NH_3^+\ (aq) + OH^-(aq)$

	$[CH_3NH_2]$	$[CH_3NH_3^+]$	$[OH^-]$
Initial	0.18	0.18	≈ 0.00
Change	$-x$	$+x$	$+x$
Equil	$0.18 - x$	$0.18 + x$	$+x$

   $K_b = \dfrac{[CH_3NH_3^+]\,[OH^-]}{[CH_3NH_2]} = 4.4 \times 10^{-4} = \dfrac{(0.18 + x)x}{0.18 - x}$

   Assume x is small (x << 0.18) so $\dfrac{(0.18 + \cancel{x})x}{0.18 - \cancel{x}} = 4.4 \times 10^{-4} = \dfrac{(0.18)x}{0.\cancel{18}}$ and $x = 4.4 \times 10^{-4} = [OH^-]$.

   Confirm that assumption is valid $\dfrac{4.4 \times 10^{-4}}{0.18} \times 100\,\% = 0.24\,\% < 5\,\%$ so assumption is valid.

   $K_w = [H_3O^+][OH^-]$ so $[H_3O^+] = \dfrac{K_w}{[OH^-]} = \dfrac{1.0 \times 10^{-14}}{4.4 \times 10^{-4}} = 2.\underline{2}727 \times 10^{-11}$ M .   Finally,

   $pH = -\log [H_3O^+] = -\log (2.\underline{2}727 \times 10^{-11}) = 10.64$.

   Check: The units (none) are correct. The magnitude of the answer makes physical sense because pH should be less than $14 + \log (0.18) = 13.3$ because this is a weak base and there is a common ion effect.

35. When an acid (such as HCl) is added is will react with the conjugate base of the buffer system as follows: $HCl + NaC_2H_3O_2 \rightarrow HC_2H_3O_2 + NaCl$. When a base (such as NaOH) is added is will react with the weak acid of the buffer system as follows: $NaOH + HC_2H_3O_2 \rightarrow H_2O + NaC_2H_3O_2$. The reaction generates the other buffer system component.

36. When an acid (such as HCl) is added is will react with the conjugate base of the buffer system as follows: $HCl + NH_3 \rightarrow NH_4Cl$. When a base (such as NaOH) is added is will react with the weak acid of the buffer system as follows: $NaOH + NH_4Cl \rightarrow H_2O + NH_3 + NaCl$. The reaction generates the other buffer system component.

37. a) **Given:** 0.15 M $HCHO_2$ and 0.10 M $NaCHO_2$ **Find:** pH   **Other:** K_a ($HCHO_2$) = 1.8×10^{-4}
   Conceptual Plan: identify acid and base components then M $NaCHO_2$ $\rightarrow$ M CHO_2^- then
   $$\text{acid} = HCHO_2 \text{ base} = CHO_2^- \qquad NaCHO_2\ (aq) \rightarrow Na^+\ (aq) + CHO_2^-\ (aq)$$
   K_a, M $HCHO_2$, M CHO_2^- $\rightarrow$ pH
   $$pH = pK_a + \log \frac{[\text{base}]}{[\text{acid}]}$$

   Solution: Acid = $HCHO_2$, so [acid] = [$HCHO_2$] = 0.15 M. Base = CHO_2^-. Since 1 CHO_2^- ion is generated for each $NaCHO_2$, [CHO_2^-] = 0.10 M CHO_2^- = [base]. then

   $$pH = pK_a + \log \frac{[\text{base}]}{[\text{acid}]} = -\log(1.8 \times 10^{-4}) + \log \frac{0.10\ M}{0.15\ M} = 3.57 .$$

   Note that in order to use the Henderson-Hasselbalch Equation, the assumption that x is small must be valid. This was confirmed in problem #29.
   Check: The units (none) are correct. The magnitude of the answer makes physical sense because pH should be less than the pK_a of the acid because there is more acid than base. The answer agrees with problem #29.

   b) **Given:** 0.12 M NH_3 and 0.18 M NH_4Cl **Find:** pH   **Other:** K_b (NH_3) = 1.79×10^{-5}
   Conceptual Plan:
   identify acid and base components then M NH_4Cl $\rightarrow$ M NH_4^+ and K_b $\rightarrow$ pK_b $\rightarrow$ pK_a
   $$\text{acid} = NH_4^+ \text{ base} = NH_3 \qquad NH_4Cl\ (aq) \rightarrow NH_4^+\ (aq) + Cl^-\ (aq) \qquad pK_b = -\log K_b \quad 14 = pK_a + pK_b$$
   then pK_a, M NH_3, M NH_4^+ $\rightarrow$ pH
   $$pH = pK_a + \log \frac{[\text{base}]}{[\text{acid}]}$$

   Solution: Base = NH_3, [base] = [NH_3] = 0.12 M   Acid = NH_4^+. Since 1 NH_4^+ ion is generated for each NH_4Cl, [NH_4^+] = 0.18 M NH_4^+ = [acid].
   Since K_b (NH_3) = 1.79×10^{-5}, $pK_b = -\log K_b = -\log(1.79 \times 10^{-5}) = 4.75$. Since

   $$14 = pK_a + pK_b, \ pK_a = 14 - pK_b = 14 - 4.75 = 9.25 \text{ then } pH = pK_a + \log \frac{[\text{base}]}{[\text{acid}]} = 9.25 + \log \frac{0.12\ M}{0.18\ M} = 9.07$$

   Note that in order to use the Henderson-Hasselbalch Equation, the assumption that x is small must be valid. This was confirmed in problem #29.
   Check: The units (none) are correct. The magnitude of the answer makes physical sense because pH should be less than the pK_a of the acid because there is more acid than base. The answer agrees with problem #29, within the error of the value.

38. a) **Given:** 0.175 M $HC_2H_3O_2$ and 0.110 M $KC_2H_3O_2$ **Find:** pH   **Other:** K_a ($HC_2H_3O_2$) = 1.8×10^{-5}
   Conceptual Plan: identify acid and base components then M $KC_2H_3O_2$ $\rightarrow$ M $C_2H_3O_2^-$ then
   $$\text{acid} = HC_2H_3O_2 \text{ base} = C_2H_3O_2^- \qquad KC_2H_3O_2\ (aq) \rightarrow K^+\ (aq) + C_2H_3O_2^-\ (aq)$$
   M $HC_2H_3O_2$, M $C_2H_3O_2^-$ $\rightarrow$ pH
   $$pH = pK_a + \log \frac{[\text{base}]}{[\text{acid}]}$$

   Solution: Acid = $HC_2H_3O_2$, so [acid] = [$HC_2H_3O_2$] = 0.175 M. Base = $C_2H_3O_2^-$. Since 1 $C_2H_3O_2^-$ ion is generated for each $KC_2H_3O_2$, [$C_2H_3O_2^-$] = 0.110 M $C_2H_3O_2^-$ = [base]. then

   $$pH = pK_a + \log \frac{[\text{base}]}{[\text{acid}]} = -\log(1.8 \times 10^{-5}) + \log \frac{0.110\ M}{0.175\ M} = 4.54 .$$

   Note that in order to use the Henderson-Hasselbalch Equation, the assumption that x is small must be valid. This was confirmed in problem #30.

Check: The units (none) are correct. The magnitude of the answer makes physical sense because pH should be less than the pK_a of the acid because there is more acid than base. The answer agrees with problem #30.

b) **Given:** 0.195 M CH_3NH_2 and 0.105 M CH_3NH_3Br **Find:** pH **Other:** K_b $(CH_3NH_2) = 4.4 \times 10^{-4}$
Conceptual Plan: identify acid and base components then M CH_3NH_3Br $\rightarrow$ M $CH_3NH_3^+$ and

acid $= CH_3NH_3^+$ base $= CH_3NH_2$ CH_3NH_3Br $(aq) \rightarrow CH_3NH_3^+$ $(aq) + Br^-$ (aq)

K_b $\rightarrow$ pK_b $\rightarrow$ pK_a **then** pK_a, M NH_3, M NH_4^+ $\rightarrow$ pH

$pK_b = -\log K_b$, $14 = pK_a + pK_b$ $pH = pK_a + \log \dfrac{[\text{base}]}{[\text{acid}]}$

Solution: Base $= CH_3NH_2$, [base] $= [CH_3NH_2] = 0.195$ M   Acid $= NH_3^+$. Since 1 $CH_3NH_3^+$ ion is generated for each CH_3NH_3Br, $[CH_3NH_3^+] = 0.105$ M $CH_3NH_3^+ =$ [acid]. Since K_b $(CH_3NH_2) = 4.4 \times 10^{-4}$, $pK_b = -\log K_b = -\log (4.4 \times 10^{-4}) = 3.36$. Since $14 = pK_a + pK_b$,

$pK_a = 14 - pK_b = 14 - 3.36 = 10.64$ then $pH = pK_a + \log \dfrac{[\text{base}]}{[\text{acid}]} = 10.64 + \log \dfrac{0.195 \text{ M}}{0.105 \text{ M}} = 10.91$.

Note that in order to use the Henderson-Hasselbalch Equation, the assumption that x is small must be valid. This was confirmed in problem #30.

Check: The units (none) are correct. The magnitude of the answer makes physical sense because pH should be greater than the pK_a of the acid because there is more base than acid. The answer agrees with problem #30.

39. a) **Given:** 0.125 M HClO and 0.150 M KClO   **Find:** pH   **Other:** K_a (HClO) $= 2.9 \times 10^{-8}$
Conceptual Plan: identify acid and base components   then   M KClO $\rightarrow$ M ClO^- then

acid = HClO base = ClO^- $KClO$ $(aq) \rightarrow K^+$ $(aq) + ClO^-$ (aq)

M HClO, M ClO^- $\rightarrow$ pH

$pH = pK_a + \log \dfrac{[\text{base}]}{[\text{acid}]}$

Solution: Acid $=$ HClO, so [acid] $=$ [HClO] $= 0.125$ M. Base $= ClO^-$. Since 1 ClO^- ion is generated for each KClO, $[ClO^-] = 0.150$ M $ClO^- =$ [base]. then

$pH = pK_a + \log \dfrac{[\text{base}]}{[\text{acid}]} = -\log (2.9 \times 10^{-8}) + \log \dfrac{0.150 \text{ M}}{0.125 \text{ M}} = 7.62$.

Check: The units (none) are correct. The magnitude of the answer makes physical sense because pH should be greater than the pK_a of the acid because there is more base than acid.

b) **Given:** 0.175 M $C_2H_5NH_2$ and 0.150 M $C_2H_5NH_3Br$ **Find:** pH **Other:** K_b $(C_2H_5NH_2) = 5.6 \times 10^{-4}$
Conceptual Plan: identify acid and base components then M $C_2H_5NH_3Br$ $\rightarrow$ M $C_2H_5NH_3^+$ and

acid $= C_2H_5NH_3^+$ base $= C_2H_5NH_2$ $C_2H_5NH_3Br$ $(aq) \rightarrow C_2H_5NH_3^+$ $(aq) + Br^-$ (aq)

K_b $\rightarrow$ pK_b $\rightarrow$ pK_a **then** pK_a, M $C_2H_5NH_2$, M $C_2H_5NH_3^+$ $\rightarrow$ pH

$pK_b = -\log K_b$, $14 = pK_a + pK_b$ $pH = pK_a + \log \dfrac{[\text{base}]}{[\text{acid}]}$

Solution: Base $= C_2H_5NH_2$, [base] $= [C_2H_5NH_2] = 0.175$ M   Acid $= C_2H_5NH_3^+$. Since 1 $C_2H_5NH_3^+$ ion is generated for each $C_2H_5NH_3Br$, $[C_2H_5NH_3^+] = 0.150$ M $C_2H_5NH_3^+ =$ [acid]. Since K_b $(C_2H_5NH_2) = 5.6 \times 10^{-4}$, $pK_b = -\log K_b = -\log (5.6 \times 10^{-4}) = 3.25$. Since $14 = pK_a + pK_b$,

$pK_a = 14 - pK_b = 14 - 3.25 = 10.48$ then $pH = pK_a + \log \dfrac{[\text{base}]}{[\text{acid}]} = 10.75 + \log \dfrac{0.175 \text{ M}}{0.150 \text{ M}} = 10.82$.

Check: The units (none) are correct. The magnitude of the answer makes physical sense because pH should be greater than the pK_a of the acid because there is more base than acid.

c) **Given:** 10.0 g $HC_2H_3O_2$ and 10.0 g $NaC_2H_3O_2$ in 150.0 mL solution **Find:** pH
Other: K_a $(HC_2H_3O_2) = 1.8 \times 10^{-5}$
Conceptual Plan:
identify acid and base components then mL $\rightarrow$ L and g $HC_2H_3O_2$ $\rightarrow$ mol $HC_2H_3O_2$

acid $= HC_2H_3O_2$ base $= C_2H_3O_2^-$ $\dfrac{1 \text{ L}}{1000 \text{ mL}}$ $\dfrac{1 \text{ mol } HC_2H_3O_2}{60.05 \text{ g } HC_2H_3O_2}$

then mol $HC_2H_3O_2$, L → M $HC_2H_3O_2$ and g $NaC_2H_3O_2$ → mol $NaC_2H_3O_2$ then

$$M = \frac{mol}{L} \qquad\qquad \frac{1 \text{ mol } NaC_2H_3O_2}{82.04 \text{ g } NaC_2H_3O_2}$$

mol $NaC_2H_3O_2$, L → M $NaC_2H_3O_2$ → M $C_2H_3O_2^-$ then M $HC_2H_3O_2$, M $C_2H_3O_2^-$ → pH

$$M = \frac{mol}{L} \qquad NaC_2H_3O_2\ (aq) \rightarrow Na^+\ (aq) + C_2H_3O_2^-\ (aq) \qquad\qquad pH = pK_a + \log\frac{[base]}{[acid]}$$

Solution: $150.0 \text{ mL} \times \dfrac{1 \text{ L}}{1000 \text{ mL}} = 0.1500 \text{ L}$ and

$10.0 \text{ g } HC_2H_3O_2 \times \dfrac{1 \text{ mol } HC_2H_3O_2}{60.05 \text{ g } HC_2H_3O_2} = 0.16\underline{6}528 \text{ mol } HC_2H_3O_2$

then $M = \dfrac{mol}{L} = \dfrac{0.16\underline{6}528 \text{ mol } HC_2H_3O_2}{0.1500 \text{ L}} = 1.1\underline{1}019 \text{ M } HC_2H_3O_2$ and

$10.0 \text{ g } NaC_2H_3O_2 \times \dfrac{1 \text{ mol } NaC_2H_3O_2}{82.04 \text{ g } NaC_2H_3O_2} = 0.12\underline{1}892 \text{ mol } NaC_2H_3O_2$ then

$M = \dfrac{mol}{L} = \dfrac{0.12\underline{1}892 \text{ mol } NaC_2H_3O_2}{0.1500 \text{ L}} = 0.81\underline{2}612 \text{ M } NaC_2H_3O_2$. So Acid $= HC_2H_3O_2$, so [acid] =

$[HC_2H_3O_2] = 1.1\underline{1}019$ M and Base $= C_2H_3O_2^-$. Since 1 $C_2H_3O_2^-$ ion is generated for each $NaC_2H_3O_2$,

$[C_2H_3O_2^-] = 0.81\underline{2}612$ M

$C_2H_3O_2^- = $ [base]. then $pH = pK_a + \log\dfrac{[base]}{[acid]} = -\log(1.8 \times 10^{-5}) + \log\dfrac{0.81\underline{2}612 \text{ M}}{1.1\underline{1}019 \text{ M}} = 4.61$.

Check: The units (none) are correct. The magnitude of the answer makes physical sense because pH should be less than the pK_a of the acid because there is more acid than base.

40. a) **Given:** 0.155 M $HC_3H_5O_2$ (propanoic acid) and 0.110 M $KC_3H_5O_2$ (potassium propanoate)
Find: pH   **Other:** $K_a (HC_3H_5O_2) = 1.3 \times 10^{-5}$
Conceptual Plan:
identify acid and base components then **M $KC_3H_5O_2$ → M $C_3H_5O_2^-$** then
acid $= HC_3H_5O_2$ base $= C_3H_5O_2^-$ $KC_3H_5O_2\ (aq) \rightarrow K^+\ (aq) + C_3H_5O_2^-\ (aq)$
M $HC_3H_5O_2$, M $C_3H_5O_2^-$ → pH

$$pH = pK_a + \log\frac{[base]}{[acid]}$$

Solution: Acid $= HC_3H_5O_2$, so [acid] $= [HC_3H_5O_2] = 0.155$ M. Base $= C_3H_5O_2^-$. Since 1 $C_3H_5O_2^-$ ion is generated for each $KC_3H_5O_2$, $[C_3H_5O_2^-] = 0.110$ M $C_3H_5O_2^- = $ [base]. then

$pH = pK_a + \log\dfrac{[base]}{[acid]} = -\log(1.3 \times 10^{-5}) + \log\dfrac{0.110 \text{ M}}{0.155 \text{ M}} = 4.74$.

Check: The units (none) are correct. The magnitude of the answer makes physical sense because pH should be less than the pK_a of the acid because there is more acid than base.

b) **Given:** 0.15 M C_5H_5N and 0.10 M C_5H_5NHCl **Find:** pH   **Other:** $K_b (C_5H_5N) = 1.7 \times 10^{-9}$
Conceptual Plan:
identify acid and base components then **M CH_3NH_3Cl → M $CH_3NH_3^+$** and
acid $= C_5H_5NH^+$ base $= C_5H_5N$ $C_5H_5NHCl\ (aq) \rightarrow C_5H_5NH^+\ (aq) + Cl^-\ (aq)$
K_b → pK_b → pK_a then **pK_a, M C_5H_5N, M $C_5H_5NH^+$ → pH**

$$pK_b = -\log K_b \quad 14 = pK_a + pK_b \qquad\qquad pH = pK_a + \log\frac{[base]}{[acid]}$$

Solution: Base $= C_5H_5N$, [base] $= [C_5H_5NH] = 0.15$ M   Acid $= C_5H_5NH^+$. Since 1 $C_5H_5NH^+$ ion is generated for each C_5H_5NHCl, $[C_5H_5NH^+] = 0.10$ M $C_5H_5NH^+ = $ [acid]. Since $K_b (C_5H_5N) =$
$= 1.7 \times 10^{-9}$, $pK_b = -\log K_b = -\log(1.7 \times 10^{-9}) = 8.77$. Since $14 = pK_a + pK_b$,

$pK_a = 14 - pK_b = 14 - 8.77 = 5.23$ then $pH = pK_a + \log\dfrac{[base]}{[acid]} = 5.23 + \log\dfrac{0.15 \text{ M}}{0.10 \text{ M}} = 5.41$.

Check: The units (none) are correct. The magnitude of the answer makes physical sense because pH should be greater than the pK_a of the acid because there is more base than acid.

c) **Given:** 15.0 g HF and 25.0 g NaF in 125 mL solution **Find:** pH   **Other:** K_a (HF) = 3.5 x 10^{-4}
Conceptual Plan:
identify acid and base components   **then**   **mL** $\rightarrow$ **L**   **and**   **g HF** $\rightarrow$ **mol HF**

$$\text{acid} = HF \text{ base} = F^-$$

$$\frac{1 \text{ L}}{1000 \text{ mL}} \qquad \frac{1 \text{ mol HF}}{20.01 \text{ g HF}}$$

then mol HF, L $\rightarrow$ **M HF   and   g NaF** $\rightarrow$ **mol NaF**   **then**

$$M = \frac{\text{mol}}{\text{L}} \qquad \frac{1 \text{ mol NaF}}{41.99 \text{ g NaF}}$$

mol NaF, L $\rightarrow$ **M NaF** $\rightarrow$ **M F$^-$**   **then   M HF, M F$^-$** $\rightarrow$ **pH**

$$M = \frac{\text{mol}}{\text{L}} \qquad NaF \, (aq) \rightarrow Na^+ \, (aq) + F^- \, (aq) \qquad pH = pK_a + \log \frac{[\text{base}]}{[\text{acid}]}$$

Solution: $125 \text{ mL} \times \dfrac{1 \text{ L}}{1000 \text{ mL}} = 0.125$ L and $10.0 \text{ g HF} \times \dfrac{1 \text{ mol HF}}{20.01 \text{ g HF}} = 0.499750$ mol HF then

$M = \dfrac{\text{mol}}{\text{L}} = \dfrac{0.499750 \text{ mol HF}}{0.125 \text{ L}} = 3.998$ M HF and $25.0 \text{ g NaF} \times \dfrac{1 \text{ mol NaF}}{41.99 \text{ g NaF}} = 0.595380$ mol NaF   then

$M = \dfrac{\text{mol}}{\text{L}} = \dfrac{0.595380 \text{ mol NaF}}{0.125 \text{ L}} = 4.76304$ M NaF . So Acid = HF, so [acid] = [HF] = 3.998 M and

Base = F$^-$. Since 1F$^-$ ion is generated for each NaF, [F$^-$] = 4.76304 M F$^-$ = [base]. then

$pH = pK_a + \log \dfrac{[\text{base}]}{[\text{acid}]} = -\log(3.5 \text{ x } 10^{-4}) + \log \dfrac{4.76304 \text{ M}}{3.998 \text{ M}} = 3.53$.

Check: The units (none) are correct.   The magnitude of the answer makes physical sense because pH should be greater than the pK$_a$ of the acid because there is more base than acid.

41. a) **Given:** 50.0 mL of 0.15 M HCHO$_2$ and 75.0 mL of 0.13 M NaCHO$_2$ **Find:** pH
   Other: K_a (HCHO$_2$) = 1.8 x 10^{-4}
   Conceptual Plan:
   identify acid and base components   **then mL HCHO$_2$, mL NaCHO$_2$** $\rightarrow$ **total mL then**

   acid = HCHO$_2$ base = CHO$_2^-$ total mL = mL HCHO$_2$ + mL NaCHO$_2$

   mL HCHO$_2$, M HCHO$_2$, total mL $\rightarrow$ **buffer M HCHO$_2$**   **and**

   $$M_1 V_1 = M_2 V_2$$

   mL NaCHO$_2$, M NaCHO$_2$, total mL $\rightarrow$ **buffer M NaCHO$_2$** $\rightarrow$ **buffer M CHO$_2^-$**   **then**

   $$M_1 V_1 = M_2 V_2 \qquad NaCHO_2 \, (aq) \rightarrow Na^+ \, (aq) + CHO_2^- \, (aq)$$

   K$_a$, M HCHO$_2$, M CHO$_2^-$ $\rightarrow$ **pH**

   $$pH = pK_a + \log \frac{[\text{base}]}{[\text{acid}]}$$

   Solution: total mL = mL HCHO$_2$ + mL NaCHO$_2$ = 50.0 mL + 75.0 mL = 125.0 mL. then Since

   $M_1 V_1 = M_2 V_2$ Rearrange to solve for M$_2$. $M_2 = \dfrac{M_1 V_1}{V_2} = \dfrac{(0.15 \text{ M})(50.0 \text{ mL})}{125.0 \text{ mL}} = 0.060$ M HCHO$_2$ and

   $M_2 = \dfrac{M_1 V_1}{V_2} = \dfrac{(0.13 \text{ M})(75.0 \text{ mL})}{125.0 \text{ mL}} = 0.078$ M NaCHO$_2$. Acid = HCHO$_2$, so [acid] = [HCHO$_2$] = 0.060 M.

   Base = CHO$_2^-$. Since 1 CHO$_2^-$ ion is generated for each NaCHO$_2$, [CHO$_2^-$] = 0.078 M CHO$_2^-$ = [base].

   then $pH = pK_a + \log \dfrac{[\text{base}]}{[\text{acid}]} = -\log(1.8 \text{ x } 10^{-4}) + \log \dfrac{0.078 \text{ M}}{0.060 \text{ M}} = 3.86$.

   Check: The units (none) are correct.   The magnitude of the answer makes physical sense because pH should be greater than the pK$_a$ of the acid because there is more base than acid.

   b) **Given:** 125.0 mL of 0.10 M NH$_3$ and 250.0 mL of 0.10 M NH$_4$Cl   **Find:** pH
   Other: K_b (NH$_3$) = 1.79 x 10^{-5}
   Conceptual Plan:
   identify acid and base components then mL NH$_3$, mL NH$_4$Cl $\rightarrow$ **total mL   then**

   acid = NH$_4^+$ base = NH$_3$ total mL = mL NH$_3$ + mL NH$_4$Cl

   mL NH$_3$, M NH$_3$, total mL $\rightarrow$ **buffer M NH$_3$**   **and**

   $$M_1 V_1 = M_2 V_2$$

   mL NH$_4$Cl, M NH$_4$Cl, total mL $\rightarrow$ **buffer M NH$_4$Cl** $\rightarrow$ **buffer M NH$_4^+$ and K$_b$** $\rightarrow$ **pK$_b$** $\rightarrow$ **pK$_a$ then**

$$M_1 V_1 = M_2 V_2 \quad NH_4Cl\ (aq) \rightarrow NH_4^+\ (aq) + Cl^-\ (aq) \qquad pK_b = -\log K_b \quad 14 = pK_a + pK_b$$

then pK_a, **M** NH_3, **M** NH_4^+ $\rightarrow$ **pH**

$$pH = pK_a + \log \frac{[base]}{[acid]}$$

Solution: total mL = mL NH_3 + mL NH_4Cl = 125.0 mL + 250.0 mL = 375.0 mL. then Since

$M_1 V_1 = M_2 V_2$ Rearrange to solve for M_2. $\quad M_2 = \dfrac{M_1 V_1}{V_2} = \dfrac{(0.10\ M)(125.0\ mL)}{375.0\ mL} = 0.03\underline{3}333\ M\ NH_3$ and

$M_2 = \dfrac{M_1 V_1}{V_2} = \dfrac{(0.10\ M)(250.0\ mL)}{375.0\ mL} = 0.06\underline{6}667\ M\ NH_4Cl$. Base = NH_3, [base] = $[NH_3]$ = 0.03\underline{3}333 M

Acid = NH_4^+. Since 1 NH_4^+ ion is generated for each NH_4Cl, $[NH_4^+]$ = 0.06\underline{6}667 M NH_4^+ = [acid].
Since K_b (NH_3) = 1.79 x 10^{-5}, $pK_b = -\log K_b = -\log (1.79\ x\ 10^{-5}) = 4.75$. Since $14 = pK_a + pK_b$,

$$pK_a = 14 - pK_b = 14 - 4.75 = 9.25 \text{ then } pH = pK_a + \log \frac{[base]}{[acid]} = 9.25 + \log \frac{0.03\underline{3}333\ M}{0.06\underline{6}667\ M} = 8.95 .$$

Check: The units (none) are correct. The magnitude of the answer makes physical sense because pH should be less than the pK_a of the acid because there is more acid than base.

42. a) **Given:** 150.0 mL of 0.25 M HF and 225.0 mL of 0.30 M NaF **Find:** pH
Other: K_a (HF) = 3.5 x 10^{-4}
Conceptual Plan:
identify acid and base components   **then**   **mL** $HCHO_2$, **mL** $NaCHO_2$ $\rightarrow$ **total mL**   **then**
         acid = HF base = F^- total mL = mL HF + mL NaF

mL HF, M HF, total mL $\rightarrow$ **buffer M HF**   **and**
       $M_1 V_1 = M_2 V_2$

mL NaF, M NaF, total mL $\rightarrow$ **buffer M NaF** $\rightarrow$ **buffer M** F^-
       $M_1 V_1 = M_2 V_2$ NaF (aq) $\rightarrow$ Na^+ (aq) + F^- (aq)

then K_a, **M** $HCHO_2$, **M** CHO_2^- $\rightarrow$ **pH**

$$pH = pK_a + \log \frac{[base]}{[acid]}$$

Solution: total mL = mL HF + mL NaF = 150.0 mL + 225.0 mL = 375.0 mL. then Since

$M_1 V_1 = M_2 V_2$ Rearrange to solve for M_2. $\quad M_2 = \dfrac{M_1 V_1}{V_2} = \dfrac{(0.25\ M)(150.0\ mL)}{375.0\ mL} = 0.10\ M\ HF$ and

$M_2 = \dfrac{M_1 V_1}{V_2} = \dfrac{(0.30\ M)(225.0\ mL)}{375.0\ mL} = 0.18\ M\ NaF$. Acid = HF, so [acid] = [HF] = 0.10 M. Base = F^-.

Since 1 F^- ion is generated for each NaF, $[F^-]$ = 0.18 M F^- = [base]. then

$$pH = pK_a + \log \frac{[base]}{[acid]} = -\log (3.5\ x\ 10^{-4}) + \log \frac{0.18\ M}{0.10\ M} = 3.71 .$$

Check: The units (none) are correct. The magnitude of the answer makes physical sense because pH should be greater than the pK_a of the acid because there is more base than acid.

b) **Given:** 175.0 mL of 0.10 M $C_2H_5NH_2$ and 275.0 mL of 0.20 M $C_2H_5NH_3Cl$
Find: pH   **Other:** K_b ($C_2H_5NH_2$) = 5.6 x 10^{-4}
Conceptual Plan:
identify acid and base components   **then**   **mL** $C_2H_5NH_2$, **mL** $C_2H_5NH_3Cl$ $\rightarrow$ **total mL**   **then**
         acid = $C_2H_5NH_3^+$ base = $C_2H_5NH_2$ total mL = mL $C_2H_5NH_2$ + mL $C_2H_5NH_3Cl$

mL NH_3, **M** $C_2H_5NH_2$, **total mL** $\rightarrow$ **buffer M** $C_2H_5NH_2$ **and**
       $M_1 V_1 = M_2 V_2$

mL NH_4Cl, **M** $C_2H_5NH_3Cl$, **total mL** $\rightarrow$ **buffer M** $C_2H_5NH_3Cl$ $\rightarrow$ **buffer M** $C_2H_5NH_3^+$ **and**
       $M_1 V_1 = M_2 V_2$ $C_2H_5NH_3Cl$ (aq) $\rightarrow$ $C_2H_5NH_3^+$ (aq) + Cl^- (aq)

K_b $\rightarrow$ pK_b $\rightarrow$ pK_a **then** pK_a, **M** $C_2H_5NH_2$, **M** $C_2H_5NH_3^+$ $\rightarrow$ **pH**

$$pK_b = -\log K_b \quad 14 = pK_a + pK_b \qquad\qquad pH = pK_a + \log \frac{[base]}{[acid]}$$

Solution: total mL = mL $C_2H_5NH_2$ + mL $C_2H_5NH_3Cl$ = 175.0 mL + 275.0 mL = 450.0 mL. then
Since $M_1 V_1 = M_2 V_2$ Rearrange to solve for M_2.

$$M_2 = \frac{M_1 V_1}{V_2} = \frac{(0.10 \text{ M})(175.0 \text{ mL})}{450.0 \text{ mL}} = 0.038889 \text{ M } C_2H_5NH_2 \text{ and}$$

$$M_2 = \frac{M_1 V_1}{V_2} = \frac{(0.20 \text{ M})(275.0 \text{ mL})}{450.0 \text{ mL}} = 0.12222 \text{ M } C_2H_5NH_3Cl. \quad \text{Base} = C_2H_5NH_2, \text{ [base]} = [C_2H_5NH_2] =$$

0.038889 M Acid $= C_2H_5NH_3^+$. Since 1 $C_2H_5NH_3^+$ ion is generated for each $C_2H_5NH_3Cl$, $[C_2H_5NH_3^+]$ $= 0.12222$ M $C_2H_5NH_3^+ = $ [acid]. Since K_b $(C_2H_5NH_2) = 5.6 \times 10^{-4}$,

$pK_b = -\log K_b = -\log (5.6 \times 10^{-4}) = 3.25$. Since $14 = pK_a + pK_b$,

$$pK_a = 14 - pK_b = 14 - 3.25 = 10.75 \text{ then } \quad pH = pK_a + \log \frac{[\text{base}]}{[\text{acid}]} = 10.75 + \log \frac{0.038889 \text{ M}}{0.12222 \text{ M}} = 10.25.$$

Check: The units (none) are correct. The magnitude of the answer makes physical sense because pH should be less than the pK_a of the acid because there is more acid than base.

43. **Given:** NaF / HF buffer at pH = 4.00   **Find:** [NaF] / [HF]   **Other:** K_a (HF) = 3.5×10^{-4}
     Conceptual Plan: identify acid and base components   **then**   **pH, K_a** $\rightarrow$ **[NaF] / [HF]**

$$\text{acid} = \text{HF base} = F^- \qquad\qquad pH = pK_a + \log \frac{[\text{base}]}{[\text{acid}]}$$

Solution: $pH = pK_a + \log \dfrac{[\text{base}]}{[\text{acid}]} = -\log(3.5 \times 10^{-4}) + \log \dfrac{[\text{NaF}]}{[\text{HF}]} = 4.00$. Solve for [NaF] / [HF].

$$\log \frac{[\text{NaF}]}{[\text{HF}]} = 4.00 - 3.46 = 0.54 \quad \rightarrow \quad \frac{[\text{NaF}]}{[\text{HF}]} = 10^{0.54} = 3.5.$$

Check: The units (none) are correct. The magnitude of the answer makes physical sense because the pH is greater than the pK_a of the acid there needs to be more base than acid.

44. **Given:** CH_3NH_2 / CH_3NH_3Cl buffer at pH = 10.24 **Find:** $[CH_3NH_2]$ / $[CH_3NH_3Cl]$
    Other: K_b (CH_3NH_2) = 4.4×10^{-4}
    Conceptual Plan: identify acid and base components   **and K_b** $\rightarrow$ **pK_b** $\rightarrow$ **pK_a**   **then**

$$\text{acid} = CH_3NH_3^+ \text{ base} = CH_3N \qquad pK_b = -\log K_b \quad 14 = pK_a + pK_b$$

pH, K_a $\rightarrow$ **$[CH_3NH_2]$ / $[CH_3NH_3Cl]$**

$$pH = pK_a + \log \frac{[\text{base}]}{[\text{acid}]}$$

Solution: Since K_b (CH_3NH_2) = 4.4×10^{-4}, $pK_b = -\log K_b = -\log (4.4 \times 10^{-4}) = 3.36$. Since

$14 = pK_a + pK_b$, $pK_a = 14 - pK_b = 14 - 3.36 = 10.64$ then

$$pH = pK_a + \log \frac{[\text{base}]}{[\text{acid}]} = 10.64 + \log \frac{[CH_3NH_2]}{[CH_3NH_3Cl]} = 10.24.$$

Solve for $[CH_3NH_2]$ / $[CH_3NH_3Cl]$.

$$\log \frac{[CH_3NH_2]}{[CH_3NH_3Cl]} = 10.24 - 10.64 = -0.40 \quad \rightarrow \quad \frac{[CH_3NH_2]}{[CH_3NH_3Cl]} = 10^{-0.40} = 0.39.$$

Check: The units (none) are correct. The magnitude of the answer makes physical sense because the pH is less than the pK_a of the acid there needs to be less base than acid.

45. **Given:** 150.0 mL buffer of 0.15 M benzoic acid at pH = 4.25   **Find:** mass sodium benzoate
    Other: K_a $(HC_7H_5O_2) = 6.5 \times 10^{-5}$
    Conceptual Plan: identify acid and base components   **then**   **pH, K_a, $[HC_7H_5O_2]$** $\rightarrow$ **$[NaC_7H_5O_2]$**

$$\text{acid} = HC_7H_5O_2 \text{ base} = C_7H_5O_2^- \qquad\qquad pH = pK_a + \log \frac{[\text{base}]}{[\text{acid}]}$$

mL $\rightarrow$ **L**   **then**   **$[NaC_7H_5O_2]$, L** $\rightarrow$ **mol $NaC_7H_5O_2$** $\rightarrow$ **g $NaC_7H_5O_2$**

$$\frac{1 \text{ L}}{1000 \text{ mL}} \qquad\qquad M = \frac{\text{mol}}{\text{L}} \qquad\qquad \frac{144.11 \text{ g } NaC_7H_5O_2}{1 \text{ mol } NaC_7H_5O_2}$$

Solution: $pH = pK_a + \log \dfrac{[\text{base}]}{[\text{acid}]} = -\log(6.5 \times 10^{-5}) + \log \dfrac{[NaC_7H_5O_2]}{0.15 \text{ M}} = 4.25$. Solve for $[NaC_7H_5O_2]$.

$$\log \frac{[NaC_7H_5O_2]}{0.15 \text{ M}} = 4.25 - 4.19 = 0.06291 \rightarrow \frac{[NaC_7H_5O_2]}{0.15 \text{ M}} = 10^{0.06291} = 1.1559 \rightarrow [NaC_7H_5O_2] = 0.17338 \text{ M}.$$

Convert to moles using $M = \dfrac{\text{mol}}{\text{L}}$.

$$\frac{0.17338 \text{ mol } NaC_7H_5O_2}{1 \text{ L}} \times 0.150 \text{ L} = 0.026007 \text{ mol } NaC_7H_5O_2 \times \frac{144.11 \text{ g } NaC_7H_5O_2}{1 \text{ mol } NaC_7H_5O_2} = 3.7 \text{ g } NaC_7H_5O_2 \ .$$

Check: The units (g) are correct. The magnitude of the answer makes physical sense because the volume of solution is small and the concentration is low, so much less than a mole is needed.

46. **Given:** 2.55 L buffer of 0.155 M NH_3 at pH = 9.55   **Find:** mass ammonium chloride
     Other: K_b (NH_3) = 1.79×10^{-5}
     Conceptual Plan: identify acid and base components   **then** $K_b \rightarrow pK_b \rightarrow pK_a$ **then**
                   acid = NH_4^+ base = NH_3 $pK_b = -\log K_b$ $14 = pK_a + pK_b$

     pH, K_a, [NH_3] $\rightarrow$ **[NH_4Cl]**   **then**   **[NH_4Cl], L** $\rightarrow$ **mol NH_4Cl** $\rightarrow$ **g NH_4Cl**
         $pH = pK_a + \log \dfrac{[base]}{[acid]}$ $M = \dfrac{mol}{L}$ $\dfrac{53.49 \text{ g } NH_4Cl}{1 \text{ mol } NH_4Cl}$

     Solution: Since K_b (NH_3) = 1.79×10^{-5}, $pK_b = -\log K_b = -\log (1.79 \times 10^{-5}) = 4.75$. Since $14 = pK_a + pK_b$,

     $pK_a = 14 - pK_b = 14 - 4.75 = 9.25$ then $pH = pK_a + \log \dfrac{[base]}{[acid]} = 9.25 + \log \dfrac{0.155 \text{ M}}{[NH_4Cl]} = 9.55$.

     Solve for [NH_4Cl]. $\log \dfrac{0.155 \text{ M}}{[NH_4Cl]} = 9.55 - 9.25 = 0.30 \rightarrow \dfrac{0.155 \text{ M}}{[NH_4Cl]} = 10^{0.30} = 1.99526 \rightarrow$

     [NH_4Cl] = 0.0776841 M . Convert to moles using $M = \dfrac{mol}{L}$.

     $\dfrac{0.0776841 \text{ mol } NH_4Cl}{1 \text{ L}} \times 2.55 \text{ L} = 0.198094 \text{ mol } NH_4Cl \times \dfrac{53.49 \text{ g } NH_4Cl}{1 \text{ mol } NH_4Cl} = 10.6 \text{ g } NH_4Cl$.

     Check: The units (g) are correct. The magnitude of the answer makes physical sense because the volume of solution is large and the concentration is low, so less than a mole is needed.

47. a) **Given:** 250.0 mL buffer 0.250 M $HC_2H_3O_2$ and 0.250 M $NaC_2H_3O_2$ **Find:** initial pH
      Other: K_a ($HC_2H_3O_2$) = 1.8×10^{-5}
      Conceptual Plan: identify acid and base components then M $NaC_2H_3O_2$ $\rightarrow$ **M $C_2H_3O_2^-$**   **then**
                 acid = $HC_2H_3O_2$ base = $C_2H_3O_2^-$ $NaC_2H_3O_2$ (aq) $\rightarrow$ Na^+ (aq) + $C_2H_3O_2^-$ (aq)
      M $HC_2H_3O_2$, M $C_2H_3O_2^-$ $\rightarrow$ **pH**
               $pH = pK_a + \log \dfrac{[base]}{[acid]}$

      Solution: Acid = $HC_2H_3O_2$, so [acid] = [$HC_2H_3O_2$] = 0.250 M. Base = $C_2H_3O_2^-$. Since 1 $C_2H_3O_2^-$
      ion is generated for each $NaC_2H_3O_2$, [$C_2H_3O_2^-$] = 0.250 M $C_2H_3O_2^-$ = [base]. Then

      $pH = pK_a + \log \dfrac{[base]}{[acid]} = -\log (1.8 \times 10^{-5}) + \log \dfrac{0.250 \text{ M}}{0.250 \text{ M}} = 4.74$.

      Check: The units (none) are correct. The magnitude of the answer makes physical sense because pH is equal to the pK_a of the acid because there are equal amounts of acid and base.

   b) **Given:**   250.0 mL buffer 0.250 M $HC_2H_3O_2$ and 0.250 M $NaC_2H_3O_2$, add 0.0050 mol HCl
      Find: pH   **Other:** K_a ($HC_2H_3O_2$) = 1.8×10^{-5}
      Conceptual Plan: Part I: Stoichiometry:
      mL $\rightarrow$ **L**   **then**   **[$NaC_2H_3O_2$], L** $\rightarrow$ **mol $NaC_2H_3O_2$**   **and**   **[$HC_2H_3O_2$], L** $\rightarrow$ **mol $HC_2H_3O_2$**
         $\dfrac{1 \text{ L}}{1000 \text{ mL}}$ $M = \dfrac{mol}{L}$ $M = \dfrac{mol}{L}$

      write balanced equation then
      $HCl + NaC_2H_3O_2 \rightarrow HC_2H_3O_2 + NaCl$
      mol $NaC_2H_3O_2$, mol $HC_2H_3O_2$, mol HCl $\rightarrow$ **mol $NaC_2H_3O_2$, mol $HC_2H_3O_2$ then**
                                set up stoichiometry table
      Part II: Equilibrium:
      mol $NaC_2H_3O_2$, mol $HC_2H_3O_2$, L, K_a $\rightarrow$ **pH**
                     $pH = pK_a + \log \dfrac{[base]}{[acid]}$

     Solution: 250.0 mL $\times \dfrac{1 \text{ L}}{1000 \text{ mL}} = 0.2500$ L then $\dfrac{0.250 \text{ mol } HC_2H_3O_2}{1 \text{ L}} \times 0.250 \text{ L} = 0.0625 \text{ mol } HC_2H_3O_2$

and $\frac{0.250 \text{ mol NaC}_2\text{H}_3\text{O}_2}{1 \text{ L}} \times 0.250 \text{ L} = 0.0625 \text{ mol NaC}_2\text{H}_3\text{O}_2$ set up table to track changes:

$$\text{HCl } (aq) + \text{NaC}_2\text{H}_3\text{O}_2 \ (aq) \rightarrow \text{HC}_2\text{H}_3\text{O}_2 \ (aq) + \text{NaCl } (aq)$$

Before addition	≈ 0.00 mol	0.0625 mol	0.0625 mol	0.00 mol
Addition	0.0050 mol	–	–	–
After addition	≈ 0.00 mol	0.0575 mol	0.0675 mol	0.0050 mol

Since the amount of HCl is small, there are still significant amounts of both buffer components, so the Henderson-Hasselbalch Equation can be used to calculate the new pH.

$$\text{pH} = \text{pK}_a + \log \frac{[\text{base}]}{[\text{acid}]} = -\log(1.8 \times 10^{-5}) + \log \frac{\dfrac{0.0575 \text{ mol}}{0.250 \text{ L}}}{\dfrac{0.0675 \text{ mol}}{0.250 \text{ L}}} = 4.68 \ .$$

Check: The units (none) are correct. The magnitude of the answer makes physical sense because the pH dropped slightly when acid was added.

c) **Given:** 250.0 mL buffer 0.250 M $\text{HC}_2\text{H}_3\text{O}_2$ and 0.250 M $\text{NaC}_2\text{H}_3\text{O}_2$, add 0.0050 mol NaOH
Find: pH   **Other:** $\text{K}_a \ (\text{HC}_2\text{H}_3\text{O}_2) = 1.8 \times 10^{-5}$
Conceptual Plan: Part I: Stoichiometry:
mL $\rightarrow$ L   then $[\text{NaC}_2\text{H}_3\text{O}_2]$, L $\rightarrow$ mol $\text{NaC}_2\text{H}_3\text{O}_2$ and $[\text{HC}_2\text{H}_3\text{O}_2]$, L $\rightarrow$ mol $\text{HC}_2\text{H}_3\text{O}_2$

$$\frac{1 \text{ L}}{1000 \text{ mL}} \qquad\qquad M = \frac{\text{mol}}{\text{L}} \qquad\qquad M = \frac{\text{mol}}{\text{L}}$$

write balanced equation then
$\text{NaOH} + \text{HC}_2\text{H}_3\text{O}_2 \rightarrow \text{H}_2\text{O} + \text{NaC}_2\text{H}_3\text{O}_2$
mol $\text{NaC}_2\text{H}_3\text{O}_2$, mol $\text{HC}_2\text{H}_3\text{O}_2$, mol NaOH $\rightarrow$ mol $\text{NaC}_2\text{H}_3\text{O}_2$, mol $\text{HC}_2\text{H}_3\text{O}_2$ then
set up stoichiometry table
Part II: Equilibrium:
mol $\text{NaC}_2\text{H}_3\text{O}_2$, mol $\text{HC}_2\text{H}_3\text{O}_2$, L, K_a $\rightarrow$ pH

$$\text{pH} = \text{pK}_a + \log \frac{[\text{base}]}{[\text{acid}]}$$

Solution: $250.0 \text{ mL} \times \dfrac{1 \text{ L}}{1000 \text{ mL}} = 0.2500 \text{ L}$ then $\dfrac{0.250 \text{ mol HC}_2\text{H}_3\text{O}_2}{1 \text{ L}} \times 0.2500 \text{ L} = 0.0625 \text{ mol HC}_2\text{H}_3\text{O}_2$

and $\dfrac{0.250 \text{ mol NaC}_2\text{H}_3\text{O}_2}{1 \text{ L}} \times 0.2500 \text{ L} = 0.0625 \text{ mol NaC}_2\text{H}_3\text{O}_2$ set up table to track changes:

$$\text{NaOH } (aq) + \text{HC}_2\text{H}_3\text{O}_2 \ (aq) \rightarrow \text{NaC}_2\text{H}_3\text{O}_2 \ (aq) + \text{H}_2\text{O } (l)$$

Before addition	≈ 0.00 mol	0.0625 mol	0.0625 mol	–
Addition	0.0050 mol	–	–	–
After addition	≈ 0.00 mol	0.0575 mol	0.0675 mol	–

Since the amount of NaOH is small, there are still significant amounts of both buffer components, so the Henderson-Hasselbalch Equation can be used to calculate the new pH.

$$\text{pH} = \text{pK}_a + \log \frac{[\text{base}]}{[\text{acid}]} = -\log(1.8 \times 10^{-5}) + \log \frac{\dfrac{0.0675 \text{ mol}}{0.2500 \text{ L}}}{\dfrac{0.0575 \text{ mol}}{0.2500 \text{ L}}} = 4.81 \ .$$

Check: The units (none) are correct. The magnitude of the answer makes physical sense because the pH rose slightly when base was added.

48. a) **Given:** 100.0 mL buffer 0.175 M HClO and 0.150 M NaClO   **Find:** initial pH
Other: $\text{K}_a \ (\text{HClO}) = 2.9 \times 10^{-8}$
Conceptual Plan: identify acid and base components   then   M NaClO $\rightarrow$ M ClO$^-$ then
acid = HClO base = ClO$^-$ NaClO $(aq) \rightarrow$ Na$^+$ (aq) + ClO$^-$ (aq)
M HClO, M ClO$^-$ $\rightarrow$ pH

$$\text{pH} = \text{pK}_a + \log \frac{[\text{base}]}{[\text{acid}]}$$

Solution: Acid = HClO, so [acid] = [HClO] = 0.175 M. Base = ClO$^-$. Since 1 ClO$^-$ ion is generated for each NaClO, [ClO$^-$] = 0.150 M ClO$^-$ = [base].

Then $pH = pK_a + \log \dfrac{[base]}{[acid]} = -\log(2.9 \times 10^{-9}) + \log \dfrac{0.150 \text{ M}}{0.175 \text{ M}} = 7.47$.

Check: The units (none) are correct. The magnitude of the answer makes physical sense because pH is greater than the pK_a of the acid because there is more base than acid.

b) **Given:** 100.0 mL buffer 0.175 M HClO and 0.150 M NaClO, add 150.0 mg HBr   **Find:** pH
Other: K_a (HClO) $= 2.9 \times 10^{-8}$
Conceptual Plan: Part I: Stoichiometry:
mL → L   then   [NaClO], L → mol NaClO and [HClO], L → mol HClO and

$$\dfrac{1 \text{ L}}{1000 \text{ mL}} \qquad\qquad M = \dfrac{mol}{L} \qquad\qquad M = \dfrac{mol}{L}$$

mg HBr → g   HBr → mol HBr   write balanced equation   then

$$\dfrac{1 \text{ g HBr}}{1000 \text{ mg HBr}} \qquad \dfrac{1 \text{ mol HBr}}{71.91 \text{ g HBr}} \qquad HBr + NaClO \rightarrow HClO + NaBr$$

mol NaClO, mol HClO, mol HBr → mol NaClO, mol   HClO   then
set up stoichiometry table

Part II: Equilibrium:
mol NaClO, mol HClO, L, K_a →   pH

$$pH = pK_a + \log \dfrac{[base]}{[acid]}$$

Solution: $100.0 \text{ mL} \times \dfrac{1 \text{ L}}{1000 \text{ mL}} = 0.1000 \text{ L}$ then $\dfrac{0.175 \text{ mol HClO}}{1 \text{ L}} \times 0.1000 \text{ L} = 0.0175 \text{ mol HClO}$ and

$\dfrac{0.150 \text{ mol NaClO}}{1 \text{ L}} \times 0.1000 \text{ L} = 0.0150 \text{ mol NaClO}$ and

$150.0 \text{ mg HBr} \times \dfrac{1 \text{ g HBr}}{1000 \text{ mg HBr}} \times \dfrac{1 \text{ mol HBr}}{71.91 \text{ g HBr}} = 0.002086 \text{ mol HBr}$ then set up table to track changes:

	HBr (aq) +	NaClO (aq) →	HClO (aq) +	NaBr (aq)
Before addition	$\approx$ 0.00 mol	0.0150 mol	0.0175 mol	0.00 mol
Addition	0.002086 mol	–	–	–
After addition	$\approx$ 0.00 mol	0.0129 mol	0.0196 mol	0.002086 mol

Since the amount of HBr is small, there are still significant amounts of both buffer components, so the Henderson-Hasselbalch Equation can be used to calculate the new pH.

$$pH = pK_a + \log \dfrac{[base]}{[acid]} = -\log(2.9 \times 10^{-8}) + \log \dfrac{\dfrac{0.0129 \text{ mol}}{0.1000 \text{ L}}}{\dfrac{0.0196 \text{ mol}}{0.1000 \text{ L}}} = 7.36$$.

Check: The units (none) are correct. The magnitude of the answer makes physical sense because the pH dropped slightly when acid was added. The pH is closer to the pK_a of the acid than at the start.

c) **Given:** 100.0 mL buffer 0.175 M HClO and 0.150 M NaClO, add 85.0 mg NaOH   **Find:** pH
Other: K_a (HClO) $= 2.9 \times 10^{-8}$
Conceptual Plan: Part I: Stoichiometry:
mL → L   then   [NaClO], L → mol NaClO and [HClO], L → mol HClO and

$$\dfrac{1 \text{ L}}{1000 \text{ mL}} \qquad\qquad M = \dfrac{mol}{L} \qquad\qquad M = \dfrac{mol}{L}$$

mg NaOH → g   NaOH → mol NaOH   the write balanced equation   then

$$\dfrac{1 \text{ g NaOH}}{1000 \text{ mg NaOH}} \qquad \dfrac{1 \text{ mol NaOH}}{40.00 \text{ g NaOH}} \qquad NaOH + HClO \rightarrow H_2O + NaClO$$

mol NaClO, mol HClO, mol NaOH → mol NaClO, mol   HClO   then
set up stoichiometry table

Part II: Equilibrium:
mol NaClO, mol HClO, L, K_a →   pH

$$pH = pK_a + \log \dfrac{[base]}{[acid]}$$

Solution: $100.0 \text{ mL} \times \dfrac{1 \text{ L}}{1000 \text{ mL}} = 0.1000 \text{ L}$ then $\dfrac{0.175 \text{ mol HClO}}{1 \text{ L}} \times 0.1000 \text{ L} = 0.0175 \text{ mol HClO}$ and

$\dfrac{0.150 \text{ mol NaClO}}{1 \text{ L}} \times 0.1000 \text{ L} = 0.0150 \text{ mol NaClO}$ and

$85.0 \text{ mg NaOH} \times \dfrac{1 \text{ g NaOH}}{1000 \text{ mg NaOH}} \times \dfrac{1 \text{ mol NaOH}}{40.00 \text{ g NaOH}} = 0.00213 \text{ mol NaOH}$ then set up table to track

$$NaOH\ (aq)\ +\ HClO\ (aq)\ \rightarrow\ NaClO\ (aq)\ +\ H_2O\ (l)$$

changes:

	NaOH	HClO	NaClO	H₂O
Before addition	≈ 0.00 mol	0.0175 mol	0.0150 mol	–
Addition	0.00213 mol	–	–	–
After addition	≈ 0.00 mol	0.0154 mol	0.0171 mol	–

Since the amount of NaOH is small, there are still significant amounts of both buffer components, so the Henderson-Hasselbalch Equation can be used to calculate the new pH.

$$pH = pK_a + \log \frac{[\text{base}]}{[\text{acid}]} = -\log(2.9 \times 10^{-8}) + \log \frac{\dfrac{0.0171 \text{ mol}}{0.1000 \text{ L}}}{\dfrac{0.0154 \text{ mol}}{0.1000 \text{ L}}} = 7.58\ .$$

Check: The units (none) are correct. The magnitude of the answer makes physical sense because the pH rose slightly when base was added.

49. a) **Given:** 500.0 mL pure water **Find:** initial pH and after adding 0.010 mol HCl
   Conceptual Plan:
   pure water has a pH of 7.00   then mL → L then mol HCl, L → $[H_3O^+]$ → pH

   $$\dfrac{1 \text{ L}}{1000 \text{ mL}} \qquad M = \dfrac{\text{mol}}{\text{L}} \qquad pH = -\log [H_3O^+]$$

   Solution: pure water has a pH of 7.00   so initial pH = 7.00   then $500.0 \text{ mL} \times \dfrac{1 \text{ L}}{1000 \text{ mL}} = 0.5000 \text{ L}$

   then $M = \dfrac{\text{mol}}{\text{L}} = \dfrac{0.010 \text{ mol HCl}}{0.5000 \text{ L}} = 0.020 \text{ M HCl}$.   Since HCl is a strong acid, it dissociates completely,

   so $pH = -\log [H_3O^+] = -\log (0.020) = 1.70$.

   Check: The units (none) are correct. The magnitudes of the answers make physical sense because the pH starts neutral and then dropped significantly when acid is added and there is no buffer present.

b) **Given:** 500.0 mL buffer 0.125 M $HC_2H_3O_2$ and 0.115 M $NaC_2H_3O_2$
    Find: initial pH and after adding 0.010 mol HCl   **Other:** $K_a\ (HC_2H_3O_2) = 1.8 \times 10^{-5}$
   Conceptual Plan: initial pH:
   identify acid and base components   then   M $NaC_2H_3O_2$ → M $C_2H_3O_2^-$ then
   acid = $HC_2H_3O_2$ base = $C_2H_3O_2^-$ $NaC_2H_3O_2\ (aq) \rightarrow Na^+\ (aq) + C_2H_3O_2^-\ (aq)$
   M $HC_2H_3O_2$, M $C_2H_3O_2^-$ → pH

   $$pH = pK_a + \log \frac{[\text{base}]}{[\text{acid}]}$$

   pH after HCl addition: Part I: Stoichiometry:
   mL → L   then [$NaC_2H_3O_2$], L → mol $NaC_2H_3O_2$ and   [$HC_2H_3O_2$], L → mol $HC_2H_3O_2$

   $$\dfrac{1 \text{ L}}{1000 \text{ mL}} \qquad\qquad M = \dfrac{\text{mol}}{\text{L}} \qquad\qquad M = \dfrac{\text{mol}}{\text{L}}$$

   write balanced equation then
   $HCl + NaC_2H_3O_2 \rightarrow HC_2H_3O_2 + NaCl$
   mol $NaC_2H_3O_2$, mol $HC_2H_3O_2$, mol HCl → mol $NaC_2H_3O_2$, mol $HC_2H_3O_2$ then
   set up stoichiometry table
   Part II: Equilibrium:
   mol $NaC_2H_3O_2$, mol $HC_2H_3O_2$, L, K_a → pH

   $$pH = pK_a + \log \frac{[\text{base}]}{[\text{acid}]}$$

   Solution: initial pH: Acid $= HC_2H_3O_2$, so [acid] = [$HC_2H_3O_2$] = 0.125 M. Base = $C_2H_3O_2^-$. Since 1 $C_2H_3O_2^-$ ion is generated for each $NaC_2H_3O_2$, [$C_2H_3O_2^-$] = 0.115 M $C_2H_3O_2^-$ = [base]. then

$pH = pK_a + \log \dfrac{[base]}{[acid]} = -\log(1.8 \times 10^{-5}) + \log \dfrac{0.115 \text{ M}}{0.125 \text{ M}} = 4.71$. pH after HCl addition:

$500.0 \text{ mL} \times \dfrac{1 \text{ L}}{1000 \text{ mL}} = 0.5000 \text{ L}$ then $\dfrac{0.125 \text{ mol HC}_2\text{H}_3\text{O}_2}{1 \text{ L}} \times 0.5000 \text{ L} = 0.0625 \text{ mol HC}_2\text{H}_3\text{O}_2$ and

$\dfrac{0.115 \text{ mol NaC}_2\text{H}_3\text{O}_2}{1 \text{ L}} \times 0.5000 \text{ L} = 0.0575 \text{ mol NaC}_2\text{H}_3\text{O}_2$ set up table to track changes:

$$HCl \, (aq) + NaC_2H_3O_2 \, (aq) \rightarrow HC_2H_3O_2 \, (aq) + NaCl \, (aq)$$

	HCl	NaC₂H₃O₂	HC₂H₃O₂	NaCl
Before addition	$\approx$ 0.00 mol	0.0575 mol	0.0625 mol	0.00 mol
Addition	0.010 mol	–	–	–
After addition	$\approx$ 0.00 mol	0.0475 mol	0.0725 mol	0.010 mol

Since the amount of HCl is small, there are still significant amounts of both buffer components, so the Henderson-Hasselbalch Equation can be used to

calculate the new pH. $pH = pK_a + \log \dfrac{[base]}{[acid]} = -\log(1.8 \times 10^{-5}) + \log \dfrac{\dfrac{0.0475 \text{ mol}}{0.5000 \text{ L}}}{\dfrac{0.0725 \text{ mol}}{0.5000 \text{ L}}} = 4.56$.

Check: The units (none) are correct. The magnitudes of the answers make physical sense because the pH started below the pK_a of the acid and it dropped slightly when acid was added.

c) **Given**: 500.0 mL buffer 0.155 M CH₃CH₂NH₂ and 0.145 M CH₃CH₂NH₃Cl
   Find: initial pH and after adding 0.010 mol HCl   **Other**: K_b (CH₃CH₂NH₂) = 5.6×10^{-4}
   Conceptual Plan: initial pH:
   identify acid and base components then M CH₃CH₂NH₃Cl → M CH₃CH₂NH₃⁺
        acid = C₂H₅NH₃⁺ base = C₂H₅NH₂   C₂H₅NH₃Cl (aq) → C₂H₅NH₃⁺ (aq) + Cl⁻ (aq)
   and K_b → pK_b → pK_a then pK_a, M CH₃CH₂NH₂, M CH₃CH₂NH₃⁺ → pH

   $pK_b = -\log K_b$ $14 = pK_a + pK_b$ $pH = pK_a + \log \dfrac{[base]}{[acid]}$

   pH after HCl addition: Part I: Stoichiometry:
   mL → L then [CH₃CH₂NH₂], L → mol CH₃CH₂NH₂ and

   $\dfrac{1 \text{ L}}{1000 \text{ mL}}$ $M = \dfrac{\text{mol}}{\text{L}}$

   [CH₃CH₂NH₃Cl], L → mol CH₃CH₂NH₃Cl   write balanced equation   then

   $M = \dfrac{\text{mol}}{\text{L}}$ HCl + CH₃CH₂NH₂ → CH₃CH₂NH₃Cl

   mol CH₃CH₂NH₂, mol CH₃CH₂NH₃Cl, mol HCl → mol CH₃CH₂NH₂, mol CH₃CH₂NH₃Cl then
                           set up stoichiometry table

   Part II: Equilibrium:
   mol CH₃CH₂NH₂, mol CH₃CH₂NH₃Cl, L, K_a → pH

   $$pH = pK_a + \log \dfrac{[base]}{[acid]}$$

   Solution: Base = CH₃CH₂NH₂, [base] = [CH₃CH₂NH₂] = 0.155 M   Acid = CH₃CH₂NH₃⁺. Since 1 CH₃CH₂NH₃⁺ ion is generated for each CH₃CH₂NH₃Cl, [CH₃CH₂NH₃⁺] = 0.145 M CH₃CH₂NH₃⁺ = [acid]. Since K_b (CH₃CH₂NH₂) = 5.6×10^{-4}, $pK_b = -\log K_b = -\log(5.6 \times 10^{-4}) = 3.25$. Since $14 = pK_a + pK_b$, $pK_a = 14 - pK_b = 14 - 3.25 = 10.48$

   then $pH = pK_a + \log \dfrac{[base]}{[acid]} = 10.75 + \log \dfrac{0.155 \text{ M}}{0.145 \text{ M}} = 10.78$.

   pH after HCl addition: $500.0 \text{ mL} \times \dfrac{1 \text{ L}}{1000 \text{ mL}} = 0.5000 \text{ L}$ then

   $\dfrac{0.155 \text{ mol CH}_3\text{CH}_2\text{NH}_2}{1 \text{ L}} \times 0.5000 \text{ L} = 0.0775 \text{ mol CH}_3\text{CH}_2\text{NH}_2$ and

   $\dfrac{0.145 \text{ mol CH}_3\text{CH}_2\text{NH}_3\text{Cl}}{1 \text{ L}} \times 0.5000 \text{ L} = 0.0725 \text{ mol CH}_3\text{CH}_2\text{NH}_3\text{Cl}$ set up table to track changes:

$$HCl \ (aq) + CH_3CH_2NH_2 \ (aq) \ \rightarrow \ CH_3CH_2NH_3Cl \ (aq)$$

Before addition	≈ 0.00 mol	0.0775 mol	0.0725 mol
Addition	0.010 mol	–	–
After addition	≈ 0.00 mol	0.06$\underline{7}$5 mol	0.08$\underline{2}$5 mol

Since the amount of HCl is small, there are still significant amounts of both buffer components, so the Henderson-Hasselbalch Equation can be used to calculate the new pH.

$$pH = pK_a + \log \frac{[base]}{[acid]} = 10.75 + \log \frac{\dfrac{0.06\underline{7}5 \ \text{mol}}{0.5000 \ \text{L}}}{\dfrac{0.08\underline{2}5 \ \text{mol}}{0.5000 \ \text{L}}} = 10.66 \ .$$

Check: The units (none) are correct. The magnitudes of the answers make physical sense because the initial pH should be greater than the pK$_a$ of the acid because there is more base than acid and the pH drops slightly when acid is added.

50. a) **Given:** 250.0 mL pure water   **Find:** initial pH and after adding 0.010 mol NaOH
Conceptual Plan:
pure water has a pH of 7.00 then mL→ L then mol NaOH, L→ [OH⁻] → [H$_3$O⁺] → pH

$$\frac{1 \ L}{1000 \ mL} \qquad M = \frac{mol}{L} \quad K_w = [H_3O^+][OH^-] \quad pH = -\log [H_3O^+]$$

Solution: pure water has a pH of 7.00   so initial pH = 7.00   then $250.0 \ \text{mL} \times \dfrac{1 \ L}{1000 \ \text{mL}} = 0.2500 \ L$

then $M = \dfrac{mol}{L} = \dfrac{0.010 \ mol \ NaOH}{0.2500 \ L} = 0.040 \ M \ NaOH$.   Since NaOH is a strong base, it dissociates

completely, so $[OH^-] == 0.020 \ M.$ $K_w = [H_3O^+][OH^-]$ so $[H_3O^+] = \dfrac{K_w}{[OH^-]} = \dfrac{1.0 \times 10^{-14}}{0.040} = 2.5 \times 10^{-13} \ M$

and $pH = -\log [H_3O^+] = -\log (2.5 \times 10^{-13}) = 12.60$.

Check: The units (none) are correct. The magnitudes of the answers make physical sense because the pH starts neutral and then rose significantly when base is added and there is no buffer present.

b) **Given:** 250.0 mL buffer 0.195 M HCHO$_2$ and 0.275 M KCHO$_2$
Find: initial pH and after adding 0.010 mol NaOH   **Other:** K$_a$ (HCHO$_2$) = 1.8 x 10^{-4}
Conceptual Plan: initial pH:
identify acid and base components   then   M KCHO$_2$ →   M CHO$_2^-$ then
acid = HCHO$_2$ base = CHO$_2^-$ KCHO$_2$ (aq) → K⁺ (aq) + CHO$_2^-$ (aq)
M HCHO$_2$, M CHO$_2^-$ →   pH

$$pH = pK_a + \log \frac{[base]}{[acid]}$$

pH after NaOH addition: Part I: Stoichiometry:
mL →   L   then [KCHO$_2$], L → mol KCHO$_2$ and   [HCHO$_2$], L → mol HCHO$_2$

$$\frac{1 \ L}{1000 \ mL} \qquad\qquad M = \frac{mol}{L} \qquad\qquad M = \frac{mol}{L}$$

write balanced equation   then
NaOH + HCHO$_2$ → NaCHO$_2$+ H$_2$O
mol CHO$_2^-$, mol HCHO$_2$, mol NaOH → mol NaCHO$_2$, mol   HCHO$_2$ then
set up stoichiometry table
Part II: Equilibrium:
mol NaC$_2$H$_3$O$_2$, mol HC$_2$H$_3$O$_2$, L, K$_a$ →   pH

$$pH = pK_a + \log \frac{[base]}{[acid]}$$

Solution: initial pH: Acid = HCHO$_2$, so [acid] = [HCHO$_2$] = 0.195 M. Base = CHO$_2^-$.
Since 1 CHO$_2^-$ ion is generated for each KCHO$_2$, [CHO$_2^-$] = 0.275 M CHO$_2^-$ = [base]. then

$$pH = pK_a + \log \frac{[base]}{[acid]} = -\log (1.8 \times 10^{-4}) + \log \frac{0.275 \ M}{0.195 \ M} = 3.89 \ .$$

pH after NaOH addition: $250.0 \ \text{mL} \times \dfrac{1 \ L}{1000 \ \text{mL}} = 0.2500 \ L$ then

$$\frac{0.195 \text{ mol HCHO}_2}{1 \text{ L}} \times 0.2500 \text{ L} = 0.048\underline{7}5 \text{ mol HCHO}_2 \text{ and}$$

$$\frac{0.275 \text{ mol KCHO}_2}{1 \text{ L}} \times 0.2500 \text{ L} = 0.068\underline{7}5 \text{ mol KCHO}_2$$

set up table to track changes:

	NaOH (aq) +	HCHO$_2$ (aq) $\rightarrow$	NaCHO$_2$ (aq) +	H$_2$O (l)
Before addition	≈ 0.00 mol	0.04875 mol	0.06875 mol	–
Addition	0.010 mol	–	–	–
After addition	≈ 0.00 mol	0.02875 mol	0.07875 mol	–

Since the amount of NaOH is small, there are still significant amounts of both buffer components, so the Henderson-Hasselbalch Equation can be used to calculate the new pH.

$$pH = pK_a + \log \frac{[\text{base}]}{[\text{acid}]} = -\log(1.8 \times 10^{-4}) + \log \frac{\dfrac{0.07875 \text{ mol}}{0.2500 \text{ L}}}{\dfrac{0.02875 \text{ mol}}{0.2500 \text{ L}}} = 4.18 .$$

Check: The units (none) are correct. The magnitudes of the answers make physical sense because the pH started below the pK_a of the acid and it dropped slightly when acid was added.

c) **Given**: 250.0 mL buffer 0.255 M CH$_3$CH$_2$NH$_2$ and 0.235 M CH$_3$CH$_2$NH$_3$Cl
Find: initial pH and after adding 0.010 mol NaOH   **Other**: K$_b$ (CH$_3$CH$_2$NH$_2$) = 5.6 x 10^{-4}
Conceptual Plan: initial pH:
identify acid and base components   **then M CH$_3$CH$_2$NH$_3$Cl** $\rightarrow$ **M CH$_3$CH$_2$NH$_3^+$**
     acid = C$_2$H$_5$NH$_3^+$ base = C$_2$H$_5$NH$_2$ C$_2$H$_5$NH$_3$Cl (aq) $\rightarrow$ C$_2$H$_5$NH$_3^+$ (aq) + Cl$^-$ (aq)
and K$_b$ $\rightarrow$ **pK$_b$** $\rightarrow$ **pK$_a$** **then pK$_a$, M CH$_3$CH$_2$NH$_2$, M CH$_3$CH$_2$NH$_3^+$** $\rightarrow$ **pH**

$$pK_b = -\log K_b \qquad 14 = pK_a + pK_b \qquad\qquad\qquad pH = pK_a + \log \frac{[\text{base}]}{[\text{acid}]}$$

pH after NaOH addition: Part I: Stoichiometry:
mL $\rightarrow$ **L**   **then**   **[CH$_3$CH$_2$NH$_2$], L** $\rightarrow$ **mol CH$_3$CH$_2$NH$_2$**   **and**

$$\frac{1 \text{ L}}{1000 \text{ mL}} \qquad\qquad M = \frac{\text{mol}}{\text{L}}$$

[CH$_3$CH$_2$NH$_3$Cl], L $\rightarrow$ **mol CH$_3$CH$_2$NH$_3$Cl**

$$M = \frac{\text{mol}}{\text{L}}$$

write balanced equation   **then**
NaOH + CH$_3$CH$_2$NH$_3$Cl $\rightarrow$ CH$_3$CH$_2$NH$_2$ + NaCl + H$_2$O
mol CH$_3$CH$_2$NH$_2$, mol CH$_3$CH$_2$NH$_3$Cl, mol NaOH $\rightarrow$ **mol CH$_3$CH$_2$NH$_2$, mol CH$_3$CH$_2$NH$_3$Cl**
                                 set up stoichiometry table
Part II: Equilibrium:
mol CH$_3$CH$_2$NH$_2$, mol CH$_3$CH$_2$NH$_3$Cl, L, K$_a$ $\rightarrow$ **pH**

$$pH = pK_a + \log \frac{[\text{base}]}{[\text{acid}]}$$

Solution: Base = CH$_3$CH$_2$NH$_2$, [base] = [CH$_3$CH$_2$NH$_2$] = 0.255 M   Acid = CH$_3$CH$_2$NH$_3^+$. Since 1 CH$_3$CH$_2$NH$_3^+$ ion is generated for each CH$_3$CH$_2$NH$_3$Cl, [CH$_3$CH$_2$NH$_3^+$] = 0.235 M CH$_3$CH$_2$NH$_3^+$ = [acid]. Since K$_b$ (CH$_3$CH$_2$NH$_2$) = 5.6 x 10^{-4}, $pK_b = -\log K_b = -\log(5.6 \times 10^{-4}) = 3.25$. Since $14 = pK_a + pK_b$, $pK_a = 14 - pK_b = 14 - 3.25 = 10.48$ then

$$pH = pK_a + \log \frac{[\text{base}]}{[\text{acid}]} = 10.75 + \log \frac{0.255 \text{ M}}{0.235 \text{ M}} = 10.79 .$$

pH after HCl addition: $250.0 \text{ mL} \times \dfrac{1 \text{ L}}{1000 \text{ mL}} = 0.2500 \text{ L}$ then

$$\frac{0.255 \text{ mol CH}_3\text{CH}_2\text{NH}_2}{1 \text{ L}} \times 0.2500 \text{ L} = 0.063\underline{7}5 \text{ mol CH}_3\text{CH}_2\text{NH}_2 \text{ and}$$

$$\frac{0.235 \text{ mol CH}_3\text{CH}_2\text{NH}_3\text{Cl}}{1 \text{ L}} \times 0.2500 \text{ L} = 0.058\underline{7}5 \text{ mol CH}_3\text{CH}_2\text{NH}_3\text{Cl} \text{ set up table to track changes:}$$

$$NaOH\,(aq) + CH_3CH_2NH_3Cl\,(aq) \rightarrow CH_3CH_2NH_2\,(aq) + NaCl\,(aq) + H_2O\,(aq)$$

Before addition	$\approx$ 0.00 mol	0.05875 mol		0.06375 mol	0.00 mol	–
Addition	0.010 mol	–		–	–	–
After addition	$\approx$ 0.00 mol	0.04875 mol		0.07375 mol		

Since the amount of NaOH is small, there are still significant amounts of both buffer components, so the Henderson-Hasselbalch Equation can be used to calculate the new pH.

$$pH = pK_a + \log \frac{[base]}{[acid]} = 10.75 + \log \frac{\dfrac{0.07375\ mol}{0.2500\ L}}{\dfrac{0.04875\ mol}{0.2500\ L}} = 10.93 \,.$$

Check: The units (none) are correct. The magnitudes of the answers make physical sense because the initial pH should be greater than the pK_a of the acid because there is more base than acid and the pH rises slightly when base is added.

51. **Given:** 350.00 mL 0.150 M HF and 0.150 M NaF buffer
    Find: mass NaOH to raise pH to 4.00 and mass NaOH to raise pH to 4.00 with buffer concentrations raised to 0.350 M
    Other: K_a (HF) = 3.5 x 10^{-4}
    Conceptual Plan: identify acid and base components   Since [NaF] = [HF]   then initial   pH = pK_a.

    acid = HF base = F⁻   pH = pK_a

    final pH, pK_a $\rightarrow$ [NaF]/[HF] and mL $\rightarrow$ L then [HF], L $\rightarrow$ mol HF and [NaF], L $\rightarrow$ mol NaF

    $pH = pK_a + \log \dfrac{[base]}{[acid]}$ $\dfrac{1\ L}{1000\ mL}$ $M = \dfrac{mol}{L}$ $M = \dfrac{mol}{L}$

    then   write balanced equation   then
    $$NaOH + HF \rightarrow NaF + H_2O$$
    mol HF, mol NaF, [NaF]/[HF] $\rightarrow$ mol NaOH $\rightarrow$ g NaOH

    set up stoichiometry table $\dfrac{40.00\ g\ NaOH}{1\ mol\ NaOH}$

    Finally, when the buffer concentrations are raised to 0.350 M, simply multiply the g NaOH by ratio of concentrations (0.350 M / 0.150 M).

    Solution: initial $pH = pK_a = -\log(3.5\ x\ 10^{-4}) = 3.64$ then

    $$pH = pK_a + \log \frac{[base]}{[acid]} = -\log(3.5\ x\ 10^{-4}) + \log \frac{[NaF]}{[HF]} = 4.00 \,. \text{ Solve for [NaF] / [HF]}.$$

    $\log \dfrac{[NaF]}{[HF]} = 4.00 - 3.46 = 0.54$ $\rightarrow$ $\dfrac{[NaF]}{[HF]} = 10^{0.54} = 3.5$. $350.0\ mL$ x $\dfrac{1\ L}{1000\ mL} = 0.3500\ L$ then

    $\dfrac{0.150\ mol\ HF}{1\ L}$ x $0.3500\ L = 0.0525\ mol\ HF$ and $\dfrac{0.150\ mol\ NaF}{1\ L}$ x $0.3500\ L = 0.0525\ mol\ NaF$

    set up table to track changes:

	NaOH (aq)	+ HF (aq)	$\rightarrow$ NaF (aq)	+ H₂O (aq)
Before addition	0.00 mol	0.0525 mol	0.0525 mol	–
Addition	x	–	–	–
After addition	$\approx$ 0.00 mol	$(0.0525 - x)$ mol	$(0.0525 + x)$ mol	–

    Since $\dfrac{[NaF]}{[HF]} = 3.5 = \dfrac{(0.0525 + x)\ mol}{(0.0525 - x)\ mol}$, solve for x. Note that the ratio of moles is the same as the ratio of

    concentrations, since the volume for both terms is the same. $3.5\,(0.0525 - x) = (0.0525 + x)$ $\rightarrow$

    $0.18375 - 3.5\,x = 0.0525 + x$ $\rightarrow$ $0.13125 = 4.5\,x$ $\rightarrow$ $x = 0.029167$ mol NaOH then

    $0.029167\ mol\ NaOH$ x $\dfrac{40.00\ g\ NaOH}{1\ mol\ NaOH} = 1.1667\ g\ NaOH = 1.2\ g\ NaOH$. Finally multiply the NaOH mass by the

    ratio of concentrations $1.1667\ g\ NaOH$ x $\dfrac{0.350\ M}{0.150\ M} = 2.7\ g\ NaOH$.

Check: The units (g) are correct. The magnitudes of the answers make physical sense because there is much less than a mole of each of the buffer components, so there must be much less than a mole of NaOH. The higher the buffer concentrations, the higher the buffer capacity and the mass of NaOH it can neutralize.

52. **Given:** 100.00 mL 0.100 M NH_3 and 0.125 M NH_4Br buffer
   Find: mass HCl to lower pH to 9.00 and mass HCl to lower pH to 9.00 with buffer concentrations raised to 0.250 M NH_3 and 0.400 M NH_4Br
   Other: $K_b (NH_3) = 1.79 \times 10^{-5}$
   Conceptual Plan: identify acid and base components   then $K_b \rightarrow pK_b \rightarrow pK_a$ then

$$acid = NH_4^+ \quad base = NH_3 \qquad\qquad pK_b = -\log K_b \qquad 14 = pK_a + pK_b$$

final pH, $pK_a \rightarrow [NH_3]/[NH_4^+]$ and mL $\rightarrow$ L then $[NH_3]$, L $\rightarrow$ mol NH_3 and

$$pH = pK_a + \log \frac{[base]}{[acid]} \qquad\qquad \frac{1\ L}{1000\ mL} \qquad\qquad M = \frac{mol}{L}$$

$[NH_4^+]$, L $\rightarrow$ mol NH_4^+

$$M = \frac{mol}{L}$$

then   write balanced equation   then

$$H^+ + NH_3 \rightarrow NH_4^+$$

mol NH_3, mol NH_4^+, $[NH_3]/[NH_4^+] \rightarrow$ mol HCl $\rightarrow$ g HCl

$$set\ up\ stoichiometry\ table \qquad \frac{36.46\ g\ HCl}{1\ mol\ HCl}$$

Solution: Since $K_b (NH_3) = 1.79 \times 10^{-5}$, $pK_b = -\log K_b = -\log (1.79 \times 10^{-5}) = 4.75$. Since $14 = pK_a + pK_b$,

$$pK_a = 14 - pK_b = 14 - 4.75 = 9.25 \text{ then } pH = pK_a + \log \frac{[base]}{[acid]} = 9.25 + \log \frac{[NH_3]}{[NH_4^+]} = 9.00.$$

Solve for $[NH_4Br]$. $\log \dfrac{[NH_3]}{[NH_4^+]} = 9.00 - 9.25 = -0.25 \rightarrow \dfrac{[NH_3]}{[NH_4^+]} = 10^{-0.25} = 0.562341$.

$100.0\ mL \times \dfrac{1\ L}{1000\ mL} = 0.1000\ L$ then $\dfrac{0.100\ mol\ NH_3}{1\ L} \times 0.1000\ L = 0.0100\ mol\ NH_3$ and

$\dfrac{0.125\ mol\ NH_4Br}{1\ L} \times 0.1000\ L = 0.0125\ mol\ NH_4Br = 0.0125\ mol\ NH_4^+$ Since HCl is a strong acid, $[HCl] = [H^+]$,

and set up table to track changes:

	H^+ (aq)	+	NH_3 (aq)	$\rightarrow$	NH_4^+ (aq)
Before addition	$\approx$ 0.00 mol		0.0100 mol		0.0125 mol
Addition	x		–		–
After addition	$\approx$ 0.00 mol		(0.0100 – x) mol		(0.0125 + x) mol

Since $\dfrac{[NH_3]}{[NH_4^+]} = 0.562341 = \dfrac{(0.0100 - x)\ mol}{(0.0125 + x)\ mol}$, solve for x. Note that the ratio of moles is the same as the

ratio of concentrations, since the volume for both terms is the same. $0.562341(0.0125 + x) = (0.0100 - x) \rightarrow$
$0.00702926 + 0.562341x = 0.0100 - x \rightarrow 1.562341x = 0.0029707 \rightarrow x = 0.0019015\ mol\ HCl$ then

$0.0019015\ mol\ HCl \times \dfrac{36.46\ g\ HCl}{1\ mol\ HCl} = 0.06932\ g\ HCl = 0.07\ g\ HCl$. For the higher concentration buffer, repeat

part of the above calculations. $\dfrac{0.250\ mol\ NH_3}{1\ L} \times 0.1000\ L = 0.0250\ mol\ NH_3$ and

$\dfrac{0.400\ mol\ NH_4Br}{1\ L} \times 0.1000\ L = 0.0400\ mol\ NH_4Br = 0.0400\ mol\ NH_4^+$ Since HCl is a strong acid, $[HCl] = [H^+]$,

and set up table to track changes:

	H^+ (aq)	+	NH_3 (aq)	$\rightarrow$	NH_4^+ (aq)
Before addition	$\approx$ 0.00 mol		0.0250 mol		0.0400 mol
Addition	x		–		–
After addition	$\approx$ 0.00 mol		(0.0250 – x) mol		(0.0400 + x) mol

Since $\dfrac{[NH_3]}{[NH_4^+]} = 0.562341 = \dfrac{(0.0250 - x)\ mol}{(0.0400 + x)\ mol}$, solve for x. Note that the ration of moles is the same as the

ratio of concentrations, since the volume for both terms is the same. $0.562341(0.0400 + x) = (0.0250 - x) \rightarrow$
$0.0224936 + 0.562341x = 0.0250 - x \rightarrow 1.562341x = 0.00250636 \rightarrow x = 0.0016042\ mol\ HCl$ then

$0.0016042\ mol\ HCl \times \dfrac{36.46\ g\ HCl}{1\ mol\ HCl} = 0.058490\ g\ HCl = 0.06\ g\ HCl$.

Check: The units (g) are correct. The magnitudes of the answers make physical sense because there is much less than a mole of each of the buffer components, so there must be much less than a mole of HCl. Also, the pH of the initial buffer is less than the pK_a of the acid, so even less acid is necessary to drop the pH below 9.00. The higher concentration buffer solution requires about the same amount of acid because the initial pH of this buffer is closer to 9.00 than the low concentration buffer.

53. a) Yes, this will be a buffer because NH_3 is a weak base and NH_4^+ is its conjugate acid. The ratio of base to acid is $0.10/0.15 = 0.67$, so the pH will be within 1 pH unit of the pK_a.

    b) No, this will not be a buffer solution because HCl is a strong acid and NaOH is a strong base.

    c) Yes, this will be a buffer because HF is a weak acid and the NaOH will convert $20.0/50.0 = 40$ % of the acid to its conjugate base.

    d) No, this will not be a buffer solution because both components are bases.

    e) No, this will not be a buffer solution because both components are bases.

54. a) Yes, this will be a buffer because HF is a weak acid and F^- is its conjugate base. The ratio of base to acid is $(55.0 \times 0.15)/(75.0 \times 0.10) = 1.1$, so the pH will be within 1 pH unit of the pK_a.

    b) No, this will not be a buffer solution because both components are acids.

    c) Yes, this will be a buffer because HF is a weak acid and the KOH will convert $(135.0 \times 0.050)/(165.0 \times 0.10) = 41$ % of the acid to its conjugate base.

    d) Yes, this will be a buffer because CH_3NH_2 is a weak base and $CH_3NH_3^+$ is its conjugate acid. The ratio of base to acid is $(125.0 \times 0.15)/(120.0 \times 0.25) = 0.63$, so the pH will be within 1 pH unit of the pK_a.

    e) Yes, this will be a buffer because CH_3NH_2 is a weak base and the HCl will convert $(95.0 \times 0.10)/(105.0 \times 0.15) = 60$ % of the base to its conjugate acid.

55. a) **Given:** blood buffer 0.024 M HCO_3^- and 0.0012 M H_2CO_3, $pK_a = 6.1$ **Find:** initial pH
    Conceptual Plan: identify acid and base components   then   M HCO_3^- , M H_2CO_3 $\rightarrow$ pH

    $$\text{acid} = H_2CO_3 \quad \text{base} = HCO_3^- \qquad\qquad pH = pK_a + \log \frac{[\text{base}]}{[\text{acid}]}$$

    Solution: Acid $= H_2CO_3$, so [acid] $= [H_2CO_3] = 0.0012$ M. Base $= HCO_3^-$, so [base] $= [HCO_3^-] =$ 0.024 M HCO_3^-. Then $pH = pK_a + \log \dfrac{[\text{base}]}{[\text{acid}]} = 6.1 + \log \dfrac{0.024 \text{ M}}{0.0012 \text{ M}} = 7.4$.

    Check: The units (none) are correct. The magnitude of the answer makes physical sense because pH is greater than the pK_a of the acid because there is more base than acid.

    b) **Given:** 5.0 L of blood buffer   **Find:** mass HCl to lower pH to 7.0
    Conceptual Plan: final pH, pK_a $\rightarrow$ $[HCO_3^-]/[H_2CO_3]$ then $[HCO_3^-]$, L $\rightarrow$ mol HCO_3^- and

    $$pH = pK_a + \log \frac{[\text{base}]}{[\text{acid}]} \qquad\qquad\qquad M = \frac{\text{mol}}{L}$$

    $[H_2CO_3]$, L $\rightarrow$ mol H_2CO_3 then   write balanced equation   then

    $$M = \frac{\text{mol}}{L} \qquad\qquad H^+ + HCO_3^- \rightarrow H_2CO_3$$

    mol HCO_3^-, mol H_2CO_3, $[HCO_3^-]/[H_2CO_3]$ $\rightarrow$ mol HCl $\rightarrow$ g HCl

    $$\text{set up stoichiometry table} \qquad \frac{36.46 \text{ g HCl}}{1 \text{ mol HCl}}$$

    Solution: $pH = pK_a + \log \dfrac{[\text{base}]}{[\text{acid}]} = 6.1 + \log \dfrac{[HCO_3^-]}{[H_2CO_3]} = 7.0$. Solve for $[HCO_3^-]/[H_2CO_3]$.

    $$\log \frac{[HCO_3^-]}{[H_2CO_3]} = 7.0 - 6.1 = 0.9 \;\rightarrow\; \frac{[HCO_3^-]}{[H_2CO_3]} = 10^{0.9} = 7.9433.$$

Then $\dfrac{0.024 \text{ mol HCO}_3^-}{1 \text{ L}}$ x 5.0 L = 0.12 mol HCO$_3^-$ and $\dfrac{0.0012 \text{ mol H}_2\text{CO}_3}{1 \text{ L}}$ x 5.0 L = 0.0060 mol H$_2$CO$_3$ Since

HCl is a strong acid, [HCl] = [H$^+$], and set up table to track changes:

$$\text{H}^+ \ (aq) \ + \ \text{HCO}_3^- \ (aq) \ \rightarrow \ \text{H}_2\text{CO}_3 \ (aq)$$

Before addition	≈ 0.00 mol	0.12 mol	0.0060 mol
Addition	x	–	–
After addition	≈ 0.00 mol	(0.12 – x) mol	(0.0060 + x) mol

Since $\dfrac{[\text{HCO}_3^-]}{[\text{H}_2\text{CO}_3]} = 7.9433 = \dfrac{(0.12 - x) \text{ mol}}{(0.0060 + x) \text{ mol}}$, solve for x. Note that the ration of moles is the same as

the ratio of concentrations, since the volume for both terms is the same. $7.9433(0.0060 + x) = (0.12 - x)$

→ $0.0476598 + 7.9433x = 0.12 - x$ → $8.9433x = 0.07234$ → $x = 0.0080888$ mol HCl then

$0.0080888 \text{ mol HCl}$ x $\dfrac{36.46 \text{ g HCl}}{1 \text{ mol HCl}}$ = 0.29492 g HCl = 0.3 g HCl .

Check: The units (g) are correct. The amount of acid needed is small because the concentrations of the buffer components are very low and the buffer starts only 0.4 pH units above the final pH.

c) **Given:** 5.0 L of blood buffer   **Find:** mass NaOH to raise pH to 7.8
Conceptual Plan: final pH, pK$_a$ → [HCO$_3^-$]/[H$_2$CO$_3$] then **[HCO$_3^-$], L → mol HCO$_3^-$** and

$$\text{pH} = \text{pK}_a + \log \dfrac{[\text{base}]}{[\text{acid}]} \qquad\qquad\qquad M = \dfrac{\text{mol}}{L}$$

[H$_2$CO$_3$], L → mol H$_2$CO$_3$ then   **write balanced equation**   then

$$M = \dfrac{\text{mol}}{L} \qquad\qquad \text{OH}^- + \text{H}_2\text{CO}_3 \rightarrow \text{HCO}_3^- + \text{H}_2\text{O}$$

mol HCO$_3^-$, mol H$_2$CO$_3$, [HCO$_3^-$]/[H$_2$CO$_3$] → mol NaOH → g NaOH

$$\text{set up stoichiometry table} \qquad \dfrac{40.00 \text{ g NaOH}}{1 \text{ mol NaOH}}$$

Solution: $\text{pH} = \text{pK}_a + \log \dfrac{[\text{base}]}{[\text{acid}]} = 6.1 + \log \dfrac{[\text{HCO}_3^-]}{[\text{H}_2\text{CO}_3]} = 7.8$.

Solve for [HCO$_3^-$]/[H$_2$CO$_3$]. $\log \dfrac{[\text{HCO}_3^-]}{[\text{H}_2\text{CO}_3]} = 7.8 - 6.1 = 1.7$ → $\dfrac{[\text{HCO}_3^-]}{[\text{H}_2\text{CO}_3]} = 10^{1.7} = 50.11872$. then

$\dfrac{0.024 \text{ mol HCO}_3^-}{1 \text{ L}}$ x 5.0 L = 0.12 mol HCO$_3^-$ and $\dfrac{0.0012 \text{ mol H}_2\text{CO}_3}{1 \text{ L}}$ x 5.0 L = 0.0060 mol H$_2$CO$_3$ Since

NaOH is a strong base, [NaOH] = [OH$^-$], and set up table to track changes:

$$\text{OH}^- \ (aq) \ + \ \text{H}_2\text{CO}_3 \ (aq) \ \rightarrow \ \text{HCO}_3^- \ (aq) + \text{H}_2\text{O} \ (l)$$

Before addition	≈ 0.00 mol	0.0060 mol	0.12 mol	–
Addition	x	–	–	
After addition	≈ 0.00 mol	(0.0060 – x) mol	(0.12 + x) mol	

Since $\dfrac{[\text{HCO}_3^-]}{[\text{H}_2\text{CO}_3]} = 50.11872 = \dfrac{(0.12 + x) \text{ mol}}{(0.0060 - x) \text{ mol}}$, solve for x. Note that the ration of moles is the same as

the ratio of concentrations, since the volume for both terms is the same.
$50.11872(0.0060 - x) = (0.12 + x)$ → $0.30071 - 50.11872x = 0.12 + x$ → $51.11872x = 0.18071$ →

$x = 0.0035351$ mol NaOH then $0.0035351 \text{ mol NaOH}$ x $\dfrac{40.00 \text{ g NaOH}}{1 \text{ mol NaOH}}$ = 0.14141 g NaOH = 0.14 g NaOH .

Check: The units (g) are correct. The amount of base needed is small because the concentrations of the buffer components are very low.

56. a) **Given:** HPO$_4^{2-}$/H$_2$PO$_4^-$ buffer at pH = 7.1   **Find:** [HPO$_4^{2-}$]/[H$_2$PO$_4^-$]
Other: K$_{a2}$ (H$_3$PO$_4$) = 6.2 x 10^{-8}

Conceptual Plan: identify acid and base components then **pH, K$_a$ → [HPO$_4^{2-}$]/[H$_2$PO$_4^-$]**

$$\text{acid} = \text{H}_2\text{PO}_4^- \quad \text{base} = \text{HPO}_4^{2-} \qquad\qquad \text{pH} = \text{pK}_a + \log \dfrac{[\text{base}]}{[\text{acid}]}$$

Solution: $pH = pK_a + \log \dfrac{[base]}{[acid]} = -\log(6.2 \times 10^{-8}) + \log \dfrac{[HPO_4^{2-}]}{[H_2PO_4^-]} = 7.1$. Solve for $[HPO_4^{2-}]/[H_2PO_4^-]$.

$\log \dfrac{[HPO_4^{2-}]}{[H_2PO_4^-]} = 7.1 - 7.2 = -0.1 \quad \rightarrow \quad \dfrac{[HPO_4^{2-}]}{[H_2PO_4^-]} = 10^{-0.1} = 0.\underline{7}9433 = 0.8$.

Check: The units (none) are correct. The magnitude of the answer makes physical sense because the pH is very close, but less than, the pK_a of the acid.

b) No, H_3PO_4 and $H_2PO_4^-$ can not be used as a buffer in the cell because the K_{a1} $(H_3PO_4) = 7.5 \times 10^{-3}$ and so the $pK_{a1} = 2.1$. In order to have an effective buffer the pK_a should be within in 1 pH unit of the desired pH (not 5.0 pH units).

57. **Given:** $HC_2H_3O_2/KC_2H_3O_2$, $HClO_2/KClO_2$, NH_3/NH_4Cl, and $HClO/KClO$ potential buffer systems to create buffer at pH = 7.20   **Find:** best buffer system and ratio of component masses   **Other:** K_a $(HC_2H_3O_2) = 1.8 \times 10^{-5}$, K_a $(HClO_2) = 1.8 \times 10^{-4}$, K_b $(NH_3) = 1.79 \times 10^{-5}$, K_a $(HClO) = 2.9 \times 10^{-8}$
Conceptual Plan:
calculate p K_a of all potential buffer acids for the base $K_b \rightarrow pK_b \rightarrow pK_a$ **then**

$$pK_a = -\log K_a \qquad\qquad pK_b = -\log K_b \quad 14 = pK_a + pK_b$$

and choose the pK_a that is closest to 7.20. then pH, K_a $\rightarrow$ **[base]/[acid]** $\rightarrow$ **mass base/mass acid**

$$pH = pK_a + \log \dfrac{[base]}{[acid]} \qquad \dfrac{\mathfrak{M}\ (base)}{\mathfrak{M}\ (acid)}$$

Solution: for $HC_2H_3O_2/KC_2H_3O_2$: $pK_a = -\log K_a = -\log(1.8 \times 10^{-5}) = 4.74$; for $HClO_2/KClO_2$:

$pK_a = -\log K_a = -\log(1.8 \times 10^{-4}) = 3.74$; for NH_3/NH_4Cl: $pK_b = -\log K_b = -\log(1.79 \times 10^{-5}) = 4.75$.

Since $14 = pK_a + pK_b$, $pK_a = 14 - pK_b = 14 - 4.75 = 9.25$; and for $HClO/KClO$:

$pK_a = -\log K_a = -\log(2.9 \times 10^{-8}) = 7.54$. So the $HClO/KClO$ buffer system has the pK_a that is the closest to

7.20. So, $pH = pK_a + \log \dfrac{[base]}{[acid]} = 7.54 + \log \dfrac{[KClO]}{[HClO]} = 7.1$. Solve for [KClO]/[HClO].

$\log \dfrac{[KClO]}{[HClO]} = 7.20 - 7.54 = -0.34 \quad \rightarrow \quad \dfrac{[KClO]}{[HClO]} = 10^{-0.34} = 0.4\underline{5}7088$. Then convert to mass ratio using

$$\dfrac{\mathfrak{M}\ (base)}{\mathfrak{M}\ (acid)}, \quad 0.4\underline{5}7088 \ \dfrac{\cancel{KClO\ mol}}{\cancel{HClO\ mol}} \times \dfrac{\dfrac{90.55\ g\ KClO}{\cancel{mol\ KClO}}}{\dfrac{52.46\ g\ HClO}{\cancel{mol\ HClO}}} = 0.79 \ \dfrac{g\ KClO}{g\ HClO}$$

Check: The units (none and g base/g acid)) are correct. The buffer system with the K_a closest to 10^{-7} is the best choice. The magnitude of the answer makes physical sense because the buffer needs more acid than base (and this fact is not overcome by the heavier molar mass of the base).

58. **Given:** HF/KF, HNO_2/KNO_2, NH_3/NH_4Cl, and $HClO/KClO$ potential buffer systems to create buffer at pH = 9.00   **Find:** best buffer system and ratio of component masses
Other: K_a $(HF) = 3.5 \times 10^{-4}$, K_a $(HNO_2) = 4.6 \times 10^{-4}$, K_b $(NH_3) = 1.79 \times 10^{-5}$, K_a $(HClO) = 2.9 \times 10^{-8}$
Conceptual Plan:
calculate p K_a of all potential buffer acids for the base $K_b \rightarrow pK_b \rightarrow pK_a$ **then**

$$pK_a = -\log K_a \qquad\qquad pK_b = -\log K_b \quad 14 = pK_a + pK_b$$

and choose the pK_a that is closest to 9.00. then pH, K_a $\rightarrow$ **[base]/[acid]** $\rightarrow$ **mass base/mass acid**

$$pH = pK_a + \log \dfrac{[base]}{[acid]} \qquad \dfrac{\mathfrak{M}\ (base)}{\mathfrak{M}\ (acid)}$$

Solution: for HF/KF: $pK_a = -\log K_a = -\log(3.5 \times 10^{-4}) = 3.46$; for HNO_2/KNO_2 :

$pK_a = -\log K_a = -\log(4.6 \times 10^{-4}) = 3.34$; for NH_3/NH_4Cl: $pK_b = -\log K_b = -\log(1.79 \times 10^{-5}) = 4.75$.

Since $14 = pK_a + pK_b$, $pK_a = 14 - pK_b = 14 - 4.75 = 9.25$; and for $HClO/KClO$:

$pK_a = -\log K_a = -\log(2.9 \times 10^{-8}) = 7.54$. So the NH_3/NH_4Cl buffer system has the pK_a that is the closest to

9.00. So, $pH = pK_a + \log \dfrac{[base]}{[acid]} = 9.25 + \log \dfrac{[NH_3]}{[NH_4Cl]} = 9.00$. Solve for [NH$_3$]/[NH$_4$Cl].

$\log \dfrac{[NH_3]}{[NH_4Cl]} = 9.00 - 9.25 = -0.25 \rightarrow \dfrac{[NH_3]}{[NH_4Cl]} = 10^{-0.25} = 0.5\underline{6}2341$ .then convert to mass ratio using $\dfrac{\mathfrak{M}\ (base)}{\mathfrak{M}\ (acid)}$,

$$0.56\underline{2}341 \frac{\dfrac{NH_3 \text{ mol}}{L}}{\dfrac{NH_4Cl \text{ mol}}{L}} \times \frac{\dfrac{17.03 \text{ g } NH_3}{\text{mol } NH_3}}{\dfrac{55.49 \text{ g } NH_4Cl}{\text{mol } NH_4Cl}} = 0.17 \frac{\text{g } NH_3}{\text{g } NH_4Cl}$$

Check: The units (none and g base/g acid)) are correct. The buffer system with the K_a closest to 10^{-9} is the best choice. The magnitude of the answer makes physical sense because the buffer needs more acid than base and the acid component has a heavier molar mass, so the mass ratio is small.

59. **Given:** 500.0 mL of 0.100 M HNO_2 / 0.150 M KNO_2 buffer and a) 250 mg NaOH, b) 350 mg KOH, c) 1.25 g HBr and d) 1.35 g HI   **Find:** if buffer capacity is exceeded
Conceptual Plan:
mL → L   then $[HNO_2]$, L → mol HNO_2 and $[KNO_2]$, L → mol KNO_2 then

$\dfrac{1 \text{ L}}{1000 \text{ mL}}$ $M = \dfrac{\text{mol}}{L}$ $M = \dfrac{\text{mol}}{L}$

then calculate moles of acid or base to be added to the buffer mg → g → mol   then

$\dfrac{1 \text{ g}}{1000 \text{ mg}}$ $\mathfrak{M}$

compare the added amount to the buffer amount of the opposite component. **Ratio of base/acid must be between 0.1 and 10 to maintain the buffer integrity.**

Solution: $500.00 \text{ mL} \times \dfrac{1 \text{ L}}{1000 \text{ mL}} = 0.5000 \text{ L}$ then $\dfrac{0.100 \text{ mol } HNO_2}{1 \text{ L}} \times 0.5000 \text{ L} = 0.0500 \text{ mol } HNO_2$ and

$\dfrac{0.150 \text{ mol } KNO_2}{1 \text{ L}} \times 0.5000 \text{ L} = 0.0750 \text{ mol } KNO_2$

a) for NaOH: $250 \text{ mg NaOH} \times \dfrac{1 \text{ g NaOH}}{1000 \text{ mg NaOH}} \times \dfrac{1 \text{ mol NaOH}}{40.00 \text{ g NaOH}} = 0.006\underline{2}5 \text{ mol NaOH}$. Since the buffer

contains 0.0500 mol acid, the amount of acid is reduced by 0.00625/0.0500 = 12.5 % and the ratio of base/acid is still between 0.1and 10. The buffer capacity is not exceeded.

b) for KOH: $350 \text{ mg KOH} \times \dfrac{1 \text{ g KOH}}{1000 \text{ mg KOH}} \times \dfrac{1 \text{ mol KOH}}{56.11 \text{ g KOH}} = 0.006\underline{2}4 \text{ mol KOH}$. Since the buffer contains

0.0500 mol acid, the amount of acid is reduced by 0.00624/0.0500 = 12.5 % and the ratio of base/acid is still between 0.1 and 10. The buffer capacity is not exceeded.

c) for HBr: $1.25 \text{ g HBr} \times \dfrac{1 \text{ mol HBr}}{80.91 \text{ g HBr}} = 0.015\underline{4}496 \text{ mol HBr}$. Since the buffer contains 0.0750 mol base,

the amount of acid is reduced by 0.0154/0.0750 = 20.6 % and the ratio of base/acid is still between 0.1and 10. The buffer capacity is not exceeded.

d) for HI: $1.35 \text{ g HI} \times \dfrac{1 \text{ mol HI}}{127.91 \text{ g HI}} = 0.010\underline{5}545 \text{ mol HI}$. Since the buffer contains 0.0750 mol base, the

amount of acid is reduced by 0.0106/0.0750 = 14.1 % and the ratio of base/acid is still between 0.1 and 10. The buffer capacity is not exceeded.

60. **Given:** 1.0 L of 0.125 M HNO_2 / 0.145 M $NaNO_2$ buffer and a. 1.5 g HCl, b. 1.5 g NaOH, c. 1.5 g HI
Find: $[HNO_2]$ and $[NaNO_2]$ after addition   **Other:** K_a (HNO_2) = 4.6 x 10^{-4}
Conceptual Plan: $[HNO_2]$, L → mol HNO_2 and $[NaNO_2]$, L → mol $NaNO_2$ (= mol NO_2^-) then

$M = \dfrac{\text{mol}}{L}$ $M = \dfrac{\text{mol}}{L}$

then calculate moles of acid or base to be added to the buffer   g → mol   then
$\mathfrak{M}$

then write balanced equation then mol HNO_2, mol NO_2^-, mol added species → mol HNO_2, mol NO_2^-
$\qquad\qquad H^+ + NO_2^- \rightarrow HNO_2$ set up stoichiometry table
$\qquad\qquad OH^- + HNO_2 \rightarrow NO_2^- + H_2O$

mol HNO_2, L → $[HNO_2]$ and   mol NO_2^- (= mol $NaNO_2$), L → $[NaNO_2]$

$M = \dfrac{\text{mol}}{L}$ $M = \dfrac{\text{mol}}{L}$

Solution: $\dfrac{0.125 \text{ mol } HNO_2}{1 \text{ L}} \times 1.0 \text{ L} = 0.125 \text{ mol } HNO_2$ and $\dfrac{0.145 \text{ mol } KNO_2}{1 \text{ L}} \times 1.0 \text{ L} = 0.145 \text{ mol } KNO_2$

a) for HCl: $1.5 \text{ g HCl} \times \dfrac{1 \text{ mol HCl}}{36.46 \text{ g HCl}} = 0.041141 \text{ mol HCl}$. Since HCl is a strong acid, $[HCl] = [H^+]$, and set up table to track changes:

	H^+ (aq)	+	NO_2^- (aq)	→	HNO_2 (aq)
Before addition	≈ 0.00 mol		0.145 mol		0.125 mol
Addition	0.041141 mol		–		–
After addition	≈ 0.00 mol		0.104 mol		0.166 mol

Because the concentrations of the acid and base components have not changed much, the buffer is still able to do its job. Finally, since there is 1.0 L of solution, $[HNO_2] = 0.17 \text{ M}$ and $[NaNO_2] = 0.10 \text{ M}$.

b) for NaOH: $1.5 \text{ g NaOH} \times \dfrac{1 \text{ mol NaOH}}{40.00 \text{ g NaOH}} = 0.0375 \text{ mol NaOH}$. Since NaOH is a strong base, $[NaOH] = [OH^-]$, and set up table to track changes:

	OH^- (aq)	+	HNO_2 (aq)	→	NO_2^- (aq)	+ H_2O (l)
Before addition	≈ 0.00 mol		0.125 mol		0.145 mol	–
Addition	0.0375 mol		–		–	–
After addition	≈ 0.00 mol		0.0875 mol		0.1825 mol	–

Because the concentrations of the acid and base components have not changed much, the buffer is still able to do its job. Finally, since there is 1.0 L of solution, $[HNO_2] = 0.09 \text{ M}$ and $[NaNO_2] = 0.18 \text{ M}$.

c) for HI: $1.5 \text{ g HI} \times \dfrac{1 \text{ mol HI}}{127.91 \text{ g HI}} = 0.011727 \text{ mol HI}$. Since HI is a strong acid, $[HI] = [H^+]$, and set up table to track changes:

	H^+ (aq)	+	NO_2^- (aq)	→	HNO_2 (aq)
Before addition	≈ 0.00 mol		0.145 mol		0.125 mol
Addition	0.011727 mol		–		–
After addition	≈ 0.00 mol		0.133 mol		0.137 mol

Because the concentrations of the acid and base components have not changed much, the buffer is still able to do its job. Finally, since there is 1.0 L of solution, $[HNO_2] = 0.14 \text{ M}$ and $[NaNO_2] = 0.13 \text{ M}$.

Check: The units (M) are correct. Since the number of moles added is small compared to the buffer components, the buffer still remains active. Adding acid increases the amount of the conjugate base. Adding base increases the amount of the weak acid.

61. (i) The equivalence point of a titration is where the pH rises sharply as base is added. The pH as the equivalence point is the midpoint of the sharp rise at ~ 50 mL added base. For (a) the pH = ~ 8 and for (b) the pH = ~ 7.

(ii) Graph (a) represents a weak acid and graph (b) represents a strong acid. A strong acid titration starts at a lower pH, has a flatter initial region and a sharper rise at the equivalence point than a weak acid. The pH at the equivalence point of a strong acid is neutral, while the pH at the equivalence point of a weak acid is basic.

62. **Given:** 25.0 mL 0.100 M HCl and 0.100 M HF titrated with 0.200 M KOH
a) **Find:** volume of base to reach equivalence point
Conceptual Plan: The answer for both titrations will be the same since the initial concentration and volumes of the acids are the same and both acids are monoprotic. Write balanced equation

$HCl + KOH \rightarrow KCl + H_2O$ and $HF + KOH \rightarrow KF + H_2O$

then mL → L then

$\dfrac{1 \text{ L}}{1000 \text{ mL}}$

[acid], L → mol acid then set mol acid = mol base and

$M = \dfrac{\text{mol}}{L}$ balanced equation has 1:1 stoichiometry

[KOH], mol KOH $\rightarrow$ L KOH $\rightarrow$ mL KOH

$$M = \frac{mol}{L} \qquad \frac{1000 \text{ mL}}{1 \text{ L}}$$

Solution: $25.0 \text{ mL acid} \times \dfrac{1 \text{ L}}{1000 \text{ mL}} = 0.0250 \text{ L acid}$ then $\dfrac{0.100 \text{ mol acid}}{1 \text{ L}} \times 0.0250 \text{ L} = 0.00250 \text{ mol acid}$.

So mol acid = 0.00250 mol = mol KOH then

$0.00250 \text{ mol KOH} \times \dfrac{1 \text{ L KOH}}{0.200 \text{ mol KOH}} = 0.0125 \text{ L KOH} \times \dfrac{1000 \text{ mL}}{1 \text{ L}} = 12.5 \text{ mL KOH}$ for both titrations.

Check: The units (mL) are correct. The volume of base is half the volume of acids because the concentration of the base is twice that of the acids. The answer for both titrations is the same because the stoichiometry is the same for both titration reactions.

b) The pH at the equivalence point will be neutral for HCl (since it is a strong acid) and it will be basic for HF (since it is a weak acid).

c) The initial pH will be lower for HCl (since it is a strong acid) and so it dissociate completely. The HF (since it is a weak acid) will only partially dissociate and not drop the pH as low as HCl at the same acid concentration.

d) The titration curves will look like:

HCl:

HF:

Important features to include are a low initial pH (if strong acid pH is 1 and higher for a weak acid), flat initial region (very flat for strong acid, not as flat for weak acid where pH half-way to equivalence point is the pK_a of the acid), sharp rise at equivalence point, pH at equivalence point (neutral for strong acid and higher for weak acid), and then flatten out at high pH.

63. **Given:** 20.0 mL 0.200 M KOH and 0.200 M CH_3NH_2 titrated with 0.100 M HI
    a) **Find:** volume of base to reach equivalence point
    Conceptual Plan: The answer for both titrations will be the same since the initial concentration and volumes of the bases are the same. Write balanced equation then mL $\rightarrow$ L then

$$HI + KOH \rightarrow KI + H_2O \text{ and } HI + KOH \rightarrow CH_3NH_3I \qquad \frac{1 \text{ L}}{1000 \text{ mL}}$$

[base], L $\rightarrow$ mol base   then   set mol base = mol acid and [HI], mol HI $\rightarrow$ L HI $\rightarrow$ mL HI

$$M = \frac{mol}{L} \qquad \text{balanced equation has 1:1 stoichiometry} \qquad M = \frac{mol}{L} \quad \frac{1000 \text{ mL}}{1 \text{ L}}$$

Solution: $20.0 \text{ mL base} \times \dfrac{1 \text{ L}}{1000 \text{ mL}} = 0.0200 \text{ L base}$ then $\dfrac{0.200 \text{ mol base}}{1 \text{ L}} \times 0.0200 \text{ L} = 0.00400 \text{ mol base}$.

So mol base = 0.00400 mol = mol HI then

$0.00400 \text{ mol HI} \times \dfrac{1 \text{ L HI}}{0.100 \text{ mol HI}} = 0.0400 \text{ L HI} \times \dfrac{1000 \text{ mL}}{1 \text{ L}} = 40.0 \text{ mL HI}$ for both titrations.

Check: The units (mL) are correct. The volume of acid is twice the volume of bases because the concentration of the base is twice that of the acid in each case. The answer for both titrations is the same because the stoichiometry is the same for both titration reactions.

b) The pH at the equivalence point will be neutral for KOH (since it is a strong base) and it will be acidic for CH_3NH_2 (since it is a weak base).

c) The initial pH will be lower for CH_3NH_2 (since it is a weak base and will only partially dissociate and not raise the pH as high as KOH (since it is a strong base and so it dissociate completely) at the same acid concentration.

d) The titration curves will look like:

Important features to include are a high initial pH (if strong base pH is over 13 and lower for a weak base), flat initial region (very flat for strong base, not as flat for weak base where pH half-way to equivalence point is the pK_b of the base), sharp drop at equivalence point, pH at equivalence point (neutral for strong base and lower for weak base), and then flatten out at low pH.

64. (i) The equivalence point of a titration is where the pH drops sharply as acid is added. The pH at the equivalence point is the midpoint of the sharp drop at ~ 25 mL added acid. For (a) the pH = ~ 7 and for (b) the pH = ~ 5.

(ii) Graph (a) represents a strong base and graph (b) represents a weak base. A strong base titration starts at a higher pH, has a flatter initial region and a sharper drop at the equivalence point than a weak base. The pH at the equivalence point of a strong base is neutral, while the pH at the equivalence point of a weak base is acidic.

65. a) The equivalence point of a titration is where the pH rises sharply as base is added. The volume at the equivalence point is ~ 30 mL. The pH as the equivalence point is the midpoint of the sharp rise at ~ 30 mL added base, which is a pH = ~ 9.

b) At 0 mL the pH is calculated by doing an equilibrium calculation of a weak acid in water (as done in chapter 15).

c) The pH one-half way to the equivalence point is equal to the pK_a of the acid, or ~ 15 mL.

d) The pH at the equivalence point, or ~ 30 mL, is calculated by doing an equilibrium problem with the K_b of the acid. At the equivalence point all of the acid has been converted to its conjugate base.

e) Beyond the equivalence point, or ~ 30 mL, there is excess base. All of the acid has been converted to its conjugate base and so the pH is calculated by focusing on this excess base concentration.

66. a) The equivalence point of a titration is where the pH drops sharply as acid is added. The volume at the equivalence point is ~ 25 mL. The pH as the equivalence point is the midpoint of the sharp drop at ~ 25 mL added acid, which is a pH = ~ 5.

b) At 0 mL the pH is calculated by doing an equilibrium calculation of a weak base in water (as done in chapter 15).

c) The pH one-half way to the equivalence point is equal to the $14 - pK_b = pK_a$ of the base, or ~ 12 mL.

d) The pH at the equivalence point, or ~ 25 mL, is calculated by doing an equilibrium problem with the K_a of the base. At the equivalence point all of the base has been converted to its conjugate acid.

e) Beyond the equivalence point, or ~ 25 mL, there is excess acid. All of the base has been converted to its conjugate acid and so the pH is calculated by focusing on this excess acid concentration.

67. **Given:** 35.0 mL of 0.175 M HBr titrated with 0.200 M KOH

a) **Find:** initial pH

Conceptual Plan: **Since HBr is a strong acid, it will dissociate completely, so initial pH = $-$ log $[H_3O^+]$ = $-$ log [HBr].**

Solution: $pH = - \log [HBr] = - \log 0.175 = 0.757$

Check: The units (none) are correct. The pH is reasonable since the concentration is greater than 0.1 M and the acid dissociates completely, the pH is less than 1.

b) **Find:** volume of base to reach equivalence point

Conceptual Plan: Write balanced equation then mL $\rightarrow$ L then [HBr], L $\rightarrow$ mol HBr then

$$HBr + KOH \rightarrow KBr + H_2O \qquad \frac{1 \text{ L}}{1000 \text{ mL}} \qquad M = \frac{mol}{L}$$

set mol acid (HBr) = mol base (KOH) and [KOH], mol KOH $\rightarrow$ L KOH $\rightarrow$ mL KOH

balanced equation has 1:1 stoichiometry $\qquad M = \dfrac{mol}{L} \qquad \dfrac{1000 \text{ mL}}{1 \text{ L}}$

Solution: $35.0 \text{ mL HBr} \times \dfrac{1 \text{ L}}{1000 \text{ mL}} = 0.0350 \text{ L HBr}$ then

$\dfrac{0.175 \text{ mol HBr}}{1 \text{ L}} \times 0.0350 \text{ L} = 0.006125 \text{ mol HBr}$.

So mol acid = mol HBr = 0.006125 mol = mol KOH then

$0.006125 \text{ mol KOH} \times \dfrac{1 \text{ L}}{0.200 \text{ mol KOH}} = 0.030625 \text{ L KOH} \times \dfrac{1000 \text{ mL}}{1 \text{ L}} = 30.6 \text{ mL KOH}$.

Check: The units (mL) are correct. The volume of base is a little less than the volume of acid because the concentration of the base is a little greater that of the acid.

c) **Find:** pH after adding 10.0 mL of base

Conceptual Plan:

Use calculations from part b. then mL $\rightarrow$ L then [KOH], L $\rightarrow$ mol KOH then

$$\frac{1 \text{ L}}{1000 \text{ mL}} \qquad M = \frac{mol}{L}$$

mol HBr, mol KOH $\rightarrow$ mol excess HBr and L HBr, L KOH $\rightarrow$ total L then

set up stoichiometry table $\qquad$ L HBr + L KOH = total L

mol excess HBr, L $\rightarrow$ [HBr] $\rightarrow$ pH

$$M = \frac{mol}{L} \qquad pH = - \log [HBr]$$

Solution: $10.0 \text{ mL KOH} \times \dfrac{1 \text{ L}}{1000 \text{ mL}} = 0.0100 \text{ L KOH}$ then

$\dfrac{0.200 \text{ mol KOH}}{1 \text{ L}} \times 0.0100 \text{ L} = 0.00200 \text{ mol KOH}$.

Since KOH is a strong base, [KOH] = [OH$^-$], and set up table to track changes:

	KOH (aq)	+ HBr (aq)	$\rightarrow$ KBr (aq)	+ H$_2$O (l)
Before addition	0.00 mol	0.006125 mol	0.00 mol	–
Addition	0.00200 mol	–	–	–
After addition	$\approx$ 0.00 mol	0.004125 mol	0.00200 mol	–

Then 0.0350 L HBr + 0.0100 L KOH = 0.0450 L total volume. So mol excess acid = mol HBr = 0.004125 mol in 0.0450 L so $[HBr] = \dfrac{0.004125 \text{ mol HBr}}{0.0450 \text{ L}} = 0.0916667 \text{ M}$ and

$pH = - \log [HBr] = - \log 0.0916667 = 1.038$.

Check: The units (none) are correct. The pH is a little higher than the initial pH, which is expected since this is a strong acid.

d) **Find:** pH at equivalence point

Solution: Since this is a strong acid – strong base titration, the pH at the equivalence point is neutral or 7.

e) **Find:** pH after adding 5.0 mL of base beyond the equivalence point

Conceptual Plan: Use calculations from parts b & c.   then   the pH is only dependent on the amount of excess base and the total solution volumes.

mL excess → L excess   then   [KOH],   L excess → mol KOH excess

$$\frac{1\,L}{1000\,mL}$$

$$M = \frac{mol}{L}$$

then   L HBr, L KOH to equivalence point, L KOH excess → total L   then

L HBr + L KOH to equivalence point + L KOH excess = total L

mol excess KOH, total L → [KOH] = [OH⁻] → [H₃O⁺] → pH

$$M = \frac{mol}{L}$$ $$K_w = [H_3O^+][OH^-]$$ $$pH = -\log[H_3O^+]$$

Solution: $5.0\ mL\ KOH \times \dfrac{1\,L}{1000\,mL} = 0.0050\ L\ KOH$ excess   then

$\dfrac{0.200\ mol\ KOH}{1\,L} \times 0.0050\ L = 0.0010\ mol\ KOH$ excess . then $0.0350\ L\ HBr + 0.0306\ L\ KOH + 0.0050\ L$

$KOH = 0.0706\ L$ total volume. $[KOH\ excess] = \dfrac{0.0010\ mol\ KOH\ excess}{0.0706\ L} = 0.01\underline{4}164\ M\ KOH$ excess

Since KOH is a strong base, [KOH] excess = [OH⁻]. $K_w = [H_3O^+][OH^-]$ so

$[H_3O^+] = \dfrac{K_w}{[OH^-]} = \dfrac{1.0 \times 10^{-14}}{0.01\underline{4}164} = 7.\underline{0}6 \times 10^{-13}\ M$. Finally, $pH = -\log[H_3O^+] = -\log(7.\underline{0}6 \times 10^{-13}) = 12.15$.

Check: The units (none) are correct. The pH is rising sharply at the equivalence point, so the pH after 5 mL past the equivalence point should be quite basic.

68. **Given:** 20.0 mL of 0.125 M H NO₃ titrated with 0.150 M NaOH

Find: pH at 5 different points and plot titration curve

Conceptual Plan: Choose points to calculate: (i) initial pH; (ii) pH after 5.0 mL; (iii) pH after 10.0 mL; (iv) pH at equivalence point; and pH at 25.0 mL. Points should be on both sides of the equivalence point.

(i) **Since HNO₃ is a strong acid, it will dissociate completely, so initial pH = − log [H₃O⁺] = − log [HNO₃].**

Solution: $pH = -\log[HNO_3] = -\log 0.125 = 0.903$

Check: The units (none) are correct. The pH is reasonable since the concentration is greater than 0.1 M and the acid dissociates completely, the pH is less than 1.

(ii) **Find:** pH after adding 5.0 mL of base

Conceptual Plan:

Write balanced equation then mL → L then [HNO₃], L → mol HNO₃   then

$HNO_3 + NaOH \rightarrow NaNO_3 + H_2O$ $\dfrac{1\,L}{1000\,mL}$ $M = \dfrac{mol}{L}$

mL → L   then   [NaOH], L → mol NaOH   then   mol HNO₃, mol NaOH → mol excess HNO₃

$\dfrac{1\,L}{1000\,mL}$ $M = \dfrac{mol}{L}$ set up stoichiometry table

and   L HNO₃, L NaOH → total L   then   mol excess HNO₃, L → [HNO₃] → pH

L HNO₃ + L NaOH = total L $M = \dfrac{mol}{L}$ $pH = -\log[HNO_3]$

Solution: $20.0\ mL\ HNO_3 \times \dfrac{1\,L}{1000\,mL} = 0.0200\ L\ HNO_3$ then

$\dfrac{0.125\ mol\ HNO_3}{1\,L} \times 0.0200\ L = 0.00250\ mol\ HNO_3$ and $5.0\ mL\ NaOH \times \dfrac{1\,L}{1000\,mL} = 0.0050\ L\ NaOH$ then

$\dfrac{0.150\ mol\ NaOH}{1\,L} \times 0.0050\ L = 0.00075\ mol\ NaOH$.

This is a strong acid – strong base titration, so set up table to track changes:

$$NaOH\ (aq)\ +\ HNO_3\ (aq)\ \rightarrow\ NaNO_3\ (aq) + H_2O\ (l)$$

	NaOH (aq)	HNO₃ (aq)	NaNO₃ (aq)	H₂O (l)
Before addition	0.00 mol	0.00250 mol	0.00 mol	–
Addition	0.00075 mol	–	–	–
After addition	≈ 0.00 mol	0.00175 mol	0.00075 mol	–

Then 0.0200 L HNO₃ + 0.0050 L NaOH = 0.0250 L total volume. So mol excess acid = mol HNO₃ = 0.00175 mol in 0.0250 L, so $[HNO_3] = \dfrac{0.00175\ mol\ HNO_3}{0.0250\ L} = 0.0700$ M and

$pH = -\log\,[HNO_3] = -\log\,0.0700 = 1.155$.

Check: The units (none) are correct. The pH remains very low in a strong acid – strong base titration before the equivalence point.

(iii) Find: pH after adding 10.0 mL of base

Conceptual Plan:

Use calculations for point (ii) then $mL \rightarrow L$ then [NaOH], $L \rightarrow$ mol NaOH then

$$\frac{1\ L}{1000\ mL} \qquad\qquad M = \frac{mol}{L}$$

mol HNO₃, mol NaOH $\rightarrow$ mol excess HNO₃ and L HNO₃, L NaOH $\rightarrow$ total L then
<small>set up stoichiometry table</small> <small>L HNO₃ + L NaOH = total L</small>

mol excess HNO₃, L $\rightarrow$ [HNO₃] $\rightarrow$ pH

$$M = \frac{mol}{L} \qquad pH = -\log\,[HNO_3]$$

Solution: $10.0\ \cancel{mL\ NaOH} \times \dfrac{1\ L}{1000\ \cancel{mL}} = 0.0100$ L NaOH then

$\dfrac{0.150\ mol\ NaOH}{1\ \cancel{L}} \times 0.0100\ \cancel{L} = 0.00150$ mol NaOH . Set up table to track changes:

$$NaOH\ (aq)\ +\ HNO_3\ (aq)\ \rightarrow\ NaNO_3\ (aq) + H_2O\ (l)$$

	NaOH (aq)	HNO₃ (aq)	NaNO₃ (aq)	H₂O (l)
Before addition	0.00 mol	0.00250 mol	0.00 mol	–
Addition	0.00150 mol	–	–	–
After addition	≈ 0.00 mol	0.00100 mol	0.00150 mol	–

Then 0.0200 L HNO₃ + 0.0100 L NaOH = 0.0300 L total volume. So mol excess acid = mol HNO₃ = 0.00100 mol in 0.0300 L, so $[HNO_3] = \dfrac{0.00100\ mol\ HNO_3}{0.0300\ L} = 0.033\underline{3}333$ M and

$pH = -\log\,[HNO_3] = -\log\,0.033\underline{3}333 = 1.477$.

Check: The units (none) are correct. The pH remains very low in a strong acid – strong base titration before the equivalence point.

(iv) Find: pH at equivalence point and volume of base to reach equivalence point

Conceptual Plan: Since this is a strong acid – strong base titration, the pH at the equivalence point is neutral or 7. Use calculations for point (ii) then

set mol acid (HNO₃) = mol base (NaOH) and
<small>balanced equation has 1:1 stoichiometry</small>

[NaOH], mol NaOH $\rightarrow$ L NaOH $\rightarrow$ mL NaOH

$$M = \frac{mol}{L} \qquad\qquad \frac{1000\ mL}{1\ L}$$

Solution: Since this is a strong acid – strong base titration, the pH at the equivalence point is neutral or 7. So mol acid = mol HNO₃ = 0.00250 mol = mol NaOH then

$0.00250\ \cancel{mol\ NaOH} \times \dfrac{1\ L}{0.150\ \cancel{mol\ NaOH}} = 0.016\underline{6}667\ \cancel{L\ NaOH} \times \dfrac{1000\ mL}{1\ \cancel{L}} = 16.7$ mL NaOH .

Check: The units (none and mL) are correct. The equivalence point pH of a strong acid – strong base titration is neutral. The volume of base is a little less than the volume of acid because the concentration of the base is a little greater that of the acid.

(v) Find: pH after adding 25.0 mL of base

Conceptual Plan:

Use calculations for point (ii) then   mL → L   then   [NaOH], L → mol NaOH   then

$$\frac{1 \text{ L}}{1000 \text{ mL}}$$

$$M = \frac{\text{mol}}{L}$$

mol HNO₃, mol NaOH → mol excess HNO₃   and   L HNO₃, L NaOH → total L   then
set up stoichiometry table   L HNO₃ + L NaOH = total L

mol excess NaOH, total L → [NaOH] = [OH⁻] → [H₃O⁺] → pH

$$M = \frac{\text{mol}}{L} \qquad K_w = [H_3O^+][OH^-] \qquad pH = -\log[H_3O^+]$$

Solution: $25.0 \text{ mL NaOH} \times \dfrac{1 \text{ L}}{1000 \text{ mL}} = 0.0250 \text{ L NaOH}$ then

$\dfrac{0.150 \text{ mol NaOH}}{1 \text{ L}} \times 0.0250 \text{ L} = 0.00375 \text{ mol NaOH}$. Set up table to track changes:

	NaOH (aq)	+ HNO₃ (aq)	→ NaNO₃ (aq)	+ H₂O (l)
Before addition	0.00 mol	0.00250 mol	0.00 mol	–
Addition	0.00375 mol	–	–	–
After addition	0.00125 mol	≈ 0.00 mol	0.00375 mol	–

Then 0.0200 L HNO₃ + 0.0250 L NaOH = 0.0450 L total volume. So mol excess acid = mol NaOH = 0.00125 mol in 0.0450 L, so. $[\text{NaOH excess}] = \dfrac{0.00125 \text{ mol NaOH excess}}{0.0450 \text{ L}} = 0.0277778$ M NaOH excess

Since NaOH is a strong base, [NaOH] excess = [OH⁻]. $K_w = [H_3O^+][OH^-]$ so

$[H_3O^+] = \dfrac{K_w}{[OH^-]} = \dfrac{1.0 \times 10^{-14}}{0.0277778} = 3.6 \times 10^{-13}$ M . Finally, $pH = -\log[H_3O^+] = -\log(3.6 \times 10^{-13}) = 12.44 \ldots$

Check: The units (none) are correct. The pH is rising sharply at the equivalence point, so the pH over 5 mL past the equivalence point should be quite basic.

Finally plotting these 5 points, the titration curve looks like:

69. **Given:** 25.0 mL of 0.115 M RbOH titrated with 0.100 M HCl

a) **Find:** initial pH

Conceptual Plan: Since RbOH is a strong base, it will dissociate completely, so
[RbOH] = [OH⁻] → [H₃O⁺] → pH

$$K_w = [H_3O^+][OH^-] \qquad pH = -\log[H_3O^+]$$

Solution: Since RbOH is a strong base, [RbOH] excess = [OH⁻]. $K_w = [H_3O^+][OH^-]$ so

$[H_3O^+] = \dfrac{K_w}{[OH^-]} = \dfrac{1.0 \times 10^{-14}}{0.115} = 8.69565 \times 10^{-14}$ M and $pH = -\log[H_3O^+] = -\log(8.69565 \times 10^{-14}) = 13.06$

Check: The units (none) are correct. The pH is reasonable since the concentration is greater than 0.1 M and the base dissociates completely, the pH is greater than 13.

b) **Find:** volume of acid to reach equivalence point

Conceptual Plan: Write balanced equation then mL → L then [RbOH], L → mol RbOH   then

$$\text{HCl} + \text{RbOH} \rightarrow \text{RbCl} + H_2O$$

$$\frac{1 \text{ L}}{1000 \text{ mL}}$$

$$M = \frac{\text{mol}}{L}$$

set mol base (RbOH) = mol acid (HCl)   and   [HCl], mol HCl → L HCl   →   mL HCl

balanced equation has 1:1 stoichiometry

$$M = \frac{\text{mol}}{L} \qquad \frac{1000 \text{ mL}}{1 \text{ L}}$$

Solution: $25.0 \text{ mL RbOH} \times \dfrac{1 \text{ L}}{1000 \text{ mL}} = 0.0250 \text{ L RbOH}$ then

$\dfrac{0.115 \text{ mol RbOH}}{1 \text{ L}} \times 0.0250 \text{ L} = 0.002875 \text{ mol RbOH}$. So mol base = mol RbOH = 0.002875 mol = mol

HCl then $0.002875 \text{ mol HCl} \times \dfrac{1 \text{ L}}{0.100 \text{ mol HCl}} = 0.02875 \text{ L HCl} \times \dfrac{1000 \text{ mL}}{1 \text{ L}} = 28.8 \text{ mL HCl}$.

Check: The units (mL) are correct. The volume of acid is a greater less than the volume of base because the concentration of the base is a little greater that of the acid.

c) **Find:** pH after adding 5.0 mL of acid

Conceptual Plan: Use calculations from part b. Then mL $\rightarrow$ L then [HCl], L $\rightarrow$ mol HCl then

$$\dfrac{1 \text{ L}}{1000 \text{ mL}} \qquad\qquad M = \dfrac{\text{mol}}{\text{L}}$$

mol RbOH, mol HCl $\rightarrow$ mol excess RbOH and L RbOH, L HCl $\rightarrow$ total L then
set up stoichiometry table $\qquad\qquad$ L RbOH + L HCl = total L

mol excess RbOH, L $\rightarrow$ [RbOH] = [OH⁻] $\rightarrow$ [H₃O⁺] $\rightarrow$ pH

$$M = \dfrac{\text{mol}}{\text{L}} \qquad\qquad K_w = [H_3O^+][OH^-] \qquad pH = -\log [H_3O^+]$$

Solution: $5.0 \text{ mL HCl} \times \dfrac{1 \text{ L}}{1000 \text{ mL}} = 0.0050 \text{ L HCl}$ then $\dfrac{0.100 \text{ mol HCl}}{1 \text{ L}} \times 0.0050 \text{ L} = 0.00050 \text{ mol HCl}$.

Since HCl is a strong acid, [HCl] = [H₃O⁺], and set up table to track changes:

$$HCl\,(aq) + RbOH\,(aq) \rightarrow RbCl\,(aq) + H_2O\,(l)$$

Before addition	0.00 mol	0.002875 mol	0.00 mol	–
Addition	0.00050 mol	–	–	–
After addition	≈ 0.00 mol	0.002375 mol	0.00050 mol	–

Then 0.0250 L RbOH + 0.0050 L HCl = 0.0300 L total volume. So mol excess base = mol RbOH =

0.002375 mol in 0.0300 L so $[RbOH] = \dfrac{0.002375 \text{ mol RbOH}}{0.0300 \text{ L}} = 0.0791667 \text{ M}$ Since RbOH is a strong

base, [RbOH] excess = [OH⁻]. $K_w = [H_3O^+][OH^-]$ so $[H_3O^+] = \dfrac{K_w}{[OH^-]} = \dfrac{1.0 \times 10^{-14}}{0.0791667} = 1.26316 \times 10^{-13} \text{ M}$ and

$pH = -\log [H_3O^+] = -\log (1.26316 \times 10^{-13}) = 12.90$.

Check: The units (none) are correct. The pH is a little lower than the initial pH, which is expected since this is a strong base.

d) **Find:** pH at equivalence point

Solution: Since this is a strong acid – strong base titration, the pH at the equivalence point is neutral or 7.

e) **Find:** pH after adding 5.0 mL of acid beyond the equivalence point

Conceptual Plan: Use calculations from parts b & c. then **the pH is only dependent on the amount of excess acid and the total solution volumes.** then

mL excess $\rightarrow$ L excess then [HCl], L excess $\rightarrow$ mol HCl excess

$$\dfrac{1 \text{ L}}{1000 \text{ mL}} \qquad\qquad M = \dfrac{\text{mol}}{\text{L}}$$

then **L RbOH, L HCl to equivalence point, L HCl excess $\rightarrow$ total L then**
L RbOH + L HCl to equivalence point + L HCl excess = total L

mol excess HCl, total L $\rightarrow$ [HCl] = [H₃O⁺] $\rightarrow$ pH

$$M = \dfrac{\text{mol}}{\text{L}} \qquad\qquad pH = -\log [H_3O^+]$$

Solution: $5.0 \text{ mL HCl} \times \dfrac{1 \text{ L}}{1000 \text{ mL}} = 0.0050 \text{ L HCl excess}$ then

$\dfrac{0.100 \text{ mol HCl}}{1 \text{ L}} \times 0.0050 \text{ L} = 0.00050 \text{ mol HCl excess}$. then 0.0250 L RbOH + 0.0288 L HCl + 0.0050 L

HCl = 0.0588 L total volume. $[HCl \text{ excess}] = \dfrac{0.00050 \text{ mol HCl excess}}{0.0588 \text{ L}} = 0.0085034 \text{ M HCl excess}$

Since HCl is a strong acid, [HCl] excess = $[H_3O^+]$. Finally, $pH = -\log[H_3O^+] = -\log(0.008\underline{5}034) = 2.07$.

Check: The units (none) are correct. The pH is dropping sharply at the equivalence point, so the pH after 5 mL past the equivalence point should be quite acidic.

70. **Given:** 15.0 mL of 0.100 M $Ba(OH)_2$ titrated with 0.125 M HCl
 Find: pH at 5 different points and plot titration curve
 Conceptual Plan: **Choose points to calculate: (i) initial pH; (ii) pH after 10.0 mL; (iii) pH after 20.0 mL; (iv) pH at equivalence point; and pH at 30.0 mL. Points should be on both sides of the equivalence point.**
 (i) **Find:** initial pH
 Conceptual Plan: Since $Ba(OH)_2$ is a strong base, it will dissociate completely, bearing in mind that $Ba(OH)_2 \rightarrow Ba^{2+} + 2\,OH^-$ so 2 hydroxide ions are generated for each barium hydroxide and $2\,[Ba(OH)_2] = [OH^-]$ $\rightarrow$ $[H_3O^+]$ $\rightarrow$ pH

$$K_w = [H_3O^+][OH^-] \qquad pH = -\log[H_3O^+]$$

 Solution: Since $Ba(OH)_2$ is a strong base, $2\,[Ba(OH)_2] = [OH^-] = 2 \times 0.100\ M = 0.200\ M$.

$$K_w = [H_3O^+][OH^-] \text{ so } [H_3O^+] = \frac{K_w}{[OH^-]} = \frac{1.0 \times 10^{-14}}{0.200} = 5.0 \times 10^{-14}\ M \text{ and}$$

$$pH = -\log[H_3O^+] = -\log(5.0 \times 10^{-14}) = 13.30$$

 Check: The units (none) are correct. The pH is reasonable since the concentration is greater than 0.1 M and the base dissociates completely, the pH is greater than 13.

 (ii) **Find:** pH after adding 10.0 mL of acid
 Conceptual Plan:
 Write balanced equation then mL $\rightarrow$ L then $[Ba(OH)_2]$, L $\rightarrow$ mol $Ba(OH)_2$ then

$$2\,HCl + Ba(OH)_2 \rightarrow BaCl_2 + 2\,H_2O \qquad \frac{1\ L}{1000\ mL} \qquad M = \frac{mol}{L}$$

 mL $\rightarrow$ L then [HCl], L $\rightarrow$ mol HCl then mol $Ba(OH)_2$, mol HCl $\rightarrow$ mol excess $Ba(OH)_2$ and

$$\frac{1\ L}{1000\ mL} \qquad M = \frac{mol}{L} \qquad\qquad \text{set up stoichiometry table}$$

 L $Ba(OH)_2$, L HCl $\rightarrow$ total L then

$$M = \frac{mol}{L}$$

 mol excess $Ba(OH)_2$, L $\rightarrow$ $2\,[Ba(OH)_2] = [OH^-]$ $\rightarrow$ $[H_3O^+]$ $\rightarrow$ pH

$$L\ Ba(OH)_2 + L\ HCl = total\ L \qquad K_w = [H_3O^+][OH^-] \qquad pH = -\log[H_3O^+]$$

 Solution: $15.0\ \cancel{mL\ Ba(OH)_2} \times \dfrac{1\ L}{1000\ \cancel{mL}} = 0.0150\ L\ Ba(OH)_2$ then

$$\frac{0.100\ mol\ Ba(OH)_2}{1\ \cancel{L}} \times 0.0150\ \cancel{L} = 0.00150\ mol\ Ba(OH)_2 \text{ and } 10.0\ \cancel{mL\ HCl} \times \frac{1\ L}{1000\ \cancel{mL}} = 0.0100\ L\ HCl \text{ then}$$

$$\frac{0.125\ mol\ HCl}{1\ \cancel{L}} \times 0.0100\ \cancel{L} = 0.00125\ mol\ HCl.$$ Since HCl is a strong acid, $[HCl] = [H_3O^+]$, and set up table to track changes:

	2 HCl (aq)	+ Ba(OH)$_2$ (aq)	$\rightarrow$	BaCl$_2$ (aq)	+ 2 H$_2$O (l)
Before addition	0.00 mol	0.00150 mol		0.00 mol	–
Addition	0.00125 mol	–		–	–
After addition	$\approx$ 0.00 mol	0.000875 mol		0.000625 mol	–

Then $0.0150\ L\ Ba(OH)_2 + 0.0100\ L\ HCl = 0.0250\ L$ total volume. So mol excess base = mol $Ba(OH)_2$ $= 0.000\underline{8}75$ mol in 0.0250 L so $[Ba(OH)_2] = \dfrac{0.000\underline{8}75\ mol\ Ba(OH)_2}{0.0250\ L} = 0.035\ M$ Since $Ba(OH)_2$ is a strong base, $2\,[Ba(OH)_2] = [OH^-] = 2 \times 0.035\ M = 0.070\ M$. $K_w = [H_3O^+][OH^-]$ so

$$[H_3O^+] = \frac{K_w}{[OH^-]} = \frac{1.0 \times 10^{-14}}{0.070} = 1.\underline{4}286 \times 10^{-13}\ M \text{ and}$$

$$pH = -\log[H_3O^+] = -\log(1.\underline{4}286 \times 10^{-13}) = 12.85.$$

 Check: The units (none) are correct. The pH is a little lower than the initial pH, which is expected since this is a strong base.

(iii) Find: pH after adding 20.0 mL of acid

Conceptual Plan:

Use calculations from part (ii) then mL $\rightarrow$ L then [HCl], L $\rightarrow$ mol   HCl then

$$\frac{1\ L}{1000\ mL} \qquad\qquad M = \frac{mol}{L}$$

mol Ba(OH)$_2$, mol HCl $\rightarrow$ mol excess Ba(OH)$_2$ and   **L Ba(OH)$_2$, L HCl $\rightarrow$ total L**   then
set up stoichiometry table   L Ba(OH)$_2$ + L HCl = total L

mol excess Ba(OH)$_2$, L $\rightarrow$ 2 [Ba(OH)$_2$] = [OH$^-$] $\rightarrow$ [H$_3$O$^+$] $\rightarrow$ pH

$$M = \frac{mol}{L} \qquad\qquad K_w = [H_3O^+][OH^-] \quad pH = -\log\,[H_3O^+]$$

Solution: $20.0\ \cancel{mL\ HCl}\ \times\ \dfrac{1\ L}{1000\ \cancel{mL}} = 0.0200\ L\ HCl$ then $\dfrac{0.125\ mol\ HCl}{1\ \cancel{L}} \times 0.0200\ \cancel{L} = 0.00250\ mol\ HCl$.

Since HCl is a strong acid, [HCl] = [H$_3$O$^+$], and set up table to track changes:

$$2\ HCl\ (aq)\ +\ Ba(OH)_2\ (aq)\ \rightarrow\ BaCl_2\ (aq) + 2\ H_2O\ (l)$$

Before addition	0.00 mol	0.00150 mol	0.00 mol	–
Addition	0.00250 mol	–	–	–	then
After addition	≈ 0.00 mol	0.00025 mol	0.00125 mol	–

0.0150 L Ba(OH)$_2$ + 0.0200 L HCl = 0.0350 L total volume. So mol excess base = mol Ba(OH)$_2$ =

0.00025 mol in 0.0350 L so $[Ba(OH)_2] = \dfrac{0.00025\ mol\ Ba(OH)_2}{0.0350\ L} = 0.007\underline{1}429\ M$ Since Ba(OH)$_2$ is a

strong base, 2 [Ba(OH)$_2$] = [OH$^-$] = 2 x 0.007$\underline{1}$429 M = 0.01$\underline{4}$286 M. K$_w$ = [H$_3$O$^+$][OH$^-$] so

$[H_3O^+] = \dfrac{K_w}{[OH^-]} = \dfrac{1.0\ x\ 10^{-14}}{0.007\underline{1}429} = 1.\underline{4}000\ x\ 10^{-12}\ M$ and $pH = -\log\,[H_3O^+] = -\log\,(1.\underline{4}000\ x\ 10^{-12}) = 11.85$.

Check: The units (none) are correct. The pH is a little lower than the initial pH, which is expected since this is a strong base.

(iv) Find: pH at equivalence point and volume of acid to reach equivalence point

Solution: Since this is a strong acid – strong base titration, the pH at the equivalence point is neutral or 7.

Conceptual Plan:

Use calculations from part (ii)   then set 2 mol base (Ba(OH)$_2$) = mol acid   (HCl) and
balanced equation has 1:2 stoichiometry

[HCl], mol HCl $\rightarrow$ L HCl $\rightarrow$ mL HCl

$$M = \frac{mol}{L} \qquad \frac{1000\ mL}{1\ L}$$

Solution: So $0.00150\ mol\ Ba(OH)_2\ \times\ \dfrac{2\ mol\ HCl}{1\ mol\ Ba(OH)_2} = 0.00300\ mol\ HCl$ then

$0.00300\ \cancel{mol\ HCl}\ \times\ \dfrac{1\ L}{0.125\ \cancel{mol\ HCl}} = 0.0240\ \cancel{L\ HCl}\ \times\ \dfrac{1000\ mL}{1\ \cancel{L}} = 24.0\ mL\ HCl$.

Check: The units (mL) are correct. The volume of acid is a greater less than the volume of base because two moles of acid are needed for each mole of the base.

(v) Find: pH after adding 30.0 mL of acid

Conceptual Plan: Use calculations from earlier parts.   then   the pH is only dependent on the amount of excess acid and the total solution volumes.

mL added, mL at equiv. pt. $\rightarrow$ mL excess $\rightarrow$ L excess   then

$$mL\ excess = mL\ added - mL\ at\ equiv.\ pt. \qquad \frac{1\ L}{1000\ mL}$$

[HCl], L excess $\rightarrow$ mol HCl excess then   L Ba(OH)$_2$, L HCl $\rightarrow$ total L   then

$$M = \frac{mol}{L} \qquad\qquad L\ Ba(OH)_2 + L\ HCl = total\ L$$

mol excess HCl, total L $\rightarrow$ [HCl] = [H$_3$O$^+$] $\rightarrow$ pH

$$M = \frac{mol}{L} \qquad pH = -\log\,[H_3O^+]$$

Solution: mL HCl excess = mL added – mL to equiv. pt. = 30.0 mL – 24.0 mL = 6.0 mL.

$6.0 \; \overline{mL \; HCl} \times \dfrac{1 \; L}{1000 \; \overline{mL}} = 0.0060 \; L \; HCl \; excess$ then $\dfrac{0.125 \; mol \; HCl}{1 \; \overline{L}} \times 0.0060 \; \overline{L} = 0.00075 \; mol \; HCl \; excess$.

Then $0.0150 \; L \; Ba(OH)_2 + 0.0300 \; L \; HCl = 0.0450 \; L$ total volume.

$[HCl \; excess] = \dfrac{0.00075 \; mol \; HCl \; excess}{0.0450 \; L} = 0.01\underline{6}667 \; M \; HCl \; excess$. Since HCl is a strong acid, [HCl] excess

$= [H_3O^+]$. Finally, $pH = -\log [H_3O^+] = -\log (0.01\underline{6}667) = 1.78$.

Check: The units (none) are correct. The pH is dropping sharply at the equivalence point, so the pH after 5 mL past the equivalence point should be quite acidic.

Finally plotting these 5 points, the titration curve looks like:

71. **Given:** 20.0 mL of 0.105 M $HC_2H_3O_2$ titrated with 0.125 M NaOH   **Other:** $K_a \; (HC_2H_3O_2) = 1.8 \times 10^{-5}$
 a) **Find:** initial pH
  Conceptual Plan:
  Since $HC_2H_3O_2$ is a weak acid, set up an equilibrium problem using the initial concentration. So M H $C_2H_3O_2$ $\rightarrow$ $[H_3O^+]$ $\rightarrow$ pH
  ICE Chart $pH = -\log [H_3O^+]$

  Solution:
  $HC_2H_3O_2 \, (aq) + H_2O \, (l) \rightleftharpoons H_3O^+ \, (aq) + C_2H_3O_2^{2-} \, (aq)$

	$[HC_2H_3O_2]$	$[H_3O^+]$	$[C_2H_3O_2^{2-}]$
Initial	0.105	≈ 0.00	0.00
Change	$-x$	$+x$	$+x$
Equil	$0.105 - x$	$+x$	$+x$

  $K_a = \dfrac{[H_3O^+] \, [C_2H_3O_2^-]}{[HC_2H_3O_2]} = 1.8 \times 10^{-5} = \dfrac{x^2}{0.105 - x}$ Assume x is small (x << 0.105) so

  $\dfrac{x^2}{0.105 - \cancel{x}} = 1.8 \times 10^{-5} = \dfrac{x^2}{0.105}$ and $x = 1.\underline{3}748 \times 10^{-3} = [H_3O^+]$. Confirm that assumption is valid

  $\dfrac{1.\underline{3}748 \times 10^{-3}}{0.105} \times 100 \% = 1.3 \% < 5 \%$ so assumption is valid. Finally,

  $pH = -\log [H_3O^+] = -\log (1.\underline{3}748 \times 10^{-3}) = 2.86$.

  Check: The units (none) are correct.   The magnitude of the answer makes physical sense because pH should be greater than $-\log (0.105) = 0.98$ because this is a weak acid.

 b) **Find:** volume of base to reach equivalence point
  Conceptual Plan:
  Write balanced equation then mL $\rightarrow$ L then $[HC_2H_3O_2]$, L $\rightarrow$ mol $HC_2H_3O_2$ then

  $HC_2H_3O_2 + NaOH \rightarrow NaC_2H_3O_2 + H_2O$ $\dfrac{1 \; L}{1000 \; mL}$ $M = \dfrac{mol}{L}$

  set mol acid($HC_2H_3O_2$) = mol base(NaOH)   and   [NaOH], mol NaOH $\rightarrow$ L NaOH $\rightarrow$ mL NaOH

  balanced equation has 1:1 stoichiometry $M = \dfrac{mol}{L}$ $\dfrac{1000 \; mL}{1 \; L}$

  Solution: $20.0 \; \overline{mL \; HC_2H_3O_2} \times \dfrac{1 \; L}{1000 \; \overline{mL}} = 0.0200 \; L \; HC_2H_3O_2$ then

  $\dfrac{0.105 \; mol \; HC_2H_3O_2}{1 \; \overline{L}} \times 0.0200 \; \overline{L} = 0.00210 \; mol \; HC_2H_3O_2$. So mol acid = mol $HC_2H_3O_2$ = 0.00210 mol =

mol NaOH then $0.00210 \text{ mol NaOH} \times \dfrac{1 \text{ L}}{0.125 \text{ mol NaOH}} = 0.0168 \text{ L NaOH} \times \dfrac{1000 \text{ mL}}{1 \text{ L}} = 16.8 \text{ mL NaOH}$.

Check: The units (mL) are correct. The volume of base is a little less than the volume of acid because the concentration of the base is a little greater that of the acid.

c) **Find:** pH after adding 5.0 mL of base

Conceptual Plan:

Use calculations from part b. then mL $\rightarrow$ L then [NaOH], L $\rightarrow$ mol NaOH then

$$\dfrac{1 \text{ L}}{1000 \text{ mL}} \qquad\qquad M = \dfrac{\text{mol}}{\text{L}}$$

mol $HC_2H_3O_2$, mol NaOH $\rightarrow$ mol excess $HC_2H_3O_2$, mol $C_2H_3O_2^-$ and

set up stoichiometry table

L $HC_2H_3O_2$, L NaOH $\rightarrow$ total L then

L $HC_2H_3O_2$ + L NaOH = total L

then mol excess $HC_2H_3O_2$, L $\rightarrow$ [$HC_2H_3O_2$] and mol excess $C_2H_3O_2^-$, L $\rightarrow$ [$C_2H_3O_2^-$] then

$$M = \dfrac{\text{mol}}{\text{L}} \qquad\qquad\qquad\qquad\qquad\qquad M = \dfrac{\text{mol}}{\text{L}}$$

M $HC_2H_3O_2$, M $C_2H_3O_2^-$ $\rightarrow$ [H_3O^+] $\rightarrow$ pH

ICE Chart $\quad pH = -\log[H_3O^+]$

Solution: $5.0 \text{ mL NaOH} \times \dfrac{1 \text{ L}}{1000 \text{ mL}} = 0.0050 \text{ L NaOH}$ then

$\dfrac{0.125 \text{ mol NaOH}}{1 \text{ L}} \times 0.0050 \text{ L} = 0.000625 \text{ mol NaOH}$. Set up table to track changes:

	NaOH (aq)	+ $HC_2H_3O_2$ (aq)	$\rightarrow$ $NaC_2H_3O_2$ (aq)	+ H_2O (l)
Before addition	0.00 mol	0.00210 mol	0.00 mol	–
Addition	0.000625 mol	–	–	–
After addition	$\approx$ 0.00 mol	0.001475 mol	0.000625 mol	–

Then 0.0200 L H $C_2H_3O_2$ + 0.0050 L NaOH = 0.0250 L total volume. then

$[HC_2H_3O_2] = \dfrac{0.001475 \text{ mol } HC_2H_3O_2}{0.0250 \text{ L}} = 0.0590 \text{ M}$ and $[NaC_2H_3O_2] = \dfrac{0.000625 \text{ mol } C_2H_3O_2^-}{0.0250 \text{ L}} = 0.025 \text{ M}$.

Since 1 $C_2H_3O_2^-$ ion is generated for each $NaC_2H_3O_2$, [$C_2H_3O_2^-$] = 0.025 M $C_2H_3O_2^-$.

$$HC_2H_3O_2 (aq) + H_2O(l) \rightleftharpoons H_3O^+ (aq) + C_2H_3O_2^- (aq)$$

	[$HC_2H_3O_2$]	[H_3O^+]	[$C_2H_3O_2^-$]
Initial	0.0590	$\approx$ 0.00	0.025
Change	$-x$	$+x$	$+x$
Equil	$0.0590 - x$	$+x$	$0.025 + x$

$K_a = \dfrac{[H_3O^+][C_2H_3O_2^-]}{[HC_2H_3O_2]} = 1.8 \times 10^{-5} = \dfrac{x(0.025 + x)}{0.0590 - x}$ Assume x is small (x << 0.025 < 0.0590) so

$\dfrac{x(0.025 + x)}{0.0590 - x} = 1.8 \times 10^{-5} = \dfrac{x(0.025)}{0.0590}$ and x = 4.248×10^{-5} = [H_3O^+]. Confirm that assumption is valid

$\dfrac{4.248 \times 10^{-5}}{0.025} \times 100 \% = 0.17 \% < 5 \%$ so assumption is valid. Finally,

$pH = -\log[H_3O^+] = -\log(4.248 \times 10^{-5}) = 4.37$.

Check: The units (none) are correct. The pH is a little higher than the initial pH, which is expected since some of the acid has been neutralized.

d) **Find:** pH at One-half of the equivalence point

Conceptual Plan: Since this is a weak acid – strong base titration, the pH at one-half the equivalence point is the pK_a of the weak acid.

Solution: $pH = pK_a = -\log K_a = -\log(1.8 \times 10^{-5}) = 4.74$.

Check: The units (none) are correct. Since this is a weak acid – strong base titration, the pH at one-half the equivalence point is the pK_a of the weak acid, so it should be a little below 5.

e) **Find:** pH at equivalence point

Conceptual Plan: **Use calculations from parts b.** **then** **since all of the weak acid has been converted to its conjugate base, the pH is only dependent on the hydrolysis reaction of the conjugate base. The mol $C_2H_3O_2^- =$ initial mol $HC_2H_3O_2$ and L $HC_2H_3O_2$, L NaOH to equivalence point $\rightarrow$ total L** **then**

$$L\ HC_2H_3O_2 + L\ NaOH = total\ L$$

mol excess $C_2H_3O_2^-$, L $\rightarrow$ $[C_2H_3O_2^-]$ **and** **$K_a \rightarrow K_b$** **then** **do equilibrium calculation:**

$$M = \frac{mol}{L} \qquad\qquad K_w = K_a\ K_b$$

$[C_2H_3O_2^-]$, K_b $\rightarrow$ $[OH^-]$ $\rightarrow$ $[H_3O^+]$ $\rightarrow$ pH

$$\text{set up ICE table} \quad K_w = [H_3O^+][OH^-] \qquad pH = -\log [H_3O^+]$$

Solution: mol $C_2H_3O_2^- =$ initial mol $HC_2H_3O_2 = 0.00210$ mol and total volume = L $HC_2H_3O_2$ + L

NaOH $= 0.020$ L $+ 0.0168$ L $= 0.0368$ L then $[C_2H_3O_2^-] = \dfrac{0.00210\ \text{mol}\ C_2H_3O_2^-}{0.0368\ L} = 0.0570652$ M and

$K_w = K_a\ K_b$. Rearrange to solve for K_b. $K_b = \dfrac{K_w}{K_a} = \dfrac{1.0\ \text{x}\ 10^{-14}}{1.8\ \text{x}\ 10^{-5}} = 5.5556\ \text{x}\ 10^{-10}$. Set up ICE table

$$C_2H_3O_2^-\ (aq) + H_2O\ (l) \rightleftharpoons HC_2H_3O_2\ (aq) + OH^-\ (aq)$$

	$[C_2H_3O_2^-]$	$[HC_2H_3O_2]$	$[OH^-]$
Initial	0.0570652	≈ 0.00	≈ 0.00
Change	$-x$	$+x$	$+x$
Equil	$0.0570652 - x$	$+x$	$+x$

$K_b = \dfrac{[HC_2H_3O_2]\ [OH^-]}{[C_2H_3O_2^-]} = 5.5556\ \text{x}\ 10^{-10} = \dfrac{x^2}{0.0570652 - x}$ Assume x is small (x << 0.057) so

$\dfrac{x^2}{0.0570652 - x} = 5.5556\ \text{x}\ 10^{-10} = \dfrac{x^2}{0.0570652}$ and x $= 5.6305\ \text{x}\ 10^{-6} = [OH^-]$.

Confirm that assumption is valid $\dfrac{5.6305\ \text{x}\ 10^{-6}}{0.0570652}$ x 100 % = 0.0099 % < 5 % so assumption is valid.

$K_w = [H_3O^+][OH^-]$ so $[H_3O^+] = \dfrac{K_w}{[OH^-]} = \dfrac{1.0\ \text{x}\ 10^{-14}}{5.6305\ \text{x}\ 10^{-6}} = 1.7760\ \text{x}\ 10^{-9}$ M . Finally,

$pH = -\log [H_3O^+] = -\log (1.7760\ \text{x}\ 10^{-9}) = 8.75$.

Check: The units (none) are correct. Since this is a weak acid – strong base titration, the pH at the equivalence point is basic.

e) **Find:** pH after adding 5.0 mL of base beyond the equivalence point

Conceptual Plan: **Use calculations from parts b & c.** **then** **the pH is only dependent on the amount of excess base and the total solution volumes.**

mL excess $\rightarrow$ L excess **then**   **[NaOH], L excess $\rightarrow$ mol NaOH excess**

$$\frac{1\ L}{1000\ mL} \qquad\qquad\qquad\qquad M = \frac{mol}{L}$$

then **L $HC_2H_3O_2$, L NaOH to equivalence point, L NaOH excess $\rightarrow$ total L** **then**

$$L\ HC_2H_3O_2 + L\ NaOH\ to\ equivalence\ point + L\ NaOH\ excess = total\ L$$

mol excess NaOH, total L $\rightarrow$ [NaOH] = [OH^-] $\rightarrow$ [H_3O^+] $\rightarrow$ pH

$$M = \frac{mol}{L} \qquad\qquad K_w = [H_3O^+][OH^-] \qquad pH = -\log [H_3O^+]$$

Solution: 5.0 mL NaOH x $\dfrac{1\ L}{1000\ mL} = 0.0050$ L NaOH excess then

$\dfrac{0.125\ \text{mol NaOH}}{1\ L}$ x 0.0050 L $= 0.000625$ mol NaOH excess . then 0.0200 L $HC_2H_3O_2$ + 0.0168 L NaOH +

0.0050 L NaOH $= 0.0418$ L total volume.

$[NaOH\ excess] = \dfrac{0.000625\ \text{mol NaOH excess}}{0.0418\ L} = 0.0149522$ M NaOH excess Since NaOH is a strong base,

$[NaOH]$ excess $= [OH^-]$. The strong base overwhelms the weak base and is insignificant in the calculation. $K_w = [H_3O^+][OH^-]$ so $[H_3O^+] = \dfrac{K_w}{[OH^-]} = \dfrac{1.0 \times 10^{-14}}{0.0149522} = 6.\underline{6}88 \times 10^{-13}$ M . Finally,

$pH = -\log[H_3O^+] = -\log(6.\underline{6}88 \times 10^{-13}) = 12.17$.

Check: The units (none) are correct. The pH is rising sharply at the equivalence point, so the pH after 5 mL past the equivalence point should be quite basic.

72. **Given:** 30.0 mL of 0.165 M $HC_3H_5O_2$ titrated with 0.300 M KOH   **Other:** K_a ($HC_3H_5O_2$) = 1.3×10^{-5}
Find: initial pH
Conceptual Plan: Since $HC_3H_5O_2$ is a weak acid, set up an equilibrium problem using the initial concentration.
So   **M $HC_3H_5O_2$** $\rightarrow$ **$[H_3O^+]$** $\rightarrow$ **pH**
                ICE Chart $pH = -\log[H_3O^+]$

Solution:

$$HC_3H_5O_2\,(aq) + H_2O\,(l) \rightleftharpoons H_3O^+\,(aq) + C_3H_5O_2{}^{2-}(aq)$$

	$[HC_3H_5O_2]$	$[H_3O^+]$	$[C_3H_5O_2{}^{2-}]$
Initial	0.165	≈ 0.00	0.00
Change	$-x$	$+x$	$+x$
Equil	$0.165-x$	$+x$	$+x$

$K_a = \dfrac{[H_3O^+][C_3H_5O_2{}^-]}{[HC_3H_5O_2]} = 1.3 \times 10^{-5} = \dfrac{x^2}{0.165-x}$ Assume x is small (x $\ll$ 0.165) so

$\dfrac{x^2}{0.165-\cancel{x}} = 1.3 \times 10^{-5} = \dfrac{x^2}{0.165}$ and $x = 1.\underline{4}646 \times 10^{-3} = [H_3O^+]$. Confirm that assumption is valid

$\dfrac{1.\underline{4}646 \times 10^{-3}}{0.165} \times 100\,\% = 0.89\,\% < 5\,\%$ so assumption is valid. Finally,

$pH = -\log[H_3O^+] = -\log(1.\underline{4}646 \times 10^{-3}) = 2.83$

Check: The units (none) are correct. The magnitude of the answer makes physical sense because pH should be greater than $-\log(0.165) = 0.78$ because this is a weak acid.

Find: pH after adding 5.0 mL of base
Conceptual Plan:
Write balanced equation then   mL $\rightarrow$ L then $[HC_3H_5O_2]$, L $\rightarrow$ mol $HC_3H_5O_2$ then

$HC_3H_5O_2 + KOH \rightarrow KC_3H_5O_2 + H_2O$ $\dfrac{1\,L}{1000\,mL}$ $M = \dfrac{mol}{L}$

mL $\rightarrow$ L then   [KOH], L $\rightarrow$ mol KOH then

$\dfrac{1\,L}{1000\,mL}$ $M = \dfrac{mol}{L}$

mol $HC_3H_5O_2$, mol KOH $\rightarrow$ mol excess $HC_3H_5O_2$, mol $C_3H_5O_2{}^-$
          set up stoichiometry table
Since there are significant concentrations of both the acid and the conjugate base species, this is a buffer solution and so Henderson-Hasselbalch Equation $\left(pH = pK_a + \log \dfrac{[base]}{[acid]} \right)$ can be used. Also note that ratio of concentrations is the same as the ration of moles, since the volume is the same for both species.

Solution: $30.0 \text{ mL } HC_3H_5O_2 \times \dfrac{1\,L}{1000\,mL} = 0.0300\text{ L } HC_3H_5O_2$ then

$\dfrac{0.165 \text{ mol } HC_3H_5O_2}{1\,L} \times 0.0300\text{ L} = 0.00495 \text{ mol } HC_3H_5O_2$ and $5.0 \text{ mL KOH} \times \dfrac{1\,L}{1000\,mL} = 0.0050\text{ L KOH}$ then

$\dfrac{0.300 \text{ mol KOH}}{1\,L} \times 0.0050\text{ L} = 0.0015 \text{ mol KOH}$. Set up table to track changes:

	KOH (aq)	+ $HC_3H_5O_2$ (aq)	$\rightarrow$	$KC_3H_5O_2$ (aq)	+ H_2O (l)
Before addition	0.00 mol	0.00495 mol		0.00 mol	–
Addition	0.0015 mol	–		–	–
After addition	≈ 0.00 mol	0.00345 mol		0.0015 mol	–

Then use Henderson-Hasselbalch Equation, since the solution is a buffer.

$$pH = pK_a + \log\frac{[base]}{[acid]} = -\log(1.3 \times 10^{-5}) + \log\frac{0.0015}{0.00345} = 4.52$$

Check: The units (none) are correct. The pH is a little higher than the initial pH, which is expected since some of the acid has been neutralized.

Find: pH after adding 10.0 mL of base

Conceptual Plan: Use calculations from above then mL → L then [KOH], L → mol KOH then

$$\frac{1\,L}{1000\,mL} \qquad\qquad M = \frac{mol}{L}$$

mol HC$_3$H$_5$O$_2$, mol KOH → mol excess HC$_3$H$_5$O$_2$, mol C$_3$H$_5$O$_2^-$

set up stoichiometry table

Since there are significant concentrations of both the acid and the conjugate base species, this is a buffer solution and so Henderson-Hasselbalch Equation $\left(pH = pK_a + \log\frac{[base]}{[acid]} \right)$ **can be used. Also note that ratio of concentrations is the same as the ration of moles, since the volume is the same for both species.**

Solution: $10.0\ \overline{mL\,KOH} \times \dfrac{1\,L}{1000\,\overline{mL}} = 0.0100\,L\,KOH$ then $\dfrac{0.300\,mol\,KOH}{1\,\overline{L}} \times 0.0100\,\overline{L} = 0.0030\,mol\,KOH$.

Set up table to track changes:

	KOH (aq)	+ HC$_3$H$_5$O$_2$ (aq)	→ KC$_3$H$_5$O$_2$ (aq)	+ H$_2$O (l)
Before addition	0.00 mol	0.00495 mol	0.00 mol	–
Addition	0.0030 mol	–	–	–
After addition	≈ 0.00 mol	0.00195 mol	0.0030 mol	–

Then use Henderson-Hasselbalch Equation, since the solution is a buffer.

$$pH = pK_a + \log\frac{[base]}{[acid]} = -\log(1.3 \times 10^{-5}) + \log\frac{0.0030}{0.00195} = 5.07$$

Check: The units (none) are correct. The pH is a little higher than the last pH, which is expected since some of the acid has been neutralized.

Find: pH at equivalence point

Conceptual Plan: Use calculations from above, then set mol acid (HC$_3$H$_5$O$_2$) = mol base (KOH)

balanced equation has 1:1 stoichiometry

and [KOH], mol KOH → L KOH   then since all of the weak acid has been converted to its

$$M = \frac{mol}{L}$$

conjugate base, the pH is only dependent on the hydrolysis reaction of the conjugate base. The mol C$_3$H$_5$O$_2^-$ = initial mol HC$_3$H$_5$O$_2$ and L HC$_3$H$_5$O$_2$, L KOH to equivalence point → total L

L HC$_3$H$_5$O$_2$ + L KOH = total L

then   mol C$_2$H$_3$O$_2^-$, L → [C$_2$H$_3$O$_2^-$]   and

$$M = \frac{mol}{L}$$

K$_a$ → K$_b$ then   do equilibrium calculation: [C$_2$H$_3$O$_2^-$], K$_b$ → [OH$^-$] → [H$_3$O$^+$] →   pH

$K_w = K_a\,K_b$ set up ICE table $K_w = [H_3O^+][OH^-]$ $pH = -\log[H_3O^+]$

Solution: mol acid = mol HC$_3$H$_5$O$_2$ = 0.00495 mol = mol KOH then

$$0.00495\ \overline{mol\,KOH} \times \frac{1\,L}{0.300\,\overline{mol\,KOH}} = 0.0165\,L\,KOH\ .\ \text{then total volume} = L\,HC_3H_5O_2 + L\,KOH =$$

$0.0300\,L + 0.0165\,L = 0.0465$ then $[C_3H_5O_2^-] = \dfrac{0.00495\,mol\,C_3H_5O_2^-}{0.0465\,L} = 0.10\underline{6}452\,M$ and $K_w = K_a\,K_b$.

Rearrange to solve for K$_b$. $K_b = \dfrac{K_w}{K_a} = \dfrac{1.0 \times 10^{-14}}{1.3 \times 10^{-5}} = 7.\underline{6}923 \times 10^{-10}\,M$. Set up ICE table

$$C_3H_5O_2^-\,(aq) + H_2O(l) \rightleftharpoons HC_3H_5O_2\,(aq) + OH^-(aq)$$

	[C$_3$H$_5$O$_2^-$]	[HC$_3$H$_5$O$_2$]	[OH$^-$]
Initial	0.10$\underline{6}$452	≈ 0.00	≈ 0.00
Change	$-x$	$+x$	$+x$
Equil	0.10$\underline{6}$452 $- x$	$+x$	$+x$

$$K_b = \frac{[HC_3H_5O_2]\,[OH^-]}{[C_3H_5O_2^-]} = 7.\underline{6}923 \times 10^{-10} = \frac{x^2}{0.10\underline{6}452 - x}$$ Assume x is small (x << 0.106) so

$$\frac{x^2}{0.10\underline{6}452 - \cancel{x}} = 7.\underline{6}923 \times 10^{-10} = \frac{x^2}{0.10\underline{6}452}$$ and x = 9.\underline{0}491 \times 10^{-6} = [OH^-].

Confirm that assumption is valid $\dfrac{9.\underline{0}491 \times 10^{-6}}{0.10\underline{6}452} \times 100\% = 0.0085\% < 5\%$ so assumption is valid.

$K_w = [H_3O^+][OH^-]$ so $[H_3O^+] = \dfrac{K_w}{[OH^-]} = \dfrac{1.0 \times 10^{-14}}{9.\underline{0}491 \times 10^{-6}} = 1.\underline{1}051 \times 10^{-9}\,M$. Finally,

$pH = -\log[H_3O^+] = -\log(1.\underline{1}051 \times 10^{-9}) = 8.96$.

Check: The units (none) are correct. Since this is a weak acid – strong base titration, the pH at the equivalence point is basic.

Find: pH at one-half of the equivalence point
Conceptual Plan: Since this is a weak acid – strong base titration, the pH at one-half the equivalence point is the pK_a of the weak acid.
Solution: $pH = pK_a = -\log K_a = -\log(1.8 \times 10^{-5}) = 4.74$ and the volume of added base is $0.5 \times 16.5\,mL = 8.3\,mL$.
Check: The units (none) are correct. Since this is a weak acid – strong base titration, the pH at one-half the equivalence point is the pK_a of the weak acid, so it should be a little below 5.

Find: pH after adding 20.0 mL of base
Conceptual Plan: Use calculations from earlier. then the pH is only dependent on the amount of excess base and the total solution volumes. mL added, mL at equiv. pt. → mL excess → L excess

mL excess = mL added – mL at equiv. pt. $\dfrac{1\,L}{1000\,mL}$

then mL excess → L excess then [KOH], L excess → mol KOH excess

$\dfrac{1\,L}{1000\,mL}$ $M = \dfrac{mol}{L}$

then L HC₃H₅O₂, L KOH to equivalence point, L KOH excess → total L then
L HC₂H₃O₂ + L KOH to equivalence point + L KOH excess = total L
mol excess KOH, total L → [KOH] = [OH⁻] → [H₃O⁺] → pH

$M = \dfrac{mol}{L}$ $K_w = [H_3O^+][OH^-]$ $pH = -\log[H_3O^+]$

Solution: mL KOH excess = mL added – mL to equiv. pt. = 20.0 mL – 16.5 mL = 3.5 mL.

$3.5\,\cancel{mL\,KOH} \times \dfrac{1\,L}{1000\,\cancel{mL}} = 0.0035\,L\,KOH\ excess$ then $\dfrac{0.300\,mol\,KOH}{1\,\cancel{L}} \times 0.0035\,\cancel{L} = 0.001\underline{0}5\,mol\,KOH\ excess$.

then $0.0300\,L\,HC_3H_5O_2 + 0.0165\,L\,KOH + 0.0035\,L\,KOH = 0.0500\,L$ total volume.

$[KOH\ excess] = \dfrac{0.001\underline{0}5\,mol\,KOH\ excess}{0.0500\,L} = 0.021\,M\,KOH\ excess$ Since KOH is a strong base, [KOH] excess =

[OH⁻]. The strong base overwhelms the weak base and is insignificant in the calculation. $K_w = [H_3O^+][OH^-]$

so $[H_3O^+] = \dfrac{K_w}{[OH^-]} = \dfrac{1.0 \times 10^{-14}}{0.021} = 4.\underline{7}619 \times 10^{-13}\,M$. Finally, $pH = -\log[H_3O^+] = -\log(4.\underline{7}619 \times 10^{-13}) = 12.32$.

Check: The units (none) are correct. The pH is rising sharply at the equivalence point, so the pH after 5 mL past the equivalence point should be quite basic.

Find: pH after adding 25.0 mL of base
Conceptual Plan: Use calculations from earlier. then the pH is only dependent on the amount of excess base and the total solution volumes. mL added, mL at equiv. pt. → mL excess → L excess

mL excess = mL added – mL at equiv. pt. $\dfrac{1\,L}{1000\,mL}$

then mL excess → L excess then [KOH], L excess → mol KOH excess

$\dfrac{1\,L}{1000\,mL}$ $M = \dfrac{mol}{L}$

then L HC₃H₅O₂, L KOH to equivalence point, L KOH excess → total L then
L HC₂H₃O₂ + L KOH to equivalence point + L KOH excess = total L

mol excess KOH, total L $\rightarrow$ **[KOH] = [OH⁻]** $\rightarrow$ **[H₃O⁺]** $\rightarrow$ **pH**

$$M = \frac{mol}{L} \qquad\qquad K_w = [H_3O^+][OH^-] \qquad pH = -\log[H_3O^+]$$

Solution: mL KOH excess = mL added – mL to equiv. pt. = 25.0 mL – 16.5 mL = 8.5 mL.

$8.5 \text{ mL KOH} \times \dfrac{1 \text{ L}}{1000 \text{ mL}} = 0.0085 \text{ L KOH excess}$ then $\dfrac{0.300 \text{ mol KOH}}{1 \text{ L}} \times 0.0085 \text{ L} = 0.00255 \text{ mol KOH excess}$.

then $0.0300 \text{ L HC}_3\text{H}_5\text{O}_2 + 0.0165 \text{ L KOH} + 0.0085 \text{ L KOH} = 0.0550 \text{ L total volume.}$

$[\text{KOH excess}] = \dfrac{0.00255 \text{ mol KOH excess}}{0.0550 \text{ L}} = 0.046364 \text{ M KOH excess}$ Since KOH is a strong base, [KOH]

excess = [OH⁻]. The strong base overwhelms the weak base and is insignificant in the calculation.

$K_w = [H_3O^+][OH^-]$ So $[H_3O^+] = \dfrac{K_w}{[OH^-]} = \dfrac{1.0 \times 10^{-14}}{0.046364} = 2.1569 \times 10^{-13}$ M . Finally,

$pH = -\log[H_3O^+] = -\log(2.1569 \times 10^{-13}) = 12.67.$

Check: The units (none) are correct. The pH is rising sharply at the equivalence point, so the pH after 5 mL past the equivalence point should be quite basic. This pH is higher than the last pH.

Plotting these data points:

73. **Given:** 25.0 mL of 0.175 M CH₃NH₂ titrated with 0.150 M HBr   **Other:** K_b (CH₃NH₂) = 4.4 × 10⁻⁴
    a) **Find:** initial pH
       Conceptual Plan: Conceptual Plan: **Since CH₃NH₂ is a weak base, set up an equilibrium problem using the initial concentration. so   M CH₃NH₂ $\rightarrow$ [OH⁻] $\rightarrow$ [H₃O⁺] $\rightarrow$ pH**

       $$\text{ICE Chart} \quad K_w = [H_3O^+][OH^-] \quad pH = -\log[H_3O^+]$$

       Solution:

       $$CH_3NH_2\,(aq) + H_2O\,(l) \rightleftharpoons CH_3NH_3^+\,(aq) + OH^-\,(aq)$$

	[CH₃NH₂]	[CH₃NH₃⁺]	[OH⁻]
Initial	0.175	0.00	≈ 0.00
Change	−x	+ x	+ x
Equil	0.175 − x	+ x	+ x

       $K_b = \dfrac{[CH_3NH_3^+][OH^-]}{[CH_3NH_2]} = 4.4 \times 10^{-4} = \dfrac{x^2}{0.175 - x}$

       Assume x is small (x << 0.175) so $\dfrac{x^2}{0.175 - x} = 4.4 \times 10^{-4} = \dfrac{x^2}{0.175}$ and x = 8.7750 × 10⁻³ = [OH⁻].

       Confirm that assumption is valid $\dfrac{8.7750 \times 10^{-3}}{0.175} \times 100\% = 5.0\%$ so assumption is valid.

       $K_w = [H_3O^+][OH^-]$ so $[H_3O^+] = \dfrac{K_w}{[OH^-]} = \dfrac{1.0 \times 10^{-14}}{8.7750 \times 10^{-3}} = 1.1396 \times 10^{-12}$ M . Finally,

       $pH = -\log[H_3O^+] = -\log(1.1396 \times 10^{-12}) = 11.94.$

       Check: The units (none) are correct.   The magnitude of the answer makes physical sense because pH should be less than 14 + log (0.175) = 13.2 because this is a weak base.

    b) **Find:** volume of acid to reach equivalence point
       Conceptual Plan: Write balanced equation   then   mL $\rightarrow$ L then [CH₃NH₂], L $\rightarrow$ mol CH₃NH₂

       $$HBr + CH_3NH_2 \rightarrow CH_3NH_3Br + H_2O \qquad\qquad \frac{1 \text{ L}}{1000 \text{ mL}} \qquad\qquad M = \frac{mol}{L}$$

586

then set mol base (CH_3NH_2) = mol acid (HBr)   and   [HBr], mol HBr $\rightarrow$ L HBr $\rightarrow$ mL HBr

balanced equation has 1:1 stoichiometry

$$M = \dfrac{mol}{L} \qquad \dfrac{1000\ mL}{1\ L}$$

Solution: $25.0\ \cancel{mL\ CH_3NH_2}$ x $\dfrac{1\ L}{1000\ \cancel{mL}}$ = 0.0250 L CH_3NH_2 then

$\dfrac{0.175\ mol\ CH_3NH_2}{1\ \cancel{L}}$ x 0.0250 $\cancel{L}$ = 0.004375 mol CH_3NH_2 . So mol base = mol CH_3NH_2 = 0.002875 mol =

mol HBr then   0.004375 $\cancel{mol\ HBr}$ x $\dfrac{1\ L}{0.150\ \cancel{mol\ HBr}}$ = 0.0291667 $\cancel{L\ HBr}$ x $\dfrac{1000\ mL}{1\ \cancel{L}}$ = 29.2 mL HBr .

Check: The units (mL) are correct. The volume of acid is a greater less than the volume of base because the concentration of the base is a little greater that of the acid.

c) **Find:** pH after adding 5.0 mL of acid
Conceptual Plan: Use calculations from part b. then mL $\rightarrow$ L then [HBr], L $\rightarrow$ mol HBr

$$\dfrac{1\ L}{1000\ mL} \qquad\qquad M = \dfrac{mol}{L}$$

then mol CH_3NH_2, mol HBr $\rightarrow$ mol excess CH_3NH_2 and L CH_3NH_2, L HBr $\rightarrow$ total L   then

set up stoichiometry table   L CH_3NH_2 + L HBr = total L

Since there are significant concentrations of both the acid and the conjugate base species, this is a buffer solution and so Henderson-Hasselbalch Equation $\left(pH = pK_a + \log \dfrac{[base]}{[acid]} \right)$ **can be used.**

Convert K_b to K_a using $K_w = K_a\, K_b$. Also note that ratio of concentrations is the same as the ration of moles, since the volume is the same for both species.

Solution: 5.0 $\cancel{mL\ HBr}$ x $\dfrac{1\ L}{1000\ \cancel{mL}}$ = 0.0050 L HBr   then $\dfrac{0.150\ mol\ HBr}{1\ \cancel{L}}$ x 0.0050 $\cancel{L}$ = 0.00075 mol HBr .

Set up table to track changes:

	HBr (*aq*)	+ CH_3NH_2 (*aq*)	$\rightarrow$	CH_3NH_3Br (*aq*)
Before addition	0.00 mol	0.004375 mol		0.00 mol
Addition	0.00075 mol	–		–
After addition	$\approx$ 0.00 mol	0.003625 mol		0.000750 mol

then $K_w = K_a\, K_b$ so

$K_a = \dfrac{K_w}{K_b} = \dfrac{1.0\ x\ 10^{-14}}{4.4\ x\ 10^{-4}}$ = 2.2727 x 10^{-11} M then use Henderson-Hasselbalch Equation, since the solution is

a buffer. $pH = pK_a + \log \dfrac{[base]}{[acid]} = - \log(2.2727\ x\ 10^{-11}) + \log \dfrac{0.003625}{0.000750} = 11.33$

Check: The units (none) are correct. The pH is a little lower than the last pH, which is expected since some of the base has been neutralized.

d) **Find:** pH at one-half of the equivalence point
Conceptual Plan: Since this is a weak base – strong acid titration, the pH at one-half the equivalence point is the pK_a of the conjugate acid of weak base.
Solution: $pH = pK_a = - \log K_a = - \log (2.2727\ x\ 10^{-11}) = 10.64$.

Check: The units (none) are correct. Since this is a weak acid – strong base titration, the pH at one-half the equivalence point is the pK_a of the conjugate acid of the weak base, so it should be a little below 11.

e) **Find:** pH at equivalence point
Conceptual Plan: Use calculations from above. Since all of the weak base has been converted to its conjugate acid, the pH is only dependent on the hydrolysis reaction of the conjugate acid. The mol $CH_3NH_3^+$ = initial mol CH_3NH_2 and
L CH_3NH_2, L HBr to equivalence point $\rightarrow$ total L then   mol $CH_3NH_3^+$, L $\rightarrow$ [$CH_3NH_3^+$]

L CH_3NH_2 + L HBr = total L $M = \dfrac{mol}{L}$

then   do equilibrium calculation: [$CH_3NH_3^+$], K_a $\rightarrow$ [H_3O^+] $\rightarrow$ pH

set up ICE table $pH = - \log [H_3O^+]$

Solution: mol base = mol acid = mol $CH_3NH_3^+$ = 0.004375 mol. then total volume = L CH_3NH_2 + L

HBr = 0.0250 L + 0.0292 L = 0.0542 then $[CH_3NH_3^+] = \dfrac{0.004375 \text{ mol mol } CH_3NH_3^+}{0.0542 \text{ L}} = 0.0807196$ M . Set

$$CH_3NH_3^+(aq) + H_2O(l) \rightleftharpoons CH_3NH_2(aq) + H_3O^+(aq)$$

	$[CH_3NH_3^+]$	$[CH_3NH_2]$	$[H_3O^+]$
Initial	0.0807196	≈ 0.00	≈ 0.00
Change	$-x$	$+x$	$+x$
Equil	0.0807196 $- x$	$+x$	$+x$

up ICE table

$K_a = \dfrac{[CH_3NH_2][H_3O^+]}{[CH_3NH_3^+]} = 2.2727 \times 10^{-11} = \dfrac{x^2}{0.0807196 - x}$ Assume x is small (x << 0.0807) so

$\dfrac{x^2}{0.0807196 - \cancel{x}} = 2.2727 \times 10^{-11} = \dfrac{x^2}{0.0807196}$ and x = 1.3544×10^{-6} = $[H_3O^+]$.

Confirm that assumption is valid $\dfrac{1.3544 \times 10^{-6}}{0.0807106} \times 100\,\% = 0.0017\,\% < 5\,\%$ so assumption is valid.

Finally, $pH = -\log[H_3O^+] = -\log(1.3544 \times 10^{-6}) = 5.87$.

Check: The units (none) are correct. Since this is a weak base – strong acid titration, the pH at the equivalence point is acidic.

f) **Find:** pH after adding 5.0 mL of acid beyond the equivalence point
    Conceptual Plan: Use calculations from parts b & c. then the pH is only dependent on the amount of excess acid and the total solution volumes.
    mL excess → L excess then [HBr], L excess → mol HBr excess

$\dfrac{1\text{ L}}{1000\text{ mL}}$ $\qquad\qquad\qquad\qquad M = \dfrac{\text{mol}}{\text{L}}$

then L CH_3NH_2, L HBr to equivalence point, L HBr excess → total L then

L CH_3NH_2 + L HBr to equivalence point + L HBr excess = total L

mol excess HBr, total L → [HBr] = $[H_3O^+]$ → pH

$M = \dfrac{\text{mol}}{\text{L}}$ $\qquad\qquad pH = -\log[H_3O^+]$

Solution: 5.0 $\cancel{\text{mL HBr}}$ x $\dfrac{1\text{ L}}{1000\ \cancel{\text{mL}}} = 0.0050$ L HBr excess then

$\dfrac{0.150\text{ mol HBr}}{1\ \cancel{\text{L}}}$ x 0.0050 $\cancel{\text{L}}$ = 0.00075 mol HBr excess . then 0.0250 L CH_3NH_2 + 0.0292 L HBr + 0.0050

L HBr = 0.0592 L total volume. [HBr excess] = $\dfrac{0.00075\text{ mol HBr excess}}{0.0592\text{ L}} = 0.012669$ M HBr excess

Since HBr is a strong acid, [HBr] excess = $[H_3O^+]$. The strong acid overwhelms the weak acid and is insignificant in the calculation. Finally, $pH = -\log[H_3O^+] = -\log(0.012669) = 1.90$.

Check: The units (none) are correct. The pH is dropping sharply at the equivalence point, so the pH after 5 mL past the equivalence point should be quite acidic.

74. **Given:** 25.0 mL of 0.125 M pyridine (C_5H_5N) titrated with 0.100 M HCl **Other:** K_b (C_5H_5N) = 1.7×10^{-9}
    Find: initial pH
    Conceptual Plan: Since C_5H_5N is a weak base, set up an equilibrium problem using the initial concentration. so M C_5H_5N → [OH⁻] → $[H_3O^+]$ → pH

ICE Chart $K_w = [H_3O^+][OH^-]$ $pH = -\log[H_3O^+]$

Solution:

$$C_5H_5N(aq) + H_2O(l) \rightleftharpoons C_5H_5NH^+(aq) + OH^-(aq)$$

	$[C_5H_5N]$	$[C_5H_5NH^+]$	$[OH^-]$
Initial	0.125	0.00	≈ 0.00
Change	$-x$	$+x$	$+x$
Equil	0.125 $- x$	$+x$	$+x$

$K_b = \dfrac{[C_5H_5NH^+][OH^-]}{[C_5H_5N]} = 1.7 \times 10^{-9} = \dfrac{x^2}{0.125 - x}$

Assume x is small (x << 0.125) so $\dfrac{x^2}{0.125 - \cancel{x}} = 1.7 \times 10^{-9} = \dfrac{x^2}{0.125}$ and x = 1.4577×10^{-5} = $[OH^-]$.

Confirm that assumption is valid $\dfrac{1.\underline{4}577 \times 10^{-5}}{0.125} \times 100\% = 0.012\% < 5.0\%$ so assumption is valid.

$K_w = [H_3O^+][OH^-]$ so $[H_3O^+] = \dfrac{K_w}{[OH^-]} = \dfrac{1.0 \times 10^{-14}}{1.\underline{4}577 \times 10^{-5}} = 6.\underline{8}601 \times 10^{-10}\ M$. Finally,

$pH = -\log[H_3O^+] = -\log(6.\underline{8}601 \times 10^{-10}) = 9.16$.

Check: The units (none) are correct. The magnitude of the answer makes physical sense because pH should be less than $14 + \log(0.125) = 13.1$ because this is a weak base.

Find: pH after adding 10.0 mL of acid

Conceptual Plan: Write balanced equation then   mL → L   then $[C_5H_5N]$, L → mol C_5H_5N then

$$HCl + C_5H_5N \to C_5H_5NHCl \qquad \dfrac{1\ L}{1000\ mL} \qquad M = \dfrac{mol}{L}$$

mL → L   then   [HCl], L → mol HCl   then   mol C_5H_5N, mol HCl → mol excess C_5H_5N and

$$\dfrac{1\ L}{1000\ mL} \qquad M = \dfrac{mol}{L} \qquad\qquad \text{set up stoichiometry table}$$

L C_5H_5N, L HCl → total L   then   Since there are significant concentrations of both the acid and
L C_5H_5N + L HCl = total L

the conjugate base species, this is a buffer solution and so Henderson-Hasselbalch Equation

$\left(pH = pK_a + \log\dfrac{[base]}{[acid]}\right)$ **can be used. Convert K_b to K_a using** $K_w = K_a K_b$. **Also note that ratio of**

concentrations is the same as the ration of moles, since the volume is the same for both species.

Solution: $25.0\ \overline{mL\ C_5H_5N} \times \dfrac{1\ L}{1000\ \overline{mL}} = 0.0250\ L\ C_5H_5N$ then

$\dfrac{0.125\ mol\ C_5H_5N}{1\ \overline{L}} \times 0.0250\ \overline{L} = 0.0031\underline{2}5\ mol\ C_5H_5N$. and $10.0\ \overline{mL\ HCl} \times \dfrac{1\ L}{1000\ \overline{mL}} = 0.0100\ L\ HCl$ then

$\dfrac{0.100\ mol\ HCl}{1\ \overline{L}} \times 0.0100\ \overline{L} = 0.00100\ mol\ HCl$. Set up table to track changes:

	$HCl\ (aq)$	+ $C_5H_5N\ (aq)$	→ $C_5H_5NHCl\ (aq)$
Before addition	0.00 mol	0.0031$\underline{2}$5 mol	0.00 mol
Addition	0.00100 mol	–	–
After addition	≈ 0.00 mol	0.0021$\underline{2}$5 mol	0.00100 mol

Then $K_w = K_a K_b$ so $K_a = \dfrac{K_w}{K_b} = \dfrac{1.0 \times 10^{-14}}{1.7 \times 10^{-9}} = 5.\underline{8}824 \times 10^{-6}\ M$ then use Henderson-Hasselbalch Equation,

since the solution is a buffer. $pH = pK_a + \log\dfrac{[base]}{[acid]} = -\log(5.\underline{8}824 \times 10^{-6}) + \log\dfrac{0.0021\underline{2}5}{0.00100} = 5.56$

Check: The units (none) are correct. The pH is lower than the last pH, which is expected since some of the base has been neutralized.

Find: pH after adding 20.0 mL of acid

Conceptual Plan: Use calculations from above. then   mL → L   then   [HCl], L → mol HCl

$$\dfrac{1\ L}{1000\ mL} \qquad\qquad M = \dfrac{mol}{L}$$

then mol C_5H_5N, mol HCl → mol excess C_5H_5N and   L C_5H_5N, L HCl → total L   then
set up stoichiometry table   L C_5H_5N + L HCl = total L

Since there are significant concentrations of both the acid and the conjugate base species, this is a

buffer solution and so Henderson-Hasselbalch Equation $\left(pH = pK_a + \log\dfrac{[base]}{[acid]}\right)$ **can be used. Convert**

K_b to K_a using $K_w = K_a K_b$. **Also note that ratio of concentrations is the same as the ration of moles, since the volume is the same for both species.**

Solution: $20.0\ \overline{mL\ HCl} \times \dfrac{1\ L}{1000\ \overline{mL}} = 0.0200\ L\ HCl$ then $\dfrac{0.100\ mol\ HCl}{1\ \overline{L}} \times 0.0200\ \overline{L} = 0.00200\ mol\ HCl$. Set

up table to track changes:

$$\text{HCl } (aq) \quad + \text{ C}_5\text{H}_5\text{N } (aq) \quad \rightarrow \quad \text{C}_5\text{H}_5\text{NHCl } (aq)$$

	HCl (aq)	C$_5$H$_5$N (aq)	C$_5$H$_5$NHCl (aq)
Before addition	0.00 mol	0.003125 mol	0.00 mol
Addition	0.00200 mol	–	–
After addition	≈ 0.00 mol	0.001125 mol	0.00200 mol

Then use Henderson-Hasselbalch Equation, since the solution is a buffer.

$$\text{pH} = \text{pK}_a + \log \frac{[\text{base}]}{[\text{acid}]} = -\log(5.\underline{8}824 \times 10^{-6}) + \log \frac{0.001125}{0.00200} = 4.98$$

Check: The units (none) are correct. The pH is lower than the last pH, which is expected since some of the base has been neutralized.

Find: pH at equivalence point
Conceptual Plan:
Use calculations from above. Since all of the weak base has been converted to its conjugate acid, the pH is only dependent on the hydrolysis reaction of the conjugate acid. The mol C$_5$H$_5$NH$^+$ = initial mol C$_5$H$_5$N then set mol base (C$_5$H$_5$N) = mol acid (HCl) and [HCl], mol HCl $\rightarrow$ L HCl then

$$\text{balanced equation has 1:1 stoichiometry} \qquad\qquad M = \frac{\text{mol}}{\text{L}}$$

L C$_5$H$_5$N, L HCl to equivalence point $\rightarrow$ total L then mol C$_5$H$_5$NH$^+$, L $\rightarrow$ [C$_5$H$_5$NH$^+$]

$$\text{L C}_5\text{H}_5\text{N} + \text{L HCl} = \text{total L} \qquad\qquad M = \frac{\text{mol}}{\text{L}}$$

then do equilibrium calculation: [C$_5$H$_5$NH$^+$], K$_a$ $\rightarrow$ [H$_3$O$^+$] $\rightarrow$ pH

$$\text{set up ICE table} \qquad pH = -\log[\text{H}_3\text{O}^+]$$

Solution: mol base = mol acid = mol C$_5$H$_5$NH$^+$ = 0.003125 mol. then

$$0.003\underline{1}25 \text{ mol HCl} \times \frac{1 \text{ L}}{0.100 \text{ mol HCl}} = 0.03125 \text{ L HCl} \times \frac{1000 \text{ mL}}{1 \text{ L}} = 31.3 \text{ mL HCl then}$$

total volume = L C$_5$H$_5$N + L HCl = 0.0250 L + 0.0313 L = 0.05632 L then

$$[\text{C}_5\text{H}_5\text{NH}^+] = \frac{0.003125 \text{ mol mol C}_5\text{H}_5\text{NH}^+}{0.0563 \text{ L}} = 0.055\underline{5}556 \text{ M}. \text{ Set up ICE table}$$

$$\text{C}_5\text{H}_5\text{NH}^+ (aq) + \text{H}_2\text{O}(l) \rightleftharpoons \text{C}_5\text{H}_5\text{N}(aq) + \text{H}_3\text{O}^+(aq)$$

	[C$_5$H$_5$NH$^+$]	[C$_5$H$_5$N]	[H$_3$O$^+$]
Initial	0.055\underline{5}556	≈ 0.00	≈ 0.00
Change	−x	+ x	+ x
Equil	0.055\underline{5}556 − x	+ x	+ x

$$K_a = \frac{[\text{C}_5\text{H}_5\text{N}][\text{H}_3\text{O}^+]}{[\text{C}_5\text{H}_5\text{NH}^+]} = 5.\underline{8}824 \times 10^{-6} = \frac{x^2}{0.055\underline{5}556 - x}$$

Assume x is small (x << 0.0556) so $\dfrac{x^2}{0.055\underline{5}556 - x} = 5.\underline{8}824 \times 10^{-6} = \dfrac{x^2}{0.055\underline{5}556}$ and x = 5.\underline{7}166 × 10^{-4} =

[H$_3$O$^+$]. Confirm that assumption is valid $\dfrac{5.\underline{7}166 \times 10^{-4}}{0.055\underline{5}556} \times 100 \% = 1.0 \% < 5 \%$ so assumption is valid.

Finally, $pH = -\log[\text{H}_3\text{O}^+] = -\log(5.\underline{7}166 \times 10^{-4}) = 3.24$.
Check: The units (none) are correct. Since this is a weak base – strong acid titration, the pH at the equivalence point is acidic.

Find: pH at one-half of the equivalence point
Conceptual Plan: Since this is a weak base – strong acid titration, the pH at one-half the equivalence point is the pK$_a$ of the conjugate acid of weak base.
Solution: $pH = pK_a = -\log K_a = -\log(5.\underline{8}824 \times 10^{-6}) = 5.23$ and the volume is 0.5 × 31.3 mL = 15.7 mL.

Check: The units (none) are correct. Since this is a weak base – strong acid titration, the pH at one-half the equivalence point is the pK$_a$ of the conjugate acid of the weak base, so it should be a little below 6.

Find: pH after adding 40.0 mL of acid
Conceptual Plan: Use calculations from above. then the pH is only dependent on the amount of excess acid and the total solution volumes.
mL added, mL at equiv. pt. $\rightarrow$ mL excess $\rightarrow$ L excess then

$$\text{mL excess} = \text{mL added} - \text{mL at equiv. pt.} \qquad \frac{1 \text{ L}}{1000 \text{ mL}}$$

mL excess → L excess   then   [HCl], L excess → mol HCl excess

$$\frac{1\,L}{1000\,mL}$$

$$M = \frac{mol}{L}$$

then L C_5H_5N, L HCl to equivalence point, L HCl excess → total L   then

L C_5H_5N + L HCl to equivalence point + L HCl excess = total L

mol excess HCl, total L → [HCl] = [H_3O^+] → pH

$$M = \frac{mol}{L}$$ $$pH = -\log[H_3O^+]$$

Solution: mL excess = mL added – mL at equiv. pt. = 40.0 mL – 31.3 mL = 8.7 mL.

8.7 mL HCl x $\frac{1\,L}{1000\,mL}$ = 0.0087 L HCl excess   then $\frac{0.100\ mol\ HCl}{1\ L}$ x 0.0087 L = 0.00087 mol HCl excess . then

0.0250 L C_5H_5N + 0.0313 L HCl + 0.0087 L HCl = 0.0650 L total volume.

$$[\text{HCl excess}] = \frac{0.00087\ mol\ HCl\ excess}{0.0650\ L} = 0.01\underline{3}385\ M\ HCl\ excess$$

Since HCl is a strong acid, [HCl] excess = [H_3O^+]. The strong acid overwhelms the weak acid and is insignificant in the calculation. Finally, $pH = -\log[H_3O^+] = -\log(0.01\underline{3}385) = 1.87$.

Check: The units (none) are correct. The pH is dropping sharply at the equivalence point, so the pH after 5 mL past the equivalence point should be quite acidic.

Find: pH after adding 50.0 mL of acid

Conceptual Plan:
Use calculations from above.   then   the pH is only dependent on the amount of excess acid and the total solution volumes.   mL added, mL at equiv. pt. →   mL excess →   L excess   then

mL excess = mL added – mL at equiv. pt. $\frac{1\,L}{1000\,mL}$

mL excess → L excess   then   [HCl], L excess → mol HCl excess

$$\frac{1\,L}{1000\,mL}$$

$$M = \frac{mol}{L}$$

then L C_5H_5N, L HCl to equivalence point, L HCl excess → total L   then

L C_5H_5N + L HCl to equivalence point + L HCl excess = total L

mol excess HCl, total L → [HCl] = [H_3O^+] → pH

$$M = \frac{mol}{L}$$ $$pH = -\log[H_3O^+]$$

Solution: mL excess = mL added – mL at equiv. pt. = 50.0 mL – 31.3 mL = 18.7 mL.

18.7 mL HCl x $\frac{1\,L}{1000\,mL}$ = 0.0187 L HCl excess   then $\frac{0.100\ mol\ HCl}{1\ L}$ x 0.0187 L = 0.00187 mol HCl excess .

then   0.0250 L C_5H_5N + 0.0313 L HCl + 0.0187 L HBr = 0.0750 L total volume.

$$[\text{HCl excess}] = \frac{0.00187\ mol\ HCl\ excess}{0.0750\ L} = 0.02\underline{4}933\ M\ HCl\ excess$$

Since HCl is a strong acid, [HCl] excess = [H_3O^+]. The strong acid overwhelms the weak acid and is insignificant in the calculation. Finally, $pH = -\log[H_3O^+] = -\log(0.02\underline{4}933) = 1.60$.

Check: The units (none) are correct. The pH is dropping sharply at the equivalence point, so the pH after 5 mL past the equivalence point should be quite acidic. The pH is lower than the last point.

Plotting these points gives:

75. i) acid a is more concentrated, since the equivalence point (where sharp pH rise occurs) is at a higher volume of added base.

   ii) acid b has the larger K_a, since the pH at a volume of added base equal to half of the equivalence point volume is lower.

76. i) acid b is more concentrated, since the equivalence point (where sharp pH rise occurs) is at a higher volume of added base.

   ii) acid b has the larger K_b, since the pH at a volume of added base equal to half of the equivalence point volume is higher.

77. **Given:** 0.229 g unknown monoprotic acid titrated with 0.112 M NaOH and curve   **Find:** molar mass and pK_a of acid
   Conceptual Plan: The equivalence point is where sharp pH rise occurs. The pK_a is the pH at a volume of added base equal to half of the equivalence point volume. then mL NaOH → L NaOH

$$\frac{1\,L}{1000\,mL}$$

   then [NaOH], L NaOH → mol NaOH = mol acid   then mol NaOH, g acid → molar mass

$$M = \frac{mol}{L} \qquad\qquad \frac{g\ acid}{mol\ acid}$$

   Solution: The equivalence point is at 25 mL NaOH. The pH at 0.5 x 25 mL = 13 mL is ~3. then

$$25\ \overline{mL\ NaOH} \times \frac{1\,L}{1000\ \overline{mL}} = 0.025\ L\ NaOH \quad then$$

$$\frac{0.112\ mol\ NaOH}{1\ \overline{L}} \times 0.025\ \overline{L} = 0.0028\ mol\ NaOH = 0.0028\ mol\ acid\ then\ Molar\ Mass = \frac{0.229\ g\ acid}{0.0028\ mol\ acid} = 82\ g/mol\ .$$

   Check: The units (none and g/mol) are correct. The pK_a is consistent with a weak acid. The molar mass is reasonable for an acid (>1 g/mol).

78. **Given:** 0.446 g unknown monoprotic acid titrated with 0.105 M KOH and curve   **Find:** molar mass and pK_a of acid
   Conceptual Plan: The equivalence point is where sharp pH rise occurs. The pK_a is the pH at a volume of added base equal to half of the equivalence point volume. then mL KOH → L KOH then

$$\frac{1\,L}{1000\,mL}$$

   [KOH], L KOH → mol KOH = mol acid   then mol KOH, g acid → molar mass

$$M = \frac{mol}{L} \qquad\qquad \frac{g\ acid}{mol\ acid}$$

   Solution: The equivalence point is at 35 mL NaOH. The pH at 0.5 x 35 mL = 18 mL is ~ 4.5. then

$$28\ \overline{mL\ KOH} \times \frac{1\,L}{1000\ \overline{mL}} = 0.028\ L\ KOH \quad then$$

$$\frac{0.105\ mol\ KOH}{1\ \overline{L}} \times 0.028\ \overline{L} = 0.00294\ mol\ KOH = 0.00294\ mol\ acid\ then$$

$$Molar\ Mass = \frac{0.446\ g\ acid}{0.00294\ mol\ acid} = 150\ g/mol\ .$$

   Check: The units (none and g/mol) are correct. The pK_a is consistent with a weak acid. The molar mass is reasonable for an acid (>1 g/mol).

79. **Given:** 20.0 mL of 0.125 M sulfurous acid (H_2SO_3) titrated with 0.1014 M KOH
    Find: volume of base added
   Conceptual Plan:
   Since this is a diprotic acid, each proton is titrated sequentially. Write balanced equations. then

$$H_2SO_3 + OH^- \rightarrow HSO_3^- + H_2O \quad and \quad HSO_3^- + OH^- \rightarrow SO_3^{2-} + H_2O$$

   mL → L then [H_2SO_3], L → mol H_2SO_3 then   set mol base (H_2SO_3) = mol acid (KOH) and

$$\frac{1\,L}{1000\,mL} \qquad\qquad M = \frac{mol}{L} \qquad\qquad balanced\ equation\ has\ 1{:}1\ stoichiometry$$

[KOH], mol KOH → L KOH → mL KOH the volume to the second equivalence point will be

$$M = \frac{mol}{L} \qquad \frac{1000 \text{ mL}}{1 \text{ L}}$$

double the volume to the first equivalence point.

Solution: 20.0 mL H₂SO₃ x $\frac{1 \text{ L}}{1000 \text{ mL}}$ = 0.0200 L H₂SO₃ then

$\frac{0.115 \text{ mol H}_2\text{SO}_3}{1 \text{ L}}$ x 0.0200 L = 0.00230 mol H₂SO₃. So mol base = mol H₂SO₃ = 0.00230 mol = mol KOH

then 0.00230 mol KOH x $\frac{1 \text{ L}}{0.1014 \text{ mol KOH}}$ = 0.02268245 L KOH x $\frac{1000 \text{ mL}}{1 \text{ L}}$ = 22.7 mL KOH to first

equivalencepoint. The volume to the second equivalence point is simply twice this amount or 45.4 mL to the second equivalence point.

Check: The units (mL) are correct. The volume of base is a greater than the volume of acid because the concentration of the acid is a little greater that of the base. The volume to the second equivalence point is twice the volume to the first equivalence point.

80. **Given:** 20.0 mL of 0.125 M diprotic acid (H₂A) titrated with 0.1019 M KOH **Find:** volume of base added
Conceptual Plan:
Since this is a diprotic acid, each proton is titrated sequentially. Write balanced equations.
$$H_2A + OH^- \rightarrow HA^- + H_2O \quad \text{and} \quad HA^- + OH^- \rightarrow A^{2-} + H_2O$$
then mL → L then [H₂A], L → mol H₂A   then   set mol base (H₂A) = mol acid (KOH) and

$\frac{1 \text{ L}}{1000 \text{ mL}}$ $\qquad M = \frac{mol}{L}$ $\qquad$ balanced equation has 1:1 stoichiometry

[KOH], mol KOH → L KOH → mL KOH the volume to the second equivalence point will be

$$M = \frac{mol}{L} \qquad \frac{1000 \text{ mL}}{1 \text{ L}}$$

double the volume to the first equivalence point.

Solution: 20.0 mL H₂A x $\frac{1 \text{ L}}{1000 \text{ mL}}$ = 0.0200 L H₂A then $\frac{0.125 \text{ mol H}_2\text{A}}{1 \text{ L}}$ x 0.0200 L = 0.00250 mol H₂A . So

mol base = mol H₂A = 0.00250 mol = mol KOH then

0.00250 mol KOH x $\frac{1 \text{ L}}{0.1019 \text{ mol KOH}}$ = 0.0245339 L KOH x $\frac{1000 \text{ mL}}{1 \text{ L}}$ = 24.5 mL KOH to first equivalence

point. The volume to the second equivalence point is simply twice this amount or 49.1 mL to the second equivalence point.

Check: The units (mL) are correct. The volume of base is a greater less than the volume of acid because the concentration of the acid is a little greater that of the base. The volume to the second equivalence point is twice the volume to the first equivalence point.

81. The indicator will be in its acid form at an acidic pH, so the color in the HCl sample will be red. The color change will occur over the pH range from pH = pKₐ – 1.0 to pH = pKₐ + 1.0, so the color will start to change at pH = 5.0 – 1.0 = 4.0 and finish changing by pH = 5.0 + 1.0 = 6.0

82. **Given:** Phenolphthalein pKₐ = 9.7, acid form = colorless, base form = pink **Find:** [In]/[HIn] and color
Conceptual Plan: calculate [In]/[HIn] using equation in chapter. If pH < (pKₐ – 1.0) then the solution

$$\frac{[In^-]}{[HIn]} = 10^{(pH - pK_a)}$$

is colorless. If pH > pKₐ + 1.0 then the solution is pink.
Solution:

a)   pH = 2.0 so $\frac{[In^-]}{[HIn]} = 10^{(pH-pK_a)} = 10^{(2.0-9.7)} = 10^{-7.7} = 2 \times 10^{-8}$ and the solution will be colorless.

b)   pH = 5.0 so $\frac{[In^-]}{[HIn]} = 10^{(pH-pK_a)} = 10^{(5.0-9.7)} = 10^{-4.7} = 2 \times 10^{-5}$ and the solution will be colorless.

c)   pH = 8.0 so $\frac{[In^-]}{[HIn]} = 10^{(pH-pK_a)} = 10^{(8.0-9.7)} = 10^{-1.7} = 2 \times 10^{-2}$ and the solution will be colorless.

d) $pH = 11.0$ so $\dfrac{[In^-]}{[HIn]} = 10^{(pH-pK_a)} = 10^{(11.0-9.7)} = 10^{+1.3} = 2 \times 10^1$ and the solution will be pink.

Check: The units (none) are correct. The ratio is less than one and the solution is colorless when the solution is more acidic than the pK_a. The ratio is greater than one and the solution is pink when the solution is more basic than the pK_a

83. Since the exact conditions of the titration are not given, a rough calculation will suffice. Looking at the pattern of earlier problems, the pH at the equivalence point of a titration of a weak acid and a strong base is the hydrolysis of the conjugate base of the weak acid that has been diluted by a factor of roughly 2 with base. If it is assumed that the initial concentration of the weak acid is ~ 0.1 M, then the conjugate base concentration will be ~ 0.05 M. From earlier calculations it can be seen that the $K_b = \dfrac{K_w}{K_a} = \dfrac{[OH^-]^2}{0.05}$ thus

$$[OH^-] = \sqrt{\dfrac{0.05\,K_w}{K_a}} = \sqrt{\dfrac{5 \times 10^{-16}}{K_a}} \text{ and the } pH = 14 + \log\sqrt{\dfrac{5 \times 10^{-16}}{K_a}}.$$

a) for HF, the $pK_a = 3.5 \times 10^{-4}$ and so the above equations approximates the pH at the equivalence point is ~ 8.0. Looking at Table 16.1, phenol red or *m*-nitrophenol will change at the appropriate pH range.

b) for HCl, the pH at the equivalence point is 7, since HCl is a strong acid. Looking at Table 16.1, alizarin, bromthymol blue or phenol red will change at the appropriate pH range.

c) for HCN, the $pK_a = 4.9 \times 10^{-10}$ and so the above equations approximates the pH at the equivalence point is ~ 11.0. Looking at Table 16.1, alizarin yellow R will change at the appropriate pH range.

84. Since the exact conditions of the titration are not given, a rough calculation will suffice. Looking at the pattern of earlier problems, the pH at the equivalence point of a titration of a weak base and a strong acid is the hydrolysis of the conjugate acid of the weak base that has been diluted by a factor of roughly 2 with acid. If it is assumed that the initial concentration of the weak base is ~ 0.1 M, then the conjugate acid concentration will be ~ 0.05 M. From earlier calculations it can be seen that the $K_a = \dfrac{K_w}{K_b} = \dfrac{[H_3O^+]^2}{0.05}$ thus

$$[H_3O^+] = \sqrt{\dfrac{0.05\,K_w}{K_b}} = \sqrt{\dfrac{5 \times 10^{-16}}{K_b}} \text{ and the } pH = -\log\sqrt{\dfrac{5 \times 10^{-16}}{K_b}}.$$

a) for CH_3NH_2, the $pK_b = 4.4 \times 10^{-4}$ and so the above equations approximates the pH at the equivalence point is ~ 6.0. Looking at Table 16.1, methyl red, Eriochrom Black T, bromeresol purple or bromthymol blue will change at the appropriate pH range.

b) for NaOH, the pH at the equivalence point is 7, since NaOH is a strong base. Looking at Table 16.1, alizarin, bromthymol blue or phenol red will change at the appropriate pH range.

c) for $C_6H_5NH_2$, the $pK_b = 3.9 \times 10^{-10}$ and so the above equations approximates the pH at the equivalence point is ~ 2.9. Looking at Table 16.1, erythrosine B will change at the appropriate pH range.

85. For the dissolution reaction, start with the ionic compound as a solid and put it in equilibrium with the appropriate cation and anion, making sure to include the appropriate stoichiometric coefficients. The K_{sp} expression is the product of the concentrations of the cation and anion concentrations raise to their stoichiometric coefficients.

a) $BaSO_4 (s) \rightleftharpoons Ba^{2+} (aq) + SO_4^{2-} (aq)$ and $K_{sp} = [Ba^{2+}][SO_4^{2-}]$.

b) $PbBr_2 (s) \rightleftharpoons Pb^{2+} (aq) + 2\,Br^- (aq)$ and $K_{sp} = [Pb^{2+}][Br^-]^2$.

c) $Ag_2CrO_4 (s) \rightleftharpoons 2\,Ag^+ (aq) + CrO_4^{2-} (aq)$ and $K_{sp} = [Ag^+]^2[CrO_4^{2-}]$.

86. For the dissolution reaction, start with the ionic compound as a solid and put it in equilibrium with the appropriate cation and anion, making sure to include the appropriate stoichiometric coefficients. The K_{sp} expression is the product of the concentrations of the cation and anion concentrations raise to their stoichiometric coefficients.

a) $CaCO_3 (s) \rightleftharpoons Ca^{2+} (aq) + CO_3^{2-} (aq)$ and $K_{sp} = [Ca^{2+}][CO_3^{2-}]$.

b) $PbCl_2 (s) \rightleftharpoons Pb^{2+} (aq) + 2\ Cl^- (aq)$ and $K_{sp} = [Pb^{2+}][Cl^-]^2$.

c) $AgI (s) \rightleftharpoons Ag^+ (aq) + I^- (aq)$ and $K_{sp} = [Ag^+][I^-]$.

87. **Given:** ionic compound formula and Table 16.2 of $K_{sp}^{'}$ values   **Find:** molar solubility (S)
     Conceptual Plan: use equation derived in problem #20 and solve for S.
$$\text{for ionic compound, } A_mX_n, \ K_{sp} = m^m\ n^n\ S^{m+n}.$$
Solution:
a)   for AgBr, $K_{sp} = 5.35 \times 10^{-13}$, $A = Ag^+$, m = 1, $X = Br^-$, and n = 1 so $K_{sp} = 5.35 \times 10^{-13} = S^2$. Rearrange
     to solve for S. $S = \sqrt{5.35 \times 10^{-13}} = 7.31 \times 10^{-7}$ M.

b)   for $Mg(OH)_2$, $K_{sp} = 2.06 \times 10^{-13}$, $A = Mg^{2+}$, m = 1, $X = OH^-$, and n = 2 so $K_{sp} = 2.06 \times 10^{-13} = 2^2 S^3$.
     Rearrange to solve for S. $S = \sqrt[3]{\dfrac{2.06 \times 10^{-13}}{4}} = 3.72 \times 10^{-5}$ M .

c)   for CaF_2, $K_{sp} = 1.46 \times 10^{-10}$, $A = Ca^{2+}$, m = 1, $X = F^-$, and n = 2 so $K_{sp} = 1.46 \times 10^{-10} = 2^2 S^3$. Rearrange
     to solve for S. $S = \sqrt[3]{\dfrac{1.46 \times 10^{-10}}{4}} = 3.32 \times 10^{-4}$ M .

Check: The units (M) are correct. The molar solubilities are much less than one and dependent not only on
the value of the K_{sp}, but also the stoichiometry of the ionic compound. The more ions that are generated, the
greater the molar solubility for the same value of the K_{sp}.

88. **Given:** ionic compound formula and Table 16.2 of K_{sp} values   **Find:** molar solubility (S)
     Conceptual Plan: use equation derived in problem #20 and solve for S.
$$\text{for ionic compound, } A_mX_n, \ K_{sp} = m^m\ n^n\ S^{m+n}.$$
Solution:
a)   for CuS, $K_{sp} = 1.27 \times 10^{-36}$, $A = Cu^{2+}$, m = 1, $X = S^{2-}$, and n = 1 so $K_{sp} = 1.27 \times 10^{-36} = S^2$. Rearrange
     to solve for S. $S = \sqrt{1.27 \times 10^{-36}} = 1.13 \times 10^{-18}$ M .

b)   for Ag_2CrO_4, $K_{sp} = 1.12 \times 10^{-12}$, $A = Ag^+$, m = 2, $X = CrO_4^{2-}$, and n = 1 so $K_{sp} = 1.12 \times 10^{-12} = 2^2 S^3$.
     Rearrange to solve for S. $S = \sqrt[3]{\dfrac{1.12 \times 10^{-12}}{4}} = 6.54 \times 10^{-5}$ M .

c)   for $Ca(OH)_2$, $K_{sp} = 4.68 \times 10^{-6}$, $A = Ca^{2+}$, m = 1, $X = OH^-$, and n = 2 so $K_{sp} = 4.68 \times 10^{-6} = 2^2 S^3$.
     Rearrange to solve for S. $S = \sqrt[3]{\dfrac{4.68 \times 10^{-6}}{4}} = 1.05 \times 10^{-2}$ M .

Check: The units (M) are correct. The molar solubilities are much less than one and dependent not only on
the value of the K_{sp}, but also the stoichiometry of the ionic compound. The more ions that are generated, the
greater the molar solubility for the same value of the K_{sp}.

89. **Given:** ionic compound formula and molar solubility (S)   **Find:** K_{sp} molar solubility (S)
     Conceptual Plan: use equation derived in problem #20.
$$\text{for ionic compound, } A_mX_n, \ K_{sp} = m^m\ n^n\ S^{m+n}.$$
Solution:
a)   for NiS, $S = 3.27 \times 10^{-11}$ M, $A = Ni^{2+}$, m = 1, $X = S^{2-}$, and n = 1 so $K_{sp} = S^2 = (3.27 \times 10^{-11})^2 = 1.07 \times 10^{-21}$.

b)   for PbF_2, $S = 5.63 \times 10^{-3}$ M, $A = Pb^{2+}$, m = 1, $X = F^-$, and n = 2 so $K_{sp} = 2^2 S^3 = 2^2 (5.63 \times 10^{-3})^3 = 7.14 \times 10^{-7}$.

c)   for MgF_2, $S = 2.65 \times 10^{-4}$ M, $A = Mg^{2+}$, m = 1, $X = F^-$, and n = 2 so $K_{sp} = 2^2 S^3 = 2^2 (2.65 \times 10^{-4})^3 = 7.44 \times 10^{-11}$.

Check: The units (none) are correct. The K_{sp} values are much less than one and dependent not only on the
value of the solubility, but also the stoichiometry of the ionic compound. The more ions that are generated,
the smaller the K_{sp} for the same value of the S.

90. **Given:** ionic compound formula and molar solubility (S) **Find:** K_{sp} molar solubility (S)
    Conceptual Plan: use equation derived in problem #20.
    $$\text{for ionic compound, } A_mX_n, \ K_{sp} = m^m \ n^n \ S^{m+n}.$$
    Solution:
    a) for $BaCrO_4$, $S = 1.08 \times 10^{-5}$ M, $A = Ba^{2+}$, $m = 1$, $X = CrO_4^{2-}$, and $n = 1$ so $K_{sp} = S^2 = (1.08 \times 10^{-5})^2 = 1.12 \times 10^{-10}$.

    b) for Ag_2SO_3, $S = 1.55 \times 10^{-5}$ M, $A = Ag^+$, $m = 2$, $X = SO_3^{2-}$, and $n = 1$ so $K_{sp} = 2^2 S^3 = 2^2 (1.55 \times 10^{-5})^3 = 1.49 \times 10^{-14}$.

    c) for $Pd(SCN)_2$, $S = 2.22 \times 10^{-8}$ M, $A = Pd^{2+}$, $m = 1$, $X = SCN^-$, and $n = 2$ so $K_{sp} = 2^2 S^3 = 2^2 (2.22 \times 10^{-8})^3 = 4.38 \times 10^{-23}$.

    Check: The units (none) are correct. The K_{sp} values are much less than one and dependent not only on the value of the solubility, but also the stoichiometry of the ionic compound. The more ions that are generated, the smaller the K_{sp} for the same value of the S.

91. **Given:** ionic compound formulas AX and AX_2 and $K_{sp} = 1.5 \times 10^{-5}$ **Find:** higher molar solubility (S)
    Conceptual Plan: use equation derived in problem #20 and solve for S, then compare S values.
    $$\text{for ionic compound, } A_mX_n, \ K_{sp} = m^m \ n^n \ S^{m+n}.$$
    Solution: for AX, $K_{sp} = 1.5 \times 10^{-5}$, $m = 1$, and $n = 1$ so $K_{sp} = 1.5 \times 10^{-5} = S^2$. Rearrange to solve for S. $S = \sqrt{1.5 \times 10^{-5}} = 3.9 \times 10^{-3}$ M . For AX_2, $K_{sp} = 1.5 \times 10^{-5}$, $m = 1$, and $n = 2$ so $K_{sp} = 1.5 \times 10^{-5} = 2^2 S^3$.

    Rearrange to solve for S. $S = \sqrt[3]{\dfrac{1.5 \times 10^{-5}}{4}} = 1.6 \times 10^{-2}$ M . Since 10^{-2} M > c. 10^{-3} M, AX_2 has a higher molar solubility.

    Check: The units (M) are correct. The more ions that are generated, the greater the molar solubility for the same value of the K_{sp}.

92. **Given:** ionic compound formula and molar solubility (S) **Find:** K_{sp} molar solubility (S)
    Conceptual Plan: use equation derived in problem #20.
    $$\text{for ionic compound, } A_mX_n, \ K_{sp} = m^m \ n^n \ S^{m+n}.$$
    Solution: AX, $S = 1.35 \times 10^{-4}$ M, $m = 1$, and $n = 1$ so $K_{sp} = S^2 = (1.35 \times 10^{-4})^2 = 1.82 \times 10^{-8}$.
    for AX_2, $S = 2.25 \times 10^{-4}$ M, $m = 1$, and $n = 2$ so $K_{sp} = 2^2 S^3 = 2^2 (2.25 \times 10^{-4})^3 = 4.56 \times 10^{-11}$.
    for AX_3, $S = 1.75 \times 10^{-4}$ M, $m = 1$, and $n = 3$ so $K_{sp} = 3^3 S^3 = 3^3 (1.75 \times 10^{-4})^3 = 1.45 \times 10^{-10}$.
    Check: The units (none) are correct. The K_{sp} values are much less than one and dependent not only on the value of the solubility, but also the stoichiometry of the ionic compound. The more ions that are generated, the smaller the K_{sp} for the same value of the S.

93. **Given:** $Fe(OH)_2$ in 100.0 mL solution **Find:** grams of $Fe(OH)_2$ **Other:** $K_{sp} = 4.87 \times 10^{-17}$
    Conceptual Plan: use equation derived in problem #20 and solve for S, then mL → L then
    $$\text{for ionic compound, } A_mX_n, \ K_{sp} = m^m \ n^n \ S^{m+n}.$$
    $$\dfrac{1 \ L}{1000 \ mL}$$

    S, L → mol $Fe(OH)_2$ → g $Fe(OH)_2$
    $$M = \dfrac{mol}{L} \qquad \dfrac{89.87 \ g \ Fe(OH)_2}{1 \ mol \ Fe(OH)_2}$$

    Solution: for $Fe(OH)_2$, $K_{sp} = 4.87 \times 10^{-17}$, $A = Fe^{2+}$, $m = 1$, $X = OH^-$, and $n = 2$ so $K_{sp} = 4.87 \times 10^{-17} = 2^2 S^3$. Rearrange to solve for S. $S = \sqrt[3]{\dfrac{4.87 \times 10^{-17}}{4}} = 2.30080 \times 10^{-6}$ M . then $100.0 \ \overline{mL} \times \dfrac{1 \ L}{1000 \ \overline{mL}} = 0.1000$ L

    then
    $$\dfrac{2.30080 \times 10^{-6} \ mol \ Fe(OH)_2}{1 \ \overline{L}} \times 0.1000 \ \overline{L} = 2.30080 \times 10^{-7} \ \overline{mol \ Fe(OH)_2} \times \dfrac{89.87 \ g \ Fe(OH)_2}{1 \ \overline{mol \ Fe(OH)_2}} = 2.07 \times 10^{-5} g \ Fe(OH)_2 \ .$$

    Check: The units (g) are correct. The solubility rules from Chapter 4 (most hydroxides are insoluble) suggest that very little $Fe(OH)_2$ will dissolve, so the magnitude of the answer is not surprising.

94. **Given:** 3.91 mg CuCl in 100.0 mL solution **Find:** K_{sp}
    Conceptual Plan: mL → L then mg CuCl → g CuCl → mol CuCl then L, mol CuCl → S then
    $$\dfrac{1 \ L}{1000 \ mL} \qquad \dfrac{1 \ g \ CuCl}{1000 \ mg \ CuCl} \qquad \dfrac{1 \ mol \ CuCl}{99.00 \ g \ CuCl} \qquad M = \dfrac{mol}{L}$$

use equation derived in problem #20

for ionic compound, A_mX_n, $K_{sp} = m^m\, n^n\, S^{m+n}$.

Solution: $100.0\ \text{mL} \times \dfrac{1\ \text{L}}{1000\ \text{mL}} = 0.1000\ \text{L}$ then

$3.91\ \text{mg CuCl} \times \dfrac{1\ \text{g CuCl}}{1000\ \text{mg CuCl}} \times \dfrac{1\ \text{mol CuCl}}{99.00\ \text{g CuCl}} = 3.9\underline{4}950 \times 10^{-5}\ \text{mol CuCl}$ then

$\dfrac{3.9\underline{4}950 \times 10^{-5}\ \text{mol CuCl}}{0.1000\ \text{L}} = 3.9\underline{4}950 \times 10^{-4}\ \text{M CuCl} = S$ then for CuCl $A = Cu^+$, $m = 1$, $X = Cl^-$, and $n = 2$ so

$K_{sp} = S^2 = = (3.9\underline{4}950 \times 10^{-4})^2 = 1.56 \times 10^{-7}$.

Check: The units (none) are correct. The value of $K_{sp} \ll 1$ since only mg dissolve in a liter of solution. The K_{sp} is not too low since CuCl dissociates into only 2 ions and S is 10^{-4}.

95. a) **Given:** BaF_2 **Find:** molar solubility (S) in pure water **Other:** $K_{sp}\ (BaF_2) = 2.45 \times 10^{-5}$
   Conceptual Plan: use equation derived in problem #20 and solve for S.

   for ionic compound, A_mX_n, $K_{sp} = m^m\, n^n\, S^{m+n}$.

   Solution: BaF_2, $K_{sp} = 2.45 \times 10^{-5}$, $A = Ba^{2+}$, $m = 1$, $X = F^-$, and $n = 2$ so $K_{sp} = 2.45 \times 10^{-5} = 2^2 S^3$.

   Rearrange to solve for S. $S = \sqrt[3]{\dfrac{2.45 \times 10^{-5}}{4}} = 1.83 \times 10^{-2}\ \text{M}$.

   b) **Given:** BaF_2 **Find:** molar solubility (S) in $0.10\ \text{M}\ Ba(NO_3)_2$ **Other:** $K_{sp}\ (BaF_2) = 2.45 \times 10^{-5}$
   Conceptual Plan: $M\ Ba(NO_3)_2 \rightarrow M\ Ba^{2+}$ then $M\ Ba^{2+}, K_{sp} \rightarrow S$

   $Ba(NO_3)_2\ (s) \rightarrow Ba^{2+}\ (aq) + 2\ NO_3^-\ (aq)$ ICE Chart

   Solution: Since 1 Ba^{2+} ion is generated for each $Ba(NO_3)_2$, $[Ba^{2+}] = 0.10\ \text{M}$.

   $BaF_2\ (s) \rightleftharpoons Ba^{2+}\ (aq) + 2\ F^-\ (aq)$

Initial	0.10	0.00
Change	S	2S
Equil	0.10 + S	2S

   $K_{sp}\ (BaF_2) = [Ba^{2+}]\ [F^-]^2 = 2.45 \times 10^{-5} = (0.10 + S\,)(2\,S\,)^2$.

   Assume $S \ll 0.10$, $2.45 \times 10^{-5} = (0.10)(2\,S)^2$, and $S = 7.83 \times 10^{-3}\ \text{M}$. Confirm that assumption is valid

   $\dfrac{7.83 \times 10^{-3}}{0.10} \times 100\ \% = 7.8\ \% > 5\ \%$ so assumption is not valid. Since expanding the expression will give a

   third order polynomial, that is not easily solved directly. Solve by successive approximations. Substitute $S = 7.83 \times 10^{-3}\ \text{M}$ for the S term that is part of a sum (i.e. the one in (0.10 + S)). Thus, $2.45 \times 10^{-5} = (0.10 + 7.83 \times 10^{-3})(2\,S)^2$ and $S = 7.53 \times 10^{-3}\ \text{M}$. Substitute this new S value again. Thus, $2.45 \times 10^{-5} = (0.10 + 7.53 \times 10^{-3})(2\,S)^2$ and $S = 7.55 \times 10^{-3}\ \text{M}$. Substitute this new S value again. Thus, $2.45 \times 10^{-5} = (0.10 + 7.55 \times 10^{-3})(2\,S)^2$ and $S = 7.55 \times 10^{-3}\ \text{M}$. So the solution has converged and $S = 7.55 \times 10^{-3}\ \text{M}$.

   c) **Given:** BaF_2 **Find:** molar solubility (S) in $0.15\ \text{M}\ NaF$ **Other:** $K_{sp}\ (BaF_2) = 2.45 \times 10^{-5}$
   Conceptual Plan: $M\ NaF \rightarrow M\ F^-$ then $M\ F^-, K_{sp} \rightarrow S$

   $NaF\ (s) \rightarrow Na^+\ (aq) + F^-\ (aq)$ ICE Chart

   Solution: Since 1 F^- ion is generated for each NaF, $[F^-] = 0.15\ \text{M}$.

   $BaF_2\ (s) \rightleftharpoons Ba^{2+}\ (aq) + 2\ F^-\ (aq)$

Initial	0.00	0.15
Change	S	2S
Equil	S	0.15 + 2S

   $K_{sp}\ (BaF_2) = [Ba^{2+}]\ [F^-]^2 = 2.45 \times 10^{-5} = (S\,)(0.15 + 2\,S)^2$.

   Since $2\,S \ll 0.15$, $2.45 \times 10^{-5} = (S)(0.15)^2$, and $S = 1.09 \times 10^{-3}\ \text{M}$. Confirm that assumption is valid

   $\dfrac{2\,(1.09 \times 10^{-3})}{0.10} \times 100\ \% = 2.2\ \% < 5\ \%$ so assumption is valid.

   Check: The units (M) are correct. The solubility of the BaF_2 decreases in the presence of a common ion. The effect of the anion is greater because the K_{sp} expression has the anion concentration squared.

96. a) **Given:** CuS **Find:** molar solubility (S) in pure water **Other:** $K_{sp}\ (CuS) = 1.27 \times 10^{-36}$
   Conceptual Plan: use equation derived in problem #20 and solve for S.

   for ionic compound, A_mX_n, $K_{sp} = m^m\, n^n\, S^{m+n}$.

   Solution: CuS, $K_{sp} = 1.27 \times 10^{-36}$, $A = Cu^{2+}$, $m = 1$, $X = S^{2-}$, and $n = 1$ so $K_{sp} = 1.27 \times 10^{-36} = S^2$.
   Rearrange to solve for S. $S = 1.13 \times 10^{-18}\ \text{M}$.

b) **Given:** CuS **Find:** molar solubility (S) in 0.25 M $CuCl_2$ **Other:** K_{sp} (CuS) = 1.27×10^{-36}
Conceptual Plan: M $CuCl_2$ → M Cu^{2+} then M Cu^{2+}, K_{sp} → S
$$CuCl_2\,(s) \rightarrow Cu^{2+}\,(aq) + 2\,Cl^-\,(aq)$$
ICE Chart
Solution: Since 1 Cu^{2+} ion is generated for each $CuCl_2$, $[Cu^{2+}]$ = 0.25 M.

$$CuS(s) \rightleftharpoons Cu^{2+}\,(aq) + S^{2-}(aq)$$

Initial	0.25	0.00
Change	S	S
Equil	0.25 + S	S

K_{sp} (CuS) = $[Cu^{2+}]\,[S^{2-}]$ = 1.27×10^{-36} = $(0.25 + S)\,S$.

Assume S ≪ 0.25, 1.27×10^{-36} = (0.25) S, and S = 5.08×10^{-36} M. Confirm that assumption is valid

$\dfrac{5.08 \times 10^{-36}}{0.25}$ x 100 % = 2.0×10^{-33} % ≪ 5 % so assumption is valid.

c) **Given:** CuS **Find:** molar solubility (S) in 0.20 M K_2S **Other:** K_{sp} (CuS) = 1.27×10^{-36}
Conceptual Plan: M K_2S → M S^{2-} then M S^{2-}, K_{sp} → S
$$K_2S\,(s) \rightarrow 2\,K^+\,(aq) + S^{2-}\,(aq)$$
ICE Chart
Solution: Since 1 S^{2-} ion is generated for each K_2S, $[S^{2-}]$ = 0.20 M.

$$CuS(s) \rightleftharpoons Cu^{2+}\,(aq) + S^{2-}(aq)$$

Initial	0.00	0.20
Change	S	S
Equil	S	0.20 + S

K_{sp} (CuS) = $[Cu^{2+}]\,[S^{2-}]$ = 1.27×10^{-36} = $(S)(0.20 + S)$.

Since S ≪ 0.20, 1.27×10^{-36} = (S)(0.20), and S = 6.35×10^{-36} M. Confirm that assumption is valid

$\dfrac{6.35 \times 10^{-36})}{0.20}$ x 100 % = 3.2×10^{-33} % ≪ 5 % so assumption is valid.

Check: The units (M) are correct. The solubility of the CuS decreases in the presence of a common ion.

97. **Given:** $Ca(OH)_2$ **Find:** molar solubility (S) in buffers at a. pH = 4, b. pH = 7, and c. pH = 9
Other: K_{sp} ($Ca(OH)_2$) = 4.68×10^{-6}
Conceptual Plan: pH → $[H_3O^+]$ → $[OH^-]$ then M OH^-, K_{sp} → S
$$[H_3O^+] = 10^{-pH} \quad K_w = [H_3O^+][OH^-]$$
set up ICE table
Solution:

a) pH = 4, so $[H_3O^+] = 10^{-pH} = 10^{-4} = 1 \times 10^{-4}$ M then $K_w = [H_3O^+][OH^-]$ so

$$Ca(OH)_2\,(s) \rightleftharpoons Ca^{2+}\,(aq) + 2\,OH^-\,(aq)$$

$[OH^-] = \dfrac{K_w}{[H_3O^+]} = \dfrac{1.0 \times 10^{-14}}{1 \times 10^{-4}} = 1 \times 10^{-10}$ M then

Initial	0.00	1×10^{-10}
Change	S	—
Equil	S	1×10^{-10}

K_{sp} ($Ca(OH)_2$) = $[Ca^{2+}]\,[OH^-]^2$ = 4.68×10^{-6} = $S\,(1 \times 10^{-10})^2$. and S = 5×10^{14} M.

b) pH = 7, so $[H_3O^+] = 10^{-pH} = 10^{-7} = 1 \times 10^{-7}$ M then $K_w = [H_3O^+][OH^-]$ so

$$Ca(OH)_2\,(s) \rightleftharpoons Ca^{2+}\,(aq) + 2\,OH^-\,(aq)$$

$[OH^-] = \dfrac{K_w}{[H_3O^+]} = \dfrac{1.0 \times 10^{-14}}{1 \times 10^{-7}} = 1 \times 10^{-7}$ M then

Initial	0.00	1×10^{-7}
Change	S	—
Equil	S	1×10^{-7}

K_{sp} ($Ca(OH)_2$) = $[Ca^{2+}]\,[OH^-]^2$ = 4.68×10^{-6} = $S\,(1 \times 10^{-7})^2$. and S = 5×10^8 M.

c) pH = 9, so $[H_3O^+] = 10^{-pH} = 10^{-9} = 1 \times 10^{-9}$ M then $K_w = [H_3O^+][OH^-]$ so

$$Ca(OH)_2\,(s) \rightleftharpoons Ca^{2+}\,(aq) + 2\,OH^-\,(aq)$$

$[OH^-] = \dfrac{K_w}{[H_3O^+]} = \dfrac{1.0 \times 10^{-14}}{1 \times 10^{-9}} = 1 \times 10^{-5}$ M then

Initial	0.00	1×10^{-5}
Change	S	—
Equil	S	1×10^{-5}

K_{sp} ($Ca(OH)_2$) = $[Ca^{2+}]\,[OH^-]^2$ = 4.68×10^{-6} = $S\,(1 \times 10^{-5})^2$. and S = 5×10^4 M.

Check: The units (M) are correct. The solubility of the $Ca(OH)_2$ decreases as the pH increases (and the hydroxide ion concentration increases). Realize that these molar solubilities are not achievable because the density of pure $Ca(OH)_2$ is ~ 30 M. The bottom line is that as long as the hydroxide concentration can be controlled with a buffer, the $Ca(OH)_2$ will be very soluble.

98. **Given:** $Mg(OH)_2$ in 1.00×10^2 mL solution   **Find:** grams of $Mg(OH)_2$ in pure water and buffer at pH = 10   **Other:** K_{sp} $(Mg(OH)_2) = 2.06 \times 10^{-13}$
Conceptual Plan: For pure water:
use equation derived in problem #20 and solve for S,   **then**   **mL $\rightarrow$ L**   **then**

for ionic compound, A_mX_n, $K_{sp} = m^m\, n^n\, S^{m+n}$. $\dfrac{1\ L}{1000\ mL}$

S, L $\rightarrow$ mol $Mg(OH)_2$ $\rightarrow$ g $Mg(OH)_2$. For buffer solution: pH $\rightarrow$ $[H_3O^+]$ $\rightarrow$ $[OH^-]$ then

$M = \dfrac{mol}{L}$ $\dfrac{58.33\ g\ Mg(OH)_2}{1\ mol\ Mg(OH)_2}$ $[H_3O^+] = 10^{-pH}$ $K_w = [H_3O^+][OH^-]$

M OH$^-$, K_{sp} $\rightarrow$ S then   **S, L $\rightarrow$ mol $Mg(OH)_2$ $\rightarrow$ g $Mg(OH)_2$**

set up ICE table $M = \dfrac{mol}{L}$ $\dfrac{58.33\ g\ Mg(OH)_2}{1\ mol\ Mg(OH)_2}$

Solution: for pure water, $K_{sp} = 2.06 \times 10^{-13}$, A = Mg^{2+}, m = 1, X = OH^-, and n = 2 so $K_{sp} = 2.06 \times 10^{-13} =$

$2^2 S^3$. Rearrange to solve for S. $S = \sqrt[3]{\dfrac{2.06 \times 10^{-13}}{4}} = 3.7\underline{2}051 \times 10^{-5}$ M . Then

$1.00 \times 10^2\ \cancel{mL} \times \dfrac{1\ L}{1000\ \cancel{mL}} = 0.100$ L then

$\dfrac{3.7\underline{2}051 \times 10^{-5}\ mol\ Mg(OH)_2}{1\ \cancel{L}} \times 0.100\ \cancel{L} = 3.7\underline{2}051 \times 10^{-6}\ \cancel{mol\ Mg(OH)_2} \times \dfrac{58.33\ g\ Mg(OH)_2}{1\ \cancel{mol\ Mg(OH)_2}} = 2.17 \times 10^{-4} g\ Mg(OH)_2$.

for pH = 10, so $[H_3O^+] = 10^{-pH} = 10^{-10} = 1 \times 10^{-10}$ M then $K_w = [H_3O^+][OH^-]$ so

	$Mg(OH)_2\,(s) \rightleftharpoons Mg^{2+}\,(aq) + OH^-(aq)$	
$[OH^-] = \dfrac{K_w}{[H_3O^+]} = \dfrac{1.0 \times 10^{-14}}{1 \times 10^{-10}} = 1 \times 10^{-4}$ M then	*Initial* 0.00 1×10^{-4}	
	Change S —	
	Equil S 1×10^{-4}	

K_{sp} $(Mg(OH)_2) = [Mg^{2+}][OH^-]^2 = 2.06 \times 10^{-13} = S\,(1 \times 10^{-4})^2$.and $S = \underline{2}.06 \times 10^{-5}$ M. then

$\dfrac{2.06 \times 10^{-5}\ mol\ Mg(OH)_2}{1\ \cancel{L}} \times 0.100\ \cancel{L} = \underline{2}.06 \times 10^{-6}\ \cancel{mol\ Mg(OH)_2} \times \dfrac{58.33\ g\ Mg(OH)_2}{1\ \cancel{mol\ Mg(OH)_2}} = 1 \times 10^{-4} g\ Mg(OH)_2$.

Check: The units (M) are correct. The solubility of the $Mg(OH)_2$ decreases as the pH increases (and the hydroxide ion concentration increases).

99. a) $BaCO_3$ will be more soluble in acidic solutions because CO_3^{2-} is basic. In acidic solutions it can be converted to HCO_3^- and $H_2CO_3^{2-}$. These species are not CO_3^{2-} so they do not appear in the K_{sp} expression.

b) CuS will be more soluble in acidic solutions because S^{2-} is basic. In acidic solutions it can be converted to HS^- and H_2S^{2-}. These species are not S^{2-} so they do not appear in the K_{sp} expression.

c) AgCl will not be more soluble in acidic solutions because Cl^- will not react with acidic solutions, because HCl is a strong acid.

d) PbI_2 will not be more soluble in acidic solutions because I^- will not react with acidic solutions, because HI is a strong acid.

100. a) Hg_2Br_2 will not be more soluble in acidic solutions because Br^- will not react with acidic solutions, because HBr is a strong acid.

b) $Mg(OH)_2$ will be more soluble in acidic solutions because OH^- is basic. In acidic solutions it can be converted to H_2O. This species are not OH^- so it does not appear in the K_{sp} expression.

c) $CaCO_3$ will be more soluble in acidic solutions because CO_3^{2-} is basic. In acidic solutions it can be converted to HCO_3^- and $H_2CO_3^{2-}$. These species are not CO_3^{2-} so they do not appear in the K_{sp} expression.

d) AgI will not be more soluble in acidic solutions because I⁻ will not react with acidic solutions, because HI is a strong acid.

101. **Given:** 0.015 M NaF and 0.010 M Ca(NO₃)₂   **Find:** will a precipitate form, if so, identify it
Other: K_{sp} (CaF₂) = 1.46 x 10⁻¹⁰
Conceptual Plan: Look at all possible combinations and consider the solubility rules from Chapter 4. Salts of alkali metals (Na) are very soluble, so NaF and NaNO₃ will be very soluble. Nitrate compounds are very soluble so NaNO₃ will be very soluble. The only possibility for a precipitate is CaF₂. Determine if a precipitate will form by determining the concentration of the Ca²⁺ and F⁻ in solution. then compute the reaction quotient, Q. If Q > K_{sp} then a precipitate will form.
Solution: Since the only possible precipitate is CaF₂, calculate the concentrations of Ca²⁺ and F⁻.
NaF (s) → Na⁺ (aq) + F⁻ (aq). Since 1 F⁻ ion is generated for each NaF, [F⁻] = 0.015 M.
Ca(NO₃)₂ (s) → Ca²⁺ (aq) + 2 NO₃⁻ (aq). Since 1 Ca²⁺ ion is generated for each Ca(NO₃)₂, [Ca²⁺] = 0.010 M. then calculate Q (CaF₂), A = Ca²⁺, m = 1, X = F⁻, and n = 2 Since Q= [Aⁿ⁺]ᵐ [Xᵐ⁻]ⁿ, then
Q (CaF₂) = [Ca²⁺] [F⁻]² = (0.010) (0.015)² = 2.3 x 10⁻⁶ > 1.46 x 10⁻¹⁰ = K_{sp} (CaF₂) , so a precipitate will form.
Check: The units (none) are correct. The solubility of the CaF₂ is low, and the concentration of ions are extremely large compared to the K_{sp}, so a precipitate will form.

102. **Given:** 0.013 M KBr and 0.0035 M Pb(C₂H₃O₂)₂   **Find:** will a precipitate form, if so, identify it
Other: K_{sp} (PbBr₂) = 4.67 x 10⁻⁶
Conceptual Plan: Look at all possible combinations and consider the solubility rules from Chapter 4. Salts of alkali metals (K) are very soluble, so KBr and KC₂H₃O₂ will be very soluble. Acetate compounds are very soluble so Pb(C₂H₃O₂)₂ and KC₂H₃O₂ will be very soluble. The only possibility for a precipitate is PbBr₂. Determine if a precipitate will form by determining the concentration of the Pb²⁺ and Br⁻ in solution. then compute the reaction quotient, Q. If Q > K_{sp} then a precipitate will form.
Solution: Since the only possible precipitate is PbBr₂, calculate the concentrations of Pb²⁺ and Br⁻.
KBr (s) → K⁺ (aq) + Br⁻ (aq). Since 1 Br⁻ ion is generated for each KBr, [Br⁻] = 0.013 M.
Pb(C₂H₃O₂)₂ (s) → Ca²⁺ (aq) + 2 C₂H₃O₂⁻ (aq). Since 1 Pb²⁺ ion is generated for each Pb(C₂H₃O₂)₂, [Pb⁺] = 0.0035 M. then calculate Q (PbBr₂), A = Pb²⁺, m = 1, X = Br⁻, and n = 2 Since Q= [Aⁿ⁺]ᵐ [Xᵐ⁻]ⁿ, then
Q (PbBr₂) = [Pb²⁺] [Br⁻]² = (0.013) (0.0035)² = 1.6 x 10⁻⁷ < 4.67 x 10⁻⁶ = K_{sp} (PbBr₂) , so a precipitate will not form.
Check: The units (none) are correct. The K_{sp} of the PbBr₂ is not too low compared to the solution ion concentrations, so a precipitate will not form.

103. **Given:** 75.0 mL of NaOH with pH = 2.58 and 125.0 mL of 0.0018 M MgCl₂
Find: will a precipitate form, if so, identify it   **Other:** K_{sp} (Mg(OH)₂) = 2.06 x 10⁻¹³
Conceptual Plan: Look at all possible combinations and consider the solubility rules from Chapter 4. Salts of alkali metals (Na) are very soluble, so NaOH and NaCl will be very soluble. Chloride compounds are generally very soluble so MgCl₂ and NaCl will be very soluble. The only possibility for a precipitate is Mg(OH)₂. Determine if a precipitate will form by determining the concentration of the Mg²⁺ and OH⁻ in solution. Since pH, not NaOH concentration, is given pOH → [OH⁻] then

$$[OH^-] = 10^{-pOH}$$

mix solutions and calculate diluted concentrations mL NaOH, mL MgCl₂ → mL total   then
mL NaOH + mL MgCl₂ = total mL
mL, initial M → final M   then compute the reaction quotient, Q.

$$M_1 V_1 = M_2 V_2$$

If Q > K_{sp} then a precipitate will form.
Solution: Since the only possible precipitate is Mg(OH)₂, calculate the concentrations of Mg²⁺ and OH⁻.
for NaOH at pOH = 2.58, so $[OH^-] = 10^{-pOH} = 10^{-2.58} = 2.\underline{6}3027$ x 10⁻³ M and
MgCl₂ (s) → Mg²⁺ (aq) + 2 Cl⁻ (aq). Since 1 Mg²⁺ ion is generated for each MgCl₂, [Mg²⁺] = 0.0018 M. then   total mL = mL NaOH + mL MgCl₂ = 75.0 mL + 125.0 mL = 200.0 mL. then $M_1 V_1 = M_2 V_2$.

Rearrange to solve for M₂. $M_2 = M_1 \dfrac{V_1}{V_2}$ = 2.\underline{6}3027 x 10⁻³ M OH⁻ x $\dfrac{75.0 \text{ mL}}{200.0 \text{ mL}}$ = 9.\underline{8}635 x 10⁻⁴ M OH⁻ and

$M_2 = M_1 \dfrac{V_1}{V_2}$ = 0.0018 M Mg⁺ x $\dfrac{125.0 \text{ mL}}{200.0 \text{ mL}}$ = 1.\underline{1}25 x 10⁻³ M Mg²⁺. Calculate Q (Mg(OH)₂), A = Mg²⁺, m = 1,

$X = OH^-$, and n = 2 Since $Q = [A^{n+}]^m [X^{m-}]^n$, then Q ($Mg(OH)_2$) = $[Mg^{2+}] [OH^-]^2$ =
$(1.125 \times 10^{-3})(9.8635 \times 10^{-4})^2 = 1.1 \times 10^{-9} > 2.06 \times 10^{-13} = K_{sp}$ ($Mg(OH)_2$), so a precipitate will form.

Check: The units (none) are correct. The solubility of the $Mg(OH)_2$ is low, and the NaOH (a base) is high enough that the product of the concentration of ions are large compared to the K_{sp}, so a precipitate will form.

104. **Given:** 175.0 mL of 0.0055 M KCl and 145.0 mL of 0.0015 M $AgNO_3$ **Find:** will a precipitate form, if so, identify it   **Other:** K_{sp} (AgCl) = 1.77×10^{-10}
Conceptual Plan: Look at all possible combinations and consider the solubility rules from Chapter 4. Salts of alkali metals (K) are very soluble, so KCl and KNO_3 will be very soluble. Nitrate compounds are very soluble so KNO_3 and Ag NO_3 will be very soluble. The only possibility for a precipitate is AgCl. Determine if a precipitate will form by determining the concentration of the Ag^+ and Cl^- in solution. Mix solutions and calculate
diluted concentrations mL KCl, mL $AgNO_3$ $\rightarrow$ mL total   then   mL, initial M $\rightarrow$ final M   then

$$mL\ KCl + mL\ AgNO_3 = total\ mL \qquad\qquad M_1 V_1 = M_2 V_2$$

compute the reaction quotient, Q. If Q > K_{sp} then a precipitate will form.
Solution: Since the only possible precipitate is AgCl, calculate the concentrations of Ag^+ and Cl^-.
KCl (s) $\rightarrow$ K^+ (aq) + Cl^- (aq). Since 1 Cl^- ion is generated for each AgCl, $[Cl^-]$ = 0.0055 M. and
$AgNO_3$ (s) $\rightarrow$ Ag^+ (aq) + NO_3^- (aq). Since 1 Ag^+ ion is generated for each $AgNO_3$, $[Ag^+]$ = 0.0015 M.
then total mL = mL KCl + mL $AgNO_3$ = 175.0 mL + 145.0 mL = 320.0. then $M_1 V_1 = M_2 V_2$. Rearrange to

solve for M2. $M_2 = M_1 \dfrac{V_1}{V_2}$ = 0.0055 M Cl^- x $\dfrac{175.0\ mL}{320.0\ mL}$ = 0.00300781 M Cl^- and

$M_2 = M_1 \dfrac{V_1}{V_2}$ = 0.0015 M Ag^+ x $\dfrac{145.0\ mL}{320.0\ mL}$ = 0.00067969 M Ag^+. Calculate Q ($AgCl_2$), A = Ag^+, m = 1, X =

Cl^-, and n = 1 Since $Q = [A^{n+}]^m [X^{m-}]^n$, then Q (AgCl) = $[Ag^+] [Cl^-]$ = (0.00067969)(0.00300781) = 2.0×10^{-6} >
$1.77 \times 10^{-10} = K_{sp}$ (AgCl), so a precipitate will form.
Check: The units (none) are correct. The solubility of the AgCl is low, and the concentrations of the ions are high enough that the product of the concentration of ions is very large compared to the K_{sp}, so a precipitate will form.

105. **Given:** KOH as precipitation agent in a) 0.015 M $CaCl_2$, b) 0.0025 M $Fe(NO_3)_2$ and c) 0.0018 M $MgBr_2$
Find: concentration of KOH necessary to form a precipitate
Other: K_{sp} ($Ca(OH)_2$) = 4.68×10^{-6}, K_{sp} ($Fe(OH)_2$) = 4.87×10^{-17}, K_{sp} ($Mg(OH)_2$) = 2.06×10^{-13}
Conceptual Plan: The solubility rules from Chapter 4 state that most hydroxides are insoluble, so all precipitate will be hydroxides. Determine the concentration of the cation in solution. Since all metals have an oxidation state of +2 and $[OH^-]$ = [KOH], all of the K_{sp} = [cation] $[KOH]^2$ and so

$$[KOH] = \sqrt{\dfrac{K_{sp}}{[cation]}}.$$

Solution:
a) $CaCl_2$ (s) $\rightarrow$ Ca^{2+} (aq) + 2 Cl^- (aq). Since 1 Ca^{2+} ion is generated for each $CaCl_2$, $[Ca^{2+}]$ = 0.015 M.

then $[KOH] = \sqrt{\dfrac{K_{sp}}{[cation]}} = \sqrt{\dfrac{4.68 \times 10^{-6}}{0.015}}$ = 0.018 M KOH.

b) $Fe(NO_3)_2$ (s) $\rightarrow$ Fe^{2+} (aq) + 2 NO_3^- (aq). Since 1 Fe^{2+} ion is generated for each $Fe(NO_3)_2$, $[Fe^{2+}]$ =

0.0025 M. then $[KOH] = \sqrt{\dfrac{K_{sp}}{[cation]}} = \sqrt{\dfrac{4.87 \times 10^{-17}}{0.0025}}$ = 1.4×10^{-7} M KOH.

c) $MgBr_2$ (s) $\rightarrow$ Mg^{2+} (aq) + 2 Br^- (aq). Since 1 Mg^{2+} ion is generated for each $MgBr_2$, $[Mg^{2+}]$ = 0.0018

M. then $[KOH] = \sqrt{\dfrac{K_{sp}}{[cation]}} = \sqrt{\dfrac{2.06 \times 10^{-13}}{0.0018}}$ = 1.1×10^{-5} M KOH.

Check: The units (none) are correct. Since all cations have an oxidation state of +2, it can be seen that the [KOH] needed to precipitate the hydroxide is lower the smaller the K_{sp}.

106. **Given:** solution and precipitation agent pairs a) 0.035 M $BaNO_3$: NaF, b) 0.085 M CaI_2 : K_2SO_4, and c) 0.0018 M $AgNO_3$:RbCl   **Find:** concentration of precipitation agent necessary to form a precipitate
Other: K_{sp} (BaF_2) = 2.45×10^{-5}, K_{sp} ($CaSO_4$) = 7.10×10^{-5}, K_{sp} (AgCl) = 1.77×10^{-10}
Conceptual Plan:

Use the solubility rules from Chapter 4 to decide on precipitate that will form. **Determine the concentration of the cation in solution.** Use equation derived in problem #19 to define K_{sp}.

for ionic compound, A_mX_n, $K_{sp} = [A^{n+}]^m [X^{m-}]^n$

Substitute in concentration of cation and solve for concentration of anion.

Solution:

a) Salts of alkali metals (Na) are very soluble, so NaF and $NaNO_3$ will be very soluble. Nitrate compounds are very soluble so $Ba(NO_3)_2$ and $NaNO_3$ will be very soluble. The only possibility for a precipitate is BaF_2.

$Ba(NO_3)_2$ (s) → Ba^{2+} (aq) + 2 NO_3^- (aq). Since 1 Ba^{2+} ion is generated for each $Ba(NO_3)_2$, $[Ba^{2+}]$ = 0.035 M. then derive expression for K_{sp} (BaF_2), A = Ba^{2+}, m = 1, X = F^-, and n = 2 Since K_{sp} = $[Ba^{2+}] [F^-]^2$, then K_{sp} (BaF_2) = 2.45 x 10^{-5} = 0.035 $[F^-]^2$. Solve for $[F^-]$. $[F^-]$ = 0.026 M F^-. Since NaF (s) → Na^+ (aq) + F^- (aq), 1 F^- ion is generated for each NaF, [NaF] = 0.026 M NaF.

b) Salts of alkali metals (K) are very soluble, so KI and K_2SO_4 will be very soluble. Sulfate compounds are very soluble, with the exception of a few cations, with Ca^{2+} being one of the insoluble exceptions. The only possibility for a precipitate is $CaSO_4$. CaI_2 (s) → Ca^{2+} (aq) + 2 I^- (aq). Since 1 Ca^{2+} ion is generated for each CaI_2, $[Ca^{2+}]$ = 0.085 M. then derive expression for K_{sp} ($CaSO_4$), A = Ca^{2+}, m = 1, X = SO_4^{2-}, and n = 1 Since K_{sp} = $[Ca^{2+}] [SO_4^{2-}]$, then K_{sp} ($CaSO_4$) = 7.10 x 10^{-5} = 0.085 $[SO_4^{2-}]$. Solve for $[SO_4^{2-}]$. $[SO_4^{2-}]$ = 0.00084 M SO_4^{2-}. Since K_2SO_4 (s) → 2 K^+ (aq) + SO_4^{2-} (aq). Since 1 SO_4^{2-} ion is generated for each K_2SO_4, $[K_2SO_4]$ = 0.00084 M K_2SO_4.

c) Salts of alkali metals (Rb) are very soluble, so RbCl and $RbNO_3$ will be very soluble. Nitrate compounds are very soluble, so $RbNO_3$ and $AgNO_3$ are very soluble. The only possibility for a precipitate is AgCl, which is insoluble according to the solubility rules. then $AgNO_3$ (s) → Ag^+ (aq) + NO_3^- (aq). Since 1 NO_3^- ion is generated for each $AgNO_3$, $[Ag^+]$ = 0.0018 M. then derive expression for K_{sp} (AgCl), A = Ag^+, m = 1, X = Cl^-, and n = 1 Since K_{sp} = $[Ag^+] [Cl^-]$, then K_{sp} (AgCl) = 1.77 x 10^{-10} = 0.0018 $[Cl^-]$. Solve for $[Cl^-]$. $[Cl^-]$ = 9.8 x 10^{-8} M Cl^-. Since RbCl (s) → Rb^+ (aq) + Cl^- (aq). Since 1 Cl^- ion is generated for each RbCl, [RbCl] = 9.8 x 10^{-8} M RbCl.

Check: The units (M) are correct. Comparing part a) and part b) the effect of the stoichiometry of the precipitate is seen and the concentration of the precipitation agent is much lower. Looking at part c) the concentration of the precipitation agent is so low because the K_{sp} is so small.

107. **Given:** solution with 0.010 M Ba^{2+} and 0.020 M Ca^{2+} add Na_2SO_4 to form precipitates
   Find: a) which ion precipitates first and minimum $[Na_2SO_4]$ needed; and b) [first cation] when second cation precipitates   **Other:** K_{sp} ($BaSO_4$) = 1.07 x 10^{-10}, K_{sp} ($CaSO_4$) = 7.10 x 10^{-5}
   Conceptual Plan: a) The precipitates that will form are $BaSO_4$ and $CaSO_4$.
   Use equation derived in problem #19 to define K_{sp}. Substitute in concentration of cation and solve for
   for ionic compound, A_mX_n, $K_{sp} = [A^{n+}]^m [X^{m-}]^n$
   concentration of anion to form precipitate. The cation with the lower anion concentration will precipitate first.
   b) Substitute the higher anion concentration into the K_{sp} expression for the first cation to precipitate and calculate the amount of this first cation to remain in solution.
   Solution:

a) Derive expression for K_{sp} ($BaSO_4$), A = Ba^{2+}, m = 1, X = SO_4^{2-}, and n = 1 Since K_{sp} = $[Ba^{2+}] [SO_4^{2-}]$, then K_{sp} ($BaSO_4$) = 1.07 x 10^{-10} = 0.010 $[SO_4^{2-}]$. Solve for $[SO_4^{2-}]$. $[SO_4^{2-}]$ = 1.07 x 10^{-8} M SO_4^{2-}. Since Na_2SO_4 (s) → 2 Na^+ (aq) + SO_4^{2-} (aq). Since 1 SO_4^{2-} ion is generated for each Na_2SO_4, $[Na_2SO_4]$ = 1.1 x 10^{-8} M Na_2SO_4 to precipitate $BaSO_4$. Derive expression for K_{sp} ($CaSO_4$), A = Ca^{2+}, m = 1, X = SO_4^{2-}, and n = 1 Since K_{sp} = $[Ca^{2+}] [SO_4^{2-}]$, then K_{sp} ($CaSO_4$) = 7.10 x 10^{-5} = 0.020 $[SO_4^{2-}]$. Solve for $[SO_4^{2-}]$. $[SO_4^{2-}]$ = 0.0036 M SO_4^{2-} = 0.0036 M Na_2SO_4 = $[Na_2SO_4]$ to precipitate $CaSO_4$. Since 1.1 x 10^{-8} M Na_2SO_4 << 0.0036 M Na_2SO_4, the Ba^{2+} will precipitate first.

b) Since Ca^{2+} will not precipitate until $[Na_2SO_4]$ = 0.00355 M Na_2SO_4, substitute this value into the K_{sp} expression for $BaSO_4$. So K_{sp} ($BaSO_4$) = $[Ba^{2+}] [SO_4^{2-}]$ = 1.07 x 10^{-10} = $[Ba^{2+}]$ 0.0035. Solve for $[Ba^{2+}]$ = 3.0 x 10^{-8} M Ba^{2+}.

Check: The units (none, M, and M) are correct. Comparing the two K_{sp} values, it can be seen that the Ba^{2+} will precipitate first since the solubility product is so much lower. Since the K_{sp} value is so low, the concentration of precipitating agent is very low. Since the $CaSO_4$ K_{sp} value is so much higher, the higher $[SO_4^{2-}]$ to precipitate Ca will force the concentration of Ba^{2+} to very low levels.

108. Given: solution with 0.022 M Fe^{2+} and 0.014 M Mg^{2+} add K_2CO_3 to form precipitates **Find:** a) which ion precipitates first and minimum $[K_2CO_3]$ needed; and b) [first cation] when second cation precipitates
Other: K_{sp} (FeCO_3) = 3.07 x 10^{-11}, K_{sp} (MgCO_3) = 6.82 x 10^{-6}
Conceptual Plan: a) The precipitates that will form are FeCO_3 and MgCO_3.
Use equation derived in problem #19 to define K_{sp}. Substitute in concentration of cation and solve for
for ionic compound, A_mX_n, $K_{sp} = [A^{n+}]^m [X^{m-}]^n$
concentration of anion to form precipitate.   The cation with the lower anion concentration will precipitate first.

b) Substitute the higher anion concentration into the K_{sp} expression for the first cation to precipitate and calculate the amount of this first cation to remain in solution.
Solution:

a)   Derive expression for K_{sp} (FeCO_3),   A = Fe^{2+}, m = 1, X = CO_3^{2-}, and n = 1 Since K_{sp} = $[Fe^{2+}]$ $[CO_3^{2-}]$, then K_{sp} (FeCO_3) = 3.07 x 10^{-11} = 0.022 $[CO_3^{2-}]$. Solve for $[CO_3^{2-}]$. $[CO_3^{2-}]$ = 1.4 x 10^{-9} M CO_3^{2-}. Since K_2CO_3 *(s)* → 2 K^+ *(aq)* + CO_3^{2-} *(aq)*. Since 1 CO_3^{2-} ion is generated for each K_2CO_3, $[K_2CO_3]$ = 1.4 x 10^{-9} M K_2CO_3 to precipitate FeCO_3.   Derive expression for K_{sp} (MgCO_3),   A = Mg^{2+}, m = 1, X = CO_3^{2-}, and n = 1 Since K_{sp} = $[Mg^{2+}]$ $[CO_3^{2-}]$, then K_{sp} (MgCO_3) = 6.82 x 10^{-6} = 0.014 $[CO_3^{2-}]$. Solve for $[CO_3^{2-}]$. $[CO_3^{2-}]$ = 4.9 x 10^{-4} M CO_3^{2-} = 4.9 x 10^{-4} M K_2CO_3 = $[K_2CO_3]$ to precipitate MgCO_3. Since 1.4 x 10^{-9} M K_2CO_3 < 4.9 x 10^{-4} M K_2CO_3, the Fe^{2+} will precipitate first.

b)   Since Mg^{2+} will not precipitate until $[K_2CO_3]$ = 4.9 x 10^{-4} M K_2CO_3, substitute this value into the K_{sp} expression for FeCO_3. So K_{sp} (FeCO_3) = $[Fe^{2+}]$ $[CO_3^{2-}]$ = 3.07 x 10^{-11} = $[Fe^{2+}]$ 4.9 x 10^{-4} . Solve for $[Fe^{2+}]$ = 6.3 x 10^{-8} M Fe^{2+}.

Check: The units (none, M, and M) are correct. Comparing the two K_{sp} values, it can be seen that the Fe^{2+} will precipitate first since the solubility product is so much lower. Since the K_{sp} value is so low, the concentration of precipitating agent is very low. Since the MgCO_3 K_{sp} value is so much higher, the higher $[CO_3^{2-}]$ to precipitate Mg will force the concentration of Fe^{2+} to very low levels.

109. Given: solution with 1.1 x 10^{-3} M $Zn(NO_3)_2$ and 0.150 M NH_3 **Find:** $[Zn^{2+}]$ at equilibrium
Other: K_f (Zn(NH_3)_4^{2+}) = 2.0 x 10^9
Conceptual Plan: Write balanced equation and expression for K_f. Use initial concentrations to set up ICE table. Since the K_f, assume that reaction essentially goes to completion. Solve for $[Zn^{2+}]$ at equilibrium.
Solution: $Zn(NO_3)_2$ *(s)* → Zn^{2+} *(aq)* + 2 NO_3^- *(aq)*. Since 1 Zn^{2+} ion is generated for each $Zn(NO_3)_2$, $[Zn^{2+}]$ = 1.1 x 10^{-3} M. Balanced equation is:

$$Zn^{2+} (aq) + 4\,NH_3\,(aq) \rightleftharpoons Zn(NH_3)_4^{2+}\,(aq) \qquad \text{Set up ICE table with initial concentrations.}$$

	$[Zn^{2+}]$	$[NH_3]$	$[Zn(NH_3)_4^{2+}]$	
Initial	1.1 x 10^{-3}	0.150	0.00	Since K_f is so large and since the initially $[NH_3] > 4[Zn^{2+}]$
Change	≈ 1.1 x 10^{-3}	≈ (0.150 − 4(1.1 x 10^{-3}))	≈ 1.1 x 10^{-3}	the reaction essentially goes to completion.
Equil	x	0.14<u>5</u>6	1.1 x 10^{-3}	then write equilibrium expression and solve for x.

K_f = $\dfrac{[Zn(NH_3)_4^{2+}]}{[Zn^{2+}][NH_3]^4}$ = 2.0 x 10^9 = $\dfrac{1.1 \times 10^{-3}}{x(0.14\underline{5}6)^4}$ So x = 1.2 x 10^{-9} M Zn^{2+}. Since x is insignificant compared to

the initial concentration, the assumption is valid.
Check: The units (M) are correct. Since K_f is so large, the reaction essentially goes to completion and $[Zn^{2+}]$ is extremely small.

110. Given: 120.0 mL of 2.8 x 10^{-3} M $AgNO_3$ mixed with 225.0 mL of 0.10 M NaCN
   Find: $[Ag^+]$ at equilibrium
   Other: K_f (Ag(CN)_2^-) = 1 x 10^{21}
   Conceptual Plan:
   Mix solutions and calculate diluted concentrations mL $AgNO_3$, mL NaCN →   mL total
   mL $AgNO_3$ + mL NaCN = total mL
   then   mL, initial M →   final M   then Write balanced equation and expression for K_f.
   $M_1 V_1 = M_2 V_2$

Use initial concentrations to set up ICE table. Since the K_f, assume that reaction essentially goes to completion. Solve for $[Ag^+]$ at equilibrium.
Solution: $AgNO_3$ *(s)* → Ag^+ *(aq)* + NO_3^- *(aq)*. Since 1 Ag^+ ion is generated for each $AgNO_3$, $[Ag^+]$ = 2.8 x 10^{-3} M. and NaCN *(s)* → Na^+ *(aq)* + CN^- *(aq)*. Since 1 CN^- ion is generated for each NaCN, $[CN^-]$ =

0.10 M. then total mL = mL $AgNO_3$ + mL NaCN = 120.0 mL + 225.0 mL = 345.0 mL. Then $M_1V_1 = M_2V_2$. Rearrange to solve for M_2. $M_2 = M_1\dfrac{V_1}{V_2} = 2.8 \times 10^{-3}$ M Ag^+ x $\dfrac{120.0 \text{ mL}}{345.0 \text{ mL}} = 0.00097391$ M Ag^+

and $M_2 = M_1\dfrac{V_1}{V_2} = 0.10$ M CN^+ x $\dfrac{225.0 \text{ mL}}{345.0 \text{ mL}} = 0.065217$ M CN^-. Balanced equation is:

$Ag^+ (aq) + 2 CN^- (aq) \rightleftharpoons Ag(CN)_2^- (aq)$ Set up ICE table with initial concentrations.

	$[Ag^+]$	$[CN^-]$	$[Ag(CN)_2^-]$	
Initial	0.00097391	0.065217	0.00	Since K_f is so large and since the initially
Change	≈ 0.00097391	$\approx (0.065217 - 2(0.00097391))$	≈ 0.00097391	$[CN^-] > 2[Ag^+]$ the reaction essentially goes
Equil	x	0.063270	0.00097391	to completion. then

write equilibrium expression and solve for x.

$K_f = \dfrac{[Ag(CN)_2^-]}{[Ag^+][CN^-]^2} = 1 \times 10^{21} = \dfrac{0.00097391}{x(0.063270)^2}$ So $x = 2 \times 10^{-22}$ M Ag^+. Since x is insignificant compared to the

initial concentration, the assumption is valid.

Check: The units (M) are correct. Since K_f is so large, the reaction essentially goes to completion and $[Ag^+]$ is extremely small.

111. **Given:** $FeS (s) + 6 CN^- (aq) \rightleftharpoons Fe(CN)_6^{4-} (aq) + S^{2-} (aq)$ use K_{sp} and K_f values   **Find:** K
Other: $K_f (Fe(CN)_6^{4-}) = 1.5 \times 10^{35}$, $K_{sp} (FeS) = 3.72 \times 10^{-19}$
Conceptual Plan: Identify the appropriate solid and complex ion. Write balanced equations for dissolving the solid and forming the complex ion. Add these two reactions to get the desired overall reaction. Using the rules from Chapter 14, multiply the individual reaction K's to get the overall K for the sum of these reactions.
Solution: Identify the solid as FeS and the complex ion as $Fe(CN)_6^{4-}$. Write the individual reactions and add them together.

$FeS (s) \rightleftharpoons Fe^{2+}(aq) + S^{2-} (aq)$ $K_{sp} = 1.5 \times 10^{-19}$

$Fe^{2+}(aq) + 6 CN^- (aq) \rightleftharpoons Fe(CN)_6^{4-}(aq)$ $K_f = 3.72 \times 10^{35}$ Since the overall reaction is the simple

$FeS (s) + 6 CN^- (aq) \rightleftharpoons Fe(CN)_6^{4-} (aq) + S^{2-} (aq)$

sum of the two reactions, the overall reaction K = K_f x K_{sp} = (1.5×10^{35}) x (3.72×10^{-19}) = 5.6×10^{16}.
Check: The units (none) are correct. Since K_f is so large, it overwhelms the K_{sp} and the overall reaction is very spontaneous.

112. **Given:** $PbCl_2 (s) + 3 OH^- (aq) \rightleftharpoons Pb(OH)_3^- (aq) + 2 Cl^- (aq)$ use K_{sp} and K_f values   **Find:** K
Other: $K_f (Pb(OH)_3^-) = 8 \times 10^{13}$, $K_{sp} (PbCl_2) = 1.17 \times 10^{-5}$
Conceptual Plan: Identify the appropriate solid and complex ion. Write balanced equations for dissolving the solid and forming the complex ion. Add these two reactions to get the desired overall reaction. Using the rules from Chapter 14, multiply the individual reaction K's to get the overall K for the sum of these reactions.
Solution: Identify the solid as $PbCl_2$ and the complex ion as $Pb(OH)_3^-$. Write the individual reactions and add them together.

$PbCl_2 (s) \rightleftharpoons Pb^{2+}(aq) + 2 Cl^- (aq)$ $K_{sp} = 1.17 \times 10^{-5}$

$Pb^{2+}(aq) + 3 OH^- (aq) \rightleftharpoons Pb(OH)_3^- (aq)$ $K_f = 8 \times 10^{13}$ Since the overall reaction is the simple

$PbCl_2 (s) + 3 OH^- (aq) \rightleftharpoons Pb(OH)_3^- (aq) + 2 Cl^- (aq)$

sum of the two reactions, the overall reaction K = K_f x K_{sp} = (8×10^{13}) x (1.17×10^{-5}) = 9×10^8.
Check: The units (none) are correct. Since K_f is so large, it overwhelms the K_{sp} and the overall reaction is very spontaneous.

113. **Given:** 150.0 mL solution of 2.05 g sodium benzoate and 2.47 g benzoic acid   **Find:** pH
Other: $K_a (HC_7H_5O_2) = 6.5 \times 10^{-5}$

Conceptual Plan: g $NaC_7H_5O_2$ → mol $NaC_7H_5O_2$ and g $HC_7H_5O_2$ → mol $HC_7H_5O_2$

$$\frac{1 \text{ mol } NaC_7H_5O_2}{144.11 \text{ g } NaC_7H_5O_2} \qquad \frac{1 \text{ mol } HC_7H_5O_2}{122.13 \text{ g } HC_7H_5O_2}$$

Since the two components are in the same solution, the ratio of [base]/[acid] = (mol base)/(mol acid).
then K_a, mol $NaC_7H_5O_2$, mol $HC_7H_5O_2$ → **pH**

$$pH = pK_a + \log \frac{[\text{base}]}{[\text{acid}]}$$

Solution: $2.05 \text{ g } NaC_7H_5O_2 \times \dfrac{1 \text{ mol } NaC_7H_5O_2}{144.11 \text{ g } NaC_7H_5O_2} = 0.0142252 \text{ mol } NaC_7H_5O_2$ and

$2.47 \text{ g } HC_7H_5O_2 \times \dfrac{1 \text{ mol } HC_7H_5O_2}{122.13 \text{ g } HC_7H_5O_2} = 0.0202244 \text{ mol } HC_7H_5O_2$ then

$$pH = pK_a + \log \frac{[\text{base}]}{[\text{acid}]} = pK_a + \log \frac{\text{mol base}}{\text{mol acid}} = -\log(6.5 \times 10^{-5}) + \log \frac{0.0142252 \text{ mol}}{0.0202244 \text{ mol}} = 4.03 \,.$$

Check: The units (none) are correct. The magnitude of the answer makes physical sense because the pH is a little lower than the pK_a of the acid because there is more acid than base in the buffer solution.

114. **Given:** 10.0 mL of 17.5 M acetic acid and 5.54 g sodium acetate diluted to 1.50 L **Find:** pH
     Other: K_a ($HC_2H_3O_2$) = 1.8 x 10^{-5}
     Conceptual Plan:
     mL → L then L, initial $HC_2H_3O_2$ M → mol $HC_2H_3O_2$ then g $NaC_2H_3O_2$ → mol $NaC_2H_3O_2$

$$\frac{1 \text{ L}}{1000 \text{ mL}} \qquad\qquad M = \frac{\text{mol}}{L} \qquad\qquad \frac{1 \text{ mol } NaC_2H_3O_2}{83.04 \text{ g } NaC_2H_3O_2}$$

then Since the two components are in the same solution, the ratio of [base]/[acid] = (mol base)/(mol acid). then K_a, mol $NaC_2H_3O_2$, mol $HC_2H_3O_2$ → **pH**

$$pH = pK_a + \log \frac{[\text{base}]}{[\text{acid}]}$$

Solution: $10.0 \text{ mL} \times \dfrac{1 \text{ L}}{1000 \text{ mL}} = 0.0100 \text{ L}$ then $0.0100 \text{ L } HC_2H_3O_2 \times \dfrac{17.5 \text{ mol } HC_2H_3O_2}{1 \text{ L } HC_2H_3O_2} = 0.175 \text{ mol } HC_2H_3O_2 \,.$

then $5.54 \text{ g } NaC_2H_3O_2 \times \dfrac{1 \text{ mol } NaC_2H_3O_2}{83.04 \text{ g } NaC_2H_3O_2} = 0.0667148 \text{ mol } NaC_2H_3O_2$ then

$$pH = pK_a + \log \frac{[\text{base}]}{[\text{acid}]} = pK_a + \log \frac{\text{mol base}}{\text{mol acid}} = -\log(1.8 \times 10^{-5}) + \log \frac{0.0667148 \text{ mol}}{0.175 \text{ mol}} = 4.32 \,.$$

Check: The units (none) are correct. The magnitude of the answer makes physical sense because the pH is a little lower than the pK_a of the acid because there is more acid than base in the buffer solution.

115. **Given:** 150.0 mL of 0.25 M $HCHO_2$ and 75.0 ml of 0.20 M NaOH   **Find:** pH   **Other:** K_a ($HCHO_2$) = 1.8 x 10^{-4}
     Conceptual Plan: In this buffer, the base is generated by converting some of the formic acid to the formate ion. Part I: Stoichiometry:
     mL → L then L, initial $HCHO_2$ M → mol $HCHO_2$ then   mL → L then

$$\frac{1 \text{ L}}{1000 \text{ mL}} \qquad\qquad M = \frac{\text{mol}}{L} \qquad\qquad \frac{1 \text{ L}}{1000 \text{ mL}}$$

L, initial NaOH M → mol NaOH   then   write balanced equation   then

$$M = \frac{\text{mol}}{L} \qquad\qquad NaOH + HCHO_2 \rightarrow H_2O + NaCHO_2$$

mol $HCHO_2$, mol NaOH → mol $NaCHO_2$, mol $HCHO_2$ then
                set up stoichiometry table
Part II: Equilibrium:
Since the two components are in the same solution, the ratio of [base]/[acid] = (mol base)/(mol acid).
then K_a, mol $NaCHO_2$, mol $HCHO_2$ → pH

$$pH = pK_a + \log \frac{[\text{base}]}{[\text{acid}]}$$

Solution: $150.0 \text{ mL} \times \dfrac{1\text{ L}}{1000\text{ mL}} = 0.1500\text{ L}$ then $0.1500\text{ L HCHO}_2 \times \dfrac{0.25\text{ mol HCHO}_2}{1\text{ L HCHO}_2} = 0.0375\text{ mol HCHO}_2$.

then $75.0 \text{ mL} \times \dfrac{1\text{ L}}{1000\text{ mL}} = 0.0750\text{ L}$ then $0.0750\text{ L NaOH} \times \dfrac{0.20\text{ mol NaOH}}{1\text{ L NaOH}} = 0.015\text{ mol NaOH}$ then

set up table to track changes:

$$\text{NaOH }(aq) + \text{HCHO}_2\,(aq) \rightarrow \text{NaCHO}_2\,(aq) + \text{H}_2\text{O }(l)$$

Before addition	0.00 mol	0.0375 mol	0.00 mol	—
Addition	0.015 mol	—	—	—
After addition	≈ 0.00 mol	0.0225 mol	0.015 mol	—

Since the amount of NaOH is small, there are significant amounts of both buffer components, so the Henderson-Hasselbalch Equation can be used to calculate the pH..

$$\text{pH} = \text{pK}_a + \log\frac{[\text{base}]}{[\text{acid}]} = \text{pK}_a + \log\frac{\text{mol base}}{\text{mol acid}} = -\log(1.8 \times 10^{-4}) + \log\frac{0.015\text{ mol}}{0.0225\text{ mol}} = 3.57 \,.$$

Check: The units (none) are correct. The magnitude of the answer makes physical sense because the pH is a little lower than the pK$_a$ of the acid because there is more acid than base in the buffer solution.

116. **Given:** 750.0 mL solution of 3.55 g NH$_3$ and 4.78 g HCl   **Find:** pH   **Other:** K$_b$ (NH$_3$) = 1.79 x 10^{-5}
Conceptual Plan: In this buffer, the acid is generated by converting some of the ammonia to the ammonium ion. Part I: Stoichiometry:
g NH$_3$ → mol NH$_3$ and   g HCl → mol HCl   write balanced equation   then

$$\frac{1\text{ mol NH}_3}{17.03\text{ g NH}_3} \qquad \frac{1\text{ mol HCl}}{36.46\text{ g HCl}} \qquad \text{NH}_3 + \text{HCl} \rightarrow \text{NH}_4\text{Cl}$$

mol NH$_3$, mol HCl → mol NH$_3$, mol NH$_4$Cl then
set up stoichiometry table
Part II: Equilibrium:
K$_b$ → pK$_b$ → pK$_a$ then Since the two components are in the same solution,
$pK_b = -\log K_b \qquad 14 = pK_a + pK_b$

the ratio of [base]/[acid] = (mol base)/(mol acid). then   pK$_a$, mol NH$_3$, mol NH$_4$Cl →   pH

$$\text{pH} = \text{pK}_a + \log\frac{[\text{base}]}{[\text{acid}]}$$

Solution: $3.55 \text{ g NH}_3 \times \dfrac{1\text{ mol NH}_3}{17.03\text{ g NH}_3} = 0.208456\text{ mol NH}_3$ and

$4.78 \text{ g HCl} \times \dfrac{1\text{ mol HCl}}{36.46\text{ g HCl}} = 0.131103\text{ mol HCl}$ then set up table to track changes:

$$\text{HCl }(aq) + \text{NH}_3\,(aq) \rightarrow \text{NH}_4\text{Cl }(aq)$$

Before addition	0.00 mol	0.208456 mol	0.00 mol
Addition	0.131103 mol	—	—
After addition	≈ 0.00 mol	0.077353 mol	0.131103 mol

Since the amount of HCl is small, there are significant amounts of both buffer components, so the Henderson-Hasselbalch Equation can be used to calculate the pH..
Since K$_b$ (NH$_3$) = 1.79 x 10^{-5}, $pK_b = -\log K_b = -\log(1.79 \times 10^{-5}) = 4.75$. Since $14 = pK_a + pK_b$,
$pK_a = 14 - pK_b = 14 - 4.75 = 9.25$ then

$$\text{pH} = \text{pK}_a + \log\frac{[\text{base}]}{[\text{acid}]} = \text{pK}_a + \log\frac{\text{mol base}}{\text{mol acid}} = 9.25 + \log\frac{0.077353\text{ mol}}{0.131103\text{ mol}} = 9.02 \,.$$

Check: The units (none) are correct. The magnitude of the answer makes physical sense because the pH is a little lower than the pK$_a$ of the acid because there is more acid than base in the buffer solution.

117. **Given:** 1.0 L of buffer of 0.25 mol NH$_3$ and 0.25 mol NH$_4$Cl; adjust to pH = 8.75
Find: mass NaOH or HCl   **Other:** K$_b$ (NH$_3$) = 1.79 x 10^{-5}
Conceptual Plan: To decide which reagent needs to be added to adjust pH, calculate the initial pH.
Since the mol NH$_3$ = mol NH$_4$Cl, the pH = pK$_a$ so   K$_b$ → pK$_b$ → pK$_a$ then

acid = NH$_4^+$ base = NH$_3$ $pK_b = -\log K_b \qquad 14 = pK_a + pK_b$

final pH, pK$_a$ $\rightarrow$ [NH$_3$]/[NH$_4^+$] then **[NH$_3$], L $\rightarrow$ mol NH$_3$** and **[NH$_4^+$], L $\rightarrow$ mol NH$_4^+$**

$$pH = pK_a + \log \frac{[base]}{[acid]}$$

$$M = \frac{mol}{L}$$

$$M = \frac{mol}{L}$$

then write balanced equation then

$$H^+ + NH_3 \rightarrow NH_4^+$$

mol NH$_3$, mol NH$_4^+$, [NH$_3$]/[NH$_4^+$] $\rightarrow$ mol HCl $\rightarrow$ g HCl

set up stoichiometry table $\quad \dfrac{36.46 \text{ g HCl}}{1 \text{ mol HCl}}$

Solution: Since K$_b$ (NH$_3$) = 1.79 x 10^{-5}, $pK_b = -\log K_b = -\log (1.79 \times 10^{-5}) = 4.75$. Since $14 = pK_a + pK_b$, $pK_a = 14 - pK_b = 14 - 4.75 = 9.25$. Since the desired pH is lower (8.75) HCl (a strong acid) needs to be

added. then $pH = pK_a + \log \dfrac{[base]}{[acid]} = 9.25 + \log \dfrac{[NH_3]}{[NH_4^+]} = 8.75$. Solve for $\dfrac{[NH_3]}{[NH_4^+]}$.

$\log \dfrac{[NH_3]}{[NH_4^+]} = 8.75 - 9.25 = -0.50 \rightarrow \dfrac{[NH_3]}{[NH_4^+]} = 10^{-0.50} = 0.31623$. then $\dfrac{0.25 \text{ mol NH}_3}{1 \text{ L}} \times 1.0 \text{ L} = 0.25$ mol NH$_3$ and

$\dfrac{0.25 \text{ mol NH}_4Cl}{1 \text{ L}} \times 1.0 \text{ L} = 0.25$ mol NH$_4$Cl = 0.25 mol NH$_4^+$ Since HCl is a strong acid, [HCl] = [H$^+$], and

set up table to track changes:

	H$^+$ (aq)	+	NH$_3$ (aq)	$\rightarrow$	NH$_4^+$ (aq)
Before addition	$\approx$ 0.00 mol		0.25 mol		0.25 mol
Addition	x		$-$		$-$
After addition	$\approx$ 0.00 mol		(0.25 $-$ x) mol		(0.25 + x) mol

Since $\dfrac{[NH_3]}{[NH_4^+]} = 0.31623 = \dfrac{(0.25 - x) \text{ mol}}{(0.25 + x) \text{ mol}}$, solve for x. Note that the ratio of moles is the same as the ratio of

concentrations, since the volume for both terms is the same. $0.31623(0.25 + x) = (0.25 - x) \rightarrow$

$0.0790575 + 0.3162 x = 0.25 - x \rightarrow 1.31623 x = 0.17094 \rightarrow x = 0.12987$ mol HCl then

0.12987 mol HCl $\times \dfrac{36.46 \text{ g HCl}}{1 \text{ mol HCl}} = 4.7$ g HCl.

Check: The units (g) are correct. The magnitude of the answer makes physical sense because there is much less than a mole of each of the buffer components, so there must be much less than a mole of HCl.

118. **Given:** 250.0 mL of buffer of 0.025 mol HCHO$_2$ and 0.025 mol NaCHO$_2$; adjust to pH = 4.10
Find: mass NaOH or HCl $\qquad$ **Other:** K$_a$ (HCHO$_2$) = 1.8 x 10^{-4}
Conceptual Plan: To decide which reagent needs to be added to adjust pH, calculate the initial pH.
Since the mol HCHO$_2$ = mol NaCHO$_2$, the pH = pK$_a$ then **final pH, pK$_a$ $\rightarrow$ [NaCHO$_2$]/[HCHO$_2$]**

acid = HCHO$_2$ base = HCHO$_2^-$ $\qquad pK_a = -\log K_a$ $\qquad\qquad pH = pK_a + \log \dfrac{[base]}{[acid]}$

then mL $\rightarrow$ L then **write balanced equation** then

$\dfrac{1 \text{ L}}{1000 \text{ mL}}$ $\qquad$ NaOH + HCHO$_2$ $\rightarrow$ NaCHO$_2$ + H$_2$O

mol NaCHO$_2$, mol HCHO$_2$, [NaCHO$_2$]/[HCHO$_2$] $\rightarrow$ mol NaOH $\rightarrow$ g NaOH

set up stoichiometry table $\quad \dfrac{40.00 \text{ g NaOH}}{1 \text{ mol NaOH}}$

Solution: Since K$_a$ (HCHO$_2$) = 1.8 x 10^{-4}, $pK_a = -\log K_a = -\log (1.8 \times 10^{-4}) = 3.74$. Since the desired pH is higher (4.105) NaOH (a strong base) needs to be added. Then

$pH = pK_a + \log \dfrac{[base]}{[acid]} = 3.74 + \log \dfrac{[NaCHO_2]}{[HCHO_2]} = 4.10$. Solve for $\dfrac{[NaCHO_2]}{[HCHO_2]}$.

$\log \dfrac{[NaCHO_2]}{[HCHO_2]} = 4.10 - 3.74 = 0.36 \rightarrow \dfrac{[NaCHO_2]}{[HCHO_2]} = 10^{+0.36} = 2.26607$. Then since NaOH is a strong base,

[NaOH] = [OH$^-$], and set up table to track changes:

	NaOH (aq)	+	HCHO$_2$ (aq)	$\rightarrow$	NaCHO$_2$ (aq)	+ H$_2$O (l)
Before addition	$\approx$ 0.00 mol		0.025 mol		0.025 mol	$-$
Addition	x		$-x$		$+x$	$-$
After addition	$\approx$ 0.00 mol		(0.025 $-$ x) mol		(0.025 + x) mol	$-$

Since $pH = pK_a + \log\dfrac{[A^-]}{[HA]}$ so $4.10 = 3.74 + \log\dfrac{0.025\ \text{mol} + x}{0.025\ \text{mol} - x}$ solve for x. Note that the ratio of moles is the same as the ratio of concentrations, since the volume for both terms is the same

$0.360 = \log\dfrac{0.025\ \text{mol} + x}{0.025\ \text{mol} - x} \rightarrow 2.29 = \dfrac{0.025\ \text{mol} + x}{0.025\ \text{mol} - x} \rightarrow 0.0573 - 2.29x = 0.025 + x \rightarrow 3.29x = 0.0323 \rightarrow$

$x = 0.00981\ \text{mol}$ then $0.00981\ \text{mol NaOH} \times \dfrac{40.00\ \text{g NaOH}}{1\ \text{mol NaOH}} = 0.39\ \text{g NaOH}$.

Check: The units (g) are correct. The magnitude of the answer makes physical sense because there is much less than a mole of each of the buffer components, so there must be much less than a mole of NaOH.

119. a) **Given:** potassium hydrogen phthalate = KHP = $KHC_8H_4O_4$ titration with NaOH
  Find: balanced equation
  Conceptual Plan: The reaction will be a titration of the acid proton, leaving the phthalate ion in tact. The K will not be titrated since it is basic.
  Solution: $NaOH\,(aq) + KHC_8H_4O_4\,(aq) \rightarrow Na^+\,(aq) + K^+\,(aq) + C_8H_4O_4^{2-}\,(aq) + H_2O\,(l)$
  Check: An acid - base reaction generates a salt (soluble here) and water. There is only on e acidic proton in KHP.

b) **Given:** 0.5527 g KHP titrated with 25.87 mL of NaOH solution **Find:** [NaOH]
  Conceptual Plan:
  g KHP → mol KHP → mol NaOH and mL → L then mol NaOH and mL → M NaOH

$\dfrac{1\ \text{mol KHP}}{204.22\ \text{g KHP}}$ 1:1 from balance equation $\dfrac{1\ \text{L}}{1000\ \text{mL}}$ $M = \dfrac{\text{mol}}{\text{L}}$

  Solution: $0.5527\ \text{g KHP} \times \dfrac{1\ \text{mol KHP}}{204.22\ \text{g KHP}} = 0.002706395\ \text{mol KHP}$ mol KHP = mol acid = mol base =

  $0.002706395\ \text{mol NaOH}$ then $25.87\ \text{mL} \times \dfrac{1\ \text{L}}{1000\ \text{mL}} = 0.02587\ \text{L}$ then

  $[NaOH] = \dfrac{0.002706395\ \text{mol NaOH}}{0.02587\ \text{L}} = 0.1046\ \text{M NaOH}$.

  Check: The units (M) are correct. The magnitude of the answer makes physical sense because there is much less than a mole of acid. The magnitude of the moles of acid and base are smaller than the volume of base in liters.

120. **Given:** 0.5224 g monoprotic acid titrated with 23.82 mL of 0.0998 M NaOH solution **Find:** molar mass of acid
  Conceptual Plan:
  mL → L then M NaOH, L → mol NaOH → mol acid then mol acid, g acid → $\mathfrak{M}$

$\dfrac{1\ \text{L}}{1000\ \text{mL}}$ $M = \dfrac{\text{mol}}{\text{L}}$ 1:1 for monoprotic acid $\mathfrak{M} = \dfrac{\text{g acid}}{\text{mol acid}}$

  Solution: $23.82\ \text{mL} \times \dfrac{1\ \text{L}}{1000\ \text{mL}} = 0.02382\ \text{L}$ then

  $0.02382\ \text{L NaOH} \times \dfrac{0.0998\ \text{mol NaOH}}{1\ \text{L NaOH}} = 0.00237724\ \text{mol NaOH}$ $0.00237724\ \text{mol NaOH}$ = mol base = mol acid =

  $0.00237724\ \text{mol acid}$ then. $M = \dfrac{\text{g acid}}{\text{mol acid}} = \dfrac{0.5224\ \text{g acid}}{0.00237724\ \text{mol acid}} = 220.\ \text{g/mol}$.

  Check: The units (g/mol) are correct. The magnitude of the answer makes physical sense because there is much less than a mole of acid and about a half a gram of acid, so the molar mass will be high. The number is reasonable for an acid (must be > 20 g/mol – lightest acid is HF).

121. **Given:** 0.25 mol weak acid with 10.0 mL of 3.00 M KOH diluted to 1.5000 L has pH = 3.85 **Find:** pK_a of acid
  Conceptual Plan: mL → L then M KOH, L → mol KOH then write balanced reaction

$\dfrac{1\ \text{L}}{1000\ \text{mL}}$ $M = \dfrac{\text{mol}}{\text{L}}$ $KOH + HA \rightarrow NaA + H_2O$

  added mol KOH, initial mol acid → equil. mol KOH, equil. mol acid then
  set up stoichiometry table

equil. mol KOH, equil. mol acid, pH → pK_a

$$pH = pK_a + \log \frac{[base]}{[acid]}$$

Solution: $10.00 \text{ mL} \times \dfrac{1 \text{ L}}{1000 \text{ mL}} = 0.01000 \text{ L}$ then $0.01000 \text{ L KOH} \times \dfrac{3.00 \text{ mol KOH}}{1 \text{ L KOH}} = 0.0300 \text{ mol KOH}$ then

Since KOH is a strong base, $[KOH] = [OH^-]$, and set up table to track changes:

$$KOH\ (aq)\ +\ HA\ (aq)\ \rightarrow\ KA\ (aq) + H_2O\ (l)$$

	KOH	HA	KA	H₂O
Before addition	≈ 0.00 mol	0.25 mol	0.00 mol	–
Addition	0.0300 mol	–	–	–
After addition	≈ 0.00 mol	0.23 mol	0.0300 mol	–

Since the ratio of base to acid is between 0.1 and 10, so it is a buffer solution. Note that the ratio of moles is the same as the ratio of concentrations, since the volume for both terms is the

same. $pH = pK_a + \log \dfrac{[base]}{[acid]} = pK_a + \log \dfrac{0.0300 \text{ mol}}{0.23 \text{ mol}} = 3.85$. Solve for pK_a. $pK_a = 3.85 - \log \dfrac{0.0300 \text{ mol}}{0.23 \text{ mol}} = 4.73$.

Check: The units (none) are correct. The magnitude of the answer makes physical sense because there is more acid than base at equilibrium, so the pK_a is higher than the pH of the solution.

122. **Given:** 5.55 g weak acid with $K_a = 1.3 \times 10^{-4}$ with 5.00 mL of 6.00 M NaOH diluted to 750 mL has pH = 4.25   **Find:** molar mass of acid

Conceptual Plan: mL → L   then   M NaOH, L → mol NaOH   then   write balanced reaction

$$\frac{1 \text{ L}}{1000 \text{ mL}} \qquad\qquad M = \frac{mol}{L} \qquad\qquad NaOH + HA \rightarrow NaA + H_2O$$

added mol NaOH, initial mol acid → equil. mol NaOH, equil. mol acid   then
set up stoichiometry table
added mol NaOH, equil. mol acid, pH, pK_a →   equil. mol NaOH, equil. mol acid then

$$pH = pK_a + \log \frac{[base]}{[acid]}$$

mol acid, g acid → $\mathfrak{M}$

$$\mathfrak{M} = \frac{g \text{ acid}}{mol \text{ acid}}$$

Solution: $5.00 \text{ mL} \times \dfrac{1 \text{ L}}{1000 \text{ mL}} = 0.00500 \text{ L}$ then $0.00500 \text{ L NaOH} \times \dfrac{6.00 \text{ mol NaOH}}{1 \text{ L NaOH}} = 0.0300 \text{ mol NaOH}$ then

Since NaOH is a strong base, $[NaOH] = [OH^-]$, and set up table to track changes:

$$NaOH\ (aq)\ +\ HA\ (aq)\ \rightarrow\ NaA\ (aq) + H_2O\ (l)$$

	NaOH	HA	NaA	H₂O
Before addition	≈ 0.00 mol	x mol	0.00 mol	–
Addition	0.0300 mol	–	–	–
After addition	≈ 0.00 mol	$x - 0.0300$ mol	0.0300 mol	–

Since the pH is within 1 unit of the pK_a, it is a buffer solution. Note that the ratio of moles is the same as the ratio of concentrations, since the volume for both terms is the same.

$$pH = pK_a + \log \frac{[base]}{[acid]} = -\log (1.3 \times 10^{-4}) + \log \frac{0.0300 \text{ mol}}{(x - 0.0300) \text{ mol}} = 4.25 \ .$$

Solve for x. $\log 0.0300 - \log (x - 0.0300) = 4.25 - 3.89$ → $-\log (x - 0.0300) = 1.88682$ →

$x - 0.0300 = 10^{-1.88682} = 0.0129771$ → $x = 0.0429771$ mol. Finally,

$$M = \frac{g \text{ acid}}{mol \text{ acid}} = \frac{5.55 \text{ g acid}}{0.0429771 \text{ mol acid}} = 129 \text{ g/mol}$$

Check: The units (g/mol) are correct. The magnitude of the answer makes physical sense because there is much less than a mole of acid and about a 6 grams of acid, so the molar mass will be high. The number is reasonable for an acid (must be > 20 g/mol – lightest acid is HF).

123. **Given:** 0.552 g ascorbic acid dissolved in 20.00 mL and titrated with 28.42 mL of 0.1103 M KOH solution; pH = 3.72 when 10.0 mL KOH added   **Find:** molar mass and K_a of acid

Conceptual Plan: mL → L then M KOH, L → mol KOH → mol acid then mol acid, g acid → $\mathfrak{M}$

$$\frac{1 \text{ L}}{1000 \text{ mL}} \qquad\qquad M = \frac{mol}{L} \qquad 1{:}1 \text{ for monoprotic acid} \qquad \mathfrak{M} = \frac{g \text{ acid}}{mol \text{ acid}}$$

For second part of problem:

mL → L   then   M KOH, L → mol KOH   then   write balanced reaction

$$\frac{1\,L}{1000\,mL}$$

$$M = \frac{mol}{L}$$

$$KOH + HA \rightarrow NaA + H_2O$$

added mol KOH, initial mol acid → equil. mol KOH, equil. mol acid   then

set up stoichiometry table

equil. mol KOH, equil. mol acid, pH   → pK_a → K_a

$$pH = pK_a + \log \frac{[base]}{[acid]} \quad pK_a = -\log K_a$$

Solution: $28.42\ mL \times \dfrac{1\,L}{1000\ mL} = 0.02842\ L$ then

$0.02842\ L\,KOH \times \dfrac{0.1103\ mol\ KOH}{1\ L\,KOH} = 0.003134726\ mol\ KOH = mol\ base = mol\ acid = 0.003134726\ mol\ ascorbic$

acid then $M = \dfrac{g\ acid}{mol\,acid} = \dfrac{0.552\ g\ acid}{0.003134726\ mol\ acid} = 176\ g/mol$.   For second part of the problem,

$10.00\ mL \times \dfrac{1\,L}{1000\ mL} = 0.01000\ L$ then $0.01000\ L\,KOH \times \dfrac{0.1103\ mol\ KOH}{1\ L\,KOH} = 0.001103\ mol\ KOH$ then

Since KOH is a strong base, $[KOH] = [OH^-]$, and set up table to track changes:

	KOH (aq)	+	HA (aq)	→	KA (aq)	+ H_2O (l)
Before addition	≈ 0.00 mol		0.003134726 mol		0.00 mol	–
Addition	0.001103 mol		–		–	–
After addition	≈ 0.00 mol		0.002031726 mol		0.001103 mol	–

Since the ratio of base to acid is between 0.1 and 10, so it is a buffer solution. Note that the ratio of moles is the same as the ratio of concentrations, since the volume for both terms is the same.

$$pH = pK_a + \log \frac{[base]}{[acid]} = pK_a + \log \frac{0.001103\ mol}{0.002031726\ mol} = 3.72 . \text{ Solve for } pK_a.$$

$pK_a = 3.72 - \log \dfrac{0.001103}{0.002031726} = 3.98529$ and so $pK_a = -\log K_a$ or $K_a = 10^{-pK_a} = 10^{-3.98529} = 1.0 \times 10^{-4}$.

Check: The units (g/mol and none) are correct. The magnitude of the answer makes physical sense because there is much less than a mole of acid and about a half a gram of acid, so the molar mass will be high. The number is reasonable for an acid (must be > 20 g/mol – lightest acid is HF). The K_a is reasonable because the pK_a is within 1 unit of the pH when the titration solution is behaving as a buffer.

124. **Given:** titration data in problem #123   **Find:** initial pH

Conceptual Plan: Since ascorbic acid is a weak acid, set up an equilibrium problem using the initial concentration. so   mL → L   then mol HA, L → M HA   → $[H_3O^+]$ → pH

$$\frac{1\,L}{1000\,mL}$$

$$M = \frac{mol}{L} \quad ICE\ Chart \quad pH = -\log [H_3O^+]$$

Solution: $20.00\ mL \times \dfrac{1\,L}{1000\ mL} = 0.02000\ L$ then $\dfrac{0.003134726\ mol\ HA}{0.02000\,L\ HA} = 0.1567363\ mol\ HA$ then

$$HA\,(aq) + H_2O\,(l) \rightleftharpoons H_3O^+\,(aq) + A^-\,(aq)$$

	[HA]	$[H_3O^+]$	$[A^-]$
Initial	0.1567363	≈ 0.00	0.00
Change	$-x$	$+x$	$+x$
Equil	$0.1567363 - x$	$+x$	$+x$

and $K_a = \dfrac{[H_3O^+]\,[A^-]}{[HA]} = 1.0 \times 10^{-4} = \dfrac{x^2}{0.1567363 - x}$

Assume x is small (x << 0.1567) so $\dfrac{x^2}{0.1567363 - x} = 1.0 \times 10^{-4} = \dfrac{x^2}{0.1567363}$ and $x = 3.9590 \times 10^{-3} =$

$= [H_3O^+]$. Confirm that assumption is valid $\dfrac{3.9590 \times 10^{-3}}{0.1567363} \times 100\,\% = 2.5\,\% < 5\,\%$ so assumption is valid.

Finally, $pH = -\log [H_3O^+] = -\log (3.9590 \times 10^{-3}) = 2.40$

Check: The units (none) are correct. The magnitude of the answer makes physical sense because pH should be greater than $-\log (0.1567) = 0.80$ because this is a weak acid.

Find: pH at One-half of the equivalence point

Conceptual Plan: Since this is a weak acid – strong base titration, the pH at one-half the equivalence point is the pK_a of the weak acid.

Solution: $pH = pK_a = -\log K_a = -\log (1.0 \times 10^{-4}) = 4.00$ and the volume of added base is 0.5×28.42 mL $= 14.21$ mL.

Check: The units (none) are correct. Since this is a weak acid – strong base titration, the pH at one-half the equivalence point is the pK_a of the weak acid, so it should be 4.

Find: pH at equivalence point

Conceptual Plan: Use calculations from above, then since all of the weak acid has been converted to its conjugate base, the pH is only dependent on the hydrolysis reaction of the conjugate base. The mol A^- = initial mol HA and L HA, L KOH to equivalence point → total L then mol A^-, L → $[A^-]$

$$L\ HA + L\ KOH = \text{total L} \qquad\qquad M = \frac{mol}{L}$$

and $K_a \rightarrow K_b$ then do equilibrium calculation: $[A], K_b \rightarrow [OH^-] \rightarrow [H_3O^+] \rightarrow$ pH

$$K_w = K_a K_b \qquad\qquad set\ up\ ICE\ table \quad K_w = [H_3O^+][OH^-] \qquad pH = -\log [H_3O^+]$$

Solution: total volume = L HA + L KOH = 0.0200 L + 0.02842 L = 0.04842 L then

$$[A^-] = \frac{0.003134726\ mol\ A^-}{0.04842\ L} = 0.0647403\ M \quad and \quad K_w = K_a K_b. \text{ Rearrange to solve for } K_b.$$

$$A^- (aq) + H_2O (l) \rightleftharpoons HA (aq) + OH^- (aq)$$

	$[A^-]$	$[HA]$	$[OH^-]$
Initial	0.0647403	≈ 0.00	≈ 0.00
Change	$-x$	$+x$	$+x$
Equil	$0.0647403 - x$	$+x$	$+x$

$K_b = \dfrac{K_w}{K_a} = \dfrac{1.0 \times 10^{-14}}{1.0 \times 10^{-4}} = 1.0 \times 10^{-10}$. Set up ICE table

$$K_b = \frac{[HA][OH^-]}{[A^-]} = 1.0 \times 10^{-10} = \frac{x^2}{0.0647403 - x} \quad \text{Assume x is small (x << 0.0647) so}$$

$$\frac{x^2}{0.0647403 - x} = 1.0 \times 10^{-10} = \frac{x^2}{0.0647403} \quad \text{and } x = 2.5444 \times 10^{-6} = [OH^-]. \text{ Confirm that assumption is valid}$$

$$\frac{2.5444 \times 10^{-6}}{0.0647403} \times 100\ \% = 0.0039\ \% << 5\ \% \quad \text{so assumption is valid. } K_w = [H_3O^+][OH^-] \text{ so}$$

$$[H_3O^+] = \frac{K_w}{[OH^-]} = \frac{1.0 \times 10^{-14}}{2.5444 \times 10^{-6}} = 3.9302 \times 10^{-9}\ M. \text{ Finally, } pH = -\log [H_3O^+] = -\log (3.9302 \times 10^{-9}) = 8.41.$$

Check: The units (none) are correct. Since this is a weak acid – strong base titration, the pH at the equivalence point is basic.

Find: pH after adding 5.0 mL of excess base

Conceptual Plan:

Use calculations from earlier. then the pH is only dependent on the amount of excess base and the total solution volumes. mL excess → L excess then [KOH], L excess → mol KOH excess

$$\frac{1\ L}{1000\ mL} \qquad\qquad M = \frac{mol}{L}$$

then L HA, L KOH to equivalence point, L KOH excess → total L then

$$L\ HA + L\ NaOH\ to\ equivalence\ point + L\ NaOH\ excess = \text{total L}$$

mol excess KOH, total L → [KOH] = $[OH^-]$ → $[H_3O^+]$ → pH

$$M = \frac{mol}{L} \qquad K_w = [H_3O^+][OH^-] \qquad pH = -\log [H_3O^+]$$

Solution: $5.0\ mL\ KOH \times \dfrac{1\ L}{1000\ mL} = 0.0050\ L\ KOH\ excess$ then

$$\frac{0.1103\ mol\ KOH}{1\ L} \times 0.0050\ L = 0.0005515\ mol\ KOH\ excess. \text{ then}$$

$0.0200\ L\ HA + 0.02842\ L\ KOH + 0.0050\ L\ KOH = 0.05342\ L$ total volume.

$$[KOH\ excess] = \frac{0.0005515\ mol\ KOH\ excess}{0.05342\ L} = 0.010324\ M\ KOH\ excess \quad \text{Since KOH is a strong base,}$$

[KOH] excess = [OH$^-$]. The strong base overwhelms the weak base and is insignificant in the calculation.

$K_w = [H_3O^+][OH^-]$ so $[H_3O^+] = \dfrac{K_w}{[OH^-]} = \dfrac{1.0 \times 10^{-14}}{0.010\underline{3}24} = 9.\underline{6}863 \times 10^{-13}$ M . Finally,

$pH = -\log [H_3O^+] = -\log (9.\underline{6}863 \times 10^{-13}) = 12.01$.

Check: The units (none) are correct. The pH is rising sharply at the equivalence point, so the pH after 5 mL past the equivalence point should be quite basic.

Given: above data   **Find:** titration curve and suitable indicator
Solution: Plotting these data points:

Since the pH at the equivalence point is 8.42, an appropriate indicator is *m*-Nitrophenol

125. **Given:** saturated CaCO$_3$ solution; precipitate 1.00×10^2 mg CaCO$_3$ **Find:** volume of solution evaporated
Other: K_{sp} (CaCO$_3$) = 4.96×10^{-9}
Conceptual Plan: mg CaCO$_3$ → g CaCO$_3$ → mol CaCO$_3$ then

$$\dfrac{1 \text{ g CaCO}_3}{1000 \text{ mg CaCO}_3} \qquad \dfrac{1 \text{ mol CaCO}_3}{100.09 \text{ g CaCO}_3}$$

Use equation derived in problem #20 and solve for S. then   mol CaCO$_3$, S → L

for ionic compound, $A_m X_n$, $K_{sp} = m^m \, n^n \, S^{m+n}$. $M = \dfrac{\text{mol}}{\text{L}}$

Solution: 1.00×10^2 mg CaCO$_3$ × $\dfrac{1 \text{ g CaCO}_3}{1000 \text{ mg CaCO}_3}$ × $\dfrac{1 \text{ mol CaCO}_3}{100.09 \text{ g CaCO}_3}$ = 9.99101×10^{-4} mol CaCO$_3$ then

$K_{sp} = 4.96 \times 10^{-9}$, A = Ca^{2+}, m = 1, X = CO$_3^{2-}$, and n = 1 so $K_{sp} = 4.96 \times 10^{-9} = S^2$. Rearrange to solve for S.

$S = \sqrt{4.96 \times 10^{-9}} = 7.0\underline{4}273 \times 10^{-5}$ M . Finally, 9.99101×10^{-4} mol CaCO$_3$ × $\dfrac{1 \text{ L}}{7.0\underline{4}273 \times 10^{-5} \text{ mol CaCO}_3}$ = 14.2 L .

Check: The units (L) are correct. The volume should be large since the solubility is low.

126. **Given:** [Na$^+$] = 0.140 M and K_{sp} (NaC$_5$H$_3$N$_4$) = 5.76×10^{-8} **Find:** [C$_5$H$_3$N$_4^-$] to form precipitate
Conceptual Plan: Write balanced equation and expression for K_{sp}. then [Na$^+$], K_{sp} → [C$_5$H$_3$N$_4^-$]
Solution: NaC$_5$H$_3$N$_4$ (s) → Na$^+$ (aq) + C$_5$H$_3$N$_4^-$ (aq). So K_{sp} = [Na$^+$] [C$_5$H$_3$N$_4^-$] = 5.76×10^{-8} = (0.140) [C$_5$H$_3$N$_4^-$]. Solve for [C$_5$H$_3$N$_4^-$]. then [C$_5$H$_3$N$_4^-$] = 4.11×10^{-7} M.
Check: The units (M) are correct. Since K_{sp} is so small and the sodium concentration is fairly high, the urate concentration is driven to a very low level.

127. **Given:** [Ca^{2+}] = 9.2 mg/dL and K_{sp} (Ca$_2$P$_2$O$_7$) = 8.64×10^{-13} **Find:** [P$_2$O$_7^{4-}$] to form precipitate
Conceptual Plan: mg Ca^{2+}/dL → g Ca^{2+}/dL → mol Ca^{2+}/dL → mol Ca^{2+}/L then

$$\dfrac{1 \text{ g Ca}^{2+}}{1000 \text{ mg Ca}^{2+}} \qquad \dfrac{1 \text{ mol Ca}^{2+}}{40.08 \text{ g Ca}^{2+}} \qquad \dfrac{10 \text{ dL}}{1 \text{ L}}$$

Write balanced equation and expression for K_{sp}. then [Ca^{2+}], K_{sp} → [P$_2$O$_7^{4-}$]

Solution: $9.2 \dfrac{\text{mg Ca}^{2+}}{\text{dL}}$ × $\dfrac{1 \text{ g Ca}^{2+}}{1000 \text{ mg Ca}^{2+}}$ × $\dfrac{1 \text{ mol Ca}^{2+}}{40.08 \text{ g Ca}^{2+}}$ × $\dfrac{10 \text{ dL}}{1 \text{ L}}$ = 2.29541×10^{-3} M Ca^{2+} then write equation

Ca$_2$P$_2$O$_7$ (s) → 2 Ca^{2+} (aq) + P$_2$O$_7^{4-}$ (aq). So K_{sp} = [Ca^{2+}]^2 [P$_2$O$_7^{4-}$] = 8.64×10^{-13} =
= $(2.\underline{2}9541 \times 10^{-3})^2$ [P$_2$O$_7^{4-}$]. Solve for [P$_2$O$_7^{4-}$]. then [P$_2$O$_7^{4-}$] = 1.6×10^{-7} M.

Check: The units (M) are correct. Since K_{sp} is so small and the sodium concentration is fairly high, the urate concentration is driven to a very low level.

128. **Given:** AgCl in 0.100 M NH_3 **Find:** molar solubility (S)
Other: K_f ($Ag(NH_3)_2^+$) = 1.7 x 10^7, K_{sp} (AgCl) = 1.77 x 10^{-10}
Conceptual Plan: Identify the appropriate solid and complex ion. Write balanced equations for dissolving the solid and forming the complex ion. Add these two reactions to get the desired overall reaction. Using the rules from Chapter 14, multiply the individual reaction K's to get the overall K for the sum of these reactions. Then M NH_3, K → S
ICE Chart
Solution: Identify the solid as AgCl and the complex ion as $Ag(NH_3)_2^+$. Write the individual reactions and add them together.

$$AgCl\ (s) \rightleftharpoons Ag^+\ (aq) + Cl^-\ (aq) \qquad K_{sp} = 1.77\ x\ 10^{-10}$$

$$\underline{Ag^+\ (aq) + 2\ NH_3\ (aq) \rightleftharpoons Ag(NH_3)_2^+\ (aq) \qquad K_f = 1.7\ x\ 10^7}$$

$$AgCl\ (s) + 2\ NH_3\ (aq) \rightleftharpoons Ag(NH_3)_2^+\ (aq) + Cl^-\ (aq)$$

Since the overall reaction is the simple sum of the two reactions, the overall reaction K = K_f x K_{sp} =
= (1.7 x 10^7) x (1.77 x 10^{-10}) = 3.009 x 10^{-3}. then. Set up ICE table

$$AgCl\ (s) + 2\ NH_3\ (aq) \rightleftharpoons Ag(NH_3)_2^+\ (aq) + Cl^-\ (aq)$$

	$[NH_3]$	$[Ag(NH_3)_2^+]$	$[Cl^-]$
Initial	0.100	0.00	0.00
Change	$-2S$	$+S$	$+S$
Equil	$0.100 - 2S$	$+S$	$+S$

$$K = \frac{[Ag(NH_3)_2^+][Cl^-]}{[NH_3]^2} = 3.009\ x\ 10^{-3} = \frac{S^2}{(0.100 - 2S)^2}.$$

Simplify by taking the square root of the expression. $\sqrt{3.009\ x\ 10^{-3}} = 5.4854\ x\ 10^{-2} = \dfrac{S}{(0.100 - 2S)}$ Solve for

S. $(5.4854\ x\ 10^{-2})(0.100 - 2S) = S$ → $5.4854\ x\ 10^{-3} = (1.10971)\ S$ → $S = 4.9431\ x\ 10^{-3} = 4.9\ x\ 10^{-3}$ M.

Check: The units (M) are correct. Since K_f is large, the overall K is larger than the original K_{sp} and the solubility of AgCl increases over that of pure water $\left(\sqrt{1.77\ x\ 10^{-10}} = 1.33\ x\ 10^{-5}\ M\right)$.

129. **Given:** CuS in 0.150 M NaCN   **Find:** molar solubility (S)
Other: K_f ($Cu(CN)_4^{2-}$) = 1.0 x 10^{25}, K_{sp} (CuS) = 1.27 x 10^{-36}
**Conceptual Plan: Identify the appropriate solid and complex ion. Write balanced equations for dissolving the solid and forming the complex ion. Add these two reactions to get the desired overall reaction. Using the rules from Chapter 14, multiply the individual reaction K's to get the overall K for the sum of these reactions. then
M NaCN, K → S**
ICE Chart
Solution: Identify the solid as CuS and the complex ion as $Cu(CN)_4^{2-}$. Write the individual reactions and add them together.

$$CuS\ (s) \rightleftharpoons Cu^{2+}\ (aq) + S^{2-}\ (aq) \qquad K_{sp} = 1.27\ x\ 10^{-36}$$

$$\underline{Cu^{2+}\ (aq) + 4\ CN^-\ (aq) \rightleftharpoons Cu(CN)_4^{2-}\ (aq) \qquad K_f = 1.0\ x\ 10^{25}}$$

$$CuS\ (s) + 4\ CN^-\ (aq) \rightleftharpoons Cu(CN)_4^{2-}\ (aq) + S^{2-}\ (aq)$$

Since the overall reaction is the simple sum of the two reactions, the overall reaction K = K_f x K_{sp} = (1.0 x 10^{25}) x (1.27 x 10^{-36}) = 1.27 x 10^{-11}. then. NaCN (s) → Na^+ (aq) + CN^- (aq). Since 1 CN^- ion is generated for each NaCN, $[CN^-]$ = 0.150 M. Set up ICE table.

$$CuS\ (s) + 4\ CN^-\ (aq) \rightleftharpoons Cu(CN)_4^{2-}\ (aq) + S^{2-}\ (aq)$$

	$[CN^-]$	$[Cu(CN)_4^{2-}]$	$[S^{2-}]$
Initial	0.150	0.00	0.00
Change	$-4S$	$+S$	$+S$
Equil	$0.150 - 4S$	$+S$	$+S$

$$K = \frac{[Cu(CN)_4^{2-}][S^{2-}]}{[CN^-]^4} = 1.27\ x\ 10^{-11} = \frac{S^2}{(0.150 - 4S)^4}.$$

Assume S is small (4S << 0.150) so $\dfrac{S^2}{(0.150 - 4S)^4} = 1.27\ x\ 10^{-11} = \dfrac{S^2}{(0.150)^4}$ and S = 8.0183 x 10^{-8} =

= 8.0 x 10^{-8} M. Confirm that assumption is valid $\dfrac{4(8.0183\ x\ 10^{-8})}{0.150}$ x 100 % = 0.00021 % << 5 % so

assumption is valid.

Check: The units (M) are correct. Since K_f is large, the overall K is larger than the original K_{sp} and the solubility of CuS increases over that of pure water $\left(\sqrt{1.27 \times 10^{-36}} = 1.13 \times 10^{-18} \text{ M}\right)$.

130. **Given:** 0.10 M φNH_2, keep $[\varphi NH_3^+] < 1.0 \times 10^{-9}$ and K_b (φNH_2) $= 4.3 \times 10^{-10}$ **Find:** [NaOH]

     Conceptual Plan: M φNH_2, maximum M φNH_3^+ → [OH⁻] = [NaOH]

$$\text{ICE Chart} \quad K_w = [H_3O^+][OH^-] \quad pH = -\log [H_3O^+]$$

Solution: Set up ICE table. Since the amount of the conjugate acid is set so small, the concnetration of the weak base is not significantly changing.

$$\phi NH_2 (aq) + H_2O(l) \rightleftharpoons \phi NH_3^+ (aq) + OH^- (aq)$$

	$[\phi NH_3]$	$[\phi NH_4^+]$	$[OH^-]$
Initial	0.10	0.00	≈ 0.00
Change	–	–	+ x
Equil	≈ 0.10	1.0×10^{-9}	+ x

$$K_b = \frac{[\phi NH_4^+][OH^-]}{[\phi NH_2]} = 4.3 \times 10^{-10} = \frac{(1.0 \times 10^{-9})x}{\approx 0.10}$$

Solve for x. So x = 0.043 M = [OH⁻]. NaOH (aq) → Na⁺ (aq) + OH⁻ (aq). Since 1 OH⁻ ion is generated for each NaOH, [NaOH] = 0.043 M NaOH.

Check: The units (M) are correct. The magnitude of the answer makes physical sense because [OH⁻] needs to be about one order of magnitue lower than the aniline concentration (comparing K_b with maximum conjugate acid concentrations).

131. **Given:** 100 mL of 0.36 M NH_2OH and 50 mL of 0.26 M HCl and K_b (NH_2OH) $= 1.10 \times 10^{-8}$ **Find:** pH

     Conceptual Plan: identify acid and base components   mL →   L   then $[NH_2OH]$, L → mol NH_2OH

$$\text{acid} = NH_3OH^+ \text{ base} = NH_2OH \qquad \frac{1 \text{ L}}{1000 \text{ mL}} \qquad M = \frac{\text{mol}}{\text{L}}$$

     then   mL →   L   then   [HCl], L → mol HCl   then   write balanced equation   then

$$\frac{1 \text{ L}}{1000 \text{ mL}} \qquad M = \frac{\text{mol}}{\text{L}} \qquad HCl + NH_2OH \rightarrow NH_3OHCl$$

     mol NH_2OH, mol HCl → mol excess NH_2OH, mol NH_3OH^+

        set up stoichiometry table

Since there are significant amounts of both the acid and the conjugate base species, this is a buffer solution and so Henderson-Hasselbalch Equation $\left(pH = pK_a + \log \frac{[\text{base}]}{[\text{acid}]} \right)$ can be used. Convert K_b to K_a using $K_w = K_a K_b$. Also note that ratio of concentrations is the same as the ratio of moles, since the volume is the same for both species.

Solution: $100 \text{ mL } NH_2OH \times \dfrac{1 \text{ L}}{1000 \text{ mL}} = 0.1 \text{ L } NH_2OH$ then $\dfrac{0.36 \text{ mol } NH_2OH}{1 \text{ L}} \times 0.1 \text{ L} = 0.036 \text{ mol } NH_2OH$.

$50 \text{ mL HCl} \times \dfrac{1 \text{ L}}{1000 \text{ mL}} = 0.05 \text{ L HCl}$ then $\dfrac{0.26 \text{ mol HCl}}{1 \text{ L}} \times 0.05 \text{ L} = 0.013 \text{ mol HCl}$.

Set up table to track changes:

	HCl (aq)	+ NH_2OH (aq)	→ NH_3OHCl (aq)
Before addition	0.00 mol	0.036 mol	0.00 mol
Addition	0.013 mol	–	–
After addition	≈ 0.00 mol	0.023 mol	0.013 mol

then $K_w = K_a K_b$ so $K_a = \dfrac{K_w}{K_b} = \dfrac{1.0 \times 10^{-14}}{1.10 \times 10^{-8}} = 9.0909 \times 10^{-7}$ M then use Henderson-Hasselbalch Equation,

since the solution is a buffer. Note that the ratio of moles is the same as the ratio of concentrations, since the volume for both terms is the same.

$$pH = pK_a + \log \frac{[\text{base}]}{[\text{acid}]} = -\log(9.0909 \times 10^{-7}) + \log \frac{0.023 \text{ mol}}{0.013 \text{ mol}} = 6.28918 = 6.3 .$$

Check: The units (none) are correct. The magnitude of the answer makes physical sense because pH should be more than the pK_a of the acid because there is more base than acid.

132. **Given:** 0.867 g diprotic acid titrated with 32.2 mL of 0.182 M $Ba(OH)_2$ solution **Find:** molar mass of acid

     Conceptual Plan:

Write balanced reaction then **mL** → **L** then **M Ba(OH)₂, L** → **mol Ba(OH)₂** → **mol acid**

$$H_2A + Ba(OH)_2 \rightarrow BaA + 2\,H_2O$$

$$\frac{1\,L}{1000\,mL} \qquad\qquad M = \frac{mol}{L} \qquad\qquad 1{:}1$$

then mol acid, g acid → 𝔐

$$\mathfrak{M} = \frac{g\ acid}{mol\ acid}$$

Solution: $32.2\ \cancel{mL} \times \dfrac{1\,L}{1000\ \cancel{mL}} = 0.0322\,L$ then

$$0.0322\ \cancel{L\ Ba(OH)_2} \times \frac{0.182\ mol\ Ba(OH)_2}{1\ \cancel{L\ Ba(OH)_2}} = 0.0058\underline{6}04\ \cancel{mol\ Ba(OH)_2} \times \frac{1\ mol\ H_2A}{1\ \cancel{mol\ Ba(OH)_2}} = 0.0058\underline{6}04\ mol\ H_2A \text{ then}$$

$$\mathfrak{M} = \frac{g\ acid}{mol\ acid} = \frac{0.867\ g\ H_2A}{0.0058\underline{6}04\ mol\ H_2A} = 148\ g/mol\ .$$

Check: The units (g/mol) are correct. The magnitude of the answer makes physical sense because there is much less than a mole of acid and about a half a gram of acid, so the molar mass will be high. The number is reasonable for an acid (must be > 20 g/mol – lightest acid is HF).

133. **Given:** 25.0 mL of NaOH titrated with 19.6 mL of 0.189 M HCl solution; 10.0 mL of H₃PO₄ titrated with 34.9 mL NaOH **Find:** concentration of H₃PO₄ solution

Conceptual Plan:

Write 1ˢᵗ balanced reaction then **mL** → **L** then **M HCl, L** → **mol HCl** → **mol NaOH**

$$HCl + NaOH \rightarrow NaCl + H_2O$$

$$\frac{1\,L}{1000\,mL} \qquad\qquad M = \frac{mol}{L} \qquad\qquad 1{:}1$$

then mL → **L then mol NaOH, L** → **M NaOH** then **Write 2ⁿᵈ balanced reaction** then **mL** → **L**

$$\frac{1\,L}{1000\,mL} \qquad H_3PO_4 + 3\,NaOH \rightarrow Na_3PO_4 + 3\,H_2O \qquad \frac{1\,L}{1000\,mL}$$

then M NaOH, L → **mol NaOH** → **mol H₃PO₄** then **mL** → **L** then **mol H₃PO₄, L** → **M H₃PO₄**

$$M = \frac{mol}{L} \qquad 3{:}1 \qquad\qquad \frac{1\,L}{1000\,mL} \qquad\qquad M = \frac{mol}{L}$$

Solution: In the first titration, $19.6\ \cancel{mL} \times \dfrac{1\,L}{1000\ \cancel{mL}} = 0.0196\,L$ then

$$0.0196\ \cancel{L\ HCl} \times \frac{0.189\ mol\ HCl}{1\ \cancel{L\ HCl}} = 0.0037\underline{0}44\ \cancel{mol\ HCl} \times \frac{1\ mol\ NaOH}{1\ \cancel{mol\ HCl}} = 0.0037\underline{0}44\ mol\ NaOH \text{ then}$$

$$25.0\ \cancel{mL} \times \frac{1\,L}{1000\ \cancel{mL}} = 0.0250\,L \text{ then } \frac{0.0037\underline{0}44\ mol\ NaOH}{0.0250\ L\ NaOH} = 0.148\underline{1}76\ M\ NaOH\ .\ \text{In the second titration,}$$

$$34.9\ \cancel{mL} \times \frac{1\,L}{1000\ \cancel{mL}} = 0.0349\,L \text{ then}$$

$$0.0349\ \cancel{L\ NaOH} \times \frac{0.148\underline{1}76\ mol\ NaOH}{1\ \cancel{L\ NaOH}} = 0.00517\underline{1}34\ \cancel{mol\ NaOH} \times \frac{1\ mol\ H_3PO_4}{3\ \cancel{mol\ NaOH}} = 0.00172\underline{3}78\ mol\ H_3PO_4 \text{ then}$$

$$10.0\ \cancel{mL} \times \frac{1\,L}{1000\ \cancel{mL}} = 0.0100\,L \text{ then } \frac{0.00172\underline{3}78\ mol\ H_3PO_4}{0.0100\ L\ H_3PO_4} = 0.172\ M\ H_3PO_4\ .$$

Check: The units (M) are correct. The magnitude of the answer makes physical sense because the concentration of NaOH is a little lower than the HCl (because the volume of NaOH is greater than HCl) and the concentration of H₃PO₄ is more than the NaOH (because the ratio of the volume of NaOH to volume of H₃PO₄ is just over 3 and H₃PO₄ is a triproitic acid).

134. The Henderson-Hasselbalch Equation is $pH = pK_a + \log \dfrac{[base]}{[acid]}$. Remember that $14 = pH + pOH$ and $14 = pK_a + pK_b$. Substituting these into the Henderson-Hasselbalch Equation :

$14 - pOH = 14 - pK_b + \log \dfrac{[base]}{[acid]}$. Simplifying thei expression gives: $pOH = pK_b - \log \dfrac{[base]}{[acid]}$

135. **Given:** 10.0 L of 75 ppm CaCO₃ and 55 ppm MgCO₃ (by mass) **Find:** mass Na₂CO₃ to precipitate 90.0 % of ions **Other:** $K_{sp}(CaCO_3) = 4.96 \times 10^{-9}$ and $K_{sp}(MgCO_3) = 6.82 \times 10^{-6}$

Conceptual Plan:

Assume that the density of water is 1.00 g/mL.   L water → mL water → g water then

$$\frac{1000 \text{ mL}}{1 \text{ L}} \qquad \frac{1.00 \text{ g water}}{1 \text{ mL}}$$

g water → g CaCO₃ → mol CaCO₃ → mol Ca²⁺ and g water → g MgCO₃ → mol MgCO₃ then

$$\frac{75 \text{ g CaCO}_3}{10^6 \text{ g water}} \quad \frac{1 \text{ mol CaCO}_3}{100.09 \text{ g CaCO}_3} \quad \frac{1 \text{ mol Ca}^{2+}}{1\text{ mol CaCO}_3} \qquad \frac{55 \text{ g MgCO}_3}{10^6 \text{ g water}} \quad \frac{1 \text{ mol MgCO}_3}{84.32 \text{ g MgCO}_3}$$

mol MgCO₃ → mol Mg²⁺ then Comparing the two K_sp values, essentially all of the of the Ca²⁺ will

$$\frac{1 \text{ mol Mg}^{2+}}{1\text{ mol MgCO}_3}$$

precipitate before the Mg²⁺ will begin to precipitate.   Since 90.0 % of the ions are to be precipitates, there will be 10.0 % of the ions left in solution (all will be Mg²⁺).

$$(0.100)(\text{mol Ca}^{2+} + \text{mol Mg}^{2+})$$

Calculate the moles of ions remaining in solution. then   mol Mg²⁺, L → M Mg²⁺ then   Use

$$M = \frac{\text{mol}}{\text{L}}$$

equation derived in problem #19 and use to M Mg²⁺, K_sp → M CO₃²⁻ then M CO₃²⁻, L → mol CO₃²⁻

$$\text{for ionic compound, } A_mX_n, \ K_{sp} = [A^{n+}]^m \ [X^{m-}]^n. \qquad M = \frac{\text{mol}}{\text{L}}$$

then   mol CO₃²⁻ → mol Na₂CO₃ → g Na₂CO₃

$$\frac{1 \text{ mol CO}_3^{2-}}{1 \text{ mol Na}_2\text{CO}_3} \qquad \frac{105.99 \text{ g Na}_2\text{CO}_3}{1 \text{ mol Na}_2\text{CO}_3}$$

Solution: $10.0 \text{ L} \times \dfrac{1000 \text{ mL}}{1 \text{ L}} \times \dfrac{1.00 \text{ g water}}{1 \text{ mL}} = 1.00 \times 10^4$ g water   then

$$1.00 \times 10^4 \text{ g water} \times \frac{75 \text{ g CaCO}_3}{10^6 \text{ g water}} \times \frac{1 \text{ mol CaCO}_3}{100.09 \text{ g CaCO}_3} \times \frac{1 \text{ mol Ca}^{2+}}{1\text{ mol CaCO}_3} = 0.007\underline{4}933 \text{ mol Ca}^{2+} \quad \text{and}$$

$$1.00 \times 10^4 \text{ g water} \times \frac{55 \text{ g MgCO}_3}{10^6 \text{ g water}} \times \frac{1 \text{ mol MgCO}_3}{84.32 \text{ g MgCO}_3} \times \frac{1 \text{ mol Mg}^{2+}}{1\text{ mol MgCO}_3} = 0.006\underline{5}228 \text{ mol Mg}^{2+} \text{ so the ions}$$

remaining in solution after 90.0 % precipitate out =

$(0.100)(\text{mol Ca}^{2+} + \text{mol Mg}^{2+}) = (0.100)(0.007\underline{4}933 \text{ mol Ca}^{2+} + 0.006\underline{5}228 \text{ mol Mg}^{2+}) = 0.001\underline{4}0607$ mol ions .

so $\dfrac{0.001\underline{4}0607 \text{ mol Ca}^{2+}}{10.0 \text{ L}} = 0.000\underline{1}40607$ M Ca²⁺ then K_sp = 6.82 × 10⁻⁶, A = Mg²⁺, m = 1, X = CO₃²⁻, and n = 1

so $K_{sp} = 6.82 \times 10^{-6} = [\text{Mg}^{2+}] [\text{CO}_3^{2-}] = (0.000\underline{1}40607) [\text{CO}_3^{2-}]$.   Rearrange to solve for [CO₃²⁻].
So [CO₃²⁻] = 0.048\underline{5}040 M. then

$$\frac{0.048\underline{5}040 \text{ mol CO}_3^{2-}}{1 \text{ L}} \times 10.0 \text{ L} \times \frac{1 \text{ mol Na}_2\text{CO}_3}{1 \text{ mol CO}_3^{2-}} \times \frac{105.99 \text{ g Na}_2\text{CO}_3}{1 \text{ mol Na}_2\text{CO}_3} = 51.6 \text{ g Na}_2\text{CO}_3.$$

Check: The units (g) are correct. The mass is reasonable to put in a washing machine load.

136. Given: 0.558 g diprotic acid with molar mass = 255.8 g/mol dissolved in 25.00 mL water and titrated saturated Ca(OH)₂ solution   Other: K_sp (Ca(OH)₂) = 4.68 × 10⁻⁶
a)   Find: volume of base to the first and second equivalence points
   Conceptual Plan:
   Calculate the [Ca(OH)₂] by using the equation derived in problem #20 and solve for S.
          for ionic compound, A_mX_n, $K_{sp} = m^m \, n^n \, S^{m+n}$.
   then Write balanced reaction for titration of both protons. (Volume to 1st equivalence point will
          $$H_2A + Ca(OH)_2 \rightarrow CaA + 2 H_2O$$
   be half of this.) then g H₂A, 𝔐 → mol H₂A → mol Ca(OH)₂ then

   $$\mathfrak{M} = \frac{\text{g acid}}{\text{mol acid}} \qquad 1:1$$

   M Ca(OH)₂, mol Ca(OH)₂ → L Ca(OH)₂ → mL Ca(OH)₂ Finally divide the volume to
          $$M = \frac{\text{mol}}{\text{L}} \qquad \frac{1000 \text{ mL}}{1 \text{ L}}$$

   the second equivalence point by 2 to get the volume to the first equivalence point.

Solution: for $Ca(OH)_2$, $K_{sp} = 4.68 \times 10^{-6}$, $A = Ca^{2+}$, $m = 1$, $X = OH^-$, and $n = 2$ so $K_{sp} = 4.68 \times 10^{-6} = 2^2S^3$. Rearrange to solve for S. $S = \sqrt[3]{\dfrac{4.68 \times 10^{-6}}{4}} = 1.05 \times 10^{-2}$ M .

$0.558 \ \cancel{g \ H_2A} \ \times \ \dfrac{1 \ mol \ H_2A}{255.8 \ \cancel{g \ H_2A}} = 0.00218139 \ mol \ H_2A$ Since the stoichiometry of the overall titration reaction is 1:1 then $0.00218139 \ mol \ H_2A = 0.00218139 \ mol \ Ca(OH)_2$.

Then $0.00218139 \ \cancel{mol \ Ca(OH)_2} \ \times \ \dfrac{1 \ \cancel{L \ Ca(OH)_2}}{0.0105 \ \cancel{mol \ Ca(OH)_2}} \ \times \ \dfrac{1000 \ mL \ Ca(OH)_2}{1 \ \cancel{L \ Ca(OH)_2}} = 208 \ mL \ Ca(OH)_2$ to reach the second equivalence point.   Then ½ (208 mL $Ca(OH)_2$) = 104 mL $Ca(OH)_2$ to reach the first equivalence point.

Check: The units (mL and mL) are correct.   The magnitude of the answer makes physical sense because the concentration of the $Ca(OH)_2$ solution is so low.

b)   **Given:** after adding 25.0 mL of $Ca(OH)_2$ solution pH = 3.82   **Find:** pK_{a1} of acid
   Conceptual Plan:
   mL $\rightarrow$ L   then   M $Ca(OH)_2$, L $\rightarrow$ mol $Ca(OH)_2$ $\rightarrow$ mol OH^- then   write a balanced reaction

   $\dfrac{1 \ L}{1000 \ mL}$ $M = \dfrac{mol}{L}$ $Ca(OH)_2 \rightarrow Ca^{2+} + 2 \ OH^-$ $OH^- + H_2A \rightarrow HA^- + H_2O$

   added mol OH^-, initial mol acid $\rightarrow$ equil. mol HA^-, equil. mol H_2A then
   set up stoichiometry table
   equil. mol HA^-, equil. mol H_2A, pH $\rightarrow$ pK_{a1}

   $pH = pK_a + \log \dfrac{[base]}{[acid]}$

   Solution: $25.0 \ \cancel{mL} \ \times \ \dfrac{1 \ L}{1000 \ \cancel{mL}} = 0.0250 \ L$ then

   $0.0250 \ \cancel{L \ Ca(OH)_2} \ \times \ \dfrac{0.0105 \ mol \ Ca(OH)_2}{1 \ \cancel{L \ Ca(OH)_2}} = 0.0002625 \ \cancel{mol \ Ca(OH)_2} \ \times \ \dfrac{2 \ mol \ OH^-}{1 \ \cancel{mol \ Ca(OH)_2}} = 0.000525 \ mol \ OH^-$

   then Set up table to track changes:

	OH^- (aq)	+	H_2A (aq)	$\rightarrow$	HA^- (aq)	+ H_2O (l)
Before addition	≈ 0.00 mol		0.00218139 mol		0.00 mol	–
Addition	0.000525 mol		–		–	–
After addition	≈ 0.00 mol		0.00165639 mol		0.000525 mol	–

   Since the ratio of base to acid is between 0.1 and 10, so it is a buffer solution. Note that the ratio of moles is the same as the ratio of concentrations, since the volume for both terms is the same. $pH = pK_a + \log \dfrac{[base]}{[acid]} = pK_{a1} + \log \dfrac{0.000525 \ \cancel{mol}}{0.00165639 \ \cancel{mol}} = 3.82$. Solve for pK_{a1}.

   $pK_{a1} = 3.82 - \log \dfrac{0.000525}{0.00165639} = 4.32$.

   Check: The units (none) are correct.   The magnitude of the answer makes physical sense because there is more acid than base at equilibrium, so the pK_{a1} is higher than the pH of the solution.

c)   **Given:** after adding 20.0 mL of $Ca(OH)_2$ solution after first equivalence point pH = 8.25
   Find: pK_{a2} of acid
   Conceptual Plan:
   mL $\rightarrow$ L   then   M $Ca(OH)_2$, L $\rightarrow$ mol $Ca(OH)_2$ $\rightarrow$ mol OH^- then   write balanced reaction

   $\dfrac{1 \ L}{1000 \ mL}$ $M = \dfrac{mol}{L}$ $Ca(OH)_2 \rightarrow Ca^{2+} + 2 \ OH^-$ $OH^- + HA^- \rightarrow A^{2-} + H_2O$

   added mol OH^-, initial mol acid $\rightarrow$ equil. mol HA^-, equil. mol A^{2-} then
   set up stoichiometry table
   equil. mol HA^-, equil. mol A^{2-}, pH $\rightarrow$ pK_{a2}

   $pH = pK_a + \log \dfrac{[base]}{[acid]}$

   Solution: $20.0 \ \cancel{mL} \ \times \ \dfrac{1 \ L}{1000 \ \cancel{mL}} = 0.0200 \ L$ then

$$0.0200 \ \cancel{L \ Ca(OH)_2} \ \times \ \frac{0.0105 \ mol \ Ca(OH)_2}{1 \ \cancel{L \ Ca(OH)_2}} = 0.000210 \ \cancel{mol \ Ca(OH)_2} \ \times \ \frac{2 \ mol \ OH^-}{1 \ \cancel{mol \ Ca(OH)_2}} = 0.000420 \ mol \ OH^-$$

then Set up table to track changes:

$$OH^- \ (aq) \ + \ HA^- \ (aq) \ \rightarrow \ A^{2-} \ (aq) + H_2O \ (l)$$

Before addition	≈ 0.00 mol	0.00218139 mol	0.00 mol	–
Addition	0.000420 mol	–	–	–
After addition	≈ 0.00 mol	0.00176139 mol	0.000420 mol	–

Since the ratio of base to acid is between 0.1 and 10, so it is a buffer solution. Note that the ratio of moles is the same as the ratio of concentrations, since the volume for both terms is the

same. $pH = pK_a + \log \frac{[base]}{[acid]} = pK_{a2} + \log \frac{0.000420 \ \cancel{mol}}{0.00176139 \ \cancel{mol}} = 8.25$. Solve for pK_{a2}.

$$pK_a = 8.25 - \log \frac{0.000420}{0.00176139} = 8.87 \ .$$

Check: The units (none) are correct. The magnitude of the answer makes physical sense because there is more acid than base at equilibrium, so the pK_{a2} is higher than the pH of the solution.

137. **Given:** excess $Mg(OH)_2$ in 1.00 L 0f 1.0 M NH_4Cl has pH = 9.00   **Find:** K_{sp} ($Mg(OH)_2$)
Other: K_b (NH_3) = 1.76 x 10^{-5}
Conceptual Plan: $M \ NH_4Cl \rightarrow M \ NH_4^+$ and $K_b \rightarrow K_a$ then final pH $\rightarrow$ $[H_3O^+]$ then

$$NH_4Cl \ (aq) \rightarrow NH_4^+ \ (aq) + Cl^- \ (aq) \qquad K_w = K_a \ K_b \qquad [H_3O^+] = 10^{-pH}$$

$M \ NH_4^+, M \ H_3O^+, K_a \rightarrow x$ **Since x is significant compared to initial M NH_4^+ this is a buffer solution.**
ICE Chart
The NH_4^+ is neutralized with $Mg(OH)_2$. Since $Mg(OH)_2 \ (s) \rightleftharpoons Mg^{2+} \ (aq) + 2 \ OH^- \ (aq)$ **there are 2 moles of OH^- generated for each mole of $Mg(OH)_2$ dissolved. Thus ½ (x mol OH^-) = mol $Mg(OH)_2$ was dissolved in 1.00 L of solution. Since there is 1.00 L solution mol $Mg(OH)_2 = [Mg^{2+}]$ and $[H_3O^+]$ $\rightarrow$ $[OH^-]$ then**

$$K_w = [H_3O^+][OH^-]$$

Finally, write expression for K_{sp} ($Mg(OH)_2$) and substitute in values for $[Mg^{2+}]$ and $[OH^-]$.
Solution: Since 1 NH_4^+ ion is generated for each NH_4Cl, $[NH_4^+]$ = 1.0 M NH_4^+. Since $K_w = K_a \ K_b$,

rearrange to solve for K_a. $K_a = \frac{K_w}{K_b} = \frac{1.0 \times 10^{-14}}{1.76 \times 10^{-5}} = 5.\underline{6}818 \times 10^{-10}$ Final pH = 9.00, so

$[H_3O^+] = 10^{-pH} = 10^{-9.00} = 1.0 \times 10^{-9} \ M$ Set up ICE Chart.

$$NH_4^+ \ (aq) + H_2O(l) \rightleftharpoons H_3O^+ \ (aq) + NH_3(aq)$$

	$[NH_4^+]$	$[H_3O^+]$	$[NH_3]$
Initial	1.0	≈ 0.00	0.00
Change	−x	+ x	+ x
Equil	1.0 − x	1.0 x 10^{-9}	+ x

$K_a = \frac{[H_3O^+] \ [NH_3]}{[NH_4^+]} = 5.\underline{6}818 \times 10^{-10} = \frac{(1.0 \times 10^{-9})x}{1.0 - x}$.

Solve for x. $5.\underline{6}818 \times 10^{-10} \ (1.0 - x) = (1.0 \times 10^{-9})x$ $\rightarrow$ $5.\underline{6}818 \times 10^{-10} = (1.0 \times 10^{-9} + 5.\underline{6}818 \times 10^{-10})x$ $\rightarrow$
x = 0.3\underline{6}2318, so this is a buffer solution. Since there is 1.00 L of solution, 0.362318 mol of NH_4^+ is neutralized with $Mg(OH)_2$. Since $Mg(OH)_2 \ (s) \rightleftharpoons Mg^{2+} \ (aq) + 2 \ OH^- \ (aq)$ there are 2 moles of OH^- generated for each mole of $Mg(OH)_2$ dissolved. Thus ½ (0.3\underline{6}2318 mol OH^-) = 0.1\underline{8}1159 mol $Mg(OH)_2$ was dissolved in 1.00 L of solution. Thus the $[Mg^{2+}]$ = 0.1\underline{8}1159 M. Since $K_w = [H_3O^+][OH^-]$ so

$$[OH^-] = \frac{K_w}{[H_3O^+]} = \frac{1.0 \times 10^{-14}}{1.0 \times 10^{-9}} = 1.0 \times 10^{-5} \ M \ \text{then}$$

K_{sp} ($Mg(OH)_2$) = $[Mg^{2+}] \ [OH^-]^2 = (0.1\underline{8}1159) \ (1.0 \times 10^{-5})^2 = 1.8 \times 10^{-11}$.
Check: The units (none) are correct. The magnitude of the answer makes physical sense because the concentration of NH_4Cl is high and so it took a significant amount of $Mg(OH)_2$ to raise the pH to 9.00. Note that this number disagrees with the accepted value for the K_{sp} ($Mg(OH)_2$). This is most likely due to errors in the measurements in this experiment.

138. Given: 1.0 L of 0.10 M H_2CO_3 titrated with NaOH to $[H^+] = 3.2 \times 10^{-11}$ M (assume no volume change)
Find: mass NaOH   **Other:** K_{a1} (H_2CO_3) $= 4.3 \times 10^{-7}$, K_{a2} (H_2CO_3) $= 5.6 \times 10^{-11}$
Conceptual Plan: Comparing the $[H^+]$ to the K_a's it can be seen that the pH is just below the pK_{a2} so the final solution is a buffer solution where the acid is HCO_3^- and the base is CO_3^{2-}. The total NaOH will be the amount needed to get to the first equivalence point and then what is needed to get to final pH. To first equivalence point,
L, M CO_3^{2-} → mol CO_3^{2-} → mol NaOH   then Use the Henderson-Hasselbalch Equation to calculate

$$M = \frac{mol}{L} \qquad \text{1:1 ratio}$$

the $[CO_3^{2-}]/[HCO_3^-]$. Then solve for $[CO_3^{2-}]$ knowing that $[CO_3^{2-}] + [HCO_3^-] =$ initial $[H_2CO_3]$.

$$pH = pK_a + \log \frac{[base]}{[acid]}$$

then L, M CO_3^{2-} → mol CO_3^{2-} → mol NaOH beyond first equivalence point   then add two NaOH

$$M = \frac{mol}{L} \qquad \text{1:1 ratio}$$

moles and finally   total mol NaOH → g NaOH

$$\frac{40.00 \text{ g NaOH}}{1 \text{ mol NaOH}}$$

Solution: To the first equivalence point,

$$1.0 \text{ L } H_2CO_3 \times \frac{0.10 \text{ mol } H_2CO_3}{1 \text{ L } H_2CO_3} \times \frac{1 \text{ mol } HCO_3^-}{1 \text{ mol } H_2CO_3} \times \frac{1 \text{ mol NaOH}}{1 \text{ mol } HCO_3^-} = 0.10 \text{ mol NaOH} \ .$$

To the final pH, $pH = pK_a + \log \frac{[base]}{[acid]}$ so $-\log [H^+] = -\log K_{a2} + \log \frac{[CO_3^{2-}]}{[HCO_3^-]}$ →

$$-\log (3.2 \times 10^{-11}) = -\log (5.6 \times 10^{-11}) + \log \frac{[CO_3^{2-}]}{[HCO_3^-]} \rightarrow 10.49 = 10.25 + \log \frac{[CO_3^{2-}]}{[HCO_3^-]} \rightarrow 0.24 = \log \frac{[CO_3^{2-}]}{[HCO_3^-]} \rightarrow$$

$$\frac{[CO_3^{2-}]}{[HCO_3^-]} = 10^{+0.24} = 1.7\underline{3}780 \quad \text{and} \quad [CO_3^{2-}] + [HCO_3^-] = \text{initial } [H_2CO_3] = 0.10 \text{ M}.$$

Thus $[HCO_3^-] = 0.10[CO_3^{2-}]$, and $\dfrac{[CO_3^{2-}]}{0.10 \text{ M} - [CO_3^{2-}]} = 1.7\underline{3}780 \rightarrow [CO_3^{2-}] = 1.7\underline{3}780 (0.10 \text{ M} - [CO_3^{2-}]) \rightarrow$

$[CO_3^{2-}] = 0.173780 \text{ M} - 1.7\underline{3}780 [CO_3^{2-}] \rightarrow 2.7\underline{3}780 [CO_3^{2-}] = 0.173780 \text{ M} \rightarrow [CO_3^{2-}] = 0.063\underline{1}090 \text{ M}$ then

$$1.0 \text{ L } CO_3^{2-} \times \frac{0.063\underline{1}090 \text{ mol } CO_3^{2-}}{1 \text{ L } CO_3^{2-}} \times \frac{1 \text{ mol NaOH}}{1 \text{ mol } CO_3^{2-}} = 0.063\underline{1}090 \text{ mol NaOH} \ . \text{ So, the total mole NaOH} = 0.10$$

mol $+ \ 0.063\underline{1}090 \text{ mol} = 0.163\underline{1}090 \text{ mol NaOH}$.   Finally, $0.163\underline{1}090 \text{ mol NaOH} \times \dfrac{40.00 \text{ g NaOH}}{1 \text{ mol NaOH}} = 6.5 \text{ g NaOH}$.

Check: The units (g) are correct. The magnitude of the answer makes physical sense because if all of the acid were fully titrated 0.20 mol of NaOH (or 8 g) would be required. The pH indicates that the titration is most of the way there.

139. a) Given: $Au(OH)_3$ in pure water   **Find:** molar solubility (S)   **Other:** $K_{sp} = 5.5 \times 10^{-46}$
Conceptual Plan: use equations derived in problems #19 and #20 and solve for S.   then
for ionic compound, A_mX_n, $K_{sp} = [A^{n+}]^m [X^{m-}]^n = m^m n^n S^{m+n}$.
Check answer for validity.
Solution: for $Au(OH)_3$, $K_{sp} = 5.5 \times 10^{-46}$, A $= Au^{3+}$, m $= 1$, X $= OH^-$, and n $= 3$ so $K_{sp} = [Au^{3+}] [OH^-]^3$

$= 5.5 \times 10^{-46} = 3^3 S^4$. Rearrange to solve for S. $S = \sqrt[4]{\dfrac{5.5 \times 10^{-46}}{27}} = 2.1 \times 10^{-12}$ M . This answer suggests

that the $[OH^-] = 3(2.1 \times 10^{-12} \text{ M}) = 6.3 \times 10^{-12}$ M . This result is lower than found in pure water (1.0×10^{-7} M), so substitute this value for $[OH^-]$, and solve for S $= [Au^{3+}]$. So $K_{sp} = [Au^{3+}] [OH^-]^3 = 5.5 \times 10^{-46} =$ S $(1.0 \times 10^{-7} \text{ M})^3$ and solving for S gives S $= 5.5 \times 10^{-25}$ M.
Check: The units (M) are correct. Since K_{sp} is so small the autoionization of water must be considered and the solubility is smaller than normally anticipated.

b) Given: $Au(OH)_3$ in 1.0 M HNO_3 **Find:** molar solubility (S)   **Other:** $K_{sp} = 5.5 \times 10^{-46}$
Conceptual Plan: Since HNO_3 is a strong acid, it will neutralize the gold (III) hydroxide (through the reaction of H^+ with OH^- to for water (the reverse of the autoionization of water equilibrium).

Write balanced equations for dissolving the solid and for the neutralization reaction. Add these two reactions to get the desired overall reaction. Using the rules from Chapter 14, multiply the individual reaction K's to get the overall K for the sum of these reactions. then M HNO_3, K → S

ICE Chart

Solution: Identify the solid as $Au(OH)_3$. Write the individual reactions and add them together.

$$Au(OH)_3\,(s) \rightleftharpoons Au^{3+}(aq) + 3\,\cancel{OH^-}(aq) \qquad K_{sp} = 5.5 \times 10^{-46}$$

$$\underline{3\,H^+(aq) + 3\,\cancel{OH^-}(aq) \rightleftharpoons 3\,H_2O(l) \qquad \left(\frac{1}{K_w}\right)^3 = \left(\frac{1}{1.0 \times 10^{-14}}\right)^3}$$

$$Au(OH)_3\,(s) + 3\,H^+(aq) \rightleftharpoons Au^{3+}(aq) + 3\,H_2O(l)$$

Since the overall reaction is the sum of the dissolution reaction and three times the reverse of the autoionization of water reaction, the overall reaction

$$K = K_{sp}\left(\frac{1}{K_w}\right)^3 = (5.5 \times 10^{-46})\left(\frac{1}{1.0 \times 10^{-14}}\right)^3 = 5.5 \times 10^{-4} = \frac{[Au^{3+}]}{[H^+]^3}$$ then Since HNO_3 is a strong acid, it will

completely dissociate to H^+ and NO_3^- Set up ICE table.

$$Au(OH)_3\,(s) + 3\,H^+(aq) \rightleftharpoons Au^{3+}(aq) + 3\,H_2O(l)$$

	$[H^+]$	$[Au^{3+}]$
Initial	1.0	0.00
Change	$-3S$	$+S$
Equil	$1.0 - 3S$	$+S$

$$K = \frac{[Au^{3+}]}{[H^+]^3} = 5.5 \times 10^{-4} = \frac{S}{(1.0 - 3S)^3}.$$

Assume S is small ($3S \ll 1.0$) so $\dfrac{S}{(1.0 - \cancel{3S})^3} = 5.5 \times 10^{-4}\,M = \dfrac{S}{(1.0)^3} = S$. Confirm that assumption is

valid $\dfrac{3(5.5 \times 10^{-4})}{1.0}$ x 100 % = 0.017 % $<<$ 5 % so assumption is valid.

Check: The units (M) are correct. Since K is much larger than the original K_{sp} and so the solubility of $Au(OH)_3$ increases over that of pure water.

140. **Given:** excess AgCl in 0.10 M KI   **Find:** $[I^-]$ **Other:** K_{sp} (AgCl) = 1.77 x 10^{-10}, K_{sp} (AgI) = 8.51 x 10^{-17}

Conceptual Plan:

Since the KI does not generate a common ion with AgCl, use equations derived in problems #19 and #20 and solve for S. and so S(AgCl) = $[Ag^+]$ then use equation derived in problem #19 to get K_{sp} (KI)

for ionic compound, A_mX_n, $K_{sp} = [A^{n+}]^m\,[X^{m-}]^n = m^m\,n^n\,S^{m+n}$.

for ionic compound, A_mX_n, $K_{sp} = [A^{n+}]^m\,[X^{m-}]^n$.

expression. Substitute value for $[Ag^+]$ into K_{sp} (KI) expression and solve for $[I^-]$.

Solution: for AgCl, K_{sp} (AgCl) = 1.77 x 10^{-10}, A = Ag^+, m = 1, X = Cl^-, and n = 1 so $K_{sp} = [Ag^+]\,[Cl^-] =$ 1.77 x $10^{-10} = S^2$. Rearrange to solve for S. S = 1.33 x 10^{-5} M. then , K_{sp} (AgI) = 8.51 x 10^{-17}, A = Ag^+, m = 1, X = I^-, and n = 1 so $K_{sp} = [Ag^+]\,[I^-] = 8.51$ x 10^{-17}. Substitute value for $[Ag^+]$ into K_{sp} (KI) expression and solve for $[I^-]$.

8.51 x 10^{-17} = (1.33 x 10^{-5}) $[I^-]$, so $[I^-]$ = 6.40 x 10^{-12} M.

Check: The units (M) are correct. Since there are silver ions generated from the excess AgCl in solution, the iodide ions are converted to AgI and the concentration of remaining iodide ions is controlled by the solubility of the AgCl.

141. If the concentration of the acid is greater than the concentration of the base, then the pH will be less than the pK_a. If the concentration of the acid is equal to the concentration of the base, then the pH will be equal to the pK_a. If the concentration of the acid is less than the concentration of the base, then the pH will be greater than the pK_a.

a) pH < pK_a

b) pH > pK_a

c) pH = pK_a, the OH^- will convert half of the acid to base

d) pH > pK_a, the OH^- will convert more than half of the acid to base

142. As long as the [base]/[acid] is between 0.1 and 10 the buffer will still be active and the buffer capacity will not have been exceeded.

a) no, the buffer capacity is not exceeded because [base]/[acid] = 0.22/0.08

b) no, the buffer capacity is not exceeded because [base]/[acid] = 0.18/0.12

c) yes, the buffer capacity will be exceeded because all of the acid is converted to base

d) no, the buffer capacity is not exceeded because [base]/[acid] = 0.19/0.11

143. Only (b) is correct. A diprotic acid will take twice as much base to fully titrate and the pH at the equivalence point decreases as the strength of the acid increases.

144. Only (c) is correct. If the volume of base is twice as high then the acid concentration is twice as high and the weaker acid has the higher pH at the equivalence point.

145. a) The solubility will be unchanged since the pH is constant and ther are no common ions added.

b) The solubility will be less because extra fluoride ions are added, suppressing the solubility of the fluoride ionic compound.

c) The solubility will increase because some of the fluoride ion will be converted to HF, and so more of the ionic compound can be dissolved.

Chapter 17
Free Energy and Thermodynamics

1. The first law of thermodynamics states that energy is conserved in chemical processes. When we burn gasoline to run a car, for example, the amount of energy produced by the chemical reaction does not vanish, nor does any new energy appear that was not present before the combustion. Some of the energy from the combustion reaction goes toward driving the car forward (about 20%), and the rest is dissipated into the surroundings as heat (just feel the engine). However, the total energy given off by the combustion reaction exactly equals the sum of the amount of energy driving the car forward and the amount dissipated as heat—energy is conserved. In other words, when it comes to energy, you can't win; you cannot create energy that was not there to begin with.

2. The second law of thermodynamics implies that, not only can we not win in an energy transaction, but we cannot even break even. In every process that involves energy, some of the energy is lost to the surroundings as heat. This means that no process is perfectly efficient. This amount of energy that must be lost to the surroundings in order for the process to occur at all is nature's heat tax, an unavoidable cut of every energy transaction.

3. A perpetual motion machine is a machine that perpetually moves without any energy input. This machine is not possible because if the machine is to be in motion, it must pay the heat tax with each cycle of its motion—over time, it will therefore run down and stop moving.

4. It is more efficient to heat your home with a natural gas furnace because you are burning the fuel in your home and using the heat from the combustion to heat the air that is circulated in your home. When you use an electric furnace, fuel is burned at the electric company's power plant, it is converted to electricity. This electricity is transmitted to your home through wires and through power substations. Once it reaches you home, the electricity then needs to be converted to heat to warm the air that circulates in your home. Each step must pay a heat tax. Using a natural gas furnace has fewer steps and so it pays a much lower tax.

5. A spontaneous process is one that occurs without ongoing outside intervention (such as the performance of work by some external force). For example, when you drop a book in a gravitational field, the book spontaneously drops to the floor.

6. In thermodynamics, the spontaneity of a reaction is the direction in which and extent to which a chemical reaction proceeds. Kinetics is the speed of the reaction—how fast a reaction takes place. A reaction may be thermodynamically spontaneous, but kinetically slow at a given temperature. For example, the conversion of diamond to graphite is thermodynamically spontaneous. But your diamonds will not become worthless anytime soon because the process is extremely slow kinetically. Although the rate of a spontaneous process can be increased by the use of a catalyst, a nonspontaneous process cannot be made spontaneous by the use of a catalyst. Catalysts affect only the rate of a reaction, not the spontaneity.

7. Entropy (S) is a thermodynamic function that is proportional to the number of energetically equivalent ways to arrange the components of a system to achieve a particular state. Entropy, like enthalpy, is a state function—its value depends only on the state of the system, not on how the system got to that state. Therefore, for any process, the change in entropy is just the entropy of the final state minus the entropy of the initial state or $\Delta S = S_{final} - S_{intitial}$.

8. The entropy of a gas increases when it expands into a vacuum because the number of possible states increases (such as, where the particle is located).

9. Microstates are the number of internal arrangements. These microstates give rise to the same external arrangement, or macrostate. If I have 3 gas particles (A, B and C) and 2 containers. The fact that the first container has 2 particles and the other container has 1 particle is a macrostate. The fact that particles A and C are in the first container and particle B is in the other container is a microstate. There are at least as many microstates as there are macrostates.

10. The entropy of a state is proportional to the number of energetically equivalent ways to arrange the components of the system to achieve a particular state. This implies the state with the highest entropy also has the greatest dispersal of energy.

11. The Second Law of Thermodynamics – For any spontaneous process, the entropy of the universe increases ($\Delta S_{univ} > 0$). The criterion for spontaneity is the entropy of the universe. Processes that increase the entropy of the universe—those that result in greater dispersal or randomization of energy— occur spontaneously. Processes that decrease the entropy of the universe do not occur spontaneously. Heat travels from a substance at higher temperature to one at lower temperature because the process disperses thermal energy. The cooler object has less thermal energy, so transferring heat from the warmer object results in greater energy randomization—the energy that was concentrated in the hot substance becomes dispersed between the two substances.

12. The entropy of a sample of matter increases as it changes state from a solid to a liquid and then to a gas, because the amount of molecular motion and the amount of thermal energy is the greatest in the gas phase and is least in the solid phase.

13. When water freezes at temperatures below 0 °C, the entropy of the water decreases, yet the process is spontaneous because the entropy of the universe increases ($\Delta S_{univ} > 0$). The entropy of the system can decrease ($\Delta S_{sys} < 0$) as long as the entropy of the surroundings increases by a greater amount ($\Delta S_{surr} > -\Delta S_{sys}$), so that the overall entropy of the universe undergoes a net increase. For liquid water freezing, the change in entropy for the system (ΔS_{sys}) is negative because the water becomes more ordered. For ΔS_{univ} to be positive, ΔS_{surr} must be positive and greater in absolute value (or magnitude) than ΔS_{sys}. We learned in chapter 6 that freezing is an exothermic process: it gives off heat to the surroundings. If we think of entropy as the dispersal or randomization of energy, then the release of heat energy by the system disperses that energy into the surroundings, increasing the entropy of the surroundings. The freezing of water below 0 °C increases the entropy of the universe because the heat given off to the surroundings increases the entropy of the surroundings to a sufficient degree to overcome the entropy decrease in the water. The freezing of water becomes nonspontaneous above 0 °C because the magnitude of the increase in the entropy of the surroundings due to the dispersal of energy into the surroundings is temperature dependent. The higher the temperature, the smaller the percent increase in entropy for a given rise in temeperature. Therefore, the impact of the heat released to the surroundings by the freezing of water depends on the temperature of the surroundings—the higher the temperature, the smaller the impact.

14. Exothermic processes ($-\Delta H_{sys}$) tend to be spontaneous at low temperatures because they increase the entropy of the surroundings ($+\Delta S_{surr}$). Since $\Delta S_{surr} = \dfrac{-\Delta H_{sys}}{T}$, as temperature increases a given negative ΔH produces a smaller positive ΔS_{surr}; therefore exothermicity becomes less of a determining factor for spontaneity as temperature increases.

15. The change in Gibbs free energy for a process is proportional to the negative of ΔS_{univ}. Since ΔS_{univ} is a criterion for spontaneity, ΔG is also a criterion for spontaneity (although opposite in sign).

16. a) ΔH negative, ΔS positive If a reaction is exothermic ($\Delta H < 0$), and if the change in entropy for the reaction is positive ($\Delta S > 0$), then the change in free energy will be negative at all temperatures and the reaction will therefore be spontaneous at all temperatures.

    b) ΔH positive, ΔS negative If a reaction is endothermic ($\Delta H > 0$), and if the change in entropy for the reaction is negative ($\Delta S < 0$), then the change in free energy will be positive at all temperatures and the reaction will therefore be nonspontaneous at all temperatures.

    c) ΔH negative, ΔS negative If a reaction is exothermic ($\Delta H < 0$), and if the change in entropy for the reaction is negative ($\Delta S < 0$), then the change in free energy will depend on temperature. The reaction will be spontaneous at low temperature, but nonspontaneous at high temperature.

    d) ΔH positive, ΔS positive If a reaction is endothermic ($\Delta H > 0$), and if the change in entropy for the reaction is positive ($\Delta S > 0$), then the change in free energy will also depend on temperature. The reaction will be nonspontaneous at low temperature, but spontaneous at high temperature.

17. The third law of thermodynamics states that the entropy of a perfect crystal at absolute zero (0 K) is zero. For enthalpy we defined a standard state, so that we could define a "zero" for the scale. This is not necessary for entropy because there is an absolute zero.

18. Gases have much greater standard entropy because; they have more energetically equivalent ways to arrange their components, which in turn results in greater energy dispersal at 25 °C.

19. The larger the molar mass, the greater its entropy at 25 °C. For a given state of matter, entropy generally increases with increasing molecular complexity.

20. To calculate ΔS_{rxn}°, subtract the standard entropies of the reactants multiplied by their stoichiometric coefficients from the standard entropies of the products multiplied by their stoichiometric coefficients or $\Delta S_{rxn}^{0} = \sum n_p S^0 (products) - \sum n_r S^0 (reactants)$ where, n_p represents the stoichiometric coefficients of the products, n_r represents the stoichiometric coefficients of the reactants, and S° represents the standard entropies. Keep in mind when using this equation that, unlike enthalpies of formation, which are equal to zero for elements in their standard states, standard entropies are always nonzero at 25 °C.

21. The three ways of calculating the ΔG_{rxn} are to:
    - use tabulated values of standard enthalpies of formation to calculate ΔH_{rxn}° and use tabulated values of standard entropies to calculate ΔS_{rxn}°; then use the values of ΔH_{rxn}° and ΔS_{rxn}° calculated in these ways to calculate the standard free energy change for a reaction by using the equation: $\Delta G_{rxn}^{\circ} = \Delta H_{rxn}^{\circ} - T \Delta S_{rxn}^{\circ}$.
    - use tabulated values of the standard free energies of formation to calculate ΔG_{rxn}° using an equation similar to that used for standard enthalpy of a reaction: $\Delta G_{rxn}^{0} = \sum n_p \Delta G_f^0 (products) - \sum n_r \Delta G_f^0 (reactants)$.
    - use a reaction pathway or stepwise reaction to sum the changes in free energy for each of the steps in a manner similar to that used in chapter 6 for enthalpy of stepwise reactions.

    The method to calculate the free energy of a reaction at temperatures other than at 25°C is the first method. (The second method is only applicable at 25°C. The third method is only applicable at the temperature of the individual reactions, generally 25°C.)

22. The change in free energy of a chemical reaction represents the maximum amount of energy available, or free, to do work (if ΔG_{rxn}° is negative).

23. The standard free energy change for a reaction (ΔG_{rxn}°) applies only to standard conditions. For a gas, standard conditions are those in which the pure gas is present at a partial pressure of 1 atmosphere. For nonstandard conditions, we need to calculate ΔG_{rxn} (not ΔG_{rxn}°) to predict spontaneity.

24. Even though ΔG_{vap}° is positive at room temperature, liquid water is in equilibrium with water vapor at a pressure of 0.0313 atm. The vapor pressure of water is just not as high as 1 atm, the standard conditions of a gas. This means that some water will evaporate.

25. The free energy of reaction under nonstandard conditions (ΔG_{rxn}) can be calculated from ΔG_{rxn}° using the relationship $\Delta G_{rxn} = \Delta G_{rxn}^{\circ} + RT \ln Q$, where Q is the reaction quotient (defined in Section 14.7), T is the temperature in K, and R is the gas constant in the appropriate units (8.314 J/mol K).

26. The relationship between ΔG_{rxn}° and K is $\Delta G_{rxn}^{\circ} = -RT \ln K$. When ΔG_{rxn}° is positive this means that the log of K is negative and $K < 1$. Under standard conditions (when $Q = 1$) the reaction is spontaneous in the reverse direction. When ΔG_{rxn}° is zero this means that the log of K is zero and $K = 1$. The reaction happens to be at equilibrium under standard conditions. When ΔG_{rxn}° is negative the log of K is positive and $K > 1$,. Under standard conditions (when $Q = 1$) the reaction is spontaneous in the forward direction.

27. a and c are spontaneous processes.

28. a and c are nonspontaneous processes. Nonspontaneous processes are not impossible. Work of some form must be added to make the process proceed.

29. Yes, the particles may also be distributed so that one is in the 0 J level and the other is in the 20 J level. The total energy is the sum of the energies of the two particles = 0 J + 20 J = 20 J. There are two such arrangements of the particles in this fashion, so this state will have the greatest entropy and be more likely.

30. Yes, the particles may also be distributed so that one is in the 0 J level, one is in the 10 J level and the last is in the 20 J level. The total energy is the sum of the energies of the three particles = 0 J + 10 J + 20 J = 30 J.

If we label the particles as A, B and C. They may be arranges as ABC, ACB, BAC, BCA, CAB, and CBA. There are six ways of arranging the particles, so this state will have the greatest entropy and be more likely.

31. a) $\Delta S > 0$ because a gas is being generated

   b) $\Delta S < 0$ because 2 moles of gas are being converted to 1 mole of gas

   c) $\Delta S < 0$ because a gas is being converted to a solid

   d) $\Delta S < 0$ because 4 moles of gas are being converted to 2 moles of gas

32. a) $\Delta S < 0$ because a gas is being converted to a solid

   b) $\Delta S < 0$ because 5 moles of gas are being converted to 4 moles of gas

   c) $\Delta S > 0$ because 2 moles of gas are being converted to 3 moles of gas

   d) $\Delta S < 0$ because 2 moles of gas are being converted to a solid

33. a) $\Delta S_{sys} > 0$, because 6 moles of gas are being converted to 7 moles of gas. Since $\Delta H < 0$ $\Delta S_{surr} > 0$ and the reaction is spontaneous at all temperatures.

   b) $\Delta S_{sys} < 0$ because 2 moles of different gases are being converted to 2 moles of one gas. Since $\Delta H > 0$ $\Delta S_{surr} < 0$ and the reaction is nonspontaneous at all temperatures.

   c) $\Delta S_{sys} < 0$, because 3 moles of gas are being converted to 2 moles of gas. Since $\Delta H > 0$ $\Delta S_{surr} < 0$ the reaction is nonspontaneous at all temperatures.

   d) $\Delta S_{sys} > 0$, because 9 moles of gas are being converted to 10 moles of gas. Since $\Delta H < 0$ $\Delta S_{surr} > 0$ the reaction is spontaneous at all temperatures.

34. a) $\Delta S_{sys} < 0$, because 3 moles of gas are being converted to 2 moles of gas. Since $\Delta H < 0$ $\Delta S_{surr} > 0$ and the reaction is spontaneous at low temperatures.

   b) $\Delta S_{sys} > 0$ because 2 moles of gas are being converted to 3 moles of gas. Since $\Delta H > 0$ $\Delta S_{surr} < 0$ and the reaction is spontaneous at high temperatures.

   c) $\Delta S_{sys} < 0$, because 3 moles of gas are being converted to 2 moles of gas. Since $\Delta H < 0$ $\Delta S_{surr} > 0$ the reaction is spontaneous at low temperatures.

   d) $\Delta S_{sys} < 0$, because 1 mole of a complicated gas are being converted to 1 mole of gas and a solid. Since $\Delta H > 0$ $\Delta S_{surr} < 0$ the reaction is nonspontaneous at all temperatures.

35. a) **Given:** $\Delta H°_{rxn} = -287$ kJ, $T = 298$ K **Find:** ΔS_{surr}
    Conceptual plan: kJ → J then $\Delta H°_{rxn}, T$ → ΔS_{surr}

    $$\frac{1000\,J}{1\,kJ} \qquad \Delta S_{surr} = \frac{-\Delta H_{sys}}{T}$$

    Solution: $-287\,\cancel{kJ} \times \frac{1000\,J}{1\,\cancel{kJ}} = -287{,}000\,J$ then $\Delta S_{surr} = \frac{-\Delta H_{sys}}{T} = \frac{-(-287{,}000\,J)}{298\,K} = 963\,\frac{J}{K}$

    Check: The units (J/K) are correct. The magnitude of the answer (10^3 J/K) makes sense because the kJ and the temperature started with very similar values and then a factor of 10^3 was applied.

   b) **Given:** $\Delta H°_{rxn} = -287$ kJ, $T = 77$ K **Find:** ΔS_{surr}
    Conceptual plan: kJ → J then $\Delta H°_{rxn}, T$ → ΔS_{surr}

    $$\frac{1000\,J}{1\,kJ} \qquad \Delta S_{surr} = \frac{-\Delta H_{sys}}{T}$$

Solution: $-287\,\cancel{kJ} \times \dfrac{1000\,J}{1\,\cancel{kJ}} = -287,000\,J$ then $\Delta S_{surr} = \dfrac{-\Delta H_{sys}}{T} = \dfrac{-(-287,000\,J)}{77\,K} = 3730\,\dfrac{J}{K} = 3.73\times10^3\,\dfrac{J}{K}$

Check: The units (J/K) are correct. The magnitude of the answer (4×10^3 J/K) makes sense because the temperature is much lower than in part a, so the answer should increase.

c) **Given:** $\Delta H^\circ_{rxn} = +127$ kJ, T = 298 K **Find:** ΔS_{surr}
   Conceptual plan: kJ → J then ΔH°_{rxn}, T → ΔS_{surr}

$$\dfrac{1000\,J}{1\,kJ} \qquad\qquad \Delta S_{surr} = \dfrac{-\Delta H_{sys}}{T}$$

Solution: $+127\,\cancel{kJ} \times \dfrac{1000\,J}{1\,\cancel{kJ}} = +127,000\,J$ then $\Delta S_{surr} = \dfrac{-\Delta H_{sys}}{T} = \dfrac{-127,000\,J}{298\,K} = -426\,\dfrac{J}{K}$

Check: The units (J/K) are correct. The magnitude of the answer (- 400 J/K) makes sense because the kJ are less and of the opposite sign than part a and so the answer should decrease.

d) **Given:** $\Delta H^\circ_{rxn} = +127$ kJ, T = 77 K **Find:** ΔS_{surr}
   Conceptual plan: kJ → J then ΔH°_{rxn}, T → ΔS_{surr}

$$\dfrac{1000\,J}{1\,kJ} \qquad\qquad \Delta S_{surr} = \dfrac{-\Delta H_{sys}}{T}$$

Solution: $+127\,\cancel{kJ} \times \dfrac{1000\,J}{1\,\cancel{kJ}} = +127,000\,J$ then $\Delta S_{surr} = \dfrac{-\Delta H_{sys}}{T} = \dfrac{-127,000\,J}{77\,K} = -1650\,\dfrac{J}{K} = -1.65\times10^3\,\dfrac{J}{K}$

Check: The units (J/K) are correct. The magnitude of the answer (- 2×10^3 J/K) makes sense because the temperature is much lower than in part c, so the answer should increase.

36. **Given:** $\Delta H^\circ_{rxn} = -127$ kJ, $\Delta S_{rxn} = 314$ J/K **Find:** T when $\Delta S^\circ_{rxn} = \Delta S_{surr}$
   Conceptual plan: kJ → J then set $\Delta S^\circ_{rxn} = \Delta S_{surr}$ then ΔH°_{rxn}, ΔS_{surr} → T

$$\dfrac{1000\,J}{1\,kJ} \qquad\qquad\qquad\qquad \Delta S_{surr} = \dfrac{-\Delta H_{sys}}{T}$$

Solution: $-127\,\cancel{kJ} \times \dfrac{1000\,J}{1\,\cancel{kJ}} = -127,000\,J$ then set $\Delta S^\circ_{rxn} = 314$ J/K $= \Delta S_{surr}$ then

$$T = \dfrac{-\Delta H_{sys}}{\Delta S_{surr}} = \dfrac{-(-127,000\,\cancel{J})}{314\,\dfrac{\cancel{J}}{K}} = +404\,K\,.$$

Check: The units (K) are correct. The magnitude of the answer (400 K) makes sense because there is almost a factor of 500 between the enthalpy and the entropy.

37. a) **Given:** $\Delta H^\circ_{rxn} = -125$ kJ, $\Delta S_{rxn} = +253$ J/K, T = 298 K **Find:** ΔS_{univ} and spontaneity
   Conceptual plan: kJ → J then ΔH°_{rxn}, T → ΔS_{surr} then ΔS_{rxn}, ΔS_{surr} → ΔS_{univ}

$$\dfrac{1000\,J}{1\,kJ} \qquad\quad \Delta S_{surr} = \dfrac{-\Delta H_{sys}}{T} \qquad\quad \Delta S_{univ} = \Delta S_{sys} + \Delta S_{surr}$$

Solution: $-125\,\cancel{kJ} \times \dfrac{1000\,J}{1\,\cancel{kJ}} = -125,000\,J$ then $\Delta S_{surr} = \dfrac{-\Delta H_{sys}}{T} = \dfrac{-(-125,000\,J)}{298\,K} = 419.463\,\dfrac{J}{K}$ then

$\Delta S_{univ} = \Delta S_{sys} + \Delta S_{surr} = +253\,\dfrac{J}{K} + 419.463\,\dfrac{J}{K} = +672\,\dfrac{J}{K}$ so the reaction is spontaneous.

Check: The units (J/K) are correct. The magnitude of the answer (700 J/K) makes sense because both terms were positive and so the reaction is spontaneous.

b) **Given:** $\Delta H^\circ_{rxn} = +125$ kJ, $\Delta S_{rxn} = -253$ J/K, T = 298 K **Find:** ΔS_{univ} and spontaneity
   Conceptual plan: kJ → J then ΔH°_{rxn}, T → ΔS_{surr} then ΔS_{rxn}, ΔS_{surr} → ΔS_{univ}

$$\dfrac{1000\,J}{1\,kJ} \qquad\quad \Delta S_{surr} = \dfrac{-\Delta H_{sys}}{T} \qquad\quad \Delta S_{univ} = \Delta S_{sys} + \Delta S_{surr}$$

Solution: $+125\,\cancel{kJ} \times \dfrac{1000\,J}{1\,\cancel{kJ}} = +125,000\,J$ then $\Delta S_{surr} = \dfrac{-\Delta H_{sys}}{T} = \dfrac{-125,000\,J}{298\,K} = -419.463\,\dfrac{J}{K}$ then

$\Delta S_{univ} = \Delta S_{sys} + \Delta S_{surr} = -253 \dfrac{J}{K} - 419.463 \dfrac{J}{K} = -672 \dfrac{J}{K}$ so the reaction is nonspontaneous.

Check: The units (J/K) are correct. The magnitude of the answer (– 700 J/K) makes sense because both terms were negative and so the reaction is nonspontaneous.

c) **Given:** $\Delta H^\circ_{rxn} = -125$ kJ, $\Delta S_{rxn} = -253$ J/K, T = 298 K   **Find:** ΔS_{univ} and spontaneity

    Conceptual plan: kJ → J then ΔH°_{rxn}, T → ΔS_{surr} then ΔS_{rxn}, ΔS_{surr} → ΔS_{univ}

$$\dfrac{1000\,J}{1\,kJ} \qquad \Delta S_{surr} = \dfrac{-\Delta H_{sys}}{T} \qquad \Delta S_{univ} = \Delta S_{sys} + \Delta S_{surr}$$

    Solution: $-125\,kJ \times \dfrac{1000\,J}{1\,kJ} = -125{,}000\,J$ then $\Delta S_{surr} = \dfrac{-\Delta H_{sys}}{T} = \dfrac{-(-125{,}000\,J)}{298\,K} = +419.463 \dfrac{J}{K}$ then

$\Delta S_{univ} = \Delta S_{sys} + \Delta S_{surr} = -253 \dfrac{J}{K} + 419.463 \dfrac{J}{K} = +166 \dfrac{J}{K}$ so the reaction is spontaneous.

Check: The units (J/K) are correct. The magnitude of the answer (200 J/K) makes sense because the larger term was positive and so the reaction is spontaneous.

d) **Given:** $\Delta H^\circ_{rxn} = -125$ kJ, $\Delta S_{rxn} = -253$ J/K, T = 555 K   **Find:** ΔS_{univ} and spontaneity

    Conceptual plan: kJ → J then ΔH°_{rxn}, T → ΔS_{surr} then ΔS_{rxn}, ΔS_{surr} → ΔS_{univ}

$$\dfrac{1000\,J}{1\,kJ} \qquad \Delta S_{surr} = \dfrac{-\Delta H_{sys}}{T} \qquad \Delta S_{univ} = \Delta S_{sys} + \Delta S_{surr}$$

    Solution: $-125\,kJ \times \dfrac{1000\,J}{1\,kJ} = -125{,}000\,J$ then $\Delta S_{surr} = \dfrac{-\Delta H_{sys}}{T} = \dfrac{-(-125{,}000\,J)}{555\,K} = +225.225 \dfrac{J}{K}$ then

$\Delta S_{univ} = \Delta S_{sys} + \Delta S_{surr} = -253 \dfrac{J}{K} + 225.225 \dfrac{J}{K} = -28 \dfrac{J}{K}$ so the reaction is nonspontaneous.

Check: The units (J/K) are correct. The magnitude of the answer (– 30 J/K) makes sense because the larger term was negative and so the reaction is nonspontaneous.

38. a) **Given:** $\Delta H^\circ_{rxn} = +85$ kJ, $\Delta S_{rxn} = +147$ J/K, T = 298 K   **Find:** ΔS_{univ} and spontaneity

    Conceptual plan: kJ → J then ΔH°_{rxn}, T → ΔS_{surr} then ΔS_{rxn}, ΔS_{surr} → ΔS_{univ}

$$\dfrac{1000\,J}{1\,kJ} \qquad \Delta S_{surr} = \dfrac{-\Delta H_{sys}}{T} \qquad \Delta S_{univ} = \Delta S_{sys} + \Delta S_{surr}$$

    Solution: $+85\,kJ \times \dfrac{1000\,J}{1\,kJ} = +85{,}000\,J$ then $\Delta S_{surr} = \dfrac{-\Delta H_{sys}}{T} = \dfrac{-85{,}000\,J}{298\,K} = -285.23 \dfrac{J}{K}$ then

$\Delta S_{univ} = \Delta S_{sys} + \Delta S_{surr} = +147 \dfrac{J}{K} - 285.23 \dfrac{J}{K} = -138 \dfrac{J}{K} = -1.4 \times 10^2 \dfrac{J}{K}$ so the reaction is nonspontaneous.

Check: The units (J/K) are correct. The magnitude of the answer (-140 J/K) makes sense because the entropy of the surroundings is negative and dominates over the entropy gain of the system, so the reaction is nonspontaneous.

b) **Given:** $\Delta H^\circ_{rxn} = +85$ kJ, $\Delta S_{rxn} = +147$ J/K, T = 755 K   **Find:** ΔS_{univ} and spontaneity

    Conceptual plan: kJ → J then ΔH°_{rxn}, T → ΔS_{surr} then ΔS_{rxn}, ΔS_{surr} → ΔS_{univ}

$$\dfrac{1000\,J}{1\,kJ} \qquad \Delta S_{surr} = \dfrac{-\Delta H_{sys}}{T} \qquad \Delta S_{univ} = \Delta S_{sys} + \Delta S_{surr}$$

    Solution: $+85\,kJ \times \dfrac{1000\,J}{1\,kJ} = +85{,}000\,J$ then $\Delta S_{surr} = \dfrac{-\Delta H_{sys}}{T} = \dfrac{-85{,}000\,J}{755\,K} = -112.58 \dfrac{J}{K}$ then

$\Delta S_{univ} = \Delta S_{sys} + \Delta S_{surr} = +147 \dfrac{J}{K} - 112.58 \dfrac{J}{K} = +34 \dfrac{J}{K} = +3 \times 10^1 \dfrac{J}{K}$ so the reaction is spontaneous.

Check: The units (J/K) are correct. The magnitude of the answer (30 J/K) makes sense because at a higher temperature, the entropy of the surroundings is reduced, so that the entropy of the system dominates and the reaction is spontaneous.

c) **Given:** $\Delta H°_{rxn} = + 85$ kJ, $\Delta S_{rxn} = - 147$ J/K, T = 298 K   **Find:** ΔS_{univ} and spontaneity

Conceptual plan: kJ → J then $\Delta H°_{rxn}$, T → ΔS_{surr} then ΔS_{rxn}, ΔS_{surr} → ΔS_{univ}

$$\frac{1000\,J}{1\,kJ}\qquad\qquad \Delta S_{surr}= \frac{-\Delta H_{sys}}{T}\qquad\qquad \Delta S_{univ} = \Delta S_{sys} + \Delta S_{surr}$$

Solution: $+85\,\cancel{kJ}\times \dfrac{1000\,J}{1\,\cancel{kJ}} = + 85{,}000\,J$ then $\Delta S_{surr}= \dfrac{-\Delta H_{sys}}{T} = \dfrac{-85{,}000\,J}{298\,K} = -2\underline{8}5.23\,\dfrac{J}{K}$ then

$\Delta S_{univ} = \Delta S_{sys} + \Delta S_{surr} = -147\,\dfrac{J}{K} - 2\underline{8}5.23\,\dfrac{J}{K} = -4\underline{3}2\,\dfrac{J}{K} = -4.3\times 10^2\,\dfrac{J}{K}$ so the reaction is nonspontaneous.

Check: The units (J/K) are correct. The magnitude of the answer (-400 J/K) makes sense because both terms are negative, so the sum is negative and the reaction is nonspontaneous.

d) **Given:** $\Delta H°_{rxn} = -85$ kJ, $\Delta S_{rxn} = + 147$ J/K, T = 398 K   **Find:** ΔS_{univ} and spontaneity

Conceptual plan: kJ → J then $\Delta H°_{rxn}$, T → ΔS_{surr} then ΔS_{rxn}, ΔS_{surr} → ΔS_{univ}

$$\frac{1000\,J}{1\,kJ}\qquad\qquad \Delta S_{surr}= \frac{-\Delta H_{sys}}{T}\qquad\qquad \Delta S_{univ} = \Delta S_{sys} + \Delta S_{surr}$$

Solution: $-85\,\cancel{kJ}\times \dfrac{1000\,J}{1\,\cancel{kJ}} = - 85{,}000\,J$ then $\Delta S_{surr}= \dfrac{-\Delta H_{sys}}{T} = \dfrac{-(-85{,}000\,J)}{398\,K} = + 2\underline{1}3.57\,\dfrac{J}{K}$ then

$\Delta S_{univ} = \Delta S_{sys} + \Delta S_{surr} = +147\,\dfrac{J}{K} + 2\underline{1}3.57\,\dfrac{J}{K} = + 3\underline{6}1\,\dfrac{J}{K} = + 3.6\times 10^2\,\dfrac{J}{K}$ so the reaction is spontaneous.

Check: The units (J/K) are correct. The magnitude of the answer (400 J/K) makes sense because both terms are positive, so the sum is positive and the reaction is spontaneous.

39. a) **Given:** $\Delta H°_{rxn} = - 125$ kJ, $\Delta S_{rxn} = + 253$ J/K, T = 298 K   **Find:** ΔG and spontaneity

Conceptual plan: J/K → kJ/K then $\Delta H°_{rxn}$, ΔS_{rxn}, T → ΔG

$$\frac{1000\,J}{1\,kJ}\qquad\qquad\qquad \Delta G = \Delta H_{rxn} - T\Delta S_{rxn}$$

Solution: $+253\,\dfrac{\cancel{J}}{K}\times \dfrac{1\,kJ}{1000\,\cancel{J}} = + 0.253\,\dfrac{kJ}{K}$ then

$\Delta G = \Delta H_{rxn} - T\Delta S_{rxn} = -125\,kJ - (298\,\cancel{K})\left(0.253\,\dfrac{kJ}{\cancel{K}}\right) = - 200.\,kJ = - 2.00\times 10^2\,kJ$ so the reaction is spontaneous.

Check: The units (kJ) are correct. The magnitude of the answer (- 200 kJ) makes sense because both terms were negative and so the reaction is spontaneous.

b) **Given:** $\Delta H°_{rxn} = + 125$ kJ, $\Delta S_{rxn} = - 253$ J/K, T = 298 K   **Find:** ΔS_{univ} and spontaneity

Conceptual plan: J/K → kJ/K then $\Delta H°_{rxn}$, ΔS_{rxn}, T → ΔG

$$\frac{1000\,J}{1\,kJ}\qquad\qquad\qquad \Delta G = \Delta H_{rxn} - T\Delta S_{rxn}$$

Solution: $-253\,\dfrac{\cancel{J}}{K}\times \dfrac{1\,kJ}{1000\,\cancel{J}} = - 0.253\,\dfrac{kJ}{K}$ then

$\Delta G = \Delta H_{rxn} - T\Delta S_{rxn} = +125\,kJ - (298\,\cancel{K})\left(-0.253\,\dfrac{kJ}{\cancel{K}}\right) = + 200.\,kJ = + 2.00\times 10^2\,kJ$ so the reaction is nonspontaneous.

Check: The units (kJ) are correct. The magnitude of the answer (200 kJ) makes sense because both terms were positive and so the reaction is nonspontaneous.

c) **Given:** $\Delta H°_{rxn} = - 125$ kJ, $\Delta S_{rxn} = - 253$ J/K, T = 298 K   **Find:** ΔS_{univ} and spontaneity

Conceptual plan: J/K → kJ/K then $\Delta H°_{rxn}$, ΔS_{rxn}, T → ΔG

$$\frac{1000\,J}{1\,kJ}\qquad\qquad\qquad \Delta G = \Delta H_{rxn} - T\Delta S_{rxn}$$

Solution: $-253\,\dfrac{\cancel{J}}{K}\times \dfrac{1\,kJ}{1000\,\cancel{J}} = - 0.253\,\dfrac{kJ}{K}$ then

$$\Delta G = \Delta H_{rxn} - T\Delta S_{rxn} = -125 \text{ kJ} - (298 \text{ K})\left(-0.253 \frac{\text{kJ}}{\text{K}}\right) = -49.606 \text{ kJ} = -5.0 \times 10^1 \text{ kJ so the reaction is}$$

spontaneous.

Check: The units (kJ) are correct. The magnitude of the answer (-50 kJ) makes sense because the larger term was negative and so the reaction is spontaneous.

  d)   **Given:** $\Delta H^\circ_{rxn} = -125$ kJ, $\Delta S_{rxn} = -253$ J/K, T = 555 K   **Find:** ΔS_{univ} and spontaneity
        Conceptual plan: $\textbf{J/K} \rightarrow \textbf{kJ/K}$ **then** $\Delta\textbf{H}^\circ_{\textbf{rxn}}, \Delta\textbf{S}_{\textbf{rxn}}, \textbf{T} \rightarrow \Delta\textbf{G}$

$$\frac{1000 \text{ J}}{1 \text{ kJ}} \qquad\qquad\qquad \Delta G = \Delta H_{rxn} - T\Delta S_{rxn}$$

        Solution: $-253 \frac{\text{J}}{\text{K}} \times \frac{1 \text{ kJ}}{1000 \text{ J}} = -0.253 \frac{\text{kJ}}{\text{K}}$ then

$$\Delta G = \Delta H_{rxn} - T\Delta S_{rxn} = -125 \text{ kJ} - (555 \text{ K})\left(-0.253 \frac{\text{kJ}}{\text{K}}\right) = +15 \text{ kJ so the reaction is nonspontaneous.}$$

        Check: The units (J/K) are correct. The magnitude of the answer (+ 15 kJ) makes sense because the larger term was positive and so the reaction is nonspontaneous.

40. a)   **Given:** $\Delta H^\circ_{rxn} = +85$ kJ, $\Delta S_{rxn} = +147$ J/K, T = 298 K   **Find:** ΔS_{univ} and spontaneity
        Conceptual plan: $\textbf{J/K} \rightarrow \textbf{kJ/K}$ **then** $\Delta\textbf{H}^\circ_{\textbf{rxn}}, \Delta\textbf{S}_{\textbf{rxn}}, \textbf{T} \rightarrow \Delta\textbf{G}$

$$\frac{1 \text{kJ}}{1000 \text{ J}} \qquad\qquad\qquad \Delta G = \Delta H_{rxn} - T\Delta S_{rxn}$$

        Solution: $+147 \frac{\text{J}}{\text{K}} \times \frac{1 \text{ kJ}}{1000 \text{ J}} = +0.147 \frac{\text{kJ}}{\text{K}}$ then

$$\Delta G = \Delta H_{rxn} - T\Delta S_{rxn} = +85 \text{ kJ} - (298 \text{ K})\left(0.147 \frac{\text{kJ}}{\text{K}}\right) = +41 \text{ kJ so the reaction is nonspontaneous.}$$

        Check: The units (kJ) are correct. The magnitude of the answer (41 kJ) makes sense because the positive enthalpy dominates over the entropy term, so the reaction is nonspontaneous.

  b)   **Given:** $\Delta H^\circ_{rxn} = +85$ kJ, $\Delta S_{rxn} = +147$ J/K, T = 755 K   **Find:** ΔS_{univ} and spontaneity
        Conceptual plan: $\textbf{J/K} \rightarrow \textbf{kJ/K}$ **then** $\Delta\textbf{H}^\circ_{\textbf{rxn}}, \Delta\textbf{S}_{\textbf{rxn}}, \textbf{T} \rightarrow \Delta\textbf{G}$

$$\frac{1 \text{kJ}}{1000 \text{ J}} \qquad\qquad\qquad \Delta G = \Delta H_{rxn} - T\Delta S_{rxn}$$

        Solution: $+147 \frac{\text{J}}{\text{K}} \times \frac{1 \text{ kJ}}{1000 \text{ J}} = +0.147 \frac{\text{kJ}}{\text{K}}$ then

$$\Delta G = \Delta H_{rxn} - T\Delta S_{rxn} = +85 \text{ kJ} - (755 \text{ K})\left(0.147 \frac{\text{kJ}}{\text{K}}\right) = -26 \text{ kJ so the reaction is spontaneous.}$$

        Check: The units (kJ) are correct. The magnitude of the answer (- 30 kJ) makes sense because at a higher temperature, the entropy term now dominates and the reaction is spontaneous.

  c)   **Given:** $\Delta H^\circ_{rxn} = +85$ kJ, $\Delta S_{rxn} = -147$ J/K, T = 298 K   **Find:** ΔS_{univ} and spontaneity
        Conceptual plan: $\textbf{J/K} \rightarrow \textbf{kJ/K}$ **then** $\Delta\textbf{H}^\circ_{\textbf{rxn}}, \Delta\textbf{S}_{\textbf{rxn}}, \textbf{T} \rightarrow \Delta\textbf{G}$

$$\frac{1 \text{kJ}}{1000 \text{ J}} \qquad\qquad\qquad \Delta G = \Delta H_{rxn} - T\Delta S_{rxn}$$

        Solution: $-147 \frac{\text{J}}{\text{K}} \times \frac{1 \text{ kJ}}{1000 \text{ J}} = -0.147 \frac{\text{kJ}}{\text{K}}$ then

$$\Delta G = \Delta H_{rxn} - T\Delta S_{rxn} = +85 \text{ kJ} - (298 \text{ K})\left(-0.147 \frac{\text{kJ}}{\text{K}}\right) = +129 \text{ kJ so the reaction is nonspontaneous.}$$

        Check: The units (kJ) are correct. The magnitude of the answer (130 kJ) makes sense because both terms are positive, so the sum is positive and the reaction is nonspontaneous.

  d)   **Given:** $\Delta H^\circ_{rxn} = -85$ kJ, $\Delta S_{rxn} = +147$ J/K, T = 398 K   **Find:** ΔS_{univ} and spontaneity
        Conceptual plan: $\textbf{J/K} \rightarrow \textbf{kJ/K}$ **then** $\Delta\textbf{H}^\circ_{\textbf{rxn}}, \Delta\textbf{S}_{\textbf{rxn}}, \textbf{T} \rightarrow \Delta\textbf{G}$

$$\frac{1 \text{kJ}}{1000 \text{ J}} \qquad\qquad\qquad \Delta G = \Delta H_{rxn} - T\Delta S_{rxn}$$

Solution: $+147 \frac{J}{K} \times \frac{1 \text{ kJ}}{1000 \text{ J}} = +0.147 \frac{kJ}{K}$ then

$$\Delta G = \Delta H_{rxn} - T\Delta S_{rxn} = -85 \text{ kJ} - (398 \text{ K})\left(0.147 \frac{kJ}{K}\right) = -144 \text{ kJ} \text{ so the reaction is spontaneous.}$$

Check: The units (kJ) are correct. The magnitude of the answer (- 140 kJ) makes sense because both terms are negative, so the sum is negative and the reaction is spontaneous.

41. **Given:** $\Delta H°_{rxn} = -2217 \text{ kJ}, \Delta S_{rxn} = +101.1 \text{ J/K}, T = 25 °C$ **Find:** ΔS_{univ} and spontaneity

    Conceptual plan: °C → K   then   J/K → kJ/K   then $\Delta H°_{rxn}, \Delta S_{rxn}, T$ → ΔG

$$K = 273.15 + °C \qquad\qquad \frac{1 kJ}{1000 J} \qquad\qquad \Delta G = \Delta H_{rxn} - T\Delta S_{rxn}$$

    Solution: $T = 273.15 + 25 °C = 298 \text{ K}$ then $+101.1 \frac{J}{K} \times \frac{1 \text{ kJ}}{1000 \text{ J}} = +0.1011 \frac{kJ}{K}$ then

$$\Delta G = \Delta H_{rxn} - T\Delta S_{rxn} = -2217 \text{ kJ} - (298 \text{ K})\left(0.1011 \frac{kJ}{K}\right) = -2247 \text{ kJ} = -2.247 \times 10^6 \text{ J} \text{ so the reaction is}$$

spontaneous.

Check: The units (kJ) are correct. The magnitude of the answer (- 2250 kJ) makes sense because both terms are negative, so the reaction is spontaneous.

42. **Given:** $\Delta H°_{rxn} = -1269,8 \text{ kJ}, \Delta S_{rxn} = -364.6 \text{ J/K}, T = 25 °C$ **Find:** ΔS_{univ} and spontaneity

    Conceptual plan: °C → K   then   J/K → kJ/K   then $\Delta H°_{rxn}, \Delta S_{rxn}, T$ → ΔG

$$K = 273.15 + °C \qquad\qquad \frac{1 kJ}{1000 J} \qquad\qquad \Delta G = \Delta H_{rxn} - T\Delta S_{rxn}$$

    Solution: $T = 273.15 + 25 °C = 298 \text{ K}$ then $-364.6 \frac{J}{K} \times \frac{1 \text{ kJ}}{1000 \text{ J}} = -0.3646 \frac{kJ}{K}$ then

$$\Delta G = \Delta H_{rxn} - T\Delta S_{rxn} = -1269.8 \text{ kJ} - (298 \text{ K})\left(-0.3646 \frac{kJ}{K}\right) = -1161.1 \text{ kJ} = -1.161 \times 10^6 \text{ J} \text{ so the reaction is}$$

spontaneous.

Check: The units (kJ) are correct. The magnitude of the answer (- 1200 kJ) makes sense because the negative enthalpy term dominates over the positive entropy term, so the reaction is spontaneous.

43.

ΔH	ΔS	ΔG	Low Temp.	High Temp.
−	+	−	Spontaneous	Spontaneous
−	−	Temp dependent	Spontaneous	Nonspontaneous
+	+	Temp dependent	Nonspontaneous	Spontaneous
+	−	+	Nonspontaneous	Nonspontaneous

44. a) $\Delta H°_{rxn}$ for a condensation is negative and ΔS_{rxn} is negative, so the reaction will be spontaneous at low temperatures (< 100 °C).

    b) $\Delta H°_{rxn}$ for a sublimation is positive and ΔS_{rxn} is positive, so the reaction will be spontaneous at high temperatures (> − 78.5 °C).

    c) $\Delta H°_{rxn}$ for a bond breaking is positive and ΔS_{rxn} is positive, so the reaction will be spontaneous at high temperatures.

    d) $\Delta H°_{rxn}$ is positive and ΔS_{rxn} is positive, so the reaction will be spontaneous at high temperatures.

45. The molar entropy of a substance increases with increasing temperatures. The kinetic energy and the molecular motion increases. The substance will have access to an increased number of energy levels.

46. The third law of thermodynamics states that the entropy of a perfect crystal at absolute zero (0 K) is zero. For enthalpy we defined a standard state so that we could define a "zero" for the scale. This is not necessary for entropy because there is an absolute zero for the entropy scale.

47. a) $CO_2 (g)$ because it has greater molar mass/complexity.

b) CH_3OH (*g*) because it is in the gas phase.

c) CO_2 (*g*) because it has greater molar mass/complexity.

d) SiH_4 (*g*) because it has greater molar mass.

e) $CH_3CH_2CH_3$ (*g*) because it has greater molar mass/complexity.

f) NaBr (*aq*) because a solution has more entropy than a solid crystal.

48. a) $NaNO_3$ (*aq*) because a solution has more entropy than a solid crystal.

b) CH_3CH_3 (*g*) because it has greater molar mass/complexity.

c) Br_2 (*g*) because it is in the gas phase.

d) Br_2 (*g*) because it has greater molar mass.

e) PCl_5 (*g*) because it has greater molar mass/complexity.

f) $CH_3CH_2CH_2CH_3$ (*g*) because it has greater complexity.

49. a) He (*g*) < Ne (*g*) < SO_2 (*g*) < NH_3 (*g*) < CH_3CH_2OH (*g*). All are in the gas phase. From He to Ne there is an increase in molar weight, beyond that, the molecules increase in complexity.

b) H_2O (*s*) < H_2O (*l*) < H_2O (*g*). Entropy increases as we go from a solid to a liquid to a gas.

c) CH_4 (*g*) < CF_4 (*g*) < CCl_4 (*g*). Entropy increases as the molar mass increases.

50. a) F (*g*) < Cl_2 (*g*) < Br_2 (*g*) < I_2 (*g*). All are in the gas phase. Entropy increases as the molar weight increases.

b) H_2O (*g*) < H_2S (*g*) < H_2O_2 (*g*). Entropy increases as the molar mass and the complexity of the molecules increases.

c) C (*s*, diamond) < C (*s*, graphite) < C (*s*, amorphous). Entropy increases as the complexity increases. The diamond structure is ordered in all three dimensions. Graphite has ordered sheets that can slide with respect to each other. The amorphous carbon has no long range order.

51. a) **Given:** C_2H_4 (*g*) + H_2 (*g*) → C_2H_6 (*g*)   **Find:** $\Delta S°_{rxn}$

Conceptual plan: $\Delta S°_{rxn} = \sum n_p S°(products) - \sum n_r S°(reactants)$

Solution:

Reactant/Product	$S°$ (J/mol K from Appendix IIB)
C_2H_4 (*g*)	219.3
H_2 (*g*)	130.7
C_2H_6 (*g*)	229.2

Be sure to pull data for the correct formula and phase.

$\Delta S°_{rxn} = \sum n_p S°(products) - \sum n_r S°(reactants)$

$= [1(S°(C_2H_6\ (g))] - [1(S°(C_2H_4\ (g)) + 1(S°(H_2\ (g))]$

$= [1(229.2\ J/mol\ K)] - [1(219.3\ J/mol\ K) + 1(130.7\ J/mol\ K)]$ The moles of gas are decreasing.

$= [229.2\ J/K] - [350.0\ J/K]$

$= -120.8\ J/K$

Check: The units (J/K) are correct.   The answer is negative, which is consistent with 2 moles of gas going to 1 mole of gas.

b) **Given:** $C\ (s)\ +\ H_2O\ (g)\ \rightarrow\ CO\ (g)\ +\ H_2\ (g)$ **Find:** $\Delta S°_{rxn}$

Conceptual plan: $\Delta S^0_{rxn} = \sum n_p S^0 (products) - \sum n_r S^0 (reactants)$

Solution:

Reactant/Product	S^0 (J/mol K from Appendix IIB)
$C\ (s)$	5.7
$H_2O\ (g)$	188.8
$CO\ (g)$	197.7
$H_2\ (g)$	130.7

Be sure to pull data for the correct formula and phase.

$\Delta S^0_{rxn} = \sum n_p S^0 (products) - \sum n_r S^0 (reactants)$

$= [1(S^0(CO\ (g)) + 1(S^0(H_2\ (g)))] - [1(S^0(C\ (s)) + 1(S^0(H_2O\ (g)))]$

$= [1(197.7\ \text{J/mol K}) + 1(130.7\ \text{J/mol K})] - [1(5.7\ \text{J/mol K}) + 1(188.8\ \text{J/mol K})]$ The moles of gas are

$= [328.4\ \text{J/K}] - [194.5\ \text{J/K}]$

$= +133.9\ \text{J/K}$

increasing.

Check: The units (J/K) are correct.   The answer is positive, which is consistent with 1 mole of gas going to 1 mole of gas.

c) **Given:** $CO\ (g)\ +\ H_2O\ (g)\ \rightarrow\ H_2\ (g)\ +\ CO_2\ (g)$ **Find:** $\Delta S°_{rxn}$

Conceptual plan: $\Delta S^0_{rxn} = \sum n_p S^0 (products) - \sum n_r S^0 (reactants)$

Solution:

Reactant/Product	S^0 (J/mol K from Appendix IIB)
$CO\ (g)$	197.7
$H_2O\ (g)$	188.8
$H_2\ (g)$	130.7
$CO_2\ (g)$	213.8

Be sure to pull data for the correct formula and phase.

$\Delta S^0_{rxn} = \sum n_p S^0 (products) - \sum n_r S^0 (reactants)$

$= [1(S^0(H_2\ (g)) + 1(S^0(CO_2\ (g)))] - [1(S^0(CO\ (g)) + 1(S^0(H_2O\ (g)))]$

$= [1(130.7\ \text{J/mol K}) + 1(213.8\ \text{J/mol K})] - [1(197.7\ \text{J/mol K}) + 1(188.8\ \text{J/mol K})]$

$= [344.5\ \text{J/K}] - [386.5\ \text{J/K}]$

$= -42.0\ \text{J/K}$

The change is small because the number of moles of gas is constant.

Check: The units (J/K) are correct.   The answer is small and negative, which is consistent with a constant number of moles of gas. Water molecules are bent and carbon dioxide molecules are linear, so the water has more complexity. Also, carbon monoxide is more complex than hydrogen gas.

d) **Given:** $2\ H_2S\ (g)\ +\ 3\ O_2\ (g)\ \rightarrow\ 2\ H_2O\ (l)\ +\ 2\ SO_2\ (g)$ **Find:** $\Delta S°_{rxn}$

Conceptual plan: $\Delta S^0_{rxn} = \sum n_p S^0 (products) - \sum n_r S^0 (reactants)$

Solution:

Reactant/Product	S^0 (J/mol K from Appendix IIB)
$H_2S\ (g)$	205.8
$O_2\ (g)$	205.2
$H_2O\ (l)$	70.0
$SO_2\ (g)$	248.2

Be sure to pull data for the correct formula and phase.

$\Delta S^0_{rxn} = \sum n_p S^0 (products) - \sum n_r S^0 (reactants)$

$= [2(S^0(H_2O\ (l)) + 2(S^0(SO_2\ (g)))] - [2(S^0(H_2S\ (g)) + 3(S^0(O_2\ (g)))]$

$= [2(70.0\ \text{J/mol K}) + 2(248.2\ \text{J/mol K})] - [2(205.8\ \text{J/mol K}) + 3(205.2\ \text{J/mol K})]$

$= [636.4\ \text{J/K}] - [1027.2\ \text{J/K}]$

$= -390.8\ \text{J/K}$

The number of moles of gas is decreasing.
Check: The units (J/K) are correct.   The answer is negative, which is consistent with a decrease in the number of moles of gas.

52. a) **Given**: $3 NO_2 (g) + H_2O (l) \rightarrow 2 HNO_3 (aq) + NO (g)$ **Find**: $\Delta S°_{rxn}$

    Conceptual plan: $\Delta S^0_{rxn} = \sum n_p S^0 (products) - \sum n_r S^0 (reactants)$

    Solution:

Reactant/Product	S^0 (J/mol K from Appendix IIB)
$NO_2 (g)$	240.1
$H_2O (l)$	70.0
$HNO_3 (aq)$	146
$NO (g)$	210.8

Be sure to pull data for the correct formula and phase.

$\Delta S^0_{rxn} = \sum n_p S^0 (products) - \sum n_r S^0 (reactants)$

     $= [2(S^0(HNO_3 (aq)) + 1(S^0(NO(g))] - [3(S^0(NO_2 (g)) + 1(S^0(H_2O (l))]$

     $= [2(146 J/mol K) + 1(210.8 J/mol K)] - [3(240.1 J/mol K) + 1(70.0 J/mol K)]$ The number of moles of

     $= [50\underline{2}.8 J/K] - [790.3 J/K]$

     $= -288 J/K$

gas is decreasing.
Check: The units (J/K) are correct.   The answer is negative, which is consistent with a decrease in the number of moles of gas.

b) **Given**: $Cr_2O_3 (s) + 3 CO (g) \rightarrow 2 Cr (s) + 3 CO_2 (g)$ **Find**: $\Delta S°_{rxn}$

    Conceptual plan: $\Delta S^0_{rxn} = \sum n_p S^0 (products) - \sum n_r S^0 (reactants)$

    Solution:

Reactant/Product	S^0 (J/mol K from Appendix IIB)
$Cr_2O_3 (s)$	81.2
$CO (g)$	197.7
$Cr (s)$	23.8
$CO_2 (g)$	213.8

Be sure to pull data for the correct formula and phase.

$\Delta S^0_{rxn} = \sum n_p S^0 (products) - \sum n_r S^0 (reactants)$

     $= [2(S^0(Cr (s)) + 3(S^0(CO_2 (g))] - [1(S^0(Cr_2O_3 (s)) + 3(S^0(CO (g))]$

     $= [2(23.8 J/mol K) + 3(213.8 J/mol K)] - [1(81.2 J/mol K) + 3(197.7 J/mol K)]$

     $= [689.0 J/K] - [674.3 J/K]$

     $= +14.7 J/K$

The change is small because the number of moles of gas is constant.
Check: The units (J/K) are correct.   The answer is small and positive, which is consistent with a constant number of moles of gas. Carbon dioxide molecules have more complexity than carbon monoxide molecules, but the chromium oxide is more complex than chromium metal.

c) **Given**: $SO_2 (g) + ½ O_2 (g) \rightarrow SO_3 (g)$ **Find**: $\Delta S°_{rxn}$

    Conceptual plan: $\Delta S^0_{rxn} = \sum n_p S^0 (products) - \sum n_r S^0 (reactants)$

    Solution:

Reactant/Product	S^0 (J/mol K from Appendix IIB)
$SO_2 (g)$	248.2
$O_2 (g)$	205.2
$SO_3 (g)$	256.8

Be sure to pull data for the correct formula and phase.

$$\Delta S^0_{rxn} = \sum n_p S^0(products) - \sum n_r S^0(reactants)$$
$$= [1(S^0(SO_3\ (g)))] - [1(S^0(SO_2\ (g)) + 1/2(S^0(O_2\ (g))]$$
$$= [1(256.8\ J/mol\ K)] - [1(248.2\ J/mol\ K) + 1/2(205.2\ J/mol\ K)]$$
$$= [256.8\ J/K] - [350.8\ J/K]$$
$$= -94.0\ J/K$$

The number of moles of gas is decreasing.

Check: The units (J/K) are correct. The answer is negative, which is consistent with a decrease in the number of moles of gas.

d) **Given**: $N_2O_4\ (g) + 4\ H_2\ (g) \rightarrow N_2\ (g) + 4\ H_2O\ (g)$ **Find**: $\Delta S°_{rxn}$

Conceptual plan: $\Delta S^0_{rxn} = \sum n_p S^0(products) - \sum n_r S^0(reactants)$

Solution:

Reactant/Product	S^0 (J/mol K from Appendix IIB)
$N_2O_4\ (g)$	304.4
$H_2\ (g)$	130.7
$N_2\ (g)$	191.6
$H_2O\ (g)$	188.8

Be sure to pull data for the correct formula and phase.

$$\Delta S^0_{rxn} = \sum n_p S^0(products) - \sum n_r S^0(reactants)$$
$$= [1(S^0(N_2\ (g)) + 4(S^0(H_2O\ (g)))] - [1(S^0(N_2O_4\ (g)) + 4(S^0(H_2\ (g))]$$
$$= [1(191.6\ J/mol\ K) + 4(188.8\ J/mol\ K)] - [1(304.4\ J/mol\ K) + 4(130.7\ J/mol\ K)]$$
$$= [946.8\ J/K] - [827.2\ J/K]$$
$$= +119.6\ J/K$$

The change is small because the number of moles of gas is constant.

Check: The units (J/K) are correct. The answer is positive, which is consistent with 1 mole of a complex gas and 4 moles of a simple gas going to 1 mole of simple gas and 4 moles of a complex gas.

53. **Given**: $CH_2Cl_2\ (g)$ formed from elements in standard states **Find**: $\Delta S°$ and rationalize sign

Conceptual plan: Write balanced reaction. then $\Delta S^0_{rxn} = \sum n_p S^0(products) - \sum n_r S^0(reactants)$

Solution: $C\ (s) + H_2\ (g) + Cl_2\ (g) \rightarrow CH_2Cl_2\ (g)$

Reactant/Product	S^0 (J/mol K from Appendix IIB)
$C\ (s)$	5.7
$H_2\ (g)$	130.7
$Cl_2\ (g)$	223.1
$CH_2Cl_2\ (g)$	270.2

Be sure to pull data for the correct formula and phase.

$$\Delta S^0_{rxn} = \sum n_p S^0(products) - \sum n_r S^0(reactants)$$
$$= [1(S^0(CH_2Cl_2\ (g)))] - [1(S^0(C\ (s)) + 1(S^0(H_2\ (g)) + 1(S^0(Cl_2\ (g))]$$
$$= [1(270.2\ J/mol\ K)] - [1(5.7\ J/mol\ K) + 1(130.7\ J/mol\ K) + 1(223.1\ J/mol\ K)]$$
$$= [270.2\ J/K] - [359.5\ J/K]$$
$$= -89.3\ J/K$$

The moles of gas are decreasing.

Check: The units (J/K) are correct. The answer is negative, which is consistent with 2 moles of gas going to 1 mole of gas.

54. **Given**: $NF_4\ (g)$ formed from elements in standard states **Find**: $\Delta S°$ and rationalize sign

Conceptual plan: Write balanced reaction. then $\Delta S^0_{rxn} = \sum n_p S^0(products) - \sum n_r S^0(reactants)$

Solution: $\frac{1}{2} N_2\ (g) + 3/2\ F_2\ (g) \rightarrow NF_3\ (g)$

Reactant/Product	S^0 (J/mol K from Appendix IIB)
N_2 (g)	191.6
F_2 (g)	202.79
NF_3 (g)	260.8

Be sure to pull data for the correct formula and phase.

$$\Delta S^0_{rxn} = \sum n_p S^0(products) - \sum n_r S^0(reactants)$$

$$= [1(S^0(NF_3\ (g)))] - [1/2(S^0(N_2\ (g))) + 3/2(S^0(F_2\ (g)))]$$

$$= [1(260.8\ \text{J/mol K})] - [1/2(191.6\ \text{J/mol K}) + 3/2(202.79\ \text{J/mol K})] \quad \text{The moles of gas are decreasing.}$$

$$= [260.8\ \text{J/K}] - [399.\underline{9}85\ \text{J/K}]$$

$$= -139.2\ \text{J/K}$$

Check: The units (J/K) are correct.   The answer is negative, which is consistent with 2 moles of simple gases going to 1 mole of a complex gas.

55. **Given:** methanol (CH_3OH) combustion at 25 °C   **Find:** $\Delta H°_{rxn}$, $\Delta S°_{rxn}$, $\Delta G°_{rxn}$, and sponteneity
Conceptual plan: write balanced reaction   then $\Delta H^o_{rxn} = \Sigma n_P \Delta H^o_f(products) - \Sigma n_R \Delta H^o_f(reactants)$ **then**

$\Delta S^0_{rxn} = \sum n_p S^0(products) - \sum n_r S^0(reactants)$ **then**   °C → K   **then**   J/K → kJ/K   **then**

$$K = 273.15 + °C \qquad \frac{1\,kJ}{1000\,J}$$

$\Delta H°_{rxn}$, $\Delta S°_{rxn}$, T → $\Delta G°$

$$\Delta G = \Delta H_{rxn} - T\Delta S_{rxn}$$

Solution: combustion is combination with oxygen to form carbon dioxide and water
$2\ CH_3OH\ (l) + 3\ O_2\ (g) → 2\ CO_2\ (g) + 4\ H_2O\ (g)$

Reactant/Product	ΔH^0_f (kJ/mol from Appendix IIB)
CH_3OH (l)	− 238.6
O_2 (g)	0.0
CO_2 (g)	− 393.5
H_2O (g)	− 241.8

Be sure to pull data for the correct formula and phase.

$\Delta H^o_{rxn} = \Sigma n_P \Delta H^o_f(products) - \Sigma n_R \Delta H^o_f(reactants)$

$$= [2(\Delta H^o_f(CO_2(g))) + 4(\Delta H^o_f(H_2O(g)))] - [2(\Delta H^o_f(CH_3OH(l))) + 3(\Delta H^o_f(O_2(g)))] \quad \text{then}$$

$$= [2(-393.5\ \text{kJ}) + 4(-241.8\ \text{kJ})] - [2(-238.6\ \text{kJ}) + 3(0.0\ \text{kJ})]$$

$$= [-1754.2\ \text{kJ}] - [-477.2\ \text{kJ}]$$

$$= -1277\ \text{kJ}$$

Reactant/Product	S^0 (J/mol K from Appendix IIB)
CH_3OH (l)	126.8
O_2 (g)	205.2
CO_2 (g)	213.8
H_2O (g)	188.8

Be sure to pull data for the correct formula and phase.

$\Delta S^o_{rxn} = \Sigma n_P S^o(products) - \Sigma n_R S^o(reactants)$

$$= [2(S^o(CO_2(g))) + 4(S^o(H_2O(g)))] - [2(S^o(CH_3OH(l))) + 3(S^o(O_2(g)))]$$

$$= [2(213.8\ \text{J/mol K}) + 4(188.8\ \text{J/mol K})] - [2(126.8\ \text{J/mol K}) + 3(205.2\ \text{J/mol K})] \quad \text{then}$$

$$= [1182.8\ \text{J/K}] - [869.2\ \text{J/K}]$$

$$= 313.6\ \text{J/K}$$

$$T = 273.15 + 25\ °C = 298\ K \quad \text{then} \quad +313.6\frac{\text{J}}{\text{K}} \times \frac{1\ kJ}{1000\ \text{J}} = +0.3136\frac{kJ}{K} \quad \text{then}$$

$$\Delta G = \Delta H_{rxn} - T\Delta S_{rxn} = -1277\ \text{kJ} - (298\ \text{K})\left(+0.3136\frac{kJ}{\text{K}}\right) = -1370.\ \text{kJ} = -1.370 \times 10^6\ \text{J} \quad \text{so the reaction is}$$

spontaneous.

Check: The units (kJ, J/K and kJ) are correct. Combustion reactions are exothermic and we see a large negative enthalpy. We expect a large positive entropy because we have an increase in the number of moles of gas. The free energy is the sum of two negative terms so we expect a large negative free energy and the reaction is spontaneous.

56. **Given:** form glucose ($C_6H_{12}O_6$) and oxygen from sunlight, carbon dioxide and water at 25 °C
   Find: $\Delta H°_{rxn}$, $\Delta S°_{rxn}$, $\Delta G°_{rxn}$, and sponteneity
   Conceptual plan: **write balanced reaction** then $\Delta H°_{rxn} = \sum n_p \Delta H°_f(products) - \sum n_r \Delta H°_f(reactants)$ **then**

   $\Delta S°_{rxn} = \sum n_p S°(products) - \sum n_r S°(reactants)$ **then** °C $\rightarrow$ K then J/K$\rightarrow$ kJ/K then $\Delta H°_{rxn}$, $\Delta S°_{rxn}$, T $\rightarrow$ $\Delta G°$

   $$K = 273.15 + °C \qquad \frac{1\,kJ}{1000\,J} \qquad \Delta G = \Delta H_{rxn} - T\Delta S_{rxn}$$

   Solution: $6\,CO_2\,(g) + 6\,H_2O\,(l) \rightarrow C_6H_{12}O_6\,(s) + 6\,O_2\,(g)$

Reactant/Product	$\Delta H°_f$(kJ/mol from Appendix IIB)
CO_2 (g)	-393.5
H_2O (l)	-285.8
$C_6H_{12}O$ (s)	-1273.3
O_2 (g)	0.0

   Be sure to pull data for the correct formula and phase.
   $\Delta H°_{rxn} = \sum n_P \Delta H°_f(products) - \sum n_R \Delta H°_f(reactants)$
   $= [1(\Delta H°_f(C_6H_{12}O\,(s)) + 6(\Delta H°_f(O_2\,(g))] - [6(\Delta H°_f(CO_2\,(g)) + 6(\Delta H°_f(H_2O\,(l))]$
   $= [1(-1273.3\,kJ) + 6(0.0\,kJ)] - [6(-393.5\,kJ) + 6(-285.8\,kJ)]$ then
   $= [-1273.3\,kJ] - [-4075.8\,kJ]$
   $= +2802.5\,kJ$

Reactant/Product	$S°$(J/mol K from Appendix IIB)
CO_2 (g)	213.8
H_2O (l)	70.0
$C_6H_{12}O$ (s)	212.1
O_2 (g)	205.2

   Be sure to pull data for the correct formula and phase.
   $\Delta S°_{rxn} = \sum n_P S°(products) - \sum n_R S°(reactants)$
   $= [1(S°(C_6H_{12}O\,(s)) + 6(S°(O_2\,(g))] - [6(S°(CO_2\,(g)) + 6(S°(H_2O\,(l))]$
   $= [1(212.1\,J/mol\,K) + 6(205.2\,J/mol\,K)] - [6(213.8\,J/mol\,K) + 6(70.0\,J/mol\,K)]$ then
   $= [1443.3\,J/K] - [1702.8\,J/K]$
   $= -259.5\,J/K$

   $T = 273.15 + 25\,°C = 298\,K$ then $-259.5\,\frac{J}{K} \times \frac{1\,kJ}{1000\,J} = -0.2595\,\frac{kJ}{K}$ then

   $\Delta G = \Delta H_{rxn} - T\Delta S_{rxn} = +2802.5\,kJ - (298\,K)\left(-0.2595\,\frac{kJ}{K}\right) = +2879.8\,kJ = +2.8798 \times 10^6\,J$ so the reaction is

   nonspontaneous.
   Check: The units (kJ, J/K and kJ) are correct. The reaction requires the input of light energy, so we expect that this will be an endothermic reaction. We expect a negative entropy change because we have going from 6 moles of a gas and 6 moles of a liquid to 6 moles of a gas and one mole of a solid. The free energy is the sum of two positive terms so we expect a large positive free energy and the reaction is nonspontaneous. Photosynthesis does not happen on its own, light energy must be added to make the process move forward.

57. a) **Given:** $N_2O_4 (g) \rightarrow 2\,NO_2 (g)$ at 25 °C

Find: $\Delta H°_{rxn}$, $\Delta S°_{rxn}$, $\Delta G°_{rxn}$, spontaneity and can temperature be changed to make it spontaneous

Conceptual plan: $\Delta H^0_{rxn} = \sum n_P \Delta H^0_f (products) - \sum n_R \Delta H^0_f (reactants)$ **then**

$\Delta S^0_{rxn} = \sum n_p S^0 (products) - \sum n_r S^0 (reactants)$ **then** °C $\rightarrow$ K then   J/K $\rightarrow$ kJ/K   **then**

$$K = 273.15 + °C \qquad \frac{1\,kJ}{1000\,J}$$

$\Delta H°_{rxn}, \Delta S_{rxn}, T \rightarrow \Delta G$

$$\Delta G = \Delta H_{rxn} - T\Delta S_{rxn}$$

Solution:

Reactant/Product	ΔH^0_f (kJ/mol from Appendix IIB)
$N_2O_4 (g)$	11.1
$NO_2 (g)$	33.2

Be sure to pull data for the correct formula and phase.

$\Delta H^0_{rxn} = \sum n_P \Delta H^0_f (products) - \sum n_R \Delta H^0_f (reactants)$

$= [2(\Delta H^0_f (NO_2\ (g)))] - [1(\Delta H^0_f (N_2O_4\ (g)))]$

$= [2(33.2\ kJ)] - [1(11.1\ kJ)]$ then

$= [66.4\ kJ] - [11.1\ kJ]$

$= +55.3\ kJ$

Reactant/Product	S^0 (J/mol K from Appendix IIB)
$N_2O_4 (g)$	304.4
$NO_2 (g)$	240.1

Be sure to pull data for the correct formula and phase.

$\Delta S^0_{rxn} = \sum n_P S^0 (products) - \sum n_R S^0 (reactants)$

$= [2(S^0 (NO_2\ (g)))] - [1(S^0 (N_2O_4\ (g)))]$

$= [2(240.1\ J/mol\ K)] - [1(304.4\ J/mol\ K)]$ then   T = 273.15 + 25 °C = 298 K   then

$= [480.2\ J/K] - [304.4\ J/K]$

$= +175.8\ J/K$

$+175.8\ \dfrac{J}{K} \times \dfrac{1\,kJ}{1000\,J} = +0.1758\ \dfrac{kJ}{K}$ then

$\Delta G^0 = \Delta H^0_{rxn} - T\Delta S^0_{rxn} = +55.3\ kJ - (298\ K)\left(+0.1758\ \dfrac{kJ}{K}\right) = +2.9\ kJ = +2.9 \times 10^3\,J$ so the reaction is

nonspontaneous. It can be made spontaneous by raising the temperature.

Check: The units (kJ, J/K and kJ) are correct.   The reaction requires the breaking of a bond, so we expect that this will be an endothermic reaction. We expect a positive entropy change because are increasing the number of moles of gas.   Since the positive enthalpy term dominates at room temperature, the reaction is nonspontaneous. The second term can dominate if we raise the temperature high enough.

b) **Given:** $NH_4Cl (s) \rightarrow HCl (g) + NH_3 (g)$ at 25 °C

Find: $\Delta H°_{rxn}$, $\Delta S°_{rxn}$, $\Delta G°_{rxn}$, spontaneity and can temperature be changed to make it spontaneous

Conceptual plan: $\Delta H^0_{rxn} = \sum n_P \Delta H^0_f (products) - \sum n_R \Delta H^0_f (reactants)$ **then**

$\Delta S^0_{rxn} = \sum n_p S^0 (products) - \sum n_r S^0 (reactants)$ **then** °C$\rightarrow$K then J/K$\rightarrow$ kJ/K then $\Delta H°_{rxn}, \Delta S_{rxn}, T \rightarrow \Delta G$

$$K = 273.15 + °C \qquad \frac{1\,kJ}{1000\,J} \qquad\qquad \Delta G = \Delta H_{rxn} - T\Delta S_{rxn}$$

Solution:

Reactant/Product	ΔH^0_f (kJ/mol from Appendix IIB)
$NH_4Cl (s)$	-314.4
$HCl (g)$	-92.3
$NH_3 (g)$	-45.9

637

Be sure to pull data for the correct formula and phase.

$$\Delta H_{rxn}^0 = \sum n_P \Delta H_f^0 (products) - \sum n_R \Delta H_f^0 (reactants)$$

$$= [1(\Delta H_f^0 (\text{HCl }(g)) + 1(\Delta H_f^0 (\text{NH}_3 \ (g))] - [1(\Delta H_f^0 (\text{NH}_4\text{Cl }(g))]$$

$$= [1(-92.3 \text{ kJ}) + 1(-45.9 \text{ kJ})] - [1(-314.4 \text{ kJ})] \qquad \text{then}$$

$$= [-138.2 \text{ kJ}] - [-314.4 \text{ kJ}]$$

$$= +176.2 \text{ kJ}$$

Reactant/Product	S^0(J/mol K from Appendix IIB)
$NH_4Cl \ (s)$	94.6
$HCl \ (g)$	186.9
$NH_3 \ (g)$	192.8

Be sure to pull data for the correct formula and phase.

$$\Delta S_{rxn}^0 = \sum n_P S^0 (products) - \sum n_R S^0 (reactants)$$

$$= [1(S^0 (\text{HCl }(g)) + 1(S^0 (\text{NH}_3 \ (g))] - [1(S^0 (\text{NH}_4\text{Cl }(g))]$$

$$= [1(186.9 \text{ J/mol K}) + 1(192.8 \text{ J/mol K})] - [1(94.6 \text{ J/mol K})] \quad \text{then T} = 273.15 + 25 \ °C = 298 \text{ K} \quad \text{then}$$

$$= [379.7 \text{ J/K}] - [94.6 \text{ J/K}]$$

$$= +285.1 \text{ J/K}$$

$$+285.1 \frac{\text{J}}{\text{K}} \times \frac{1 \text{ kJ}}{1000 \text{ J}} = +0.2851 \frac{\text{kJ}}{\text{K}} \text{ then}$$

$$\Delta G^0 = \Delta H_{rxn}^0 - T\Delta S_{rxn}^0 = +176.2 \text{ kJ} - (298 \text{ K}) \left(+0.2851 \frac{\text{kJ}}{\text{K}} \right) = +91.2 \text{ kJ} = +9.12 \times 10^4 \text{ J} \quad \text{so the reaction is}$$

nonspontaneous. It can be made spontaneous by raising the temperature.

Check: The units (kJ, J/K and kJ) are correct. The reaction requires the breaking of a bond, so we expect that this will be an endothermic reaction. We expect a positive entropy change because are increasing the number of moles of gas. Since the positive enthalpy term dominates at room temperature, the reaction is nonspontaneous. The second term can dominate if we raise the temperature high enough.

c) **Given:** $3 \text{ H}_2 \ (g) + \text{Fe}_2\text{O}_3 \ (s) \rightarrow 2 \text{ Fe }(s) + 3 \text{ H}_2\text{O} \ (g)$ at 25 °C

Find: $\Delta H°_{rxn}$, $\Delta S°_{rxn}$, $\Delta G°_{rxn}$, spontaneity and can temperature be changed to make it spontaneous

Conceptual plan: $\Delta H_{rxn}^0 = \sum n_P \Delta H_f^0 (products) - \sum n_R \Delta H_f^0 (reactants)$ **then**

$\Delta S_{rxn}^0 = \sum n_P S^0 (products) - \sum n_R S^0 (reactants)$ **then** **°C → K** **then** **J/K → kJ/K** **then**

$$K = 273.15 + °C \qquad \frac{1 \text{ kJ}}{1000 \text{ J}}$$

$\Delta H°_{rxn}$, ΔS_{rxn}, T → ΔG

$$\Delta G = \Delta H_{rxn} - T\Delta S_{rxn}$$

Solution:

Reactant/Product	ΔH_f^0(kJ/mol from Appendix IIB)
$H_2 \ (g)$	0.0
$Fe_2O_3 \ (s)$	− 824.2
$Fe \ (s)$	0.0
$H_2O \ (g)$	− 241.8

Be sure to pull data for the correct formula and phase.

$$\Delta H_{rxn}^0 = \sum n_P \Delta H_f^0 (products) - \sum n_R \Delta H_f^0 (reactants)$$

$$= [2(\Delta H_f^0 (\text{Fe }(s)) + 3(\Delta H_f^0 (\text{H}_2\text{O} \ (g))] - [3(\Delta H_f^0 (\text{H}_2 \ (g)) + 1(\Delta H_f^0 (\text{Fe}_2\text{O}_3 \ (s))]$$

$$= [2(0.0 \text{ kJ}) + 3(-241.8 \text{ kJ})] - [3(0.0 \text{ kJ}) + 1(-824.2 \text{ kJ})] \qquad \text{then}$$

$$= [-725.4 \text{ kJ}] - [-824.2 \text{ kJ}]$$

$$= +98.8 \text{ kJ}$$

Reactant/Product	S^0 (J/mol K from Appendix IIB)
H_2 (g)	130.7
Fe_2O_3 (s)	87.4
Fe (s)	27.3
H_2O (g)	188.8

Be sure to pull data for the correct formula and phase.

$$\Delta S^0_{rxn} = \sum n_P S^0 (products) - \sum n_R S^0 (reactants)$$

$$= [2(S^0(Fe\ (s)) + 3(S^0(H_2O\ (g))] - [3(S^0(H_2\ (g)) + 1(S^0(Fe_2O_3\ (s))]$$

$$= [2(27.3\ J/mol\ K) + 3(188.8\ J/mol\ K)] - [3(130.7\ J/mol\ K) + 1(87.4\ J/mol\ K)] \quad then$$

$$= [621.0\ J/K] - [479.5\ J/K]$$

$$= +141.5\ J/K$$

$T = 273.15 + 25\ °C = 298\ K$ then $+141.5\ \dfrac{J}{K} \times \dfrac{1\ kJ}{1000\ J} = +0.1415\ \dfrac{kJ}{K}$ then

$\Delta G^0 = \Delta H^0_{rxn} - T\Delta S^0_{rxn} = +98.8\ kJ - (298\ K)\left(+0.1415\ \dfrac{kJ}{K} \right) = +56.6\ kJ = +5.66 \times 10^4\ J$ so the reaction is

nonspontaneous. It can be made spontaneous by raising the temperature.

Check: The units (kJ, J/K and kJ) are correct. The reaction requires the breaking of a bond, so we expect that this will be an endothermic reaction. We expect a positive entropy change because there is no change in the number of moles of gas, but the product gas is more complex. Since the positive enthalpy term dominates at room temperature, the reaction is nonspontaneous. The second term can dominate if we raise the temperature high enough. This process is the opposite of rusting, so we are not surprised that it is nonspontaneous.

d) **Given:** N_2 (g) + 3 H_2 (g) $\rightarrow$ 2 NH_3 (g) at 25 °C

Find: $\Delta H°_{rxn}$, $\Delta S°_{rxn}$, $\Delta G°_{rxn}$, spontaneity and can temperature be changed to make it spontaneous

Conceptual plan: $\Delta H^0_{rxn} = \sum n_P \Delta H^0_f (products) - \sum n_R \Delta H^0_f (reactants)$ **then**

$\Delta S^0_{rxn} = \sum n_P S^0 (products) - \sum n_R S^0 (reactants)$ **then** °C $\rightarrow$ K **then** J/K $\rightarrow$ kJ/K **then**

$$K = 273.15 + °C \qquad \dfrac{1\ kJ}{1000\ J}$$

$\Delta H°_{rxn}$, ΔS_{rxn}, T $\rightarrow$ ΔG

$$\Delta G = \Delta H_{rxn} - T\Delta S_{rxn}$$

Solution:

Reactant/Product	ΔH^0_f (kJ/mol from Appendix IIB)
N_2 (g)	0.0
H_2 (g)	0.0
NH_3 (g)	$-$ 45.9

Be sure to pull data for the correct formula and phase.

$$\Delta H^0_{rxn} = \sum n_P \Delta H^0_f (products) - \sum n_R \Delta H^0_f (reactants)$$

$$= [2(\Delta H^0_f(NH_3\ (g))] - [1(\Delta H^0_f(N_2\ (g)) + 3(\Delta H^0_f(H_2\ (g))]$$

$$= [2(-45.9\ kJ)] - [1(0.0\ kJ) + 3(0.0\ kJ)] \qquad then$$

$$= [-91.8\ kJ] - [0.0\ kJ]$$

$$= -91.8\ kJ$$

Reactant/Product	S^0 (J/mol K from Appendix IIB)
N_2 (g)	191.6
H_2 (g)	130.7
NH_3 (g)	192.8

Be sure to pull data for the correct formula and phase.

$$\Delta S^0_{rxn} = \sum n_P S^0(products) - \sum n_R S^0(reactants)$$

$$= [2(S^0(NH_3\ (g))] - [1(S^0(N_2\ (g)) + 3(S^0(H_2\ (g))]$$

$$= [2(192.8\ J/mol\ K)] - [1(191.6\ J/mol\ K) + 3(130.7\ J/mol\ K)]\quad then$$

$$= [385.6\ J/K] - [583.7\ J/K]$$

$$= -198.1\ J/K$$

$T = 273.15 + 25\ ^\circ C = 298\ K$ then $-198.1\frac{J}{K} \times \frac{1\ kJ}{1000\ J} = -0.1981\frac{kJ}{K}$ then

$\Delta G^0 = \Delta H^0_{rxn} - T\Delta S^0_{rxn} = -91.8\ kJ - (298\ K)\left(-0.1981\frac{kJ}{K}\right) = -32.8\ kJ = -3.28\ x\ 10^4\ J$ so the reaction is spontaneous.

Check: The units (kJ, J/K and kJ) are correct.   The reaction requires the breaking of a bond, so we expect that this will be an endothermic reaction. We expect a positive entropy change because are increasing the number of moles of gas.   Since the negative enthalpy term dominates at room temperature, the reaction is spontaneous. The second term can dominate if we raise the temperature high enough.

58. a) **Given:** $2\ CH_4\ (g) \rightarrow C_2H_6\ (g) + H_2\ (g)$ at 25 °C
   Find: ΔH°_{rxn}, ΔS°_{rxn}, ΔG°_{rxn}, spontaneity and can temperature be changed to make it spontaneous
   Conceptual plan: $\Delta H^0_{rxn} = \sum n_p \Delta H^0_f(products) - \sum n_R \Delta H^0_f(reactants)$ **then**

   $\Delta S^0_{rxn} = \sum n_p S^0(products) - \sum n_r S^0(reactants)$ **then** °C $\rightarrow$ K **then** J/K $\rightarrow$ kJ/K **then**

   $$K = 273.15 + ^\circ C \qquad \frac{1\ kJ}{1000\ J}$$

   ΔH°_{rxn}, ΔS_{rxn}, T $\rightarrow$ ΔG
      $\Delta G = \Delta H_{rxn} - T\Delta S_{rxn}$

   Solution:

Reactant/Product	ΔH^0_f(kJ/mol from Appendix IIB)
$CH_4\ (g)$	-74.6
$C_2H_6\ (g)$	-84.6
$H_2\ (g)$	0.0

   Be sure to pull data for the correct formula and phase.
   $$\Delta H^0_{rxn} = \sum n_P \Delta H^0_f(products) - \sum n_R \Delta H^0_f(reactants)$$

   $$= [1(\Delta H^0_f(C_2H_6\ (g)) + 1(\Delta H^0_f(H_2\ (g))] - [2(\Delta H^0_f(CH_4\ (g))]$$

   $$= [1(-84.6\ kJ) + 1(0.0\ kJ)] - [2(-74.6\ kJ)] \qquad then$$

   $$= [-84.6\ kJ] - [-149.2\ kJ]$$

   $$= +64.6\ kJ$$

Reactant/Product	S^0(J/mol K from Appendix IIB)
$CH_4\ (g)$	186.3
$C_2H_6\ (g)$	229.2
$H_2\ (g)$	130.7

   Be sure to pull data for the correct formula and phase.
   $$\Delta S^0_{rxn} = \sum n_P S^0(products) - \sum n_R S^0(reactants)$$

   $$= [1(S^0(C_2H_6\ (g)) + 1(S^0(H_2\ (g))] - [2(S^0(CH_4\ (g))]$$

   $$= [1(229.2\ J/mol\ K) + 1(130.7\ J/mol\ K)] - [2(186.3\ J/mol\ K)]\quad then$$

   $$= [359.9\ J/K] - [372.6\ J/K]$$

   $$= -12.7\ J/K$$

   $T = 273.15 + 25\ ^\circ C = 298\ K$ then $-12.7\frac{J}{K} \times \frac{1\ kJ}{1000\ J} = -0.0127\frac{kJ}{K}$ then

   $\Delta G^0 = \Delta H^0_{rxn} - T\Delta S^0_{rxn} = +64.6\ kJ - (298\ K)\left(-0.0127\frac{kJ}{K}\right) = +68.4\ kJ = +6.84\ x\ 10^4\ J$ so the reaction is

   spontaneous.

Check: The units (kJ, J/K and kJ) are correct. The two moles of methane has a lower enthalpy than one mole of ethane, so we expect that this will be an endothermic reaction. We expect a very small entropy change because the number of moles of gas is unchanged. Since the both terms are positive, the reaction is nonspontaneous. Since both terms are positive, this reaction can not be spontaneous at any temperature.

b) **Given:** $2 NH_3 (g) \rightarrow N_2H_4 (g) + H_2 (g)$ at 25 °C

   Find: $\Delta H°_{rxn}$, $\Delta S°_{rxn}$, $\Delta G°_{rxn}$, spontaneity and can temperature be changed to make it spontaneous

   Conceptual plan: $\Delta H^0_{rxn} = \sum n_p \Delta H^0_f (products) - \sum n_R \Delta H^0_f (reactants)$ **then**

   $\Delta S^0_{rxn} = \sum n_p S^0 (products) - \sum n_r S^0 (reactants)$ **then** °C $\rightarrow$ K **then** J/K $\rightarrow$ kJ/K **then**

$$K = 273.15 + °C \qquad\qquad \frac{1 kJ}{1000 J}$$

   $\Delta H°_{rxn}, \Delta S_{rxn}, T \rightarrow \Delta G$

   $\Delta G = \Delta H_{rxn} - T\Delta S_{rxn}$

   Solution:

Reactant/Product	ΔH^0_f(kJ/mol from Appendix IIB)
$NH_3 (g)$	$-$ 45.9
$N_2H_4 (g)$	95.4
$H_2 (g)$	0.0

   Be sure to pull data for the correct formula and phase.

   $\Delta H^0_{rxn} = \sum n_P \Delta H^0_f (products) - \sum n_R \Delta H^0_f (reactants)$

   $\quad = [1(\Delta H^0_f(N_2H_4 (g)) + 1(\Delta H^0_f(H_2 (g))] - [2(\Delta H^0_f(NH_3 (g))]$

   $\quad = [1(95.4 kJ) + 1(0.0 kJ)] - [2(-45.9 kJ)]$ then

   $\quad = [95.4 kJ] - [-91.8 kJ]$

   $\quad = + 187.2 kJ$

Reactant/Product	S^0(J/mol K from Appendix IIB)
$NH_3 (g)$	192.8
$N_2H_4 (g)$	238.5
$H_2 (g)$	130.7

   Be sure to pull data for the correct formula and phase.

   $\Delta S^0_{rxn} = \sum n_P S^0 (products) - \sum n_R S^0 (reactants)$

   $\quad = [1(S^0(N_2H_4 (g)) + 1(S^0(H_2 (g))] - [2(S^0(NH_3 (g))]$

   $\quad = [1(238.5 J/mol K) + 1(130.7 J/mol K)] - [2(192.8 J/mol K)]$ then

   $\quad = [369.2 J/K] - [385.6 J/K]$

   $\quad = -16.4 J/K$

   $T = 273.15 + 25 °C = 298 K$ then $-16.4 \frac{J}{K} \times \frac{1 kJ}{1000 J} = -0.0164 \frac{kJ}{K}$ then

   $\Delta G^0 = \Delta H^0_{rxn} - T\Delta S^0_{rxn} = +187.2 kJ - (298 \text{ K})\left(-0.0164 \frac{kJ}{K}\right) = +192.1 kJ = +1.921 \times 10^5 J$ so the reaction is nonspontaneous.

   Check: The units (kJ, J/K and kJ) are correct. The N_2H_4 has such a high enthalpy of formation compared to ammonia, so we expect that this will be an endothermic reaction. We expect a very small entropy change because the number of moles of gas is unchanged. Since the both terms are positive, the reaction is nonspontaneous. Since both terms are positive, this reaction can not be spontaneous at any temperature.

c) **Given:** $N_2 (g) + O_2 (g) \rightarrow 2 NO (g)$ at 25 °C

   Find: $\Delta H°_{rxn}$, $\Delta S°_{rxn}$, $\Delta G°_{rxn}$, spontaneity and can temperature be changed to make it spontaneous

   Conceptual plan: $\Delta H^0_{rxn} = \sum n_p \Delta H^0_f (products) - \sum n_R \Delta H^0_f (reactants)$ **then**

   $\Delta S^0_{rxn} = \sum n_p S^0 (products) - \sum n_r S^0 (reactants)$ **then** °C $\rightarrow$ K **then** J/K $\rightarrow$ kJ/K **then** $\Delta H°_{rxn}, \Delta S_{rxn}, T \rightarrow \Delta G$

$$K = 273.15 + °C \quad \frac{1 kJ}{1000 J} \qquad\qquad \Delta G = \Delta H_{rxn} - T\Delta S_{rxn}$$

Solution:

Reactant/Product	ΔH_f^0(kJ/mol from Appendix IIB)
N_2 (g)	0.0
O_2 (g)	0.0
NO (g)	91.3

Be sure to pull data for the correct formula and phase.

$$\Delta H_{rxn}^0 = \sum n_P \Delta H_f^0(products) - \sum n_R \Delta H_f^0(reactants)$$

$$= [2(\Delta H_f^0(NO\ (g))] - [1(\Delta H_f^0(N_2\ (g)) + 1(\Delta H_f^0(O_2\ (g))]$$

$$= [2(91.3\ kJ)] - [1(0.0\ kJ) + 1(0.0\ kJ)] \qquad \text{then}$$

$$= [182.6\ kJ] - [0.0\ kJ]$$

$$= +182.6\ kJ$$

Reactant/Product	S^0(J/mol K from Appendix IIB)
N_2 (g)	191.6
O_2 (g)	205.2
NO (g)	210.8

Be sure to pull data for the correct formula and phase.

$$\Delta S_{rxn}^0 = \sum n_P S^0(products) - \sum n_R S^0(reactants)$$

$$= [2(S^0(NO\ (g))] - [1(S^0(N_2\ (g)) + 1(S^0(O_2\ (g))]$$

$$= [2(210.8\ J/mol\ K)] - [1(191.6\ J/mol\ K) + 1(205.2\ J/mol\ K)] \quad \text{then}$$

$$= [421.6\ J/K] - [396.8\ J/K]$$

$$= +24.8\ J/K$$

$$T = 273.15 + 25\ ^\circ C = 298\ K \quad \text{then} \quad +24.8\ \frac{J}{K} \times \frac{1\ kJ}{1000\ J} = +0.0248\ \frac{kJ}{K} \quad \text{then}$$

$$\Delta G^0 = \Delta H_{rxn}^0 - T\Delta S_{rxn}^0 = +182.6\ kJ - (298\ K)\left(0.0248\ \frac{kJ}{K}\right) = +175.2\ kJ = +1.752 \times 10^5\ J \quad \text{so the reaction is}$$

nonspontaneous.

Check: The units (kJ, J/K and kJ) are correct. The enthalpy is twice the enthalpy of formation of NO. We expect a very small entropy change because the number of moles of gas is unchanged. Since the positive enthalpy term dominates at room temperature, the reaction is nonspontaneous. The second term can dominate if we raise the temperature high enough.

d) **Given:** $2\ KClO_3\ (s) \rightarrow 2\ KCl\ (s) + O_2\ (g)$ at 25 °C

Find: ΔH°_{rxn}, ΔS°_{rxn}, ΔG°_{rxn}, spontaneity and can temperature be changed to make it spontaneous

Conceptual plan: $\Delta H_{rxn}^0 = \sum n_P \Delta H_f^0(products) - \sum n_R \Delta H_f^0(reactants)$ **then**

$\Delta S_{rxn}^0 = \sum n_P S^0(products) - \sum n_R S^0(reactants)$ **then** $\degree C \rightarrow K$ then $J/K \rightarrow kJ/K$ then $\Delta H^\circ_{rxn}, \Delta S_{rxn}, T \rightarrow \Delta G$

$$K = 273.15 + \degree C \qquad \frac{1 kJ}{1000\ J} \qquad \Delta G = \Delta H_{rxn} - T\Delta S_{rxn}$$

Solution:

Reactant/Product	ΔH_f^0(kJ/mol from Appendix IIB)
$KClO_3$ (s)	− 397.7
KCl (s)	− 436.5
O_2 (g)	0.0

Be sure to pull data for the correct formula and phase.

$$\Delta H_{rxn}^0 = \sum n_P \Delta H_f^0(products) - \sum n_R \Delta H_f^0(reactants)$$

$$= [2(\Delta H_f^0(KCl\ (s)) + 1(\Delta H_f^0(O_2\ (g))] - [2(\Delta H_f^0(KClO_3\ (s))]$$

$$= [2(-436.5\ kJ) + 3(0.0\ kJ)] - [2(-397.7\ kJ)] \qquad \text{then}$$

$$= [-873.0\ kJ] - [-795.4\ kJ]$$

$$= -77.6\ kJ$$

Reactant/Product	S^0 (J/mol K from Appendix IIB)
$KClO_3$ (s)	143.1
KCl (s)	82.6
O_2 (g)	205.2

Be sure to pull data for the correct formula and phase.

$$\Delta S_{rxn}^0 = \sum n_P S^0(products) - \sum n_R S^0(reactants)$$
$$= [2(S^0(KCl\ (s)) + 3(S^0(O_2\ (g)))] - [2(S^0(KClO_3\ (s)))]$$
$$= [2(82.6\ J/mol\ K) + 3(205.2\ J/mol\ K)] - [2(143.1\ J/mol\ K)] \quad then$$
$$= [780.8\ J/K] - [286.2\ J/K]$$
$$= +494.6\ J/K$$

$T = 273.15 + 25\ °C = 298\ K$ then $+494.6 \frac{J}{K} \times \frac{1\ kJ}{1000\ J} = +0.4946 \frac{kJ}{K}$ then

$$\Delta G^0 = \Delta H^0_{rxn} - T\Delta S^0_{rxn} = -77.6\ kJ - (298\ K)\left(0.4946 \frac{kJ}{K}\right) = -225.0\ kJ = -2.250 \times 10^6\ J \text{ so the reaction is}$$

spontaneous.

Check: The units (kJ, J/K and kJ) are correct. The reaction is exothermic because the enthalpy of formation of KCl is less than that for $KClO_3$. We expect a positive entropy change because the number of moles of gas is increasing. Since both terms are negative, the reaction is spontaneous at all temperatures.

59. a) **Given:** N_2O_4 (g) → 2 NO_2 (g) at 25 °C
   Find: $\Delta G°_{rxn}$, spontaneity and compare to #57

   Conceptual plan: $\Delta G_{rxn}^0 = \sum n_P \Delta G_f^0(products) - \sum n_R \Delta G_f^0(reactants)$ **then compare to #57**
   Solution:

Reactant/Product	ΔG_f^0 (kJ/mol from Appendix IIB)
N_2O_4 (g)	99.8
NO_2 (g)	51.3

Be sure to pull data for the correct formula and phase.

$$\Delta G_{rxn}^0 = \sum n_P \Delta G_f^0(products) - \sum n_R \Delta G_f^0(reactants)$$
$$= [2(\Delta G_f^0(NO_2\ (g)))] - [1(\Delta G_f^0(N_2O_4\ (g)))]$$
$$= [2(51.3\ kJ)] - [1(99.8\ kJ)] \qquad \text{so the reaction is nonspontaneous.}$$
$$= [102.6\ kJ] - [99.8\ kJ]$$
$$= +2.8\ kJ$$

The value is similar to in #57.

Check: The units (kJ) are correct. The free energy of the products is greater than the reactants, so the answer is positive and the reaction is nonspontaneous. The answer is the same as in #57 within the error of the calculation.

b) **Given:** NH_4Cl (s) → HCl (g) + NH_3 (g) at 25 °C
   Find: $\Delta G°_{rxn}$, spontaneity and compare to #57

   Conceptual plan: $\Delta G_{rxn}^0 = \sum n_P \Delta G_f^0(products) - \sum n_R \Delta G_f^0(reactants)$ **then compare to #57**
   Solution:

Reactant/Product	ΔG_f^0 (kJ/mol from Appendix IIB)
NH_4Cl (s)	– 202.9
HCl (g)	– 95.3
NH_3 (g)	– 16.4

Be sure to pull data for the correct formula and phase.

$$\Delta G_{rxn}^0 = \sum n_P \Delta G_f^0(products) - \sum n_R \Delta G_f^0(reactants)$$
$$= [1(\Delta G_f^0(HCl\ (g)) + 1(\Delta G_f^0(NH_3\ (g))] - [1(\Delta G_f^0(NH_4Cl\ (g))]$$
$$= [1(-95.3\ kJ) + 1(-16.4\ kJ)] - [1(-202.9\ kJ)] \qquad \text{so the reaction is nonspontaneous.}$$
$$= [-111.7\ kJ] - [-202.9\ kJ]$$
$$= +91.2\ kJ$$

The result is the same as in #57.
Check: The units (kJ) are correct. The answer matches #57.

c) **Given:** $3\ H_2\ (g) + Fe_2O_3\ (s) \rightarrow 2\ Fe\ (s) + 3\ H_2O\ (g)$ at 25 °C
Find: $\Delta G°_{rxn}$, spontaneity and compare to #57

Conceptual plan: $\Delta G_{rxn}^0 = \sum n_P \Delta G_f^0(products) - \sum n_R \Delta G_f^0(reactants)$ **then compare to #57**

Solution:

Reactant/Product	ΔG_f^0(kJ/mol from Appendix IIB)
$H_2\ (g)$	0.0
$Fe_2O_3\ (s)$	-742.2
$Fe\ (s)$	0.0
$H_2O\ (g)$	-228.6

Be sure to pull data for the correct formula and phase.
$$\Delta G_{rxn}^0 = \sum n_P \Delta G_f^0(products) - \sum n_R \Delta G_f^0(reactants)$$
$$= [2(\Delta G_f^0(Fe\ (s)) + 3(\Delta G_f^0(H_2O\ (g))] - [3(\Delta G_f^0(H_2\ (g)) + 1(\Delta G_f^0(Fe_2O_3\ (s))]$$
$$= [2(0.0\ kJ) + 3(-228.6\ kJ)] - [3(0.0\ kJ) + 1(-742.2\ kJ)]$$
$$= [-685.8\ kJ] - [-742.2\ kJ]$$
$$= +56.4\ kJ$$

so the reaction is nonspontaneous. The value is similar to that in #57.
Check: The units (kJ) are correct. The answer is the same as in #57 within the error of the calculation.

d) **Given:** $N_2\ (g) + 3\ H_2\ (g) \rightarrow 2\ NH_3\ (g)$ at 25 °C
Find: $\Delta G°_{rxn}$, spontaneity and compare to #57

Conceptual plan: $\Delta G_{rxn}^0 = \sum n_P \Delta G_f^0(products) - \sum n_R \Delta G_f^0(reactants)$ **then compare to #57**

Solution:

Reactant/Product	ΔG_f^0(kJ/mol from Appendix IIB)
$N_2\ (g)$	0.0
$H_2\ (g)$	0.0
$NH_3\ (g)$	-16.4

Be sure to pull data for the correct formula and phase.
$$\Delta G_{rxn}^0 = \sum n_P \Delta G_f^0(products) - \sum n_R \Delta G_f^0(reactants)$$
$$= [2(\Delta G_f^0(NH_3\ (g))] - [1(\Delta G_f^0(N_2\ (g)) + 3(\Delta G_f^0(H_2\ (g))]$$
$$= [2(-16.4\ kJ)] - [1(0.0\ kJ) + 3(0.0\ kJ)]$$
$$= [-32.8\ kJ] - [0.0\ kJ]$$
$$= -32.8\ kJ$$

so the reaction is spontaneous. The result is the same as in #57.
Check: The units (kJ) are correct. The answer matches #57.

Values calculated by the two methods are comparable. The method using $\Delta H°$ and $\Delta S°$ is longer, but it can be used to determine how $\Delta G°$ changes with temperature.

60. a) **Given:** $2\ CH_4\ (g) \rightarrow C_2H_6\ (g) + H_2\ (g)$ at 25 °C
Find: $\Delta G°_{rxn}$, spontaneity and compare to #58

Conceptual plan: $\Delta G_{rxn}^0 = \sum n_P \Delta G_f^0(products) - \sum n_R \Delta G_f^0(reactants)$ **then compare to #58**

Solution:

Reactant/Product	ΔG_f^0(kJ/mol from Appendix IIB)
CH_4 (g)	$-$ 50.5
C_2H_6 (g)	$-$ 32.0
H_2 (g)	0.0

Be sure to pull data for the correct formula and phase.

$\Delta G_{rxn}^0 = \sum n_P \Delta G_f^0(products) - \sum n_R \Delta G_f^0(reactants)$

$= [1(\Delta G_f^0(C_2H_6\ (g)) + 1(\Delta G_f^0(H_2\ (g))] - [2(\Delta G_f^0(CH_4\ (g))\ ]$

$= [1(-32.0\ kJ) + 1(0.0\ kJ)] - [2(-50.5\ kJ)]$

$= [-32.0\ kJ] - [-101.0\ kJ]$

$= +69.0\ kJ$

so the reaction is spontaneous. The value is similar to that in #58.

Check: The units (kJ) are correct. The answer is the same as in #58 within the error of the calculation.

b) **Given:** $2\ NH_3\ (g) \rightarrow N_2H_4\ (g) +\ H_2\ (g)$ at 25 °C
Find: $\Delta G°_{rxn}$, spontaneity and compare to #58

Conceptual plan: $\Delta G_{rxn}^0 = \sum n_P \Delta G_f^0(products) - \sum n_R \Delta G_f^0(reactants)$ **then compare to #58**
Solution:

Reactant/Product	ΔG_f^0(kJ/mol from Appendix IIB)
NH_3 (g)	$-$ 16.4
N_2H_4 (g)	159.4
H_2 (g)	0.0

Be sure to pull data for the correct formula and phase.

$\Delta G_{rxn}^0 = \sum n_P \Delta G_f^0(products) - \sum n_R \Delta G_f^0(reactants)$

$= [1(\Delta G_f^0(N_2H_4\ (g)) + 1(\Delta G_f^0(H_2\ (g))] - [2(\Delta G_f^0(NH_3\ (g))]$

$= [1(159.4\ kJ) + 1(0.0\ kJ)] - [2(-16.4\ kJ)]$

$= [159.4\ kJ] - [-32.8\ kJ]$

$= +192.2\ kJ$

so the reaction is nonspontaneous. The value is similar to in #58.

Check: The units (kJ) are correct. The answer is the same as in #58 within the error of the calculation.

c) **Given:** $N_2\ (g) +\ O_2\ (g) \rightarrow 2\ NO\ (g)$ at 25 °C
Find: $\Delta G°_{rxn}$, spontaneity and compare to #58

Conceptual plan: $\Delta G_{rxn}^0 = \sum n_P \Delta G_f^0(products) - \sum n_R \Delta G_f^0(reactants)$ **then compare to #58**
Solution:

Reactant/Product	ΔG_f^0(kJ/mol from Appendix IIB)
N_2 (g)	0.0
O_2 (g)	0.0
NO (g)	87.6

Be sure to pull data for the correct formula and phase.

$\Delta G_{rxn}^0 = \sum n_P \Delta G_f^0(products) - \sum n_R \Delta G_f^0(reactants)$

$= [2(\Delta G_f^0(NO\ (g))] - [1(\Delta G_f^0(N_2\ (g)) + 1(\Delta G_f^0(O_2\ (g))]$

$= [2(87.6\ kJ)] - [1(0.0\ kJ) + 1(0.0\ kJ)]$

$= [175.2\ kJ] - [0.0\ kJ]$

$= +175.2\ kJ$

so the reaction is nonspontaneous. The result is the same as in #57.

Check: The units (kJ) are correct. The answer matches #57.

d) **Given:** $2\ KClO_3\ (s) \rightarrow 2\ KCl\ (s) +\ 3\ O_2\ (g)$ at 25 °C
Find: $\Delta G°_{rxn}$, spontaneity and compare to #58

Conceptual plan: $\Delta G_{rxn}^0 = \sum n_P \Delta G_f^0(products) - \sum n_R \Delta G_f^0(reactants)$ **then compare to #58**
Solution:

Reactant/Product	ΔG_f^0 (kJ/mol from Appendix IIB)
$KClO_3$ (s)	-296.3
KCl (s)	-408.5
O_2 (g)	0.0

Be sure to pull data for the correct formula and phase.

$\Delta G_{rxn}^0 = \sum n_P \Delta G_f^0 (products) - \sum n_R \Delta G_f^0 (reactants)$

$= [2(\Delta G_f^0(KCl\ (s)) + 1(\Delta G_f^0(O_2\ (g))] - [2(\Delta G_f^0(KClO_3\ (s))]$

$= [2(-408.5\ kJ) + 3(0.0\ kJ)] - [2(-296.3\ kJ)]$

$= [-817.0\ kJ] - [-592.6\ kJ]$

$= -224.4\ kJ$

so the reaction is spontaneous. The value is similar to in #58.

Check: The units (kJ) are correct. The answer is the same as in #58 within the error of the calculation.

Values calculated by the two methods are comparable. The method using $\Delta H°$ and $\Delta S°$ is longer, but it can be used to determine how $\Delta G°$ changes with temperature.

61. **Given:** $2\ NO\ (g) + O_2\ (g) \rightarrow 2\ NO_2\ (g)$ **Find:** $\Delta G°_{rxn}$ and spontaneity at a) 298 K, b) 715 K, and 855 K

Conceptual plan: $\Delta H_{rxn}^0 = \sum n_p \Delta H_f^0 (products) - \sum n_R \Delta H_f^0 (reactants)$ **then**

$\Delta S_{rxn}^0 = \sum n_p S^0(products) - \sum n_r S^0(reactants)$ **then J/K $\rightarrow$ kJ/K then** $\Delta H°_{rxn}, \Delta S_{rxn}, T \rightarrow \Delta G$

$$\frac{1\ kJ}{1000\ J}$$

$$\Delta G = \Delta H_{rxn} - T\Delta S_{rxn}$$

Solution:

Reactant/Product	ΔH_f^0 (kJ/mol from Appendix IIB)
NO (g)	91.3
O_2 (g)	0.0
NO_2 (g)	33.2

Be sure to pull data for the correct formula and phase.

$\Delta H_{rxn}^0 = \sum n_P \Delta H_f^0 (products) - \sum n_R \Delta H_f^0 (reactants)$

$= [2(\Delta H_f^0(NO_2\ (g))] - [2(\Delta H_f^0(NO\ (g)) + 1(\Delta H_f^0(O_2\ (g))]$

$= [2(33.2\ kJ)] - [2(91.3\ kJ) + 1(0.0\ kJ)]$ then

$= [66.4\ kJ] - [182.6\ kJ]$

$= -116.2\ kJ$

Reactant/Product	S^0 (J/mol K from Appendix IIB)
NO (g)	210.8
O_2 (g)	205.2
NO_2 (g)	240.1

Be sure to pull data for the correct formula and phase.

$\Delta S_{rxn}^0 = \sum n_P S^0 (products) - \sum n_R S^0 (reactants)$

$= [2(S^0(NO_2\ (g))] - [2(S^0(NO\ (g)) + 1(S^0(O_2\ (g))]$

$= [2(240.1\ J/mol\ K)] - [2(210.8\ J/mol\ K) + 1(205.2\ J/mol\ K)]$ then $-146.6\ \frac{J}{K} \times \frac{1\ kJ}{1000\ J} = -0.1466\ \frac{kJ}{K}$ then

$= [480.2\ J/K] - [626.8\ J/K]$

$= -146.6\ J/K$

a) $\Delta G° = \Delta H°_{rxn} - T\Delta S°_{rxn} = -116.2\ kJ - (298\ K)\left(-0.1466\ \frac{kJ}{K}\right) = -72.5\ kJ = -7.25 \times 10^4\ J$ so the reaction is

spontaneous.

b) $\Delta G° = \Delta H°_{rxn} - T\Delta S°_{rxn} = -116.2\ kJ - (715\ K)\left(-0.1466\ \frac{kJ}{K}\right) = -11.4\ kJ = -1.14 \times 10^4\ J$ so the reaction is

spontaneous.

b) $\Delta G^0 = \Delta H^0_{rxn} - T\Delta S^0_{rxn} = -116.2 \text{ kJ} - (855 \text{ K})\left(-0.1466 \dfrac{\text{kJ}}{\text{K}}\right) = +9.1 \text{ kJ} = +9.1 \times 10^3 \text{ J}$ so the reaction is

nonspontaneous.

Check: The units (kJ) are correct.   The enthalpy term dominates at low temperatures making the reaction spontaneous. As the temperature increases, the decrease in entropy starts to dominate and the last case the reaction is nonspontaneous.

62. **Given**: $CaCO_3 (s) \rightarrow$ CaO (s) + $CO_2 (g)$ **Find**: ΔG°_{rxn} and spontaneity at a) 298 K, b) 1055 K, and 1455 K
Conceptual plan: $\Delta H^0_{rxn} = \sum n_p \Delta H^0_f (products) - \sum n_r \Delta H^0_f (reactants)$ **then**

$\Delta S^0_{rxn} = \sum n_p S^0 (products) - \sum n_r S^0 (reactants)$ **then   J/K $\rightarrow$ kJ/K   then $\Delta H^\circ_{rxn}, \Delta S_{rxn}, T \rightarrow$ ΔG**

$$\dfrac{1 \text{kJ}}{1000 \text{ J}} \qquad\qquad \Delta G = \Delta H_{rxn} - T\Delta S_{rxn}$$

Solution:

Reactant/Product	ΔH^0_f (kJ/mol from Appendix IIB)
$CaCO_3 (s)$	-1207.6
CaO (s)	-634.9
$CO_2 (g)$	-393.5

Be sure to pull data for the correct formula and phase.

$\Delta H^0_{rxn} = \sum n_P \Delta H^0_f (products) - \sum n_R \Delta H^0_f (reactants)$

$\qquad = [1(\Delta H^0_f (\text{CaO} (g)) + 1(\Delta H^0_f (CO_2 (g))] - [1(\Delta H^0_f (CaCO_2 (g))]$ then

$\qquad = [1(-634.9 \text{ kJ}) + 1(-393.5 \text{ kJ})] - [1(-1207.6 \text{ kJ})]$

$\qquad = [-1028.4 \text{ kJ}] - [-1207.6 \text{ kJ}]$

$\qquad = +179.2 \text{ kJ}$

Reactant/Product	S^0 (J/mol K from Appendix IIB)
$CaCO_3 (s)$	91.7
CaO (s)	38.1
$CO_2 (g)$	213.8

Be sure to pull data for the correct formula and phase.

$\Delta S^0_{rxn} = \sum n_P S^0 (products) - \sum n_R S^0 (reactants)$

$\qquad = [1(S^0 (\text{CaO} (g)) + 1(S^0 (CO_2 (g))] - [1(S^0 (CaCO_2 (g))]$

$\qquad = [1(38.1 \text{ J/mol K}) + 1(213.8 \text{ J/mol K})] - [1(91.7 \text{ J/mol K})]$ then $+160.2 \dfrac{\text{J}}{\text{K}} \times \dfrac{1 \text{ kJ}}{1000 \text{ J}} = +0.1602 \dfrac{\text{kJ}}{\text{K}}$ then

$\qquad = [251.9 \text{ J/K}] - [91.7 \text{ J/K}]$

$\qquad = +160.2 \text{ J/K}$

a) $\Delta G^0 = \Delta H^0_{rxn} - T\Delta S^0_{rxn} = +179.2 \text{ kJ} - (298 \text{ K})\left(+0.1602 \dfrac{\text{kJ}}{\text{K}}\right) = +131.5 \text{ kJ} = +1.315 \times 10^5 \text{ J}$ so the reaction is

nonspontaneous.

b) $\Delta G^0 = \Delta H^0_{rxn} - T\Delta S^0_{rxn} = +179.2 \text{ kJ} - (1055 \text{ K})\left(+0.1602 \dfrac{\text{kJ}}{\text{K}}\right) = +10.2 \text{ kJ} = +1.02 \times 10^4 \text{ J}$ so the reaction is

nonspontaneous.

b) $\Delta G^0 = \Delta H^0_{rxn} - T\Delta S^0_{rxn} = +179.2 \text{ kJ} - (1455 \text{ K})\left(+0.1602 \dfrac{\text{kJ}}{\text{K}}\right) = -53.9 \text{ kJ} = -5.39 \times 10^4 \text{ J}$ so the reaction is

spontaneous.
Check: The units (kJ) are correct.   The enthalpy term dominates at low temperatures making the reaction nonspontaneous. As the temperature increases, the increase in entropy starts to dominate and the last case the reaction is spontaneous.

63. Since the first reaction has Fe_2O_3 as a product and the reaction of interest has it as a reactant, we need to reverse the first reaction. When the reaction direction is reversed ΔG changes.

$\qquad Fe_2O_3 (s) \rightarrow 2 \text{ Fe} (s) + 3/2 \, O_2 (g)$ $\Delta G^0 = +742.2 \text{ kJ}$

Since the second reaction has 1 mole CO as a reactant and the reaction of interest has 3 moles of CO as a reactant, we need to multiply the second reaction and the ΔG by 3.

$3\,[CO\,(g) + 1/2\,O_2\,(g) \rightarrow CO_2\,(g)]$ $\qquad\qquad\qquad$ $\Delta G^0 = 3(-257.2\text{ kJ}) = -771.6\text{ kJ}$

Hess' Law states the ΔG of the net reaction is the sum of the ΔG of the steps.
The rewritten reactions are:

$Fe_2O_3\,(s) \rightarrow 2\,Fe\,(s) + \cancel{3/2\,O_2\,(g)}$	$\Delta G^0 = +742.2\text{ kJ}$
$3\,CO\,(g) + \cancel{3/2\,O_2\,(g)} \rightarrow 3\,CO_2\,(g)$	$\Delta G^0 = -771.6\text{ kJ}$
$Fe_2O_3\,(s) + 3\,CO\,(g) \rightarrow 2\,Fe\,(s) + 3\,CO_2\,(g)$	$\Delta G^0_{rxn} = -29.4\text{ kJ}$

64. Since the first reaction has $CaCO_3$ as a product and the reaction of interest has it as a reactant, we need to reverse the first reaction. When the reaction direction is reversed ΔG changes.

$CaCO_3\,(s) \rightarrow Ca\,(s) + CO_2\,(g) + 1/2\,O_2\,(g)$ $\qquad$ $\Delta G^0 = +734.4\text{ kJ}$

Since the second reaction has 2 moles CaO as a product and the reaction of interest has 1 mole of CaO as a product, we need to multiply it by ½. The ΔG the second reaction is multiplied by ½.

$1/2[2\,Ca\,(s) + O_2\,(g) \rightarrow 2\,CaO\,(s)]$ $\qquad\qquad\qquad$ $\Delta G^0 = 1/2(-1206.6\text{ kJ}) = -603.3\text{ kJ}$

Hess' Law states the ΔH of the net reaction is the sum of the ΔH of the steps.
The rewritten reactions are:

$CaCO_3\,(s) \rightarrow \cancel{Ca\,(s)} + CO_2\,(g) + \cancel{1/2\,O_2\,(g)}$	$\Delta G^0 = +734.4\text{ kJ}$
$1/2[\cancel{2\,Ca\,(s)} + \cancel{O_2\,(g)} \rightarrow 2\,CaO\,(s)]$	$\Delta G^0 = -603.3\text{ kJ}$
$CaCO_3\,(s) \rightarrow CaO\,(s) + CO_2\,(g)$	$\Delta G^0_{rxn} = +131.1\text{ kJ}$

65. a) **Given:** $I_2\,(s) \rightarrow I_2\,(g)$ $\qquad$ at 25.0 °C $\qquad\qquad\qquad\qquad\qquad\qquad\qquad$ **Find:** ΔG°_{rxn}

Conceptual plan: $\Delta G^0_{rxn} = \sum n_P \Delta G^0_f(products) - \sum n_R \Delta G^0_f(reactants)$

Solution:

Reactant/Product	ΔG^0_f(kJ/mol from Appendix IIB)
$I_2\,(s)$	0.0
$I_2\,(g)$	19.3

Be sure to pull data for the correct formula and phase.

$\Delta G^0_{rxn} = \sum n_P \Delta G^0_f(products) - \sum n_R \Delta G^0_f(reactants)$

$\qquad = [1(\Delta G^0_f(I_2\,(g))] - [1(\Delta G^0_f(I_2\,(s))]$ $\qquad\qquad$ so the reaction is nonspontaneous.

$\qquad = [1(19.3\text{ kJ})] - [1(0.0\text{ kJ})]$

$\qquad = +19.3\text{ kJ}$

Check: The units (kJ) are correct. The answer is positive because gases have higher free energy than solids and the free energy change of the reaction is the same as free energy of formation of gaseous iodine.

b) **Given:** $I_2\,(s) \rightarrow I_2\,(g)$ at 25.0 °C (i) $P_{I2} = 1.00$ mm Hg; (ii) $P_{I2} = 0.100$ mm Hg $\qquad$ **Find:** ΔG_{rxn}

Conceptual plan: °C $\rightarrow$ K $\quad$ and $\quad$ mm Hg $\rightarrow$ atm $\quad$ then $\Delta G^\circ_{rxn}, P_{I2}, T \rightarrow \Delta G_{rxn}$

$K = 273.15 + °C$ $\qquad$ $\dfrac{1\,\text{atm}}{760\,\text{mm Hg}}$ $\qquad$ $\Delta G_{rxn} = \Delta G^0_{rxn} + RT\ln Q$ where $Q = P_{I_2}$

Solution: $T = 273.15 + 25.0\ °C = 298.2$ K and (i) $1.00\ \cancel{\text{mm Hg}} \times \dfrac{1\,\text{atm}}{760\,\cancel{\text{mm Hg}}} = 0.0013\underline{1}579$ atm $\qquad$ then

$\Delta G_{rxn} = \Delta G^0_{rxn} + RT\ln Q = \Delta G^0_{rxn} + RT\ln P_{I_2} = +19.3\text{ kJ} + \left(8.314\,\dfrac{\cancel{J}}{\cancel{K}\,\text{mol}}\right)\left(\dfrac{1\,\text{kJ}}{1000\,\cancel{J}}\right)(298.2\,\cancel{K})\ln(0.0013\underline{1}579) =$

$= +2.9\text{ kJ}$ so the reaction is nonspontaneous. then (ii) $0.100\ \cancel{\text{mm Hg}} \times \dfrac{1\,\text{atm}}{760\,\cancel{\text{mm Hg}}} = 0.00013\underline{1}579$ atm

then

$\Delta G_{rxn} = \Delta G^0_{rxn} + RT\ln Q = \Delta G^0_{rxn} + RT\ln P_{I_2} = +19.3\text{ kJ} + \left(8.314\,\dfrac{\cancel{J}}{\cancel{K}\,\text{mol}}\right)\left(\dfrac{1\,\text{kJ}}{1000\,\cancel{J}}\right)(298.2\,\cancel{K})\ln(0.00013\underline{1}579) =$

$= -2.9\text{ kJ}$ so the reaction is spontaneous.

Check: The units (kJ) are correct. The answer is positive at high pressures because the pressure is higher than the vapor pressure of iodine. Once the desired pressure is below the vapor pressure (0.31 mm Hg at 25.0 °C), the reaction becomes spontaneous.

c) Iodine sublimes at room temperature because there is an equilibrium between the solid and the gas phases. The vapor pressure is low (0.31 mm Hg at 25.0 °C), so a small amount of iodine can remain in the gas phase, which is consistent with the free energy values.

66. a) **Given**: CH_3OH (*l*) $\rightarrow$ CH_3OH (*g*)　　　at 25.0 °C　　　　　　　　**Find**: $\Delta G°_{rxn}$

Conceptual plan: $\Delta G^0_{rxn} = \sum n_P \Delta G^0_f (products) - \sum n_R \Delta G^0_f (reactants)$

Solution:

Reactant/Product	ΔG^0_f (kJ/mol from Appendix IIB)
CH_3OH (*l*)	-166.6
CH_3OH (*g*)	-162.3

Be sure to pull data for the correct formula and phase.

$\Delta G^0_{rxn} = \sum n_P \Delta G^0_f (products) - \sum n_R \Delta G^0_f (reactants)$

$= [1(\Delta G^0_f (CH_3OH\ (g))] - [1(\Delta G^0_f (CH_3OH\ (l))]$　so the reaction is nonspontaneous.

$= [1(-162.3\ kJ)] - [1(-166.6\ kJ)]$

$= +4.3\ kJ$

Check: The units (kJ) are correct. The answer is positive because gases have higher free energy than liquids.

b) **Given**: CH_3OH (*l*) $\rightarrow$ CH_3OH (*g*) at 25.0 °C (i) P_{CH3OH} = 150.0 mm Hg; (ii) P_{CH3OH} = 100.0 mm Hg and (ii) P_{CH3OH} = 10.0 mm Hg　　　**Find**: ΔG_{rxn}

Conceptual plan: °C $\rightarrow$ K　　and　　mm Hg $\rightarrow$ atm　　then　$\Delta G°_{rxn}$, P_{CH3OH}, T $\rightarrow$　ΔG_{rxn}

$$K = 273.15 + °C \qquad \frac{1\ atm}{760\ mm\ Hg} \qquad \Delta G_{rxn} = \Delta G^0_{rxn} + RT \ln Q \quad where \quad Q = P_{CH3OH}$$

Solution: T = 273.15 + 25.0 °C = 298.2 K and (i) 150.0 mm Hg x $\dfrac{1\ atm}{760\ mm\ Hg}$ = 0.197\underline{3}684 atm　　then

$\Delta G_{rxn} = \Delta G^0_{rxn} + RT \ln Q = \Delta G^0_{rxn} + RT \ln P_{CH3OH} = +4.3\ kJ + \left(8.314\ \dfrac{J}{K\ mol} \right) \left(\dfrac{1\ kJ}{1000\ J} \right) (298.2\ K) \ln (0.197\underline{3}684) =$

$= +0.3\ kJ$ so the reaction is nonspontaneous. then (ii) 100.0 mm Hg x $\dfrac{1\ atm}{760\ mm\ Hg}$ = 0.131\underline{5}79 atm　　then

$\Delta G_{rxn} = \Delta G^0_{rxn} + RT \ln Q = \Delta G^0_{rxn} + RT \ln P_{CH3OH} = +4.3\ kJ + \left(8.314\ \dfrac{J}{K\ mol} \right) \left(\dfrac{1\ kJ}{1000\ J} \right) (298.2\ K) \ln (0.131\underline{5}79) =$

$= -0.7\ kJ$ so the reaction is spontaneous. then (iii) 10.0 mm Hg x $\dfrac{1\ atm}{760\ mm\ Hg}$ = 0.0131\underline{5}79 atm　　then

$\Delta G_{rxn} = \Delta G^0_{rxn} + RT \ln Q = \Delta G^0_{rxn} + RT \ln P_{CH3OH} = +4.3\ kJ + \left(8.314\ \dfrac{J}{K\ mol} \right) \left(\dfrac{1\ kJ}{1000\ J} \right) (298.2\ K) \ln (0.0131\underline{5}79) =$

$= -6.4\ kJ$ so the reaction is spontaneous.

Check: The units (kJ) are correct. The answer is positive at high pressures because the pressure is higher than the vapor pressure of methanol. Once the desired pressure is below the vapor pressure (143 mm Hg at 25.0 °C), the reaction becomes spontaneous.

c) Methanol evaporates at room temperature because there is an equilibrium between the liquid and the gas phases. The vapor pressure is moderate (143 mm Hg at 25.0 °C), so a moderate amount of methanol can remain in the gas phase, which is consistent with the free energy values.

67. **Given:** $CH_3OH\ (g) \rightleftharpoons CO\ (g) + 2\ H_2\ (g)$ at 25 °C, $P_{CH3OH} = 0.855$ atm, $P_{CO} = 0.125$ atm, $P_{H2} = 0.183$ atm
   Find: ΔG
   Conceptual plan:

   $\Delta G^0_{rxn} = \sum n_P \Delta G^0_f (products) - \sum n_R \Delta G^0_f (reactants)$ **then** °C$\rightarrow$ K **then** ΔG°_{rxn}, P_{CH3OH}, P_{CO}, P_{H2}, T $\rightarrow \Delta G$

   $K = 273.15 + °C \quad \Delta G_{rxn} = \Delta G^0_{rxn} + RT \ln Q \quad$ where $Q = \dfrac{P_{CO} P^2_{H2}}{P_{CH3OH}}$

   Solution:

Reactant/Product	ΔG^0_f (kJ/mol from Appendix IIB)
$CH_3OH\ (g)$	-162.3
$CO\ (g)$	-137.2
$H_2\ (g)$	0.0

   B

   Be sure to pull data for the correct formula and phase.

   $\Delta G^0_{rxn} = \sum n_P \Delta G^0_f (products) - \sum n_R \Delta G^0_f (reactants)$

   $= [1(\Delta G^0_f (CO\ (g)) + 2(\Delta G^0_f (H_2\ (g))] - [1(\Delta G^0_f (CH_3OH\ (g))]$

   $= [1(-137.2\ kJ) + 2(0.0\ kJ)] - [1(-162.3\ kJ)] \qquad\qquad$ T = 273.15 + 25 °C = 298 K then

   $= [-137.2\ kJ] - [-162.3\ kJ]$

   $= + 25.1\ kJ$

   $Q = \dfrac{P_{CO} P^2_{H2}}{P_{CH3OH}} = \dfrac{(0.125)(0.183)^2}{0.855} = 0.00489605$ then

   $\Delta G_{rxn} = \Delta G^0_{rxn} + RT \ln Q = +25.1\ kJ + \left(8.314\ \dfrac{J}{K\ mol}\right)\left(\dfrac{1\ kJ}{1000\ J}\right)(298\ K) \ln(0.00489605) = + 11.9\ kJ$

   so the reaction is nonspontaneous.
   Check: The units (kJ) are correct. The standard free energy for the reaction was positive and the fact that Q was less than one made the free energy smaller, but the reaction at these conditions is still not spontaneous.

68. **Given:** $CO_2\ (g) + CCl_4\ (g) \rightleftharpoons 2\ COCl_2\ (g)$ at 25 °C, $P_{CO2} = 0.112$ atm, $P_{CCl4} = 0.174$ atm, $P_{COCl2} = 0.744$ atm   **Find:** ΔG
   Conceptual plan:

   $\Delta G^0_{rxn} = \sum n_P \Delta G^0_f (products) - \sum n_R \Delta G^0_f (reactants)$ **then** °C$\rightarrow$K **then** ΔG°_{rxn}, P_{CO2}, P_{CCl4}, P_{COCl2}, T $\rightarrow \Delta G$

   $K = 273.15 + °C \quad \Delta G_{rxn} = \Delta G^0_{rxn} + RT \ln Q \quad$ where $Q = \dfrac{P^2_{COCl2}}{P_{CO2} P_{CCl4}}$

   Solution:

Reactant/Product	ΔG^0_f (kJ/mol from Appendix IIB)
$CO_2\ (g)$	-394.4
$CCl_4\ (g)$	-62.3
$COCl_2\ (g)$	-204.9

   Be sure to pull data for the correct formula and phase.

   $\Delta G^0_{rxn} = \sum n_P \Delta G^0_f (products) - \sum n_R \Delta G^0_f (reactants)$

   $= [2(\Delta G^0_f (COCl_2\ (g))] - [1(\Delta G^0_f (CO_2\ (g)) + 1(\Delta G^0_f (CCl_4\ (g))]$

   $= [2(-204.9\ kJ)] - [1(-394.4\ kJ) + 1(-62.3\ kJ)] \qquad\qquad$ T = 273.15 + 25 °C = 298 K then

   $= [-409.8\ kJ] - [-456.7\ kJ]$

   $= + 46.9\ kJ$

   $Q = \dfrac{P^2_{COCl2}}{P_{CO2} P_{CCl4}} = \dfrac{(0.744)^2}{(0.112)(0.174)} = 28.4039$ then

   $\Delta G_{rxn} = \Delta G^0_{rxn} + RT \ln Q = +46.9\ kJ + \left(8.314\ \dfrac{J}{K\ mol}\right)\left(\dfrac{1\ kJ}{1000\ J}\right)(298\ K) \ln(28.4039) = + 55.2\ kJ$

   so the reaction is nonspontaneous.
   Check: The units (kJ) are correct. The standard free energy for the reaction was positive and the fact that Q was greater than one made the free energy larger, so the reaction is less spontaneous in the forward direction at these conditions than at standard conditions.

69. a) **Given:** $2 CO\,(g) + O_2\,(g) \rightleftharpoons 2 CO_2\,(g)$ at 25 °C   **Find:** K

   Conceptual plan: $\Delta G^0_{rxn} = \sum n_P \Delta G^0_f (products) - \sum n_R \Delta G^0_f (reactants)$ **then** °C $\rightarrow$ K **then** $\Delta G°_{rxn}$, T $\rightarrow$ K

$$K = 273.15 + °C \qquad \Delta G^0_{rxn} = -RT \ln K$$

   Solution:

Reactant/Product	ΔG^0_f (kJ/mol from Appendix IIB)
CO (g)	− 137.2
O_2 (g)	0.0
CO_2 (g)	− 394.4

Be sure to pull data for the correct formula and phase.

$\Delta G^0_{rxn} = \sum n_P \Delta G^0_f (products) - \sum n_R \Delta G^0_f (reactants)$

$\quad = [2(\Delta G^0_f(CO_2\,(g)))] - [2(\Delta G^0_f(CO\,(g))) + 1(\Delta G^0_f(O_2\,(g)))]$

$\quad = [2(-394.4\ kJ)] - [2(-137.2\ kJ) + 1(0.0\ kJ)]$ $T = 273.15 + 25\ °C = 298\ K$ then

$\quad = [-788.8\ kJ] - [-274.4\ kJ]$

$\quad = -514.4\ kJ$

$\Delta G^0_{rxn} = -RT \ln K$

Rearrange to solve for K. $K = e^{\frac{-\Delta G^0_{rxn}}{RT}} = e^{\frac{-(-514.4\ \cancel{kJ}) \times \frac{1000\ \cancel{J}}{1\ \cancel{kJ}}}{\left(8.314\ \frac{\cancel{J}}{K\ mol}\right)(298\ \cancel{K})}} = e^{207.623} = 1.48 \times 10^{90}$.

Check: The units (none) are correct. The standard free energy for the reaction was very negative and so we expect a very large K. The reaction is spontaneous and so mostly products are present at equilibrium.

   b) **Given:** $2 H_2S\,(g) \rightleftharpoons 2 H_2\,(g) + S_2\,(g)$ at 25 °C   **Find:** K

   Conceptual plan: $\Delta G^0_{rxn} = \sum n_P \Delta G^0_f (products) - \sum n_R \Delta G^0_f (reactants)$ **then** °C $\rightarrow$ K **then** $\Delta G°_{rxn}$, T $\rightarrow$ K

$$K = 273.15 + °C \qquad \Delta G^0_{rxn} = -RT \ln K$$

   Solution:

Reactant/Product	ΔG^0_f (kJ/mol from Appendix IIB)
H_2S (g)	− 33.4
H_2 (g)	0.0
S_2 (g)	79.7

Be sure to pull data for the correct formula and phase.

$\Delta G^0_{rxn} = \sum n_P \Delta G^0_f (products) - \sum n_R \Delta G^0_f (reactants)$

$\quad = [2(\Delta G^0_f(H_2\,(g))) + 1(\Delta G^0_f(S_2\,(g)))] - [2(\Delta G^0_f(H_2S\,(g)))]$

$\quad = [2(0.0\ kJ)] + 1(79.7\ kJ)] - [2(-33.4\ kJ)]$ $T = 273.15 + 25\ °C = 298\ K$ then

$\quad = [79.7\ kJ] - [-66.8\ kJ]$

$\quad = +146.5\ kJ$

$\Delta G^0_{rxn} = -RT \ln K$

Rearrange to solve for K. $K = e^{\frac{-\Delta G^0_{rxn}}{RT}} = e^{\frac{-146.5\ \cancel{kJ} \times \frac{1000\ \cancel{J}}{1\ \cancel{kJ}}}{\left(8.314\ \frac{\cancel{J}}{K\ mol}\right)(298\ \cancel{K})}} = e^{-59.1305} = 2.09 \times 10^{-26}$.

Check: The units (none) are correct. The standard free energy for the reaction was positive and so we expect a small K. The reaction is nonspontaneous and so mostly reactants are present at equilibrium.

70. a) **Given:** $2 NO_2\,(g) \rightleftharpoons N_2O_4\,(g)$ at 25 °C   **Find:** K

   Conceptual plan: $\Delta G^0_{rxn} = \sum n_P \Delta G^0_f (products) - \sum n_R \Delta G^0_f (reactants)$ **then** °C $\rightarrow$ K **then** $\Delta G°_{rxn}$, T $\rightarrow$ K

$$K = 273.15 + °C \qquad \Delta G^0_{rxn} = -RT \ln K$$

   Solution:

Reactant/Product	ΔG_f^0(kJ/mol from Appendix IIB)
NO_2 (g)	51.3
N_2O_4 (g)	99.8

Be sure to pull data for the correct formula and phase.

$$\Delta G_{rxn}^0 = \sum n_P \Delta G_f^0(products) - \sum n_R \Delta G_f^0(reactants)$$
$$= [1(\Delta G_f^0(N_2O_4\ (g))] - [2(\Delta G_f^0(NO_2\ (g))]$$
$$= [1(99.8\ kJ)] - [2(51.3\ kJ)] \qquad\qquad T = 273.15 + 25\ °C = 298\ K \text{ then } \Delta G_{rxn}^0 = -RT \ln K$$
$$= [99.8\ kJ] - [102.6\ kJ]$$
$$= -2.8\ kJ$$

Rearrange to solve for K. $K = e^{\frac{-\Delta G_{rxn}^0}{RT}} = e^{\left(\frac{-(-2.8\ kJ)\ \times \frac{1000\ J}{1\ kJ}}{\left(8.314 \frac{J}{K\ mol}\right)(298\ K)}\right)} = e^{1.1301} = 3.1$.

Check: The units (none) are correct. The standard free energy for the reaction was very slightly negative and so we expect a K just over 1. The reaction is spontaneous and so mostly products are present at equilibrium.

b) **Given:** Br_2 (g) + Cl_2 (g) $\rightleftharpoons$ 2 BrCl (g) at 25 °C **Find: K**

Conceptual plan: $\Delta G_{rxn}^0 = \sum n_P \Delta G_f^0(products) - \sum n_R \Delta G_f^0(reactants)$ **then °C → K then $\Delta G°_{rxn}$, T → K**

$$K = 273.15 + °C \qquad \Delta G_{rxn}^0 = -RT \ln K$$

Solution:

Reactant/Product	ΔG_f^0(kJ/mol from Appendix IIB)
Br_2 (g)	3.1
Cl_2 (g)	0.0
BrCl (g)	−1.0

Be sure to pull data for the correct formula and phase.

$$\Delta G_{rxn}^0 = \sum n_P \Delta G_f^0(products) - \sum n_R \Delta G_f^0(reactants)$$
$$= [2(\Delta G_f^0(BrCl\ (g))] - [1(\Delta G_f^0(Br_2\ (g)) + 1(\Delta G_f^0(Cl_2\ (g))]$$
$$= [2(-1.0\ kJ)] - [1(3.1\ kJ) + 1(0.0\ kJ)] \qquad\qquad T = 273.15 + 25\ °C = 298\ K \text{ then}$$
$$= [-2.0\ kJ] - [3.1\ kJ]$$
$$= -5.1\ kJ$$

$\Delta G_{rxn}^0 = -RT \ln K$

Rearrange to solve for K. $K = e^{\frac{-\Delta G_{rxn}^0}{RT}} = e^{\left(\frac{-(-5.1\ kJ)\ \times \frac{1000\ J}{1\ kJ}}{\left(8.314 \frac{J}{K\ mol}\right)(298\ K)}\right)} = e^{2.0585} = 7.8$.

Check: The units (none) are correct. The standard free energy for the reaction was very slightly negative and so we expect a K just over 1. The reaction is spontaneous.

71. a) **Given:** CO (g) + 2 H_2 (g) $\rightleftharpoons$ CH_3OH (g) K_p = 2.26 x 10^4 at 25 °C

Find: $\Delta G°_{rxn}$ at a)standard conditions, b)at equilibrium, and c)P_{CH3OH} = 1.0 atm, P_{CO} = P_{H2} = 0.010 atm

Conceptual plan: °C → K then a) K, T → $\Delta G°_{rxn}$ then b) at equilibrium ΔG_{rxn} = 0 then

$$K = 273.15 + °C \qquad \Delta G_{rxn}^0 = -RT \ln K$$

c) $\Delta G°_{rxn}$, P_{CH3OH}, P_{CO}, P_{H2}, T → ΔG

$$\Delta G_{rxn} = \Delta G_{rxn}^0 + RT \ln Q \quad \text{where } Q = \frac{P_{CH3OH}}{P_{CO} P_{H2}^2}$$

Solution: T = 273.15 + 25 °C = 298 K then

a) $\Delta G_{rxn}^0 = -RT \ln K = -\left(8.314 \frac{J}{K\ mol}\right)\left(\frac{1\ kJ}{1000\ J}\right)(298\ K) \ln(2.26 \times 10^4) = -24.8\ kJ$;

652

b) at equilibrium $\Delta G_{rxn} = 0$

c) $Q = \dfrac{P_{CH3OH}}{P_{CO}P_{H2}^2} = \dfrac{1.0}{(0.010)(0.010)^2} = 1.0 \times 10^6$ then

$$\Delta G_{rxn} = \Delta G_{rxn}^0 + RT\ln Q = -24.8 \text{ kJ} + \left(8.314\dfrac{\text{J}}{\text{K mol}}\right)\left(\dfrac{1\text{ kJ}}{1000\text{ J}}\right)(298\text{ K})\ln(1.0 \times 10^6) = +9.4 \text{ kJ}$$

Check: The units (kJ) are correct. The K was greater than one so we expect a negative standard free energy for the reaction. At equilibrium, by definition, the free energy change is zero. Since the conditions give a Q > K then the reactions needs to proceed in the reverse direction, which means that the reaction is spontaneous in the reverse direction.

72. **Given:** $I_2 (g) + Cl_2 (g) \rightleftharpoons 2\ ICl\ (g)$ $K_p = 81.9$ at 25 °C   **Find:** ΔG°_{rxn} at a) standard conditions,
b) at equilibrium, and c) $P_{ICl} = 2.55$ atm, $P_{I2} = 0.325$ atm, $P_{Cl2} = 0.221$ atm
Conceptual plan: °C → K then a) K, T → ΔG°_{rxn} then b) at equilibrium $\Delta G_{rxn} = 0$ then

$$K = 273.15 + °C \qquad\qquad \Delta G_{rxn}^0 = -RT\ln K$$

c) **$\Delta G^\circ_{rxn}, P_{ICl}, P_{I2}, P_{Cl2}, T$ → ΔG**

$\Delta G_{rxn} = \Delta G_{rxn}^0 + RT\ln Q$ where $Q = \dfrac{P_{ICl}^2}{P_{I2}P_{Cl2}}$

Solution: T = 273.15 + 25 °C = 298 K then

a) $\Delta G_{rxn}^0 = -RT\ln K = -\left(8.314\dfrac{\text{J}}{\text{K mol}}\right)\left(\dfrac{1\text{ kJ}}{1000\text{ J}}\right)(298\text{ K})\ln(81.9) = -10.9 \text{ kJ}$;

b) at equilibrium $\Delta G_{rxn} = 0$

c) $Q = \dfrac{P_{ICl}^2}{P_{I2}P_{Cl2}} = \dfrac{(2.55)^2}{(0.325)(0.221)} = 90.\underline{5}325$ then

$$\Delta G_{rxn} = \Delta G_{rxn}^0 + RT\ln Q = -10.9 \text{ kJ} + \left(8.314\dfrac{\text{J}}{\text{K mol}}\right)\left(\dfrac{1\text{ kJ}}{1000\text{ J}}\right)(298\text{ K})\ln(90.\underline{5}325) = +0.3 \text{ kJ}$$

Check: The units (kJ) are correct. The K was greater than one so we expect a negative standard free energy for the reaction. At equilibrium, by definition, the free energy change is zero. Since the conditions give a Q just greater than K then the reactions needs to proceed in the reverse direction, which means that the reaction is slightly spontaneous.

73. a) **Given:** $2\ CO\ (g) + O_2\ (g) \rightleftharpoons 2\ CO_2\ (g)$ at 25 °C   **Find:** K at 525 K
Conceptual plan: $\Delta H_{rxn}^0 = \sum n_p \Delta H_f^\circ(products) - \sum n_R \Delta H_f^\circ(reactants)$ **then**

$\Delta S_{rxn}^0 = \sum n_p S^\circ(products) - \sum n_r S^\circ(reactants)$ **then J/K → kJ/K   then $\Delta H^\circ_{rxn}, \Delta S_{rxn}, T$ → ΔG**

$$\dfrac{1\text{ kJ}}{1000\text{ J}} \qquad\qquad \Delta G = \Delta H_{rxn} - T\Delta S_{rxn}$$

then $\Delta G^\circ_{rxn}, T$ → K

$\Delta G_{rxn}^0 = -RT\ln K$

Solution:

Reactant/Product	ΔH_f^0(kJ/mol from Appendix IIB)
CO (g)	−110.5
O_2 (g)	0.0
CO_2 (g)	−393.5

Be sure to pull data for the correct formula and phase.

$$\Delta H^0_{rxn} = \sum n_P \Delta H^0_f(products) - \sum n_R \Delta H^0_f(reactants)$$

$$= [2(\Delta H^0_f(CO_2\ (g))] - [2(\Delta H^0_f(CO\ (g)) + 1(\Delta H^0_f(O_2\ (g))]$$

$$= [2(-393.5\ kJ)] - [2(-110.5\ kJ) + 1(0.0\ kJ)] \qquad then$$

$$= [-787.0\ kJ] - [-221.0\ kJ]$$

$$= -566.0\ kJ$$

Reactant/Product	S^0 (J/mol K from Appendix IIB)
CO (g)	197.7
O$_2$ (g)	205.2
CO$_2$ (g)	213.8

Be sure to pull data for the correct formula and phase.

$$\Delta S^0_{rxn} = \sum n_P S^0(products) - \sum n_R S^0(reactants)$$

$$= [2(S^0(CO_2\ (g))] - [2(S^0(CO\ (g)) + 1(S^0(O_2\ (g))]$$

$$= [2(213.8\ J/mol\ K)] - [2(197.7\ J/mol\ K) + 1(205.2\ J/mol\ K)] \quad then \quad -173.0\ \frac{J}{K} \times \frac{1\ kJ}{1000\ J} = -0.1730\ \frac{kJ}{K}$$

$$= [427.6\ J/K] - [600.6\ J/K]$$

$$= -173.0\ J/K$$

then $\quad \Delta G^0 = \Delta H^0_{rxn} - T\Delta S^0_{rxn} = -566.0\ kJ - (525\ K)\left(-0.1730\ \frac{kJ}{K}\right) = -475.2\ kJ = -4.752 \times 10^5\ J \qquad then$

$\Delta G^0_{rxn} = -RT \ln K$ Rearrange to solve for K.

$$K = e^{\frac{-\Delta G^0_{rxn}}{RT}} = e^{\frac{-(-4.752 \times 10^5\ J)}{\left(8.314\ \frac{J}{K\ mol}\right)(525\ K)}} = e^{108.864} = 1.90 \times 10^{47}\ .$$

Check: The units (none) are correct. The free energy change is very negative, indicating a spontaneous reaction. This results in a very large K.

b) **Given:** $2\ H_2S\ (g) \rightleftharpoons 2\ H_2\ (g) + S_2\ (g)$ at 25 °C $\qquad$ **Find:** K at 525 K

Conceptual plan: $\Delta H^0_{rxn} = \sum n_P \Delta H^0_f(products) - \sum n_R \Delta H^0_f(reactants)$ **then**

$\Delta S^0_{rxn} = \sum n_P S^0(products) - \sum n_R S^0(reactants)$ **then** J/K $\rightarrow$ kJ/K **then** $\Delta H°_{rxn}, \Delta S_{rxn}, T \rightarrow \Delta G$

$$\frac{1\ kJ}{1000\ J} \qquad\qquad \Delta G = \Delta H_{rxn} - T\Delta S_{rxn}$$

then $\Delta G°_{rxn}, T \rightarrow$ K

$$\Delta G^0_{rxn} = -RT \ln K$$

Solution:

Reactant/Product	ΔH^0_f (kJ/mol from Appendix IIB)
H$_2$S (g)	-20.6
H$_2$ (g)	0.0
S$_2$ (g)	128.6

Be sure to pull data for the correct formula and phase.

$$\Delta H^0_{rxn} = \sum n_P \Delta H^0_f(products) - \sum n_R \Delta H^0_f(reactants)$$

$$= [2(\Delta H^0_f(H_2\ (g)) + 1(\Delta H^0_f(S_2\ (g))] - [2(\Delta H^0_f(H_2S\ (g))]$$

$$= [2(0.0\ kJ) + 1(128.6\ kJ)] - [2(-20.6\ kJ)] \qquad then$$

$$= [128.6\ kJ] - [-41.2\ kJ]$$

$$= +169.8\ kJ$$

Reactant/Product	S^0 (J/mol K from Appendix IIB)
H$_2$S (g)	205.8
H$_2$ (g)	130.7
S$_2$ (g)	228.2

Be sure to pull data for the correct formula and phase.

$$\Delta S^0_{rxn} = \sum n_P S^0(products) - \sum n_R S^0(reactants)$$

$$= [2(S^0(\text{H}_2\ (g)) + 1(S^0(\text{S}_2\ (g))] - [2(S^0(\text{H}_2\text{S}\ (g))\ ]$$

$$= [2(130.7\ \text{J/mol K}) + 1(228.2\ \text{J/mol K})] - [2(205.8\ \text{J/mol K})] \qquad \text{then} \quad +78.0\ \frac{\text{J}}{\text{K}} \times \frac{1\ \text{kJ}}{1000\ \text{J}} = +0.0780\ \frac{\text{kJ}}{\text{K}}$$

$$= [489.6\ \text{J/K}] - [411.6\ \text{J/K}]$$

$$= +78.0\ \text{J/K}$$

then

$$\Delta G^0 = \Delta H^0_{rxn} - T\Delta S^0_{rxn} = +169.8\ \text{kJ} - (525\ \text{K})\left(+0.0780\ \frac{\text{kJ}}{\text{K}}\right) = +128.\underline{8}5\ \text{kJ} = +1.28\underline{8}5 \times 10^5\ \text{J} \qquad \text{then}$$

$$\Delta G^0_{rxn} = -RT\ln K \qquad \text{Rearrange to solve for K.}$$

$$K = e^{\frac{-\Delta G^0_{rxn}}{RT}} = e^{\frac{-1.28\underline{8}5 \times 10^5\ \text{J}}{\left(8.314\frac{\text{J}}{\text{K mol}}\right)(525\ \text{K})}} = e^{-29.\underline{5}199} = 1.51 \times 10^{-13}.$$

Check: The units (none) are correct. The free energy change is positive, indicating a nonspontaneous reaction. This results in a very small K.

74. a) **Given:** $2\ \text{NO}_2\ (g) \rightleftharpoons \text{N}_2\text{O}_4\ (g)$ at 25 °C **Find:** K at 655 K

Conceptual plan: $\Delta H^0_{rxn} = \sum n_P \Delta H^0_f(products) - \sum n_R \Delta H^0_f(reactants)$ **then**

$\Delta S^0_{rxn} = \sum n_P S^0(products) - \sum n_R S^0(reactants)$ **then** J/K → kJ/K **then** **ΔH°$_{rxn}$, ΔS$_{rxn}$, T → ΔG**

$$\frac{1\text{kJ}}{1000\ \text{J}} \qquad\qquad \Delta G = \Delta H_{rxn} - T\Delta S_{rxn}$$

then ΔG°$_{rxn}$, T → K

$$\Delta G^0_{rxn} = -RT\ln K$$

Solution:

Reactant/Product	ΔH^0_f(kJ/mol from Appendix IIB)
$\text{NO}_2\ (g)$	33.2
$\text{N}_2\text{O}_4\ (g)$	11.1

Be sure to pull data for the correct formula and phase.

$$\Delta H^0_{rxn} = \sum n_P \Delta H^0_f(products) - \sum n_R \Delta H^0_f(reactants)$$

$$= [1(\Delta H^0_f(\text{N}_2\text{O}_4\ (g))] - [2(\Delta H^0_f(\text{NO}_2\ (g))]$$

$$= [1(11.1\ \text{kJ})] - [2(33.2\ \text{kJ})] \qquad \text{then}$$

$$= [11.1\ \text{kJ}] - [66.4\ \text{kJ}]$$

$$= -55.3\ \text{kJ}$$

Reactant/Product	S^0 (J/mol K from Appendix IIB)
$\text{NO}_2\ (g)$	240.1
$\text{N}_2\text{O}_4\ (g)$	304.4

Be sure to pull data for the correct formula and phase.

$$\Delta S^0_{rxn} = \sum n_P S^0(products) - \sum n_R S^0(reactants)$$

$$= [1(S^0(\text{N}_2\text{O}_4\ (g))] - [2(S^0(\text{NO}_2\ (g))]$$

$$= [1(304.4\ \text{J/mol K})] - [2(240.1\ \text{J/mol K})] \quad \text{then} \quad -175.8\ \frac{\text{J}}{\text{K}} \times \frac{1\ \text{kJ}}{1000\ \text{J}} = -0.1758\ \frac{\text{kJ}}{\text{K}} \quad \text{then}$$

$$= [304.4\ \text{J/K}] - [480.2\ \text{J/K}]$$

$$= -175.8\ \text{J/K}$$

$$\Delta G^0 = \Delta H^0_{rxn} - T\Delta S^0_{rxn} = -55.3\ \text{kJ} - (655\ \text{K})\left(-0.1758\ \frac{\text{kJ}}{\text{K}}\right) = +59.\underline{8}\ \text{kJ} = +5.9\underline{8}49 \times 10^4\ \text{J} \quad \text{then}$$

$$\Delta G^0_{rxn} = -RT\ln K \text{ Rearrange to solve for K. } K = e^{\frac{-\Delta G^0_{rxn}}{RT}} = e^{\frac{-5.9\underline{8}49 \times 10^4\ \text{J}}{\left(8.314\frac{\text{J}}{\text{K mol}}\right)(655\ \text{K})}} = e^{-10.\underline{9}902} = 1.69 \times 10^{-5}.$$

Check: The units (none) are correct. The free energy change is positive, indicating a nonspontaneous reaction. This results on a very K.

b) **Given:** $Br_2\ (g) + Cl_2\ (g) \rightleftharpoons 2\ BrCl\ (g)$ at 25 °C   **Find:** K at 655 K

Conceptual plan: $\Delta H^0_{rxn} = \sum n_p \Delta H^0_f (products) - \sum n_r \Delta H^0_f (reactants)$ **then**

$\Delta S^0_{rxn} = \sum n_p S^0 (products) - \sum n_r S^0 (reactants)$ **then** **J/K** → **kJ/K** **then** $\Delta H^\circ_{rxn}, \Delta S_{rxn}, T$ → **ΔG**

$$\frac{1\,kJ}{1000\,J}$$ $\Delta G = \Delta H_{rxn} - T\Delta S_{rxn}$

then $\Delta G^\circ_{rxn}, T$ → **K**

$\Delta G^0_{rxn} = -RT\ln K$

Solution:

Reactant/Product	ΔH^0_f(kJ/mol from Appendix IIB)
$Br_2\ (g)$	30.9
$Cl_2\ (g)$	0.0
$BrCl\ (g)$	14.6

Be sure to pull data for the correct formula and phase.

$\Delta H^0_{rxn} = \sum n_p \Delta H^0_f (products) - \sum n_R \Delta H^0_f (reactants)$

$= [2(\Delta H^0_f (BrCl\ (g)))] - [1(\Delta H^0_f (Br_2\ (g)) + 1(\Delta H^0_f (Cl_2\ (g))]$

$= [2(14.6\ kJ)] - [1(30.9\ kJ) + 1(0.0\ kJ)]$ then

$= [29.2\ kJ] - [30.9\ kJ]$

$= -1.7\ kJ$

Reactant/Product	S^0(J/mol K from Appendix IIB)
$Br_2\ (g)$	245.5
$Cl_2\ (g)$	223.1
$BrCl\ (g)$	240.0

Be sure to pull data for the correct formula and phase.

$\Delta S^0_{rxn} = \sum n_p S^0 (products) - \sum n_R S^0 (reactants)$

$= [2(S^0 (BrCl\ (g)))] - [1(S^0 (Br_2\ (g)) + 1(S^0 (Cl_2\ (g))]$

$= [2(240.0\ J/mol\ K)] - [1(245.5\ J/mol\ K) + 1(223.1\ J/mol\ K)]$ then $+11.4\ \frac{\cancel{J}}{K} \times \frac{1\,kJ}{1000\,\cancel{J}} = +0.0114\ \frac{kJ}{K}$

$= [480.0\ J/K] - [468.6\ J/K]$

$= +11.4\ J/K$

then $\Delta G^0 = \Delta H^0_{rxn} - T\Delta S^0_{rxn} = -1.7\ kJ - (655\ \cancel{K})\left(+0.0114\ \frac{kJ}{\cancel{K}}\right) = -9.\underline{1}67\ kJ = -9.\underline{1}67 \times 10^3\ J$ then

$\Delta G^0_{rxn} = -RT\ln K$ Rearrange to solve for K. $K = e^{\frac{-\Delta G^0_{rxn}}{RT}} = e^{\left(\dfrac{-9.\underline{1}67 \times 10^3\ \cancel{J}}{\left(8.314\frac{\cancel{J}}{\cancel{K}\,mol}\right)(655\ \cancel{K})}\right)} = e^{-1.\underline{6}834} = 0.19$.

Check: The units (none) are correct.   The free energy change is positive, indicating a nonspontaneous reaction. This results on a small K.

75. **Given:** table of K_p versus temperature   **Find:** $\Delta H^\circ_{rxn}, \Delta S^\circ_{rxn}$
Conceptual Plan: Plot ln K verus 1/T. The slope will be -ΔH°_{rxn}/R and the intercept will be ΔS°_{rxn}/R.
Solution: Plot ln K verus 1/T.   Since

$ln\ K = -\dfrac{\Delta H^0_{rxn}}{R}\dfrac{1}{T} + \dfrac{\Delta S^0_{rxn}}{R}$, the negative of the

slope will be $-\dfrac{\Delta H^0_{rxn}}{R}$ and the intercept will be

$\dfrac{\Delta S^0_{rxn}}{R}$.   The slope can be determined by

measuring $\Delta y/\Delta x$ on the plot or by using functions, such as "add trendline" in Excel. Since the slope is $-6092.2\ K^{-1}$,

$y = -6092.2x + 27.136$

656

$$\Delta H^0_{rxn} = -\,slope\ R = -\left(\dfrac{-6092.2}{K}\right)\left(8.314\dfrac{\cancel{J}}{K\ mol}\right)\left(\dfrac{1\ kJ}{1000\ \cancel{J}}\right) = 50.\underline{6}1\ \dfrac{kJ}{mol} = 50.6\ \dfrac{kJ}{mol}\ .$$ Since the intercept is

27.$\underline{1}$36, $\Delta S^0_{rxn} =\ intercept\ R = \left(\dfrac{27.\underline{1}36}{K}\right)\left(8.314\dfrac{\cancel{J}}{K\ mol}\right) = 22\underline{5}.609\ \dfrac{J}{K} = 226\ \dfrac{J}{K}\ .$

Check: The units are correct (kJ/mole and J/K). The plot is very linear. The numbers are typical for reactions. Since the slope is negative, the enthalpy change must be positive.

76. **Given:** table of K_p versus temperature **Find:** $\Delta H°_{rxn}$, $\Delta S°_{rxn}$
 Conceptual Plan: Plot ln K verus 1/T. The slope will be -$\Delta H°_{rxn}$/R and the intercept will be $\Delta S°_{rxn}$/R.
 Solution: Plot ln K verus 1/T. Since

$ln\ K = -\dfrac{\Delta H^0_{rxn}}{R}\dfrac{1}{T} + \dfrac{\Delta S^0_{rxn}}{R}$, the negative of the slope will

be $-\dfrac{\Delta H^0_{rxn}}{R}$ and the intercept will be $\dfrac{\Delta S^0_{rxn}}{R}$. The slope

can be determined by measuring $\Delta y/\Delta x$ on the plot or by using functions, such as "add trendline" in Excel. Since the slope is $-13\underline{7}04\ K^{-1}$,

$\Delta H^0_{rxn} = -\,slope\ R =$

$= -\left(\dfrac{-13\underline{7}04}{K}\right)\left(8.314\dfrac{\cancel{J}}{K\ mol}\right)\left(\dfrac{1\ kJ}{1000\ \cancel{J}}\right) = \ .$

$= 11\underline{3}.935\ \dfrac{kJ}{mol} = 114\ \dfrac{kJ}{mol}$

Since the intercept is 75.$\underline{0}$42, $\Delta S^0_{rxn} =\ intercept\ R = \left(\dfrac{75.\underline{0}42}{K}\right)\left(8.314\dfrac{\cancel{J}}{K\ mol}\right) = 62\underline{3}.899\ \dfrac{J}{K} = 624\ \dfrac{J}{K}\ .$

Check: The units are correct (kJ/mole and J/K). The plot is very linear. The numbers are typical for reactions. Since the slope is negative, the enthalpy change must be positive.

77. a) +, since vapors have higher entropy than liquids.

 b) –, since solids have less entropy than liquids.

 c) –, since there is only one microstate for the final macrostate and there are six microstates for the initial macrostate.

78. a) +, since vapors have higher entropy than solids.

 b) –, since liquids have less entropy than vapors.

 c) +, since there are twenty microstates for the final macrostate and there are only six microstates for the initial macrostate.

79. a) **Given:** $N_2\ (g) + O_2\ (g) \rightarrow 2\ NO\ (g)$ **Find:** $\Delta G°_{rxn}$, and K_p at 25 °C
 Conceptual plan: $\Delta H^0_{rxn} = \sum n_p \Delta H^0_f (products) - \sum n_r \Delta H^0_f (reactants)$ **then**
  $\Delta S^0_{rxn} = \sum n_p S^0 (products) - \sum n_r S^0 (reactants)$ **then** °C → K **then** J/K → kJ/K **then** $\Delta H°_{rxn}$, ΔS_{rxn}, T → ΔG

 $$K = 273.15 + °C \qquad \dfrac{1\ kJ}{1000\ J} \qquad \Delta G = \Delta H_{rxn} - T\Delta S_{rxn}$$

 then $\Delta G°_{rxn}$, T → K
  $\Delta G^0_{rxn} = -\,RT\ ln\ K$

 Solution:

Reactant/Product	ΔH^0_f (kJ/mol from Appendix IIB)
$N_2\ (g)$	0.0
$O_2\ (g)$	0.0
$NO\ (g)$	91.3

 Be sure to pull data for the correct formula and phase.

$$\Delta H^0_{rxn} = \sum n_P \Delta H^0_f(products) - \sum n_R \Delta H^0_f(reactants)$$

$$= [2(\Delta H^0_f(NO\ (g))] - [1(\Delta H^0_f(N_2\ (g)) + 1(\Delta H^0_f(O_2\ (g))]$$

$$= [2(91.3\ kJ)] - [1(0.0\ kJ) + 1(0.0\ kJ)] \qquad \text{then}$$

$$= [182.6\ kJ] - [0.0\ kJ]$$

$$= +182.6\ kJ$$

Reactant/Product	S^0 (J/mol K from Appendix IIB)
N_2 (g)	191.6
O_2 (g)	205.2
NO (g)	210.8

Be sure to pull data for the correct formula and phase.

$$\Delta S^0_{rxn} = \sum n_P S^0(products) - \sum n_R S^0(reactants)$$

$$= [2(S^0(NO\ (g))] - [1(S^0(N_2\ (g)) + 1(S^0(O_2\ (g))]$$

$$= [2(210.8\ J/mol\ K)] - [1(191.6\ J/mol\ K) + 1(205.2\ J/mol\ K)] \quad \text{then}$$

$$= [421.6\ J/K] - [396.8\ J/K]$$

$$= +24.8\ J/K$$

$$T = 273.15 + 25\ °C = 298\ K \quad \text{then} \quad +24.8\ \frac{J}{K} \times \frac{1\ kJ}{1000\ J} = +0.0248\ \frac{kJ}{K} \quad \text{then}$$

$$\Delta G^0 = \Delta H^0_{rxn} - T\Delta S^0_{rxn} = +182.6\ kJ - (298\ K)\left(0.0248\ \frac{kJ}{K}\right) = +175.2\ kJ = +1.752 \times 10^5\ J \quad \text{then}$$

$$\Delta G^0_{rxn} = -RT \ln K \quad \text{Rearrange to solve for K.}$$

$$K = e^{\frac{-\Delta G^0_{rxn}}{RT}} = e^{\frac{-1.752 \times 10^5\ J}{\left(8.314\frac{J}{K\ mol}\right)(298\ K)}} = e^{-70.7144} = 1.95 \times 10^{-31}\ \text{so the reaction is nonspontaneous and at}$$

equilibrium mostly reactants are present.

Check: The units (kJ and none) are correct. The enthalpy is twice the enthalpy of formation of NO. We expect a very small entropy change because the number of moles of gas is unchanged. Since the positive enthalpy term dominates at room temperature, the free energy change is very positive and the reaction in the forward direction is nonspontaneous. This results in a very small K.

b) **Given:** N_2 (g) + O_2 (g) → 2 NO (g)   **Find:** $\Delta G°_{rxn}$ at 2000 K

Conceptual plan: use results from part a) $\Delta H°_{rxn}, \Delta S_{rxn}, T$ → ΔG then $\Delta G°_{rxn}, T$ → K

$$\Delta G = \Delta H_{rxn} - T\Delta S_{rxn} \qquad\qquad \Delta G^0_{rxn} = -RT \ln K$$

Solution: $\Delta G = \Delta H_{rxn} - T\Delta S_{rxn} = +182.6\ kJ - (2000\ K)\left(0.0248\ \frac{kJ}{K}\right) = +133.0\ kJ = +1.330 \times 10^5\ J$ then

$\Delta G^0_{rxn} = -RT \ln K$ Rearrange to solve for K. $K = e^{\frac{-\Delta G^0_{rxn}}{RT}} = e^{\frac{-1.330 \times 10^5\ J}{\left(8.314\frac{J}{K\ mol}\right)(2000\ K)}} = e^{-7.998557} = 3.36 \times 10^{-4}$ so

the forward reaction is becoming more spontaneous.

Check: The units (kJ and none) are correct. As the temperature rises, the entropy term becomes more significant. The free energy change is reduced and the K increases. The reaction is still nonspontaneous.

80. **Given:** 3 NO_2 (g) + H_2O (l) → 2 HNO_3 (aq) + NO (g)   **Find:** $\Delta G°_{rxn}$, and K_p at 25 °C

Conceptual plan: $\Delta G^0_{rxn} = \sum n_P \Delta G^0_f(products) - \sum n_R \Delta G^0_f(reactants)$ then $\Delta G°_{rxn}, T$ → K

$$\Delta G^0_{rxn} = -RT \ln K$$

Solution:

Reactant/Product	ΔG^0_f (kJ/mol from Appendix IIB)
NO_2 (g)	51.3
H_2O (l)	−237.1
HNO_3 (aq)	−110.9
NO (g)	87.6

Be sure to pull data for the correct formula and phase.

$\Delta G_{rxn}^0 = \sum n_P \Delta G_f^0 (products) - \sum n_R \Delta G_f^0 (reactants)$

$\qquad = [2(\Delta G_f^0 (HNO_3\ (g)) + 1(\Delta G_f^0 (NO\ (g))] - [3(\Delta G_f^0 (NO_2\ (g)) + 1(\Delta G_f^0 (H_2O\ (l))]$

$\qquad = [2(-110.9\ kJ) + 1(87.6\ kJ)] - [3(51.3\ kJ) + 1(-237.1\ kJ)]$ $\qquad\qquad$ then $\Delta G_{rxn}^0 = -RT\ln K$

$\qquad = [-134.2\ kJ] - [-83.2\ kJ]$

$\qquad = -51.0\ kJ = +5.10 \times 10^4\ J$

Rearrange to solve for K. $K = e^{\frac{-\Delta G_{rxn}^0}{RT}} = e^{\dfrac{-\left(-5.10 \times 10^4\ J\right)}{\left(8.314\frac{J}{K\ mol}\right)(298\ K)}} = e^{20.5847} = 8.71 \times 10^8$ so the reaction is spontaneous.

Check: The units (kJ and none) are correct. The free energy change is negative and the reaction is spontaneous. This results in a large K.

81. **Given:** $C_2H_4\ (g) + X_2\ (g) \rightarrow C_2H_4X_2\ (g)$ where X = Cl, Br and I
    Find: $\Delta H^{\circ}_{rxn}, \Delta S^{\circ}_{rxn}, \Delta G^{\circ}_{rxn}$ and K at 25 °C and spontaneity trends with X and temperature

    Conceptual plan: $\Delta H_{rxn}^0 = \sum n_P \Delta H_f^0 (products) - \sum n_R \Delta H_f^0 (reactants)$ **then**

    $\Delta S_{rxn}^0 = \sum n_P S^0 (products) - \sum n_r S^0 (reactants)$ **then** °C → K **then** J/K → kJ/K **then**

    $\qquad\qquad\qquad\qquad\qquad K = 273.15 + °C \qquad\qquad \dfrac{1\ kJ}{1000\ J}$

    $\Delta H^{\circ}_{rxn}, \Delta S_{rxn}, T \rightarrow \Delta G$

    $\qquad \Delta G = \Delta H_{rxn} - T\Delta S_{rxn}$

    Solution:

Reactant/Product	ΔH_f^0(kJ/mol from Appendix IIB)
$C_2H_4\ (g)$	52.4
$Cl_2\ (g)$	0.0
$C_2H_4Cl_2\ (g)$	−129.7

Be sure to pull data for the correct formula and phase.

$\Delta H_{rxn}^0 = \sum n_P \Delta H_f^0 (products) - \sum n_R \Delta H_f^0 (reactants)$

$\qquad = [1(\Delta H_f^0 (C_2H_4Cl_2\ (g))] - [1(\Delta H_f^0 (C_2H_4\ (g)) + 1(\Delta H_f^0 (Cl_2\ (g))]$

$\qquad = [1(-129.7\ kJ)] - [1(52.4\ kJ) + 1(0.0\ kJ)]$ $\qquad\qquad$ then

$\qquad = [-129.7\ kJ] - [52.4\ kJ]$

$\qquad = -182.1\ kJ$

Reactant/Product	S^0(J/mol K from Appendix IIB)
$C_2H_4\ (g)$	219.3
$Cl_2\ (g)$	223.1
$C_2H_4Cl_2\ (g)$	308.0

Be sure to pull data for the correct formula and phase.

$\Delta S_{rxn}^0 = \sum n_P S^0 (products) - \sum n_R S^0 (reactants)$

$\qquad = [1(S^0 (C_2H_4Cl_2\ (g))] - [1(S^0 (C_2H_4\ (g)) + 1(S^0 (Cl_2\ (g))]$

$\qquad = [1(308.0\ J/mol\ K)] - [1(219.3\ J/mol\ K) + 1(223.1\ J/mol\ K)]$ then T = 273.15 + 25 °C = 298 K then

$\qquad = [308.0\ J/K] - [442.4\ J/K]$

$\qquad = -134.4\ J/K$

$-134.4\ \dfrac{J}{K} \times \dfrac{1\ kJ}{1000\ J} = -0.1344\ \dfrac{kJ}{K}$ then

$\Delta G^0 = \Delta H^{\circ}_{rxn} - T\Delta S^{\circ}_{rxn} = -182.1\ kJ - (298\ K)\left(-0.1344\ \dfrac{kJ}{K}\right) = -142.0\ kJ = -1.420 \times 10^5\ J$ then $\Delta G_{rxn}^0 = -RT\ln K$

Rearrange to solve for K. $K = e^{\frac{-\Delta G_{rxn}^0}{RT}} = e^{\dfrac{-\left(-1.420 \times 10^5\ J\right)}{\left(8.314\frac{J}{K\ mol}\right)(298\ K)}} = e^{57.334} = 7.94 \times 10^{24}$ so the reaction is spontaneous.

659

Reactant/Product	ΔH^0_f(kJ/mol from Appendix IIB)
C_2H_4 (g)	52.4
Br_2 (g)	30.9
$C_2H_4Br_2$ (g)	-38.3

Be sure to pull data for the correct formula and phase.

$\Delta H^0_{rxn} = \sum n_P \Delta H^0_f(products) - \sum n_R \Delta H^0_f(reactants)$

$= [1(\Delta H^0_f(C_2H_4Br_2\ (g)))] - [1(\Delta H^0_f(C_2H_4\ (g)) + 1(\Delta H^0_f(Br_2\ (g)))]$

$= [1(-38.3\ kJ)] - [1(52.4\ kJ) + 1(30.9\ kJ)]$ then

$= [-38.3\ kJ] - [83.3\ kJ]$

$= -121.6\ kJ$

Reactant/Product	S^0(J/mol K from Appendix IIB)
C_2H_4 (g)	219.3
Br_2 (g)	245.5
$C_2H_4Br_2$ (g)	330.6

Be sure to pull data for the correct formula and phase.

$\Delta S^0_{rxn} = \sum n_P S^0(products) - \sum n_R S^0(reactants)$

$= [1(S^0(C_2H_4Br_2\ (g)))] - [1(S^0(C_2H_4\ (g)) + 1(S^0(Br_2\ (g)))]$

$= [1(330.6\ J/mol\ K)] - [1(219.3\ J/mol\ K) + 1(245.5\ J/mol\ K)]$ then $-134.2\ \dfrac{J}{K} \times \dfrac{1\ kJ}{1000\ J} = -0.1342\ \dfrac{kJ}{K}$ then

$= [330.6\ J/K] - [464.8\ J/K]$

$= -134.2\ J/K$

$\Delta G^0 = \Delta H^0_{rxn} - T\Delta S^0_{rxn} = -121.6\ kJ - (298\ K)\left(-0.1342\ \dfrac{kJ}{K}\right) = -81.6\ kJ = -8.16 \times 10^4\ J$ then $\Delta G^0_{rxn} = -RT \ln K$

Rearrange to solve for K. $K = e^{\frac{-\Delta G^0_{rxn}}{RT}} = e^{\dfrac{-(-8.16 \times 10^4\ J)}{\left(8.314\frac{J}{K\ mol}\right)(298\ K)}} = e^{32.9389} = 2.02 \times 10^{14}$ so the reaction is spontaneous.

Reactant/Product	ΔH^0_f(kJ/mol from Appendix IIB)
C_2H_4 (g)	52.4
I_2 (g)	62.42
$C_2H_4I_2$ (g)	66.5

Be sure to pull data for the correct formula and phase.

$\Delta H^0_{rxn} = \sum n_P \Delta H^0_f(products) - \sum n_R \Delta H^0_f(reactants)$

$= [1(\Delta H^0_f(C_2H_4I_2\ (g)))] - [1(\Delta H^0_f(C_2H_4\ (g)) + 1(\Delta H^0_f(I_2\ (g)))]$

$= [1(66.5\ kJ)] - [1(52.4\ kJ) + 1(62.42\ kJ)]$ then

$= [66.5\ kJ] - [114.82\ kJ]$

$= -48.32\ kJ$

Reactant/Product	S^0(J/mol K from Appendix IIB)
C_2H_4 (g)	219.3
I_2 (g)	260.69
$C_2H_4I_2$ (g)	347.8

Be sure to pull data for the correct formula and phase.

$\Delta S^0_{rxn} = \sum n_P S^0(products) - \sum n_R S^0(reactants)$

$= [1(S^0(C_2H_4I_2\ (g)))] - [1(S^0(C_2H_4\ (g)) + 1(S^0(I_2\ (g)))]$

$= [1(347.8\ J/mol\ K)] - [1(219.3\ J/mol\ K) + 1(260.69\ J/mol\ K)]$ then $-132.2\ \dfrac{J}{K} \times \dfrac{1\ kJ}{1000\ J} = -0.1322\ \dfrac{kJ}{K}$ then

$= [347.8\ J/K] - [479.99\ J/K]$

$= -132.2\ J/K$

$\Delta G^0 = \Delta H^0_{rxn} - T\Delta S^0_{rxn} = -48.32\ kJ - (298\ K)\left(-0.1322\ \dfrac{kJ}{K}\right) = -8.9244\ kJ = -8.9244 \times 10^3\ J$ then

$\Delta G_{rxn}^0 = -RT \ln K$ **Rearrange to solve for K.** $K = e^{\frac{-\Delta G_{rxn}^0}{RT}} = e^{\frac{-\left(-8.9244 \times 10^3 \text{ J}\right)}{\left(8.314\frac{\text{J}}{\text{K mol}}\right)(298 \text{ K})}} = e^{3.6021} = 37$ and the

reaction is spontaneous.

Cl_2 is the most spontaneous in the forward direction, I_2 is the least. The entropy change in the reactions is very constant. The spontaneity is determined by the standard enthalpy of formation of the dihalogenated ethane. Higher temperatures make the forward reactions less spontaneous.

Check: The units (kJ and none) are correct. The enthalpy change becomes less negative as we move to larger halogens. The enthalpy term dominates at room temperature, the free energy change is the same sign as the enthalpy change. The more negative the free energy change, the larger the K.

82. **Given:** $H_2 (g) + X_2 (g) \rightarrow 2 HX (g)$ where X = Cl, Br and I

Find: ΔH°_{rxn}, ΔS°_{rxn}, ΔG°_{rxn} and K at 25 °C and spontaneity trends with X and temperature

Conceptual plan: $\Delta H_{rxn}^0 = \sum n_p \Delta H_f^0 (products) - \sum n_R \Delta H_f^0 (reactants)$ **then**

$\Delta S_{rxn}^0 = \sum n_p S^0 (products) - \sum n_r S^0 (reactants)$ **then** °C $\rightarrow$ K **then** J/K $\rightarrow$ kJ/K **then**

$$K = 273.15 + °C \qquad\qquad \frac{1 \text{kJ}}{1000 \text{ J}}$$

ΔH°_{rxn}, ΔS_{rxn}, T $\rightarrow$ ΔG

$\Delta G = \Delta H_{rxn} - T\Delta S_{rxn}$

Solution:

Reactant/Product	ΔH_f^0 (kJ/mol from Appendix IIB)
$H_2 (g)$	0.0
$Cl_2 (g)$	0.0
HCl (g)	– 92.3

Be sure to pull data for the correct formula and phase.

$\Delta H_{rxn}^0 = \sum n_p \Delta H_f^0 (products) - \sum n_R \Delta H_f^0 (reactants)$

$= [2(\Delta H_f^0 (\text{HCl} (g)))] - [1(\Delta H_f^0 (H_2 (g)) + 1(\Delta H_f^0 (Cl_2 (g)))]$

$= [2(-92.3 \text{ kJ})] - [1(0.0 \text{ kJ}) + 1(0.0 \text{ kJ})]$ **then**

$= [-184.6 \text{ kJ}] - [0.0]$

$= -184.6 \text{ kJ}$

Reactant/Product	S^0 (J/mol K from Appendix IIB)
$H_2 (g)$	130.7
$Cl_2 (g)$	223.1
HCl (g)	186.9

Be sure to pull data for the correct formula and phase.

$\Delta S_{rxn}^0 = \sum n_p S^0 (products) - \sum n_R S^0 (reactants)$

$= [2(S^0 (\text{HCl} (g)))] - [1(S^0 (H_2 (g)) + 1(S^0 (Cl_2 (g)))]$

$= [2(186.9 \text{ J/mol K})] - [1(130.7 \text{ J/mol K}) + 1(223.1 \text{ J/mol K})]$ then T = 273.15 + 25 °C = 298 K   then

$= [373.8 \text{ J/K}] - [353.8 \text{ J/K}]$

$= + 20.0 \text{ J/K}$

$+ 20.0 \frac{\text{J}}{\text{K}} \times \frac{1 \text{ kJ}}{1000 \text{ J}} = + 0.0200 \frac{\text{kJ}}{\text{K}}$ then

$\Delta G^0 = \Delta H^0_{rxn} - T\Delta S^0_{rxn} = -184.6 \text{ kJ} - (298 \text{ K})\left(+ 0.0200 \frac{\text{kJ}}{\text{K}}\right) = -190.6 \text{ kJ} = -1.906 \times 10^5 \text{ J}$ then $\Delta G_{rxn}^0 = -RT \ln K$

Rearrange to solve for K. $K = e^{\frac{-\Delta G_{rxn}^0}{RT}} = e^{\frac{-\left(-1.906 \times 10^5 \text{ J}\right)}{\left(8.314\frac{\text{J}}{\text{K mol}}\right)(298 \text{ K})}} = e^{76.9140} = 2.53 \times 10^{33}$ so the reaction is spontaneous.

Reactant/Product	ΔH_f^0 (kJ/mol from Appendix IIB)
$H_2\ (g)$	0.0
$Br_2\ (g)$	30.9
$HBr\ (g)$	-36.3

Be sure to pull data for the correct formula and phase.

$$\Delta H_{rxn}^0 = \sum n_P \Delta H_f^0 (products) - \sum n_R \Delta H_f^0 (reactants)$$

$$= [2(\Delta H_f^0 (HBr\ (g)))] - [1(\Delta H_f^0 (H_2\ (g))) + 1(\Delta H_f^0 (Br_2\ (g)))]$$

$$= [2(-36.3\ kJ)] - [1(0.0\ kJ) + 1(30.9\ kJ)] \qquad\qquad then$$

$$= [-72.6\ kJ] - [30.9\ kJ]$$

$$= -103.5\ kJ$$

Reactant/Product	S^0 (J/mol K from Appendix IIB)
$H_2\ (g)$	130.7
$Br_2\ (g)$	245.5
$HBr\ (g)$	198.7

Be sure to pull data for the correct formula and phase.

$$\Delta S_{rxn}^0 = \sum n_P S^0 (products) - \sum n_R S^0 (reactants)$$

$$= [2(S^0 (HBr\ (g)))] - [1(S^0 (H_2\ (g))) + 1(S^0 (Br_2\ (g)))]$$

$$= [2(198.7\ J/mol\ K)] - [1(130.7\ J/mol\ K) + 1(245.5\ J/mol\ K)] \quad then\ +21.2 \tfrac{\cancel{J}}{K} \times \tfrac{1\ kJ}{1000\ \cancel{J}} = +0.0212 \tfrac{kJ}{K} \ then$$

$$= [397.4\ J/K] - [376.2\ J/K]$$

$$= +21.2\ J/K$$

$$\Delta G^0 = \Delta H^0{}_{rxn} - T\Delta S^0{}_{rxn} = -103.5\ kJ - (298\ \cancel{K})\left(+0.0212 \frac{kJ}{\cancel{K}}\right) = -109.8176\ kJ = -1.098176 \times 10^5\ J\ then$$

$$\Delta G_{rxn}^0 = -RT \ln K \quad \text{Rearrange to solve for K.}$$

$$K = e^{\frac{-\Delta G_{rxn}^0}{RT}} = e^{\frac{-(-1.098176 \times 10^5\ \cancel{J})}{\left(8.314 \frac{\cancel{J}}{\cancel{K}\ mol}\right)(298\ \cancel{K})}} = e^{44.3247} = 1.78 \times 10^{19} \text{ so the reaction is spontaneous.}$$

Reactant/Product	ΔH_f^0 (kJ/mol from Appendix IIB)
$H_2\ (g)$	0.0
$I_2\ (g)$	62.42
$HI\ (g)$	26.5

Be sure to pull data for the correct formula and phase.

$$\Delta H_{rxn}^0 = \sum n_P \Delta H_f^0 (products) - \sum n_R \Delta H_f^0 (reactants)$$

$$= [2(\Delta H_f^0 (HI\ (g)))] - [1(\Delta H_f^0 (H_2\ (g))) + 1(\Delta H_f^0 (I_2\ (g)))]$$

$$= [2(26.5\ kJ)] - [1(0.0\ kJ) + 1(62.42\ kJ)] \qquad\qquad then$$

$$= [53.0\ kJ] - [62.42\ kJ]$$

$$= -9.42\ kJ$$

Reactant/Product	S^0 (J/mol K from Appendix IIB)
$H_2\ (g)$	130.7
$I_2\ (g)$	260.69
$HI\ (g)$	206.6

Be sure to pull data for the correct formula and phase.

$$\Delta S_{rxn}^0 = \sum n_P S^0 (products) - \sum n_R S^0 (reactants)$$

$$= [2(S^0 (HI\ (g)))] - [1(S^0 (H_2\ (g))) + 1(S^0 (I_2\ (g)))]$$

$$= [2(206.6\ J/mol\ K)] - [1(130.7\ J/mol\ K) + 1(260.69\ J/mol\ K)] \quad then\ 21.8 \tfrac{\cancel{J}}{K} \times \tfrac{1\ kJ}{1000\ \cancel{J}} = +0.0218 \tfrac{kJ}{K} \ then$$

$$= [413.2\ J/K] - [391.39\ J/K]$$

$$= +21.8\ J/K$$

$$\Delta G^0 = \Delta H^0{}_{rxn} - T\Delta S^0{}_{rxn} = -9.42\ kJ - (298\ \cancel{K})\left(+0.0218 \frac{kJ}{\cancel{K}}\right) = -15.9164\ kJ = -1.59164 \times 10^4\ J\ then$$

$\Delta G^0_{rxn} = -RT \ln K$ Rearrange to solve for K.

$$K = e^{\frac{-\Delta G^0_{rxn}}{RT}} = e^{\frac{-(-1.59164 \times 10^4 \text{ J})}{\left(8.314\frac{\text{J}}{\text{K mol}}\right)(298 \text{ K})}} = e^{6.42419} = 6.17 \times 10^2 = 617$$. The reaction is spontaneous.

Cl_2 is the most spontaneous, I_2 is the least. The entropy change in the reactions is very constant. The spontaneity is determined by the standard enthalpy of formation of the acid. Higher temperatures make the reactions more spontaneous.

Check: The units (kJ and none) are correct. The enthalpy is twice the enthalpy of formation of the acid. We expect a very small entropy change because the number of moles of gas is unchanged. Since both terms are negative, the free energy change is negative and the reaction is spontaneous. The more negative the free energy change, the larger the K.

83. a) **Given**: $N_2O (g) + NO_2 (g) \rightleftharpoons 3 NO (g)$ at 298 K   **Find**: $\Delta G°_{rxn}$

   Conceptual plan: $\Delta G^0_{rxn} = \sum n_p \Delta G^0_f (products) - \sum n_R \Delta G^0_f (reactants)$

   Solution:

Reactant/Product	ΔG^0_f(kJ/mol from Appendix IIB)
$N_2O (g)$	103.7
$NO_2 (g)$	51.3
$NO (g)$	87.6

   Be sure to pull data for the correct formula and phase.

   $\Delta G^0_{rxn} = \sum n_p \Delta G^0_f (products) - \sum n_R \Delta G^0_f (reactants)$

   $= [3(\Delta G^0_f (NO (g))] - [1(\Delta G^0_f (N_2O (g)) + 1(\Delta G^0_f (NO_2 (g))]$

   $= [3(87.6 kJ)] - [1(103.7 kJ) + 1(51.3 kJ)]$

   $= [262.8 kJ] - [155.0 kJ]$

   $= +107.8 kJ$

   The reaction is nonspontaneous.

   Check: The units (kJ) are correct. The standard free energy for the reaction was positive and so the reaction is nonspontaneous.

   b) **Given**: $P_{N2O} = P_{NO2} = 1.0$ atm initially   **Find**: P_{N2O} when reaction ceases to be spontaneous

   Conceptual Plan: Reaction will not longer be spontaneous when $Q = K$ so then $\Delta G°_{rxn}, T \rightarrow K$

   $$\Delta G^0_{rxn} = -RT \ln K$$

   then solve equilibrium problem to get gas pressures, since $K \ll 1$ the amount of NO generated will be very, very small   compared to 1.0 atm, so, within experimental error, $P_{N2O} = P_{NO2} = 1.0$ atm. Simply solve of P_{NO}.

   $$K = \frac{P^3_{NO}}{P_{N2O} P_{NO2}}$$

   Solution: $\Delta G^0_{rxn} = -RT \ln K$ Rearrange to solve for K.

   $$K = e^{\frac{-\Delta G^0_{rxn}}{RT}} = e^{\frac{-107.8 \text{ kJ} \times \frac{1000 \text{ J}}{1 \text{ kJ}}}{\left(8.314\frac{\text{J}}{\text{K mol}}\right)(298 \text{ K})}} = e^{-43.5103} = 1.27 \times 10^{-19}$$. Since $K = \frac{P^3_{NO}}{P_{N2O} P_{NO2}}$, rearrange to solve

   for P_{NO}. $P^3_{NO} = \sqrt[3]{K P_{N2O} P_{NO2}} = \sqrt[3]{(1.27 \times 10^{-19})(1.0)(1.0)} = 5.0 \times 10^{-7}$ atm .

   Note that that assumption that P_{N2O} was very, very small was valid.

   Check: The units (atm) are correct. Since the free energy change was positive, the K was very small. This leads us to expect that very little NO will be formed.

c) **Given:** $N_2O\ (g) + NO_2\ (g) \rightleftharpoons 3\ NO\ (g)$ **Find:** temperature for spontaneity

Conceptual plan: $\Delta H^0_{rxn} = \sum n_P \Delta H^0_f(products) - \sum n_R \Delta H^0_f(reactants)$ **then**

$\Delta S^0_{rxn} = \sum n_P S^0(products) - \sum n_r S^0(reactants)$ **then J/K** $\rightarrow$ **kJ/K** **then** $\Delta H^\circ_{rxn}, \Delta S_{rxn} \rightarrow$ **T**

$$\frac{1\,kJ}{1000\,J}$$

$$\Delta G = \Delta H_{rxn} - T\Delta S_{rxn}$$

Solution:

Reactant/Product	ΔH^0_f(kJ/mol from Appendix IIB)
$N_2O\ (g)$	81.6
$NO_2\ (g)$	33.2
$NO\ (g)$	91.3

Be sure to pull data for the correct formula and phase.

$\Delta H^0_{rxn} = \sum n_P \Delta H^0_f(products) - \sum n_R \Delta H^0_f(reactants)$

$= [3(\Delta H^0_f(NO\ (g))] - [1(\Delta H^0_f(N_2O\ (g)) + 1(\Delta H^0_f(NO_2\ (g))]$

$= [3(91.3\ kJ)] - [1(81.6\ kJ) + 1(33.2\ kJ)]$ **then**

$= [273.9\ kJ] - [114.8\ kJ]$

$= +159.1\ kJ$

Reactant/Product	S^0(J/mol K from Appendix IIB)
$N_2O\ (g)$	220.0
$NO_2\ (g)$	240.1
$NO\ (g)$	210.8

Be sure to pull data for the correct formula and phase.

$\Delta S^0_{rxn} = \sum n_P S^0(products) - \sum n_R S^0(reactants)$

$= [3(S^0(NO\ (g))] - [1(S^0(N_2O\ (g)) + 1(S^0(NO_2\ (g))]$

$= [3(210.8\ J/mol\ K)] - [1(220.0\ J/mol\ K) + 1(240.1\ J/mol\ K)]$ **then** $+172.3\ \dfrac{J}{K} \times \dfrac{1\ kJ}{1000\ J} = +0.1723\ \dfrac{kJ}{K}$.

$= [632.4\ J/K] - [460.1\ J/K]$

$= +172.3\ J/K$

Since $\Delta G = \Delta H_{rxn} - T\Delta S_{rxn}$, set $\Delta G = 0$ and rearrange to solve for T.

$$T = \frac{\Delta H_{rxn}}{\Delta S_{rxn}} = \frac{+159.1\ kJ}{0.1723\ \dfrac{kJ}{K}} = +923.4\ K\ .$$

Check: The units (K) are correct. The reaction can be made more spontaneous by raising the temperature, because the entropy change is positive (increase in the number of moles of gas).

84. a) **Given:** $BaCO_3\ (s) \rightleftharpoons BaO\ (s) + CO_2\ (g)$ at 298 K   **Find:** ΔG°_{rxn}

Conceptual plan: $\Delta G^0_{rxn} = \sum n_P \Delta G^0_f(products) - \sum n_R \Delta G^0_f(reactants)$

Solution:

Reactant/Product	ΔG^0_f(kJ/mol from Appendix IIB)
$BaCO_3\ (s)$	-1134.4
$BaO\ (s)$	-520.3
$CO_2\ (g)$	-394.4

Be sure to pull data for the correct formula and phase.

$\Delta G^0_{rxn} = \sum n_P \Delta G^0_f(products) - \sum n_R \Delta G^0_f(reactants)$

$= [1(\Delta G^0_f(BaO\ (s)) + 1(\Delta G^0_f(CO_2\ (g))] - [1(\Delta G^0_f(BaCO_3\ (s))]$

$= [1(-520.3\ kJ) + 1(-394.4\ kJ)] - [1(-1134.4\ kJ)]$

$= [-914.7\ kJ] - [-1134.4\ kJ]$

$= +219.7\ kJ$

The reaction is nonspontaneous.

Check: The units (kJ) are correct. The standard free energy for the reaction was positive and so the reaction is nonspontaneous.

b) **Given:** $BaCO_3$ (s) initially in container   **Find:** P_{CO2} at equilibrium

     Conceptual Plan: **Reaction will be at equilibrium when Q = K so then $\Delta G°_{rxn}$, T → K→ P_{CO2}**

$$\Delta G^0_{rxn} = -RT \ln K \quad K = P_{CO2}$$

     Solution: $\Delta G^0_{rxn} = -RT \ln K$ Rearrange to solve for K.

$$K = e^{\frac{-\Delta G^0_{rxn}}{RT}} = e^{\left(\frac{-219.7 \text{ kJ} \times \frac{1000 \text{ J}}{1 \text{ kJ}}}{8.314 \frac{\text{J}}{\text{K mol}} (298 \text{ K})}\right)} = e^{-88.\underline{6}755} = 3.08 \times 10^{-39}. \quad \text{So } P_{CO2} = 3.08 \times 10^{-39} \text{ atm.}$$

     Check: The units (atm) are correct. Since the free energy change was very positive, the K was very, very small. This leads us to expect that very little carbon dioxide will be formed.

c) **Given:** $BaCO_3$ (s) $\rightleftharpoons$ BaO (s) + CO_2 (g)   **Find:** temperature for P_{CO2} = 1.0 atm

     Conceptual plan: $\Delta H^0_{rxn} = \sum n_p \Delta H^0_f (products) - \sum n_R \Delta H^0_f (reactants)$ **then**

$\Delta S^0_{rxn} = \sum n_p S^0 (products) - \sum n_r S^0 (reactants)$ **then J/K → kJ/K**   **then** $\Delta H°_{rxn}, \Delta S_{rxn}$ →   **T**

$$\frac{1 kJ}{1000 J} \qquad\qquad \Delta G = \Delta H_{rxn} - T\Delta S_{rxn}$$

     Solution:

Reactant/Product	ΔH^0_f (kJ/mol from Appendix IIB)
$BaCO_3$ (s)	− 1213.0
BaO (s)	− 548.0
CO_2 (g)	− 393.5

Be sure to pull data for the correct formula and phase.

$\Delta H^0_{rxn} = \sum n_p \Delta H^0_f (products) - \sum n_R \Delta H^0_f (reactants)$

$\quad = [1(\Delta H^0_f (BaO\ (s)) + 1(\Delta H^0_f (CO_2\ (g))] - [1(\Delta H^0_f (BaCO_3\ (s))]$

$\quad = [1(-548.0 kJ) + 1(-393.5\ kJ)] - [1(-1213.0\ kJ)]$ then

$\quad = [-941.5\ kJ] - [-1213.0\ kJ]$

$\quad = +271.5\ kJ$

Reactant/Product	S^0 (J/mol K from Appendix IIB)
$BaCO_3$ (s)	112.1
BaO (s)	72.1
CO_2 (g)	213.8

Be sure to pull data for the correct formula and phase.

$\Delta S^0_{rxn} = \sum n_p S^0 (products) - \sum n_R S^0 (reactants)$

$\quad = = [1(S^0 (BaO\ (s)) + 1(S^0 (CO_2\ (g))] - [1(S^0 (BaCO_3\ (s))]$

$\quad = [1(72.1\ J/mol\ K) + 1(213.8\ J/mol\ K)] - [1(112.1\ J/mol\ K)]$ then $+173.8 \frac{J}{K} \times \frac{1\ kJ}{1000\ J} = +0.1738 \frac{kJ}{K}$.

$\quad = [285.9\ J/K] - [112.1\ J/K]$

$\quad = +173.8\ J/K$

Since $\Delta G = \Delta H_{rxn} - T\Delta S_{rxn}$, set $\Delta G = 0$ and rearrange to solve for T.

$$T = \frac{\Delta H_{rxn}}{\Delta S_{rxn}} = \frac{+271.5\ kJ}{0.1738\ \frac{kJ}{K}} = +1562\ K.$$ When $\Delta G = 0\ K = 1$, so at 1562 K $P_{CO2} = 1.0$ atm.

     Check: The units (K) are correct. The reaction can be made more spontaneous by raising the temperature, because the entropy change is positive (increase in the number of moles of gas). We expect a high temperature because the enthalpy change is so positive.

85. a) **Given:** ATP (aq) + H_2O (l) → ADP (aq) + P_i (aq) $\Delta G°_{rxn}$ = − 30.5 kJ at 298 K   **Find:** K

     Conceptual plan: $\Delta G°_{rxn}$, T →   K

$$\Delta G^0_{rxn} = -RT \ln K$$

Solution: $\Delta G^0_{rxn} = -RT \ln K$ Rearrange to solve for K.

$$K = e^{\frac{-\Delta G^0_{rxn}}{RT}} = e^{\frac{-(-30.5 \cancel{kJ}) \times \frac{1000 \cancel{J}}{1 \cancel{kJ}}}{\left(8.314 \frac{\cancel{J}}{K \cdot mol}\right)(298 \cancel{K})}} = e^{12.3104} = 2.22 \times 10^5.$$

Check: The units (none) are correct.   The free energy change is negative and the reaction is spontaneous. This results in a large K.

b) **Given:** oxidation of glucose drives reforming of ATP
   Find: $\Delta G°_{rxn}$ of oxidation of glucose and moles ATP formed per mole of glucose
   Conceptual plan: write balanced reaction for glucose oxidation then

$$\Delta G^0_{rxn} = \sum n_p \Delta G^0_f (products) - \sum n_R \Delta G^0_f (reactants) \quad \textbf{then } \Delta\textbf{G}°_{rxn}\textbf{'s} \rightarrow \textbf{ moles ATP/ mole glucose}$$

$$\frac{\Delta G^0_{rxn} \; glucose \; oxidation}{\Delta G^0_{rxn} \; ATP \; hydrolysis}$$

Solution: Solution: $C_6H_{12}O_6 \, (s) + 6\,O_2 \, (g) \rightarrow 6\,CO_2 \, (g) + 6\,H_2O \, (l)$

Reactant/Product	ΔG^0_f(kJ/mol from Appendix IIB)
$C_6H_{12}O_6 \, (s)$	-910.4
$O_2 \, (g)$	0.0
$CO_2 \, (g)$	-394.4
$H_2O \, (l)$	-237.1

Be sure to pull data for the correct formula and phase.

$$\Delta G^0_{rxn} = \sum n_p \Delta G^0_f (products) - \sum n_R \Delta G^0_f (reactants)$$
$$= [6(\Delta G^0_f(CO_2 \, (g)) + 6(\Delta G^0_f(H_2O \, (l))] - [1(\Delta G^0_f(C_6H_{12}O_6 \, (s)) + 6(\Delta G^0_f(O_2 \, (g))]$$
$$= [6(-394.4 \, kJ) + 6(-237.1 \, kJ)] - [1(-910.4 \, kJ) + 6(0.0 \, kJ)]$$
$$= [-3789.0 \, kJ] - [-910.4 \, kJ]$$
$$= -2878.6 \, kJ$$

So the reaction is very spontaneous. $\dfrac{2878.6 \dfrac{kJ \; generated}{mole \; glucose \; oxidized}}{30.5 \dfrac{kJ \; needed}{mole \; ATP \; reformed}} = 94.4 \dfrac{mole \; ATP \; reformed}{mole \; glucose \; oxidized}$

Check: The units (mol) are correct.   The free energy change for the glucose oxidation is large compared to the ATP hydrolysis, so we expect to reform many moles of ATP.

86. **Given:**   ATP (aq) + $H_2O \, (l) \rightarrow$ ADP (aq) + $P_i \, (aq)$ $\Delta G°_{rxn} = -30.5 \, kJ$ at 298 K
   Find: ΔG_{rxn} when [ATP] = 0.0031 M, [ADP] = 0.0014 M and [P_i] = 0.0048 M
   Conceptual plan: $\Delta\textbf{G}°_{\textbf{rxn}}$**, [ATP], [ADP], [$P_i$], T** $\rightarrow$ $\Delta\textbf{G}$

$$\Delta G_{rxn} = \Delta G^0_{rxn} + RT \ln Q \quad \text{where } Q = \frac{[ADP][P_i]}{[ATP]}$$

Solution: $Q = \dfrac{[ADP][P_i]}{[ATP]} = \dfrac{(0.0014)(0.0048)}{0.0031} = 0.00216774$ then

$$\Delta G_{rxn} = \Delta G^0_{rxn} + RT \ln Q = -30.5 \, kJ + \left(8.314 \frac{\cancel{J}}{K \cdot mol}\right)\left(\frac{1 \, kJ}{1000 \cancel{J}}\right)(298 \cancel{K}) \ln(0.00216774) = -45.7 \, kJ$$

Check: The units (kJ) are correct.   The Q is less than one so we expect a free energy more negative than at standard conditions.

87. a) **Given:** $2\,CO \, (g) + 2\,NO \, (g) \rightarrow N_2 \, (g) + 2\,CO_2 \, (g)$ **Find:** $\Delta G°_{rxn}$ and effect of increasing T on ΔG
   Conceptual plan: $\Delta G^0_{rxn} = \sum n_p \Delta G^0_f (products) - \sum n_R \Delta G^0_f (reactants)$
   Solution: Solution:

Reactant/Product	ΔG_f^0 (kJ/mol from Appendix IIB)
CO (g)	-137.2
NO (g)	87.6
N_2 (g)	0.0
CO_2 (g)	-394.4

Be sure to pull data for the correct formula and phase.

$\Delta G_{rxn}^0 = \sum n_P \Delta G_f^0(products) - \sum n_R \Delta G_f^0(reactants)$

$= [1(\Delta G_f^0(N_2\ (g)) + 2(\Delta G_f^0(CO_2\ (g))] - [2(\Delta G_f^0(CO\ (g)) + 2(\Delta G_f^0(NO\ (g))]$

$= [1(0.0\ kJ) + 2(-394.4\ kJ)] - [2(-137.2\ kJ) + 2(87.6\ kJ)]$

$= [-788.8\ kJ] - [-99.2\ kJ]$

$= -689.6\ kJ$

Since the number of moles of gas is decreasing, the entropy change is negative and so ΔG will become more positive with increasing temperature.

Check: The units (kJ) are correct. The free energy change is negative since the carbon dioxide has such a low free energy of formation.

b) **Given:** $5\ H_2\ (g) + 2\ NO\ (g) \rightarrow 2\ NH_3\ (g) + 2\ H_2O\ (g)$ **Find:** $\Delta G°_{rxn}$ and effect of increasing T on ΔG

Conceptual plan: $\Delta G_{rxn}^0 = \sum n_P \Delta G_f^0(products) - \sum n_R \Delta G_f^0(reactants)$

Solution: Solution:

Reactant/Product	ΔG_f^0 (kJ/mol from Appendix IIB)
H_2 (g)	0.0
NO (g)	87.6
NH_3 (g)	-16.4
H_2O (g)	-228.6

Be sure to pull data for the correct formula and phase.

$\Delta G_{rxn}^0 = \sum n_P \Delta G_f^0(products) - \sum n_R \Delta G_f^0(reactants)$

$= [2(\Delta G_f^0(NH_3\ (g)) + 2(\Delta G_f^0(H_2O\ (g))] - [5(\Delta G_f^0(H_2\ (g)) + 2(\Delta G_f^0(NO\ (g))]$

$= [2(-16.4\ kJ) + 2(-228.6\ kJ)] - [5(0.0\ kJ) + 2(87.6\ kJ)]$

$= [-490.0\ kJ] - [175.2\ kJ]$

$= -665.2\ kJ$

Since the number of moles of gas is decreasing, the entropy change is negative and so ΔG will become more positive with increasing temperature.

Check: The units (kJ) are correct. The free energy change is negative since ammonia and water have such a low free energy of formation.

c) **Given:** $2\ H_2\ (g) + 2\ NO\ (g) \rightarrow N_2\ (g) + 2\ H_2O\ (g)$ **Find:** $\Delta G°_{rxn}$ and effect of increasing T on ΔG

Conceptual plan: $\Delta G_{rxn}^0 = \sum n_P \Delta G_f^0(products) - \sum n_R \Delta G_f^0(reactants)$

Solution: Solution:

Reactant/Product	ΔG_f^0 (kJ/mol from Appendix IIB)
H_2 (g)	0.0
NO (g)	87.6
N_2 (g)	0.0
H_2O (g)	-228.6

Be sure to pull data for the correct formula and phase.

$\Delta G_{rxn}^0 = \sum n_P \Delta G_f^0(products) - \sum n_R \Delta G_f^0(reactants)$

$= [1(\Delta G_f^0(N_2\ (g)) + 2(\Delta G_f^0(H_2O\ (g))] - [2(\Delta G_f^0(H_2\ (g)) + 2(\Delta G_f^0(NO\ (g))]$

$= [1(0.0\ kJ) + 2(-228.6\ kJ)] - [2(0.0\ kJ) + 2(87.6\ kJ)]$

$= [-457.2\ kJ] - [175.2\ kJ]$

$= -632.4\ kJ$

Since the number of moles of gas is decreasing, the entropy change is negative and so ΔG will become more positive with increasing temperature.

Check: The units (kJ) are correct. The free energy change is negative since water has such a low free energy of formation.

d) **Given**: $2 NH_3 (g) + 2 O_2 (g) \rightarrow N_2O (g) + 3 H_2O (g)$ **Find**: $\Delta G°_{rxn}$ and effect of increasing T on ΔG

Conceptual plan: $\Delta G^0_{rxn} = \sum n_p \Delta G^0_f (products) - \sum n_R \Delta G^0_f (reactants)$

Solution: Solution:

Reactant/Product	ΔG^0_f(kJ/mol from Appendix IIB)
$NH_3 (g)$	-16.4
$O_2 (g)$	0.0
$N_2O (g)$	103.7
$H_2O (g)$	-228.6

Be sure to pull data for the correct formula and phase.

$\Delta G^0_{rxn} = \sum n_P \Delta G^0_f (products) - \sum n_R \Delta G^0_f (reactants)$

$= [1(\Delta G^0_f (N_2O\ (g)) + 3(\Delta G^0_f (H_2O\ (g))] - [2(\Delta G^0_f (NH_3\ (g)) + 2(\Delta G^0_f (O_2\ (g))]$

$= [1(103.7\ kJ) + 3(-228.6\ kJ)] - [2(-16.4\ kJ) + 2(0.0\ kJ)]$

$= [-582.1\ kJ] - [-32.8\ kJ]$

$= -549.3\ kJ$

Since the number of moles of gas is constant the entropy change will be small and slightly negative and so the magnitude of ΔG will decrease with increasing temperature.

Check: The units (kJ) are correct. The free energy change is negative since water has such a low free energy of formation. The entropy change is negative once the S° values are reviewed ($\Delta S_{rxn} = -9.6$ J/K).

88. a) **Given**: $NH_3 (g) + HBr (g) \rightarrow NH_4Br (s)$ **Find**: $\Delta G°_{rxn}$ effect of decreasing T on ΔG

Conceptual plan: $\Delta G^0_{rxn} = \sum n_p \Delta G^0_f (products) - \sum n_R \Delta G^0_f (reactants)$

Solution:

Reactant/Product	ΔG^0_f(kJ/mol from Appendix IIB)
$NH_3 (g)$	-16.4
$HBr (g)$	-53.4
$NH_4Br (s)$	-175.2

Be sure to pull data for the correct formula and phase.

$\Delta G^0_{rxn} = \sum n_P \Delta G^0_f (products) - \sum n_R \Delta G^0_f (reactants)$

$= [1(\Delta G^0_f (NH_4Br\ (s))] - [1(\Delta G^0_f (NH_3\ (g)) + 1(\Delta G^0_f (HBr\ (g))]$

$= [1(-175.2\ kJ)] - [1(-16.4\ kJ) + 1(-53.4\ kJ)]$

$= [-175.2\ kJ] - [-69.8\ kJ]$

$= -105.4\ kJ$

Since the number of moles of gas decreases, the entropy change will be negative and ΔG will become more negative with decreasing temperature.

Check: The units (kJ) are correct. The free energy change is negative since ammonium bromide has such a low free energy of formation.

b) **Given**: $CaCO_3 (s) \rightarrow CaO (s) + CO_2 (g)$ **Find**: $\Delta G°_{rxn}$ effect of decreasing T on ΔG

Conceptual plan: $\Delta G^0_{rxn} = \sum n_p \Delta G^0_f (products) - \sum n_R \Delta G^0_f (reactants)$

Solution:

Reactant/Product	ΔG^0_f(kJ/mol from Appendix IIB)
$CaCO_3 (s)$	-1129.1
$CaO (s)$	-603.3
$CO_2 (g)$	-394.4

Be sure to pull data for the correct formula and phase.

$$\Delta G^0_{rxn} = \sum n_P \Delta G^0_f (products) - \sum n_R \Delta G^0_f (reactants)$$
$$= [1(\Delta G^0_f (CaO\ (s)) + 1(\Delta G^0_f (CO_2\ (g))] - [1(\Delta G^0_f (CaCO_3\ (s))]$$
$$= [1(-603.3kJ) + 1(-394.4\ kJ)] - [1(-1129.1\ kJ)]$$
$$= [-997.7\ kJ] - [-1129.1\ kJ]$$
$$= +131.4\ kJ$$

Since the number of moles of gas decreases, the entropy change will be negative and ΔG will become more positive with decreasing temperature.

Check: The units (kJ) are correct. The free energy change is negative since calcium carbonate has such a low free energy of formation.

c) **Given:** $CH_4\ (g) + 3\ Cl_2\ (g) \rightarrow CHCl_3\ (g) + 3\ HCl\ (g)$ **Find:** $\Delta G°_{rxn}$ effect of decreasing T on ΔG

Conceptual plan: $\Delta G^0_{rxn} = \sum n_P \Delta G^0_f (products) - \sum n_R \Delta G^0_f (reactants)$

Solution:

Reactant/Product	ΔG^0_f(kJ/mol from Appendix IIB)
$CH_4\ (g)$	-50.5
$Cl_2\ (g)$	0.0
$CHCl_3\ (g)$	-70.4
$HCl\ (g)$	-95.3

Be sure to pull data for the correct formula and phase.

$$\Delta G^0_{rxn} = \sum n_P \Delta G^0_f (products) - \sum n_R \Delta G^0_f (reactants)$$
$$= [1(\Delta G^0_f (CHCl_3\ (g)) + 3(\Delta G^0_f (HCl\ (g))] - [1(\Delta G^0_f (CH_4\ (g)) + 1(\Delta G^0_f (Cl_2\ (g))]$$
$$= [1(-70.4\ kJ) + 3(-95.3\ kJ)] - [1(-50.5\ kJ) + 3(0.0\ kJ)]$$
$$= [-356.3\ kJ] - [-50.5\ kJ]$$
$$= -305.8\ kJ$$

Since the number of moles of gas is constant, the entropy change will be small. The entropy change is so small that the magnitude of ΔG will remain constant with decreasing temperature.

Check: The units (kJ) are correct. The free energy change is negative since chloroform and hydrogen chloride have such low free energies of formation. The entropy change is slightly positive once the S° values are reviewed ($\Delta S_{rxn} = +0.7$ J/K).

89. With one exception, the formation of any oxide of nitrogen at 298 K requires more moles of gas as reactants than are formed as products. For example 1 mole of N_2O requires 0.5 moles of O_2 and 1 mole of N_2; 1 mole of N_2O_3 requires 1 mole of N_2 and 1.5 moles of O_2 and so on. The exception is NO, where 1 mole of NO requires 0.5 moles of O_2 and 0.5 moles of N_2: $\frac{1}{2} N_2(g) + \frac{1}{2} O_2(g) \rightarrow NO(g)$ This reaction has a positive ΔS because what is essentially mixing of the N and O has taken place in the product.

90. $\Delta G°_f$ becomes less negative as the atomic number increases because the bond length increases and the bond strength decreases. There is less chemical energy stored in the longer bonds. The $\Delta S°_f$ increases as the atomic number increases because the halides in the hydrogen halides. This is because the hydrogen halide has a low entropy component (hydrogen) and a high entropy component (the halide, which increases as the atomic number of the halide increases).

91. a) **Given:**glutamate (aq) + $NH_3\ (aq)$ → glutamine (aq) + $H_2O\ (l)$ $\Delta G°_{rxn} = +14.2$ kJ at 298 K   **Find:** K

Conceptual plan: $\Delta G°_{rxn}, T \rightarrow K$

$$\Delta G^0_{rxn} = -RT \ln K$$

Solution: $\Delta G^0_{rxn} = -RT \ln K$ Rearrange to solve for K.

$$K = e^{\frac{-\Delta G^0_{rxn}}{RT}} = e^{\frac{-14.2\ kJ \times \frac{1000\ J}{1\ kJ}}{\left(8.314 \frac{J}{K\ mol}\right)(298\ K)}} = e^{-5.73142} = 3.24 \times 10^{-3}.$$

Check: The units (none) are correct. The free energy change is positive and the reaction is nonspontaneous. This results in a small K.

b) **Given:** pair ATP hydrolysis with glutamate/NH_3 reaction **Find:** show coupled reactions, $\Delta G°_{rxn}$ and K
Conceptual plan: use reaction mechanism shown, where A = NH_3 and B = glutamate
($C_5H_8O_4N^-$), then calculate $\Delta G°_{rxn}$ by adding free energies of reactions then $\Delta G°_{rxn}$, T $\rightarrow$ K

$$\Delta G^0_{rxn} = -RT \ln K$$

Solution:

$NH_3 (aq) + ATP (aq) + \cancel{H_2O (l)} \rightarrow \cancel{NH_3\text{-}P_i (aq)} + ADP (aq)$ $\qquad\qquad$ $\Delta G^0_{rxn} = -30.5$ kJ

$\cancel{NH_3\text{-}P_i (aq)} + C_5H_8O_4N^- (aq) \rightarrow C_5H_9O_3N_2^- (aq) + \cancel{H_2O (l)} + P_i (aq)$ $\qquad$ $\Delta G^0_{rxn} = +14.2$ kJ then

---

$NH_3 (aq) + C_5H_8O_4N^- (aq) + ATP (aq) \rightarrow C_5H_9O_3N_2^- (aq) + ADP (aq) + P_i (aq)$ $\quad \Delta G^0_{rxn} = -16.3$ kJ

$\Delta G^0_{rxn} = -RT \ln K$ Rearrange to solve for K. $K = e^{\frac{-\Delta G^0_{rxn}}{RT}} = e^{\left(\frac{-(-16.3 \,\cancel{kJ}) \times \frac{1000\,\cancel{J}}{1\,\cancel{kJ}}}{\left(8.314 \frac{\cancel{J}}{\cancel{K}\,mol}\right)(298\,\cancel{K})}\right)} = e^{6.57902} = 7.20 \times 10^2$.

Check: The units (none) are correct. The free energy change is negative and the reaction is spontaneous. This results in a large K.

92. **Given:** flask configurations **Find:** entropy and rank as increasing entropy
Conceptual Plan: calculate the number of possible states then W $\rightarrow$ S then rank

$$W = \frac{n!}{(n-r)!\,r!} \text{ where n = \# particles and r = \# particle in one flask} \qquad S = k \ln W$$

Solution:

a) $W = \dfrac{n!}{(n-r)!\,r!} = \dfrac{5!}{(0)!\,5!} = 1$ then $S = k \ln W = \left(1.38 \times 10^{-23} \dfrac{J}{K}\right) \ln 1 = 0$;

b) $W = \dfrac{n!}{(n-r)!\,r!} = \dfrac{5!}{(2)!\,3!} = 10$ then $S = k \ln W = \left(1.38 \times 10^{-23} \dfrac{J}{K}\right) \ln 10 = 3.18 \times 10^{-23} \dfrac{J}{K}$; and

c) $W = \dfrac{n!}{(n-r)!\,r!} = \dfrac{5!}{(1)!\,4!} = 5$ then $S = k \ln W = \left(1.38 \times 10^{-23} \dfrac{J}{K}\right) \ln 5 = 2.22 \times 10^{-23} \dfrac{J}{K}$. So a) < c) < b).

Check: The units (J/K) are correct. The more possibilities for rearranging particles the higher the entropy.

93. a) **Given:** ½ $H_2 (g)$ + ½ $Cl_2 (g)$ $\rightarrow$ HCl (g), define standard state as 2 atm **Find:** $\Delta G°_f$
Conceptual plan: $\Delta G°_f$, P_{H2}, P_{Cl2}, P_{HCl}, T $\rightarrow$ new $\Delta G°_f$

$$\Delta G_{rxn} = \Delta G^0_{rxn} + RT \ln Q \quad \text{where } Q = \frac{P_{HCl}}{P_{H2}^{1/2} P_{Cl2}^{1/2}}$$

Solution: $\Delta G°_f = -95.3$ kJ/mol and $Q = \dfrac{P_{HCl}}{P_{H2}^{1/2} P_{Cl2}^{1/2}} = \dfrac{2}{2^{1/2}\,2^{1/2}} = 1$ then

$$\Delta G_{rxn} = \Delta G^0_{rxn} + RT \ln Q = -95.3 \frac{kJ}{mol} + \left(8.314 \frac{\cancel{J}}{\cancel{K}\,mol}\right)\left(\frac{1\,kJ}{1000\,\cancel{J}}\right)(298\,\cancel{K}) \ln(1) = -95.3 \frac{kJ}{mol} = -95,300 \frac{J}{mol}.$$

Since the number of moles of reactants and products are the same, the decrease in volume affects the entropy of both equally, so there is no change in $\Delta G°_f$.
Check: The units (kJ) are correct. The Q is one so $\Delta G°_f$ is unchanged under the new standard conditions.

b) **Given:** $N_2 (g)$ + ½ $O_2 (g)$ $\rightarrow$ $N_2O (g)$, define standard state as 2 atm **Find:** $\Delta G°_f$
Conceptual plan: $\Delta G°_f$, P_{N2}, P_{O2}, P_{N2O}, T $\rightarrow$ new $\Delta G°_f$

$$\Delta G_{rxn} = \Delta G^0_{rxn} + RT \ln Q \quad \text{where } Q = \frac{P_{N2O}}{P_{N2} P_{O2}^{1/2}}$$

Solution: $\Delta G°_f = +103.7$ kJ/mol and $Q = \dfrac{P_{N2O}}{P_{N2} P_{O2}^{1/2}} = \dfrac{2}{2\,2^{1/2}} = \dfrac{1}{\sqrt{2}}$ then

$$\Delta G_{rxn} = \Delta G_{rxn}^0 + RT \ln Q = +103.7 \, \frac{kJ}{mol} + \left(8.314 \frac{\cancel{J}}{K \, mol}\right)\left(\frac{1 \, kJ}{1000 \, \cancel{J}}\right)(298 \, \cancel{K}) \ln\left(\frac{1}{\sqrt{2}}\right) = +102.8 \, \frac{kJ}{mol} =$$

$$= +102,800 \, \frac{J}{mol}$$

The entropy of the reactants (1.5 mol) is decreased more than the entropy of the product (1 mol). Since the product is relatively more favored at lower volume, $\Delta G°_f$ is less positive.

Check: The units (kJ) are correct. The Q is less than one so $\Delta G°_f$ is reduced under the new standard conditions.

c) **Given:** ½ H_2 (g) → H (g), define standard state as 2 atm   **Find:** $\Delta G°_f$

Conceptual plan: $\Delta G°_f, P_{H2}, P_H, T$ → new $\Delta G°_f$

$$\Delta G_{rxn} = \Delta G_{rxn}^0 + RT \ln Q \quad \text{where} \quad Q = \frac{P_H}{P_{H2}^{1/2}}$$

Solution: $\Delta G°_f = +203.3 \, kJ/mol$ and $Q = \frac{P_H}{P_{H2}^{1/2}} = \frac{2}{2^{1/2}} = \sqrt{2}$ then

$$\Delta G_{rxn} = \Delta G_{rxn}^0 + RT \ln Q = +203.3 \, \frac{kJ}{mol} + \left(8.314 \frac{\cancel{J}}{K \, mol}\right)\left(\frac{1 \, kJ}{1000 \, \cancel{J}}\right)(298 \, \cancel{K}) \ln\left(\sqrt{2}\right) = +204.2 \, \frac{kJ}{mol} =$$

$$= +204,200 \, \frac{J}{mol}$$

The entropy of the product (1 mol) is decreased more than the entropy of the reactant (1/2 mol). Since the product is relatively less favored, $\Delta G°_f$ is more positive.

Check: The units (kJ) are correct. The Q is greater than one so $\Delta G°_f$ is increased under the new standard conditions.

94. **Given:** H_2O (l) → H_2O (s) at −10 °C $\Delta G_{freezing} = -210 \, J/mol$, $\Delta H_{fusion} = +5610 \, J/mol$ **Find:** $\Delta S_{freezing}$ at −10 °C

Conceptual plan: °C → K   then $\Delta G_{freezing}, \Delta H_{fus}, T$ → $\Delta S_{freezing}$

K = 273.15 + °C $\Delta G = \Delta H_{rxn} - T\Delta S_{rxn}$

Solution: T = −10 °C + 273.15 = 263 K, $\Delta H_{freezing} = -5610 \, J/mol = -\Delta H_{fusion}$ then $\Delta G = \Delta H_{rxn} - T\Delta S_{rxn}$.

Rearrange to solve for ΔS. $\Delta S_{freezing} = \frac{\Delta H_{freezing} - \Delta G_{freezing}}{T} = \frac{-5610 \, J - (-210 \, J)}{263 \, K} = -20.5 \, \frac{J}{K}$.

Check: The units (J/K) are correct. The entropy for freezing should be negative since the solid has a more ordered structure.

95. **Given:** K = 3.9 x 10^5 at 300 K and K = 1.2 x 10^{-1} at 500 K   **Find:** $\Delta H°_{rxn}$, $\Delta S°_{rxn}$

Conceptual Plan: Plot ln K verus 1/T. The slope will be $-\Delta H°_{rxn}/R$ and the intercept will be $\Delta S°_{rxn}/R$.

Solution: Plot ln K verus 1/T. Since $\ln K = -\frac{\Delta H_{rxn}^0}{R}\frac{1}{T} + \frac{\Delta S_{rxn}^0}{R}$, the negative of the slope will be $-\frac{\Delta H_{rxn}^0}{R}$ and

the intercept will be $\frac{\Delta S_{rxn}^0}{R}$. The slope can be determined by measuring $\Delta y/\Delta x$ on the plot or by using functions, such as "add trendline" in Excel. Since the slope is   + 11246 K^{-1},

$\Delta H_{rxn}^0 = -slope \, R =$

$$= -\left(\frac{+11246}{K}\right)\left(8.314 \frac{\cancel{J}}{K \, mol}\right)\left(\frac{1 \, kJ}{1000 \, \cancel{J}}\right) = .$$

$$= -93.499 \, \frac{kJ}{mol} = -93 \, \frac{kJ}{mol}$$

Since the intercept is −24.612,

$$\Delta S_{rxn}^0 = intercept \, R = \left(\frac{-24.612}{K}\right)\left(8.314 \frac{\cancel{J}}{K \, mol}\right) = -204.62 \, \frac{J}{K} = -2.0 \, x \, 10^2 \, \frac{J}{K} .$$

Check: The units are correct (kJ/mole and J/K mol). The numbers are typical for reactions. Since the slope is positive, the enthalpy change must be negative. The entropy change is expected to be negative since the number of moles of gas is decreasing.

96. a) **Given:** $NH_4NO_3\,(s) \rightarrow HNO_3\,(g) + NH_3\,(g)$ **Find:** ΔG°_{rxn}

Conceptual plan: $\Delta G^0_{rxn} = \sum n_P \Delta G^0_f(products) - \sum n_R \Delta G^0_f(reactants)$

Solution:

Reactant/Product	ΔG^0_f (kJ/mol from Appendix IIB)
$NH_4NO_3\,(s)$	-183.9
$HNO_3\,(g)$	-73.5
$NH_3\,(g)$	-16.4

Be sure to pull data for the correct formula and phase.

$\Delta G^0_{rxn} = \sum n_P \Delta G^0_f(products) - \sum n_R \Delta G^0_f(reactants)$

$\qquad = [1(\Delta G^0_f(HNO_3\,(g)) + 1(\Delta G^0_f(NH_3\,(g))] - [1(\Delta G^0_f(NH_4NO_3\,(s))]$

$\qquad = [1(-73.5\,kJ) + 1(-16.4\,kJ)] - [1(-183.9\,kJ)]$

$\qquad = [-89.9\,kJ] - [-183.9\,kJ]$

$\qquad = +94.0\,kJ$

Check: The units (kJ) are correct. The free energy change is positive since ammonium nitrate has such a low free energy of formation.

b) **Given:** $NH_4NO_3\,(s) \rightarrow N_2O\,(g) + 2\,H_2O\,(g)$ **Find:** ΔG°_{rxn}

Conceptual plan: $\Delta G^0_{rxn} = \sum n_P \Delta G^0_f(products) - \sum n_R \Delta G^0_f(reactants)$

Solution:

Reactant/Product	ΔG^0_f (kJ/mol from Appendix IIB)
$NH_4NO_3\,(s)$	-183.9
$N_2O\,(g)$	103.7
$H_2O\,(g)$	-228.6

Be sure to pull data for the correct formula and phase.

$\Delta G^0_{rxn} = \sum n_P \Delta G^0_f(products) - \sum n_R \Delta G^0_f(reactants)$

$\qquad = [1(\Delta G^0_f(N_2O\,(g)) + 2(\Delta G^0_f(H_2O\,(g))] - [1(\Delta G^0_f(NH_4NO_3\,(s))]$

$\qquad = [1(103.7\,kJ) + 2(-228.6\,kJ)] - [1(-183.9\,kJ)]$

$\qquad = [-353.5\,kJ] - [-183.9\,kJ]$

$\qquad = -169.6\,kJ$

Check: The units (kJ) are correct. The free energy change is negative since water has such a low free energy of formation.

c) **Given:** $NH_4NO_3\,(s) \rightarrow N_2\,(g) + \tfrac{1}{2}\,O_2\,(g) + 2\,H_2O\,(g)$ **Find:** ΔG°_{rxn}

Conceptual plan: $\Delta G^0_{rxn} = \sum n_P \Delta G^0_f(products) - \sum n_R \Delta G^0_f(reactants)$

Solution:

Reactant/Product	ΔG^0_f (kJ/mol from Appendix IIB)
$NH_4NO_3\,(s)$	-183.9
$N_2\,(g)$	0.0
$O_2\,(g)$	0.0
$H_2O\,(g)$	-228.6

Be sure to pull data for the correct formula and phase.

$\Delta G^0_{rxn} = \sum n_P \Delta G^0_f(products) - \sum n_R \Delta G^0_f(reactants)$

$\qquad = [1(\Delta G^0_f(N_2\,(g)) + 1/2(\Delta G^0_f(O_2\,(g)) + 2(\Delta G^0_f(H_2O\,(g))] - [1(\Delta G^0_f(NH_4NO_3\,(s))]$

$\qquad = [1(0.0\,kJ) + 1/2(0.0\,kJ) + 2(-228.6\,kJ)] - [1(-183.9\,kJ)]$

$\qquad = [-457.2\,kJ] - [-183.9\,kJ]$

$\qquad = -273.3\,kJ$

Check: The units (kJ) are correct. The free energy change is negative since water has such a low free energy of formation.

The second and third reactions are spontaneous and so we would expect decomposition products of N_2O, N_2, O_2, and H_2O in the gas phase. It is still possible for ammonium nitrate to remain as a solid because the thermodynamics of the reaction says nothing of the kinetics of the reaction (reaction can be extremely slow). Since all of the products are gasses, the decomposition of ammonium nitrate will result in a large increase in volume (explosion). Some of the products aid in combustion, which could facilitate the combustion of materials near the ammonium nitrate. Also, N_2O is known as laughing gas, which has anesthetic and toxic effects on humans. The solid should not be kept in tightly sealed containers.

97. A butane lighter is more efficient than an electric lighter since the butane lighter process is accomplished in one step. When you use an electric lighter, fuel is burned to generate electricity. This electricity is transmitted to the lighter through wires. Once it reaches the lighter, the electricity then needs to be converted to heat. Each step must pay a heat tax. Using a butane lighter has fewer steps and so it pays a much lower tax.

98. c) The spontaneity of a reaction says nothing about the speed of a reaction. It only states which direction the reaction will go as it approaches equilibrium.

99. a) and c) will both increase the entropy of the surroundings because they are both exothermic reactions (adding thermal energy to the surroundings).

100. b) has the largest decrease in the number of microstates from the initial to the final state. In a) there are initially $\dfrac{9!}{4!\,4!\,1!} = 90$ microstates and $\dfrac{9!}{3!\,3!\,3!} = 1680$ microstates at the end, so $\Delta S > 0$. In b) there are initially $\dfrac{9!}{4!\,2!\,3!} = 1260$ microstates and $\dfrac{9!}{6!\,3!\,0!} = 84$ microstates at the end, so $\Delta S < 0$. In c) there are initially $\dfrac{9!}{3!\,4!\,2!} = 1260$ microstates and $\dfrac{9!}{3!\,4!\,2!} = 1260$ microstates at the end, so $\Delta S = 0$. Also the final state in b) has the lease entropy.

101. c) If the entropy of a system is increasing, the enthalpy of a reaction can be overcome (if necessary) by the entropy change as long as the temperature is high enough. If the entropy change of the system is decreasing, the reaction must be exothermic in order to be spontaneous since the entropy is working against spontaneity.

102. c) Since the vapor pressure of water at 298 K is 23.78 mm Hg or 0.03129 atm. As long as the desired pressure (0.010 atm) is less than the equilibrium vapor pressure of water, the reaction will be spontaneous.

103. a) and b) are both true. Since $\Delta G_{rxn} = \Delta G_{rxn}^0 + RT\ln Q$ and $\Delta G_{rxn}^\circ = -42.5$ kJ, in order for $\Delta G_{rxn} = 0$ the second term must be positive. This necessitates that $Q > 1$ or that we have more product than reactant. Any reaction at equilibrium has $\Delta G_{rxn} = 0$.

Chapter 18
Electrochemistry

1. Electrochemistry uses spontaneous redox reactions to generate electrical energy.

2. Electricity can be used to drive non-spontaneous redox reactions, such as those that occur in gold or silver plating.

3. Oxidation is the loss of electrons and corresponds to an increase in oxidation state. Reduction is the gain of electrons and corresponds to a decrease in oxidation state. Balancing redox reactions can be more complicated than balancing other types of reactions because both the mass (or number of each type of atom) and the charge must be balanced. Redox reactions occurring in aqueous solutions can be balanced by using a special procedure called the half-reaction method of balancing. In this procedure, the overall equation is broken down into two half-reactions: one for oxidation and one for reduction. The half-reactions are balanced individually and then added together so that the number of electrons generated in the oxidation half-reaction is the same as the number of electrons consumed in the reduction half-reaction.

4. A voltaic (or galvanic) cell produces electrical current from a spontaneous chemical reaction. An electrochemical cell, called an eletrolytic cell, uses electrical current to drive a nonspontaneous chemical reaction.

5. In all electrochemical cells, the electrode where oxidation occurs is called the anode. In a voltaic cell, the anode is labeled with a negative (–) sign. The anode is negative because the oxidation reaction that occurs at the anode releases electrons. Electrons flow from the anode to the cathode (from negative to positive) through the wires connecting the electrodes.

6. In all electrochemical cells, the electrode where reduction occurs is called the cathode. The cathode of a voltaic cell is labeled with a (+) sign. The cathode is positive because the reduction reaction that occurs at the cathode takes up electrons. Electrons flow from the anode to the cathode (from negative to positive) through the wires connecting the electrodes.

7. A salt bridge is a pathway by which ions can flow between the half-cells, completing the electrical circuit, without the solutions in the half-cells totally mixing.

8. Electrical current is measured in units of amperes (A). One ampere, or amp, represents the flow of one coulomb (a measure of electrical charge) per second: $1 \, A = 1 \, C/s$. Potential difference is a measure of the difference in potential energy (usually in joules) per unit of charge (coulombs). The SI unit of potential difference is the volt (V), which is equal to one joule per coulomb: $1 \, V = 1 \, J/C$. The potential difference is the drop in potential energy and the current is a measure of how many electrons travel across this potential difference.

9. The standard cell potential (E°_{cell}) or standard emf is the cell potential under standard conditions (1 M concentration for reactants in solution and 1 atm pressure for gaseous reactants). The cell potential is a measure of the overall tendency of the redox reaction to occur spontaneously. The more positive the cell potential, the more spontaneous the reaction. A negative cell potential indicates a nonspontaneous reaction.

10. Electrochemical cells are often represented with a compact notation called a cell diagram or line notation. In this representation, the oxidation half-reaction is always written on the left and the reduction on the right. A double vertical line (‖), indicating the salt bridge, separates the two half-reactions. Substances in different phases are separated by a single vertical line (|), which represents the boundary between the phases. For some redox reactions, the reactants and products of one or both of the half-reactions may be in the same phase. In these cases, the reactants and products are simply separated from each other with a comma in the line diagram. Such cells use an inert electrode, such as platinum (Pt) or graphite, as the anode or cathode (or both).

11. Inert electrode, such as platinum (Pt) or graphite, are used as the anode or cathode (or both) when the reactants and products of one or both of the half-reactions are in the same phase.

12. The standard hydrogen electrode (SHE) half-cell is the half-cell that is normally chosen to have a potential of zero. This cell consists of an inert platinum electrode imersed in 1 M HCl with hydrogen gas at 1 atm

bubbling through the solution. When the SHE acts as the cathode, the following half-reaction occurs: $2\,H^+$ $(aq) + 2\,e^- \rightarrow H_2(g)$ $E^{\circ}_{red} = 0.00$ V. If we combine the standard hydrogen electrode half-cell with another half-cell of interest, we can measure the voltage and assign it to the half-cell of interest.

13. The overall cell potential for any electrochemical cell will always be the sum of the half-cell potential for the oxidation reaction and the half-cell potential for the reduction reaction or $E^{\circ}_{cell} = E^{\circ}_{ox} + E^{\circ}_{red.}$

14. Half-reactions with large positive reduction half-cell potentials have a strong tendency to have the reduction reaction occur in the forward direction and the reactants are therefore excellent oxidzing agents. Half-reactions with large negative reduction half-cell potentials have a strong tendency for the reduction reaction to occur in the reverse direction and so they have a strong tendency to be oxidized. These are excellent reducing agents.

15. In general, any reduction half-reaction will be spontaneous when paired with the reverse of a half-reaction below it in the table.

16. In general, metals whose reduction half-reactions lie below the reduction of H^+ to H_2 in Table 18.1 will dissolve in acids, while metals above it will not. An important exception to this rule is nitric acid (HNO_3) which can oxidize metals through the following reduction half-reaction: NO_3^- $(aq) + 4\,H^+(aq) + 3\,e^- \rightarrow NO$ $(g) + 2\,H_2O$ (l) $E^{\circ}_{red} = 0.96$ V. Since this half-reaction is above the reduction of H^+ in Table 18.1, HNO_3 can oxidize metals (such as copper, for example) that can't be oxidizied by HCl.

17. We have seen that a positive standard cell potential (E^{0}_{cell}) corresponds to a spontaneous oxidation-reduction reaction. We also know (from Chapter 17) that the spontaneity of a reaction is determined by the sign of ΔG°. Therefore, E°_{cell} and ΔG° must be related. We also know from Section 17.9 that ΔG° for a reaction is related to the equilibrium constant (K) for the reaction. Since E°_{cell} and ΔG° are related, then E°_{cell} and K must also be related. The equation that relates the three quantities is: $\Delta G^{0}_{rxn} = -RT \ln K = -n\,F\,E^{0}_{cell}$.

18. A redox reaction with a small equilibrium constant (K < 1) will not be spontaneous and so will have a negative E^{0}_{cell} and a negative ΔG°_{rxn}.

19. The Nernst equation relates concentration and cell potential as follows: $E_{cell} = E^{\circ}_{cell} - \dfrac{0.0592\ V}{n} \log Q$,

    where E_{cell} is the cell potential in V, E°_{cell} is the standard cell potential in V, n is the number of moles of electrons transferred in the redox reaction, and Q is the reaction quotient. Increasing the concentration of the reactants decreases the value of Q and so it increases the cell potential. Increasing the concentration of the products increases the value of Q and so it decreases the cell potential.

20. The Nernst equation states that: $E_{cell} = E^{\circ}_{cell} - \dfrac{0.0592\ V}{n} \log Q$. Under standard conditions, $Q = 1$, and (since $\log 1 = 0$) the second term drops out and $E_{cell} = E^{\circ}_{cell}$.

21. A concentration cell is a voltaic cell in which both half reactions are the same, but in which a difference in concentration drives the current flow (since the cell potential depends, not only on the half-reactions occurring in the cell, but also on the concentrations of the reactants and products in those half-reactions). Therefore $E_{cell} = -\dfrac{0.0592\ V}{n} \log Q$.

22. In an inexpensive dry-cell battery zinc is oxidized at the anode according to the following reaction: Zn (s) $\rightarrow Zn^{2+}$ $(aq) + 2\,e^-$. The cathode is a carbon rod immersed in a moist paste of MnO_2 that also contains NH_4Cl. The MnO_2 is reduced to Mn_2O_3 according to the following reaction: $2\,MnO_2$ $(s) + 2\,NH_4^+$ $(aq) + 2$ $e^- \rightarrow Mn_2O_3$ $(s) + 2\,NH_3(aq) + H_2O$ (l). These two half-reactions produce a voltage of about 1.5 volts.

    The more common alkaline batteries employ slightly different half-reactions that use a base (therefore the name alkaline). The anode reaction is: Zn $(s) + 2\,OH^-$ $(aq) \rightarrow Zn(OH)_2$ $(s) + 2\,e^-$. The cathode reaction is: $2\,MnO_2$ $(s) + 2\,H_2O$ $(l) + 2\,e^- \rightarrow 2\,MnO(OH)$ $(s) + 2\,OH^-$ (aq).

23. Lead-acid storage batteries consist of six electrochemical cells wired in series, in which each cell produces 2 V for a total of 12 V. Each cell contains a porous lead anode where oxidation occurs according to: Pb $(s) +$

HSO_4^- *(aq)* $\rightarrow$ $PbSO_4$ *(s)* + H^+ *(aq)* + 2 e^- and a lead(IV) oxide cathode where reduction occurs according to: PbO_2 *(s)* + HSO_4^- *(aq)* + 3 H^+ *(aq)* + 2 e^- $\rightarrow$ $PbSO_4$ *(s)* + 2 H_2O *(l)*. As electrical current is drawn from the battery, both the anode and the cathode become coated with $PbSO_4$ *(s)* and the solution becomes depleted of HSO_4^- (aq). If the battery is run for a long time without recharging, too much $PbSO_4$ *(s)* develops on the surface of the electrodes and the battery goes dead. The lead-acid storage battery can be recharged, however, by running electrical current through it in reverse. The electrical current, which must come from an external source such as an alternator in a car, causes the preceding reaction to occur in reverse, converting the $PbSO_4$ *(s)* back to Pb *(s)* and PbO_2 *(s)*, recharging the battery.

24. The most common types of portable rechargeable batteries include the nickel-cadmium (NiCad) battery, the nickel metal hydride (NiMH) battery, and the lithium ion battery.

    The Nickel-Cadmium (NiCad) battery consists of an anode composed of solid cadmiun and a cathode composed of NiO(OH)(s). The electrolyte is usually KOH(aq). During operation, the cadmium is oxidized and the NiO(OH) is reduced according to the following equations:
    Anode reaction: Cd *(s)* + 2 OH⁻ *(aq)* $\rightarrow$ $Cd(OH)_2$ *(s)* + 2 e⁻
    Cathode reaction: 2NiO(OH) *(s)* + 2 H_2O *(l)* + 2e⁻ $\rightarrow$ 2 $Ni(OH)_2$ *(s)* + 2 OH⁻ *(aq)*
    The overall reaction produces about 1.30 V. As current is drawn from the NiCad battery, solid cadmium hydroxide accumulates on the anode and solid nickel(II) hydroxide accumulates on the cathode. By running current in the opposite direction, the reactants can be regenerated from the products.

    The NiMH battery uses the same cathode reaction as the NiCad battery but a different anode reaction. In the anode of a NiMH battery, hydrogen atoms held in a metal alloy are oxidized. If we let M represent the metal alloy, we can write the half-reactions as follows:
    Anode reaction: M $\cdot$ H *(s)* + OH⁻ *(aq)* $\rightarrow$ M *(s)* + H_2O *(l)* + e⁻
    Cathode reaction: NiO(OH) *(s)* + H_2O *(l)* + e⁻ $\rightarrow$ $Ni(OH)_2$ *(s)* + OH⁻ *(aq)*.

    The Lithium-Ion Battery is the newest and most expensive common type of rechargeable battery. The lithium battery works differently than the other batteries we have examined so far, and the details of its operation are beyond our current scope. Briefly, we can think of the operation of the lithium battery as being due primarily to the motion of lithium ions from the anode to the cathode. The anode is composed of graphite into which lithium ions are incorporated between layers of carbon atoms. Upon discharge, the lithium ions spontaneously migrate to the cathode, which consists of a lithium transition metal oxide such as $LiCoO_2$ or $LiMn_2O_4$. The transition metal is reduced during this process. Upon recharging, the transition metal is oxidized, forcing the lithium to migrate back into the graphite. The flow of lithium ions from the anode to the cathode causes a corresponding flow of electrons in the external circuit.

25. Fuel cells are like batteries, but the reactants must be constantly replenished. Normal batteries lose their ability to generate voltage with use because the reactants become depleted as electrical current is drawn from the battery. In a fuel cell, the reactants—the fuel—constantly flow through the battery, generating electrical current as they undergo a redox reaction.

    The most common fuel cell is the hydrogen–oxygen fuel cell. In the cell, hydrogen gas flows past the anode (a screen coated with platinum catalyst) and undergoes oxidation: 2 H_2 *(g)* + 4 OH⁻ *(aq)* $\rightarrow$ 4 H_2O *(l)* + 4 e⁻ . Oxygen gas flows past the cathode (a similar screen) and undergoes reduction: O_2 *(g)* + 2 H_2O *(l)* + 4 e⁻ $\rightarrow$ 4 OH⁻ *(aq)*. The half-reactions sum to the following overall reaction: 2 H_2 *(g)* + O_2 *(g)* $\rightarrow$ 2 H_2O *(l)*. Notice that the only product is water.

26. Breathalyzers work because the quantity of ethyl alcohol (CH_3CH_2OH) in the breath is proportional to the quantity of ethyl alcohol in the bloodstream. One type of breathalyzer employs a fuel cell to measure the quantity of alcohol in the breath. When a suspect blows into the breathalyzer, ethyl alcohol is oxidized to acetic acid ($HC_2H_3O_2$) at the anode according to the following reaction: CH_3CH_2OH *(g)* + OH⁻ *(aq)* $\rightarrow$ $HC_2H_3O_2$ *(g)* + 3 H_2O *(l)* + 4 e⁻. At the cathode, oxygen is reduced according to the following reaction: O_2 *(g)* + 2 H_2O *(l)* + 4 e⁻ $\rightarrow$ 4 OH⁻ *(aq)*. The overall reaction is simply the oxidation of ethyl alcohol to acetic acid and water as follows: CH_3CH_2OH *(g)* + O_2 *(g)* $\rightarrow$ $HC_2H_3O_2$ *(g)* + H_2O *(l)*. The magnitude of electrical current produced depends on the quantity of alcohol in the breath. A higher current reveals a higher blood alcohol level. When calibrated correctly, the fuel-cell breathalyzer can precisely measure the blood alcohol level of a suspected drunk driver.

27. Applications of electrolysis include breaking water into hydrogen and oxygen; converting metal oxides to

pure metals; production of sodium from molten sodium chloride; and plating metals onto other metals (for example, silver can be plated onto a less expensive metal).

28. In an electrolytic cell, the source of the electrons is the external power source. The external power source must draw electrons away from the anode; thus, the anode must be connected to the positive terminal of the battery (as shown in Figure 18.22). Similarly, the power source drives electrons towards the cathode (where they will be used in reduction), so the cathode must be connected to the negative terminal of the battery. The charge labels (+ and -) on an electrolytic cell are therefore opposite of what they are in a voltaic cell.

29. The anion is oxidized. The cation is reduced to the metal.

30. In the electrolysis of a mixture of ions: the cation that is most easily reduced (the one with the least negative, or most positive, reduction half-cell potential) is reduced first; and the anion that is most easily oxidized (the one that has the least negative, or most positive, oxidation half-cell potential) will be oxidized first.

31. In the electrolysis of aqueous NaCl solutions, two different reduction half-reactions are possible at the cathode, the reduction of Na^+ and the reduction of water:
$$2\ Na^+ (l) + 2\ e^- \rightarrow 2\ Na\ (s) \qquad\qquad E^\circ_{red} = -2.71\ V$$
$$2\ H_2O\ (l) + 2\ e^- \rightarrow H_2\ (g) + 2\ OH^-\ (aq) \qquad E_{red} = -0.41\ V\ ([OH^-] = 10^{-7}\ M)$$
The half-reaction that occurs most easily (the one with the least negative, or most positive, half-cell potential) will be the one that actually occurs.

32. An overvoltage is an additional voltage that must be applied in order to get some non-spontaneous reactions to occur. Overvoltages are important because the desired reaction may not occur.

33. We can determine the number of moles of electrons that have flowed in a given electrolysis cell by measuring the total charge that has flowed through cell, which in turn depends on the magnitude of current and the time that the current has run. Since 1 Amphere = 1 C/s, if we multiply the amount of current (in A) flowing through the cell by the time (in s) that the current flowed, we can find the total charge that passed through the cell in that time: current (C/s) × time (s) = charge (C). The relationship between charge and the number of moles of electrons is given by Faraday's constant, which corresponds to the charge in coulombs of 1 mol of electrons, so F = 96,485 C/mole e⁻. These relationships can be used to solve problems involving the stoichiometry of electrolytic cells.

34. Corrosion is the (usually) gradual nearly always undesired oxidation of metals that occurs when they are exposed to oxidizing agents in the environment. This metal oxidation will be spontaneous when the half-reaction for the reduction of the metal ion lies below the half-reactions for the reduction of oxygen (+ 1.23 V) in Table 18.1. Many metals, such as aluminum, form oxides that coat the surface of the metal and prevent further corrosion.

35. Moisture must be present for many corrosion reactions to occur. The presence of water is necessary because water is a reactant in many oxidation reactions (such as $4\ Fe^{2+}\ (aq) + O_2\ (g) + (4 + 2n)\ H_2O\ (l) \rightarrow 2Fe_2O_3 \cdot nH_2O\ (s) + 8\ H^+\ (aq)$, and also because charge (either electrons or ions) must be free to flow between the anodic and cathodic regions.

Additional electrolytes promote more corrosion. The presence of an electrolyte (such as sodium chloride) on the surface of iron promotes rusting because it enhances current flow. This is why cars rust so quickly in cold climates where roads are salted, or in areas directly adjacent to beaches where salt water mist is present.

The presence of acids promotes corrosion. Since H^+ ions are involved in the reduction of oxygen, lower pH enhances the cathodic reaction and leads to faster corrosion.

36. The most obvious way to prevent rust formation is to keep iron dry. Without water, the redox reaction cannot occur. Another way of preventing rust formaation is to coat the iron with a substance that is impervious to water. Cars, for example, are painted and sealed to prevent rust. A scratch in the paint, however, can lead to rusting of the underlying iron . Rust can also be prevented by placing a sacrificial electrode in electrical contact with the iron. The sacrificial electrode must be composed of a metal that oxidizes more easily than iron (that is, it must be below iron in Table 18.1). The sacrificial electrode then oxidizes in place of the iron (just as the more easily oxidizable species in a mixture will be the one to

oxidize), protecting the iron from oxidation. Another way to protect iron from rusting is to coat it with a metal that oxidizes more easily than iron. Galvanized nails, for example, are coated with a thin layer of zinc. Since zinc has a more positive half-cell potential for oxidation, it will oxidize in place of the underlying iron (just as a sacrificial electrode does). The oxide of zinc is not crumbly and remains on the nail as a protective coating.

37. **Conceptual Plan: Separate the overall reaction into two half-reactions: one for oxidation and one for reduction. → Balance each half-reaction with respect to mass in the following order: 1) balance all elements other than H and O; 2) balance O by adding H_2O; and 3) balance H by adding H^+. → Balance each half reaction with respect to charge by adding electrons. (The sum of the charges on both sides of the equation should be made equal by adding electrons as necessary.) → Make the number of electrons in both half-reactions equal by multiplying one or both half-reactions by a small whole number. → Add the two half-reactions together, canceling electrons and other species as necessary. → Verify that the reaction is balanced both with respect to mass and with respect to charge.**
Solution:

a) Separate: $K\ (s) \rightarrow K^+\ (aq)$ and $Cr^{3+}\ (aq) \rightarrow Cr\ (s)$
   Balance elements: $K\ (s) \rightarrow K^+\ (aq)$ and $Cr^{3+}\ (aq) \rightarrow Cr\ (s)$
   Add electrons: $K\ (s) \rightarrow K^+\ (aq) + e^-$ and $Cr^{3+}\ (aq) + 3\ e^- \rightarrow Cr\ (s)$
   Equalize electrons: $3\ K\ (s) \rightarrow 3\ K^+\ (aq) + 3\ e^-$ and $Cr^{3+}\ (aq) + 3\ e^- \rightarrow Cr\ (s)$

   Add half-reactions: $3\ K\ (s) +\ Cr^{3+}\ (aq) +\ \cancel{3e^-} \rightarrow 3\ K^+\ (aq) +\ \cancel{3e^-} +\ Cr\ (s)$

   Cancel electrons: $3\ K\ (s) +\ Cr^{3+}\ (aq) \rightarrow 3\ K^+\ (aq) +\ Cr\ (s)$
   Check:

Reactants	Products
3 K atoms	3 K atoms
1 Cr atom	1 Cr atom
+3 charge	+3 charge

b) Separate: $Al\ (s) \rightarrow Al^{3+}\ (aq)$ and $Fe^{2+}\ (aq) \rightarrow Fe\ (s)$
   Balance elements: $Al\ (s) \rightarrow Al^{3+}\ (aq)$ and $Fe^{2+}\ (aq) \rightarrow Fe\ (s)$
   Add electrons: $Al\ (s) \rightarrow Al^{3+}\ (aq) + 3\ e^-$ and $Fe^{2+}\ (aq) + 2\ e^- \rightarrow Fe\ (s)$
   Equalize electrons: $2\ Al\ (s) \rightarrow 2\ Al^{3+}\ (aq) + 6\ e^-$ and $3\ Fe^{2+}\ (aq) + 6\ e^- \rightarrow 3\ Fe\ (s)$

   Add half-reactions: $2\ Al\ (s) +\ 3\ Fe^{2+}\ (aq) +\ \cancel{6e^-} \rightarrow 2\ Al^{3+}\ (aq) +\ \cancel{6e^-} +\ 3\ Fe\ (s)$

   Cancel electrons: $2\ Al\ (s) +\ 3\ Fe^{2+}\ (aq) \rightarrow 2\ Al^{3+}\ (aq) +\ 3\ Fe\ (s)$
   Check:

Reactants	Products
2 Al atoms	2 Al atoms
3 Fe atom	3 Fe atom
+6 charge	+6 charge

c) Separate: $BrO_3^-\ (aq) \rightarrow Br^-\ (aq)$ and $N_2H_4\ (g) \rightarrow N_2\ (g)$
   Balance non H & O elements: $BrO_3^-\ (aq) \rightarrow Br^-\ (aq)$ and $N_2H_4\ (g) \rightarrow N_2\ (g)$
   Balance O with H_2O: $BrO_3^-\ (aq) \rightarrow Br^-\ (aq) + 3\ H_2O\ (l)$ and $N_2H_4\ (g) \rightarrow N_2\ (g)$
   Balance H with H^+: $BrO_3^-\ (aq) + 6\ H^+\ (aq) \rightarrow Br^-\ (aq) + 3\ H_2O\ (l)$ and $N_2H_4\ (g) \rightarrow N_2\ (g) + 4\ H^+$ (aq)
   Add electrons: $BrO_3^-\ (aq) + 6\ H^+\ (aq) + 6\ e^- \rightarrow Br^-\ (aq) + 3\ H_2O\ (l)$ and $N_2H_4\ (g) \rightarrow N_2\ (g) + 4\ H^+\ (aq)$ $+ 4\ e^-$
   Equalize electrons:
   $2\ BrO_3^-\ (aq) + 12\ H^+\ (aq) + 12\ e^- \rightarrow 2\ Br^-\ (aq) + 6\ H_2O\ (l)$ and $3\ N_2H_4\ (g) \rightarrow 3\ N_2\ (g) + 12\ H^+\ (aq) + 12\ e^-$
   Add half-reactions:

   $2\ BrO_3^-\ (aq) +\ \cancel{12\ H^+ (aq)} +\ 3\ N_2H_4\ (g) +\ \cancel{12e^-} \rightarrow 2\ Br^-\ (aq) + 6\ H_2O\ (l) + 3\ N_2\ (g) +$

   $\cancel{12\ H^+ (aq)} +\ \cancel{12e^-}$

   Cancel electrons & others: $2\ BrO_3^-\ (aq) + 3\ N_2H_4\ (g) \rightarrow 2\ Br^-\ (aq) + 6\ H_2O\ (l) + 3\ N_2\ (g)$
   Check:

Reactants	Products
3 Br atoms	3 Br atoms
6 O atoms	6 O atoms
12 H atoms	12 H atoms
6 N atoms	6 N atoms
–2 charge	–2 charge

38. **Conceptual Plan: Separate the overall reaction into two half-reactions: one for oxidation and one for reduction. → Balance each half-reaction with respect to mass in the following order: 1) balance all elements other than H and O; 2) balance O by adding H_2O; and 3) balance H by adding H^+. → Balance each half reaction with respect to charge by adding electrons. (The sum of the charges on both sides of the equation should be made equal by adding electrons as necessary.) → Make the number of electrons in both half-reactions equal by multiplying one or both half-reactions by a small whole number. → Add the two half-reactions together, canceling electrons and other species as necessary. → Verify that the reaction is balanced both with respect to mass and with respect to charge.**

Solution:

a) Separate: $\quad\quad\quad\quad$ $Zn\ (s) \rightarrow Zn^{+2}\ (aq)$ $\quad$ and $\quad$ $Sn^{2+}\ (aq) \rightarrow Sn\ (s)$

$\quad$ Balance elements: $\quad$ $Zn\ (s) \rightarrow Zn^{+2}\ (aq)$ $\quad$ and $\quad$ $Sn^{2+}\ (aq) \rightarrow Sn\ (s)$

$\quad$ Add electrons: $\quad\quad$ $Zn\ (s) \rightarrow Zn^{+2}\ (aq) + 2\ e^-$ and $\quad$ $Sn^{2+}\ (aq) + 2\ e^- \rightarrow Sn\ (s)$

$\quad$ Equalize electrons: $\quad$ $Zn\ (s) \rightarrow Zn^{+2}\ (aq) + 2\ e^-$ and $\quad$ $Sn^{2+}\ (aq) + 2\ e^- \rightarrow Sn\ (s)$

$\quad$ Add half-reactions: $\quad$ $Zn\ (s) + Sn^{2+}\ (aq) + \cancel{2e^-} \rightarrow Zn^{+2}\ (aq) + \cancel{2e^-} + Sn\ (s)$

$\quad$ Cancel electrons: $\quad\quad$ $Zn\ (s) + Sn^{2+}\ (aq) \rightarrow Zn^{+2}\ (aq) + Sn\ (s)$

$\quad$ **Check:**

Reactants	Products
1 Zn atom	1 Zn atom
1 Sn atom	1 Sn atom
+2 charge	+2 charge

b) Separate: $\quad\quad\quad\quad$ $Mg\ (s) \rightarrow Mg^{2+}\ (aq)$ $\quad$ and $\quad$ $Cr^{3+}\ (aq) \rightarrow Cr\ (s)$

$\quad$ Balance elements: $\quad$ $Mg\ (s) \rightarrow Mg^{2+}\ (aq)$ $\quad$ and $\quad$ $Cr^{3+}\ (aq) \rightarrow Cr\ (s)$

$\quad$ Add electrons: $\quad\quad$ $Mg\ (s) \rightarrow Mg^{2+}\ (aq) + 2\ e^-$ and $\quad$ $Cr^{3+}\ (aq) + 3\ e^- \rightarrow Cr\ (s)$

$\quad$ Equalize electrons: $\quad$ $3\ Mg\ (s) \rightarrow 3\ Mg^{2+}\ (aq) + 6\ e^-$ and $\quad$ $2\ Cr^{3+}\ (aq) + 6\ e^- \rightarrow 2\ Cr\ (s)$

$\quad$ Add half-reactions: $\quad$ $3\ Mg\ (s) + 2\ Cr^{3+}\ (aq) + \cancel{6e^-} \rightarrow 3\ Mg^{2+}\ (aq) + \cancel{6e^-} + 2\ Cr\ (s)$

$\quad$ Cancel electrons: $\quad\quad$ $3\ Mg\ (s) + 2\ Cr^{3+}\ (aq) \rightarrow 3\ Mg^{2+}\ (aq) + 2\ Cr\ (s)$

$\quad$ **Check:**

Reactants	Products
3 Mg atoms	3 Mg atoms
2 Cr atoms	2 Cr atoms
+6 charge	+6 charge

c) Separate: $\quad\quad\quad\quad$ $MnO_4^-\ (aq) \rightarrow Mn^{2+}\ (aq)$ $\quad$ and $\quad$ $Al\ (s) \rightarrow Al^{3+}\ (aq)$

$\quad$ Balance non H & O elements: $MnO_4^-\ (aq) \rightarrow Mn^{2+}\ (aq)$ $\quad$ and $\quad$ $Al\ (s) \rightarrow Al^{3+}\ (aq)$

$\quad$ Balance O with H_2O: $\quad$ $MnO_4^-\ (aq) \rightarrow Mn^{2+}\ (aq) + 4\ H_2O\ (l)$ and $\quad$ $Al\ (s) \rightarrow Al^{3+}\ (aq)$

$\quad$ Balance H with H^+: $\quad$ $MnO_4^-\ (aq) + 8\ H^+\ (aq) \rightarrow Mn^{2+}\ (aq) + 4\ H_2O\ (l)$ and $\quad$ $Al\ (s) \rightarrow Al^{3+}\ (aq)$

$\quad$ Add electrons: $MnO_4^-\ (aq) + 8\ H^+\ (aq) + 5\ e^- \rightarrow Mn^{2+}\ (aq) + 4\ H_2O\ (l)$ and $Al\ (s) \rightarrow Al^{3+}\ (aq) + 3\ e^-$

$\quad$ Equalize electrons:

$\quad$ $3\ MnO_4^-\ (aq) + 24\ H^+\ (aq) + 15\ e^- \rightarrow 3\ Mn^{2+}\ (aq) + 12\ H_2O\ (l)$ and $\ 5\ Al\ (s) \rightarrow 5\ Al^{3+}\ (aq) + 15\ e^-$

$\quad$ Add half-reactions:

$\quad\quad$ $3\ MnO_4^-\ (aq) + 24\ H^+\ (aq) + \cancel{15\ e^-} + 5\ Al\ (s) \rightarrow 3\ Mn^{2+}\ (aq) + 12\ H_2O\ (l) + 5\ Al^{3+}\ (aq) + \cancel{15\ e^-}$

$\quad$ Cancel electrons: $\quad$ $3\ MnO_4^-\ (aq) + 24\ H^+\ (aq) + 5\ Al\ (s) \rightarrow 3\ Mn^{2+}\ (aq) + 12\ H_2O\ (l) + 5\ Al^{3+}\ (aq)$

$\quad$ **Check:**

Reactants	Products
3 Mn atoms	3 Mn atoms
12 O atoms	12 O atoms
24 H atoms	24 H atoms
5 Al atoms	5 Al atoms
+21 charge	+21 charge

39. **Conceptual Plan: Separate the overall reaction into two half-reactions: one for oxidation and one for reduction. → Balance each half-reaction with respect to mass in the following order: 1) balance all elements other than H and O; 2) balance O by adding H_2O; and 3) balance H by adding H^+. → Balance each half reaction with respect to charge by adding electrons. (The sum of the charges on both sides of the equation should be made equal by adding electrons as necessary.) → Make the number of electrons in both half-reactions equal by multiplying one or both half-reactions by a small whole number. → Add the two half-reactions together, canceling electrons and other species as necessary. → Verify that the reaction is balanced both with respect to mass and with respect to charge.**

Solution:

a) Separate: PbO_2 (s) → Pb^{2+} (aq)   and I^- (aq) → I_2 (s)

Balance non H & O elements: PbO_2 (s) → Pb^{2+} (aq)   and $2 I^-$ (aq) → I_2 (s)

Balance O with H_2O: PbO_2 (s) → Pb^{2+} (aq) + $2 H_2O$ (l)   and $2 I^-$ (aq) → I_2 (s)

Balance H with H^+: PbO_2 (s) + $4 H^+$ (aq) → Pb^{2+} (aq) + $2 H_2O$ (l)   and $2 I^-$ (aq) → I_2 (s)

Add electrons: PbO_2 (s) + $4 H^+$ (aq) + $2 e^-$ → Pb^{2+} (aq) + $2 H_2O$ (l) and $2 I^-$ (aq) → I_2 (s) + $2 e^-$

Equalize electrons: PbO_2 (s) + $4 H^+$ (aq) + $2 e^-$ → Pb^{2+} (aq) + $2 H_2O$ (l) and $2 I^-$ (aq) → I_2 (s) + $2 e^-$

Add half-reactions: PbO_2 (s) + $4 H^+$ (aq) + $\cancel{2e^-}$ + $2 I^-$ (aq) → Pb^{2+} (aq) + $2 H_2O$ (l) + I_2 (s) + $\cancel{2e^-}$

Cancel electrons & others: PbO_2 (s) + $4 H^+$ (aq) + $2 I^-$ (aq) → Pb^{2+} (aq) + $2 H_2O$ (l) + I_2 (s)

Check:

Reactants	Products
1 Pb atom	1 Pb atom
2 O atoms	2 O atoms
4 H atoms	4 H atoms
2 I atoms	2 I atoms
+2 charge	+2 charge

b) Separate: MnO_4^- (aq) → Mn^{2+} (aq)   and SO_3^{2-} (aq) → SO_4^{2-} (aq)

Balance non H & O elements: MnO_4^- (aq) → Mn^{2+} (aq)   and SO_3^{2-} (aq) → SO_4^{2-} (aq)

Balance O with H_2O: MnO_4^- (aq) → Mn^{2+} (aq) + $4 H_2O$ (l)   and SO_3^{2-} (aq) + H_2O (l) → SO_4^{2-} (aq)

Balance H with H^+:MnO_4^- (aq) + $8 H^+$ (aq)→ Mn^{2+} (aq) + $4 H_2O$ (l)and SO_3^{2-} (aq)+ H_2O (l)→SO_4^{2-} (aq)+ $2 H^+$ (aq)

Add electrons:

MnO_4^- (aq) + $8 H^+$ (aq) + $5 e^-$ → Mn^{2+} (aq) + $4 H_2O$ (l) and SO_3^{2-} (aq)+ H_2O (l)→SO_4^{2-} (aq)+ $2 H^+$ (aq) + $2 e^-$

Equalize electrons:

$2 MnO_4^-$ (aq) + $16 H^+$ (aq) + $10 e^-$ → $2 Mn^{2+}$ (aq) + $8 H_2O$ (l)   and $5 SO_3^{2-}$ (aq) + $5 H_2O$ (l) → $5 SO_4^{2-}$ (aq) + $10 H^+$ (aq) + $10 e^-$

Add half-reactions: $2 MnO_4^-$ (aq) + $6 \cancel{16} H^+$ (aq) + $\cancel{10e^-}$ + $5 SO_3^{2-}$ (aq) + $\cancel{5 H_2O(l)}$ →

$2 Mn^{2+}$ (aq) + $3 \cancel{8} H_2O(l)$ + $5 SO_4^{2-}$ (aq) + $\cancel{10 H^+}$ (aq) + $\cancel{10e^-}$

Cancel electrons: $2 MnO_4^-$ (aq) + $6 H^+$ (aq) + $5 SO_3^{2-}$ (aq) → $2 Mn^{2+}$ (aq)+ $3 H_2O$ (l) + $5 SO_4^{2-}$ (aq)

Check:

Reactants	Products
2 Mn atoms	2 Mn atoms
23 O atoms	23 O atoms
6 H atoms	6 H atoms
5 S atoms	5 S atoms
–6 charge	–6 charge

c) Separate: $S_2O_3^{2-}$ (aq) → SO_4^{2-} (aq)   and Cl_2 (g) → Cl^- (aq)

Balance non H & O elements: $S_2O_3^{2-}$ (aq) → $2 SO_4^{2-}$ (aq)   and Cl_2 (g) → $2 Cl^-$ (aq)

Balance O with H_2O: $S_2O_3^{2-}$ (aq) + $5 H_2O$ (l) → $2 SO_4^{2-}$ (aq)   and Cl_2 (g) → $2 Cl^-$ (aq)

Balance H with H^+: $S_2O_3^{2-}$ (aq) + $5 H_2O$ (l) → $2 SO_4^{2-}$ (aq) + $10 H^+$ (aq)   and Cl_2 (g) → $2 Cl^-$ (aq)

Add electrons:$S_2O_3^{2-}$(aq) + $5 H_2O$ (l) → $2 SO_4^{2-}$ (aq) + $10 H^+$ (aq) + $8 e^-$ and Cl_2 (g) + $2 e^-$ → $2 Cl^-$ (aq)

Equalize electrons: $S_2O_3^{2-}$ (aq) + $5 H_2O$ (l) → $2 SO_4^{2-}$ (aq) + $10 H^+$ (aq) + $8 e^-$ and $4 Cl_2$ (g) + $8 e^-$ → $8 Cl^-$ (aq)

Add half-reactions: $S_2O_3^{2-}$ (aq) + $5 H_2O$ (l) + $4 Cl_2$ (g) + $\cancel{8e^-}$ → $2 SO_4^{2-}$ (aq) + $10 H^+$ (aq) + $\cancel{8e^-}$ + $8 Cl^-$ (aq)

Cancel electrons: $S_2O_3^{2-}$ (aq) + $5 H_2O$ (l) + $4 Cl_2$ (g) → $2 SO_4^{2-}$ (aq) + $10 H^+$ (aq) + $8 Cl^-$ (aq)

Check:

Reactants	Products
2 S atoms	2 S atoms
8 O atoms	8 O atoms
10 H atoms	10 H atoms
8 Cl atoms	8 Cl atoms
–2 charge	–2 charge

40. **Conceptual Plan: Separate the overall reaction into two half-reactions: one for oxidation and one for reduction. → Balance each half-reaction with respect to mass in the following order: 1) balance all elements other than H and O; 2) balance O by adding H_2O; and 3) balance H by adding H^+. →**

Balance each half reaction with respect to charge by adding electrons. (The sum of the charges on both sides of the equation should be made equal by adding electrons as necessary.) → Make the number of electrons in both half-reactions equal by multiplying one or both half-reactions by a small whole number. → Add the two half-reactions together, canceling electrons and other species as necessary. → Verify that the reaction is balanced both with respect to mass and with respect to charge.

Solution:

a) Separate: NO_2^- (aq) → NO (g) and I^- (aq) → I_2 (s)

Balance non H & O elements: NO_2^- (aq) → NO (g) and $2 I^-$ (aq) → I_2 (s)

Balance O with H_2O: NO_2^- (aq) → NO (g) + H_2O (l) and $2 I^-$ (aq) → I_2 (s)

Balance H with H^+: NO_2^- (aq) + $2 H^+$ (aq) → NO (g) + H_2O (l) and $2 I^-$ (aq) → I_2 (s)

Add electrons: NO_2^- (aq) + $2 H^+$ (aq) + e^- → NO (g) + H_2O (l) and $2 I^-$ (aq) → I_2 (s) + $2 e^-$

Equalize electrons: $2 NO_2^-$ (aq) + $4 H^+$ (aq) + $2 e^-$ → $2 NO$ (g) + $2 H_2O$ (l) and $2 I^-$ (aq) → I_2 (s) + $2 e^-$

Add half-reactions: $2 NO_2^-$ (aq) + $4 H^+$ (aq) + $2 e^-$ + $2 I^-$ (aq) → $2 NO$ (g) + $2 H_2O$ (l) + I_2 (s) + $2 e^-$

Cancel electrons: $2 NO_2^-$ (aq) + $4 H^+$ (aq) + $2 I^-$ (aq) → $2 NO$ (g) + $2 H_2O$ (l) + I_2 (s)

Check:

Reactants	Products
2 N atoms	2 N atoms
4 O atoms	4 O atoms
4 H atoms	4 H atoms
2 I atoms	2 I atoms
0 charge	0 charge

b) Separate: ClO_4^- (aq) → ClO_3^- (aq) and Cl^- (aq) → Cl_2 (g)

Balance non H & O elements: ClO_4^- (aq) → ClO_3^- (aq) and $2 Cl^-$ (aq) → Cl_2 (g)

Balance O with H_2O: ClO_4^- (aq) → ClO_3^- (aq) + H_2O (l) and $2 Cl^-$ (aq) → Cl_2 (g)

Balance H with H^+: ClO_4^- (aq) + $2 H^+$ (aq) → ClO_3^- (aq) + H_2O (l) and $2 Cl^-$ (aq) → Cl_2 (g)

Add electrons: ClO_4^- (aq) + $2 H^+$ (aq) + $2 e^-$ → ClO_3^- (aq) + H_2O (l) and $2 Cl^-$ (aq) → Cl_2 (g) + $2 e^-$

Equalize electrons: ClO_4^- (aq) + $2 H^+$ (aq) + $2 e^-$ → ClO_3^- (aq) + H_2O (l) and $2 Cl^-$ (aq) → Cl_2 (g) + $2 e^-$

Add half-reactions: ClO_4^- (aq) + $2 H^+$ (aq) + $2 e^-$ + $2 Cl^-$ (aq) → ClO_3^- (aq) + H_2O (l) + Cl_2 (g) + $2 e^-$

Cancel electrons: ClO_4^- (aq) + $2 H^+$ (aq) + $2 Cl^-$ (aq) → ClO_3^- (aq) + H_2O (l) + Cl_2 (g)

Check:

Reactants	Products
3 Cl atoms	3 Cl atoms
4 O atoms	4 O atoms
2 H atoms	2 H atoms
−1 charge	−1 charge

c) Separate: NO_3^- (aq) → NO (g) and Sn^{2+} (aq) → Sn^{4+} (aq)

Balance non H & O elements: NO_3^- (aq) → NO (g) and Sn^{2+} (aq) → Sn^{4+} (aq)

Balance O with H_2O: NO_3^- (aq) → NO (g) + $2 H_2O$ (l) and Sn^{2+} (aq) → Sn^{4+} (aq)

Balance H with H^+: NO_3^- (aq) + $4 H^+$ (aq) → NO (g) + $2 H_2O$ (l) and Sn^{2+} (aq) → Sn^{4+} (aq)

Add electrons: NO_3^- (aq) + $4 H^+$ (aq) + $3 e^-$ → NO (g) + $2 H_2O$ (l) and Sn^{2+} (aq) → Sn^{4+} (aq) + $2 e^-$

Equalize electrons: $2 NO_3^-$ (aq) + $8 H^+$ (aq) + $6 e^-$ → $2 NO$ (g) + $4 H_2O$ (l) and $3 Sn^{2+}$ (aq) → $3 Sn^{4+}$ (aq) + $6 e^-$

Add half-reactions: $2 NO_3^-$ (aq) + $8 H^+$ (aq) + $6 e^-$ + $3 Sn^{2+}$ (aq) → $2 NO$ (g) + $4 H_2O$ (l) + $3 Sn^{4+}$ (aq) + $6 e^-$

Cancel electrons: $2 NO_3^-$ (aq) + $8 H^+$ (aq) + $3 Sn^{2+}$ (aq) → $2 NO$ (g) + $4 H_2O$ (l) + $3 Sn^{4+}$ (aq)

Check:

Reactants	Products
2 N atoms	2 N atoms
6 O atoms	6 O atoms
8 H atoms	8 H atoms
3 Sn atoms	3 Sn atoms
+12 charge	+12 charge

41. **Conceptual Plan:** Separate the overall reaction into two half-reactions: one for oxidation and one for reduction. → Balance each half-reaction with respect to mass in the following order: 1) balance all elements other than H and O; 2) balance O by adding H_2O; 3) balance H by adding H^+; and 4) Neutralize H^+ by adding enough OH^- to neutralize each H^+. Add the same number of OH^- ions to each side of the equation. → Balance each half reaction with respect to charge by adding electrons. (The

sum of the charges on both sides of the equation should be made equal by adding electrons as necessary.) → **Make the number of electrons in both half-reactions equal by multiplying one or both half-reactions by a small whole number.** → **Add the two half-reactions together, canceling electrons and other species as necessary.** → **Verify that the reaction is balanced both with respect to mass and with respect to charge.**

Solution:

a) Separate: $\quad\quad\quad\quad\quad\quad\quad\quad$ $ClO_2\ (aq) \rightarrow ClO_2^-\ (aq)$ $\quad\quad$ and $\quad\quad$ $H_2O_2\ (aq) \rightarrow O_2\ (g)$

Balance non H & O elements: $ClO_2\ (aq) \rightarrow ClO_2^-\ (aq)$ $\quad\quad$ and $\quad\quad$ $H_2O_2\ (aq) \rightarrow O_2\ (g)$

Balance O with H_2O: $\quad\quad\quad$ $ClO_2\ (aq) \rightarrow ClO_2^-\ (aq)$ $\quad\quad$ and $\quad\quad$ $H_2O_2\ (aq) \rightarrow O_2\ (g)$

Balance H with H^+: $\quad\quad\quad\quad$ $ClO_2\ (aq) \rightarrow ClO_2^-\ (aq)$ and $H_2O_2\ (aq) \rightarrow O_2\ (g) + 2\ H^+\ (aq)$

Neutralize H^+ with OH^-: $ClO_2\ (aq) \rightarrow ClO_2^-\ (aq)$ and $\quad$ $H_2O_2\ (aq) + 2\ OH^-\ (aq) \rightarrow O_2\ (g) +$ $\underbrace{2\ H^+\ (aq) + 2\ OH^-\ (aq)}_{2\ H_2O\ (l)}$

Add electrons: $ClO_2\ (aq) + e^- \rightarrow ClO_2^-\ (aq)$ and $H_2O_2\ (aq) + 2\ OH^-\ (aq) \rightarrow O_2\ (g) + 2\ H_2O\ (l)\ + 2\ e^-$

Equalize electrons: $2\ ClO_2\ (aq) + 2\ e^- \rightarrow 2\ ClO_2^-\ (aq)$ and $H_2O_2\ (aq) + 2\ OH^-\ (aq) \rightarrow O_2\ (g) + 2\ H_2O\ (l)\ + 2\ e^-$

Add half-reactions: $2\ ClO_2\ (aq) + \cancel{2e^-} + H_2O_2\ (aq) + 2\ OH^-\ (aq) \rightarrow 2\ ClO_2^-\ (aq) + O_2\ (g) + 2\ H_2O\ (l) + \cancel{2e^-}$

Cancel electrons: $\quad\quad$ $2\ ClO_2\ (aq) + H_2O_2\ (aq) + 2\ OH^-\ (aq) \rightarrow 2\ ClO_2^-\ (aq) + O_2\ (g) + 2\ H_2O\ (l)$

Check:

Reactants	Products
2 Cl atoms	2 Cl atoms
8 O atoms	8 O atoms
4 H atoms	4 H atoms
–2 charge	–2 charge

b) Separate: $\quad\quad\quad\quad\quad\quad\quad\quad$ $MnO_4^-\ (aq) \rightarrow MnO_2\ (s)$ $\quad\quad$ and $\quad\quad$ $Al\ (s) \rightarrow Al(OH)_4^-\ (aq)$

Balance non H & O elements: $MnO_4^-\ (aq) \rightarrow MnO_2\ (s)$ $\quad\quad$ and $\quad\quad$ $Al\ (s) \rightarrow Al(OH)_4^-\ (aq)$

Balance O with H_2O: $\quad\quad\quad$ $MnO_4^-\ (aq) \rightarrow MnO_2\ (s) + 2\ H_2O\ (l)$ $\quad$ and $\quad$ $Al\ (s) + 4\ H_2O\ (l) \rightarrow$ $Al(OH)_4^-\ (aq)$

Balance H with H^+:

$MnO_4^-\ (aq) + 4\ H^+\ (aq) \rightarrow MnO_2\ (s) + 2\ H_2O\ (l)$ and $Al\ (s) + 4\ H_2O\ (l) \rightarrow Al(OH)_4^-\ (aq) + 4\ H^+\ (aq)$

Neutralize H^+ with OH^-: $\quad$ $MnO_4^-\ (aq) + \underbrace{4\ H^+\ (aq) + 4\ OH^-\ (aq)}_{2\ \cancel{4}\ H_2O\ (l)} \rightarrow MnO_2\ (s) + \cancel{2\ H_2O}(l) + 4\ OH^-\ (aq)$

and

$\quad\quad\quad\quad$ $Al\ (s) + \cancel{4\ H_2O}(l) + 4\ OH^-\ (aq) \rightarrow Al(OH)_4^-\ (aq) + \underbrace{4\ H^+\ (aq) + 4\ OH^-\ (aq)}_{4\ H_2O\ (l)}$

Add electrons: $\quad$ $MnO_4^-\ (aq) + 2\ H_2O\ (l) + 3\ e^- \rightarrow MnO_2\ (s) + 4\ OH^-\ (aq)$ and $\quad\quad\quad\quad\quad\quad\quad$ $Al\ (s) + 4\ OH^-\ (aq) \rightarrow Al(OH)_4^-\ (aq) + 3\ e^-$

Equalize electrons: $MnO_4^-\ (aq) + 2\ H_2O\ (l) + 3\ e^- \rightarrow MnO_2\ (s) + 4\ OH^-\ (aq)$ and $\quad\quad\quad\quad\quad\quad\quad\quad$ $Al\ (s) + 4\ OH^-\ (aq) \rightarrow Al(OH)_4^-\ (aq) + 3\ e^-$

Add half-reactions:

$MnO_4^-\ (aq) + 2\ H_2O\ (l) + \cancel{3e^-} + Al\ (s) + \cancel{4\ OH^-(aq)} \rightarrow MnO_2\ (s) + \cancel{4\ OH^-(aq)} + Al(OH)_4^-\ (aq) + \cancel{3e^-}$

Cancel electrons: $\quad\quad$ $MnO_4^-\ (aq) + 2\ H_2O\ (l) + Al\ (s) \rightarrow MnO_2\ (s) + Al(OH)_4^-\ (aq)$

Check:

Reactants	Products
1 Mn atom	1 Mn atom
6 O atoms	6 O atoms
4 H atoms	4 H atoms
1 Al atom	1 Al atom
–1 charge	–1 charge

c) Separate: $\quad\quad\quad\quad\quad\quad\quad\quad$ $Cl_2\ (g) \rightarrow Cl^-\ (aq)$ $\quad\quad$ and $\quad\quad$ $Cl_2\ (g) \rightarrow ClO^-\ (aq)$

Balance non H & O elements: $Cl_2\ (g) \rightarrow 2\ Cl^-\ (aq)$ $\quad\quad$ and $\quad\quad$ $Cl_2\ (g) \rightarrow 2\ ClO^-\ (aq)$

Balance O with H_2O: $\quad\quad\quad$ $Cl_2\ (g) \rightarrow 2\ Cl^-\ (aq)$ $\quad\quad$ and $\quad$ $Cl_2\ (g) + 2\ H_2O\ (l) \rightarrow 2\ ClO^-\ (aq)$

Balance H with H^+: $Cl_2\ (g) \rightarrow 2\ Cl^-\ (aq)$ $\quad\quad$ and $\quad$ $Cl_2\ (g) + 2\ H_2O\ (l) \rightarrow 2\ ClO^-\ (aq) + 4\ H^+\ (aq)$

Neutralize H^+ with OH^-:

Cl_2 (g) → 2 Cl^- (aq) and Cl_2 (g) + $\cancel{2H_2O(l)}$ + 4 OH^- (aq) → 2 ClO^- (aq) + $\underbrace{4H^+\ (aq) + 4\ OH^-\ (aq)}_{\cancel{2}4\ H_2O\ (l)}$

Add electrons: Cl_2 (g) + 2 e^- → 2 Cl^- (aq) and Cl_2 (g) + 4 OH^- (aq) → 2 ClO^- (aq) + 2 H_2O (l) + 2 e^-

Equalize electrons: Cl_2 (g) + 2 e^- → 2 Cl^- (aq) and Cl_2 (g) + 4 OH^- (aq) → 2 ClO^- (aq) + 2 H_2O (l) + 2 e^-

Add half-reactions: Cl_2 (g) + $\cancel{2e^-}$ + Cl_2 (g) + 4 OH^- (aq) → 2 Cl^- (aq) + 2 ClO^- (aq) + 2 H_2O (l)

+ $\cancel{2e^-}$

Cancel electrons: 2 Cl_2 (g) + 4 OH^- (aq) → 2 Cl^- (aq) + 2 ClO^- (aq) + 2 H_2O (l)
Simplify: Cl_2 (g) + 2 OH^- (aq) → Cl^- (aq) + ClO^- (aq) + H_2O (l)

Check:

Reactants	Products
2 Cl atoms	2 Cl atoms
2 O atoms	2 O atoms
2 H atoms	2 H atoms
–2 charge	–2 charge

42. **Conceptual Plan: Separate the overall reaction into two half-reactions: one for oxidation and one for reduction. → Balance each half-reaction with respect to mass in the following order: 1) balance all elements other than H and O; 2) balance O by adding H_2O; 3) balance H by adding H^+; and 4) Neutralize H^+ by adding enough OH^- to neutralize each H^+. Add the same number of OH^- ions to each side of the equation. → Balance each half reaction with respect to charge by adding electrons. (The sum of the charges on both sides of the equation should be made equal by adding electrons as necessary.) → Make the number of electrons in both half-reactions equal by multiplying one or both half-reactions by a small whole number. → Add the two half-reactions together, canceling electrons and other species as necessary. → Verify that the reaction is balanced both with respect to mass and with respect to charge.**

Solution:

a) Separate: MnO_4^- (aq) → MnO_2 (s) and Br^- (aq) → BrO_3^- (aq)
   Balance non H & O elements: MnO_4^- (aq) → MnO_2 (s) and Br^- (aq) → BrO_3^- (aq)
   Balance O with H_2O: MnO_4^- (aq) → MnO_2 (s) + 2 H_2O (l) and Br^- (aq) + 3 H_2O (l) → BrO_3^- (aq)
   Balance H with H^+:
   MnO_4^- (aq) + 4 H^+ (aq) → MnO_2 (s) + 2 H_2O (l) and Br^- (aq) + 3 H_2O (l) → BrO_3^- (aq) + 6 H^+ (aq)
   Neutralize H^+ with OH^-: MnO_4^- (aq) + $\underbrace{4\ H^+\ (aq) + 4\ OH^-\ (aq)}_{\cancel{2}4\ H_2O\ (l)}$ → MnO_2 (s) + $\cancel{2\ H_2O(l)}$ + 4 OH^- (aq)

and

Br^- (aq) + $\cancel{3\ H_2O(l)}$ + 6 OH^- (aq) → BrO_3^- (aq) + $\underbrace{6\ H^+\ (aq) + 6\ OH^-\ (aq)}_{\cancel{3}6\ H_2O\ (l)}$

Add electrons: MnO_4^- (aq) + 2 H_2O (l) + 3 e^- → MnO_2 (s) + 4 OH^- (aq) and
   Br^- (aq) + 6 OH^- (aq) → BrO_3^- (aq) + 3 H_2O (l) + 6 e^-

Equalize electrons: 2 MnO_4^- (aq) + 4 H_2O (l) + 6 e^- → 2 MnO_2 (s) + 8 OH^- (aq) and
   Br^- (aq) + 6 OH^- (aq) → BrO_3^- (aq) + 3 H_2O (l) + 6 e^-

Add half-reactions: 2 MnO_4^- (aq) + 1 $\cancel{4}$ H_2O (l) + $\cancel{6e^-}$ + Br^- (aq) + 6 $\cancel{OH^-(aq)}$ →

   2 MnO_2 (s) + 2 $\cancel{8}$ $OH^-(aq)$ + BrO_3^- (aq) + $\cancel{3H_2O(l)}$ + $\cancel{6e^-}$

Cancel electrons & others: 2 MnO_4^- (aq) + H_2O (l) + Br^- (aq) → 2 MnO_2 (s) + 2 OH^- (aq) + BrO_3^- (aq)

Check:

Reactants	Products
2 Mn atoms	2 Mn atoms
9 O atoms	9 O atoms
2 H atoms	2 H atoms
1 Br atom	1 Br atom
–3 charge	–3 charge

b) Separate: Ag (s) + CN^- (aq) → $Ag(CN)_2^-$ (aq) and O_2 (g) →
   Balance non H & O elements: Ag (s) + 2 CN^- (aq) → $Ag(CN)_2^-$ (aq) and O_2 (g) →
   Balance O with H_2O: Ag (s) + 2 CN^- (aq) → $Ag(CN)_2^-$ (aq) and O_2 (g) → 2 H_2O (l)
   Balance H with H^+: Ag (s) + 2 CN^- (aq) → $Ag(CN)_2^-$ (aq) and O_2 (g) + 4 H^+ (aq) → 2 H_2O (l)
   Neutralize H^+ with OH^-:

$Ag\ (s) + 2\ CN^-\ (aq) \rightarrow Ag(CN)_2^-\ (aq)$ and $O_2\ (g) + \underbrace{4\ H^+\ (aq) + 4\ OH^-\ (aq)}_{2\cancel{4}\,H_2O\ (l)} \rightarrow \cancel{2}\cancel{H_2O}\ (l) + 4\ OH^-\ (aq)$

Add electrons: $Ag\ (s) + 2\ CN^-\ (aq) \rightarrow Ag(CN)_2^-\ (aq) + e^-$ and $O_2\ (g) + 2\ H_2O\ (l)\,) + 4\ e^- \rightarrow 4\ OH^-\ (aq)$

Equalize electrons: $4\ Ag\ (s) + 8\ CN^-\ (aq) \rightarrow 4\ Ag(CN)_2^-\ (aq) + 4\ e^-$ and $O_2\ (g) + 2\ H_2O\ (l) + 4\ e^- \rightarrow 4\ OH^-\ (aq)$

Add half-reactions: $4\ Ag\ (s) + 8\ CN^-\ (aq) + O_2\ (g) + 2\ H_2O\ (l) + \cancel{4e^-} \rightarrow 4\ Ag(CN)_2^-\ (aq) + \cancel{4e^-} + 4\ OH^-\ (aq)$

Cancel electrons: $\quad 4\ Ag\ (s) + 8\ CN^-\ (aq) + O_2\ (g) + 2\ H_2O\ (l) \rightarrow 4\ Ag(CN)_2^-\ (aq) + 4\ OH^-\ (aq)$

Check:

Reactants	Products
4 Ag atoms	4 Ag atoms
8 C atoms	8 C atoms
8 N atoms	8 N atoms
4 O atoms	4 O atoms
4 H atoms	4 H atoms
–8 charge	–8 charge

c) Separate: $\quad NO_2^-\ (aq) \rightarrow NH_3\ (g)$ and $Al\ (s) \rightarrow AlO_2^-\ (aq)$

Balance non H & O elements: $NO_2^-\ (aq) \rightarrow NH_3\ (g)$ and $Al\ (s) \rightarrow AlO_2^-\ (aq)$

Balance O with H_2O: $\quad NO_2^-\ (aq) \rightarrow NH_3\ (g) + 2\ H_2O\ (l)$ and $Al\ (s) + 2\ H_2O\ (l) \rightarrow AlO_2^-\ (aq)$

Balance H with H^+: $NO_2^-\ (aq) + 7\ H^+\ (aq) \rightarrow NH_3\ (g) + 2\ H_2O\ (l)$ and $Al\ (s) + 2\ H_2O\ (l) \rightarrow AlO_2^-\ (aq) + 4\ H^+\ (aq)$

Neutralize H^+ with OH^-: $NO_2^-\ (aq) + \underbrace{7\ H^+\ (aq) + 7\ OH^-\ (aq)}_{5\cancel{7}\,H_2O\ (l)} \rightarrow NH_3\ (g) + \cancel{2}\cancel{H_2O}\ (l) + 7\ OH^-\ (aq)$ and

$Al\ (s) + \cancel{2}\cancel{H_2O}\ (l) + 4\ OH^-\ (aq) \rightarrow AlO_2^-\ (aq) + \underbrace{4\ H^+\ (aq) + 4\ OH^-\ (aq)}_{2\cancel{4}\,H_2O\ (l)}$

Add electrons:

$NO_2^-\ (aq) + 5\ H_2O\ (l) + 6\ e^- \rightarrow NH_3\ (g) + 7\ OH^-\ (aq)$ and $Al\ (s) + 4\ OH^-\ (aq) \rightarrow AlO_2^-\ (aq) + 2\ H_2O\ (l) + 3\ e^-$

Equalize electrons:

$NO_2^-\ (aq) + 5\ H_2O\ (l) + 6\ e^- \rightarrow NH_3\ (g) + 7\ OH^-\ (aq)$ and $2\ Al\ (s) + 8\ OH^-\ (aq) \rightarrow 2\ AlO_2^-\ (aq) + 4\ H_2O\ (l) + 6\ e^-$

Add half-reactions: $\quad NO_2^-\ (aq) + 1\,\cancel{5}\ H_2O\ (l) + \cancel{6e^-} + 2\ Al\ (s) + 1\,\cancel{8}\,OH^-(aq) \rightarrow$

$NH_3\ (g) + 7\,\cancel{OH^-(aq)} + 2\ AlO_2^-\ (aq) + \cancel{4}\cancel{H_2O}\ (l) + \cancel{6e^-}$

Cancel electrons & others: $\quad NO_2^-\ (aq) + H_2O\ (l) + 2\ Al\ (s) + OH^-\ (aq) \rightarrow NH_3\ (g) + 2\ AlO_2^-\ (aq)$

Check:

Reactants	Products
1 N atom	1 N atom
4 O atoms	4 O atoms
3 H atoms	3 H atoms
2 Al atoms	2 Al atoms
–2 charge	–2 charge

43. **Given:** voltaic cell overall redox reaction

Find: Sketch voltaic cell, labeling anode, cathode, all species and direction of electron flow

Conceptual plan: Separate overall reaction into 2 half-cell reactions and add electrons as needed to balance reactions. Put anode reaction on the left (oxidation = electrons as product) and cathode reaction on the right (reduction = electrons as reactant). Electrons flow from anode to cathode.

Solution:

a) $2\ Ag^+\ (aq) + Pb\ (s) \rightarrow 2\ Ag\ (s) + Pb^{2+}\ (aq)$ separates to $2\ Ag^+\ (aq) \rightarrow 2\ Ag\ (s)$ and $Pb\ (s) \rightarrow Pb^{2+}\ (aq)$ then add electrons to balance to get the cathode reaction: $2\ Ag^+\ (aq) + 2\ e^- \rightarrow 2\ Ag\ (s)$ and the anode reaction: $Pb\ (s) \rightarrow Pb^{2+}\ (aq) + 2\ e^-$.

Since we have Pb (s) as the reactant for the oxidation, it will be our anode. Since we have Ag (s) as the product for the reduction, it will be our cathode. Simplify the cathode reaction, dividing all terms by 2.

b) 2 ClO$_2$ (g)+ 2 I$^-$ (aq) → 2 ClO$_2^-$ (aq) + I$_2$ (s)   separates to 2 ClO$_2$ (g) → 2 ClO$_2^-$ (aq) and 2 I$^-$ (aq) → I$_2$ (s) then   add electrons to balance to get the cathode reaction: 2 ClO$_2$ (g) + 2 e$^-$ → 2 ClO$_2^-$ (aq) and the anode reaction: 2 I$^-$ (aq) → I$_2$ (s) + 2 e$^-$.

Since we have I$^-$ (aq) as the reactant for the oxidation, we will need to use Pt as our anode. Since we have ClO$_2^-$ (aq) as the product for the reduction, we will need to use Pt as our cathode. Since ClO$_2$ (g) is our reactant for the reduction, we need to use an electrode assembly like that is used for a SHE. Simplify the cathode reaction, dividing all terms by 2.

c) O$_2$ (g)+ 4 H$^+$ (aq) + 2 Zn (s) → 2 H$_2$O (l) + 2 Zn^{2+} (aq) separates to O$_2$ (g)+ 4 H$^+$ (aq) → 2 H$_2$O (l) and 2 Zn (s) → 2 Zn^{2+} (aq) then   add electrons to balance to get the cathode reaction: O$_2$ (g)+ 4 H$^+$ (aq) + 4 e$^-$ → 2 H$_2$O (l) and the anode reaction: 2 Zn (s) → 2 Zn^{2+} (aq) + 4 e$^-$.

Since we have Zn (s) as the reactant for the oxidation, it will be our anode. Since we have H$_2$O (l) as the product for the reduction, we will need to use Pt as our cathode. Since O$_2$ (g) is our reactant for the reduction, we need to use an electrode assembly like what is used for a SHE. Simplify the anode reaction, dividing all terms by 2.

44. **Given:** voltaic cell overall redox reaction
Find: Sketch voltaic cell, labeling anode, cathode, all species and direction of electron flow
Conceptual plan: Separate overall reaction into 2 half-cell reactions and add electrons as needed to balance reactions. Put anode reaction on the left (oxidation = electrons as product) and cathode reaction on the right (reduction = electrons as reactant). Electrons flow from anode to cathode.
Solution:

a) Ni^{2+} *(aq)*+ Mg *(s)* → Ni *(s)* + Mg^{2+} *(aq)* separates to Ni^{2+} *(aq)* → Ni *(s)* and Mg *(s)* → Mg^{2+} *(aq)* then add electrons to balance to get the cathode reaction: Ni^{2+} *(aq)* + 2 e⁻ → Ni *(s)* and the anode reaction: Mg *(s)* → Mg^{2+} *(aq)* + 2 e⁻.

Since we have Mg (s) as the reactant for the oxidation, it will be our anode. Since we have Ni (s) as the product for the reduction, it will be our cathode.

b) 2 H^+ *(aq)* + Fe *(s)* → H_2 *(g)* + Fe^{2+} *(aq)* separates to 2 H^+ *(aq)* → H_2 *(g)* and Fe *(s)* → Fe^{2+} *(aq)* then add electrons to balance to get the cathode reaction: 2 H^+ *(aq)* + 2 e⁻ → H_2 *(g)* and the anode reaction: Fe *(s)* → Fe^{2+} *(aq)* + 2 e⁻.

Since we have Fe *(s)* as the reactant for the oxidation, it will be our anode. Since we have H_2 *(g)* as the product for the reduction, we will need to use Pt as our cathode and the product can leave using an electrode assembly like what is used for a SHE.

c) 2 NO_3^- *(aq)* + 8 H^+ *(aq)* + 3 Cu *(s)* → 2 NO *(g)* + 4 H_2O *(l)* + 3 Cu^{2+} *(aq)* separates to 2 NO_3^- *(aq)* + 8 H^+ *(aq)* → 2 NO *(g)* + 4 H_2O *(l)* and 3 Cu *(s)* → 3 Cu^{2+} *(aq)* then add electrons to balance to get the cathode reaction: 2 NO_3^- *(aq)* + 8 H^+ *(aq)* + 6 e⁻ → 2 NO *(g)* + 4 H_2O *(l)* and the anode reaction: 3 Cu *(s)* → 3 Cu^{2+} *(aq)* + 6 e⁻.

Since we have Cu *(s)* as the reactant for the oxidation, it will be our anode. Since we have H_2O *(l)* and NO *(g)* as the products for the reduction, we will need to use Pt as our cathode and the gaseous product can leave using an electrode assembly like what is used for a SHE.

45. **Given:** overall reactions from #43   **Find:** $E°_{cell}$
Conceptual plan: Look up half-reactions from solution of problem #43 in Table 18.1. In order to determine the cell potential of the oxidation reaction, reverse the sign of the standard reduction potential ($E°_{ox} = -E°_{red}$) then add the two half-cell potentials: $E°_{cell} = E°_{ox} + E°_{red}$.
Solution:
a) Ag^+ *(aq)* $+ e^- \rightarrow$ Ag *(s)* $E°_{red} = 0.80$ V and Pb *(s)* $\rightarrow Pb^{2+}$ *(aq)* $+ 2 e^- \; E°_{ox} = -E°_{red} = -(-0.13$ V) $= 0.13$ V. Then $E°_{cell} = E°_{ox} + E°_{red} = 0.80$ V $+ 0.13$ V $= 0.93$ V.

b) ClO_2 *(g)* $+ e^- \rightarrow ClO_2^-$ *(aq)* $E°_{red} = 0.95$ V and $2 I^-$ *(aq)* $\rightarrow I_2$ *(s)* $+ 2 e^- \; E°_{ox} = -E°_{red} = -0.54$ V. Then $E°_{cell} = E°_{ox} + E°_{red} = 0.95$ V $- 0.54$ V $= 0.41$ V.

c) O_2 *(g)* $+ 4 H^+$ *(aq)* $+ 4 e^- \rightarrow 2 H_2O$ *(l)* $E°_{red} = 1.23$ V and Zn *(s)* $\rightarrow Zn^{2+}$ *(aq)* $+ 2 e^- \; E°_{ox} = -E°_{red} = -(-0.76$ V).
Then $E°_{cell} = E°_{ox} + E°_{red} = 1.23$ V $+ 0.76$ V $= 1.99$ V.
Check: The units (V) are correct. All of the voltages are positive, which is consistent with a voltaic cell.

46. **Given:** overall reactions from #44   **Find:** $E°_{cell}$
Conceptual plan: Look up half-reactions from solution of problem #44 in Table 18.1. In order to determine the cell potential of the oxidation reaction, reverse the sign of the standard reduction potential ($E°_{ox} = -E°_{red}$) then add the two half-cell potentials: $E°_{cell} = E°_{ox} + E°_{red}$.
Solution:
a) Ni^{2+} *(aq)* $+ 2 e^- \rightarrow$ Ni *(s)* $E°_{red} = -0.23$ V and Mg *(s)* $\rightarrow Mg^{2+}$ *(aq)* $+ 2 e^- \; E°_{ox} = -E°_{red} = -(-2.37$ V) $= 2.37$ V. Then $E°_{cell} = E°_{ox} + E°_{red} = -0.23$ V $+ 2.37$ V $= 2.14$ V.

b) $2 H^+$ *(aq)* $+ 2 e^- \rightarrow H_2$ *(g)* $E°_{red} = 0.00$ V and Fe *(s)* $\rightarrow Fe^{2+}$ *(aq)* $+ 2 e^- \quad E°_{ox} = -E°_{red} = -(-0.45$ V) $= 0.45$ V.
Then $E°_{cell} = E°_{ox} + E°_{red} = 0.00$ V $+ 0.45$ V $= 0.45$ V.

c) NO_3^- *(aq)* $+ 4 H^+$ *(aq)* $+ 3 e^- \rightarrow$ NO *(g)* $+ 2 H_2O$ *(l)* $E°_{red} = 0.96$ V and Cu *(s)* $\rightarrow Cu^{2+}$ *(aq)* $+ 2 e^- \; E°_{ox} = -E°_{red} = -0.34$ V. Then $E°_{cell} = E°_{ox} + E°_{red} = 0.96$ V $- 0.34$ V $= 0.62$ V.
Check: The units (V) are correct. All of the voltages are positive, which is consistent with a voltaic cell.

47. **Given:** voltaic cell drawing   **Find:** a) determine electron flow direction, anode and cathode; b) write balanced overall reaction and calculate $E°_{cell}$; c) label electrodes as + and −; and d) directions of anions and cations from salt bridge
Conceptual plan: Look at each half-cell and write a reduction reaction, by using electrode and solution composition and adding electrons to balance. Look up half-reactions standard reduction potentials in Table 18.1. Since this is a voltaic cell, the cell potentials must be assigned to give a positive $E°_{cell}$ (One reaction must be reversed to become the oxidation half-cell reaction and $E°_{ox} = -E°_{red}$.) then add the two half-cell potentials: $E°_{cell} = E°_{ox} + E°_{red}$.
a) Label electrode where the oxidation occurs as the anode. Label the electrode where the reduction as the cathode. Electrons flow from anode to cathode.
b) Take two half-cell reactions and multiply the reactions as necessary to equalize the number of electrons transferred. Add the two half-cell reactions and cancel electrons and any other species.
c) Label anode as (−) and cathode as (+).
d) Cations will flow from the salt bridge towards the cathode and the anions will flow from salt bridge towards the anode.
Solution:
left side: Fe^{3+} *(aq)* $\rightarrow$ Fe *(s)* and right side: Cr^{3+} *(aq)* $\rightarrow$ Cr *(s)* add electrons to balance Fe^{3+} *(aq)* $+ 3 e^- \rightarrow$ Fe *(s)* and right side: Cr^{3+} *(aq)* $+ 3 e^- \rightarrow$ Cr *(s)*. Look up cell standard reduction potentials: Fe^{3+} *(aq)* $+ 3 e^- \rightarrow$ Fe *(s)* $E°_{red} = -0.036$ V and Cr^{3+} *(aq)* $+ 3 e^- \rightarrow$ Cr *(s)* $E°_{red} = -0.73$ V. In order to get a positive cell potential, the second reaction is the oxidation reaction. $E°_{cell} = E°_{ox} + E°_{red} = -(-0.73$ V) $- 0.036$ V $= +0.69$ V.a, c, d)

b) Add two half-reactions with the second reaction reversed.

$Fe^{3+} (aq) + \cancel{3e^-} + Cr (s) \rightarrow Fe (s) + Cr^{3+} (aq) + \cancel{3e^-}$.

Cancel electrons to get:

$Fe^{3+} (aq) + Cr (s) \rightarrow Fe (s) + Cr^{3+} (aq)$.

Check: All atoms and charge are balanced. The units (V) are correct. The cell potential is positive which is consistent with a voltaic cell.

48. **Given:** voltaic cell drawing **Find:** a) determine electron flow direction, anode and cathode; b) write balanced overall reaction and calculate E°_{cell}; c) label electrodes as + and −; and d) directions of anions and cations from salt bridge

    Conceptual plan: Look at each half-cell and write a reduction reaction, by using electrode and solution composition and adding electrons to balance. Look up half-reactions standard reduction potentials in Table 18.1. Since this is a voltaic cell, the cell potentials must be assigned to give a positive E°_{cell} (One reaction must be reversed to become the oxidation half-cell reaction and $E^\circ_{ox} = -E^\circ_{red}$.) then add the two half-cell potentials: $E^\circ_{cell} = E^\circ_{ox} + E^\circ_{red}$.

    a) Label electrode where the oxidation occurs as the anode. Label the electrode where the reduction as the cathode. Electrons flow from anode to cathode.

    b) Take two half-cell reactions and multiply the reactions as necessary to equalize the number of electrons transferred. Add the two half-cell reactions and cancel electrons and any other species.

    c) Label anode as (−) and cathode as (+).

    d) Cations will flow from the salt bridge towards the cathode and the anions will flow from salt bridge towards the anode.

    Solution:

    left side: $Pb^{2+} (aq) \rightarrow Pb (s)$ and right side: $Cl_2 (g) \rightarrow 2 Cl^- (aq)$ add electrons to balance $Pb^{2+} (aq) + 2 e^- \rightarrow Pb (s)$ and right side: $Cl_2 (g) + 2 e^- \rightarrow 2 Cl^- (aq)$. Look up cell standard reduction potentials: $Pb^{2+} (aq) + 2 e^- \rightarrow Pb (s)$ $E^\circ_{red} = -0.13$ V and $Cl_2 (g) + 2 e^- \rightarrow 2 Cl^- (aq)$ $E^\circ_{red} = 1.36$ V. In order to get a positive cell potential, the first reaction is the oxidation reaction. $E^\circ_{cell} = E^\circ_{ox} + E^\circ_{red} = -(-0.13 \text{ V}) + 1.36$ V = + 1.49 V.

    a, c, d)

    b) Add two half-reactions with the first reaction reversed.

    $Pb (s) + Cl_2 (g) + \cancel{2e^-} \rightarrow Pb^{2+} (aq) + \cancel{2e^-} + 2 Cl^- (aq)$.

    Cancel electrons to get:

    $Pb (s) + Cl_2 (g) \rightarrow Pb^{2+} (aq) + 2 Cl^- (aq)$.

Check: All atoms and charge are balanced. The units (V) are correct. The cell potential is positive which is consistent with a voltaic cell.

49. **Given:** overall reactions from #43 **Find:** line notation

Conceptual plan: Use solution from problem #43. Write the oxidation half-reaction components on the left and the reduction on the right. A double vertical line ($\|$), indicating the salt bridge, separates the two half-reactions. Substances in different phases are separated by a single vertical line ($|$), which represents the boundary between the phases. For some redox reactions, the reactants and products of one or both of the half-reactions may be in the same phase. In these cases, the reactants and products are simply separated from each other with a comma in the line diagram. Such cells use an inert electrode, such as platinum (Pt) or graphite, as the anode or cathode (or both).
Solution:

a) Reduction reaction: Ag^+ *(aq)* $+ e^- \rightarrow$ Ag *(s)* and the oxidation reaction: Pb *(s)* $\rightarrow$ Pb^{2+} *(aq)* $+ 2\ e^-$ so
Pb *(s)*$|Pb^{2+}$ *(aq)*$\|Ag^+$ *(aq)* $|$Ag *(s)*

b) Reduction reaction: ClO_2 *(g)* $+\ e^- \rightarrow ClO_2^-$ *(aq)* and the oxidation reaction: $2\ I^-$ *(aq)* $\rightarrow$ I_2 *(s)* $+ 2\ e^-$
so Pt *(s)*$|I^-$ *(aq)* $|\ I_2$ *(s)*$\|\ ClO_2$ *(g)*$|ClO_2^-$ *(aq)*$|$Pt *(s)*

c) Reduction reaction: O_2 *(g)*$+ 4\ H^+$ *(aq)* $+ 4\ e^- \rightarrow 2\ H_2O$ *(l)* and the oxidation reaction: Zn *(s)* $\rightarrow Zn^{2+}$ *(aq)* $+ 2\ e^-$ so Zn *(s)*$|Zn^{2+}$ *(aq)* $\|O_2$ *(g)*$|H^+$ *(aq)*, H_2O *(l)*$|$Pt *(s)*

50. **Given:** overall reactions from #44   **Find:** line notation
    Conceptual plan: Use solution from problem #44. Write the oxidation half-reaction components on the left and the reduction on the right. A double vertical line ($\|$), indicating the salt bridge, separates the two half-reactions. Substances in different phases are separated by a single vertical line ($|$), which represents the boundary between the phases. For some redox reactions, the reactants and products of one or both of the half-reactions may be in the same phase. In these cases, the reactants and products are simply separated from each other with a comma in the line diagram. Such cells use an inert electrode, such as platinum (Pt) or graphite, as the anode or cathode (or both).
    Solution:

    a) Reduction reaction: Ni^{2+} *(aq)* $+ 2\ e^- \rightarrow$ Ni *(s)* and the oxidation reaction: Mg *(s)* $\rightarrow$ Mg^{2+} *(aq)* $+ 2\ e^-$
    so Mg *(s)*$|Mg^{2+}$ *(aq)*$\|Ni^{2+}$ *(aq)* $|$Ni *(s)*

    b) Reduction reaction: $2\ H^+$ *(aq)* $+ 2\ e^- \rightarrow\ H_2$ *(g)* and the oxidation reaction: Fe *(s)* $\rightarrow$ Fe^{2+} *(aq)* $+ 2\ e^-$
    so Fe *(s)*$|Fe^{2+}$ *(aq)*$\|\ H^+$ *(aq)*$|\ H_2$ *(g)*$|$Pt *(s)*

    c) Reduction reaction: NO_3^- *(aq)* $+ 4\ H^+$ *(aq)* $+ 3\ e^- \rightarrow$ NO *(g)* $+ 2\ H_2O$ *(l)* and the oxidation reaction:
    Cu *(s)* $\rightarrow Cu^{2+}$ *(aq)* $+ 2\ e^-$ so Cu *(s)*$|Cu^{2+}$ *(aq)* $\| NO_3^-$ *(aq)*, H^+ *(aq)* $)$, H_2O *(l)*$|$NO *(g)*$|$Pt *(s)*

51. **Given:** Sn *(s)*$|Sn^{2+}$ *(aq)* $\| NO_3^-$ *(aq)*, H^+ *(aq)* $)$, H_2O *(l)*$|$NO *(g)*$|$Pt *(s)*
    Find: Sketch voltaic cell, labeling anode, cathode all species and direction of electron flow and E°_{cell}
    Conceptual plan: Separate overall reaction into 2 half-cell reactions knowing that the oxidation half-reaction components on the left and the reduction on the right. Add electrons as needed to balance reactions. Multiply the half-reactions by the appropriate factors to have an equal number of electrons transferred. Add the half-cell reactions and cancel electrons. Put anode reaction on the left (oxidation = electrons as product) and cathode reaction on the right (reduction = electrons as reactant). Electrons flow from anode to cathode. Look up half-reactions from solution of problem #44 in Table 18.1. In order to determine the cell potential of the oxidation reaction, reverse the sign of the standard reduction potential ($E^{\circ}_{ox} = - E^{\circ}_{red}$) then add the two half-cell potentials: $E^{\circ}_{cell} = E^{\circ}_{ox} + E^{\circ}_{red}$.
    Solution: Oxidation reaction (anode): Sn *(s)* $\rightarrow Sn^{2+}$ *(aq)* $+ 2\ e^-$ $E^{\circ}_{ox} = - E^{\circ}_{red} = - (- 0.14\ V) = 0.14\ V$ and Reduction reaction (cathode): NO_3^- *(aq)* $+ 4\ H^+$ *(aq)* $+ 3\ e^- \rightarrow$ NO *(g)* $+ 2\ H_2O$ *(l)* $E^{\circ}_{red} = 0.96\ V$. E°_{cell} $= E^{\circ}_{ox} + E^{\circ}_{red} = 0.14\ V + 0.96\ V = 1.10\ V$. Multiply first reaction by 3 and the second reaction by 2 so that 6 electrons are transferred. 3 Sn *(s)* $\rightarrow$ 3 Sn^{2+} *(aq)* $+ 6\ e^-$ and 2 NO_3^- *(aq)* $+ 8\ H^+$ *(aq)* $+ 6\ e^- \rightarrow$ 2 NO *(g)* $+$ 4 H_2O *(l)*. Add the two half-reactions and cancel electrons 3 Sn *(s)*$+ 2\ NO_3^-$ *(aq)* $+ 8\ H^+$ *(aq)* $+$ $\cancel{6\ e^-}$ $\rightarrow$3

    Sn^{2+} *(aq)* $+$ $\cancel{6\ e^-}$ $+ 2$ NO *(g)* $+$ 4 H_2O *(l)*. So balanced reaction is: 3 Sn *(s)*$+ 2\ NO_3^-$ *(aq)* $+ 8\ H^+$ *(aq)* $\rightarrow$ 3 Sn^{2+} *(aq)* $+ 2$ NO *(g)* $+$ 4 H_2O *(l)*.

Check: All atoms and charge are balanced. The units (V) are correct. The cell potential is positive which is consistent with a voltaic cell.

52. **Given:** Mn (s)|Mn^{2+} (aq) || ClO$_2$ (g)|ClO$_2^-$ (aq)|Pt (s)

 Find: Sketch voltaic cell, labeling anode, cathode all species and direction of electron flow and $E°_{cell}$

 Conceptual plan: Separate overall reaction into 2 half-cell reactions knowing that the oxidation half-reaction components on the left and the reduction on the right. Add electrons as needed to balance reactions. Multiply the half-reactions by the appropriate factors to have an equal number of electrons transferred. Add the half-cell reactions and cancel electrons. Put anode reaction on the left (oxidation = electrons as product) and cathode reaction on the right (reduction = electrons as reactant). Electrons flow from anode to cathode. Look up half-reactions from solution of problem #44 in Table 18.1. In order to determine the cell potential of the oxidation reaction, reverse the sign of the standard reduction potential ($E°_{ox}$ $= - E°_{red}$) then add the two half-cell potentials: $E°_{cell} = E°_{ox} + E°_{red}$.

 Solution: Oxidation reaction (anode): Mn (s) → Mn^{2+} (aq) + 2 e$^-$ $E°_{ox}$ $= - E°_{red} = - (- 1.18 \text{ V}) = 1.18$ V and Reduction reaction (cathode): ClO$_2$ (g) + e$^-$ → ClO$_2^-$ (aq) $E°_{red} = 0.95$ V. $E°_{cell} = E°_{ox} + E°_{red} = 1.18$ V + 0.95 V = 2.13 V. Multiply the second reaction by 2 so that 2 electrons are transferred. Mn (s) → Mn^{2+} (aq) + 2 e$^-$ and
2 ClO$_2$ (g) + 2 e$^-$ → 2 ClO$_2^-$ (aq). Add the two half-reactions and cancel electrons Mn (s)+ 2 ClO$_2$ (g) + 2e$^-$ → Mn^{2+} (aq) + 2e$^-$ + 2 ClO$_2^-$ (aq). So balanced reaction is: Mn (s)+ 2 ClO$_2$ (g) → Mn^{2+} (aq) + 2 ClO$_2^-$ (aq).

Check: All atoms and charge are balanced. The units (V) are correct. The cell potential is positive which is consistent with a voltaic cell.

53. **Given:** overall reactions   **Find:** spontaneity in forward direction

 Conceptual plan: Separate overall reaction into 2 half-cell reactions and add electrons as needed to balance reactions. Look up half-reactions in Table 18.1. In order to determine the cell potential of the oxidation reaction, reverse the sign of the standard reduction potential ($E°_{ox}$ $= - E°_{red}$) then add the two half-cell potentials: $E°_{cell} = E°_{ox} + E°_{red}$. **If $E°_{cell} > 0$ the reaction is spontaneous in the forward direction.**

 Solution:
 a) Ni (s) + Zn^{2+} (aq) → Ni^{2+} (aq) + Zn (s) separates to Ni (s) → Ni^{2+} (aq) and Zn^{2+} (aq) → Zn (s) add electrons Ni (s) → Ni^{2+} (aq) + 2 e$^-$ and Zn^{2+} (aq) + 2 e$^-$ → Zn (s). Look up cell potentials. Ni is oxidized so $E°_{ox}$ $= - E°_{red} = - (- 0.23 \text{ V}) = 0.23$ V. Zn^{2+} is reduced so $E°_{red} = - 0.76$ V. Then $E°_{cell} = E°_{ox} + E°_{red} = 0.23$ V – 0.76 V = – 0.53 V and so the reaction is nonspontaneous.

 b) Ni (s) + Pb^{2+} (aq) → Ni^{2+} (aq) + Pb (s) separates to Ni (s) → Ni^{2+} (aq) and Pb^{2+} (aq) → Pb (s) add electrons Ni (s) → Ni^{2+} (aq) + 2 e$^-$ and Pb^{2+} (aq) + 2 e$^-$ → Pb (s). Look up cell potentials. Ni is oxidized so $E°_{ox}$ $= - E°_{red} = - (- 0.23 \text{ V}) = 0.23$ V. Pb^{2+} is reduced so $E°_{red} = - 0.13$ V. Then $E°_{cell} = E°_{ox} + E°_{red} = 0.23$ V – 0.13 V = + 0.10 V and so the reaction is spontaneous.

c) Al (s) + 3 Ag$^+$ (aq) → Al^{3+} (aq) + 3 Ag (s) separates to Al (s) → Al^{3+} (aq) and 3 Ag$^+$ (aq) → 3 Ag (s) add electrons Al (s) → Al^{3+} (aq) + 3 e$^-$ and 3 Ag$^+$ (aq) + 3 e$^-$ → 3 Ag (s). Simplify the Ag reaction to: Ag$^+$ (aq) + e$^-$ → Ag (s). Look up cell potentials. Al is oxidized so $E°_{ox}$ = − $E°_{red}$ = − (− 1.66 V) = 1.66 V. Ag$^+$ is reduced so $E°_{red}$ = 0.80 V. Then $E°_{cell}$ = $E°_{ox}$ + $E°_{red}$ = 1.66 V + 0.80 V = + 2.46 V and so the reaction is spontaneous.

d) Pb (s) + Mn^{2+} (aq) → Pb^{2+} (aq) + Mn (s) separates to Pb (s) → Pb^{2+} (aq) and Mn^{2+} (aq) → Mn (s) add electrons Pb (s) → Pb^{2+} (aq) + 2 e$^-$ and Mn^{2+} (aq) + 2 e$^-$ → Mn (s). Look up cell potentials. Pb is oxidized so $E°_{ox}$ = − $E°_{red}$ = − (− 0.13 V) = 0.13 V. Mn^{2+} is reduced so $E°_{red}$ = − 1.18 V. Then $E°_{cell}$ = $E°_{ox}$ + $E°_{red}$ = 0.13 V − 1.18 V = − 1.05 V and so the reaction is nonspontaneous.

Check: The units (V) are correct. If the voltage is positive, the reaction is spontaneous.

54. **Given:** overall reactions   **Find:** spontaneity in forward direction
     Conceptual plan: Separate overall reaction into 2 half-cell reactions and add electrons as needed to balance reactions. Look up half-reactions in Table 18.1. In order to determine the cell potential of the oxidation reaction, reverse the sign of the standard reduction potential ($E°_{ox}$ = − $E°_{red}$) then add the two half-cell potentials: $E°_{cell}$ = $E°_{ox}$ + $E°_{red}$. **If $E°_{cell}$ > 0 the reaction is spontaneous in the forward direction.**

Solution:
a) Ca^{2+} (aq) + Zn (s) → Ca (s) + Zn^{2+} (aq) separates to Ca^{2+} (aq) → Ca (s) and Zn (s) → Zn^{2+} (aq) add electrons Ca^{2+} (aq) + 2 e$^-$ → Ca (s) and Zn (s) → Zn^{2+} (aq) + 2 e$^-$. Look up cell potentials. Zn is oxidized so $E°_{ox}$ = − $E°_{red}$ = − − 0.76 V = 0.76 V. Ca^{2+} is reduced so $E°_{red}$ = − 2.76 V. Then $E°_{cell}$ = $E°_{ox}$ + $E°_{red}$ = 0.76 V − 2.76 V = − 2.00 V and so the reaction is spontaneous in the reverse direction.

b) 2 Ag$^+$ (aq) + Ni (s) → 2 Ag (s) + Ni^{2+} (aq) separates to 2 Ag$^+$ (aq) → 2 Ag (s) and Ni (s) → Ni^{2+} (aq) add electrons 2 Ag$^+$ (aq) + 2 e$^-$ → 2 Ag (s) and Ni (s) → Ni^{2+} (aq) + 2 e$^-$. Simplify the Ag reaction to: Ag$^+$ (aq) + e$^-$ → Ag (s). Look up cell potentials. Ni is oxidized so $E°_{ox}$ = − $E°_{red}$ = − − 0.23 V = 0.23 V. Ag$^+$ is reduced so $E°_{red}$ = 0.80 V. Then $E°_{cell}$ = $E°_{ox}$ + $E°_{red}$ = 0.23 V + 0.80 V = + 1.03 V and so the reaction is nonspontaneous in the reverse direction.

c) Fe (s) + Mn^{2+} (aq) → Fe^{2+} (aq) + Mn (s) separates to Fe (s) → Fe^{2+} (aq) and Mn^{2+} (aq) → Mn (s) add electrons Fe (s) → Fe^{2+} (aq) + 2 e$^-$ and Mn^{2+} (aq) + 2 e$^-$ → Mn (s). Look up cell potentials. Fe is oxidized so $E°_{ox}$ = − $E°_{red}$ = − − 0.45 V = 0.45 V. Mn^{2+} is reduced so $E°_{red}$ = − 1.18 V. Then $E°_{cell}$ = $E°_{ox}$ + $E°_{red}$ = 0.45 V − 1.18 V = + 0.73 V and so the reaction is nonspontaneous in the reverse direction.

d) 2 Al (s) + 3 Pb^{2+} (aq) → 2 Al^{3+} (aq) + 3 Pb (s) separates to 2 Al (s) → 2 Al^{3+} (aq) and 3 Pb^{2+} (aq) → 3 Pb (s) add electrons 2 Al (s) → 2 Al^{3+} (aq) + 6 e$^-$ and 3 Pb^{2+} (aq) + 6 e$^-$ → 2 Pb (s). Simplify the reactions to Al (s) → Al^{3+} (aq) + 3 e$^-$ and Pb^{2+} (aq) + 2 e$^-$ → Pb (s). Look up cell potentials. Al is oxidized so $E°_{ox}$ = − $E°_{red}$ = − − 1.66 V = 1.66 V. Pb^{2+} is reduced so $E°_{red}$ = − 0.13 V. Then $E°_{cell}$ = $E°_{ox}$ + $E°_{red}$ = 1.66 V − 0.13 V = + 1.53 V and so the reaction is nonspontaneous in the reverse direction.

Check: The units (V) are correct. If the voltage is negative, the reaction is spontaneous in the reverse direction.

55. In order for a metal to be able to reduce an ion, it must be above it in Table 18.1 (need positive $E°_{cell}$ = $E°_{ox}$ + $E°_{red}$). So we need a metal that is above Mn^{2+}, but below Mg^{2+}. Aluminum is the only one in the table that meets these criteria.

56. In order for a metal to be able to oxidized an ion, it must be below it in Table 18.1 (need positive $E°_{cell}$ = $E°_{ox}$ + $E°_{red}$). So we need a metal that is above Fe^{2+}, but below Sn^{2+}. Nickel and cadmium meet these criteria.

57. In general, metals whose reduction half-reactions lie below the reduction of H$^+$ to H$_2$ in Table 18.1 will dissolve in acids, while metals above it will not. a) Al and c) Pb meet this criterion. To write the balanced redox reactions, pair the oxidation of the metal with the reduction of H$^+$ to H$_2$ (2 H$^+$$(aq)$ + 2 e$^-$ → H$_2(g)$). For Al, Al (s) → Al^{3+} (aq) + 3 e$^-$. In order to balance the number of electrons transferred we need to multiply the Al reaction by 2 and the H$^+$ reaction by 3. So, 2 Al (s) → 2 Al^{3+} (aq) + 6 e$^-$ and 6 H$^+$$(aq)$ + 6 e$^-$ → 3 H$_2(g)$. Adding the two reactions: 2 Al (s) + 6 H$^+$$(aq)$ + 6 e$^-$ → 2 Al^{3+} (aq) + 6 e$^-$ + 3 H$_2(g)$. Simplify to 2 Al (s) + 6 H$^+$$(aq)$ → 2 Al^{3+} (aq) + 3 H$_2(g)$. For Pb, Pb (s) → Pb^{2+} (aq) + 2 e$^-$. Since each

reaction involves 2 electrons we can add the two reactions. Pb (s) + 2 H$^+$$(aq)$ + $\cancel{2e^-}$ → Pb^{2+} (aq) + $\cancel{2e^-}$ + H$_2$$(g)$. Simplify to Pb (s) + 2 H$^+$$(aq)$ → Pb^{2+} (aq) + H$_2$$(g)$.

58. In general, metals whose reduction half-reactions lie below the reduction of H$^+$ to H$_2$ in Table 18.1 will dissolve in acids, while metals above it will not. Only b) Fe meets this criterion. To write the balanced redox reactions, pair the oxidation of the metal with the reduction of H$^+$ to H$_2$ (2 H$^+$$(aq)$ + 2 e$^-$ → H$_2$$(g)$). For Fe there are two possible reactions, Fe (s) → Fe^{3+} (aq) + 3 e$^-$ and Fe (s) → Fe^{2+} (aq) + 2 e$^-$. Since the second reaction is lower in Table 18.1, the cell potential will be more positive. This means that this reaction will be more spontaneous and thus preferred. Since each reaction involves 2 electrons we can add the two reactions. Fe (s) + 2 H$^+$$(aq)$ + $\cancel{2e^-}$ → Fe^{2+} (aq) + $\cancel{2e^-}$ + H$_2$$(g)$. Simplify to Fe (s) + 2 H$^+$$(aq)$ → Fe^{2+} (aq) + H$_2$$(g)$.

59. Nitric acid (HNO$_3$) oxidizes metals through the following reduction half-reaction: NO$_3^-$ (aq) + 4 H$^+$ (aq) + 3 e$^-$ → NO (g) + 2 H$_2$O (l) E$^°_{red}$ = 0.96 V. Since this half-reaction is above the reduction of H$^+$ in Table 18.1, HNO$_3$ can oxidize metals (such as copper, for example) that can't be oxidizied by HCl. a) Cu will be oxidized, but b) Au (which has a reduction potential of 1.50 V will not be oxidized. To write the balanced redox reactions, pair the oxidation of the metal with the reduction of nitric acid (NO$_3^-$ (aq) + 4 H$^+$ (aq) + 3 e$^-$ → NO (g) + 2 H$_2$O (l)). For Cu, Cu (s) → Cu^{2+} (aq) + 2 e$^-$. In order to balance the number of electrons transferred we need to multiply the Cu reaction by 3 and the nitric acid reaction by 2. So, 3 Cu (s) → 3 Cu^{2+} (aq) + 6 e$^-$ and 2 NO$_3^-$ (aq) + 8 H$^+$ (aq) + 6 e$^-$ → 2 NO (g) + 4 H$_2$O (l). Adding the two reactions: 3 Cu (s)+ 2 NO$_3^-$ (aq) + 8 H$^+$ (aq) + $\cancel{6e^-}$ → 3 Cu^{2+} (aq) + $\cancel{6e^-}$ + 2 NO (g) + 4 H$_2$O (l). Simplify to 3 Cu (s)+ 2 NO$_3^-$ (aq) + 8 H$^+$ (aq) → 3 Cu^{2+} (aq) + 2 NO (g) + 4 H$_2$O (l).

60. Iodic acid (HIO$_3$) oxidizes metals through the following reduction half-reaction: IO$_3^-$ (aq) + 6 H$^+$ (aq) + 5 e$^-$ → ½ I$_2$ (aq) + 3 H$_2$O (l) E$^°_{red}$ = 1.20 V. Since this half-reaction is above the reduction of H$^+$ in Table 18.1, HNO$_3$ can oxidize metals (such as copper, for example) that can't be oxidizied by HCl. a) Au (which has a reduction potential of 1.50 V) will not be oxidized, but b) Cr (which has a reduction potential of – 0.50 V) will be oxidized. To write the balanced redox reactions, pair the oxidation of the metal with the reduction of iodic acid (IO$_3^-$ (aq) + 6 H$^+$ (aq) + 5 e$^-$ → ½ I$_2$ (aq) + 3 H$_2$O (l)). For Cr, Cr (s) → Cr^{3+} (aq) + 3 e$^-$. In order to balance the number of electrons transferred we need to multiply the Cr reaction by 5 and the iodic acid reaction by 3. So, 5 Cr (s) → 5 Cr^{3+} (aq) + 15 e$^-$ and 3 IO$_3^-$ (aq) + 18 H$^+$ (aq) + 15 e$^-$ → 3/2 I$_2$ (aq) + 9 H$_2$O (l). Adding the two reactions: 5 Cr (s)+ 3 IO$_3^-$ (aq) + 18 H$^+$ (aq) + $\cancel{15e^-}$ → 5 Cr^{3+} (aq) + $\cancel{15e^-}$ + 3/2 I$_2$ (aq) + 9 H$_2$O (l). Simplify to 5 Cr (s)+ 3 IO$_3^-$ (aq) + 18 H$^+$ (aq) → 5 Cr^{3+} (aq) + 3/2 I$_2$ (aq) + 9 H$_2$O (l).

61. **Given:** overall reactions $\qquad\qquad$ **Find:** $E^°_{cell}$ and spontaneity in forward direction
    Conceptual plan: Separate overall reaction into 2 half-cell reactions and add electrons as needed to balance reactions. Look up half-reactions in Table 18.1. In order to determine the cell potential of the oxidation reaction, reverse the sign of the standard reduction potential ($E^°_{ox}$ = – $E^°_{red}$) then add the two half-cell potentials: $E^°_{cell} = E^°_{ox} + E^°_{red}$. If $E^°_{cell} > 0$ the reaction is spontaneous in the forward direction.
    Solution:
    a) 2 Cu (s) + Mn^{2+} (aq) → 2 Cu$^+$ (aq) + Mn (s) separates to 2 Cu (s) → 2 Cu$^+$ (aq) and Mn^{2+} (aq) → Mn (s) add electrons 2 Cu (s) → 2 Cu$^+$ (aq) + 2 e$^-$ and Mn^{2+} (aq) + 2 e$^-$ → Mn (s). Simplify the Cu reaction to: Cu (s) → Cu$^+$ (aq) + e$^-$. Look up cell potentials. Cu is oxidized so $E^°_{ox}$ = – $E^°_{red}$ = – 0.52 V. Mn^{2+} is reduced so $E^°_{red}$ = – 1.18 V. Then $E^°_{cell} = E^°_{ox} + E^°_{red}$ = – 0.52 V – 1.18 V = – 1.70 V and so the reaction is nonspontaneous.

    b) MnO$_2$ (s) + 4 H$^+$$(aq)$ + Zn (s) → Mn^{2+} (aq) + 2 H$_2$O (l) + Zn^{2+} (aq) separates to MnO$_2$ (s) + 4 H$^+$$(aq)$ → Mn^{2+} (aq) + 2 H$_2$O (l) and Zn (s) → Zn^{2+} (aq) add electrons MnO$_2$ (s) + 4 H$^+$$(aq)$ + 2 e$^-$ → Mn^{2+} (aq) + 2 H$_2$O (l) and Zn (s) → Zn^{2+} (aq) + 2 e$^-$. Look up cell potentials. Zn is oxidized so $E^°_{ox}$ = – $E^°_{red}$ = – – 0.76 V = 0.76 V. Mn is reduced so $E^°_{red}$ = 1.21 V. Then $E^°_{cell} = E^°_{ox} + E^°_{red}$ = 0.76 V + 1.21 V = + 1.97 V and so the reaction is spontaneous.

    c) Cl$_2$ (g) + 2 F$^-$ (aq) → 2 Cl$^-$ (aq) + F$_2$ (g) separates to Cl$_2$ (g) → 2 Cl$^-$ (aq) and 2 F$^-$ (aq) → F$_2$ (g) add electrons Cl$_2$ (g) + 2 e$^-$ → 2 Cl$^-$ (aq) and 2 F$^-$ (aq) → F$_2$ (g) + 2 e$^-$. Look up cell potentials. F is oxidized so $E^°_{ox}$ = – $E^°_{red}$ = – 2.87 V. Cl is reduced so $E^°_{red}$ = 1.36 V. Then $E^°_{cell} = E^°_{ox} + E^°_{red}$ = – 2.87 V + 1.36 V = – 1.51 V and so the reaction is nonspontaneous.
    Check: The units (V) are correct. If the voltage is positive, the reaction is spontaneous.

62. **Given:** overall reactions   **Find:** $E°_{cell}$ and spontaneity in forward direction

    Conceptual plan: Separate overall reaction into 2 half-cell reactions and add electrons as needed to balance reactions. Look up half-reactions in Table 18.1. In order to determine the cell potential of the oxidation reaction, reverse the sign of the standard reduction potential ($E°_{ox} = - E°_{red}$) then add the two half-cell potentials: $E°_{cell} = E°_{ox} + E°_{red}$. **If $E°_{cell} > 0$ the reaction is spontaneous in the forward direction.**

    Solution:

    a) $O_2 (g) + 2 H_2O (l) + 4 Ag (s) \rightarrow 4 OH^- (aq) + 4 Ag^+ (aq)$ separates to $O_2 (g) + 2 H_2O (l) \rightarrow 4 OH^-$ (aq) and $4 Ag (s) \rightarrow 4 Ag^+ (aq)$ add electrons $O_2 (g) + 2 H_2O (l) + 4 e^- \rightarrow 4 OH^- (aq)$ and $4 Ag (s)$ $\rightarrow 4 Ag^+ (aq) + 2 e^-$. Simplify the Ag reaction to: $Ag (s) \rightarrow Ag^+ (aq) + e^-$. Look up cell potentials. Ag is oxidized so $E°_{ox} = - E°_{red} = - 0.80$ V. O is reduced so $E°_{red} = 0.40$ V. Then $E°_{cell} = E°_{ox} + E°_{red}$ $= - 0.80$ V $+ 0.40$ V $= - 0.40$ V and so the reaction is nonspontaneous.

    b) $Br_2 (l) + 2 I^- (aq) \rightarrow 2 Br^- (aq) + I_2 (g)$ separates to $Br_2 (g) \rightarrow 2 Br^- (aq)$ and $2 I^- (aq) \rightarrow I_2 (g)$ add electrons $Br_2 (g) + 2 e^- \rightarrow 2 Br^- (aq)$ and $2 I^- (aq) \rightarrow I_2 (g) + 2 e^-$. Look up cell potentials. I is oxidized so $E°_{ox} = - E°_{red} = - 0.54$ V. Br is reduced so $E°_{red} = 1.09$ V. Then $E°_{cell} = E°_{ox} + E°_{red} = -$ 0.54 V $+ 1.09$ V $= + 0.55$ V and so the reaction is spontaneous.

    c) $PbO_2 (s) + 4 H^+(aq) + Sn (s) \rightarrow Pb^{2+} (aq) + 2 H_2O (l) + Sn^{2+} (aq)$ separates to $PbO_2 (s) + 4 H^+(aq) \rightarrow$ $Pb^{2+} (aq) + 2 H_2O (l)$ and $Sn (s) \rightarrow Sn^{2+} (aq)$ add electrons $PbO_2 (s) + 4 H^+(aq) + 2 e^- \rightarrow Pb^{2+} (aq) + 2$ $H_2O (l)$ and $Sn (s) \rightarrow Sn^{2+} (aq) + 2 e^-$. Look up cell potentials. Sn is oxidized so $E°_{ox} = - E°_{red} = -(-$ 0.14 V$) = 0.14$ V. Pb is reduced so $E°_{red} = 1.46$ V. Then $E°_{cell} = E°_{ox} + E°_{red} = 0.14$ V $+ 1.46$ V $= +$ 1.60 V and so the reaction is spontaneous.

    Check: The units (V) are correct. If the voltage is positive, the reaction is spontaneous.

63.   a) Pb^{2+}. The strongest oxidizing agent is the one with the reduction reaction that is closest to the top of Table 18.1.

64.   b)   Al. The strongest reducing agent is the one with the reduction reaction that yields the metal that is closest to the bottom of Table 18.1.

65. **Given:** overall reactions   **Find:** $\Delta G°_{rxn}$ and spontaneity in forward direction

    Conceptual plan: Separate overall reaction into 2 half-cell reactions and add electrons as needed to balance reactions. Look up half-reactions in Table 18.1. In order to determine the cell potential of the oxidation reaction, reverse the sign of the standard reduction potential ($E°_{ox} = - E°_{red}$) then add the two half-cell potentials: $E°_{cell} = E°_{ox} + E°_{red}$. **then calculate $\Delta G°_{rxn}$ using** $\Delta G^0_{rxn} = - n F E^0_{cell}$ **.**

    Solution:

    a) $Pb^{2+} (aq) + Mg (s) \rightarrow Pb (s) + Mg^{2+} (aq)$ separates to $Pb^{2+} (aq) \rightarrow Pb (s)$ and $Mg (s) \rightarrow Mg^{2+} (aq)$ add electrons $Pb^{2+} (aq) + 2 e^- \rightarrow Pb (s)$ and $Mg (s) \rightarrow Mg^{2+} (aq) + 2 e^-$. Look up cell potentials. Mg is oxidized so $E°_{ox} = - E°_{red} = - (- 2.37$ V$) = 2.37$ V. Pb^{2+} is reduced so $E°_{red} = - 0.13$ V. Then $E°_{cell} =$ $E°_{ox}$ $+$ $E°_{red}$ $=$ 2.37 V $-$ 0.13 V $=$ $+$ 2.24 V. n $=$ 2 so

$$\Delta G^0_{rxn} = - n F E^0_{cell} = -2 \text{ mole}^- \times \frac{96,485 \text{ C}}{\text{mole}^-} \times 2.24 \text{ V} = -2 \times 96,485 \text{ C} \times 2.24 \frac{\text{J}}{\text{C}} = - 4.32 \times 10^5 \text{ J} = - 432 \text{ kJ} .$$

    b) $Br_2 (l) + 2 Cl^- (aq) \rightarrow 2 Br^- (aq) + Cl_2 (g)$ separates to $Br_2 (g) \rightarrow 2 Br^- (aq)$ and $2 Cl^- (aq) \rightarrow Cl_2$ (g) add electrons $Br_2 (g) + 2 e^- \rightarrow 2 Br^- (aq)$ and $2 Cl^- (aq) \rightarrow Cl_2 (g) + 2 e^-$. Look up cell potentials. Cl is oxidized so $E°_{ox} = - E°_{red} = - 1.36$ V. Br is reduced so $E°_{red} = 1.09$ V. Then $E°_{cell} =$ $E°_{ox}$ $+$ $E°_{red}$ $=$ $-$ 1.36 V $+$ 1.09 V $=$ $-$ 0.27 V. n $=$ 2 so

$$\Delta G^0_{rxn} = - n F E^0_{cell} = -2 \text{ mole}^- \times \frac{96,485 \text{ C}}{\text{mole}^-} \times -0.27 \text{ V} = -2 \times 96,485 \text{ C} \times -0.27 \frac{\text{J}}{\text{C}} = 5.2 \times 10^4 \text{ J} = 52 \text{ kJ} .$$

    c) $MnO_2 (s) + 4 H^+(aq) + Cu (s) \rightarrow Mn^{2+} (aq) + 2 H_2O (l) + Cu^{2+} (aq)$ separates to $MnO_2 (s) + 4 H^+(aq)$ $\rightarrow Mn^{2+} (aq) + 2 H_2O (l)$ and $Cu (s) \rightarrow Cu^{2+} (aq)$ add electrons $MnO_2 (s) + 4 H^+(aq) + 2 e^- \rightarrow Mn^{2+}$ $(aq) + 2 H_2O (l)$ and $Cu (s) \rightarrow Cu^{2+} (aq) + 2 e^-$. Look up cell potentials. Cu is oxidized so $E°_{ox} = -$ $E°_{red} = - 0.34$ V. Mn is reduced so $E°_{red} = 1.21$ V. Then $E°_{cell} = E°_{ox} + E°_{red} = - 0.34$ V $+ 1.21$ V $= +$ 0.87 V. n $=$ 2 so

$$\Delta G^0_{rxn} = - n F E^0_{cell} = -2 \text{ mole}^- \times \frac{96,485 \text{ C}}{\text{mole}^-} \times 0.87 \text{ V} = -2 \times 96,485 \text{ C} \times 0.87 \frac{\text{J}}{\text{C}} = -1.7 \times 10^5 \text{ J} = -1.7 \times 10^2 \text{ kJ} .$$

Check: The units (kJ) are correct. If the voltage is positive, the reaction is spontaneous and the free energy change is negative.

66. **Given:** overall reactions   **Find:** ΔG°_{rxn} and spontaneity in forward direction
Conceptual plan: **Separate overall reaction into 2 half-cell reactions and add electrons as needed to balance reactions. Look up half-reactions in Table 18.1. In order to determine the cell potential of the oxidation reaction, reverse the sign of the standard reduction potential ($E^\circ_{ox} = -E^\circ_{red}$) then add the two half-cell potentials:** $E^\circ_{cell} = E^\circ_{ox} + E^\circ_{red}.$ **then calculate** ΔG°_{rxn} **using** $\Delta G^0_{rxn} = -nFE^0_{cell}$.
Solution:

a) $2\,Fe^{3+}\,(aq) + 3\,Sn\,(s) \rightarrow 2\,Fe\,(s) + 3\,Sn^{2+}\,(aq)$ separates to $2\,Fe^{3+}\,(aq) \rightarrow 2\,Fe\,(s)$ and $3\,Sn\,(s) \rightarrow 3\,Sn^{2+}\,(aq)$ add electrons $2\,Fe^{3+}\,(aq) + 6\,e^- \rightarrow 2\,Fe\,(s)$ and $3\,Sn\,(s) \rightarrow 3\,Sn^{2+}\,(aq) + 6\,e^-$. Simplify reactions to $Fe^{3+}\,(aq) + 3\,e^- \rightarrow Fe\,(s)$ and $Sn\,(s) \rightarrow Sn^{2+}\,(aq) + 2\,e^-$. Look up cell potentials. Sn is oxidized so $E^\circ_{ox} = -E^\circ_{red} = -(-0.14\,V) = 0.14\,V$. Fe^{3+} is reduced so $E^\circ_{red} = -0.036\,V$. Then $E^\circ_{cell} = E^\circ_{ox} + E^\circ_{red} = 0.14\,V - 0.036\,V = +0.10\underline{4}\,V.$ $n = 6$ so

$$\Delta G^0_{rxn} = -nFE^0_{cell} = -6\ \cancel{mole^-}\ \times \frac{96,485\ C}{\cancel{mole^-}} \times 0.10\underline{4}\,V = -6 \times 96,485\ \cancel{C} \times 0.10\underline{4}\,\frac{J}{\cancel{C}} = -6.0 \times 10^4\,J = -6.0 \times 10^1\,kJ\ .$$

b) $O_2\,(g) + 2\,H_2O\,(l) + 2\,Cu\,(s) \rightarrow 4\,OH^-\,(aq) + 2\,Cu^{2+}\,(aq)$ separates to $O_2\,(g) + 2\,H_2O\,(l) \rightarrow 4\,OH^-\,(aq)$ and $2\,Cu\,(s) \rightarrow 2\,Cu^{2+}\,(aq)$ add electrons $O_2\,(g) + 2\,H_2O\,(l) + 4\,e^- \rightarrow 4\,OH^-\,(aq)$ and $2\,Cu\,(s) \rightarrow 2\,Cu^{2+}\,(aq) + 4\,e^-$. Simplify the Cu reaction to: $Cu\,(s) \rightarrow Cu^{2+}\,(aq) + 2\,e^-$. Look up cell potentials. Cu is oxidized so $E^\circ_{ox} = -E^\circ_{red} = -0.34\,V$. O is reduced so $E^\circ_{red} = 0.40\,V$. Then $E^\circ_{cell} = E^\circ_{ox} + E^\circ_{red} =$
$-\quad\quad 0.34\quad V\quad +\quad 0.40\quad V\quad =\quad +\quad 0.06\quad V.\quad n\quad =\quad 4\quad$ so

$$\Delta G^0_{rxn} = -nFE^0_{cell} = -4\ \cancel{mole^-}\ \times \frac{96,485\ C}{\cancel{mole^-}} \times 0.06\,V = -4 \times 96,485\ \cancel{C} \times 0.06\,\frac{J}{\cancel{C}} = -2 \times 10^4\,J = -2 \times 10^1\,kJ\ .$$

c) $Br_2\,(l) + 2\,I^-\,(aq) \rightarrow 2\,Br^-\,(aq) + I_2\,(g)$ separates to $Br_2\,(g) \rightarrow 2\,Br^-\,(aq)$ and $2\,I^-\,(aq) \rightarrow I_2\,(g)$ add electrons $Br_2\,(g) + 2\,e^- \rightarrow 2\,Br^-\,(aq)$ and $2\,I^-\,(aq) \rightarrow I_2\,(g) + 2\,e^-$. Look up cell potentials. I is oxidized so $E^\circ_{ox} = -E^\circ_{red} = -0.54\,V$. Br is reduced so $E^\circ_{red} = 1.09\,V$. Then $E^\circ_{cell} = E^\circ_{ox} + E^\circ_{red} = -$
$0.54\quad V\quad +\quad 1.09\quad V\quad =\quad +\quad 0.55\quad V.\quad n\quad =\quad 2\quad$ so

$$\Delta G^0_{rxn} = -nFE^0_{cell} = -2\ \cancel{mole^-}\ \times \frac{96,485\ C}{\cancel{mole^-}} \times 0.55\,V = -2 \times 96,485\ \cancel{C} \times 0.55\,\frac{J}{\cancel{C}} = -1.1 \times 10^5\,J = -1.1 \times 10^2\,kJ\ .$$

Check: The units (kJ) are correct. If the voltage is positive, the reaction is spontaneous and the free energy change is negative.

67. **Given:** overall reactions from #65   **Find:** K
Conceptual plan: °C $\rightarrow$ K   then ΔG°_{rxn}, T $\rightarrow$ K
$$K = 273.15 + °C \qquad\qquad \Delta G^0_{rxn} = -RT\ln K$$
Solution: T = 273.15 + 25 °C = 298 K then

a) $\Delta G^0_{rxn} = -RT\ln K$ Rearrange to solve for K. $K = e^{\frac{-\Delta G^0_{rxn}}{RT}} = e^{\frac{-(-432)\ \cancel{kJ}\ \times\frac{1000\ \cancel{J}}{1\ \cancel{kJ}}}{\left(8.314\frac{\cancel{J}}{K\ mol}\right)(298\ \cancel{K})}} = e^{174.364} = 5.31 \times 10^{75}$.

b) $\Delta G^0_{rxn} = -RT\ln K$ Rearrange to solve for K. $K = e^{\frac{-\Delta G^0_{rxn}}{RT}} = e^{\frac{-52\ \cancel{kJ}\ \times\frac{1000\ \cancel{J}}{1\ \cancel{kJ}}}{\left(8.314\frac{\cancel{J}}{K\ mol}\right)(298\ \cancel{K})}} = e^{-20.988} = 7.7 \times 10^{-10}$.

c) $\Delta G^0_{rxn} = -RT\ln K$ Rearrange to solve for K. $K = e^{\frac{-\Delta G^0_{rxn}}{RT}} = e^{\frac{-(-170\ \cancel{kJ})\ \times\frac{1000\ \cancel{J}}{1\ \cancel{kJ}}}{\left(8.314\frac{\cancel{J}}{K\ mol}\right)(298\ \cancel{K})}} = e^{68.616} = 6.3 \times 10^{29}$.

Check: The units (none) are correct. If the voltage is positive, the reaction is spontaneous and the free energy change is negative and the equilibrium constant is large.

68. **Given:** overall reactions from #66   **Find:** K

Conceptual plan: °C $\rightarrow$ K   then $\Delta G°_{rxn}$, T $\rightarrow$ K

$$K = 273.15 + °C \qquad \Delta G^0_{rxn} = -RT \ln K$$

Solution: T = 273.15 + 25 °C = 298 K then

a) $\Delta G^0_{rxn} = -RT \ln K$ Rearrange to solve for K. $K = e^{\frac{-\Delta G^0_{rxn}}{RT}} = e^{\left(\frac{-(-60 \text{ kJ}) \times \frac{1000 \text{ J}}{1 \text{ kJ}}}{\left(8.314 \frac{J}{K \text{ mol}}\right)(298 \text{ K})}\right)} = e^{24.217} = 3.3 \times 10^{10}$.

b) $\Delta G^0_{rxn} = -RT \ln K$ Rearrange to solve for K. $K = e^{\frac{-\Delta G^0_{rxn}}{RT}} = e^{\left(\frac{-(-20 \text{ kJ}) \times \frac{1000 \text{ J}}{1 \text{ kJ}}}{\left(8.314 \frac{J}{K \text{ mol}}\right)(298 \text{ K})}\right)} = e^{8.072} = 3 \times 10^3$.

c) $\Delta G^0_{rxn} = -RT \ln K$ Rearrange to solve for K. $K = e^{\frac{-\Delta G^0_{rxn}}{RT}} = e^{\left(\frac{-(-110 \text{ kJ}) \times \frac{1000 \text{ J}}{1 \text{ kJ}}}{\left(8.314 \frac{J}{K \text{ mol}}\right)(298 \text{ K})}\right)} = e^{44.398} = 1.9 \times 10^{19}$.

Check: The units (none) are correct. If the voltage is positive, the reaction is spontaneous and the free energy change is negative and the equilibrium constant is large.

69. **Given:** $Ni^{2+} (aq) + Cd (s) \rightarrow$ **Find:** K

Conceptual plan: **Write 2 half-cell reactions and add electrons as needed to balance reactions. Look up half-reactions in Table 18.1. In order to determine the cell potential of the oxidation reaction, reverse the sign of the standard reduction potential ($E°_{ox}$ $= -E°_{red}$) then add the two half-cell potentials:** $E°_{cell} = E°_{ox} + E°_{red.}$ **then**
°C $\rightarrow$ K   **then** $E°_{cell}$, n, T $\rightarrow$ K

$$K = 273.15 + °C \qquad \Delta G^0_{rxn} = -RT \ln K = -n F E°_{cell} .$$

Solution:
a) $Ni^{2+} (aq) + 2 e^- \rightarrow Ni (s)$ and $Cd (s) \rightarrow Cd^{2+} (aq) + 2 e^-$. Look up cell potentials. Cd is oxidized so $E°_{ox} = -E°_{red} = -(-0.40 \text{ V}) = 0.40 \text{ V}$. Ni^{2+} is reduced so $E°_{red} = -0.23 \text{ V}$. Then $E°_{cell} = E°_{ox} + E°_{red} = 0.40 \text{ V} - 0.23 \text{ V} = +0.17 \text{ V}$. The overall reaction is $Ni^{2+} (aq) + Cd (s) \rightarrow Ni (s) + Cd^{2+} (aq)$. n = 2 and T = 273.15 + 25 °C = 298 K   then $\Delta G^0_{rxn} = -RT \ln K = -n F E°_{cell}$. Rearrange to solve for K.

$$K = e^{\frac{n F E°_{cell}}{RT}} = e^{\left(\frac{2 \text{ mole}^- \times \frac{96,485 \text{ C}}{\text{mole}^-} \times 0.17 \frac{J}{C}}{\left(8.314 \frac{J}{K \text{ mol}}\right)(298 \text{ K})}\right)} = e^{13.241} = 5.6 \times 10^5 .$$

Check: The units (none) are correct. If the voltage is positive, the reaction is spontaneous and the equilibrium constant is large.

70. **Given:** $Fe^{2+} (aq) + Zn (s) \rightarrow$ **Find:** K

Conceptual plan: **Write 2 half-cell reactions and add electrons as needed to balance reactions. Look up half-reactions in Table 18.1. In order to determine the cell potential of the oxidation reaction, reverse the sign of the standard reduction potential ($E°_{ox}$ $= -E°_{red}$) then add the two half-cell potentials:** $E°_{cell} = E°_{ox} + E°_{red.}$ **then**
°C $\rightarrow$ K   **then** $E°_{cell}$, n, T $\rightarrow$ K

$$K = 273.15 + °C \qquad \Delta G^0_{rxn} = -RT \ln K = -n F E°_{cell} .$$

Solution:
a) $Fe^{2+} (aq) + 2 e^- \rightarrow Fe (s)$ and $Zn (s) \rightarrow Zn^{2+} (aq) + 2 e^-$. Look up cell potentials. Zn is oxidized so $E°_{ox} = -E°_{red} = -(-0.76 \text{ V}) = 0.76 \text{ V}$. Fe^{2+} is reduced so $E°_{red} = -0.45 \text{ V}$. Then $E°_{cell} = E°_{ox} + E°_{red} = 0.76 \text{ V} - 0.45 \text{ V} = +0.31 \text{ V}$. The overall reaction is $Fe^{2+} (aq) + Zn (s) \rightarrow Fe (s) + Zn^{2+} (aq)$. n = 2

and $T = 273.15 + 25\ ^\circ C = 298\ K$ then $\Delta G^0_{rxn} = -RT \ln K = -nFE^0_{cell}$.   Rearrange to solve for K.

$$K = e^{\frac{nFE^0_{cell}}{RT}} = e^{\dfrac{2\ \cancel{mole^-} \times \frac{96,485\ \cancel{C}}{\cancel{mole^-}} \times 0.31\frac{\cancel{J}}{\cancel{C}}}{\left(8.314\frac{\cancel{J}}{\cancel{K}\ mol}\right)(298\ \cancel{K})}} = e^{24.145} = 3.1 \times 10^{10}.$$

Check: The units (none) are correct. If the voltage is positive, the reaction is spontaneous and the equilibrium constant is large.

71. **Given:** $n = 2$ and $K = 25$ **Find:** ΔG°_{rxn} and E°_{cell}
   Conceptual plan: $\mathbf{K, T \rightarrow \Delta G^\circ_{rxn}}$ **and** $\mathbf{\Delta G^\circ_{rxn}, n \rightarrow E^\circ_{cell}}$

   $$\Delta G^0_{rxn} = -RT \ln K \qquad\qquad \Delta G^0_{rxn} = -nFE^0_{cell}$$

   Solution: $\Delta G^0_{rxn} = -RT \ln K = -\left(8.314\dfrac{J}{K\ mol}\right)(298\ \cancel{K}) \ln 25 = -7.\underline{9}7500 \times 10^3\ J = -8.0\ kJ$ and

   $\Delta G^0_{rxn} = -nFE^0_{cell}$.

   Rearrange to solve for E°_{cell}. $E^0_{cell} = \dfrac{\Delta G^0_{rxn}}{-nF} = \dfrac{-7.\underline{9}7500 \times 10^3\ J}{-2\ \cancel{mole^-} \times \dfrac{96,485\ C}{\cancel{mole^-}}} = 0.041\ \dfrac{V\ \cancel{C}}{\cancel{C}} = 0.041\ V$.

   Check: The units (kJ and V) are correct. If $K > 1$ then the voltage is positive, the free energy change is negative.

72. **Given:** $n = 3$ and $K = 0.050$ **Find:** ΔG°_{rxn} and E°_{cell}
   Conceptual plan: $\mathbf{K, T \rightarrow \Delta G^\circ_{rxn}}$ **and** $\mathbf{\Delta G^\circ_{rxn}, n \rightarrow E^\circ_{cell}}$

   $$\Delta G^0_{rxn} = -RT \ln K \qquad\qquad \Delta G^0_{rxn} = -nFE^0_{cell}$$

   Solution: $\Delta G^0_{rxn} = -RT \ln K = -\left(8.314\dfrac{J}{K\ mol}\right)(298\ \cancel{K}) \ln 0.050 = 7.\underline{4}221 \times 10^3\ J = 7.4\ kJ$ and $\Delta G^0_{rxn} = -nFE^0_{cell}$.

   Rearrange to solve for E°_{cell}. $E^0_{cell} = \dfrac{\Delta G^0_{rxn}}{-nF} = \dfrac{7.\underline{4}221 \times 10^3\ J}{-3\ \cancel{mole^-} \times \dfrac{96,485\ C}{\cancel{mole^-}}} = -0.026\ \dfrac{V\ \cancel{C}}{\cancel{C}} = -0.026\ V$.

   Check: The units (kJ and V) are correct. If $K < 1$ then the voltage is negative, the free energy change is positive.

73. **Given:** $Sn^{2+}\ (aq) + Mn\ (s) \rightarrow Sn\ (s) + Mn^{2+}\ (aq)$ **Find:** a) E°_{cell}; b) E_{cell} when $[Sn^{2+}] = 0.0100$ M; $[Mn^{2+}] = 2.00$ M; and c) E_{cell} when $[Sn^{2+}] = 2.00$ M; $[Mn^{2+}] = 0.0100$ M
   Conceptual plan: a) Separate overall reaction into 2 half-cell reactions and add electrons as needed to balance reactions. Look up half-reactions in Table 18.1. In order to determine the cell potential of the oxidation reaction, reverse the sign of the standard reduction potential ($E^\circ_{ox} = -E^\circ_{red}$) then add the two half-cell potentials: $E^\circ_{cell} = E^\circ_{ox} + E^\circ_{red}$. **b) and c)** $E^\circ_{cell}, [Sn^{2+}], [Mn^{2+}], n \rightarrow E_{cell}$

   $$E_{cell} = E^\circ_{cell} - \frac{0.0592\ V}{n} \log Q \text{ where } Q = \frac{[Mn^{2+}]}{[Sn^{2+}]}$$

   Solution: a) separate overall reaction to: $Sn^{2+}\ (aq) \rightarrow Sn\ (s)$ and $Mn\ (s) \rightarrow Mn^{2+}\ (aq)$ add electrons $Sn^{2+}\ (aq) + 2\ e^- \rightarrow Sn\ (s)$ and $Mn\ (s) \rightarrow Mn^{2+}\ (aq) + 2\ e^-$. Look up cell potentials. Mn is oxidized so $E^\circ_{ox} = -E^\circ_{red} = -(-1.18\ V) = 1.18\ V$. Sn^{2+} is reduced so $E^\circ_{red} = -0.14\ V$. Then $E^\circ_{cell} = E^\circ_{ox} + E^\circ_{red} = 1.18\ V - 0.14\ V = +1.04\ V$.

   b) $Q = \dfrac{[Mn^{2+}]}{[Sn^{2+}]} = \dfrac{2.00\ \cancel{M}}{0.0100\ \cancel{M}} = 200.$ and n =   2   then

       $E_{cell} = E^0_{cell} - \dfrac{0.0592\ V}{n} \log Q = 1.04\ V - \dfrac{0.0592\ V}{2} \log 200. = +0.97\ V$

   c) $Q = \dfrac{[Mn^{2+}]}{[Sn^{2+}]} = \dfrac{0.0100\ \cancel{M}}{2.00\ \cancel{M}} = 0.00500$ and n =   2   then

       $E_{cell} = E^0_{cell} - \dfrac{0.0592\ V}{n} \log Q = 1.04\ V - \dfrac{0.0592\ V}{2} \log 0.00500 = +1.11\ V$

Check: The units (V, V and V) are correct. The Sn^{2+} reduction reaction is above the Mn^{2+} reduction reaction, so the standard cell potential will be positive. Having more products than reactants reduces the cell potential. Having more reactants than products raises the cell potential.

74. **Given:** $2 Fe^{3+} (aq) + 3 Mg (s) \rightarrow 2 Fe (s) + 3 Mg^{2+} (aq)$ **Find:** a) $E°_{cell}$; b) E_{cell} when $[Fe^{3+}] = 1.0 \times 10^{-3}$ M; $[Mg^{2+}] = 2.50$ M; and c) E_{cell} when $[Fe^{3+}] = 2.00$ M; $[Mg^{2+}] = 1.5 \times 10^{-3}$ M

Conceptual plan: a) **Separate overall reaction into 2 half-cell reactions and add electrons as needed to balance reactions. Look up half-reactions in Table 18.1. In order to determine the cell potential of the oxidation reaction, reverse the sign of the standard reduction potential ($E°_{ox} = -E°_{red}$) then add the two half-cell potentials:** $E°_{cell} = E°_{ox} + E°_{red}$. b) and c) $E°_{cell}, [Fe^{3+}], [Mg^{2+}], n \rightarrow E_{cell}$

$$E_{cell} = E°_{cell} - \frac{0.0592 \ V}{n} \log Q \quad \text{where} \quad Q = \frac{[Mg^{2+}]^3}{[Fe^{3+}]^2}$$

Solution: a) separate overall reaction to: $2 Fe^{3+} (aq) \rightarrow 2 Fe (s)$ and $3 Mg (s) \rightarrow 3 Mg^{2+} (aq)$ add electrons $2 Fe^{3+} + 6 e^- (aq) \rightarrow 2 Fe (s)$ and $3 Mg (s) \rightarrow 3 Mg^{2+} (aq) + 6 e^-$. Look up cell potentials. Mg is oxidized so $E°_{ox} = -E°_{red} = -(-2.37 \ V) = 2.37 \ V$. Fe^{3+} is reduced so $E°_{red} = -0.036 \ V$. Then $E°_{cell} = E°_{ox} + E°_{red} = 2.37 \ V - 0.036 \ V = +2.3\underline{3}4 \ V = +2.33 \ V$.

b) $Q = \frac{[Mg^{2+}]^3}{[Fe^{3+}]^2} = \frac{(2.50)^3}{(1.0 \times 10^{-3})^2} = 1.\underline{5}625 \times 10^7$ and $n = 6$ then

$E_{cell} = E°_{cell} - \frac{0.0592 \ V}{n} \log Q = 2.3\underline{3}4 \ V - \frac{0.0592 \ V}{6} \log 1.\underline{5}625 \times 10^7 = +2.26 \ V$

c) $Q = \frac{[Mg^{2+}]^3}{[Fe^{3+}]^2} = \frac{(1.5 \times 10^{-3})^3}{(2.00)^2} = 8.\underline{4}375 \times 10^{-10}$ and $n = 6$ then

$E_{cell} = E°_{cell} - \frac{0.0592 \ V}{n} \log Q = 2.3\underline{3}4 \ V - \frac{0.0592 \ V}{6} \log 8.\underline{4}375 \times 10^{-10} = +2.42 \ V$

Check: The units (V, V and V) are correct. The Fe^{3+} reduction reaction is above the Mg^{2+} reduction reaction, so the standard cell potential will be positive. Having more products than reactants reduces the cell potential. Having more reactants than products raises the cell potential.

75. **Given:** $Pb (s) \rightarrow Pb^{2+} (aq, 0.10 \ M) + 2 e^-$ and $MnO_4^- (aq, 1.50 \ M) + 4 H^+ (aq, 2.0 \ M) + 3 e^- \rightarrow MnO_2 (s) + 2 H_2O (l)$ **Find:** E_{cell}

Conceptual plan: **Look up half-reactions in Table 18.1. In order to determine the cell potential of the oxidation reaction, reverse the sign of the standard reduction potential ($E°_{ox} = -E°_{red}$) then add the two half-cell potentials:** $E°_{cell} = E°_{ox} + E°_{red}$. **Equalize the number of electrons transferred by multiplying the first reaction by 3 and the second reaction by 2. Add the two half-cell reactions and cancel the electrons.**

Then $E°_{cell}, [Pb^{2+}], [MnO_4^-], [H^+], n \rightarrow E_{cell}$

$$E_{cell} = E°_{cell} - \frac{0.0592 \ V}{n} \log Q \quad \text{where} \quad Q = \frac{[Pb^{2+}]^3}{[MnO_4^-]^2[H^+]^8}$$

Solution: Pb is oxidized so $E°_{ox} = -E°_{red} = --0.13 \ V = 0.13 \ V$. Mn is reduced so $E°_{red} = 1.68 \ V$. Then $E°_{cell} = E°_{ox} + E°_{red} = 0.13 \ V + 1.68 \ V = +1.81 \ V$. Equalizing the electrons: $3 Pb (s) \rightarrow 3 Pb^{2+} (aq) + 6 e^-$ and $2 MnO_4^- (aq) + 8 H^+ (aq) + 6 e^- \rightarrow 2 MnO_2 (s) + 4 H_2O (l)$. Adding the two reactions: $3 Pb (s) + 2 MnO_4^- (aq) + 8 H^+ (aq) + 6 e^- \rightarrow 3 Pb^{2+} (aq) + 6 e^- + 2 MnO_2 (s) + 4 H_2O (l)$. Cancel the electrons: $3 Pb (s) + 2 MnO_4^- (aq) + 8 H^+ (aq) \rightarrow 3 Pb^{2+} (aq) + 2 MnO_2 (s) + 4 H_2O (l)$. So $n = 6$ and

$Q = \frac{[Pb^{2+}]^3}{[MnO_4^-]^2[H^+]^8} = \frac{(0.10)^3}{(1.50)^2(2.0)^8} = 1.\underline{7}361 \times 10^{-6}$ then

$E_{cell} = E°_{cell} - \frac{0.0592 \ V}{n} \log Q = 1.81 \ V - \frac{0.0592 \ V}{6} \log 1.\underline{7}361 \times 10^{-6} = +1.87 \ V$.

Check: The units (V) are correct. The MnO_4^- reduction reaction is above the Pb^{2+} reduction reaction, so the standard cell potential will be positive. Having more reactants than products raises the cell potential.

76. **Given:** $Sn (s) \rightarrow Sn^{2+} (aq, 2.00 \ M) + 2 e^-$ and $ClO_2 (g, 0.100 \ atm) + e^- \rightarrow ClO_2^- (aq, 2.00 \ M)$ **Find:** E_{cell}

Conceptual plan: Look up half-reactions in Table 18.1. In order to determine the cell potential of the oxidation reaction, reverse the sign of the standard reduction potential ($E^\circ_{ox} = -E^\circ_{red}$) then add the two half-cell potentials: $E^\circ_{cell} = E^\circ_{ox} + E^\circ_{red}$. Equalize the number of electrons transferred by multiplying the second reaction by 2. Add the two half-cell reactions and cancel the electrons. Then E°_{cell}, [Sn^{2+}], P_{ClO2}, [ClO_2^-], n → E_{cell}

$$E_{cell} = E^\circ_{cell} - \frac{0.0592\ V}{n} \log Q \quad \text{where} \quad Q = \frac{[Sn^{2+}][ClO_2^-]^2}{P_{ClO_2}^2}$$

Solution: Sn is oxidized so $E^\circ_{ox} = -E^\circ_{red} = -(-0.14\ V) = 0.14\ V$. ClO_2 is reduced so $E^\circ_{red} = 0.95\ V$. Then $E^\circ_{cell} = E^\circ_{ox} + E^\circ_{red} = 0.14\ V + 0.95\ V = +1.09\ V$. Equalizing the electrons: Sn (s) → Sn^{2+} (aq) + 2 e^- and 2 ClO_2 (g) + 2 e^- → 2 ClO_2^- (aq). Adding the two reactions: Sn (s)+ 2 ClO_2 (g) + 2̶e̶⁻ → Sn^{2+} (aq) + 2̶e̶⁻ + 2 ClO_2^- (aq). Cancel the electrons: Sn (s)+ 2 ClO_2 (g) → Sn^{2+} (aq) + 2 ClO_2^- (aq). So n = 2

and
$$Q = \frac{[Sn^{2+}][ClO_2^-]^2}{P_{ClO2}^2} = \frac{(2.00)(2.00)^2}{(0.100)^2} = 800.$$
then

$$E_{cell} = E^0_{cell} - \frac{0.0592\ V}{n} \log Q = 1.09\ V - \frac{0.0592\ V}{2} \log 800. = +1.00\ V\ .$$

Check: The units (V) are correct. The ClO_2 reduction reaction is above the Sn^{2+} reduction reaction, so the standard cell potential will be positive. Having more products than reactants lowers the cell potential.

77. **Given:** Zn/Zn^{2+} and Ni/Ni^{2+} half-cells in voltaic cell; initially [Ni^{2+}] = 1.50 M, and [Zn^{2+}] = 0.100 M
Find: a) initial E_{cell}; b) E_{cell} when [Ni^{2+}] = 0.500 M; and c) [Ni^{2+}] and [Zn^{2+}] when E_{cell} = 0.45 V
Conceptual plan: a) Write 2 half-cell reactions and add electrons as needed to balance reactions. Look up half-reactions in Table 18.1. In order to determine the cell potential of the oxidation reaction, reverse the sign of the standard reduction potential ($E^\circ_{ox} = -E^\circ_{red}$) then add the two half-cell potentials: $E^\circ_{cell} = E^\circ_{ox} + E^\circ_{red}$. Choose the direction of the half-cell reactions so that $E^\circ_{cell} > 0$. Add two half-cell reactions and cancel electrons to generate overall reaction. Define Q based on overall reaction. Then E°_{cell}, [Ni^{2+}], [Zn^{2+}], n → E_{cell}

$$E_{cell} = E^\circ_{cell} - \frac{0.0592\ V}{n} \log Q$$

b) When [Ni^{2+}] = 0.500 M, then [Zn^{2+}] = 1.100 M (since the stoichiometric coefficients for Ni^{2+}: Zn^{2+} are 1:1, and the [Ni^{2+}] drops by 1.00 M, the other concentration must rise by 1.00 M). Then E°_{cell}, [Ni^{2+}], [Zn^{2+}], n → E_{cell}

$$E_{cell} = E^\circ_{cell} - \frac{0.0592\ V}{n} \log Q$$

c) E°_{cell}, E_{cell}, n → [Zn^{2+}] / [Ni^{2+}] → [Ni^{2+}], [Zn^{2+}]

$$E_{cell} = E^\circ_{cell} - \frac{0.0592\ V}{n} \log Q \qquad [Ni^{2+}] + [Zn^{2+}] = 1.50\ M + 0.100\ M = 1.60\ M$$

Solution: a) Zn^{2+} (aq) + 2 e^- → Zn (s) and Ni^{2+} (aq) + 2 e^- → Ni (s). Look up cell potentials. For Zn, $E^\circ_{red} = -0.76\ V$. For Ni, $E^\circ_{red} = -0.23\ V$. In order to get a positive E°_{cell} the sign of the Zn potential must be reversed. Zn is oxidized so $E^\circ_{ox} = -E^\circ_{red} = -(-0.76\ V) = 0.76\ V$. Ni^{2+} is reduced so $E^\circ_{red} = -0.23\ V$. Then $E^\circ_{cell} = E^\circ_{ox} + E^\circ_{red} = 0.76\ V - 0.23\ V = +0.53\ V$. Adding the two half-cell reactions: Zn (s)+ Ni^{2+} (aq) + 2̶e̶⁻ → Zn^{2+} (aq) + 2̶e̶⁻ + Ni (s). The overall reaction is: Zn (s)+ Ni^{2+} (aq) → Zn^{2+} (aq) + Ni (s).

Then $\qquad Q = \frac{[Zn^{2+}]}{[Ni^{2+}]} = \frac{0.100}{1.50} = 0.0666667 \qquad$ and $\qquad n = 2 \qquad$ then

$$E_{cell} = E^0_{cell} - \frac{0.0592\ V}{n} \log Q = 0.53\ V - \frac{0.0592\ V}{2} \log 0.0666667 = +0.56\ V\ .$$

b) $\quad Q = \frac{[Zn^{2+}]}{[Ni^{2+}]} = \frac{1.100}{0.500} = 2.20$ then $E_{cell} = E^0_{cell} - \frac{0.0592\ V}{n} \log Q = 0.53\ V - \frac{0.0592\ V}{2} \log 2.20 = +0.52\ V\ .$

c) $E_{cell} = E^0_{cell} - \dfrac{0.0592 \text{ V}}{n} \log Q$ so $0.45 \text{ V} = 0.53 \text{ V} - \dfrac{0.0592 \text{ V}}{2} \log Q$ → $0.08 \text{ V} = \dfrac{0.0592 \text{ V}}{2} \log Q$ →

$\log Q = 2.\underline{7}0270$ → $Q = 10^{2.70270} = 50\underline{4}.32$ then $Q = 50\underline{4}.32 = \dfrac{[Zn^{2+}]}{1.60 \text{ M} - [Zn^{2+}]}$ solving for $[Zn^{2+}]$

$(50\underline{4}.32)(1.60 \text{ M} - [Zn^{2+}]) = [Zn^{2+}]$ → $[Zn^{2+}] = \dfrac{80\underline{6}.906 \text{ M}}{50\underline{5}.32} = 1.\underline{5}9628 \text{ M} = 1.60 \text{ M}$ then

$[Ni^{2+}] = 1.60 \text{ M} - 1.\underline{5}9628 \text{ M} = 0.003 \text{ M}$.

Check: The units (V, V and V) are correct. The standard cell potential is positive and since there are more reactants than products this raises the cell potential. As the reaction proceeds, reactants are converted to products so the cell potential drops for parts b) and c).

78. **Given:** Pb/Pb^{2+} and Cu/Cu^{2+} half-cells in voltaic cell; initially $[Pb^{2+}] = 0.0500$ M, and $[Cu^{2+}] = 1.50$ M
Find: a) initial E_{cell}; b) E_{cell} when $[Cu^{2+}] = 0.200$ M; and c) $[Pb^{2+}]$ and $[Cu^{2+}]$ when $E_{cell} = 0.35$ V
Conceptual plan: a) Write 2 half-cell reactions and add electrons as needed to balance reactions. Look up half-reactions in Table 18.1. In order to determine the cell potential of the oxidation reaction, reverse the sign of the standard reduction potential ($E^{\circ}_{ox} = - E^{\circ}_{red}$) then add the two half-cell potentials: $E^{\circ}_{cell} = E^{\circ}_{ox} + E^{\circ}_{red}$. Choose the direction of the half-cell reactions so that $E^{\circ}_{cell} > 0$. Add two half-cell reactions and cancel electrons to generate overall reaction. Define Q based on overall reaction. Then E°_{cell}, $[Pb^{2+}]$, $[Cu^{2+}]$, n → E_{cell}

$$E_{cell} = E^{\circ}_{cell} - \dfrac{0.0592 \text{ V}}{n} \log Q$$

b) When $[Cu^{2+}] = 0.200$ M, then $[Pb^{2+}] = 1.35$ M (since the stoichiometric coefficients for Pb^{2+}: Cu^{2+} are 1:1, and the $[Cu^{2+}]$ drops by 1.30 M, the other concentration must rise by 1.30 M). Then E°_{cell}, $[Pb^{2+}]$, $[Cu^{2+}]$, n → E_{cell}

$$E_{cell} = E^{\circ}_{cell} - \dfrac{0.0592 \text{ V}}{n} \log Q$$

c) E°_{cell}, E_{cell}, n → $[Pb^{2+}]/[Cu^{2+}]$ → $[Pb^{2+}]$, $[Cu^{2+}]$
$E_{cell} = E^{\circ}_{cell} - \dfrac{0.0592 \text{ V}}{n} \log Q$ $[Pb^{2+}] + [Cu^{2+}] = 0.0500 \text{ M} + 1.50 \text{ M} = 1.55 \text{ M}$

Solution: a) Pb^{2+} (aq) + 2 e⁻ → Pb (s) and Cu^{2+} (aq) + 2 e⁻ → Cu (s). Look up cell potentials. For Pb, $E^{\circ}_{red} = - 0.13$ V. For Cu, $E^{\circ}_{red} = + 0.34$ V. In order to get a positive E°_{cell} the sign of the Pb potential must be reversed. Pb is oxidized so $E^{\circ}_{ox} = - E^{\circ}_{red} = - (- 0.13 \text{ V}) = 0.13$ V. Cu^{2+} is reduced so $E^{\circ}_{red} = 0.34$ V. Then $E^{\circ}_{cell} = E^{\circ}_{ox} + E^{\circ}_{red} = 0.13 \text{ V} + 0.34 \text{ V} = + 0.47$ V. Adding the two half-cell reactions: Pb (s) + Cu^{2+} (aq) + 2e⁻ → Pb^{2+} (aq) + 2e⁻ + Cu (s). The overall reaction is: Pb (s) + Cu^{2+} (aq) → Pb^{2+} (aq) + Cu

(s). Then $Q = \dfrac{[Pb^{2+}]}{[Cu^{2+}]} = \dfrac{0.050}{1.50} = 0.03\underline{3}333$ and $n = 2$ then

$E_{cell} = E^0_{cell} - \dfrac{0.0592 \text{ V}}{n} \log Q = 0.47 \text{ V} - \dfrac{0.0592 \text{ V}}{2} \log 0.03\underline{3}333 = +0.51 \text{ V}$.

b) $Q = \dfrac{[Pb^{2+}]}{[Cu^{2+}]} = \dfrac{1.35}{0.200} = 6.75$ then $E_{cell} = E^0_{cell} - \dfrac{0.0592 \text{ V}}{n} \log Q = 0.47 \text{ V} - \dfrac{0.0592 \text{ V}}{2} \log 6.75 = +0.45 \text{ V}$.

c) $E_{cell} = E^0_{cell} - \dfrac{0.0592 \text{ V}}{n} \log Q$ so $0.35 \text{ V} = 0.47 \text{ V} - \dfrac{0.0592 \text{ V}}{2} \log Q$ → $0.12 \text{ V} = \dfrac{0.0592 \text{ V}}{2} \log Q$ →

$\log Q = 4.\underline{0}540$ → $Q = 10^{4.0540} = 1.\underline{1}325 \times 10^4$ then $Q = 1.\underline{1}325 \times 10^4 = \dfrac{[Pb^{2+}]}{1.55 \text{ M} - [Pb^{2+}]}$ solving for $[Pb^{2+}]$

$(1.\underline{1}325 \times 10^4)(1.55 \text{ M} - [Pb^{2+}]) = [Pb^{2+}]$ → $[Pb^{2+}] = \dfrac{1.\underline{7}554 \times 10^4 \text{ M}}{1.\underline{1}335 \times 10^4} = 1.\underline{5}487 \text{ M} = 1.5 \text{ M}$ then

$[Cu^{2+}] = 1.55 \text{ M} - 1.\underline{5}487 \text{ M} = 0.0\underline{0}1345 \text{ M} = 0.001 \text{ M}$.

Check: The units (V, V and V) are correct. The standard cell potential is positive and since there are more reactants than products this raises the cell potential. As the reaction proceeds, reactants are converted to products so the cell potential drops for parts b) and c).

79. **Given:** Zn/Zn²⁺ concentration cell, with [Zn²⁺] = 2.0 M in one half-cell and [Zn²⁺] = 1.0 x 10⁻³ M in other half-cell
Find: Sketch voltaic cell, labeling anode, cathode, reactions at electrodes, all species and direction of electron flow
Conceptual plan: In a concentration cell, the half-cell with the higher concentration is always the half-cell where the reduction takes place (contains the cathode). The 2 half-cell reactions are the same, only reversed. Put anode reaction on the left (oxidation = electrons as product) and cathode reaction on the right (reduction = electrons as reactant). Electrons flow from anode to cathode.

Solution:

Check: The figure looks similar to the right side of Figure 18.12.

80. **Given:** Pb/Pb²⁺ concentration cell sketch **Find:** a) Label anode and cathode; b) Indicate direction of electron flow; and c) Indicate what happens to [Pb²⁺] in each half-cell with time
Conceptual plan: a) In a concentration cell, the half-cell with the higher concentration is always the half-cell where the reduction takes place (contains the cathode). b) Electrons flow from anode to cathode. c) Each half cell reaction moves forward, so concentration change direction can be determined.
Solution:
c) As the reaction proceeds, the left half-cell (cathode = reduction reaction) will decrease in concentration; and the right half-cell (anode = oxidation reaction) will increase in concentration. Eventually the two concentrations will be the same and the flow of electrons will stop.

Check: The figure looks similar to the right side of Figure 18.12.

81. **Given:** Sn/Sn²⁺ concentration cell with E_{cell} = 0.10 V **Find:** ratio of [Sn²⁺] in two half-cells
Conceptual plan: Determine n, then $E°_{cell}, E_{cell}, n$ → Q = ratio of [Sn²⁺] in two half-cells

$$E_{cell} = E°_{cell} - \frac{0.0592\ V}{n} \log Q$$

Solution: Since Sn²⁺ (aq) + 2 e⁻ → Sn (s), n = 2. In a concentration cell, $E°_{cell}$ = 0 V. So

$$E_{cell} = E°_{cell} - \frac{0.0592\ V}{n} \log Q \quad so \quad 0.10\ V = 0.00\ V - \frac{0.0592\ V}{2} \log Q \rightarrow 0.10\ V = -\frac{0.0592\ V}{2} \log Q \rightarrow$$

$$\log Q = -3.\underline{3}784 \rightarrow Q = 10^{-3.3784} = 4.2\ x\ 10^{-4} = \frac{[Sn^{2+}](ox)}{[Sn^{2+}](red)}.$$

Check: The units (none) are correct. Since the concentration in the reduction reaction half-cell is always greater that the concentration in the oxidation half-cell in a voltaic concentration cell, the Q or ratio of two cells is less than 1.

82. **Given:** Cu/Cu^{2+} concentration cell with $E_{cell} = 0.22$ V; and $[Cu^{2+}] = 1.5 \times 10^{-3}$ M **Find:** $[Cu^{2+}]$ in other half-cell

   Conceptual plan: Determine n, then E°_{cell}, E_{cell}, $n \rightarrow Q$ = ratio of $[Cu^{2+}]$ in two half-cells   then

$$E_{cell} = E^{\circ}_{cell} - \frac{0.0592\ V}{n} \log Q$$

   $[Cu^{2+}]$ one side, Q $\rightarrow [Cu^{2+}]$ other side

$$Q = \frac{[Cu^{2+}](ox)}{[Cu^{2+}](red)}$$

   Solution: Since Sn^{2+} *(aq)* $+ 2\ e^- \rightarrow Sn$ *(s)*, $n = 2$. In a concentration cell, $E^{\circ}_{cell} = 0$ V. So

$$E_{cell} = E^0_{cell} - \frac{0.0592\ V}{n} \log Q \quad \text{so} \quad 0.22\ V = 0.00\ V - \frac{0.0592\ V}{2} \log Q \quad \rightarrow \quad 0.22\ V = -\frac{0.0592\ V}{2} \log Q \quad \rightarrow$$

   $\log Q = -7.\underline{4}324$ $\rightarrow$ $Q = 10^{-7.4324} = 3.\underline{6}946 \times 10^{-8} = \dfrac{[Cu^{2+}](ox)}{[Cu^{2+}](red)}$. If we assume that the concentration of the

   copper solution given is the lower of the two, so $[Cu^{2+}](red) = \dfrac{[Cu^{2+}](ox)}{Q} = \dfrac{1.5 \times 10^{-3}\ M}{3.\underline{6}946 \times 10^{-8}} = 4.0 \times 10^4$ M , which

   is impossible.

   So it must be the higher concentration or
   $[Cu^{2+}](ox) = [Cu^{2+}](red) \times Q = (1.5 \times 10^{-3}\ M)(3.\underline{6}946 \times 10^{-8}) = 5.5 \times 10^{-11}$ M , which is low, but possible.

   Check: The units (M) are correct. Since the voltage is fairly high for a concentration cell, there must be an very small Q, which leads to an extremely low concentration on the oxidation side.

83. **Given:** alkaline battery   **Find:** optimum mass ratio of Zn to MnO_2

   Conceptual plan: Look up alkaline battery reactions. Use stoichiometry to get mole ratio.   then

$$\frac{1\ mol\ Zn}{2\ mol\ MnO_2}$$

$$Zn\ (s) + 2\ OH^-\ (aq) \rightarrow Zn(OH)_2\ (s) + 2\ e^-$$

$$2\ MnO_2\ (s) + 2\ H_2O\ (l) + 2\ e^- \rightarrow 2\ MnO(OH)\ (s) + 2\ OH^-\ (aq).$$

   mol Zn $\rightarrow$ g Zn then mol MnO_2 $\rightarrow$ g MnO_2

$$\frac{65.41\ g\ Zn}{1\ mol\ Zn} \qquad \frac{1\ mol\ MnO_2}{86.94\ g\ MnO_2}$$

   Solution: $\dfrac{1\ mol\ Zn}{2\ mol\ MnO_2} \times \dfrac{65.41\ g\ Zn}{1\ mol\ Zn} \times \dfrac{1\ mol\ MnO_2}{86.94\ g\ MnO_2} = 0.3762\ \dfrac{g\ Zn}{g\ MnO_2}$.

   Check: The units (mass ratio) are correct. Since more moles of MnO_2 are needed and the molar mass is larger, the ratio is less than 1.

84. **Given:** lead storage battery, 1.00 g Pb oxidizes   **Find:** mass $PbSO_4$

   Conceptual plan: Look up lead acid battery reactions. then g Pb $\rightarrow$ mol Pb $\rightarrow$ mol $PbSO_4$ $\rightarrow$ g $PbSO_4$

$$\frac{1\ mol\ Pb}{207.2\ g\ Pb} \qquad \frac{2\ mol\ PbSO_4}{1\ mol\ Pb} \qquad \frac{303.27\ g\ PbSO_4}{1\ mol\ PbSO_4}$$

$$Pb\ (s) + HSO_4^-\ (aq) \rightarrow PbSO_4\ (s) + H^+\ (aq) + 2\ e^-$$

$$PbO_2\ (s) + HSO_4^-\ (aq) + 3\ H^+\ (aq) + 2\ e^- \rightarrow PbSO_4\ (s) + 2\ H_2O\ (l).$$

   Solution: $1.00\ g\ Pb \times \dfrac{1\ mol\ Pb}{207.2\ g\ Pb} \times \dfrac{2\ mol\ PbSO_4}{1\ mol\ Pb} \times \dfrac{303.27\ g\ PbSO_4}{1\ mol\ PbSO_4} = 2.93\ g\ PbSO_4$.

   Check: The units (g) are correct. Since more moles of $PbSO_4$ are generated and the molar mass is larger, the mass is larger.

85. **Given:** $CH_4\ (g) + 2\ O_2\ (g) \rightarrow CO_2\ (g) + 2\ H_2O\ (g)$ **Find:** E°_{cell}

   Conceptual plan: $\Delta G^{\circ}_{rxn} = \sum n_p \Delta G^{\circ}_f (products) - \sum n_R \Delta G^{\circ}_f (reactants)$ **and determine n then ΔG°_{rxn}, $n \rightarrow E^{\circ}_{cell}$**

$$\Delta G^0_{rxn} = -n F E^0_{cell}$$

Solution:

Reactant/Product	ΔG_f^0(kJ/mol from Appendix IIB)
CH_4 (g)	− 50.5
O_2 (g)	0.0
CO_2 (g)	− 394.4
H_2O (g)	− 228.6

Be sure to pull data for the correct formula and phase.

$$\Delta G_{rxn}^0 = \sum n_P \Delta G_f^0 (products) - \sum n_R \Delta G_f^0 (reactants)$$

$$= [1(\Delta G_f^0 (CO_2\ (g)) + 2(\Delta G_f^0 (H_2O\ (g))] - [1(\Delta G_f^0 (CH_4\ (g)) + 2(\Delta G_f^0 (O_2\ (g))]$$

$$= [1(-394.4\ kJ) + 2(-228.6\ kJ)] - [1(-50.5\ kJ) + 2(0.0\ kJ)]$$

$$= [-851.6\ kJ] - [-50.5\ kJ]$$

$$= -801.1\ kJ = -8.011 \times 10^5\ J$$

and since one C atoms goes from an oxidation state of -4 to +4 and 4 O atoms are going from 0 to -2, then n = 8 and

$\Delta G_{rxn}^0 = - nF E_{cell}^0$. Rearrange to solve for $E°_{cell}$. $E_{cell}^0 = \dfrac{\Delta G_{rxn}^0}{-nF} = \dfrac{-8.011 \times 10^5\ J}{-8\ mole^- \times \dfrac{96{,}485\ C}{mole^-}} = 1.038\ \dfrac{V\cdot C}{C} = 1.038\ V$.

Check: The units (V) are correct. The cell voltage is positive which is consistent with a spontaneous reaction.

86. **Given:** CH_3CH_2OH (g) + O_2 (g) → $HC_2H_3O_2$ (g) + H_2O (g)   **Find:** $E°_{cell}$

   Conceptual plan: $\Delta G_{rxn}^0 = \sum n_P \Delta G_f^0 (products) - \sum n_R \Delta G_f^0 (reactants)$ **and determine n then** $\Delta G°_{rxn}, n \rightarrow E°_{cell}$

$$\Delta G_{rxn}^0 = - nF E_{cell}^0$$

Solution:

Reactant/Product	ΔG_f^0(kJ/mol from Appendix IIB)
CH_3CH_2OH (g)	− 167.9
O_2 (g)	0.0
$HC_2H_3O_2$ (g)	− 374.2
H_2O (g)	− 228.6

Be sure to pull data for the correct formula and phase.

$$\Delta G_{rxn}^0 = \sum n_P \Delta G_f^0 (products) - \sum n_R \Delta G_f^0 (reactants)$$

$$= [1(\Delta G_f^0 (HC_2H_3O_2\ (g)) + 1(\Delta G_f^0 (H_2O\ (g))] - [1(\Delta G_f^0 (CH_3CH_2OH\ (g)) + 1(\Delta G_f^0 (O_2\ (g))]$$

$$= [1(-374.2\ kJ) + 1(-228.6\ kJ)] - [1(-167.9\ kJ) + 1(0.0\ kJ)]$$

$$= [-602.8\ kJ] - [-167.9\ kJ]$$

$$= -434.9\ kJ = -4.349 \times 10^5\ J$$

and since 2 O atoms are going from 0 to -2 so n = 4   then $\Delta G_{rxn}^0 = - nF E_{cell}^0$. Rearrange to solve for $E°_{cell}$.

$E_{cell}^0 = \dfrac{\Delta G_{rxn}^0}{-nF} = \dfrac{-4.349 \times 10^5\ J}{-4\ mole^- \times \dfrac{96{,}485\ C}{mole^-}} = 1.127\ \dfrac{V\cdot C}{C} = 1.127\ V$.

Check: The units (V) are correct. The cell voltage is positive which is consistent with a spontaneous reaction.

87. In order for a metal to be able to protect iron, it must more easily oxidized than iron or be below it in Table 18.1. a) Zn and c) Mn meet this criterion.

88. In order for a metal to be able to protect iron, it must more easily oxidized than iron or be below it in Table 18.1. a) Mg and b) Cr meet this criterion.

89. **Given:** electrolytic cell sketch **Find:** a) Label anode and cathode and indicate half-reactions; b) Indicate direction of electron flow; and c) Label battery terminals and calculate minimum voltage to drive reaction

Conceptual plan: a) Write 2 half-cell reactions and add electrons as needed to balance reactions. Look up half-reactions in Table 18.1. In order to determine the cell potential of the oxidation reaction, reverse the sign of the standard reduction potential ($E^o_{ox} = - E^o_{red}$) then add the two half-cell potentials: $E^o_{cell} = E^o_{ox} + E^o_{red}$. Choose the direction of the half-cell reactions so that $E^o_{cell} < 0$. b) Electrons flow from anode to cathode. c) Each half cell reaction moves forward, so concentration change direction can be determined.

Solution:

a) Ni^{2+} (aq) + 2 e⁻ → Ni (s) and Cd^{2+} (aq) + 2 e⁻ → Cd (s). Look up cell potentials. For Ni, $E^o_{red} = -0.23$ V. For Cd, $E^o_{red} = -0.40$ V. In order to get a negative cell potential, Ni is oxidized so $E^o_{ox} = -E^o_{red} = -(-0.23$ V$) = 0.23$ V. Cd^{2+} is reduced so $E^o_{red} = -0.23$ V. Then $E^o_{cell} = E^o_{ox} + E^o_{red} = 0.23$ V $- 0.40$ V $= -0.17$ V. Since oxidation occurs at the anode, the Ni is the anode and the reaction is Ni (s) → Ni^{2+} (aq) + 2 e⁻. Since reduction takes place at the cathode, Cd is the cathode and the reaction is Cd^{2+} (aq) + 2 e⁻ → Cd (s).

c) Since reduction is occurring at the cathode, the battery terminal closest to the cathode is the negative terminal. Since the cell potential from part a) is $= -0.17$ V, a minimum of 0.17 V must be applied by the battery.

Check: The reaction is nonspontaneous, since the reduction of Ni^{2+} is above Cd^{2+}. Electrons still flow from the anode to the cathode. The reaction can be made spontaneous with the application of electrical energy.

90. **Given:** electrolytic cell Mn^{2+} reduced to Mn and Sn oxidized to Sn^{2+} **Find:** Draw cell labeling anode and cathode; write half-reactions; indicate direction of electron flow; and calculate minimum voltage to drive reaction

Conceptual plan: Write 2 half-cell reactions and add electrons as needed to balance reactions. Look up half-reactions in Table 18.1. In order to determine the cell potential of the oxidation reaction, reverse the sign of the standard reduction potential for Sn ($E^o_{ox} = -E^o_{red}$) then add the two half-cell potentials: $E^o_{cell} = E^o_{ox} + E^o_{red}$. Anode is where oxidation occurs, so Sn is anode and Sn is cathode. Electrons flow f----- ar--'- to cathode. The minimum potential needed is E^o_{cell}.

Solution:

Mn^{2+} (aq) + 2 e⁻ → Mn (s) and Sn^{2+} (aq) + 2 e⁻ → Sn (s). Look up cell potentials. For Mn^{2+}, $E^o_{red} = -1.18$ V. For Sn, $E^o_{red} = -0.14$ V. Since Sn is oxidized, $E^o_{ox} = -E^o_{red} = -(-0.14$ V$) = 0.14$ V. Then $E^o_{cell} = E^o_{ox} + E^o_{red} = -1.18$ V $+ 0.14$ V $= -1.04$ V. Since oxidation occurs at the anode, the Sn is the anode and the reaction is Sn (s) → Sn^{2+} (aq) + 2 e⁻. Since reduction takes place at the cathode, Mn is the cathode and the reaction is Mn^{2+} (aq) + 2 e⁻ → Mn (s). Electrons flow from the anode to the cathode. Since the cell potential is -1.04 V, a minimum of 1.04 V must be applied by the battery.

Check: The reaction is nonspontaneous, since the reduction of Sn^{2+} is above Mn^{2+}. Electrons still flow from the anode to the cathode. The reaction can be made spontaneous with the application of electrical energy.

91. **Given:** electrolysis of molten KBr   **Find:** write half-reactions
    Conceptual plan: Write 2 half-cell reactions taking the cation and the anion to their elemental forms at high temperatures, adding electrons as needed to balance reactions.
    Solution: KBr breaks apart to K^+ and Br^-. $K^+ (l) + e^- \rightarrow K (l)$ and $2 Br^- (l) \rightarrow Br_2 (g) + 2 e^-$.
    Check: The cation is reduced and the anion is oxidized. Mass and charge are balanced in the reactions.

92. **Given:** electrolysis of molten NaI   **Find:** products
    Conceptual plan: The products are the cation and the anion in their elemental forms at high temperatures.
    Solution: NaI breaks apart to Na^+ and I^-, so the elemental forms are $Na (l)$ and $I_2 (g)$.
    Check: The cation is reduced and the anion is oxidized.

93. **Given:** electrolysis of mixture of molten KBr and molten LiBr   **Find:** write half-reactions
    Conceptual plan: Write 2 half-cell reactions taking the cation and the anion to their elemental forms at high temperatures, adding electrons as needed to balance reactions. Look up cation cell potentials to see which one generates the mores spontaneous reaction.
    Solution: KBr breaks apart to K^+ and Br^-. $K^+ (l) + e^- \rightarrow K (l)$ and $2 Br^- (l) \rightarrow Br_2 (g) + 2 e^-$. LiBr breaks apart to Li^+ and Br^-. $Li^+ (l) + e^- \rightarrow Li (l)$ and $2 Br^- (l) \rightarrow Br_2 (g) + 2 e^-$. The anions are the same so the anode reaction is $2 Br^- (l) \rightarrow Br_2 (g) + 2 e^-$. Looking up the cation reduction potentials, for K^+ E°_{red} = $- 2.92$ V and for Li^+ $E^\circ_{red} = - 3.04$ V. Since the reduction potential is more positive for K^+, the reaction at the cathode is $K^+ (l) + e^- \rightarrow K (l)$.
    Check: The cation is reduced and the anion is oxidized. Mass and charge are balanced in the reactions. The cation that is higher in Table 18.1 will be the reaction at cathode.

94. **Given:** electrolysis of mixture of molten KI and molten KBr   **Find:** products
    Conceptual plan: Write 2 half-cell reactions taking the cation and the anion to their elemental forms at high temperatures, adding electrons as needed to balance reactions. Look up anion cell potentials to see which one generates the mores spontaneous reaction.
    Solution: KI breaks apart to K^+ and I^-. $K^+ (l) + e^- \rightarrow K (l)$ and $2 I^- (l) \rightarrow I_2 (g) + 2 e^-$. KBr breaks apart to K^+ and Br^-. $K^+ (l) + e^- \rightarrow K (l)$ and $2 Br^- (l) \rightarrow Br_2 (g) + 2 e^-$. The cations are the same so the cathode reaction is $K^+ (l) + e^- \rightarrow K (l)$ and the product will be K (l). Looking up the anion reduction potentials, for Br^- $E^\circ_{ox} = - E^\circ_{red} = - 1.09$ V and for I^- $E^\circ_{ox} = - E^\circ_{red} = - 0.54$ V. Since the oxidation potential is more positive for I^-, the reaction at the anode is $2 I^- (l) \rightarrow I_2 (g) + 2 e^-$ and the product will be $I_2 (g)$.
    Check: The cation is reduced and the anion is oxidized. The anion that is lower in Table 18.1 will be the reaction at the anode.

95. **Given:** electrolysis of aqueous solutions   **Find:** write half-reactions
    Conceptual plan: Write 2 half-cell reactions taking the cation and the anion to their elemental forms at standard conditions, adding electrons as needed to balance reactions. Look up cell potentials and compare to the cell potentials for the electrolysis of water to see which one generates the more spontaneous reaction.
    Solution: The hydrolysis of water reactions are: $2 H_2O (l) \rightarrow O_2 (g) + 4 H^+ (aq) + 4 e^-$ where $E^\circ_{ox} = - 0.82$ V; and
    $2 H_2O (l) + 2 e^- \rightarrow H_2 (g) + OH^- (aq)$ where $E^\circ_{red} = - 0.41$ V.
    a) NaBr breaks apart to Na^+ and Br^-. $Na^+ (aq) + e^- \rightarrow Na (s)$ and $2 Br^- (aq) \rightarrow Br_2 (l) + 2 e^-$. Looking up the half-cell potentials, for Na^+ $E^\circ_{red} = - 2.71$ V and for Br^- $E^\circ_{ox} = - E^\circ_{red} = - 1.09$ V. Since $- 0.82$ V is more positive than $= - 1.09$ V, the oxidation reaction will be: $2 H_2O (l) \rightarrow O_2 (g) + 4 H^+ (aq) + 4 e^-$ at the anode. Since $- 0.41$ V is more positive than $= - 2.71$ V, the reduction reaction will be: $2 H_2O (l) + 2 e^- \rightarrow H_2 (g) + OH^- (aq)$ at the cathode.

    b) PbI_2 breaks apart to Pb^{2+} and I^-. $Pb^{2+} (aq) + 2 e^- \rightarrow Pb (s)$ and $2 I^- (aq) \rightarrow I_2 (s) + 2 e^-$. Looking up the half-cell potentials, for Pb^{2+} $E^\circ_{red} = - 0.13$ V and for I^- $E^\circ_{ox} = - E^\circ_{red} = - 0.54$ V. Since $- 0.13$ V is more positive than $= - 0.82$ V, the oxidation reaction will be: $2 I^- (l) \rightarrow I_2 (s) + 2 e^-$ at the anode. Since $- 0.13$ V is more positive than $= - 0.41$ V, the reduction reaction will be: $Pb^{2+} (aq) + 2 e^- \rightarrow Pb (s)$ at the cathode.

c) $NaSO_4$ breaks apart to Na^+ and SO_4^{2-}. Na^+ (aq) + e^- → Na (s) and SO_4^{2-} (aq) + 4 H^+ (aq) + 2 e^- → H_2SO_3 (aq) + H_2O (l). Notice that both of these are reductions. Since S is in such a high oxidation state (+6) it can not be oxidized. Looking up the half-cell potentials, for Na^+ $E°_{red}$ = − 2.71 V and for SO_4^{2-} $E°_{red}$ = 0.20 V. Since sodium sulfate solutions are neutral and not acidic, even though 0.20 V is more positive than − 0.41 V and − 2.71 V, the reduction reaction will not be: SO_4^{2-} (aq) + 4 H^+ (aq) + 2 e^- → H_2SO_3 (aq) + H_2O (l) at the cathode, which only occurs in acidic solutions. Thus, the reduction reaction will be Na^+ (aq) + e^- → Na (s). Since the only one oxidation reaction is possible, the oxidation reaction will be: 2 H_2O (l) → O_2 (g) + 4 H^+ (aq) + 4 e^- at the anode.

Check: The most positive reactions are the reactions that will occur.

96. **Given:** electrolysis of aqueous solutions   **Find:** write half-reactions
    Conceptual plan: Write 2 half-cell reactions taking the cation and the anion to their elemental forms at standard conditions, adding electrons as needed to balance reactions. Look up cell potentials and compare to the cell potentials for the electrolysis of water to see which one generates the more spontaneous reaction.
    Solution: The hydrolysis of water reactions are: 2 H_2O (l) → O_2 (g) + 4 H^+ (aq) + 4 e^- where $E°_{ox}$ = − 0.82 V; and
    2 H_2O (l) + 2 e^- → H_2 (g) + OH^- (aq) where $E°_{red}$ = − 0.41 V.

    a) $Ni(NO_3)_2$ breaks apart to Ni^{2+} and NO_3^-. Ni^{2+} (aq) + 2 e^- → Ni (s) and NO_3^- (aq) + 4 H^+ (aq) + 3 e^- → NO (g) + 2 H_2O (l). Notice that both of these are reductions. Since N is in such a high oxidation state (+5) it can not be oxidized. Looking up the half-cell potentials, for Ni^{2+} $E°_{red}$ = − 0.23 V and for NO_3^- $E°_{red}$ = + 0.96 V. Since 0.96 V is more positive than − 0.23 V and − 0.41 V, the reduction reaction will be: NO_3^- (aq) + 4 H^+ (aq) + 3 e^- → NO (g) + 2 H_2O (l) at the cathode. Since the only one oxidation reaction is possible, the oxidation reaction will be: 2 H_2O (l) → O_2 (g) + 4 H^+ (aq) + 4 e^- at the anode.

    b) KCl breaks apart to K^+ and Cl^-. K^+ (aq) + e^- → K (s) and 2 Cl^- (aq) → Cl_2 (s) + 2 e^-. Looking up the half-cell potentials, for K^+ $E°_{red}$ = − 2.92 V and for Cl^- $E°_{ox}$ = − $E°_{red}$ = − 1.36 V. Since − 0.82 V is more positive than = − 1.36 V, the oxidation reaction will be: 2 H_2O (l) → O_2 (g) + 4 H^+ (aq) + 4 e^- at the anode. Since − 0.41 V is more positive than = − 2.92 V, the reduction reaction will be: 2 H_2O (l) + 2 e^- → H_2 (g) + OH^- (aq) at the cathode.

    c) $CuBr_2$ breaks apart to Cu^{2+} and Br^-. Cu^{2+} (aq) + 2 e^- → Cu (s) and 2 Br^- (aq) → Br_2 (l) + 2 e^-. Looking up the half-cell potentials, for Cu^{2+} $E°_{red}$ = + 0.34 V and for Br^- $E°_{ox}$ = − $E°_{red}$ = − 1.09 V. Since − 0.82 V is more positive than = − 1.09 V, the oxidation reaction will be: 2 H_2O (l) → O_2 (g) + 4 H^+ (aq) + 4 e^- at the anode. Since + 0.34 V is more positive than = − 0.41 V, the reduction reaction will be: Cu^{2+} (aq) + 2 e^- → Cu (s) at the cathode.

    Check: The most positive reactions are the reactions that will occur.

97. **Given:** electrolysis cell to electroplate Cu onto a metal surface   **Find:** Draw cell, labeling anode and cathode; and write half-reactions
    Conceptual plan: Write 2 half-cell reactions and add electrons as needed to balance reactions. The cathode reaction will be the reduction of Cu^{2+} to the metal. The anode will be the reverse reaction.
    Solution:

Check: The metal to be plated is the cathode, since metal ions are converted to Cu (s) on the surface of the metal.

98. **Given:** electrolysis cell to electroplate Ni onto a metal surface   **Find:** Draw cell, labeling anode and cathode; and write half-reactions

Conceptual plan: Write 2 half-cell reactions and add electrons as needed to balance reactions. The cathode reaction will be the reduction of Ni^{2+} to the metal. The anode will be the reverse reaction.

Solution:

Check: The metal to be plated is the cathode, since metal ions are converted to Ni *(s)* on the surface of the metal.

99. **Given:** Cu electroplating of 225 mg Cu at a current of 7.8 A; Cu^{2+} *(aq)* + 2 e^- → Cu *(s)*
    Find: time

Conceptual plan: mg Cu → g Cu → mol Cu → mol e^- → C → s

$$\frac{1\ g}{1000\ mg} \quad \frac{1\ mol\ Cu}{63.55\ g\ Cu} \quad \frac{2\ mol\ e^-}{1\ mol\ Cu} \quad \frac{96,485\ C}{1\ mol\ e^-} \quad \frac{1\ s}{7.8\ C}$$

Solution: $225\ mg\ Cu \times \dfrac{1\ g\ Cu}{1000\ mg\ Cu} \times \dfrac{1\ mol\ Cu}{63.55\ g\ Cu} \times \dfrac{2\ mol\ e^-}{1\ mol\ Cu} \times \dfrac{96,485\ C}{1\ mol\ e^-} \times \dfrac{1\ s}{7.8\ C} = 88\ s$.

Check: The units (s) are correct. Since far less than a mole of Cu is electroplated, the time is short.

100. **Given:** Ag electroplating at a current of 5.8 A for 55 min; Ag^+ *(aq)* + e^- → Ag *(s)*   **Find:** mass of Ag

Conceptual plan: min → s → C → mol e^- → mol Ag → g Ag

$$\frac{60\ s}{1\ min} \quad \frac{5.8\ C}{1\ s} \quad \frac{1\ mol\ e^-}{96,485\ C} \quad \frac{1\ mol\ Ag}{1\ mol\ e^-} \quad \frac{107.87\ g\ Ag}{1\ mol\ Ag}$$

Solution: $55\ min \times \dfrac{60\ s}{1\ min} \times \dfrac{5.8\ C}{1\ s} \times \dfrac{1\ mol\ e^-}{96,485\ C} \times \dfrac{1\ mol\ Ag}{1\ mol\ e^-} \times \dfrac{107.87\ g\ Ag}{1\ mol\ Ag} = 21\ g\ Ag$.

Check: The units (g) are correct. Since less than a mole of electrons is used, the mass is less than the molar mass of Ag.

101. **Given:** Na electrolysis, 1.0 kg in one hour   **Find:** current

Conceptual plan: Na^+ *(l)* + e^- → Na *(l)* $\dfrac{kg\ Na}{hr} \rightarrow \dfrac{g\ Na}{hr} \rightarrow \dfrac{mol\ Na}{hr} \rightarrow \dfrac{mol\ e^-}{hr} \rightarrow \dfrac{C}{hr} \rightarrow \dfrac{C}{min} \rightarrow \dfrac{C}{s}$

$$\frac{1000\ g}{1\ kg} \quad \frac{1\ mol\ Na}{22.99\ g\ Na} \quad \frac{1\ mol\ e^-}{1\ mol\ Na} \quad \frac{96,485\ C}{1\ mol\ e^-} \quad \frac{1\ hr}{60\ min} \quad \frac{1\ min}{60\ s}$$

Solution:
$$\frac{1.0\ kg\ Na}{1\ hr} \times \frac{1000\ g\ Na}{1\ kg\ Na} \times \frac{1\ mol\ Na}{22.99\ g\ Na} \times \frac{1\ mol\ e^-}{1\ mol\ Na} \times \frac{96,485\ C}{1\ mol\ e^-} \times \frac{1\ hr}{60\ min} \times \frac{1\ min}{60\ s} = 1.2 \times 10^3\ \frac{C}{s} = 1.2 \times 10^3\ A$$.

Check: The units (A) are correct. Since the amount per hour is so large we expect a very large current.

102. **Given:** Al electrolysis at a current of 25 A for 1 hour; Al^{3+} *(aq)* + 3 e^- → Al *(s)*   **Find:** mass of Al

Conceptual plan: hr → min → s → C → mol e⁻ → mol Al → g Al

$$\dfrac{60\ \text{min}}{1\ \text{hr}} \qquad \dfrac{60\ \text{s}}{1\ \text{min}} \qquad \dfrac{25\ \text{C}}{1\ \text{s}} \qquad \dfrac{1\ \text{mol e}^-}{96{,}485\ \text{C}} \qquad \dfrac{1\ \text{mol Al}}{3\ \text{mol e}^-} \qquad \dfrac{26.98\ \text{g Al}}{1\ \text{mol Al}}$$

Solution: $1\ \text{hr} \times \dfrac{60\ \text{min}}{1\ \text{hr}} \times \dfrac{60\ \text{s}}{1\ \text{min}} \times \dfrac{25\ \text{C}}{1\ \text{s}} \times \dfrac{1\ \text{mol e}^-}{96{,}485\ \text{C}} \times \dfrac{1\ \text{mol Al}}{3\ \text{mol e}^-} \times \dfrac{26.98\ \text{g Al}}{1\ \text{mol Al}} = 8.4\ \text{g Al}$.

Check: The units (g) are correct. Since more than a mole of electrons is used per Al^{3+}, the mass is less than the molar mass of Al.

103. **Given:** MnO_4^- (aq) + Zn (s) → Mn^{2+} (aq) + Zn^{2+} (aq) 0.500 M $KMnO_4$ and 2.85 g Zn

Find: balance equation and volume $KMnO_4$ solution

Conceptual plan: Separate the overall reaction into two half-reactions: one for oxidation and one for reduction. → Balance each half-reaction with respect to mass in the following order: 1) balance all elements other than H and O; 2) balance O by adding H_2O; and 3) balance H by adding H^+. → Balance each half reaction with respect to charge by adding electrons. (The sum of the charges on both sides of the equation should be made equal by adding electrons as necessary.) → Make the number of electrons in both half-reactions equal by multiplying one or both half-reactions by a small whole number. → Add the two half-reactions together, canceling electrons and other species as necessary. → Verify that the reaction is balanced both with respect to mass and with respect to charge. then g Zn → mol Zn → mol MnO_4^- → L MnO_4^- → mL MnO_4^-

$$\dfrac{1\ \text{mol Zn}}{65.41\ \text{g Zn}} \qquad \dfrac{2\ \text{mol MnO}_4^-}{5\ \text{mol Zn}} \qquad \dfrac{1\ \text{L MnO}_4^-}{0.500\ \text{mol MnO}_4^-} \qquad \dfrac{1000\ \text{mL MnO}_4^-}{1\ \text{L MnO}_4^-}$$

Solution:

Separate: $\qquad\qquad\qquad MnO_4^-$ (aq) → Mn^{2+} (aq) $\quad$ and $\qquad$ Zn (s) → Zn^{2+} (aq)

Balance non H & O elements: MnO_4^- (aq) → Mn^{2+} (aq) $\quad$ and $\qquad$ Zn (s) → Zn^{2+} (aq)

Balance O with H_2O: $\quad MnO_4^-$ (aq) → Mn^{2+} (aq) + 4 H_2O (l) $\;$ and $\qquad$ Zn (s) → Zn^{2+} (aq)

Balance H with H^+: $\; MnO_4^-$ (aq) + 8 H^+ (aq) → Mn^{2+} (aq) + 4 H_2O (l) $\;$ and $\;$ Zn (s) → Zn^{2+} (aq)

Add electrons: MnO_4^- (aq) + 8 H^+ (aq) + 5 e⁻ → Mn^{2+} (aq) + 4 H_2O (l) and Zn (s) → Zn^{2+} (aq) + 2 e⁻

Equalize electrons:

2 MnO_4^- (aq) + 16 H^+ (aq) + 10 e⁻ → 2 Mn^{2+} (aq) + 8 H_2O (l) and 5 Zn (s) → 5 Zn^{2+} (aq) + 10 e⁻

Add half-reactions:

2 MnO_4^- (aq) + 16 H^+ (aq) + 10 e⁻ + 5 Zn (s) → 2 Mn^{2+} (aq) + 8 H_2O (l) + 5 Zn^{2+} (aq) + 10 e⁻

Cancel electrons: $\quad$ 2 MnO_4^- (aq) + 16 H^+ (aq) + 5 Zn (s) → 2 Mn^{2+} (aq) + 8 H_2O (l) + 5 Zn^{2+} (aq)

$2.85\ \text{g Zn} \times \dfrac{1\ \text{mol Zn}}{65.41\ \text{g Zn}} \times \dfrac{2\ \text{mol MnO}_4^-}{5\ \text{mol Zn}} \times \dfrac{1\ \text{L MnO}_4^-}{0.500\ \text{mol MnO}_4^-} \times \dfrac{1000\ \text{mL MnO}_4^-}{1\ \text{L MnO}_4^-} = 34.9\ \text{mL MnO}_4^- =$

$= 34.9\ \text{mL KMnO}_4$.

Check:

Reactants	Products
2 Mn atoms	2 Mn atoms
8 O atoms	8 O atoms
16 H atoms	16 H atoms
5 Zn atoms	5 Zn atoms
+14 charge	+14 charge

The units (mL) are correct. Since far less than a mole of Zinc is used, less than a mole of permanganate is consumed, so the volume is less than a liter.

104. **Given:** $Cr_2O_7^{2-}$ (aq) + Cu (s) → Cr^{3+} (aq) + Cu^{2+} (aq) 0.850 M $K_2Cr_2O_7$ and 5.25 g Zn

Find: balance equation and volume $K_2Cr_2O_7$ solution

Conceptual plan: Separate the overall reaction into two half-reactions: one for oxidation and one for reduction. → Balance each half-reaction with respect to mass in the following order: 1) balance all elements other than H and O; 2) balance O by adding H_2O; and 3) balance H by adding H^+. → Balance each half reaction with respect to charge by adding electrons. (The sum of the charges on both sides of the equation should be made equal by adding electrons as necessary.) → Make the number of electrons in both half-reactions equal by multiplying one or both half-reactions by a small whole number. → Add the two half-reactions together, canceling electrons and other species as necessary. → Verify that the reaction is balanced both with respect to mass and with respect to charge. then $g\ Cu$ → $mol\ Cu$ → $mol\ Cr_2O_7^{2-}$ → $L\ Cr_2O_7^{2-}$ → $mL\ Cr_2O_7^{2-}$

$$\frac{1\ mol\ Cu}{63.55\ g\ Cu} \qquad \frac{1\ mol\ Cr_2O_7^{2-}}{3\ mol\ Cu} \qquad \frac{1\ L\ Cr_2O_7^{2-}}{0.850\ mol\ Cr_2O_7^{2-}} \qquad \frac{1000\ mL\ Cr_2O_7^{2-}}{1\ L\ Cr_2O_7^{2-}}$$

Solution:

Separate: $\qquad\qquad\qquad\qquad\qquad Cr_2O_7^{2-}\ (aq) \to Cr^{3+}\ (aq) \qquad$ and $\qquad Cu\ (s) \to Cu^{2+}\ (aq)$

Balance non H & O elements: $Cr_2O_7^{2-}\ (aq) \to 2\ Cr^{3+}\ (aq) \qquad$ and $\qquad Cu\ (s) \to Cu^{2+}\ (aq)$

Balance O with H_2O: $\quad Cr_2O_7^{2-}\ (aq) \to 2\ Cr^{3+}\ (aq) + 7\ H_2O\ (l)$ and $\qquad Cu\ (s) \to Cu^{2+}\ (aq)$

Balance H with H^+: $\quad Cr_2O_7^{2-}\ (aq) + 14\ H^+\ (aq) \to 2\ Cr^{3+}\ (aq) + 7\ H_2O\ (l)$ and $\quad Cu\ (s) \to Cu^{2+}\ (aq)$

Add electrons: $Cr_2O_7^{2-}\ (aq) + 14\ H^+\ (aq) + 6\ e^- \to 2\ Cr^{3+}\ (aq) + 7\ H_2O\ (l)$ and $Cu\ (s) \to Cu^{2+}\ (aq) + 2e^-$

Equalize electrons:

$Cr_2O_7^{2-}\ (aq) + 14\ H^+\ (aq) + 6\ e^- \to 2\ Cr^{3+}\ (aq) + 7\ H_2O\ (l)$ and $\quad 3\ Cu\ (s) \to 3\ Cu^{2+}\ (aq) + 6\ e^-$

Add half-reactions:

$Cr_2O_7^{2-}\ (aq) + 14\ H^+\ (aq) + \cancel{6\ e^-} + 3\ Cu\ (s) \to 2\ Cr^{3+}\ (aq) + 7\ H_2O\ (l) + 3\ Cu^{2+}\ (aq) + \cancel{6\ e^-}$

Cancel electrons: $Cr_2O_7^{2-}\ (aq) + 14\ H^+\ (aq) + 3\ Cu\ (s) \to 2\ Cr^{3+}\ (aq) + 7\ H_2O\ (l) + 3\ Cu^{2+}\ (aq)$

$5.25\ \cancel{g\ Cu} \times \dfrac{1\ \cancel{mol\ Cu}}{63.55\ \cancel{g\ Cu}} \times \dfrac{1\ \cancel{mol\ Cr_2O_7^{2-}}}{3\ \cancel{mol\ Cu}} \times \dfrac{1\ \cancel{L\ Cr_2O_7^{2-}}}{0.850\ \cancel{mol\ Cr_2O_7^{2-}}} \times \dfrac{1000\ mL\ Cr_2O_7^{2-}}{1\ \cancel{L\ Cr_2O_7^{2-}}} = 32.4\ mL\ Cr_2O_7^{2-} =$

$= 32.4\ mL\ K_2Cr_2O_7$.

Check:

Reactants	Products
2 Cr atoms	2 Cr atoms
7 O atoms	7 O atoms
14 H atoms	14 H atoms
3 Cu atoms	3 Cu atoms
+12 charge	+12 charge

The units (mL) are correct. Since far less than a mole of Copper is used, less than a mole of dichromate is consumed, so the volume is less than a liter.

105. **Given:** beaker with Al strip and Zn^{2+} ions   **Find:** draw sketch after Al is submerged for a few minutes

Conceptual plan: Write 2 half-cell reactions and add electrons as needed to balance reactions. Look up half-reactions in Table 18.1. In order to determine the cell potential of the oxidation reaction, reverse the sign of the standard reduction potential ($E^\circ_{ox} = - E^\circ_{red}$) then add the two half-cell potentials: $E^\circ_{cell} = E^\circ_{ox} + E^\circ_{red}$. If $E^\circ_{cell} > 0$ the reaction is spontaneous in the forward direction and Al will dissolve and Cu will deposit.

Solution: $Al\ (s) \to Al^{3+}\ (aq)$ and $Cu^{2+}\ (aq) \to Cu\ (s)$ add electrons $Al\ (s) \to Al^{3+}\ (aq) + 3\ e^-$ and $Cu^{2+}\ (aq) + 2\ e^- \to Cu\ (s)$. Look up cell potentials. Al is oxidized so $E^\circ_{ox} = - E^\circ_{red} = - - 1.66\ V = 1.66\ V$. Cu^{2+} is reduced so $E^\circ_{red} = 0.34\ V$. Then $E^\circ_{cell} = E^\circ_{ox} + E^\circ_{red} = 1.66\ V + 0.34\ V = + 2.00\ V$ and so the reaction is spontaneous. Al will dissolve to generate $Al^{3+}\ (aq)$ and Cu (s) will deposit.

Check: The units (V) are correct. If the voltages is positive, the reaction is spontaneous so Al will dissolve and Cu will deposit.

106. **Given:** Zn/Zn^{2+} and Ni/Ni^{2+} half-cells in voltaic cell **Find:** draw sketch after substantial amount of current generated

Conceptual plan: Write 2 half-cell reactions and add electrons as needed to balance reactions. Look up half-reactions in Table 18.1. In order to determine the cell potential of the oxidation reaction, reverse the sign of the standard reduction potential ($E°_{ox} = -E°_{red}$) then add the two half-cell potentials: $E°_{cell} = E°_{ox} + E°_{red}$. Choose the direction of the half-cell reactions so that $E°_{cell} > 0$. Add two half-cell reactions and cancel electrons to generate overall reaction. Since reaction is spontaneous it will move forward.

Solution: $Zn^{2+} (aq) + 2 e^- \rightarrow Zn (s)$ and $Ni^{2+} (aq) + 2 e^- \rightarrow Ni (s)$. Look up cell potentials. For Zn, $E°_{red} = -0.76$ V. For Ni, $E°_{red} = -0.23$ V. In order to get a positive $E°_{cell}$ the sign of the Zn potential must be reversed. Zn is oxidized so $E°_{ox} = -E°_{red} = --0.76$ V = 0.76 V. Ni^{2+} is reduced so $E°_{red} = -0.23$ V. Then $E°_{cell} = E°_{ox} + E°_{red} = 0.76$ V $- 0.23$ V $= +0.53$ V. Adding the two half-cell reactions: $Zn (s) + Ni^{2+} (aq) + 2e^- \rightarrow Zn^{2+} (aq) + 2e^- + Ni (s)$. The overall reaction is: $Zn (s) + Ni^{2+} (aq) \rightarrow Zn^{2+} (aq) + Ni (s)$. Zn will dissolve to generate $Zn^{2+} (aq)$ and Ni (s) will deposit.

Check: The units (V) are correct. Since Ni is above Zn in Table 18.1, Ni is reduced. If the voltages is positive, the reaction is spontaneous so Zn will dissolve and Ni will deposit.

107. **Given:** a) 2.15 g Al; b) 4.85 g Cu; and c) 2.42 g Ag in 3.5 M HI

Find: if metal dissolves, write balanced reaction and minimum amount of HI needed to dissolve metal

Conceptual Plan: In general, metals whose reduction half-reactions lie below the reduction of H^+ to H_2 in Table 18.1 will dissolve in acids, while metals above it will not. Stop here if metal does not dissolve. To write the balanced redox reactions, pair the oxidation of the metal with the reduction of H^+ to H_2 ($2 H^+(aq) + 2 e^- \rightarrow H_2(g)$). Balance the number of electrons transferred. Add the two reactions. Cancel electrons. then

g metal → mol metal → mol H^+ → L HI → mL HI

$$\underset{\mathfrak{M}}{} \qquad \frac{x \text{ mol } H^+}{y \text{ mol metal}} \qquad \frac{1 \text{ L HI}}{3.5 \text{ mol HI}} \qquad \frac{1000 \text{ mL HI}}{1 \text{ L HI}}$$

Solution: a) Al meets this criterion. For Al, $Al (s) \rightarrow Al^{3+} (aq) + 3 e^-$. we need to multiply the Al reaction by 2 and the H^+ reaction by 3. So, $2 Al (s) \rightarrow 2 Al^{3+} (aq) + 6 e^-$ and $6 H^+(aq) + 6 e^- \rightarrow 3 H_2(g)$. Adding the half-reactions together: $2 Al (s) + 6 H^+(aq) + 6e^- \rightarrow 2 Al^{3+} (aq) + 6e^- + 3 H_2(g)$. Simplify to

$$2 \quad Al \quad (s) + \quad 6 \quad H^+(aq) \rightarrow \quad 2 \quad Al^{3+} \quad (aq) \quad + \quad 3 \quad H_2(g). \qquad \text{then}$$

$$2.15 \text{ g Al} \times \frac{1 \text{ mol Al}}{26.98 \text{ g Al}} \times \frac{6 \text{ mol } H^+}{2 \text{ mol Al}} \times \frac{1 \text{ L HI}}{3.5 \text{ mol HI}} \times \frac{1000 \text{ mL HI}}{1 \text{ L HI}} = 68.3 \text{ mL HI }.$$

b) Cu does not meet this criterion, so it will not dissolve in HI.

c) Ag does not meet this criterion, so it will not dissolve in HI.

Check: Only metals with negative reduction potentials will dissolve. The volume of acid needed is fairly small since the amount of metal is much less than 1 mole and the concentration of acid is high.

108. **Given:** a) 5.90 g Au; b) 2.55 g Cu; and c) 4.83 g Sn in 6.0 M HNO_3

Find: if metal dissolves, write balanced reaction and minimum amount of HNO_3 needed to dissolve metal

Conceptual Plan: Nitric acid (HNO_3) oxidizes metals through the following reduction half-reaction: $NO_3^- (aq) + 4 H^+ (aq) + 3 e^- \rightarrow NO (g) + 2 H_2O (l)$ $E°_{red} = 0.96$ V. Since this half-reaction is above the reduction of H^+ in Table 18.1, HNO_3 can oxidize metals that can't be oxidized by HCl.

Solution: a) Au (which has a reduction potential of 1.50 V) will not be oxidized, so it will not dissolve in HNO_3.

b) Cu will be oxidized (which has a reduction potential of 0.34 V). To write the balanced redox reactions, pair the oxidation of the copper (Cu (s) → Cu^{2+} (aq) + 2 e^-) with the reduction of nitric acid (NO_3^- (aq) + 4 H^+ (aq) + 3 e^- → NO (g) + 2 H_2O (l)). In order to balance the number of electrons transferred we need to multiply the Cu reaction by 3 and the nitric acid reaction by 2. So, 3 Cu (s) → 3 Cu^{2+} (aq) + 6 e^- and 2 NO_3^- (aq) + 8 H^+ (aq) + 6 e^- → 2 NO (g) + 4 H_2O (l). Adding the two reactions: 3 Cu (s)+ 2 NO_3^- (aq) + 8 H^+ (aq) + $\cancel{6e^-}$ → 3 Cu^{2+} (aq) + $\cancel{6e^-}$ + 2 NO (g) + 4 H_2O (l). Simplify to 3 Cu (s)+ 2 NO_3^- (aq) + 8 H^+ (aq) → 3 Cu^{2+} (aq) + 2 NO (g) + 4 H_2O (l). then

$$2.55 \ \cancel{g \ Cu} \ \times \ \frac{1 \ \cancel{mol \ Cu}}{63.55 \ \cancel{g \ Cu}} \ \times \ \frac{8 \ \cancel{mol \ H^+}}{3 \ \cancel{mol \ Cu}} \ \times \ \frac{1 \ \cancel{L \ HNO_3}}{6.0 \ \cancel{mol \ HNO_3}} \ \times \ \frac{1000 \ mL \ HNO_3}{1 \ \cancel{L \ HNO_3}} = 18 \ mL \ HNO_3 \ .$$

Use stoichiometric coefficient of H^+ since it is larger than the NO_3^- stoichiometric coefficient.

c) Sn will be oxidized (which has a reduction potential of – 0.14 V). To write the balanced redox reactions, pair the oxidation of the tin (Sn (s) → Sn^{2+} (aq) + 2 e^-) with the reduction of nitric acid (NO_3^- (aq) + 4 H^+ (aq) + 3 e^- → NO (g) + 2 H_2O (l)). In order to balance the number of electrons transferred we need to multiply the Sn reaction by 3 and the nitric acid reaction by 2. So, 3 Sn (s) → 3 Sn^{2+} (aq) + 6 e^- and 2 NO_3^- (aq) + 8 H^+ (aq) + 6 e^- → 2 NO (g) + 4 H_2O (l). Adding the two reactions: 3 Sn (s)+ 2 NO_3^- (aq) + 8 H^+ (aq) + $\cancel{6e^-}$ → 3 Sn^{2+} (aq) + $\cancel{6e^-}$ + 2 NO (g) + 4 H_2O (l). Simplify to 3 Sn (s)+ 2 NO_3^- (aq) + 8 H^+ (aq) → 3 Sn^{2+} (aq) + 2 NO (g) + 4 H_2O (l). then

$$4.83 \ \cancel{g \ Sn} \ \times \ \frac{1 \ \cancel{mol \ Sn}}{118.71 \ \cancel{g \ Sn}} \ \times \ \frac{8 \ \cancel{mol \ H^+}}{3 \ \cancel{mol \ Sn}} \ \times \ \frac{1 \ \cancel{L \ HNO_3}}{6.0 \ \cancel{mol \ HNO_3}} \ \times \ \frac{1000 \ mL \ HNO_3}{1 \ \cancel{L \ HNO_3}} = 18 \ mL \ HNO_3 \ .$$

Use stoichiometric coefficient of H^+ since it is larger than the NO_3^- stoichiometric coefficient.
Check: Only metals with reduction potentials less than 0.96 V will dissolve. The volume of acid needed is fairly small since the amount of metal is much less than 1 mole and the concentration of acid is high.

109. **Given:** Pt (s)|H_2 $(g, 1 \ atm)$|H^+ $(aq, ? \ M)$||Cu^{2+} $(aq, 1.0 \ M)$|Cu (s), $E_{cell} = 355 \ mV$ **Find:** pH
Conceptual plan: Write half reactions from line notation. Look up half-reactions in Table 18.1. The reaction on the left is the oxidation so reverse the sign of the standard reduction potential ($E^o_{ox} = - E^o_{red}$) then add the two half-cell potentials: $E^o_{cell} = E^o_{ox} + E^o_{red}$. **Add the two half-cell reactions and cancel the electrons.**
Then mV → V $E^o_{cell}, E_{cell}, P_{H2}, [Cu^{2+}], n$ → $[H^+]$ → pH

$$\frac{1 \ V}{1000 \ mV} \qquad E_{cell} = E^o_{cell} - \frac{0.0592 \ V}{n} \log Q \qquad pH = - \log [H^+]$$

Solution: The half-reactions are: $H_2(g)$ → 2 $H^+(aq)$ + 2 e^- and Cu^{2+} (aq) + 2 e^- → Cu (s). H is oxidized so $E^o_{ox} = - E^o_{red} = -(- 0.00 \ V) = 0.00 \ V$. Cu is reduced so $E^o_{red} = 0.34 \ V$. Then $E^o_{cell} = E^o_{ox} + E^o_{red} = 0.00 \ V + 0.34 \ V = + 0.34 \ V$. Adding the two reactions: $H_2(g)$+ Cu^{2+} (aq) + $\cancel{2e^-}$ → 2 $H^+(aq)$ + $\cancel{2e^-}$ + Cu

(s). Cancel the electrons: $H_2(g)$+ Cu^{2+} (aq) → 2 $H^+(aq)$ + Cu (s). then $355 \ \cancel{mV} \ \times \ \frac{1 \ V}{1000 \ \cancel{mV}} = 0.355 \ V$.

So $n = 2$ and $Q = \dfrac{[H^+]^2}{P_{H2}[Cu^{2+}]} = \dfrac{(x)^2}{(1)(1.0)} = x^2$ then $E_{cell} = E^0_{cell} - \dfrac{0.0592 \ V}{n} \log Q$ substitute in values and solve

for x. $0.355 \ V = 0.34 \ V - \dfrac{0.0592 \ V}{2} \log x^2$ → $0.015 \ \cancel{V} = - \dfrac{0.0592 \ \cancel{V}}{2} \log x^2$ → $- 0.50676 = \log x^2$ →

$x^2 = 10^{- 0.50676} = 0.31135$ → $x = 0.55798$ then $pH = - \log [H^+] = - \log [0.55798] = 0.25338 = 0.3$.
Check: The units (none) are correct. The pH is acidic, which is consistent with dissolving a metal in acid.

110. **Given:** Pt (s)|H_2 $(g, 1 \ atm)$|H^+ $(aq, 1.0 \ M)$||Au^{3+} $(aq, ? \ M)$|Au (s), $E_{cell} = 1.22 \ V$ **Find:** $[Au^{3+}]$

Conceptual plan: Write half reactions from line notation. Look up half-reactions in Table 18.1. The reaction on the left is the oxidation so reverse the sign of the standard reduction potential ($E°_{ox} = -E°_{red}$). add the two half-cell potentials: $E°_{cell} = E°_{ox} + E°_{red}$. Equalize the number of electrons transferred and then add the two half-cell reactions and cancel the electrons. Then $E°_{cell}$, E_{cell}, P_{H2}, $[H^+]$, n → $[Au^{3+}]$

$$E_{cell} = E°_{cell} - \frac{0.0592\ V}{n} \log Q$$

Solution: The half-reactions are: $H_2(g)$ → $2\ H^+(aq) + 2\ e^-$ and $Au^{3+}\ (aq) + 3\ e^-$ → $Au\ (s)$. H is oxidized so $E°_{ox} = -E°_{red} = -(-0.00\ V) = 0.00\ V$. Au is reduced so $E°_{red} = 1.50\ V$. Then $E°_{cell} = E°_{ox} + E°_{red} = 0.00\ V + 1.50\ V = +1.50\ V$. Equalize the number of electrons transferred by multiplying the first reaction by 3 and the second reaction by 2 so $3\ H_2(g)$ → $6\ H^+(aq) + 6\ e^-$ and $2\ Au^{3+}\ (aq) + 6\ e^-$ → $2\ Au\ (s)$. Adding the two reactions: $3\ H_2(g) + 2\ Au^{3+}\ (aq) + 6\ e^-$ → $6\ H^+(aq) + 6\ e^- + 2\ Au\ (s)$. Cancel the electrons: $3\ H_2(g) + 2\ Au^{3+}\ (aq)$ → $6\ H^+(aq) + 2\ Au\ (s)$. So $n = 6$ and $Q = \frac{[H^+]^6}{P_{H2}^3[Au^{3+}]^2} = \frac{(1.0)^6}{(1)^3\ (x)^2} = x^{-2}$ then $E_{cell} = E°_{cell} - \frac{0.0592\ V}{n} \log Q$ substitute in values and solve for x. $1.22\ V = 1.50\ V - \frac{0.0592\ V}{6} \log x^{-2}$ → $0.28\ V = \frac{0.0592\ V}{6} \log x^{-2}$ → $28.3784 = \log x^{-2}$ → $x^{-2} = 10^{28.3784} = 2.3899 \times 10^{28}$ → $x = 6.4686 \times 10^{-15}\ M$.

Check: The units (none) are correct. The concentration is expected to be low because the cell potential must be reduced.

111. You should be wary of the battery because the most a pairing of half-cell reactions can generate is 5 to 6 V, not 24 V.

112. **Given:** Lithium oxidizing and Fluorine gas reducing   **Find:** $E°_{cell}$ and why is the battery hard to produce
    Conceptual plan: Write 2 half-cell reactions taking the elemental forms to cations and anions, adding electrons as needed to balance reactions. Look up half-reactions in Table 18.1. In order to determine the cell potential of the oxidation reaction, reverse the sign of the standard reduction potential ($E°_{ox} = -E°_{red}$) then add the two half-cell potentials: $E°_{cell} = E°_{ox} + E°_{red}$.
    Solution: $Li\ (l)$ → $Li^+\ (l) + e^-$ and $F_2\ (g) + 2\ e^-$ → $2\ F^-\ (l)$. Looking up the reduction potentials, for Li $E°_{ox} = -E°_{red} = -(-3.04\ V) = 3.04\ V$. and for F_2 $E°_{red} = +2.87\ V$. So $E°_{cell} = E°_{ox} + E°_{red} = 3.05\ V + 2.87\ V = 5.92\ V$. The problem with using this system is getting a high concentration of F_2, since it is a gas and gases have low densities.
    Check: The units (V) are correct. The metal is oxidized and the nonmetal is reduced, so we expect a high cell potential.

113. **Given:** Mg oxidation and Cu^{2+} reduction; initially $[Mg^{2+}] = 1.0 \times 10^{-4}\ M$ and $[Cu^{2+}] = 1.5\ M$ in 1.0 L half-cells   **Find:** a) initial E_{cell}; b) E_{cell} after 5.0 A for 8.0 hr; and c) how long can battery deliver 5.0 A

Conceptual plan: a) Write the 2 half-cell reactions and add electrons as needed to balance reactions. Look up half-reactions in Table 18.1. In order to determine the cell potential of the oxidation reaction, reverse the sign of the standard reduction potential ($E^\circ_{ox} = -E^\circ_{red}$) then add the two half-cell potentials: $E^\circ_{cell} = E^\circ_{ox} + E^\circ_{red}$. Add the two half-cell reactions and cancel electrons and determine n. then E°_{cell}, $[Mg^{2+}]$, $[Cu^{2+}]$, $n \rightarrow E_{cell}$

$$E_{cell} = E^\circ_{cell} - \frac{0.0592\ V}{n} \log Q$$

b) $hr \rightarrow min \rightarrow s \rightarrow C \rightarrow mol\ e^- \rightarrow mol\ Cu\ reduced \rightarrow [Cu^{2+}]$ and

$$\frac{60\ min}{1\ hr} \quad \frac{60\ s}{1\ min} \quad \frac{5.0\ C}{1\ s} \quad \frac{1\ mol\ e^-}{96,485\ C} \quad \frac{1\ mol\ Cu^{2+}}{2\ mol\ e^-} \quad since\ V = 1.0L \quad [Cu^{2+}] = [Cu^{2+}] - \frac{mol\ Cu^{2+}\ reduced}{1.0\ L}$$

$mol\ Cu\ reduced \rightarrow mol\ Mg\ oxidized \rightarrow [Mg^{2+}]$

$$\frac{1\ mol\ Mg\ oxidized}{1\ mol\ Cu^{2+}reduced} \quad since\ V = 1.0L \quad [Mg^{2+}] = [Mg^{2+}] + \frac{mol\ Mg\ oxidized}{1.0\ L}$$

c) $[Cu^{2+}] \rightarrow mol\ e^- \rightarrow C \rightarrow s \rightarrow min \rightarrow hr$

$$\frac{1\ mol\ e^-}{2\ mol\ Cu^{2+}} \quad \frac{96,485\ C}{1\ mol\ e^-} \quad \frac{1\ s}{5.0\ C} \quad \frac{1\ min}{60\ s} \quad \frac{1\ hr}{60\ min}$$

Solution: a) write half-reactions and add electrons $Cu^{2+}\ (aq) + 2\ e^- \rightarrow Cu\ (s)$ and $Mg\ (s) \rightarrow Mg^{2+}\ (aq) + 2\ e^-$. Look up cell potentials. Mg is oxidized so $E^\circ_{ox} = -E^\circ_{red} = -(-2.37\ V) = 2.37\ V$. Cu^{2+} is reduced so $E^\circ_{red} = 0.34\ V$. Then $E^\circ_{cell} = E^\circ_{ox} + E^\circ_{red} = 2.37\ V + 0.34\ V = +2.71\ V$. Add the two half-cell reactions: $Cu^{2+}\ (aq) + 2e^- + Mg\ (s) \rightarrow Cu\ (s) + Mg^{2+}\ (aq) + 2e^-$. Simplify to $Cu^{2+}\ (aq) + Mg\ (s) \rightarrow Cu\ (s) + Mg^{2+}\ (aq)$. So $Q = \frac{[Mg^{2+}]}{[Cu^{2+}]} = \frac{1.0 \times 10^{-4}}{1.5} = 6.\underline{6}667 \times 10^{-5}$ and $n = 2$ then

$$E_{cell} = E^0_{cell} - \frac{0.0592\ V}{n} \log Q = 2.71\ V - \frac{0.0592\ V}{2} \log 6.\underline{6}667 \times 10^{-5} = +2.8\underline{3}361\ V = +2.83\ V\ .$$

b)
$$8.0\ hr \times \frac{60\ min}{1\ hr} \times \frac{60\ s}{1\ min} \times \frac{5.0\ C}{1\ s} \times \frac{1\ mol\ e^-}{96,485\ C} \times \frac{1\ mol\ Cu^{2+}}{2\ mol\ e^-} = 0.7\underline{4}623\ mol\ Cu^{2+} \quad and$$

$$[Cu^{2+}] = [Cu^{2+}] - \frac{mol\ Cu^{2+}\ reduced}{1.0\ L} = 1.5\ M - \frac{0.7\underline{4}623\ mol\ Cu^{2+}}{1.0\ L} = 0.7\underline{5}377\ M\ Cu^{2+} \quad and$$

$$0.7\underline{4}623\ mol\ Cu^{2+} \times \frac{1\ mol\ Mg\ oxidized}{1\ mol\ Cu^{2+}\ reduced} = 0.7\underline{4}623\ mol\ Mg\ oxidized \quad and$$

$$[Mg^{2+}] = [Mg^{2+}] + \frac{mol\ Mg\ oxidized}{1.0\ L} = 1.0 \times 10^{-4}\ M + \frac{0.7\underline{4}623\ mol\ Mg\ oxidized}{1.0\ L} = 0.7\underline{4}633\ M\ Mg^{2+}$$

$$Q = \frac{[Mg^{2+}]}{[Cu^{2+}]} = \frac{0.7\underline{4}633}{0.7\underline{5}377} = 0.9\underline{9}013 \quad and \quad n = 2 \quad then$$

$$E_{cell} = E^0_{cell} - \frac{0.0592\ V}{n} \log Q = 2.71\ V - \frac{0.0592\ V}{2} \log 0.9\underline{9}013 = +2.7\underline{1}013\ V = +2.71\ V\ .$$

c) In 1.0 L there are initially 1.5 moles of Cu^{2+}. So

$$1.5\ mol\ Cu^{2+} \times \frac{2\ mol\ e^-}{1\ mol\ Cu^{2+}} \times \frac{96,485\ C}{1\ mol\ e^-} \times \frac{1\ s}{5.0\ C} \times \frac{1\ min}{60\ s} \times \frac{1\ hr}{60\ min} = 16\ hr\ .$$

Check: The units (V, V and hr) are correct. The Cu^{2+} reduction reaction is above the Mg^{2+} reduction reaction, so the standard cell potential will be positive. Having more reactants than products increases the cell potential. As the reaction proceeds the potential drops. The concentrations drop by ½ in 8 hours (part b), so it is all consumed in 16 hours.

114. **Given:** Ag/Ag^+ concentration cell; initially $[Ag^+] = 1.25\ M$ and $1.0 \times 10^{-3}\ M$ in 2.0 L half-cells
Find: a) how long can battery deliver 2.5A; b) mass of Ag plated after 3.5 A for 5.5 hr; and c) how long can battery deliver 5.0A   to redissolve 1.00×10^2 g Ag with 10.0 A

Conceptual plan: a) Write the 2 half-cell reactions and add electrons as needed to balance reactions. then

$[Ag^+], V \rightarrow$ mol $Ag^+ \rightarrow$ mol $e^- \rightarrow C \rightarrow s \rightarrow$ min $\rightarrow$ hr

$$M = \frac{\text{mol } Ag^+}{L} \quad \frac{1 \text{ mol } e^-}{1 \text{ mol } Ag^+} \quad \frac{96,485 \text{ C}}{1 \text{ mol } e^-} \quad \frac{1 \text{ s}}{2.5 \text{ C}} \quad \frac{1 \text{ min}}{60 \text{ s}} \quad \frac{1 \text{ hr}}{60 \text{ min}}$$

b) hr $\rightarrow$ min $\rightarrow$ s $\rightarrow C \rightarrow$ mol $e^- \rightarrow$ mol Ag $\rightarrow$ g Ag

$$\frac{60 \text{ min}}{1 \text{ hr}} \quad \frac{60 \text{ s}}{1 \text{ min}} \quad \frac{3.5 \text{ C}}{1 \text{ s}} \quad \frac{1 \text{ mol } e^-}{96,485 \text{ C}} \quad \frac{1 \text{ mol Ag}}{1 \text{ mol } e^-} \quad \frac{107.87 \text{ g Ag}}{1 \text{ mol Ag}}$$

c) g Ag $\rightarrow$ mol Ag $\rightarrow$ mol $e^- \rightarrow C \rightarrow s \rightarrow$ min $\rightarrow$ hr

$$\frac{1 \text{ mol Ag}}{107.87 \text{ g Ag}} \quad \frac{1 \text{ mol } e^-}{1 \text{ mol Ag}} \quad \frac{96,485 \text{ C}}{1 \text{ mol } e^-} \quad \frac{1 \text{ s}}{10.0 \text{ C}} \quad \frac{1 \text{ min}}{60 \text{ s}} \quad \frac{1 \text{ hr}}{60 \text{ min}}$$

Solution: a) write half-reactions and add electrons $Ag^+ (aq) + e^- \rightarrow Ag \ (s)$. $\quad M = \dfrac{\text{mol } Ag^+}{L}$ so

$$\text{mol } Ag^+ = M \times L = 1.25 \frac{\text{mol } Ag^+}{L} \times 2.0 \text{ L} = 2.50 \text{ mol } Ag^+ \quad \text{then}$$

$$2.50 \text{ mol } Ag^+ \times \frac{1 \text{ mol } e^-}{1 \text{ mol } Ag^+} \times \frac{96,485 \text{ C}}{1 \text{ mol } e^-} \times \frac{1 \text{ s}}{2.5 \text{ C}} \times \frac{1 \text{ min}}{60 \text{ s}} \times \frac{1 \text{ hr}}{60 \text{ min}} = 27 \text{ hr} \quad .$$

b) $\quad 5.5 \text{ hr} \times \dfrac{60 \text{ min}}{1 \text{ hr}} \times \dfrac{60 \text{ s}}{1 \text{ min}} \times \dfrac{3.5 \text{ C}}{1 \text{ s}} \times \dfrac{1 \text{ mol } e^-}{96,485 \text{ C}} \times \dfrac{1 \text{ mol Ag}}{1 \text{ mol } e^-} \times \dfrac{107.87 \text{ g Ag}}{1 \text{ mol Ag}} = 77 \text{ g Ag} \quad .$

c) $\quad 1.00 \times 10^2 \text{ g Ag} \times \dfrac{1 \text{ mol Ag}}{107.87 \text{ g Ag}} \times \dfrac{1 \text{ mol } e^-}{1 \text{ mol Ag}} \times \dfrac{96,485 \text{ C}}{1 \text{ mol } e^-} \times \dfrac{1 \text{ s}}{10.0 \text{ C}} \times \dfrac{1 \text{ min}}{60 \text{ s}} \times \dfrac{1 \text{ hr}}{60 \text{ min}} = 2.48 \text{ hr} \quad .$

Check: The units (hr, g and hr) are correct. Since 2.5 moles needs to be plated, we expect it to take a long time. The time is shorter by a factor of ~30 and the current is larger by about 1.5 so we expect less Ag to be plated in part b) as compared to part a). We expect a shorter time in part c) than in part b) because the current is so much larger. In parts b) and c) we are not exhausting the 2.5 moles initially in the half-cell.

115. **Given:** water electrolysis at 7.8 A; $H_2 (g)$: V = 25.0 L, P = 25.0 atm; T = 25 °C   **Find:** time

Conceptual plan: °C $\rightarrow$ K   then V, P, T $\rightarrow$ n   then write half-reactions

$$K = °C + 273.15 \qquad\qquad PV = nRT$$

mol $H_2 \rightarrow$ mol $e^- \rightarrow C \rightarrow s \rightarrow$ min $\rightarrow$ hr

$$\frac{2 \text{ mol } e^-}{1 \text{ mol } H_2} \quad \frac{96,485 \text{ C}}{1 \text{ mol } e^-} \quad \frac{1 \text{ s}}{7.8 \text{ C}} \quad \frac{1 \text{ min}}{60 \text{ s}} \quad \frac{1 \text{ hr}}{60 \text{ min}}$$

Solution: T = 25 °C + 273.15 = 298 K, then $PV = nRT$ Rearrange to solve for n.

$$n = \frac{PV}{RT} = \frac{25.0 \text{ atm} \times 25.0 \text{ L}}{0.08206 \frac{\text{L} \cdot \text{atm}}{\text{mol} \cdot \text{K}} \times 298 \text{ K}} = 25.5583 \text{ mol } H_2 \quad \text{The hydrolysis of water reactions are: } 2 \text{ H}_2\text{O} \ (l) \rightarrow O_2$$

$(g) + 4 \text{ H}^+ (aq) + 4 \text{ e}^-$ and $2 \text{ H}_2\text{O} \ (l) + 2 \text{ e}^- \rightarrow H_2 \ (g) + \ OH^- \ (aq)$.

$$25.5583 \text{ mol } H_2 \times \frac{2 \text{ mol } e^-}{1 \text{ mol } H_2} \times \frac{96,485 \text{ C}}{1 \text{ mol } e^-} \times \frac{1 \text{ s}}{7.8 \text{ C}} \times \frac{1 \text{ min}}{60 \text{ s}} \times \frac{1 \text{ hr}}{60 \text{ min}} = 176 \text{ hr} \ .$$

Check: The units (hr) are correct. Since we have 25 L of gas at 25 atm and 25 °C we expect ~25 moles of gas (remember 1 mole of gas at STP = 22.4 L). A very long time is expected since we have so many moles of gas to generate.

116. **Given:** A fuel-cell breathalyzer test; 188 mL yields 324 mA for 10 s; P = 1.0 atm, T = 25 °C

    Find: percent by volume ethanol in breath

Conceptual plan: Write the reaction and determine n, and $mA \rightarrow A$ then

$$\frac{1\,A}{1000\,mA}$$

$s \rightarrow C \rightarrow mol\ e^- \rightarrow mol\ CH_3CH_2OH$ and $°C \rightarrow K$ and $mL \rightarrow L$ then $V, n, T \rightarrow P_{CH3CH2OH}$

$$\frac{0.324\,C}{1\,s} \quad \frac{1\,mole^-}{96,485\,C} \quad \frac{1\,mol\,CH_3CH_2OH}{4\,mol\,e^-} \qquad K = °C + 273.15 \qquad \frac{1\,L}{1000\,mL} \qquad PV = nRT$$

then $P_{CH3CH2OH}$, P_{Total}, $\rightarrow$ **percent by volume CH_3CH_2OH**

$$\text{percent by volume } CH_3CH_2OH = \frac{P_{CH_3CH_2OH}}{P_{Total}} \times 100\%$$

Solution: $CH_3CH_2OH\,(g) + O_2\,(g) \rightarrow HC_2H_3O_2\,(g) + H_2O\,(g)$ since 2 O atoms are going from 0 to -2 so $n = 4$

and $324\,mA \times \dfrac{1\,A}{1000\,mA} = 0.324\,A$ then

$10\,s \times \dfrac{0.324\,C}{1\,s} \times \dfrac{1\,mole^-}{96,485\,C} \times \dfrac{1\,mol\,CH_3CH_2OH}{4\,mol\,e^-} = 8.3951 \times 10^{-6}\,mol\,CH_3CH_2OH$ and $T = 25\ °C + 273.15 =$

298 K,

and $188\,mL \times \dfrac{1\,L}{1000\,mL} = 0.188\,L$ then $PV = nRT$ Rearrange to solve for P.

$$P = \frac{nRT}{V} = \frac{8.3951 \times 10^{-6}\,mol \times 0.08206\,\frac{L\cdot atm}{mol\cdot K} \times 298\,K}{0.188\,L} = 1.09198 \times 10^{-3}\,atm\,CH_3CH_2OH \text{ then}$$

$$\text{percent by volume } CH_3CH_2OH = \frac{P_{CH_3CH_2OH}}{P_{Total}} \times 100\% = \frac{1.09198 \times 10^{-3}\,atm}{1.0\,atm} \times 100\% = 0.109198\% = 0.1\%.$$

Check: The units (%) are correct. Since the volume and current are so low we expect a small percent by volume. This number is typical for a failing blood alcohol test.

---

117. **Given:** $Cu\,(s)|CuI\,(s)|I^-\,(aq, 1.0\,M)\|Cu^+\,(aq, 1.0\,M)|Cu\,(s)$, $K_{sp}\,(CuI) = 1.1 \times 10^{-12}$ **Find:** E_{cell}
    Conceptual plan: Write half reactions from line notation. Since this is a concentration cell $E°_{cell} = 0.00$ V. then $K_{sp}, [I^-] \rightarrow [Cu^+](ox)$ then $E°_{cell}, [Cu^+](ox), [Cu^+](red), n \rightarrow E_{cell}$

    $$K_{sp} = [Cu^+][I^-] \qquad\qquad E_{cell} = E°_{cell} - \frac{0.0592\,V}{n} \log Q$$

    Solution: The half-reactions are: $Cu\,(s) \rightarrow Cu^+(aq) + e^-$ and $Cu^+\,(aq) + e^- \rightarrow Cu\,(s)$. Since this is a concentration cell $E°_{cell} = 0.00$ V and $n = 1$. Since $K_{sp} = [Cu^+][I^-]$, rearrange to solve for $[Cu^+](ox)$.

    $[Cu^+]\,(ox) = \dfrac{K_{sp}}{[I^-]} = \dfrac{1.1 \times 10^{-12}}{1.0} = 1.1 \times 10^{-12}\,M$ then $Q = \dfrac{[Cu^+](ox)}{[Cu^+](red)} = \dfrac{1.1 \times 10^{-12}}{1.0} = 1.1 \times 10^{-12}$ then

    $$E_{cell} = E°_{cell} - \frac{0.0592\,V}{n} \log Q = 0.00\,V - \frac{0.0592\,V}{1} \log(1.1 \times 10^{-12}) = 0.71\,V.$$

    Check: The units (V) are correct. Since $[Cu^+](ox)$ is so low and $[Cu^+](red)$ is high, the Q is very small so the voltage increase is significant.

---

118. **Given:** $Zn(OH)_2\,(s) + 2\,e^- \rightarrow Zn\,(s) + 2\,OH^-\,(aq)$, $K_{sp}\,(Zn(OH)_2) = 1.8 \times 10^{-14}$ **Find:** E for half-cell
    Conceptual plan: Look up half-reaction for the Zn reduction ($E°_{red}$) in Table 18.1, determine n, then $K_{sp} \rightarrow [OH^-]$ then $E°_{cell}, [OH^-], n \rightarrow E_{cell}$

    $$K_{sp} = [Zn^{2+}][OH^-]^2 \qquad E_{cell} = E°_{cell} - \frac{0.0592\,V}{n} \log Q$$

    Solution: The reduction half-reaction is: $Zn^{2+}\,(aq) + 2\,e^- \rightarrow Zn\,(s)$ and $E°_{red} = -0.76$ V and $n = 2$. Since $K_{sp} = [Zn^{2+}][OH^-]^2 = s\,(2s)^2 = 4\,s^3$, rearrange to solve for $s = [OH^-]$.

    $$s = [OH^-] = \sqrt[3]{\frac{K_{sp}}{4}} = \sqrt[3]{\frac{1.8 \times 10^{-14}}{4}} = 1.65096 \times 10^{-5}\,M \text{ then } Q = [OH^-]^2 = \left(1.65096 \times 10^{-5}\right)^2 = 2.7257 \times 10^{-10}$$

    then $E_{cell} = E°_{cell} - \dfrac{0.0592\,V}{n} \log Q = -0.76\,V - \dfrac{0.0592\,V}{2} \log(2.7257 \times 10^{-10}) = -0.48\,V.$

    Check: The units (V) are correct. Since $[OH^-]$ is so low, the Q is very small so the voltage increase is significant, but the half-reaction is nonspontanous.

119. **Given:** a) dispropotionation of Mn^{2+} (aq) to Mn (s) and MnO_2 (s); and b) dispropotionation of MnO_2 (s) to Mn^{2+} (aq) and MnO_4^- (s) in acidic solution   **Find:** ΔG°_{rxn} and K

Conceptual plan: Separate the overall reaction into two half-reactions: one for oxidation and one for reduction. → **Balance each half-reaction with respect to mass in the following order: 1) balance all elements other than H and O; 2) balance O by adding H_2O; and 3) balance H by adding H^+.** → **Balance each half reaction with respect to charge by adding electrons. (The sum of the charges on both sides of the equation should be made equal by adding electrons as necessary.)** → **Make the number of electrons in both half-reactions equal by multiplying one or both half-reactions by a small whole number.** → **Add the two half-reactions together, canceling electrons and other species as necessary.** → **Verify that the reaction is balanced both with respect to mass and with respect to charge. Look up half-reactions in Table 18.1. In order to determine the cell potential of the oxidation reaction, reverse the sign of the standard reduction potential ($E^\circ_{ox} = -E^\circ_{red}$) then add the two half-cell potentials:** $E^\circ_{cell} = E^\circ_{ox} + E^\circ_{red}$. **then calculate ΔG°_{rxn} using** $\Delta G^0_{rxn} = -nFE^0_{cell}$. **Finally** °C → K **then** ΔG°_{rxn}, T → K

$$K = 273.15 + °C \qquad\qquad \Delta G^0_{rxn} = -RT\ln K$$

Solution:

a) Separate: Mn^{2+} (aq) → MnO_2 (s)   and Mn^{2+} (aq) → Mn (s)

Balance non H & O elements: Mn^{2+} (aq) → MnO_2 (s)   and Mn^{2+} (aq) → Mn (s)

Balance O with H_2O: Mn^{2+} (aq) + 2 H_2O (l) → MnO_2 (s) and Mn^{2+} (aq) → Mn (s)

Balance H with H^+: Mn^{2+} (aq) + 2 H_2O (l) → MnO_2 (s) + 4 H^+ (aq) and Mn^{2+} (aq) → Mn (s)

Add electrons: Mn^{2+} (aq) + 2 H_2O (l) → MnO_2 (s) + 4 H^+ (aq) + 2 e^- and Mn^{2+} (aq) + 2 e^- → Mn (s)

Equalize electrons: Mn^{2+} (aq) + 2 H_2O (l) → MnO_2 (s) + 4 H^+ (aq) + 2 e^- and Mn^{2+} (aq) + 2 e^- → Mn (s)

Add half-reactions: Mn^{2+} (aq) + 2 H_2O (l) + Mn^{2+} (aq) + 2̶e̶⁻ → MnO_2 (s) + 4 H^+ (aq) + 2̶e̶⁻ + Mn (s)

Cancel electrons: 2 Mn^{2+} (aq) + 2 H_2O (l) → MnO_2 (s) + 4 H^+ (aq) + Mn (s)

Look up cell potentials. Mn is oxidized in the first half-cell reaction so $E^\circ_{ox} = -E^\circ_{red} = -1.21$ V. Mn is reduced in the second half-cell reaction so $E^\circ_{red} = -1.18$ V. Then $E^\circ_{cell} = E^\circ_{ox} + E^\circ_{red} = -1.21$ V -1.18 V $= -2.39$ V. $n = 2$ so

$$\Delta G^0_{rxn} = -nFE^0_{cell} = -2 \; \text{mol e}^- \; x \; \frac{96,485 \, C}{\text{mol e}^-} \; x -2.39 \, V = -2 \; x \; 96,485 \; C \; x -2.39 \frac{J}{C} = 4.6\underline{1}198 \; x \; 10^5 \; J = 461 \; kJ \;.$$

T = 273.15 + 25 °C = 298 K then $\Delta G^0_{rxn} = -RT\ln K$ Rearrange to solve for K.

$$K = e^{\frac{-\Delta G^0_{rxn}}{RT}} = e^{\frac{-4.6\underline{1}198 \; x \; 10^5 \; J}{\left(8.314 \frac{J}{K \, mol}\right)(298 \, K)}} = e^{-18\underline{6}.149} = 1.43 \; x \; 10^{-81} \;.$$

Check:

Reactants	Products
2 Mn atoms	2 Mn atoms
2 O atoms	2 O atoms
4 H atoms	4 H atoms
+4 charge	+4 charge

The units (kJ and none) are correct. If the voltage is negative, the reaction is nonspontaneous and the free energy change is very positive and the equilibrium constant is extremely small.

b) Separate: MnO_2 (s) → Mn^{2+} (aq)   and MnO_2 (s) → MnO_4^- (aq)

Balance non H & O elements: MnO_2 (s) → Mn^{2+} (aq)   and MnO_2 (s) → MnO_4^- (aq)

Balance O with H_2O: MnO_2 (s) → Mn^{2+} (aq) + 2 H_2O (l) and MnO_2 (s) + 2 H_2O (l) → MnO_4^- (aq)

Balance H with H^+:

MnO_2 (s) + 4 H^+ (aq) → Mn^{2+} (aq) + 2 H_2O (l) and MnO_2 (s) + 2 H_2O (l) → MnO_4^- (aq) + 4 H^+ (aq)

Add electrons:

MnO_2 (s) + 4 H^+ (aq) + 2 e^- → Mn^{2+} (aq) + 2 H_2O (l) and MnO_2 (s) + 2 H_2O (l) → MnO_4^- (aq) + 4 H^+ (aq) +3e^-

Equalize electrons: 3 MnO_2 (s) + 12 H^+ (aq) + 6 e^- → 3 Mn^{2+} (aq) + 6 H_2O (l) and

2 MnO_2 (s) + 4 H_2O (l) → 2 MnO_4^- (aq) + 8 H^+ (aq) + 6 e^-

Add half-reactions: 3 MnO_2 (s) + 4̶ 12 H^+(aq) + 6̶e̶⁻ + 2 MnO_2 (s) + 4̶H̶₂̶O̶(l) →

3 Mn^{2+} (aq) + 2̶ 4̶ H̶₂̶O̶(l) + 2 MnO_4^- (aq) + 8 H̶⁺̶(aq) + 6̶e̶⁻

Cancel electrons & species: 5 MnO_2 (s) + 4 H^+ (aq) → 3 Mn^{2+} (aq) + 2 H_2O (l) + 2 MnO_4^- (aq)

715

Look up cell potentials. Mn is reduced in the first half-cell reaction so $E^{\circ}_{red} = 1.21$ V. Mn is oxidized in the second half-cell reaction so $E^{\circ}_{ox} = -E^{\circ}_{red} = -1.68$ V. Then $E^{\circ}_{cell} = E^{\circ}_{ox} + E^{\circ}_{red} = 1.21$ V $- 1.68$ V $= -0.47$ V. n $= $ 6   so

$$\Delta G^{0}_{rxn} = -nFE^{0}_{cell} = -6 \text{ mole}^- \times \frac{96,485 \text{ C}}{\text{mole}^-} \times -0.47 \text{ V} = -6 \times 96,485 \text{ C} \times -0.47 \frac{\text{J}}{\text{C}} = 2.7209 \times 10^5 \text{ J} = 270 \text{ kJ}$$

$= 2.7 \times 10^2$ kJ .   T $= 273.15 + 25$ °C $= 298$ K then $\Delta G^{0}_{rxn} = -RT \ln K$ Rearrange to solve for K.

$$K = e^{\frac{-\Delta G^{0}_{rxn}}{RT}} = e^{\left(\frac{-2.7209 \times 10^5 \text{ J}}{8.314 \frac{\text{J}}{\text{K mol}}\right)(298 \text{ K})}} = e^{-10.982} = 2.0 \times 10^{-48}.$$

Check:

Reactants	Products
5 Mn atoms	5 Mn atoms
10 O atoms	10 O atoms
4 H atoms	4 H atoms
+4 charge	+4 charge

The units (kJ and none) are correct. If the voltage is negative, the reaction is nonspontaneous and the free energy change is very positive and the equilibrium constant is extremely small. The voltage is less than in part a) so the free energy change is not as large and the equilibrium constant is not as small.

120. **Given:** a) reaction of Cr^{2+} *(aq)* with $Cr_2O_7^{2-}$ *(aq)* in acidic solution to form Cr^{3+} *(aq)*; and b) reaction of Cr^{3+} *(aq)* with Cr *(s)* to form Cr^{2+} *(aq)*   **Find:** ΔG°_{rxn} and K
Conceptual plan: Separate the overall reaction into two half-reactions: one for oxidation and one for reduction. → Balance each half-reaction with respect to mass in the following order: 1) balance all elements other than H and O; 2) balance O by adding H_2O; and 3) balance H by adding H^+. → Balance each half reaction with respect to charge by adding electrons. (The sum of the charges on both sides of the equation should be made equal by adding electrons as necessary.) → Make the number of electrons in both half-reactions equal by multiplying one or both half-reactions by a small whole number. → Add the two half-reactions together, canceling electrons and other species as necessary. → Verify that the reaction is balanced both with respect to mass and with respect to charge. Look up half-reactions in Table 18.1. In order to determine the cell potential of the oxidation reaction, reverse the sign of the standard reduction potential ($E^{\circ}_{ox} = -E^{\circ}_{red}$) then add the two half-cell potentials: $E^{\circ}_{cell} = E^{\circ}_{ox} + E^{\circ}_{red}$.   then calculate ΔG°_{rxn} using $\Delta G^{0}_{rxn} = -nFE^{0}_{cell}$. Finally °C → K then ΔG°_{rxn}, T → K

$$K = 273.15 + °C \qquad\qquad \Delta G^{0}_{rxn} = -RT \ln K$$

Solution:
a) Separate: Cr^{2+} *(aq)* → Cr^{3+} *(aq)*   and $Cr_2O_7^{2-}$ *(aq)* → Cr^{3+} *(aq)*
Balance non H & O elements: Cr^{2+} *(aq)* → Cr^{3+} *(aq)*   and $Cr_2O_7^{2-}$ *(aq)* → 2 Cr^{3+} *(aq)*
Balance O with H_2O: Cr^{2+} *(aq)* → Cr^{3+} *(aq)*   and $Cr_2O_7^{2-}$ *(aq)* → 2 Cr^{3+} *(aq)* + 7 H_2O *(l)*
Balance H with H^+: Cr^{2+} *(aq)* → Cr^{3+} *(aq)*   and $Cr_2O_7^{2-}$ *(aq)* + 14 H^+ *(aq)* → 2 Cr^{3+} *(aq)* + 7 H_2O *(l)*
Add electrons: Cr^{2+} *(aq)* → Cr^{3+} *(aq)* + e^- and $Cr_2O_7^{2-}$ *(aq)* + 14 H^+ *(aq)* + 6 e^- → 2 Cr^{3+} *(aq)* + 7 H_2O *(l)*
Equalize electrons: 6 Cr^{2+} *(aq)* → 6 Cr^{3+} *(aq)* + 6 e^- and $Cr_2O_7^{2-}$ *(aq)* + 14 H^+ *(aq)* + 6 e^- → 2 Cr^{3+} *(aq)* + 7 H_2O *(l)*

Add half-reactions: 6 Cr^{2+} *(aq)* + $Cr_2O_7^{2-}$ *(aq)* + 14 H^+ *(aq)* + 6 e^- → 6 Cr^{3+} *(aq)* + 6 e^- + 2 Cr^{3+} *(aq)* + 7 H_2O *(l)*
Cancel electrons: 6 Cr^{2+} *(aq)* + $Cr_2O_7^{2-}$ *(aq)* + 14 H^+ *(aq)* → 8 Cr^{3+} *(aq)* + 7 H_2O *(l)*
Look up cell potentials. Cr is oxidized in the first half-cell reaction so $E^{\circ}_{ox} = -E^{\circ}_{red} = --0.50$ V $= 0.50$ V. Cr is reduced in the second half-cell reaction so $E^{\circ}_{red} = 1.33$ V. Then $E^{\circ}_{cell} = E^{\circ}_{ox} + E^{\circ}_{red} = 0.50$ V $+ 1.33$ V $= +1.83$ V.
n $=$ 6   so

$$\Delta G^{0}_{rxn} = -nFE^{0}_{cell} = -6 \text{ mole}^- \times \frac{96,485 \text{ C}}{\text{mole}^-} \times 1.83 \text{ V} = -6 \times 96,485 \text{ C} \times 1.83 \frac{\text{J}}{\text{C}} = -1.05941 \times 10^6 \text{ J} = -1.06 \times 10^3 \text{ kJ}$$

T $=$ 273.15 $+$ 25 °C $=$ 298 K then $\Delta G^{0}_{rxn} = -RT \ln K$ Rearrange to solve for K.

$$K = e^{\frac{-\Delta G^{0}_{rxn}}{RT}} = e^{\left(\frac{--1.05941 \times 10^6 \text{ J}}{8.314 \frac{\text{J}}{\text{K mol}}\right)(298 \text{ K})}} = e^{427.598} = 5.05 \times 10^{185}.$$

Check:

Reactants	Products
8 Cr atoms	8 Cr atoms

7 O atoms	7 O atoms
14 H atoms	14 H atoms
+24 charge	+24 charge

The units (kJ and none) are correct. If the voltage is positive, the reaction is spontaneous and the free energy change is very negative and the equilibrium constant is extremely large.

b) Separate: Cr^{3+} (aq) → Cr^{2+} (aq)   and   Cr (s) → Cr^{2+} (aq)

Balance: Cr^{3+} (aq) → Cr^{2+} (aq)   and   Cr (s) → Cr^{2+} (aq)

Add electrons: Cr^{3+} (aq) + e^- → Cr^{2+} (aq)   and   Cr (s) → Cr^{2+} (aq) + 2 e^-

Equalize electrons: 2 Cr^{3+} (aq) + 2 e^- → 2 Cr^{2+} (aq)   and   Cr (s) → Cr^{2+} (aq) + 2 e^-

Add half-reactions: 2 Cr^{3+} (aq) + 2e^- + Cr (s) → 2 Cr^{2+} (aq) + Cr^{2+} (aq) + 2e^-

Cancel electrons & species: 2 Cr^{3+} (aq) + Cr (s) → 3 Cr^{2+} (aq)

Look up cell potentials. Cr is reduced in the first half-cell reaction so E°_{red} = − 0.50 V. Cr is oxidized in the second half-cell reaction so E°_{ox} = − E°_{red} = − − 0.91 V = 0.91 V. Then E°_{cell} = E°_{ox} + E°_{red} = − 0.50 V + 0.91 V = + 0.41 V. n = 2 so

$$\Delta G^0_{rxn} = - n F E^0_{cell} = -2 \text{ mole}^- \times \frac{96,485 \text{ C}}{\text{mole}^-} \times 0.41 \text{ V} = -2 \times 96,485 \text{ C} \times 0.41 \frac{J}{C} = -7.9118 \times 10^4 \text{ J} = 79 \text{ kJ}$$

$= 2.7 \times 10^2$ kJ .   T = 273.15 + 25 °C = 298 K then $\Delta G^0_{rxn} = - RT \ln K$ Rearrange to solve for K.

$$K = e^{\frac{-\Delta G^0_{rxn}}{RT}} = e^{\frac{--7.9118 \times 10^4 \text{ J}}{\left(8.314 \frac{J}{K \text{ mol}}\right)(298 \text{ K})}} = e^{31.934} = 7.4 \times 10^{13} .$$

Check:

Reactants	Products
3 Cr atoms	3 Cr atoms
+6 charge	+6 charge

The units (kJ and none) are correct. If the voltage is positive, the reaction is spontaneous and the free energy change is negative and the equilibrium constant is large. The voltage anf n are less than in part a) so the free energy change is not as negative and the equilibrium constant is not as large.

121. **Given:** Metal, M, 50.9 g/mol, 1.20 g of metal reduced in 23.6 minutes at 6.42 A from molten chloride

Find: empirical formula of chloride

Conceptual plan: min → s → C → mol e^- and g M → mol M   then mol e^-, mol M → charge → MCl_x

$$\frac{60 \text{ s}}{1 \text{ min}} \quad \frac{6.42 \text{ C}}{1 \text{ s}} \quad \frac{1 \text{ mol } e^-}{96,485 \text{ C}} \qquad \frac{1 \text{ mol M}}{50.9 \text{ g M}} \qquad\qquad \frac{1 \text{ mol } e^-}{1 \text{ mol M}}$$

Solution: $23.6 \text{ min} \times \frac{60 \text{ s}}{1 \text{ min}} \times \frac{6.42 \text{ C}}{1 \text{ s}} \times \frac{1 \text{ mol } e^-}{96,485 \text{ C}} = 0.0942190 \text{ mol } e^-$ and

$1.20 \text{ g M} \times \frac{1 \text{ mol M}}{50.9 \text{ g M}} = 0.0235756 \text{ mol M}$ then $\frac{0.0942190 \text{ mol } e^-}{0.02357561 \text{ mol M}} = 3.99646 \frac{e^-}{M}$ so the empirical formula is

MCl_4.

Check: The units (none) are correct. The result was an integer within the error of the measurements. The formula is typical for a metal salt. It could be vanadium, which has a +4 oxidation state.

122. **Given:** molten MCl_3 electrolysis, 1.25 g of metal reduced in 16.2 minutes at 3.86 A   **Find:** molar mass of metal

Conceptual plan: min → s → C → mol e^- → mol M   then   g M, mol M → molar mass

$$\frac{60 \text{ s}}{1 \text{ min}} \quad \frac{6.42 \text{ C}}{1 \text{ s}} \quad \frac{1 \text{ mol } e^-}{96,485 \text{ C}} \quad \frac{1 \text{ mol M}}{3 \text{ mol } e^-} \qquad\qquad \mathfrak{M} = \frac{\text{g M}}{\text{mol M}}$$

Solution: $16.2 \text{ min} \times \frac{60 \text{ s}}{1 \text{ min}} \times \frac{3.86 \text{ C}}{1 \text{ s}} \times \frac{1 \text{ mol } e^-}{96,485 \text{ C}} \times \frac{1 \text{ mol M}}{3 \text{ mol } e^-} = 0.0129620 \text{ mol M}$ then

$\mathfrak{M} = \frac{1.20 \text{ g M}}{0.0129620 \text{ mol M}} = 92.6 \frac{g}{mol}$.

Check: The units (g/mol) are correct. The result was a number typical for meatls and it could be niobium, which is know to have a +3 oxidation state.

123. **Given:** hydrogen-oxygen fuel cell; 1.2×10^3 kWh of electricity/month   **Find:** V of H_2 (g) at STP/month

Conceptual plan: Write half reactions. Look up half-reactions in Table 18.1. The reaction on the left is the oxidation so reverse the sign of the standard reduction potential ($E^\circ_{ox} = -E^\circ_{red}$) then add the two half-cell potentials: $E^\circ_{cell} = E^\circ_{ox} + E^\circ_{red}$. Add the two half-cell reactions and cancel the electrons. then kWh $\rightarrow$ J $\rightarrow$ C $\rightarrow$ mol e$^-$ $\rightarrow$ mol H_2 $\rightarrow$ V

$$\frac{3.60 \times 10^6 \text{ J}}{1 \text{kWh}} \quad \frac{1 \text{ C}}{0.41 \text{ J}} \quad \frac{1 \text{ mole}^-}{96{,}485 \text{ C}} \quad \frac{2 \text{ mol } H_2}{4 \text{ mol } e^-} \quad \text{at STP} \frac{22.414 \text{ L}}{1 \text{ mol } H_2}$$

Solution: $2 H_2$ (g) $+ 4 OH^-$ (aq) $\rightarrow 4 H_2O$ (l) $+ 4 e^-$ where $E^\circ_{ox} = -E^\circ_{red} = -(-0.83 \text{ V}) = 0.83$ V; and O_2 (g) $+ 2 H_2O$ (l) $+ 4 e^- \rightarrow 4 OH^-$ (aq) where $E^\circ_{red} = 0.40$ V. $E^\circ_{cell} = E^\circ_{ox} + E^\circ_{red} = 0.83 \text{ V} + 0.40 \text{ V} = 1.23$ V $= 1.23$ J/C and $n = 4$. Net reaction is: $2 H_2$ (g) $+ O_2$ (g) $\rightarrow 2 H_2O$ (l). then

$$1.2 \times 10^3 \text{ kWh} \times \frac{3.60 \times 10^6 \text{ J}}{1 \text{ kWh}} \times \frac{1 \text{ C}}{1.23 \text{ J}} \times \frac{1 \text{ mole}^-}{96{,}485 \text{ C}} \times \frac{2 \text{ mol} H_2}{4 \text{ mole}^-} \times \frac{22.414 \text{ L}}{1 \text{ mol} H_2} = 4.1 \times 10^6 \text{ L}.$$

Check: The units (L) are correct. A large volume is expected since we are trying to generate a large amount of electricity.

124. **Given:** voltaic cell to measure $[Cu^{2+}]$; SHE electrode paired with Cu^{2+}/Cu cell

Find: parameters to plot for a calibrations curve and what is the slope of the curve

Conceptual plan: Write the 2 half-cell reactions and add electrons as needed to balance reactions. Look up half-reactions in Table 18.1. In order to determine the cell potential of the oxidation reaction, reverse the sign of the standard reduction potential ($E^\circ_{ox} = -E^\circ_{red}$) then add the two half-cell potentials: $E^\circ_{cell} = E^\circ_{ox} + E^\circ_{red}$. Add the two half-cell reactions and cancel electrons and determine n. then $E^\circ_{cell}, P_{H2}, [H^+], [Cu^{2+}], n \rightarrow E_{cell}$

$$E_{cell} = E^\circ_{cell} - \frac{0.0592 \text{ V}}{n} \log Q$$

Solution: write half-reactions and add electrons H_2 (g) $\rightarrow 2 H^+$ (aq) $+ 2 e^-$ and Cu^{2+} (aq) $+ 2 e^- \rightarrow Cu$ (s). Look up cell potentials. H is oxidized so $E^\circ_{ox} = -E^\circ_{red} = -0.00 \text{ V} = 0.00$ V. Cu^{2+} is reduced so $E^\circ_{red} = 0.34$ V. Then $E^\circ_{cell} = E^\circ_{ox} + E^\circ_{red} = 2.37 \text{ V} + 0.34 \text{ V} = +2.71$ V. Add the two half-cell reactions: H_2 (g) $+ Cu^{2+}$ (aq) $+ 2e^- \rightarrow 2 H^+$ (aq) $+ 2e^- + Cu$ (s). Simplify to H_2 (g) $+ Cu^{2+}$ (aq) $\rightarrow 2 H^+$ (aq) $+ Cu$ (s). So

$Q = \dfrac{[H^+]^2}{P_{H2}[Cu^{2+}]}$ and $n = 2$ then $E_{cell} = E^0_{cell} - \dfrac{0.0592 \text{ V}}{n} \log Q = 0.34 \text{ V} - \dfrac{0.0592 \text{ V}}{2} \log \dfrac{[H^+]^2}{P_{H2}[Cu^{2+}]}$. If the anode

half-cell is buffered at a constant pH and a constant P_{H2} is used then two of the terms in Q are constant and can be pulled out of the expression so that

$E_{cell} = 0.34 \text{ V} - \dfrac{0.0592 \text{ V}}{2} \left(\log \dfrac{[H^+]^2}{P_{H2}} - \log [Cu^{2+}] \right) = \left(0.34 \text{ V} - \dfrac{0.0592 \text{ V}}{2} \log \dfrac{[H^+]^2}{P_{H2}} \right) + (0.0296 \text{ V}) \log [Cu^{2+}]$. If we

plot $\log [Cu^{2+}]$ versus E°_{cell}, the slope will be 0.026 V.

125. **Given:** Au^{3+}/Au electroplating; surface area $= 49.8$ cm^2, Au thickness $= 1.00 \times 10^{-3}$ cm, density $= 19.3$ g/cm^3; at 3.25 A **Find:** time

Conceptual plan: Write the half-cell reaction and add electrons as needed to balance reactions. then surface area, thickness $\rightarrow$ V $\rightarrow$ g Au $\rightarrow$ mol Au $\rightarrow$ mol e$^-$ $\rightarrow$ C $\rightarrow$ s

$$V = surface\,area \times thickness \quad \frac{19.3 \text{ g Au}}{1 \text{ cm}^3 \text{ Au}} \quad \frac{1 \text{ mol Au}}{196.97 \text{ g Au}} \quad \frac{3 \text{ mole}^-}{1 \text{ mol Au}} \quad \frac{96{,}485 \text{ C}}{1 \text{ mole}^-} \quad \frac{1 \text{ s}}{3.25 \text{ C}}$$

Solution: write half-reaction and add electrons Au^{3+} (aq) $+ 3$ e$^- \rightarrow$ Au (s).
$V = surface\,area \times thickness = (49.8 \text{ cm}^2)(1.00 \times 10^{-3} \text{ cm}) = 0.0498$ cm^3 then

$$0.0498 \text{ cm}^3 \text{Au} \times \frac{19.3 \text{ g Au}}{1 \text{ cm}^3 \text{ Au}} \times \frac{1 \text{ mol Au}}{196.97 \text{ g Au}} \times \frac{3 \text{ mole}^-}{1 \text{ mol Au}} \times \frac{96{,}485 \text{ C}}{1 \text{ mole}^-} \times \frac{1 \text{ s}}{3.25 \text{ C}} = 435 \text{ s}.$$

Check: The units (s) are correct. Since the layer is so thin there is far less than a mole of gold, so the time is not very long. In order to be an economical process, it must be fairly quick.

126. **Given:** electrodeposit mixture Cu and Cd with 1.20 F (1 F = 1 mol e$^-$); total mass $= 50.36$ g   **Find:** mass of $CuSO_4$

Conceptual plan: Write the half-cell reaction and add electrons as needed to balance reactions. then F $\rightarrow$ mol e$^-$ $\rightarrow$ mol (Cu + Cd) then let x = g Cu so that (50.36 g $-$ x g) = g Cd then g Cu $\rightarrow$ mol Cu and

$$\frac{1 \text{ mol e}^-}{1 \text{ F}} \qquad\qquad\qquad\qquad \frac{1 \text{ mol (Cu+Cd)}}{2 \text{ mol e}^-}$$

$$\frac{1 \text{ mol Cu}}{63.55 \text{ g Cu}}$$

g Cu → mol Cu   then solve for x = g Cu → g CuSO₄

$$\frac{1 \text{ mol Cd}}{112.41 \text{ g Cd}} \qquad\qquad\qquad\qquad \frac{159.62 \text{ g CuSO}_4}{63.55 \text{ g Cu}}$$

Solution: Cu^{2+} *(aq)* + 2 e⁻ → Cu *(s)*   and Cd^{2+} *(aq)* + 2 e⁻ → Cd *(s)*, so *n* = 2 for both metals.

$$1.20 \text{ F} \times \frac{1 \text{ mol e}^-}{1 \text{ F}} \times \frac{1 \text{ mol (Cu+Cd)}}{2 \text{ mol e}^-} = 0.600 \text{ mol (Cu+Cd)} \quad \text{then let } x = \text{g Cu so that } (50.36 \text{ g} - x \text{ g}) = \text{g Cd} \quad \text{then}$$

$$x \text{ g Cu} \times \frac{1 \text{ mol Cu}}{63.55 \text{ g Cu}} = \frac{x}{63.55} \text{ mol Cu} \quad \text{and} \quad (50.36 - x) \text{ g Cd} \times \frac{1 \text{ mol Cd}}{112.41 \text{ g Cd}} = \frac{(50.36 - x)}{112.41} \text{ mol Cd} \qquad \text{then}$$

$$0.600 \text{ mol (Cu+Cd)} = \frac{x}{63.55} \text{ mol Cu} + \frac{(50.36 - x)}{112.41} \text{ mol Cd} \qquad\qquad \text{Solve} \qquad \text{for} \qquad \text{x.}$$

$$0.600 = 0.01573564\, x + 0.4480028 - 0.08896006\, x \qquad \rightarrow \qquad x = 22.\underline{2}2300 \text{ g Cu} \qquad \rightarrow$$

$$22.\underline{2}2300 \text{ g Cu} \times \frac{159.62 \text{ g CuSO}_4}{63.55 \text{ g Cu}} = 55.8 \text{ g CuSO}_4 .$$

Check: The units (g) are correct. The result is reasonable since 0.600 mol Cu = 38.1 g and 0.600 mol Cd = 67.4 g and the amount deposited is in between the two values.

127. **Given:** $C_2O_4^{2-}$ → CO_2 and MnO_4^- *(aq)* → Mn^{2+} *(aq)*; 50.1 mL of MnO_4^- to titrate 0.339 g $Na_2C_2O_4$; and 4.62 g U sample titrated by 32.3 mL MnO_4^-; and UO^{2+} → UO_2^{2+} **Find:** percent U in sample

Conceptual plan: Separate the overall reaction into two half-reactions: one for oxidation and one for reduction. → Balance each half-reaction with respect to mass in the following order: 1) balance all elements other than H and O; 2) balance O by adding H_2O; and 3) balance H by adding H^+. → Balance each half reaction with respect to charge by adding electrons. (The sum of the charges on both sides of the equation should be made equal by adding electrons as necessary.) → Make the number of electrons in both half-reactions equal by multiplying one or both half-reactions by a small whole number. → Add the two half-reactions together, canceling electrons and other species as necessary. → Verify that the reaction is balanced both with respect to mass and with respect to charge.   then   mL MnO_4^- → L MnO_4^- and   g $Na_2C_2O_4$ → mol $Na_2C_2O_4$ → mol MnO_4^- then then

$$\frac{1 \text{ L MnO}_4^-}{1000 \text{ mL MnO}_4^-} \qquad \frac{1 \text{ mol Na}_2\text{C}_2\text{O}_4}{134.00 \text{ g Na}_2\text{C}_2\text{O}_4} \qquad \frac{2 \text{ mol MnO}_4^-}{5 \text{ mol Zn}} \qquad \frac{1 \text{ L MnO}_4^-}{0.500 \text{ mol MnO}_4^-}$$

L MnO_4^-, mol MnO_4^- → M MnO_4^- then write U half-reactions and balance as above. →

$$M = \frac{\text{mol MnO}_4^-}{\text{L}}$$

Make the number of electrons in both half-reactions equal by multiplying one or both half-reactions by a small whole number. → Add the two half-reactions together, canceling electrons and other species as necessary. → Verify that the reaction is balanced both with respect to mass and with respect to charge.   then   mL MnO_4^-, M MnO_4^- → mol MnO_4^- → mol U → g U then g U, g sample → % U

$$M = \frac{\text{mol MnO}_4^-}{\text{L}} \qquad \frac{5 \text{ mol U}}{2 \text{ mol MnO}_4^-} \qquad \frac{238.03 \text{ g U}}{1 \text{ mol U}} \qquad\qquad \text{percent U} = \frac{\text{g U}}{\text{g sample}} \times 100\%$$

Solution:

Separate: MnO_4^- *(aq)* → Mn^{2+} *(aq)*   and $C_2O_4^{2-}$ *(aq)* → CO_2 *(g)*

Balance non H & O elements: MnO_4^- *(aq)* → Mn^{2+} *(aq)*   and $C_2O_4^{2-}$ *(aq)* → 2 CO_2 *(g)*

Balance O with H_2O: MnO_4^- *(aq)* → Mn^{2+} *(aq)* + 4 H_2O *(l)*   and $C_2O_4^{2-}$ *(aq)* → 2 CO_2 *(g)*

Balance H with H^+: MnO_4^- *(aq)* + 8 H^+ *(aq)* → Mn^{2+} *(aq)* + 4 H_2O *(l)*   and $C_2O_4^{2-}$ *(aq)* → 2 CO_2 *(g)*

Add electrons: MnO_4^- (aq) $+ 8 H^+$ $(aq) + 5 e^- \rightarrow Mn^{2+}$ $(aq) + 4 H_2O$ (l) and $C_2O_4^{2-}$ $(aq) \rightarrow 2 CO_2$ $(g) + 2 e^-$

Equalize electrons:

$2 MnO_4^-$ (aq) $+ 16 H^+$ $(aq) + 10 e^- \rightarrow 2 Mn^{2+}$ $(aq) + 8 H_2O$ (l) and $5 C_2O_4^{2-}$ $(aq) \rightarrow 10 CO_2$ $(g) + 10 e^-$

Add half-reactions:

$2 MnO_4^-$ (aq) $+ 16 H^+$ (aq) + $\overline{10 e^-}$ $+ 5 C_2O_4^{2-}$ $(aq) \rightarrow 2 Mn^{2+}$ $(aq) + 8 H_2O$ (l) $+ 10 CO_2$ (g) +

$\overline{10 e^-}$

Cancel electrons: $2 MnO_4^-$ (aq) $+ 16 H^+$ $(aq) + 5 C_2O_4^{2-}$ $(aq) \rightarrow 2 Mn^{2+}$ $(aq) + 8 H_2O$ (l) $+ 10 CO_2$ (g)

$$50.1 \text{ mL MnO}_4^- \times \frac{1 \text{ L MnO}_4^-}{1000 \text{ mL MnO}_4^-} = 0.0501 \text{ L MnO}_4^-$$

$$0.339 \text{ g Na}_2C_2O_4 \times \frac{1 \text{ mol Na}_2C_2O_4}{134.00 \text{ g Na}_2C_2O_4} \times \frac{2 \text{ mol MnO}_4^-}{5 \text{ mol Na}_2C_2O_4} = 0.00101194 \text{ mol MnO}_4^- \qquad \text{then}$$

$$M = \frac{0.00101194 \text{ mol MnO}_4^-}{0.0501 \text{ L}} = 0.0201984 \text{ M MnO}_4^- \ .$$

Separate: $\qquad\qquad\qquad\qquad$ MnO_4^- $(aq) \rightarrow Mn^{2+}$ (aq) $\qquad$ and $\qquad\qquad$ UO^{2+} $(aq) \rightarrow UO_2^{2+}$ (aq)

Balance non H & O elements: MnO_4^- $(aq) \rightarrow Mn^{2+}$ (aq) $\qquad$ and $\qquad\qquad$ UO^{2+} $(aq) \rightarrow UO_2^{2+}$ (aq)

Balance O with H_2O: MnO_4^- $(aq) \rightarrow Mn^{2+}$ $(aq) + 4 H_2O$ (l) $\quad$ and $\qquad\qquad$ UO^{2+} $(aq) + H_2O$ $(l) \rightarrow$ UO_2^{2+} (aq)

Balance H with H^+:

MnO_4^- $(aq) + 8 H^+$ $(aq) \rightarrow Mn^{2+}$ $(aq) + 4 H_2O$ (l) and UO^{2+} $(aq) + H_2O$ $(l) \rightarrow UO_2^{2+}$ $(aq) + 2 H^+$ (aq)

Add electrons: MnO_4^- (aq) $+ 8 H^+$ $(aq) + 5 e^- \rightarrow Mn^{2+}$ $(aq) + 4 H_2O$ (l) and

$\qquad\qquad\qquad\qquad\qquad\qquad\qquad$ UO^{2+} $(aq) + H_2O$ (l) $\rightarrow UO_2^{2+}$ $(aq) + 2 H^+$ (aq)

$+ 2 e^-$

Equalize electrons: $2 MnO_4^-$ (aq) $+ 16 H^+$ $(aq) + 10 e^- \rightarrow 2 Mn^{2+}$ $(aq) + 8 H_2O$ (l) and

$\qquad\qquad\qquad\qquad\qquad\qquad\qquad$ $5 UO^{2+}$ $(aq) + 5 H_2O$ $(l) \rightarrow 5 UO_2^{2+}$ $(aq) + 10 H^+$ (aq)

$+ 10 e^-$

Add half-reactions: $2 MnO_4^-$ (aq) $+ \overline{6 \; 10 \; H^+(aq)}$ $+ \overline{10 e^-}$ $+ 5 UO^{2+}$ $(aq) + \overline{5 H_2O(l)}$ $\rightarrow$

$\qquad\qquad\qquad\qquad\qquad$ $2 \; Mn^{2+}$ (aq) $+ \; 3\;\overline{5 H_2O(l)}$ $+ \; 5 \; UO_2^{2+}$ (aq)

$+ \overline{10 H^+(aq)}$ $+ \overline{10 e^-}$

Cancel electrons & species: $2 MnO_4^-$ (aq) $+ 6 H^+$ $(aq) + 5 UO^{2+}$ $(aq) \rightarrow 2 Mn^{2+}$ $(aq) + 3 H_2O$ (l) $+ 5$ UO_2^{2+} (aq)

$$32.3 \text{ mL MnO}_4^- \times \frac{0.0201984 \text{ mol MnO}_4^-}{1000 \text{ mL MnO}_4^-} \times \frac{5 \text{ mol U}}{2 \text{ mol MnO}_4^-} \times \frac{238.03 \text{ g U}}{1 \text{ mol U}} = 0.388232 \text{ g U} \qquad \text{then}$$

$$\text{percent U} = \frac{\text{g U}}{\text{g sample}} \times 100\% = \frac{0.388232 \text{ g U}}{4.63 \text{ g sample}} \times 100\% = 8.39 \% \ .$$

Check: first reaction

Reactants	Products
2 Mn atoms	2 Mn atoms
28 O atoms	28 O atoms
16 H atoms	16 H atoms
10 C atoms	10 C atoms
+4 charge	+4 charge

second reaction

Reactants	Products
2 Mn atoms	2 Mn atoms
13 O atoms	13 O atoms
6 H atoms	6 H atoms
5 U atoms	5 U atoms
+14 charge	+14 charge

The reactions are balqance. The units (%) are correct. The percentage is between 0 and 100 %.

720

128. b) If $E^{\circ}_{cell} > 0$ and $E_{cell} = E^{\circ}_{cell} - \dfrac{0.0592\ V}{n} \log Q < 0$ this means that the second term dominates and is negative. This means that $Q > 1$. If $E_{cell} < 0$ then $K < 1$, since the reaction is nonspontaneous or $Q > K$.

129. a) Looking for anion reductions that are in between the reduction potentials of Cl_2 and Br_2. The only one that meets this criterion is the dichromate ion.

130. b) If the free energy change is negative this is a spontaneous reaction. This translates to a positive cell potential and a large equilibrium constant.

Chapter 19
Radioactivity and Nuclear Chemistry

1. Radioactivity is the emission of subatomic particles or high-energy electromagnetic radiation by the nuclei of certain atoms. Radioactivity was discovered in 1896 by a French scientist named Antoine-Henri Becquerel (1852-1908). Becquerel placed crystals—composed of potassium uranyl sulfate, a compound known to phosphoresce—on top of a photographic plate wrapped in black cloth. The photographic plate showed a bright exposure spot where the crystals had been. Becquerel, Marie Curie and Pierre Curie received the Nobel Prize for the discovery of radioactivity.

2. Marie Curie discovered that elements besides uranium emitted radiation, discovering Polonium and Radium. She changed the name uranic rays to radiation.

3. A is the mass number (number of protons + neutrons); Z is the atomic number (number of protons) and X is the chemical symbol of the element.

4. A proton is described as ^1_1p, a neutron as ^1_0n, and an electron as $^0_{-1}e$.

5. An alpha particle has the same symbol as a Helium nucleus, ^4_2He. When an element emits an alpha particle, the number of protons in its nucleus decreases by 2 and the mass number decreases by 4, transforming it into a different element.

6. An beta particle has the same symbol as an electron, $^0_{-1}e$. When an atom emits a beta particle, its atomic number increases by one because it now has an additional proton. The mass number is unchanged.

7. Gamma rays are high-energy (short-wavelength) photons and has a symbol of $^0_0\gamma$. A gamma ray has no charge and no mass. When a gamma-ray photon is emitted from a radioactive atom, it does not change the mass number or the atomic number of the element. Gamma rays, however, are usually emitted in conjunction with other types of radiation.

8. A positron is the anti-particle of the electron: that is, it has the same mass, but opposite charge. It has a symbol of $^0_{+1}e$. When an atom emits a positron, its atomic number decreases by one because it now has one fewer protons.

9. Electron capture occurs when a nucleus assimilates an electron from an inner orbital of its electron cloud. Like positron emission, the net effect of electron capture is the conversion of a proton into a neutron: $^1_1p +$ $^0_{-1}e \rightarrow ^1_0n$. When an atom undergoes electron capture, its atomic number decreases by one because it has one less proton, and its mass number is unchanged.

10. a) Ionizing power: gamma rays < beta particles ~ positrons < alpha particles.

    b) Penetrating power: alpha particles < beta particles ~ positrons < gamma rays

11. For the lighter elements, the N/Z ratio of stable isotopes is about one (equal numbers of neutrons and protons). However, beyond about Z = 20, the N/Z ratio of stable nuclei begins to get larger (reaching about 1.5). Above Z = 83, stable nuclei do not exist.

12. The type of radioactivity emitted by a nuclide, also shown in Figure 19.5, depends in part on the N/Z ratio with the following possibilities: 1) N/Z too high – Nuclides that lie above the valley of stability have too many neutrons and will tend to convert neutrons to protons via beta decay. and 2) N/Z too low – Nuclides that lie below the valley of stability have too many protons and will tend to convert protons to neutrons via positron emission or electron capture. (Alpha decay also raises the N/Z ratio for nuclides in which N/Z > 1, but the effect is smaller than for positron emission or electron capture.)

13. Magic numbers are certain numbers of nucleons (N or Z = 2, 8, 20, 28, 50, 82, and N= 126) that have unique stability. Nuclei containing a magic number of protons or neutrons are particularly stable.

14. a) Film-badge dosimeters consist of photographic film held in a small case that is pinned to clothing and are standard for most people working with or near radioactive substances. These badges are collected and processed (or developed) regularly as a way to monitor a person's exposure. The more exposed the film has become in a given period of time, the more radioactivity the person has been exposed to.

   b) A Geiger-Müller counter (commonly referred to simply as a Geiger counter) is an instrument that can detect radioactivity instantaneously. Particles emitted by radioactive nuclei pass through an argon-filled chamber. The energetic particles create a trail of ionized argon atoms. An applied high voltage between a wire within the chamber and the chamber itself causes these newly formed ions to produce an electrical signal that can be detected on a meter or turned into an audible click. Each click corresponds to a radioactive particle passing through the argon gas chamber. This clicking is the stereotypical sound most people associate with a radiation detector.

   c) A scintillation counter is another instrument that can detect radioactivity instantaneously. In this device, the radioactive emissions pass through a material (such as NaI or CsI) that emits ultraviolet or visible light in response to excitation by energetic particles. The radioactivity excites the atoms to a higher energy state. The atoms release this energy as light, which is then detected and turned into an electrical signal that can be read on a meter.

15. The half-life is the time it takes for one-half of the parent nuclides in a radioactive sample to decay to the daughter nuclides, and is identical to the concept of half-life for chemical reactions that we covered in Chapter 13. Thus, the relationship between the half-life of a nuclide and its rate constant is given by the same expression (Equation 13.19) that we derived for a first-order reaction in Section 13.4: $t_{1/2} = \dfrac{0.693}{k}$.

   Nuclides that decay quickly have short half-lives and large rate constants—they are considered very active (many decay events per unit time). Nuclides that decay slowly have long half-lives and are less active (fewer decay events per unit time).

16. Radiocarbon dating, a technique devised in 1949 by Willard Libby at the University of Chicago, is used by archeologists, geologists, anthropologists, and other scientists to estimate the ages of fossils and artifacts. Carbon-14 is constantly formed in the upper atmosphere by the neutron bombardment of nitrogen and then decays back to nitrogen by beta emission with a half-life of 5,730 years. The continuous formation of carbon-14 in the atmosphere and its continuous decay back to nitrogen-14 produces a nearly constant equilibrium amount of atmospheric carbon-14, which is oxidized to carbon dioxide and incorporated into plants by photosynthesis. The C-14 then makes its way up the food chain and ultimately into all living organisms. As a result, all living plants, animals, and humans contain the same ratio of carbon-14 to carbon-12 (^{14}C:^{12}C) as is found in the atmosphere. When a living organism dies, however, it stops incorporating new carbon-14 into its tissues. The ^{14}C:^{12}C ratio then decreases with a half-life of 5,730 years. The accuracy of carbon-14 dating can be checked against objects whose ages are known from historical sources.

   In order to make C-14 dating more accurate, scientists have studied the carbon-14 content of western bristlecone pine trees, which can live up to 5,000 years. The tree trunk contains growth rings corresponding to each year of the tree's life, and the wood laid down in each ring incorporates carbon derived from the carbon dioxide in the atmosphere at that time. The rings thus provide a record of the historical atmospheric carbon-14 content and allow for corrections to carbon-14 concentrations due to atmospheric changes.

   The maximum age that can be estimated from carbon-14 dating is about 50,000 years—beyond that, the amount of carbon-14 becomes too low to measure accurately.

17. The ratio of uranium-238 to lead-206 within igneous rocks (rocks of volcanic origin) measures the time that has passed since the rock solidified (at which point the "radiometric clock" was reset). Since U-238 decays into Pb-206 with a half-life of 4.5×10^9 years, the relative amounts of U-238 and Pb-206 in a uranium-containing rock reveal its age. The method uses similar half-life calculations as the carbon dating method, only the half-life is much longer, so much older materials can be dated. The oldest rocks have an age of approximately 4.0 billion years, establishing a lower bound for the age of the Earth (the Earth must be at least as old as its oldest rocks). The ages of about 70 meteorites that have struck the earth have also been extensively studied and have been found to be about 4.5 billion years old. Since the meteorites were formed at the same time as our solar system (which includes the Earth), the best estimate for the age of the Earth is therefore about 4.5 billion years.

18. Nuclear fission is the splitting of an atom into smaller products. The process emits enormous amounts of energy. Three researchers in Germany—Lise Meitner (1878-1968), Fritz Strassmann (1902-1980), and Otto Hahn (1879-1968), repeating uranium bombardment experiments by Fermi, performed careful chemical analysis of the products. The nucleus of the neutron-bombarded uranium atom is split into barium, krypton, and other smaller products. A nuclear equation for a fission reaction, showing how uranium breaks apart into the daughter nuclides, is: $^{235}_{92}U + ^{1}_{0}n \rightarrow ^{140}_{56}Ba + ^{93}_{36}Kr + 3\,^{1}_{0}n + energy$. The process produces three neutrons, which have the potential to initiate fission in three other U-235 atoms. Scientists quickly realized that a sample rich in U-235 could undergo a chain reaction in which neutrons produced by the fission of one uranium nucleus would induce fission in other uranium nuclei. The result would be a self-amplifying reaction capable of producing an enormous amount of energy—an atomic bomb. However, to make a bomb, a critical mass of U-235—enough U-235 to produce a self-sustaining reaction—would be necessary.

19. The Manhattan Project was a top-secret endeavor with the main goal of building an atomic bomb before the Germans did. The project was led by physicist J.R. Oppenheimer (1904-1967) at a high-security research facility in Los Alamos, New Mexico. Four years later, on July 16, 1945, the world's first nuclear weapon was successfully detonated at a test site in New Mexico. The first atomic bomb exploded with a force equivalent to 18,000 tons of dynamite. Ironically, the Germans—who had not made a successful nuclear bomb—had already been defeated by this time. Instead, the atomic bomb was used on Japan. One bomb was dropped on Hiroshima and a second bomb was dropped on Nagasaki. Together, the bombs killed approximately 200,000 people and forced Japan to surrender.

20. Nuclear reactions, such as fission, generate enormous amounts of energy. A nuclear-powered electricity generation plant can produce a lot of electricity from a small amount of fuel by harnessing the heat created by fission. The heat is used to boil water and make steam, which then turns the turbine on a generator to produce electricity. The fission reaction itself occurs in the nuclear core of the power plant. The core consists of uranium fuel rods, enriched to about 3.5% U-235, interspersed between retractable neutron-absorbing control rods. When the control rods are fully retracted from the fuel rod assembly, the chain reaction can occur. However, when the control rods are fully inserted into the fuel assembly, they absorb the neutrons that would otherwise induce fission, shutting down the chain reaction. By retracting or inserting the control rods, the operator can increase or decrease the rate of fission. In this way, the fission reaction is controlled to produce the right amount of heat needed for electricity generation. In case of a power failure, the fuel rods automatically drop into the fuel rod assembly, shutting down the fission reaction.

21. The advantages of using fission to generate electricity are: 1) a typical nuclear power plant generates enough electricity for a city of about 1 million people and uses about 50 kg of fuel per day as opposed to a coal-burning power plant using about 2,000,000 kg of fuel to generate the same amount of electricity); and 2) a nuclear power plant generates no air pollution and no greenhouse gases. (Coal-burning power plants also emit carbon dioxide, a greenhouse gas.) The disadvantages are: 1) the danger of nuclear accidents, such as overheating and the release of radiation; and 2) waste disposal, since the products of the reaction are radioactive and have long half-lives.

22. The mass of the products is usually different than the mass of the reactants because in nuclear reactions, matter can be converted to energy. The relationship between the amount of matter that is lost and the amount of energy formed is given by Einstein's famous equation relating the two quantities, $E = mc^2$, where E is the energy produced, m is the mass lost, and c is the speed of light.

23. This difference in mass between the products and the reactants is known as the mass defect. The energy corresponding to the mass defect, obtained by substituting the mass defect into the equation $E = mc^2$, is known as the nuclear binding energy, the amount of energy that would be required to break apart the nucleus into its component nucleons. The nuclear binding energy per nucleon peaks at a mass number of 60. The significance of this is that the nuclides with mass numbers of about 60 are among the most stable.

24. Nuclear fusion is the combination of two light nuclei to form a heavier one. Both fusion and fission emit large amounts of energy because, they both form daughter nuclides with greater binding energies per nucleon than the parent nuclides.

25. Extremely high temperature required for fusion to occur. To date no material can withstand these temperatures. The U.S. Congress has reduced funding for these projects so that it is less likely that a viable process will be developed.

26. Transmutation is a process that results in the transformation of one element into another. Examples are: $_7^{12}\text{N} + _2^4\text{He} \rightarrow _8^{17}\text{O} + _1^1\text{H}$ and $_{13}^{27}\text{Al} + _2^4\text{He} \rightarrow _{15}^{30}\text{O} + _0^1\text{n}$.

27. In a single stage linear accelerator, a charged particle such as a proton is accelerated in an evacuated tube. The accelerating force is provided by a potential difference between the ends of the tube. In multi-stage linear accelerators, such as the Stanford Linear Accelerator (SLAC) at Stanford University (Figure 19.14), a series of tubes of increasing length are connected to a source of alternating voltage, as shown in Figure 19.15. The voltage alternates in such a way that, as a positively charged particle leaves a particular tube, that tube becomes positively charged, repelling the particle to the next tube. At the same time, the tube the particle is now approaching becomes negatively charged, pulling the particle towards it. This continues throughout the linear accelerator, allowing the particle to be accelerated to velocities up to 90% of the speed of light. Linear accelerators can be used to conduct nuclear transmutations, making nuclides that don't normally exist in nature.

28. In a cyclotron, a similarly alternating voltage as used in linear accelerators, is used to accelerate a charged particle, only this time the alternating voltage is applied between the two semi-circular halves of the cyclotron (Figure 19.16). A charged particle originally in the middle of the two semi-circles is accelerated back and forth between them. Additional magnets cause the particle to move in a spiral path. As the charged particles spirals out from the center, it gains speed and eventually exits the cyclotron aimed at the target.

29. The energy associated with radioactivity can ionize molecules. When radiation ionizes important molecules in living cells, problems can develop. The ingestion of radioactive materials, especially alpha and beta emitters, is particularly dangerous because the radioactivity is then inside the body and can do even more damage. The effects of radiation can be divided into three different types: acute radiation damage, increased cancer risk, and genetic effects.

30. Different type of radiation have different ionizing power (gamma rays < beta particles ~ positrons < alpha particles) and different penetrating power (alpha particles < beta particles ~ positrons < gamma rays).

31. The biological effectiveness factor, or RBE, (for relative biological effectiveness), correct the dosage (in rads) for the type of radiation. It is a correction factor that is usually multiplied by the dose in rads to obtain the dose in a unit called the rem for roentgen equivalent man. So, dose in rads × biological effectiveness factor = dose in rem. The biological effectiveness factor for alpha radiation for example, is much higher than for gamma radiation.

32. The use of radioactivity in diagnosis usually involves a radiotracer, a radioactive nuclide that has been attached to a compound or introduced into a mixture in order to track the movement of the compound or mixture within the body. Tracers are useful in the diagnosis of disease because of two main factors: 1) the sensitivity with which radioactivity can be detected, and 2) the identical chemical behavior of a radioactive nucleus and its non-radioactive counterpart. Since different elements are taken up preferentially by different organs or tissues, various radiotracers can be used to monitor metabolic activity and image a variety of organs and structures, including the kidneys, heart, brain, gallbladder, bones, and arteries. Radiotracers can also be used to locate infections or cancer within the body. Cancerous tumors can be detected because they naturally concentrate phosphorus. When a patient is given phosphorus-32 (a radioactive isotope of phosphorus), the tumors concentrate the radioactive phosphorous and become sources of radioactivity that can be detected.

Because radiation kills cells, and because it is particularly effective at killing rapidly dividing cells, it is often used as a therapy for cancer (cancer cells reproduce much faster than normal cells). Gamma rays are focused on internal tumors to kill them.

33. **Conceptual Plan: Begin with the symbol for parent nuclide on the left side of the equation and the symbol for a particle on the right side (except for electron capture). → Equalize the sum of the mass numbers and the sum of the atomic numbers on both sides of the equation by writing the appropriate**

mass number and atomic number for the unknown daughter nuclide. → Using the periodic table, deduce the identity of the unknown daughter nuclide from the atomic number and write its symbol.

Solution:

a) U-234 (alpha decay) $^{234}_{92}U \rightarrow \, ^?_?? + \, ^4_2He$ then $^{234}_{92}U \rightarrow \, ^{230}_{90}? + \, ^4_2He$ then $^{234}_{92}U \rightarrow \, ^{230}_{90}Th + \, ^4_2He$

b) Th-230 (alpha decay) $^{230}_{90}Th \rightarrow \, ^?_?? + \, ^4_2He$ then $^{230}_{90}Th \rightarrow \, ^{226}_{88}? + \, ^4_2He$ then $^{230}_{90}Th \rightarrow \, ^{226}_{88}Ra + \, ^4_2He$

c) Pb-214 (beta decay) $^{214}_{82}Pb \rightarrow \, ^?_?? + \, ^0_{-1}e$ then $^{214}_{82}Pb \rightarrow \, ^{214}_{83}? + \, ^0_{-1}e$ then $^{214}_{82}Pb \rightarrow \, ^{214}_{83}Bi + \, ^0_{-1}e$

d) N-13 (positron emission) $^{13}_{7}N \rightarrow \, ^?_?? + \, ^0_{+1}e$ then $^{13}_{7}N \rightarrow \, ^{13}_{6}? + \, ^0_{+1}e$ then $^{13}_{7}N \rightarrow \, ^{13}_{6}C + \, ^0_{+1}e$

e) Cr-51 (electron capture) $^{51}_{24}Cr + \, ^0_{-1}e \rightarrow \, ^?_??$ then $^{51}_{24}Cr + \, ^0_{-1}e \rightarrow \, ^{51}_{23}?$ then $^{51}_{24}Cr + \, ^0_{-1}e \rightarrow \, ^{51}_{23}V$

Check: a) 234 = 230 + 4, 92 = 90 + 2, and Thorium is atomic number 90. b) 230 = 226 + 4, 90 = 88 + 2, and Radium is atomic number 88. c) 214 = 214 + 0, 82 = 83 – 1, and Bismuth is atomic number 83. d) 13 = 13 + 0, 7 = 6 + 1, and Carbon is atomic number 6. e) 51 + 0 = 51, 24 – 1 = 23, and Vanadium is atomic number 23.

34. **Conceptual Plan:** Begin with the symbol for parent nuclide on the left side of the equation and the symbol for a particle on the right side (except for electron capture). → Equalize the sum of the mass numbers and the sum of the atomic numbers on both sides of the equation by writing the appropriate mass number and atomic number for the unknown daughter nuclide. → Using the periodic table, deduce the identity of the unknown daughter nuclide from the atomic number and write its symbol.

Solution:

a) Po-210 (alpha decay) $^{210}_{84}Po \rightarrow \, ^?_?? + \, ^4_2He$ then $^{210}_{84}Po \rightarrow \, ^{206}_{82}? + \, ^4_2He$ then $^{210}_{84}Po \rightarrow \, ^{206}_{82}Pb + \, ^4_2He$

b) Ac-227 (beta decay) $^{227}_{89}Ac \rightarrow \, ^?_?? + \, ^0_{-1}e$ then $^{227}_{89}Ac \rightarrow \, ^{227}_{90}? + \, ^0_{-1}e$ then $^{227}_{89}Ac \rightarrow \, ^{227}_{90}Th + \, ^0_{-1}e$

c) Tl-207 (beta decay) $^{207}_{81}Tl \rightarrow \, ^?_?? + \, ^0_{-1}e$ then $^{207}_{81}Tl \rightarrow \, ^{207}_{82}? + \, ^0_{-1}e$ then $^{207}_{81}Tl \rightarrow \, ^{207}_{82}Pb + \, ^0_{-1}e$

d) O-15 (positron emission) $^{15}_{8}O \rightarrow \, ^?_?? + \, ^0_{+1}e$ then $^{15}_{8}O \rightarrow \, ^{15}_{7}? + \, ^0_{+1}e$ then $^{15}_{8}O \rightarrow \, ^{15}_{7}N + \, ^0_{+1}e$

e) Pd-103 (electron capture) $^{103}_{46}Pd + \, ^0_{-1}e \rightarrow \, ^?_??$ then $^{103}_{46}Pd + \, ^0_{-1}e \rightarrow \, ^{103}_{45}?$ then $^{103}_{46}Pd + \, ^0_{-1}e \rightarrow \, ^{103}_{45}Rh$

Check: a) 210 = 210 + 4, 84 = 82 + 2, and Lead is atomic number 82. b) 227 = 227 + 0, 89 = 90 - 1, and Thorium is atomic number 90. c) 207 = 207 + 0, 81 = 82 – 1, and Lead is atomic number 82. d) 15 = 15 + 0, 8 = 7 + 1, and Nitrogen is atomic number 7. e) 103 + 0 = 103, 46 – 1 = 45, and Rhodium is atomic number 45.

35. **Given:** Th-232 decay series: α, β, β, α   **Find:** balanced decay reactions
Conceptual Plan: Begin with the symbol for parent nuclide on the left side of the equation and the symbol for a particle on the right side (except for electron capture). → Equalize the sum of the mass numbers and the sum of the atomic numbers on both sides of the equation by writing the appropriate mass number and atomic number for the unknown daughter nuclide. → Using the periodic table, deduce the identity of the unknown daughter nuclide from the atomic number and write its symbol. → Use the product of this reaction to write the next reaction.

Solution:

Th-232 (alpha decay) $^{232}_{90}Th \rightarrow \, ^?_?? + \, ^4_2He$ then $^{232}_{90}Th \rightarrow \, ^{228}_{88}? + \, ^4_2He$ then $^{232}_{90}Th \rightarrow \, ^{228}_{88}Ra + \, ^4_2He$

Ra-228 (beta decay) $^{228}_{88}Ra \rightarrow \, ^?_?? + \, ^0_{-1}e$ then $^{228}_{88}Ra \rightarrow \, ^{228}_{89}? + \, ^0_{-1}e$ then $^{228}_{88}Ra \rightarrow \, ^{228}_{89}Ac + \, ^0_{-1}e$

Ac-228 (beta decay) $^{228}_{89}Ac \rightarrow \, ^?_?? + \, ^0_{-1}e$ then $^{228}_{89}Ac \rightarrow \, ^{228}_{90}? + \, ^0_{-1}e$ then $^{228}_{89}Ac \rightarrow \, ^{228}_{90}Th + \, ^0_{-1}e$

Th-228 (alpha decay) $^{228}_{90}Th \rightarrow \, ^?_?? + \, ^4_2He$ then $^{228}_{90}Th \rightarrow \, ^{224}_{88}? + \, ^4_2He$ then $^{228}_{90}Th \rightarrow \, ^{224}_{88}Ra + \, ^4_2He$

Thus the decay series is: $^{232}_{90}Th \rightarrow \, ^{228}_{88}Ra + \, ^4_2He$, $^{228}_{88}Ra \rightarrow \, ^{228}_{89}Ac + \, ^0_{-1}e$, $^{228}_{89}Ac \rightarrow \, ^{228}_{90}Th + \, ^0_{-1}e$,

$^{228}_{90}Th \rightarrow \, ^{224}_{88}Ra + \, ^4_2He$.

Check: 232 = 228 + 4, 90 = 88 + 2, and Radium is atomic number 88. 228 = 228 + 0, 88 = 89 - 1, and Actinium is atomic number 89. 228 = 228 + 0, 89 = 90 – 1, and Thorium is atomic number 90. 228 = 224 + 4, 90 = 88 + 2, and Radium is atomic number 88.

36. **Given:** Rn-220 decay series: α, α, β, α   **Find:** balanced decay reactions

Conceptual Plan: Begin with the symbol for parent nuclide on the left side of the equation and the symbol for a particle on the right side (except for electron capture). → Equalize the sum of the mass numbers and the sum of the atomic numbers on both sides of the equation by writing the appropriate mass number and atomic number for the unknown daughter nuclide. → Using the periodic table, deduce the identity of the unknown daughter nuclide from the atomic number and write its symbol. → Use the product of this reaction to write the next reaction.

Solution:

Rn-220 (alpha decay) $^{220}_{86}Rn \rightarrow\ ^{?}_{?}? + ^{4}_{2}He$ then $^{220}_{86}Rn \rightarrow\ ^{216}_{84}? + ^{4}_{2}He$ then $^{220}_{86}Rn \rightarrow\ ^{216}_{84}Po + ^{4}_{2}He$

Po-216 (alpha decay) $^{216}_{84}Po \rightarrow\ ^{?}_{?}? + ^{4}_{2}He$ then $^{216}_{84}Po \rightarrow\ ^{212}_{82}? + ^{4}_{2}He$ then $^{216}_{84}Po \rightarrow\ ^{212}_{82}Pb + ^{4}_{2}He$

Pb-212 (beta decay) $^{212}_{82}Pb \rightarrow\ ^{?}_{?}? + ^{0}_{-1}e$ then $^{212}_{82}Pb \rightarrow\ ^{212}_{83}? + ^{0}_{-1}e$ then $^{212}_{82}Pb \rightarrow\ ^{212}_{83}Bi + ^{0}_{-1}e$

Bi-212 (alpha decay) $^{212}_{83}Bi \rightarrow\ ^{?}_{?}? + ^{4}_{2}He$ then $^{212}_{83}Bi \rightarrow\ ^{208}_{81}? + ^{4}_{2}He$ then $^{212}_{83}Bi \rightarrow\ ^{208}_{81}Tl + ^{4}_{2}He$

Thus the decay series is: $^{220}_{86}Rn \rightarrow\ ^{216}_{84}Po + ^{4}_{2}He$, $^{216}_{84}Po \rightarrow\ ^{212}_{82}Pb + ^{4}_{2}He$, $^{212}_{82}Pb \rightarrow\ ^{212}_{83}Bi + ^{0}_{-1}e$, $^{212}_{83}Bi \rightarrow\ ^{208}_{81}Tl + ^{4}_{2}He$.

Check: $220 = 216 + 4$, $86 = 84 + 2$, and Polonium is atomic number 84. $216 = 212 + 4$, $84 = 82 + 2$, and Lead is atomic number 82. $212 = 212 + 0$, $82 = 83 - 1$, and Bismuth is atomic number 83. $220 = 208 + 4$, $83 = 81 + 2$, and Thalium is atomic number 81.

37. **Conceptual Plan:** Equalize the sum of the mass numbers and the sum of the atomic numbers on both sides of the equation by writing the appropriate mass number and atomic number for the unknown species. → Using the periodic table and the list of particles, deduce the identity of the unknown species from the atomic number and write its symbol.

Solution:

a) $^{?}_{?}? \rightarrow\ ^{217}_{85}At + ^{4}_{2}He$ becomes $^{221}_{87}? \rightarrow\ ^{217}_{85}At + ^{4}_{2}He$ then $^{221}_{87}Fr \rightarrow\ ^{217}_{85}At + ^{4}_{2}He$

b) $^{241}_{94}Pu \rightarrow\ ^{241}_{95}Am + ^{?}_{?}?$ becomes $^{241}_{94}Pu \rightarrow\ ^{241}_{95}Am + ^{0}_{-1}?$ then $^{241}_{94}Pu \rightarrow\ ^{241}_{95}Am + ^{0}_{-1}e$

c) $^{19}_{11}Na \rightarrow\ ^{19}_{10}Ne + ^{?}_{?}?$ becomes $^{19}_{11}Na \rightarrow\ ^{19}_{10}Ne + ^{0}_{1}?$ then $^{19}_{11}Na \rightarrow\ ^{19}_{10}Ne + ^{0}_{+1}e$

d) $^{75}_{34}Se + ^{?}_{?}? \rightarrow\ ^{75}_{33}As$ becomes $^{75}_{34}Se + ^{0}_{-1}? \rightarrow\ ^{75}_{33}As$ then $^{75}_{34}Se + ^{0}_{-1}e \rightarrow\ ^{75}_{33}As$

Check: a) $221 = 210 + 4$, $87 = 85 + 2$, and Francium is atomic number 87. b) $241 = 241 + 0$, $94 = 95 - 1$, and the particle is a beta particle. c) $19 = 19 + 0$, $11 = 80 + 1$, and the particle is a positron. d) $75 = 75 + 0$, $34 - 1 = 33$, and the particle is an electron.

38. **Conceptual Plan:** Equalize the sum of the mass numbers and the sum of the atomic numbers on both sides of the equation by writing the appropriate mass number and atomic number for the unknown species. → Using the periodic table and the list of particles, deduce the identity of the unknown species from the atomic number and write its symbol.

Solution:

a) $^{241}_{95}Am \rightarrow\ ^{237}_{93}Np + ^{?}_{?}?$ becomes $^{241}_{95}Am \rightarrow\ ^{237}_{93}Np + ^{4}_{2}?$ then $^{241}_{95}Am \rightarrow\ ^{237}_{93}Np + ^{4}_{2}He$

b) $^{?}_{?}? \rightarrow\ ^{233}_{92}U + ^{0}_{-1}e$ becomes $^{233}_{91}? \rightarrow\ ^{233}_{92}U + ^{0}_{-1}e$ then $^{233}_{91}Pa \rightarrow\ ^{233}_{92}U + ^{0}_{-1}e$

c) $^{237}_{93}Np \rightarrow\ ^{?}_{?}? + ^{4}_{2}He$ becomes $^{237}_{93}Np \rightarrow\ ^{233}_{91}? + ^{4}_{2}He$ then $^{237}_{93}Np \rightarrow\ ^{233}_{91}Pa + ^{4}_{2}He$

d) $^{75}_{35}Br \rightarrow\ ^{?}_{?}? + ^{0}_{+1}e$ becomes $^{75}_{35}Br \rightarrow\ ^{75}_{34}? + ^{0}_{+1}e$ then $^{75}_{35}Br \rightarrow\ ^{75}_{34}Se + ^{0}_{+1}e$

Check: a) $241 = 237 + 4$, $95 = 93 + 2$, and the particle is an alpha particle. b) $233 = 233 + 0$, $91 = 92 - 1$, and Protactinium is atomic number 91. c) $237 = 233 + 4$, $93 = 91 + 2$, and Protactinium is atomic number 91. d) $75 = 75 + 0$, $35 = 34 + 1$, and Selenium is atomic number 34.

39. a)   stable, N/Z ratio is close to 1, acceptable for low Z atoms

b)   not stable, N/Z ratio much too high for low Z atom

c)   not stable, N/Z ratio is less than 1, much too low

d)   stable, N/Z ratio is acceptable for this Z

40. a) stable, N/Z ratio is acceptable for this Z

    b) not stable, N/Z ratio much too high for this Z

    c) not stable, N/Z ratio is close to 1, much too low for this Z

    d) stable, N/Z ratio is acceptable for this Z

41. Sc, V, and Mn, each have odd numbers of protons. Atoms with an odd number of protons typically have fewer stable isotopes than those with an even number of protons.

42. Aluminum and sodium both have an odd Z , which have fewer stable isotopes. These atoms are both small Z atoms and so the N/Z should be close to 1. There is only one option that meets both criteria. Neon and Magnesium have an even Z and so they have more options.

43. a) beta decay, since N/Z is too high

    b) positron emission, since N/Z is too low

    c) positron emission, since N/Z is too low

    d) positron emission, since N/Z is too low

44. a) beta decay, since N/Z is too high

    b) beta decay, since N/Z is too high

    c) positron emission, since N/Z is too low

    d) positron emission, since N/Z is too low

45. a) Cs-125, since it is closer to the proper N/Z

    b) Fe-62, since it is closer to the proper N/Z

46. a) Cs-139, since it is closer to the proper N/Z

    b) Fe-52, since it is closer to the proper N/Z

47. Since the half-life of U-235 is 703 million years, 1/2 will be present after 703 million years, 1/4 will be present after 2 half-lives and 1/8 will be present after 3 half-lives or 2110 million years or 2.11×10^9 years.

48. **Given:** initially 0.050 mg Tc-99m, $t_{1/2}$ for radioactive decay = 6.0 hr   **Find:** t to 6.3×10^{-3} mg
    Conceptual plan: radioactive decay implies first order kinetics, $t_{1/2} \rightarrow k$ then
    $$t_{1/2} = \frac{0.693}{k}$$

    [Tc-99m]$_0$, [Tc-99m]$_t$, k $\rightarrow$ t
    $$ln\,N_t = -kt + ln\,N_0$$

    Solution: $t_{1/2} = \dfrac{0.693}{k}$ rearrange to solve for k. $k = \dfrac{0.693}{t_{1/2}} = \dfrac{0.693}{6.0\ hr} = 0.1155\ hr^{-1}$. Since

    $ln[\text{Tc-99m}]_t = -kt + ln[\text{Tc-99m}]_0$ rearrange to solve for t

    $$t = -\frac{1}{k}\,ln\frac{[\text{Tc-99m}]_t}{[\text{Tc-99m}]_0} = -\frac{1}{0.1155\ hr^{-1}}\,ln\frac{6.3 \times 10^{-3}\ mg}{0.050\ mg} = 18\ hr\ .$$

    Check: The units (hr) are correct.   The time is 3 half-lives and the amount is 1/8 or $1/2^3$ of the original amount.

49. **Given:** $t_{1/2}$ for isotope decay = 3.8 days; 1.55 g isotope initially **Find:** mass of isotope after 5.5 days
    Conceptual plan: radioactive decay implies first order kinetics, $t_{1/2} \rightarrow k$ then

$$t_{1/2} = \frac{0.693}{k}$$

[isotope]$_0$, t, k → [isotope]$_t$

$$ln\,N_t = -kt + ln\,N_0$$

Solution: $t_{1/2} = \frac{0.693}{k}$ rearrange to solve for k. $k = \frac{0.693}{t_{1/2}} = \frac{0.693}{3.8\text{ days}} = 0.1\underline{8}237\text{ day}^{-1}$. Since

$ln[A]_t = -kt + ln[A]_0 = -(0.1\underline{8}237\text{ day}^{-1})\,(5.5\text{ day}) + ln\,(1.55\text{ g}) = -0.5\underline{6}478$ → $[A]_t = e^{-0.56478} = 0.57\text{ g}$.

Check: The units (g) are correct. The amount is consistent with a time between one and two half-lives.

50. **Given:** $t_{1/2}$ for I-131 = 8 days; 58 mg dose at 8:00 am **Find:** mass of I-131 at 5:00 pm next day
   Conceptual plan: radioactive decay implies first order kinetics, $t_{1/2}$ → k and determine days since dose

$$t_{1/2} = \frac{0.693}{k}$$

then [I-131]$_0$, t, k → [I-131]$_t$

$$ln\,N_t = -kt + ln\,N_0$$

Solution: $t_{1/2} = \frac{0.693}{k}$ rearrange to solve for k. $k = \frac{0.693}{t_{1/2}} = \frac{0.693}{8\text{ days}} = 0.0\underline{8}6625\text{ day}^{-1}$. The time since the dose

is one day plus 9 hours or $(1 + 9/24)$ days = 1.375 days. Since

$ln[I\text{-}131]_t = -kt + ln[I\text{-}131]_0 = -(0.0\underline{8}6625\text{ day}^{-1})\,(1.375\text{ day}) + ln\,(58\text{ mg}) = 3.\underline{9}413$ → $[A]_t = e^{3.9413} = 51\text{ mg}$.

Check: The units (mg) are correct. The amount is consistent with a time less than one half-life.

51. **Given:** F-18 initial decay rate = 1.5×10^5 /s, $t_{1/2}$ for F-18 = 1.83 hr **Find:** t to decay rate of 1.0×10^2 /s
   Conceptual plan: radioactive decay implies first order kinetics, $t_{1/2}$ → k then Rate$_0$, Rate$_t$, k → t

$$t_{1/2} = \frac{0.693}{k} \qquad\qquad ln\frac{Rate_t}{Rate_0} = -kt$$

Solution: $t_{1/2} = \frac{0.693}{k}$ rearrange to solve for k. $k = \frac{0.693}{t_{1/2}} = \frac{0.693}{1.83\text{ hr}} = 0.37\underline{8}689\text{ hr}^{-1}$. Since $ln\frac{Rate_t}{Rate_0} = -kt$

rearrange to solve for t $t = -\frac{1}{k}\,ln\frac{Rate_t}{Rate_0} = -\frac{1}{0.37\underline{8}689\text{ hr}^{-1}}\,ln\frac{1.0 \times 10^2\text{ /s}}{1.5 \times 10^5\text{ /s}} = 19.3\text{ hr}$.

Check: The units (hr) are correct. The time is between 10 and 11 half-lives and the rate is just under $1/2^{10}$ of the original amount.

52. **Given:** Tl-201 initial decay rate = 5.88×10^4 /s, $t_{1/2}$ for Tl-201 = 3.042 days **Find:** t to decay rate of 55 /s
   Conceptual plan: radioactive decay implies first order kinetics, $t_{1/2}$ → k then Rate$_0$, Rate$_t$, k → t

$$t_{1/2} = \frac{0.693}{k} \qquad\qquad ln\frac{Rate_t}{Rate_0} = -kt$$

Solution: $t_{1/2} = \frac{0.693}{k}$ rearrange to solve for k. $k = \frac{0.693}{t_{1/2}} = \frac{0.69315}{3.042\text{ days}} = 0.227\underline{8}590\text{ day}^{-1}$. Since

$ln\frac{Rate_t}{Rate_0} = -kt$ rearrange to solve for t

$t = -\frac{1}{k}\,ln\frac{Rate_t}{Rate_0} = -\frac{1}{0.227\underline{8}590\text{ day}^{-1}}\,ln\frac{55\text{ /s}}{5.88 \times 10^4\text{ /s}} = 3\underline{0}.609\text{ days} = 31\text{ days}$.

Check: The units (days) are correct. The time is between 10 and 11 half-lives and the rate is just under $1/2^{10}$ of the original amount.

53. **Given:** boat analysis, C-14/C-12 = 72.5 % of living organism **Find:** t **Other:** $t_{1/2}$ for decay of C-14 = 5730 years
   Conceptual plan: radioactive decay implies first order kinetics, $t_{1/2}$ → k then 72.5 % of [C-14]$_0$, k → t

$$t_{1/2} = \frac{0.693}{k} \qquad\qquad ln\,N_t = -kt + ln\,N_0$$

Solution: $t_{1/2} = \frac{0.693}{k}$ rearrange to solve for k. $k = \frac{0.693}{t_{1/2}} = \frac{0.693}{5730\text{ yr}} = 1.2\underline{0}942 \times 10^{-4}\text{ yr}^{-1}$ then

$[C\text{-}14]_t \quad = \quad 0.725 \quad [C\text{-}14]_0.$ Since $ln[C\text{-}14]_t = -kt + ln[C\text{-}14]_0$ rearrange to solve for t.

$$t = -\frac{1}{k} \ln\frac{[C\text{-}14]_t}{[C\text{-}14]_0} = -\frac{1}{1.20942 \times 10^{-4} \text{ yr}^{-1}} \ln\frac{0.725 \,[C\text{-}14]_0}{[C\text{-}14]_0} = 2.66 \times 10^3 \text{ yr}.$$

Check: The units (yr) are correct. The time to 72.5 % decay is consistent a time less than one half-life.

54. **Given:** peat analysis, C-14/C-12 = 22.8 % of living organism   **Find:** t
    Other: $t_{1/2}$ for decay of C-14 = 5730 years
    Conceptual plan: radioactive decay implies first order kinetics, $t_{1/2} \rightarrow$ k then 72.5 % of [C-14]$_0$, k $\rightarrow$ t

$$t_{1/2} = \frac{0.693}{k} \qquad\qquad ln\,N_t = -kt + ln\,N_0$$

Solution: $t_{1/2} = \dfrac{0.693}{k}$ rearrange to solve for k. $k = \dfrac{0.693}{t_{1/2}} = \dfrac{0.693}{5730 \text{ yr}} = 1.20942 \times 10^{-4} \text{ yr}^{-1}$ then

$[C\text{-}14]_t = 0.228\,[C\text{-}14]_0.$ Since $ln[C\text{-}14]_t = -kt + ln[C\text{-}14]_0$, rearrange to solve for t.

$$t = -\frac{1}{k} \ln\frac{[C\text{-}14]_t}{[C\text{-}14]_0} = -\frac{1}{1.20942 \times 10^{-4} \text{ yr}^{-1}} \ln\frac{0.228 \,[C\text{-}14]_0}{[C\text{-}14]_0} = 1.22 \times 10^4 \text{ yr}.$$

Check: The units (yr) are correct. The time to 22.8 % decay is consistent a time just more than two half-lives.

55. **Given:** skull analysis, C-14 decay rate = 15.3 dis/min·gC in living organisms and 0.85 dis/min·gC in skull
    Find: t   **Other:** $t_{1/2}$ for decay of C-14 = 5730 years
    Conceptual plan: radioactive decay implies first order kinetics, $t_{1/2} \rightarrow$ k then Rate$_0$, Rate$_t$, $k \rightarrow$ t

$$t_{1/2} = \frac{0.693}{k} \qquad\qquad ln\frac{\text{Rate}_t}{\text{Rate}_0} = -kt$$

Solution: $t_{1/2} = \dfrac{0.693}{k}$ rearrange to solve for k. $k = \dfrac{0.693}{t_{1/2}} = \dfrac{0.693}{5730 \text{ yr}} = 1.20942 \times 10^{-4} \text{ yr}^{-1}$

Since $ln\dfrac{\text{Rate}_t}{\text{Rate}_0} = -kt$, rearrange to solve for t.

$$t = -\frac{1}{k} \ln\frac{\text{Rate}_t}{\text{Rate}_0} = -\frac{1}{1.20942 \times 10^{-4} \text{ yr}^{-1}} \ln\frac{0.85 \text{ dis/min·gC}}{15.3 \text{ dis/min·gC}} = 2.39 \times 10^4 \text{ yr}.$$

Check: The units (yr) are correct. The rate is 6 % of initial value and the time is consistent a time just more than four half-lives.

56. **Given:** mammoth analysis, C-14 decay rate = 15.3 dis/min·gC in living organisms and 0.48 dis/min·gC in mammoth   **Find:** when did the mammoth live   **Other:** $t_{1/2}$ for decay of C-14 = 5730 years
    Conceptual plan: radioactive decay implies first order kinetics, $t_{1/2} \rightarrow$ k then Rate$_0$, Rate$_t$, $k \rightarrow$ t

$$t_{1/2} = \frac{0.693}{k} \qquad\qquad ln\frac{\text{Rate}_t}{\text{Rate}_0} = -kt$$

Solution: $t_{1/2} = \dfrac{0.693}{k}$ rearrange to solve for k. $k = \dfrac{0.693}{t_{1/2}} = \dfrac{0.693}{5730 \text{ yr}} = 1.20942 \times 10^{-4} \text{ yr}^{-1}$

Since $ln\dfrac{\text{Rate}_t}{\text{Rate}_0} = -kt$, rearrange to solve for t.

$$t = -\frac{1}{k} \ln\frac{\text{Rate}_t}{\text{Rate}_0} = -\frac{1}{1.20942 \times 10^{-4} \text{ yr}^{-1}} \ln\frac{0.48 \text{ dis/min·gC}}{15.3 \text{ dis/min·gC}} = 2.9 \times 10^4 \text{ yr ago}.$$

Check: The units (yr) are correct. The rate is 3 % of initial value and the time is consistent a time just more than five half-lives.

57. **Given:** rock analysis, 0.438 g Pb-206 to every 1.00 g U-238, no Pb-206 initially   **Find:** age of rock
    Other: $t_{1/2}$ for decay of U-238 to Pb-206 = 4.5×10^9 years
    Conceptual plan: radioactive decay implies first order kinetics, $t_{1/2} \rightarrow$ k then

$$t_{1/2} = \frac{0.693}{k}$$

g Pb-206 $\rightarrow$ mol Pb-206 $\rightarrow$ mol U-238 $\rightarrow$ g U-238 then [U-238]$_0$, [U-238]$_t$, $k \rightarrow$ t

$$\frac{1 \text{ mol Pb-206}}{206 \text{ g Pb-206}} \qquad \frac{1 \text{ mol U-238}}{1 \text{ mol Pb-206}} \qquad \frac{238 \text{ g U-238}}{1 \text{ mol U-238}} \qquad\qquad ln\,N_t = -kt + ln\,N_0$$

Solution: $t_{1/2} = \dfrac{0.693}{k}$ rearrange to solve for k. $k = \dfrac{0.693}{t_{1/2}} = \dfrac{0.693}{4.5 \times 10^9 \text{ yr}} = 1.\underline{5}4 \times 10^{-10} \text{ yr}^{-1}$ then

$0.438 \text{ g Pb-206} \times \dfrac{1 \text{ mol Pb-206}}{206 \text{ g Pb-206}} \times \dfrac{1 \text{ mol U-238}}{1 \text{ mol Pb-206}} \times \dfrac{238 \text{ g U-238}}{1 \text{ mol U-238}} = 0.50\underline{6}039 \text{ g U-238}$. Since $ln\dfrac{[\text{U-238}]_t}{[\text{U-238}]_0} = -kt$,

rearrange to solve for t. $t = -\dfrac{1}{k} ln\dfrac{[\text{U-238}]_t}{[\text{U-238}]_0} = -\dfrac{1}{1.\underline{5}4 \times 10^{-10} \text{ yr}^{-1}} ln\dfrac{1.00 \text{ g U-238}}{(1.00 + 0.506039) \text{ g U-238}} = 2.7 \times 10^9 \text{ yr}$.

Check: The units (yr) are correct. The amount of Pb-206 is less than half of the initial U-238 amount and time is less than one half-life.

58. **Given:** meteor analysis, 0.855 g Pb-206 : 1.00 g U-238, no Pb-206 initially   **Find:** age of meteor
Other: $t_{1/2}$ for decay of U-238 to Pb-206 = 4.5 x 10^9 years
Conceptual plan: radioactive decay implies first order kinetics, $t_{1/2} \rightarrow k$ then
$$t_{1/2} = \frac{0.693}{k}$$

g Pb-206 $\rightarrow$ mol Pb-206 $\rightarrow$ mol U-238 $\rightarrow$ g U-238 then [U-238]$_0$, [U-238]$_t$, k $\rightarrow$ t

$$\frac{1 \text{ mol Pb-206}}{206 \text{ g Pb-206}} \qquad \frac{1 \text{ mol U-238}}{1 \text{ mol Pb-206}} \qquad \frac{238 \text{ g U-238}}{1 \text{ mol U-238}} \qquad\qquad ln\,N_t = -kt + ln\,N_0$$

Solution: $t_{1/2} = \dfrac{0.693}{k}$ rearrange to solve for k. $k = \dfrac{0.693}{t_{1/2}} = \dfrac{0.693}{4.5 \times 10^9 \text{ yr}} = 1.\underline{5}4 \times 10^{-10} \text{ yr}^{-1}$ then

$0.855 \text{ g Pb-206} \times \dfrac{1 \text{ mol Pb-206}}{206 \text{ g Pb-206}} \times \dfrac{1 \text{ mol U-238}}{1 \text{ mol Pb-206}} \times \dfrac{238 \text{ g U-238}}{1 \text{ mol U-238}} = 0.98\underline{7}816 \text{ g U-238}$. Since $ln\dfrac{[\text{U-238}]_t}{[\text{U-238}]_0} = -kt$,

rearrange to solve for t. $t = -\dfrac{1}{k} ln\dfrac{[\text{U-238}]_t}{[\text{U-238}]_0} = -\dfrac{1}{1.\underline{5}4 \times 10^{-10} \text{ yr}^{-1}} ln\dfrac{1.00 \text{ g U-238}}{(1.00 + 0.987816) \text{ g U-238}} = 4.5 \times 10^9 \text{ yr}$.

Check: The units (yr) are correct. The amount of Pb-206 is just less than the initial U-238 amount and time is just under one half-life.

59. **Given:** U-235 fission induced by neutrons to Xe-144 and Sr-90   **Find:** number of neutrons produced
Conceptual Plan: Write species given on the appropriate side of the equation. $\rightarrow$Equalize the sum of the mass numbers and the sum of the atomic numbers on both sides of the equation by writing the stoichiometric coefficient in front of the desired species.
Solution: ${}^{235}_{92}\text{U} + {}^{1}_{0}\text{n} \rightarrow {}^{144}_{54}\text{Xe} + {}^{90}_{38}\text{Sr} + ?{}^{1}_{0}\text{n}$ becomes ${}^{235}_{92}\text{U} + {}^{1}_{0}\text{n} \rightarrow {}^{144}_{54}\text{Xe} + {}^{90}_{38}\text{Sr} + 2{}^{1}_{0}\text{n}$ so 2 neutrons are produced.
Check: 235 + 1 = 144 + 90 + 2, 92 + 0 = 54 + 38 + 0, and no other particle is necessary to balance the equation.

60. **Given:** U-235 fission to Te-137 and Zr-97   **Find:** number of neutrons produced
Conceptual Plan: Write species given on the appropriate side of the equation. $\rightarrow$Equalize the sum of the mass numbers and the sum of the atomic numbers on both sides of the equation by writing the stoichiometric coefficient in front of the desired species.
Solution: ${}^{235}_{92}\text{U} + {}^{1}_{0}\text{n} \rightarrow {}^{137}_{52}\text{Te} + {}^{97}_{40}\text{Zr} + ?{}^{1}_{0}\text{n}$ becomes ${}^{235}_{92}\text{U} + {}^{1}_{0}\text{n} \rightarrow {}^{137}_{52}\text{Te} + {}^{97}_{40}\text{Zr} + 2{}^{1}_{0}\text{n}$ so 2 neutrons are produced.
Check: 235 + 1 = 137 + 97 + 2, 92 + 0 = 52 + 40 + 0, and no other particle is necessary to balance the equation.

61. **Given:** fusion of 2 H-2 atoms to form He-3 and 1 neutron   **Find:** balanced equation
Conceptual Plan: Write species given on the appropriate side of the equation. $\rightarrow$Equalize the sum of the mass numbers and the sum of the atomic numbers on both sides of the equation by writing the stoichiometric coefficient in front of the desired species.
Solution: $2{}^{2}_{1}\text{H} \rightarrow {}^{3}_{2}\text{He} + {}^{1}_{0}\text{n}$.
Check: 2(2) = 3 + 1, 2(1) = 2 + 0, and no other particle is necessary to balance the equation.

62. **Given:** fusion of H-3 and H-1 atoms to form He-4   **Find:** balanced equation

Conceptual Plan: Write species given on the appropriate side of the equation. →Equalize the sum of the mass numbers and the sum of the atomic numbers on both sides of the equation by writing the stoichiometric coefficient in front of the desired species.

Solution: $^{3}_{1}H + ^{1}_{1}H \rightarrow ^{4}_{2}He$.

Check: $3 + 1 = 4$, $1 + 1 = 2$, and no other particle is necessary to balance the equation.

63. **Given:** U-238 bombarded by neutrons to form U-239 which undergoes 2 beta decays to form Pu-239
    Find: balanced equations
    Conceptual Plan: Write species given on the appropriate side of the equation. →Equalize the sum of the mass numbers and the sum of the atomic numbers on both sides of the equation by writing the stoichiometric coefficient in front of the desired species. → Use the product of this reaction to write the next reaction until process is complete.
    Solution: $^{238}_{92}U + ?^{1}_{0}n \rightarrow ^{239}_{92}U$ becomes $^{238}_{92}U + ^{1}_{0}n \rightarrow ^{239}_{92}U$. then

    beta decay $^{239}_{92}U \rightarrow ^{?}_{?}? + ^{0}_{-1}e$ becomes $^{239}_{92}U \rightarrow ^{239}_{93}? + ^{0}_{-1}e$ then $^{239}_{92}U \rightarrow ^{239}_{93}Np + ^{0}_{-1}e$. then

    beta decay $^{239}_{93}Np \rightarrow ^{?}_{?}? + ^{0}_{-1}e$ becomes $^{239}_{93}Np \rightarrow ^{239}_{94}? + ^{0}_{-1}e$ then $^{239}_{93}Np \rightarrow ^{239}_{94}Pu + ^{0}_{-1}e$.

    The entire process is $^{238}_{92}U + ^{1}_{0}n \rightarrow ^{239}_{92}U$, $^{239}_{92}U \rightarrow ^{239}_{93}Np + ^{0}_{-1}e$, $^{239}_{93}Np \rightarrow ^{239}_{94}Pu + ^{0}_{-1}e$.

    Check: $238 + 1 = 239$, $92 + 0 = 92$, and no other particle is necessary to balance the equation. $239 = 239 + 0$, $92 = 93 - 1$, and Neptunium is atomic number 93. $239 = 239 + 0$, $93 = 94 - 1$, and Plutonium is atomic number 94.

64. **Given:** Al-27 bombarded by a neutron and then undergoes an alpha decay and a beta decay   **Find:** balanced equations
    Conceptual Plan: Write species given on the appropriate side of the equation. →Equalize the sum of the mass numbers and the sum of the atomic numbers on both sides of the equation by writing the stoichiometric coefficient in front of the desired species. → Use the product of this reaction to write the next reaction until process is complete.
    Solution: $^{27}_{13}Al + ^{1}_{0}n \rightarrow ^{?}_{?}?$ becomes $^{27}_{13}Al + ^{1}_{0}n \rightarrow ^{28}_{13}?$ then $^{27}_{13}Al + ^{1}_{0}n \rightarrow ^{28}_{13}Al$ then

    alpha decay $^{28}_{13}Al \rightarrow ^{?}_{?}? + ^{4}_{2}He$ becomes $^{28}_{13}Al \rightarrow ^{24}_{11}? + ^{4}_{2}He$ then $^{28}_{13}Al \rightarrow ^{24}_{11}Na + ^{4}_{2}He$. then

    beta decay $^{24}_{11}Na \rightarrow ^{?}_{?}? + ^{0}_{-1}e$ becomes $^{24}_{11}Na \rightarrow ^{24}_{12}? + ^{0}_{-1}e$ then $^{24}_{11}Na \rightarrow ^{24}_{12}Mg + ^{0}_{-1}e$.

    The entire process is $^{27}_{13}Al + ^{1}_{0}n \rightarrow ^{28}_{13}Al$, $^{28}_{13}Al \rightarrow ^{24}_{11}Na + ^{4}_{2}He$, $^{24}_{11}Na \rightarrow ^{24}_{12}Mg + ^{0}_{-1}e$.

    Check: $27 + 1 = 28$, $13 + 0 = 13$, and Aluminum is atomic number 13. $28 = 24 + 4$, $13 = 11 + 2$, and Sodium is atomic number 11. $24 = 24 + 0$, $11 = 12 - 1$, and Magnesium is atomic number 12.

65. **Given:** Rf-257 synthesized by bombarding Cf-249 with C-12   **Find:** balanced equation
    Conceptual Plan: Write species given on the appropriate side of the equation. →Equalize the sum of the mass numbers and the sum of the atomic numbers on both sides of the equation by writing the stoichiometric coefficient in front of the desired species. → Use the product of this reaction to write the next reaction until process is complete.
    Solution: $^{249}_{98}Cf + ^{12}_{6}C \rightarrow ^{257}_{?}Rf + ?^{?}_{?}?$ becomes $^{249}_{98}Cf + ^{12}_{6}C \rightarrow ^{257}_{104}Rf + 4^{1}_{0}n$.

    Check: $249 + 12 = 257 = 4$, $98 + 6 = 104 + 0$, and Rutherfordium is atomic number 104 and 4 neutrons are needed (they have no protons) to balance the equation.

66. **Given:** Bi-209 bombarded by Cr-54 to form Bh and 1 neutron   **Find:** balanced equations
    Conceptual Plan: Write species given on the appropriate side of the equation. →Equalize the sum of the mass numbers and the sum of the atomic numbers on both sides of the equation by writing the stoichiometric coefficient in front of the desired species. → Use the product of this reaction to write the next reaction until process is complete.
    Solution: $^{209}_{83}Bi + ^{54}_{24}Cr \rightarrow ^{?}_{107}Bh + ^{1}_{0}n$ becomes $^{209}_{83}Bi + ^{54}_{24}Cr \rightarrow ^{262}_{107}Bh + ^{1}_{0}n$.

    Check: $209 + 54 = 262 + 1$, $83 + 24 = 107 + 0$, and Bhorium is atomic number 107 and no other particles are needed to balance the equation.

67. **Given:** 1.0 g of matter converted to energy   **Find:** energy
    Conceptual plan: g → kg → E

$$\frac{1 kg}{1000 g} \qquad E = m c^2$$

Solution: $1.0 \cancel{g} \times \dfrac{1\,kg}{1000\,\cancel{g}} = 0.0010\,kg$ then $E = m\,c^2 = (0.0010\,kg)\left(2.9979 \times 10^8\,\dfrac{m}{s}\right)^2 = 9.0 \times 10^{13}\,J$

Check: The units (J) are correct. The magnitude of the answer makes physical sense because we are converting a highe quantity of amu's to energy.

68. **Given:** 1.0×10^3 kWh of electricity/month from nuclear reaction **Find:** mass converted to energy / year
   Conceptual plan: kWh → J → kg → g then g/month → g/year

   $$\dfrac{3.60 \times 10^6\,J}{1\,kWh} \qquad E = m\,c^2 \qquad \dfrac{1000\,g}{1\,kg} \qquad\qquad \dfrac{12\,months}{1\,year}$$

   Solution: $1.0 \times 10^3\,\cancel{kWh} \times \dfrac{3.60 \times 10^6\,J}{1\,\cancel{kWh}} = 3.6 \times 10^9\,J$. Since $E = m\,c^2$, rearrange to solve for m.

   $$m = \dfrac{E}{c^2} = \dfrac{3.6 \times 10^9\,kg\,\dfrac{\cancel{m^2}}{\cancel{s^2}}}{\left(2.9979 \times 10^8\,\dfrac{\cancel{m}}{\cancel{s}}\right)^2} = 4.0 \times 10^{-8}\,\cancel{kg} \times \dfrac{1000\,g}{1\,\cancel{kg}} = 4.0 \times 10^{-5}\,g.\ \text{Then}$$

   $$\dfrac{4.0 \times 10^{-5}\,g}{1\,\cancel{month}} \times \dfrac{12\,\cancel{months}}{1\,year} = \dfrac{4.8 \times 10^{-4}\,g}{1\,year}$$

   Check: The units (g) are correct. A small mass is expected since nuclear reactions to generate a large amount of energy.

69. **Given:** a) O-16 = 15.9949145 amu; b) Ni-58 = 57.935346 amu; and c) Xe-129 = 128.904780 amu
   Find: mass defect and nuclear binding energy per nucleon
   Conceptual plan: $_{Z}^{A}X$, isotope mass → mass defect → nuclear binding energy per nucleon

   $$\text{mass defect} = Z(\text{mass }_{1}^{1}H) + (A - Z)(\text{mass }_{0}^{1}n) - \text{mass of isotope} \qquad \dfrac{931.5\,MeV}{(1\,amu)(A\,nucleons)}$$

   Solution: mass defect $= Z(\text{mass }_{1}^{1}H) + (A - Z)(\text{mass }_{0}^{1}n) - \text{mass of isotope}$.

   a) O-16 mass defect $= 8(1.00783\,amu) + (16 - 8)(1.00866\,amu) - 15.9949145\,amu = 0.1370055\,amu = 0.13701\,amu$

   and $0.1370055\,\cancel{amu} \times \dfrac{931.5\,MeV}{(1\,\cancel{amu})(16\,nucleons)} = 7.976\,\dfrac{MeV}{nucleons}$.

   b) Ni-58 mass defect $= 28(1.00783\,amu) + (58 - 28)(1.00866\,amu) - 57.935346\,amu = 0.543694\,amu = 0.54369\,amu$

   and $0.543694\,\cancel{amu} \times \dfrac{931.5\,MeV}{(1\,\cancel{amu})(58\,nucleons)} = 8.732\,\dfrac{MeV}{nucleons}$.

   c) Xe-129 mass defect $= 54(1.00783\,amu) + (129 - 54)(1.00866\,amu) - 128.904780\,amu = 1.16754\,amu$

   and $1.16754\,\cancel{amu} \times \dfrac{931.5\,MeV}{(1\,\cancel{amu})(129\,nucleons)} = 8.431\,\dfrac{MeV}{nucleons}$.

   Check: The units (amu and MeV/nucleon) are correct. The mass defect increases with an increasing number of nucleons, but the MeV/nucleon does not change by as much (on a relative basis).

70. **Given:** a) Li-7 = 17.016003 amu; b) Ti-48 = 47.947947 amu; and c) Ag-107 = 106.905092 amu
   Find: mass defect and nuclear binding energy per nucleon
   Conceptual plan: $_{Z}^{A}X$, isotope mass → mass defect → nuclear binding energy per nucleon

   $$\text{mass defect} = Z(\text{mass }_{1}^{1}H) + (A - Z)(\text{mass }_{0}^{1}n) - \text{mass of isotope} \qquad \dfrac{931.5\,MeV}{(1\,amu)(A\,nucleons)}$$

   Solution: mass defect $= Z(\text{mass }_{1}^{1}H) + (A - Z)(\text{mass }_{0}^{1}n) - \text{mass of isotope}$.

   a) Li-7 mass defect $= 3(1.00783\,amu) + (7 - 3)(1.00866\,amu) - 7.016003\,amu = 0.042127\,amu = 0.04213\,amu$

   and $0.042127\,\cancel{amu} \times \dfrac{931.5\,MeV}{(1\,\cancel{amu})(7\,nucleons)} = 5.606\,\dfrac{MeV}{nucleons}$.

   b) Ti-48 mass defect $= 22(1.00783\,amu) + (48 - 22)(1.00866\,amu) - 47.947947\,amu = 0.449473\,amu = 0.44947\,amu$

and 0.449473 amu $\times \dfrac{931.5 \text{ MeV}}{(1 \text{ amu})(48 \text{ nucleons})} = 8.723 \dfrac{\text{MeV}}{\text{nucleons}}$.

c)   Ag-107 mass defect $= 47(1.00783 \text{ amu}) + (107 - 47)(1.00866 \text{ amu}) - 106.905092 \text{ amu} = 0.982518 \text{ amu} =$

   $= 0.98252 \text{ amu}$ and 0.982518 amu $\times \dfrac{931.5 \text{ MeV}}{(1 \text{ amu})(107 \text{ nucleons})} = 8.553 \dfrac{\text{MeV}}{\text{nucleons}}$.

Check: The units (amu and MeV/nucleon) are correct. The mass defect increases with an increasing number of nucleons, but the MeV/nucleon does not change by as much (on a relative basis).

71. **Given:** $^{235}_{92}\text{U} + ^{1}_{0}\text{n} \rightarrow ^{144}_{54}\text{Xe} + ^{90}_{38}\text{Sr} + 2\,^{1}_{0}\text{n}$, U-235 $= 235.043922 \text{ amu}$, Xe-144 $= 143.9385 \text{ amu}$, and Sr-90 $=$
   89.907738 amu **Find:** energy per g of U-235
   Conceptual plan: mass of products & reactants → mass defect → mass defect / g of U-235   then

$$\text{mass defect} = \textstyle\sum \text{mass of reactants} - \sum \text{mass of products} \qquad \dfrac{\text{mass defect}}{235.043922 \text{ g U-235}}$$

g   →   kg   →   E

$$\dfrac{1 \text{ kg}}{1000 \text{ g}} \qquad E = m\,c^2$$

Solution: mass defect $= \sum$ mass of reactants $- \sum$ mass of products notice that we can cancel a neutron from each side to get: $^{235}_{92}\text{U} \rightarrow ^{144}_{54}\text{Xe} + ^{90}_{38}\text{Sr} + ^{1}_{0}\text{n}$ and

   mass defect $= 235.043922 \text{ g} - (143.9385 \text{ g} + 89.907738 \text{ g} + 1.00866 \text{ g}) = 0.189024 \text{ g}$

then $\dfrac{0.189024 \text{ g}}{235.043922 \text{ g U-235}} \times \dfrac{1 \text{ kg}}{1000 \text{ g}} = 8.04207 \times 10^{-7} \dfrac{\text{kg}}{\text{g U-235}}$ then

$$E = m\,c^2 = \left(8.04207 \times 10^{-7} \dfrac{\text{kg}}{\text{g U-235}}\right)\left(2.9979 \times 10^{8} \dfrac{\text{m}}{\text{s}}\right)^2 = 7.228 \times 10^{10} \dfrac{\text{J}}{\text{g U-235}}$$.

Check: The units (J) are correct. A large amount of energy is expected per gram of fuel in a nuclear reactor.

72. **Given:** $^{235}_{92}\text{U} + ^{1}_{0}\text{n} \rightarrow ^{137}_{52}\text{Te} + ^{97}_{40}\text{Zr} + 2\,^{1}_{0}\text{n}$, U-235 $= 235.043922 \text{ amu}$, Te-137 $= 136.9253 \text{ amu}$, and Zr-97 $=$
   96.910950 amu **Find:** energy per g of U-235
   Conceptual plan: mass of products & reactants → mass defect → mass defect / g of U-235   then

$$\text{mass defect} = \textstyle\sum \text{mass of reactants} - \sum \text{mass of products} \qquad \dfrac{\text{mass defect}}{235.043922 \text{ g U-235}}$$

g   →   kg   →   E

$$\dfrac{1 \text{ kg}}{1000 \text{ g}} \qquad E = m\,c^2$$

Solution: mass defect $= \sum$ mass of reactants $- \sum$ mass of products notice that we can cancel a neutron from each side to get: $^{235}_{92}\text{U} \rightarrow ^{137}_{52}\text{Te} + ^{97}_{40}\text{Zr} + ^{1}_{0}\text{n}$ and

   mass defect $= 235.043922 \text{ g} - (136.9253 \text{ g} + 96.910950 \text{ g} + 1.00866 \text{ g}) = 0.199012 \text{ g}$

then $\dfrac{0.199012 \text{ g}}{235.043922 \text{ g U-235}} \times \dfrac{1 \text{ kg}}{1000 \text{ g}} = 8.467013 \times 10^{-7} \dfrac{\text{kg}}{\text{g U-235}}$ then

$$E = m\,c^2 = \left(8.467013 \times 10^{-7} \dfrac{\text{kg}}{\text{g U-235}}\right)\left(2.9979 \times 10^{8} \dfrac{\text{m}}{\text{s}}\right)^2 = 7.610 \times 10^{10} \dfrac{\text{J}}{\text{g U-235}}$$.

Check: The units (J) are correct. A large amount of energy is expected per gram of fuel in a nuclear reactor.

73. **Given:** $2\,{}^{2}_{1}\text{H} \rightarrow {}^{3}_{2}\text{He} + {}^{1}_{0}\text{n}$, H-2 = 2.014102 amu, and He-3 = 3.016029 amu   **Find:** energy per g reactant
   Conceptual plan: **mass of products & reactants → mass defect → mass defect / g of H-2 then**

$$\text{mass defect} = \sum \text{mass of reactants} - \sum \text{mass of products} \qquad \frac{\text{mass defect}}{2(2.014102 \ \text{g H-2})}$$

   g → kg → E

   $$\frac{1\,\text{kg}}{1000\ \text{g}} \qquad E = m\,c^2$$

   Solution: $\text{mass defect} = \sum \text{mass of reactants} - \sum \text{mass of products}$ and

   $\text{mass defect} = 2(2.014102 \ \text{g}) - (3.016029 \ \text{g} + 1.00866 \ \text{g}) = 0.003515 \ \text{g}$

   then $\dfrac{0.003515 \ \text{g}}{2(2.014102 \ \text{g H-2})} \times \dfrac{1\,\text{kg}}{1000 \ \text{g}} = 8.72597 \times 10^{-7} \dfrac{\text{kg}}{\text{g H-2}}$ then

   $E = m\,c^2 = \left(8.72597 \times 10^{-7} \dfrac{\text{kg}}{\text{g H-2}} \right) \left(2.9979 \times 10^{8} \dfrac{\text{m}}{\text{s}} \right)^2 = 7.84 \times 10^{10} \dfrac{\text{J}}{\text{g H-2}}$.

   Check: The units (J) are correct. A large amount of energy is expected per gram of fuel in a nuclear reactor.

74. **Given:** ${}^{3}_{1}\text{H} + {}^{1}_{1}\text{H} \rightarrow {}^{4}_{2}\text{He}$, H-3 = 3.016049 amu, H-1 = 1.007825 amu, and He-4 = 4.002603 amu
   Find: energy per g reactant
   Conceptual plan: **mass of products & reactants → mass defect → mass defect / g reactant then**

$$\text{mass defect} = \sum \text{mass of reactants} - \sum \text{mass of products} \qquad \frac{\text{mass defect}}{\text{g reactant}}$$

   g → kg → E

   $$\frac{1\,\text{kg}}{1000\ \text{g}} \qquad E = m\,c^2$$

   Solution: $\text{mass defect} = \sum \text{mass of reactants} - \sum \text{mass of products}$ and

   $\text{mass defect} = (3.016049 \ \text{g} + 1.007825 \ \text{g}) - 4.002603 \ \text{g} = 4.023874 \ \text{g} - 4.002603 \ \text{g} = 0.021271 \ \text{g}$

   then $\dfrac{0.021271 \ \text{g}}{4.023874 \ \text{g reactants}} \times \dfrac{1\,\text{kg}}{1000 \ \text{g}} = 5.2861993 \times 10^{-6} \dfrac{\text{kg}}{\text{g reactants}}$ then

   $E = m\,c^2 = \left(5.2861993 \times 10^{-6} \dfrac{\text{kg}}{\text{g H-2}} \right) \left(2.9979 \times 10^{8} \dfrac{\text{m}}{\text{s}} \right)^2 = 4.7509 \times 10^{11} \dfrac{\text{J}}{\text{g reactants}}$.

   Check: The units (J) are correct. A large amount of energy is expected per gram of fuel in a nuclear reactor.

75. **Given:** 75 kg human exposed to 32.8 rad and falling from chair **Find:** energy absorbed in each case
   Conceptual plan: **rad, kg →   J and   assume d = 0.50 m chair height then   mass, d →   J**

   $$\frac{0.01\,\text{J}}{1\ \text{kg body tissue}} \qquad\qquad E = F \cdot d = m\,g\,d$$

   Solution: $32.8 \ \text{rad} = 32.8 \ \dfrac{0.01\,\text{J}}{1 \ \text{kg body tissue}} \times 75 \ \text{kg} = 25 \ \text{J}$ and

   $E = F \cdot d = m\,g\,d = 75 \ \text{kg} \times 9.8 \ \dfrac{\text{m}}{\text{s}^2} \times 0.50 \ \text{m} = 370 \ \text{kg} \dfrac{\text{m}^2}{\text{s}^2} = 370 \ \text{J}$.

   Check: The units (J and J) are correct. Allowable radiation exposures are low, since the radiation is very ionizing and, thus, damaging to tissue. Falling may have more energy, but it is not ionizing.

76. **Given:** 55 g mouse exposed to 20.5 rad   **Find:** energy absorbed
   Conceptual plan: g → kg then   rad, kg → J

   $$\frac{1\,\text{kg}}{1000\ \text{g}} \qquad\qquad \frac{0.01\,\text{J}}{1\ \text{kg body tissue}}$$

Solution: $55 \, \cancel{g} \times \dfrac{1 \, \text{kg}}{1000 \, \cancel{g}} = 0.055 \, \text{kg}$ then $20.5 \, \text{rad} = 20.5 \, \dfrac{0.01 \, \text{J}}{1 \, \text{kg body tissue}} \times 0.055 \, \cancel{\text{kg}} = 0.011 \, \text{J}$.

Check: The units (J) are correct. Allowable radiation exposures are low, since the radiation is very ionizing and, thus, damaging to tissue.

77. **Given:** $t_{1/2}$ for F-18 = 1.83 hr, 65 % of F-18 makes it to the hospital traveling at 60.0 miles/hour
    Find: distance between hospital and cyclotron
    Conceptual plan: $t_{1/2} \rightarrow k$ then $[\text{F-18}]_0, [\text{F-18}]_t, k \rightarrow t$ then hr $\rightarrow$ mi

$$t_{1/2} = \dfrac{0.693}{k} \qquad ln\dfrac{[\text{F-18}]_t}{[\text{F-18}]_0} = -kt \qquad \dfrac{60.0 \, \text{mi}}{1 \, \text{hr}}$$

Solution: $t_{1/2} = \dfrac{0.693}{k}$ rearrange to solve for k. $k = \dfrac{0.693}{t_{1/2}} = \dfrac{0.693}{1.83 \, \text{hr}} = 0.378689 \, \text{hr}^{-1}$. Since $ln\dfrac{[\text{F-18}]_t}{[\text{F-18}]_0} = -kt$

rearrange to solve for t $t = -\dfrac{1}{k} \, ln\dfrac{[\text{F-18}]_t}{[\text{F-18}]_0} = -\dfrac{1}{0.378689 \, \text{hr}^{-1}} \, ln\dfrac{0.65 \, [\text{F-18}]_0}{[\text{F-18}]_0} = 1.1376 \, \text{hr}$. then

$1.1376 \, \cancel{\text{hr}} \times \dfrac{60.0 \, \text{mi}}{1 \, \cancel{\text{hr}}} = 68 \, \text{mi}$.

Check: The units (mi) are correct. The time less than one half-life, so the distance is less than 1.83 times the speed of travel.

78. **Given:** I-131, 155 mg, $t_{1/2}$ = 8.0 days   **Find:** exposure (in Ci) after 4.0 hr
    Conceptual plan: hr $\rightarrow$ day and $\quad t_{1/2} \rightarrow k$ then $[\text{I-131}]_0, t, k \rightarrow [\text{I-131}]_t$

$$\dfrac{1 \, \text{day}}{24 \, \text{hr}} \qquad\qquad t_{1/2} = \dfrac{0.693}{k} \qquad\qquad ln \, N_t = -kt + ln \, N_0$$

then $mg_0, mg_t \rightarrow$ mg decayed $\rightarrow$ g decayed $\rightarrow$ mol decayed $\rightarrow$ beta decays then hr $\rightarrow$ min $\rightarrow$ s

$$mg_0 - mg_t = \text{mg decayed} \qquad \dfrac{1 \, \text{g}}{1000 \, \text{mg}} \qquad \dfrac{1 \, \text{mol I-131}}{131 \, \text{g I-131}} \qquad \dfrac{6.022 \times 10^{23} \, \text{beta decays}}{1 \, \text{mol I-131}} \qquad \dfrac{60 \, \text{min}}{1 \, \text{hr}} \qquad \dfrac{60 \, \text{s}}{1 \, \text{min}}$$

then beta decays, s $\rightarrow$ beta decays / s $\rightarrow$ Ci

$$\text{take ratio} \qquad \dfrac{1 \, \text{Ci}}{\dfrac{3.7 \times 10^{10} \, \text{decays}}{\text{s}}}$$

Solution: $4.0 \, \cancel{\text{hr}} \times \dfrac{1 \, \text{day}}{24 \, \cancel{\text{hr}}} = 0.16667 \, \text{day}$ then $t_{1/2} = \dfrac{0.693}{k}$ rearrange to solve for k.

$k = \dfrac{0.693}{t_{1/2}} = \dfrac{0.693}{8.0 \, \text{days}} = 0.086625 \, \text{day}^{-1}$.

Since $\qquad\qquad\qquad ln[\text{I-131}]_t = -kt + ln[\text{I-131}]_0 = -(0.086625 \, \text{day}^{-1})(0.16667 \, \text{day}) + ln \, (155 \, \text{mg}) = 5.02899 \rightarrow$

$[\text{I-131}]_t = e^{5.02899} = 152.778 \, \text{mg}$. then $mg_0 - mg_t = \text{mg decayed} = 155 \, \text{mg} - 152.778 \, \text{mg} = 2.222 \, \text{mg I-131}$ then

$2.222 \, \cancel{\text{mg I-131}} \times \dfrac{1 \, \cancel{\text{g I-131}}}{1000 \, \cancel{\text{mg I-131}}} \times \dfrac{1 \, \cancel{\text{mol I-131}}}{131 \, \cancel{\text{g I-131}}} \times \dfrac{6.022 \times 10^{23} \, \text{beta decays}}{1 \, \cancel{\text{mol I-131}}} = 1.0213 \times 10^{19} \, \text{beta decays}$ then

$4.0 \, \cancel{\text{hr}} \times \dfrac{60 \, \cancel{\text{min}}}{1 \, \cancel{\text{hr}}} \times \dfrac{60 \, \text{s}}{1 \, \cancel{\text{min}}} = 1.44 \times 10^4 \, \text{s}$ then

$\dfrac{1.0213 \times 10^{19} \, \cancel{\text{beta decays}}}{1.44 \times 10^4 \, \cancel{\text{s}}} \times \dfrac{1 \, \text{Ci}}{\dfrac{3.7 \times 10^{10} \, \cancel{\text{decays}}}{\cancel{\text{s}}}} = 1.9169 \times 10^4 \, \text{Ci} = 2 \times 10^4 \, \text{Ci}$

Check: The units (Ci) are correct. The amount that decays is large since the half life is fairly short and so the dose is high.

79. **Given:** Incomplete reactions   **Find:** balanced reaction and energy (in J/mol reactant)

Conceptual Plan: **Equalize the sum of the mass numbers and the sum of the atomic numbers on both sides of the equation by writing the appropriate mass number and atomic number for the unknown species. → Using the periodic table and the list of particles, deduce the identity of the unknown species from the atomic number and write its symbol.   then**

mass of products & reactants   →   mass defect in g   →   mass defect in kg   →   E

$$\text{mass defect} = \sum \text{mass of reactants} - \sum \text{mass of products} \qquad \frac{1\,\text{kg}}{1000\,\text{g}} \qquad\qquad E = m\,c^2$$

Solution:

a) $^?_?? + {}^9_4\text{Be} \rightarrow {}^6_3\text{Li} + {}^4_2\text{He}$ becomes $^1_1? + {}^9_4\text{Be} \rightarrow {}^6_3\text{Li} + {}^4_2\text{He}$ then ${}^1_1\text{H} + {}^9_4\text{Be} \rightarrow {}^6_3\text{Li} + {}^4_2\text{He}$

mass defect $= \sum \text{mass of reactants} - \sum \text{mass of products}$ and

mass defect $= (1.00783\ \text{g} + 9.012182\ \text{g}) - (6.015122\ \text{g} + 4.002603\ \text{g}) = 0.002287\ \text{g}$

then $\dfrac{0.002287\ \text{g}}{2\ \text{mol reactants}} \times \dfrac{1\,\text{kg}}{1000\ \text{g}} = 1.1435 \times 10^{-6}\ \dfrac{\text{kg}}{\text{mol reactants}}$ then

$E = m\,c^2 = \left(1.1435 \times 10^{-6}\ \dfrac{\text{kg}}{\text{mol reactants}}\right)\left(2.9979 \times 10^8\ \dfrac{\text{m}}{\text{s}}\right)^2 = 1.03 \times 10^{11}\ \dfrac{\text{J}}{\text{mol reactants}}$.

Check: $1 + 9 = 6 + 4$, $1 + 4 = 3 + 2$. The units (J) are correct.

b) ${}^{209}_{83}\text{Bi} + {}^{64}_{28}\text{Ni} \rightarrow {}^{272}_{111}\text{Rg} + {}^?_??$ becomes ${}^{209}_{83}\text{Bi} + {}^{64}_{28}\text{Ni} \rightarrow {}^{272}_{111}\text{Rg} + {}^1_0?$ then ${}^{209}_{83}\text{Bi} + {}^{64}_{28}\text{Ni} \rightarrow {}^{272}_{111}\text{Rg} + {}^1_0\text{n}$

mass defect $= (208.980384\ \text{g} + 63.927969\ \text{g}) - (272.1535\ \text{g} + 1.00866\ \text{g}) = -0.253807\ \text{g}$ (Note: Since this is negative energy must be put in.)

then $\dfrac{0.253807\ \text{g}}{2\ \text{mol reactants}} \times \dfrac{1\,\text{kg}}{1000\ \text{g}} = 1.269035 \times 10^{-4}\ \dfrac{\text{kg}}{\text{mol reactants}}$ then

$E = m\,c^2 = \left(1.269035 \times 10^{-4}\ \dfrac{\text{kg}}{\text{mol reactants}}\right)\left(2.9979 \times 10^8\ \dfrac{\text{m}}{\text{s}}\right)^2 = 1.141 \times 10^{13}\ \dfrac{\text{J}}{\text{mol reactants}}$

Check: $209 + 64 = 272 + 1$, $83 + 28 = 111 + 0$. The units (J) are correct.

c) ${}^{179}_{74}\text{W} + {}^?_??? \rightarrow {}^{179}_{73}\text{Ta}$ becomes ${}^{179}_{74}\text{W} + {}^0_{-1}? \rightarrow {}^{179}_{73}\text{Ta}$ then ${}^{179}_{74}\text{W} + {}^0_{-1}\text{e} \rightarrow {}^{179}_{73}\text{Ta}$

mass defect $= (178.94707\ \text{g} + 0.00055\ \text{g}) - 178.94593\ \text{g} = 0.00169\ \text{g}$ then

$\dfrac{0.00169\ \text{g}}{2\ \text{mol reactants}} \times \dfrac{1\,\text{kg}}{1000\ \text{g}} = 8.45 \times 10^{-7}\ \dfrac{\text{kg}}{\text{mol reactants}}$ then

$E = m\,c^2 = \left(8.45 \times 10^{-7}\ \dfrac{\text{kg}}{\text{mol reactants}}\right)\left(2.9979 \times 10^8\ \dfrac{\text{m}}{\text{s}}\right)^2 = 7.59 \times 10^{10}\ \dfrac{\text{J}}{\text{mol reactants}}$

Check: $179 + 0 = 179$, $74 - 1 = 73$. The units (J) are correct.

80. **Given:** Incomplete reactions   **Find:** balanced reaction and energy (in J/mol reactant)
Conceptual Plan: **Equalize the sum of the mass numbers and the sum of the atomic numbers on both sides of the equation by writing the appropriate mass number and atomic number for the unknown species. → Using the periodic table and the list of particles, deduce the identity of the unknown species from the atomic number and write its symbol. then**

mass of products & reactants   →   mass defect in g   → mass defect in kg →   E

$$\text{mass defect} = \sum \text{mass of reactants} - \sum \text{mass of products} \qquad \frac{1\,\text{kg}}{1000\,\text{g}} \qquad\qquad E = m\,c^2$$

Solution:

a) ${}^{27}_{13}\text{Al} + {}^4_2\text{He} \rightarrow {}^{30}_{15}\text{P} + {}^?_??$ becomes ${}^{27}_{13}\text{Al} + {}^4_2\text{He} \rightarrow {}^{30}_{15}\text{P} + {}^1_0?$ then ${}^{27}_{13}\text{Al} + {}^4_2\text{He} \rightarrow {}^{30}_{15}\text{P} + {}^1_0\text{n}$

mass defect $= \sum \text{mass of reactants} - \sum \text{mass of products}$ and

mass defect $= (26.981538\ \text{g} + 4.002603\ \text{g}) - (29.981801\ \text{g} + 1.00866\ \text{g}) = -0.00632\ \text{g}$ (Note: Since this is negative energy must be put in.) then $\dfrac{0.00632\ \text{g}}{2\ \text{mol reactants}} \times \dfrac{1\,\text{kg}}{1000\ \text{g}} = 3.16 \times 10^{-6}\ \dfrac{\text{kg}}{\text{mol reactants}}$ then

$E = m\,c^2 = \left(3.16 \times 10^{-6}\ \dfrac{\text{kg}}{\text{mol reactants}}\right)\left(2.9979 \times 10^8\ \dfrac{\text{m}}{\text{s}}\right)^2 = 2.84 \times 10^{11}\ \dfrac{\text{J}}{\text{mol reactants}}$.

Check: $27 + 4 = 30 + 1$, $13 + 2 = 15 + 0$. The units (J) are correct.

737

b) $^{32}_{16}\text{S} + {}^{?}_{?}? \rightarrow {}^{29}_{14}\text{Li} + {}^{4}_{2}\text{He}$ becomes $^{32}_{16}\text{S} + {}^{1}_{0}? \rightarrow {}^{29}_{14}\text{Li} + {}^{4}_{2}\text{He}$ then $^{32}_{16}\text{S} + {}^{1}_{0}\text{n} \rightarrow {}^{29}_{14}\text{Li} + {}^{4}_{2}\text{He}$

mass defect = $(31.972071 \text{ g} + 1.00866 \text{ g}) - (28.976495 \text{ g} + 4.002603 \text{ g}) = 0.001633 \text{ g}$

then $\dfrac{0.001633 \text{ g}}{2 \text{ mol reactants}} \times \dfrac{1 \text{kg}}{1000 \text{ g}} = 8.165 \times 10^{-7} \dfrac{\text{kg}}{\text{mol reactants}}$ then

$E = m\,c^2 = \left(8.165 \times 10^{-7} \dfrac{\text{kg}}{\text{mol reactants}}\right)\left(2.9979 \times 10^8 \dfrac{\text{m}}{\text{s}}\right)^2 = 7.34 \times 10^{10} \dfrac{\text{J}}{\text{mol reactants}}$

Check: $32 + 1 = 29 + 4$, $16 + 0 = 14 + 2$. The units (J) are correct.

c) $^{241}_{95}\text{Am} \rightarrow {}^{237}_{93}\text{Np} + {}^{?}_{?}?$ becomes $^{241}_{95}\text{Am} \rightarrow {}^{237}_{93}\text{Np} + {}^{4}_{2}?$ then $^{241}_{95}\text{Am} \rightarrow {}^{237}_{93}\text{Np} + {}^{4}_{2}\text{He}$

mass defect = $241.056822 \text{ g} - (237.048166 \text{ g} + 4.002603 \text{ g}) = 0.006053 \text{ g}$ then

$\dfrac{0.006053 \text{ g}}{1 \text{ mol reactants}} \times \dfrac{1\text{kg}}{1000 \text{ g}} = 6.053 \times 10^{-6} \dfrac{\text{kg}}{\text{mol reactants}}$ then

$E = m\,c^2 = \left(6.053 \times 10^{-6} \dfrac{\text{kg}}{\text{mol reactants}}\right)\left(2.9979 \times 10^8 \dfrac{\text{m}}{\text{s}}\right)^2 = 5.440 \times 10^{11} \dfrac{\text{J}}{\text{mol reactants}}$

Check: $241 = 237 + 4$, $95 = 93 + 2$. The units (J) are correct.

81. **Given:** a) Ru-114, b) Ra-216, c) Zn-58, and d) Ne-31   **Find:** write nuclear equation for most likely decay
Conceptual Plan: Decide on most likely decay mode depending on N/Z (too large = beta decay, too low = positron emission) → **Write the symbol for parent nuclide on the left side of the equation and the symbol for a particle on the right side.** → **Equalize the sum of the mass numbers and the sum of the atomic numbers on both sides of the equation by writing the appropriate mass number and atomic number for the unknown daughter nuclide.** → **Using the periodic table, deduce the identity of the unknown daughter nuclide from the atomic number and write its symbol.**
Solution:

a) Ru-114 will undergo beta decay $^{114}_{44}\text{Ru} \rightarrow {}^{?}_{?}? + {}^{0}_{-1}\text{e}$ then $^{114}_{44}\text{Ru} \rightarrow {}^{114}_{45}? + {}^{0}_{-1}\text{e}$ then $^{114}_{44}\text{Ru} \rightarrow {}^{114}_{45}\text{Rh} + {}^{0}_{-1}\text{e}$

b) Ra-216 will undergo positron emission $^{216}_{88}\text{Ra} \rightarrow {}^{?}_{?}? + {}^{0}_{+1}\text{e}$ then $^{216}_{88}\text{Ra} \rightarrow {}^{216}_{87}? + {}^{0}_{+1}\text{e}$ then
$^{216}_{88}\text{Ra} \rightarrow {}^{216}_{87}\text{Fr} + {}^{0}_{+1}\text{e}$

c) Zn-58 will undergo positron emission $^{58}_{30}\text{Zn} \rightarrow {}^{?}_{?}? + {}^{0}_{+1}\text{e}$ then $^{58}_{30}\text{Zn} \rightarrow {}^{58}_{29}? + {}^{0}_{+1}\text{e}$ then $^{58}_{30}\text{Zn} \rightarrow {}^{58}_{29}\text{Cu} + {}^{0}_{+1}\text{e}$

d) Ne-31 will undergo beta decay $^{31}_{10}\text{Ne} \rightarrow {}^{?}_{?}? + {}^{0}_{-1}\text{e}$ then $^{31}_{10}\text{Ne} \rightarrow {}^{31}_{11}? + {}^{0}_{-1}\text{e}$ then $^{31}_{10}\text{Ne} \rightarrow {}^{31}_{11}\text{Na} + {}^{0}_{-1}\text{e}$
Check: a) $114 = 114 + 0$, $44 = 45 - 1$, and Rhodium is atomic number 45. b) $216 = 216 + 0$, $88 = 87 + 1$, and Francium is atomic number 87. c) $58 = 58 + 0$, $30 = 29 + 1$, and Copper is atomic number 29. d) $31 = 31 + 0$, $10 = 11 - 1$, and Sodium is atomic number 11.

82. **Given:** a) Kr-74, b) Th-221, c) Ar-44, and d) Nb-85   **Find:** write nuclear equation for most likely decay
Conceptual Plan: Decide on most likely decay mode depending on N/Z (too large = beta decay, too low = positron emission) → **Write the symbol for parent nuclide on the left side of the equation and the symbol for a particle on the right side.** → **Equalize the sum of the mass numbers and the sum of the atomic numbers on both sides of the equation by writing the appropriate mass number and atomic number for the unknown daughter nuclide.** → **Using the periodic table, deduce the identity of the unknown daughter nuclide from the atomic number and write its symbol.**
Solution:

a) Kr-74 will undergo positron emission $^{74}_{36}\text{Kr} \rightarrow {}^{?}_{?}? + {}^{0}_{+1}\text{e}$ then $^{74}_{36}\text{Kr} \rightarrow {}^{74}_{35}? + {}^{0}_{+1}\text{e}$ then $^{74}_{36}\text{Kr} \rightarrow {}^{74}_{35}\text{Br} + {}^{0}_{+1}\text{e}$

b) Th-221 will undergo positron emission $^{221}_{90}\text{Th} \rightarrow {}^{?}_{?}? + {}^{0}_{+1}\text{e}$ then $^{221}_{90}\text{Th} \rightarrow {}^{221}_{89}? + {}^{0}_{+1}\text{e}$ then $^{221}_{90}\text{Th} \rightarrow {}^{221}_{89}\text{Ac} + {}^{0}_{+1}\text{e}$

c) Ar-44 will undergo beta decay $^{44}_{18}\text{Ar} \rightarrow {}^{?}_{?}? + {}^{0}_{-1}\text{e}$ then $^{44}_{18}\text{Ar} \rightarrow {}^{44}_{19}? + {}^{0}_{-1}\text{e}$ then $^{44}_{18}\text{Ar} \rightarrow {}^{44}_{19}\text{K} + {}^{0}_{-1}\text{e}$

d) Nb-85 will undergo positron emission $^{85}_{41}\text{Nb} \rightarrow {}^{?}_{?}? + {}^{0}_{+1}\text{e}$ then $^{85}_{41}\text{Nb} \rightarrow {}^{85}_{40}? + {}^{0}_{+1}\text{e}$ then $^{85}_{41}\text{Nb} \rightarrow {}^{85}_{40}\text{Zr} + {}^{0}_{+1}\text{e}$

Check: a) $74 = 74 + 0$, $36 = 35 + 1$, and Bromine is atomic number 35. b) $221 = 221 + 0$, $90 = 89 + 1$, and Actinium is atomic number 89. c) $44 = 44 + 0$, $18 = 19 - 1$, and Potassium is atomic number 19. d) $85 = 85 + 0$, $41 = 40 + 1$, and Zirconium is atomic number 40.

83. **Given:** Bi-210, $t_{1/2} = 5.0$ days, 1.2 g Bi-210, 209.984105 amu, 5.5 % absorbed
    Find: beta emissions in 15.5 days and dose (in Ci)
    Conceptual plan: $t_{1/2} \rightarrow k$ then $[\text{Bi-210}]_0, t, k \rightarrow [\text{Bi-210}]_t$ then

$$t_{1/2} = \frac{0.693}{k} \qquad\qquad\qquad ln\,N_t = -kt + ln\,N_0$$

g_0, g_t $\rightarrow$ **g decayed** $\rightarrow$ **mol decayed** $\rightarrow$ **beta decays** then **day** $\rightarrow$ **hr** $\rightarrow$ **min** $\rightarrow$ **s** then

$$g_0 - g_t = g \text{ decayed} \qquad \frac{1 \text{ mol Bi-210}}{209.984105 \text{ g Bi-210}} \qquad \frac{6.022 \times 10^{23} \text{ beta decays}}{1 \text{ mol Bi-210}} \qquad \frac{1 \text{ day}}{24 \text{ hr}} \quad \frac{60 \text{ min}}{1 \text{ hr}} \quad \frac{60 \text{ s}}{1 \text{ min}}$$

beta decays, s $\rightarrow$ **beta decays / s** $\rightarrow$ **Ci available** $\rightarrow$ **Ci absorbed**

$$\text{take ratio} \qquad \frac{1 \text{ Ci}}{\dfrac{3.7 \times 10^{10} \text{ decays}}{s}} \qquad\qquad \frac{5.5 \text{ Ci absorbed}}{100 \text{ Ci emitted}}$$

Solution: $t_{1/2} = \dfrac{0.693}{k}$ rearrange to solve for k. $k = \dfrac{0.693}{t_{1/2}} = \dfrac{0.693}{5.0 \text{ days}} = 0.1386 \text{ day}^{-1}$. Since

$ln[\text{Bi-210}]_t = -kt + ln[\text{Bi-210}]_0 = -(0.1386 \text{ day}^{-1})(13.5 \text{ day}) + ln\,(1.2 \text{ g}) = -1.6888$ $\rightarrow$

$[\text{Bi-210}]_t = e^{-1.6888} = 0.18475 \text{ g}$. then $g_0 - g_t = g$ decayed $= 1.2 \text{ g} - 0.18475 \text{ g} = 1.0153 \text{ g Bi-210}$ then

$1.0153 \text{ g Bi-210} \times \dfrac{1 \text{ mol Bi-210}}{209.984105 \text{ g Bi-210}} \times \dfrac{6.022 \times 10^{23} \text{ beta decays}}{1 \text{ mol Bi-210}} = 2.9116 \times 10^{21}$ beta decays $= 2.9 \times 10^{21}$ beta decays

then $13.5 \text{ day} \times \dfrac{24 \text{ hr}}{1 \text{ day}} \times \dfrac{60 \text{ min}}{1 \text{ hr}} \times \dfrac{60 \text{ s}}{1 \text{ min}} = 1.1664 \times 10^6 \text{ s}$ then

$\dfrac{2.9116 \times 10^{21} \text{ beta decays}}{1.1664 \times 10^6 \text{ s}} \times \dfrac{1 \text{ Ci}}{\dfrac{3.7 \times 10^{10} \text{ decays}}{s}} = 6.7466 \times 10^4 \text{ Ci emitted} \times \dfrac{5.5 \text{ Ci absorbed}}{100 \text{ Ci emitted}} = 3700 \text{ Ci}$.

Check: The units (decays and Ci) are correct. The amount that decays is large since the time is over 3 half-lives and we have a relatively large amount of the isotope. Since the decay is large, the dosage is large.

84. **Given:** Po-218, $t_{1/2} = 3.0$ minutes, 55 mg Po-218, 218.008965 amu **Find:** alpha emissions in 25.0 min and dose (in Ci)
    Conceptual plan: $t_{1/2} \rightarrow k$ then $[\text{Po-218}]_0, t, k \rightarrow [\text{Po-218}]_t$ then

$$t_{1/2} = \frac{0.693}{k} \qquad\qquad\qquad ln\,N_t = -kt + ln\,N_0$$

mg_0, mg_t $\rightarrow$ **mg decayed** $\rightarrow$ **g decayed** $\rightarrow$ **mol decayed** $\rightarrow$ **alpha decays** then **min** $\rightarrow$ **s**

$$mg_0 - mg_t = mg \text{ decayed} \qquad \frac{1 \text{ g}}{1000 \text{ mg}} \qquad \frac{1 \text{ mol Po-218}}{218.008965 \text{ g Po-218}} \qquad \frac{6.022 \times 10^{23} \text{ beta decays}}{1 \text{ mol Po-218}} \qquad \frac{60 \text{ s}}{1 \text{ min}}$$

then **beta decays, s** $\rightarrow$ **beta decays / s** $\rightarrow$ **Ci**

$$\text{take ratio} \qquad \frac{1 \text{ Ci}}{\dfrac{3.7 \times 10^{10} \text{ decays}}{s}}$$

Solution: $t_{1/2} = \dfrac{0.693}{k}$ rearrange   to   solve   for k. $k = \dfrac{0.693}{t_{1/2}} = \dfrac{0.693}{3.0 \text{ min}} = 0.231 \text{ min}^{-1}$.   Since

$ln[\text{Po-218}]_t = -kt + ln[\text{Po-218}]_0 = -(0.231 \text{ min}^{-1})(25.0 \text{ day}) + ln\,(55 \text{ mg}) = -1.7677$ $\rightarrow$

$[\text{Po-218}]_t = e^{-1.7677} = 0.17073 \text{ mg}$. then $mg_0 - mg_t = mg$ decayed $= 55 \text{ mg} - 0.17073 \text{ mg} = 54.829 \text{ mg Po-218}$ then
54.829 mg Po-218

$$54.\underline{8}29 \text{ mg Po-218} \times \frac{1 \text{ g Po-218}}{1000 \text{ mg Po-218}} \times \frac{1 \text{ mol Po-218}}{218.008965 \text{ g Po-218}} \times \frac{6.022 \times 10^{23} \text{ alpha decays}}{1 \text{ mol Po-218}} = 1.\underline{5}145 \times 10^{20} \text{ alpha decays} =$$

$$= 1.5 \times 10^{20} \text{ alpha decays then } 25.0 \text{ min} \times \frac{60 \text{ s}}{1 \text{ min}} = 1.5 \times 10^{3} \text{ s then}$$

$$\frac{1.\underline{5}145 \times 10^{20} \text{ alpha decays}}{1.5 \times 10^{3} \text{ s}} \times \frac{1 \text{ Ci}}{3.7 \times 10^{10} \frac{\text{decays}}{\text{s}}} = 2.7 \times 10^{6} \text{ Ci}.$$

Check: The units (decays and Ci) are correct. The amount that decays is large since the time is over 8 half-lives, so almost the entire isotope has decayed. Since the decay rate is large (small half-life), the dosage is large.

85. **Given:** Ra-226 (226.05402 amu) decays to Rn-224, $t_{1/2} = 1.6 \times 10^{3}$ yr, 25.0 g Ra-226, T = 25.0 °C, P = 1.0 atm   **Find:** V of Rn-224 gas produced in 5.0 day
Conceptual plan: day $\rightarrow$ **yr then** $t_{1/2} \rightarrow k$ **then** $[\text{Ra-226}]_0, t, k \rightarrow [\text{Ra-226}]_t$

$$\frac{1 \text{ yr}}{365.24 \text{ day}} \qquad\qquad t_{1/2} = \frac{0.693}{k} \qquad\qquad ln\, N_t = -kt + ln\, N_0$$

then $g_0, g_t \rightarrow$ **g decayed** $\rightarrow$ **mol decayed** $\rightarrow$ **mol Rn-224 formed then** °C $\rightarrow$ K   **then**

$$g_0 - g_t = \text{g decayed} \qquad \frac{1 \text{ mol Ra-226}}{226.05402 \text{ g Ra-226}} \qquad \frac{1 \text{ mol Rn-224}}{1 \text{ mol Ra-226}} \qquad\qquad K = °C + 273.15$$

then P, n, T $\rightarrow$ V
$$PV = nRT$$

Solution: $5.0 \text{ day} \times \frac{1 \text{ yr}}{365.24 \text{ day}} = 0.01\underline{3}690 \text{ yr then } t_{1/2} = \frac{0.693}{k}$ rearrange to solve for k.

$$k = \frac{0.693}{t_{1/2}} = \frac{0.693}{1.6 \times 10^{3} \text{ yr}} = 4.\underline{3}3125 \times 10^{-4} \text{ yr}^{-1}. \text{ Since}$$

$$ln[\text{Ra-226}]_t = -kt + ln[\text{Ra-226}]_0 = -(4.\underline{3}3125 \times 10^{-4} \text{ yr}^{-1})(0.01\underline{3}690 \text{ yr}) + ln\,(25.0 \text{ g}) = 3.2\underline{1}887 \rightarrow$$

$$[\text{Ra-226}]_t = e^{3.21887} = 24.\underline{9}999 \text{ g}. \quad \text{then} \quad mg_0 - mg_t = \text{mg decayed} = 25.0 \text{ g} - 24.\underline{9}999 \text{ g} = 0.\underline{0}00148 \text{ g Ra-226} \quad \text{then}$$

$$0.\underline{0}00148 \text{ g Ra-226} \times \frac{1 \text{ mol Ra-226}}{226.05402 \text{ g Ra-226}} \times \frac{1 \text{ mol Rn-224}}{1 \text{ mol Ra-226}} = \underline{6}.5576 \times 10^{-7} \text{ mol Rn-224 then}$$

and T = 25.0 °C + 273.15 = 298.2 K, then $PV = nRT$ Rearrange to solve for V.

$$V = \frac{nRT}{P} = \frac{\underline{6}.5576 \times 10^{-7} \text{ mol} \times 0.08206 \frac{\text{L} \cdot \text{atm}}{\text{mol} \cdot \text{K}} \times 298.2 \text{ K}}{1.0 \text{ atm}} = 1.\underline{6}047 \times 10^{-5} \text{ L} = 1.6 \times 10^{-5} \text{ L}. \text{ Two significant}$$

figures are reported as requested in problem.
Check: The units (L) are correct. The amount that gas is small since the time is so small compared to the half-life.

86. **Given:** U-235 (235.043922 amu) neutron- induced fission to Ba-140 and Kr-93, 1.00 g U-235, T = 25.0 °C, P = 1.0 atm   **Find:** V of Kr-93 gas produced
Conceptual Plan: Write species given on the appropriate side of the equation. $\rightarrow$ **Equalize the sum of the mass numbers and the sum of the atomic numbers on both sides of the equation by writing the stoichiometric coefficient in front of the desired species.   then**
g U-235 $\rightarrow$ **mol U-235** $\rightarrow$ **mol Kr-93 formed then** °C $\rightarrow$ K   **then** P, n, T $\rightarrow$ V

$$\frac{1 \text{ mol U-235}}{235.043922 \text{ g U-235}} \qquad \frac{1 \text{ mol Kr-93}}{1 \text{ mol U-235}} \qquad\qquad K = °C + 273.15 \qquad\qquad PV = nRT$$

Solution: $^{235}_{92}\text{U} + ^{1}_{0}\text{n} \rightarrow\ ^{140}_{56}\text{Ba} + ^{93}_{36}\text{Kr} + ?^{1}_{0}\text{n}$ becomes $^{235}_{92}\text{U} + ^{1}_{0}\text{n} \rightarrow\ ^{140}_{56}\text{Ba} + ^{93}_{36}\text{Kr} + 3^{1}_{0}\text{n}$. then

$$1.00 \text{ g U-235} \times \frac{1 \text{ mol U-235}}{235.043922 \text{ g U-235}} \times \frac{1 \text{ mol Kr-93}}{1 \text{ mol U-235}} = 4.2\underline{5}452 \times 10^{-3} \text{ mol Kr-93 then}$$

and T = 25.0 °C + 273.15 = 298.2 K, then $PV = nRT$ Rearrange to solve for V.

$$V = \frac{nRT}{P} = \frac{4.2\underline{5}452 \times 10^{-3} \text{ mol} \times 0.08206 \frac{\text{L} \cdot \text{atm}}{\text{mol} \cdot \text{K}} \times 298.2 \text{ K}}{1.0 \text{ atm}} = 0.1\underline{0}4109 \text{ L} = 0.10 \text{ L}.$$

Check: $235 + 1 = 140 + 93 + 3(1)$, $92 + 0 = 56 + 36 + 3(0)$, and no other particle is necessary to balance the equation. The units (L) are correct. About 1/200 mole of gas is generated so we expect the volume to be about 22/200 L.

87. **Given:** $_{+1}^{0}e + _{+1}^{0}e \rightarrow 2\,_{0}^{0}\gamma$ **Find:** a) energy (in kJ/mol) and b) wavelength of gamma ray photons
    Conceptual plan:
    a) **mass of products & reactants → mass defect (g) → kg → kg/mol → E (J/mol) → E (kJ/mol)**

    mass defect = $\sum$ mass of reactants - $\sum$ mass of products $\dfrac{1\,kg}{1000\,g}$ $\div 2\,mol$ $E = m\,c^2$ $\dfrac{1\,kJ}{1000\,J}$

    b) **Answer in part a) is for 2 moles of γ, so E (J/2 mol γ) → E (J/ γ photon) → λ**

    $\dfrac{1\,mol\,photons}{6.022 \times 10^{23}\,photons}$ $E = \dfrac{hc}{\lambda}$

    Solution: a) mass defect = $\sum$ mass of reactants - $\sum$ mass of products = $(0.00055\,g + 0.00055\,g) - 0\,g = 0.00110\,g$

    then $\dfrac{0.00110\,g}{2\,mol} \times \dfrac{1\,kg}{1000\,g} = 5.50 \times 10^{-7}\,\dfrac{kg}{mol}$ then

    $E = m\,c^2 = \left(5.50 \times 10^{-7}\,\dfrac{kg}{mol}\right)\left(2.9979 \times 10^8\,\dfrac{m}{s}\right)^2 = 4.94307 \times 10^{10}\,\dfrac{J}{mol} \times \dfrac{1\,kJ}{1000\,J} = 4.94 \times 10^7\,\dfrac{kJ}{mol}$.

    b) $E = 4.94307 \times 10^{10}\,\dfrac{J}{mol\,\gamma} \times \dfrac{1\,mol\,\gamma}{6.022 \times 10^{23}\,\gamma\,photons} = 8.20835 \times 10^{-14}\,\dfrac{J}{\gamma\,photons}$.   Then $E = \dfrac{hc}{\lambda}$.   Rearrange to

    solve for λ. $\lambda = \dfrac{hc}{E} = \dfrac{\left(6.626 \times 10^{-34}\,J \cdot s\right)\left(2.9979 \times 10^8\,\dfrac{m}{s}\right)}{8.20835 \times 10^{-14}\,\dfrac{J}{\gamma\,photons}} = 2.42 \times 10^{-12}\,m = 2.42\,pm$.

    Check: The units (kJ/mol and pm) are correct. A large amount of energy is expected per mole of mass lost. The photon is in the gamma ray region of the electromagnetic spectrum.

88. **Given:** 1.0 MW power/day   **Find:** minimum rate of mass loss required
    Conceptual plan: MW → MWh → kWh → J → kg → g

    $\dfrac{24\,hr}{1\,day}$ $\dfrac{1000\,kWh}{1\,MWh}$ $\dfrac{3.60 \times 10^6\,J}{1\,kWh}$ $E = m\,c^2$ $\dfrac{1000\,g}{1\,kg}$

    Solution: $1.0\,MW \times \dfrac{24\,hr}{1\,day} \times \dfrac{1000\,kWh}{1\,MWh} \times \dfrac{3.60 \times 10^6\,J}{1\,kWh} = 8.64 \times 10^{10}\,\dfrac{J}{day}$.   Since $E = m\,c^2$, rearrange to solve for m.

    $m = \dfrac{E}{c^2} = \dfrac{8.64 \times 10^{10}\,\dfrac{kg\,m^2}{day\,s^2}}{\left(2.9979 \times 10^8\,\dfrac{m}{s}\right)^2} = 9.6 \times 10^{-7}\,\dfrac{kg}{day} \times \dfrac{1000\,g}{1\,kg} = 9.6 \times 10^{-4}\,\dfrac{g}{day}$.

    Check: The units (g/day) are correct. A large amount of energy is expected per gram of mass lost.

89. **Given:** ^{3}He = 3.016030 amu   **Find:** nuclear binding energy per nucleon
    Conceptual plan: $_{Z}^{A}X$, **isotope mass**   →   **mass defect**   →   **nuclear binding energy per nucleon**

    mass defect = Z(mass $_1^1$H) + (A - Z)(mass $_0^1$n) - mass of isotope $\dfrac{931.5\,MeV}{(1\,amu)(A\,nucleons)}$

    Solution: mass defect = Z(mass $_1^1$H) + (A - Z)(mass $_0^1$n) - mass of isotope .

    He-3 mass defect = 2(1.00783 amu) + (3 - 2)(1.00866 amu) - 3.016030 amu = 0.00829 amu

    and $0.00829\,amu \times \dfrac{931.5\,MeV}{1\,amu} = 7.72\,MeV$.

    Check: The units (MeV) are correct. The number of nucleons is small, so the MeV is not that large.

90. **Given:** $4\,_1^1H \rightarrow\,_2^4He$ **Find:** energy (in J/mol reactant)

Conceptual Plan: mass of products & reactants → mass defect in g → mass defect in kg → E

$$\text{mass defect} = \sum \text{mass of reactants} - \sum \text{mass of products} \qquad \frac{1\,kg}{1000\,g} \qquad E = m\,c^2$$

Solution:

$$\text{mass defect} = \sum \text{mass of reactants} - \sum \text{mass of products} = 4(1.00783\,g) - 4.002603\,g = 0.028717\,g \quad \text{then}$$

$$\frac{0.028717\,\cancel{g}}{4\ \text{mol reactants}} \times \frac{1\,kg}{1000\,\cancel{g}} = 7.179\underline{2}5 \times 10^{-6}\ \frac{kg}{\text{mol reactants}} \quad \text{then}$$

$$E = m\,c^2 = \left(7.179\underline{2}5 \times 10^{-6}\ \frac{kg}{\text{mol reactants}}\right)\left(2.9979 \times 10^8\ \frac{m}{s}\right)^2 = 6.4523 \times 10^{11}\ \frac{J}{\text{mol reactants}}.$$

Check: The units (J/mol) are correct.

91. **Given:** ^{247}Es and 5 neutrons made by bombarding ^{238}U   **Find:** identity of bombarding particle
Conceptual Plan: Begin with the symbols for nuclides given. → Equalize the sum of the mass numbers and the sum of the atomic numbers on both sides of the equation by writing the appropriate mass number and atomic number for the unknown daughter nuclide. → Using the periodic table, deduce the identity of the unknown nuclide from the atomic number and write its symbol.
Solution:
$$^{238}_{92}U + ^{?}_{?}? \rightarrow ^{247}_{99}Es + 5\,^{1}_{0}n \quad \text{then} \quad ^{238}_{92}U + ^{14}_{7}? \rightarrow ^{247}_{99}Es + 5\,^{1}_{0}n \quad \text{then} \quad ^{238}_{92}U + ^{14}_{7}N \rightarrow ^{247}_{99}Es + 5\,^{1}_{0}n$$
Check: $238 + 14 = 247 + 5(1)$, $92 + 7 = 99 + 5(0)$, and Nitrogen is atomic number 7.

92. **Given:** ^{6}Li reacts with ^{2}H to for 2 identical particles   **Find:** identity of product particles
Conceptual Plan: Begin with the symbols for nuclides given. → Equalize the sum of the mass numbers and the sum of the atomic numbers on both sides of the equation by writing the appropriate mass number and atomic number for the unknown daughter nuclide. → Using the periodic table, deduce the identity of the unknown nuclide from the atomic number and write its symbol.
Solution:
$$^{6}_{3}Li + ^{2}_{1}H \rightarrow 2\,^{?}_{?}? \quad \text{then} \quad ^{6}_{3}Li + ^{2}_{1}H \rightarrow 2\,^{4}_{2}? \quad \text{then} \quad ^{6}_{3}Li + ^{2}_{1}H \rightarrow 2\,^{4}_{2}He \ \text{ or 2 alpha particles.}$$
Check: $6 + 2 = 2(4)$, $3 + 1 = 2(2)$, and Helium is atomic number 2.

93. **Given:** $t_{1/2}$ for decay of ^{238}U $= 4.5 \times 10^9$ years, 1.6 g rock, 29 dis/s all radioactivity from U-238
Find: percent by mass ^{238}U in rock
Conceptual plan:
$$t_{1/2} \rightarrow k \ \text{ and } s \rightarrow \min \rightarrow hr \rightarrow day \rightarrow yr \ \text{ then Rate}, k \rightarrow N \rightarrow \text{mol}\,^{238}U \rightarrow g\,^{238}U$$

$$t_{1/2} = \frac{0.693}{k} \qquad \frac{1\,\min}{60\,s}\ \frac{1\,hr}{60\,\min}\ \frac{1\,day}{24\,hr}\ \frac{1\,yr}{365.24\,day} \qquad \text{Rate} = k\,N \qquad \frac{1\,\text{mol dis}}{6.022 \times 10^{23}\,\text{dis}}\ \frac{238\,g\ ^{238}U}{1\,\text{mol}\ ^{238}U}$$

then $g\,^{238}U$, g rock → **percent by mass** ^{238}U

$$\text{percent by mass}\ ^{238}U = \frac{g\ ^{238}U}{g\ \text{rock}} \times 100\,\%$$

Solution: $t_{1/2} = \dfrac{0.693}{k}$ rearrange to solve for k. $\quad k = \dfrac{0.693}{t_{1/2}} = \dfrac{0.693}{4.5 \times 10^9\,yr} = 1.\underline{5}4 \times 10^{-10}\,yr^{-1}$ and

$$1\,\cancel{s} \times \frac{1\,\cancel{\min}}{60\,\cancel{s}} \times \frac{1\,\cancel{hr}}{60\,\cancel{\min}} \times \frac{1\,\cancel{day}}{24\,\cancel{hr}} \times \frac{1\,yr}{365.24\,\cancel{day}} = 3.168\underline{8}9554 \times 10^{-8}\,yr. \qquad \text{Rate} = k\,N \ \text{Rearrange to solve for } N.$$

$$N = \frac{\text{Rate}}{k} = \frac{29\ \dfrac{\text{dis}}{3.168\underline{8}9554 \times 10^{-8}\,\cancel{yr}}}{1.\underline{5}4 \times 10^{-10}\,\cancel{yr^{-1}}} = 5.\underline{9}425 \times 10^{18}\,\text{dis} \quad \text{then}$$

$$5.\underline{9}425 \times 10^{18}\,\cancel{\text{dis}} \times \frac{1\,\cancel{\text{mol dis}}}{6.022 \times 10^{23}\,\cancel{\text{dis}}} \times \frac{238\,g\ ^{238}U}{1\,\cancel{\text{mol}\ ^{238}U}} = 2.\underline{3}486 \times 10^{-3}\,g\ ^{238}U \quad \text{then}$$

$$\text{percent by mass}\ ^{238}U = \frac{g\ ^{238}U}{g\ \text{rock}} \times 100\,\% = \frac{2.\underline{3}486 \times 10^{-3}\,g\ ^{238}U}{1.6\,g\ \text{rock}} \times 100\,\% = 0.15\,\%.$$

Check: The units (%) are correct. The mass percent is low because the dis/s is low.

94. **Given:** $t_{1/2}$ for decay of ^{232}Th $= 1.4 \times 10^{10}$ years   **Find:** number of dis/hr emitted by 1.0 mol ^{232}Th in 1 min

Conceptual plan: $t_{1/2} \rightarrow k$ then N, k $\rightarrow$ Rate (dis/yr) $\rightarrow$ dis/day $\rightarrow$ dis/hr

$$t_{1/2} = \frac{0.693}{k} \qquad\qquad \text{Rate} = k\,N \qquad\qquad \frac{1\ \text{yr}}{365.24\ \text{day}} \qquad \frac{1\ \text{day}}{24\ \text{hr}}$$

Solution: $t_{1/2} = \dfrac{0.693}{k}$ rearrange to solve for k. $\quad k = \dfrac{0.693}{t_{1/2}} = \dfrac{0.693}{1.4 \times 10^{10}\ \text{yr}} = 4.\underline{9}5 \times 10^{-11}\ \text{yr}^{-1}$ then

$$\text{Rate} = k\,N = \left(4.\underline{9}5 \times 10^{-11}\ \text{yr}^{-1}\right)\left(6.0\underline{2}2 \times 10^{23}\ \text{dis}\right) \times \frac{1\ \text{yr}}{365.24\ \text{day}} \times \frac{1\ \text{day}}{24\ \text{hr}} = 3.4 \times 10^{9}\ \text{dis/min}$$

Check: The units (dis/hr) are correct. The rate is high since the amount of ^{232}Th is high.

95. a) **Given:** 72,500 kg Al *(s)* and 10 Al *(s)* + 6 NH$_4$ClO$_4$ *(s)* $\rightarrow$ 4 Al$_2$O$_3$ *(s)* + 2 AlCl$_3$ *(s)* + 12 H$_2$O *(g)* + 3 N$_2$ *(g)* and 608,000 kg O$_2$ *(g)* that reacts with hydrogen to form gaseous water

Find: energy generated ($\Delta H^\circ_{\text{rxn}}$)

Conceptual plan: write balanced reaction for O$_2$ *(g)* then

$$\Delta H^0_{rxn} = \sum n_p \Delta H^0_f (products) - \sum n_R \Delta H^0_f (reactants) \quad \textbf{then}$$

kg $\rightarrow$ g $\rightarrow$ mol $\rightarrow$ energy then add the results from the two reactions

$$\frac{1000\ \text{g}}{1\ \text{kg}} \qquad \mathfrak{M} \qquad \Delta H^\circ_{\text{rxn}}$$

Solution:

Reactant/Product	ΔH^0_f (kJ/mol from Appendix IIB)
Al *(s)*	0.0
NH$_4$ClO$_4$ *(s)*	−295
Al$_2$O$_3$ *(s)*	−1675.7
AlCl$_3$ *(s)*	−704.2
H$_2$O *(g)*	−241.8
N$_2$ *(g)*	0.0

Be sure to pull data for the correct formula and phase.

$$\Delta H^0_{rxn} = \sum n_P \Delta H^0_f (products) - \sum n_R \Delta H^0_f (reactants)$$
$$= [4(\Delta H^0_f (\text{Al}_2\text{O}_3\ (s)) + 2(\Delta H^0_f (\text{AlCl}_3\ (s)) + 12(\Delta H^0_f (\text{H}_2\text{O}\ (g)) + 3(\Delta H^0_f (\text{N}_2\ (g))] +$$
$$- [10(\Delta H^0_f (\text{Al}\ (s)) + 6(\Delta H^0_f (\text{NH}_4\text{ClO}_4\ (s))]$$
$$= [4(-1675.7\ \text{kJ}) + 2(-704.2\ \text{kJ}) + 12(-241.8\ \text{kJ}) + 3(0.0\ \text{kJ})] - [10(0.0\ \text{kJ}) + 6(-295\ \text{kJ})]$$
$$= [-11012.8\ \text{kJ}] - [-1770.\ \text{kJ}]$$
$$= -924\underline{2}.8\ \text{kJ}$$

then $72{,}500\ \cancel{\text{kg Al}} \times \dfrac{1000\ \cancel{\text{g Al}}}{1\ \cancel{\text{kg Al}}} \times \dfrac{1\ \cancel{\text{mol Al}}}{26.98\ \cancel{\text{g Al}}} \times \dfrac{9242.8\ \text{kJ}}{10\ \cancel{\text{mol Al}}} = 2.4\underline{8}3703 \times 10^{9}\ \text{kJ}$.

balanced reaction: H$_2$ *(g)* + ½ O$_2$ *(g)* $\rightarrow$ H$_2$O *(g)* $\quad \Delta H^\circ_{\text{rxn}} = \Delta H^\circ_f (\text{H}_2\text{O}\ (g)) = -241.8$ kJ/mol then

$608{,}000\ \cancel{\text{kg O}_2} \times \dfrac{1000\ \cancel{\text{g O}_2}}{1\ \cancel{\text{kg O}_2}} \times \dfrac{1\ \cancel{\text{mol O}_2}}{32.00\ \cancel{\text{g O}_2}} \times \dfrac{241.8\ \text{kJ}}{0.5\ \cancel{\text{mol O}_2}} = 9.1\underline{8}84 \times 10^{9}\ \text{kJ}$. So the total is

$2.4\underline{8}3703 \times 10^{9}\ \text{kJ} + 9.1\underline{8}84 \times 10^{9}\ \text{kJ} = 1.16\underline{7}2103 \times 10^{10}\ \text{kJ} = 1.167 \times 10^{10}\ \text{kJ}$.

Check: The units (kJ) are correct. The answer very large because the reactions are very exothermic and the weight of reactants is so large.

b) **Given:** $^1_1\text{H} + ^{-1}_{-1}\text{p} + ^{0}_{+1}\text{e} \rightarrow ^{0}_{0}\gamma$ **Find:** mass of antimatter to give same energy as part a)

Conceptual plan: since the reaction is an annihilation reaction, no matter will be left, so the mass of antimatter is the same as the mass of the hydrogen. so kJ $\rightarrow$ J $\rightarrow$ kg $\rightarrow$ g

$$\frac{1000\ \text{J}}{1\ \text{kJ}} \qquad E = m\,c^2 \qquad \frac{1000\ \text{g}}{1\ \text{kg}}$$

Solution: $1.16\underline{7}2103 \times 10^{10}\ \cancel{\text{kJ}} \times \dfrac{1000\ \text{J}}{1\ \cancel{\text{kJ}}} = 1.16\underline{7}2103 \times 10^{13}\ \text{J}$. Since $E = m\,c^2$, rearrange to solve for m.

743

$$m = \frac{E}{c^2} = \frac{1.16\underline{7}2103 \times 10^{13} \text{ kg} \frac{m^2}{s^2}}{\left(2.9979 \times 10^8 \frac{m}{s}\right)^2} = 1.299 \times 10^{-4} \text{ kg} \times \frac{1000 \text{ g}}{1 \text{ kg}} = 0.1299 \text{ g} .$$

Check: The units (g) are correct. A small mass is expected since nuclear reactions to generate a large amount of energy.

96. **Given:** 85.0 g animal, ingests 10.0 mg of substance with 2.55 % by mass Pu-239, alpha emitter, $t_{1/2}$ = 24,110 years   **Find:** a) initial exposure in Ci, and b) all radiation absorbed and 7.77×10^{-12} J/emission, RBE = 20, dose in rads in the first 4.0 hours and dose in rems in the first 4.0 hours

Conceptual plan: a) $t_{1/2} \rightarrow k$ and mg $\rightarrow$ g $\rightarrow$ g Pu-239 $\rightarrow$ mol Pu-239 $\rightarrow$ atoms Pu-239

$$t_{1/2} = \frac{0.693}{k} \qquad \frac{1 \text{ g}}{1000 \text{ mg}} \quad \frac{2.22 \text{ g Pu-239}}{100 \text{ g substance}} \quad \frac{1 \text{ mol Pu-239}}{239 \text{ g Pu-239}} \quad \frac{6.022 \times 10^{23} \text{ Pu-239 atoms}}{1 \text{ mol Pu-239}}$$

then N, k $\rightarrow$ Rate (dis/yr) $\rightarrow$ dis/day $\rightarrow$ dis/hr $\rightarrow$ dis/min $\rightarrow$ dis/s $\rightarrow$ Ci

$$\text{Rate} = k\, N \qquad \frac{1 \text{ yr}}{365.24 \text{ day}} \quad \frac{1 \text{ day}}{24 \text{ hr}} \quad \frac{1 \text{ hr}}{60 \text{ min}} \quad \frac{1 \text{ min}}{60 \text{ s}} \quad \frac{1 \text{ Ci}}{3.7 \times 10^{10} \frac{\text{decays}}{\text{s}}}$$

b) hr $\rightarrow$ min $\rightarrow$ s then dis/s, s $\rightarrow$ alpha decays $\rightarrow$ J and g $\rightarrow$ kg then J, animal mass $\rightarrow$ rad $\rightarrow$ rem

$$\frac{60 \text{ min}}{1 \text{ hr}} \quad \frac{1 \text{ s}}{60 \text{ min}} \quad \text{multiply terms} \qquad \frac{7.77 \times 10^{-12} \text{ J}}{\text{decay}} \quad \frac{1 \text{ kg}}{1000 \text{ g}} \qquad \frac{1 \text{ rad}}{0.01 \text{ J}} \qquad \text{rem} = \text{RBE} \times \text{rad}$$
$$\frac{}{\text{kg animal}}$$

Solution: $t_{1/2} = \frac{0.693}{k}$ rearrange to solve for k. $k = \frac{0.693}{t_{1/2}} = \frac{0.693}{24,110 \text{ yr}} = 2.87\underline{4}326 \times 10^{-5} \text{ yr}^{-1}$ then

$$10.0 \text{ mg} \times \frac{1 \text{ g}}{1000 \text{ mg}} \times \frac{2.55 \text{ g Pu-239}}{100 \text{ g substance}} \times \frac{1 \text{ mol Pu-239}}{239 \text{ g Pu-239}} \times \frac{6.022 \times 10^{23} \text{ Pu-239 atoms}}{1 \text{ mol Pu-239}} = 6.4\underline{2}5146 \times 10^{17} \text{ Pu-239 atoms}$$

$$\text{Rate} = k\, N = \left(2.87\underline{4}326 \times 10^{-5} \text{ yr}^{-1}\right)\left(6.4\underline{2}5146 \times 10^{17} \text{ Pu-239 atoms}\right) \times \frac{1 \text{ yr}}{365.24 \text{ day}} \times \frac{1 \text{ day}}{24 \text{ hr}} \times \frac{1 \text{ hr}}{60 \text{ min}} \times \frac{1 \text{ min}}{60 \text{ s}} =$$

$$= 5.8\underline{5}230 \times 10^5 \frac{\text{dis}}{\text{s}} \times \frac{1 \text{ Ci}}{3.7 \times 10^{10} \frac{\text{decays}}{\text{s}}} = 1.5\underline{8}170 \times 10^{-5} \text{ Ci}$$

b) $4.0 \text{ hr} \times \frac{1 \text{ day}}{24 \text{ hr}} \times \frac{1 \text{ yr}}{365.24 \text{ day}} = 4.\underline{5}632 \times 10^{-4} \text{ yr}$ Since the time is so much less than the $t_{1/2}$ (10^{-6} %) the concentration is essentially constant. Use dis/s and time to get dose, so

$$4.0 \text{ hr} \times \frac{60 \text{ min}}{1 \text{ hr}} \times \frac{60 \text{ s}}{1 \text{ min}} = 1.44 \times 10^4 \text{ s}$$

$$5.8\underline{5}230 \times 10^5 \frac{\text{dis}}{\text{s}} \times 1.44 \times 10^4 \text{ s} = 8.4\underline{2}731 \times 10^9 \text{ decays} \times \frac{7.77 \times 10^{-12} \text{ J}}{\text{decay}} = 6.5\underline{4}802 \times 10^{-2} \text{ J} \qquad \text{and}$$

$$85.0 \text{ g} \times \frac{1 \text{ kg}}{1000 \text{ g}} = 0.0850 \text{ kg then} \quad \frac{6.5\underline{4}802 \times 10^{-2} \text{ J}}{0.0850 \text{ kg}} \times \frac{1 \text{ rad}}{\frac{0.01 \text{ J}}{\text{kg animal}}} = 77 \text{ rad and}$$

rem = RBE × rad = 20 × 77 rad = 1.5×10^3 rem and the animal will die.

Check: The units (Ci, rem and rad) are correct. The number of Curies is small because of the conversion factor. The dose in rems and rad are high because it is an alpha emitter and the isotope was ingested.

97. **Given:** $^{235}_{92}\text{U} \rightarrow {}^{206}_{82}\text{Pb}$ and $^{232}_{90}\text{Th} \rightarrow {}^{206}_{82}\text{Pb}$ **Find:** decay series

Conceptual Plan: Write species given on the appropriate side of the equation. $\rightarrow$ Equalize the sum of the mass numbers and the sum of the atomic numbers on both sides of the equation by writing the stoichiometric coefficient in front of the desired species.

Solution: $^{235}_{92}\text{U} \rightarrow {}^{?}_{82}\text{Pb} + ?{}^{4}_{2}\text{He} + ?{}^{0}_{-1}\text{e}$ becomes $^{235}_{92}\text{U} \rightarrow {}^{207}_{82}\text{Pb} + 7{}^{4}_{2}\text{He} + 4{}^{0}_{-1}\text{e} .$

$^{232}_{90}\text{Th} \rightarrow ^{?}_{82}\text{Pb} + ?^4_2\text{He} + ?^0_{-1}\text{e}$ becomes $^{232}_{90}\text{Th} \rightarrow ^{208}_{82}\text{Pb} + 6^4_2\text{He} + 4^0_{-1}\text{e}$.

U-235 forms Pb-207 in 7 α-decays and 4 β-decays and Th-232 forms Pb-208 in 6 α-decays and 4 β-decays. **Check:** 235 = 207 + 7(4) + 4(0), and 92 = 82 + 7(2) + 4(-1). 232 = 208 + 6(4) + 4(0), and 90 = 82 + 6(2) + 4(-1). The mass of the Pb can be determined because alpha particles are large and need to be included as integer values.

98. **Given:** $^{21}_{9}\text{F} \rightarrow ^{?}_{?}? + ^0_{-1}\text{e}$ **Find:** missing nucleus

     Conceptual Plan: Write species given on the appropriate side of the equation. →**Equalize the sum of the mass numbers and the sum of the atomic numbers on both sides of the equation by writing the stoichiometric coefficient in front of the desired species.**

     Solution: $^{21}_{9}\text{F} \rightarrow ^{?}_{?}? + ^0_{-1}\text{e}$ becomes $^{21}_{9}\text{F} \rightarrow ^{21}_{10}\text{Ne} + ^0_{-1}\text{e}$.

     Check: 21 = 21 + 0, and 9 = 10 + -1, Neon is atomic number 10 and no other species are needed to balance the equation.

99. 7. Since $1/2^6 = 1.6\%$ and $1/2^7 = 0.8\%$.

100. Nuclide A is more dangerous because the half-life is shorter (18.5 days) and so it decays faster.

101. The gamma emitter is a greater threat while you sleep because it can penetrate more tissue. The alpha emitter is a greater threat if you ingest it since it is more ionizing.

102. Iodine is used by the thyroid gland to make hormones. Normally we ingest iodine in foods, especially iodized salt. The thyroid gland cannot tell the difference between stable and radioactive iodine and will absorb both. KI tables work by blocking radioactive iodine from entering the thyroid. When a person takes KI, the stable iodine in the tablet gets absorbed by the thyroid. Because KI contains so much stable iodine, the thyroid gland becomes "full" and cannot absorb any more iodine—either stable or radioactive—for the next 24 hours.

Chapter 20
Organic Chemistry

1. Most common smells are caused by organic molecules, molecules containing carbon combined with several other elements including hydrogen, nitrogen, oxygen, and sulfur.

2. Organic chemistry is the study of compounds containing carbon combined with one or more of the elements mentioned previously (that is, hydrogen, nitrogen, oxygen, and sulfur), including their properties and their reactions.

3. Carbon is unique in the vast number of compounds that it can form. Life needs diversity to exist and carbon has the ability to form more compounds than any other element.

4. Carbon is unique in its ability to form four covalent bonds, its ability to form double and triple bonds, and its tendency to catenate (that is, to form chains).

5. Silicon can form chains with itself. However, silicon's affinity for oxygen—the Si-O bond is 142 kJ/mol stronger than the Si-Si bond—coupled with the prevalence of oxygen in our atmosphere means that silicon-silicon chains are readily oxidized to form silicates (the silicon-oxygen compounds that compose a significant proportion of minerals). By contrast, the C-C bond (347 kJ/mol) and the C-O bond (359 kJ/mole) are nearly the same strength, allowing carbon chains to exist relatively peacefully in an oxygen rich environment. In other words, silicon's affinity for oxygen robs it of the rich diversity that catenation provides to carbon.

6. a) When carbon forms four single bonds the hybridization is sp^3 and the geometry is tetrahedral.

    b) When carbon forms two single bonds and one double bond the hybridization is sp^2 and the geometry is trigonal planar.

    c) When carbon forms one single bond and one triple bond the hybridization is sp^1 and the geometry is linear.

7. Hydrocarbons—compounds that contain only carbon and hydrogen—are the simplest organic compounds. However, because of the uniqueness of carbon (just discussed), many different kinds of hydrocarbons exist. Hydrocarbons are commonly used as fuels. Candle wax, oil, gasoline, liquid propane (LP) gas, and natural gas are all composed of hydrocarbons. Hydrocarbons are also the starting materials in the synthesis of many different consumer products including fabrics, soaps, dyes, cosmetics, drugs, plastic, and rubber.

8. Hydrocarbons can be classified into four different types: alkanes, alkenes, alkynes, and aromatic hydrocarbons. Their generic formulas are: C_nH_{2n+2}, C_nH_{2n}, C_nH_{2n-2}, and formulas containing a benzene ring, respectively, where n = the number of carbon atoms.

9. A structural formula shows not only the numbers of each kind of atoms, but also how the atoms are bonded together. The condensed structural formula groups the hydrogen atoms together with the carbon atom to which they are bonded. Condensed structural formulas may show some of the bonds or none at all. The carbon skeleton formula shows the carbon-carbon bonds only as lines. Each end or bend of a line represents a carbon atom bonded to as many hydrogen atoms as necessary to form a total of four bonds. Space-filling or ball-and-stick models are three-dimensional representations that show how atoms are bonded together. The space-filling models show the relative size of the atoms that are bonded together.

10. Structural isomers are molecules with the same molecular formula but different structures. The different structure can lead to different boiling points, melting points, based on the types of intermolecular interactions that are possible (as discussed in Chapter 11).

11. Optical isomers are two molecules that are nonsuperimposable mirror images of one another. Optical isomers contain a carbon atom with four different substituent groups. Most properties of optical isomers are the same. The differences appear when they interact with polarized light and when they are placed in environments that can interact with one isomer and not the other.

12. Enantiomers are molecules that are nonsuperimposable mirror images and are therefore optical isomers of one other.

Any molecule that exhibits optical isomerism is said to be chiral. Every chiral molecule must have a chiral center, a carbon atom with four different substituents in a tetrahedral arrangement.

A dextrorotatory isomer (or the d isomer) is an optical isomers that rotates the polarization of the light clockwise.

A levorotatory isomer (or the l isomer) is an optical isomers that rotates the polarization of the light counterclockwise.

A racemic mixture is an equimolar mixture of both optical isomers does not rotate the polarization of light at all.

13. Alkanes are often called saturated hydrocarbons because they are saturated (loaded to capacity) with hydrogen. Unsaturated hydrocarbons contain multiple bonds and, therefore, contain fewer hydrogen atoms.

14. The main difference in the way that alkanes, alkenes and alkynes are names is in the ending of the name. Alkane names end in –ane, alkene names end in –ene and alkyne names end in –yne. The multiple bonds must also have their location in the molecule designated. If there are multiple bonds in a molecule, the multiple bond must be included in the longest continuous carbon chain.

15. Since double bonds are composed of a sigma bond and a pi bond. Sigma bonds allow for free rotation about the bond. The pi bond restricts the rotational motion about the bond, resulting in isomers that are referred to as geometric isomers (same connectivity, but different geometric positions). The two isomers are designated as cis (meaning "same side") and trans (meaning "opposite sides"). Cis-trans isomerism is common in alkenes and results in different boiling points and melting points and in different abilities to interact with rigid molecules.

16. Hydrocarbon combustion reactions are the burning of hydrocarbons in the presence of oxygen to form carbon dioxide and water. An example is C_8H_{18} (l) + 25/2 O_2 (g) $\rightarrow$ 8 CO_2 (g) + 9 H_2O (g).

17. The most common types of reactions of alkanes are:
   - Hydrocarbon combustion in the presence of oxygen to form carbon dioxide and water. An example is C_8H_{18} (l) + 25/2 O_2 (g) $\rightarrow$ 8 CO_2 (g) + 9 H_2O (g); and
   - Halogen substitution in the presence of a halogen gas to form a halogenated alkane and a hydrohalic acid. An example is CH_4 (g) + Cl_2 (g) $\rightarrow$ CH_3Cl (g) + HCl (g).

18. a) Substitution reactions involve replacing a hydrogen atom in a molecule with another functional group, such as a halogen.

   b) Addition reactions involving converting a pi bond to two sigma bonds, where two functional groups are added to a molecule where the multiple bond once existed.

   c) Elimination reactions involves using concentrated acids to convert an alcohol to an alkene, eliminating water. It is also referred to as a dehydration reaction where and OH from one carbon combines with an H from an adjacent carbon to form water. The removal of these atoms from the carbons allows the formation of a pi bond between the carbons involved.

19. The most common types of reactions of alkenes are:
   - Hydrocarbon combustion in the presence of oxygen to form carbon dioxide and water. An example is C_2H_4 (g) + 3 O_2 (g) $\rightarrow$ 2 CO_2 (g) + 2 H_2O (g);
   - Hydrogenation in the presence of hydrogen to form an alkane. An example is C_2H_4 (g) + H_2 (g) $\rightarrow$ C_2H_6 (g); and
   - Halogen addition in the presence of a halogen gas or hydrohalic acid to form an halogenated alkane. An example is $CH_2CHCH_2CH_3$ (g) + HCl (g) $\rightarrow$ $CH_3CClHCH_2CH_3$ (g).

20. Markovnikov's rule states that when a polar reagent is added to an unsymmetrical alkene, the positive end (the least electronegative part) of the reagent adds to the carbon atom that has the most hydrogen atoms. In most reactions of this type, the positive end of the reagent is hydrogen; therefore, the hydrogen atom goes to the carbon atom that already contains the most hydrogen atoms. An example is $CH_2CHCH_2CH_3$ (g) + HCl (g) → $CH_3CHClCH_2CH_3$ (g).

21. The structure of benzene, C_6H_6, is a six member ring where three pi bonds are delocalized on all six of the C-C bonds that form the ring. Benzene rings are represented as one or both of the Kekulé structures :

, in a shorthand notation:

or as a ball and stick diagram with molecular orbitals:

22. The most common reactions for aromatic compounds are substitution reactions. An example is C_6H_6 + Cl_2 → C_6ClH_5 + HCl.

23. A functional group is a characteristic atom or group of atoms that is inserted into a hydrocarbon. Examples of functional groups are alcohols (-OH), halogens (-X, where X = F, Cl, Br and I), and carboxylic acid (-COOH).

24. The generic structure for alcohols is R-OH, where R represents a hydrocarbon group. Methyl alcohol is CH_3OH and ethyl alcohol is CH_3CH_2OH.

25. In organic chemistry, we think of oxidation and reduction from the point of view of the carbon atoms in the organic molecule. Thus, oxidation is the gaining of oxygen or the losing of hydrogen by a carbon atom. Reduction is then the loss of oxygen or the gaining of hydrogen by a carbon atom.

26. Alcohols undergo a number of reactions including substitution, elimination (or dehydration), and oxidation. Alcohols also react with active metals to form strong bases. In a substitution reaction an alcohol reacts with an acid, such as HBr, to form halogenated hydrocarbons as follows. CH_3OH + HBr → CH_3Br + H_2O. In an elimination (or dehydration) reaction, concentrated acids, such as H_2SO_4, react with alcohols to eliminate water, forming an alkene. For example, ethanol eliminates water to form ethene according to the following reaction: CH_3CH_2OH $\xrightarrow{H_2SO_4}$ CH_2CH_2 + H_2O. In an oxidation reaction carbon atoms gain oxygen atoms and/or lose hydrogen atoms. For example, ethanol becomes acetic acid according to the following reaction: CH_3CH_2OH $\xrightarrow[H_2SO_4]{Na_2Cr_2O_7}$ CH_3COOH. Alcohols react with active metals, such as alkali metals, forming an organic base and hydrogen gas. For example, CH_3OH + Na → CH_3ONa + H_2.

27. Aldehydes and ketones have the following general structural formulas of RCHO and RCOR, respectively, where R represents a hydrocarbon group. Both aldehydes and ketones contain a carbonyl group, an oxygen double bonded to a carbon atom $\left(\begin{smallmatrix} O \\ \| \\ -C- \end{smallmatrix} \right)$. Ketones have an R group attached to both sides of the carbonyl, while aldehydes have one R group and a hydrogen atom. An exception is formaldehyde, which is an aldehyde with two H atoms attached to the carbonyl group. Acetaldehyde is $CH_3 - \overset{\overset{\displaystyle O}{\|}}{C} - H$ and propanone is

$CH_3 - \overset{\overset{\displaystyle O}{\|}}{C} - CH_3$.

28. Since oxidation reactions are used to generate aldehydes and ketones, reduction reactions can reverse these reactions and are common. Thus butanone can be reduces to butanol: $CH_3CH_2COCH_2$ $\xrightarrow{reduction}$

$CH_3CH_2COHCH_2$. Addition reactions are also common, where the carbon oxygen pi bond is broken and functional groups are added to the carbon and oxygen. An example is $CH_2O + HCN \xrightarrow{NaCN}$ $NCC(OH)H_2$. Aldehydes can be further oxidized to carboxylic acids: $CH_3CH_2CHO \xrightarrow[oxidation]{}$ CH_3CH_2COOH.

29. Carboxylic acids and esters have the following general structural formulas of RCOOH and RCOOR, respectively, where R represents a hydrocarbon group. Both carboxylic acids and esters contain a carbonyl group, an oxygen double bonded to a carbon atom $\left(\begin{array}{c} O \\ \parallel \\ -C- \end{array} \right)$. In carboxylic acids the molecule ends in

    $\begin{array}{c} O \\ \parallel \\ -C-O-H \end{array}$ and esters have $\begin{array}{c} O \\ \parallel \\ -C-O- \end{array}$ inserted into a hydrocarbon chain. Acetic acid is $\begin{array}{c} O \\ \parallel \\ CH_3-C-O-H \end{array}$ and

    ethylethanoate is $\begin{array}{c} O \\ \parallel \\ CH_3-C-O-CH_2-CH_3 \end{array}$.

30. Since carboxylic acids are acids, they can undergo dissociate in water ($CH_3COOH \rightleftharpoons CH_3COO^- + H^+$) and acid-base reactions, such as CH_3COOH *(aq)* + NaOH *(aq)* → CH_3COO^- Na^+*(aq)* + H_2O *(l)*. An important reaction between carboxylic acids and alcohols is to form as an ester and water through a condensation reaction. An example is CH_3COOH *(aq)* + CH_3CH_2OH *(aq)* →$CH_3COOCH_2CH_3$ *(aq)* + H_2O *(l)*.

31. Ethers have the following general structural formula of ROR', where R and R' represents hydrocarbon groups. The two hydrocarbon groups are linked though an oxygen atom. Diethyl ether is $CH_3-CH_2-O-CH_2-CH_3$ and ethyl propyl ether is $CH_3-CH_2-O-CH_2-CH_2-CH_3$.

32. Amines are organic compounds that contain nitrogen. One or more of the hydrogen atoms on an ammonia molecule are replaced by hydrocarbon groups. The simplest amines have the following general structural formula of RNH_2, where R represents a hydrocarbon groups. All three hydrogen atoms can be replaced by different alkyl groups to give a formula of NRR'R". Methyl amine is CH_3NH_2 and diethylamine is $(CH_3CH_2)_2NH$.

33. Polymers are long chainlike molecules composed of repeating units called monomers. Copolymers are long chainlike molecules composed of two different monomers.

34. Addition polymers are polymers in which the monomers simply link together without the elimination of any atoms. Condensation polymers are polymers that eliminate an atom or a small group of atoms during the polymerization.

35. a) C_5H_{12} is an alkane, since it follows the general formula C_nH_{2n+2}, where n = 5.

    b) C_3H_6 is an alkene, since it follows the general formula C_nH_{2n}, where n = 3.

    c) C_7H_{12} is an alkyne, since it follows the general formula C_nH_{2n-2}, where n = 7.

    d) $C_{11}H_{22}$ is an alkene, since it follows the general formula C_nH_{2n}, where n = 11.

36. a) C_8H_{16} is an alkene, since it follows the general formula C_nH_{2n}, where n = 8.

    b) C_4H_6 is an alkyne, since it follows the general formula C_nH_{2n-2}, where n = 4.

    c) C_7H_{16} is an alkane, since it follows the general formula C_nH_{2n+2}, where n = 7.

    d) C_2H_2 is an alkyne, since it follows the general formula C_nH_{2n-2}, where n = 2.

37. $CH_3-CH_2-CH_2-CH_2-CH_2-CH_2-CH_3$,

$$CH_3-\underset{\underset{CH_3}{|}}{CH}-CH_2-CH_2-CH_2-CH_3 ,$$

$$CH_3-CH_2-\underset{\underset{CH_3}{|}}{CH}-CH_2-CH_2-CH_3 ,$$

$$CH_3-\overset{\overset{CH_3}{|}}{\underset{\underset{CH_3}{|}}{C}}-CH_2-CH_2-CH_3 ,$$

$$CH_3-\underset{\underset{CH_3}{|}}{CH}-\underset{\underset{CH_3}{|}}{CH}-CH_2-CH_3 ,$$

$$CH_3-CH_2-\overset{\overset{CH_3}{|}}{\underset{\underset{CH_3}{|}}{C}}-CH_2-CH_3 ,$$

$$CH_3-\underset{\underset{CH_3}{|}}{CH}-CH_2-\underset{\underset{CH_3}{|}}{CH}-CH_3 ,$$

$$CH_3-CH_2-\underset{\underset{CH_2-CH_3}{|}}{CH}-CH_2-CH_3 , \qquad \text{and}$$

$$CH_3-\overset{\overset{CH_3}{|}}{\underset{\underset{CH_3}{|}\underset{}{\,}}{\underset{CH_3}{}}C}-\underset{\underset{CH_3}{|}}{CH}-CH_3 .$$

38. The 18 isomers are $CH_3-CH_2-CH_2-CH_2-CH_2-CH_2-CH_2-CH_3$,

$$CH_3-\underset{\underset{CH_3}{|}}{CH}-CH_2-CH_2-CH_2-CH_2-CH_3 ,$$

$$CH_3-CH_2-\underset{\underset{CH_3}{|}}{CH}-CH_2-CH_2-CH_2-CH_3 ,$$

$$CH_3-CH_2-CH_2-\underset{\underset{CH_3}{|}}{CH}-CH_2-CH_2-CH_3 ,$$

$$CH_3-\overset{\overset{CH_3}{|}}{\underset{\underset{CH_3}{|}}{C}}-CH_2-CH_2-CH_2-CH_3 ,$$

$$CH_3-\underset{\underset{CH_3}{|}}{CH}-\underset{\underset{CH_3}{|}}{CH}-CH_2-CH_2-CH_3 ,$$

$$CH_3-\underset{\underset{CH_3}{|}}{CH}-CH_2-\underset{\underset{CH_3}{|}}{CH}-CH_2-CH_3 ,$$

$$CH_3-CH_2-\overset{\overset{CH_3}{|}}{\underset{\underset{CH_3}{|}}{C}}-CH_2-CH_2-CH_3 ,$$

$$CH_3-CH_2-\underset{\underset{CH_3}{|}}{CH}-\underset{\underset{CH_3}{|}}{CH}-CH_2-CH_3 ,$$

$$CH_3-\underset{\underset{CH_3}{|}}{CH}-CH_2-CH_2-\underset{\underset{CH_3}{|}}{CH}-CH_3 ,$$

$$CH_3-\underset{\underset{CH_3}{|}}{CH}-\underset{\underset{CH_3}{|}}{CH}-\underset{\underset{CH_3}{|}}{CH}-CH_3 ,$$

$$CH_3-CH_2-\underset{\underset{CH_2-CH_3}{|}}{CH}-CH_2-CH_2-CH_3 ,$$

$$CH_3-\overset{\overset{CH_3\;CH_3}{|\;\;|}}{\underset{\underset{CH_3\;CH_3}{|\;\;|}}{C-C}}-CH_3 ,$$

$$CH_3-\underset{\underset{CH_3}{|}}{CH}-\overset{\overset{CH_3}{|}}{\underset{\underset{CH_3}{|}}{C}}-CH_2-CH_3 ,$$

$$CH_3-CH_2-\overset{\overset{CH_3}{|}}{\underset{\underset{CH_2-CH_3}{|}}{C}}-CH_2-CH_3 ,$$

$$CH_3-CH_2-\underset{\underset{CH_2-CH_3}{|}}{CH}-\overset{\overset{CH_3}{|}}{\underset{}{CH}}-CH_3 ,$$

$$CH_3-\overset{\overset{CH_3}{|}}{\underset{\underset{CH_3}{|}}{C}}-CH_2-\underset{\underset{CH_3}{|}}{CH}-CH_3 , \qquad \text{and}$$

$$CH_3-\overset{\overset{CH_3}{|}}{\underset{\underset{CH_3\;CH_3}{|\;\;|}}{C}}-CH-CH_2-CH_3 .$$

39. a) No, this molecule will not because all four of the substituents are Cl atoms.

  b) Yes, this molecule will because the third carbon has four different substituents groups.

  c) Yes, this molecule will because the second carbon has four different substituents groups.

  d) No, each carbon has at most three different substituents groups.

40. a) Yes, this molecule will because the third carbon from the left has four different substituents groups.

  b) No, each carbon has at most two different substituents groups.

  c) Yes, this molecule will because two carbons (the one with the amino and the bromine groups) have four different substituents groups.

d)   Yes, this molecule will because the middle carbon has four different substituents groups.

41. a)   They are enantiomers, because they are mirror images of each other.

    b)   They are the same, because you can get the second molecule by rotating the first molecule counterclockwise about the C-H bond.

    c)   They are enantiomers, because they are mirror images of each other.

42. a)   They are the same, because two of the substituents groups on the central carbon are the same.

    b)   They are enantiomers, because they are mirror images of each other.

    c)   They are the same, because you can get the second molecule by rotating the first molecule counterclockwise about the C-H bond of the optically active carbon (the one with the CCl_3 group attached).

43. **Given:** alkane structures   **Find:** name
    Conceptual plan: **Count the number of carbon atoms in the longest continuous carbon chain to determine the base name of the compound. Find the prefix corresponding to this number of atoms in Table 20. 5 and add the ending –ane to form the base name. → Consider every branch from the base chain to be a substituent. Name each substituent according to Table 20.6. →Beginning with the end closest to the branching, number the base chain and assign a number to each substituent. (If two substituents occur at equal distances from each end, go to the next substituent to determine from which end to start numbering.) →Write the name of the compound in the following format: (subst. #)-(subst. name)(base name). → If there are two or more substituents, give each one a number and list them alphabetically with hyphens between words and numbers. →If a compound has two or more identical substituents, designate the number of identical substituents with the prefix di- (2), tri- (3), or tetra- (4) before the substituent's name. Separate the numbers indicating the positions of the substituents relative to each other with a comma. The prefixes are not taken into account when alphabetizing.**
    Solution:
    a) $CH_3-CH_2-CH_2-CH_2-CH_3$ has 5 carbons as the longest continuous chain. The prefix for 5 is penta-. There are no substituent groups on any of the carbons, so the name is pentane.

    b) $\boxed{CH_3-CH_2-CH-CH_3}$ has 4 carbons as the longest continuous chain. The prefix for 4 is but- and the
          |
         CH_3

    base name is butane. The only substituent group is a methyl group. $\boxed{C^4H_3-C^3H_2-C^2H-C^1H_3}$ If we start
                                                                                                           |
                                                                                                        $\boxed{CH_3}$

    numbering the chain at the end closest to the methyl group, the methyl substituent is assigned the number 2. The name of the compound is 2-methylbutane.

    c) CH_3
                                 |
              CH_3 $CH-CH_3$ has 7 carbons as the longest continuous chain. The prefix for 7
               | |
         $\boxed{CH_3-CH-CH_2-CH-CH_2-CH_2-CH_3}$
    is hept- and the base name is heptane. The substituent groups are methyl and isopropyl groups.

                                        $\boxed{CH_3}$
                                          |
                    $\boxed{CH_3}$ $\boxed{CH-CH_3}$
                       | |
         $\boxed{C^1H_3-C^2H-C^3H_2-C^4H-C^5H_2-C^6H_2-C^7H_3}$ If we start numbering the chain at the end closest to
    the methyl group, the methyl substituent is assigned the number 2 and the isopropyl group is assigned the number 4. Since i comes before m, the name of the compound is 4-isopropyl-2-methylheptane.

d) has 6 carbons as the longest continuous chain. The prefix for 6 is hex- and the base name is hexane. The only substituent groups are methyl and ethyl groups.

$$C^1H_3 - C^2H - C^3H_2 - C^4H - C^5H_2 - C^6H_3$$
$$\quad\quad\quad |\quad\quad\quad\quad\quad |$$
$$\quad\quad CH_3 \quad\quad CH_2 - CH_3$$

If we start numbering the chain at the end closest to the methyl group, the methyl substituent is assigned the number 2 and the ethyl group is assigned the number 4. Since e comes before m, the name of the compound is 4-ethyl-2-methylhexane.

44. **Given:** alkane structures   **Find:** name

Conceptual plan: **Count the number of carbon atoms in the longest continuous carbon chain to determine the base name of the compound. Find the prefix corresponding to this number of atoms in Table 20. 5 and add the ending –ane to form the base name. → Consider every branch from the base chain to be a substituent. Name each substituent according to Table 20.6. →Beginning with the end closest to the branching, number the base chain and assign a number to each substituent. (If two substituents occur at equal distances from each end, go to the next substituent to determine from which end to start numbering.) →Write the name of the compound in the following format: (subst. #)-(subst. name)(base name). → If there are two or more substituents, give each one a number and list them alphabetically with hyphens between words and numbers. →If a compound has two or more identical substituents, designate the number of identical substituents with the prefix di- (2), tri- (3), or tetra- (4) before the substituent's name. Separate the numbers indicating the positions of the substituents relative to each other with a comma. The prefixes are not taken into account when alphabetizing.**

Solution:

a)
$$\boxed{CH_3 - CH - CH_3}$$
$$\quad\quad\;\; |$$
$$\quad\quad CH_3$$
has 3 carbons as the longest continuous chain. The prefix for 3 is prop- and the base

name is propane. The only substituent group is a methyl group.
$$\boxed{C^1H_3 - C^2H - C^3H_3}$$
$$\quad\quad\quad |$$
$$\quad\quad\; \boxed{CH_3}$$
Since the branching

is in the middle, it does not matter which end we start numbering. The methyl substituent is assigned the number 2. The name of the compound is 2-methylpropane.

b)
$$\quad\quad CH_3 \quad\quad\quad CH_3$$
$$\quad\quad\; | \quad\quad\quad\quad | $$
$$\boxed{CH_3 - CH - CH_2 - CH - CH_2}$$
$$\quad\quad\quad\quad\quad\quad\quad\quad\quad |$$
$$\quad\quad\quad\quad\quad\quad\quad\quad \boxed{CH_3}$$
has 6 carbons as the longest continuous chain. The prefix for 6 is hex- and the base name is hexane. The substituent groups are two methyl groups.
$$\quad\; \boxed{CH_3} \quad\quad \boxed{CH_3}$$
$$\quad\quad\; | \quad\quad\quad\quad | $$
$$\boxed{C^1H_3 - C^2H - C^3H_2 - C^4H - C^5H_2}$$
$$\quad\quad\quad\quad\quad\quad\quad\quad\quad |$$
$$\quad\quad\quad\quad\quad\quad\quad\quad \boxed{C^6H_3}$$
If we start numbering the chain at the end closest to the left methyl group, the methyl substituents are assigned the numbers 2 and 4. The name of the compound is 2, 4-dimethylhexane.

c)
$$\quad\quad CH_3\; CH_3$$
$$\quad\quad\; |\quad\;\; |$$
$$\boxed{CH_3 - C - C - CH_3}$$
$$\quad\quad\; |\quad\;\; |$$
$$\quad\quad CH_3\; CH_3$$
has 4 carbons as the longest continuous chain. The prefix for 4 is but- and the base

name is butane. The substituent groups are 4 methyl groups.
$$\quad\quad\quad\quad \boxed{CH_3}\boxed{CH_3}$$
$$\quad\quad\quad\quad\quad | \quad\; |$$
$$\boxed{C^1H_3 - C^2 - C^3 - C^4H_3}$$
$$\quad\quad\quad\quad\quad | \quad\; |$$
$$\quad\quad\quad\quad \boxed{CH_3}\boxed{CH_3}$$
Since the branching

is in the middle and symmetric in the molecule, it does not matter which end we start numbering. The methyl substituents are assigned the numbers 2, 2, 3 and 3. The name of the compound is 2,2,3,3-tetramethylbutane.

d)

has 8 carbons as the longest continuous chain. The prefix

for 8 is oct- and the base name is octane. The only substituent groups are two methyl and one ethyl

$$\underset{\quad\quad\quad\quad\quad\boxed{CH_3}}{\boxed{CH_3}\quad\quad\quad\quad\boxed{CH_2}}$$
$$\boxed{C^1H_3-C^2H-C^3H_2-C^4H-C^5H-C^6H_2-C^7H_2-C^8H_3}$$
$$\boxed{CH_3}$$

groups. If we start numbering the chain at the end closest to the left methyl group, the methyl substituents are assigned the numbers 2 and 4 and the ethyl group is assigned the number 5. Since e comes before m, the name of the compound is 5-ethyl-2,4-dimethyloctane.

45. **Given:** alkane names   **Find:** structure
Conceptual plan: Find the number of carbon atoms corresponding to prefix of the base name in Table 20. 5. → Draw the base chain and number the carbons from left to right. → Using Table 20.6 and the prefix di- (2), tri- (3), or tetra- (4) before the substituent's name, determine each substituent. → Add the substituent to the proper carbon position in the chain. → Add hydrogen atoms to the base chain so that each carbon has 4 bonds.
Solution:
a) 3-ethylhexane. The base name hexane designates that there are 6 carbon atoms in the base chain. $C^1-C^2-C^3-C^4-C^5-C^6$. 3-ethyl designates that a -CH$_2$CH$_3$ group in the 3rd position.

$$C^1-C^2-C^3-C^4-C^5-C^6$$
$$\boxed{CH_2-CH_3}$$

.   Add hydrogens to the base chain to get the final molecule

$$CH_3-CH_2-CH-CH_2-CH_2-CH_3$$
$$CH_2-CH_3$$

b) 3-ethyl-3-methylpentane. The base name pentane designates that there are 5 carbon atoms in the base chain. $C^1-C^2-C^3-C^4-C^5$. 3-ethyl designates that a -CH$_2$CH$_3$ group in the 3rd position; and 3 methyl

designates that a -CH$_3$ group in the 3rd position . $C^1-C^2-\overset{\boxed{CH_3}}{C^3}-C^4-C^5$. Add hydrogens to the base chain
$$\boxed{CH_2-CH_3}$$

to get the final molecule $CH_3-CH_2-\overset{CH_3}{\underset{CH_2-CH_3}{CH}}-CH_2-CH_3$.

c) 2,3-dimethylbutane. The base name butane designates that there are 4 carbon atoms in the base chain. $C^1-C^2-C^3-C^4$.   2,3-dimethyl designates that are -CH$_3$ groups in the 2nd and 3rd positions.

$$C^1-C^2-C^3-C^4$$
$$\boxed{CH_3}\boxed{CH_3}$$

. Add hydrogens to the base chain to get the final molecule $\underset{CH_3\ CH_3}{CH_3-CH-CH-CH_3}$.

d) 4,7-diethyl-2,2-dimethylnonane. The base name nonane designates that there are 9 carbon atoms in the base chain. $C^1-C^2-C^3-C^4-C^5-C^6-C^7-C^8-C^9$. 4,7-diethyl designates that are -CH$_2$CH$_3$ groups in the 4th and 7th positions; and 2,2-dimethyl designates that are two -CH$_3$ groups in the 2nd position .

$$CH_3$$

$$C^1-C^2-C^3-C^4-C^5-C^6-C^7-C^8-C^9 \ .$$ Add hydrogens to the base chain to get the final molecule

$$\boxed{CH_3} \quad \boxed{CH_2-CH_3} \ \boxed{CH_2-CH_3}$$

$$
\begin{array}{ccccccc}
& CH_3 & & & & & \\
& | & & & & & \\
CH_3-&C&-CH_2-CH-CH_2-CH_2-CH-CH_2-CH_3 \ . & & & & \\
& | & & | & & | & \\
& CH_3 & & CH_2-CH_3 & & CH_2-CH_3 &
\end{array}
$$

46. **Given:** alkane names   **Find:** structure

Conceptual plan: **Find the number of carbon atoms corresponding to prefix of the base name in Table 20. 5.** → **Draw the base chain and number the carbons from left to right.** → **Using Table 20.6 and the prefix di- (2), tri- (3), or tetra- (4) before the substituent's name, determine each substituent.** → **Add the substituent to the proper carbon position in the chain.** → **Add hydrogen atoms to the base chain so that each carbon has 4 bonds.**

Solution:

a) 2,2-dimethylpentane. The base name pentane designates that there are 5 carbon atoms in the base chain. $C^1-C^2-C^3-C^4-C^5$. 2,2-dimethyl designates that are two $-CH_3$ group in the 2nd position .

$$\boxed{CH_3}$$

$$C^1-C^2-C^3-C^4-C^5 \ .$$ Add hydrogens to the base chain to get the final molecule

$$\boxed{CH_3}$$

$$
\begin{array}{c}
CH_3 \\
| \\
CH_3-C-CH_2-CH_2-CH_3 \ . \\
| \\
CH_3
\end{array}
$$

b) 3-isopropylheptane. The base name pentane designates that there are 7 carbon atoms in the base chain. $C^1-C^2-C^3-C^4-C^5-C^6-C^7$. 3-isopropyl designates that a $-CH(CH_3)_2$ group in the 3rd position.

$$C^1-C^2-C^3-C^4-C^5-C^6-C^7$$ Add hydrogens to the base chain to get the final molecule

$$
\begin{array}{c}
\boxed{\begin{array}{c} CH-CH_3 \\ | \\ CH_3 \end{array}}
\end{array}
$$

$$CH_3-CH_2-CH-CH_2-CH_2-CH_2-CH_3$$

$$
\boxed{\begin{array}{c} CH-CH_3 \\ | \\ CH_3 \end{array}}
$$

c) 4-ethyl-2,2-dimethylhexane. The base name hexane designates that there are 6 carbon atoms in the base chain. $C^1-C^2-C^3-C^4-C^5-C^6$. 4-ethyl designates that is a $-CH_2CH_3$ group in the 4th position; and

2,2-dimethyl designates that are two $-CH_3$ groups in the 2nd position . $C^1-C^2-C^3-C^4-C^5-C^6$. Add

$$\boxed{CH_3} \qquad \qquad \qquad \boxed{CH_3} \quad \boxed{CH_2-CH_3}$$

hydrogens to the base chain to get the final molecule
$$
\begin{array}{ccc}
CH_3 & & \\
| & & \\
CH_3-C-CH_2-CH-CH_2-CH_3 \ . & & \\
| & | & \\
CH_3 & CH_2-CH_3 &
\end{array}
$$

d) 4,4-diethyloctane. The base name octane designates that there are 8 carbon atoms in the base chain. $C^1-C^2-C^3-C^4-C^5-C^6-C^7-C^8$. 4,4-diethyl designates that are two $-CH_2CH_3$ groups in the 4th

position. $\boxed{CH_2 - CH_3}$

$C^1 - C^2 - C^3 - C^4 - C^5 - C^6 - C^7 - C^8$. Add hydrogens to the base chain to get the final molecule

$\boxed{CH_2 - CH_3}$

$$CH_3 - CH_2 - CH_2 - \underset{\underset{CH_2 - CH_3}{|}}{\overset{\overset{CH_2 - CH_3}{|}}{C}} - CH_2 - CH - CH_2 - CH_3 .$$

47. Hydrocarbon combustion in the presence of oxygen forms carbon dioxide and water. Balance the reaction.
   a) $CH_3CH_2CH_3$ (g) + 5 O_2 (g) → 3 CO_2 (g) + 4 H_2O (g).

   b) $CH_3CH_2CH=CH_2$ (g) + 6 O_2 (g) → 4 CO_2 (g) + 4 H_2O (g).

   c) 2 $CH\equiv CH$ (g) + 5 O_2 (g) → 4 CO_2 (g) + 2 H_2O (g).

48. Hydrocarbon combustion in the presence of oxygen forms carbon dioxide and water. Balance the reaction.
   a) 2 $CH_3CH_2CH_2CH_3$ (g) + 13 O_2 (g) → 8 CO_2 (g) + 10 H_2O (g).

   b) 2 $CH_2=CHCH_3$ (g) + 9 O_2 (g) → 6 CO_2 (g) + 6 H_2O (g).

   c) 2 $CH\equiv CCH_2CH_3$ (g) + 11 O_2 (g) → 8 CO_2 (g) + 6 H_2O (g).

49. Halogen substitution reactions remove a hydrogen atom from the alkane and replace it with a halogen atom and generate a hydrohalic acid. Assume one substitution on the hydrocarbon.
   a) $CH_3CH_3 + Br_2$ → CH_3CH_2Br + HBr. Only one carbon-containing product is possible since the C-C bond freely rotates.

   b) $CH_3CH_2CH_3 + Cl_2$ → [$CH_3CH_2CH_2Cl$ and $CH_3CHClCH_3$] + HCl. Two carbon-containing products are possible, either on the end carbon or the middle carbon, since the C-C bond freely rotates and the end carbons are equivalent before reaction.

   c) $CH_2Cl_2 + Br_2$ → $CHBrCl_2$ + HBr. Only one carbon-containing product is possible since halogen substitution reactions only remove hydrogen atoms.

   d) $\underset{\underset{CH_3}{|}}{CH_3 - CH - CH_3} + Cl_2$ → $\left[\underset{\underset{CH_3}{|}}{\overset{\overset{H}{|}}{CH_3 - C - CH_2Cl}} \text{ and } \underset{\underset{CH_3}{|}}{\overset{\overset{Cl}{|}}{CH_3 - C - CH_3}} \right]$ + HCl. Two carbon-containing products are possible, either on the end carbon or the middle carbon, since the C-C bond freely rotates and the end carbons are all equivalent before reaction.

50. Halogen substitution reactions remove a hydrogen atom from the alkane and replace it with a halogen atom and generate a hydrohalic acid. Assume one substitution on the hydrocarbon.
   a) $CH_4 + Cl_2$ → CH_3Cl + HCl. Only one carbon-containing product is possible since all of the hydrogens are equivalent.

   b) $CH_3CH_2Br + Br_2$ → [CH_2BrCH_2Br and CH_3CHBr_2] + HBr. Two carbon-containing products are possible, either on the left carbon or the right carbon, since the C-C bond freely rotates.

   c) $CH_3CH_2CH_2CH_3 + Cl_2$ → [$CH_3CH_2CH_2CH_2Cl$ and $CH_3CHClCH_2CH_3$] + HCl. Two carbon-containing products are possible, either on the end carbons or the middle carbons, since the C-C bond freely rotates and the end carbons are equivalent and the middle carbons are equivalent before reaction.

   d) $CH_3CHBr_2 + Br_2$ → [$CH_2BrCHBr_2$ and CH_3CBr_3] + HBr. Two carbon-containing products are possible, either on the left carbon or the right carbon, since the C-C bond freely rotates.

51. $CH_2=CH-CH_2-CH_2-CH_2-CH_3$, $CH_3-CH=CH-CH_2-CH_2-CH_3$ and $CH_3-CH_2-CH=CH-CH_2-CH_3$ are the only structural isomers. Remember that cis-trans isomerism generates geometric isomers, not structural isomers.

52. $HC\equiv C-CH_2-CH_2-CH_3$ and $CH_3-C\equiv C-CH_2-CH_3$ are the only structural isomers.

53. **Given:** alkene structures   **Find:** name
Conceptual plan: Count the number of carbon atoms in the longest continuous carbon chain that contains the
multiple bond to determine the base name of the compound. Find the prefix corresponding to this number of
atoms in Table 20. 5 and add the ending –ene to form the base name. → Consider every branch from the base chain to be a substituent. Name each substituent according to Table 20.6. →Beginning with the end closest to the multiple bond, number the base chain and assign a number to each substituent. →Write the name of the compound in the following format: (subst. #)-(subst. name)(base name). → If there are two or more substituents, give each one a number and list them alphabetically with hyphens between words and numbers. →If a compound has two or more identical substituents, designate the number of identical substituents with the prefix di- (2), tri- (3), or tetra- (4) before the substituent's name. Separate the numbers indicating the positions of the substituents relative to each other with a comma. The prefixes are not taken into account when alphabetizing.
Solution:

a) $\boxed{CH_2=CH-CH_2-CH_3}$ has 4 carbons as the longest continuous chain. The prefix for 4 is but- and the base name is butene. There are no substituent groups. $\boxed{C^1H_2=C^2H-C^3H_2-C^4H_3}$ Start numbering on the left since it is closer to the double bond. Since the double bond is between position number 1 and 2, the name of the compound is 1-butene.

b)
$$\begin{array}{cc} CH_3 & CH_3 \\ | & | \end{array}$$
$\boxed{CH_3-CH-C=CH-CH_3}$ has 5 carbons as the longest continuous chain. The prefix for 5 is pent- and

the base name is pentene. The substituent groups are two methyl groups.
$\boxed{CH_3}\ \boxed{CH_3}$

$\boxed{C^5H_3-C^4H-C^3=C^2H-C^1H_3}$ If we start numbering the chain at the end closest to the double bond, the

double bond is between position number 2 and 3, and the methyl substituents are assigned the numbers 3 and 4. The name of the compound is 3, 4-dimethyl-2-pentene.

$\boxed{CH_2=HC-CH-CH_2-CH_2-CH_3}$

c) CH_3-CH has 6 carbons as the longest continuous chain. The prefix for 6 is hex-
             |
            CH_3

and the base name is hexene. The only substituent group is an isopropyl group.
$\boxed{C^1H_2=HC^2-C^3H-C^4H_2-C^5H_2-C^6H_3}$

$\boxed{\begin{array}{c} CH_3-CH \\ | \\ CH_3 \end{array}}$ Start numbering on the left since it is closer to the double bond.

Since the double bond is between position number 1 and 2, and the isopropyl group is at position 3, the name of the compound is 3-isopropyl-1-hexene.

d)
$$\begin{array}{c} CH_3 \\ | \end{array}$$
$\boxed{CH_3-CH-CH_2=C-CH_3}$
             $\boxed{CH_2-CH_3}$ has 6 carbons as the longest continuous chain. The prefix for 6 is hex-
and the base name is hexene. The only substituent groups are two methyl groups.

$$\boxed{CH_3}$$
$$\boxed{C^1H_3-C^2H-C^3H_2=C^4}\boxed{-CH_3}$$
$$\boxed{C^5H_2-C^6H_3}$$ Since the double bond is in the middle of the chain, it will be at position 3 in both numbering schemes. If we start numbering the chain at the end closest to the left methyl group (closest to an end), the methyl substituents are assigned the numbers 2 and 4. The name of the compound is 2,4-dimethyl-3-hexene.

54. **Given:** alkene structures   **Find:** name
Conceptual plan: Count the number of carbon atoms in the longest continuous carbon chain that contains the multiple bond to determine the base name of the compound. Find the prefix corresponding to this number of atoms in Table 20. 5 and add the ending –ene to form the base name. → Consider every branch from the base chain to be a substituent. Name each substituent according to Table 20.6. →Beginning with the end closest to the multiple bond, number the base chain and assign a number to each substituent. →Write the name of the compound in the following format: (subst. #)-(subst. name)(base name). → If there are two or more substituents, give each one a number and list them alphabetically with hyphens between words and numbers. →If a compound has two or more identical substituents, designate the number of identical substituents with the prefix di- (2), tri- (3), or tetra- (4) before the substituent's name. Separate the numbers indicating the positions of the substituents relative to each other with a comma. The prefixes are not taken into account when alphabetizing.
Solution:

a) $\boxed{CH_2-CH_2-CH=CH-CH_2-CH_3}$ has 6 carbons as the longest continuous chain. The prefix for 6 is hex- and the base name is hexene. There are no substituent groups. $\boxed{C^1H_2-C^2H_2-C^3H=C^4H-C^5H_2-C^6H_3}$ Since the double bond is in the middle of the molecule it does not matter which end the numbering is started. Since the double bond is between position number 3 and 4, the name of the compound is 3-hexene.

b) $\boxed{CH_3-CH-CH=CH-CH_3}$
$\quad\quad\quad | $
$\quad\quad CH_3$ has 5 carbons as the longest continuous chain. The prefix for 5 is pent- and the base name is pentene. The only substituent group is a methyl group. $\boxed{C^5H_3-C^4H-C^3H=C^2H-C^1H_3}$
$\quad\quad\quad\quad |$
$\quad\quad\quad \boxed{CH_3}$ If we start numbering the chain at the end closest to the double bond, the double bond is between position number 2 and 3, and the methyl substituent is assigned the number 4. The name of the compound is 4-methyl-2-pentene.

c)
$\quad\quad\quad CH_3 \quad\quad CH_2-CH_3$
$\quad\quad\quad | \quad\quad\quad\quad |$
$\boxed{CH_3-CH-CH=C-CH-CH_3}$ has 6 carbons as the longest continuous chain. The prefix for 6 is hex-
$\quad\quad\quad\quad\quad\quad\quad\quad\quad |$
$\quad\quad\quad\quad\quad\quad\quad\quad CH_3$
and the base name is hexene. The substituent groups are two methyl groups and one ethyl group.
$\quad\quad\quad \boxed{CH_3} \quad\quad \boxed{CH_2-CH_3}$
$\quad\quad\quad\quad |\quad\quad\quad\quad\quad\quad |$
$\boxed{C^6H_3-C^5H-C^4H=C^3-C^2H-C^1H_3}$ Since the double bond is in the middle of the chain, it will be at
$\quad\quad\quad\quad\quad\quad\quad\quad\quad\quad |$
$\quad\quad\quad\quad\quad\quad\quad\quad\quad \boxed{CH_3}$
position 3 in both numbering schemes. If we start numbering the chain at the end closest to the right methyl group (since there are two substituents on this end), the methyl substituents are assigned the numbers 2 and 5; and the ethyl substituent is assigned number 3. Since e comes before m, the name of the compound is 3-ethyl-2,5-dimethyl-3-hexene.

$$\boxed{CH_3}$$
$$\boxed{C^1H_3-C^2H-C^3H_2=C^4}\boxed{-CH_3}$$
An alternative name could be 4-isopropyl-2-methyl-3-hexene: $\boxed{C^5H_2-C^6H_3}$.

d)
$$CH_3 - \underset{\underset{CH_3}{|}}{\overset{\overset{CH_3}{|}}{C}} - CH = \underset{\underset{CH_3}{|}}{C} - CH_2 - CH_3$$
has 6 carbons as the longest continuous chain. The prefix for 6 is hex-

and the base name is hexene. The substituent groups are three methyl groups.

$$C^1H_3 - \underset{\underset{[CH_3]}{|}}{\overset{\overset{[CH_3]}{|}}{C^2}} - C^3H = C^4 - C^5H - C^6H_3$$
Since the double bond is in the middle of the chain, it will be at

position 3 in both numbering schemes. If we start numbering the chain at the end closest to the left methyl groups (closest to an end), the methyl substituents are assigned the numbers 2, 2 and 4. The name of the compound is 2,2,4-trimethyl-3-hexene.

55. **Given:** alkyne structures   **Find:** name
Conceptual plan: Count the number of carbon atoms in the longest continuous carbon chain that contains the multiple bond to determine the base name of the compound. Find the prefix corresponding to this number of atoms in Table 20. 5 and add the ending –yne to form the base name. → Consider every branch from the base chain to be a substituent. Name each substituent according to Table 20.6. →Beginning with the end closest to the multiple bond, number the base chain and assign a number to each substituent. →Write the name of the compound in the following format: (subst. #)-(subst. name)(base name). → If there are two or more substituents, give each one a number and list them alphabetically with hyphens between words and numbers. →If a compound has two or more identical substituents, designate the number of identical substituents with the prefix di- (2), tri- (3), or tetra- (4) before the substituent's name. Separate the numbers indicating the positions of the substituents relative to each other with a comma. The prefixes are not taken into account when alphabetizing.
Solution:

a)
$$CH_2 - C \equiv C - CH_3$$
has 4 carbons as the longest continuous chain. The prefix for 4 is but- and the base

name is butyne. There are no substituent groups. $C^1H_2 - C^2 \equiv C^3 - C^4H_3$ Since the triple bond is in the middle of the molecule it does not matter which end the numbering is started. Since the triple bond is between position number 2 and 3, the name of the compound is 2-butyne.

b)
$$CH_3 - C \equiv C - \underset{\underset{CH_3}{|}}{\overset{\overset{CH_3}{|}}{C}} - CH_2 - CH_3$$
has 6 carbons as the longest continuous chain. The prefix for 6 is hex-

and the base name is hexyne. The only substituent groups are two methyl groups.

$$C^1H_3 - C^2 \equiv C^3 - \underset{\underset{[CH_3]}{|}}{\overset{\overset{[CH_3]}{|}}{C^4}} - C^5H_2 - C^6H_3$$
If we start numbering the chain at the end closest to the triple bond,

the triple bond is between position number 2 and 3, and the methyl substituents are assigned the numbers 4 and 4. The name of the compound is 4,4-dimethyl-2-hexyne.

c)
$$CH \equiv C - \underset{\underset{\underset{CH_3}{|}}{\overset{|}{CH}}}{CH} - CH_2 - CH_2 - CH_3$$
has 6 carbons as the longest continuous chain. The prefix for 6 is hex-

and the base name is hexyne. The only substituent group is an isopropyl group.

758

$$C^1H \equiv C^2 - C^3H - C^4H_2 - C^5H_2 - C^6H_3$$
$$\quad\quad\quad | $$
$$\quad\quad\quad CH - CH_3$$
$$\quad\quad\quad | $$
$$\quad\quad\quad CH_3$$

Start numbering at the end closest to the triple bond. The isopropyl substituent is assigned number 3. The name of the compound is 3-isopropyl-1-hexyne.

d) has 9 carbons as the longest continuous chain. The prefix for 9 is non- and the base name is nonyne. The substituent groups are two methyl groups.

$$\boxed{CH_3} - \boxed{C^3H - C^4 \equiv C^5 - C^6H - C^7H_2}$$

Start numbering at the bottom left and count clockwise along the chain. The triple bond is between positions 4 and 5 and the methyl substituents are assigned the numbers 3 and 6. The name of the compound is 3,6-dimethyl-4-nonyne.

56. **Given:** alkyne structures   **Find:** name
Conceptual plan: Count the number of carbon atoms in the longest continuous carbon chain that contains the multiple bond to determine the base name of the compound. Find the prefix corresponding to this number of atoms in Table 20. 5 and add the ending –yne to form the base name. → Consider every branch from the base chain to be a substituent. Name each substituent according to Table 20.6. →Beginning with the end closest to the multiple bond, number the base chain and assign a number to each substituent. →Write the name of the compound in the following format: (subst. #)-(subst. name)(base name). → If there are two or more substituents, give each one a number and list them alphabetically with hyphens between words and numbers. →If
a compound has two or more identical substituents, designate the number of identical substituents with the prefix
di- (2), tri- (3), or tetra- (4) before the substituent's name. Separate the numbers indicating the positions of the substituents relative to each other with a comma. The prefixes are not taken into account when alphabetizing.
Solution:

a) $$\boxed{CH \equiv C - CH - CH_3}$$
$$\quad\quad\quad | $$
$$\quad\quad\quad CH_3$$

has 4 carbons as the longest continuous chain. The prefix for 4 is but- and the base name is butyne. The only substituent group is a methyl group. Start numbering at the end closest to the triple bond. The triple bond is between numbers 1 and 2; and the methyl substituent is assigned number 3. The name of the compound is 3-methyl-1-butyne.

b) $$\boxed{CH_3 - C \equiv C - CH - CH - CH_2 - CH_3}$$
$$\quad\quad\quad\quad\quad | $$
$$\quad\quad\quad\quad\quad CH_3$$
with a CH_3 above

has 7 carbons as the longest continuous chain. The prefix for 7 is hept- and the base name is heptyne. The only substituent groups are two methyl groups.

$$\boxed{C^1H_3 - C^2 \equiv C^3 - C^4H - C^5H - C^6H_2 - C^7H_3}$$ If we start numbering the chain at the end closest to the triple

bond, the triple bond is between position number 2 and 3, and the methyl substituents are assigned the numbers 4 and 5. The name of the compound is 4,5-dimethyl-2-heptyne.

$$\boxed{CH \equiv C - C - CH_2 - CH_3}$$

c) (with CH_3 above and $CH_2 - CH_3$ below the boxed chain) has 5 carbons as the longest continuous chain. The prefix for 5 is pent- and the base name is pentyne. The substituent groups are a methyl group and an ethyl group.

$$\boxed{C^1H \equiv C^2 - C^3 - C^4H_2 - C^5H_3}$$

(with CH_3 above and $CH_2 - CH_3$ below) Start numbering at the end closest to the triple bond. The triple bond is between position numbers 1 and 2, the methyl and ethyl groups are both assigned number 3. Since e is before m, the name of the compound is 3-ethyl-3-methyl-1-pentyne.

$$CH_3 - C \equiv C - CH - C - CH_3$$

d) (with CH_3 substituents, CH_2, CH_3) has 6 carbons as the longest continuous chain. The prefix for 6 is hex- and the base name is hexyne. The only substituent group is an tert-butyl group.

$$C^1H_3 - C^2 \equiv C^3 - C^4H - C - CH_3$$

Start numbering at the end nearest the triple bond and count clockwise along the chain. The triple bond is between positions 2 and 3 and the tert-butyl substituent is assigned the number 4. The name of the compound is 4-tert-butyl-2-hexyne. An alternate name is 4-ethyl-5,5-dimethyl-2-hexyne.

57. **Given:** hydrocarbon names   **Find:** structure
    Conceptual plan: **Find the number of carbon atoms corresponding to prefix of the base name in Table 20. 5.** → **Draw the base chain and number the carbons from left to right.** → **Determine the multiply bond type from the ending of the base name (-ene = double bond, and –yne = triple bond) and place it in the appropriate position in the chain.** → **Using Table 20.6 and the prefix di- (2), tri- (3), or tetra- (4) before the substituent's name, to determine each substituent.** → **Add the substituent to the proper carbon position in the chain.** → **Add hydrogen atoms to the base chain so that each carbon has 4 bonds.**
    Solution:
    a) 4-octyne. The base name octyne designates that there are 8 carbon atoms in the base chain. $C^1 - C^2 - C^3 - C^4 - C^5 - C^6 - C^7 - C^8$. The -yne ending designates that there is a triple bond and the 4 prefix designates that it is between the 4th and 5th positions. $C^1 - C^2 - C^3 - C^4 \equiv C^5 - C^6 - C^7 - C^8$. Add hydrogens to the base chain to get the final molecule $CH_3 - CH_2 - CH_2 - C \equiv C - CH_2 - CH_2 - CH_3$.

    b) 3-nonene. The base name nonene designates that there are 9 carbon atoms in the base chain. $C^1 - C^2 - C^3 - C^4 - C^5 - C^6 - C^7 - C^8 - C^9$. The -ene ending designates that there is a double bond and the 3 prefix designates that it is between the 3rd and 4th positions. $C^1 - C^2 - C^3 = C^4 - C^5 - C^6 - C^7 - C^8 - C^9$. Add hydrogens to the base chain to get the final molecule $CH_3 - CH_2 - CH = CH - CH_2 - CH_2 - CH_2 - CH_2 - CH_3$.

c) 3,3-dimethyl-1-pentyne. The base name pentyne designates that there are 5 carbon atoms in the base chain. $C^1 - C^2 - C^3 - C^4 - C^5$. The -yne ending designates that there is a triple bond and the 1 prefix designates that it is between the 1st and 2nd positions. $C^1 \equiv C^2 - C^3 - C^4 - C^5$ 3,3-dimethyl designates that

are two -CH_3 groups in the 3rd position . $C^1 \equiv C^2 - \overset{\overset{\boxed{CH_3}}{|}}{C^3}_{\underset{\boxed{CH_3}}{|}} - C^4 - C^5$. Add hydrogens to the base chain to get

the final molecule $CH \equiv C - \overset{\overset{CH_3}{|}}{C}_{\underset{CH_3}{|}} - CH_2 - CH_3$.

d) 5-ethyl-3,6-dimethyl-2-heptene. The base name heptene designates that there are 7 carbon atoms in the base chain. $C^1 - C^2 - C^3 - C^4 - C^5 - C^6 - C^7$. The -ene ending designates that there is a double bond and the 2 prefix designates that it is between the 2nd and 3rd positions. $C^1 - C^2 = C^3 - C^4 - C^5 - C^6 - C^7$. 5-ethyl designates that is a -CH_2CH_3 group in the 5th position; and 3,6-dimethyl designates that are -CH_3 groups

in the 3rd and 6th positions. $C^1 - C^2 = \overset{\overset{\boxed{CH_3}}{|}}{C^3} - C^4 - \overset{\overset{\boxed{CH_2 - CH_3}}{|}}{C^5} - \overset{\overset{\boxed{CH_3}}{|}}{C^6} - C^7$. Add hydrogens to the base chain to get the

final molecule $CH_3 - CH = \overset{\overset{CH_3}{|}}{C} - CH_2 - \overset{\overset{CH_2-CH_3}{|}}{CH} - CH - CH_3$.

58. **Given:** hydrocarbon names   **Find:** structure
Conceptual plan: Find the number of carbon atoms corresponding to prefix of the base name in Table 20. 5. → Draw the base chain and number the carbons from left to right. → Determine the multiply bond type from the ending of the base name (-ene = double bond, and –yne = triple bond) and place it in the appropriate position in the chain. → Using Table 20.6 and the prefix di- (2), tri- (3), or tetra- (4) before the substituent's name, to determine each substituent. → Add the substituent to the proper carbon position in the chain. → Add hydrogen atoms to the base chain so that each carbon has 4 bonds.
Solution:
a) 2-hexene. The base name hexene designates that there are 6 carbon atoms in the base chain. $C^1 - C^2 - C^3 - C^4 - C^5 - C^6$. The -ene ending designates that there is a double bond and the 2 prefix designates that it is between the 2nd and 3rd positions. $C^1 - C^2 = C^3 - C^4 - C^5 - C^6$. Add hydrogens to the base chain to get the final molecule $CH_3 - CH = CH - CH_2 - CH_2 - CH_3$.

b) 1-heptyne. The base name heptyne designates that there are 7 carbon atoms in the base chain. $C^1 - C^2 - C^3 - C^4 - C^5 - C^6 - C^7$. The -ene ending designates that there is a double bond and the 3 prefix designates that it is between the 3rd and 4th positions. $C^1 \equiv C^2 - C^3 - C^4 - C^5 - C^6 - C^7$. Add hydrogens to the base chain to get the final molecule $CH \equiv C - CH_2 - CH_2 - CH_2 - CH_2 - CH_3$.

c) 4,4-dimethyl-2-hexene. The base name pentyne designates that there are 6 carbon atoms in the base chain. $C^1 - C^2 - C^3 - C^4 - C^5 - C^6$. The -ene ending designates that there is a double bond and the 2 prefix designates that it is between the 2nd and 3rd positions. $C^1 - C^2 = C^3 - C^4 - C^5 - C^6$ 4,4-dimethyl designates that are two -CH_3 groups in the 4th position . $C^1-C^2=C^3-\overset{\overset{\boxed{CH_3}}{|}}{\underset{\underset{\boxed{CH_3}}{|}}{C^4}}-C^5-C^6$. Add hydrogens to

the base chain to get the final molecule $CH_3-CH=CH-\overset{\overset{CH_3}{|}}{\underset{\underset{CH_3}{|}}{C}}-CH_2-CH_3$.

d) 3-ethyl-4-methyl-2-pentene. The base name pentene designates that there are 5 carbon atoms in the base chain. $C^1-C^2-C^3-C^4-C^5$. The -ene ending designates that there is a double bond and the 2 prefix designates that it is between the 2nd and 3rd positions. $C^1-C^2=C^3-C^4-C^5$. 3-ethyl designates that is a -CH_2CH_3 group in the 3rd position; and 4-methyl designates that is a -CH_3 group in the 4th

position. $C^1-C^2=\overset{\overset{\boxed{CH_3}}{|}}{\underset{\underset{\boxed{CH_2-CH_3}}{|}}{C^3}}-C^4-C^5$. Add hydrogens to the base chain to get the final molecule

$CH_3-CH=\overset{\overset{CH_3}{|}}{\underset{\underset{CH_2-CH_3}{|}}{C}}-CH-CH_3$.

59. Alkene addition reactions convert a double bond to a single bond and places the two halves of the other reactant on the two carbons that were in the double bond. If the other reactant is not a homonuclear diatomic, place the hydrogen atom on the carbon that has the greater number of hydrogens (Markovnikov's rule).

a) $CH_3-CH=CH-CH_3 + Cl_2 \rightarrow$ $\overset{}{CH_3-\underset{\underset{Cl}{|}}{CH}-\underset{\underset{Cl}{|}}{CH}-CH_3}$.

b) $CH_3-\underset{\underset{CH_3}{|}}{CH}-CH=CH-CH_3 + HBr \rightarrow$ $CH_3-\underset{\underset{CH_3}{|}}{CH}-\underset{\underset{H}{|}}{CH}-\underset{\underset{Br}{|}}{CH}-CH_3$ and $CH_3-\underset{\underset{CH_3}{|}}{CH}-\underset{\underset{Br}{|}}{CH}-\underset{\underset{H}{|}}{CH}-CH_3$. Two

carbon-containing products are possible, since both carbons on the double bond had one hydrogen each.

c) $CH_3-CH_2-CH=CH-CH_3 + Br_2 \rightarrow$ $CH_3-CH_2-\underset{\underset{Br}{|}}{CH}-\underset{\underset{Br}{|}}{CH}-CH_3$.

d) $CH_3-\underset{\underset{CH_3}{|}}{CH}-CH=\overset{\overset{CH_3}{|}}{C}-CH_3 + HCl \rightarrow CH_3-\underset{\underset{CH_3}{|}}{CH}-CH_2-\overset{\overset{CH_3}{|}}{\underset{\underset{Cl}{|}}{C}}-CH_3$. Only one product is formed according to Markovnikov's rule .

60. Alkene addition reactions convert a double bond to a single bond and places the two halves of the other reactant on the two carbons that were in the double bond. If the other reactant is not a homonuclear diatomic, place the hydrogen atom on the carbon that has the greater number of hydrogens (Markovnikov's rule).

a) $CH_3-\underset{\underset{CH_3}{|}}{CH}-CH=CH_2 + Br_2 \rightarrow$ $CH_3-\underset{\underset{CH_3}{|}}{CH}-\underset{\underset{Br}{|}}{CH}-\underset{\underset{Br}{|}}{CH_2}$.

b) $CH_2=CH-CH_3 + Cl_2 \rightarrow$ $\underset{\underset{Cl}{|}}{CH_2}-\underset{\underset{Cl}{|}}{CH}-CH_3$.

c)
$$CH_3 - \underset{\underset{CH_3}{|}}{\overset{\overset{CH_3}{|}}{C}} - CH=CH_2 + HCl \rightarrow CH_3 - \underset{\underset{CH_3}{|}}{\overset{\overset{CH_3}{|}}{C}} - \underset{\underset{Cl}{|}}{CH} - CH_3$$
Only one product is formed according to Markovnikov's rule.

d)
$$CH_3 - \underset{\underset{CH_2-CH_3}{|}}{CH} - CH=\overset{\overset{CH_3}{|}}{C} - CH_3 + HBr \rightarrow CH_3 - \underset{\underset{CH_2-CH_3}{|}}{CH} - CH_2 - \underset{\underset{Br}{|}}{\overset{\overset{CH_3}{|}}{C}} - CH_3$$
Only one product is formed according to Markovnikov's rule.

61. Hydrogenation reactions convert a double bond to a single bond and places the hydrogen atoms on each of the two carbons that were in the double bond.
   a) $CH_2=CH-CH_3 + H_2 \rightarrow CH_3 - CH_2 - CH_3$.

   b)
   $$CH_3 - \underset{\underset{CH_3}{|}}{CH} - CH=CH_2 + H_2 \rightarrow CH_3 - \underset{\underset{CH_3}{|}}{CH} - CH_2 - CH_3.$$

   c)
   $$CH_3 - \underset{\underset{CH_3}{|}}{CH} - \underset{\underset{CH_3}{|}}{C}=CH_2 + H_2 \rightarrow CH_3 - \underset{\underset{CH_3}{|}}{CH} - \underset{\underset{CH_3}{|}}{CH} - CH_3.$$

62. Hydrogenation reactions convert a double bond to a single bond and places the hydrogen atoms on each of the two carbons that were in the double bond.
   a) $CH_3 - CH_2 - CH=CH_2 + H_2 \rightarrow CH_3 - CH_2 - CH_2 - CH_3$.

   b)
   $$CH_3 - CH_2 - \underset{\underset{CH_3}{|}}{C}=\underset{\underset{CH_3}{|}}{C} - CH_3 + H_2 \rightarrow CH_3 - CH_2 - \underset{\underset{CH_3}{|}}{CH} - \underset{\underset{CH_3}{|}}{CH} - CH_3.$$

   c)
   $$CH_3 - CH_2 - \underset{\underset{CH_3}{|}}{C}=CH_2 + H_2 \rightarrow CH_3 - CH_2 - \underset{\underset{CH_3}{|}}{CH} - CH_3.$$

63. **Given:** monosubstituted benzene structures   **Find:** name
    Conceptual plan: Consider the branch from the benzene ring to be a substituent. Name the substituent according to Table 20.6 or with the base name of a halogen with a "o" added at the end. →Write the name of the compound in the following format: (name of substituent)benzene.
    Solution:
    a) -CH₃ or methyl is the substituent group, so the name is methylbenzene.

    b) –Br or bromo is the substituent, so the name is bromobenzene.

    c) –Cl or chloro is the substituent, so the name is chlorbenzene.

64. **Given:** monosubstituted benzene structures   **Find:** name
    Conceptual plan: Consider the branch from the benzene ring to be a substituent. Name the substituent according to Table 20.6 or with the base name of a halogen with a "o" added at the end. →Write the name of the compound in the following format: (name of substituent)benzene.
    Solution:
    a) -CH₂CH₃ or ethyl is the substituent group, so the name is ethylbenzene.

    b) –F or fluoro is the substituent, so the name is fluorobenzene.

    c) –C(CH₃)₃ or *tert*-butyl is the substituent, so the name is *tert*-butylbenzene.

65. **Given:** hydrocarbon structures **Find:** name

Conceptual plan: Count the number of carbon atoms in the longest continuous carbon chain (if a multiple bond is present, make sure that this chain contains the multiple bond) to determine the base name of the compound. Find the prefix corresponding to this number of atoms in Table 20.5 and add the ending –ane for an alkane, -ene for an alkene and –yne for an alkyne to form the base name. → Consider every branch from the base chain to be a substituent. Name each substituent according to Table 20.6. If a benzene ring is a substituent, use the phenyl group name. →Beginning with the end closest to the multiple bond, number the base chain and assign a number to each substituent. →Write the name of the compound in the following format: (subst. #)-(subst. name)(base name). → If there are two or more substituents, give each one a number and list them alphabetically with hyphens between words and numbers. →If a compound has two or more identical substituents, designate the number of identical substituents with the prefix di- (2), tri- (3), or tetra- (4) before the substituent's name. Separate the numbers indicating the positions of the substituents relative to each other with a comma. The prefixes are not taken into account when alphabetizing.

Solution: Note: $\varnothing = \bigcirc$

a)

has 9 carbons as the longest continuous chain. The prefix for 9 is non- and the base name is nonane. The substituent groups are two methyl groups and a phenyl group.

$CH_3\text{—}C^3H\text{—}C^4H_2\text{—}C^5H\text{—}C^6H_2\text{—}C^7H\text{—}C^8H_2\text{—}C^9H_3$ with CH_3 on C^5 and $\varnothing$ on C^7, and $C^2H_2\text{—}C^1H_3$ on C^3.

Start numbering at the end closest to the methyl group. The substituent groups are two methyl groups at positions 3 and 5; and a phenyl group at position 7. Since m comes before p, the name of the compound is 3, 5-dimethyl-7-phenylnonane. If the numbering is in the opposite direction, the name will be 5,7-dimethyl-3-phenylnonane.

b)

$CH_3 - CH - CH = CH - CH_2 - CH_2 - CH_2 - CH_3$ with $\varnothing$ on the second carbon.

has 8 carbons as the longest continuous chain. The prefix for 8 is oct- and since there is a double bond, the base name is octene. The only substituent group is a phenyl group.

$C^1H_3 - C^2H - C^3H = C^4H - C^5H_2 - C^6H_2 - C^7H_2 - C^8H_3$ with $\varnothing$ on C^2.

If we start numbering the chain at the end closest to the double bond, the double bond is between position number 3 and 4, and the phenyl substituent is assigned the numbers 2. The name of the compound is 2-phenyl-3-octene.

c)

$CH_3 - C \equiv C - CH - CH - CH - CH_2 - CH_3$ with $\varnothing$ on one carbon and CH_3, CH_3 below.

has 8 carbons as the longest continuous chain. The prefix for 8 is oct-and since there is a triple bond, the base name is octyne. The substituent groups are two methyl groups and a phenyl group.

$C^1H_3 - C^2 \equiv C^3 - C^4H - C^5H - C^6H - C^7H_2 - C^8H_3$ with $\varnothing$ on C^6 and CH_3, CH_3 on C^4, C^5.

Start numbering at the end closest to the triple bond. The triple bond is between position numbers 2 and 3, the methyl groups are assigned numbers 4 and 5, and the phenyl group is assigned number 6. Since m is before p, the name of the compound is 4,5-dimethyl-6-phenyl-2-octyne.

66. **Given:** hydrocarbon structures **Find:** name

Conceptual plan: Count the number of carbon atoms in the longest continuous carbon chain (if a multiple bond is present, make sure that this chain contains the multiple bond) to determine the base name of the compound. Find the prefix corresponding to this number of atoms in Table 20.5 and add the ending –ane for an alkane, -ene for an alkene and –yne for an alkyne to form the base name. →

Consider every branch from the base chain to be a substituent. Name each substituent according to Table 20.6. If a benzene ring is a substituent, use the phenyl group name. →Beginning with the end closest to the multiple bond, number the base chain and assign a number to each substituent. →Write the name of the compound in the following format: (subst. #)-(subst. name)(base name). → If there are two or more substituents, give each one a number and list them alphabetically with hyphens between words and numbers. →If a compound has two or more identical substituents, designate the number of identical substituents with the prefix di- (2), tri- (3), or tetra- (4) before the substituent's name. Separate the numbers indicating the positions of the substituents relative to each other with a comma. The prefixes are not taken into account when alphabetizing.

Solution: Note: $\varnothing = \bigcirc$

a) $\varnothing$ above, $\boxed{CH_3 - CH_2 - CH - CH - CH_2 - CH_3}$ with H_3C below, has 6 carbons as the longest continuous chain. The prefix for 6 is

hex- and the base name is hexane. The substituent groups are a methyl group and a phenyl group. $\boxed{\varnothing}$ above, $\boxed{C^6H_3 - C^5H_2 - C^4H - C^3H - C^2H_2 - C^1H_3}$ with $\boxed{H_3C}$ below. Start numbering at the end closest to the methyl group. The

substituent groups are a methyl group at positions 3 and a phenyl group at position 4. Since m comes before p, the name of the compound is 3-methyl-4-phenylhexane. If the numbering is in the opposite direction, the name will be 4-methyl-3-phenylhexane.

b) $\varnothing$ above $\boxed{CH_2 - CH_2 - CH_2 - CH_2 - C \equiv C - CH_3}$ has 7 carbons as the longest continuous chain. The prefix for 7

is hept- and since there is a triple bond, the base name is heptyne. The only substituent group is a

phenyl group. $\varnothing$ above $\boxed{C^7H_2 - C^6H_2 - C^5H_2 - C^4H_2 - C^3 \equiv C^2 - C^1H_3}$ If we start numbering the chain at the end

closest to the triple bond, the triple bond is between position number 2 and 3, and the phenyl substituent is assigned the numbers 7. The name of the compound is 7-phenyl-2-heptyne.

c) CH_3 and $\varnothing$ above, $\boxed{CH_3 - CH - CH - C = CH - CH - CH_2 - CH_3}$ with CH_3 CH_3 below, has 8 carbons as the longest continuous chain. The prefix

for 8 is oct- and since there is a double bond, the base name is octene. The substituent groups are three

methyl groups and a phenyl group. CH_3 and $\varnothing$ above, $\boxed{C^1H_3 - C^2H - C^3H - C^4 = C^5H - C^6H - C^7H_2 - C^8H_3}$ with CH_3 CH_3 below. Since the double

bond is in the middle of the molecule, start numbering at the end closest to the methyl group. The double bond is between position numbers 4 and 5, the methyl groups are assigned numbers 2, 3 and 4, and the phenyl group is assigned number 6. Since m is before p, the name of the compound is 2,3,4-trimethyl-6-phenyl-2-octene.

67. **Given:** disubstituted benzene structures   **Find:** name
Conceptual plan: Consider the branches from the benzene ring to be substituents. Name the substituent according to Table 20.6 or with the base name of a halogen with a "o" added at the end. → Number the benzene ring starting with the substituent that is first alphabetically and count in the direction that gets to the second substituent with the lower position number. → Write the name of the compound in the following format: (name of substituent)benzene, listing them alphabetically with hyphens between words and numbers. →If a compound has two identical substituents, designate the number of identical substituents with the prefix di- (2) before the substituent's name. Separate the

numbers indicating the positions of the substituents relative to each other with a comma. → Alternate names are 1,2 = *ortho* or *o*; 1,3 = *meta* or *m*; and 1,4 = *para* or *p* replacing the numbers.
Solution:

a) Both of the substituent groups are -Br or bromo groups. Start by giving one bromo an assignment of 1 and count in either direction to give the second bromo group an assignment of 4. The name is 1,4-dibromobenzene or *p*- dibromobenzene.

b) Both of the substituent groups are -CH$_2$CH$_3$ or ethyl is the substituent groups. Start by giving the top ethyl an assignment of 1 and count in the clockwise direction to give the second ethyl group an assignment of 3. The name is 1,3-diethylbenzene or *m*-diethylbenzene.

c) One substituent group is –Cl or chloro and the other is –F or fluoro. Start by giving the chloro group an assignment of 1 and count in the counterclockwise direction to give the fluoro group an assignment of 2. The name is 1-chloro-2-fluorobenzene or *o*-chlorofluorobenzene.

68. **Given:** disubstituted benzene structures   **Find:** name
Conceptual plan: Consider the branches from the benzene ring to be substituents. Name the substituent according to Table 20.6 or with the base name of a halogen with a "o" added at the end. → Number the benzene ring starting with the substituent that is first alphabetically and count in the direction that gets to the second substituent with the lower position number. → Write the name of the compound in the following format: (name of substituent)benzene, listing them alphabetically with hyphens between words and numbers. →If a compound has two identical substituents, designate the number of identical substituents with the prefix di- (2) before the substituent's name. Separate the numbers indicating the positions of the substituents relative to each other with a comma. → Alternate names are 1,2 = *ortho* or *o*; 1,3 = *meta* or *m*; and 1,4 = *para* or *p* replacing the numbers.
Solution:

a) One substituent group is –Br or bromo and the other is –Cl or chloro. Start by giving the bromo group an assignment of 1 and count in the clockwise direction to give the chloro group an assignment of 2. The name is 1-bromo-2-chlorobenzene or *o*-bromochlorobenzene.

b) One substituent group is –Cl or chloro and the other is -CH$_2$CH$_3$ or ethyl. Start by giving the chloro group an assignment of 1 and count in either direction to give the ethyl group an assignment of 4. The name is 1-chloro-4-ethylbenzene or *p*-chloroethylbenzene.

c) Both of the substituent groups are -I or iodo groups. Start by giving the top iodo an assignment of 1 and count in the clockwise direction to give the second iodo group an assignment of 3. The name is 1,3-diiodobenzene or *m*- diiodobenzene.

69. **Given:** substituted benzene names   **Find:** structures
Conceptual plan: Start with a benzene ring. Identify the structure of the substituent(s) according to Table 20.6 or with the base name of a halogen with a "o" added at the end. → If only one substituent is present, simply attach it to the benzene ring. →If a compound has two identical substituents, they are designated with the prefix di- (2) before the substituent's name. → If there are two substituents, place the first one on the benzene ring and count clockwise around the ring to determine the location to attach the second substituent. Note, 1,2 = *ortho* or *o*; 1,3 = *meta* or *m*; and 1,4 = *para* or *p* replacing the numbers.
Solution:

a) isopropylbenzene. The isopropyl group is
$$-CH-CH_3 \atop \quad | \atop \quad CH_3$$
. Attach this to a benzene ring to make :

b) *meta*-dibromobenzene. There are two bromo or –Br groups. The positions are 1 and 3, since the designation is *meta*. Attach the –Br's at the 1st and 3rd positions to make

c) 1-chloro-4-methylbenzene. One substituent group is –Cl or chloro and the other is –CH$_3$ or methyl. Start by giving the chloro group an assignment of 1 and count in the clockwise direction to give the methyl group an assignment of 4. Attach the two groups to make .

70. **Given:** substituted benzene names **Find:** structures
Conceptual plan: Start with a benzene ring. Identify the structure of the substituent(s) according to Table 20.6 or with the base name of a halogen with a "o" added at the end. → If only one substituent is present, simply attach it to the benzene ring. →If a compound has two identical substituents, they are designated with the prefix di- (2) before the substituent's name. → If there are two substituents, place the first one on the benzene ring and count clockwise around the ring to determine the location to attach the second substituent. Note, 1,2 = *ortho* or *o*; 1,3 = *meta* or *m*; and 1,4 = *para* or *p* replacing the numbers.
Solution:
a) ethylbenzene. The ethyl group is-CH$_2$CH$_3$. Attach this to a benzene ring to make .

b) 1-iodo-2-methylbenzene. The iodo group is –I and the methyl group is -CH$_3$. The –I to the benzene ring and then attach the -CH$_3$ to the adjacent carbon to make $\bigcirc$–CH$_3$.

c) *para*-diethylbenzene. There are two ethyl or -CH$_2$CH$_3$ groups. The positions are 1 and 4, since the designation is *para*-. Attach the -CH$_2$CH$_3$'s at the 1st and 4th positions to make CH$_2$CH$_3$.

CH$_2$CH$_3$

71. Aromatic substitution reaction substitute a halogen or alkyl group for a hydrogen (with a preference for the alkyl group) to generate a monosubstituted benzene and a hydrohalic acid.
a)
$+ Br_2 \xrightarrow{FeBr_3}$ **Br** $+$ HBr

b) $\bigcirc$ $+$ CH$_3$–CH–Cl (CH$_3$) $\xrightarrow{AlCl_3}$ $+$ HCl

72. Aromatic substitution reaction substitute a halogen or alkyl group for a hydrogen (with a preference for the alkyl group) to generate a monosubstituted benzene and a hydrohalic acid.

a)
$+ Cl_2 \xrightarrow{FeCl_3}$ **Cl** $+$ HCl

b) $\bigcirc$ $+$ CH$_3$–C–Cl (CH$_3$)(CH$_3$) $\xrightarrow{AlCl_3}$ $+$ HCl

73. **Given:** alcohol structures   **Find:** name

     Conceptual plan: Alcohols are named like alkanes with the following differences: (1) The base chain is the longest continuous carbon chain that contains the -OH functional group; (2) The base name has the ending –ol; (3) The base chain is numbered to give the -OH group the lowest possible number; and (3) A number indicating the position of the -OH group is inserted just before the base name.

     Solution:

a) $\boxed{CH_3-CH_2-CH_2}$ –OH The longest carbon chain has 3 carbons. The prefix for 3 is prop-, so the base name is propanol. The alcohol group is on the end, or 1st carbon, so the name is 1-propanol.

b)

The longest carbon chain has 6 carbons. The prefix for 6 is hex-, so the

base name is hexanol. There is a methyl substituent group. Start numbering at the end closest to the alcohol group. The alcohol group is assigned number 2 and the methyl group is assigned number 4. The name is 4-methyl-2-hexanol.

c)   The longest carbon chain has 7 carbons. The prefix for 7 is hept-, so the base name is heptanol. There are two methyl substituent groups.

It does not matter which end the numbering is started, since substitutions are symmetrically attached. The alcohol group is assigned number 4 and the methyl groups are assigned numbers 2 and 6. The name is 2,6-dimethyl-4-heptanol.

d)   The longest carbon chain has 5 carbons. The prefix for 5 is pent-, so the base name is pentanol. There is a methyl substituent group.

It does not matter which end the numbering is started, since substitutions are symmetrically attached. The alcohol group is assigned number 3 and the methyl group is assigned number 3. The name is 3-methyl-3-pentanol.

74. **Given:** alcohol names   **Find:** structure

     Conceptual plan: Find the number of carbon atoms corresponding to prefix of the base name in Table 20. 5. → Draw the base chain and number the carbons from left to right. → Add an –OH group to the specified position. → Using Table 20.6 and the prefix di- (2), tri- (3), or tetra- (4) before the substituent's name, determine each substituent. → Add the substituent to the proper carbon position in the chain. → Add hydrogen atoms to the base chain so that each carbon has 4 bonds.

     Solution:

a)   2-butanol. The base name butanol designates that there are 4 carbon atoms in the base chain. $C^1 - C^2 - C^3 - C^4$. The 2- prefix designates that the -OH group in the 2nd position . $C^1 - C^2 - C^3 - C^4$ with OH below C^2 . Add

hydrogens to the base chain to get the final molecule $CH_3 - CH - CH_2 - CH_3$ with OH below the CH .

b)   2-methyl-1-propanol. The base name propanol designates that there are 3 carbon atoms in the base chain. $C^1 - C^2 - C^3$. 2-methyl designates that a –CH_3 group is in the 2nd position, and the 1- prefix of the base name designates that the -OH group in the 1st position. $HO - C^1 - C^2 - C^3$ with $\boxed{CH_3}$ below C^2 . Add hydrogens to the

base chain to get the final molecule. $HO - CH_2 - CH - CH_3$ with $\boxed{CH_3}$ below the CH .

c)   3-ethyl-1-hexanol. The base name hexanol designates that there are 6 carbon atoms in the base chain. $C^1 - C^2 - C^3 - C^4 - C^5 - C^6$. 3-ethyl designates that a – CH_2CH_3 group is in the 3rd position, and the 1- prefix of the base name designates that the -OH group in the 1st position. $HO - C^1 - C^2 - C^3 - C^4 - C^5 - C^6$ with $\boxed{CH_2CH_3}$ below C^3 .

Add hydrogens to the base chain to get the final molecule. $HO - CH_2 - CH_2 - CH - CH_2 - CH_2 - CH_3$ with CH_2CH_3 below the CH .

d)   2-methyl-3-pentanol. The base name pentanol designates that there are 5 carbon atoms in the base chain. $C^1 - C^2 - C^3 - C^4 - C^5$. 2-methyl designates that a – CH_3 group is in the 2nd position, and the 3- prefix of the base name designates that the -OH group in the 3rd position. $C^1 - C^2 - C^3 - C^4 - C^5$ with $\boxed{CH_3}$ below C^2 and $\boxed{OH}$ below C^3 . Add

hydrogens to the base chain to get the final molecule. $CH_3 - CH - CH - CH_2 - CH_3$ with CH_3 below the first CH and OH below the second CH .

75. In a substitution reaction an alcohol reacts with an acid, such as HBr, to form halogenated hydrocarbons and water. In an elimination (or dehydration) reaction, concentrated acids, such as H_2SO_4, react with alcohols to eliminate water, forming an alkene. In an oxidation reaction carbon atoms gain oxygen atoms and/or lose hydrogen atoms. In these reactions, the alcohol becomes a carboxylic acid. Alcohols react with active metals, such as alkali metals, forming an organic base and hydrogen gas.
a)   This is a substitution reaction, so $CH_3 - CH_2 - CH_2 - OH + HBr \rightarrow CH_3 - CH_2 - CH_2 - Br + H_2O$.

b)   This is an elimination reaction, so $CH_3 - CH - CH_2 - OH$ (with CH_3 below the CH) $\xrightarrow{H_2SO_4}$ $CH_3 - C = CH_2$ (with CH_3 below the C) $+ H_2O$.

c)   Sodium is an active metal, so $CH_3 - CH_2 - OH + Na \rightarrow CH_3 - CH_2 - ONa + 1/2 \, H_2$.

d)   This is an oxidation reaction, so $CH_3 - \underset{\underset{CH_3}{|}}{\overset{\overset{CH_3}{|}}{C}} - CH_2 - CH_2 - OH \xrightarrow[H_2SO_4]{Na_2Cr_2O_7} CH_3 - \underset{\underset{CH_3}{|}}{\overset{\overset{CH_3}{|}}{C}} - CH_2 - \overset{\overset{O}{\|}}{C} - OH$.

76. In a substitution reaction an alcohol reacts with an acid, such as HBr, to form halogenated hydrocarbons and water. In an elimination (or dehydration) reaction, concentrated acids, such as H_2SO_4, react with alcohols to eliminate water, forming an alkene. In an oxidation reaction carbon atoms gain oxygen atoms and/or lose hydrogen atoms. In these reactions, the alcohol becomes a carboxylic acid. Alcohols react with with active metals, such as alkali metals, forming an organic base and hydrogen gas.

a) This is an elimination reaction, so
$$CH_3-\underset{\underset{CH_3}{|}}{\overset{\overset{CH_3}{|}}{C}}H-OH \xrightarrow{H_2SO_4} CH_3-\underset{\underset{CH_3}{|}}{C}=CH_2 + H_2O.$$

b) This is an oxidation reaction, so
$$CH_3-\underset{\underset{CH_3}{|}}{C}H-CH_2-CH_2-OH \xrightarrow[H_2SO_4]{Na_2Cr_2O_7} CH_3-\underset{\underset{CH_3}{|}}{C}H-CH_2-\overset{\overset{O}{||}}{C}-OH .$$

c) This is a substitution reaction, so $CH_3-CH_2-OH + HCl \rightarrow CH_3-CH_2-Cl + H_2O$.

d) Sodium is an active metal, so
$$CH_3-\underset{\underset{CH_3}{|}}{C}H-CH_2-OH + Na \rightarrow CH_3-\underset{\underset{CH_3}{|}}{C}H-CH_2-ONa + 1/2\,H_2 .$$

77. **Given:** aldehyde or ketone structures **Find:** name
Conceptual Plan: Simple aldehydes are systematically named according to the number of carbon atoms in the longest continuous carbon chain that contains the carbonyl group. Form the base name from the name of the corresponding alkane by dropping the -e and add the ending -al. Simple ketones are systematically named according to the longest continuous carbon chain containing the carbonyl group. Form the base name from the name of the corresponding alkane by dropping the letter -e and adding the ending -one. For ketones, number the chain to give the carbonyl group the lowest possible number.
Solution:

a) $\boxed{CH_3-\overset{\overset{O}{||}}{C}-CH_2-CH_3}$ The longest carbon chain has 4 carbons. The prefix for 4 is but-, since this is a

ketone the base name is butanone. The position of the carbonyl carbon does not need to be specified, since there is only one place for it to be in the molecule (if it were on the end carbon it would be an aldehyde, not a ketone). Since there are no other substituent groups, the name is butanone.

b) $\boxed{CH_3-CH_2-CH_2-CH_2-\overset{\overset{O}{||}}{C}H}$ The longest carbon chain has 5 carbons. The prefix for 5 is pent-, since

this is an aldehyde the base name is pentanal. Since there are no other substituent groups, the name is pentanal.

c) $\boxed{CH_3-\underset{\underset{CH_3}{|}}{\overset{\overset{CH_3}{|}}{C}}-CH_2-\overset{\overset{CH_3}{|}}{C}H-CH_2-\overset{\overset{O}{||}}{C}}$-H The longest carbon chain has 6 carbons. The prefix for 6 is hex-, since

this is an aldehyde the base name is hexanal. There are 3 methyl substituent groups.

$\boxed{C^6H_3-\underset{\underset{\boxed{CH_3}}{|}}{\overset{\overset{\boxed{CH_3}}{|}}{C^5}}-C^4H_2-\overset{\overset{\boxed{CH_3}}{|}}{C^3}H-C^2H_2-C^1}$-H Start numbering at the carbonyl carbon. The methyl groups are

at positions 3, 5, and 5. The name of the molecule is 3,5,5-trimethylhexanal.

d) $CH_3-\boxed{\underset{\underset{CH_2-CH_3}{|}}{C}H-CH_2-\overset{\overset{O}{||}}{C}-CH_3}$ The longest carbon chain has 6 carbons. The prefix for 6 is hex-, since this

is a ketone the base name is hexanone. There is one methyl substituent group.

$$CH_3 \boxed{CH - CH_2 - \overset{\overset{\displaystyle O}{\|}}{C} - CH_3}$$
$$\boxed{CH_2 - CH_3}$$

Start numbering at the end closest to the carbonyl carbon. The carbonyl carbon is in position 2 and the methyl group is at positions 4. The name of the molecule is 4-methyl-2-hexanal.

78. **Given:** aldehyde and ketone names   **Find:** structure

Conceptual plan: Find the number of carbon atoms corresponding to prefix of the base name in Table 20. 5. → Draw the base chain and number the carbons from left to right. → Add an =O to the specified position (If none is specified, put it at the end.). → Using Table 20.6 and the prefix di- (2), tri- (3), or tetra- (4) before the substituent's name, to determine each substituent. → Add the substituent to the proper carbon position in the chain. → Add hydrogen atoms to the base chain so that each carbon has 4 bonds.

Solution:

a) hexanal. The base name hexanal designates that there are 6 carbon atoms in the base chain. $C^1 - C^2 - C^3 - C^4 - C^5 - C^6$. The –al ending specifies that it is an aldehyde and the carbonyl carbon is on the end. There are no substituent groups, so add hydrogens to the base chain to get the final molecule

$$CH_3 - CH_2 - CH_2 - CH_2 - CH_2 - \overset{\overset{\displaystyle O}{\|}}{CH}.$$

b) 2-pentanone. The base name pentanone designates that there are 5 carbon atoms in the base chain. $C^1 - C^2 - C^3 - C^4 - C^5$. The –one ending specifies that it is a ketone. The 2- prefix of the base name designates that the =O group in the 2nd position. There are no substituent groups, so add hydrogens to the base chain to get the final molecule

$$CH_3 - \overset{\overset{\displaystyle O}{\|}}{C} - CH_2 - CH_2 - CH_3.$$

c) 2-methylbutanal. The base name butanal designates that there are 4 carbon atoms in the base chain. $C^1 - C^2 - C^3 - C^4$. 2-methyl designates that a $- CH_3$ group is in the 2nd position. The –al ending specifies that it is an aldehyde, and so the =O group in the 1st position.

$$\overset{\overset{\displaystyle O \quad CH_3}{\| \quad\quad |}}{C^1 - C^2 - C^3 - C^4}.$$ Add hydrogens to the base chain to get the final molecule.

$$\overset{\overset{\displaystyle O \quad CH_3}{\| \quad\quad |}}{H - C - CH - CH_2 - CH_3}.$$

d) 4-heptanone. The base name heptanone designates that there are 7 carbon atoms in the base chain. $C^1 - C^2 - C^3 - C^4 - C^5 - C^6 - C^7$. The –one ending specifies that it is a ketone. The 4- prefix of the base name designates that the =O group in the 4th position. There are no substituent groups, so add hydrogens to the base chain to get the final molecule

$$CH_3 - CH_2 - CH_2 - \overset{\overset{\displaystyle O}{\|}}{C} - CH_2 - CH_2 - CH_3.$$

79. This is an addition reaction, $CH_3 - CH_2 - CH_2 - \overset{\overset{\displaystyle O}{\|}}{C} - H + H - C \equiv N \xrightarrow{NaCN} CH_3 - CH_2 - CH_2 - \overset{\overset{\displaystyle OH}{|}}{\underset{\underset{\displaystyle H}{|}}{C}} - C \equiv N.$

80. This is an addition reaction, $CH_3 - \overset{\overset{\displaystyle O}{\|}}{C} - CH_2 - CH_3 + H - C \equiv N \xrightarrow{NaCN} CH_3 - \overset{\overset{\displaystyle OH}{|}}{\underset{\underset{\displaystyle CH_2 - CH_3}{|}}{C}} - C \equiv N .$

81. **Given:** carboxylic acid or ester structures   **Find:** name

Conceptual Plan: Carboxylic acids are systematically named according to the number of carbon atoms in the longest chain containing the -COOH functional group. Form the base name by dropping the -e from the name of the corresponding alkane, and adding the ending –oic acid. Esters are

systematically named as if they were derived from a carboxylic acid by replacing the H on the OH with an alkyl group. The R group from the parent acid forms the base name of the compound. Change the –ic on the name of the corresponding carboxylic acid to –ate, and drop "acid". The R group that replaced the H on the carboxylic acid is named as an alkyl group with the ending –yl.
Solution:

a)
$$CH_3-CH_2-CH_2-\overset{\overset{\displaystyle O}{\|}}{C}-O-CH_3$$
The carbon chain that has the carbonyl carbon has 4 carbons. The prefix for 4 is but-, so the base name is butanoate. The R group that replaces the H of the carboxylic acid is a methyl group. The name is methylbutanoate.

b)
$$CH_3-CH_2-\overset{\overset{\displaystyle O}{\|}}{C}-OH$$
The carbon chain has 3 carbons. The prefix for 3 is prop-, since this is a carboxylic acid, and there are no other substituents, the name is propanoic acid.

c)
$$CH_3-\underset{\underset{\displaystyle CH_3}{|}}{CH}-CH_2-CH_2-CH_2-\overset{\overset{\displaystyle O}{\|}}{C}-OH$$
The carbon chain has 6 carbons. The prefix for 6 is hex-, since this is a carboxylic acid, the base name is hexanoic acid. There is one methyl substituent group.

$$C^6H_3-\underset{\underset{\displaystyle CH_3}{|}}{C^5H}-C^4H_2-C^3H_2-C^2H_2-\overset{\overset{\displaystyle O}{\|}}{C^1}-OH$$
Number the chain starting with the carbonyl carbon. The methyl is in the 5th position. The name of the molecule is 5-methylhexanoic acid.

d)
$$CH_3-CH_2-CH_2-CH_2-\overset{\overset{\displaystyle O}{\|}}{C}-O-CH_2-CH_3$$
The carbon chain that has the carbonyl carbon has 5 carbons. The prefix for 5 is pent-, so the base name is pentanoate. The R group that replaces the H of the carboxylic acid is an ethyl group. The name is ethylpentanoate.

82. **Given:** carboxylic acid and ester names   **Find:** structure
Conceptual plan: Find the number of carbon atoms corresponding to prefix of the base name in Table 20. 5. → Draw the base chain and number the carbons from right to. → Add an =O and a –O to the last carbon on the right. → If the molecule is a carboxylic acid, add a hydrogen atom to the non-carbonyl oxygen. If the molecule is an ester, determine the length of the carbon chain using Table 20.5 and add this to the non-carbonyl oxygen. → Using Table 20.6 and the prefix di- (2), tri- (3), or tetra- (4) before the substituent's name, to determine each substituent. → Add the substituent to the proper carbon position in the chain. → Add hydrogen atoms to the base chain so that each carbon has 4 bonds.
Solution:
a) pentanoic acid. The base name pentanoic acid designates that there are 5 carbon atoms in the base chain. $C^5-C^4-C^3-C^2-C^1$. The –oic acid ending specifies that it is a carboxylic acid. There are no substituent groups, so add hydrogens to the base chain to get the final molecule

$$CH_3-CH_2-CH_2-CH_2-\overset{\overset{\displaystyle O}{\|}}{C}-OH$$.

b) methyl hexanoate. The base name hexanoate designates that there are 6 carbon atoms in the base chain. $C^6-C^5-C^4-C^3-C^2-C^1$. Adding the two oxygens to the 1st carbon, $C^6-C^5-C^4-C^3-C^2-\overset{\overset{\displaystyle O}{\|}}{C^1}-O$ The methyl prefix indicates that there is a methyl group on the non-carbonyl oxygen.

$$C^6-C^5-C^4-C^3-C^2-\overset{\overset{\displaystyle O}{\|}}{C^1}-O-\boxed{CH_3}$$ There are no substituent groups, so add hydrogens to the base chain

to get the final molecule $CH_3-CH_2-CH_2-CH_2-CH_2-\overset{\overset{\displaystyle O}{\|}}{C}-O-CH_3$.

c) 3-ethylheptanoic acid. The base name heptanoic acid designates that there are 7 carbon atoms in the base chain. $C^7-C^6-C^5-C^4-C^3-C^2-C^1$. The -oic acid ending designates that this is a carboxylic acid, with a –COOH ending. 3-ethyl designates that a $-CH_2CH_3$ group is in the 3rd position.

$$\underset{\displaystyle C^7-C^6-C^5-C^4-\underset{\displaystyle |}{C^3}-C^2-\overset{\overset{\displaystyle O}{\|}}{C^1}-OH}{\overset{\displaystyle \boxed{CH_3-CH_2}}{}}$$ Add hydrogens to the base chain to get the final molecule.

$$CH_3-CH_2-CH_2-CH_2-\underset{\overset{\displaystyle |}{\underset{\displaystyle CH_3-CH_2}{}}}{CH}-CH_2-\overset{\overset{\displaystyle O}{\|}}{C}-OH.$$

d) butyl ethanoate. The base name ethanoate designates that there are 2 carbon atoms in the base chain. C^2-C^1. Adding the two oxygens to the 1st carbon, $\overset{\overset{\displaystyle O}{\|}}{C^2-C^1}-O$ The butyl prefix indicates that there is a

butyl (4 carbon) group on the non-carbonyl oxygen. $\overset{\overset{\displaystyle O}{\|}}{C^2-C^1}-O-\boxed{CH_2-CH_2-CH_2-CH_3}$ There are no

substituent groups, so add hydrogens to the base chain to get the final molecule

$$CH_3-\overset{\overset{\displaystyle O}{\|}}{C}-O-CH_2-CH_2-CH_2-CH_3.$$

83. The reactions are condensation reactions that link the two molecules (or parts of a molecule) where the non-carbonyl oxygens are in the reactants and generate water.

a) $CH_3-CH_2-CH_2-CH_2-\overset{\overset{\displaystyle O}{\|}}{C}-OH + CH_3-CH_2-OH \xrightarrow{H_2SO_4} CH_3-CH_2-CH_2-CH_2-\overset{\overset{\displaystyle O}{\|}}{C}-O-CH_2-CH_3 + H_2O.$

b)

84. a) This is an acid-base reaction, $CH_3-CH_2-\overset{\overset{\displaystyle O}{\|}}{C}-OH + NaOH \rightarrow CH_3-CH_2-\overset{\overset{\displaystyle O}{\|}}{C}-ONa + H_2O.$

b) The reaction is a condensation reaction that links the two molecules where the non-carbonyl oxygens are in the reactants and generates water.

$$CH_3-CH_2-CH_2-\overset{\overset{\displaystyle O}{\|}}{C}-OH + CH_3-CH_2-CH_2-OH \xrightarrow{H_2SO_4} CH_3-CH_2-CH_2-\overset{\overset{\displaystyle O}{\|}}{C}-O-CH_2-CH_2-CH_3 + H_2O.$$

85. **Given:** ether structures   **Find:** name
   Conceptual Plan: Common names for ethers have the following format: (R group 1)(R group 2) ether, where the alkyl groups are those found in Table 20.5. List the names alphabetically. If the two R groups are different, use each of their names. If the two R groups are the same, use the prefix di-.
   Solution:

a) $\boxed{CH_3-CH_2-CH_2}-O-\boxed{CH_2-CH_3}$ The left carbon chain has 3 carbons and so it is a propyl group. The right carbon chain has 2 carbons and so it is an ethyl group. Listing them alphabetically the name is ethyl propyl ether.

b) $\boxed{CH_3-CH_2-CH_2-CH_2-CH_2}-O-\boxed{CH_2-CH_3}$ The left carbon chain has 5 carbons and so it is a pentyl group. The right carbon chain has 2 carbons and so it is an ethyl group. Listing them alphabetically the name is ethyl pentyl ether.

c) $\boxed{CH_3-CH_2-CH_2}-O-\boxed{CH_2-CH_2-CH_3}$ Both carbon chains have 3 carbons and so they are propyl groups. The name is dipropyl ether.

d) $\boxed{CH_3-CH_2}-O-\boxed{CH_2-CH_2-CH_2-CH_3}$ The left carbon chain has 2 carbons and so it is an ethyl group. The right carbon chain has 4 carbons and so it is an butyl group. Listing them alphabetically the name is butyl ethyl ether.

86. **Given:** ether names   **Find:** structure
Conceptual plan: Find the number of carbon atoms corresponding to prefix of the two alkyl groups using Table 20. 5. → Draw the two alkyl groups connecting them with a –O- linkage.
Solution:
  a) ethyl propyl ether. The ethyl group has 2 carbons and the propyl group has 3 carbons. Linking the alkyl groups with an –O- linkage the structure is $CH_3-CH_2-O-CH_2-CH_2-CH_3$.

  b) dibutyl ether. Each alkyl group is a butyl group with 4 carbons each. Linking the alkyl groups with an –O- linkage the structure is $CH_3-CH_2-CH_2-CH_2-O-CH_2-CH_2-CH_2-CH_3$.

  c) methyl hexyl ether. The methyl group has 1 carbon and the hexyl group has 6 carbons. Linking the alkyl groups with an –O- linkage the structure is $CH_3-O-CH_2-CH_2-CH_2-CH_2-CH_2-CH_3$.

  d) dipentyl ether. Each alkyl group is a pentyl group with 5 carbons each. Linking the alkyl groups with an –O- linkage the structure is $CH_3-CH_2-CH_2-CH_2-CH_2-O-CH_2-CH_2-CH_2-CH_2-CH_3$.

87. **Given:** amine structures   **Find:** name
Conceptual Plan: Amines are systematically named by alphabetically listing the alkyl groups that area attached to the nitrogen atom and adding an –amine ending. The alkyl groups are those found in Table 20.5. Use a prefix of di- or tri- if the alkyl groups are the same.
Solution:
  a) $\boxed{CH_3-CH_2}-\underset{H}{N}-\boxed{CH_2-CH_3}$ Both carbon chains have 2 carbons and so they are ethyl groups. The name is diethylamine.

  b) $\boxed{CH_3-CH_2-CH_2}-\underset{H}{N}-\boxed{CH_3}$ The left carbon chain has 3 carbons and so it is a propyl group. The right carbon chain has 1 carbon and so it is a methyl group. Listing them alphabetically the name is methylpropylamine.

  c) $\boxed{CH_3-CH_2-CH_2}-\overset{\overset{\textstyle CH_3}{|}}{N}-\boxed{CH_2-CH_2-CH_2-CH_3}$ The left carbon chain has 3 carbons and so it is a propyl group. The top carbon chain has 1 carbon and so it is a methyl group. The right carbon chain has 4 carbons and so it is a butyl group. Listing them alphabetically the name is butyl methylpropylamine.

88. **Given:** amine names   **Find:** structure
Conceptual plan: Find the number of carbon atoms corresponding to prefix of the two alkyl groups using Table 20. 5. → Draw the alkyl groups around a central nitrogen atom and add any necessary hydrogens to have three bonds to the nitrogen.
Solution:

a) isopropylamine. The isopropyl group is $-CH-CH_3$ with CH_3 below. Attach it to a nitrogen and add 2 hydrogen atoms to the nitrogen to get the final structure

$$H-N-CH-CH_3$$
$$|\quad\ |$$
$$H\quad CH_3$$

b) triethylamine. All three alkyl groups are ethyl groups with 2 carbons each. Linking the alkyl groups around a nitrogen gives the structure

$$CH_3-CH_2-N-CH_2-CH_3$$
$$|$$
$$CH_2-CH_3$$

c) butylethylamine. The first alkyl group is a butyl group with 4 carbons and the other alkyl group is an ethyl group with 2 carbons. Attach the alkyls groups to a nitrogen and add a hydrogen atom to the nitrogen the final structure

$$CH_3-CH_2-CH_2-CH_2-N-CH_2-CH_3$$
$$|$$
$$H$$

89. a) This reaction is an acid-base reaction, CH_3NHCH_3 *(aq)* + HCl *(aq)* → $(CH_3)_2NH_2^+$ *(aq)* + Cl^- *(aq)*.

b) Since the acid is a carboxylic acid, this reaction is a condensation reaction, $CH_3CH_2NH_2$ *(aq)* + CH_3CH_2COOH *(aq)* → $CH_3CH_2CONHCH_2CH_3$ *(aq)* + $H_2O(l)$.

c) This reaction is an acid-base reaction, CH_3NH_2 *(aq)* + H_2SO_4 *(aq)* → $CH_3NH_3^+$ *(aq)* + HSO_4^- *(aq)*.

90. a) This reaction is an acid-base reaction, $N(CH_2CH_3)_3$ *(aq)* + HNO_3 *(aq)* → $(CH_3CH_2)_3NH^+$ *(aq)* + NO_3^- *(aq)*.

b) This reaction is an addition reaction,

$$CH_3-N-CH-CH_3$$
$$|\quad\ |$$
$$H\quad CH_3$$

(aq) + HCN *(aq)* →

$$CH_3-N-CH-CH_3$$
$$|\quad\quad\ |$$
$$H-N=CH\ CH_3$$

(aq).

c) Since the acid is a carboxylic acid, this reaction is a condensation reaction,

$$CH_3-N-CH-CH_3$$
$$|\quad\ |$$
$$H\quad CH_3$$

(aq) +

$$CH_3\quad\quad\ O$$
$$|\quad\quad\quad\ ||$$
$$CH_3-CH-CH_2-C-OH$$

(aq) →

$$CH_3\quad\quad O\quad\quad CH_3$$
$$|\quad\quad\quad ||\quad\quad |$$
$$CH_3-CH-CH_2-C-N-CH-CH_3$$
$$|$$
$$CH_3$$

(aq) + $H_2O(l)$.

91. Since the monomer is

$$F\quad\ F$$
$$\backslash\ /$$
$$C=C$$
$$/\ \ \backslash$$
$$F\quad\ F$$

, as the polymer forms the double bond breaks to link with another monomer. The structure is

```
F  FF  FF  FF  FF
 \ / \ / \ / \ / \
  C   C   C   C   C
 / \ / \ / \ / \ /
  C   C   C   C   C
 \ / \ / \ / \ / \
 FF  FF  FF  FF  FF
```

92. The monomers

$$H\quad\ Cl$$
$$\backslash\ /$$
$$C=C$$
$$/\ \ \backslash$$
$$H\quad\ Cl$$

and

$$H\quad\ H$$
$$\backslash\ /$$
$$C=C$$
$$/\ \ \backslash$$
$$H\quad\ Cl$$

alternate and as the polymer forms the double bond breaks to link with another monomer. The structure is

```
Cl ClH HCl ClH HCl ClH HCl ClH HCl
 \ / \ / \ / \ / \ / \ / \ / \ / \
  C   C   C   C   C   C   C   C   C
 / \ / \ / \ / \ / \ / \ / \ / \ /
  C   C   C   C   C   C   C   C   C
 \ / \ / \ / \ / \ / \ / \ / \ / \
 HCl HH  HCl HH  HCl HH  HCl HH  H
```

93. In a condensation polymer atoms are eliminated. Here water is eliminated. The structure is

94. In a condensation polymer atoms are eliminated. Here water is eliminated. The structure is

95. **Given:** structures   **Find:** identify molecule type and name

Conceptual Plan: Look for functional groups to identify molecule type. Review appropriate set of naming rules to name molecule.

Solution:

a) $CH_3-CH_2-CH_2-\overset{\overset{\displaystyle O}{\|}}{C}-O-CH_3$ The compound has the formula of RCOOR', so it is an ester.

$\boxed{CH_3-CH_2-CH_2-\overset{\overset{\displaystyle O}{\|}}{\underset{\underset{\displaystyle CH_3}{|}}{C}}}-O-\boxed{CH_3}$ The left carbon chain has 4 carbons, which translates to but- and a base

name of butanoate. There is a methyl substituent on this chain. The right carbon chain has 2 carbons,

so it is a methyl group. $\boxed{C^4H_3-C^3H_2-C^2H_2-\overset{\overset{\displaystyle O}{\|}}{\underset{\underset{\displaystyle \boxed{CH_3}}{|}}{C^1}}}-O-\boxed{CH_3}$ Number the left chain starting with the

carbonyl carbon. The methyl group is at position 3. The name of the compound is methyl-3-methylbutanoate.

b) $\boxed{CH_3-CH_2-\overset{\overset{\displaystyle CH_3}{|}}{CH}-CH_2}-O-\boxed{CH_2-CH_3}$ The compound has the formula of ROR', so it is an ether. The

left carbon chain has 4 carbons and so it is a butyl group. There is a methyl substituent on this chain. The right carbon chain has 2 carbons and so it is an ethyl group.

$\boxed{C^4H_3-C^3H_2-\overset{\overset{\displaystyle \boxed{CH_3}}{|}}{C^2H}-C^1H_2}-O-\boxed{CH_2-CH_3}$ Number the left chain starting with the carbon next to the

oxygen. The methyl substituent is in position 2, so the alkyl group is 2-methylbutyl. Listing the alkyl group alphabetically the name is ethyl 2-methylbutyl ether.

c) $H_2C–CH_3$ The molecule is a disubstituted benzene, so it is an aromatic hydrocarbon. The substituents are an ethyl group and a methyl group. If the ethyl position is assigned the 1st position, then the methyl group is in the 3rd position. Listing the functional groups alphabetically the name is 1-ethyl-3-methylbenzene or m-ethylmethylbenzene.

d)
$$CH_3 - C \equiv C - CH - CH - CH_2 - CH_3$$
with CH$_2$–CH$_3$ above and CH$_3$ below

The molecule contains a triple bond, so it is an alkyne. The longest carbon chain is 7. The prefix for 7 is hept- and the base name is heptyne. The substituent groups are a methyl and an ethyl group.

$$C^1H_3 - C^2 \equiv C^3 - C^4H - C^5H - C^6H_2 - C^7H_3$$
with CH$_2$–CH$_3$ above and CH$_3$ below

If we start numbering the chain at the end closest to the triple bond, the triple bond is between position number 2 and 3, and the methyl substituent is assigned the number 4 and the ethyl substituent is assigned number 5. Since e is before m, the name of the compound is 5-ethyl-4-methyl-2-heptyne.

e)
$$CH_3 - CH_2 - CH_2 - CH_2 - \overset{\displaystyle O}{\overset{\|}{C}}H$$

The molecule has the formula RCHO, is it is an aldehyde. The longest carbon chain has 4 carbons. The prefix for 4 is but-, since this is an aldehyde the base name is butanal. Since there are no other substituent groups, the name is butanal.

f)
$$CH_3 - \overset{\displaystyle OH}{\overset{\|}{C}}H - CH_2$$
with H$_3$C below

The molecule has the formula ROH, so is it is an alcohol. The longest carbon chain has 3 carbons. The prefix for 3 is prop-, so the base name is propanol. There is a methyl substituent group.

$$C^3H_3 - \overset{\displaystyle OH}{\overset{\|}{C^2}}H - C^1H_2$$
with H$_3$C below

Start numbering with the carbon with the –OH group. The alcohol group is assigned number 1 and the methyl group is assigned number 2. The name is 2-methyl-1-propanol.

96. **Given:** structures **Find:** identify molecule type and name
Conceptual Plan: Look for functional groups to identify molecule type. Review appropriate set of naming rules to name molecule.
Solution:

a)
$$CH_3 - HC - C = C - CH_3$$
with CH$_3$ above and CH$_3$, CH$_3$ below

The molecule contains a double bond, so it is an alkene. The longest continuous chain has 5 carbons. The prefix for 5 is pent- and the base name is pentene. The substituent groups are three methyl groups.

$$C^5H_3 - HC^4 - C^3 = C^2 - C^1H_3$$
with CH$_3$ above and CH$_3$, CH$_3$ below

Start numbering on the right end of the molecule. The double bond is between position number 2 and 3. The methyl substituents are assigned the numbers 2, 3 and 4. The name of the compound is 2,3,4-trimethyl-2-pentene.

b)
$$CH_3 - C - CH_2 - CH - CH_2 - CH_3$$
with CH$_3$, CH$_3$ above and CH$_3$ below

The molecule contains only single bonds, so it is an alkane. The longest continuous chain has 6 carbons. The prefix for 6 is hex- and the base name is hexane. The only substituent groups are three methyl groups. $\boxed{C^1H_3-C^2-C^3H_2-C^4H-C^5H_2-C^6H_3}$ If we start

the CH₃ groups are above C² (two) and above C⁴.

numbering the chain at the end closest to the left methyl groups, the methyl substituents are assigned the numbers 2, 2 and 4. The name of the compound is 2,2,4-trimethylhexane.

c) $\boxed{CH_3-CH_2-CH-CH_2-\overset{O}{\overset{\|}{C}}}-OH$ The compound has the formula of RCOOH, so it is a carboxylic acid.

The carbon chain has 5 carbons. The prefix for 5 is pent-, since this is a carboxylic acid, the base name

is pentanoic acid. There is one methyl substituent group. $\boxed{C^5H_3-C^4H_2-C^3H-C^2H_2-\overset{O}{\overset{\|}{C^1}}}-OH$ Number

the chain starting with the carbonyl carbon. The methyl is in the 3rd position. The name of the molecule is 3-methylpentanoic acid.

d) $\boxed{CH_3-CH}-\overset{H}{\overset{|}{N}}-\boxed{CH_2-CH_2-CH_2-CH_3}$ The compound has the formula of RR'NH, so it is an amine.

with CH₃ below CH on the left group.

The left carbon chain is an isopropyl group. The right carbon chain has 4 carbons and so it is a butyl group. Listing them alphabetically the name is butyl isopropylamine.

e) $CH_3-\boxed{CH-CH_2-CH}-CH_3$ with CH_2-OH above the right CH and CH_2-CH_3 below the left CH.

The molecule has the formula ROH, so is it is an alcohol. The longest carbon chain has 6 carbons. The prefix for 6 is hex-, so the base name is hexanol. There are two

$CH_3-\boxed{C^4H-C^3H_2-C^2H}-\boxed{CH_3}$ with C^1H_2-OH above and $C^5H_2-C^6H_3$ below.

methyl substituent groups. Start numbering with the carbon with the – OH group. The alcohol group is assigned number 1 and the methyl groups are assigned numbers 2 and 4. The name is 2,4-dimethyl-1-hexanol.

f) $\boxed{CH_3-CH_2-CH_2-\overset{O}{\overset{\|}{C}}-CH-CH_3}$ with CH_3 below the CH. The molecule contains a carbonyl carbon in the interior of the

molecule and so it is a ketone. The longest carbon chain has 6 carbons. The prefix for 6 is hex-, since this is an ketone the base name is hexanone. There is one methyl substituent group.

$\boxed{C^6H_3-C^5H_2-C^4H_2-\overset{O}{\overset{\|}{C^3}}-C^2H-C^1H_3}$ with CH_3 below. Start numbering at the right side of the molecule. The carbonyl

carbon is at position number 3. The methyl group is at position 2. The name of the molecule is 2-methyl-3-hexanone.

97. **Given:** structures   **Find:** name
Conceptual Plan: Look for functional groups to identify molecule type. Review appropriate set of naming rules to name molecule.
Solution:

a)

$$CH_3$$
$$|$$
$$\boxed{CH_3-CH_2-CH-CH_2-CH-CH_2-CH_2-CH_2-CH_3}$$
$$|$$
$$HC-CH_3$$
$$|$$
$$CH_2$$
$$|$$
$$CH_3$$

The molecule contains only single bonds, so it is

an alkane. The longest continuous chain has 9 carbons. The prefix for 9 is non- and the base name is nonane. The substituent groups are a methyl group and a isobutyl group.

$$\boxed{CH_3}$$
$$|$$
$$\boxed{C^1H_3-C^2H_2-C^3H-C^4H_2-C^5H-C^6H_2-C^7H_2-C^8H_2-C^9H_3}$$ If we start numbering the chain at the end
$$|$$
$$\boxed{HC-CH_3}$$
$$\boxed{|}$$
$$\boxed{CH_2}$$
$$\boxed{|}$$
$$\boxed{CH_3}$$

closest to the methyl group, the methyl substituent is assigned the numbers 3 and the isobutyl group is assigned the number 5. List the groups alphabetically to get the name of the compound is 5-isobutyl-3-methylnonane.

b)

$$O$$
$$\parallel$$
$$\boxed{CH_3-CH-CH_2-C-CH_2-CH_3}$$ The molecule contains a carbonyl carbon in the interior of the
$$|$$
$$CH_3$$

molecule and so it is a ketone. The longest carbon chain has 6 carbons. The prefix for 6 is hex-, since this is a ketone the base name is hexanone. There is one methyl substituent group.

$$O$$
$$\parallel$$
$$\boxed{C^6H_3-C^5H-C^4H_2-C^3-C^2H_2-C^1H_3}$$ Start numbering at the right side of the molecule. The carbonyl
$$|$$
$$CH_3$$

carbon is at position number 3. The methyl group is at position 5. The name of the molecule is 5-methyl-3-hexanone.

c)

$$OH$$
$$|$$
$$\boxed{CH_3-CH-CH-CH_3}$$ The molecule has the formula ROH, so is it is an alcohol. The longest carbon
$$|$$
$$CH_3$$

chain has 4 carbons. The prefix for 4 is but-, so the base name is butanol. The only substituent group is

a methyl group.
$$OH$$
$$|$$
$$\boxed{C^4H_3-C^3H-C^2H-C^1H_3}$$ Start numbering with the end with the –OH group. The
$$|$$
$$\boxed{CH_3}$$

alcohol group is assigned number 2 and the methyl group is assigned number 3. The name is 3-methyl-2-butanol.

d)

$$CH_3$$
$$|$$
$$CH_2 \quad CH_3$$
$$| \qquad |$$
$$\boxed{CH_3-CH-\ CH-\ CH-C \equiv C-H}$$
$$|$$
$$CH_3$$

The molecule contains a triple bond, so it is an alkyne. The longest

carbon chain is 6. The prefix for 6 is hex- and the base name is hexyne. The substituent groups are two methyl and an ethyl groups.   CH₃   If we start numbering the chain at the end closest to the triple bond, the triple bond is between position number 1 and 2, and the methyl substituents are assigned the numbers 3 and 5 and the ethyl substituent is assigned number 4. Since e is before m, the name of the compound is 4-ethyl-3,5-dimethyl-1-hexyne.

98. **Given:** structures   **Find:** name
Conceptual Plan: Look for functional groups to identify molecule type. Review appropriate set of naming rules to name molecule.
Solution:

a) The molecule contains a double bond, so it is an alkene. The longest continuous chain has 7 carbons. The prefix for 7 is hept- and the base name is heptene. The substituent groups are two methyl groups and an ethyl group.

Start numbering on the left end of the molecule. The double bond is between position number 2 and 3. The methyl substituents are assigned the numbers 4 and 5 and the ethyl substituent is assigned number 4. Listing the groups alphabetically, the name of the compound is 4-ethyl-4,5-dimethyl-2-heptene.

b) Br   The molecule is a disubstituted benzene, so it is an aromatic hydrocarbon. The substituents are an ethyl group and a bromo group. If the bromo position is assigned the 1st position, then CH_2–CH_3 the ethyl group is in the 3rd position. Listing the functional groups alphabetically the name is 1-bromo-3-ethylbenzene or m-bromoethylbenzene.

c) The compound has the formula of RCOOR', so it is an ester. The left carbon chain has 5 carbons, which translates to pent- and a base name of pentanoate. There is a methyl substituent on this chain. The right carbon chain has 3 carbons and is an isopropyl group. Number the left chain starting with the carbonyl carbon. The methyl group is at position 3. The name of the compound is isopropyl-3-methylpentanoate.

d) The molecule has the formula RCHO, is it is an aldehyde. The longest carbon chain has 4 carbons. The prefix for 4 is but-, since this is an aldehyde the base name is butanal. There is a methyl substituent. $\boxed{C^4H_3 - C^3H - C^2H_2 - C^1H}$ Start numbering with the carbonyl carbon. The methyl

with O double bonded above C^1H and $\boxed{CH_3}$ below C^3H.

group is assigned number 3. The name is 3-methylbutanal.

99. a)   These structures are structural isomers. The methyl and ethyl groups have been swapped.

   b)   These structures are isomers. The iodo second group has been moved.

   c)   These structures are the same molecule. The first methyl group is simply drawn in a different orientation.

100. a)   These structures are the same molecule. The alkyl groups are drawn in different orientations.

   b)   These structures are isomers. In the first structure, there is a methyl substituent to the left carbon chain. There is no methyl substituent on the second structure.

   c)   These structures are the same molecule. The methyl group is drawn in a different orientation and the orientation of the right carbon is changed.

101. **Given:** 15.5 kg 2-butene hydrogenation   **Find:** minimum g of H_2 gas

   Conceptual Plan: Write a balanced equation. kg C_4H_8 → g C_4H_8 → mol C_4H_8 → mol H_2 → g H_2

$$\frac{1000\,g}{1\,kg} \qquad \frac{1\,mol\,C_4H_8}{56.10\,g\,C_4H_8} \qquad \frac{1\,mol\,H_2}{1\,mol\,C_4H_8} \qquad \frac{2.02\,g\,H_2}{1\,mol\,H_2}$$

   Solution: $C_4H_8\,(g) + H_2\,(g) \rightarrow C_4H_{10}\,(g)$ then

$$15.5\,kg\,C_4H_8 \times \frac{1000\,g\,C_4H_8}{1\,kg\,C_4H_8} \times \frac{1\,mol\,C_4H_8}{56.10\,g\,C_4H_8} \times \frac{1\,mol\,H_2}{1\,mol\,C_4H_8} \times \frac{2.02\,g\,H_2}{1\,mol\,H_2} = 558\,g\,H_2$$

   Check: The units (g) are correct. The magnitude of the answer (600) makes physical sense because we are reacting 15,500 g of butane. Hydrogen is lighter and the molar ratio is 1:1 so the amount of hydrogen will be significant, but less than the mass of butene.

102. **Given:** 3.8 kg *n*-octane combustion   **Find:** kg of CO_2 gas
   Conceptual Plan: Write a balanced equation.
   kg C_9H_{18} → g C_9H_{18} → mol C_8H_{18} → mol CO_2 → g CO_2 → kg CO_2

$$\frac{1000\,g}{1\,kg} \qquad \frac{1\,mol\,C_8H_{18}}{114.22\,g\,C_8H_{18}} \qquad \frac{1\,mol\,H_2}{1\,mol\,C_4H_8} \qquad \frac{44.01\,g\,CO_2}{1\,mol\,CO_2} \qquad \frac{1\,kg}{1000\,g}$$

   Solution: $C_8H_{18}\,(g) + 25/2\,O_2\,(g) \rightarrow 8\,CO_2\,(g) + 9\,H_2O\,(g)$ then

$$3.8\,kg\,C_8H_{18} \times \frac{1000\,g\,C_8H_{18}}{1\,kg\,C_8H_{18}} \times \frac{1\,mol\,C_8H_{18}}{114.22\,g\,C_8H_{18}} \times \frac{8\,mol\,CO_2}{1\,mol\,C_8H_{18}} \times \frac{44.01\,g\,CO_2}{1\,mol\,CO_2} \times \frac{1\,kg\,CO_2}{1000\,g\,CO_2} = 11.7\,kg\,CO_2$$

   Check: The units (g) are correct. The magnitude of the answer (12) makes physical sense because we are reacting 4 kg of octane. Since all of the carbon is now bound to oxygen, which is much heavier than hydrogen, the weight will increase dramatically.

103. a)   Combustion reaction – reaction with oxygen to form CO_2 and H_2O.

   b)   Alkane (halogen) substitution – reaction with halogen gas to substitute a hydrogen with a halogen.

   c)   Alcohol elimination – ROH reaction with concentrated acid to eliminate water from the alcohol.

   d)   Aromatic (halogen) substitution – benzene reaction with halogen gas to substitute a hydrogen with a halogen.

104. a)   Hydrogenation reaction – $\begin{array}{c}CH_3 - CH_2 - C = CH_2 \\ | \\ CH_3\end{array} + H_2 \rightarrow \begin{array}{c}CH_3 - CH_2 - CH - CH_3 \\ | \\ CH_3\end{array}$.

b) Halogen substitution – $CH_3-CH_2-CH_2-CH_2-OH + HBr \rightarrow CH_3-CH_2-CH_2-CH_2-Br + H_2O$.

c) Condensation reaction –

$$\begin{matrix} & CH_3 & O \\ & | & \parallel \\ CH_3-CH_2-CH-CH_2-C-OH \end{matrix} + CH_3-CH_2-OH \rightarrow$$

$$\begin{matrix} CH_3 & O \\ | & \parallel \\ CH_3-CH_2-CH-CH_2-C-O-CH_2-CH_3 \end{matrix} + H_2O.$$

d) No reaction – both reactants are bases.

105. **Given:** alkene names   **Find:** structure

Conceptual plan: Find the number of carbon atoms corresponding to prefix of the base name in Table 20. 5. → Draw the base chain and number the carbons from left to right. → Place the double bond in the appropriate position in the chain. → Using Table 20.6 and the prefix di- (2), tri- (3), or tetra- (4) before the substituent's name, determine each substituent. → Add the substituent to the proper carbon position in the chain. → Add hydrogen atoms to the base chain so that each carbon has 4 bonds. → Look for substitution around double bond to determine if cis-trans isomerism is applicable and look for carbons with four different alkyl groups attached.

Solution:

a) 3-methyl-1-pentene. The base name pentene designates that there are 5 carbon atoms in the base chain. $C^1-C^2-C^3-C^4-C^5$. The -ene ending designates that there is a double bond and the 1 prefix designates that it is between the 1st and 2nd positions. $C^1=C^2-C^3-C^4-C^5$ 3-methyl designates that is a $-CH_3$ group in the 3rd position.

$$\begin{matrix} & & \boxed{CH_3} \\ & & | \\ C^1 & =C^2 & -C^3 & -C^4 & -C^5 \end{matrix}$$

. Add hydrogens to the base chain to get the final molecule

$$\begin{matrix} & & CH_3 \\ & & | \\ CH_2 & = CH & -CH & -CH_2 & -CH_3 \end{matrix}$$

. There are stereoisomerism since the 3rd carbon has four different groups attached.

b) 3,5-dimethyl-2-hexene. The base name hexene designates that there are 6 carbon atoms in the base chain. $C^1-C^2-C^3-C^4-C^5-C^6$. The -ene ending designates that there is a double bond and the 2 prefix designates that it is between the 2nd and 3rd positions. $C^1-C^2=C^3-C^4-C^5-C^6$. 3,5-dimethyl designates that are $-CH_3$ groups in the 3rd and 5th positions.

$$\begin{matrix} & & \boxed{CH_3} & & \boxed{CH_3} \\ & & | & & | \\ C^1 & -C^2 & =C^3 & -C^4 & -C^5 & -C^6 \end{matrix}$$

. Add hydrogens to the base chain to get the final molecule

$$\begin{matrix} & & CH_3 & & CH_3 \\ & & | & & | \\ CH_3 & -CH=C & -CH_2 & -CH & -CH_3 \end{matrix}$$

. Cis-trans isomerism is possible around the double bond since all of the groups surrounding the double bond are different.

c) 3-propyl-2-hexene. The base name hexene designates that there are 6 carbon atoms in the base chain. $C^1-C^2-C^3-C^4-C^5-C^6$. The -ene ending designates that there is a double bond and the 2 prefix designates that it is between the 2nd and 3rd positions. $C^1-C^2=C^3-C^4-C^5-C^6$. 3-propyl designates that is a $-CH_2CH_2CH_3$ group in the 3rd position.

$$\begin{matrix} & & \boxed{CH_2-CH_2-CH_3} \\ & & | \\ C^1 & -C^2 & =C^3 & -C^4 & -C^5 & -C^6 \end{matrix}$$

. Add hydrogens to the base chain to get the final molecule

$$\begin{matrix} & & CH_2-CH_2-CH_3 \\ & & | \\ CH_3 & -CH=C & -CH_2 & -CH & -CH_3 \end{matrix}$$

. Cis-trans isomerism is not possible around the double bond since the two groups on the 3rd carbon are the same.

106. c) and d) exhibit stereoisomerism, because there are carbons that have four different groups attached. The

structures are:
$$\underset{\overset{|}{CH_3} - \overset{\overset{OH}{|}}{CH} - \overset{\overset{CH_3}{|}}{CH} - CH_2 - CH_3}{}$$
for 3-methyl-2-pentanol (carbon #2 and #3 are both optically

active) and
$$\underset{CH_3 - \overset{\overset{CH_3}{|}}{CH} - \overset{\overset{OH}{|}}{CH} - CH_2 - CH_3}{}$$
for 2-methyl-3-pentanol (carbon #3 is optically active).

107. The 11 isomers are
$$\underset{HC - CH_2 - CH_2 - CH_3}{\overset{\overset{O}{\|}}{}}$$
= aldehyde,
$$\underset{CH_3 - \overset{\overset{O}{\|}}{C} - CH_2 - CH_3}{}$$
= ketone,

$CH_2 = C - CH_2 - CH_2 - OH$ = alcohol & alkene, $CH_3 - CH = CH - CH_2 - OH$ = alcohol & alkene,

$CH_3 - CH_2 - CH = CH - OH$ = alcohol & alkene, $CH_3 - CH_2 - O - CH = CH_2$ = ether & alkene,

$CH_3 - O - CH_2 - CH = CH_2$ = ether & alkene, $CH_3 - O - CH = CH - CH_3$ = ether & alkene,

$$\underset{CH_3 - CH_2 - \overset{\overset{OH}{|}}{C} = CH_2}{}$$
= alcohol & alkene,
$$\underset{CH_3 - \overset{\overset{OH}{|}}{CH} - CH = CH_2}{}$$
= alcohol & alkene, and
$$\underset{CH_3 - \overset{\overset{OH}{|}}{C} = CH - CH_3}{}$$

= alcohol & alkene. There is also a 12th isomer that is cyclic:
$$\underset{\overset{}{\underset{O}{\diagdown\diagup}}}{\overset{H_2C - CH_2}{\underset{|\qquad|}{H_2C\quad CH_2}}}$$
= ether.

108. The 7 isomers are all amines and are
$$\underset{HC - CH_2 - CH_2 - NH_2}{\overset{\overset{O}{\|}}{}}$$
= aldehyde,
$$\underset{CH_3 - \overset{\overset{O}{\|}}{C} - CH_2 - NH_2}{}$$
= ketone,

$$\underset{CH_3 - CH_2 - \overset{\overset{O}{\|}}{C} - NH_2}{}$$
= ketone,
$$\underset{HC - CH_2 - \overset{}{\underset{H}{N}} - CH_3}{\overset{\overset{O}{\|}}{}}$$
= aldehyde,
$$\underset{HC - \overset{}{\underset{CH_3}{N}} - CH_3}{\overset{\overset{O}{\|}}{}}$$
= aldehyde,

$$\underset{HC - \overset{}{\underset{H}{N}} - CH_2 - CH_3}{\overset{\overset{O}{\|}}{}}$$
= aldehyde, and
$$\underset{CH_3 - \overset{\overset{O}{\|}}{C} - \overset{}{\underset{H}{N}} - CH_3}{}$$
= ketone.

109. a) This is a internal condensation reaction. It only requires heat to cause it to happen.

b) This is a dehydration reaction,
$$\underset{\overset{|}{\underset{CH_2 - CH_3}{}}}{CH_3 - CH - CH_2 - \overset{\overset{CH_2 - OH}{|}}{CH} - CH_3}$$
$\xrightarrow{H_2SO_4}$
$$\underset{\overset{|}{\underset{CH_2 - CH_3}{}}}{CH_3 - CH - CH_2 - \overset{\overset{CH_2}{\|}}{C} - CH_3}$$
+ H_2O.

c) This is an addition reaction that follows Markovnikov's rule,
$$\underset{\overset{|}{CH_3}}{CH_3 - CH_2 - C = CH_2}$$
+ HBr →

$$\underset{\overset{|}{\underset{CH_3}{}}}{CH_3 - CH_2 - \overset{\overset{Br}{|}}{C} - CH_3}$$.

110.
$$\underset{\overset{|}{CH_3}}{CH_3 - CH - CH_2 - CH_2 - OH}$$
$\xrightarrow[H_2SO_4]{Na_2Cr_2O_7}$
$$\underset{\overset{|}{CH_3}}{CH_3 - CH - CH_2 - \overset{\overset{O}{\|}}{C} - OH}$$
+ $CH_3 - CH_2 - OH$ →

$$CH_3-CH-CH_2-\overset{\displaystyle O}{\overset{\|}{C}}-O-CH_2-CH_3 + Cl_2 \rightarrow CH_3-\overset{\displaystyle Cl}{\overset{|}{CH}}-CH_2-\overset{\displaystyle O}{\overset{\|}{C}}-O-CH_2-CH_3 + HCl.$$
$$\underset{\displaystyle CH_3}{|}\qquad\qquad\qquad\qquad\qquad\underset{\displaystyle CH_3}{|}$$

111. a) Since there are 6 primary hydrogen atoms and 2 secondary hydrogen atoms, if they are equally reactive we expect a ration of 6:2 or 3:1.

b) Assume that we generate 100 product molecules. The yield = (# hydrogen atoms)(reactivity). So $1° = 45$ = (3)(reactivity $1°$) and $2° = 55 = (1)$(reactivity $2°$). Taking the ratio, $2°: 1° = 55: (45/3) = 55 : 15 = 11: 3$. The $2°$ hydrogens are much more reactive.

112. The two isomers are: $CH_3-CH_2-CH_2-CH_3$ and $\underset{\displaystyle CH_3-CH-CH_3}{\overset{\displaystyle CH_3}{\overset{|}{}}}$. The products are

$CHCl_2-CH_2-CH_2-CH_3$, $CH_3-CCl_2-CH_2-CH_3$, $CH_2Cl-CHCl-CH_2-CH_3$, $CH_2Cl-CH_2-CHCl-CH_3$, $CH_2Cl-CH_2-CH_2-CH_2Cl$, and $CH_3-CHCl-CHCl-CH_3$. There are 6 products from the first isomer. The

other products are $\underset{\displaystyle CHCl_2-CH-CH_3}{\overset{\displaystyle CH_3}{\overset{|}{}}}$, $\underset{\displaystyle CH_2Cl-CH-CH_3}{\overset{\displaystyle CH_2Cl}{\overset{|}{}}}$, and $\underset{\displaystyle CH_2Cl-CCl-CH_3}{\overset{\displaystyle CH_3}{\overset{|}{}}}$. There are 3 products from

the second isomer. There are a total of $6 + 3 = 9$ products.

113. The chiral products have four different groups on a carbon are: $CH_2Cl-CHCl-CH_2-CH_3$ (2nd carbon), $CH_2Cl-CH_2-CHCl-CH_3$ (3rd carbon), and $CH_3-CHCl-CHCl-CH_3$ (2nd and 3rd carbons).

114. a) $\underset{\displaystyle CH_3-CH}{\overset{\displaystyle O}{\overset{\|}{}}}$ is more oxidized since the oxygen is double bonded to the carbon.

b) CH_3-CH_2-OH is more oxidized since it has an oxygen.

c) $\underset{\displaystyle CH_3-CH_2-C-OH}{\overset{\displaystyle O}{\overset{\|}{}}}$ is more oxidized since it has more oxygens.

115. In order for the structure to have only one product after a single bromination, it must have all of the

hydrogens be equivalent. The structure is $CH_3-\overset{\displaystyle CH_3}{\underset{\displaystyle CH_3}{\overset{|}{\underset{|}{C}}}}-\overset{\displaystyle CH_3}{\underset{\displaystyle CH_3}{\overset{|}{\underset{|}{C}}}}-CH_3$. To name it, find the longest carbon chain:

$\boxed{CH_3-\overset{\displaystyle CH_3}{\underset{\displaystyle CH_3}{\overset{|}{\underset{|}{C}}}}-\overset{\displaystyle CH_3}{\underset{\displaystyle CH_3}{\overset{|}{\underset{|}{C}}}}-CH_3}$. Since there are 4 carbons in this chain and it is an alkane, the base name is butane.

There are 4 methyl substituent groups. $\boxed{C^1H_3-\overset{\boxed{CH_3}\boxed{CH_3}}{\underset{\boxed{CH_3}\boxed{CH_3}}{\overset{|\,|}{\underset{|\,|}{C^2-C^3}}}}-C^4H_3}$ It does not matter how the chain is numbered

since it is symmetrically substituted. The methyl groups are assigned the numbers 2, 2, 3, and 3. The name is 2,2,3,3-tetramethylbutane.

116. b) and d) are chiral since thy have carbons with four different groups attached.

Chapter 21
Biochemistry

1. Biochemistry is that area at the interface between chemistry and biology that strives to understand living organisms at the molecular level. It is the study of the chemistry occurring in living organisms. To help diabetics, Frederick Sanger discovered the detailed chemical structure of human insulin. This allowed the synthesis of insulin. This was further enhanced by biotechnology advances, particularly by Genentech, that allowed researchers to insert the human gene for insulin into the DNA of bacterial cells. This new way to manufacture human insulin revolutionized the treatment of diabetes since the human insulin is now readily available.

2. Lipids are the chemical components of the cell that are insoluble in water but soluble in nonpolar solvents. Lipids include fatty acids, fats, oils, phospholipids, glycolipids, and steroids. Their insolubility in water makes lipids ideal as the structural components of cell membranes, which must separate the aqueous interior of the cell from its aqueous environment in the body.

3. A fatty acid is a carboxylic acid with a long hydrocarbon tail. The general structure for a fatty acid is:

$$R - \overset{\overset{\textstyle O}{\|}}{C} - OH$$

where R represents a hydrocarbon chain containing 3 to 19 carbon atoms.

4. The double bond puts a bend in the carbon chain of a fatty acid or fat that makes it more difficult for neighboring molecules to interact over the entire length of the carbon chain, thus lowering the melting point.

5. Fats and oils or triglycerides, are triesters composed of glycerol with three fatty acids attached. The general structure of a triglyceride is:

$$
\begin{array}{l}
\phantom{R - \overset{O}{C} - O - } H_2C - O - \overset{\overset{\textstyle O}{\|}}{C} - R \\
R - \overset{\overset{\textstyle O}{\|}}{C} - O - CH O \\
\phantom{R - \overset{O}{C} - O - } H_2C - O - \overset{\overset{\textstyle \|}{}}{C} - R
\end{array}
$$

6. A saturated fat occurs when the fatty acids in a triglyceride are saturated. Saturated fats tend to be solids at room temperature. Triglycerides from warm – blooded animals are generally saturated. An unsaturated fat occurs when the fatty acids in a triglyceride are unsaturated. An unsaturated fat, or an oil, tends to be a liquid at room temperature. Triglycerides for plants or from cold – blooded animals are generally unsaturated.

7. Phospholipids have the same basic structure as triglycerides, except that one of the fatty acid groups is replaced with a phosphate group. Unlike a fatty acid, which is nonpolar, the phosphate group is polar. The phospholipid molecule has a polar region and a nonpolar region. The polar part of the molecule is hydrophilic while the nonpolar part is hydrophobic.
Glycolipids have similar structures and properties. The nonpolar section of a glycolipid is composed of a fatty acid chain and a hydrocarbon chain. However, the polar section is a sugar molecule.
The structure of phospholipids and glycolipids makes them ideal as components of cell membranes, where the polar parts can interact with the aqueous environments inside and outside the cell and the nonpolar parts interact with each other, forming a double – layered structure called a lipid bilayer. Lipid bilayers encapsulate cells and many cellular structures.

8. Steroids are lipids with the following four – ring structure:

Some common steroids include cholesterol, testosterone, and β – estradiol. Cholesterol for example is part of cell membranes. It also serves as a starting material for the body to synthesize other steroids such as testosterone and β – estradiol.

9. Carbohydrates have the general formula $(CH_2O)_n$. Structurally, carbohydrates are polyhydroxy aldehydes or ketones. Carbohydrates are responsible for short – term storage of energy in living organisms, and they make up the main structural components of plants.

10. Monosaccharides are the simplest carbohydrates. They contain between three and eight carbon atoms and have only one aldehyde or ketone functional group. Two monosaccharides can link together via a glycosidic linkage to form a disaccharide, a carbohydrate that can be decomposed into two simpler sugars. An aldose is a sugar with an aldehyde group and a ketose is a sugar that has a ketone group.

11. Simple carbohydrates are the simple sugars, monosaccharides and disaccharides. Polysaccharides, which are long, chainlike molecules composed of many monosaccharide units bonded together, are complex carbohydrates.

12. Cellulose consists of glucose units bonded together by ß – glycosidic linkages. This structure allows neighboring cellulose molecules to form multiple hydrogen bonds with one another, resulting in the rigid and structurally stable properties we associate with wood and fiber. Cellulose is the main structural component of plants.
    Starch is composed of two slightly different polysaccharides, amylose and amylopectin. Both are composed of glycose units bonded together by α – glycosidic linkages, but amylopectin contains branches in the chains. Starch is the main energy storage medium for plants.
    Glycogen is similar in structure to amylopectin, but the chain is even more highly branched. Animals use glycogen to store glucose in the muscles. Glycogens's highly branched structure leaves many end groups that can be quickly hydrolyzed to meet energy needs.

13. Proteins are the workhorse molecules in living organisms and are involved in virtually all facets of cell structure and function. Most of the chemical reactions that occur in living organisms are enabled by enzymes, proteins that act as catalysts in biochemical reactions. Proteins are also the structural elements of muscle, skin, and cartilage. Proteins transport oxygen in the blood, act as antibodies to fight disease, and function as hormones to regulate metabolic processes.

14. Amino acids contain a carbon atom – called the α carbon – bonded to four different groups: an amine group, an R group (also called a side chain), a carboxylic acid group, and a hydrogen atom. Amino acids link together through the reaction of the amine end of one amino acid with the carboxylic end of another resulting in a peptide bond.

15. The R groups, or side chains, differ chemically from one amino acid to another. When amino acids are strung together to make a protein, the chemical properties of the R group determine the structure and properties of the protein.

16. Since all amino acids except glycine contain four different groups attached to a tetrahedral carbon (the α carbon), all amino acids are chiral about that carbon.

17.

Alanine (Ala)

18. alanine + valine

$$H_2N - \overset{\overset{\displaystyle H}{|}}{C} - \overset{\overset{\displaystyle O}{\|}}{C} - OH \quad + \quad H_2N - \overset{\overset{\displaystyle H}{|}}{C} - \overset{\overset{\displaystyle O}{\|}}{C} - OH \quad \longrightarrow$$
$$\qquad\quad\; \underset{\displaystyle CH_3}{|} \qquad\qquad\qquad\quad H_3C - \underset{\displaystyle \underset{\displaystyle CH_3}{|}}{\overset{\displaystyle |}{C}} - H$$

$$\underset{\displaystyle N-terminal}{H_2N} - \overset{\overset{\displaystyle H}{|}}{\underset{\underset{\displaystyle CH_3}{|}}{C}} - \overset{\overset{\displaystyle O}{\|}}{C} - O - \overset{\overset{\displaystyle H}{|}}{N} - \overset{\overset{\displaystyle H}{|}}{\underset{\displaystyle H_3C - \underset{\displaystyle \underset{\displaystyle CH_3}{|}}{\overset{\displaystyle |}{C}} - H}{C}} - \overset{\overset{\displaystyle O}{\|}}{C} - OH \quad + \; H_2O \qquad \text{C – terminal}$$

19. The 10 essential amino acids are phenylalanine, tryptophan, isoleucine, histidine, lysine, valine, threonine, methionine, arginine, and leucine. These amino acids are called essential amino acids because they can not be synthesized in the body. They must come from food and in the proportions that match the needs of protein synthesis.

20. Fibrous proteins tend to have relatively simple linear structures and tend to be insoluble in aqueous solutions. They serve primarily structural functions within living organisms.
Globular proteins tend to have more complex structures that are highly complicated and specific but often roughly spherical in overall shape. Globular proteins are generally structured so that polar side chains on amino acids are oriented toward the exterior of the protein, while nonpolar side chains are oriented toward the interior of the protein. Consequently, globular proteins tend to be soluble in water, but they maintain a nonpolar environment with the protein that excludes water.

21. The primary structure is simply the amino acid sequence.
The secondary structure refers to the repeating patterns in the arrangement of protein chains.
The tertiary structure refers to the large – scale twists and folds of globular proteins.
The quarternary structure refers to the arrangement of subunits in proteins that have more than one polypeptide chain.

22. The primary structure is maintained by the peptide bonds that hold amino acids together.
The secondary structure is maintained by interactions between the peptide backbones of amino acids that are close together in the chain sequence or adjacent to each other on neighboring chains.
The tertiary structure is maintained by interactions between the R groups on amino acids that are separated by long distances in the chain sequence.
The quarternary structure is maintained by interactions between amino acids on the different subunits.

23. In the α – helix structure, the amino acid chain is wrapped into a tight coil in which the side chains extend outward from the coil. The structure is maintained by hydrogen bonding interaction between NH and CO groups along the peptide backbone of the protein.
In the β – pleated sheet the chain is extended and forms a zigzag pattern. The peptide backbones of neighboring chains interact with one another through hydrogen bonding to form zigzag shaped sheets.

24. The nucleic acids are molecules that serve as blueprints for making proteins. Nucleic acids employ a chemical code to specify the correct amino acid sequences for proteins.

25. Nucleic acids are polymers. The individual units composing nucleic acids are called nucleotides. Each nucleotide has three parts: a sugar, a base, and a phosphate groups, which serves as a link between sugars.

26. The bases in nucleic acids are complementary – that is, they are capable of precise pairing. That is, guanine specifically pairs with cytosine and adenine specifically pairs with thymine. This base pairing is central to DNA replication.

27. A codon is a sequence of three bases that codes for one amino acid.
    A gene is a sequence of codons within a DNA molecule that codes for a single protein.
    Genes are contained in structures called chromosomes. There are 46 chromosomes in the nuclei of human cells.

28. Most of the cells in our bodies contain all of the genes required to make all of the proteins that we need – the DNA within any one cell is complete. However, any particular cell does not express all those genes; it does not synthesize all those proteins. Cells synthesize only the proteins that are important to their function.

29. When a cell is about to divide, the DNA unwinds and the hydrogen bonds joining the complementary bases break, forming two daughter strands. With the help of the enzyme DNA polymerase, a complement to each daughter strand with the correct complementary bases in the correct sequence is formed. The hydrogen bonds between the strands then re – form, resulting in two complete copies of the original DNA, one for each daughter cell.

30. When a cell needs to make a particular protein, the gene – the section of the DNA that codes for that particular protein – unravels. Complementary copies of that gene are then synthesized as single strands of messenger RNA (or mRNA). The mRNA moves out of the cell's nucleus to structures in the cytoplasm called ribosomes. At the ribosome, protein synthesis occurs. The ribosome moves along the mRNA chain that codes for the protein, 'reading' the sequence of codons. At each codon, the specified amino acid is brought into place and a peptide bond is formed with the previous amino acid. As the ribosome moves along the mRNA, the protein is formed. All of this is orchestrated by enzymes that catalyze the necessary reactions.

31. a) No. It is an alkane chain.
    b) No. It is an amino acid.
    c) Yes. It is a saturated fatty acid.
    d) Yes. It is the steroid, cholesterol.

32. a) Yes. It is an unsaturated triglyceride.
    b) No. It is an alkane chain.
    c) Yes. It is a phospholipid.
    d) No. It is a dipeptide.

33. a) Yes. It is a saturated fatty acid.
    b) No. It is an alkane.
    c) No. It is an ether.
    d) Yes. It is a monounsaturated fatty acid.

34. a) It is a saturated fatty acid but it is a short chain and is most likely not a solid at room temperature.
    b) It is a long chain saturated fatty acid and is most likely a solid at room temperature.
    c) It is an unsaturated fatty acid and is most likely not a solid at room temperature.
    d) It is an unsaturated fatty acid and is most likely not a solid at room temperature.

35.

$$H_2C-OH$$
$$HO-CH \quad + \quad 3\left[HOOC(CH_2)_6\left(CH_2CH=CH\right)_2(CH_2)_4CH_3\right]$$
$$H_2C-OH$$

$$\longrightarrow$$

$$H_2C-O-\overset{\overset{\displaystyle O}{\|}}{C}-(CH_2)_6\left(CH_2CH=CH\right)_2(CH_2)_4CH_3$$

$$HC-O-\overset{\overset{\displaystyle O}{\|}}{C}-(CH_2)_6\left(CH_2CH=CH\right)_2(CH_2)_4CH_3$$

$$H_2C-O-\overset{\overset{\displaystyle O}{\|}}{C}-(CH_2)_6\left(CH_2CH=CH\right)_2(CH_2)_4CH_3$$

The double bonds in the linoleic acid would most likely make this triglyceride form an oil.

36.

$$H_2C-OH$$
$$HO-CH \quad + \quad 3\left[HOOC(CH_2)_{14}CH_3\right] \quad \longrightarrow$$
$$H_2C-OH$$

$$H_2C-O-\overset{\overset{\displaystyle O}{\|}}{C}-(CH_2)_{14}CH_3$$

$$HC-O-\overset{\overset{\displaystyle O}{\|}}{C}-(CH_2)_{14}CH_3$$

$$H_2C-O-\overset{\overset{\displaystyle O}{\|}}{C}-(CH_2)_{14}CH_3$$

This triglyceride would most likely be a solid fat since myristic acid contains no double bonds.

37. a) Yes, it is a carbohydrate, it is a monosaccharide.
   b) No, it is not a carbohydrate, it is a steroid: β – estridiol.
   c) Yes, it is a carbohydrate, it is a disaccharide.
   d) No, it is not a carbohydrate, it is a peptide.

38. a) Yes, it is a carbohydrate, it is a trisaccharide.
   b) Yes, it is a carbohydrate, it is a monosaccharide.
   c) No, it is not a carbohydrate, it is an unsaturated fatty acid.
   d) Yes, it is a carbohydrate, it is a monosaccharide.

39. a) The C – O double bond is on a terminal carbon, so it is an aldose, there are six carbon atoms, so it is a hexose.
   b) The C – O double bond is on a terminal carbon, so it is an aldose, there are five carbon atoms, so it is a pentose.
   c) The C – O double bond is NOT on a terminal carbon, so it is a ketose, there are four carbon atoms, so it is a tetrose.
   d) The C – O double bond is on a terminal carbon, so it is an aldose, there are four carbon atoms, so it is a tetrose.

40. a) The C – O double bond is on a terminal carbon, so it is an aldose, there are six carbon atoms, so it is a hexose.
   b) The C – O double bond is on a terminal carbon, so it is an aldose, there are five carbon atoms, so it is a pentose.
   c) The C – O double bond is on a terminal carbon, so it is an aldose, there are three carbon atoms, so it is a triose.

d) The C – O double bond is on a terminal carbon, so it is an aldose, there are six carbon atoms, so it is a hexose.

41. a) Five of the six carbon atoms have 4 different substituents attached; therefore, there are five chiral centers.
    b) Three of the five carbon atoms have 4 different substituents attached; therefore, there are three chiral centers.
    c) Only one of the four carbon atoms has 4 different substituents attached; therefore, there is only one chiral center.
    d) Three of the four carbon atoms have 4 different substituents attached; therefore, there are four chiral centers.

42. a) Four of the six carbon atoms have 4 different substituents attached, therefore, there are four chiral centers.
    b) Four of the five carbon atoms have 4 different substituents attached, therefore, there are four chiral centers.
    c) Only one of the three carbon atoms has 4 different substituents attached, therefore, there is only one chiral center.
    d) Five of the six carbon atoms have 4 different substituents attached, therefore, there are five chiral centers.

43. Glucose

44. Fructose

45. Hydrolysis reacts with H_2O to split the glycosidic linkage and makes monosaccharides.

46. Hydrolysis reacts with H_2O to split the glycosidic linkage and makes monosaccharides.

47.

glucose

fructose

48.

galactose + glucose → lactose

49. a) Thr = Threonine

b) Ala = Alanine

c) Leu = Leucine

d) Lys = Lysine

$$^+H_3N - \overset{\overset{\displaystyle H}{|}}{\underset{\underset{\underset{\underset{\underset{NH_2}{|}}{CH_2}}{|}}{\underset{\underset{CH_2}{|}}{\underset{\underset{CH_2}{|}}{CH_2}}}}{C}} - \overset{\overset{\displaystyle O}{\|}}{C} - O^-$$

50. a) Val = Valine

$$^+H_3N - \overset{\overset{\displaystyle H}{|}}{\underset{\underset{CH_3}{|}}{\underset{H_3C - C - H}{|}}}C - \overset{\overset{\displaystyle O}{\|}}{C} - O^-$$

b) Phe = Phenylalanine

$$^+H_3N - C - C - O^-$$
with H above C, O double bond on second C, CH_2 below connected to benzene ring

c) Tyr = Tyrosine

$$^+H_3N - C - C - O^-$$
with H above C, O double bond on second C, CH_2 below connected to benzene ring with OH

d) Cys = Cysteine

$$^+H_3N - C - C - O^-$$
with H above C, O double bond on second C, CH_2 below connected to SH

792

51. L – Alanine   D – Alanine

52. L – Cysteine   D – Cysteine

53. Because the N – terminal end and the C – terminal end are specific in a peptide, six tripeptides can be made from the three amino acids: serine, glycine, and cysteine.

Ser – Gly – Cys   Ser – Cys – Gly   Gly – Cys – Ser   Gly – Ser – Cys
Cys – Ser – Gly   Cys – Gly – Ser

54. Because the N – terminal end and the C – terminal end are specific in a peptide, two dipeptides can be made from the amino acids: leucine and serine.

Leu – Ser   Ser – Leu

55. Peptide bonds are formed when the carboxylic end of one amino acid reacts with the amine end of another amino acid.

Serine   Tyrosine

N – terminal   C – terminal end

56. Peptide bonds are formed when the carboxylic end of one amino acid reacts with the amine end of another amino acid.

Valine

$$H_2N-C-C-OH$$

with H and O at the carbonyl; side chain H_3C-C-H and CH_3

Asparagine

$$H_2N-C-C-OH$$

with H and O; side chain CH_2, $C=O$, NH_2

+

N – terminal   C – terminal

$$H_2N-C-C-N-C-C-OH + H_2O$$

Valine residue with H_3C-C-H, CH_3 side chain; Asparagine residue with CH_2, $C=O$, NH_2 side chain

57. Peptide bonds are formed when the carboxylic end of one amino acid reacts with the amine end of another amino acid.

a)   Gln – Met – Cys

$$H_2N-C-C-N-C-C-NH-C-C-OH$$

Gln: CH_2, CH_2, $C=O$, NH_2
Met: CH_2, CH_2, S, CH_3
Cys: CH_2, SH

b)   Ser – Leu – Cys

$$H_2N-C-C-N-C-C-NH-C-C-OH$$

Ser: CH_2, OH
Leu: CH_2, H_3C-CH, CH_3
Cys: CH_2, SH

c) Cys – Leu – Ser

$$H_2N-C-C-N-C-C-NH-C-C-OH$$

Cys: CH_2, SH
Leu: CH_2, H_3C-CH, CH_3
Ser: CH_2, OH

58. a) Ser – Ala – Leu – Cys

H_2N—C(H)(CH$_2$OH)—C(=O)—N—C(H)(CH$_3$)—C(=O)—N(H)—C(H)(CH$_2$—CH(CH$_3$)CH$_3$)—C(=O)—N(H)—C(H)(CH$_2$SH)—C(=O)—OH

b) Gln – Met – Cys – Gly

H_2N—C(H)(CH$_2$CH$_2$C(=O)NH$_2$)—C(=O)—N—C(H)(CH$_2$CH$_2$SCH$_3$)—C(=O)—N(H)—C(H)(CH$_2$SH)—C(=O)—N(H)—C(H)(H)—C(=O)—OH

c) Gly – Cys – Met – Gln

H_2N—C(H)(H)—C(=O)—N—C(H)(CH$_2$SH)—C(=O)—N(H)—C(H)(CH$_2$CH$_2$SCH$_3$)—C(=O)—N(H)—C(H)(CH$_2$CH$_2$C(=O)NH$_2$)—C(=O)—OH

59. This would be a tertiary structure. Tertiary structure refers to the large – scale twists and folds of globular proteins. These are maintained by interactions between the R groups of amino acids that are separated by long distances in the chain sequence.

60. This would be a secondary structure. Secondary structure refers to the repeating patterns in the arrangement of protein chains. These are maintained by interactions between the peptide backbones of amino acids that are close together in the chain sequence or adjacent to each other on neighboring chains.

61. This would be a primary structure. Primary structure is simply the amino acid sequence. It is maintained by the peptide bonds that hold amino acids together.

62. This would be a quarternary structure. Quarternary structure refers to the arrangement of subunits in proteins that have more than one polypeptide chain. Quarternary structure is maintained by interactions between amino acids on the different subunits.

63. a)   Yes, it is a nucleotide and the base is adenine.

    b)   No, it is not a nucleotide, it is the base adenine.

    c)   Yes, it is a nucleotide, and the base is thymine.

    d)   No, it is not a nucleotide, it is the amino acid methionine.

64. a)   No, it is not a nucleotide, it is the base guanine.

    b)   No, it is not a nucleotide, it is a sugar.

c)   Yes, it is a nucleotide and the base is guanine.

d)   No, it is not a nucleotide, it is a dipeptide.

65. The two purine bases are:

Adenine

Guanine

66. The three pyrimidine bases are:

Thymine   Cytosine   Uracil(in RNA)

67. The bases pair in the specific arrangement: adenine always pairs with thymine and guanine always pairs with cytosine.
    The sequence:
    T G T A C G C

    Would have the complementary sequence:

    A C A T G C G

68. The bases pair in the specific arrangement: adenine always pairs with thymine and guanine always pairs with cytosine.
    The sequence:
    A T G A C T G

    Would have the complementary sequence:

    T A C T G A C

69. Every amino acid has a specific codon that is comprised of three nucleotides. So, 154 amino acids, would need 154 codons and 462 nucleotides.

70. Every amino acid has a specific codon that is comprised of three nucleotides. So, the 142 amino acid strand would have 142 codons and 426 nucleotides and the 148 amino acid strand would have 148 codons and 444 nucleotides.

71. a)   Peptide bonds link amino acids to form proteins.
    b)   A glycosidic linkage is the connection between sugar molecules to form carbohydrates.
    c)   An ester linkage forms between the glycol molecule and a fatty acid to form lipids.

72. a)   A nuclotide makes up nucleic acids.
    b)   Amino acids join to make proteins
    c)   Saccharides combine to make complex carbohydrates.

73. A codon is a sequence of three nucleotides with their associated bases. A codon codes for one amino acid.

A nucleotide is a combination of a sugar group, a phosphate group, and a base. While a gene is a sequence of codons that codes for a specific protein.

74. A fatty acid is a long chain carboxylic acid. A triglyceride is a triester formed from the reaction of glyerol and three fatty acid molecules. A phospholipid is similar to a triglyceride but one of the fatty acid groups is replaced with a phosphate group.

75. Write the Lewis structure:

Determine the VSEPR geometry:
   N has three bonding pair and one lone pair which is trigonal pyramidal molecular geometry.
   C_1 has four bonding pair of electrons which gives tetrahedral molecular geometry.
   C_2 has three bonding pair of electrons which gives trigonal planar molecular geometry.
   C_3 has four bonding pair of electrons which gives tetrahedral molecular geometry.
   O has two bonding pair of electrons and two lone pair which gives bent molecular geometry.

76. Write the Lewis structure:

Determine the VSEPR geometry:
   N has three bonding pair and one lone pair which is trigonal pyramidal molecular geometry.
   C_1 has four bonding pair of electrons which gives tetrahedral molecular geometry.
   C_2 has three bonding pair of electrons which gives trigonal planar molecular geometry.
   C_3 has four bonding pair of electrons which gives tetrahedral molecular geometry.
   O_1 has two bonding pair of electrons and two lone pair which gives bent molecular geometry.
   O_2 has two bonding pair of electrons and two lone pair which gives bent molecular geometry.

77. Amino acids which are most likely to be involved in hydrophobic interactions would be ones that have a non polar R group. These would be: valine, leucine, isolucine, phenylalanine.

78. Valine   Glutamic acid

When valine replaces the glutamic acid, the valine has a nonpolar R group. This would decrease the solubility because water is polar. The polar R group of glutamic acid makes it more soluble in water.

79. The reagents added break up the polypeptide but do not rearrange it. Therefore, by comparing the fragments from the two reagents we can deduce the structure of the polypeptide.
   Reagent 1:   Ala – Leu – Phe – Gly – Asn – Lys Trp – Glu – Cys   Gly – Arg
   Reagent 2:   Gly – Arg – Ala – Leu – Phe   Gly – Asn – Lys – Trp   Glu – Cys
   So: the sequence is: Gly – Arg – Ala – Leu – Phe – Gly – Asn – Lys – Trp – Glu – Cys

80. The reagents added break up the polypeptide but do not rearrange it. Therefore, by comparing the fragments from the two reagents we can deduce the structure of the polypeptide.
   Reagent 1:   Gly – Glu – Ser – Lys   Trp – Arg   Leu – Thr – Ala – Trp
   Reagent 2:   Gly – Glu   Ser – Lys – Trp – Arg – Leu   Thr – Ala – Trp
   So: the sequence is: Gly – Glu – Ser – Lys – Trp – Arg – Leu – Thr – Ala – Trp

81. The DNA chain forms with a phosphate linkage between the C_5 carbon on one sugar and the C_3 carbon on the next sugar. When the fake thymine is introduced into the cell, DNA replication cannot occur because the N chain is attached at the C_3 position instead of the – OH group and this will keep future phosphate linkages from forming between the sugars and stop the replication.

82. a)   ribose

C_1, C_2, C_3, and C_4 all have four different groups attached, therefore they are all chiral. C_5 has two hydrogen groups attached, therefore it is not chiral.

b) galactose

C_1, C_2, C_3, C_4 and C_5 all have four different groups attached, therefore they are all chiral. C_6 has two hydrogen groups attached, therefore it is not chiral.

c) 5 – deoxyribose

C_1, C_2, C_3, and C_4 all have four different groups attached, therefore they are all chiral. C_5 has two hydrogen groups attached, therefore it is not chiral.

83. First rearrange the Michaelis – Menton equation to the form of a straight line: $y = mx + b$

$$V_o = \frac{V_{max}[\text{glucose}]}{K_f + [\text{glucose}]} \qquad \frac{1}{V_o} = \frac{K_f + [\text{glucose}]}{V_{max}[\text{glucose}]} \qquad \frac{1}{V_o} = \frac{K_f}{V_{max}[\text{glucose}]} + \frac{[\text{glucose}]}{V_{max}[\text{glucose}]}$$

$$\frac{1}{V_o} = \frac{K_f}{V_{max}[\text{glucose}]} + \frac{1}{V_{max}} \qquad \text{So: } y = \frac{1}{V_o}; \ x = \frac{1}{[\text{glucose}]}; \ m = \frac{K_f}{V_{max}}; \ b = \frac{1}{V_{max}}$$

[glucose]	Vo	1/[glucose]	1/Vo
0.5	12	2.0	0.083
1.0	19	1.0	0.053
2.0	27	0.50	0.037
3.0	32	0.33	0.031
4.0	35	0.25	0.029
		0	

Glucose Transport

$$y = 0.021 = \frac{1}{V_{max}}; \ m = 0.0353 = \frac{K_f}{V_{max}}; \ \text{So } V_{max} = 47.6 \text{ and } K_f = 1.68$$

84. During DNA replication the telomers shorten with each replication. The continual shortening of the telomers causes a limited lifespan of the DNA. The telomerase enzyme synthesizes new telomers. The increased amount of telomerase in cancer cells allows continual reproduction of the cancer DNA and a proliferation of the cancer cells. Future research into stopping the formation of this enzyme or altering its structure may give a way to stop the reproduction of the cancer cells and give a way to treat cancer.

85. Four different amino acids could produce 4 factorial different tetrapeptides which is 24 different tetrapeptides.

86. A three base codon codes for a single amino acid. If there are only three bases, there could only be six different three base codon arrangements. Therefore, you could only code for six different amino acids, and you could not get the 20 different amino acids needed.

87. A completely different genetic code would mean that there is no commonality between the life on another planet and the life on Earth. A genetic code that is similar would mean that there is commonality and the origin of the different lifeforms is the same.

Chapter 22
Chemistry of the Nonmetals

1. Boron nitride contains BN units that are isoelectronic with carbon in the sense that each BN unit contains 8 valence electrons, or 4 per atom (just like carbon). Also the size and electronegativity of the carbon atom is almost equal to the average of a boron atom and nitrogen atom. Therefore, BN forms a number of structures that are similar to those formed by carbon, including nanotubes.

2. The main-group elements are identified as a group by their valence electrons and their electron configuration (s and p block elements).

3. The metallic character of the main-group elements increases going down each column due to the increasing size of the atoms.

4. Silicon does not form a double bond (one sigma and one pi) like carbon, because the silicon atom is too large for there to be substantial overlap between the p orbitals on the two atoms.

5. Silica melts when heated above 1500 °C. After melting, if cooled quickly, silica does not crystallize back into the quartz structure. Instead, the Si atoms and O atoms form a randomly ordered or amorphous structure called a glass. A slow cooling will result in the crystalline quartz structure.

6. A mineral is a naturally occurring, inorganic solid with a definite chemical composition and a crystalline structure. A rock is mixture composed of minerals and/or noncrystalline materials, including organic remains.

7. a) Orthosilicates (or nesosilicates) are minerals, where silicon bonds to oxygen in tetrahedral SiO_4^{4-} polyatomic anions (four electrons are gained, satisfying the octet rule for the oxygen atoms) that are isolated in the structure (not bonded to other tetrahedrons). The minerals require cations that have a total charge of 4+ to neutralize the negative charge.

   b) Amphiboles are minerals with double silicate chains and the repeating unit in the crystal is $Si_4O_{11}^{6-}$. Half of the tetrahedrons are bonded by two of the four corner O atoms, and half of the tetrahedrons are bonded by three of the four corners, bonding the two chains together. The bonding within the double chains is very strong, but the bonding between the double chains is not as strong, often resulting in fibrous-type minerals such as asbestos.

   c) Pyroxenes (or inosilicates) are minerals in which many of the silica tetrahedrons are bonded together forming chains. The formula unit for these chains is the SiO_3^{2-} unit, and the repeating unit in the structure is two formula units ($Si_2O_6^{4-}$). Two of the oxygen atoms are bonded to two silicon atoms (and thus to two other tetrahedrons) on two of the four corners of each tetrahedron. The silicate chains are held together by ionic bonding to metal cations that lie between the chains.

   d) Pyrosilicates (or sorosilicates) are minerals in which the silicate tetrahedrons can also form structures in which two tetrahedrons share one corner, forming the disilicate ion, which has the formula $Si_2O_7^{6-}$. This group requires cations that balance the 6- charge on $Si_2O_7^{6-}$.

   e) Feldspar is a common aluminosilicate where SiO_2 units becomes AlO_2^- upon substitution of aluminum. The negative charge is balanced by a positive counter ion. This leads to a covalent network of $AlSi_3O_8^-$ or $Al_2Si_2O_8^{2-}$ units.

8. Adding boron oxide to silicon oxide glass changes the thermal expansion characteristics of the glass, which is important if glassware intended to be heated. When glass is heated, the outer edge of the glass warms and expands more quickly than the inside edge, creating stress that can result in cracking. Adding boron oxide to glass reduces its thermal expansion, allowing the glass to be heated without cracking.

9. Boron tends to form electron-deficient compounds (compounds in which boron lacks an octet) because it has only three valence electrons. Examples of these compounds are boron halides, such as BF_3 and BCl_3.

10. Three crystalline allotropes of carbon are graphite, diamond and fullerenes.

11. Solid carbon dioxide is referred to as dry ice because at 1 atmosphere it goes directly from a solid to a gas, without going through a liquid or wet phase.

12. The main commercial uses of nitric acid are the production of compounds such as ammonium nitrate that are used as fertilizers and explosives. Phosphoric acid is used to remove rust in steel production; in fertilizer production; and as a flavoring agent and bacterial growth suppressor in soft drinks.

13. About 21% of Earth's atmosphere is composed of O_2.

14. Nitrogen can be separated from air by two methods: (1) by cooling air to below -196 °C, which liquefies it, and then slightly warming it which allows the nitrogen to boils off; and (2) by passing air through certain silicate materials, called zeolites, that have specific size channels that can separate gases of different sizes.

15. Earth's early atmosphere was reducing (instead of oxidizing) and contained hydrogen, methane, ammonia, and carbon dioxide. About 2.7 billion years ago, cyanobacteria (blue-green algae) began to convert the carbon dioxide and water to oxygen by photosynthesis.

16. Ozone is beneficial in its ability to absorb ultraviolet radiation in the upper atmospheres. It is hazardous because of its ability to damage skin and lung tissue. Commercial uses of ozone include killing bacteria, water purification and as a strong oxidizing agent.

17. a) +4. In SiO_2, (Si ox state) + 2(O ox state) = 0. Since O ox state = -2, Si ox state = - 2 (-2) = +4.

   b) +4. In SiO_4^{4-}, (Si ox state) + 4(O ox state) = - 4. Since O ox state = -2, Si ox state = - 4 - 4 (-2) = +4.

   c) +4. In $Si_2O_7^{6-}$, 2(Si ox state) + 7(O ox state) = - 6. Since O ox state = -2, Si ox state = ½ (- 6 - 7 (-2)) = +4.

18. a) +4. In SiO_3^{2-}, (Si ox state) + 3(O ox state) = - 2. Since O ox state = -2, Si ox state = - 2 - 3(-2) = +4.

   b) +4. In $Si_4O_{11}^{6-}$, 4(Si ox state) + 11(O ox state) = - 6. Since O ox state = -2, Si ox state = ¼ (- 6 - 11 (-2)) = +4.

   c) +4. In $Si_2O_5^{2-}$, 2(Si ox state) + 5(O ox state) = - 2. Since O ox state = -2, Si ox state = ½ (- 2 - 5 (-2)) = +4.

19. Three SiO_4^{4-} units have a total charge of – 12. In trying to combine Ca^{2+} and Al^{3+} to get a total charge of + 12, the only possible combination is to use 3 Ca^{2+} and 2 Al^{3+} ions. The formula unit is $Ca_3Al_2(SiO_4)_3$.

20. Two SiO_3^{2-} units have a total charge of – 4. In trying to combine Mn^{2+} and Mg^{2+} to get a total charge of + 4, the only possible combination is to use one of each ion. The formula unit is $MgMn(SiO_3)_2$. Because both cations have the same charge, the real requirement is that 2 cations are present for every 2 anions.

21. Since OH has a -1 charge, Al has a +3 charge and Si_2O_5 has a -2 charge, 2(Al ox state) + 1(Si_2O_5 charge) + x (OH⁻ charge) = 0 so 2(+3) + 1(-2) + x(-1) = 0 and x = 4.

22. Since OH has a -1 charge, Ca has a +2 charge, Mg has a +2 charge, and amphiboles have $Si_4O_{11}^{6-}$, 2(Ca ox state) + 5(Mg ox state) + 2(Si_4O_{11} charge) + x (OH⁻ charge) = 0 so 2(+2) + 5(+2) + 2(-6) + x(-1) = 0 and x = 2.

23. In Table 22.2, SiO_4 has a - 4 charge and it belongs to the class of orthosilicates, where the silicate tetrahedra stand alone, not linked to each other. The – 4 charge balances with a common oxidation state of Zr of +4.

24. In Table 22.2, SiO_3 has a - 2 charge and it belongs to the class of pyroxenes, where the silicate tetrahedra form single chains. The – 2 charge balances with a oxidation state of Ca of +2.

25. Ca has a +2 charge, Mg has a +2 charge, Fe commonly has a charge of +2 or +3, and OH has a charge of – 1. So far the charge balance is 2(+2) + 4(+2) + 1(+2 or +3) + (Si_7AlO_{22} charge) + 2(-1) = 0 or Si_7AlO_{22} charge = - 12 or – 13. Looking at Table 22.2, $Si_4O_{11}^{6-}$ units are the best match. If we double the unit and

replaced 1/8th of the Si's by Al, the new unit will be Si_7AlO_{22} and the charge will be 2(- 6) -1 = -13. The charge on Fe will be +3 and the class is amphibole, with a double chain structure.

26. Ca has a +2 charge, Fe commonly has a charge of +2 or +3, and SiO_3 has a - 2 charge. So far the charge balance is 1(+2) + 1(+2 or +3) + 2(- 2) = 0 and the charge on Fe will be +2. It belongs to the class of pyroxenes, where the silicate tetrahedra form single chains.

27. **Given:** $Na_2[B_4O_5(OH)_4] \cdot 3 H_2O$ = kernite, 1.0×10^3 kg of kernite-bearing ore, 0.98 % by mass kernite, 65 % B recovery   **Find:** g boron recovered

   Conceptual plan: kg ore → g ore → g kernite → g B possible → g B recovered

$$\frac{1000\,g}{1\,kg} \qquad \frac{0.98\,g\,kernite}{100\,g\,ore} \qquad \frac{4(10.81)\,g\,B}{291.23\,g\,kernite} \qquad \frac{65\,g\,B\,recovered}{100\,g\,B}$$

   Solution:

$$1.0 \times 10^3\,\cancel{kg\,ore} \times \frac{1000\,\cancel{g\,ore}}{1\,\cancel{kg\,ore}} \times \frac{0.98\,\cancel{g\,kernite}}{100\,\cancel{g\,ore}} \times \frac{4(10.81)\,\cancel{g\,B}}{291.23\,\cancel{g\,kernite}} \times \frac{65\,g\,B\,recovered}{100\,\cancel{g\,B}} = 950\,g\,B\,recovered$$

   Check: The units (g) are correct. The magnitude of the answer makes physical sense because there is very little mineral in the ore, a low recovery and little B in the ore.

28. **Given:** $NaCaB_5O_9 \cdot 8 H_2O$ = ulexite, 5.00×10^3 kg of ulexite-bearing ore, 0.032 % by mass ulexite, 88 % B recovery   **Find:** g boron recovered

   Conceptual plan: kg ore → g ore → g ulexite → g B possible → g B recovered

$$\frac{1000\,g}{1\,kg} \qquad \frac{0.032\,g\,ulexite}{100\,g\,ore} \qquad \frac{5(10.81)\,g\,B}{405.14\,g\,ulexite} \qquad \frac{88\,g\,B\,recovered}{100\,g\,B}$$

   Solution:

$$5.00 \times 10^3\,\cancel{kg\,ore} \times \frac{1000\,\cancel{g\,ore}}{1\,\cancel{kg\,ore}} \times \frac{0.032\,\cancel{g\,ulexite}}{100\,\cancel{g\,ore}} \times \frac{5(10.81)\,\cancel{g\,B}}{405.14\,\cancel{g\,ulexite}} \times \frac{88\,g\,B\,recovered}{100\,\cancel{g\,B}} = 190\,g\,B\,recovered$$

   Check: The units (g) are correct. The magnitude of the answer makes physical sense because there is very little mineral in the ore, and little B in the ore.

29. The bond angles are different in BCl_3 versus NCl_3 because there B has 3 valence electrons and N has 5 valence electrons. The boron compound does not obey the octet rule and B has sp^2 hybridization and a trigonal planar geometry. The nitrogen compound does obey the octet rule, has a lone pair of electrons and N has sp^3 hybridization and a trigonal pyramidal geometry (based on a tetrahedral geometry).

30. The boron atom uses sp^2 hybridized orbitals to form sigma bonds with the three halogen atoms. Because boron's three valence electrons are used to form the sigma bonds, the third p orbital of boron is an empty orbital that is perpendicular to the trigonal plane of the molecule. Each halogen atom has a filled p orbital, also perpendicular to the trigonal plane molecule. The empty p orbital on the boron atom can overlap with the full p orbitals on the halogens, forming a coordinate-covalent type bond that, like a normal double bond, is shorter and stronger than a single bond.

31. a) Looking at Figure 22.11, $B_6H_6^{2-}$ has 6 vertices and 8 faces, since it has an octahedral shape.

   b) $B_{12}H_{12}^{2-}$ has the formula of a *closo*-borane $(B_nH_n^{2-})$ has 12 vertices and 20 faces, since it has an icosohedral shape.

32. a) $B_4H_4^{2-}$ has the formula of a *closo*-borane $(B_nH_n^{2-})$ has 4 vertices and 4 faces, since it has a tetrahedral shape.

   b) $B_9H_9^{2-}$ has the formula of a *closo*-borane $(B_nH_n^{2-})$ has 9 vertices and 14 faces, since it has a triaugmented triangular prism.

33. *Closo*-boranes have the formula $B_nH_n^{2-}$ and form fully closed polyhedra with triangular sides. Each of the vertices in the polyhedra is a boron atom with an attached hydrogen atom. *Nido*-boranes, named from the Latin word for *net*, have the formula B_nH_{n+4}. They consist of a cage of boron atoms missing one corner. *Arachno*-boranes, named from the Greek word for *web*, have the formula B_nH_{n+6}. They consist of a cage of boron atoms that is missing two or three corners.

34. Elemental boron is also used in the nuclear energy industry, because boron readily absorbs neutrons and is therefore used in the control rods of nuclear reactors. When the nuclear reaction needs to be slowed down, the rods are inserted into the reactor to absorb the neutrons.

35. Graphite is a good lubricant, because the structure has strong covalent bonds within the sheets of the structure, but weak interactions between the sheets. The diamond structure consists of carbon atoms connected to four other carbon atoms at the corners of a tetrahedron. This bonding extends throughout three dimensions, making giant molecules described as network covalent solids. There are no weak interactions in the diamond structure.

36. The electrons in the extended pi bonding network within a sheet make graphite a good electric conductor in the direction of the plane of the sheets. Because the diamond structure is a three dimensional network, this overlap of orbitals is not possible.

37. Regular charcoal is in large chunks that still resemble the wood from which it is made. Activated charcoal is treated with steam to break up the chunks into a finely divided powder with a high surface area.

38. The amorphous low density structure of activated charcoal results in a large surface area (greater than 10^3 m^2/g) that makes the particles extremely efficient at absorbing other molecules onto their surfaces. The diamond structure is ordered and dense with very little surface area.

39. Ionic carbides are composed of carbon and low-electronegativity metals such as the alkali metals and alkaline earth metals. Most of the ionic carbides contain the dicarbide ion, C_2^{2-}, commonly called the acetylide ion. Covalent carbides are composed of carbon and low-electronegativity nonmetals or metalloids. The most important covalent carbide is silicon carbide (SiC) a very hard material.

40. Write all species involved in the reaction. Balance reaction by balancing Si then C then H to get:
$$[(CH_3)_2Si]_8 \ (s) \xrightarrow{\text{Heat}} 8\,CH_4 \ (g) \ + \ 8\,H_2 \ (g) \ + 8\,SiC \ (s).$$

41. a)   As the pressure is reduced, the solid will be converted directly to a gas.

    b)   As the temperature is reduced, the gas will be converted to a liquid and then to a solid.

    c)   As the temperature is increased, the solid will be converted directly to a gas.

42. a)   As the temperature is reduced, the supercritical fluid will be converted to a liquid and then a solid.

    b)   As the pressure is increased, the gas will be converted to a liquid and then to a solid.

c) As the temperature is increased, the solid will be converted to a liquid and then to a gas.

43. a) The reaction will be similar to that of iron oxide and carbon monoxide: $CO\ (g)\ +\ CuO\ (s)\ \xrightarrow{\text{Heat}}$ $CO_2\ (g)\ +\ Cu\ (s)$. Note that the oxidation state of carbon increases by 2 and the oxidation state of Cu decreases by 2.

   b) This reaction is discussed in section 22.5, $SiO_2\ (s)\ +\ 3\ C\ (s)\ \xrightarrow{\text{Heat}}\ SiC\ (s)\ +\ 2\ CO\ (g)$.

   c) This reaction is discussed in section 22.5, $CO\ (g)\ +\ S\ (s)\ \xrightarrow{\text{Heat}}\ COS\ (g)$.

44. a) This reaction is discussed in section 22.5, $CO\ (g)\ +\ Cl_2\ (g)\ \rightarrow\ COCl_2\ (g)$.

   b) In this reaction the Mg must be oxidized (it can only have oxidation states of 0 and +2) and so the carbon is reduced: $CO_2\ (g)\ +\ 2\ Mg\ (s)\ \rightarrow\ C\ (s)\ +\ 2\ MgO\ (s)$. Note that the oxidation state of carbon decreases by 4 and the oxidation state of Mg increases by 2 so we need twice as many Mg atoms as C atoms.

   c) This reaction is a combination reaction. Remember that sulfur will form the sulfide ion with a -2 charge, since it is Group 6A. The product then becomes CS_2, where carbon has an oxidation state of + 4. Two sulfurs must be reduced for every carbon oxidized so the reaction is: $2\ S\ (s)\ +\ C\ (s)\ \rightarrow\ CS_2$ (g).

45. a) +2. In CO, (C ox state) + (O ox state) = 0. Since O ox state = -2, C ox state = +2.

   b) +4. In CO_2, (C ox state) + 2(O ox state) = 0. Since O ox state = -2, C ox state = - 2 (-2) = +4.

   c) +4/3. In C_3O_2, 3(C ox state) + 2(O ox state) = 0. Since O ox state = -2, C ox state = 1/3 (- 2 (-2)) = +4/3.

46. Citric acid ($C_6H_8O_7$) is an organic triprotic acid, with three –COOH groups. Sodium bicarbonate ($NaHCO_3$) will dissociate into Na^+ and HCO_3^-. The three acidic protons of the acid will react with three bicarbonate ions to generate carbon dioxide and water. The overall reaction is: $C_6H_8O_7\ (aq)\ +\ 3\ NaHCO_3\ (aq)\ \rightarrow$ $Na_3C_6H_5O_7\ +\ 3\ CO_2\ (g)\ +\ 3\ H_2O\ (l)$.

47. Even though there is a tremendous amount of N_2 gas in the atmosphere, the strong triple bond in elemental nitrogen renders it unusable by plants. In order to be used as fertilizer, elemental nitrogen has to be fixed, which means that it has to be converted into a nitrogen-containing compound such as NH_3.

48. Diatomic nitrogen is unusable by plants because the nitrogen – nitrogen triple bond is so strong. A major source of nitrogen for plants is fertilizers, such as ammonium nitrate.

49. White phosphorus consists of P_4 molecules in a tetrahedral shape, with the phosphorus atoms at the corners of the tetrahedron as shown in Figure 22.19. The bond angles between the three P atoms on any one face of the tetrahedron is small (60°) and strained, making the P_4 molecule unstable and reactive. When heated to

about 300 °C in the absence of air, white phosphorus slightly changes its structure to a different allotrope called red phosphorus, which is amorphous. The general structure of red phosphorus is similar to that of white phosphorus, except that one of the bonds between two phosphorus atoms in the tetrahedron is broken, as shown in Figure 22.20. These two phosphorus atoms then link to other phosphorus atoms making chains that can vary in structure. The red phosphorous structure is more stable because there is less strain when the linkage is changed.

50. Red phosphorus is made by heating white phosphorous to about 300 °C in the absence of air. Black phosphorus is made by heating white phosphorous under pressure.

51. **Given:** saltpeter (KNO_3) and Chile saltpeter ($NaNO_3$)   **Find:** mass percent N in each mineral
   Conceptual plan: mineral formula → mass percent nitrogen

$$\text{mass percent nitrogen} = \frac{14.01 \text{ g}}{\text{formula weight of mineral}} \times 100 \%$$

Solution: for KNO_3 :

$$\text{mass percent nitrogen} = \frac{14.01 \text{ g}}{\text{formula weight of mineral}} \times 100 \% = \frac{14.01 \text{ g}}{101.11 \text{ g}} \times 100 \% = 13.86 \%$$

and for $NaNO_3$: $\text{mass percent nitrogen} = \dfrac{14.01 \text{ g}}{\text{formula weight of mineral}} \times 100 \% = \dfrac{14.01 \text{ g}}{85.00 \text{ g}} \times 100 \% = 16.48 \%$.

Check: The units (%) are correct. The relative magnitudes of the answers make physical sense because K is heavier than Na.

52. **Given:** apatite ($Ca_3(PO_4)_2$)   **Find:** mass percent P in mineral
   Conceptual plan: mineral formula → mass percent nitrogen

$$\text{mass percent phosphorous} = \frac{2 (30.97 \text{ g})}{\text{formula weight of mineral}} \times 100 \%$$

Solution: for $Ca_3(PO_4)_2$:

$$\text{mass percent phosphorous} = \frac{2 (30.97 \text{ g})}{\text{formula weight of mineral}} \times 100 \% = \frac{61.94 \text{ g}}{310.18 \text{ g}} \times 100 \% = 19.97 \% .$$

Check: The units (%) are correct. The magnitude of the answer makes physical sense because there is a lot of Ca and O in the mineral.

53. **Given:** decomposition of hydrogen azide (HN_3) to its elements
   Find: stability at room temperature, stability at any temperature   **Other:** Appendix IIB
   Conceptual plan: Write reaction. Evaluate $\Delta G°_{rxn}$ then determine if $\Delta G_{rxn} > 0$ at any T.
   $$\Delta G = \Delta H_{rxn} - T\Delta S_{rxn}$$
   Solution: $HN_3 (g) \rightarrow 3/2 \ N_2 (g) + 1/2 \ H_2 (g)$, at 25 °C $\Delta G°_{rxn} = - \Delta G°_f (HN_3 (g)) = - 1422$ kJ/mol so the decomposition is spontaneous at room temperature. $\Delta H°_{rxn} = - \Delta H°_f (HN_3 (g)) = - 1447$ kJ/mol, and $\Delta S°_{rxn} > 0$ since the decomposition generates more moles of gas. Since $\Delta G = \Delta H_{rxn} - T\Delta S_{rxn}$ we see that both the enthalpy and the entropy term favor decomposition and so ΔG_{rxn} is always negative and hydrogen azide is unstable at all temperature.
   Check: Azides are used as explosives, so it is not surprising that they are unstable.

54. **Given:** decomposition of dinitrogen monoxide (N_2O) to its elements
   Find: stability at room temperature, stability at any temperature   **Other:** Appendix IIB
   Conceptual plan: Write reaction. Evaluate $\Delta G°_{rxn}$ then determine if $\Delta G_{rxn} > 0$ at any T.
   $$\Delta G = \Delta H_{rxn} - T\Delta S_{rxn}$$
   Solution: $N_2O (g) \rightarrow N_2 (g) + 1/2 \ O_2 (g)$, at 25 °C $\Delta G°_{rxn} = - \Delta G°_f (N_2O (g)) = - 103.7$ kJ/mol so the decomposition is spontaneous at room temperature. $\Delta H°_{rxn} = - \Delta H°_f (N_2O (g)) = - 81.6$ kJ/mol, and $\Delta S°_{rxn} > 0$ since the decomposition generates more moles of gas. Since $\Delta G = \Delta H_{rxn} - T\Delta S_{rxn}$ we see that both the enthalpy and the entropy term favor decomposition and so ΔG_{rxn} is always negative and dinitrogen monoxide is unstable at all temperature.
   Check: Dinitrogen monoxide is a good oxidizing agent and, so it is not surprising that it is unstable.

55. a)   This reaction is a decomposition reaction, $NH_4NO_3 (aq) + \text{heat} \rightarrow N_2O (g) + 2 \ H_2O (l)$.

b) This reaction is discussed in section 22.6, $3 NO_2 (g) + H_2O (l) \rightarrow 2 HNO_3 (aq) + NO (g)$.

c) This reaction is discussed in section 22.6, $2 PCl_3 (g) + O_2 (g) \rightarrow 2 POCl_3 (l)$.

56. a) This reaction is discussed in section 22.6, $NO (g) + NO_2 (g) \rightarrow N_2O_3 (l)$.

b) This reaction is discussed in section 22.6, $4 PH_3 (g) + heat \rightarrow P_4 (s) + 6 H_2 (g)$.

c) This reaction is discussed in section 22.6, $P_4 (s) + 5 O_2 (g) \rightarrow P_4O_{10} (s)$.

57. For N_3^-: 3(N ox state) = - 1, so N ox state = - 1/3.
For $N_2H_5^+$: 2(N ox state) + 5(H ox state) = +1. Since H ox state = +1, N ox state = ½ (1 - 5(+1)) = - 2.
For NO_3^-: 1(N ox state) + 3(O ox state) = -1. Since O ox state = - 2, N ox state = - 1 - 3(-2) = +5.
For NH_4^+: 1(N ox state) + 4(H ox state) = +1. Since H ox state = +1, N ox state = +1 - 4(+1) = - 3.
For NO_2^-: 1(N ox state) + 2(O ox state) = -1. Since O ox state = - 2, N ox state = - 1 - 2(-2) = +3.
So $NO_3^- > NO_2^- > N_3^- > N_2H_5^+ > NH_4^+$.

58. For NO_2: 1(N ox state) + 2(O ox state) = 0. Since O ox state = - 2, N ox state = - 2(-2) = + 4.
For HNO_3: 1(H ox state) + 1(N ox state) + 3(O ox state) = 0. Since H ox state = +1 and O ox state = - 2, N ox state =   - 1 - 3(-2) = +5.
For NO: 1(N ox state) + (O ox state) = 0. Since O ox state = - 2, N ox state = - 1(-2) = +2.
So N is being oxidized and reduced and NO_2 is both the oxidizing agent and the reducing agent.

59. P has 5 valence electrons and Cl has 7 valence electrons and so PCl_3 has 5 + 3(7) = 26 valence electrons and PCl_5 has 5 + 5(7) = 40 valence electrons. Since the electronegativity of P is less than the electronegativity of Cl, the P is in the middle. So the Lewis Dot structures are :

Notice that the PCl_5 violates the octet rule, which is allowed since P is in the 3rd row of the periodic table and Cl is a fairly small atom.
Since the PCl_3 has four electron groups surrounding the P atom, the orbital geometry is tetrahedral. Since there is one lone pair the VSEPR geometry is trigonal pyramidal.

Since the PCl_5 has five electron groups surrounding the P atom, the VSEPR geometry is trigonal bipyramidal.

60. For NO_2^+: 1(N ox state) + 2(O ox state) = +1. Since O ox state = - 2, N ox state = 1 - 2(-2) = +5.
For NO_3^-: 1(N ox state) + 3(O ox state) = -1. Since O ox state = - 2, N ox state = - 1 - 3(-2) = +5.
N has 5 valence electrons and O has 6 valence electrons and so NO_2^+ has 5 + 2(6) -1 = 16 valence electrons and NO_3^- has 5 + 3(6) + 1 = 24 valence electrons. Since the electronegativity of N is less than the electronegativity of O, the N is in the middle. So the Lewis Dot structures are :

Notice that the N in both structures has a formal charge of +1 (since it has 4 bonds) and oxygens with only 1 bond have a formal charge of – 1; and resonance structures are necessary for the nitrate ion (as seen in Example 9.7). Since the NO_2^+ has two electron groups surrounding the N atom, the VSEPR geometry is linear.
Since the NO_3^- has three electron groups surrounding the N atom, the VSEPR geometry is trigonal planar.

61. **Given:** urea ($CO(NH_2)_2$) react with water to produce 23 g ammonium carbonate   **Find:** g of urea needed
Conceptual Plan: Write a balanced equation.
g $(NH_4)_2CO_3$ → mol $(NH_4)_2CO_3$ → mol $CO(NH_2)_2$ → g $CO(NH_2)_2$

$$\frac{1 \text{ mol } (NH_4)_2CO_3}{96.04 \text{ g } (NH_4)_2CO_3} \quad \frac{1 \text{ mol } CO(NH_2)_2}{1 \text{ mol } (NH_4)_2CO_3} \quad \frac{60.03 \text{ g } CO(NH_2)_2}{1 \text{ mol } CO(NH_2)_2}$$

Solution: $CO(NH_2)_2 (aq) + 2 H_2O (l) \rightarrow (NH_4)_2CO_3 (aq)$ then

$$23 \text{ g } (NH_4)_2CO_3 \times \frac{1 \text{ mol } (NH_4)_2CO_3}{96.04 \text{ g } (NH_4)_2CO_3} \times \frac{1 \text{ mol } CO(NH_2)_2}{1 \text{ mol } (NH_4)_2CO_3} \times \frac{60.03 \text{ g } CO(NH_2)_2}{1 \text{ mol } CO(NH_2)_2} = 14 \text{ g } CO(NH_2)_2$$

Check: The units (g) are correct. The magnitude of the answer (14) makes physical sense because we are generating 23 g of $(NH_4)_2CO_3$. Since we are adding water to the urea, the amount of urea must be less than 23 g.

62. Phosphine is less polar than ammonia because P has a lower electronegativity than N, so the P – H bonds are less polar.

63. Tetraphosphorus hexaoxide, P_4O_6 (s), forms when the amount of oxygen is limited, and tetraphosphorus decaoxide, P_4O_{10} (s), is formed when greater amounts of oxygen are available.

64. In each reaction the P_4O_{10} will extract water from the other reagent and make phosphoric acid and the other desired component.
    a) P_4O_{10} (s) + 12 HNO_3 (aq) → 4 H_3PO_4 (aq) + 6 N_2O_5 (s). Notice that this is not a redox reaction.

    b) P_4O_{10} (s) + 6 H_2SO_4 (aq) → 4 H_3PO_4 (aq) + 6 SO_3 (g). Notice that this is not a redox reaction.

65. The major commercial production method of elemental oxygen is the fractionation of air. Air is cooled until its components liquefy. Then the air is warmed, and components such as N_2 and Ar are separated, leaving oxygen behind.

66. Oxygen is critical for life since the oxidation of biomolecules by oxygen provides energy for most living systems on Earth. A drop in the concentration of molecular oxygen would limit these vital reactions. We need to breathe oxygen to live. Fire fighters, mountain climbers and scuba divers take oxygen tanks with them when they go into environments that are low in oxygen. Henry's Law describes the amount of dissolved oxygen decreases with decreasing oxygen pressures, so fish will not have access to the oxygen they need to live if the amount of oxygen in the air above the body of water drops significantly. A drastic increase in the concentration of oxygen can be unhealthy as well, since high concentration of oxygen in blood can lead to oxygen poisoning. It is for this reason that scuba divers under certain conditions use helium/oxygen blends when they dive.

67. In oxides the oxidation state of O is -2, in peroxides it is -1 and in superoxides it is – ½. Alkali metals and alkaline earth metals have only two possible oxidation states 0 and +1 for the alkali metals and +2 for alkaline earth metals.
    a) LiO_2 is a superoxide, since 1(Li ox state) + 2(O ox state) = 0 and O ox state = - ½(1) = - 1/2.

    b) CaO is an oxide, since 1(Ca ox state) + 2(O ox state) = 0 and O ox state = - 1(+2) = - 2.

    c) K_2O_2 is a peroxide, since 2(K ox state) + 2(O ox state) = 0 and O ox state = - ½(2(+1)) = - 1.

68. In oxides the oxidation state of O is -2, in peroxides it is -1 and in superoxides it is – ½. Alkali metals and alkaline earth metals have only two possible oxidation states 0 and +1 for the alkali metals and +2 for alkaline earth metals.
    a) MgO is an oxide, since 1(Mg ox state) + 2(O ox state) = 0 and O ox state = - 1(+2) = - 2.

    b) Na_2O_2 is a peroxide, since 2(Na ox state) + 2(O ox state) = 0 and O ox state = - ½(2(+1)) = - 1.

    c) CsO_2 is a superoxide, since 1(Cs ox state) + 2(O ox state) = 0 and O ox state = - ½(1) = - 1/2.

69. Initially, liquid sulfur becomes less viscous when heated because the S_8 rings have greater thermal energy which overcomes intermolecular forces. Above 150 °C the rings break and the broken rings entangle one another, causing greater viscosity. Above 180 °C the intermolecular forces weaken and the solution becomes less viscous.

70. A natural source of SO_2 is volcanic activity. The largest commercial source of SO_2 is the Claus process which oxidizes H_2S in a two-step process.

71. **Given**: 1.0 L of 5.00 x 10^{-5} M Na_2S **Find**: maximum g of metal sulfide that can dissolve
    Other: K_{sp} (PbS) = 9.04 x 10^{-29}, K_{sp} (PbS) = 2 x 10^{-25}
    Conceptual Plan: M Na_2S → M S^{2-} → **M metal sulfide** → **mol metal sulfide** → **g metal sulfide**

Na_2S (s) → 2 Na^+(aq) + S^{2-} (aq) ICE Chart $M = \dfrac{mol}{L}$ $\mathfrak{M}$

Solution: Since 1 S^{2-} ion is generated for each Na_2S, $[S^{2-}] = 5.00 \times 10^{-5}$ M Na_2S.

a)

	$PbS(s) \rightleftharpoons Pb^{2+}(aq) + S^{2-}(aq)$	
Initial	0.00	5.00×10^{-5}
Change	S	S
Equil	S	$5.00 \times 10^{-5} + S$

K_{sp} (PbS) = $[Pb^{2+}][S^{2-}] = 9.04 \times 10^{-29} = S(5.00 \times 10^{-5} + S)$.

Since $S \ll 5.00 \times 10^{-5}$, $9.04 \times 10^{-29} = S(5.00 \times 10^{-5})$, and $S = 1.81 \times 10^{-24}$ M. (Note that assumption that S was very small was good.) Since there is 1.0 L of solution we can dissolve at most 1.8×10^{-24} moles of PbS then 1.8×10^{-24} mol PbS $\times \dfrac{239.3 \text{ g PbS}}{1 \text{ mol PbS}} = 4.3 \times 10^{-22}$ g PbS.

b)

	$ZnS(s) \rightleftharpoons Zn^{2+}(aq) + S^{2-}(aq)$	
Initial	0.00	5.00×10^{-5}
Change	S	S
Equil	S	$5.00 \times 10^{-5} + S$

K_{sp} (ZnS) = $[Zn^{2+}][S^{2-}] = 2 \times 10^{-25} = S(5.00 \times 10^{-5} + S)$.

Since $S \ll 5.00 \times 10^{-5}$, $2 \times 10^{-25} = S(5.00 \times 10^{-5})$, and $S = 4 \times 10^{-21}$ M. (Note that assumption that S was very small was good.) Since there is 1.0 L of solution we can dissolve at most 4×10^{-21} moles of ZnS then

4×10^{-21} mol ZnS $\times \dfrac{97.48 \text{ g ZnS}}{1 \text{ mol ZnS}} = 4 \times 10^{-19}$ g ZnS.

Check: The units (g) are correct. The magnitude of the answer makes physical sense because the solubility constants are so small. The amount of PBS that can dissolve is less than the amount of ZnS because the solubility constant is much smaller.

72. **Given:** coal 1.1 % by mass S, 2.0×10^4 kg of coal   **Find:** g $CaSO_4$ produced
    Conceptual plan: kg coal $\rightarrow$ g coal $\rightarrow$ g S $\rightarrow$ mol S $\rightarrow$ mol $CaSO_4 \rightarrow$ g $CaSO_4$

$$\frac{1000 \text{ g}}{1 \text{ kg}} \quad \frac{1.1 \text{ g S}}{100 \text{ g coal}} \quad \frac{1 \text{ mol S}}{32.07 \text{ g S}} \quad \frac{1 \text{ mol } CaSO_4}{1 \text{ mol S}} \quad \frac{136.15 \text{ g } CaSO_4}{1 \text{ mol } CaSO_4}$$

Solution:

2.0×10^4 kg coal $\times \dfrac{1000 \text{ g coal}}{1 \text{ kg coal}} \times \dfrac{1.1 \text{ g S}}{100 \text{ g coal}} \times \dfrac{1 \text{ mol S}}{32.07 \text{ g S}} \times \dfrac{1 \text{ mol } CaSO_4}{1 \text{ mol S}} \times \dfrac{136.15 \text{ g } CaSO_4}{1 \text{ mol } CaSO_4} = 9.3 \times 10^5$ g $CaSO_4$.

Check: The units (g) are correct. The magnitude of the answer makes physical sense because even though calcium sulfate is heavier than sulfur, the sulfur content in the coal is lower.

73. **Given:** iron pyrite (FeS_2) roasted generating S_2 (g), 5.5 kg of iron pyrite   **Find:** balanced reaction and V S_2 at STP
    Conceptual plan: Write reaction then kg FeS_2 $\rightarrow$ g FeS_2 $\rightarrow$ mol FeS_2 $\rightarrow$ mol $S_2 \rightarrow$ V S_2

$$\frac{1000 \text{ g}}{1 \text{ kg}} \quad \frac{1 \text{ mol } FeS_2}{119.99 \text{ g } FeS_2} \quad \frac{1 \text{ mol } S_2}{2 \text{ mol } FeS_2} \quad \frac{22.414 \text{ L } S_2}{1 \text{ mol } S_2}$$

Solution: $2 FeS_2 (s) \xrightarrow{\text{Heat}} 2 FeS (s) + S_2 (g)$, then

5.5 kg $FeS_2 \times \dfrac{1000 \text{ g } FeS_2}{1 \text{ kg } FeS_2} \times \dfrac{1 \text{ mol } FeS_2}{119.99 \text{ g } FeS_2} \times \dfrac{1 \text{ mol } S_2}{2 \text{ mol } FeS_2} \times \dfrac{22.414 \text{ L } S_2}{1 \text{ mol } S_2} = 510$ L S_2.

Check: The units (L) are correct. The magnitude of the answer makes physical sense because there is much more than a mole of iron pyrite, so the volume of gas is many time 22 L.

74. **Given:** Claus process, 1.0 kg of S (s) produced   **Find:** overall balanced reaction and V H_2S at STP
    Conceptual plan: Write reaction then kg S $\rightarrow$ g S $\rightarrow$ mol S $\rightarrow$ mol H_2S $\rightarrow$ V H_2S

$$\frac{1000 \text{ g}}{1 \text{ kg}} \quad \frac{1 \text{ mol S}}{32.07 \text{ g S}} \quad \frac{1 \text{ mol } S_2}{2 \text{ mol } FeS_2} \quad \frac{22.414 \text{ L } H_2S}{1 \text{ mol } H_2S}$$

Solution:

$$2\,H_2S\,(g) + 3\,O_2\,(g) \rightarrow \overline{2\,SO_2\,(g)} + H_2O\,(g)$$

$$\underline{4\,H_2S\,(g) + \overline{2\,SO_2\,(g)} \rightarrow 6\,S\,(s) + H_2O\,(g)} \quad \text{then}$$

$$6\,H_2S\,(g) + 3\,O_2\,(g) \rightarrow 6\,S\,(s) + 2\,H_2O\,(g)$$

$$1.0\,\cancel{kg\,S} \times \frac{1000\,\cancel{g\,S}}{1\,\cancel{kg\,S}} \times \frac{1\,\cancel{mol\,S}}{32.07\,\cancel{g\,S}} \times \frac{6\,\cancel{mol\,H_2S}}{6\,\cancel{mol\,S}} \times \frac{22.414\,L\,H_2S}{1\,\cancel{mol\,H_2S}} = 7.0 \times 10^2\,L\,H_2S.$$

Check: The units (L) are correct. The magnitude of the answer makes physical sense because there is much more than a mole of sulfur generated, so the volume of gas is many time 22 L.

75. a) + 2. In XeF_2, 1(Xe ox state) + 2(F ox state) = 0. Since F ox state = - 1, Xe ox state = - 2(- 1) = + 2. Xe has 8 valence electrons and F has 7 valence electrons and so XeF_2 has 8 + 2(7) = 22. Since the electronegativity of Xe is less than the electronegativity of F, the Xe is in the middle. So the Lewis Dot structure is :

Notice that the XeF_2 violates the octet rule, which is allowed since Xe is in the 5th row of the periodic table and F is a fairly small atom. Since there are five electron groups surrounding the Xe atom, the orbital geometry is trigonal bipyramidal. Since there are three lone pairs the VSEPR geometry is linear.

b) +6. In XeF_6, 1(Xe ox state) + 6(F ox state) = 0. Since F ox state = - 1, Xe ox state = - 6(- 1) = + 6. Xe has 8 valence electrons and F has 7 valence electrons and so XeF_6 has 8 + 6(7) = 50. Since the electronegativity of Xe is less than the electronegativity of F, the Xe is in the middle. So the Lewis Dot structure is shown to the right. Notice that the XeF_6 violates the octet rule, which is allowed since Xe is in the 5th row of the periodic table and F is a fairly small atom. Since there are six electron groups surrounding the Xe atom, the VSEPR geometry is octahedral.

c) +6. In $XeOF_4$, 1(Xe ox state) + 1(O ox state) + 4(F ox state) = 0. Since F ox state = - 1, and O ox state = -2, Xe ox state = - (1(-2) + 4(- 1) = + 6. Xe has 8 valence electrons, O has 6 valence electrons, and F has 7 valence electrons and so $XeOF_4$ has 8 + 1(6) + 4(7) = 42. Since the electronegativity of Xe is less than the electronegativity of F, the Xe is in the middle. Oxygen needs a double bond. So the Lewis Dot structure is shown to the right. Notice that the $XeOF_4$ violates the octet rule, which is allowed since Xe is in the 5th row of the periodic table and O and F are fairly small atoms. Since there are six electron groups surrounding the Xe atom, the orbital geometry is octahedral. Since there is one lone pair the VSEPR geometry is square pyramidal.

76. a) Br has 7 valence electrons and F has 7 valence electrons and so BrF_4^- has 7 + 4(7) +1 = 36. Since the electronegativity of Br is less than the electronegativity of F, the Br is in the middle. So the Lewis Dot structure is shown on the right. Notice that the BrF_4^- violates the octet rule, which is allowed since Br is in the 4th row of the periodic table and F is a fairly small atom. Br has a formal charge of -1. Since there are six electron groups surrounding the Br atom, the orbital geometry is octahedral. Since there are two lone pairs the VSEPR geometry is square planar. **Note: Figure needs brackets and charge.**

b)I has 7 valence electrons and F has 7 valence electrons and so IF_3 has 7 + 3(7) = 28. Since the electronegativity of I is less than the electronegativity of F, the I is in the middle. So the Lewis Dot structure is shown to the right. Notice that the IF_3 violates the octet rule, which is allowed since I is in the 5th row of the periodic table and F is a fairly small atom. Since there are five electron groups surrounding the Xe atom, orbital geometry is trigonal bipyramidal. Since here are two lone pairs the VSEPR geometry is T-shaped.

c) Br has 7 valence electrons, O has 6 valence electrons, and so BrO_2^- has 7 + 2(6) + 1 = 20. Since the electronegativity of Br is less than the electronegativity of O, the Br is in the middle. The oxygens need double bonds. So the Lewis Dot structure is $\left[\ddot{O} = \ddot{B}r = \ddot{O}\right]^-$. The formal charge on Br is -1. Since there are four electron groups surrounding the Br atom, the orbital geometry is tetrahedral. Since there are two lone pairs the VSEPR geometry is bent.

d) Cl has 7 valence electrons, O has 6 valence electrons, and so ClO_4^- has $7 + 4(6) + 1 = 32$. Since the electronegativity of Cl is less than the electronegativity of O, the Cl is in the middle. The oxygens need double bonds. So the Lewis Dot structure is $\begin{bmatrix} :\ddot{O}: \\ \| \\ \ddot{O} = Cl = \ddot{O} \\ \| \\ :\ddot{O}: \end{bmatrix}^-$. The formal charge on Cl is -1. Since there are four electron groups surrounding the Cl atom, the VSEPR geometry is tetrahedral.

77. The red color is from molecular bromine (Br_2), so $Cl_2\ (g) + 2\ Br^-\ (aq) \rightarrow 2\ Cl^-\ (aq) + Br_2\ (l)$. Cl is being reduced and Br is being oxidized, so is the Cl_2 oxidizing agent and Br^- is the reducing agent.

78. $3\ Cl_2\ (g) + CS_2\ (g) \xrightarrow{\text{Catlayst}} S_2Cl_2\ (s) + CCl_4\ (g)$. Cl is being reduced and S is being oxidized.

79. **Given:** 55 g SiO_2 and 111 L of 0.032 M HF
Find: limiting reagent and amount of excess reagent left
Conceptual plan: Write reaction then M HF, L HF → mol HF → mol SiO_2 → g SiO_2 then

$$M = \frac{mol}{L} \qquad \frac{1\ mol\ SiO_2}{4\ mol\ HF} \qquad \frac{60.09\ g\ SiO_2}{1\ mol\ SiO_2}$$

determine limiting reagent then determine amount of excess reagent left

amount of excess reacent = inital amount - amount reacted

Solution: $4\ HF\ (g) + SiO_2\ (s) \rightarrow SiF_4\ (g) + 2\ H_2O\ (l)$ then $\frac{0.032\ mol\ HF}{1\ L} \times 111\ L\ HF = 3.552\ mol\ HF$

then $3.552\ mol\ HF \times \frac{1\ mol\ SiO_2}{4\ mol\ HF} \times \frac{60.09\ g\ SiO_2}{1\ mol\ SiO_2} = 53.3599\ g\ SiO_2$. Since 55 g of SiO_2 is available, HF is the limiting reagent. The amount of excess SiO_2 is $55\ g - 53.3599\ g = 2\ g\ SiO_2$.

Check: The units (g) are correct. The magnitude of the answer makes physical sense because the amount required to react all of the HF is just under the amount of glass available.

80. For ICl_4^-: I has 7 valence electrons and Cl has 7 valence electrons and so ICl_4^- has $7 + 4(7) + 1 = 36$. Since the electronegativity of I is less than the electronegativity of Cl, the I is in the middle. So the Lewis Dot structure is shown on the right. Notice that the ICl_4^- violates the octet rule, which is allowed since I is in the 5th row of the periodic table and Cl is a fairly small atom. I has a formal charge of -1. All bonds are single bonds. Since there are six electron groups surrounding the I atom, the orbital geometry is octahedral. Since there are two lone pairs the VSEPR geometry is square planar. **Note: Figure needs brackets and charge.**

For IO_4^-: I has 7 valence electrons, O has 6 valence electrons, and so IO_4^- has $7 + 4(6) + 1 = 32$. Since the electronegativity of I is less than the electronegativity of O, the Cl is in the middle. The oxygens need double bonds. So the Lewis Dot structure is $\begin{bmatrix} :O: \\ \| \\ \ddot{O} = I = \ddot{O} \\ \| \\ :O: \end{bmatrix}^-$. Notice that the IO_4^- violates the octet rule, which is allowed since I is in the 5th row of the periodic table and O is a fairly small atom. The formal charge on I is -1. Since there are four electron groups surrounding the I atom, the VSEPR geometry is tetrahedral.

81. **Given:** lignite coal 1 mol % S and bituminous coal 5 mol, % S, 1.00×10^2 kg of coal
Find: g H_2SO_4 produced

Conceptual plan: Table 22.3 Composition $\rightarrow$ $\mathfrak{M}$ **then**

$$\mathfrak{M} = \frac{(\text{mol}\%\,C)(12.01\text{ g/mol}) + (\text{mol }\%\text{ H})(1.001\text{ g/mol}) + (\text{mol }\%\text{ O})(16.00\text{ g/mol}) + (\text{mol }\%\text{ S})(32.07\text{g/mol})}{100\,\%}$$

kg coal $\rightarrow$ **g coal** $\rightarrow$ **mol coal** $\rightarrow$ **mol S** $\rightarrow$ **mol H$_2$SO$_4$** $\rightarrow$ **g H$_2$SO$_4$**

$$\frac{1000\,g}{1\text{ kg}} \qquad \mathfrak{M} \qquad \frac{1\text{ or }5\text{ mol S}}{100\,\text{mol coal}} \qquad \frac{1\text{ mol H}_2\text{SO}_4}{1\text{ mol S}} \qquad \frac{98.07\text{ g H}_2\text{SO}_4}{1\text{ mol H}_2\text{SO}_4}$$

Solution: lignite:

$$\mathfrak{M} = \frac{(\text{mol}\%\,C)(12.01\text{ g/mol}) + (\text{mol }\%\text{ H})(1.001\text{ g/mol}) + (\text{mol }\%\text{ O})(16.00\text{ g/mol}) + (\text{mol }\%\text{ S})(32.07\text{g/mol})}{100\,\%} =$$

$$= \frac{(71\text{ mol}\%\,C)(12.01\text{ g/mol}) + (4\text{ mol }\%\text{ H})(1.001\text{ g/mol}) + (23\text{ mol }\%\text{ O})(16.00\text{ g/mol}) + (1\text{ mol }\%\text{ S})(32.07\text{g/mol})}{100\,\%} =$$

$$= 12.5678\text{ g/mol}$$

$$1.00 \times 10^2\text{ kg coal} \times \frac{1000\text{ g coal}}{1\text{ kg coal}} \times \frac{1\text{ mol coal}}{12.5678\text{ g coal}} \times \frac{1\text{ mol S}}{100\text{ mol coal}} \times \frac{1\text{ mol H}_2\text{SO}_4}{1\text{ mol S}} \times \frac{98.07\text{ g H}_2\text{SO}_4}{1\text{ mol H}_2\text{SO}_4} =$$

$$= 7.803 \times 10^3\text{ g H}_2\text{SO}_4 = 8\text{ kg H}_2\text{SO}_4$$

bitumenous:

$$\mathfrak{M} = \frac{(\text{mol}\%\,C)(12.01\text{ g/mol}) + (\text{mol }\%\text{ H})(1.001\text{ g/mol}) + (\text{mol }\%\text{ O})(16.00\text{ g/mol}) + (\text{mol }\%\text{ S})(32.07\text{g/mol})}{100\,\%} =$$

$$= \frac{(80\text{ mol}\%\,C)(12.01\text{ g/mol}) + (6\text{ mol }\%\text{ H})(1.001\text{ g/mol}) + (8\text{ mol }\%\text{ O})(16.00\text{ g/mol}) + (5\text{ mol }\%\text{ S})(32.07\text{g/mol})}{100\,\%} =$$

$$= 12.55156\text{ g/mol}$$

$$1.00 \times 10^2\text{ kg coal} \times \frac{1000\text{ g coal}}{1\text{ kg coal}} \times \frac{1\text{ mol coal}}{12.55156\text{ g coal}} \times \frac{5\text{ mol S}}{100\text{ mol coal}} \times \frac{1\text{ mol H}_2\text{SO}_4}{1\text{ mol S}} \times \frac{98.07\text{ g H}_2\text{SO}_4}{1\text{ mol H}_2\text{SO}_4} =$$

$$= 3.9067 \times 10^4\text{ g H}_2\text{SO}_4 = 40\text{ kg H}_2\text{SO}_4$$

Check: The units (kg and kg) are correct. The magnitude of the answer makes physical sense because sulfuric acid is heavier than sulfur and it more than balances out the sulfur content in the coal.

82. **Given:** 88 g sodium bicarbonate (NaHCO$_3$) decomposed   **Find:** V CO$_2$ at STP
   Conceptual plan: Write reaction then g NaHCO$_3$ $\rightarrow$ **mol NaHCO$_3$** $\rightarrow$ **mol CO$_2$** $\rightarrow$ **V CO$_2$**

$$\frac{1\text{ mol NaHCO}_3}{84.00\text{ g NaHCO}_3} \qquad \frac{1\text{ mol CO}_2}{1\text{ mol NaHCO}_3} \qquad \frac{22.414\text{ L CO}_2}{1\text{ mol CO}_2}$$

Solution: NaHCO$_3$ (s) $\xrightarrow{\text{Heat}}$ NaOH $(s) + $ CO$_2$ (g), then

$$88\text{ g NaHCO3} \times \frac{1\text{ mol NaHCO}_3}{84.00\text{ g NaHCO}_3} \times \frac{1\text{ mol NaHCO}_3}{1\text{ mol CO}_2} \times \frac{22.414\text{ L CO}_2}{1\text{ mol CO}_2} = 23\text{ L CO}_2.$$

Check: The units (L) are correct. The magnitude of the answer makes physical sense because there is about a mole of NaHCO$_3$, so the volume of gas is about 22 L.

83. The strength of an acid is determined by the strength of the bond of the H to the rest of the molecule – the weaker the bond, the stronger the acid. Since Cl is more electronegative than I, it pulls density away from the O more than I does and so the O can not interact with the H as strongly.

84. The strength of an acid is determined by the strength of the bond of the H to the rest of the molecule – the weaker the bond, the stronger the acid. The oxidation state of the Cl increases as the number of oxygens increases. This increased oxidation state increases the strength of the Cl – O bonds, thus decreasing the strength of the H – O bond.

85. **Given:** HCl versus X = a) Cl$_2$, b) HF, and c) HI   **Find:** ratio of effusion rates HCl / X
   Conceptual plan: $\mathfrak{M}$ **(HCl)** , $\mathfrak{M}$ **(X)** $\rightarrow$ **Rate (HCl) / Rate (X)**

$$\frac{Rate\,(HCl)}{Rate\,(X)} = \sqrt{\frac{\mathfrak{M}(X)}{\mathfrak{M}(HCl)}}$$

Solution: HCl: $\mathfrak{M} = \frac{36.45\text{ g}}{1\text{ mol}} \times \frac{1\text{ kg}}{1000\text{ g}} = 0.03645\text{ kg/mol}$, a) Cl$_2$: $\mathfrak{M} = \frac{70.90\text{ g}}{1\text{ mol}} \times \frac{1\text{ kg}}{1000\text{ g}} = 0.07090\text{ kg/mol}$,

$$\frac{Rate(HCl)}{Rate(Cl_2)} = \sqrt{\frac{\mathfrak{M}(Cl_2)}{\mathfrak{M}(HCl)}} = \sqrt{\frac{0.07090 \ kg / mol}{0.03645 \ kg / mol}} = 1.395 \ .$$

b) HF: $\mathfrak{M} = \dfrac{20.00 \ g}{1 \ mol} \times \dfrac{1 \ kg}{1000 \ g} = 0.02000 \ kg/mol$, $\dfrac{Rate(HCl)}{Rate(HF)} = \sqrt{\dfrac{\mathfrak{M}(HF)}{\mathfrak{M}(HCl)}} = \sqrt{\dfrac{0.02000 \ kg / mol}{0.03645 \ kg / mol}} = 0.7407$.

b) HI: $\mathfrak{M} = \dfrac{127.90 \ g}{1 \ mol} \times \dfrac{1 \ kg}{1000 \ g} = 0.012790 \ kg/mol$, $\dfrac{Rate(HCl)}{Rate(HI)} = \sqrt{\dfrac{\mathfrak{M}(HI)}{\mathfrak{M}(HCl)}} = \sqrt{\dfrac{0.012790 \ kg / mol}{0.03645 \ kg / mol}} = 0.5924$.

Check: The units (none) are correct. The magnitudes of the answers make sense because; the heavier molecules have the lower effusion rate (because they move slower).

86. **Given:** $^{238}UF_6$ versus X = a) ClF and b) $^{235}UF_6$ **Find:** ratio of effusion rates $^{238}UF_6$ / X
Other: U-235 = 235.054 amu, U-238 = 238.051 amu
Conceptual plan: $\mathfrak{M} (^{238}UF_6)$, $\mathfrak{M} (X)$ → **Rate ($^{238}UF_6$) / Rate (X)**

$$\frac{Rate(^{238}UF_6)}{Rate(X)} = \sqrt{\frac{\mathfrak{M}(X)}{\mathfrak{M}(^{238}UF_6)}}$$

Solution: $^{238}UF_6$: $\mathfrak{M} = \dfrac{352.05 \ g}{1 \ mol} \times \dfrac{1 \ kg}{1000 \ g} = 0.35205 \ kg/mol$,

a) $^{235}UF_6$: $\mathfrak{M} = \dfrac{349.05 \ g}{1 \ mol} \times \dfrac{1 \ kg}{1000 \ g} = 0.34905 \ kg/mol$,

$$\frac{Rate(^{238}UF_6)}{Rate(^{235}UF_6)} = \sqrt{\frac{\mathfrak{M}(^{235}UF_6)}{\mathfrak{M}(^{238}UF_6)}} = \sqrt{\frac{0.34905 \ kg / mol}{0.35205 \ kg / mol}} = 0.99574 \ .$$

b) ClF: $\mathfrak{M} = \dfrac{54.45 \ g}{1 \ mol} \times \dfrac{1 \ kg}{1000 \ g} = 0.5445 \ kg/mol$, $\dfrac{Rate(^{238}UF_6)}{Rate(ClF)} = \sqrt{\dfrac{\mathfrak{M}(ClF)}{\mathfrak{M}(^{238}UF_6)}} = \sqrt{\dfrac{0.05445 \ kg / mol}{0.35205 \ kg / mol}} = 0.3933$.

Check: The units (none) are correct. The magnitudes of the answers make sense because; the heavier molecules have the lower effusion rate (because they move slower).

87. Sodium peroxide is Na_2O_2, so the reaction is $4 \ Na_2O_2 + 3 \ Fe$ → $4 \ Na_2O + Fe_3O_4$. Note that the oxidation state of O is decreasing from -1 to -2, needing 8 electrons and the oxidation state of Fe is increasing from 0 to + 8/3 generating 8 electrons.

88. The red color is from molecular bromine (Br_2), so $SO_2 \ (g) + Br_2 \ (l) + 2 \ H_2O \ (l)$ → $2 \ Br^- \ (aq) + H_2SO_4 \ (aq)$. Note that the oxidation state of Br is decreasing from 0 to -1, needing 2 electrons and the oxidation state of S is increasing from + 4 to + 6 generating 2 electrons. Since Br is being reduced, Br_2 oxidizing agent. Since S is being oxidized, SO_2 is the reducing agent.

89. **Given:** O_2^+, O_2, O_2^-, O_2^{2-} and MO Theory   **Find:** Explain bond lengths and state which are diamagnetic
Conceptual Plan: Use diagram from chapter 10 and fill with appropriate number of electrons to determine bond order and if diamagnetic
Solution: O_2^+ has 11 electrons in n = 2 shell and so its MO configuration σ_{2s}^2, σ_{2s}^{*2}, σ_{2p}^2, π_{2p}^4, π_{2p}^{*1}, the bond

order = $\dfrac{\text{bonding electrons - antibonding electrons}}{2} = \dfrac{8 - 3}{2} = 2.5$ and it is paramagnetic (unpaired electrons).

O_2 has 12 electrons in n = 2 shell and so its MO configuration σ_{2s}^2, σ_{2s}^{*2}, σ_{2p}^2, π_{2p}^4, π_{2p}^{*2}, the bond order =
$\dfrac{\text{bonding electrons - antibonding electrons}}{2} = \dfrac{8 - 4}{2} = 2$ and it is paramagnetic (unpaired electrons).

O_2^- has 13 electrons in n = 2 shell and so its MO configuration σ_{2s}^2, σ_{2s}^{*2}, σ_{2p}^2, π_{2p}^4, π_{2p}^{*3}, the bond order =
$\dfrac{\text{bonding electrons - antibonding electrons}}{2} = \dfrac{8 - 5}{2} = 1.5$ and it is paramagnetic (unpaired electrons).

O_2^{2-} has 14 electrons in n = 2 shell and so its MO configuration σ_{2s}^2, σ_{2s}^{*2}, σ_{2p}^2, π_{2p}^4, π_{2p}^{*4}, the bond order =
$\dfrac{\text{bonding electrons - antibonding electrons}}{2} = \dfrac{8 - 6}{2} = 1$ and it is diamagnetic (all paired electrons).

The bond order is decreasing because the electrons are being added to an antibonding orbital. As expected, the higher the bond order, the shorter the bond.

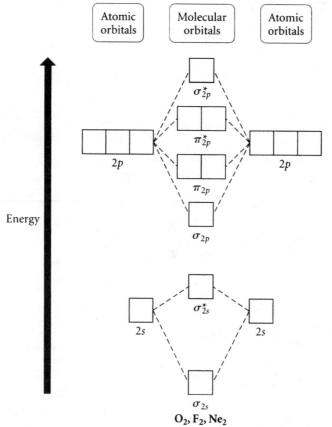

σ_{2p}^*

π_{2p}^*

2p

2p

Energy

π_{2p}

σ_{2p}

σ_{2s}^*

2s

2s

σ_{2s}

O_2, F_2, Ne_2

Check: The higher the bond order, the more electron orbital overlap and the shorter and stronger the bond. Molecular oxygen is paramagnetic and because of the number of π_{2p} and $\pi_{2p}{}^*$ orbitals, many configurations are paramagnetic.

90. a) $B_4H_4{}^{2-}$ has the formula of a *closo*-borane ($B_nH_n{}^{2-}$) has n = 4 vertices and (2n – 4) = 2(4) – 4 = 4 faces, since it has an tetrahedral shape as seen is problem #32 a.

   b) $B_{12}H_{12}{}^{2-}$ has the formula of a *closo*-borane ($B_nH_n{}^{2-}$) has n = 12 vertices and (2n – 4) = 2(12) – 4 = 20 faces.

91. **Given:** iron oxides + CO (g) $\rightarrow$ Fe (s) + CO_2 (g), where a) Fe_3O_4, b) FeO, and c) Fe_2O_3 **Find:** $\Delta H°_{rxn}$
   Conceptual plan: Write reaction. then $\Delta H°_{rxn} = \sum n_p \Delta H_f° (products) - \sum n_R \Delta H_f° (reactants)$
   Solution: a) Fe_3O_4 (s) + 4 CO (g) $\rightarrow$ 3 Fe (s) + 4 CO_2 (g)

Reactant/Product	ΔH_f^0(kJ/mol from Appendix IIB)
Fe_3O_4 (s)	−1118.4
CO (g)	−110.5
Fe (s)	0.0
CO_2 (g)	−393.5

Be sure to pull data for the correct formula and phase.

$\Delta H_{rxn}^0 = \sum n_P \Delta H_f^0 (products) - \sum n_R \Delta H_f^0 (reactants)$

     $= [3(\Delta H_f^0(\text{Fe }(s)) + 4(\Delta H_f^0(CO_2\ (g))] - [1(\Delta H_f^0(Fe_3O_4\ (s)) + 4(\Delta H_f^0(CO\ (g))]$

     $= [3(0.0\ \text{kJ}) + 4(-393.5\ \text{kJ})] - [1(-1118.4\ \text{kJ}) + 4(-110.5\ \text{kJ})]$

     $= [-1574.0\ \text{kJ}] - [-1560.4\ \text{kJ}]$

     $= -13.6\ \text{kJ}$

   b) FeO (s) + CO (g) $\rightarrow$ Fe (s) + CO_2 (g)

Reactant/Product	ΔH_f^0 (kJ/mol from Appendix IIB)
FeO (s)	− 272.0
CO (g)	−110.5
Fe (s)	0.0
CO_2 (g)	− 393.5

Be sure to pull data for the correct formula and phase.

$\Delta H_{rxn}^0 = \sum n_P \Delta H_f^0 (products) - \sum n_R \Delta H_f^0 (reactants)$

$= [1(\Delta H_f^0(\text{Fe }(s)) + 1(\Delta H_f^0(CO_2\ (g))] - [1(\Delta H_f^0(\text{FeO }(s)) + 1(\Delta H_f^0(\text{CO }(g))]$

$= [1(0.0\ \text{kJ}) + 1(-393.5\ \text{kJ})] - [1(-272.0\ \text{kJ}) + 1(-110.5\ \text{kJ})]$

$= [-393.5\ \text{kJ}] - [-382.5\ \text{kJ}]$

$= -11.0\ \text{kJ}$

c) Fe_2O_3 (s) + 3 CO (g) → 2 Fe (s) + 3 CO_2 (g)

Reactant/Product	ΔH_f^0 (kJ/mol from Appendix IIB)
Fe_2O_3 (s)	− 824.2
CO (g)	−110.5
Fe (s)	0.0
CO_2 (g)	− 393.5

Be sure to pull data for the correct formula and phase.

$\Delta H_{rxn}^0 = \sum n_P \Delta H_f^0 (products) - \sum n_R \Delta H_f^0 (reactants)$

$= [2(\Delta H_f^0(\text{Fe }(s)) + 3(\Delta H_f^0(CO_2\ (g))] - [1(\Delta H_f^0(Fe_2O_3\ (s)) + 3(\Delta H_f^0(\text{CO }(g))]$

$= [2(0.0\ \text{kJ}) + 3(-393.5\ \text{kJ})] - [1(-824.2\ \text{kJ}) + 3(-110.5\ \text{kJ})]$

$= [-1180.5\ \text{kJ}] - [-1155.7\ \text{kJ}]$

$= -24.8\ \text{kJ}$

Fe_2O_3 is the most exothermic because it has the highest oxidation state and therefore oxidizes the most CO per mole of Fe.

Check: The units (kJ) are correct.   The answers are negative, which means that the reactions are exothermic.

92. **Given:** calcium carbide + water → acetylene, burn acetylene → water + CO_2 (g), 18 g calcium carbide
    Find: acetylene generation balanced reaction and $\Delta H°_{rxn}$

    Conceptual plan: Write reactions. then $\Delta H_{rxn}^0 = \sum n_P \Delta H_f^0 (products) - \sum n_R \Delta H_f^0 (reactants)$ **then**
    g calcium carbide → mol calcium carbide → kJ

$$\frac{1\ \text{mol CaC}_2}{64.10\ \text{g CaC}_2} \qquad \Delta H°_{rxn}$$

    Solution:

CaC_2 (s) + 2 H_2O (l) → C_2H_2 (g) + $Ca(OH)_2$ (s)

C_2H_2 (g) + 5/2 O_2 (g) → 2 CO_2 (g) + H_2O (g)

CaC_2 (s) + 2 H_2O (l) + 5/2 O_2 (g) → 2 CO_2 (g) + H_2O (g) + $Ca(OH)_2$ (s)

Reactant/Product	ΔH_f^0 (kJ/mol from Appendix IIB)
CaC_2 (s)	− 59.8
H_2O (l)	−285.8
O_2 (g)	0.0
CO_2 (g)	− 393.5
H_2O (g)	−241.8
$Ca(OH)_2$ (s)	− 985.2

Be sure to pull data for the correct formula and phase.

$$\Delta H^0_{rxn} = \sum n_P \Delta H^0_f(products) - \sum n_R \Delta H^0_f(reactants)$$

$$= [2(\Delta H^0_f(CO_2\ (g)) + 1(\Delta H^0_f(H_2O\ (g)) + 1(\Delta H^0_f(Ca(OH)_2\ (s))] +$$

$$- [1(\Delta H^0_f(CaC_2\ (s)) + 2(\Delta H^0_f(H_2O\ (l)) + 5/2(\Delta H^0_f(O_2\ (g))]\ \text{then}$$

$$= [2(-393.5\ \text{kJ}) + 1(-241.8\ \text{kJ}) + 1(-985.2\ \text{kJ})] - [1(-59.8\ \text{kJ}) + 2(-285.8\ \text{kJ}) + 5/2(0.0\ \text{kJ})]$$

$$= [-2014.0\ \text{kJ}] - [-631.4\ \text{kJ}]$$

$$= -1382.6\ \text{kJ}$$

$$18\ \text{g CaC}_2 \times \frac{1\ \text{mol CaC}_2}{64.10\ \text{g CaC}_2} \times \frac{-1382.6\ \text{kJ}}{1\ \text{mol CaC}_2} = -390\ \text{kJ}\ \text{or}\ 390\ \text{kJ heat released.}$$

Check: The units (kJ) are correct. Since 18 g is less than 1 mole of calcium carbide the heat released will be less than the ΔH°_{rxn}.

93. a) This is a linear molecule. Each C has 4 valence electrons and each O has 6 valence electrons, so C_3O_2 has 3(4) + 2(6) = 24 valence electrons. All of the bonds are double bonds so the Lewis structure is:
$\ddot{O} = C = C = C = \ddot{O}$.

b) Since each carbon has two electron groups and needs to make 2 pi bonds, the hybridization is sp.

c) $\ddot{O} = C = C = C = \ddot{O} + 2\ H - \ddot{O} - H \rightarrow H - O - \overset{\overset{\displaystyle O}{\|}}{C} - \overset{\overset{\displaystyle H}{|}}{\underset{\underset{\displaystyle H}{|}}{C}} - \overset{\overset{\displaystyle O}{\|}}{C} - O - H$ The reaction involves breaking 2 C=C bonds

and
2 O – H bonds and making 2 C – H bonds, 2 C – C bonds and 2 C – O bonds. Thus,
$$\Delta H^0_{rxn} = \sum \Delta H's(bonds\ broken) - \sum \Delta H's(bonds\ formed)$$
$$= [2(611\ \text{kJ}) + 2(464\ \text{kJ})] + [2(-414\ \text{kJ}) + 2(-347\ \text{kJ}) + 2(-360\ \text{kJ})] = [2150\ \text{kJ}] + [-2242\ \text{kJ}] = -92\ \text{kJ}$$

94. **Given:** $CaCO_3\ (s) + HCl\ (aq)$ reaction   **Find:** ΔH°_{rxn}, ΔS°_{rxn}, and ΔG°_{rxn}
Conceptual plan: write balanced reaction then $\Delta H^0_{rxn} = \sum n_P \Delta H^0_f(products) - \sum n_R \Delta H^0_f(reactants)$ **then**

$\Delta S^0_{rxn} = \sum n_P S^0(products) - \sum n_r S^0(reactants)$ **then** °C → K   **then**   J/K → kJ/K   **then**

$$K = 273.15 + °C \qquad \frac{1\ \text{kJ}}{1000\ \text{J}}$$

ΔH°_{rxn}, ΔS_{rxn}, T → ΔG
$$\Delta G = \Delta H_{rxn} - T\Delta S_{rxn}$$

Solution: $CaCO_3\ (s) + 2\ HCl\ (aq) \rightarrow Ca^{2+}(aq) + 2\ Cl^-\ (aq) + CO_2\ (g) + H_2O\ (g)$

Reactant/Product	ΔH^0_f(kJ/mol from Appendix IIB)
$CaCO_3\ (s)$	-1207.6
$HCl\ (aq)$	-167.2
$Ca^{2+}\ (aq)$	-542.8
$Cl^{2-}\ (aq)$	-167.1
$CO_2\ (g)$	-393.5
$H_2O\ (l)$	-285.8

Be sure to pull data for the correct formula and phase.
$$\Delta H^0_{rxn} = \sum n_P \Delta H^0_f(products) - \sum n_R \Delta H^0_f(reactants)$$
$$= [1(\Delta H^0_f(Ca^{2+}\ (aq)) + 2(\Delta H^0_f(Cl^-\ (aq)) + 1(\Delta H^0_f(CO_2\ (g)) + 1(\Delta H^0_f(H_2O\ (l))] +$$
$$- [1(\Delta H^0_f(CaCO_3\ (s)) + 2(\Delta H^0_f(HCl\ (aq))]\ \text{then}$$
$$= [1(-542.8\ \text{kJ}) + 2(-167.1\ \text{kJ}) + 1(-393.5\ \text{kJ}) + 1(-285.8\ \text{kJ})] - [1(-1207.6\ \text{kJ}) + 2(-167.2\ \text{kJ})]$$
$$= [-1556.3\ \text{kJ}] - [-1542.0\ \text{kJ}]$$
$$= -14.3\ \text{kJ}$$

Reactant/Product	S^0 (J/mol K from Appendix IIB)
$CaCO_3$ (s)	91.7
HCl (aq)	56.5
Ca^{2+} (aq)	– 53.1
Cl^{2-} (aq)	56.6
CO_2 (g)	213.8
H_2O (l)	70.0

Be sure to pull data for the correct formula and phase.

$$\Delta S^0_{rxn} = \sum n_P \Delta S^0 (products) - \sum n_R \Delta S^0 (reactants)$$

$$= [1(\Delta S^0(Ca^{2+} (aq)) + 2(\Delta S^0(Cl^- (aq)) + 1(\Delta S^0(CO_2 (g)) + 1(\Delta S^0(H_2O (l))] +$$

$$- [1(\Delta S^0(CaCO_3 (s)) + 2(\Delta S^0(HCl (aq))] \quad \text{then}$$

$$= [1(-53.1 \text{ J/K}) + 2(56.6 \text{ J/K}) + 1(213.8 \text{ J/K}) + 1(70.0 \text{ J/K})] - [1(91.7 \text{ J/K}) + 2(56.5 \text{ J/K})]$$

$$= [343.9 \text{ J/K}] - [204.7 \text{ J/K}]$$

$$= + 139.2 \text{ k/K}$$

$$T = 273.15 + 25 \text{ °C} = 298 \text{ K} \quad \text{then} \quad +139.2 \frac{J}{K} \times \frac{1 \text{ kJ}}{1000 \text{ J}} = + 0.1392 \frac{kJ}{K} \quad \text{then}$$

$$\Delta G = \Delta H_{rxn} - T\Delta S_{rxn} = -14.3 \text{ kJ} - (298 \text{ K}) \left(+ 0.1392 \frac{kJ}{K} \right) = -55.8 \text{ kJ} \quad \text{so the reaction is}$$

spontaneous. Both the enthalpy and the entropy help the reaction to be spontaneous. The entropy term is the larger of the two, because we are generating a gaseous product.

Check: The units (kJ, J/K and kJ) are correct. The reaction does form heat when done in the lab, so it is exothermic. We expect a large positive entropy because we have an increase in the number of moles of gas. The free energy is the sum of two negative terms so we expect a negative free energy and the reaction is spontaneous.

95. a) K_b for the overall reaction will be the product of the two individual K_b's, so $K_b = K_{b1} \cdot K_{b2} =$
$= (8.5 \times 10^{-7})(8.9 \times 10^{-16}) = 7.6 \times 10^{-22}$.

b) $K_{a1} = K_w / K_{b1} = (1.0 \times 10^{-14})/(8.5 \times 10^{-7}) = 1.2 \times 10^{-8}$.

c) **Given**: pH = 8.5, 0.012 mol N_2H_4 in 1.0 L   **Find**: $[N_2H_4]$, $[N_2H_5^+]$, and $[N_2H_6^+]$
     Other: $K_{b1} = 8.5 \times 10^{-7}$, $K_{b2} = 8.9 \times 10^{-16}$
     Conceptual Plan: pH → pOH → $[OH^-]$ and mol N_2H_4, L → M N_2H_4 then

$$pH + pOH = 14 \quad pOH = - \log [OH^-] \qquad M = \frac{mol}{L} \qquad ICE$$

$[OH^-]$, $[N_2H_4]_0$ → $[N_2H_4]$, $[N_2H_5^+]$ and $[OH^-]$, $[N_2H_4]_0$ → $[N_2H_5^+]$, $[N_2H_6^{2+}]$
   ICE Chart   ICE Chart

Solution: $pH + pOH = 14$ so $pOH = 14 - pH = 14.0 - 8.5 = 5.5$ then $[OH^-] = 10^{-[OH^-]} = 10^{-5.5} =$
$= 3.16 \times 10^{-6}$. There are 0.012 mol N_2H_4 in 1.0 L so $[N_2H_4]_0 = 0.012$ M. Set up first ICE Chart.

N_2H_4 (aq) + H_2O (l) $\rightleftharpoons$ $N_2H_5^+$ (aq) + OH^-(aq)		
Initial 0.012	0.00	3.16×10^{-6}
Change $- x$	x	
Equil $0.012 - x$	x	3.16×10^{-6}

Since the solution is buffered, $[OH^-]$ will be unchanged.

$$K_{b1} = \frac{[N_2H_5^+][OH^-]}{[N_2H_4]} = \frac{(x)(3.16 \times 10^{-6})}{0.012 - x} = 8.5 \times 10^{-7} \text{ Solve for x.} \quad (x)(3.16 \times 10^{-6}) = 8.5 \times 10^{-7}(0.012 - x) \rightarrow$$

$x(3.16 \times 10^{-6} + 8.5 \times 10^{-7}) = 1.02 \times 10^{-8} \rightarrow x = 0.0025$ so $[N_2H_4] = 0.012$ M $- 0.0025$ M $= 0.009$ M and
$[N_2H_5^+] = 0.0025$ M.   then   Set up second ICE Chart.

$N_2H_5^+$ (aq) + H_2O (l) $\rightleftharpoons$ $N_2H_6^{2+}$ (aq) + OH^-(aq)		
Initial 0.0025	0.00	3.16×10^{-6}
Change $- x$	x	
Equil $0.0025 - x$	x	3.16×10^{-6}

Since the solution is buffered, $[OH^-]$ will be unchanged.

$K_{b2} = \dfrac{[\text{N}_2\text{H}_6^{2+}][\text{OH}^-]}{[\text{N}_2\text{H}_5^+]} = \dfrac{(x)\,(3.16 \times 10^{-6})}{0.0025 - x} = 8.9 \times 10^{-16}$ Since x << 0.0025 then $\dfrac{(x)\,(3.16 \times 10^{-6})}{0.0025} = 8.9 \times 10^{-16}$ and

$x = 7.0 \times 10^{-13}\,\text{M} = [\text{N}_2\text{H}_6^{2+}]$ (Note that assumption that x was very small was good.)

Check: The units (M) are correct. The magnitude of the answer makes physical sense because the only a portion of the hydrazine dissociates and the product concentrations get smaller and smaller.

96. **Given:** 2.200×10^3 kg Al (s) and $3\,\text{NH}_4\text{ClO}_4$ (s) + 3 Al (s) → Al_2O_3 (s) + AlCl_3 (s) + 6 H_2O (g) + 3 NO (g)

    Find: energy generated ($\Delta H°_{rxn}$) in J

    Conceptual plan: $\Delta H^\circ_{rxn} = \sum n_p \Delta H^\circ_f (products) - \sum n_R \Delta H^\circ_f (reactants)$ **then** kg Al → g Al → mol Al → kJ → J

$$\dfrac{1000\ \text{g}}{1\ \text{kg}} \qquad \dfrac{1\ \text{mol Al}}{26.98\ \text{g Al}} \qquad \Delta H°_{rxn} \qquad \dfrac{1000\ \text{J}}{1\ \text{kJ}}$$

then mol Al → mol gas → V gas

$$\dfrac{9\ \text{mol gas}}{3\ \text{mol Al}} \qquad PV = nRT$$

Solution:

Reactant/Product	ΔH^0_f (kJ/mol from Appendix IIB)
NH_4ClO_4 (s)	−293.5
Al (s)	0.0
Al_2O_3 (s)	−1675.7
AlCl_3 (s)	−704.2
H_2O (g)	−241.8
NO (g)	91.3

Be sure to pull data for the correct formula and phase.

$\Delta H^0_{rxn} = \sum n_P \Delta H^0_f (products) - \sum n_R \Delta H^0_f (reactants)$

$= [1(\Delta H^0_f(\text{Al}_2\text{O}_3\ (s)) + 1(\Delta H^0_f(\text{AlCl}_3\ (s)) + 6(\Delta H^0_f(\text{H}_2\text{O}\ (g)) + 3(\Delta H^0_f(\text{NO}\ (g))] +$

$\qquad\qquad\qquad\qquad\qquad -[3(\Delta H^0_f(\text{NH}_4\text{ClO}_4\ (s)) + 3(\Delta H^0_f(\text{Al}\ (s))]$

$= [1(-1675.7\ \text{kJ}) + 1(-704.2\ \text{kJ}) + 6(-241.8\ \text{kJ}) + 3(91.3\ \text{kJ})] - [3(-293.5\ \text{kJ}) + 3(0.0\ \text{kJ})]$

$= [-3556.8\ \text{kJ}] - [-880.5\ \text{kJ}]$

$= -2676.3\ \text{kJ}$

then $2.200 \times 10^3\ \text{kg Al} \times \dfrac{1000\ \text{g Al}}{1\ \text{kg Al}} \times \dfrac{1\ \text{mol Al}}{26.98\ \text{g Al}} \times \dfrac{2676.3\ \text{kJ}}{3\ \text{mol Al}} \times \dfrac{1000\ \text{J}}{1\ \text{kJ}} = 7.274 \times 10^{10}\ \text{J}$. then

$8.154188 \times 10^4\ \text{mol Al} \times \dfrac{9\ \text{mol gas}}{3\ \text{mol Al}} = 2.446256 \times 10^5\ \text{mol gas}$. Since $PV = nRT$, rearrange to solve for V

$V = \dfrac{2.446256 \times 10^5\ \text{mol} \times 0.08206\ \dfrac{\text{L} \cdot \text{atm}}{\text{mol} \cdot \text{K}} \times 298\ \text{K}}{1\ \text{atm}} = 5.98 \times 10^6\ \text{L gas}$.

Check: The units (J and L) are correct. We expect the amount of energy and the volume to be extremely large to launch a rocket.

97. Fine particles of activated charcoal have a much greater total surface area than does a charcoal briquette, allowing it to interact with more impurities.

98. The triple bond is nitrogen is much stronger than the double bond in oxygen, so it is much harder to break. This makes it less likely that the bond in nitrogen will be broken.

99. Nitrogen can either gain three electrons or lose five electrons to obtain an octet, giving it the possibility of oxidation states between −3 and +5.

100. Sodium dihydrogen phosphate (NaH_2PO_4) can act as a weak base or a weak acid. A buffer can be made by mixing it with either Na_2HPO_4 or with Na_3PO_4, depending on the desired pH of the buffer solution.

101. H_2S has a different bond angle than H_2O because S is larger than O and since S is less electronegative than O. H_2S is more reactive because the O – H bond is much shorter and stronger than the S – H bond.

102. F is extremely small and so there is a huge driving force to fill the octet by adding an electron, giving a -1 oxidation state. Other halogens have access to d orbital, which allows for more hybridization and oxidation state options.

103. Fluorine has a greater electronegativity than oxygen and is more reactive.

104. SO_3 can not be a reducing agent, because the oxidation state of S is + 6, the highest possible oxidation state for S. Reducing agents need to be able to be oxidized. SO_2 can be a reducing agent or an oxidizing agent, because the oxidation state of S is + 4.

105. Cl is small enough to fit around Br, but Br is too large to fit around Cl and form stable bonds.

Chapter 23
Metals and Metallurgy

1. The source of vanadium in some crude oil is the very animals from which the oil was formed. It appears that some extinct animals used vanadium for oxygen transport.

2. The categories of metallurgical processes are pyrometallurgy, hydrometallurgy, electrometallurgy, and powder metallurgy.

3. Even though over 2 % of the Earth's mass is nickel, most of this is in the Earth's core, and because the core is so far from the surface, it is not accessible.

4. Minerals are homogenous, naturally occurring, crystalline inorganic solids. A rock that contains a high concentration of a specific mineral is called an ore.

5. The mineral is the phase that contains the desired element(s) and the gangue is the undesired material. These are generally separated by physical methods.

6. In pyrometallurgy, heat is used to extract a metal from its mineral. Calcination is the heating of an ore in order to decompose it and drive off a volatile product, such as carbon dioxide or water. Heating that causes a chemical reaction between the furnace atmosphere and the mineral is called roasting. Roasting is particularly important in processing sulfide ores. When roasting forms a liquid product, which often helps in separation, it is called smelting.

7. Sodium cyanide has been traditionally used to leach gold by forming a soluble gold complex ($Au(CN)_2^-$). The problem with this process is that cyanide is very toxic and has often resulted in the contamination of streams and rivers with cyanide. New alternatives, using the thiosulfate ion ($S_2O_3^-$), are being investigated to replace it.

8. Powder metallurgy offers several advantages over traditional casting or milling of metal: (1) there is no scrap involved in making metal components through powder metallurgy—the part can be pressed directly into the desired shape; (2) the process is quicker since intricate details such as teeth on gears and multiple holes can be designed into the press and do not have to be machined after production; and (3) using the powder avoids the need for high temperatures.

9. The body-centered cubic unit cell consists of a cube with one atom at each corner and one atom in the very center of the cube. In the body-centered unit cell, the atoms do not touch along each edge of the cube, but rather touch along the diagonal line that runs from one corner, through the middle of the cube, to the opposite corner. The body-centered unit cell contains two atoms per unit cell because the center atom is not shared with any other neighboring cells. The coordination number of the body-centered cubic unit cell is 8, and the packing efficiency is 68%. The face-centered cubic unit cell is characterized by a cube with one atom at each corner and one atom in the center of each cube face. In the face-centered unit cell (like the body-centered unit cell), the atoms do not touch along each edge of the cube. Instead, the atoms touch along the face diagonal. The face-centered unit cell contains four atoms per unit cell because the center atoms on each of the six faces are shared between two unit cells. So there are ½ x 6 = 3 face-centered atoms plus 1/8 x 8 = 1 corner atoms, for a total of four atoms per unit cell. The coordination number of the face-centered cubic unit cell is 12 and its packing efficiency is 74%. In the face-centered structure, any one atom strongly interacts with more atoms than in either the simple cubic unit cell or the body-centered cubic unit cell.

10. In a substitutional alloy, one metal atom substitutes for another in the crystal structure. The crystal structure may either stay the same upon the substitution, or it may change to accommodate the differences between the atoms. In an interstitial alloy, small, usually nonmetallic, atoms fit in between the metallic atoms of a crystal. The alloy still maintains it metallic properties with these interstitial atoms in the structure.

11. Copper was one of the first metals used because it can be found in nature in its elemental form.

12. Bronze was one of the first alloys ever produced because it had a low enough melting point so that it could be made in the low heat of a Stone Age campfire.

13. Bronze is an alloy of copper and tin. Brass is an alloy of copper and zinc.

14. Properties that are useful for use in electrical wires are that copper is ductile and has high electrical and heat conductivity. For making water pipes, copper pipes are easily soldered together and copper alloys are useful because they do not spark when struck.

15. Metals are typically opaque, are good conductors of heat and electricity, and are ductile and malleable, meaning that they can be drawn into wires and flattened into sheets.

16. a)   Metals have a higher thermal conductivity than nonmetals.

    b)   Nonmetals have a higher electrical resistivity than metals.

    c)   Nonmetals have a higher transparency than metals.

    d)   Metals have a higher ductility than nonmetals.

17. Aluminum, iron, calcium, magnesium, sodium and potassium are all over 1 % of the Earth's crust.

18. Nickel, copper, palladium, silver, platinum, and gold are found naturally as elements.

19. Hematite (Fe_2O_3) and magnetite (Fe_3O_4) are important mineral sources of iron. Cinnabar (HgS) is an important mineral source of mercury. Vanadite [$Pb_5(VO_4)Cl$], carnotite [$K_2(UO_2)_2(VO_4)_2 \cdot 3H_2O$] are important mineral sources of vanadium. Columbite [$Fe(NbO_3)_2$] is an important mineral source of niobium.

20. Rutile (TiO_2) is an important mineral source of titanium. Sphalerite (ZnS) is an important mineral source of zinc. carnotite [$K_2(UO_2)_2(VO_4)_2 \cdot 3H_2O$] is an important mineral source of uranium. Tantalite [$Fe(TaO_3)_2$] is an important mineral source of tantalum.

21. $MgCO_3\ (s) \xrightarrow{\text{Heat}} MgO\ (s) + CO_2\ (g)$ and $Mg(OH)_2\ (s) \xrightarrow{\text{Heat}} MgO\ (s) + H_2O\ (g)$.

22. $CuO\ (s) + C\ (s) \xrightarrow{\text{Heat}} Cu\ (l) + CO\ (g)$ and $CuS\ (s) + 3/2\ O_2\ (g) \xrightarrow{\text{Heat}} CuO\ (s) + SO_2\ (g)$.

23. A flux is a material that will react with the gangue to form a substance with a low melting point. MgO is the flux.

24. A slag is the waste liquid solution that is formed between the flux and gangue. It is usually a silicate material. $MgSiO_3$ is the slag.

25. Hydrometallurgy is used to separate metals from ores by selectively dissolving the metal in a solution, filtering out impurities, and then reducing the metal to its elemental form.

26. In electrometallurgy, electrolysis is used to produce metals from their compounds or impure metals. The material to be purified is dissolved (by dissolving the material in a liquid or molten solution or by using it as the anode (where oxidation occurs from the elemental form to a soluble ion) in an electrolysis cell, the desired metal ions are reduced at the cathode and are removed as the cathode or as material that has dropped off of the cathode.

27. The Bayer process is a hydrometallurgical process by which Al_2O_3 is selectively dissolved, leaving other oxides as solids. The soluble form of aluminum is $Al(OH)_4^-$.

28. The impure copper is the anode and the purified copper is the cathode. The sludge at the bottom of the electrolysis cell contains many precious metals, including gold and silver.

29. Sponge powdered iron contains many small holes in the iron particles due to escaping of oxygen when the iron is reduced. Water atomized powdered iron has much more smooth and dense particles as the powder is formed from molten iron.

30. In the production of sponge powdered iron, iron powder from mill scrap (which is primarily iron oxide that would fall off the steel as it was being milled) is heated in a hydrogen atmosphere to reduce the oxide to iron

particles. In the production of water atomization iron, pure metal is melted and a small stream of the liquid is allowed to flow from the bottom of the container of molten metal, then a high pressure blast of cold water hits the stream, breaking it into small droplets that quickly solidify.

31. a) When one-half of the V atoms are replaced by Cr atoms, the composition will be 50 % Cr by moles and 50 % V by moles. To get percent by mass assume 100 moles of alloy, so

percent by mass Cr $= \dfrac{(\text{mol\% Cr})(52.00 \text{ g/mol})}{(\text{mol \% Cr})(52.00 \text{ g/mol}) + (\text{mol \% V})(50.94 \text{ g/mol})} \times 100 \% =$

$= \dfrac{(50 \text{ mol})(52.00 \text{ g/mol})}{(50 \text{ mol})(52.00 \text{ g/mol}) + (50 \text{ mol})(50.94 \text{ g/mol})} \times 100 \% = 50.5 \%$ Cr by mass and percent by mass V $=$ 100.0 % - 50.5 % = 49.5 % V.

b) When one-fourth of the V atoms are replaced by Fe atoms, the composition will be 25 % Fe by moles and 75 % V by moles. To get percent by mass assume 100 moles of alloy, so

percent by mass Fe $= \dfrac{(\text{mol\% Fe})(55.85 \text{ g/mol})}{(\text{mol \% Fe})(55.85 \text{ g/mol}) + (\text{mol \% V})(50.94 \text{ g/mol})} \times 100 \% =$

$= \dfrac{(25 \text{ mol})(55.85 \text{ g/mol})}{(25 \text{ mol})(55.85 \text{ g/mol}) + (75 \text{ mol})(50.94 \text{ g/mol})} \times 100 \% = 26.8 \%$ Fe by mass and percent by mass V $=$ 100.0 % - 26.8 % = 73.2 % V.

c) When one-fourth of the V atoms are replaced by Cr atoms and one-fourth of the V atoms are replaced by Fe atoms, the composition will be 25 % Cr by moles, 25 % Fe by moles and 50 % V by moles. To get percent by mass assume 100 moles of alloy, so

percent by mass Cr $= \dfrac{(\text{mol\% Cr})(52.00 \text{ g/mol})}{(\text{mol\% Cr})(52.00 \text{ g/mol}) + (\text{mol\% Fe})(55.85 \text{ g/mol}) + (\text{mol \% V})(50.94 \text{ g/mol})} \times 100 \% =$

$= \dfrac{(25 \text{ mol})(52.00 \text{ g/mol})}{(25 \text{ mol})(52.00 \text{ g/mol}) + (25 \text{ mol})(55.85 \text{ g/mol}) + (50 \text{ mol})(50.94 \text{ g/mol})} \times 100 \% = 24.8 \%$ Cr by mass ,

percent by mass Fe $= \dfrac{(\text{mol\% Fe})(55.85 \text{ g/mol})}{(\text{mol\% Cr})(52.00 \text{ g/mol}) + (\text{mol\% Fe})(55.85 \text{ g/mol}) + (\text{mol \% V})(50.94 \text{ g/mol})} \times 100 \% =$

$= \dfrac{(25 \text{ mol})(55.85 \text{ g/mol})}{(25 \text{ mol})(52.00 \text{ g/mol}) + (25 \text{ mol})(55.85 \text{ g/mol}) + (50 \text{ mol})(50.94 \text{ g/mol})} \times 100 \% = 26.6 \%$ Fe by mass and

percent by mass V = 100.0 % - (24.8 % + 26.6 %) = 48.6 % V.

32. a) When one-third of the Co atoms are replaced by Zn atoms, the composition will be 33.3 % Zn by moles and 66.7 % Co by moles. To get percent by mass assume 100 moles of alloy, so

percent by mass Zn $= \dfrac{(\text{mol\% Zn})(65.41 \text{ g/mol})}{(\text{mol\% Zn})(65.41 \text{ g/mol}) + (\text{mol \% Co})(58.93 \text{ g/mol})} \times 100 \% =$

$= \dfrac{(33.3 \text{ mol})(65.41 \text{ g/mol})}{(33.3 \text{ mol})(65.41 \text{ g/mol}) + (66.7 \text{ mol})(58.93 \text{ g/mol})} \times 100 \% = 35.7 \%$ Zn by mass and percent by mass Co = 100.0 % - 35.7 % = 64.3 % Co.

b) When one-eighth of the Co atoms are replaced by Ti atoms, the composition will be 12.5 % Ti by moles and 87.5 % Co by moles. To get percent by mass assume 100 moles of alloy, so

percent by mass Ti $= \dfrac{(\text{mol\% Ti})(47.88 \text{ g/mol})}{(\text{mol\% Ti})(47.88 \text{ g/mol}) + (\text{mol \% Co})(58.93 \text{ g/mol})} \times 100 \% =$

$= \dfrac{(12.5 \text{ mol})(47.88 \text{ g/mol})}{(12.5 \text{ mol})(47.88 \text{ g/mol}) + (87.5 \text{ mol})(58.93 \text{ g/mol})} \times 100 \% = 10.4 \%$ Fe by mass and percent by mass Co = 100.0 % - 10.4 % = 89.6 % Co.

c) When one-third of the Co atoms are replaced by Zn atoms and one-sixth of the Co atoms are replaced by Ti atoms, the composition will be 33.3 % Zn by moles, 16.7 % Ti by moles and 50 % Co by moles. To get percent by mass assume 100 moles of alloy, so

$$\text{percent by mass Zn} = \frac{(\text{mol \% Zn})(65.41 \text{ g/mol})}{(\text{mol \% Zn})(65.41 \text{ g/mol}) + (\text{mol \% Ti})(47.88 \text{ g/mol}) + (\text{mol \% Co})(58.93 \text{ g/mol})} \times 100 \% =$$

$$= \frac{(33.3 \text{ mol})(65.41 \text{ g/mol})}{(33.3 \text{ mol})(65.41 \text{ g/mol}) + (16.7 \text{ mol})(47.88 \text{ g/mol}) + (50 \text{ mol})(58.93 \text{ g/mol})} \times 100 \% =$$

$$= 42.5 \% \text{ Zn by mass}$$

$$\text{percent by mass Ti} = \frac{(\text{mol \% Ti})(47.88 \text{ g/mol})}{(\text{mol \% Zn})(65.41 \text{ g/mol}) + (\text{mol \% Ti})(47.88 \text{ g/mol}) + (\text{mol \% Co})(58.93 \text{ g/mol})} \times 100 \% =$$

$$= \frac{(16.7 \text{ mol})(47.88 \text{ g/mol})}{(33.3 \text{ mol})(65.41 \text{ g/mol}) + (16.7 \text{ mol})(47.88 \text{ g/mol}) + (50 \text{ mol})(58.93 \text{ g/mol})} \times 100 \% =$$

$$= 13.5 \% \text{ Ti by mass}$$

and percent by mass Co = 100.0 % - (42.5 % + 13.5 %) = 44.0 % Co.

33. Cr and Fe are very close together in the periodic table (atomic numbers 24 and 26, respectively), so there respective atomic radii are probably close enough to form an alloy. Also, both form body-centered cubic structures.

34. Even though Co and Cu are close together in the periodic table (and so have similar atomic radii), Co forms a hexagonal closest packed structure and Cu forms a face-centered cubic structure. This difference in preferred structure type would lead to them no forming a miscible alloy.

35. This phase diagram indicates that the solid and liquid phases are completely miscible. The composition is determined by determining the x-axis value at the point.

   A: solid with 20 % Cr and 100 % - 20 % = 80 % Fe.

   B: liquid with 50 % Cr and 100 % - 50 % = 50 % Fe.

36. This phase diagram indicates that the solid and liquid phases are completely miscible. The composition is determined by determining the x-axis value at the point.

   C: solid with 70 % Cr and 100 % - 70 % = 30 % Fe.

   D: liquid with 20 % Cr and 100 % - 20 % = 80 % Fe.

37. This phase diagram indicates that the solid and liquid phases are not completely miscible. Single phases only exist between the pure component and the red line. The composition will be a mixture of the two structures. The composition of the two phases is determined by moving to the left and right until reaching the red lines. The x-axis value is the composition of that structure. According to the lever rule, the phase that is closer to the point is the dominant phase.

   A: solid with 20 % Co and 100 % − 20 % = 80 % Cu overall composition. One phase will be the copper structure with ~ 4 % Co; and the other phase will be the Co structure with ~ 7 % Cu. According to the lever rule there will be more of the Cu structure, since point A is closer to the Cu structure phase boundary line.

   B: solid single phase with Co structure and composition of 90 % Co and 100 % - 90 % = 10 % Cu.

38. This phase diagram indicates that the solid and liquid phases are not completely miscible. Single phases only exist between the pure component and the red line. The composition will be a mixture of the two structures. The composition of the two phases is determined by moving to the left and right until reaching the red lines. The x-axis value is the composition of that structure. According to the lever rule, the phase that is closer to the point is the dominant phase.

   C: solid single phase with Co structure and composition of 95 % Co and 100 % - 95 % = 5 % Cu.

   D: solid with 50 % Co and 100 % -50 % = 50 % Cu overall composition. One phase will be the copper structure with ~ 3 % Co; and the other phase will be the Co structure with ~ 5 % Cu. According to the lever rule there will be slightly more of the Co structure, since point D is closer to the Co structure phase boundary line.

39. Since C (77 pm) is much smaller than Fe (126 pm), it will fill interstitial holes. Since Mn (130 pm) and Si (118 pm) are close to the same size as Fe, they will substitute for Fe in the lattice.

40. Since N (70 pm) is much smaller than Fe (126 pm), it will fill interstitial holes. Since P (110 pm) and Si (118 pm) are close to the same size as Fe, they will substitute for Fe in the lattice.

41. a) Since there are the same number of octahedral holes as there are metal atoms in a closest packed structure and half are filled with N, the formula is Mo_2N.

    b) Since there twice as many tetrahedral holes as there are metal atoms, and all of the tetrahedral holes are occupied, the formula is CrH_2.

42. a) Since there are the same number of octahedral holes as there are metal atoms in a closest packed structure and one-fourth are filled with N, the formula is Fe_4N.

    b) Since there twice as many tetrahedral holes as there are metal atoms, and half of the tetrahedral holes are occupied, the formula is TiH.

43. a) Zn, since Sphalerite is ZnS.

    b) Cu, since malachite is $Cu_2(OH)_2CO_3$.

    c) Mn, since hausmannite is Mn_3O_4.

44. a) Hematite (Fe_2O_3) and magnetite (Fe_3O_4) are important mineral sources of iron.

    b) Cobaltite (CoAsS) is an important mineral source of cobalt.

    c) Chromite ($FeCr_2O_3$) is an important mineral source of chromium.

45. **Given:** Calcination of rhodochrosite ($MnCO_3$)   **Find:** heat of reaction
    Conceptual Plan: Write reaction. then $\Delta H^{\circ}_{rxn} = \sum n_p \Delta H^{\circ}_f(products) - \sum n_R \Delta H^{\circ}_f(reactants)$
    Solution: $MnCO_3(s) + \frac{1}{2}O_2(g) \xrightarrow{\text{Heat}} MnO_2(s) + CO_2(g)$

Reactant/Product	ΔH^0_f (kJ/mol from Appendix IIB)
$MnCO_3(s)$	-894.1
$O_2(g)$	0.0
$MnO_2(s)$	-520.0
$CO_2(g)$	-393.5

Be sure to pull data for the correct formula and phase.

$\Delta H^0_{rxn} = \sum n_P \Delta H^0_f(products) - \sum n_R \Delta H^0_f(reactants)$

$\quad = [1\Delta H^0_f(MnO_2(s)) + 1\Delta H^0_f(CO_2(g))] - [1\Delta H^0_f(MnCO_3(s)) + 1/2\Delta H^0_f(O_2(g))]$

$\quad = [1(-520.0\text{ kJ}) + 1(-393.5\text{ kJ})] - [1(-894.1\text{ kJ}) + 1/2(0.0\text{ kJ})]$

$\quad = [-913.5\text{ kJ}] - [-894.1\text{ kJ}]$

$\quad = -19.4\text{ kJ}$

Check: The units (kJ) are correct. The answer is negative, which means that the reactions are exothermic.

46. **Given:** Extraction of Mn from pyrolusite with Al   **Find:** heat of reaction
    Conceptual Plan: Write reaction. then $\Delta H^{\circ}_{rxn} = \sum n_p \Delta H^{\circ}_f(products) - \sum n_R \Delta H^{\circ}_f(reactants)$
    Solution: $MnO_2(s) + 4Al(s) \xrightarrow{\text{Heat}} 3Mn(s) + Al_2O_3(s)$

Reactant/Product	ΔH^0_f (kJ/mol from Appendix IIB)
$MnO_2(s)$	-520.0
$Al(s)$	0.0
$Mn(s)$	0.0
$Al_2O_3(s)$	-1675.7

Be sure to pull data for the correct formula and phase.

$$\Delta H^0_{rxn} = \sum n_P \Delta H^0_f(products) - \sum n_R \Delta H^0_f(reactants)$$
$$= [3\Delta H^0_f(Mn\ (s)) + 1\Delta H^0_f(Al_2O_3\ (s))] - [1\Delta H^0_f(MnO_2\ (s)) + 4\Delta H^0_f(Al\ (s))]$$
$$= [3(0.0\ kJ) + 1(-1675.7\ kJ)] - [1(-520.0\ kJ) + 4(0.0\ kJ)]$$
$$= [-1675.7\ kJ] - [-520.0\ kJ]$$
$$= -1155.7\ kJ$$

Check: The units (kJ) are correct. The answer is negative, which means that the reactions are exothermic. The heat of formation of alumina is so low that the heat of reaction is negative.

47. When Cr is added to steel it reacts with oxygen in steel to prevent it from rusting. A Cr steel alloy would be used in any situation where a steel might be easily oxidized, such as when it comes in contact with water.

48. Mn is added to steel to change physical properties, such as making steel easier to deform at high temperatures, helping the rolling and forging steps of steel production. Manganese strengthens steel alloys for military and industrial uses.

49. rutile = TiO_2: The composition will be 33.3 % Ti by moles and 66.7 % O by moles. To get percent by mass assume 100 moles of atoms, so

$$\text{percent by mass Ti} = \frac{(mol\%Ti)(47.88\ g/mol)}{(mol\%Ti)(47.88\ g/mol) + (mol\%O)(16.00\ g/mol)} \times 100\% =$$

$$= \frac{(33.3\ mol)(47.88\ g/mol)}{(33.3\ mol)(47.88\ g/mol) + (66.7\ mol)(16.00\ g/mol)} \times 100\% = 59.9\ \%\ Ti\ by\ mass.$$

ilmenite = $FeTiO_3$: The composition will be 20.0 % Ti by moles, 20.0 % Fe by moles, and 60.0 % O by moles. To get percent by mass assume 100 moles of atoms, so

$$\text{percent by mass Ti} = \frac{(mol\%Ti)(47.88\ g/mol)}{(mol\%Ti)(47.88\ g/mol) + (mol\%Fe)(55.85\ g/mol) + (mol\%O)(16.00\ g/mol)} \times 100\% =$$

$$= \frac{(20.0\ mol)(47.88\ g/mol)}{(20.0\ mol)(47.88\ g/mol) + (20.0\ mol)(55.85\ g/mol) + (60.0\ mol)(16.00\ g/mol)} \times 100\% = 31.6\ \%\ Ti\ by\ mass.$$

50. pyrolusite = MnO_2: The composition will be 33.3 % Mn by moles and 66.7 % O by moles. To get percent by mass assume 100 moles of atoms, so

$$\text{percent by mass Mn} = \frac{(mol\%Mn)(54.94\ g/mol)}{(mol\%Ti)(54.94\ g/mol) + (mol\%O)(16.00\ g/mol)} \times 100\% =$$

$$= \frac{(33.3\ mol)(54.94\ g/mol)}{(33.3\ mol)(54.94\ g/mol) + (66.7\ mol)(16.00\ g/mol)} \times 100\% = 63.2\ \%\ Mn\ by\ mass.$$

rhodochrosite = $MnCO_3$: The composition will be 20.0 % Mn by moles, 20.0 % C by moles, and 60.0 % O by moles. To get percent by mass assume 100 moles of atoms, so

$$\text{percent by mass Mn} = \frac{(mol\%Mn)(54.94\ g/mol)}{(mol\%Mn)(54.94\ g/mol) + (mol\%C)(12.01\ g/mol) + (mol\%O)(16.00\ g/mol)} \times 100\% =$$

$$= \frac{(20.0\ mol)(54.94\ g/mol)}{(20.0\ mol)(54.94\ g/mol) + (20.0\ mol)(12.01\ g/mol) + (60.0\ mol)(16.00\ g/mol)} \times 100\% = 47.8\ \%\ Mn\ by\ mass$$

51. Titanium must be arc-melted in an inert atmosphere because the high temperature and flow of electrons would cause the metal to oxidize in a normal atmosphere.

52. Despite its reactivity, solid titanium is highly resistant to corrosion in air, acid, and seawater because it quickly reacts with oxygen to form an oxide that coats the surface, preventing further oxidation of the underlying metal. Consequently, titanium is often used in the production of ship components such as propeller shafts and rigging. Titanium is also very strong and light; it is stronger than steel, but less than half as dense.

53. TiO_2 is the most important industrial product of titanium and is often used as a pigment in white paint.

54. Zinc is commonly used as an anticorrosion coating for steel products in a process called galvanizing. Galvanizing a steel object (such as a nail) involves simply dipping the object into a molten bath of zinc. The zinc, which is more reactive than the iron in steel, preferentially oxidizes, forming a tough protective coating.

55. The Bayer process is a hydrometallurgical process used to separate the bauxite (Al_2O_3 n H_2O) from the iron and silicon oxide with which it is usually found. In this process, the bauxite is digested with a hot concentrated aqueous NaOH solution under high pressure. The basic aluminum solution is separated from the oxide solids, and then the aluminum oxide is precipitated out of solution by neutralizing it. Calcination of the precipitate at temperatures greater than 1000 $^{\circ}$C yields anhydrous alumina (Al_2O_3).

56. The Mond process is a process of refining nickel. The sulfides are roasted in air to form metal oxides, and then they are reduced to the elemental metals with carbon. The metal mixture is then heated in the presence of carbon monoxide, forming nickel carbonyl, which has a boiling point of 43 $^{\circ}$C and can therefore be collected as a gas. When the nickel carbonyl is heated past 200 $^{\circ}$C, it decomposes back to nickel metal and carbon monoxide.

57. Carbaloy steel contains cobalt and tungsten.

58. Monel contains nickel, copper, and iron.

59. **Given:** ilmenite, 2.0 x 10^4 kg of ore, 0.051 % by mass ilmenite, 87 % Fe recovery and 63 % Ti recovery
Find: g Fe and Ti recovered
Conceptual plan: ilmenite = $FeTiO_3$ kg ore → g ore → g ilmenite → g Ti possible → g Ti recovered

$$\frac{1000\,g}{1\,kg} \quad \frac{0.051\,g\,ilmenite}{100\,g\,ore} \quad \frac{1(47.88)\,g\,Ti}{151.73\,g\,ilmenite} \quad \frac{63\,g\,Ti\,recovered}{100\,g\,Ti}$$

and   g ilmenite → g Fe possible → g Fe recovered

$$\frac{1(55.85)\,g\,Fe}{151.73\,g\,ilmenite} \quad \frac{87\,g\,Fe\,recovered}{100\,g\,Fe}$$

Solution: 2.0×10^4 kg ore $\times \dfrac{1000\,g\,ore}{1\,kg\,ore} \times \dfrac{0.051\,g\,ilmenite}{100\,g\,ore} = 1.02 \times 10^4\,g$ ilmenite then

1.02×10^4 g ilmenite $\times \dfrac{1(47.88)\,g\,Ti}{151.73\,g\,ilmenite} \times \dfrac{63\,g\,Ti\,recovered}{100\,g\,Ti} = 2.0 \times 10^3$ g Ti recovered$= 2.0$ kg Ti recovered and

1.02×10^4 g ilmenite $\times \dfrac{1(55.85)\,g\,Fe}{151.73\,g\,ilmenite} \times \dfrac{87\,g\,Fe\,recovered}{100\,g\,Ti} = 3.3 \times 10^3$ g Fe recovered$= 3.3$ kg Fe recovered .

Check: The units (g) are correct. The magnitudes of the answers make physical sense because there is very little mineral in the ore. The amount of Fe recovered is higher than Ti recovered because the atomic weight of Fe and the percent recovery of Fe are both higher than Ti.

60. **Given:** chromite = 5.00×10^2 g   **Find:** g Al needed and Cr recovered
**Conceptual plan: chromite = $FeCr_2O_3$ write balanced reaction   then
g chromite → mol chromite → mol Al → g Al and   mol chromite → mol Cr → g Cr**

$$\frac{1\,mol\,chromite}{207.85\,g\,chromite} \quad \frac{8\,mol\,Al}{3\,mol\,chromite} \quad \frac{26.98\,g\,Al}{1\,mol\,Al} \qquad \frac{2\,mol\,Cr}{1\,mol\,chromite} \quad \frac{52.00\,g\,Cr}{1\,mol\,Cr}$$

Solution: $3\,FeCr_2O_3\,(s) + 8\,Al\,(s) \xrightarrow{\text{Heat}} 4\,Al_2O_3\,(s) + 6\,Cr\,(s) + 3\,Fe\,(s)$

5.00×10^2 g chromite $\times \dfrac{1\,mol\,chromite}{207.85\,g\,chromite} = 2.40558\,g$ chromite then

2.40558 g chromite $\times \dfrac{8\,mol\,Al}{3\,mol\,chromite} \times \dfrac{26.98\,g\,Al}{1\,mol\,Al} = 173\,g$ Al and

2.40558 g chromite $\times \dfrac{2\,mol\,Cr}{1\,mol\,chromite} \times \dfrac{52.00\,g\,Cr}{1\,mol\,Cr} = 250.\,g$ Cr .

Check: The units (g) are correct. The magnitudes of the answers make physical sense because there is over 2 moles of mineral. The amount of Cr is larger than Al because the atomic weight of Al is about half of the atomic weight of Cr. There are over 4 moles of Cr and over 6 moles of Al.

61. Four atoms surround a tetrahedral hole and six atoms surround an octahedral hole. The octahedral hole is larger because it is surrounded by a greater number of atoms.

62. The crystal structures of the two elements are important in determining the phase diagram because they are more likely to be miscible. If the crystal structures are different then they will not form a substitutional alloy. If the sizes of the two elements are within 15 % of each other then they are likely to be able to form a substitutional alloy. If one element is much smaller than the other, the smaller element can form an interstitial alloy (if it can fit in the octahedral or tetrahedral holes).

63. Manganese has one more electron orbital available for bonding than chromium.

64. MnO_2 is added to glass to counteract the color that is imparted by iron oxide impurities in the glass, which impart a green color. Normally MnO_2 is brown or black, depending on the level of hydration. The manganese acts as an oxidizing agent and converts the iron from its reduced state (which is a strong greenish blue colorant) to an oxidized state (which has a yellowish, but much less intense, color).

65. Ferromagnetic atoms, like paramagnetic atoms, have unpaired electrons. However, in ferromagnetic atoms, these electrons align with their spin oriented in the same direction, resulting in a permanent magnetic field.

66. In an acidic solution (below pH = 6), the orange-red dichromate ion, $Cr_2O_7^{2-}$, is more stable. In more basic solutions (above pH = 6), the yellow chromate ion, CrO_4^{2-}, dominates. The dichromate ion has a higher Cr:O ratio (2:7 or 0.285:1) than the chromate ion (1:4 or 0.25:1). Both the chromate and dichromate ions have a chromium oxidation state of +6.

67. **Given:** cylinder, h = 5.62 cm after pressing, r = 4.00 cm; d (before pressing) = 2.41 g/mL, d (after pressing) = 6.85 g/mL, d (solid iron) = 7.78 g/mL   **Find:** a) original height, b) theoretical height if d = d(solid iron), and c) % voids in component

    Conceptual plan: **a) Since** $d = \dfrac{m}{V}$, $V = \pi r^2 h$, **and the mass of iron is constant, this means that**

    $d \propto \dfrac{1}{h}$. **So d (before pressing), d (after pressing), h(after pressing) → h (before pressing)**

    $$\frac{d_1}{d_2} = \frac{h_2}{h_1}$$

    b) d (solid iron), d (after pressing), h(after pressing) → h (solid iron)

    $$\frac{d_1}{d_2} = \frac{h_2}{h_1}$$

    c) Assume d (air) = 0, so d (solid iron), d (after pressing) → % voids

    $$\% \; voids = \frac{d_{after\,pressing} - d_{solid\,iron}}{d_{after\,pressing}} \times 100 \;\%$$

    Solution: a) $\dfrac{d_1}{d_2} = \dfrac{h_2}{h_1}$ Rearrange to solve for h_2. $h_2 = \dfrac{d_1 h_1}{d_2} = \dfrac{6.85 \;\frac{g}{mL} \times 5.62 \;cm}{2.41 \;\frac{g}{mL}} = 16.0 \;cm$.

    b) $\dfrac{d_1}{d_2} = \dfrac{h_2}{h_1}$ Rearrange to solve for h_2. $h_2 = \dfrac{d_1 h_1}{d_2} = \dfrac{6.85 \;\frac{g}{mL} \times 5.62 \;cm}{7.78 \;\frac{g}{mL}} = 4.95 \;cm$.

    c) $\% \; voids = \dfrac{d_{solid\,iron} - d_{after\,pressing}}{d_{after\,pressing}} \times 100 \;\% = \dfrac{7.78 \;\frac{g}{mL} - 6.85 \;\frac{g}{mL}}{6.85 \;\frac{g}{mL}} \times 100 \;\% = 14 \;\%$

Check: The units (cm, cm and %) are correct. The higher the density, the smaller the height, so the answer for a) is greater than 5.62 cm and the answer for b) is smaller than 5.62 cm. Since the density of the pressed component is close to the density of solid iron, the volume of voids is low.

68. **Given:** producing circular part (10.0 cm diameter) from pressing versus cutting from square part (10.0 cm side length) **Find:** percentage of scrap metal is starting with square and percentage of scrap is making 6.0 cm diameter center hole
    Conceptual plan: Since we are calculating percentage of scrap and not mass of scrap, the height of the part is not needed. Calculate the volume of the original square and

$$V = l^2 h$$

the final product (remember that r = ½ d). then

$$V = \pi r^2 h$$

V (square), V (final part) → % scrap and calculate volume of hole and then

$$\% \ scrap = \frac{V(square) - V(finalpart)}{V(square)} \times 100 \ \% \qquad\qquad V = \pi r^2 h$$

V (solid part), V (hole) → % scrap

$$\% \ scrap = \frac{V(hole)}{V(solid \ part)} \times 100 \ \%$$

and the total scrap from the original square is the sum of the two sources of waste, keeping the original square as reference.
Solution: $V = l^2 h = (10.0 \ cm)^2 \ h = 100. \ cm^2 \ h$ and $r = ½ \ d = ½ \ (10.0 \ cm) = 5.00 \ cm$ then

$V = \pi r^2 h = \pi (5.00 \ cm)^2 \ h = 78.\underline{5}398 \ cm^2 \ h$ and

$$\% \ scrap = \frac{V(square) - V(finalpart)}{V(square)} \times 100 \ \% = \frac{100. \ cm^2 \ h - 78.\underline{5}398 \ cm^2 \ h}{100. \ cm^2 \ h} \times 100 \ \% = 21 \ \% \ .$$

For hole $r = ½ \ d = ½ \ (6.0 \ cm) = 3.0 \ cm$ then $V = \pi r^2 h = \pi (3.0 \ cm)^2 \ h = 28.\underline{2}743 \ cm^2 \ h$ and

$$\% \ scrap = \frac{V(hole)}{V(solid \ part)} \times 100 \ \% = \frac{28.\underline{2}743 \ cm^2 \ h}{78.\underline{5}398 \ cm^2 \ h} \times 100 \ \% = 36 \ \% \ \text{in last step. The scrap from the original}$$

square then $\% \ scrap = \dfrac{V(hole)}{V(original square)} \times 100 \ \% = \dfrac{28.\underline{2}743 \ cm^2 \ h}{100 \ cm^2 \ h} \times 100 \ \% = 28 \ \% \ \text{from hole so the}$

total scrap is $21 \ \% + 28 \ \% = 49 \ \%.$
Check: The units (%) are correct. The amount of scrap is quite high since the corners contain a large amount of the volume and the hole in the center is large.

69. Since there are the same number of octahedral holes as there are metal atoms in a closest packed structure and twice as many tetrahedral holes as there are metal atoms there are a total of three holes for each metal atom and the formula would be LaH_3. Since the formula is $LaH_{2.76}$, the percentage of holes filled is (2.76/3) x 100 % = 92.0 % filled.

70. Nickel is recovered from a high nickel deposits in few locations that are believed to be the site of meteor impacts. Since the deposits are high in nickel content and the deposits are well defined, it is economical the recover. It is economical to use because in many applications only a thin surface coating is necessary.

    Cobalt is economical to mine and use because it is collected as a by-product in the extraction process of other metal ores.

71. Gold and silver are found in their elemental forms because of their low reactivity. Sodium and calcium are Group 1A and Group 2A metals, respectively, and are highly reactive as they readily lose their valence electrons to obtain octets.

Chapter 24
Transition Metals and Coordination Compounds

1. A transition metal atom forms an ion by losing the ns^2 (valence shell) electrons first.

2. Transition metals can have multiple oxidation states because they lose the ns^2 (valence shell) electrons and then can lose $(n-1)d^x$ electrons.

3. The +2 oxidation state is common because most of the transition metals have two electrons occupying the ns orbitals. These electrons are lost first by the metal.

4. The reason that the third transition row elements are not large than the second row transition elements is because 14 of the 32 electrons added have gone into a $(n-2)f$ sublevel, and while electrons in f orbitals are in lower principal quantum levels, they are not very effective at shielding the outer electrons from nuclear charge. Consequently, the outer electrons are held more tightly by the nucleus, offsetting the typical increases in size between the periods – an effect called the lanthanide contraction.

5. The electronegativity of the transition elements generally increases across a row, following the main group trend. However, in contrast to main – group trend, electronegativity increases from the first transition row to the second. There is little electronegativity difference between the second and third transition row. There is a slight increase from silver to gold. Therefore, Au is the most electronegative of the transition metals.

6. a) The coordination number is the number of molecules or ions directly bound to the metal atom. It is the secondary balance of the metal atom.

    b) A ligand is a Lewis base (or electron donor) that forms a bond with the metal.

    c) Bidentate ligands can donate two pairs of electrons from two different atoms to the metal. Polydentate ligands can donate even more than two electron pairs from more than two atoms, to the metal.

    d) A complex ion contains the metal ion in the center and the ligands – which can be neutral molecules or ions – arranged around it.

    e) A chelating agent is ligand that is either a bidentate or polydentate ligand.

7. A ligand can be considered a Lewis base because it donates a pair of electrons. The transition metal ion would be a Lewis acid because it accepts the pair of electrons.

8. a) A structural isomers are those in which atoms are connected to one another in different ways, whereas stereoisomers are those in which atoms are connected in the same way but the ligands have a different spatial arrangement about the metal atom.

    b) Linkage isomers occur when the ligands can coordinate to the metal in different ways. Coordination isomers occur when a coordinated ligand exchanges places with the uncoordinated counterion.

    c) Geometric isomers result when the ligands bonded to the metal have a different spatial arrangement. Optical isomers are nonsuperimposable mirror images of one another.

9. Cis – trans isomerism occurs in square planar complexes of the general formula MA_2B_2 or octahedral complexes of the general formula MA_4B_2.

10. A complex ion will be optically active if the mirror image is nonsuperimposable on the original molecule.

11. Because of the spatial arrangement of the ligands, the normally degenerate d orbitals are split in energy. The difference between these split d orbitals is the crystal field splitting energy. The magnitude of the splitting depends on the particular complex. In strong – field complexes, the splitting is large, and in weak – field complexes, the splitting is small. The magnitude of the crystal field splitting depends in large part on the ligands attached to the central metal ion.

12. Sc^{3+} has an electron configuration of [Ar], while Ti^{3+} has an electron configuration of $[Ar]3d^1$. It is the presence of d electrons that give Ti^{3+} compounds their color.

13. Zn^{2+} has a filled d subshell, while Cu^{2+} has 9 d electrons. Since Zn^{2+} has this filled d subshell, the color of the compounds will be white. Cu^{2+} has an incomplete d subshell, so different ligands will cause a different crystal field splitting and the compounds will have color.

14. Strong field ligands cause a large split in the d orbitals and it will take more nergy to occupy the higher energy level than it does to pair the electrons in the lower energy level. Weak field ligands cause a small split in the d orbital energy, so the electron pairing energy is greater than the energy of the split. So, complexes with strong field ligands have fewer unpaired electrons relative to the free metal ion, and are called low – spin complexes. Complexes with weak – field ligand have the same number of unpaired electrons as the free metal ion and are called high – spin complexes.

15. Almost all tetrahedral complexes are high – spin because of reduced ligand – metal interactions. The d orbitals in a tetrahedral complex are interacting with only four ligands, as opposed to six in the octahedral complex, so the value of Δ is generally smaller.

16. According to crystal field theory, the ligands cause the normally degenerate d orbitals to split in energy. The energy difference, the crystal field splitting energy, Δ, is the energy absorbed by the complex. The color seen is the complementary color to the color absorbed.

17. Identify the noble gas that precedes the element and put it in square brackets.
Determine the outer principal quantum level for the s orbital. Subtract one to obtain the quantum level for the d orbital. If the element is in the third or fourth transition series, include $(n - 2)f$ electrons in the configuration.
Count across the row to see how many electrons are in the neutral atom.
For an ion, remove the required number of electrons, first from the s and then from the d orbitals.
   a) Ni; Ni^{2+}
      The noble gas that precedes Ni is Ar, Ni is in the fourth period so the orbitals we use are 4s and 3d and Ni has 10 more electrons than Ar.
      Ni $[Ar]4s^23d^8$
      Ni will lose electrons from the 4s and then from the 3d
      Ni^{2+} $[Ar]4s^03d^8$

   b) Mn; Mn^{4+}
      The noble gas that precedes Mn is Ar, Mn is in the fourth period so the orbitals we use are 4s and 3d and Mn has 7 more electrons than Ar.
      Mn $[Ar]4s^23d^5$
      Mn will lose electrons from the 4s and then from the 3d
      Mn^{4+} $[Ar]4s^03d^3$

   c) Y; Y^+
      The noble gas that precedes Y is Kr, Y is in the fifth period so the orbitals we use are 5s and 4d and Y has 3 more electrons than Kr.
      Y $[Kr]5s^24d^1$
      Y will lose electrons from the 5s and then from the 4d
      Y^+ $[Kr]5s^14d^1$

   d) Ta; Ta^{2+}
      The noble gas that precedes Ta is Xe, Ta is in the sixth period so the orbitals we use are 6s, 5d and 4f and Ta has 19 more electrons than Xe.
      Ta $[Xe]6s^24f^{14}5d^3$

      Ta will lose electrons from the 6s and then from the 5d
      Ta^{2+} $[Xe]6s^04f^{14}5d^3$

18. Identify the noble gas that precedes the element and put it in square brackets.
Determine the outer principal quantum level for the s orbital. Subtract one to obtain the quantum level for the d orbital. If the element is in the third or fourth transition series, include $(n - 2)f$ electrons in the configuration.

Count across the row to see how many electrons are in the neutral atom.

For an ion, remove the required number of electrons, first from the *s* and then from the *d* orbitals.

a) Zr; Zr^{2+}

The noble gas that precedes Zr is Kr, Zr is in the fifth period so the orbitals we use are 5s and 4d and Zr has 4 more electrons than Kr.

Zr $[Kr]5s^2 4d^2$

Zr will lose electrons from the 5s and then from the 4d

Zr^{2+} $[Kr]5s^0 4d^2$

b) Co; Co^{2+}

The noble gas that precedes Co is Ar, Co is in the fourth period so the orbitals we use are 4s and 3d and Co has 9 more electrons than Ar.

Co $[Ar]5s^2 4d^7$

Co will lose electrons from the 5s and then from the 4d

Co^{2+} $[Ar]5s^0 4d^7$

c) Tc; Tc^{3+}

The noble gas that precedes Tc is Kr, Tc is in the fifth period so the orbitals we use are 5s and 4d and Tc has 7 more electrons than Kr.

Tc $[Kr]5s^2 4d^5$

Tc will lose electrons from the 5s and then from the 4d

Tc^{3+} $[Kr]5s^0 4d^4$

d) Os; Os^{4+}

The noble gas that precedes Os is Xe, Os is in the sixth period so the orbitals we use are 6s, 5d and 4f and Os has 22 more electrons than Xe.

Os $[Xe]6s^2 4f^{14} 5d^6$

Os will lose electrons from the 6s and then from the 5d

Os^{4+} $[Xe]6s^0 4f^{14} 5d^4$

19. a) V   Highest oxidation state = +5. V = $[Ar]4s^2 3d^3$. Since V is to the left of Mn, it can lose   all of the 3s and 3d electrons so the highest oxidation state is +5

b) Re   Highest oxidation state = +7. Re = $[Xe]6s^2 4f^{14} 5d^5$. Re can lose all of the 6s and 5d electrons, so the highest oxidation state is +7.

c) Pd   Highest oxidation state = +4. Pd = $[Kr]5s^2 4d^8$. Pd can lose the 5s and then 2 electrons from the 4d orbitals, so the highest oxidation state is +4.

20. a) +3   In the first row transition metals the elements that can have a highest oxidation state of +3 are scandium, nickel, and copper.

b) +7   In the first row transition metals the element that can have a highest oxidation state of +7 is manganese.

c) +4   In the first row transition metals the elements that can have a highest oxidation state of +4 are titanium and cobalt.

21. a) $[Cr(H_2O)_6]^{3+}$ H_2O is neutral, so Cr has an oxidation state of +3, there are 6 H_2O molecules attached to each Cr, so the coordination number is 6

b) $[Co(NH_3)_3Cl_3]^-$ NH_3 is neutral and Cl has charge of – 1. The sum of the oxidation state of Co and the charge of chloride ion = 1–. x+(3(–1)) = –1, x = +2, therefore the oxidation state of Co is +2. The 3 NH_3 molecules and the 3 Cl^- ions are bound directly to the Co atom, therefore the coordination number is 6.

c) $[Cu(CN)_4]^{2-}$ CN has a charge of –1. The sum of the oxidation state of Cu and the charge of the cyanide ion = 2–. x+(4(–1)) = 2–, x = +2, therefore, the oxidation state of Cu is +2. The 4 cyanide ions are directly bound to the Cu atom, therefore, the coordination number is 4.

d) $[Ag(NH_3)_2]^+$ NH_3 is neutral, so Ag has an oxidation number of +1, there are 2 NH_3 molecules attached to each Ag atom so the coordination number is 2.

22. a) $[Co(NH_3)_5Br]^{2+}$ NH_3 is neutral and Br has charge of -1. The sum of the oxidation state of Co and the charge of bromide ion = 2+. $x+(1(1-)) = 2+$, $x = +3$, therefore the oxidation state of Co is +3. The 5 NH_3 molecules and the bromide ion are directly bound to the Co atom, therefore, the coordination number is 6.

b) $[Fe(CN)_6]^{4-}$ CN has a charge of -1. The sum of the oxidation state of Fe and the charge of the cyanide ions = 4$-$. $x+(6(1-)) = 4-$, $x = +2$, therefore, the oxidation state of Fe is +2. The 6 cyanide ions are directly bound to the Fe atom, therefore, the coordination number is 6.

c) $[Co(ox)_3]^{4-}$ ox (oxalate ion) has a charge of -2. The sum of the oxidation state of Co and the charge of the oxalate ion = 4$-$, $x+(3(-2)) = 4-$, $x = +2$, therefore, the oxidation state of Co is +2. Oxalate ion is a bidentate ligand, and the oxalate ions are directly bound to the Co atom, therefore, the coordination number is 6.

d) $[PdCl_4]^{2-}$ Cl has a charge of -1. The sum of the oxidation state of Pd and the charge on the chloride ions = -1. $x+(4(-1)) = 2-$, $x = +2$, therefore, the oxidation state of Pd is +2. The 4 chloride ions are directly bound to the Pd atom, therefore the coordination number is 4.

23. a) $[Cr(H_2O)_6]^{3+}$ is hexaaquachromium(III) ion.
$[Cr(H_2O)_6]^{3+}$ is a complex cation
Name the ligand: H_2O is aqua
Name the metal ion: Cr^{3+} is chromium(III)
Name the complex ion by adding the prefixes to indicate the number of each ligand, followed by the name of each ligand, followed by the name of the metal ion: hexaaquachromium(III) ion.

b) $[Cu(CN)_4]^{2-}$ is tetracyanocuprate(II) ion.
$[Cu(CN)_4]^{2-}$ is a complex anion
Name the ligand: CN^- is cyano
Name the metal ion: Cu^{2+} is cuprate(II) because the complex is an anion
Name the complex ion by adding the prefix to indicate the number of each ligand, followed by the name of each ligand, followed by the name of the metal ion: tetracyanocuprate(II) ion.

c) $[Fe(NH_3)_5Br]SO_4$ is pentaamminebromoiron(III) sulfate
$[Fe(NH_3)_5Br]^{2+}$ is a complex cation, SO_4^{2-} is sulfate.
Name the ligands in alphabetical order: NH_3 is ammine, Br^{1-} is bromo
Name the metal cation: Fe^{3+} is iron(III)
Name the complex ion by adding prefixes to indicate the number of each ligand, followed by the name of the ligand, followed by the name of the metal ion: pentaamminebromoiron(III)
Name the compound by writing the name of the cation before the anion. The only space is between the ion names: pentaamminebromoiron(III) sulfate

d) $[Co(H_2O)_4(NH_3)(OH)]Cl_2$ is amminetetraaquahydroxycobalt(III) chloride
$[Co(H_2O)_4(NH_3)(OH)]^{2+}$ is a complex cation, Cl^{1-} is chloride.
Name the ligands in alphabetical order: NH_3 is ammine, H_2O is aqua, OH^- is hydroxo
Name the metal cation: Co^{3+} is cobalt(III)
Name the complex ion by adding prefixes to indicate the number of each ligand, followed by the name of the ligand, followed by the metal ion: amminetetraaquahydroxocobalt(III)
Name the compound by writing the name of the cation before the anion. The only space is between the ion names: amminetetraaquahydroxycobalt(III) chloride

24. a) $[Co(en)_2]^{2+}$ is bis(ethylenediamine)cobalt(II) ion
$[Co(en)_2]^{2+}$ is a complex cation
Name the ligand: en is ethylenediamine
Name the metal cation: Co^{2+} is cobalt(II)
Name the complex ion by adding a prefix to indicate the number of ligands, followed by the name of the ligand, followed by the metal ion: bis(ethylenediamine)cobalt(II) ion

b) $[Mn(CO)_3(NO_2)_3]^{2+}$ is tricarbonyltrinitromanganese(V) ion
$[Mn(CO)_3(NO_2)_3]^{2+}$ is a complex cation
Name the ligands in alphabetical order: CO is carbonyl, NO_2^{1-} is nitro
Name the metal cation: Mn^{5+} is manganese(V)
Name the complex ion by adding the prefixes to indicate the number of each ligand, followed by the name of the ligand, followed by the metal ion: tricarbonyltrinitromanganese(V) ion

c) $Na[Cr(H_2O)_2(ox)_2]$ is sodium diaquadioxalatochromate(III)
Na^+ is sodium ion, $[Cr(H_2O)_2(ox)_2]^{1-}$ is a complex anion
Name the ligands in alphabetical order: H_2O is aqua, ox (oxalate) is oxalato
Name the metal ion: Cr^{3+} is chromate(III) because the complex is an anion
Name the complex ion by adding the prefixes to indicate the number of each ligand, followed by the name of the ligand, followed by the metal ion: diaquadoxalatochromate(III)
Name the compound by writing the name of the cation before the anion. The only space is between the ion names: sodium diaquadioxalatochromate(III)

d) $[Co(en)_3][Fe(CN)_6]$ is trisethylenediamiecobalt(III) hexacyanoferrate(III)
$[Co(en)_3]^{3+}$ is a complex cation and $[Fe(CN)_6]^{3-}$ is a complex anion
Name the complex cation:
Name the ligand: en is ethylenediamine
Name the metal ion: Co^{3+} is cobalt(III)
Name the complex ion by adding the prefix to indicate the number of ligand, followed by the name of the ligand, followed by the metal ion: trisethylenediamiecobalt(III)
Name the complex anion:
Name the ligand: CN^{1-} is cyano
Name the metal ion: Fe^{3+} is ferrate(III) because the complex is an anion
Name the complex ion by adding the prefix to indicate the number of ligand, followed by the name of the ligand, followed by the metal ion: hexacyanoferrate(III) ion
Name the compound by writing the name of the cation before the anion. The only space is between the ion names: trisethylenediaminecobalt(III) hexacyanoferrate(III)

25. a) hexamminechromium(III) is a complex ion with Cr^{3+} metal ion and 6 NH_3 ligands.
$[Cr(NH_3)_6]^{3+}$

b) potassium hexacyanoferrate(III) is a compound with a $3K^+$ cations and a complex anion with Fe^{3+} metal ion and 6 CN^- ligands. $K_3[Fe(CN)_6]$

c) ethylenediaminedithiocyanatocopper(II) is a compound with a Cu^{2+} metal ion, a ethylenediamine ligand and two SCN^- ligands. $[Cu(en)(SCN)_2]$

d) tetraaquaplatinum(II) hexachloroplatinate(IV) is a complex compound with a complex cation that contains a Pt^{2+} metal ion, and 4 H_2O ligands and a complex anion that contains a Pt^{4+} metal ion and 6 Cl^- ligands.
$[Pt(H_2O)_4][PtCl_6]$

26. a) hexaaquanickel(II) chloride is a compound with a complex cation that contains a Ni^{2+} metal ion and 6 H_2O ligands and 2 Cl^- counterions. $[Ni(H_2O)_6]Cl_2$

b) pentacarbonylchloromanganese(I) is a coordination compound than contains a Mn^+ metal ion, 5 CO ligands and 1 Cl^- ligand.
$[Mn(CO)_5Cl]$

c) ammonium diaquatetrabromovanadate(III) is a coordination compound with an ammonium cation and a complex anion that contains V^{3+} metal ion, 2 H_2O ligands and 4 Br^- ligands. $NH_4[V(H_2O)_2Br_4]$

d) tris(ethylenediamine)cobalt(III) trioxalatoferrate(III) is a coordination compound with a complex cation that contains Co^{3+} metal ion and three ethylenediamine ligands and a complex anion that contains an Fe^{3+} metal ion and 3 oxalate ligands. $[Co(en)_3][Fe(ox)_3]$

27. a) $[Co(NH_3)_3(CN)_3]$ is triamminetricyanocobalt(III)

b) Since ethylenediamine is a bidentate ligand, you need three to have a coordination number of six. $[Cr(en)_3]^{3+}$ is tris(ethylenediamine)chromium(III) ion

28. a) $[Fe(H_2O)_4(ONO)_2]^+$ is the tetraaquadinitritoiron(III) ion

b) The complex cation is: $[V(en)_2Cl_2]^+$; the complex anion is $[NiCl_4]^{2-}$, the coordination compound is $[V(en)_2Cl_2]_2[NiCl_4]$ and is named dichlorobis(ethylenediamine)vanadium(III) tetrachloroferrate(II).

29. In linkage isomers the ligand coordinates to the metal in different ways.

pentaamminenitromanganese(III) ion   pentaamminenitritomanganese(III) ion

30. In linkage isomers the ligand coordinates to the metal in different ways.

trichlorothiocyanatoplatinum(II) ion   trichloroisothiocyanatoplatinum(II) ion

31. Coordination isomers occur when a coordinated ligand exchanges places with the uncoordinated counterion.
$[Fe(H_2O)_5Cl]Cl \cdot H_2O$ pentaaquachloroiron(II) chloride monohydrate

$[Fe(H_2O)_4Cl_2] \cdot 2H_2O$ tetraaquadichloroiron(II) dihydrate

32. Coordination isomers occur when a coordinated ligand exchanges places with the uncoordinated counterion.
$[Co(en)_2(ox)][Cr(en)(ox)_2]$
    bis(ethylenediamine)oxalatocobalt(III) ethylenediaminedioxalatochromate(III)

$[Cr(en)_2(ox)][Co(en)(ox)_2]$
    bis(ethylenediamine)oxalatochromium(III) ethylenediamindioxalatocobaltate(III)

$[Cr(en)_3][Co(ox)_3]$
    tris(ethylenediamine)chromium(III) trioxalatocobaltate(III)

33. Geometric isomers result when the ligands bonded to the metal have a different spatial arrangement.
a) No, an octahedral complex has to have at least two different ligands to have geometric isomers.

b) Yes, there will be cis – trans isomers.

c) Yes, there will be fac – mer isomers.

d) No, a square planar complex has to have at least two different ligands to have geometric isomers.

e) Yes, there will be cis – trans isomers.

34. Geometric isomers result when the ligands bonded to the metal have a different spatial arrangement.
a) Yes, there will be cis – trans isomers.

b) No, an octahedral complex has to have at least two different ligands to have geometric isomers.

c) Yes, there will be cis – trans isomers.

d) Yes, there will be cis – trans isomers.

e) Yes, there will be cis – trans isomers.

35. a) square – planar $[NiWXYZ]^{2+}$ would have 3 geometric isomers.

b) tetrahedral $[ZnWXYZ]^{2+}$ would have 2 geometric isomers.

36. a) $[Fe(CO)_3(Cl)_3]$ would have 2 geometric isomers. (fac and mer)

    fac   mer

b) $[Mn(CO)_2Cl_2Br_2]^+$ would have 5 isomers

  all trans   CO trans, Cl,Br cis: Cl trans, CO,Br cis:

            Br trans, CO, Cl cis   all cis

37. a) $[Cr(CO)_3(NH_3)_3]^{3+}$ has a coordination number of 6, and is octahedral. There will be fac and mer isomers and no optical isomers because rotation of the mirror images are superimposable upon each other.

    fac   mer

b) $[Pd(CO)_2(H_2O)Cl]^+$ has a coordination number of 4, and is d^8 complex so it is square – planar. There will be cis and trans isomers. There will be no optical isomers because rotation of the mirror images are superimposable upon each other.

    cis   trans

38. a) $[Fe(CO)_4Cl_2]^+$ has a coordination number of 6 and is octahedral. There will be cis and trans isomers.

    trans   cis

b) $[Pt(en)Cl_2]$ has a coordination number of 4, Pt is d^8 so it is square – planar.

39. $[Cr(CO)_2(ox)_2]^-$ has a coordination number of 6 and is octahedral. There will be cis and trans isomers. The cis isomer has a mirror image that is nonsuperimposable.

trans   cis

40. $[Fe(CO)_3Cl_3]$ has a coordination number of 6 and is octahedral. There will be fac and mer isomers. There are no optical isomers.

fac   mer

41. a) Zn^{2+} d^{10} b) Fe^{3+} d^5 high spin   low spin

c) V^{3+} d^2 d) Co^{2+} d^7 high spin

42. a) Cr^{3+} d^3 b) Cu^{2+} d^9

c) Mn^{3+} d^4 high spin   low spin   d) Fe^{2+} d^6 low spin

43. **Given:** $[CrCl_6]^{3-}$; $\lambda = 735$ absorbance maximum **Find:** crystal field energy
Conceptual Plan: $\lambda \rightarrow \Delta \ (J) \rightarrow$ kJ/ion $\rightarrow$ kJ/mol

$$\Delta = \frac{hc}{\lambda} \quad \frac{kJ}{1000\ J} \quad \frac{6.02 \times 10^{23}\ ions}{mol}$$

Solution: $\dfrac{(6.626 \times 10^{-34}\ J \cdot \cancel{s})(3.00 \times 10^{8}\ \frac{\cancel{m}}{\cancel{s}})}{(735\ \cancel{nm})\left(\dfrac{1 \times 10^{-9}\ \cancel{m}}{\cancel{nm}}\right)} = 2.7\underline{0}4 \times 10^{-19}$ J/ion

$2.7\underline{0}4 \times 10^{-19}\ \dfrac{\cancel{J}}{\cancel{ion}} \times \dfrac{6.02 \times 10^{23}\ \cancel{ions}}{mol} \times \dfrac{kJ}{1000\ \cancel{J}} = 163$ kJ/mol

Check: Cl is a weak field ligand and would be expected to have a relatively small Δ which is consistent with a value of 163 kJ.

44. **Given:** $[Rh(NH_3)_6]^{3+}$; $\lambda = 295$ absorbance maximum   **Find:** crystal field energy, Δ
Conceptual Plan: $\lambda \rightarrow \Delta \ (J) \rightarrow$ kJ/ion $\rightarrow$ kJ/mol

$$\Delta = \frac{hc}{\lambda} \quad \frac{kJ}{1000\ J} \quad \frac{6.02 \times 10^{23}\ ions}{mol}$$

Solution: $\dfrac{(6.626 \times 10^{-34}\ J \cdot \cancel{s})(3.00 \times 10^{8}\ \frac{\cancel{m}}{\cancel{s}})}{(295\ \cancel{nm})\left(\dfrac{1 \times 10^{-9}\ \cancel{m}}{\cancel{nm}}\right)} = 6.7\underline{3}8 \times 10^{-19}$ J/ion

$6.7\underline{3}8 \times 10^{-19}\ \dfrac{\cancel{J}}{\cancel{ion}} \times \dfrac{6.02 \times 10^{23}\ \cancel{ions}}{mol} \times \dfrac{kJ}{1000\ \cancel{J}} = 405$ kJ/mol

Check: NH_3 is a strong field ligand and would be expected to have a relatively large Δ which is consistent with a value of 405 kJ.

45. The crystal field ligand strength would be $CN^- > NH_3 > F^-$. The smaller the wavelength, the larger the energy, the greater the crystal field splitting that would be observed. So $[Co(CN)_6]^{3-}$ would have a smaller wavelength than $[Co(NH_3)_6]^{3+}$ which would have a smaller wavelength than $[CoF_6]^{3-}$.
So: $[Co(CN)_6]^{3-} = 290$ nm which absorbs in the UV, and would have a colorless solution.
$[Co(NH_3)_6]^{3+} = 440$ nm which absorbs in the blue and would have a yellow solution.
$[CoF_6]^{3-} = 770$ nm which absorbs in the red and would have a green solution.

46. The green solution absorbs in the red, the yellow solution absorbs in the violet, and the purple solution absorbs in the yellow. So the green solution has the smallest Δ, the next would be the purple solution and the largest Δ would be the yellow solution. The crystal field ligand strength would be $NH_3 > H_2O > Cl^-$.
So, the green solution which absorbs in the red would have the smallest Δ, and would be $[Cr(H_2O)_4Cl_2]^+$.
The purple solution which absorbs in the yellow would have the next Δ, and would be $[Cr(H_2O)_6]^{3+}$.
The yellow solution which absorbs in the violet and would have the largest Δ, and would be $[Cr(NH_3)_6]^{3+}$.

47. Mn^{2+} is d^5 and there are 5 unpaired electrons so the crystal field splitting energy, Δ, is small compared to the energy to pair the electrons. Therefore, NH_3 induces a weak field with Mn^{2+}.

48. Fe^{2+} is d^6, to be paramagnetic there must be unpaired electrons. For all the electrons to be unpaired, the crystal field splitting energy must be smaller than the energy to pair the electrons. Therefore, H_2O induces a weak field with Fe^{2+}

49. a) $[RhCl_6]^{3-}$ Rh^{3+} d^6 Cl^- is a weak field ligand, so the value of Δ will be small, so there are 4 unpaired electrons.

b) $[Co(OH)_6]^{4-}$ Co^{2+} d^7 OH^- is a weak field ligand, so the value of Δ will be small, so there are 3 unpaired electrons.

c) cis - $[Fe(en)(NO_2)_2]^+$ Fe^{3+} d^5 en and NO_2^- are strong field ligands, so the value of Δ will be large, so there is 1 unpaired electrons.

50. a) $[Cr(CN)_6]^{4-}$ Cr^{2+} d^4 CN^- is a strong field ligand, so the value of Δ will be large, so there are 2 unpaired electrons.

b) $[MnF_6]^{4-}$ Mn^{2+} d^5 F^- is a weak field ligand, so the value of Δ will be small, so there are 5 unpaired electrons.

c) $[Ru(en)_3]^{2+}$ Ru^{2+} d^6 en is a strong field ligand, so the value of Δ will be large, so there are 0 unpaired electrons.

51. $[CoCl_4]^{2-}$ Co^{2+} is d^7, Cl^- is a weak field ligand, so the value of Δ will be small and there will be 3 unpaired electrons. The crystal field splitting for a tetrahedral structure is:

52. $[PdCl_4]^{2-}$ is known to be diamagnetic. Pd complexes are low spin complexes. Pd^{2+} is d^8. Use the crystal field splitting for a tetrahedral structure and a square – planar structure and determine which would be diamagnetic.

tetrahedral (2 unpaired electrons)   square – planar (0 unpaired electrons)

The tetrahedral structure would be paramagnetic and the square – planar would be diamagnetic, since the compound is diamagnetic it must be square – planar.

53. Hemoglobin, cytochrome c, and chlorlphyll all contain a porphyrin ligand.

54. a) hemoglobin contains Fe metal.

838

b) carbonic anhydrase contains Zn^{2+}.

c) chlorophyll contains Mg metal

d) iron blue contains Fe^{2+} and Fe^{3+}.

55. Oxyhemoglobin is low spin and a red color. Since it is low spin, the crystal field splitting energy must be large. The red color means that the complex absorbs in the green region (~500 nm) which also indicates a large crystal field splitting energy, therefore, O_2 must be a strong field ligand.
Deoxyhemoglobin is high spin and a blue color. Since it is high spin, the crystal field splitting energy must be small. The blue color means that the complex absorbs in the orange region (~600 nm) which also indicates a small crystal field splitting energy. Both of these are consistent with H_2O as a weak field ligand.

56. To calculate the equilibrium constant for the new reaction:

Reverse reaction 1:	HbO_2	$\leftrightarrows$	$Hb + O_2$	$K = 1/K_1 = 1/(2 \times 10^{12})$
Add reaction 2:	$Hb + CO$	$\leftrightarrows$	$HbCO$	$K_2 = 1 \times 10^{14}$
	$HbO_2 + CO$	$\leftrightarrows$	$HbCO + O_2$	$K_3 = 5 \times 10^1$

Since $K > 1$, the reaction favors the products.

57. a)
Cr	$[Ar]4s^1 3d^5$
Cr^+	$[Ar]4s^0 3d^5$
Cr^{2+}	$[Ar]4s^0 3d^4$
Cr^{3+}	$[Ar]4s^0 3d^3$

b)
Cu	$[Ar]4s^1 3d^{10}$
Cu^+	$[Ar]4s^0 3d^{10}$
Cu^{2+}	$[Ar]4s^0 3d^9$

58. a)
Mo	$[Kr]5s^1 4d^5$
Mo^+	$[Kr]5s^0 4d^5$

Ag	$[Ar]4s^1 3d^{10}$
Ag^+	$[Ar]4s^0 3d^{10}$

b)
Ru	$[Kr]5s^1 4d^7$
Ru^{3+}	$[Kr]5s^0 4d^5$

c)
Rh	$[Kr]5s^1 4d^8$
Rh^{2+}	$[Kr]5s^0 4d^7$

d)
Pd	$[Kr]4d^{10}$
Pd^+	$[Kr]4d^9$
Pd^{2+}	$[Kr]4d^8$

59. a)

b)

ligand can bond from either end.

c)

60. a)

ligand can bond from either end.

b)

bipyridal is a bidentate ligand.

c)

ligand can bond from the N or the O.

61. An octahedral complex has 6 ligands.

MA$_2$B$_2$C$_2$ will have cis/trans isomers: all cis; A trans, B,C cis; B trans, A,C cis; C trans, A,B cis; all trans

MAB$_2$C$_3$ will have fac/mer isomers

MA$_2$B$_3$C   will have fac/mer isomers

MAB$_3$C$_2$ will have fac/mer isomers

MA$_3$B$_2$C   will have fac/mer isomers

MA$_2$BC$_3$ will have fac.mer isomers

MA$_3$BC$_2$ will have fac/mer isomers

MABC$_4$ will have AB cis and trans

MAB$_4$C   will AC have cis and trans

MA$_4$BC   will BC have cis and trans

62. a) [Ni(gly)$_2$] Ni^{2+} d^8 square – planar cis/trans isomers, no optical isomers

cis – diglycinenickel(II)   trans – diglycinenickel(II)

b) [Zn(gly)$_2$]Zn^{2+} d^{10} tetrahedral, optical isomers

diglycinezinc

c) [Fe(gly)$_3$] Fe^{3+} d^5 octahedral, fac isomer, optical isomers

fac – triglycineiron(III)

mer – triglycineiron(III)

mer isomer, optical isomers

63. $[Fe(ox)_3]^{3-}$ Fe^{3+} d^5 coordination number = 6, octahedral, structure has a nonsuperimposable mirror image.

64. a) square – planar $[NiWXYZ]^{2+}$ would have 3 geometric isomers.

none of the isomers will be optically active. The mirror image of each can be rotated to superimpose on the

original structure. e.g.   flip the ion right to left and the will match.

   b) tetrahedral $[ZnWXYZ]^{2+}$ will have an optical isomer.

the structures are nonsuperimposable, the ion is optically active

65. $[Mn(CN)_6]^{3-}$ Mn^{3+} d^4 has a coordination number of 6 and is octahedral. CN^- is a strong field ligand and will cause a large crystal field splitting energy so the ion is low spin.

The ion will be paramagnetic with 2 unpaired electrons.

66. a) a blue solution will absorb most strongly in the orange region so the wavelength will be between 580 and   650 nm.

   b) a red solution will absorb most strongly in the green region so the wavelength will be between 490 and   560 nm.

   c) a yellow solution will absorb most strongly in the violet region so the wavelength will be between 400   and 430 nm.

67. **Given:** 46.7% Pt, 17.0% Cl, 14.8% P, 17.2% C, 4.34% H; **Find:** formula, structures, and names for both compounds.
   Conceptual Plan: % compostion → pseudoformula → formula

$$n = \frac{g}{molar\ mass}$$ divide by smallest

Solution: 46.7 $\cancel{g\ Pt}$ x $\dfrac{1\ mol\ Pt}{195.1\ \cancel{g}}$ = 0.23936 mol Pt   17.0 $\cancel{g\ Cl}$ x $\dfrac{1\ mol\ Cl}{35.45\ \cancel{g\ Cl}}$ = 0.47955 mol Cl

14.8 $\cancel{g\ P}$ x $\dfrac{1\ mol\ P}{30.97\ \cancel{g}}$ = 0.47788 mol P   17.2 $\cancel{g\ C}$ x $\dfrac{1\ mol\ C}{12.01\ \cancel{g\ C}}$ = 1.4321 mol C

4.34 $\cancel{g\ H}$ x $\dfrac{1\ mol\ H}{1.008\ \cancel{g}}$ = 4.3056 mol H

$$Pt_{0.23936}Cl_{0.47955}P_{0.47788}C_{1.4321}H_{4.3056}$$

$$\frac{Pt_{0.23936}}{0.23936}\frac{Cl_{0.47955}}{0.23936}\frac{P_{0.47788}}{0.23936}\frac{C_{1.4321}}{0.23936}\frac{H_{4.3056}}{0.23936}$$

$$PtCl_2P_2C_6H_{18}$$

$$[Pt(P(CH_3)_3)_2Cl_2]$$

cis – dichlorobis(trimethylphosphine)platinum(II)   trans – dichlorobis(trimethylphosphine)platinum(II)

68.

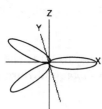

The trigonal planar complex ion has lobes along the x axis and between the x and y axes. So, the ligands will interact most strongly with the $x^2 - y^2$ and the xy orbitals and will not interact with the z^2, the xz , or the yz orbitals. So the crystal field splitting would look like:

_____$x^2 - y^2$ _____xy

_____z^2 _____xz   _____yz

69.

The trigonal bipyramidal complex ion has lobes along the x axis and between the x and y axes and along the z axis.. So, the ligands will interact most strongly with z^2 orbital and then with the $x^2 - y^2$ and the xy orbitals and will not interact with the xz , or the yz orbitals. So the crystal field splitting would look like:

_____z^2

_____$x^2 - y^2$ _____xy

_____xz   _____yz

70. $[Ni(NH_3)_4]^{2+}$ Ni^{2+} is d^8 and square – planar and paramagnetic

$[Ni(CN)_4]^{2-}$ Ni^{2+} is d^8 and square – planar and dimagnetic

_____ $x^2 - y^2$

842

The CN⁻ ligand is a stronger field ligand then NH_3 ligand, so there is a greater splitting between the $x^2 - y^2$ orbital and the xy orbital in the tetracyanonickel(II) complex ion than if the tetraamminenickel(II) complex ion.

71. a) **Given:** $K_{sp}(NiS) = 3 \times 10^{-16}$ **Find:** Solubility in water
Conceptual plan: write the reaction, prepare an ICE table, substitute into the equilibrium expression and solve for S(molar solubility).
Solution: $NiS(s) \leftrightarrows Ni^{2+}(aq) + S^{2-}(aq)$

I	0.0	0.0
C	S	S
E	S	S

$K_{sp} = [Ni^{2+}][S^{2-}]$ $3 \times 10^{-16} = S^2$

$S = 1.7 \times 10^{-8} = 2 \times 10^{-8}$

b) **Given:** $K_{sp}(NiS) = 3 \times 10^{-16}$ $K_f [Ni(NH_3)_6]^{2+} = 2.0 \times 10^8$ **Find:** Solubility in 3.0 M NH_3
Conceptual Plan: Sum the reaction, prepare an ICE table, substitute into the equilibrium expression and solve for S(molar solubility).
Solution:

Reaction 1: $NiS(s)$ $\leftrightarrows$ $\cancel{Ni^{2+}}(aq) + S^{2-}(aq)$ $K_{sp}(NiS) = 3 \times 10^{-16}$
Reaction 2: $\cancel{Ni^{2+}}(aq) + 6NH_3$ $\leftrightarrows$ $Ni(NH_3)_6^{2+}(aq)$ $K_f = 2.0 \times 10^8$

Reaction 3: $NiS(s) + 6NH_3$ $\leftrightarrows$ $Ni(NH_3)_6^{2+} + S^{2-}(aq)$ $K = K_{sp} K_f = 6.0 \times 10^{-8}$

I	3.0 M	0.0	0.0
C	− 6S	S	S
E	3.0 − 6S	S	S

$K = \dfrac{[Ni(NH_3)_6]^{2+}[S^{2-}]}{[NH_3]^6}$ $6.0 \times 10^{-8} = \dfrac{(S)(S)}{(3.0 - S)^6}$

Assume S is small compared to 3.0

$S^2 = 4.37 \times 10^{-5}$

$S = 6.6 \times 10^{-3}$

c) NiS is more soluble in ammonia because the formation of the $[Ni(NH_3)_6]^{2+}$ complex ion is highly favorable. The formation removes Ni^{2+} ion from the solution, causing more of the NiS to dissolve.

72. M with ligand A forms a green solution. This means that the solution is absorbing red which is a long wavelength, lower energy, and small Δ.
M with ligand B forms a violet solution. This means that the solution is absorbing yellow, which is a shorter wavelength and higher energy, this would have a larger Δ.
So, ligand B results in the larger Δ.

73. Au would have the higher ionization energy. Ionization energy increases as you go down a group in the transition metals. Because there is a large increase in the number of protons and not a large increase in size, the ionization energy increases.

74. Fe^{3+} has a coordination number of 6 and is octahedral.
Fe [Ar]$4s^2 3d^6$
The octahedral splitting would be:

_____ _____

_____ _____ _____

If the electrons are lost from 3d orbitals first the electron configuration would be:
Fe^{3+} [Ar]$4s^2 3d^3$ and there would be 3 d electrons,

_____ _____

Since there are only 3 d electrons, it would not matter if the complex was high spin or low spin there would always be 3 unpaired electrons.

If the electrons are lost from the 4s orbitals first the electron configuration would be:

$Fe^{3+}[Ar]4s^03d^5$ and there would be 5 d electrons,

high spin (all electrons unpaired)   low spin (electrons will pair)

There are 5 unpaired electrons when the compound is high spin and only 1 unpaired electron when the compound is low spin. This influences the magnetic properties of the various complexes. This supports the idea that the electrons are lost from the 4s orbitals first.